Organic Electronic Spectral Data
Volume XV 1973

Organic Electronic Spectral Data

Volume XV 1973

JOHN P. PHILLIPS, DALLAS BATES
HENRY FEUER & B. S. THYAGARAJAN

EDITORS

CONTRIBUTORS

Dallas Bates
H. Feuer
L. D. Freedman
C. M. Martini
F. C. Nachod
J. P. Phillips

AN INTERSCIENCE ® PUBLICATION

JOHN WILEY & SONS
New York • Chichester • Brisbane • Toronto

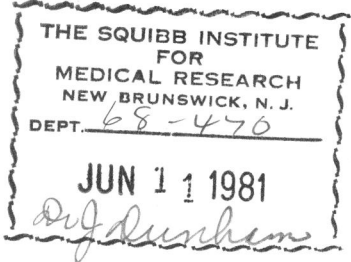

An Interscience® Publication

Library of Congress Catalog Card Number: 60-16428

ISBN 0-471-05572-7

Printed in the United States of America

10 9 8 7 6 5 4 3 2 1

INTRODUCTION TO THE SERIES

In 1956 a cooperative effort to abstract and publish in formula order all the ultraviolet-visible spectra of organic compounds presented in the journal literature was organized through the enterprise and leadership of M.J. Kamlet and H.E. Ungnade. Organic Electronic Spectral Data was incorporated in 1957 to create a formal structure for the venture, and coverage of the literature from 1946 onward was then carried out by chemists with special interests in spectrophotometry through a page by page search of the major chemical journals. After the first two volumes (covering the literature from 1946 through 1955) were produced, a regular schedule of one volume for each subsequent period of two years was inaugurated. In 1966 an annual schedule began. Fifteen volumes have now been published.

Altogether, more than fifty chemists have searched a group of journals totalling more than a hundred titles during the course of this sustained project. Additions and subtractions from both the lists of contributors and of journals have occurred from time to time, and it is estimated that the effort to cover all the literature containing spectra may not be more than 95% successful. However, the total collection is by far the largest ever assembled, amounting to more than 300,000 spectra through the volumes so far.

Volume XVI is in preparation.

PREFACE

Processing of the data provided by the contributors to Volume XV as to the last several volumes was performed at the University of Louisville.

John P. Phillips
Dallas Bates
Henry Feuer
B.S. Thyagarajan

ORGANIZATION AND USE OF THE DATA

The data in this volume were abstracted from the journals listed in the reference section at the end. Although a few exceptions were made, the data generally had to satisfy the following requirements: the compound had to be pure enough for satisfactory elemental analysis and for a definite empirical formula; solvent and phase had to be given; and sufficient data to calculate molar absorptivities had to be available. Later it was decided to include spectra even if solvent was not mentioned. Experience has shown that the most probable solvent in such circumstances is ethanol.

All entries in the compilation are organized according to the molecular formula index system used by Chemical Abstracts. Most of the compound names have been made to conform with the Chemical Abstracts system of nomenclature.

Solvent or phase appears in the second column of the data lists, often abbreviated according to standard practice; there is a key to less obvious abbreviations on the next page. Anion and cation are used in this column if the spectra are run in relatively basic or acidic conditions respectively but exact specifications cannot be ascertained.

The numerical data in the third column present wavelength values in millimicrons (or nanometers) for all maxima, shoulders and inflections, with the logarithms of the corresponding molar absorptivities in parentheses. Shoulders and inflections are marked with a letter s. In spectra with considerable fine structure in the bands a main maximum is listed and labelled with a letter f. Numerical values are given to the nearest nanometer for wavelength and nearest 0.01 unit for the logarithm of the molar absorptivity. Spectra that change with time or other common conditions are labelled "anom." or "changing", and temperatures are indicated if unusual.

The reference column contains the code number of the journal, the initial page number of the paper, and in the last two digits, the year (1973). A letter is added for journals with more than one volume or section in a year. The complete list of all articles and authors thereof appears in the References at the end of the volume.

Several journals that were abstracted for previous volumes in this series have been omitted, usually for lack of useful data, and several new ones have been added. Most Russian journals have been abstracted in the form of English translation editions.

ABBREVIATIONS

s	shoulder or inflection
f	fine structure
n.s.g.	no solvent given in original reference
C_5H_5N	pyridine
$C_6H_{11}Me$	methylcyclohexane
C_6H_{12}	cyclohexane
DMF	dimethylformamide
DMSO	dimethylsulfoxide
THF	tetrahydrofuran

Other solvent abbreviations generally follow the practice of Chemical Abstracts.

Underlined data were estimated from graphs.

JOURNALS ABSTRACTED

Journal	No.
Acta Chem. Scand.	1
Indian J. Chem.	2
Anal. Chem.	3
J. Heterocyclic Chem.	4
Ann. Chem. Liebigs	5
Ann. Chim. (Paris)	6
Ann. chim. (Rome)	7
Manufacturing Chemists Assoc. Research Project	8
Arch. Biochem. Biophys.	10
Australian J. Chem.	12
Steroids	13
Bull. Chem. Soc. Japan	18
Bull. Acad. Polon. Sci.	19
Bull. soc. chim. Belges	20
Bull. soc. chim. France	22
Can. J. Chem.	23
Chem. Ber.	24
Chem and Ind. (London)	25
Chimia	27
Compt. rend.	28
Doklady Akad. Nauk S.S.S.R.	30
Experientia	31
Gazz. chim. ital.	32
Helv. Chim. Acta	33
J. Chem. Eng. Data	34
J. Am. Chem. Soc.	35
J. Pharm. Sci.	36
J. Chem. Soc., Perkin Trans. II	39B
J. Chem. Soc., Perkin Trans. I	39C
Nippon Kagaku Kaishi	40
J. Indian Chem. Soc.	42
J. Org. Chem.	44
J. Phys. Chem.	46
J. Polymer Sci., Pt. A-1	47
J. prakt. Chem.	48
Monatsh. Chem.	49
Rec. trav. chim.	54
Roczniki Chem.	56
Science	57
Spectrochim. Acta	59
J. Chem. Soc., Faraday Trans. I	60
Ber. Bunsengesellschaft Phys. Chem.	61
Z. phys. Chem. (Leipzig)	62
Z. physiol. Chem.	63
Z. Naturforsch.	64
Zhur. Obshchei Khim.	65
J. Structural Chem. S.S.S.R.	67
Biochemistry	69
Izvest. Akad. Nauk. S.S.S.R.	70
Coll. Czech. Chem. Comm.	73
J. Chem. Soc., Chem. Comm.	77
Tetrahedron	78
Revue Roumaine Chim.	80
J. Mol. Spectr.	82
Arch. Pharm.	83
J. Med. Chem.	87
Tetrahedron Letters	88
Angew. Chem.	89
J. Applied Chem. S.S.S.R.	93
Chem. Pharm. Bull. (Japan)	94
J. Pharm. Soc. Japan	95
Z. Chemie	97
J. Agr. Food Chem.	98
Theor. Exptl. Chem.	99
Lloydia	100
J. Organometallic Chem.	101
Phytochemistry	102
Khim. Geterosikl. Soedin.	103
Zhur. Organ. Khim.	104
Khim. Prirodn. Soedin.	105
Die Pharmazie	106
Synthetic Comm.	107
Israel J. Chem.	108
Russian J. Phys. Chem.	110
Chim. ther.	111
Spectroscopy Letters	112
Acta Chim. Acad. Sci. Hung.	114
Egyptian J. Chem.	115
Macromolecules	116
Org. Preps. and Procedures	117
Synthesis	118
South African Chem. Inst. J.	119
Pakistan J. Sci. Ind. Research	120
J. Macromol. Sci.	121
Ukrain. Khim. Zhur.	124
Makromol. Chem.	126
Croatica Chim. Acta	128
Syn. Inorg. Metal-Org. Chem.	129
Bioorganic Chem.	130
J. Mol. Structure	131
Anales Assoc. Quim. Argentina	132
Pharm. Acta Helv.	133
J. Appl. Spectroscopy S.S.S.R.	135
Carbohydrate Research	136
Chemistry Letters	138
Phosphorus	139
J. Anal. Chem. S.S.S.R.	140
Acta Univ. Palackianae Olomucensis Fac. Med., Suppl. XIII	141
Heterocycles	142
Int. J. Sulfur Chem.	143

Compound	Solvent	$\lambda_{max}(\log \epsilon)$	Ref.
CCl_2S			
Carbonothioic dichloride	gas	254.0f(3.5)	82-0419-73B
$CHBr_3$			
Methane, tribromo-	MeOH	210s(3.2),221(3.3)	8-0172-73
$CH_2Cl_2O_3S$			
Chlorosulfuric acid, chloromethyl ester	heptane	206.1(2.40)	33-1483-73
CH_3ClO_3S			
Chlorosulfuric acid, methyl ester	heptane	205.9(2.39)	33-1483-73
CH_4N_2O			
Hydrazinecarboxaldehyde	H_2O	188(3.7),189(3.8), 192(3.8),193(3.7)	18-1366-73
	0.58M NaOH	220(3.3)	18-1371-73
	aq HCl	188(3.6),189(3.6)	18-1366-73
	MeOH	203(3.5)	18-1366-73
	dioxan	212(3.1)	18-1366-73
CH_4N_2S			
Thiourea	H_2O	235(4.05)	1-0209-73
	H_2SO_4	end absorption	1-0209-73
CO_2			
Carboxylate radical	pH 0.0	250(3.0)	60-0555-73
	pH 8.4	none	60-0555-73
CS_2			
Carbon disulfide	C_6H_{12}	209.6(5.0)	33-1752-73

Compound	Solvent	$\lambda_{max}(\log \epsilon)$	Ref.
$C_2Cl_3F_3$			
Ethane, 1,2,2-trichloro-1,1,2-trifluoro-	MeOH	none above 210 nm	8-0171-73
C_2Cl_4			
Ethene, tetrachloro-	MeOH	none above 240 nm	8-0168-73
$C_2H_2N_2S_3$			
1,3,4-Thiadiazolidine-2,5-dithione	n.s.g.	260(3.71),335(4.15)	48-0915-73
$C_2H_3N_3O$			
Cyanamide, methylnitroso-	CH_2Cl_2	253(3.51),373(2.08), 385(2.21),401(2.16)	44-1325-73
$C_2H_3N_3S$			
1,3,4-Thiadiazol-2-amine	EtOH	255(3.72)	80-1777-73
	EtOH-HCl	243(3.78)	80-1777-73
$C_2H_4Cl_2$			
Ethene, 1,2-dichloro-	MeOH	none above 200 nm	8-0170-73
$C_2H_4N_2O_2$			
Ethanediamide	H_2O	200(3.96),272(1.95)	82-0469-73C
$C_2H_4N_4S_2$			
1,2,4-Triazolidine-3,5-dithione, 4-amino-	EtOH	225(2.7),250s(2.3)	103-0518-73
C_2H_4O			
Acetaldehyde	hexane	293(1.26)	35-6685-73
	H_2O	274(0.91)	35-6685-73
$C_2H_4O_2$			
Acetic acid, Mn(III) salt	HOAc	460(2.52)	65-0121-73
Formic acid, methyl ester	MeOH	221(1.9)	8-0157-73
$C_2H_5ClO_3S$			
Chlorosulfuric acid, ethyl ester	heptane	204.7(2.43)	33-1483-73
C_2H_5NS			
Ethanethioamide	H_2O	262(4.14)	1-0209-73
protonated	H_2SO_4	234(4.02)	1-0209-73
$C_2H_5NS_2$			
Carbamodithioic acid, N-methyl-	pH 1	233(3.90),265(4.06)	94-0329-73
	pH 13	248(4.06),281(4.15)	94-0329-73
	80% H_2SO_4	242(4.02)	94-0329-73
	15M KOH	246(4.18)	94-0329-73
$C_2H_5N_3OS$			
Ethanethioamide, amino(hydroxyimino)-	EtOH	289(3.98)	39-0047-73C
$C_2H_6N_2$			
Diazine, dimethyl-, trans	n.s.g.	357(1.11)	89-0224-73
C_2H_6OS			
Dimethylsulfoxide	MeOH	none above 220 nm	8-0173-73
$C_2H_{18}CoN_6$			
Cobalt(3+), (acetonitrile)(pentammine)-(OC-6-22)-, triperchlorate	pH 3	333(1.75),467(1.80)	35-5649-73

Compound	Solvent	$\lambda_{max}(\log \epsilon)$	Ref.
$C_3Cl_5N_2P$			
1,3,2-Diazaphosphorine, 2,2,4,5,6-pentachloro-2,2-dihydro-	hexane	209(4.04),357(3.87)	112-0621-73
$C_3HCl_4N_2P$			
1,3,2-Diazaphosphorine, 2,2,4,6-tetrachloro-2,2-dihydro-	hexane	332(3.86)	112-0621-73
C_3HN_2			
Propanedinitrile, ion(1-), tetrabutylammonium salt	$CHCl_3$	244(3.45)	1-0258-73
$C_3HN_5O_2$			
1,2,4-Oxadiazole-3-carbonyl azide	EtOH	241(3.66)	39-0047-73C
$C_3H_2N_2O_2$			
Propanedial, diazo-	EtOH	227(4.15),241s(4.04),256(3.94)	73-2641-73
$C_3H_2N_2O_3$			
Imidazolidinetrione (parabanic acid)	H_2O	247s(--),298(--)	35-6928-73
	EtOH	248s(3.18),310(1.77)	35-6928-73
	ether	316.0(1.73)	35-6928-73
	MeCN	248s(3.15),312(1.78)	35-6928-73
$C_3H_2N_4O_4$			
1H-Pyrazole, 3,4-dinitro-	0.05M HCl	267(3.73)	4-1055-73
	0.05M NaOH	312(3.77)	4-1055-73
1H-Pyrazole, 3,5-dinitro-	0.05M HCl	244(4.09),270s(--)	4-1055-73
	0.05M NaOH	280(4.03),305s(--)	4-1055-73
$C_3H_2OS_2$			
3H-1,2-Dithiol-3-one	n.s.g.	310(3.60)	97-0026-73
$C_3H_2O_2S$			
1,3-Dioxole-2-thione	EtOH	207(3.34),263(4.16)	35-7161-73
$C_3H_2S_3$			
3H-1,2-Dithiole-3-thione	n.s.g.	229(3.88),251(3.92),336(3.80),415(3.83),498(2.00),531(1.91)	97-0026-73
$C_3H_3Cl_3OS$			
Ethanethioic acid, trichloro-, S-methyl ester	MeCN	251.5(3.60)	35-3994-73
$C_3H_3HgN_3$			
Mercury, (cyanodiazomethyl)methyl-	MeOH	208(4.33),262(3.97),400(1.81)	44-3937-73
$C_3H_3NOS_2$			
Rhodanine	EtOH	253(4.15),295(4.24)	94-1431-73
$C_3H_3NO_2S$			
2,4-Thiazolidinedione	EtOH	225(3.54)	132-0113-73
	EtOH-NaOH	242(3.77)	132-0113-73
$C_3H_3NO_4$			
Propanedial, nitro-	C_6H_{12}	248(3.90),270(3.86)	104-2245-73

Compound	Solvent	λ max (log ε)	Ref.
Propanedial, nitro- (cont.)	H_2O	230(3.85),270(3.89), 327(3.97)	104-2245-73
	ether	250(3.90),270(3.88)	104-2245-73
	CH_2Cl_2	257(3.87),275(3.87)	104-2245-73
	$CHCl_3$	253(3.85),278(3.87)	104-2245-73
anion	H_2O	227(3.89),268(3.93), 328(3.98)	104-2245-73
C_3H_3NSe			
Isoselenazole	EtOH	212(3.29),266(3.69)	4-0267-73
$C_3H_3N_3OS$			
1,2,4-Oxadiazole-3-carbothioamide	EtOH	306(3.81)	39-0047-73C
$C_3H_3N_3OS_2$			
1,2,5-Thiadiazole-4-carboxamide, 3-mercapto- (dicyclohexylamine salt)	EtOH	209s(3.76),233(4.11), 268(4.15),359(3.53)	23-2349-73
$C_3H_3N_3O_2$			
1H-Pyrazole, 3-nitro-	0.05M HCl	261(3.79)	4-1055-73
	0.05M NaOH	316(3.86)	4-1055-73
Pyrazole, 4-nitro-	0.05M HCl	274(3.92)	4-1055-73
	0.05M NaOH	319(4.06)	4-1055-73
1,2,4-Triazin-3(2H)-one, 1-oxide	pH 1	264(3.85),337(3.73)	44-3277-73
	H_2O	256(3.83),337(3.77)	44-3277-73
	pH 11	252(3.86),335(3.80)	44-3277-73
$C_3H_3N_5$			
1H-1,2,3-Triazole-4-carbonitrile, 5-amino-	EtOH	225(3.93),280(3.78)	22-3442-73
1H-1,2,3-Triazole-5-carbonitrile, 4-amino-	pH 3	251(3.77)	39-1629-73C
	pH 9	252(3.79)	39-1629-73C
$C_3H_3S_2$			
1,2-Dithiolium	MeOH	247(3.52),287(3.45)	78-3399-73
	MeCN	243(3.72),285(3.67)	78-3399-73
$C_3H_4Cl_2OS$			
Ethanethioic acid, dichloro-, S-methyl ester	MeCN	246(3.58)	35-3994-73
$C_3H_4F_2OS$			
Ethanethioic acid, difluoro-, S-methyl ester	MeCN	241(3.59)	35-3994-73
$C_3H_4N_2$			
Acrylonitrile, 3-amino-	EtOH	260(4.14)	73-3479-73
$C_3H_4N_2O$			
3-Pyrazolol	MeOH	219(3.66),250(3.15)	48-0382-73
	50% MeOH	221(3.43),241(3.53)	48-0382-73
	10% MeOH	240(3.64)	48-0382-73
$C_3H_4N_2OS$			
4-Thiazolidinone, 2-imino-	EtOH	220(4.26),249(3.94)	132-0113-73
	EtOH-NaOH	231(4.27)	132-0113-73
$C_3H_4N_2O_3$			
2-Propenal, 3-amino-2-nitro-	$CHCl_3$	270(3.78),328(3.83)	104-0477-73

Compound	Solvent	$\lambda_{max}(\log \epsilon)$	Ref.
$C_3H_4N_2S$			
2-Thiazolamine	pH 1	254(3.52)	80-0677-73
	EtOH	257(3.87)	80-0677-73
$C_3H_4N_2S_3$			
1,3,4-Thiadiazole-2(3H)-thione, 5-(methylthio)-	n.s.g.	322(4.18)	48-0915-73
1,3,4-Thiadiazolidine-2,5-dithione, 3-methyl-	n.s.g.	260(3.82),333(4.11)	48-0915-73
$C_3H_4N_4O_2$			
1,2,4-Oxadiazole-3-carboximidamide, N-hydroxy-	EtOH	243(3.60)	39-0047-73C
1,2,4-Oxadiazole-3-carboxylic acid, hydrazide	EtOH	243(3.60)	39-0047-73C
$C_3H_4O_3$			
1,3-Dioxolan-3-one	MeOH	none above 200 nm	8-0158-73
C_3H_5ClOS			
Ethanethioic acid, chloro-, S-methyl ester	MeCN	230(3.38)	35-3994-73
$C_3H_5NO_2$			
3-Isoxazolidinone	H_2O	218(3.60)	103-0001-73
1-Propene, 1-nitro-	nonane	226(3.98),307s(1.90), 317(1.87)	65-2164-73
	EtOH	233(3.98)	19-0351-73
sodium salt	EtOH	276(4.26)	19-0351-73
$C_3H_5NS_2$			
2-Thiazolidinethione	EtOH	275(4.0)	22-0971-73
$C_3H_5N_3O$			
Cyanamide, ethylnitroso-	H_2O	257(3.56),376(2.02), 388(2.10),402(2.00)	44-1325-73
	CH_2Cl_2	256(3.53),362s(1.86), 377(2.06),390(2.19), 406(2.13)	44-1325-73
1,2,4-Triazin-3(2H)-one, 4,5-dihydro-	MeOH	243(3.41)	44-3277-73
$C_3H_5N_3O_2$			
1,2,4-Triazolidine-3,5-dione, 1-methyl-	EtOH	207.5(3.60)	88-5123-73
1,2,4-Triazolidine-3,5-dione, 4-methyl-	CCl_4	289(3.24),542(2.40)	35-0721-73
$C_3H_5N_3S$			
1,3,4-Thiadiazol-2-amine, 5-methyl-	EtOH-HCl	245(3.79)	80-1777-73
3(2H)-Thiazolamine, 2-imino-	dioxan	248s(3.63),265(3.79)	4-0947-73
$C_3H_5N_3S_2$			
1,3,4-Thiadiazol-2-amine, 5-(methylthio)-	EtOH	282(4.08)	104-2631-73
hydrochloride	EtOH	281(3.75)	104-2631-73
hydroiodide	EtOH	288(3.83)	104-2631-73
1,3,4-Thiadiazole-2(3H)-thione, 5-(methylamino)-	EtOH	322(4.16)	104-2631-73
$C_3H_6N_2O_2$			
Ethenamine, N-methyl-N-nitro-	heptane	272(3.96)	104-0044-73

Compound	Solvent	λ_{max}(log ϵ)	Ref.
$C_3H_6N_2O_4$			
Propane, 2,2-dinitro-	$CHCl_3$	650(1.26)	78-3579-73
$C_3H_6N_2O_5$			
1-Propanol, 3,3-dinitro-, K salt	H_2O	375(4.21)	104-0922-73
$C_3H_6N_4$			
1,2,3-Triazol-4-amine, 1-methyl-	pH 0	262(3.17)	39-1629-73C
	pH 5	241(3.49)	39-1629-73C
1,2,4-Triazol-2-amine, 1-methyl-	n.s.g.	215(3.47)	22-1849-73
1,2,4-Triazol-3-amine, 1-methyl-	n.s.g.	227(3.47)	22-1849-73
1,2,4-Triazol-5-amine, 1-methyl-	n.s.g.	213(3.47)	22-1849-73
s-Triazole, 3-(methylamino)-	n.s.g.	213(3.67)	22-1849-73
$C_3H_6N_4S_2$			
3H-1,2,4-Triazole-3-thione, 4-amino-2,4-dihydro-5-(methylthio)-	EtOH	210(3.6),260(3.5)	103-0518-73
C_3H_6O			
Acetone, tetracyanoethylene complex	CH_2Cl_2	360(1.74)	46-2652-73
Propanal	hexane	292(1.32)	35-6685-73
	H_2O	278(0.99)	35-6685-73
$C_3H_6OS_2$			
Carbonodithioic acid, S,S-dimethyl ester	EtOH	215(3.40),248(3.65)	44-1641-73
$C_3H_6O_3$			
Propanal, 2,3-dihydroxy-	H_2O	273(0.70)	35-6685-73
	EtOH	272(1.26)	35-6685-73
2-Propanone, 1,3-dihydroxy-	H_2O	192.5(2.13)	136-0165-73D
	H_2O	275(1.38)	130-0197-73
$C_3H_7ClO_3S$			
Chlorosulfuric acid, propyl ester	heptane	203.9(2.45)	33-1483-73
C_3H_7NS			
Ethanethioamide, N-methyl-	H_2O	255(4.21)	1-0209-73
	H_2SO_4	230(3.98)	1-0209-73
Ethanimidothioic acid, methyl ester	H_2O	226(4.20)	1-0209-73
protonated	H_2O	228(4.42)	1-0209-73
$C_3H_7NS_2$			
Carbamodithioic acid, N-ethyl-	pH 1	235(3.92),267(4.06)	94-0329-73
	pH 13	251(4.08),282(4.16)	94-0329-73
	80% H_2SO_4	243(4.05)	94-0329-73
	15M KOH	248(4.16)	94-0329-73
$C_3H_7N_3O_2$			
Urea, N-ethyl-N-nitroso-	CH_2Cl_2	237(3.85),382(1.90), 396(2.08),414(2.05)	44-1325-73
$C_3H_8N_2O_2$			
Methanamine, 1-methoxy-N-methyl-N-nitroso-	isooctane	227(3.80),358(1.90), 370(2.02),383(1.94)	88-2671-73
$C_3H_8N_2S$			
Thiourea, N,N-dimethyl-	EtOH	242(4.25)	48-0144-73

Compound	Solvent	$\lambda_{max}(\log \epsilon)$	Ref.
$C_3H_8N_3O_4P$			
Phosphoramidic acid, [(acetylamino)-iminomethyl]-	H_2O	224(4.26)	35-8080-73
$C_3H_9BrCuO_3P$			
Copper, bromo(trimethyl phosphite-P)-	MeCN	230(4.01)(end abs.)	44-3893-73

Compound	Solvent	λmax(log ε)	Ref.
$C_4Br_2O_2S$			
2,5-Thiophenedione, 3,4-dibromo-	C_6H_{12}	268(4.0),326(2.7)	64-0662-73B
$C_4Cl_2O_2S$			
2,5-Thiophenedione, 3,4-dichloro-	C_6H_{12}	257(4.0),324(2.3)	64-0662-73B
$C_4HBr_2NO_2$			
1H-Pyrrole-2,5-dione, 3,4-dibromo-	MeCN	243f(3.8),302(3.1)	64-0662-73B
C_4HClN_2S			
5-Thiazolecarbonitrile, 2-chloro-	EtOH	241(3.80),256(3.94)	39-2769-73C
$C_4HCl_2NO_2$			
1H-Pyrrole-2,5-dione, 3,4-dichloro-	MeCN	236f(4.1),287(2.8)	64-0662-73B
$C_4HCl_3N_3P$			
1,3,2-Diazaphosphorine-5-carbonitrile, 2,2,4-trichloro-2,2-dihydro-	hexane	238(4.01),336(3.71)	112-0621-73
C_4HCl_5			
1,3-Butadiene, 1,1,2,3,4-pentachloro-	hexane	248(3.7)	104-0887-73
1,3-Butadiene, 1,1,2,4,4-pentachloro-	hexane	264(3.8)	104-0887-73
$C_4HI_2NO_2$			
1H-Pyrrole-2,5-dione, 3,4-diiodo-	$CHCl_3$	244(4.0),336(3.2)	64-0662-73B
$C_4HN_3O_2S$			
5-Thiazolecarbonitrile, 2-nitro-	EtOH	250(3.90),303(4.00)	39-2769-73C
$C_4H_2BrCl_2N_3$			
2-Pyrimidinamine, 5-bromo-4,6-dichloro-	MeOH	238(4.26),314(3.62)	44-4386-73
$C_4H_2BrN_3O_4$			
3(2H)-Pyridazinone, 6-bromo-4-nitro-, 1-oxide	MeOH	230(3.8),255s(3.6), 285s(3.4),372(3.23)	4-0835-73
$C_4H_2O_2S$			
2,5-Thiophenedione	C_6H_{12}	230(3.91),320(2.55)	64-0662-73B
$C_4H_2O_3$			
Maleic anhydride	C_6H_{12}	207(4.08),308(1.15)	64-0662-73B
	H_2O	210(4.45)	23-3539-73
	EtOH	203(3.92)	23-3539-73
	dioxan	206(3.89)	23-3539-73
triethylamine salt	H_2O	212(4.53),350(--), 403(--),510(--), 540(--)	23-3539-73
	EtOH	212(4.06)	23-3539-73
	dioxan	220(4.57)	23-3539-73
$C_4H_2O_4$			
3-Cyclobutene-1,2-dione, 3,4-dihydroxy-	pH 1.08	240(4.3),252s(4.3)	1-3499-73
(squaric acid)	pH 6.21	270(4.5)	1-3499-73
Bis(triphenylphosphine)iminium salt	CH_2Cl_2	268(4.46),275(4.45)	46-2652-73
$C_4H_3Cl_4N_2P$			
1,3,2-Diazaphosphorine, 2,2,4,6-tetrachloro-2,2-dihydro-5-methyl-	hexane	346(3.90)	112-0621-73

Compound	Solvent	λ_{max}(log ϵ)	Ref.
$C_4H_3NO_2$			
1H-Pyrrole-2,5-dione	C_6H_{12}	216(4.23),268(3.04), 346(1.34)	64-0662-73B
$C_4H_3NO_2S$			
Thiophene, 2-nitro-	isooctane	270s(3.8),298(3.85)	33-1787-73
Thiophene, 3-nitro-	isooctane	260(3.92)	33-1787-73
$C_4H_3N_3O_2$			
2,4-Pyrrolidinedione, 3-diazo-	EtOH	210(4.54),240(4.56), 290s(3.82)	39-2907-73C
$C_4H_3N_3O_3S$			
4(1H)-Pyrimidinone, 2,3-dihydro-5-nitro-2-thioxo-	MeOH	209(4.0),255s(3.8), 272(3.9),349(4.1)	24-3039-73
1,2,4-Triazine-6-carboxylic acid, 2,3,4,5-tetrahydro-5-oxo-3-thioxo-	EtOH	221(3.91),278(4.21), 312s(3.67)	22-3178-73
Violuric acid, thio-, anion	pH 6.5-7.0	340(4.48),570(2.45)	140-0395-73
dianion	n.s.g.	350(4.39),570(2.49)	140-0395-73
$C_4H_3N_3O_4$			
Violuric acid, anion	pH 6.5-7.0	310(4.16),542(1.70)	140-0395-73
dianion	pH 11	520(1.70)	140-0395-73
$C_4H_3N_3S$			
Cyanamide, 2-thiazolyl-	EtOH	230(3.36),284(4.13)	94-2408-73
5-Thiazolecarbonitrile, 2-amino-	EtOH	290.5(4.13)	39-2769-73C
$C_4H_3N_5OS$			
[1,2,4]Triazolo[1,5-a][1,3,5]triazin-5(4H)-one, 6,7-dihydro-7-thioxo-	pH 12	237(3.30),280(3.43)	103-0256-73
[1,2,4]Triazolo[1,5-a][1,3,5]triazin-7(4H)-one, 5,6-dihydro-5-thioxo-	pH 12	240(3.24),282(3.28)	103-0256-73
$C_4H_3N_5O_2$			
[1,2,4]Triazolo[1,5-a][1,3,5]triazine-5,7(1H,6H)-dione	EtOH	225(3.76),257(3.59)	39-1209-73C
$C_4H_3N_5S$			
Imidazo[4,5-d][1,2,3]thiadiazin-4(5H)-one	n.s.g.	220(4.18),253(4.11), 280(3.63),327(3.59)	103-1173-73
4H-Imidazo[4,5-d]-1,2,3-triazine-4-thione, 1,5-dihydro-	n.s.g.	237(3.87),315(4.18)	103-1173-73
C_4H_4			
1-Buten-3-yne	isooctane	221(3.76),227s(3.80)	135-1521-73
$C_4H_4BrClN_4$			
2,4-Pyrimidinediamine, 5-bromo-6-chloro-	MeOH	233(4.05),294(3.78)	44-4386-73
$C_4H_4ClN_3O$			
2-Pyrazinamine, 3-chloro-, 1-oxide	pH 1	230(4.29),255s(--), 337(3.80)	87-0643-73
	pH 13	232(4.29),263s(--), 338(3.77)	87-0643-73
	MeOH	235(4.32),263s(--), 340(3.86)	87-0643-73
$C_4H_4ClN_3OS$			
5-Thiazolecarboximidamide, 2-chloro-N-hydroxy-	EtOH	253(3.73),295(3.69)	39-2769-73C

Compound	Solvent	λ_{max}(log ε)	Ref.
$C_4H_4NO_2$			
Acetonitrile, (acetyloxy)-, Na salt	EtOH	246(4.10)	1-0258-73
$C_4H_4N_2$			
Pyrazine	pH 7.0	261(3.77),267(3.69), 302(2.90)	114-0069-73B
	7N H_2SO_4	267(3.85)	114-0069-73B
	15N H_2SO_4	268(3.83)	114-0069-73B
	20N H_2SO_4	270(3.81)	114-0069-73B
	25N H_2SO_4	273(3.78)	114-0069-73B
	30N H_2SO_4	284(3.86)	114-0069-73B
	36N H_2SO_4	284(3.97)	114-0069-73B
Pyridazine	pH 7.0	242(3.15),247(3.14), 300(2.52)	114-0069-73B
	N H_2SO_4	238(3.21),241(3.24)	114-0069-73B
	10N H_2SO_4	216(3.25),238(3.22)	114-0069-73B
	23N H_2SO_4	216(3.25),238(3.22)	114-0069-73B
	33N H_2SO_4	216(3.25),236(3.22)	114-0069-73B
	36N H_2SO_4	216(3.25),236(3.23)	114-0069-73B
$C_4H_4N_2O_2S_2$			
Acetic acid, (1,2,5-thiadiazol-3-yl-thio)-	EtOH	208(3.71),297(3.93)	23-2349-73
$C_4H_4N_2O_3$			
Imidazolidinetrione, 1-methyl- (also qualitative spectrum in water)	EtOH	215(4.11),255s(3.09), 307(1.80)	35-6928-73
	MeCN	214(--),253(--), 310(1.84)	35-6928-73
	ether	213(--),253s(--), 316(1.76)	35-6928-73
2,4,5(3H)-Pyrimidinetrione, dihydro-	n.s.g.	210(3.90),278(3.83)	103-0253-73
$C_4H_4N_2O_4$			
Sydnone, 3-(carboxymethyl)-	EtOH	204(3.59),298(3.84)	103-0441-73
$C_4H_4N_4O_3S$			
5-Thiazolecarboximidamide, N-hydroxy-2-nitro-	EtOH	248(3.84),303(3.63), 371(3.48)	39-2769-73C
$C_4H_4N_4O_4$			
1H-Pyrazole, 3-methyl-4,5-dinitro-	0.05M HCl	273(3.77)	4-1055-73
	0.05M NaOH	317(3.86)	4-1055-73
2(1H)-Pyrimidinone, 6-amino-1-hydroxy-5-nitro-	pH 2.0	245s(3.76),270(3.82), 330(3.99)	44-0703-73
	pH 10	240s(3.90),276(3.95), 347(4.10)	44-0703-73
$C_4H_4OS_2$			
1,3-Dithiol-2-one, 4-methyl-	EtOH	239(3.45),272(3.44)	143-0273-73
$C_4H_4O_2$			
1,3-Cyclobutanedione	EtOH	237(4.07)	44-1451-73
$C_4H_4O_2S$			
2,4(3H,5H)-Thiophenedione	0.025M HCl	233(4.13),262(3.79)	56-1735-73
	96% EtOH	228(3.97),283(4.22)	56-1735-73
	99.8% EtOH	230(4.05),282(4.02)	56-1735-73
	ether	228(4.06)	56-1735-73

Compound	Solvent	λmax(log ε)	Ref.
$C_4H_4O_3$			
Fumaraldehydic acid	EtOH	216(4.04)	44-0815-73
Malealdehydic acid	EtOH	202(3.84)	44-0815-73
Tetronic acid	EtOH	222(4.10)	78-4251-73
$C_4H_4S_3$			
3H-1,2-Dithiole-3-thione, 5-methyl-	heptane	231(3.74),252(3.89), 333(3.73),411(3.81), 492(2.04),514(2.03)	78-3599-73
	H_2O	225(3.99),272(3.87), 307(3.56),396(4.12)	78-3599-73
	MeOH	229(3.99),246(3.83), 266(3.85),318(3.76), 404(4.06),470s(--)	78-3599-73
	MeCN	229(3.98),247(3.83), 268(3.83),317(3.76), 406(4.05),470(2.30)	78-3599-73
	10N H_2SO_4	224(3.95),272(3.86), 305(3.49),394(4.11)	78-3599-73
	11N H_2SO_4	224(3.86),273(3.80), 305(3.40),394(4.04)	78-3599-73
	12N H_2SO_4	224(3.81),274(3.77), 302(3.37),344s(3.36), 393(4.00)	78-3599-73
and other sulfuric acid concentrations	20N H_2SO_4	209(3.76),231s(3.15), 279(3.84),340(4.27)	78-3599-73
$C_4H_5ClN_2$			
2-Butenenitrile, 3-amino-2-chloro-	MeCN	254(4.22)	44-2287-73
C_4H_5ClO			
Cyclobutanone, 2-chloro-	gas	300(1.79)	35-4320-73
$(C_4H_5NO)_n$			
Poly(1,2-azetidinediylcarbonyl), (S)-	H_2O	206(3.74)	116-0517-73
	EtOH	209(3.93)	116-0517-73
$C_4H_5NO_2$			
2,4-Pyrrolidinedione	H_2O	240s(4.82),257s(3.79), 320s(3.59)	39-2907-73C
$C_4H_5NO_2S$			
2,5-Thiazolidinedione, 5-methyl-	EtOH	220(3.58)	132-0113-73
	EtOH-NaOH	242(3.73)	132-0113-73
C_4H_5NS			
Thiazole, 2-methyl-	n.s.g.	236(3.83)	124-0353-73
hydrochloride	n.s.g.	242(3.91)	124-0353-73
Thiazole, 4-methyl-	n.s.g.	242(3.66)	124-0353-73
hydrochloride	n.s.g.	249(3.70)	124-0353-73
Thiazole, 5-methyl-	n.s.g.	241.5(3.56)	124-0353-73
hydrochloride	n.s.g.	248.5(3.56)	124-0353-73
C_4H_5NSe			
Isoselenazole, 5-methyl-	EtOH	224(3.51),266(3.72)	4-0267-73
$C_4H_5N_3O$			
2(1H)-Pyrimidinone, 4-amino-	pH 7.0	267(3.79)	39-1101-73B
1,2,4-Triazine, 3-methoxy-	n.s.g.	218(3.11),255s(3.00), 310s(2.54)	22-2493-73

Compound	Solvent	$\lambda_{max}(\log \epsilon)$	Ref.
1,2,4-Triazin-3(2H)-one, 2-methyl-	pH 1	243(3.52),310(2.78)	44-3277-73
	pH 11	243(3.48),310(2.55)	44-3277-73
	EtOH	243(3.42),309(2.82)	44-3277-73
1,2,4-Triazin-5(4H)-one, 6-methyl-	EtOH	238(4.05),266s(3.79)	22-2126-73
$C_4H_5N_3OS$			
4(1H)-Pyrimidinone, 5-amino-2,3-dihydro-2-thioxo-	MeOH	226(4.0),297(4.2)	24-3039-73
	MeOH-HCl	211(4.1),273(4.2), 293s(4.1)	24-3039-73
5-Thiazolecarboxaldehyde, 2-amino-, oxime	EtOH	244(3.34),300(4.23)	39-2769-73C
5-Thiazolecarboximidamide, N-hydroxy-	EtOH	284(3.61)	39-2769-73C
$C_4H_5N_3O_2$			
Pyrazole, 3-methyl-4-nitro-	0.05M HCl	282(3.91)	4-1055-73
	0.05M NaOH	322(4.08)	4-1055-73
1H-Pyrazole, 3-methyl-5-nitro-	0.05M HCl	265(3.82)	4-1055-73
	0.05M NaOH	321(3.84)	4-1055-73
Pyrazole, 4-methyl-3-nitro-	0.05M HCl	266(3.80)	4-1055-73
	0.05M NaOH	318(3.90)	4-1055-73
$C_4H_5N_3O_4$			
2,4,6(1H,3H,5H)-Pyrimidinetrione, 5-(hydroxyamino)-	EtOH	250(3.71)	103-0247-73
$C_4H_5N_3S$			
1,2,4-Triazine, 3-(methylthio)-	n.s.g.	225s(3.26),255(3.53), 325(3.20)	22-2493-73
$C_4H_5N_5$			
1H-1,2,3-Triazole-5-carbonitrile, 4-amino-1-methyl-	EtOH	215s(3.76),283(3.74)	39-1634-73C
2H-1,2,3-Triazole-5-carbonitrile, 4-amino-2-methyl-	pH 7.0	216s(3.74),269(3.73)	39-1634-73C
$C_4H_5S_3$			
3H-1,2-Dithiol-3-ylium, 3-(methylthio)-, iodide	H_2O	217(4.20),257(3.46), 295(3.36),351(4.18)	78-3599-73
	MeOH	220(4.22),269(3.40), 310s(--),360(4.10)	78-3599-73
$C_4H_6Cl_2OS$			
Ethanethioic acid, dichloro-, S-ethyl ester	10% MeCN	249(3.65)	35-3994-73
$C_4H_6HgN_2O$			
Mercury, (1-diazo-2-oxopropyl)methyl-	MeOH	288(3.92),366(1.90)	44-3937-73
$C_4H_6HgN_2O_2$			
Mercury, (1-diazo-2-methoxy-2-oxoethyl)methyl-	MeOH	269(4.00),377(1.64)	44-3937-73
$C_4H_6N_2$			
2-Butenenitrile, 3-amino-	EtOH	258(4.24)	73-3479-73
	MeCN	255(4.09)	44-2287-73
$C_4H_6N_2O$			
5-Pyrazolone, 1-methyl-	MeOH	222(3.62),247(3.62)	48-0382-73
	50% MeOH	243(3.92)	48-0382-73
	10% MeOH	241(3.92)	48-0382-73

Compound	Solvent	$\lambda_{max}(\log \epsilon)$	Ref.
$C_4H_6N_2OS$			
4-Thiazolidinone, 2-imino-5-methyl-	EtOH	220(4.25),250(3.93)	132-0113-73
	EtOH-NaOH	232(4.20)	132-0113-73
$C_4H_6N_2O_2$			
2,3-Piperazinedione	H_2O	210(3.81),270s(1.0)	82-0469-73C
$C_4H_6N_2O_3$			
2-Propenal, 3-(methylamino)-2-nitro-	$CHCl_3$	284(4.02),320(4.12)	104-0477-73
$C_4H_6N_2S_3$			
1,3,4-Thiadiazole, 2,5-bis(methylthio)-	n.s.g.	289(3.99)	48-0915-73
1,3,4-Thiadiazole-2(3H)-thione, 3-methyl-5-(methylthio)-	n.s.g.	319(4.17)	48-0915-73
1,3,4-Thiadiazolidine-2,5-dithione, 3,4-dimethyl-	n.s.g.	268(4.09),328(4.08)	48-0915-73
$C_4H_6N_4O$			
2,6-Pyrazinediamine, 1-oxide	EtOH	231(4.34),282(3.34), 336(3.98)	39-0606-73C
1H-1,2,3-Triazole-4-carboxaldehyde, 5-amino-1-methyl-	pH -4	241(3.67),301(3.91)	39-1629-73C
	pH 2	237(3.60),287(3.96)	39-1629-73C
1H-1,2,3-Triazole-5-carboxaldehyde, 4-amino-1-methyl-	pH 3	243(3.64),316(3.83)	39-1629-73C
2H-1,2,3-Triazole-4-carboxaldehyde, 5-amino-2-methyl-	pH -4	241(3.90)	39-1629-73C
	pH 2	236(3.60),302(3.79)	39-1629-73C
$C_4H_6N_4OS$			
5-Thiazolecarboximidamide, 2-amino-N-hydroxy-	EtOH	292.5(4.05)	39-2769-73C
$C_4H_6N_4O_2$			
1H-Imidazol-5-amine, 1-methyl-4-nitro-	pH 1	218(3.99),257s(3.59), 364(4.14)	39-0244-73C
	pH 11	268(3.77),369(4.13)	39-0244-73C
	MeOH	220(4.04),360(4.13)	39-0244-73C
2,6-Pyrazinediamine, N-hydroxy-, 1-oxide	EtOH	235(4.39),285(3.46), 338(3.74)	39-0606-73C
$C_4H_6N_4O_2S$			
2-Pyrazinesulfonamide, 3-amino-	EtOH	240(4.03),335(3.68)	18-1890-73
$C_4H_6N_4O_5S$			
4(1H)-Pyrimidinone, 2,6-diamino-5-sulfooxy-	H_2O	210(4.17),236(2.51), 273(3.94)	70-2308-73
$C_4H_6N_6OS$			
Thiourea, [5-[(hydroxyimino)methyl]-1H-1,2,3-triazol-4-yl]-	MeOH	248(4.19),268(4.16), 280s(4.13)	39-1625-73C
$C_4H_6N_6O_2$			
8-Azapurin-2(3H)-one, 1,6-dihydro-6-(hydroxyamino)-	pH 2	209(3.79),242(3.84)	39-1625-73C
Methanimidamide, N-hydroxy-N'-[5-(hydroxyimino)methyl]-1H-1,2,3-triazol-4-yl]-	MeOH	261(3.75),290s(3.44)	39-1625-73C
C_4H_6O			
Cyclobutanone	gas	270(1.2),280f(1.3), 290f(1.2)	35-0682-73

Compound	Solvent	λ_{max}(log ϵ)	Ref.
Cyclobutanone (cont.)	hexane	2815(1.28)	46-1830-73
$C_4H_6O_2$			
2,3-Butanedione	hexane	420(1.18)	35-6685-73
	H_2O	404(1.30)	35-6685-73
$C_4H_6O_2S_2$			
Ethanebis(thioic) acid, S,S-dimethyl ester	MeCN	278(3.75)	35-3994-73
$C_4H_6O_3S_2$			
1,2-Dithiolane-4-carboxylic acid, 1-oxide, anti	MeOH	248(3.1)	88-1073-73
syn	MeOH	248(3.1)	88-1073-73
$C_4H_7ClN_2O_2$			
Ethenamine, N-(2-chloroethyl)-N-nitro-	heptane	273(3.87)	104-0044-73
C_4H_7NO			
Isoxazole, 4,5-dihydro-3-methyl-	EtOH	214(3.65)	22-1390-73
$C_4H_7NO_2$			
1-Butene, 1-nitro-	EtOH	234(3.74)	19-0351-73
sodium salt	EtOH	265(4.19)	19-0351-73
2-Butene, 2-nitro-	EtOH	240(3.76)	19-0351-73
sodium salt	EtOH	263(4.23)	19-0351-73
1-Propene, 2-methyl-1-nitro-	EtOH	242(3.94)	19-0351-73
sodium salt	EtOH	278(4.20)	19-0351-73
$C_4H_7NO_2S_2$			
Ethene, 1,1-bis(methylthio)-2-nitro-	heptane	335(4.12)	1-1183-73
	EtOH	291(3.78),355(4.17)	1-1183-73
$C_4H_7NO_4S_2$			
Dithiocarbamic acid, N-(3-sulfooxy-propyl)-, disodium salt	EtOH	305(4)	22-0971-73
$C_4H_7N_3O_2$			
1,2,4-Triazolidine-3,5-dione, 4-ethyl-	CCl_4	287(4.32),544(2.36)	35-0721-73
$C_4H_7N_3S$			
1,3,4-Thiadiazol-2-amine, 5-ethyl-	EtOH	256(3.77)	80-1777-73
	EtOH-HCl	245(3.89)	80-1777-73
1,2,4-Triazolidine-3-thione, 1,4-dimeth-yl-, meso-ionic didehydro deriv.	MeCN	248(4.35)	103-1048-73
$C_4H_7N_3S_2$			
1,3,4-Thiadiazol-2-amine, N-methyl-5-(methylthio)-	EtOH	286(3.97)	104-2631-73
hydriodide	EtOH	285(4.03)	104-2631-73
1,3,4-Thiadiazole-2(3H)-thione, 5-(dimethylamino)-	EtOH	322(4.07)	104-2631-73
$C_4H_7N_5O$			
1H-Imidazole-4-carboxamide, 5-hydra-zino-, hydrochloride	H_2O	198(4.02),269(3.99)	103-0083-73
$C_4H_7N_5O_2$			
Ethenamine, N-(2-azidoethyl)-N-nitro-	heptane	273(3.90)	104-0044-73

Compound	Solvent	$\lambda_{max}(\log \epsilon)$	Ref.
$C_4H_7N_7O$			
Guanidine, [5-(hydroxyimino)methyl]-1H-1,2,3-triazol-4-yl]-	MeOH	218(4.24),272(3.86)	39-1625-73C
C_4H_8BrS			
Thiophenium, 1-bromotetrahydro-, bromide	CH_2Cl_2	285(3.26)	44-2156-73
$C_4H_8IN_3S_2$			
1,3,4-Thiadiazolium, 2-amino-3-methyl-5-(methylthio)-, iodide	EtOH	278(3.95)	104-2631-73
$C_4H_8N_2$			
Acetaldehyde azine	C_6H_{12}	225(3.2),280(2.0)	65-2005-73
	EtOH	215(3.7),280s(2.3)	65-2005-73
$C_4H_8N_2O_2$			
Ethanediamide, N,N'-dimethyl-	H_2O	211(3.99),270s(1.91)	82-0469-73C
	MeCN	208(4.10),272(1.92), 280s(1.91),294s(1.57)	82-0469-73C
	gas	203(--)	82-0469-73C
Ethenamine, N,N-dimethyl-2-nitro-	n.s.g.	240(3.57),350(4.35)	135-1299-73
$C_4H_8N_4O$			
2H-1,2,3-Triazole-4-methanol, 5-amino-2-methyl-	pH -2	220(3.81)	39-1629-73C
	pH 4	210s(3.43),252(3.76)	39-1629-73C
$C_4H_8N_8$			
Methanimidic acid, N-[5-(hydrazonomethyl)-1H-1,2,3-triazol-4-yl]-, hydrazide	MeOH	276(4.06)	39-1625-73C
C_4H_8O			
Butanal	hexane	293(1.27)	35-6685-73
	H_2O	281(1.09)	35-6685-73
Ethene, ethoxy-	heptane	210(3.22)	135-1154-73
	MeOH	198(3.94)	135-1154-73
	isoPrOH	198(4.05)	135-1154-73
	ether	197(3.86)	135-1154-73
	$C_2H_4Cl_2$	217(3.31)	135-1154-73
Furan, tetrahydro-	H_2O	186.0(2.08)	136-0165-73D
Propanal, 2-methyl-	hexane	293(1.26)	35-6685-73
	H_2O	280(1.08)	35-6685-73
$C_4H_8O_2$			
Acetic acid, ethyl ester	MeOH	210(1.8)	8-0160-73
1,4-Dioxane	H_2O	189.5(2.13)	136-0165-73D
	MeOH	none above 210 nm	8-0159-73
$C_4H_9ClO_3S$			
Chlorosulfuric acid, butyl ester	heptane	203.6(2.45)	33-1483-73
C_4H_9NO			
Acetamide, N,N-dimethyl-	MeOH	none above 210 nm	8-0174-73
$C_4H_9NO_3$			
Nitric acid, tert-butyl ester	heptane	265(1.2)	44-2281-73
C_4H_9NS			
Ethanethioamide, N,N-dimethyl-	H_2O	264(4.26)	1-0209-73

Compound	Solvent	λ max (log ε)	Ref.
Ethanethioamide, N,N-dimethyl- (cont.)	H_2SO_4	237(4.11)	1-0209-73
Ethanimidothioic acid, N-methyl-, methyl ester	H_2O	226(4.28)	1-0209-73
protonated	H_2O	228(4.40)	1-0209-73
C_4H_9NSe			
Ethaneselenamide, N,N-dimethyl-	EtOH	298(4.14),379(2.22)	143-0519-73
Propaneselenamide, N-methyl-	EtOH	291(4.05),368(2.20)	143-0519-73
$C_4H_9N_5$			
1H-1,2,3-Triazole-5-methanamine, 4-amino-1-methyl-	pH -1.2	266(3.46)	39-1634-73C
	pH 4.0	249(3.56)	39-1634-73C
	pH 10.0	249(3.62)	39-1634-73C
2H-1,2,3-Triazole-4-methanamine, 5-amino-2-methyl-	pH 5.0	249(3.73)	39-1634-73C
	pH 11.0	250(3.81)	39-1634-73C
$C_4H_{10}N_2O_2$			
2-Butanone, 4-(hydroxyamino)-, oxime, hydrochloride	EtOH	204(3.38)	104-0793-73
$C_4H_{10}N_2O_4Si$			
Methane, nitro[(trimethylsilyl)-aci-nitro]-	CH_2Cl_2	303(3.85)	65-1699-73
$C_4H_{10}N_4$			
1,2,3,4-Tetrazine, 1,4,5,6-tetrahydro-1,4-dimethyl-	MeOH	223(3.4),275(3.7)	89-0495-73
$C_4H_{10}N_4O$			
Carbamimidic acid, (aminoiminomethyl)-, ethyl ester	EtOH	204(3.8),230(3.7)	94-0478-73
at 60-70°	EtOH	203(3.9),230(3.6)	94-0478-73
1,2,3,4-Tetrazine, 1,4,5,6-tetrahydro-1,4-dimethyl-, 2-oxide	MeOH	291(4.08)	89-0495-73
$C_4H_{10}O$			
1-Propanol, 2-methyl-	MeOH	205(-1.0)	8-0184-73
$C_4H_{11}PS$			
Phosphine sulfide, diethyl-	C_6H_{12}	222(3.90)	18-1803-73
	MeCN	209(3.61)	18-1803-73
$C_4H_{12}N_4$			
2-Tetrazene, 1,1,4,4-tetramethyl-	hexane	280(3.98)	126-0311-73D
	DMF	283(3.95)	126-0311-73D
	acrylonitrile	283(3.90)	126-0311-73D
$C_4I_2O_2S$			
2,5-Thiophenedione, 3,4-diiodo-	C_6H_{12}	284(3.9),366(3.3)	64-0662-73B

Compound	Solvent	λmax(log ε)	Ref.
C_5BrCl_5Hg			
Mercury, bromo(1,2,3,4,5-pentachloro-2,4-cyclopentadien-1-yl)-	C_6H_{12}	217(4.2),270(4.0), 335(3.1)	35-8658-73
	glyme	220s(4.3),276(4.0), 329s(3.1)	35-8658-73
$C_5Br_4N_2$			
1,3-Cyclopentadiene, 1,2,3,4-tetra-bromo-5-diazo-	hexane	310(4.24),318s(4.21)	44-1340-73
C_5Br_6O			
3-Cyclopenten-1-one, 2,2,3,4,5,5-hexa-bromo-	C_6H_{12}	241(4.17)	44-0153-73
C_5Cl_6Hg			
Mercury, chloro(1,2,3,4,5-pentachloro-2,4-cyclopentadien-1-yl)-	C_6H_{12}	215(4.1),265(3.9), 330(3.1)	35-8658-73
	glyme	212(4.0),270(3.9), 323s(3.1)	35-8658-73
$C_5Cl_6N_3P$			
1,3,2-Diazaphosphorine-5-carbonitrile, 2,2,6-trichloro-2,2-dihydro-4-(tri-chloromethyl)-	hexane	249(4.02),349(3.84)	112-0621-73
C_5HBr_7			
Cyclopentene, heptabromo-	C_6H_{12}	244(4.11)	44-0153-73
$C_5HCl_5N_2O$			
4(3H)-Pyrimidinone, 5,5,6-trichloro-2-(dichloromethylene)-2,5-dihydro-	C_6H_{12}	242(3.60),275s(3.49), 295(3.54)	18-0299-73
$C_5HF_3N_4O_2$			
3,3'-Bi-1,2,4-oxadiazole, 5-(trifluoro-methyl)-	EtOH	none from 220 to 350 nm	39-0047-73C
$C_5H_2BrClO_2$			
2-Furancarbonyl chloride, 5-bromo-	heptane	284(--)	103-0546-73
	dioxan	288(4.23)	103-0546-73
$C_5H_2Br_2O_2$			
4-Cyclopentene-1,3-dione, 4,5-dibromo-	$CHCl_3$	280(4.0)	64-0662-73B
$C_5H_2Br_4N_2$			
2,4-Cyclopentadien-1-one, 2,3,4,5-tetrabromo-, hydrazone	MeOH	343(4.33)	44-1340-73
$C_5H_2ClIO_2$			
2-Furancarbonyl chloride, 5-iodo-	heptane	290(--)	103-0546-73
	dioxan	295(4.27)	103-0546-73
$C_5H_2ClNO_4$			
2-Furancarbonyl chloride, 5-nitro-	heptane	286(--)	103-0546-73
	dioxan	299(4.06)	103-0546-73
$C_5H_2ClN_3OS$			
1,2,4-Oxadiazole, 3-(2-chloro-5-thiazo-lyl)-	EtOH	265(4.06)	39-2769-73C

Compound	Solvent	λ_{max}(log ε)	Ref.
$C_5H_2Cl_2O_2$			
4-Cyclopentene-1,3-dione, 4,5-dichloro-	$CHCl_3$	264(4.1)	64-0662-73B
2-Furancarbonyl chloride, 5-chloro-	heptane	275(--)	103-0546-73
	dioxan	285(4.25)	103-0546-73
$C_5H_2Cl_4N_2$			
Pyrimidine, 4,5,6-trichloro-2-(chloromethyl)-	C_6H_{12}	232(4.13),268(3.88), 275s(3.82)	18-0299-73
$C_5H_2F_2N_4$			
1-Cyclobutene-1-carbonitrile, 2-azido-3,3-difluoro-	MeOH	266(4.15)	24-3544-73
$C_5H_2I_2O_2$			
4-Cyclopentene-1,3-dione, 4,5-diiodo-	$CHCl_3$	310(3.8)	64-0662-73B
$C_5H_2N_4O_3S$			
1,2,4-Oxadiazole, 3-(2-nitro-5-thiazolyl)-	EtOH	221(3.76),319(3.56)	39-2769-73C
$C_5H_2O_5$			
1-Cyclopentene-3,4,5-trione, 1,2-dihydroxy- (croconic acid)	H_2SO_4	275(4.08),290s(4.03)	22-2209-73
bis(triphenylphosphine)iminium salt	CH_2Cl_2	262(4.04),268(4.11), 275(4.00),373(4.54)	46-2652-73
$C_5H_3BrO_2$			
2-Furancarboxaldehyde, 5-bromo-	heptane	275(--)	103-0546-73
	H_2O	290(--)	103-0546-73
	EtOH	285(--)	103-0546-73
	dioxan	282(4.20)	103-0546-73
$C_5H_3BrO_3$			
2-Furancarboxylic acid, 5-bromo-	heptane	263(--)	103-0546-73
	H_2O	256(--)	103-0546-73
	EtOH	250(--)	103-0546-73
	dioxan	256(4.24)	103-0546-73
$C_5H_3ClO_2$			
2-Furancarbonyl chloride	heptane	268(--)	103-0546-73
	dioxan	272(4.16)	103-0546-73
2-Furancarboxaldehyde, 5-chloro-	heptane	273(--)	103-0546-73
	H_2O	288(--)	103-0546-73
	EtOH	282(--)	103-0546-73
	dioxan	280(4.17)	103-0546-73
$C_5H_3ClO_3$			
2-Furancarboxylic acid, 5-chloro-	heptane	261(--)	103-0546-73
	H_2O	253(--)	103-0546-73
	EtOH	248(--)	103-0546-73
	dioxan	254(4.22)	103-0546-73
$C_5H_3F_2N_3O_2$			
1-Cyclobutene-1-carboxylic acid, 2-azido-3,3-difluoro-	MeOH	268(3.97)	24-3544-73
$C_5H_3F_3N_4O_3$			
1,2,4-Oxadiazole-3-carboximidamide, N-[(trifluoroacetyl)oxy]-	EtOH	261(3.58)	39-0047-73C

Compound	Solvent	$\lambda_{max}(\log \epsilon)$	Ref.
$C_5H_3F_6N$			
1,2-Propadien-1-amine, N,N-bis(trifluoromethyl)-	n.s.g.	207(2.46),232s(2.2)	39-1066-73C
$C_5H_3IO_2$			
2-Furancarboxaldehyde, 5-iodo-	heptane	283(--)	103-0546-73
	H_2O	299(--)	103-0546-73
	EtOH	296(--)	103-0546-73
	dioxan	291(4.20)	103-0546-73
$C_5H_3IO_3$			
2-Furancarboxylic acid, 5-iodo-	heptane	269(--)	103-0546-73
	H_2O	259(--)	103-0546-73
	EtOH	253(--)	103-0546-73
	dioxan	264(4.20)	103-0546-73
$C_5H_3NO_4$			
2-Furancarboxaldehyde, 5-nitro-	heptane	292(--)	103-0546-73
	H_2O	310(--)	103-0546-73
	EtOH	310(--)	103-0546-73
	dioxan	302(4.06)	103-0546-73
$C_5H_3NO_5$			
2-Furancarboxylic acid, 5-nitro-	heptane	289(--)	103-0546-73
	H_2O	315(--)	103-0546-73
	EtOH	314(--)	103-0546-73
	dioxan	299(4.04)	103-0546-73
$C_5H_3N_3OS$			
Formamide, N-(5-cyano-2-thiazolyl)-	EtOH	284(4.10)	39-2769-73C
1,2,4-Oxadiazole, 3-(5-thiazolyl)-	EtOH	255(4.00)	39-2769-73C
$C_5H_3N_3O_5$			
Pyridine, 2,5-dinitro-, N-oxide	EtOH	352(4.06)	104-2622-73
$C_5H_3N_5O_3$			
Pyrimido[5,4-e]-1,2,4-triazine-3,5,7(4H,6H,8H)-trione	pH 1.2	231(3.88),273(3.83), 420(2.79)	12-1689-73
	pH 10.9	242(4.24),272s(3.83), 425(3.59),469s(3.27)	12-1689-73
$C_5H_4BrN_3O_4$			
Pyridazine, 6-bromo-3-methoxy-4-nitro-, 1-oxide	MeOH	250(3.6),285(3.6), 285[sic](3.2),367(4.2)	4-0835-73
$C_5H_4ClN_5$			
1H-1,2,3-Triazolo[4,5-b]pyridin-5-amine	pH 7	265s(3.71),293(3.87)	44-1095-73
$C_5H_4ClN_5O_2$			
Pyridazine, 4-azido-6-chloro-3-methoxy-, 1-oxide	MeOH	230(3.8),290(4.3), 345(4.1)	4-0835-73
$C_5H_4Cl_2N_2O_2$			
Pyridazine, 4,6-dichloro-3-methoxy-, 1-oxide	MeOH	220(4.32),267(4.01), 340(3.7)	4-0835-73
C_5H_4FN			
Pyridine, 4-fluoro-	EtOH	244(3.04),249(3.07), 255(2.90)	39-1865-73C

Compound	Solvent	$\lambda_{max}(\log \epsilon)$	Ref.
C_5H_4FNO			
2(1H)-Pyridinone, 5-fluoro-	pH 1	290(3.63)	4-0779-73
	pH 14.0	304(3.75)	4-0779-73
	MeOH	307(3.67)	4-0779-73
C_5H_4FNO			
2(1H)-Pyridinone, 5-fluoro-4-hydroxy-	pH 1.0	268(3.63)	87-0524-73
	pH 3.2	285(3.60)	87-0524-73
	pH 7.2	254(3.84),270s(3.73)	87-0524-73
	pH 14.0	254(3.67),270s(3.56)	87-0524-73
$C_5H_4F_2N_4O$			
1-Cyclobutene-1-carboxamide, 2-azido-3,3-difluoro-	MeOH	268(4.03)	24-3544-73
$C_5H_4N_2OS$			
Acetonitrile, (4-oxo-2-thiazolylidene)-	EtOH	272(4.28)	1-1923-73
$C_5H_4N_2S_2$			
Thieno[2,3-c]isothiazol-3-amine	MeOH	239(4.43),310(4.03)	48-0539-73
$C_5H_4N_4O$			
1H-Imidazo[4,5-b]pyrazine, 4-oxide	pH 1	215(4.11),303(4.08)	87-0643-73
	pH 13	220(4.21),246(3.75), 317(4.11)	87-0643-73
	MeOH	221(4.31),305(4.16)	87-0643-73
$C_5H_4N_4OS$			
2-Thiazolamine, 5-(1,2,4-oxadiazol-3-yl)-	EtOH	299.5(4.21)	39-2769-73C
$C_5H_4N_4O_2$			
1H-Imidazo[4,5-b]pyrazine, 4,7-dioxide	pH 1	227(3.85),260(3.28), 331(3.79)	87-0643-73
	pH 13	220(3.80),258(3.37), 337(3.46)	87-0643-73
	MeOH	225(3.67),264(3.36), 348(3.67)	87-0643-73
$C_5H_4N_4O_2S$			
2H-Pyrazino[2,3-e][1,2,4]thiadiazine, 1,1-dioxide	EtOH	233(3.58),256(3.54), 300(3.82)	18-1890-73
$C_5H_4N_8$			
1H-1,2,3-Triazolo[4,5-b]pyridin-5-amine, 7-azido-	pH 7	284(4.10),307s(3.98)	44-1095-73
$C_5H_4O_2$			
4-Cyclopentene-1,3-dione	C_6H_{12}	216(4.15),390(1.28)	64-0662-73B
2-Furancarboxaldehyde	heptane	265(--)	103-0546-73
	H_2O	278(--)	103-0546-73
	EtOH	272(--)	103-0546-73
	dioxan	268(4.13)	103-0546-73
$C_5H_4O_3$			
2-Furancarboxylic acid	heptane	250(--)	103-0546-73
	H_2O	245(--)	103-0546-73
	EtOH	241(--)	103-0546-73
	dioxan	246(4.10)	103-0546-73

Compound	Solvent	$\lambda_{max}(\log \epsilon)$	Ref.
$C_5H_4O_5$			
2,4-Cyclopentadien-1-one, 2,3,4,5-tetrahydroxy-	11M H_2SO_4	228(3.79),286(3.92)	22-2209-73
4-Cyclopentene-1,3-dione, 2,4,5-trihydroxy-, diprotonated ion	H_2SO_4	230(3.94),300(4.02)	22-2209-73
2H-Pyran-2,5-dione, 4,5-dihydro-3,4-dihydroxy-	18M H_2SO_4	275(4.07),290s(3.97)	22-2214-73
	dil H_2SO_4	252(3.90)	22-2214-73
$C_5H_5BrClN_3$			
2-Pyrimidinamine, 5-bromo-4-chloro-6-methyl-	MeOH	237(4.22),310(3.57)	44-4386-73
$C_5H_5ClN_2O$			
2-Butenoyl chloride, 3-amino-2-cyano-	MeCN	288(4.21)	44-2287-73
$C_5H_5ClN_2O_2S$			
4-Pyridazinethiol, 6-chloro-3-methoxy-, 1-oxide	MeOH	285(3.8)	4-0835-73
$C_5H_5ClN_2S$			
2(1H)-Pyridinethione, 3-amino-6-chloro-	MeOH	256(3.90),355(3.55)	44-4383-73
$C_5H_5Cl_4N_2P$			
1,3,2-Diazaphosphorine, 2,2,4,6-tetrachloro-5-ethyl-2,2-dihydro-	hexane	345(3.85)	112-0621-73
$C_5H_5IN_2O_2$			
2,4(1H,3H)-Pyrimidinedione, 6-iodo-5-methyl-	pH 2	270(3.95)	22-2719-73
	pH 7	270.5(3.95)	22-2719-73
	N NH_3	295(4.00)	22-2719-73
C_5H_5N			
Pyridine	H_2O	199(3.46),256(3.61)	103-0888-73
	H_o 1.09	202(3.40),256(3.69)	103-0888-73
	-2.12	202(3.39),256(3.65)	103-0888-73
	-4.78	202(3.38),256(3.69)	103-0888-73
	-7.58	202(3.44),256(3.71)	103-0888-73
	-9.06	202(3.42),256(3.74)	103-0888-73
	-11.98	205(3.13),256(3.67)	103-0888-73
C_5H_5NO			
Pyridine N-oxide	H_2O	207(4.20),255(3.99)	103-0888-73
	H_o 1.09	207(4.06),255(3.95)	103-0888-73
	-2.12	219(3.70),259(3.43)	103-0888-73
	-4.78	219(3.70),259(3.48)	103-0888-73
	-7.58	216(3.58),257(3.43)	103-0888-73
	-9.06	216(3.42),257(3.27)	103-0888-73
	-11.98	217(3.60),257(3.55)	103-0888-73
hydrochloride	H_2O	255(4.10)	59-0139-73
	6M HCl	259(3.50)	59-0139-73
3-Pyridinol	H_o 1.09	202(4.12),284(3.83)	103-0888-73
	-2.12	198(4.25),282(3.72)	103-0888-73
	-4.78	198(4.27),282(3.83)	103-0888-73
	-7.58	198(4.23),280(3.76)	103-0888-73
	-9.06	198(4.27),280(3.82)	103-0888-73
	-11.98	210(3.22),261(3.73)	103-0888-73
$C_5H_5NO_2$			
2,3-Pyridinediol	H_2O	240(3.47),300(3.87)	103-0051-73
	pH 1	234(3.54),297(3.81)	103-0051-73

Compound	Solvent	$\lambda_{max}(\log \epsilon)$	Ref.
2,3-Pyridinediol (cont.)	N HCl	290(4.25)	103-0051-73
	acid	222(3.45),290(3.92)	103-0051-73
	pH 13	252(3.81),310(3.96)	103-0051-73
	N NaOH	253(4.21),310(4.40)	103-0051-73
	EtOH	240(3.47),300(3.87)	103-0051-73
	DMSO	300(4.22)	103-0051-73
2,5-Pyridinediol	pH 1	229(3.81),313(3.64)	103-0051-73
	pH 13	230(4.63),290(4.40), 347(3.84)	103-0051-73
	EtOH	230(4.06),330(3.84)	103-0051-73
	DMSO	336(4.07)	103-0051-73
3-Pyridinol N-oxide	H_2O	220(4.16),253(3.94), 295(2.98)	99-0417-73
	N HCl	220(3.94),255(3.49), 289(3.74)	99-0417-73
	N NaOH	234(4.56),314(3.90)	99-0417-73
	EtOH	224(3.56),244(3.75), 262(3.97),302(2.98)	99-0417-73
	H_o 1.09	206(4.17),254(3.74)	103-0888-73
	-2.12	203(4.34),285(3.70)	103-0888-73
	-4.78	202(4.37),285(3.75)	103-0888-73
	-7.58	201(4.31),283(3.75)	103-0888-73
	-9.06	201(4.37),282(3.77)	103-0888-73
	-11.98	218(3.61),263(3.61)	103-0888-73
2(1H)-Pyridinone, 4-hydroxy-	pH 1	257(3.63)	87-0294-73
	pH 11	253(3.0),261(3.78)	87-0294-73
	MeOH	277(3.66)	87-0294-73
$C_5H_5NO_3$			
2H-1,3-Oxazine-2,6(3H)-dione, 5-methyl-	EtOH	271(3.81)	88-3493-73
$C_5H_5N_3O_2$			
2-Pyridinamine, 3-nitro-	80.4% DMSO	396(3.86)	22-1225-73
anion	80.4% DMSO	510(3.97)	22-1225-73
2-Pyridinamine, 5-nitro-	80.4% DMSO	360(4.18)	22-1225-73
anion	80.4% DMSO	440(4.43)	22-1225-73
$C_5H_5N_3O_3S$			
1,2,4-Triazine-6-carboxylic acid, 2,5-dihydro-3-(methylthio)-5-oxo-	EtOH	227(3.85),244s(3.94), 325(3.91)	22-3178-73
1,2,4-Triazine-6-carboxylic acid, 2,3,4,5-tetrahydro-2-methyl-5-oxo-3-thioxo-	EtOH	234(4.05),274(4.31), 318(3.78)	22-3178-73
1,2,4-Triazine-6-carboxylic acid, 2,3,4,5-tetrahydro-4-methyl-5-oxo-3-thioxo-	EtOH	225(3.95),276(4.18), 315s(3.68)	22-3178-73
1,2,4-Triazine-6-carboxylic acid, 2,3,4,5-tetrahydro-5-oxo-3-thioxo-, methyl ester	EtOH	233(3.65),278(4.00)	22-3178-73
$C_5H_5N_3O_4$			
1H-Imidazole-5-carboxylic acid, 1-methyl-2-nitro-	n.s.g.	243(3.77),305(3.80)	87-0557-73
$C_5H_5N_3S$			
Thiazolo[3,2-b][1,2,4]triazole, 2-methyl-	MeOH	206(--),242(--)	4-0947-73

Compound	Solvent	λ_{max}(log ε)	Ref.
$C_5H_5N_5OS$			
[1,2,4]Triazolo[1,5-a][1,3,5]triazin-5(1H)-one, 5,6-dihydro-2-methyl-7-thioxo-	pH 12	237(3.30),280(3.43)	103-0256-73
[1,2,4]Triazolo[1,5-a][1,3,5]triazin-7(1H)-one, 5,6-dihydro-2-methyl-5-thioxo-	pH 12	239(3.19),282(3.27)	103-0256-73
[1,2,4]Triazolo[1,5-a][1,3,5]triazin-7(3H)-one, 5,6-dihydro-3-methyl-5-thioxo-	pH 12	223(3.04),240(3.07), 290(3.40)	103-0256-73
$C_5H_5N_5S$			
1H-Imidazo[4,5-d]-1,2,3-triazine, 4-(methylthio)-	n.s.g.	234(4.07),290(3.98)	103-1173-73
$C_5H_5N_7$			
Pyrimido[5,4-e]-1,2,4-triazine-3,5-diamine	pH 1.0	217(4.21),270(4.03), 295(3.72),415(3.71)	12-1689-73
	pH 8.5	215(4.31),228s(4.18), 268(4.11),421(3.68)	12-1689-73
$C_5H_6I_2S$			
1,3-Butadiene, 1,2-diiodo-1-(methylthio)-	n.s.g.	255(3.7),268(3.7), 288s(3.6)	104-1822-73
$C_5H_6NO_3P$			
Phosphonic acid, 2-pyridinyl-	pH 2	263(3.93)	44-1306-73
	pH 6	264(3.82)	44-1306-73
	pH 10	256(3.67),262(3.75), 268(3.61)	44-1306-73
$C_5H_6N_2$			
1H-Imidazole, 1-ethenyl-	EtOH	230(4.09)	103-1517-73
Et_3SnBr complex	EtOH	230(4.25)	103-1517-73
Et_3SnCl complex	EtOH	230(4.17)	103-1517-73
Ph_3SnCl complex	EtOH	216(4.57)	103-1517-73
Pr_3SnCl complex (also other complexes)	EtOH	230(4.25)	103-1517-73
$C_5H_6N_2O$			
2(1H)-Pyridinone, 4-amino-	pH 1	209(4.26),252(4.20)	87-0294-73
	H_2O	210(4.33),259(3.90), 265s(3.89)	87-0294-73
	pH 11	260(3.88),268s(3.87)	87-0294-73
2(1H)-Pyrimidinone, 1-methyl-	H_2O	303(3.72)	73-1381-73
$C_5H_6N_2OS$			
4(1H)-Pyrimidinone, 2,3-dihydro-1-methyl-2-thioxo-	MeOH	216(4.2),267(4.1), 292(4.0)	24-3039-73
	MeOH-NaOH	238(4.3),254s(4.2), 271(4.2)	24-3039-73
4(1H)-Pyrimidinone, 2-(methylthio)-	MeOH	228(3.9),286(3.9), 308s(3.5)	24-3039-73
	MeOH-HCl	221(4.0),248(3.9), 269s(3.8),308s(3.2)	24-3039-73
	MeOH-NaOH	222(4.2),243(3.9), 278(3.8)	24-3039-73
$C_5H_6N_2O_2$			
2,4-Diazabicyclo[4.1.0]heptane-3,5-dione, cis-(±)	H_2O	196(3.96),245s(2.90)	49-0415-73

Compound	Solvent	λmax(log ε)	Ref.
1H-Pyrazole-3-carboxylic acid, methyl ester	MeOH	217(4.08)	88-2655-73
2,4(1H,3H)-Pyrimidinedione, dihydro-5-methylene-	H_2O	208(4.02)(changing)	49-0415-73
2,4(1H,3H)-Pyrimidinedione, 1-methyl-	H_2O	268(4.03)	39-0391-73C
	neutral	262(3.98)	46-0482-73
$C_5H_6N_2O_3$			
Imidazolidinetrione, dimethyl-	EtOH	218(4.09),260(2.86), 313s(1.78)	35-6928-73
	MeCN	218(--),263(--), 310s(1.95)	35-6928-73
	ether	217(--),256(--), 314(1.82)	35-6928-73
Isoxazole, 3,5-dimethyl-4-nitro-	EtOH	218(4.05),265(4.10)	2-1074-73
$C_5H_6N_2O_4$			
Propanedioic acid, diazo-, dimethyl ester	EtOH	250(3.90)	22-2065-73
Sydnone, 3-(2-carboxyethyl)-	EtOH	203(3.48),295(3.86)	103-0441-73
$C_5H_6N_2S_2$			
3-Thiophenecarbothioamide, 2-amino-	MeOH	246(4.20),287(3.81), 351(3.88)	48-0539-73
$C_5H_6N_4$			
Pyrazolo[4,3-c]pyrazole, 1,4-dihydro-3-methyl-	EtOH	223(--),265(3.75)	88-1189-73
$C_5H_6N_4O$			
1,2,4-Oxadiazole, 3-(1H-imidazol-2-yl)-, hydrochloride	EtOH	268(3.42)	39-0047-73C
$C_5H_6N_4O_2S$			
5-Thiazolecarboximidamide, 2-(formyl-amino)-N-hydroxy-	EtOH	295.5(3.98)	39-2769-73C
$C_5H_6N_4O_4$			
1H-Pyrazole, 4-ethyl-3,5-dinitro-	0.05M HCl	254(4.10),280s(--)	4-1055-73
	0.05M NaOH	290(4.10),310s(--)	4-1055-73
$C_5H_6N_6$			
1H-1,2,3-Triazolo[4,5-b]pyridine-5,7-diamine	pH 7	280s(4.19),293(4.26)	44-1095-73
1H-1,2,3-Triazolo[4,5-c]pyridine-4,6-diamine	pH 7	225(4.43),275(3.68), 314(3.73)	44-1095-73
7H-1,2,3-Triazolo[4,5-d]pyrimidin-7-imine, 1,6-dihydro-6-methyl-	pH 1	261(3.96)	39-2659-73C
	pH 7	268(3.95)	39-2659-73C
	pH 12	272(4.08)	39-2659-73C
$C_5H_6OS_2$			
1,3-Dithiol-2-one, 4,5-dimethyl-	EtOH	218(3.57),238(3.48), 276(3.44)	143-0273-73
$C_5H_6O_3$			
Tetronic acid, 3-methyl-	EtOH	228(4.08)	78-4251-73
Tetronic acid, 5-methyl-	EtOH	221(4.12)	78-4251-73

Compound	Solvent	λ_{max}(log ε)	Ref.
$C_5H_6O_4$			
Propanoic acid, 2-formyl-3-oxo-, methyl ester	EtOH	268(3.90)	35-0540-73
	EtOH-base	241(4.17),278(4.11)	35-0540-73
C_5H_6S			
1-Buten-3-yne, 4-(methylthio)-	heptane	222(4.06),252(3.93), 266(3.89),288(3.28)	135-1521-73
	H_2O	220(--),249(--), 261(--)	135-1521-73
	EtOH	222(3.99),251(3.89), 264(3.81),286(3.30)	135-1521-73
	n.s.g.	252(3.9),267(3.8), 293(3.3)	104-1822-73
C_5H_6Se			
1-Buten-3-yne, 4-(methylseleno)-	heptane	225(4.00),255(3.84), 268(3.85),299(3.15)	135-1521-73
	H_2O	224(--),248(--), 261(--),290(--)	135-1521-73
	EtOH	225(3.98),253(3.79), 265(3.79),296(3.18)	135-1521-73
C_5H_6Te			
1-Buten-3-yne, 4-(methyltelluro)-	heptane	270(3.86),284(3.93), 350(2.95)	135-1521-73
	H_2O	265(--),279(--), 332(--)	135-1521-73
	EtOH	270(3.74),284(3.83), 340(2.90)	135-1521-73
C_5H_7ClO			
2-Butenal, 3-chloro-2-methyl- (10% cis)	EtOH	244(4.10)	78-4241-73
3-Buten-2-one, 4-chloro-3-methyl- (20% trans)	EtOH	231(4.18)	78-4241-73
3-Penten-2-one, 4-chloro- (20% cis)	EtOH	238(3.87)	78-4241-73
$C_5H_7IN_2$			
Pyridinium, 1-amino-, iodide	EtOH	211(4.28),255(3.90)	103-1108-73
	acetone	240(4.22)	103-1108-73
	HOAc	245(3.86),290(3.41)	103-1108-73
	H_2SO_4	255(3.93)	103-1108-73
	MeCN	247(4.29)	103-1108-73
	DMSO	241(4.17),260(3.91)	103-1108-73
C_5H_7NO			
2H-Pyrrol-2-one, 3,4-dihydro-5-methyl-, (hexachloroantimonate)	MeCN	234(3.54),269(3.93)	24-1423-73
	H_2SO_4	205(3.95),290(3.75)	24-1423-73
$C_5H_7NO_2$			
5-Isoxazolone, 3,4-dimethyl-	EtOH	261(4.0)	1-2802-73
3-Pyrrolin-2-one, 5-hydroxy-4-methyl-	MeOH	230s(3.06)	36-1206-73
$C_5H_7NO_2S$			
2,4-Thiazolidinedione, 5,5-dimethyl-	EtOH	221(3.56)	132-0113-73
	EtOH-NaOH	242(3.53)	132-0113-73
2,4-Thiazolidinedione, 5-ethyl-	EtOH	222(2.73)	132-0113-73
	EtOH-NaOH	243(3.94)	132-0113-73
$C_5H_7NO_3$			
Carbamic acid, (3-oxo-1-propenyl)-, methyl ester	EtOH	266(4.52)	104-0908-73

Compound	Solvent	$\lambda_{max}(\log \epsilon)$	Ref.
$C_5H_7NO_4$			
Butanoic acid, 2-(hydroxyimino)-3-oxo-, methyl ester	EtOH	231(3.77)	107-0225-73
C_5H_7NSe			
Isoselenazole, 4,5-dimethyl-	EtOH	225(3.48),272(3.71)	4-0267-73
$C_5H_7N_3O$			
1,2,4-Triazine, 3-methoxy-5-methyl-	n.s.g.	215(3.45),285(3.38), 360(2.90)	22-2493-73
1,2,4-Triazine, 5-methoxy-6-methyl-	EtOH	259(3.63)	22-2126-73
1,2,4-Triazin-5(2H)-one, 2,6-dimethyl-	EtOH	245(4.08),265s(3.81)	22-2126-73
1,2,4-Triazin-5(4H)-one, 4,6-dimethyl-	EtOH	273(3.66)	22-2126-73
$C_5H_7N_3OS$			
Acetamide, N-(3-amino-2(3H)-thiazolylidene)-	dioxan	296(4.11)	4-0947-73
$C_5H_7N_3OS_2$			
Carbamothioic acid, dimethyl-, O-1,2,5-thiadiazol-3-yl ester	EtOH	206(3.68),253(4.24)	23-2349-73
Carbamothioic acid, dimethyl-, S-1,2,5-thiadiazol-3-yl ester	EtOH	210(3.87),278(3.94)	23-2349-73
$C_5H_7N_3O_2$			
1H-Pyrazole, 3,5-dimethyl-4-nitro-	0.05M HCl	284(3.93)	4-1055-73
	0.05M NaOH	321(4.10)	4-1055-73
1H-Pyrazole, 4-ethyl-3-nitro-	0.05M HCl	269(3.77)	4-1055-73
	0.05M NaOH	319(3.90)	4-1055-73
$C_5H_7N_3S$			
2(1H)-Pyrazinethione, 3-amino-6-methyl-	EtOH	236(3.60),278(3.63), 387(3.80)	18-1890-73
1,2,4-Triazine, 5-methyl-3-(methylthio)-	n.s.g.	222(3.70),257(4.10), 322(2.91)	22-2493-73
1,2,4-Triazine, 6-methyl-3-(methylthio)-	n.s.g.	225(3.62),255(4.14), 330(2.60)	22-2493-73
$C_5H_7O_2$			
2,4-Pentanedione, ion(1-), tetrabutylammonium salt	$CHCl_3$	245(3.42),274(3.95)	1-0258-73
$C_5H_7O_3$			
Butanoic acid, 3-oxo-, methyl ester, ion(1-), sodium salt	EtOH	272(4.26)	1-0258-73
$C_5H_7O_4$			
Propanedioic acid, dimethyl ester, ion(1-), sodium salt	EtOH	258(3.51)	1-0258-73
C_5H_8			
1,2-Butadiene, 3-methyl-	gas	143(4.00),146(4.06), 150(4.04),151(4.04), 152(4.14),153(4.16), 156(4.28),158(4.29), 163(4.22),165(4.25), 170(4.40),173(4.41), 176(4.31),181(4.09), 198(3.13),210(2.88)	35-1429-73
Spiropentane	C_6H_{12}	232(1.62)	89-0334-73

Compound	Solvent	$\lambda_{max}(\log \epsilon)$	Ref.
C_5H_8BrNO			
3-Penten-2-one, 4-amino-3-bromo-	hexane	306(3.99)	40-2152-73
C_5H_8ClNO			
3-Penten-2-one, 4-amino-3-chloro-	hexane	303.5(3.94)	40-2152-73
$C_5H_8HgN_2O_2$			
Mercury, (1-diazo-2-ethoxy-2-oxoethyl)-methyl-	MeOH	269(4.04),377(1.68)	44-3937-73
Mercury, (1-diazo-2-methoxy-2-oxoethyl)-ethyl-	MeOH	272(3.97),377(1.70)	44-3937-73
$C_5H_8NOS_2$			
4-Morpholinecarbodithioic acid, ion(1-)	aq base	262(4.21),286(4.23), 341(2.09)	44-0560-73
C_5H_8NS			
Thiazolium, 2,3-dimethyl-, methosulfate	n.s.g.	242(3.69)	124-0353-73
Thiazolium, 2,4-dimethyl-, methosulfate	n.s.g.	249(3.56)	124-0353-73
Thiazolium, 2,5-dimethyl-, methosulfate	n.s.g.	248.5(3.56)	124-0353-73
$C_5H_8NS_3$			
4-Thiomorpholinecarbodithioic acid, ion(1-)	aq base	261(4.18),286(4.23), 349(1.80)	44-0560-73
$C_5H_8N_2O$			
2-Imidazolidinone, 1,5-dimethyl-	EtOH	207(5.02)	70-1380-73
3H-Pyrazol-3-one, 2,4-dihydro-2,4-dimethyl-	H_2O	247.5(3.95)	20-0215-73
	MeOH	252(3.88)	20-0215-73
	EtOH	252.5(3.82)	20-0215-73
	isoPrOH	255(3.76)	20-0215-73
	tert-BuOH	228(3.53),256(3.64)	20-0215-73
	dioxan	257(2.90)	20-0215-73
	THF	257(3.00)	20-0215-73
	MeCN	258(3.46)	20-0215-73
	DMSO	263(3.13)	20-0215-73
	CF_3CH_2OH	247(3.97)	20-0215-73
$C_5H_8N_2OS$			
4(1H)-Pyrimidinone, tetrahydro-6-methyl-2-thioxo-	H_2O	228(3.98),271(4.14)	44-1963-73
4-Thiazolidinone, 5,5-dimethyl-2-imino-	EtOH	220(4.27),249(3.94)	132-0113-73
	EtOH-NaOH	232(4.22)	132-0113-73
4-Thiazolidinone, 5-ethyl-2-imino-	EtOH	219(4.31),249(3.95)	132-0113-73
	EtOH-NaOH	232(4.10)	132-0113-73
$C_5H_8N_2O_2$			
1H-Pyrazole-3-carboxylic acid, 4,5-dihydro-, methyl ester	MeOH	291(4.02)	88-2655-73
$C_5H_8N_2O_3$			
Butanamide, 2-(hydroxyimino)-N-methyl-3-oxo-	EtOH	232(3.89)	107-0225-73
Cyclopropane, (1-nitro-1-nitrosoethyl)-	CH_2Cl_2	652(1.15)	78-3579-73
2-Propenal, 3-(ethylamino)-2-nitro-	$CHCl_3$	285(4.06),320(4.17)	104-0477-73
$C_5H_8N_2O_5S$			
5-Pyrimidinemethanesulfonic acid, hexahydro-2,4-dioxo-, Na salt	H_2O	196(4.09)	49-0415-73

Compound	Solvent	$\lambda_{max}(\log \epsilon)$	Ref.
$C_5H_8N_4O$			
Hydrazinecarboxamide, 2-(2-cyano-1-methylethylidene)-	MeOH	228(4.05),250s(3.60)	28-1457-73A
Methanimidamide, N,N-dimethyl-N'-1,2,4-oxadiazol-3-yl-	EtOH	253(4.30)	39-0047-73C
$C_5H_8N_4OS$			
Urea, N-ethyl-N-(1,3,4-thiadiazol-2-yl)-	EtOH	222(3.62),254(3.96)	44-3868-73
$C_5H_8N_4O_2$			
Carbamic acid, 1H-1,2,4-triazol-3-yl-, ethyl ester	EtOH	210(4.05)	39-1209-73C
1H-1,2,4-Triazole-1-carboxylic acid, 3-amino-, ethyl ester	EtOH	263(3.76)	39-1209-73C
1H-1,2,4-Triazole-1-carboxylic acid, 5-amino-, ethyl ester	EtOH	243(3.72)	39-1209-73C
$C_5H_8N_4O_2S$			
Carbamic acid, (3-amino-1,2,4-thiadiazol-5-yl)-, ethyl ester	EtOH	272(3.49)	94-2396-73
2-Pyrazinesulfonamide, 3-amino-6-methyl-	EtOH	242(4.08),345(3.69)	18-1890-73
$C_5H_8N_4O_{12}$			
Pentaerythritol tetranitrate	MeCN	194(4.31),260s(1.88), 290s(1.34)	46-0910-73
$C_5H_8N_4S_2$			
1,2,4-Thiadiazol-3(2H)-imine, 2-(1-iminoethyl)-5-(methylthio)-	H_2O	243(4.36)	138-0917-73
$C_5H_8N_6O_2$			
8-Azapurin-2(3H)-one, 1,6-dihydro-6-(methoxyamino)-	pH 2	210(3.79),241(3.88)	39-1625-73C
C_5H_8O			
Cyclopentanone	hexane	300f(1.26)	46-1830-73
	C_6H_{12}	290(1.15),300(1.19), 311(1.11)	22-2231-73
	heptane	290(1.23),300(1.24), 312(1.15)	22-2231-73
	H_2O	280(--)	22-2231-73
	MeOH	287(1.27)	22-2231-73
	EtOH	288(1.26)	22-2231-73
	MeCN	287(1.20),294(1.23), 304(1.15)	22-2231-73
	CCl_4	289(1.32),290(1.36), 309(1.28)	22-2231-73
	$CHCl_3$	294(1.23)	22-2231-73
	CH_2Cl_2	287(1.26),295(1.27), 305(1.20)	22-2231-73
3-Penten-2-one, cis	hexane	221(3.93)	35-7345-73
3-Penten-2-one, trans	hexane	214(4.07)	35-7345-73
C_5H_8OS			
2-Pentanone, 4-thioxo-	C_6H_{12}	238(3.43),297(3.69), 355(4.06),456(1.60)	78-2449-73
	EtOH	238(3.26),293(3.85), 357(3.86),448s(1.48)	78-2449-73
	isoPrOH	294(3.85),355(4.00), 445s(1.48)	78-2449-73

Compound	Solvent	$\lambda_{max}(\log \epsilon)$	Ref.
2-Pentanone, 4-thioxo- (cont.)	dioxan	291(3.73),358(3.96), 446(1.60)	78-2449-73
	THF	294(3.71),356(3.94), 445(1.60)	78-2449-73
	MeCN	239(3.40),288(3.85), 358(3.88),444s(1.48)	78-2449-73
	CCl_4	296(3.74),359(4.02), 455(1.70)	78-2449-73
	$CHCl_3$	294(3.89),357(3.92), 446s(1.48)	78-2449-73
	DMF	291(3.79),361(3.94), 443s(1.60)	78-2449-73
	DMSO	290(3.77),362(3.97), 440s(1.60)	78-2449-73
anion	EtOH-KOH	352(4.44)	78-2449-73
	DMF-Et_3N	366(4.47)	78-2449-73
C_5H_9BrOS			
Thiophene, 3-bromotetrahydro-2-methoxy-	EtOH	212(2.86)	44-2156-73
C_5H_9NO			
2-Isoxazoline, 3,5-dimethyl-	EtOH	212(3.62)	22-1390-73
2H-Pyrrole, 3,4-dihydro-5-methyl-, 1-oxide	EtOH	227(3.94)	44-2236-73
$C_5H_9NO_2$			
1-Butene, 3-methyl-1-nitro-	EtOH	235(3.83)	19-0351-73
sodium salt	EtOH	250(4.18)	19-0351-73
2-Butene, 2-methyl-3-nitro-	EtOH	253(3.92)	19-0351-73
sodium salt	EtOH	277(4.21)	19-0351-73
2-Pentene, 2-nitro-	EtOH	243(3.79)	19-0351-73
sodium salt	EtOH	254(4.25)	19-0351-73
2-Pentene, 3-nitro-	EtOH	244(3.86)	19-0351-73
sodium salt	EtOH	260(4.15)	19-0351-73
Propanamide, N,N-dimethyl-3-oxo-	CH_2Cl_2	247(3.71)	33-1318-73
Propanedial, (dimethylamino)-	EtOH	262(4.42)	73-1168-73
2-Pyrrolidinone, 5-hydroxy-5-methyl-	H_2SO_4	260(2.79)	24-1423-73
$C_5H_9NO_3$			
Butanoic acid, 2-amino-3-oxo-, methyl ester, hydrochloride	EtOH	238(3.23)	107-0225-73
$C_5H_9N_2$			
1H-1,4-Diazepinium, 2,3-dihydro-, perchlorate	MeOH	331(4.10)	118-0791-73
1H-Imidazolium, 1,3-dimethyl-, dihydrogen phosphate	H_2O	208.5(3.51)	39-2506-73C
$C_5H_9N_2S_2$			
1-Piperazinecarbodithioic acid, ion(1-)	aq base	269s(4.39),283(4.35), 350(1.94)	44-0560-73
$C_5H_9N_3O$			
1,2,4-Triazine, 2,5-dihydro-3-methoxy-5-methyl-	n.s.g.	221(4.07),255(3.89)	22-2493-73
$C_5H_9N_3S$			
1,3,4-Thiadiazol-2-amine, 5-isopropyl-	EtOH	256(3.74)	80-1777-73
	EtOH-HCl	245(3.85)	80-1777-73
1,3,4-Thiadiazol-2-amine, 5-propyl-	EtOH	256(3.80)	80-1777-73

Compound	Solvent	λmax(log ε)	Ref.
1,3,4-Thiadiazol-2-amine, 5-propyl- (cont.)	EtOH-HCl	247(3.89)	80-1777-73
1,2,4-Triazine, 2,5-dihydro-5-methyl-3-(methylthio)-	n.s.g.	221(3.77),265s(3.18), 326s(2.30)	22-2493-73
$C_5H_9N_3S_2$			
1,3,4-Thiadiazol-2-amine, N,N-dimethyl-5-(methylthio)-	EtOH	290(4.03)	104-2631-73
hydrochloride	EtOH	290(4.12)	104-2631-73
hydroiodide	EtOH	293(4.10)	104-2631-73
1,3,4-Thiadiazole-2(3H)-thione, 5-(dimethylamino)-3-methyl-	EtOH	321(4.18)	104-2631-73
$C_5H_9N_4$			
Pyrimidinium, 2,4-diamino-1-methyl-, chloride	pH 9	235(4.02),270(3.83)	94-1451-73
	N NaOH	297(2.45)	94-1451-73
$C_5H_{10}IN_3S_2$			
1,3,4-Thiadiazolium, 2-(methylamino)-3-methyl-5-(methylthio)-, iodide	EtOH	290(3.78)	104-2631-73
$C_5H_{10}NO$			
Isoxazolium, 4,5-dihydro-2,3-dimethyl-, perchlorate	EtOH	225(3.55)	22-1390-73
$C_5H_{10}N_2O$			
2-Propenal, 2-amino-3-(dimethylamino)-	CH_2Cl_2	320(4.27)	33-0944-73
$C_5H_{10}N_2OS$			
4-Morpholinecarbothioamide	EtOH	250(4.17)	48-0144-73
$C_5H_{10}N_2OS_2$			
Carbamothioic acid, (3-amino-3-thioxopropyl)-, O-methyl ester	n.s.g.	246(4.25),263s(4.14)	128-0495-73
$C_5H_{10}N_2O_2S$			
Carbamic acid, N-[2-(thiocarbamoyl)ethyl]-, methyl ester	n.s.g.	215(3.51),276(4.10)	128-0495-73
Ethenamine, N,N-dimethyl-1-(methylthio)-2-nitro-	heptane	348(4.09)	1-1183-73
	EtOH	370(4.28)	1-1183-73
Thiocarbamic acid, N-[2-(carbamoyl)ethyl]-, methyl ester	EtOH	242.5(4.14)	128-0495-73
$C_5H_{10}N_2S$			
1-Pyrrolidinecarbothioamide	EtOH	259(4.29)	48-0144-73
$C_5H_{10}N_3S_2$			
1,3,4-Thiadiazolium, 2-(methylamino)-3-methyl-5-(methylthio)-, iodide	EtOH	290(3.78)	104-2631-73
$C_5H_{10}O$			
Pentanal	hexane	293(1.37)	35-6685-73
	H_2O	283(1.21)	35-6685-73
Pivalaldehyde	hexane	294(1.18)	35-6685-73
	H_2O	284(1.16)	35-6685-73
$C_5H_{10}O_2$			
Propanoic acid, ethyl ester	MeOH	210(1.8)	8-0161-73

Compound	Solvent	$\lambda_{max}(\log \epsilon)$	Ref.
$C_5H_{11}Cl$			
Propane, 1-chloro-2,2-dimethyl-	MeOH	none above 210 nm	8-0169-73
$C_5H_{11}NSe$			
Propaneselenoamide, N,N-dimethyl-	EtOH	300(4.10),380(2.20)	143-0519-73
$C_5H_{12}N_2O_2$			
Hydroxylamine, N-(3-hydroxyimino-1-pentyl)-	EtOH	206(3.38)	104-0793-73
$C_5H_{12}N_2S$			
Thiourea, N,N-diethyl-	EtOH	246(4.16)	48-0144-73
$C_5H_{12}N_4$			
1,2-Ethanediamine, N-(4,5-dihydro-1H-imidazol-2-yl)-, dihydriodide	EtOH	218(4.50)	44-1641-73
$C_5H_{12}O$			
Butanol, 3-methyl-	neat	none above 205 nm	8-0164-73
$C_5H_{13}N_9$			
1,3,5-Triazine-2,4(1H,3H)-dione, 1-amino-6-(dimethylamino)-, dihydrazone	MeOH	252(4.16),294(3.99)	114-0419-73C
$C_5H_{14}N_3O$			
Ethanaminium, 2-hydrazino-N,N,N-trimethyl-2-oxo-, chloride	pH 10.8	217s(3.85)	35-1323-73
$C_5H_{14}SSi$			
Ethanethiol, 2-(trimethylsilyl)-	hexane	199(3.17)	67-0061-73
C_5N_6			
2H-Imidazole-4,5-dicarbonitrile, 2-diazo-	n.s.g.	232(3.97),315(4.35)	35-2695-73

Compound	Solvent	λ_{max}(log ε)	Ref.
C_6BrClF_4O 2,4-Cyclohexadien-1-one, 4-bromo-6-chloro-2,3,5,6-tetrafluoro-	C_6H_{12}	215(3.71),247s(3.56), 355(3.12)	104-1246-73
C_6BrF_5O 2,5-Cyclohexadien-1-one, 4-bromo-2,3,4,5,6-pentafluoro-	C_6H_{12}	233(3.84)	104-1256-73
C_6ClF_5O 2,4-Cyclohexadien-1-one, 6-chloro-2,3,4,5,6-pentafluoro- (95%)	C_6H_{12}	220(3.88),330(3.58)	104-1246-73
$C_6Cl_3F_4P$ Phosphonous dichloride, (4-chloro-2,3,5,6-tetrafluorophenyl)-	heptane	223(3.75),288(3.42)	104-1729-73
$C_6Cl_4O_2$ 1,2-Benzoquinone, tetrachloro-	MeOAc	430(3.3)	23-0089-73
C_6Cl_6 Fulvene, hexachloro-	benzene	295(4.12),303(4.19), 314(4.19),326(4.00), 444(2.62)	1-1735-73
	EtOH	290(4.16),299(4.28), 310(4.26),322(4.03), 435(2.65)	1-1735-73
C_6Cl_8 1,3-Cyclopentadiene, 1,2,3,4,5-pentachloro-5-(trichloromethyl)-	EtOH	204(4.3),237s(3.4), 327(3.4)	35-8658-73
C_6F_6O 2,5-Cyclohexadien-1-one, 2,3,4,4,5,6-hexafluoro-	heptane	219(3.67)	104-0578-73
$C_6F_8N_2$ Pyridazine, 3,4,6-trifluoro-5-(pentafluoroethyl)-	C_6H_{12}	262.5(3.41)	39-1405-73C
$C_6HCl_2F_4P$ Phosphonous dichloride, (2,3,5,6-tetrafluorophenyl)-	heptane	219(2.70),282(3.21)	104-1729-73
C_6HF_6P Phosphonous difluoride, (2,3,5,6-tetrafluorophenyl)-	heptane	209(3.80),286(3.36)	104-1729-73
C_6HF_8P Phosphorane, tetrafluoro(2,3,5,6-tetrafluorophenyl)-	heptane	211(3.76),268(3.31)	104-1729-73
$C_6H_2Cl_4N_2$ 1-Cyclobutene-1-carbonitrile, 2-amino-3,3-dichloro-4-(dichloromethylene)-	n.s.g.	262(3.93),314(3.46)	44-1470-73
$C_6H_2Cl_4O_2$ 1,2-Benzenediol, 3,4,5,6-tetrachloro-	$CHCl_3$	305(3.7)	25-0089-73
$C_6H_2F_3N_3OS$ Acetamide, N-(5-cyano-2-thiazolyl)-2,2,2-trifluoro-	EtOH	287(4.06)	39-2769-73C

Compound	Solvent	$\lambda_{max}(\log \epsilon)$	Ref.
$C_6H_2N_6$			
Propanedinitrile, [(dicyanomethylene)-hydrazino]-	H_2O	280(4.18)	22-3442-73
$C_6H_2N_6O_{10}$			
Aniline, 2,3,4,5,6-pentanitro-	EtOH	212(4.48),300s(3.86), 371(4.21)	114-0035-73B
$C_6H_2O_6$			
Rhodizonic acid, bis(triphenylphosphine)iminium salt	CH_2Cl_2	262(4.04),268(4.11), 275(4.00),487(4.60)	46-2652-73
$C_6H_3BrN_2S$			
Isothiazolo[3,4-b]pyridine, 3-bromo-	EtOH	213(4.29),303(4.00), 330(3.86)	23-1741-73
Isothiazolo[4,3-b]pyridine, 3-bromo-	EtOH	213(4.29),306(4.14), 324(4.00)	23-1741-73
$C_6H_3ClN_2O_5$			
Phenol, 2-chloro-4,6-dinitro-	EtOH	260(3.91),371(3.99)	110-0627-73
diethylamine complex	EtOH	258(3.86),372(4.23)	110-0627-73
Phenol, 4-chloro-2,6-dinitro-	EtOH	266(3.79),356(3.56), 424(2.52)	110-0627-73
diethylamine complex	EtOH	337(4.36),425(3.80)	110-0627-73
$C_6H_3ClN_2S$			
Isothiazolo[3,4-b]pyridine, 3-chloro-	EtOH	216(4.06),303(3.83), 328s(3.67)	23-1741-73
Pyridine, 2-chloro-3-isothiocyanato-	EtOH	221(4.40),276(4.04), 287(4.06)	2-0744-73
$C_6H_3ClN_4$			
Pyrido[2,3-e]-1,2,4-triazine, 3-chloro-	EtOH	273(3.66),327(4.00), 336(3.97)	4-0575-73
$C_6H_3Cl_2NO_2$			
Benzene, 1,4-dichloro-2-nitro-	DMF	305(3.165)	39-1430-73B
$C_6H_3Cl_5N_3P$			
1,3,2-Diazaphosphorine-5-carbonitrile, 2,2,4-trichloro-6-(1,1-dichloroethyl)-2,2-dihydro-	hexane	248(4.19),344(3.89)	112-0621-73
$C_6H_3F_7O$			
2-Hexenal, 4,4,5,5,6,6,6-heptafluoro-, (E)-	hexane	213(3.35)	44-0632-73
$C_6H_3N_5O_8$			
Aniline, 2,3,4,6-tetranitro-	C_6H_{12}	250s(--),299(--), 370(--)	114-0035-73B
	EtOH	208(4.41),298(4.06), 350(4.12),406(3.91)	114-0035-73B
	dioxan	262s(4.05),320(4.06), 394(3.76)	114-0035-73B
	MeCN	266(4.01),324(4.05), 383(4.01)	114-0035-73B
	DMF	286(4.0),324s(4.06), 378(4.15),418(4.18)	114-0035-73B

Compound	Solvent	$\lambda_{max}(\log \epsilon)$	Ref.
$C_6H_3N_7O$			
Pyrido[2,3-e]-1,2,4-triazine, 3-azido-, 1-oxide	EtOH	265(4.29),370(3.75)	4-0575-73
$C_6H_4BrNO_2$			
Benzene, 1-bromo-4-nitro-	DMF	280(4.02)	32-0723-73
$C_6H_4BrN_3OS_2$			
4H-Thiazolo[3,2-a]-1,3,5-triazin-4-one, 7-bromo-2-(methylthio)-	EtOH	271(3.92),316(4.31), 324s(--)	94-0074-73
$C_6H_4BrN_3O_2$			
Imidazo[1,2-a]pyrimidine-5,7-diol,	pH 1	219(4.45),273(4.01)	4-1021-73
6-bromo-	pH 11	227(4.54),270(3.90)	4-1021-73
$C_6H_4BrN_3O_4$			
Aniline, 2-bromo-4,6-dinitro-	95.5% DMSO	355(4.12)	22-1225-73
anion	95.5% DMSO	400(4.27),530(4.13)	22-1225-73
C_6H_4ClNO			
3-Pyridinecarboxaldehyde, 2-chloro-	EtOH	210(3.52),238(2.97), 265(3.09),272(3.01), 290s(2.44)	23-1741-73
$C_6H_4ClNO_2$			
Benzene, 1-chloro-2-nitro-	DMF	294s(3.129)	39-1430-73B
$C_6H_4ClNO_3$			
Phenol, 2-chloro-4-nitro-	EtOH	233(3.91),314(3.95), 400(3.37)	110-0627-73
diethylamine complex	EtOH	269(3.52),303(3.26), 403(4.28)	110-0627-73
$C_6H_4ClN_3$			
1H-Imidazo[4,5-c]pyridine, 4-chloro-	pH 1	268(3.90)	124-0703-73
	pH 13	277(3.81)	124-0703-73
	MeOH	250(3.76),265(3.81)	124-0703-73
1H-Pyrazolo[3,4-b]pyridine, 4-chloro-	EtOH	212(4.29),270(3.64), 296(3.85)	104-1294-73
$C_6H_4ClN_3S$			
Thiazolo[5,4-b]pyridin-2-amine,	MeOH	272(4.16),310(3.92)	44-4383-73
5-chloro-	MeOH-HCl	260(4.07),297(4.08)	44-4383-73
	MeOH-NaOH	272(4.19),310(3.95)	44-4383-73
$C_6H_4Cl_2N_2O_2$			
Aniline, 2,4-dichloro-6-nitro-	70.5% DMSO	420(3.71)	22-1225-73
anion	70.5% DMSO	503(3.93),528(3.94)	22-1225-73
Aniline, 2,6-dichloro-4-nitro-	95.5% DMSO	370(4.19)	22-1225-73
anion	95.5% DMSO	467(4.54)	22-1225-73
1-Cyclobutene-1,2-dicarbonyl dichloride	MeCN	258(3.99)	33-3004-73
$C_6H_4Cl_2O_3S$			
Chlorosulfuric acid, 4-chlorophenyl ester	heptane	213(3.84),228(3.99), 269(2.71),274(2.62), 278(2.60),287(2.49), 289(2.49),293(2.45), 296(2.43)	33-1483-73

Compound	Solvent	$\lambda_{max}(\log \epsilon)$	Ref.
$C_6H_4F_6OS_2$			
1,3-Dithiole, 2-methoxy-4,5-bis(trifluoromethyl)-	isooctane	212(3.56),269(3.59), 287s(3.51)	35-4379-73
$C_6H_4F_6O_2S$			
Carbonothioic acid, O-methyl S-[3,3,3-trifluoro-1-(trifluoromethyl)-1-propenyl] ester, (Z)-	isooctane	215s(3.33),260(2.91)	35-4379-73
$C_6H_4F_7NO$			
2-Hexenamide, 4,4,5,5,6,6,6-heptafluoro-, (E)-	EtOH	209(3.53),229(3.43)	44-0632-73
$C_6H_4N_2$			
Butanedinitrile, bis(methylene)-	MeOH	226(4.23)	33-3004-73
	MeOH	226(4.23)	88-0999-73
1-Cyclobutene-1,2-dicarbonitrile	MeOH	235(4.06),247s(3.91)	33-3004-73
$C_6H_4N_2O_2S$			
5-Thiazolecarbonitrile, 2-acetoxy-	EtOH	265(3.89)	39-2769-73C
$C_6H_4N_2O_5$			
Phenol, 2,4-dinitro-	EtOH	252(3.99),294(3.94), 396(3.29)	110-0627-73
diethylamine complex	EtOH	252(3.90),359(4.20), 396(4.12)	110-0627-73
Phenol, 2,6-dinitro-	EtOH	240(3.92),340(3.60), 434(3.47)	110-0627-73
diethylamine complex	EtOH	224(4.31),434(3.92)	110-0627-73
$C_6H_4N_2O_6$			
1,3-Benzenediol, 4,6-dinitro-	hexane	216(4.14),261(4.13), 285s(4.02),334(3.88)	124-1265-73
	EtOH	276(4.18),340(3.89)	124-1265-73
	dioxan	235s(3.77),283(4.32), 347(3.86)	124-1265-73
$C_6H_4N_2O_7$			
2-Propenal, 3,3'-oxybis[2-nitro-	$CHCl_3$	260(4.16)	104-2245-73
$C_6H_4N_2S$			
Isothiazolo[3,4-b]pyridine	EtOH	213(4.03),296(3.86)	23-1741-73
Isothiazolo[5,4-b]pyridine	EtOH	228(4.19),298(3.46), 307s(3.40)	23-1741-73
$C_6H_4N_2S_2$			
Isothiazolo[3,4-b]pyridine-3-thiol	EtOH	211(3.79),248s(3.38), 306(3.59),314(3.56)	23-1741-73
$C_6H_4N_4$			
Pyrimido[4,5-d]pyrimidine	EtOH	248(4.03),310(3.78)	24-3743-73
	MeCN	248(3.83),311(3.67)	24-3743-73
$C_6H_4N_4O_2$			
Benzene, 1-azido-4-nitro-	C_6H_{12}	218(3.9),300(4.0)	115-0077-73A
2,4(1H,3H)-Pteridinedione (lumazine)	pH 5.8	228(4.03),325(3.86)	24-3149-73
	pH 10.0	215(3.97),236(4.03), 269(3.98),346(3.71)	24-3149-73
2(1H)-Pteridinone, 1-hydroxy-	pH 5.0	227s(3.83),241(3.88), 289s(3.63),311(3.87)	44-0703-73

Compound	Solvent	$\lambda_{max}(\log \epsilon)$	Ref.
2(1H)-Pteridinone, 1-hydroxy- (cont.)	pH 12	258(4.18),275(4.24), 415(3.52)	44-0703-73
$C_6H_4N_4O_2S$			
Formamide, N-[5-(1,2,4-oxadiazol-3-yl)-2-thiazolyl]-	EtOH	291(4.17)	39-2769-73C
$C_6H_4N_4O_3$			
2,4(1H,3H)-Pteridinedione, 1-hydroxy-	pH 3.0	232(4.06),252s(3.88), 332(3.83)	44-0703-73
	pH 7.9	234(3.99),261(4.01), 302(3.84)	44-0703-73
	pH 12.0	238(3.93),271(4.30), 307s(3.39)	44-0703-73
2,4(1H,3H)-Pteridinedione, 8-oxide	pH 2.0	234(4.26),244(4.27), 270(3.73),345(3.84)	24-3149-73
	pH 8.0	245(4.10),266(4.23), 285s(3.95),387(3.86)	24-3149-73
$C_6H_4N_4O_3S$			
1,2,4-Oxadiazole, 5-methyl-3-(2-nitro-5-thiazolyl)-	EtOH	320(3.99)	39-2769-73C
$C_6H_4N_4O_4$			
Imidazo[1,2-a]pyrimidine-5,7-diol, 6-nitro-	pH 1	228(4.15),312(3.85)	4-1021-73
	pH 11	217(4.43),333(3.86)	4-1021-73
$C_6H_4N_4O_6$			
Aniline, 2,4,6-trinitro-	EtOH	238(4.24),316(4.10), 406(3.91)	114-0035-73B
$C_6H_4N_6$			
1H-1,2,3-Triazolo[4,5-b]pyridine-6-carbonitrile, 5-amino-	MeOH	238(4.29),340(3.99)	39-1620-73C
$C_6H_4N_6O_2$			
[5,5'-Bi-1,2,4-triazine]-3,3'(2H,2'H)-dione	n.s.g.	230(4.16),360(3.80)	22-2493-73
$C_6H_4O_4$			
5H-1,4-Dioxepin-2-carboxaldehyde, 5-oxo-	EtOH	229(4.10),308(3.89)	73-2641-73
2H-Pyran-5-carboxylic acid, 2-oxo-	EtOH	243(3.7),288(3.5)	23-3263-73
$C_6H_4S_4$			
1,3-Dithiole, 2-(1,3-dithiol-2-ylidene)-	MeCN	308(4.09),316(4.09), 357s(--),446(2.42)	5-0310-73
semiquinone perchlorate	MeCN	266(2.99),338(3.78), 403s(--),434(4.27), 493s(--),579(3.70)	5-0310-73
$C_6H_5BrN_4O$			
1H-Purine, 6-(bromomethyl)-, 3-oxide	pH 3	227(4.36),303(4.06)	87-0984-73
	pH 9	228(4.45),301(3.98)	87-0984-73
	pH 13	228(4.46),305(3.98)	87-0984-73
3H-Purine, 6-(bromomethyl)-, 1-oxide	pH 3	248(4.31),273s(3.65), 327(3.80)	87-0984-73
	pH 7	237(4.35),327(3.68)	87-0984-73
	pH 13	236(4.37),328(3.89)	87-0984-73

Compound	Solvent	$\lambda_{max}(\log \epsilon)$	Ref.
$C_6H_5BrO_2$			
Ethanone, 1-(5-bromo-2-furanyl)-	heptane	273(--)	103-0546-73
	H_2O	286(--)	103-0546-73
	EtOH	281(--)	103-0546-73
	dioxan	280(4.28)	103-0546-73
$C_6H_5ClN_2O$			
Diazene, 1-chloro-2-phenyl-, 2-oxide	C_6H_{12}	256(5.40)	118-0106-73
$C_6H_5ClO_2$			
Ethanone, 1-(5-chloro-2-furanyl)-	heptane	272(--)	103-0546-73
	H_2O	285(--)	103-0546-73
	EtOH	280(--)	103-0546-73
	dioxan	278(4.27)	103-0546-73
2-Furancarbonyl chloride, 5-methyl-	heptane	280(--)	103-0546-73
	dioxan	288(4.26)	103-0546-73
$C_6H_5Cl_3$			
1,3-Cyclopentadiene, x-(trichlorometh-yl)- (isomer mixture)	hexane	258(3.26)	101-0243-73C
$C_6H_5FN_2O_4$			
Pyridine, 5-fluoro-2-methoxy-4-nitro-, 1-oxide	MeOH	260(3.39),357(3.28)	4-0779-73
$C_6H_5F_2N_3O_2$			
1-Cyclobutene-1-carboxylic acid, 2-azido-3,3-difluoro-, methyl ester	MeOH	273(4.04)	24-3544-73
$C_6H_5F_3$			
Cyclobutene, 1-ethenyl-2,3,3-trifluoro-	EtOH	225(4.45)	35-0146-73
C_6H_5IO			
Benzene, iodosyl-	10% EtOH	223(3.85)	139-0277-73B
$C_6H_5IO_2$			
Ethanone, 1-(5-iodo-2-thienyl)-	heptane	275(--)	103-0546-73
	H_2O	292(--)	103-0546-73
	EtOH	285(--)	103-0546-73
	dioxan	282(4.30)	103-0546-73
$C_6H_5NO_2$			
Benzene, nitro-	C_6H_{12}	251(3.97),287(3.08), 345(2.09)	114-0035-73B
	EtOH	260(3.92),297(3.18), 344(2.24)	114-0035-73B
1-Cyclobutene-1-carboxylic acid, 2-cyano-	MeOH	235(4.04)	33-3004-73
$C_6H_5NO_3$			
Furan, 2-(2-nitroethenyl)-	MeOH	237(3.65),340(4.27)	48-0419-73
Phenol, 2-nitro-	hexane	213(4.21),346(3.59)	124-1265-73
	EtOH	272(3.82),346(3.50)	110-0627-73
diethylamine complex	EtOH	279(3.61),415(3.70)	110-0627-73
diisopropylamine complex	EtOH	278(3.62),417(3.71)	110-0627-73
Phenol, 3-nitro-	EtOH	230(3.96),270(3.75), 334(3.32)	110-0627-73
diethylamine complex	EtOH	229(4.14),257(3.95), 395(3.06)	110-0627-73
Phenol, 4-nitro-	hexane	219(3.99),296(4.00)	124-1265-73

Compound	Solvent	$\lambda_{max}(\log \epsilon)$	Ref.
Phenol, 4-nitro- (cont.)	EtOH	228(3.90),317(4.06)	110-0627-73
diethylamine complex	EtOH	297(3.12),399(4.34)	110-0627-73
ethylenediamine complex (1:1)	H_2O	405(4.52)	59-0365-73
	MeOH	395(4.42)	59-0365-73
	isoPrOH	410(4.41)	59-0365-73
	50% MeOH	405(4.57)	59-0365-73
and other solvent mixtures	50% dioxan	410(4.62)	59-0365-73
pyridine complex	C_6H_5Cl	317.5(4.04)	19-0593-73
	o-$C_6H_4Cl_2$	320(4.05)	19-0593-73
triethylamine complex	C_6H_5Cl	324.5(4.02)	19-0593-73
	o-$C_6H_4Cl_2$	328.5(4.00)	19-0593-73
$C_6H_5NO_4$			
1H-Pyrrole-3,4-dicarboxylic acid	MeOH	240(3.90),259(3.88)	23-1089-73
$C_6H_5N_3$			
Benzene, azido-	C_6H_{12}	246(4.4),275(3.8), 285(3.6)	115-0077-73A
4,7-Diazaindole	EtOH	209(4.18),311(3.90)	103-0792-73
Imidazo[1,5-a]pyrazine	EtOH	260s(3.41),263s(3.43), 269(3.52),280(3.50), 331(3.33)	44-2049-73
1H-Pyrazolo[3,4-c]pyridine	EtOH	235(3.37),298(3.75), 309(3.63)	39-2901-73C
Pyrrolo[1,2-d][1,2,4]triazine	EtOH	223(4.57),232s(4.50), 262(3.80),268(3.82), 278(3.74),322(3.46)	77-0035-73
$C_6H_5N_3O$			
Isoxazolo[4,5-b]pyrazine, 3-methyl-	C_6H_{12}	241(3.34),287(3.98), 293(4.00)	4-0181-73
$C_6H_5N_3OS$			
1,2,4-Oxadiazole, 5-methyl-3-(5-thiazolyl)-	EtOH	257(3.98)	39-2769-73C
$C_6H_5N_3OS_2$			
Thiazolo[4,5-d]pyridazin-7(6H)-one, 2-mercapto-6-methyl-	$CHCl_3$	242(--),299(4.14), 316(4.16)	22-3324-73
4H-Thiazolo[3,2-a]-1,3,5-triazin-4-one, 2-(methylthio)-	EtOH	226(3.97),245(3.86), 268(3.90),308(4.29), 316(4.28)	94-0074-73
$C_6H_5N_3O_2$			
Imidazo[1,2-a]pyrimidine-5,7-diol	pH 1	263(4.03)	4-1021-73
	pH 11	263(4.07)	4-1021-73
$C_6H_5N_3O_2S_2$			
Carbamic acid, 2H-thiazolo[3,2-b]-[1,2,4]thiadiazol-2-ylidene-, methyl ester	EtOH	252(3.48),308(4.35)	94-2408-73
$C_6H_5N_3O_4$			
Aniline, 2,4-dinitro-	EtOH	226(4.02),258(3.98), 337(4.17),380s(3.87)	114-0035-73B
	80.4% DMSO	345(4.18)	22-1225-73
anion	80.4% DMSO	385(4.27),530(4.13)	22-1225-73
Aniline, 2,6-dinitro-	C_6H_{12}	222(4.39),246(4.07), 307(2.95),408(3.95)	114-0035-73B

Compound	Solvent	$\lambda_{max}(\log \epsilon)$	Ref.
Aniline, 2,6-dinitro- (cont.)	EtOH	223(4.36),250(4.02), 316(2.88),422(3.95)	114-0035-73B
Aniline, 3,5-dinitro-	EtOH	228(4.46),257(4.12), 330s(3.18),398(3.34)	114-0035-73B
$C_6H_5N_3S$			
Isothiazolo[3,4-b]pyridin-3-amine	EtOH	228(4.52),245(4.45), 293(3.93),302(3.89), 400(3.98)	23-1741-73
Isothiazolo[4,3-b]pyridin-3-amine	EtOH	226(4.08),245(4.09), 297(3.47),307(3.38), 390(3.54)	23-1741-73
1H-Pyrazolo[3,4-b]pyridine-4-thiol (glycoside)	EtOH	251(3.71),357(3.91)	104-1294-73
$C_6H_5N_5O$			
4(1H)-Pteridinone, 2-amino-	pH 0.0	229s(4.03),242s(3.94), 314(3.89)	24-3175-73
	pH 5.0	233(4.04),270(4.08), 339(3.79)	24-3175-73
	pH 10.0	251(4.33),360(3.85)	24-3175-73
$C_6H_5N_5O_2$			
4(1H)-Pteridinone, 2-amino-, 8-oxide	pH -2.0	252(4.29),273s(3.87), 342(3.71),390s(3.19)	24-3175-73
	pH 4.0	242(4.05),268(4.33), 291(4.01),376(3.87)	24-3175-73
	pH 10.0	259(4.50),285s(3.78), 383(3.95)	24-3175-73
1H-Purine-6-carboxaldehyde, oxime,	pH 3	227(4.31),298(3.93)	87-0984-73
3-oxide	pH 13	230(4.17),342(4.20)	87-0984-73
Pyrazinecarbonitrile, 3-amino-6-[(hydroxyimino)methyl]-, 4-oxide	MeOH	276s(4.33),390(3.72)	35-6413-73
$C_6H_5N_7$			
Pyrido[2,3-e]tetrazolo[5,1-c][1,2,4]-triazine, 4,5-dihydro-	DMSO	326(3.74)	4-0575-73
C_6H_6			
Benzene (partial spectrum)	MeOH	254.3(2.43)	35-4489-73
Benzene	EtOH	207s(3.76),243(2.15), 249(2.34),255(2.35), 260(2.28)	141-0001-73
	dioxan	243(2.15),249(2.33), 255(2.36),261(2.27)	141-0001-73
$C_6H_6BrClN_2O_2$			
Pyrimidine, 5-bromo-4-chloro-2,6-dimethoxy-	MeOH	223(3.97),273(3.84)	44-4386-73
C_6H_6BrNO			
1H-Pyrrole-2-carboxaldehyde, 4-bromo-5-methyl-	$CHCl_3$	253(3.81),307(4.23)	39-2281-73C
C_6H_6ClN			
Aniline, 4-chloro-	EtOH	244(3.38),298(3.89)	27-0099-73
	EtOH-HCl	216(3.99),244(2.98), 274(2.29)	27-0099-73
C_6H_6ClNO			
3-Pyridinemethanol, 2-chloro-	MeOH	265.5(3.62)	18-2187-73

Compound	Solvent	$\lambda_{max}(\log \epsilon)$	Ref.
C_6H_6FNO			
Pyridine, 5-fluoro-2-methoxy-	MeOH	280(3.45)	4-0779-73
2(1H)-Pyridinone, 5-fluoro-1-methyl-	pH 1.0	295(3.74)	4-0779-73
	MeOH	312(3.71)	4-0779-73
$C_6H_6FNO_2$			
Pyridine, 5-fluoro-2-methoxy-, N-oxide	MeOH	257(3.88),312(3.72)	4-0779-73
2(1H)-Pyridinone, 5-fluoro-4-hydroxy-1-methyl-	pH 1.0	285(3.31)	4-0779-73
	pH 3.2	290(3.61)	4-0779-73
	pH 7.2	257(3.86),275s(3.67)	4-0779-73
	pH 14.0	257(3.89),275s(3.72)	4-0779-73
4(1H)-Pyridinone, 5-fluoro-2-methoxy-	pH 1.0	259(3.79)	4-0779-73
	H O	253(4.14)	4-0779-73
	pH 14.0	269(3.59)	4-0779-73
$C_6H_6IO_3P$			
Phosphonic acid, (2-iodophenyl)-	10% EtOH	230s(3.81),266s(2.97), 273(3.00),281(2.93)	139-0277-73B
Phosphonic acid, (4-iodophenyl)-	10% EtOH	238(4.47)	139-0277-73B
$C_6H_6IO_4P$			
1,3,2-Benziodoxaphosphole, 1,3-dihydro-1,3-dihydroxy-, 3-oxide	10% EtOH	220s(3.95),261(2.81), 267(2.81),273(2.72)	139-0277-73B
$C_6H_6N_2$			
7,8-Diazatetracyclo[3.3.0.0^{2,4}.0^{3,6}]-oct-7-ene	C_6H_{12}	357s(2.37),363(2.46), 368(2.46),372(2.49), 381(2.40)	35-7813-73
3-Pyridinecarbonitrile, 1,4-dihydro-	EtOH	330(3.75)	94-1914-73
$C_6H_6N_2O$			
1-Cyclobutene-1-carboxamide, 2-cyano-	MeOH	234(4.13)	33-3004-73
$C_6H_6N_2OS$			
Acetonitrile, (3-methyl-4-oxo-2-thiazolidinylidene)-, (E)-	EtOH	272(4.26)	1-1923-73
(Z)-	EtOH	272(4.27)	1-1923-73
Thiazolo[3,2-c]pyrimidin-5-one, 2,3-dihydro-	MeOH	207(3.82),225(3.86), 322(4.05)	39-2022-73C
$C_6H_6N_2OS_3$			
4-Thiazolidinone, 5-(2-thiazolidinylidene)-2-thioxo-	EtOH	274(4.09),391(4.56)	94-1431-73
$C_6H_6N_2O_2$			
Aniline, N-hydroxy-N-nitroso-, ammonium salt (cupferron)	MeOH	220(4.06),285(4.03)	64-0610-73B
Co chelate	MeOH	216(4.82),275(4.69)	64-0610-73B
Cu chelate	MeOH	212(4.12),245(3.92), 280s(3.84),290s(3.84)	64-0610-73B
Mn chelate	MeOH	215(4.62),276(4.53)	64-0610-73B
Ni chelate	MeOH	210(5.02),245s(4.57)	64-0610-73B
Zn chelate	MeOH	218(4.80),274(4.72)	64-0610-73B
Aniline, 2-nitro-	C_6H_{12}	228(4.28),270(3.62), 378(3.63)	114-0035-73B
	EtOH	230(4.28),278(3.72), 406(3.74)	114-0035-73B
	95.5% DMSO	420(3.74)	22-1225-73
anion	95.5% DMSO	520(3.91)	22-1225-73
Aniline, 3-nitro-	C_6H_{12}	228(4.24),270s(3.61), 346(3.31)	114-0035-73B

Compound	Solvent	λ_{max}(log ε)	Ref.
Aniline, 3-nitro- (cont.)	EtOH	234(4.24),280s(3.62), 374(3.22)	114-0035-73B
Aniline, 4-nitro-	C_6H_{12}	227(3.89),322(4.17)	114-0035-73B
	EtOH	230(3.83),376(4.20)	114-0035-73B
	95.5% DMSO	392(4.28)	22-1225-73
anion	95.5% DMSO	470(4.51)	22-1225-73
Furo[2,3-d]pyrimidin-2(3H)-one, 5,6-di-hydro-	pH 7	206(4.24),280(3.66)	44-0264-73
	pH 13	226(3.91),290(3.82)	44-0264-73
2,4(1H,3H)-Pyrimidinedione, 5-ethenyl-	pH 1	239(4.01),288(3.84)	78-1611-73
	pH 7	238(4.06),286(3.83)	44-0264-73
	pH 11.5	251(4.09),307(3.91)	44-0264-73
	pH 14	252(4.09),309(3.90)	78-1611-73
$C_6H_6N_2O_2S_2$			
2,4-Thiazolidinedione, 5-(2-thiazoli-dinylidene)-	EtOH	250(3.61),335(4.34)	94-1431-73
$C_6H_6N_2O_3$			
4(5H)-Benzofuranone, 6,7-dihydro-, 1-oxide	MeOH	212(3.79),268(3.63)	39-0351-73C
4(5H)-Benzofuranone, 6,7-dihydro-, 3-oxide	MeOH	215(3.95),252(3.30), 284(3.60)	39-0351-73C
2,4(1H,3H)-Pyrimidinedione, 5-acetyl-	pH 1	277(4.05)	78-1611-73
	pH 13	253(3.99),308(4.18)	78-1611-73
$C_6H_6N_2O_4S$			
2H-Pyrrole-3-carboxylic acid, 5-(hy-droxyamino)-4-(methylthio)-2-oxo-	EtOH	340(4.08)	94-1667-73
$C_6H_6N_2S_2$			
Propanedinitrile, [bis(methylthio)-methylene]-	C_6H_{12}	292s(3.95),324(4.12)	1-0258-73
	EtOH	300s(3.95),330(4.14)	1-0258-73
Thieno[2,3-d]thiazol-2-amine, 5-methyl-	MeCN	267(3.34),291(3.90)	48-0539-73
$C_6H_6N_4$			
Imidazo[4,5-b]pyrazine, 1-methyl-	pH 1	241(3.21),284(4.00)	87-0643-73
	pH 13	245s(--),290(3.98)	87-0643-73
	MeOH	255s(--),290(4.14)	87-0643-73
Pyrazinecarbonitrile, 3-amino-6-methyl-	MeOH	249(4.17),358(3.88)	35-6413-73
1H-Pyrazolo[3,4-b]pyridin-4-amine	EtOH	306(4.05)	104-1294-73
$C_6H_6N_4O$			
Imidazo[4,5-b]pyrazine, 1-methyl-, 4-oxide	pH 1	220(4.32),245s(--), 305(4.24)	87-0643-73
	pH 13	236s(--),310(3.77)	87-0643-73
	MeOH	227(4.30),304(4.24)	87-0643-73
Pyrazinecarbonitrile, 3-amino-6-meth-yl-, 4-oxide	EtOH	224(4.08),252(4.29), 285s(3.63),380(3.81)	35-6413-73
1H-Pyrazolo[3,4-d]pyrimidin-4-ol, 6-methyl-	pH 1	252(3.93)	4-0887-73
	pH 11	260(3.93)	4-0887-73
Pyrimido[4,5-d]pyrimidin-4-ol, 3,4-di-hydro-	EtOH	215(3.91),285(3.94)	24-3743-73
$C_6H_6N_4OS$			
Hypoxanthine, 2-(methylthio)-	neutral	262(4.19)	39-2647-73C
	anion	271(4.16)	39-2647-73C
	cation	264.5(4.21)	39-2647-73C
	dianion	275(4.17)	39-2647-73C
2H-Purin-2-one, 1,3-dihydro-6-(methyl-thio)-	neutral	268(3.94),316(4.09)	39-2445-73C
	anion	256(3.92),318(4.10)	39-2445-73C

Compound	Solvent	λ_{max}(log ε)	Ref.
2H-Purin-2-one, 1,3-dihydro-6-(methylthio)- (cont.)	cation	258(3.81),338(4.18)	39-2445-73C
	dianion	240(3.97),319(4.08)	39-2445-73C
2-Thiazolamine, 5-(5-methyl-1,2,4-oxadiazol-3-yl)-	EtOH	298.5(4.20)	39-2769-73C
$C_6H_6N_4OS_2$			
Carbamothioic acid, O-(4-cyano-1,2,5-thiadiazol-3-yl) ester	EtOH	206(3.71),256(4.30)	23-2349-73
Carbamothioic acid, S-(4-cyano-1,2,5-thiadiazol-3-yl) ester	EtOH	209(4.00),274(3.81)	23-2349-73
5H-1,3,4-Thiadiazolo[3,2-a][1,3,5]triazin-5-one, 8-ethyl-6,7,8,8a-tetrahydro-7-thioxo-, meso-ionic didehydro deriv.	H_2O	217(4.02),277(4.45)	44-3868-73
$C_6H_6N_4O_2$			
Oxazolo[4,5-d]pyrimidin-2(3H)-one, 5-amino-7-methyl-	EtOH	302(4.04)	95-0817-73
1H-Purine-8-methanol, 6,9-dihydro-6-oxo-	pH 1	249(4.09)	39-1855-73C
	pH 4.5	251(4.08)	39-1855-73C
	pH 11	261(4.11)	39-1855-73C
Pyrazinecarbonitrile, 3-amino-6-methyl-, 1,4-dioxide	MeOH	238(4.37),256(4.16), 310(3.91)	35-6413-73
$C_6H_6N_4O_2S$			
1H-Purine-2,6-dione, 3,7,8,9-tetrahydro-1-methyl-8-thioxo-	pH 1	243(4.07),295(4.42)	44-3367-73
	pH 6	299(4.30)	44-3367-73
	pH 8.0	253(4.30)	44-3367-73
1H-Purine-2,6-dione, 3,7,8,9-tetrahydro-9-methyl-8-thioxo-	pH 1	259(3.84),356(4.18)	44-3367-73
	pH 8.0	349(4.43)	44-3367-73
2H-Pyrazino[2,3-e]-1,2,4-thiadiazine, 7-methyl-, 1,1-dioxide	EtOH	233(3.60),267(3.66), 317(3.83)	18-1890-73
5H-1,3,4-Thiadiazolo[3,2-a][1,3,5]triazine-5,7(6H)-dione, 8-ethyl-8,8a-dihydro-, meso-ionic didehydro deriv.	H_2O	221(3.96),267(4.46)	44-3868-73
$C_6H_6N_6$			
2,4-Pteridinediamine	pH 3.0	239(4.10),282(3.71), 331(3.92)	24-3175-73
	pH 9.0	225(4.03),254(4.31), 363(3.86)	24-3175-73
$C_6H_6N_6O$			
2,4-Pteridinediamine, 8-oxide	pH 0.0	250(4.55),279(4.10), 351(4.04),365(4.00)	24-3175-73
	pH 6.0	224s(4.09),261(4.63), 290(3.94),390(4.07)	24-3175-73
1H-Purin-2-amine, N-methyl-N-nitroso-	pH 5	242(3.99),286(4.08)	87-0365-73
	pH 13	258(4.05),282(4.01)	87-0365-73
1H-Purin-6-amine, N-methyl-N-nitroso-	pH 1	216(4.03),252(3.76), 295(4.03)	87-0365-73
	pH 7	216(4.06),262(3.83), 300(4.01)	87-0365-73
	pH 13	225(4.11),310(3.88)	87-0365-73
1H-Purin-8-amine, N-methyl-N-nitroso-	pH 1	300(4.19)	87-0365-73
	pH 7	296.5(4.07)	87-0365-73
	pH 13	302(4.17)	87-0365-73
3H-Purine-6-carboxaldehyde, hydrazone, 1-oxide	pH 3	244(4.03),346(4.34)	87-0984-73
	pH 9	252(4.19),341(4.22)	87-0984-73
	pH 14	253(4.21),340(4.21)	87-0984-73

Compound	Solvent	$\lambda_{max}(\log \epsilon)$	Ref.
$C_6H_6N_6O_2$			
2,4-Pteridinediamine, 5,8-dioxide	pH -1.0	217(4.21),258(4.33), 292s(3.92),383(3.88)	24-3175-73
	pH 4.0	213(4.37),266(4.53), 283s(4.07),378(3.97), 390s(3.94)	24-3175-73
7H-Purin-6-amine, N-methyl-N-nitroso-, 3-oxide	pH 1	246(3.81),288(3.95), 323(4.07)	87-0365-73
	pH 7	241(4.06),322(4.02)	87-0365-73
	pH 13	246(4.16),327(4.08)	87-0365-73
6H-Purin-6-one, 1,7-dihydro-2-(methyl-nitrosamino)-	pH 1	254(3.96),288(3.69)	87-0365-73
	pH 7	243(3.97),261(3.89)	87-0365-73
	pH 13	245(4.00),263(3.82), 319(3.40)	87-0365-73
C_6H_6O			
Phenol	EtOH	219(3.77),266s(3.18), 273(3.28),280s(3.16)	141-0001-73
	EtOH-NaOH	239(3.99),290(3.45)	141-0001-73
	dioxan	274(3.32),280(3.24)	126-0039-73L
	dioxan	220(3.74),268s(3.18), 274(3.31),281(3.22)	141-0001-73
$C_6H_6OS_2$			
2H-Pyran-2-thione, 4-mercapto-6-methyl-	MeOH	271(4.11),387(3.39)	7-0269-73
2H-Thiopyran-2-one, 4-mercapto-6-meth-yl-	MeOH	237(4.13),295(3.87), 332(3.92),360(3.92)	7-0269-73
2H-Thiopyran-2-thione, 4-hydroxy-6-methyl-	MeOH	215(3.95),269(4.31)	7-0269-73
$C_6H_6O_2$			
1,2-Benzenediol	EtOH	218(3.80),278(3.46), 284s(3.39)	141-0001-73
	EtOH-NaOH	241(3.82),292(3.62), 406(3.09)	141-0001-73
	dioxan	218(3.79),231s(3.45), 279(3.46),286s(3.32)	141-0001-73
1,3-Benzenediol	MeOH	207(4.10),222(3.80), 278(3.33)	106-0129-73
	EtOH	207(4.08),219s(3.85), 271s(3.30),276(3.38), 283(3.32)	141-0001-73
	EtOH-NaOH	239(3.86),288(3.47)	141-0001-73
	dioxan	221(3.83),269s(3.22), 277(3.36),283(3.30)	141-0001-73
1,4-Benzenediol	EtOH	225(3.79),295(3.50)	141-0001-73
	EtOH-NaOH	225s(3.63),245(3.71), 273(3.70),380s(2.93)	141-0001-73
	dioxan	227(3.77),296(3.54)	141-0001-73
Ethanone, 1-(2-furanyl)-	heptane	262(--)	103-0546-73
	H_2O	273(--)	103-0546-73
	EtOH	269(--)	103-0546-73
	dioxan	265(4.19)	103-0546-73
2-Furancarboxaldehyde, 3-methyl-	n.s.g.	265(4.08)	103-0939-73
2-Furancarboxaldehyde, 5-methyl-	heptane	277(--)	103-0546-73
	H_2O	292(--)	103-0546-73
	EtOH	284(--)	103-0546-73
	dioxan	282(4.23)	103-0546-73
2-Penten-4-ynoic acid, methyl ester, cis	EtOH	243(4.25),249(4.22)	39-0743-73

Compound	Solvent	$\lambda_{max}(\log \epsilon)$	Ref.
$C_6H_6O_2S$			
2H-Pyran-2-one, 4-mercapto-6-methyl-	MeOH	216(4.09),322(3.96)	7-0269-73
2H-Pyran-2-thione, 4-hydroxy-6-methyl-	MeOH	231(4.25),278(3.82), 340(4.04)	7-0269-73
2H-Thiopyran-2-one, 4-hydroxy-6-methyl-	MeOH	228(4.33),313(3.72)	7-0269-73
$C_6H_6O_3$			
1,2,3-Benzenetriol	EtOH	209(4.20),225s(3.85), 268(2.95)	141-0001-73
	EtOH-NaOH	240(3.62),265s(3.58), 354(3.61),430s(3.48)	141-0001-73
	dioxan	225s(3.86),268(2.90)	141-0001-73
1,2,4-Benzenetriol	EtOH	243(4.11),310(3.44)	141-0001-73
	EtOH-NaOH	243(4.10),307(3.43)	141-0001-73
	dioxan	252(4.10),327(3.48)	141-0001-73
1,3,5-Benzenetriol	EtOH	210(4.22),225s(3.79), 256s(2.60),269(2.70), 273(2.64),276s(2.54)	141-0001-73
	EtOH-NaOH	227(4.17),254(4.23), 270s(3.16),354(3.83)	141-0001-73
	dioxan	224s(3.81),268(2.69), 273(2.62),277s(2.49)	141-0001-73
2-Furancarboxaldehyde, 5-(hydroxy-methyl)-	EtOH	227(3.39),282(4.18)	94-1155-73
2-Furancarboxylic acid, 5-methyl-	heptane	264(--)	103-0546-73
	H_2O	256(--)	103-0546-73
	EtOH	250(--)	103-0546-73
	dioxan	256(4.15)	103-0546-73
2(5H)-Furanone, 3-ethenyl-5-hydroxy-	EtOH	245(3.94)	39-1349-73C
Ba salt	EtOH	276(4.53)	39-1349-73C
Na salt	EtOH	273(4.29)	39-1349-73C
C_6H_6S			
Benzenethiol	C_6H_{12}	205(4.26),236(3.94), 280f(2.82)	39-1125-73B
	EtOH	205(4.20),237(3.92), 279(2.92)	39-1125-73B
	EtOH-base	269(4.08)	39-1125-73B
	5% EtOH	202(4.20),236(3.81), 262(3.30)	39-1125-73B
	5% EtOH-base	216(3.99),264(4.03)	39-1125-73B
$C_6H_6S_3$			
2H-Thiopyran-2-thione, 4-mercapto-6-methyl-	MeOH	299(4.27),364(4.08), 425(4.21)	7-0269-73
$C_6H_7BrN_2OS$			
Ethanone, 1-(2-amino-4-methyl-5-thiazolyl)-2-bromo-	pH 1	295(4.01)	80-0677-73
	EtOH	220(3.45),328(3.95)	80-0677-73
$C_6H_7BrN_2O_3$			
2,4(1H,3H)-Pyrimidinedione, 5-bromo-1-(2-hydroxyethyl)-	H_2O	212(3.97),281(3.95)	18-1762-73
$C_6H_7ClNO_4P$			
3-Pyridinemethanol, 2-chloro-, dihydrogen phosphate	EtOH	266(3.50),272(3.45)	18-2187-73

Compound	Solvent	$\lambda_{max}(\log \epsilon)$	Ref.
$C_6H_7ClN_2O_2S$			
Pyridazine, 6-chloro-3-methoxy-4-(methylthio)-, 1-oxide	MeOH	237(3.8),274(4.1), 304(4.0),360(3.57)	4-0835-73
$C_6H_7IN_2O_3$			
2,4(1H,3H)-Pyrimidinedione, 1-(2-hydroxyethyl)-5-iodo-	H_2O	217(4.02),290(3.91)	18-1762-73
C_6H_7N			
Aniline	C_6H_{12}	234(3.95),288(3.27)	114-0035-73B
	EtOH	235(3.90),286(3.18)	114-0035-73B
2,3-Pentadienenitrile, 4-methyl-	EtOH	207(4.00)	22-2301-73
Pyridine, 2-methyl-	H_2O	202(3.51),262(3.57)	103-0888-73
	H_o 1.09	204(3.41),263(3.75)	103-0888-73
	-2.12	204(3.66),262(3.90)	103-0888-73
	-4.78	205(3.53),264(3.80)	103-0888-73
	-7.58	205(3.42),264(3.84)	103-0888-73
	-9.06	204(3.42),263(3.80)	103-0888-73
	-11.98	208(3.11),263(3.65)	103-0888-73
C_6H_7NO			
1-Cyclobutene-1-carbonitrile, 2-methoxy-	MeCN	232(4.00)	44-0475-73
1,3-Pentadiene, 1-isocyanato-	heptane	247(4.4)	44-2982-73
Pyridine, 2-methyl-, 1-oxide	H_2O	252(4.05)	59-0139-73
	H_2O	208(3.98),252(3.63)	103-0888-73
	H_o 1.09	209(4.04),254(3.69)	103-0888-73
	-2.12	219(3.50),265(3.55)	103-0888-73
	-4.78	214(3.50),265(3.55)	103-0888-73
	-7.58	211(3.58),264(3.63)	103-0888-73
	-9.06	206(3.83),263(3.62)	103-0888-73
	-11.98	213(3.67),265(3.86)	103-0888-73
	6M HCl	265(3.69)	59-0139-73
Pyridine, 3-methyl-, 1-oxide	H_2O	255(4.08)	59-0139-73
	6M HCl	266(3.56)	59-0139-73
Pyridine, 4-methyl-, 1-oxide	H_2O	256(4.17)	59-0139-73
	6M HCl	256(3.40)	59-0139-73
3-Pyridinol, 2-methyl-	H_o 1.09	202(4.13),286(3.87)	103-0888-73
	-2.12	199(4.32),287(3.94)	103-0888-73
	-4.78	199(4.36),286(3.98)	103-0888-73
	-7.58	199(4.26),285(3.74)	103-0888-73
	-9.06	199(4.47),285(4.02)	103-0888-73
	-11.98	210(4.53),268(4.83)	103-0888-73
3-Pyridinol, 6-methyl-	H_o 1.09	202(4.35),291(3.94)	103-0888-73
	-2.12	200(4.43),290(3.95)	103-0888-73
	-4.78	200(4.45),289(3.96)	103-0888-73
	-7.58	200(4.45),288(3.88)	103-0888-73
	-9.06	200(4.44),286(3.99)	103-0888-73
	-11.98	211(4.40),269(3.98)	103-0888-73
Pyrrole, 1-acetyl-	hexane	232(4.0)	18-1437-73
$C_6H_7NO_2$			
3-Pyridinol, 2-methoxy-	H_2O	221(3.76),280(3.76)	103-0051-73
	acid	229(3.60),292(3.92)	103-0051-73
3-Pyridinol, 2-methyl-, N-oxide	H_o 1.09	206(4.33),254(3.65)	103-0888-73
	-2.12	203(4.48),290(3.91)	103-0888-73
	-4.78	203(4.45),288(3.95)	103-0888-73
	-7.58	202(4.42),286(3.76)	103-0888-73
	-9.06	202(4.40),287(3.91)	103-0888-73
	-11.98	214(3.91),272(4.12)	103-0888-73
3-Pyridinol, 6-methyl-, N-oxide	H_o 1.09	205(4.31),251(3.65)	103-0888-73

Compound	Solvent	λ_{max}(log ϵ)	Ref.
3-Pyridinol, 6-methyl-, N-oxide (cont.)	H_o -2.12	203(4.42),292(3.77)	103-0888-73
	-4.78	202(4.42),289(3.78)	103-0888-73
	-7.58	201(4.32),288(3.78)	103-0888-73
	-9.06	203(4.46),290(3.81)	103-0888-73
	-11.98	213(4.57),271(4.58)	103-0888-73
2(1H)-Pyridinone, 3-hydroxy-1-methyl-	M HCl	290(4.44)	103-0051-73
	pH 1	235(3.55),298(3.84)	103-0051-73
	pH 13	256(3.82),310(4.00)	103-0051-73
	M NaOH	259(4.30),310(4.35)	103-0051-73
	EtOH	300(3.80)	103-0051-73
	DMSO	320(4.31)	103-0051-73
2(1H)-Pyridinone, 4-hydroxy-5-methyl-	pH 1.0	265(3.59)	87-0524-73
	pH 14.0	256(3.63)	87-0524-73
	MeOH	280(3.57)	87-0524-73
	MeOH	278(3.68)	88-3079-73
2(3H)-Pyridinone, 3-(hydroxymethyl)-	MeOH	230(3.79),299(3.77)	18-2187-73
$C_6H_7NO_2S_2$			
2-Propenoic acid, 2-cyano-3-mercapto-3-(methylthio)-, K salt	EtOH	345(4.37)	54-1169-73
$C_6H_7NO_3S$			
Acetic acid, (4-oxo-2-thiazolidinylidene)-, methyl ester, (E)-	EtOH	283(4.32)	1-1914-73
(Z)-	EtOH	283(4.30)	1-1914-73
$C_6H_7NO_4$			
3-Pyrrolidinecarboxylic acid, 2,4-dioxo-, methyl ester	H_2O	228(4.40),262(4.38)	39-2907-73C
$C_6H_7NS_2$			
6H-[1,2]Dithiolo[5,1-e]isothiazole-7-S^{IV}, 6-methyl-	C_6H_{12}	214(4.20),232(4.31), 261s(3.68),418(3.99)	39-2351-73C
	MeOH	208(4.15),235(4.46), 263s(3.89),415(4.08)	39-2351-73C
C_6H_7NSe			
4H-Cyclopenta[d]isoselenazole, 5,6-dihydro-	EtOH	202(3.48),226(3.59), 272(3.69)	4-0267-73
$C_6H_7N_3$			
5H-Imidazo[1,2-b]pyrazole, 6-methyl- (also gas spectrum)	isooctane	221(--),257s(--)	4-0411-73
	H_2O	219(4.53),246(3.99)	4-0411-73
	MeOH	248(3.94)	4-0411-73
	EtOH	246.5(3.87)	4-0411-73
	ether	247(3.97)	4-0411-73
$C_6H_7N_3O_3$			
1(2H)-Pyrimidineacetic acid, 4-amino-2-oxo-	pH 2	280(4.08)	78-2293-73
	pH 12	274(3.93)	78-2293-73
$C_6H_7N_3O_3S$			
2-Butenamide, 2-cyano-3-(methylthio)-4-nitro-	EtOH	323(4.07)	94-1667-73
2H-Pyrrole-3-carboxamide, 5-(hydroxyamino)-4-(methylthio)-2-oxo-	EtOH	362(4.13)	94-1667-73
1,2,4-Triazine-6-carboxylic acid, 4,5-dihydro-4-methyl-3-(methylthio)-5-oxo-	EtOH	218(3.65),245s(3.74), 283(3.92),312s(3.81)	22-3178-73
1,2,4-Triazine-6-carboxylic acid, 2,5-dihydro-3-(methylthio)-5-oxo-, methyl ester	EtOH	228(3.82),239s(3.58), 319(3.51)	22-3178-73

Compound	Solvent	λ_{max}(log ε)	Ref.
1,2,4-Triazine-6-carboxylic acid, 2,3,4,5-tetrahydro-2,4-dimethyl-5-oxo-3-thioxo-	EtOH	228(3.94),271(4.12), 318(3.60)	22-3178-73
1,2,4-Triazine-6-carboxylic acid, 2,3,4,5-tetrahydro-2-methyl-5-oxo-3-thioxo-, methyl ester	EtOH	216(3.51),237(3.78), 278(4.09)	22-3178-73
1,2,4-Triazine-6-carboxylic acid, 2,3,4,5-tetrahydro-4-methyl-5-oxo-3-thioxo-, methyl ester	EtOH	221(4.06),275(4.08), 377(4.00)	22-3178-73
$C_6H_7N_3O_3S_2$			
Acetic acid, [[4-[(aminocarbonyl)-1,2,5-thiadiazol-3-yl]thio]-, methyl ester	EtOH	208s(3.48),231(4.05), 242s(3.97),315(3.75)	23-2349-73
$C_6H_7N_3O_4$			
1H-1,2,3-Triazole-4,5-dicarboxylic acid, dimethyl ester	anion	247(3.91)	78-3271-73
$C_6H_7N_3O_4S_2$			
1,2,4-Dithiazolidine, 3,5-bis(methoxycarbonylimino)-	EtOH	225(3.92),269(4.22), 302(4.05),320s(3.98)	94-2396-73
$C_6H_7N_3O_5$			
5-Pyrimidinecarboxylic acid, hexahydro-2,4,6-trioxo-, 2-oxime	EtOH	264(4.23)	103-0247-73
$C_6H_7N_3S$			
2-Pyridinecarbothioamide, 3-amino-	EtOH	223(4.30),264(3.89), 311(3.75),372(3.87)	23-1741-73
3-Pyridinecarbothioamide, 2-amino-	EtOH	217(4.25),268(3.83), 299(3.72),345(3.65)	23-1741-73
3-Pyridinecarbothioamide, 4-amino-	EtOH	228(4.19),257(3.87), 294(3.67),335s(--)	23-1741-73
$C_6H_7N_5$			
Adenine, 7-methyl-	0.05M HCl	269(4.16)	94-0034-73
	0.05M NaOH	269(4.16)	94-0034-73
Adenine, 9-methyl-	0.05M HCl	260(4.15)	94-0034-73
	0.05M NaOH	260(4.17)	94-0034-73
1H-Pyrazolo[3,4-b]pyridine, 4-hydrazino-	EtOH	218(4.06),231(4.07), 310(4.03)	104-1294-73
$C_6H_7N_5O$			
Guanine, 7-methyl-	pH 1	250(4.04),270s(--)	103-0377-73
	pH 6	248(--),283(3.87)	103-0377-73
	pH 13	280(3.89)	103-0377-73
9H-Purine-8-methanol, 6-amino-	pH 1	265(4.10)	39-1855-73C
	pH 4.5	262(4.09)	39-1855-73C
	pH 11	270(4.06)	39-1855-73C
$C_6H_7N_5OS$			
Thiazolo[4,5-d]pyridazine-2,7(3H,6H)-dione, 6-methyl-, 2-hydrazone	$CHCl_3$	247(4.40),306s(3.63)	22-3324-73
$C_6H_7N_5O_2$			
3,6-Pyridazinedione, 4-azido-1,2-dihydro-1,2-dimethyl-	EtOH	228(4.12),278(4.17), 334(3.52)	78-0529-73

Compound	Solvent	$\lambda_{max}(\log \epsilon)$	Ref.
$C_6H_7N_7$			
Pyrimido[5,4-e]-1,2,4-triazine-3,5-diamine, 7-methyl-	pH 1.0	218(4.26),233s(4.12), 265(4.08),269(4.08), 295s(3.69),424(3.70)	12-1689-73
	pH 8.5	213(4.30),232s(4.14), 269(4.17),429(3.68)	12-1689-73
$C_6H_7N_7O$			
Pyrimido[5,4-e]-1,2,4-triazine-3,5-diamine, 7-methoxy-	MeOH	220s(4.11),251s(4.19), 261(4.24),320s(3.04), 430(3.67),470s(3.40)	12-1689-73
C_6H_8			
1,3,4-Hexatriene	hexane	214(4.34)	104-1815-73
$C_6H_8BrN_2O_6P$			
2,4(1H,3H)-Pyrimidinedione, 5-bromo-1-[2-(phosphonooxy)ethyl]-	H_2O	212(3.93),281(3.91)	18-1762-73
$C_6H_8BrN_3O$			
Carbonocyanimidic bromide, 4-morpholinyl-	EtOH	230(3.54),282(3.94)	87-0691-73
$C_6H_8Br_2$			
1,3-Butadiene, 2,3-bis(bromomethyl)-	isooctane	225(4.03)	88-2361-73
$C_6H_8Br_4$			
2-Butene, 1,4-dibromo-2,3-bis(bromomethyl)-	pentane	218(4.09),251(4.03)	44-1367-73
$C_6H_8ClN_2O_6P$			
2,4(1H,3H)-Pyrimidinedione, 5-chloro-1-[2-(phosphonooxy)ethyl]-	H_2O	213(4.08),280(3.99)	18-1762-73
$C_6H_8Cl_3N_2P$			
1,3,2-Diazaphosphorine, 2,2,4-trichloro-6-ethyl-2,2-dihydro-5-methyl-	hexane	344(4.00)	112-0621-73
$C_6H_8N_2$			
3-Pyridinecarbonitrile, 1,4,5,6-tetrahydro-	EtOH	265(4.16)	94-1914-73
$C_6H_8N_2O$			
3-Pyridinemethanol, 2-amino-	MeOH	236(3.97),296(3.66)	18-2187-73
2(1H)-Pyrimidinone, 1,5-dimethyl-	H_2O	314(3.67)	73-1381-73
$C_6H_8N_2OS$			
2(1H)-Pyridinethione, 3-amino-6-methoxy-	MeOH	270(3.81),388(4.09)	44-4383-73
4(1H)-Pyrimidinone, 1-methyl-2-(methylthio)-	MeOH	231(4.2),267s(3.5)	24-3039-73
Thiazole, 4-acetyl-2-amino-5-methyl-	EtOH	201(3.52),223(3.86), 310(4.03)	34-0099-73
Thiazole, 5-acetyl-2-amino-4-methyl-	EtOH	225(3.49),325(4.15)	80-0677-73
	pH 1	246(3.32),295(4.05)	80-0677-73
Thiocyanic acid, 1-acetyl-2-amino-1-propenyl ester	EtOH	286.5(4.12)	40-2152-73
$C_6H_8N_2O_2$			
1H-Pyrazole-4-carboxylic acid, 3-methyl-, methyl ester	MeOH	223(3.99)	44-2949-73

Compound	Solvent	$\lambda_{max}(\log \epsilon)$	Ref.
2,4(1H,3H)-Pyrimidinedione, 1,3-di-methyl-	H_2O	276(4.04)	39-0391-73C
2,4(1H,3H)-Pyrimidinedione, 1,5-di-methyl-	H_2O	272(4.00)	39-0391-73C
2,4(1H,3H)-Pyrimidinedione, 1-ethyl-	H_2O	268.0(4.04)	39-0391-73C
$C_6H_8N_2O_2S$			
Pyridinium, 1-[(methylsulfonyl)amino]-, hydroxide, inner salt	EtOH	245(3.92),308(3.30)	44-3311-73
4(1H)-Pyrimidinone, 2,3-dihydro-1-(meth-oxymethyl)-2-thioxo-	MeOH	217(4.2),275(4.2)	24-3039-73
	MeOH-NaOH	238(4.3),275(4.2)	24-3039-73
$C_6H_8N_2O_3$			
2,4(1H,3H)-Pyrimidinedione, 5-(1-hy-droxyethyl)-	pH 1	263(3.88)	78-1611-73
	pH 13	287(3.96)	78-1611-73
$C_6H_8N_2O_3S$			
Sulfonium, dimethyl-, hexahydro-2,4,6-trioxo-5-pyrimidinylide	EtOH	236(4.12)	104-2213-73
$C_6H_8N_2O_4$			
Sydnone, 3-(1-carboxypropyl)-	EtOH	205(3.55),298(3.78)	103-0441-73
Sydnone, 3-(3-carboxypropyl)-	EtOH	203(3.48),295(3.80)	103-0441-73
$C_6H_8N_2O_5$			
Cyclohexanone, 2,6-dinitro-	pH 13	235(3.92),325(3.51) (changing)	18-3462-73
	MeOH	310(2.67)	18-3462-73
	MeOH-NaOH	236(3.89),325(3.52) (changing)	18-3462-73
after heating	MeOH-NaOH	234(3.95),310s(3.55)	18-3462-73
disodium deriv.	MeOH	205(2.98),280s(2.62), 308(2.98)	18-3462-73
$C_6H_8N_2S$			
3(2H)-Cyclopenta[c]pyrazolethione, 1,4,5,6-tetrahydro-	EtOH	235(3.42),286(3.88)	39-1009-73C
$C_6H_8N_4O_2$			
Acetamide, N-(4-amino-1,6-dihydro-6-oxo-5-pyrimidinyl)-	pH 1	260(3.84)	39-1855-73C
	pH 11	257(3.94)	39-1855-73C
Pyrazinecarboxamide, 3-amino-6-methyl-, 4-oxide	EtOH	228(4.05),246(4.24), 378(3.88)	35-6407-73
$C_6H_8N_4O_3$			
Acetamide, N-(4-amino-1,6-dihydro-6-oxo-5-pyrimidinyl)-2-hydroxy-	pH 1	258(3.91)	39-1855-73C
	pH 4.5	258(3.89)	39-1855-73C
	pH 11	255(3.70)	39-1855-73C
$C_6H_8N_4O_4S$			
Carbamic acid, 1,2,4-thiadiazole-3,5-diylbis-, dimethyl ester	EtOH	257(3.60)	94-2396-73
$C_6H_8N_6$			
1,3-Butadiene, 2,3-bis(azidomethyl)-	isooctane	220(4.19),282(1.69)	88-2361-73
1H-Imidazo[4,5-d]-1,2,3-triazin-4-amine, N,N-dimethyl-	n.s.g.	249(4.08),316(3.50)	103-1173-73
7H-1,2,3-Triazolo[4,5-d]pyrimidin-7-imine, 1,6-dihydro-1,6-dimethyl-	pH 2	208(4.25),277(3.88)	39-2659-73C
	pH 8	210(4.07),277(3.98)	39-2659-73C
	pH 9	210(4.16),290(4.05)	39-2659-73C

Compound	Solvent	$\lambda_{max}(\log \epsilon)$	Ref.
$C_6H_8N_6O$			
Urea, N,N-dimethyl-N'-(1H-1,2,3-triazol-5-yl)-	EtOH	220(4.03),250(3.81)	22-3442-73
$C_6H_8N_8$			
1H,6H-Bis[1,2,4]triazolo[4,3-b:4',3'-e]-[1,2,4,5]tetrazine, 1,6-dimethyl-	MeOH	286(3.98)	48-1131-73
$C_6H_8N_{10}$			
1H-1,2,3-Triazole-4-carboxaldehyde, 5-amino-, [(5-amino-1H-1,2,3-triazol-4-yl)methylene]hydrazone	MeOH-4% DMSO	249(3.85),346(4.37)	39-1625-73C
C_6H_8O			
2-Cyclohexen-1-one	MeOH	275(1.4),281(1.5),317(1.5)	8-0162-73
	CH_2Cl_2	223(4.00),329(1.46)	88-3251-73
BF$_3$ complex	CH_2Cl_2	250(3.95)	88-3251-73
3-Hexen-1-yn-5-ol	EtOH	223(4.07)	22-2331-73
2-Penten-4-yn-1-ol, 3-methyl-	EtOH	224(3.96)	22-2331-73
(E)-	EtOH	224(4.12)	104-1868-73
(Z)-	EtOH	223(4.04)	104-1868-73
C_6H_8OS			
Thiophene, tetrahydro-3,4-bis(methylene)-, 1-oxide	EtOH	244(3.79)	88-2365-73
$C_6H_8O_2$			
1,3-Cyclobutanedione, 2,2-dimethyl-	EtOH	241(4.15)	44-1451-73
2-Cyclobuten-1-one, 3-ethoxy-	EtOH	233(4.10)	44-1451-73
2(3H)-Furanone, 3-ethylidene-, cis	C_6H_{12}	215(4.0)	18-2181-73
	MeOH	220(4.0)	18-2181-73
	MeCN	220(4.0)	18-2181-73
$C_6H_8O_2S$			
Thiophene, tetrahydro-3,4-bis(methylene)-, 1,1-dioxide	EtOH	244(3.82)	88-2365-73
$C_6H_8O_3$			
Tetronic acid, 3,5-dimethyl-	EtOH	227(4.07)	78-4251-73
Tetronic acid, 5-ethyl-	EtOH	221(4.13)	78-4251-73
$C_6H_8O_3S$			
1,2-Oxathiin, 4,6-dimethyl-, 2,2-dioxide	EtOH	267.5(3.72)	44-2257-73
$C_6H_8O_3S_2$			
1,3-Dithiole-4-carboxylic acid, 2-methoxy-, methyl ester	EtOH	230s(3.61),304(3.82)	35-4379-73
$C_6H_8O_4$			
Pentanoic acid, 2,4-dioxo-, methyl ester	isooctane	287(3.90)	18-0880-73
	EtOH	288(3.83)	18-0880-73
$C_6H_8O_4S$			
2-Propenoic acid, 3-[(2-carboxyethyl)-thio]-, cis	H_2O	283(4.03)	44-3507-73
trans	H_2O	275(4.20)	44-3507-73

Compound	Solvent	$\lambda_{max}(\log \epsilon)$	Ref.
$C_6H_8O_9S$			
L-Ascorbic acid, 2-(hydrogen sulfate),	pH 2.1	232(4.15)	136-0259-73D
K salt	pH 7.2	255(4.34)	136-0259-73D
C_6H_8S			
Thiophene, tetrahydro-3,4-bis(methyl-ene)-	EtOH	240(3.78)	88-2365-73
$C_6H_9ClN_2O$			
Cyclohexanone, 2-(chloroimino)-, oxime	H_2O	265(3.99)	18-1816-73
hydrochloride	EtOH	224(4.66),265(4.46)	18-1816-73
C_6H_9ClO			
3-Penten-2-one, 4-chloro-3-methyl-	EtOH	244(3.78)	78-4241-73
C_6H_9Cu			
Copper, (3,3-dimethyl-1-butynyl)-	heptane	235s(3.73),316s(3.43)	44-3893-73
$C_6H_8IN_2O_6P$			
2,4(1H,3H)-Pyrimidinedione, 5-iodo-1-[2-(phosphonooxy)ethyl]-	H_2O	217(4.03),290(3.91)	18-1762-73
$C_6H_9NO_2$			
3(2H)-Isoxazolone, 5-ethyl-4-methyl-	EtOH	end absorption	1-2802-73
5(4H)-Isoxazolone, 3-ethyl-4-methyl-	EtOH	264(3.91)	1-2802-73
2H-Pyrrol-2-one, 5-ethoxy-3,4-dihydro-	C_6H_{12}	273(1.74)	35-3957-73
	EtOH	265(1.65)	35-3957-73
$C_6H_9NO_2S$			
2,4-Thiazolidinedione, 5-isopropyl-	EtOH	224(3.52)	132-0113-73
2,4-Thiazolidinedione, 5-propyl-	EtOH	223(3.60)	132-0113-73
	EtOH-NaOH	244(3.63)	132-0113-73
$C_6H_9NO_3$			
Butanamide, N-acetyl-3-oxo-	MeOH	267(3.4)	104-2034-73
	EtOH	268(3.5)	104-2034-73
	EtOH-NaOH	300(4.20)	104-2034-73
	MeCN	265(3.1)	104-2034-73
Carbamic acid, (2-methyl-3-oxo-1-pro-penyl)-, methyl ester	EtOH	268(4.50)	104-0908-73
Fumaranic acid, 2-methyl-, methyl ester	MeOH	221(4.00)	44-1841-73
$C_6H_9NO_3S$			
2H-1,4-Thiazine-6-carboxylic acid, 3,4-dihydro-, methyl ester, 1-oxide	EtOH	273(4.17)	78-3023-73
$C_6H_9NO_5$			
L-Ascorbic acid, 2-amino-2-deoxy-	H_2O	246.5(4.19)	98-0676-73
$C_6H_9NO_6$			
Butanedioic acid, nitro-, dimethyl ester	MeOH	275(2.46)	18-0337-73
$C_6H_9N_2O_4P$			
3-Pyridinemethanol, 2-amino-, dihydro-gen phosphate	H_2O	233(3.91),303(3.83)	18-2187-73
$C_6H_9N_3$			
4-Pyrimidinamine, 2,6-dimethyl-	MeOH	235(4.11)	18-2804-73
3,6,9-Triazatetracyclo[6.1.0.0^{2,4}.0^{5,7}]-nonane	EtOH	220(2.60)(end abs.)	89-0989-73

Compound	Solvent	$\lambda_{max}(\log \epsilon)$	Ref.
1,2,4-Triazine-4-^{15}N, 3,5,6-trimethyl-	MeOH	263(3.64),362(2.60)	5-1963-73
$C_6H_9N_3O$			
1,2,4-Triazine, 3-methoxy-5,6-dimethyl-	n.s.g.	216(3.60),257(3.40), 289(3.44),360(2.78)	22-2493-73
$C_6H_9N_3OS_2$			
1,3,4-Thiadiazole-2(3H)-thione, 5-(4-morpholinyl)-	EtOH	322(4.17)	104-2631-73
$C_6H_9N_3O_2$			
5(3)-Pyrazolecarboxamide, 3(5)-ethyl-4-hydroxy-	pH 1	267(3.74)	4-0843-73
	pH 11	235(3.87),310(3.88)	4-0843-73
	pH 12	233(3.83),311(3.87)	4-0843-73
$C_6H_9N_3S$			
2(1H)-Pyrazinethione, 3-amino-5,6-dimethyl-	EtOH	228(3.66),275(3.45), 392(3.65)	18-1890-73
1,2,4-Triazine, 5,6-dimethyl-3-(methylthio)-	n.s.g.	225(3.73),257(4.03), 325(3.11)	22-2493-73
$C_6H_9N_5O_3$			
Carbamic acid, [(5-amino-1H-1,2,4-triazol-1-yl)carbonyl]-, ethyl ester	EtOH	250(3.42)	39-1209-73C
Carbamic acid, [(1H-1,2,4-triazol-3-ylamino)carbonyl]-, ethyl ester	EtOH	219(4.08)	39-1209-73C
$C_6H_9N_9O_3$			
L-chiro-Inositol, 1,2,4-triazido-1,2,4-trideoxy-	EtOH	281(1.90)	89-0989-73
$C_6H_9S_2$			
1,2-Dithiol-1-ium, 3-ethyl-4-methyl-, perchlorate	HOAc	255(3.66),304(3.83)	39-2351-73C
$C_6H_9S_3$			
Cyclopropenylium, tris(methylthio)-, perchlorate	MeCN	273(4.39)	88-3409-73
$C_6H_{10}BrNO$			
3-Penten-2-one, 3-bromo-4-(methylamino)-	hexane	325(4.13)	40-2152-73
$C_6H_{10}ClNO$			
3-Penten-2-one, 3-chloro-4-(methylamino)-	hexane	325(4.12)	40-2152-73
$C_6H_{10}HgN_2O_2$			
Mercury, (1-diazo-2-methoxy-2-oxoethyl)-(1-methylethyl)-	MeOH	274(3.94),376(1.72)	44-3937-73
$C_6H_{10}NS_2$			
1-Piperidinecarbodithioic acid, ion(1-)	aq base	261(4.20),280(4.20), 346(1.83)	44-0560-73
$C_6H_{10}N_2$			
1H-Pyrazole, 3,4,5-trimethyl-	EtOH	223(3.67)	78-4159-73
$C_6H_{10}N_2O$			
5-Pyrazolinone, 1,3,4-trimethyl-	H_2O	246.5(3.97)	20-0215-73
	MeOH	250(3.96)	20-0215-73

Compound	Solvent	$\lambda_{max}(\log \epsilon)$	Ref.
5-Pyrazolinone, 1,3,4-trimethyl- (cont.)	EtOH	251(3.95)	20-0215-73
	isoPrOH	252.5(3.94)	20-0215-73
	tert-BuOH	254(3.92)	20-0215-73
	acetone	257(3.66)	20-0215-73
	dioxan	257(3.54)	20-0215-73
	THF	257.5(3.39)	20-0215-73
	MeCN	256.5(3.74)	20-0215-73
	DMSO	260.5(3.64)	20-0215-73
	CF_3CH_2OH	244.5(4.00)	20-0215-73
3-Pyrazolol, 1-isopropyl-	MeOH	227(3.78),255(2.79)	48-0382-73
	50% MeOH	228(3.68),253(3.24)	48-0382-73
	10% MeOH	230(3.59),250(3.44)	48-0382-73
$C_6H_{10}N_2OS$			
5-Thiazolemethanol, 2-amino-α,4-dimethyl-	pH 1	270(3.74)	80-0677-73
	EtOH	273(3.82)	80-0677-73
4-Thiazolidinone, 2-imino-5-isopropyl-	EtOH	221(4.28),250(3.92)	132-0113-73
4-Thiazolidinone, 2-imino-5-propyl-	EtOH	220(4.18),240(3.85)	132-0113-73
	EtOH-NaOH	236(4.36)	132-0113-73
$C_6H_{10}N_2O_3$			
Butanamide, 2-(hydroxyimino)-N,N-dimethyl-3-oxo-	EtOH	229(3.91)	107-0225-73
Cyclohexane, 1-nitro-1-nitroso-	$CHCl_3$	649(1.28)	78-3579-73
2-Propenal, 3-[(1-methylethyl)amino]-2-nitro-	$CHCl_3$	286(4.10),321(4.21)	104-0477-73
$C_6H_{10}N_3O$			
Pyrimidinium, 2-amino-4-methoxy-1-methyl-, chloride	H_2O	272(3.59)	94-1451-73
	N NaOH	307(3.26)	94-1451-73
Pyrimidinium, 4-amino-2-methoxy-1-methyl-, chloride	H_2O	233(3.85),267(3.88)	94-1451-73
$C_6H_{10}N_3S$			
Pyrimidinium, 2-amino-1-methyl-4-(methylthio)-, iodide	H_2O	221(4.39),278s(3.98), 301(4.09),310s(4.01)	94-1451-73
	N NaOH	277(3.97),333(3.46)	94-1451-73
Pyrimidinium, 4-amino-1-methyl-2-(methylthio)-, chloride	H_2O	242(4.45)	94-1451-73
$C_6H_{10}N_4O_2S$			
Carbamic acid, (3-amino-1,2,4-thiadiazol-5-yl)-, propyl ester	EtOH	272(3.49)	94-2396-73
Pyrazinesulfonamide, 3-amino-5,6-dimethyl-	EtOH	246(4.11),340(3.86)	18-1890-73
$C_6H_{10}N_4S$			
2-Imidazolidinethione, 1-(4,5-dihydro-1H-imidazol-2-yl)-, monohydriodide	EtOH	223(4.43),265(4.10)	44-1641-73
$C_6H_{10}N_6O_2$			
Methanimidamide, N-methoxy-N'-[5-(methoxyimino)methyl]-1H-1,2,3-triazol-4-yl]-	MeOH	223(4.19),262(4.11), 290s(3.91)	39-1625-73C
$C_6H_{10}O$			
Cyclobutanone, 2,3-dimethyl-, cis	gas	280(1.3)	35-0682-73
trans	gas	290(1.3)	35-0682-73
Cyclobutanone, 2,4-dimethyl-, cis	gas	295(1.5)	35-0682-73
trans	gas	295(1.3)	35-0682-73

Compound	Solvent	$\lambda_{max}(\log \epsilon)$	Ref.
Cyclohexanone	C_6H_{12}	291(1.15)	22-2231-73
	hexane	290(1.18)	46-1830-73
	heptane	291(1.15)	22-2231-73
	H_2O	277(--)	22-2231-73
	MeOH	282(1.20)	22-2231-73
	EtOH	283(1.22)	22-2231-73
	CCl_4	293(1.30)	22-2231-73
	$CHCl_3$	287(1.28)	22-2231-73
	CH_2Cl_2	287(1.23)	22-2231-73
	MeCN	287(1.20)	22-2231-73
Cyclopentanone, 2-methyl-	C_6H_{12}	288(1.18),299(1.20), 310(1.11)	22-2231-73
	hexane	300f(1.20)	46-1830-73
	heptane	289(1.26),299(1.28), 310(1.18)	22-2231-73
	H_2O	283(--)	22-2231-73
	MeOH	288(1.32)	22-2231-73
	EtOH	290(1.32)	22-2231-73
	CCl_4	298(1.38),307(1.30)	22-2231-73
	$CHCl_3$	294(1.38)	22-2231-73
	CH_2Cl_2	294(1.32)	22-2231-73
	MeCN	293(1.30)	22-2231-73
Cyclopentanone, 3-methyl-	hexane	301(1.23)	46-1830-73
2-Cyclopenten-1-ol, 1-methyl-	n.s.g.	244(3.67)	70-0034-73
2-Cyclopenten-1-ol, 2-methyl-	n.s.g.	243.5(3.48)	70-0034-73
2-Cyclopenten-1-ol, 3-methyl-	n.s.g.	238.5(3.80)	70-0034-73
4-Hexen-2-one, cis	hexane	221(4.01)	35-7345-73
trans	hexane	215(4.09)	35-7345-73
2,4-Pentadien-1-ol, 3-methyl-, cis	EtOH	230.5(4.27)	39-0584-73C
trans	EtOH	229.5(4.39)	39-0584-73C
$C_6H_{10}OS$			
3-Penten-2-one, 4-(methylthio)-	C_6H_{12}	287(4.22)	78-2449-73
	EtOH	298(4.20)	78-2449-73
2H-Thiopyran-3(4H)-one, dihydro-6-methyl-, (S)-	isooctane	248(2.54),296(2.13), 305(2.25),316(2.25), 327(2.00)	35-3678-73
	MeOH	306(2.35)	35-3678-73
$C_6H_{10}O_2$			
1,4-Butanediol, 2,3-bis(methylene)-	EtOH	223(4.15)	88-2361-73
2H-Pyran-2-one, tetrahydro-6-methyl-, (R)-	MeOH	211(2.32)	39-1487-73C
2H-Pyran-3(4H)-one, dihydro-6-methyl-, (S)-	isooctane	298(1.21),307(1.21), 318(1.12)	35-3678-73
	MeOH	296(1.16)	35-3678-73
	EPA	306(1.11)	35-3678-73
$C_6H_{10}O_2S$			
2H-Thiopyran-3(4H)-one, dihydro-6-methyl-, 1-oxide, (6S)-	MeOH	240(2.80),302(2.56)	35-3678-73
$C_6H_{10}O_3S$			
Cyclopentanone, 2-(methylsulfonyl)-	EtOH	210(2.34),271(2.13)	44-0741-73
2H-Thiopyran-3(4H)-one, dihydro-6-methyl-, 1,1-dioxide, (6S)-	MeOH	296(1.48)	35-3678-73
$C_6H_{10}S$			
2H-Thiopyran, 3,6-dihydro-4-methyl-	pentane	228(3.78),248(3.43)	35-6120-73

Compound	Solvent	$\lambda_{max}(\log \epsilon)$	Ref.
$C_6H_{11}Cl_2O_2P$			
Phosphonic dichloride, 2-(butoxyethen-yl)-	nonane	216.5(4.10)	65-2164-73
$C_6H_{11}N$			
Propanamine, N-allylidene-	EtOH	213(3.83)	78-4111-73
$C_6H_{11}NO$			
Isoxazole, 4,5-dihydro-3,5,5-trimethyl-	EtOH	212(3.60)	22-1390-73
2H-1,4-Oxazine, 3,4-dihydro-4,6-dimeth-yl-	heptane	199(3.12)	135-1154-73
	MeOH	200(3.1)	135-1154-73
	isoPrOH	211(2.79)	135-1154-73
	ether	203(3.22)	135-1154-73
	$C_2H_4Cl_2$	241(2.28)	135-1154-73
$C_6H_{11}NO_2$			
1-Butene, 2,3-dimethyl-1-nitro-	EtOH	251(3.85)	19-0351-73
sodium salt	EtOH	273(4.15)	19-0351-73
3-Buten-2-one, 4-methoxy-4-(methyl-amino)-	MeOH	286(4.31)	138-0111-73
3-Hexene, 3-nitro-	EtOH	247(3.93)	19-0351-73
sodium salt	EtOH	252(4.20)	19-0351-73
2-Pentene, 4-methyl-2-nitro-	EtOH	250(3.86)	19-0351-73
sodium salt	EtOH	243(4.24)	19-0351-73
2-Pyrrolidinone, 5-hydroxy-1,5-dimethyl-	H_2SO_4	255(2.30)	24-1423-73
$C_6H_{11}N_2S_2$			
1-Piperazinecarbodithioic acid, 4-meth-yl-, ion(1-)	aq base	261(4.24),285(4.23), 347(2.00)	44-0560-73
$C_6H_{11}N_3O$			
1,2,4-Triazine, 2,5-dihydro-3-methoxy-5,5-dimethyl-	n.s.g.	219(4.10),252(3.94), 324(3.35)	22-2493-73
$C_6H_{11}N_3O_2$			
Imidazolidine, 1,3-dimethyl-2-(nitro-methylene)-	heptane	332(4.19)	1-1183-73
	EtOH	333.5(4.22)	1-1183-73
1,2,4-Triazolidine-3,5-dione, 4-butyl-	CCl_4	296(3.24),544(2.38)	35-0721-73
$C_6H_{11}N_3S$			
1,3,4-Thiadiazol-2-amine, 5-butyl-	EtOH	256(3.85)	80-1777-73
	EtOH-HCl	247(3.91)	80-1777-73
1,3,4-Thiadiazol-2-amine, 5-tert-butyl-	EtOH	257(3.72)	80-1777-73
	EtOH-HCl	247(3.81)	80-1777-73
1,3,4-Thiadiazol-2-amine, 5-isobutyl-	EtOH	257(3.79)	80-1777-73
	EtOH-HCl	247(3.88)	80-1777-73
1,2,4-Triazine, 2,5-dihydro-5,5-dimeth-yl-3-(methylthio)-	n.s.g.	217(3.70),269s(3.23), 327s(2.18)	22-2493-73
1,2,4-Triazine, 2,5-dihydro-5,6-dimeth-yl-3-(methylthio)-	n.s.g.	216(3.80),267s(3.30)	22-2493-73
$C_6H_{11}N_5O$			
Acetamide, N-[(4-amino-1-methyl-1H-1,2,3-triazol-5-yl)methyl]-	pH 0.5	264(3.54)	39-1634-73C
	pH 7.0	248(3.63)	39-1634-73C
$C_6H_{11}N_7O$			
Urea, [5-(dimethylhydrazono)methyl]-1H-1,2,4-triazol-4-yl]-	pH 0.5	207(4.03),236(3.73), 283(3.90)	39-1625-73C
	pH 5	230(3.92),292(4.05)	39-1625-73C
	pH 10	226(3.78),289(4.02)	39-1625-73C

Compound	Solvent	λ_{max}(log ε)	Ref.
$C_6H_{11}N_7S$			
Thiourea, [5-(dimethylhydrazono)methyl]-1H-1,2,3-triazol-4-yl]-	anion	260(4.38),300s(4.17)	39-1625-73C
$C_6H_{12}Cl_2N_3$			
Methylium, chloro[[chloro(dimethyl-amino)methylene]amino](dimethyl-amino)-, chloride	CH_2Cl_2	282(4.51)	89-0074-73
$C_6H_{12}IN_3S_2$			
1,3,4-Thiadiazolium, 2-(dimethylamino)-3-methyl-5-(methylthio)-, iodide	EtOH	288(4.16)	104-2631-73
1,3,4-Thiadiazolium, 5-(dimethylamino)-3-methyl-2-(methylthio)-, iodide	EtOH	320(4.16)	104-2631-73
$C_6H_{12}NO$			
Isoxazolium, 4,5-dihydro-2,3,5-trimeth-yl-, perchlorate	EtOH	225(3.55)	22-1390-73
$C_6H_{12}N_2$			
1,4-Butanediamine, 2,3-bis(methylene)-	EtOH	224(4.11)	88-2361-73
2-Propanone, (1-methylethylidene)hydra-zone	C_6H_{12}	227(3.8),295(2.1)	65-2005-73
	EtOH	210(3.8),227s(3.7)	65-2005-73
1H-Pyrazole, 4,5-dihydro-3,5,5-trimeth-yl-	heptane	205(3.43),231(3.73)	135-1154-73
	MeOH	194(3.28),238(3.57)	135-1154-73
	isoPrOH	190(3.78),233(3.85)	135-1154-73
	ether	214(3.62)	135-1154-73
	$C_2H_4Cl_2$	205(3.44),237(3.43)	135-1154-73
$C_6H_{12}N_2O$			
3-Buten-2-one, 4-amino-4-(dimethyl-amino)-	CH_2Cl_2	291(4.41)	33-0944-73
1,2-Diazete, 3,4-dihydro-3,3,4,4-tetra-methyl-, 1-oxide	MeOH	219(3.91)	35-1677-73
2-Propenal, 3-(dimethylamino)-2-(meth-ylamino)-	CH_2Cl_2	311(4.24)	33-0944-73
2-Propenal, 3-(dimethylamino)-3-(meth-ylamino)-	CH_2Cl_2	239(3.73),304(4.29)	33-0944-73
$C_6H_{12}N_2OS_2$			
Carbamothioic acid, [3-(methylamino)-3-thioxopropyl]-, O-methyl ester	n.s.g.	250(4.31),269s(4.12)	128-0495-73
$C_6H_{12}N_2O_2$			
Ethanediamide, tetramethyl-	C_6H_{12}	207.5(--)	82-0469-73C
	H_2O	197.5(4.13)	82-0469-73C
2-Propenoic acid, 3-amino-3-(dimethyl-amino)-, methyl ester	CH_2Cl_2	274(4.46)	33-0944-73
$C_6H_{12}N_2O_2S$			
Carbamic acid, [(dimethylamino)thioxo-methyl]-, ethyl ester	EtOH	271(4.22),330(2.67)	48-0144-73
Carbamic acid, N-methyl-N-[2-(thiocarb-amoyl)ethyl]-, methyl ester	n.s.g.	207(3.77),269(3.96)	128-0495-73
Thiocarbamic acid, N-methyl-N-[2-carb-amoyl)ethyl]-, methyl ester	n.s.g.	247(4.25)	128-0495-73
$C_6H_{12}N_2S$			
1-Piperidinecarbothioamide	EtOH	248(4.27)	48-0144-73

Compound	Solvent	$\lambda_{max}(\log \epsilon)$	Ref.
$C_6H_{12}N_3S_2$			
1,3,4-Thiadiazolium, 2-(dimethylamino)-3-methyl-5-(methylthio)-, perchlorate	EtOH	284(3.95)	104-2631-73
$C_6H_{12}N_6O_3$			
1-Piperazineethanimidamide, N-hydroxy-3,5-bis(hydroxyimino)-	EtOH	234(4.19)	39-0606-73C
$C_6H_{12}O$			
Butane, 1-(ethenyloxy)-	C_6H_{12}	194(3.99)	65-2164-73
$C_6H_{12}O_2$			
Acetic acid, butyl ester	MeOH	209(1.6)	8-0163-73
$C_6H_{12}O_5$			
D-Galactose, 2-deoxy-	H_2O	186.8(2.10)	136-0165-73D
D-Galactose, 6-deoxy-	H_2O	188.0(2.11)	136-0165-73D
$C_6H_{12}O_5$			
D-Galactose	H_2O	188(2.12),228(0.60), 278(0.23)	136-0165-73D
	EtOH	197(0.79),282(-0.03)	136-0165-73D
D-Fructose	H_2O	189(2.13),278(0.05)	136-0165-73D
	EtOH	198(1.36),284(-0.12)	136-0165-73D
D-Glucose	H_2O	186(2.09),228(0.53), 280(0.02)	136-0165-73D
	EtOH	197(0.66),282(-0.05)	136-0165-73D
Inositol	H_2O	185.5(2.04)	136-0165-73D
D-Mannose	H_2O	188(2.12),225(0.38), 278(0.18)	136-0165-73D
$C_6H_{12}S$			
Butane, 2-(ethenylthio)-	heptane	230(3.84),237s(3.79), 250s(3.61)	143-0019-73
$C_6H_{13}NO_4Si$			
Acetic acid, [(trimethylsilyl)-aci-nitro]-, methyl ester	CH_2Cl_2	265(4.04)	65-1699-73
$C_6H_{13}N_3O_2$			
1,1-Ethenediamine, N,N,N',N'-tetramethyl-2-nitro-	heptane	333.5(4.21)	1-1183-73
	EtOH	345(4.33)	1-1183-73
$C_6H_{13}OP$			
Phosphine, acetyldiethyl-	C_6H_{12}	247(3.13),332(2.58)	18-1803-73
	CH_2Cl_2	333(3.78)	18-1803-73
	MeCN	205(3.49),245(3.44), 328(2.71)	18-1803-73
$C_6H_{13}OPS$			
Phosphine sulfide, acetyldiethyl-	C_6H_{12}	264(2.74),357(2.49)	18-1803-73
	CH_2Cl_2	256(2.65),352(2.46)	18-1803-73
	MeCN	207(4.20),234(3.79), 257(2.68),350(2.52)	18-1803-73
$C_6H_{13}O_3P$			
Phosphonic acid, ethenyl-, diethyl ester	nonane	less than 190(c.3.5)	65-2164-73

Compound	Solvent	$\lambda_{max}(\log \epsilon)$	Ref.
$C_6H_{14}N_2O_2$			
2-Pentanone, 4-(hydroxyamino)-4-methyl-, oxime	EtOH	207(3.34)	70-2318-73
oxalate	EtOH	204(3.62)	70-2318-73
$C_6H_{14}OS$			
Propane, 2,2'-sulfinylbis-	heptane	262(2.18)	143-0217-73
$C_6H_{14}OS_3$			
Disulfide, [(1,1-dimethylethyl)sulfinyl]methyl methyl	EtOH	246(2.65)	35-5048-73
$C_6H_{14}O_3$			
Bis(2-methoxyethyl) ether	MeOH	210(1.4),225(0.2)	8-0165-73
$C_6H_{14}O_6$			
D-Glucitol	H_2O	187.0(2.11)	136-0165-73D
$C_6H_{14}S$			
Propane, 1,1'-thiobis-	hexane	199(3.17),210s(--)	67-0061-73
$C_6H_{16}SSi$			
Methanethiol, (diethylmethylsilyl)-	hexane	198.5(3.08)	67-0061-73

Compound	Solvent	λ_{max}(log ε)	Ref.
$C_7Cl_2F_7P$			
Phosphonous dichloride, [2,3,5,6-tetra-fluoro-4-(trifluoromethyl)phenyl]-	heptane	224(3.96),294(3.46)	104-1729-73
C_7F_9N			
Pyridine, 2,3,5,6-tetrafluoro-4-(penta-fluoroethyl)-	C_6H_{12}	280.5(3.59)	39-1405-73C
C_7F_9P			
Phosphonous difluoride, [2,3,5,6-tetra-fluoro-4-(trifluoromethyl)phenyl]-	heptane	228(3.63),288(3.34)	104-1729-73
$C_7F_{11}P$			
Phosphorane, tetrafluoro[2,3,5,6-tetra-fluoro-4-(trifluoromethyl)phenyl]-	heptane	220(3.72),288(3.48)	104-1729-73
$C_7H_2F_{12}N_2$			
1,2-Propadiene-1,1-diamine, N,N,N',N'-tetrakis(trifluoromethyl)-	n.s.g.	209(2.77),221s(2.65)	39-1066-73C
1,2-Propadiene-1,3-diamine, N,N,N',N'-tetrakis(trifluoromethyl)-	n.s.g.	211(2.75),229s(2.54)	39-1066-73C
$C_7H_3ClN_2O_4$			
4H,5H-Pyrano[3,4-e]-1,3-oxazine-4,5-di-one, 2-amino-7-chloro-	MeCN	291(4.07),334(4.23)	39-2432-73C
$C_7H_3Cl_2F_4OP$			
Phosphonous dichloride, (2,3,5,6-tetra-fluoro-4-methoxyphenyl)-	heptane	226(3.89),253(3.92)	104-1729-73
$C_7H_3F_6OP$			
Phosphonous difluoride, (2,3,5,6-tetra-fluoro-4-methoxyphenyl)-	heptane	217(3.71),278(3.77)	104-1729-73
$C_7H_3F_8OP$			
Phosphorane, tetrafluoro(2,3,5,6-tetra-fluoro-4-methoxyphenyl)-	heptane	209(3.78),257(3.78)	104-1729-73
$C_7H_3N_3O_5$			
1,2-Benzisoxazole, 5,7-dinitro-	pH 3	255(4.15),305(3.61)	44-2294-73
Benzonitrile, 2-hydroxy-3,5-dinitro-	30% H_2SO_4	226(4.30),255(4.16), 328(3.76)	44-2294-73
	pH 10	326(4.03),359(4.18)	44-2294-73
$C_7H_3N_5O_2S$			
Benzothiazole, 2-azido-4-nitro-	n.s.g.	224(4.18),266(4.22)	124-0215-73
Benzothiazole, 2-azido-5-nitro-	n.s.g.	232(4.16),269(4.52)	124-0215-73
Benzothiazole, 2-azido-6-nitro-	n.s.g.	313(4.23)	124-0215-73
Benzothiazole, 2-azido-7-nitro-	n.s.g.	270(4.31)	124-0215-73
$C_7H_4BrIO_3$			
2-Propenoic acid, 3-(4-bromo-5-iodo-2-furanyl)-	MeOH	339(4.37)	103-0802-73
$C_7H_4BrN_5$			
3,5-Pyridinedicarbonitrile, 2,4-diamino-6-bromo-	EtOH	212(3.91),241(4.55), 249(4.48),315(3.74)	12-2567-73
$C_7H_4Br_2O_3$			
2-Propenoic acid, 3-(4,5-dibromo-2-fur-anyl)-	MeOH	298(4.29)	103-0802-73

Compound	Solvent	λ_{max}(log ε)	Ref.
C_7H_4ClNO			
1,2-Benzisoxazole, 5-chloro-	H_2O	236(3.95),293(3.50)	44-2294-73
1,2-Benzisoxazole, 6-chloro-	H_2O	244(4.00),284(3.47)	44-2294-73
Benzonitrile, 4-chloro-2-hydroxy-	pH 2	240(4.13),299(3.68)	44-2294-73
	pH 10	246(3.94),327(3.83)	44-2294-73
Benzonitrile, 5-chloro-2-hydroxy-	pH 2	232(4.00),308(3.60)	44-2294-73
	pH 10	251(3.98),339(3.75)	44-2294-73
$C_7H_4ClNS_2$			
2(3H)-Benzothiazolethione, 4-chloro-	$CHCl_3$	250(4.13),334(4.46)	22-3044-73
2(3H)-Benzothiazolethione, 5-chloro-	$CHCl_3$	246(4.25),249(--), 335(4.52),336(--)	22-3044-73
2(3H)-Benzothiazolethione, 6-chloro-	$CHCl_3$	244(4.09),336(4.37)	22-3044-73
2(3H)-Benzothiazolethione, 7-chloro-	$CHCl_3$	246(4.12),335(4.45)	22-3044-73
$C_7H_4Cl_2OS$			
4H-Cyclopenta[c]thiophen-4-one, 1,3-dichloro-5,6-dihydro-	EtOH	218(4.11),265(4.05), 307(3.6)	22-0335-73
$C_7H_4Cl_6N_2$			
Pyrimidine, 4,5,6-trichloro-5-(chloromethyl)-2-(1,2-dichloroethylidene)-2,5-dihydro-	C_6H_{12}	232(3.93),258s(3.59)	18-0299-73
$C_7H_4N_2OS$			
Thiocyanic acid, 3-formyl-2-pyridinyl ester	MeOH	226(4.01),266(3.61), 302s(3.07)	23-1741-73
$C_7H_4N_2O_3$			
1,2-Benzisoxazole, 6-nitro-	H_2O	275(4.18)	44-2294-73
Benzonitrile, 2-hydroxy-4-nitro-	pH 2	214(4.10),237(3.85), 271(3.95),342(3.50)	44-2294-73
	pH 10	234(4.23),264(4.01), 404(4.46)	44-2294-73
Benzonitrile, 2-hydroxy-5-nitro-	pH 2	219(4.28),223(4.27), 306(4.04)	44-2294-73
	pH 10	327(3.91),380(4.20)	44-2294-73
$C_7H_4N_4O_3S$			
1,2,4-Oxadiazole, 3-[2-(2-nitro-5-thiazolyl)ethenyl]-, (E)-	EtOH	261(3.98),358(4.14)	39-2769-73C
$C_7H_4N_6$			
Pyrido[2,3-e][1,2,4]triazolo[3,4-c]-[1,2,4]triazine	EtOH	323(3.97)	4-0575-73
$C_7H_4N_6O$			
Pyrido[2,3-e][1,2,4]triazolo[3,4-c]-[1,2,4]triazine 5-oxide	EtOH	328(3.99),336(3.98)	4-0575-73
$C_7H_4O_3S$			
2-Propynoic acid, 3-(4-hydroxy-2-thienyl)-	ether	260(4.03),309(3.98)	24-0497-73
$C_7H_4O_4$			
4H-Furo[3,2-c]pyran-2,4(6H)-dione	EtOH	294(3.90)	130-0134-73
$C_7H_5BF_2O_2$			
Boron, difluoro(2-hydroxybenzaldehydato-O,O')-(T-4)-	$C_2H_4Cl_2$	258(4.0),327(3.45)	24-2427-73

Compound	Solvent	$\lambda_{max}(\log \epsilon)$	Ref.
$C_7H_5BrCl_4N_2O$			
1-Cyclobutene-1-carbonitrile, 2-amino-4-(bromodichloromethyl)-3,3-dichloro-4-methoxy-	n.s.g.	268(3.88)	44-1470-73
$C_7H_5BrO_2S$			
2-Propenoic acid, 3-(5-bromo-2-thienyl)-, cis	EtOH	310(4.08)	94-2070-73
trans	EtOH	312(4.28)	94-2070-73
$C_7H_5BrO_3S$			
2-Furanethanethioic acid, 5-bromo-α-oxo-, S-methyl ester	EtOH	318(4.45)	103-0374-73
C_7H_5ClO			
Benzaldehyde, 3-chloro-	1% EtOH	249(4.00)	39-0786-73B
Benzaldehyde, 4-chloro-	1% EtOH	260(4.20)	39-0786-73B
C_7H_5ClOS			
4H-Cyclopenta[c]thiophen-4-one, 1-chloro-5,6-dihydro-	EtOH	218(3.93),264(4.15), 288s(3.50)	22-0335-73
$C_7H_5ClO_2$			
Benzoic acid, 4-chloro-, anion	H_2O	235(4.13)	104-2111-73
$C_7H_5Cl_2NO_2$			
1H-Pyrrole-3,4-dicarboxaldehyde, 2,5-dichloro-1-methyl-	EtOH	245(4.3),295(4.0)	103-0467-73
$C_7H_5Cl_3O_3$			
1,4-Dioxaspiro[4.4]non-8-en-7-one, 6,8,9-trichloro-	n.s.g.	243(3.99)	88-3059-73
$C_7H_5D_3N_2OS_3$			
Rhodanine, 5-(N-methyl-d_3-2-thiazolidinylidene)-	EtOH	282(4.10),393(4.54)	94-1431-73
C_7H_5NO			
Benzonitrile, 2-hydroxy-	pH 2	232(3.92),295(3.61)	44-2294-73
	pH 10	241(3.85),325(3.78)	44-2294-73
C_7H_5NOS			
2,1-Benzisothiazol-3-ol	EtOH	217(4.79),230s(--), 353(3.67)	4-0413-73
$C_7H_5NO_3$			
Benzaldehyde, 3-nitro-	1% EtOH	270(3.45)	39-0786-73B
Benzaldehyde, 4-nitro-	1% EtOH	268(4.15)	39-0786-73B
$C_7H_5NO_4$			
Benzoic acid, 3-nitro-, anion	H_2O	265(3.86)	104-2111-73
Benzoic acid, 4-nitro-, anion	H_2O	274(4.03)	104-2111-73
$C_7H_5NO_4S$			
2-Propenoic acid, 3-(5-nitro-2-thienyl)-, cis	EtOH	245(3.82),355(4.03)	94-2070-73
trans	EtOH	246(3.86),356(4.14)	94-2070-73
C_7H_5NS			
2-Propenenitrile, 3-(2-thienyl)-	EtOH	272s(3.94),283s(4.01), 308(4.24)	39-2241-73C

Compound	Solvent	λ_{max}(log ε)	Ref.
2-Propenenitrile, 3-(2-thienyl)-, cis	EtOH	280(3.96),306(4.12)	39-2241-73C
2-Propenenitrile, 3-(3-thienyl)-, cis	EtOH	231s(3.72),240s(3.60), 277(3.99)	39-2241-73C
$C_7H_5NS_2$			
2(3H)-Benzothiazolethione	$CHCl_3$	244(4.00),329(4.43)	22-3044-73
C_7H_5NSe			
1,2-Benzisoselenazole	EtOH	203(4.15),228(4.30), 318(3.67)	4-0267-73
$C_7H_5N_5O_3S$			
1,3,5-Triazin-2(1H)-one, 4-amino-6-(5-nitro-2-thienyl)-, hydrochloride	MeOH	327(4.22)	39-2499-73C
$C_7H_5N_5O_6$			
Formaldehyde, nitro-, 2,4-dinitrophenylhydrazone	$CHCl_3$	349(4.20),378s(--)	78-3929-73
$C_7H_5N_7$			
Methanimidamide, N-[5-(2,2-dicyanoethenyl)-1H-1,2,3-triazol-4-yl]-	MeOH	239(3.87),260s(3.60), 340(3.49)	39-1620-73C
$C_7H_5N_7O$			
Urea, [5-(2,2-dicyanoethenyl)-1H-1,2,3-triazol-4-yl]-	MeOH	212(4.16),238(4.29), 340(3.99)	39-1620-73C
$C_7H_6BrNO_2$			
Benzene, 1-bromo-2-methyl-4-nitro-	DMF	283(4.07)	32-0723-73
$C_7H_6BrN_3O_2S_2$			
Carbamic acid, (5-bromo-2H-thiazolo-[3,2-b][1,2,4]thiadiazol-2-ylidene)-, ethyl ester	EtOH	250(3.60),316(4.39)	94-2408-73
$C_7H_6Br_2O$			
Phenol, 2,6-dibromo-4-methyl-	dioxan	286(3.53)	126-0039-73L
$C_7H_6Br_2O_2$			
Benzenemethanol, 3,5-dibromo-4-hydroxy-	dioxan	284.5(3.48)	126-0039-73L
$C_7H_6ClF_2N_3O_2$			
1-Cyclobutene-1-carboxylic acid, 2-azido-3,3-difluoro-, 2-chloroethyl ester	MeOH	274(4.04)	24-3544-73
$C_7H_6ClNO_2$			
Benzene, 1-chloro-4-methyl-2-nitro-	DMF	302(3.162)	39-1430-73B
$C_7H_6ClNO_3$			
Benzene, 4-chloro-1-methoxy-2-nitro-	DMF	333(3.194)	39-1430-73B
1H-Pyrrole-3,4-dicarboxaldehyde, 5-chloro-2,3-dihydro-1-methyl-2-oxo-	C_6H_{12}	250(3.6),280(3.5), 315(3.5)	103-0467-73
	EtOH	227(4.1),278(4.1), 385(4.4)	103-0467-73
$C_7H_6ClN_3$			
1H-Imidazo[4,5-c]pyridine, 4-chloro-1-methyl-	pH 1	271(4.01)	124-0703-73
	pH 13	268(3.96)	124-0703-73
	MeOH	257(3.90),267(3.88)	124-0703-73
1H-Imidazo[4,5-c]pyridine, 4-chloro-2-methyl-	pH 1	268(3.77)	124-0703-73
	pH 13	277(3.75)	124-0703-73

Compound	Solvent	$\lambda_{max}(\log \epsilon)$	Ref.
1H-Imidazo[4,5-c]pyridine, 4-chloro-2-methyl- (cont.)	MeOH	250(3.81),267(3.83)	124-0703-73
$C_7H_6ClN_3S$			
Benzothiazole, 4-chloro-2-hydrazino-	$CHCl_3$	246(4.17),273(4.11)	22-3044-73
Benzothiazole, 5-chloro-2-hydrazino-	$CHCl_3$	242(4.13),268(4.04)	22-3044-73
Benzothiazole, 6-chloro-2-hydrazino-	$CHCl_3$	242(3.81),268(4.13)	22-3044-73
Benzothiazole, 7-chloro-2-hydrazino-	$CHCl_3$	242(4.03),265(4.08)	22-3044-73
$C_7H_6Cl_2O$			
Phenol, 2,6-dichloro-4-methyl-	dioxan	286.5(3.48)	126-0039-73L
$C_7H_6Cl_2O_2$			
Benzenemethanol, 3,5-dichloro-4-hydroxy-	dioxan	282.5(3.45)	126-0039-73L
$C_7H_6Cl_4N_2$			
Pyrimidine, 4,6-dichloro-2-(2-chloroethyl)-5-(chloromethyl)-	C_6H_{12}	225(3.86)	18-0299-73
Pyrimidine, 4,5,6-trichloro-2-(1-chloroethylidene)-2,5-dihydro-5-methyl-	C_6H_{12}	226(3.76),260(3.59)	18-0299-73
$C_7H_6Cl_4N_2O$			
1-Cyclobutene-1-carbonitrile, 2-amino-3,3-dichloro-4-(dichloromethyl)-	n.s.g.	267(4.06)	44-1470-73
$C_7H_6F_3NO_3$			
Acetamide, 2,2,2-trifluoro-N-(2,5-dioxo-1-cyclopentyl)-	MeOH	255(4.34)	5-0407-73
	MeOH-HCl	243(4.16)	5-0407-73
	MeOH-NaOH	258(4.36)	5-0407-73
$C_7H_6F_6OS_2$			
1,3-Dithiole, 2-ethoxy-4,5-bis(trifluoromethyl)-	isooctane	272(3.59),287s(3.51)	35-4379-73
$C_7H_6IN_2O_5$			
1,3-Cyclohexadiene, 1-iodo-6-methoxy-	DMSO	363(4.20),513(4.40)	39-0710-73B
C_7H_6NS			
Isothiazolo[2,3-a]pyridinium, perchlorate	EtOH	212(3.85),230(4.25), 318(4.07),331(4.11)	77-0150-73
$C_7H_6N_2$			
3H-Diazirine, 3-phenyl-	hexane	265(2.52),362(2.48)	35-5072-73
$C_7H_6N_2OS$			
Isothiazolo[3,4-b]pyridine, 3-methoxy-	EtOH	219(4.18),289(3.66), 297s(3.62),352(3.58)	23-1741-73
$C_7H_6N_2O_2$			
Benzoic acid, o-diazeno-	pH 6.8	271(3.70),405(2.16)	78-3497-73
Benzoic acid, p-diazeno-	pH 6.8	216(4.00),274(4.02), 405(2.32)	78-3497-73
$C_7H_6N_2O_4$			
4-Cyclopentene-1,3-dione, 2-diazo-4,5-dimethoxy-	CH_2Cl_2	239(4.02),256(4.00), 291(3.58),380(3.08)	78-0253-73
2-Propenoic acid, 3-(1,2,3,4-tetrahydro-2,4-dioxo-5-pyrimidinyl)-	pH 1	270s(4.13),296(4.27)	44-0264-73
	pH 6	260(4.13),293(4.13)	44-0264-73
	pH 11.5	278(4.10),319(4.25)	44-0264-73

Compound	Solvent	λ_{max}(log ϵ)	Ref.
$C_7H_6N_2O_5$			
Phenol, 2-methyl-4,6-dinitro-	acid	273(4.15)	49-1315-73
	anion	262(3.81),373(4.16)	49-1315-73
$C_7H_6N_2O_6$			
Phenol, 5-methoxy-2,4-dinitro-	hexane	216(4.14),261(3.13), 285s(4.02),334(3.88)	124-1265-73
	EtOH	221(4.09),270(4.16), 290s(4.08),331(3.91)	124-1265-73
	dioxan	223(4.06),273(4.18), 290s(4.14),334(3.91)	124-1265-73
$C_7H_6N_2O_8S$			
1,3-Cyclohexadiene-1-sulfonic acid, 6-methoxy-3,5-dinitro-, ion(2-)	DMSO	360(4.15),520(4.34)	39-0710-73B
isomer	DMSO	360(--),530(--), 600(--)	39-0710-73B
$C_7H_6N_2S$			
Isothiazolo[5,4-c]pyridine, 3-methyl-	EtOH	209(4.15),224s(4.01), 313(3.74),326s(3.69)	23-1741-73
$C_7H_6N_3O_7$			
1,3-Cyclohexadiene, 6-methoxy-1,3,5-tri-nitro-, ion(1-)	DMSO	431(4.45),505(4.29)	39-0710-73B
1,5-Cyclohexadiene, 4-methoxy-1,3,5-tri-nitro-, ion(1-)	DMSO	431(4.45),505(4.29)	39-0710-73B
$C_7H_6N_4O$			
Pteridine, 7-methoxy-	MeOH	293s(3.92),301(4.04), 313(3.98)	24-0317-73
7(8H)-Pteridinone, 8-methyl-	MeOH	215(4.33),251(3.63), 259(3.63),270s(3.53), 309(4.00)	24-0317-73
$C_7H_6N_4O_2$			
2,4(1H,3H)-Pteridinedione, 1-methyl-	pH 6.3	232(4.07),329(3.86)	24-1401-73 +24-3149-73
	pH 10.5	242(4.19),281(3.54), 339(3.89)	24-1401-73 +24-3149-73
2,4(1H,3H)-Pteridinedione, 3-methyl-	pH 5.8	231(4.15),326(3.88)	24-1401-73
	pH 10.0	215(4.02),244(4.25), 268(3.98),362(3.81)	24-3149-73
4(3H)-Pteridinone, 6-methyl-, 8-oxide	H_2O	228(4.05),225s(4.05), 265s(4.13),272(4.13), 300s(3.86),345(3.86), 358(3.86)	35-6407-73
1H-Pyrazolo[4,3-b]pyridine, 5-methyl-3-nitro-	EtOH	250(3.80),295(3.96)	39-2901-73C
$C_7H_6N_4O_3$			
1H-Benzotriazole, 1-methoxy-4-nitro-	EtOH	302(3.92)	39-0160-73B
1H-Benzotriazole, 1-methyl-7-nitro-, 3-oxide	EtOH	243(3.97),370(3.74)	39-0160-73B
2,4(1H,3H)-Pteridinedione, 1-methyl-, 5-oxide	pH 5.0	242(4.36),288(3.82), 348(3.69)	24-3149-73
	pH 11.0	247(4.35),292(3.92), 353(3.74)	24-3149-73
2,4(1H,3H)-Pteridinedione, 3-methyl-, 8-oxide	pH 2.0	241(4.39),272s(3.79), 347(3.88)	24-3149-73

Compound	Solvent	λ_{max}(log ε)	Ref.
2,4(1H,3H)-Pteridinedione, 3-methyl-, 8-oxide (cont.)	pH 9.0	208(4.18),253(4.36), 287s(3.91),387(3.91)	24-3149-73
2,4(1H,3H)-Pteridinedione, 6-methyl-, 8-oxide	H_2O	248s(4.40),268(4.47), 290s(4.08),385(3.99)	35-6407-73
9H-Purine-9-acetic acid, 6-hydroxy-	pH 2	250(4.04)	78-2293-73
	pH 13	252(4.11)	78-2293-73
$C_7H_6N_4O_5S$			
2,4(1H,3H)-Pteridinedione, 1-[(methyl-sulfonyl)oxy]-	pH 5.0	229(4.05),315(3.83)	44-0703-73
$C_7H_6N_6$			
Pyrido[2,3-e][1,2,4]triazolo[3,4-c]-[1,2,4]triazine, 5,6-dihydro-	EtOH	315(3.71),338(3.78)	4-0575-73
Tetrazolo[5,1-c][1,2,4]benzotriazine, 1,5-dihydro-	EtOH	309(3.80),390(3.27)	4-0575-73
$C_7H_6N_6O$			
1H-Tetrazol-5-amine, N-nitroso-1-phenyl-	pH 13	276(3.98)	39-1357-73C
	MeOH	245(3.62)	39-1357-73C
$C_7H_6N_6O_2S$			
1,3,5-Triazine-2,4-diamine, 6-(5-nitro-2-thienyl)-	MeOH	333(3.75)	39-2499-73C
C_7H_6O			
Benzaldehyde	EtOH	246(4.09),281(3.10), 287s(3.05)	141-0001-73
	dioxan	244(4.11),280(3.15), 286s(3.08)	141-0001-73
at -75°	FSO_3H	296(4.34),330s(<3.5)	59-0807-73
C_7H_6OS			
4H-Cyclopenta[c]thiophen-4-one, 5,6-dihydro-	EtOH	259(4.15)	22-0335-73
$C_7H_6OS_2$			
Cyclopenta-1,2-dithiole-6-carboxaldehyde, 4,5-dihydro-	n.s.g.	416(4.19),434(4.12)	97-0026-73
$C_7H_6O_2$			
Benzaldehyde, 2-hydroxy-	EtOH	215(4.23),255(4.06), 327(3.60)	141-0001-73
	EtOH-NaOH	230(4.24),266(3.86), 382(3.83)	141-0001-73
	dioxan	218(4.22),254(4.04), 324(3.56)	141-0001-73
Benzaldehyde, 3-hydroxy-	H_2O	266(3.78)	39-0786-73B
	EtOH	221(4.27),255(3.96), 317(3.47)	141-0001-73
	EtOH-NaOH	241(4.41),267s(3.78), 365(3.43)	141-0001-73
	dioxan	219(4.25),251(3.98), 313(3.52)	141-0001-73
Benzaldehyde, 4-hydroxy-	EtOH	222(4.09),286(4.21), 291s(4.19),330s(2.51)	141-0001-73
	EtOH-NaOH	241(3.88),296s(3.72), 336(4.48)	141-0001-73
	dioxan	219(4.17),270(4.25), 283s(4.15)	141-0001-73

Compound	Solvent	$\lambda_{max}(\log \epsilon)$	Ref.
1,3-Benzodioxole	EtOH	232(3.68),282(3.50)	141-0001-73
	dioxan	233(3.62),283(3.49)	141-0001-73
Benzoic acid	EtOH	228(4.06),269s(2.96), 272(3.00),280(2.91)	141-0001-73
	EtOH-NaOH	223(3.98),262(2.95), 269(2.89),276(2.82)	141-0001-73
	dioxan	228(4.06),267s(2.97), 273(3.06),280(2.98)	141-0001-73
	$C_2H_4Cl_2$	274(3.1),282(3.1)	8-0166-73
	neutral	231(4.08),274(3.05)	3-0415-73
$C_7H_6O_2S$			
2-Propenoic acid, 3-(2-thienyl)-, cis	EtOH	298(3.93)	94-2070-73
2-Propenoic acid, 3-(2-thienyl)-, trans	EtOH	302(4.18)	94-2070-73
$C_7H_6O_2S_2$			
5H-Cyclopenta-1,4-dithiin-5,7(6H)-dione, 2,3-dihydro-	MeOH	249(4.73),368(4.68)	49-1224-73
$C_7H_6O_3$			
Benzaldehyde, 2,4-dihydroxy-	EtOH	213(4.16),216s(4.15), 233(3.99),281(4.20), 314(3.88)	141-0001-73
	EtOH-NaOH	220(4.10),230s(4.08), 250(3.89),336(4.32)	141-0001-73
	dioxan	218(4.20),231(4.09), 277(4.24),313(3.85)	141-0001-73
Benzaldehyde, 2,5-dihydroxy-	EtOH	210(4.01),231(4.20), 259(3.88),367(3.61)	141-0001-73
	EtOH-NaOH	223(4.14),240s(4.06), 268s(3.84),417(3.63)	141-0001-73
	dioxan	231(4.20),258(3.81), 365(3.57)	141-0001-73
Benzaldehyde, 3,4-dihydroxy-	EtOH	209(4.17),234(4.15), 281(4.01),315(3.97), 360s(3.05)	141-0001-73
	EtOH-NaOH	253(3.96),275s(3.58), 297s(3.56),353(4.33), 400s(3.09)	141-0001-73
	dioxan	229(4.18),272(4.05), 307(3.92)	141-0001-73
Benzaldehyde, 3,5-dihydroxy-	EtOH	220(4.18),255(4.00), 334(3.54)	141-0001-73
Benzoic acid, 2-hydroxy-	EtOH	212(4.14),234(3.87), 302(3.62)	141-0001-73
	EtOH-NaOH	223s(3.87),228(3.91), 297(3.62)	141-0001-73
	dioxan	237(3.92),307(3.64)	141-0001-73
Benzoic acid, 3-hydroxy-	EtOH	213(4.24),234(3.84), 296(3.44)	141-0001-73
	EtOH-NaOH	242s(3.89),314(3.45)	141-0001-73
	dioxan	215(4.17),236(3.88), 296(3.50)	141-0001-73
Benzoic acid, 4-hydroxy-	EtOH	212(4.03),254(4.15), 274s(3.77),283s(3.30)	141-0001-73
	EtOH-NaOH	279(4.25)	141-0001-73
	dioxan	252(4.20),273s(3.61), 283s(3.03)	141-0001-73

Compound	Solvent	$\lambda_{max}(\log \epsilon)$	Ref.
$C_7H_6O_4$			
Benzaldehyde, 2,3,5-trihydroxy-	EtOH	276(4.00),332(3.30)	141-0001-73
Benzaldehyde, 2,4,6-trihydroxy-	EtOH	293(4.40),340s(3.40)	141-0001-73
Benzoic acid, 2,3-dihydroxy-	EtOH	216(4.30),246(3.81), 314(3.51)	141-0001-73
	EtOH-NaOH	229(4.34),250s(3.85), 329(3.62)	141-0001-73
	dioxan	219(4.25),250(3.91), 323(3.54)	141-0001-73
Benzoic acid, 2,4-dihydroxy-	EtOH	212(4.29),218s(4.16), 255(4.07),295(3.74)	141-0001-73
	EtOH-NaOH	220(4.12),232(4.11), 272(4.20),299(4.12)	141-0001-73
	dioxan	215(4.23),221s(4.14), 258(4.16),297(3.77)	141-0001-73
Benzoic acid, 2,5-dihydroxy-	EtOH	215(4.28),234s(3.81), 332(3.62)	141-0001-73
	EtOH-NaOH	223(4.22),236s(3.97), 320(3.55)	141-0001-73
	dioxan	219(4.27),238(3.83), 340(3.68)	141-0001-73
Benzoic acid, 2,6-dihydroxy-	EtOH	217(4.26),249(3.83), 304(3.56)	141-0001-73
	EtOH-NaOH	216(4.28),235s(3.81), 246(3.79),273(3.37), 303(3.64)	141-0001-73
	dioxan	222(4.19),254(4.00), 310s(3.47),323(3.50)	141-0001-73
Benzoic acid, 3,4-dihydroxy-	EtOH	211(4.24),254(3.89), 293(3.63)	141-0001-73
	EtOH-NaOH	222(4.13),273(3.85), 296(3.79),424(3.33)	141-0001-73
	dioxan	219(4.20),257(3.98), 291(3.64)	141-0001-73
Benzoic acid, 3,5-dihydroxy-	EtOH	215(4.26),251(3.77), 310(3.43)	141-0001-73
	EtOH-NaOH	223(4.31),265s(3.47), 320(3.45)	141-0001-73
	dioxan	250(3.83),307(3.52)	141-0001-73
$C_7H_6O_4S$			
2H-Thiopyran-5-carboxylic acid, 4-hydroxy-6-methyl-2-oxo-	MeOH	240(4.44),322(3.49)	7-0269-73
$C_7H_6O_5$			
Benzoic acid, 2,4,6-trihydroxy-	EtOH	220(4.44),261(4.08), 295(3.41)	141-0001-73
	EtOH-NaOH	222(4.18),228s(4.13), 277(4.20)	141-0001-73
	dioxan	223(4.41),266(4.21), 305(3.48)	141-0001-73
Benzoic acid, 3,4,5-trihydroxy-	EtOH	216(4.41),271(3.92)	141-0001-73
	dioxan	221(4.32),269(3.97)	141-0001-73
$C_7H_6O_5S$			
3-Furancarboxylic acid, 2,5-dihydro-4-(methylthio)-2,5-dioxo-, methyl ester	EtOH	299(4.14)	95-1008-73

Compound	Solvent	λ_{max}(log ϵ)	Ref.
$C_7H_6S_3$			
Cyclopenta-1,2-dithiole-6-carbothioaldehyde, 4,5-dihydro-	n.s.g.	514(3.83)	97-0026-73
C_7H_7			
2,4,6-Cycloheptatrien-1-ylium, tetrafluoroborate	MeCN	218(4.54),273(3.72), 279s(3.65)	33-2796-73
	H_2SO_4	220(4.60),266s(3.62), 272(3.75),278(3.72)	33-2796-73
C_7H_7Br			
3,4-Hexadien-1-yne, 1-bromo-5-methyl-	n.s.g.	206(3.95),217(3.94), 227(3.94),237(3.89), 279(3.22)	70-1029-73
$C_7H_7BrN_2O$			
Benzoic acid, 4-bromo-, hydrazide	neutral	242(4.15)	23-0811-73
	cation	247(4.19)	23-0811-73
$C_7H_7BrN_2S$			
1H-Thieno[2,3-c]pyrazole, 5-bromo-1,3-dimethyl-	EtOH	256(4.0)	104-2216-73
$C_7H_7BrN_2Se$			
1H-Selenolo[2,3-c]pyrazole, 5-bromo-1,3-dimethyl-	EtOH	260(3.8)	104-2216-73
$C_7H_7BrO_3$			
2-Furancarboxylic acid, 5-bromo-, ethyl ester	heptane	259(--)	103-0546-73
	H_2O	266(--)	103-0546-73
	EtOH	262(--)	103-0546-73
	dioxan	261(4.30)	103-0546-73
$C_7H_7ClN_2O$			
Benzoic acid, 4-chloro-, hydrazide	neutral	237(4.12)	23-0811-73
	cation	241(4.17)	23-0811-73
$C_7H_7ClO_3$			
2-Furancarboxylic acid, 5-chloro-, ethyl ester	heptane	255(--)	103-0546-73
	H_2O	263(--)	103-0546-73
	EtOH	258(--)	103-0546-73
	dioxan	257(4.29)	103-0546-73
$C_7H_7ClO_3S$			
Chlorosulfuric acid, p-tolyl ester	heptane	205(4.03),223(3.77), 264(2.82),270(2.64), 274(2.53)	33-1483-73
$C_7H_7FN_2O$			
Benzoic acid, 4-fluoro-, hydrazide	neutral	229(3.95)	23-0811-73
	cation	233(4.01)	23-0811-73
$C_7H_7F_2N_3O_2$			
1-Cyclobutene-1-carboxylic acid, 2-azido-3,3-difluoro-, ethyl ester	MeOH	273(4.0)	24-3544-73
$C_7H_7IN_2O$			
Benzoic acid, 4-iodo-, hydrazide	neutral	252(4.18)	23-0811-73
	cation	257(4.16)	23-0811-73

Compound	Solvent	$\lambda_{max}(\log \epsilon)$	Ref.
$C_7H_7IO_3$			
2-Furancarboxylic acid, 5-iodo-, ethyl ester	heptane	264(--)	103-0546-73
	H_2O	269(--)	103-0546-73
	EtOH	267(--)	103-0546-73
	dioxan	267(4.33)	103-0546-73
C_7H_7NO			
Benzaldehyde oxime	pH 6.61	253(3.68)	36-1381-73
	EtOH	210(4.18),214(4.08), 252(4.15),282(3.32), 292(3.07)	36-1381-73
	dioxan	215(4.07),253(4.16), 283(3.32),293(3.11)	36-1381-73
Benzamide	H_2SO_4	244(4.14),275(3.22)	3-0415-73
	neutral	227(3.98),269(2.90)	3-0415-73
$C_7H_7NO_2$			
Benzoic acid, 4-amino-, anion	H_2O	265(4.11)	104-2111-73
Cyclohexanecarbonitrile, 2,6-dioxo-	EtOH	236(3.84),273(4.19)	70-0811-73
3(2H)-Isoxazolone, 5-methyl-4-(2-propynyl)-	EtOH	229(3.54)	1-2802-73
5(2H)-Isoxazolone, 3-methyl-4-(2-propynyl)-	EtOH	259(3.95)	1-2802-73
$C_7H_7NO_3$			
Benzene, 1-methoxy-2-nitro-	MeOH	323(3.36)	39-0055-73B
Benzene, 1-methoxy-4-nitro-	MeOH	305(4.09)	39-0055-73B
Cyclopenta[c]pyrrole-1,3(2H,4H)-dione, 5,6-dihydro-4-hydroxy-	H_2O	225(4.15),230s(--)	69-4992-73
Phenol, 2-methyl-4-nitro-	acid	325(3.96)	49-1315-73
	anion	232(3.67),416(4.29)	49-1315-73
$C_7H_7NO_4$			
1H-Pyrrole-3,4-dicarboxylic acid, 3-methyl ester	EtOH	245(3.90),260(3.87)	23-1089-73
$C_7H_7NO_4S$			
1H-Pyrrole-3-carboxylic acid, 2,5-dihydro-4-(methylthio)-2,5-dioxo-, methyl ester	EtOH	265(4.84),375(4.79)	94-1667-73
$C_7H_7NO_5$			
2-Furancarboxylic acid, 5-nitro-, ethyl ester	heptane	291(--)	103-0546-73
	H_2O	310(--)	103-0546-73
	EtOH	295(--)	103-0546-73
	dioxan	298(4.10)	103-0546-73
$C_7H_7NO_5S$			
3-Furancarboxylic acid, 2,5-dihydro-5-(hydroxyimino)-4-(methylthio)-2-oxo-, methyl ester	EtOH	299(3.92),380(3.61)	95-1008-73
C_7H_7NS			
Benzenecarbothioamide	H_2O	287(3.94)	1-0209-73
	H_2SO_4	271(4.20)	1-0209-73
$C_7H_7NS_2$			
Carbamodithioic acid, phenyl-	pH 13	257(3.99),291(4.26)	94-0329-73
	15M KOH	260(4.20)	94-0329-73
	H_2SO_4	253(4.07),273s(3.79)	94-0329-73

Compound	Solvent	λ max(log ε)	Ref.
$C_7H_7N_2O_5$			
1,3-Cyclohexadiene, 1-methoxy-2,4-dinitro-, ion(1-)	DMSO	520(4.43)	39-0710-73B
$C_7H_7N_2O_7P$			
Phosphonic acid, [(2,4-dinitrophenyl)-methyl]-	H_2O	256(4.07)	78-2553-73
$C_7H_7N_3$			
Imidazo[1,5-a]pyrazine, 3-methyl-	EtOH	260s(3.55),265s(3.57), 270(3.65),281(3.61), 340(3.43)	44-2049-73
1H-Pyrazolo[4,3-b]pyridine, 5-methyl-	C_6H_{12}	258(3.60),294(3.68), 298(3.68),306(3.57)	39-2901-73C
	EtOH	288(3.74)	39-2901-73C
$C_7H_7N_3O$			
Benzene, 1-azido-4-methoxy-	C_6H_{12}	254(4.8),295(4.1)	115-0077-73A
2H-Benzotriazole, 2-methyl-, 1-oxide	EtOH	326(3.70)	39-0160-73B
2-Butyn-1-one, 1-(5-methyl-1H-1,2,3-triazol-4-yl)-	EtOH	260(3.88)	78-3271-73
anion	EtOH	293(4.02)	78-3271-73
$C_7H_7N_3OS$			
Thiazolo[5,4-b]pyridin-2-amine, 5-methoxy-	MeOH	267(4.10),314(3.86)	44-4383-73
	MeOH-HCl	270(3.95),302(4.04)	44-4383-73
	MeOH-NaOH	267(4.12),314(3.82)	44-4383-73
$C_7H_7N_3OS_2$			
Thiazolo[4,5-d]pyridazin-7(6H)-one, 6-methyl-2-(methylthio)-	$CHCl_3$	267(4.38),296(4.00)	22-3324-73
2H-Thiazolo[3,2-a]-1,3,5-triazin-2-one, 1-ethyl-1,3,4,8a-tetrahydro-4-thioxo-, meso-ionic didehydro deriv.	EtOH	225(3.92),274(3.96), 320(4.11)	44-3868-73
4H-Thiazolo[3,2-a]-1,3,5-triazin-4-one, 1-ethyl-1,2,3,8a-tetrahydro-2-thioxo-, meso-ionic didehydro deriv.	H_2O	216(4.23),239s(4.05), 276(4.01),298(4.02)	44-3868-73
4H-Thiazolo[3,2-a]-1,3,5-triazin-4-one, 2-(ethylthio)-	dioxan	247(3.69),270(3.90), 309(4.27),318(4.26)	94-0074-73
4H-Thiazolo[3,2-a]-1,3,5-triazin-4-one, 6-methyl-2-(methylthio)-	EtOH	225(3.98),250(3.92), 267(3.94),320(4.26)	94-0074-73
4H-Thiazolo[3,2-a]-1,3,5-triazin-4-one, 7-methyl-2-(methylthio)-	EtOH	246(3.86),267(3.92), 314(4.31),320s(--)	94-0074-73
$C_7H_7N_3O_2$			
Ethanediamide, 3-pyridinyl-	EtOH	267(3.95)	103-0621-73
Imidazo[1,2-a]pyrimidine-5,7-diol, 6-methyl-	pH 1	275(4.08)	4-1021-73
	pH 11	275(4.07)	4-1021-73
2,4-Pyridinedicarboxaldehyde dioxime	0.5M HCl	310(4.07)	73-2788-73
	pH 6	295(4.74)	73-2788-73
	pH 13	282(4.42)	73-2788-73
2,5-Pyridinedicarboxaldehyde dioxime	0.5M HCl	317(4.07)	73-2788-73
	pH 6	295(4.03)	73-2788-73
	pH 11	318(4.17)	73-2788-73
	pH 13	327(4.15)	73-2788-73
$C_7H_7N_3O_2S$			
5H-1,3,4-Thiadiazolo[3,2-a]pyrimidine-5,7(6H)-dione, 8-ethyl-8,8a-dihydro-, meso-ionic didehydro deriv.	H_2O	214(4.35),283(3.82)	44-3868-73

Compound	Solvent	$\lambda_{max}(\log \epsilon)$	Ref.
$C_7H_7N_3O_2S_2$			
Carbamic acid, 2H-thiazolo[3,2-b]-[1,2,4]thiadiazol-2-ylidene-, ethyl ester	EtOH	308(4.23)	94-2408-73
$C_7H_7N_3S$			
3(2H)-Benzothiazolamine, 2-imino-	dioxan	234(3.84),265(3.84), 298(3.65)	4-0947-73
Benzothiazole, 2-hydrazino-	$CHCl_3$	242(3.91),266(4.09)	22-3044-73
1H-Pyrazolo[3,4-b]pyridine, 4-(methyl-thio)-	EtOH	233(3.88),312(3.99), 319(3.96)	104-1294-73
Thiocyanic acid, 2-amino-6-methyl-3-pyridinyl ester	MeOH	256(4.20),302(3.75)	44-4383-73
$C_7H_7N_5O$			
Isopterin, 1-methyl-	pH 0.0	205(4.21),239(4.14), 342(3.91)	33-1225-73
	pH 7.0	245(4.18),287(3.60), 344(3.93)	33-1225-73
4-Pteridinamine, 2-methoxy-	pH 0.0	234(4.08),262s(3.59), 329(3.97)	33-1225-73
	pH 7.0	243(4.24),272s(3.47), 340(3.81)	33-1225-73
$C_7H_7N_5O_2$			
4,7(1H,8H)-Pteridinedione, 2-amino-	pH 4.0	218(4.40),290(3.91), 342(4.07)	24-1952-73
	pH 11.0	257(3.96),280(3.44), 358(4.07)	24-1952-73
4(3H)-Pteridinone, 2-amino-6-methyl-, 8-oxide	pH -1.85	257(4.29),287s(3.93), 352(3.73)	35-6407-73
	pH -2.0	253(4.29),275s(3.97), 344(3.74),395(3.18)	24-3175-73
	pH 4.0	241(4.05),270(4.37), 290s(4.08),381(3.85)	24-3175-73
	pH 4.82	270(4.35),290s(4.10), 378(3.85)	35-6407-73
	pH 10	260(4.50),285s(3.89), 390(3.90)	24-3175-73
	pH 13	260(4.54),287s(3.92), 387(3.94)	35-6407-73
4(3H)-Pteridinone, 2-amino-7-methyl-, 8-oxide	pH -2.0	251(4.38),280(3.89), 332(3.80),380(3.15)	24-3175-73
	pH 3.0	211(4.22),240(4.16), 268(4.45),290s(3.99), 365(3.90)	24-3175-73
	pH 10.0	258(4.48),285s(3.74), 373(3.94)	24-3175-73
3H-Purine-3-acetic acid, 6-amino-	pH 2	276(4.24)	78-2293-73
	pH 12	274(4.09)	78-2293-73
9H-Purine-9-acetic acid, 6-amino-	pH 2	258(4.15)	78-2293-73
	pH 12	261(4.14)	78-2293-73
Pyrimido[5,4-e]-1,2,4-triazine, 5,7-di-methoxy-	C_6H_{12}	214(4.01),236(4.15), 253s(3.66),259s(3.56), 263s(3.44),278(2.94), 321s(3.43),327s(3.53), 335(3.67),343(3.72), 350(3.80),359(3.67), 367(3.68),480(2.44), 508s(2.22),520s(2.04)	12-1689-73

Compound	Solvent	$\lambda_{max}(\log \epsilon)$	Ref.
$C_7H_7N_5O_3$			
Pyrimido[5,4-e]-1,2,4-triazine-5,7(6H,8H)-dione, 3-ethoxy-	MeOH	216s(3.63),221s(4.00), 236(4.28),264s(3.32), 267s(3.27),272(3.19), 379(3.70)	12-1689-73
$C_7H_7N_7OS$			
Purine-6-carboxaldehyde, thiosemicarbazone, 1-oxide	pH 3	247(4.29),361(4.48)	87-0984-73
	pH 13	255(4.23),405(4.43)	87-0984-73
Purine-6-carboxaldehyde, thiosemicarbazone, 3-oxide	pH 1	245(4.11),297(3.75), 362(4.52),373(4.54)	87-0984-73
	pH 13	232(4.19),398(4.44)	87-0984-73
$C_7H_7N_7O_2$			
6-Pteridinecarboxaldehyde, 2,4-diamino-, oxime, 8-oxide	pH 13	275(4.29),313(4.41)	35-6413-73
C_7H_8			
3,4-Hexadien-1-yne, 5-methyl-	n.s.g.	210(4.00),220(4.02)	70-1029-73
Spiro[2.4]hepta-4,6-diene	EtOH	257(3.43)	89-0577-73
$C_7H_8BrN_5O$			
9H-Purine-9-ethanol, 6-amino-8-bromo-	H_2O	268(4.20)	121-1297-73
C_7H_8ClNO			
2H-Azepin-2-one, 6-chloro-1,3-dihydro-1-methyl-	EtOH	274(3.59)	39-1079-73C
$C_7H_8ClN_4$			
7H-Purinium, 6-chloro-7,9-dimethyl-, perchlorate	H_2O	266(4.10)	104-1308-73
$C_7H_8ClN_5$			
3H-Purin-6-amine, 8-chloro-3-ethyl-	pH 1	222s(4.12),228s(4.00), 278(4.28),285s(4.20)	94-1954-73
	pH 7	224s(4.08),281(4.20)	94-1954-73
	pH 13	224s(4.08),281(4.19)	94-1954-73
	EtOH	227s(4.03),284(4.17)	94-1954-73
$C_7H_8Cl_2N_2$			
Pyrimidine, 4,6-dichloro-2-ethyl-5-methyl-	C_6H_{12}	260(3.64)	18-0299-73
$C_7H_8FNO_2$			
Pyridine, 5-fluoro-2,4-dimethoxy-	MeOH	267(3.49)	87-0524-73
$C_7H_8FNO_3$			
Pyridine, 5-fluoro-2,4-dimethoxy-, 1-oxide	MeOH	257(3.95),300s(3.59)	4-0779-73
$C_7H_8N_2$			
4,5,6-Methenocyclopentapyrazole, 3,3a,4,5,6,6a-hexahydro-	C_6H_{12}	330(2.45)	89-0660-73
2-Tolyldiazene	pH 6.8	275(3.74),404(2.27)	78-3497-73
3-Tolyldiazene	pH 6.8	274(3.83),399(3.20)	78-3497-73
4-Tolyldiazene	pH 6.8	221(3.91),283(3.95), 397(2.32)	78-3497-73
$C_7H_8N_2O$			
Acetamide, N-2-pyridinyl-, hydrochloride	MeOH	236(4.02),275(3.72)	4-0821-73

Compound	Solvent	$\lambda_{max}(\log \epsilon)$	Ref.
Benzoic acid hydrazide	neutral	226(3.94)	23-0811-73
	cation	230(3.98)	23-0811-73
Ethanone, 1-(3-amino-4-pyridinyl)-	EtOH	223(4.20),252(3.68), 373(3.69)	23-1741-73
$C_7H_8N_2OS$			
2-Propenimidamide, N-hydroxy-3-(2-thienyl)-, cis	EtOH	272(3.94)	39-2241-73C
trans	EtOH	308(4.26)	39-2241-73C
picrate	EtOH	343(4.23)	39-2241-73C
2-Propenimidamide, N-hydroxy-3-(3-thienyl)-, cis	EtOH	230s(3.79),254s(3.70), 265s(3.67),275s(3.64)	39-2241-73C
picrate	EtOH	299(4.01),355(4.14)	39-2241-73C
trans	EtOH	234(4.05),241(4.03), 279(4.23)	39-2241-73C
5H-Thiazolo[3,2-a]pyrimidin-5-one, 2,3-dihydro-6-methyl-	EtOH	232(3.81),289(3.93), 297s(--)	94-1305-73
$C_7H_8N_2OS_3$			
Rhodanine, 3-methyl-5-(2-thiazolidinylidene)-	EtOH	275(4.13),393(4.51)	94-1431-73
Rhodanine, 5-(N-methyl-2-thiazolidinylidene)-	EtOH	278(4.10),394(4.51)	94-1431-73
$C_7H_8N_2O_2$			
Benzoic acid, 2-hydrazino-	pH 6.8	210(4.41),243(3.85), 312(3.42)	78-3497-73
Benzoic acid, 4-hydrazino-	pH 6.8	268.4(4.17)	78-3497-73
$C_7H_8N_2O_4$			
1H-Imidazole-4,5-dicarboxylic acid, dimethyl ester	EtOH	211(4.01),254(4.10)	95-0893-73
1(2H)-Pyrimidineacetic acid, 3,4-dihydro-5-methyl-2,4-dioxo-	pH 2	268(3.97)	78-2293-73
	pH 12	271(3.86)	78-2293-73
1(2H)-Pyrimidinepropanoic acid, 3,4-dihydro-2,4-dioxo-	H_2O	264(3.97)	138-0967-73
$C_7H_8N_2O_4S$			
2-Butenoic acid, 2-cyano-3-(methylthio)-4-nitro-, methyl ester	EtOH	239(4.32),316(4.41)	95-0612-73
3-Furancarboxylic acid, 2,5-dihydro-5-(hydroxyimino)-2-imino-4-(methylthio)-, methyl ester	EtOH	240(3.94),303(3.89)	95-1008-73
$C_7H_8N_2O_5$			
Pyridine, 2,5-dimethoxy-4-nitro-, 1-oxide	MeOH	267(3.74),310(3.73), 370(3.86)	4-0779-73
$C_7H_8N_4$			
1H-Imidazo[4,5-b]pyrazine, 5,6-dimethyl-	pH 1	285s(3.90),304(4.08)	39-0244-73C
	pH 11	302s(3.86),323(4.13)	39-0244-73C
	MeOH	241(3.12),295s(3.96), 309(4.02)	39-0244-73C
Pyrazolo[1,5-a]-1,3,5-triazine, 2,4-dimethyl-	pH 1	205(4.06),238(3.82)	4-0885-73
	pH 11	222(4.42),266(3.48), 275s(--)	4-0885-73
$C_7H_8N_4O$			
Pyrazolo[3,4-d]pyrimidin-4-ol, 1,5-dimethyl-	EtOH	257(3.79),267(3.76)	103-1280-73

Compound	Solvent	λ_{max}(log ϵ)	Ref.
Pyrazolo[3,4-d]pyrimidin-4-ol, 2,5-di-methyl-	EtOH	260(3.89),267(3.89)	103-1280-73
Pyrimido[4,5-d]pyrimidine, 3,4-dihydro-4-methoxy-	MeCN	213(3.92),266(3.64), 341(3.26)	24-3743-73
1H-1,2,3-Triazole, 4-methyl-5-(3-methyl-5-isoxazolyl)-	EtOH	254(4.19)	78-3271-73
	anion	264(4.16)	78-3271-73
1H-1,2,4-Triazolo[4,3-b]pyridazin-4-ium, 8-hydroxy-1,6-dimethyl-, hydroxide, inner salt	n.s.g.	223(3.54),280(3.82), 306(4.02)	48-0097-73
$C_7H_8N_4OS$			
2H-Purin-2-one, dihydro-1-methyl-6-(methylthio)-	neutral	246(3.85),335(4.09)	39-2445-73C
	anion	280(3.73),342(3.97)	39-2445-73C
	cation	264(3.95),335(3.86)	39-2445-73C
2H-Purin-2-one, 1,7-dihydro-1-methyl-8-(methylthio)-	pH 1	346(4.45)	44-2066-73
	pH 6	330(4.04)	44-2066-73
	pH 12	286(4.06),330(4.06)	44-2066-73
2H-Purin-2-one, dihydro-3-methyl-6-(methylthio)-	neutral	268(4.06),317(4.19)	39-2445-73C
	anion	260(4.03),320(4.21)	39-2445-73C
	cation	256(3.85),341(4.28)	39-2445-73C
2H-Purin-2-one, dihydro-7-methyl-6-(methylthio)-	neutral	270(4.05),317(4.15)	39-2445-73C
	anion	255(3.91),322(4.07)	39-2445-73C
	cation	259(3.96),339(4.06)	39-2445-73C
2H-Purin-2-one, dihydro-9-methyl-6-(methylthio)-	neutral	252(3.88),332(4.07)	39-2445-73C
	anion	242(4.05),314(4.12)	39-2445-73C
	cation	258(3.89),331(4.14)	39-2445-73C
6H-Purin-6-one, 1,7-dihydro-1-methyl-2-(methylthio)-	neutral	262(4.06)	39-2647-73C
	anion	272(4.06)	39-2647-73C
	cation	265.5(4.14)	39-2647-73C
6H-Purin-6-one, 1,7-dihydro-7-methyl-2-(methylthio)-	pH 1	266(4.27)	44-2066-73
	pH 6	225(4.12),265(4.22)	44-2066-73
	neutral	265(4.22)	39-2647-73C
	pH 12	233(4.45),275(4.15)	44-2066-73
	anion	274.5(4.15)	39-2647-73C
6H-Purin-6-one, 1,9-dihydro-9-methyl-2-(methylthio)-	pH 1	266(4.32)	44-2066-73
	pH 6	263(4.20)	44-2066-73
	pH 12	273(4.20)	44-2066-73
	anion	272.5(4.20)	39-2647-73C
6H-Purin-6-one, 3,7-dihydro-3-methyl-2-(methylthio)-	neutral	238(4.14),279(4.20)	39-2647-73C
	anion	234(4.31),283(4.13)	39-2647-73C
	cation	233(4.06),278(4.04)	39-2647-73C
6H-Purin-6-one, 1,2,3,7-tetrahydro-1,3-dimethyl-2-thioxo-	MeOH	286(4.25)	39-2647-73C
6H-Purin-6-one, 1,2,3,7-tetrahydro-3,7-dimethyl-2-thioxo-	MeOH	286(4.24)	39-2647-73C
$C_7H_8N_4OS_2$			
6H-Purin-6-one, 1,7-dihydro-2,8-bis-(methylthio)-	neutral	280(4.30)	39-2647-73C
	anion	289(4.26)	39-2647-73C
	dianion	291.5(4.26)	39-2647-73C
	cation	283(4.36)	39-2647-73C
$C_7H_8N_4O_2$			
6H-Purin-6-one, 1,7-dihydro-1-methoxy-7-methyl-	pH 0	250(3.91)	44-2397-73
	pH 9	213(4.40),256(3.88)	44-2397-73
$C_7H_8N_4O_2S$			
1H-Purine-2,6-dione, 3,7-dihydro-1-methyl-8-(methylthio)-	pH 1.0	289(4.17)	44-3367-73
	pH 6.0	293(4.14)	44-3367-73
	pH 12.0	295(4.16)	44-3367-73

Compound	Solvent	$\lambda_{max}(\log \epsilon)$	Ref.
1H-Purine-2,6-dione, 3,7-dihydro-3-methyl-8-(methylthio)-	pH 1.0	291(4.25)	44-3367-73
	pH 6.0	295(4.15)	44-3367-73
	pH 12.0	294(4.43)	44-3367-73
2H-Pyrazino[2,3-e]-1,2,4-thiadiazine, 6,7-dimethyl-, 1,1-dioxide	EtOH	231(3.63),276(3.61), 315(3.94)	18-1890-73
$C_7H_8N_4O_3$			
2(1H)-Pteridinone, 3,4-dihydro-1-hydroxy-4-methoxy-	MeOH	228s(3.83),242(3.90), 290s(3.74),312(3.82)	44-0703-73
	MeOH-NaOH	260(4.05),278(4.10), 415(3.32)	44-0703-73
$C_7H_8N_4S_2$			
[4,5'-Bithiazole]-2,2'-diamine, 4'-methyl-	pH 1	266(4.21)	80-0677-73
	EtOH	262(4.08),313(4.20)	80-0677-73
$C_7H_8N_6$			
2,4-Pteridinediamine, 6-methyl-	0.12M HCl	242(4.16),281(3.63), 338(3.99),349(3.93)	35-6413-73
$C_7H_8N_6O$			
Methanone, bis(5-methyl-1H-1,2,3-triazol-4-yl)-	EtOH	264(4.07)	78-3271-73
anion	EtOH	291(4.17)	78-3271-73
2,4-Pteridinediamine, 6-methyl-, 8-oxide	H_2O	213(4.12),228s(3.89), 263(4.48),293s(3.84), 392(3.84)	35-6413-73
Pyrimido[5,4-e]-1,2,4-triazin-3-amine, 5-methoxy-7-methyl-	MeOH	222s(4.04),259(4.17), 310s(3.04),394(3.71)	12-1689-73
Pyrimido[5,4-e]-1,2,4-triazin-5-amine, 3-ethoxy-	MeOH	218(4.04),261(4.11), 296s(3.27),392(3.73)	12-1689-73
Urea, N-methyl-N'-1H-purin-6-yl-	pH 1-2	277(4.33)	87-0139-73
	pH 5-7	269(4.28),277s(--)	87-0139-73
	pH 11.5	277(4.24)	87-0139-73
C_7H_8O			
Anisole	EtOH	219(3.76),267s(3.16), 273(3.25),278s(3.17)	141-0001-73
	dioxan	220(3.70),268s(3.11), 273(3.25),280(3.15)	141-0001-73
2-Cyclobuten-1-one, 4-(1-methylethylidene)-	C_6H_{12}	223(4.42),305(2.73)	35-0274-73
2,4-Cycloheptadien-1-one	MeOH	294(3.8)	35-3289-73
3,5-Cycloheptadien-1-one	MeOH	227(3.62)	35-3289-73
at -50°	FSO_3H	318(3.3)	35-3289-73
4,6-Heptadiyn-3-ol	EtOH	217(2.77),226(2.88), 238(2.83),252(2.64)	39-2785-73C
8-Oxabicyclo[5.1.0]octa-2,5-diene	C_6H_{12}	280(2.78)	89-0580-73
Phenol, 2-methyl-	dioxan	274(3.35),280(3.30)	126-0039-73L
Phenol, 4-methyl-	dioxan	282(3.35),288(3.26)	126-0039-73L
$C_7H_8OS_2$			
2H-Pyran-2-thione, 6-methyl-4-(methylthio)-	MeOH	279(4.45),384(4.18)	7-0269-73
4H-Pyran-4-thione, 6-methyl-2-(methylthio)-	MeOH	222(4.10),298(4.03), 355(4.44)	7-0269-73
2H-Thiopyran-2-one, 6-methyl-4-(methylthio)-	MeOH	237(4.16),303(4.21)	7-0269-73
4H-Thiopyran-4-one, 2-methyl-6-(methylthio)-	MeOH	248(4.04),293(4.20)	7-0269-73

Compound	Solvent	$\lambda_{max}(\log \epsilon)$	Ref.
2H-Thiopyran-2-thione, 4-methoxy-6-methyl-	MeOH	268(4.35),311(3.81) 405(3.87)	7-0269-73
$C_7H_8O_2$			
Benzenemethanol, 2-hydroxy-	dioxan	274(3.37),279s(3.34)	126-0039-73L
Benzenemethanol, 4-hydroxy-	dioxan	278(3.28),283s(3.22)	126-0039-73L
Ethanone, 1-(3-methyl-2-furanyl)-	n.s.g.	284(4.16)	103-0939-73
Ethanone, 1-(5-methyl-2-furanyl)-	heptane	272(--)	103-0546-73
	H_2O	289(--)	103-0546-73
	EtOH	283(--)	103-0546-73
	dioxan	280(4.29)	103-0546-73
$C_7H_8O_2S$			
2H-Pyran-2-one, 6-methyl-4-(methylthio)-	MeOH	227(4.19),273(4.15), 300(3.94)	7-0269-73
4H-Pyran-4-one, 2-methyl-6-(methylthio)-	MeOH	215(4.13),276(4.12)	7-0269-73
2H-Pyran-2-thione, 4-methoxy-6-methyl-	MeOH	231(4.33),277(3.94), 353(4.16)	7-0269-73
2H-Thiopyran-2-one, 4-methoxy-6-methyl-	MeOH	228(4.45),255(3.74), 313(3.68)	7-0269-73
4H-Thiopyran-4-one, 2-methoxy-6-methyl-	MeOH	207(--),235(3.93), 280(4.28)	7-0269-73
$C_7H_8O_3$			
2-Cyclopenten-1-one, 2-acetoxy-	EtOH	228(3.97),308(1.71)	44-2117-73
Desoxyepoxidon	MeOH	242(3.67)	130-0134-73
2-Furancarboxylic acid, ethyl ester	heptane	248(--)	103-0546-73
	H_2O	254(--)	103-0546-73
	EtOH	251(--)	103-0546-73
	dioxan	249(4.22)	103-0546-73
C_7H_8S			
Benzene, (methylthio)-	C_6H_{12}	206(4.19),255(4.02), 284(3.00)	39-1125-73B
	EtOH	207(4.11),253(3.99), 283(2.93)	39-1125-73B
	5% EtOH	203(4.23),251(3.99), 280(2.97)	39-1125-73B
Benzenethiol, 2-methyl-	C_6H_{12}	208(4.32),235(3.91), 277f(2.89)	39-1125-73B
	EtOH	208(4.36),239(3.85), 277f(2.86)	39-1125-73B
	EtOH-base	266(3.99)	39-1125-73B
	5% EtOH	205(4.18),237(3.86), 277s(3.06)	39-1125-73B
	+ base	216(4.14),262(4.08)	39-1125-73B
Benzenethiol, 3-methyl-	C_6H_{12}	209(4.32),237(3.84), 280s(2.86)	39-1125-73B
	EtOH	208(4.36),240(3.86), 280s(2.92)	39-1125-73B
	EtOH-base	269(3.99)	39-1125-73B
	5% EtOH	207(4.30),240(3.84)	39-1125-73B
	+ base	263(4.00)	39-1125-73B
Benzenethiol, 4-methyl-	C_6H_{12}	208(4.30),239(3.99), 285s(2.85)	39-1125-73B
	EtOH	206(4.30),239(3.96), 284s(2.92)	39-1125-73B
	EtOH-base	268(4.10)	39-1125-73B
	5% EtOH	203(4.32),240(3.91)	39-1125-73B
	+ base	265(4.07)	39-1125-73B

Compound	Solvent	λ_{max}(log ε)	Ref.
$C_7H_8S_3$			
[1,2]Dithiolo[1,5-b][1,2]dithiole-7-S^{IV}, 3,4-dimethyl-	C_6H_{12}	205(4.11),236(4.28), 264(4.69),492(3.73)	39-2351-73C
2H-Thiopyran-2-thione, 6-methyl-4-(methylthio)-	MeOH	307(4.47),436(4.00)	7-0269-73
$C_7H_9BrN_2O_4$			
2,4(1H,3H)-Pyrimidinedione, 5-bromo-1-(2,3-dihydroxypropyl)-	H_2O	211(3.99),283(3.96)	18-1572-73
$C_7H_9BrN_5O_4P$			
9H-Purine-9-ethanol, 6-amino-8-bromo-, dihydrogen phosphate	H_2O	268(4.18)	121-1297-73
$C_7H_9ClN_2$			
Hydrazine, 2-(2-chloro-2,4-cyclopentadien-1-ylidene)-1,1-dimethyl-	hexane	266(3.25),330(4.44)	88-5101-73
$C_7H_9ClN_2O_2S$			
Pyridazine, 6-chloro-4-(ethylthio)-3-methoxy-, 1-oxide	MeOH	237(3.85),274(4.15), 304(4.07),360(3.6)	4-0835-73
$C_7H_9ClN_2O_4$			
2,4(1H,3H)-Pyrimidinedione, 5-chloro-1-(2,3-dihydroxypropyl)-	H_2O	213(3.89),280(3.92)	126-0019-73J
C_7H_9ClO			
Cyclohexanone, 2-(chloromethylene)-	EtOH	245(3.89)	78-4241-73
2-Cyclohexen-1-one, 3-chloro-2-methyl-	EtOH	241(4.08)	78-4241-73
$C_7H_9FN_2O_4$			
2,4(1H,3H)-Pyrimidinedione, 1-(2,3-dihydroxypropyl)-5-fluoro-	H_2O	210(3.99),275(3.95)	18-1572-73
$C_7H_9IN_2O_4$			
2,4(1H,3H)-Pyrimidinedione, 1-(2,3-dihydroxypropyl)-5-iodo-	H_2O	219(4.08),292(3.99)	18-1572-73
C_7H_9NO			
Oxazole, 2-ethynyl-4,5-dihydro-4,4-dimethyl-	MeOH	219(3.60)	18-0540-73
Pyridine, 2,4-dimethyl-, 1-oxide, hydrochloride	6M HCl	261(3.62)	59-0139-73
	H_2O	254(4.13)	59-0139-73
Pyridine, 2,5-dimethyl-, 1-oxide, hydrochloride	6M HCl	272(3.68)	59-0139-73
	H_2O	252(4.02)	59-0139-73
Pyridine, 2,6-dimethyl-, 1-oxide, hydrochloride	6M HCl	270(3.84)	59-0139-73
	H_2O	251(4.00)	59-0139-73
Pyridine, 3,4-dimethyl-, 1-oxide, hydrochloride	6M HCl	262(3.61)	59-0139-73
	H_2O	256(4.26)	59-0139-73
Pyridine, 3,5-dimethyl-, 1-oxide, hydrochloride	6M HCl	271(3.62)	59-0139-73
	H_2O	255(4.08)	59-0139-73
Pyridine, 2-ethyl-, 1-oxide	H_2O	253(4.02)	59-1069-73
	cation	266(3.71)	59-1069-73
Pyridine, 3-ethyl-, 1-oxide	H_2O	255(4.07)	59-1069-73
	cation	266(3.58)	59-1069-73
3-Pyridinol, 2,6-dimethyl-	H_o 1.09	202(4.25),295(4.06)	103-0888-73
	-2.12	200(4.51),295(4.14)	103-0888-73
	-4.78	200(4.44),295(4.18)	103-0888-73
	-7.58	201(3.34),291(4.28)	103-0888-73
	-9.06	199(3.91),294(3.65)	103-0888-73

Compound	Solvent	λ max(log ε)	Ref.
3-Pyridinol, 2,6-dimethyl- (cont.)	H_o -11.98	213(4.33),276(4.66)	103-0888-73
2(1H)-Pyridinone, 1,3-dimethyl-	MeOH	226(3.74),299(3.68)	94-2695-73
2(1H)-Pyridinone, 1,5-dimethyl-	MeOH	227(3.88),311(3.63)	94-2695-73
Pyrrole, 3-acetyl-2-methyl-	EtOH	206(4.17),243(3.96), 281(3.82)	12-1551-73
Pyrrole, 3-acetyl-4-methyl-	H_2O	248(4.10),280(3.59)	103-1355-73
	20N H_2SO_4	276(4.36),330(3.32)	103-1355-73
1H-Pyrrole-2-carboxaldehyde, 3,4-dimethyl-	H_2O	270(3.93),304(4.18)	103-1355-73
	16N H_2SO_4	292(4.26),340(3.75)	103-1355-73
1H-Pyrrole-2-carboxaldehyde, 3,5-dimethyl-	H_2O	260(3.62),309(4.33)	103-1355-73
	25N H_2SO_4	298(4.25)	103-1355-73
1H-Pyrrole-3-carboxaldehyde, 2,4-dimethyl-	H_2O	257(4.10),295(3.67)	103-1355-73
	14N H_2SO_4	272(4.29),335(3.46)	103-1355-73
C_7H_9NOS			
2(1H)-Pyridinethione, 3-(hydroxymethyl)-1-methyl-	EtOH	210(4.12),280(4.08), 353(3.90)	94-2590-73
2(1H)-Pyridinethione, 5-(hydroxymethyl)-1-methyl-	EtOH	210(4.10),288(4.20), 360(3.92)	94-2590-73
$C_7H_9NO_2$			
2,1-Benzisoxazol-3(1H)-one, 4,5,6,7-tetrahydro-	EtOH	262(3.99)	1-2802-73
2,4(1H,3H)-Pyridinedione, 3,5-dimethyl-	EtOH	283(4.02)	94-1047-73
3-Pyridinol, 2,6-dimethyl-, 1-oxide	H_o 1.09	204(4.31),251(3.05)	103-0888-73
	-2.12	203(4.41),296(3.95)	103-0888-73
	-4.78	203(4.63),298(3.90)	103-0888-73
	-7.58	202(4.63),292(4.10)	103-0888-73
	-9.06	204(4.23),291(4.02)	103-0888-73
	-11.98	214(4.49),278(4.74)	103-0888-73
1H-Pyrrole-1-carboxylic acid, ethyl ester	$CHCl_3$	241(3.81)	39-2281-73C
1H-Pyrrole-2-carboxylic acid, ethyl ester	$CHCl_3$	264(4.33)	39-2281-73C
1H-Pyrrole-2,5-dione, 3-ethyl-4-methyl-	dioxan	222(4.26),272(2.68)	24-0803-73
2,5-Pyrrolidinedione, 3-ethylidene-4-methyl-, (E)-	dioxan	219(4.23),269(1.91)	24-0803-73
(Z)-	dioxan	224(4.14),273(2.48)	24-0803-73
$C_7H_9NO_2S$			
2-Propenoic acid, 2-cyano-3-(methylthio)-, ethyl ester, (E)-	EtOH	304(4.21)	18-0699-73
$C_7H_9NO_2S_2$			
2-Propenoic acid, 2-cyano-3,3-bis(methylthio)-, methyl ester	C_6H_{12}	300s(3.92),327(4.09)	1-0258-73
	EtOH	307(4.16)	1-0258-73
$C_7H_9NO_3$			
Acetamide, N-(2-hydroxy-5-oxo-1-cyclopenten-1-yl)-	MeOH	257(4.30)	5-0407-73
	MeOH-HCl	243(4.08)	5-0407-73
	MeOH-NaOH	258(4.43)	5-0407-73
2,6-Piperidinedione, 3-acetyl-	EtOH	283(3.76)	95-1437-73
$C_7H_9NO_3S$			
Acetic acid, (3-methyl-4-oxo-2-thiazolidinylidene)-, methyl ester	EtOH	282(4.30)	1-1923-73
Acetic acid, (4-oxo-2-thiazolidinylidene)-, ethyl ester	MeOH	233(4.04),284(4.34)	44-3615-73
(E)-	EtOH	283(4.33)	1-1914-73
(Z)-	EtOH	283(4.33)	1-1914-73

Compound	Solvent	$\lambda_{max}(\log \epsilon)$	Ref.
Carbamic acid, (4-methylene-1,3-oxathiolan-2-ylidene)-, ethyl ester	EtOH	259.5(3.83)	94-0062-73
Thioimidodicarbonic acid, O-ethyl S-1,2-propadienyl ester	dioxan	238(3.81)	94-0062-73
Thioimidodicarbonic acid, O-ethyl O'-2-propynyl ester	EtOH	259(3.88)	94-0062-73
$C_7H_9NO_5S$			
2H-1,4-Thiazine-3,6-dicarboxylic acid, 3,4-dihydro-, 6-methyl ester, 1-oxide, (3R)-	EtOH	273(4.14)	78-3023-73
$C_7H_9NS_2$			
6H-[1,2]Dithiolo[5,1-e]isothiazole-7-S^{IV}, 2,6-dimethyl-	MeOH	209(4.17),234(4.46), 265s(3.82),414(4.14)	39-2351-73C
C_7H_9NSe			
1,2-Benzisoselenazole, 4,5,6,7-tetrahydro-	EtOH	203(3.43),226(3.55), 272(3.72)	4-0267-73
$C_7H_9N_3O_2$			
Glycine, N-(6-methyl-4-pyrimidinyl)-	pH 1	258(4.25)	94-2349-73
	pH 7	246(4.13),263s(3.91)	94-2349-73
	pH 12	244(4.18),267s(3.62)	94-2349-73
$C_7H_9N_3O_2S_2$			
Carbamic acid, [(methylthio)(2-thiazolylimino)methyl]-, methyl ester	dioxan	242(3.83),315(4.32)	94-0074-73
$C_7H_9N_3O_3$			
1(2H)-Pyrimidinecarboxylic acid, 4-amino-2-oxo-, ethyl ester	pH 1	211(3.99),271(4.02)	35-2677-73
	pH 13	281(3.86)	35-2677-73
1(2H)-Pyrimidinepropanoic acid, 3,6-dihydro-6-imino-2-oxo-	H_2O	278(4.00)	138-0967-73
$C_7H_9N_3O_3S$			
Carbamic acid, [(2-thiazolylamino)carbonyl]-, ethyl ester	EtOH	262(4.06)	94-0074-73
1,2,4-Triazine-6-carboxylic acid, 2,5-dihydro-2-methyl-3-(methylthio)-5-oxo-, methyl ester	EtOH	244(4.37),280s(3.77)	22-3178-73
1,2,4-Triazine-6-carboxylic acid, 4,5-dihydro-4-methyl-3-(methylthio)-5-oxo-, methyl ester	EtOH	229(3.91),330(4.02)	22-3178-73
1,2,4-Triazine-6-carboxylic acid, 2,3,4,5-tetrahydro-2,4-dimethyl-5-oxo-3-thioxo-, methyl ester	EtOH	231(3.95),275(4.17), 337(3.84)	22-3178-73
$C_7H_9N_3S$			
Propanedicarbonitrile, [(dimethylamino)-(methylthio)methylene]-	C_6H_{12}	262(3.78),310(4.12)	1-0258-73
	EtOH	268s(3.78),307(4.19)	1-0258-73
$C_7H_9N_5$			
Adenine, 3,9-dimethyl-, perchlorate	pH 1	270(4.19)	77-0917-73
	pH 7	270(4.19)	77-0917-73
	EtOH	272(4.11)	77-0917-73
Adenine, 7,9-dimethyl-, perchlorate	pH 1	268(4.08)	88-4873-73
	pH 7	269(4.08)	88-4873-73
	pH 13	257(3.76)	88-4873-73
	EtOH	273(4.06)	88-4873-73

Compound	Solvent	$\lambda_{max}(\log \epsilon)$	Ref.
Adenine, 3-ethyl-	pH 1	220s(4.05),275(4.24)	94-1954-73
	pH 7	274.5(4.12)	94-1954-73
	pH 13	274(4.11)	94-1954-73
	EtOH	275(4.09)	94-1954-73
1H-1,2,3-Triazole, 4-methyl-5-(5-methyl-1H-pyrazol-3-yl)-	EtOH	238(4.05)	78-3271-73
	anion	252(4.16)	78-3271-73
$C_7H_9N_5O$			
Adenine, N^6-methoxy-7-methyl-	pH 1	228(3.83),278(4.02)	88-4873-73
	pH 7	275(4.14)	88-4873-73
	pH 13	296(4.12)	88-4873-73
	EtOH	277(4.13)	88-4873-73
Methanimidic acid, N-(5-cyano-1-methyl-1H-1,2,3-triazol-4-yl)-, ethyl ester	C_6H_{12}	208(4.05),255(4.04)	39-2659-73C
Methanimidic acid, N-(5-cyano-2-methyl-1,2,3-triazol-4-yl)-, ethyl ester	C_6H_{12}	247(4.07)	39-2659-73C
8H-Purin-8-one, 6-amino-3-ethyl-3,7-dihydro-	pH 1	218(4.35),287(4.25)	94-1954-73
	pH 7	229(4.29),294(4.26)	94-1954-73
	pH 13	232s(3.95),307(4.12)	94-1954-73
	EtOH	234(4.25),299(4.22)	94-1954-73
$C_7H_9N_5OS$			
Thiazolo[4,5-d]pyridazine-2,7(3H,6H)-dione, 3,6-dimethyl-, 2-hydrazone	$CHCl_3$	256(4.28),351(3.31)	22-3324-73
$C_7H_9N_5O_2$			
2,6-Pyridinedicarboxylic acid dihydrazide	pH 2.8	224(4.02),273(3.74)	35-1323-73
	pH 6.2	223(4.02),274s(3.79)	35-1323-73
	pH 10.8	220s(4.01),273(3.79)	35-1323-73
$C_7H_9N_5O_4S$			
Hydrazinecarbothioamide, 2-(5-acetoxytetrahydro-4,6-dioxo-2(1H)-pyrimidinylidene)-	EtOH	241(4.26)	103-0247-73
$C_7H_9N_5O_5$			
Hydrazinecarboxamide, 2-(5-acetoxy-1,4,5,6-tetrahydro-4,6-dioxo-2-pyrimidinyl)-	EtOH	260(4.09)	103-0247-73
$C_7H_9N_7$			
Pyrimido[5,4-e]-1,2,4-triazine-3,5-diamine, N,N'-dimethyl-	pH 1	226(4.28),284(4.03), 295s(4.00),312s(3.85), 450(3.72)	12-1689-73
	pH 9.0	223(4.40),281(4.14), 445(3.72)	12-1689-73
$C_7H_9N_7O$			
Pyrimido[5,4-e]-1,2,4-triazine-3,5-diamine, 7-ethoxy-	MeOH	221s(4.11),253s(4.24), 260(4.27),318s(3.08), 433(3.69),475s(3.30)	12-1689-73
C_7H_9O			
Cycloheptadienylium, 1-hydroxy-	FSO_3H	375(3.89)	35-3289-73
C_7H_{10}			
1,3-Cyclohexadiene, 1-methyl-	heptane	265(3.81)	70-1984-73
1,3-Cyclohexadiene, 2-methyl-	heptane	261(3.81)	70-1984-73
	isooctane	261(3.51)	35-4346-73
1,3-Cyclohexadiene, 5-methyl-	heptane	259(3.62)	70-1984-73

Compound	Solvent	$\lambda_{max}(\log \epsilon)$	Ref.
Cyclohexene, 3-methylene-	heptane	231(4.30)	70-1984-73
1,3-Cyclopentadiene, 1,3-dimethyl-	heptane	254(3.52)	70-0034-73
1,3-Cyclopentadiene, 5,5-dimethyl-	heptane	250(3.52)	70-0346-73
	EtOH	250(3.46)	89-0577-73
Dispiro[2.0.2.1]heptane	C_6H_{12}	202(1.18),210(1.20), 262(0.48)	89-0334-73
1,3,5-Hexatriene, 2-methyl-, (E)-	heptane	248(4.49),258(4.63), 268(4.54)	78-1393-73
1,3,5-Hexatriene, 2-methyl-, (Z)-	heptane	249(4.27),259(4.35), 269(4.22)	78-1393-73
1,3,5-Hexatriene, 3-methyl-, 3-cis	isooctane	252(4.35),262(4.46), 272(4.35)	44-2478-73
1,3,5-Hexatriene, 3-methyl-, 3-trans	isooctane	244s(--),253(4.51), 263(4.64),274(4.54)	44-2478-73
$C_7H_{10}CuF_3O_3S$			
Norbornylenecopper(I) trifluoroacetate	n.s.g.	236(3.53),272(3.30)	35-1889-73
$C_7H_{10}INO$			
2-Pyrrolidinone, 5-(iodomethylene)-4,4-dimethyl-	EtOH	238(4.15)	89-0910-73
trans	EtOH	240(4.27)	89-0910-73
$C_7H_{10}NO_3P$			
Phosphonic acid, (2,6-dimethyl-4-pyridinyl)-	pH 3.0	278(3.87),283s(3.81)	44-1306-73
	pH 6.30	278(3.87),283s(3.81)	44-1306-73
	pH 10.0	273(3.64),280(3.41)	44-1306-73
$C_7H_{10}N_2$			
Hydrazine, (2-methylphenyl)-	pH 6.8	231(3.87),279(3.17)	78-3497-73
Hydrazine, (3-methylphenyl)-	pH 6.8	235(3.89),281(3.13)	78-3497-73
Hydrazine, (4-methylphenyl)-	pH 6.8	234(3.97),284(3.14)	78-3497-73
4-Pyridinamine, N-ethyl-	n.s.g.	356(4.41)	88-2807-73
2-Pyridinemethanamine, α-methyl-, (S)-	MeOH-KOH	256s(3.56),261(3.60), 267s(3.46)	35-0811-73
dihydrochloride	MeOH-KOH	261(3.88)	35-0811-73
3-Pyridinemethanamine, α-methyl-, (R)-	MeOH-KOH	257s(3.43),261(3.46), 267s(3.32)	35-0811-73
dihydrochloride	MeOH-KOH	260(3.81)	35-0811-73
4-Pyridinemethanamine, α-methyl-, (S)-	MeOH-KOH	252s(3.28),256(3.32), 262s(3.20)	35-0811-73
dihydrochloride	MeOH-KOH	257(3.71)	35-0811-73
$C_7H_{10}N_2O$			
Phenol, 3-(hydrazinomethyl)-, hydrochloride	EtOH	275(3.09)	39-0471-73C
$C_7H_{10}N_2OS$			
2(1H)-Pyrimidinethione, 4-ethoxy-1-methyl-	M HCl	277(4.03)	94-1451-73
	H_2O	276(3.99)	94-1451-73
Thiocyanic acid, 1-acetyl-2-(methylamino)-1-propenyl ester	hexane	297(4.13)	40-2152-73
$C_7H_{10}N_2O_2$			
1H-Imidazole-2-carboxylic acid, 1-methyl-, ethyl ester	EtOH	219(3.56),261(3.45)	12-0415-73
3H-Isoxazolo[3,4-d]azepin-3-one, 1,4,5,6,7,8-hexahydro-	EtOH	255(3.95)	1-3251-73
2,6-Piperidinedione, 3-(1-aminoethylidene)-	EtOH	312(4.17)	95-1437-73

Compound	Solvent	$\lambda_{max}(\log \epsilon)$	Ref.
2,4(1H,3H)-Pyrimidinedione, 1-ethyl-5-methyl-	H_2O	273.5(3.88)	39-0391-73C
2,4(1H,3H)-Pyrimidinedione, 1,3,5-tri-methyl-	H_2O	271(3.94)	39-0391-73C
$C_7H_{10}N_2O_2S$			
4(1H)-Pyrimidinone, 2,3-dihydro-5-(1-methoxyethyl)-2-thioxo-	H_2O	214(4.14),274(4.19), 285s(4.18)	44-1963-73
	anion	209(4.05),234(4.02), 260(4.08),315(3.96)	44-1963-73
	dianion	260(4.09),292(3.96)	44-1963-73
$C_7H_{10}N_2O_3$			
Acetic acid, (4-oxoimidazolidinyli-dene)-, ethyl ester	EtOH	213(4.08),278(4.48)	1-2221-73
1H-Pyrazole-4-carboxylic acid, 3-acetyl-4,5-dihydro-, methyl ester	MeOH	280(4.29)	88-2655-73
5-Pyrimidinecarboxylic acid, 1,2,3,4-tetrahydro-4-methyl-2-oxo-, methyl ester	H_2O	284(3.97)	44-1963-73
$C_7H_{10}N_2O_4$			
1,2-Benzisoxazole, 3a,4,5,6,7,7a-hexa-hydro-3-nitro-, 2-oxide	EtOH	322(3.89)	104-0931-73
$C_7H_{10}N_2S$			
2-Benzothiazolamine, 4,5,6,7-tetra-hydro-, hydrobromide	EtOH	202(2.96),220(3.20), 262(3.95)	34-0099-73
$C_7H_{10}N_3O$			
Pyridinium, 3-(hydrazinocarbonyl)-1-methyl-, iodide	pH 2.8	264(3.72)	35-1323-73
	pH 6.2	264(3.72)	35-1323-73
	pH 10.8	255(3.85),305(3.66)	35-1323-73
Pyridinium, 4-(hydrazinocarbonyl)-1-methyl-, iodide	pH 2.8	268(3.78)	35-1323-73
	pH 6.2	268(3.78)	35-1323-73
	pH 10.8	253(3.72),372(3.70)	35-1323-73
Pyridinium, 1-(2-hydrazino-2-oxoethyl)-, chloride	pH 2.8	259(3.68)	35-1323-73
	pH 6.2	259(3.68)	35-1323-73
	pH 10.8	258(3.66)	35-1323-73
$C_7H_{10}N_4OS_2$			
Thiourea, [1-(1,2,3,4-tetrahydro-4-oxo-2-thioxo-5-pyrimidinyl)ethyl]-	H_2O	238(4.13),276(4.23), 294s(4.18)	44-1963-73
$C_7H_{10}N_4O_2S$			
2H-Pyrazino[2,3-e]-1,2,4-thiadiazine, 3,4-dihydro-6,7-dimethyl-, 1,1-di-oxide	EtOH	251(4.00),348(3.85)	18-1890-73
$C_7H_{10}N_4S_2$			
Carbamodithioic acid, (4-amino-2-methyl-5-pyrimidinyl)methyl-	pH 1	243(4.32),257s(4.24)	94-0329-73
	pH 13	233(4.18),253(4.16), 285(4.29)	94-0329-73
	15M KOH	249(4.34)	94-0329-73
	H_2SO_4	243(4.37)	94-0329-73
$C_7H_{10}N_6$			
2,4-Pteridinediamine, 7,8-dihydro-6-methyl-	pH 1	232(4.28),288(4.06)	35-6413-73

Compound	Solvent	$\lambda_{max}(\log \epsilon)$	Ref.
$C_7H_{10}O$			
Bicyclo[3.1.0]hexan-2-one, 1-methyl-	EtOH	200(3.64)	35-0468-73
Bicyclo[3.1.0]hexan-2-one, 5-methyl-	EtOH	194(3.57),280(1.75)	35-0468-73
2-Cyclohexen-1-one, 2-methyl-	CH_2Cl_2	235(3.93),325(1.52)	88-3251-73
BF_3 complex	CH_2Cl_2	272.6(3.83)	88-3251-73
2-Cyclohexen-1-one, 3-methyl-	CH_2Cl_2	233(4.10),323(1.53)	88-3251-73
BF_3 complex	CH_2Cl_2	269.9(4.02)	88-3251-73
2-Cyclohexen-1-one, 4-methyl-	CH_2Cl_2	226(4.00),330(1.45)	88-3251-73
BF_3 complex	CH_2Cl_2	252.3(3.92)	88-3251-73
2-Cyclopenten-1-one, 2,3-dimethyl-	EtOH	206(4.11)	35-0468-73
$C_7H_{10}OS$			
Cyclopentanethione, 2-acetyl-	C_6H_{12}	245s(3.31),297(3.52), 369(3.72),465(1.40)	78-2449-73
	EtOH	304(3.62),367(3.44), 453(1.14)	78-2449-73
$C_7H_{10}OS_2$			
1,3-Dithiole-2-one, 4-(1,1-dimethylethyl)-	EtOH	239(3.49),270(3.48)	143-0273-73
$C_7H_{10}O_2$			
1,2-Cyclopentanedione, 3,5-dimethyl-	MeOH	258(4.05)	24-2255-73
Cyclopentanone, 2-acetyl-	EtOH	284(3.42)	44-0514-73
1-Cyclopentene-1-carboxylic acid, methyl ester	EtOH	224(3.99)	44-4348-73
2-Cyclopenten-1-one, 3,5-dimethyl-2-hydroxy-	EtOH	261(4.08)	44-0551-73
4H-Pyran-4-one, 2,3-dihydro-2,6-dimethyl-	EtOH	263(4.15)	23-1267-73
$C_7H_{10}O_2S_2$			
2,4-Pentanedione, 3-[mercapto(methylthio)methylene]-, anion	EtOH	311(3.93),371(3.75)	54-1169-73
$C_7H_{10}O_3$			
Homofuraneol (isomer mixture)	EtOH	293(3.87)	33-1882-73
3-Penten-2-one, 3-acetoxy-	EtOH	238(3.07)	33-1882-73
2H-Pyran-2-one, 5,6-dihydro-4-methoxy-6-methyl-	EtOH	220(3.24),234(3.39)	28-1131-73A
$C_7H_{10}O_3S_2$			
1,3-Dithiole-4-carboxylic acid, 2-methoxy-, ethyl ester	EtOH	230s(3.63),304(3.78)	35-4379-73
$C_7H_{10}O_4$			
2H-Pyran-3(6H)-one, 6-(hydroxymethyl)-2-methoxy-, (2S-trans)-	MeOH	225.2(3.98)	23-3357-73
$C_7H_{10}O_4S$			
Butanoic acid, 4-[(2-carboxyethenyl)-thio]-, cis	H_2O	283(4.03)	44-3507-73
trans	H_2O	276(4.16)	44-3507-73
2-Propenoic acid, 3-[(3-methoxy-3-oxopropyl)thio]-, (Z)-	H_2O	275(4.00)	44-3507-73
$C_7H_{10}S$			
Thiophene, 2,3,4-trimethyl-	EtOH	238(3.77)	35-1285-73

Compound	Solvent	$\lambda_{max}(\log \epsilon)$	Ref.
$C_7H_{11}F_3O_2$ 3-Hexanone, 6,6,6-trifluoro-5-hydroxy-4-methyl-, threo	EtOH	216(1.90),273(1.54)	23-3177-73
$C_7H_{11}IO$ 3,4-Hexadien-2-ol, 3-iodo-5-methyl-	EtOH	212(4.11),247(3.90)	22-2506-73
$C_7H_{11}N$ Pyrrole, 2-ethyl-5-methyl- Pyrrolidine, 1-methyl-3,4-bis(methylene)-	MeOH isooctane	216(3.80) 240s(3.92),245(3.94)	35-4356-73 88-2361-73
$C_7H_{11}NO$ 2,3-Hexadienamide, 4-methyl-	EtOH	210(4.17)	88-0209-73
$C_7H_{11}NO_2$ 2(3H)-Pyridinone, 6-ethoxy-4,5-dihydro-	C_6H_{12} tert-BuOH	275(1.78) 275s(2.11)	35-3957-73 35-3957-73
$C_7H_{11}NO_2S$ 2-Propenethioamide, 3-acetoxy-N,N-dimethyl-, (Z)- 2,4-Thiazolidinedione, 5-butyl-	ether EtOH	228(<u>4.1</u>),287(<u>3.9</u>) 222(3.52)	27-0073-73 132-0113-73
$C_7H_{11}NO_3$ Carbamic acid, (2-methyl-3-oxo-1-propenyl)-, ethyl ester	EtOH	267(4.49)	104-0908-73
$C_7H_{11}NO_4S$ 2H-1,4-Thiazine-6-carboxylic acid, 3,4-dihydro-3-(hydroxymethyl)-, methyl ester, 1-oxide, (3R)- (S)-	EtOH EtOH	273(4.17) 276(4.15)	78-3023-73 78-3023-73
$C_7H_{11}NS_2$ Cyclopentanecarbodithioic acid, 2-imino-3-methyl-	EtOH	303(3.90),392(4.26)	39-1009-73C
$C_7H_{11}N_3OS_2$ Morpholine, 4-[5-(methylthio)-1,3,4-thiadiazol-2-yl]- hydriodide 1,3,4-Thiadiazole-2(3H)-thione, 3-methyl-5-(4-morpholinyl)-	EtOH EtOH EtOH	288(4.05) 286(3.77) 320(4.04)	104-2631-73 104-2631-73 104-2631-73
$C_7H_{11}N_3O_2$ 1H-Pyrazole, 3-tert-butyl-4-nitro- 1H-Pyrazole, 3-tert-butyl-5-nitro-	0.05M HCl 0.05M NaOH 0.05M HCl 0.05M NaOH	288(3.86) 326(4.04) 264(3.86) 324(3.89)	4-1055-73 4-1055-73 4-1055-73 4-1055-73
$C_7H_{11}N_3O_3$ Glycine, N-(4,5-dihydro-1-methyl-4-oxo-1H-imidazol-2-yl)-N-methyl- hydrochloride Sydnone imine, 1-(4-carboxybutyl)- hydrochloride	pH 12 pH 12 EtOH EtOH	229(4.34) 227(4.25) 206(3.82),298(3.81) 205(3.91),300(3.87)	44-1591-73 44-1591-73 103-1327-73 103-1327-73
$C_7H_{11}N_5O$ 1H-Imidazole-4-carboxamide, 5-[(1-methylethylidene)hydrazino]-	H_2O	204(4.33),286(4.07)	103-0083-73

Compound	Solvent	λ_{max}(log ϵ)	Ref.
$C_7H_{11}N_5O_4$			
1,3-Propanediol, 2-[(6-amino-5-nitro-4-pyrimidinyl)amino]-	pH 1	339(3.78)	103-0117-73
	H_2O	341(4.22)	103-0117-73
	pH 13	341(3.87)	103-0117-73
C_7H_{12}			
2,3-Pentadiene, 2,4-dimethyl-	gas	152(4.10),156(4.22), 158(4.27),161(4.41), 166(4.45),167(4.45), 168(4.45),169(4.46), 173(4.33),177(4.15), 181(3.94),191(3.97), 196(4.09),216(3.13)	35-1429-73
$C_7H_{12}ClN_3$			
Acetonitrile, (1-chloroisopropyldiazo)-dimethyl-	C_6H_{12}	353(1.27)	108-0819-73
	MeCN	348(1.30)	108-0819-73
$C_7H_{12}Cl_3N_4$			
Ammonium, dimethyl[1,3,5-trichloro-5-(dimethylamino)-2,4-diaza-2,4-pentadienylidene]-, chloride	$CHCl_3$	247(4.22),310(4.28)	114-0081-73A
$C_7H_{12}N_2$			
6,7-Diazabicyclo[3.2.2]non-6-ene	hexane	396(2.08)	35-6478-73
$C_7H_{12}N_2O$			
2-Cyclopropen-1-one, 2,3-bis(dimethyl-amino)-	MeCN	232(4.03),265s(3.33)	88-2619-73
2-Propenal, 3-(1-aziridinyl)-3-(dimeth-ylamino)-	CH_2Cl_2	228(3.83),303(4.42)	33-0944-73
4H-Pyrazol-4-one, 3,5-dihydro-3,3,5,5-tetramethyl-	n.s.g.	357(2.40)	89-0224-73
$C_7H_{12}N_2OS$			
4(5H)-Thiazolone, 3-butyl-2-imino-	EtOH	220(4.14),248(3.90)	132-0113-73
$C_7H_{12}N_2O_2$			
Piperidine, 1-methyl-2-(nitromethylene)-	EtOH	219(3.68),244s(3.45), 352(4.43)	103-0880-73
$C_7H_{12}N_2O_3$			
2-Propenal, 3-(diethylamino)-2-nitro-	$CHCl_3$	294(4.01),343(4.10)	104-0477-73
$C_7H_{12}N_2O_3S$			
Cysteinamide, N,S-diacetyl-	H_2O	226(3.74)	44-0270-73
$C_7H_{12}N_2O_6$			
Hexanoic acid, 2,6-dinitro-, methyl ester	MeOH	270(1.89)	18-3462-73
	MeOH-NaOMe	233(4.09)	18-3462-73
$C_7H_{12}N_4O_2S$			
Carbamic acid, (3-amino-1,2,4-thiadia-zol-5-yl)-, butyl ester	EtOH	272(3.51)	94-2396-73
Carbamic acid, [4-methyl-3-(methyl-amino)-1,2,4-thiadiazol-5(4H)-ylidene]-, ethyl ester	EtOH	287.5(3.91)	94-2396-73
$C_7H_{12}N_4S$			
1,2'-Bi-1H-imidazole, 4,4',5,5'-tetra-hydro-2-(methylthio)-, hydriodide	EtOH	218(4.16)	44-1641-73

Compound	Solvent	λ_{max}(log ϵ)	Ref.
1,2'-Bi-1H-imidazole, 4,4',5,5'-tetrahydro-2-(methylthio)-, methanethiol adduct	EtOH	219(4.68)	44-1641-73
3H-Imidazo[2,1-b][1,3,5]triazepine, 2,7,8,9-tetrahydro-5-(methylthio)-, hydriodide	EtOH	219(4.42)	44-1641-73
$C_7H_{12}O$			
Cycloheptanone	hexane	292(1.18)	46-1830-73
Cyclohexanone, 2-methyl-	hexane	290(1.20)	46-1830-73
	C_6H_{12}	290(1.22)	22-2231-73
	heptane	289(1.23)	22-2231-73
	H_2O	279(--)	22-2231-73
	MeOH	284(1.30)	22-2231-73
	EtOH	285(1.28)	22-2231-73
	MeCN	287(1.26)	22-2231-73
	CCl_4	293(1.36)	22-2231-73
	$CHCl_3$	287(1.34)	22-2231-73
	CH_2Cl_2	289(1.26)	22-2231-73
Cyclohexanone, 3-methyl-	hexane	290(1.15)	46-1830-73
	C_6H_{12}	290(1.18)	22-2231-73
	heptane	290(1.18)	22-2231-73
	H_2O	277(--)	22-2231-73
	MeOH	282(1.23)	22-2231-73
	EtOH	284(1.26)	22-2231-73
	MeCN	287(1.23)	22-2231-73
	CCl_4	294(1.33)	22-2231-73
	$CHCl_3$	287(1.32)	22-2231-73
	CH_2Cl_2	288(1.32)	22-2231-73
Cyclohexanone, 4-methyl-	hexane	290(1.20)	46-1830-73
	C_6H_{12}	291(1.18)	22-2231-73
	heptane	291(1.18)	22-2231-73
	H_2O	278(--)	22-2231-73
	MeOH	282(1.15)	22-2231-73
	EtOH	283(1.20)	22-2231-73
	MeCN	287(1.18)	22-2231-73
	CCl_4	293(1.30)	22-2231-73
	$CHCl_3$	287(1.31)	22-2231-73
	CH_2Cl_2	287(1.20)	22-2231-73
Cyclopentanone, 2,2-dimethyl-	C_6H_{12}	291(1.28),299(1.30), 309(1.23)	22-2231-73
	heptane	291(1.26),299(1.29), 309(1.20)	22-2231-73
	H_2O	287(--)	22-2231-73
	MeOH	292(1.38)	22-2231-73
	EtOH	292(1.36)	22-2231-73
	MeCN	295(1.34)	22-2231-73
	CCl_4	298(1.38)	22-2231-73
	$CHCl_3$	294(1.38)	22-2231-73
	CH_2Cl_2	295(1.36)	22-2231-73
Cyclopentanone, 2,3-dimethyl-	C_6H_{12}	289(1.26),298(1.30), 308(1.22)	22-2231-73
	heptane	289(1.28),298(1.30), 308(1.23)	22-2231-73
	H_2O	284(--)	22-2231-73
	MeOH	290(1.34)	22-2231-73
	EtOH	290(1.34)	22-2231-73
	MeCN	293(1.34)	22-2231-73
	CCl_4	297(1.42),306(1.34)	22-2231-73
	$CHCl_3$	293(1.42)	22-2231-73
	CH_2Cl_2	294(1.32)	22-2231-73

Compound	Solvent	λ_{max}(log ϵ)	Ref.
Cyclopentanone, 2,5-dimethyl-	C_6H_{12}	299(1.28),309(1.20)	22-2231-73
	hexane	300(1.28)	46-1830-73
	heptane	290(1.23),299(1.28), 309(1.22)	22-2231-73
	H_2O	288(--)	22-2231-73
	MeOH	293(1.33)	22-2231-73
	EtOH	294(1.33)	22-2231-73
	MeCN	295(1.30)	22-2231-73
	CCl_4	298(1.38),307(1.34)	22-2231-73
	$CHCl_3$	295(1.36)	22-2231-73
	CH_2Cl_2	295(1.32)	22-2231-73
Cyclopentanone, 3,4-dimethyl-, cis	hexane	301(1.30)	46-1830-73
trans	hexane	301(1.28)	46-1830-73
2-Cyclopenten-1-ol, 1,2-dimethyl-	n.s.g.	240.5(3.61)	70-0034-73
2-Cyclopenten-1-ol, 2,4-dimethyl-	n.s.g.	253(3.49)	70-0034-73
2-Cyclopenten-1-ol, 2,5-dimethyl-	n.s.g.	252(3.51)	70-0034-73
Cyclopropane, 1-acetyl-2,2-dimethyl-	EtOH	227(1.91)	22-2301-73
2-Hepten-4-one, cis	hexane	222(3.98)	35-7345-73
trans	hexane	216(4.09)	35-7345-73
4-Hexen-3-one, 2-methyl-, cis	hexane	222(3.98)	35-7345-73
trans	hexane	218(4.04)	35-7345-73
$C_7H_{12}O_3$			
2-Pentenal, 5,5-dimethoxy-	hexane	217(4.10)	104-0074-73
$C_7H_{12}O_4$			
2-Propenoic acid, 3-methoxy-2-(methoxymethyl)-, methyl ester	MeOH	237(4.18)	18-0580-73
$C_7H_{13}B_6Co$			
Cobalt, (η^5-2,4-cyclopentadien-1-yl)-[(3,5,6,7,8-η-octahydro-dicarbaoctaborato(2-)]-	MeCN	250(4.01),274s(3.84), 350(3.56),460(2.32)	35-4565-73
$C_7H_{13}B_6Fe$			
Iron, (η^5-2,4-cyclopentadien-1-yl)-[(1,3,6,8-η)-octahydro-1,8-dicarbaoctaborato(2-)]-	MeCN	226(4.28),294(3.92), 344s(3.10),460(2.97), 670(2.17)	35-4565-73
isomer	MeCN	228(4.18),284(3.78), 346(3.56),464(2.95)	35-4565-73
$C_7H_{13}N$			
3-Buten-1-amine, N,3-dimethyl-2-methylene-	EtOH	225(4.24)	44-1483-73
tert-Butylamine, N-allylidene-	EtOH	214(4.38)	78-4111-73
$C_7H_{13}NO$			
3-Piperidinone, 1,6-dimethyl-, (S)-	isooctane	297(1.52)	35-3678-73
$C_7H_{13}NO_2$			
3-Buten-2-one, 4-(dimethylamino)-4-methoxy-	CH_2Cl_2	296(4.24)	33-0944-73
2-Pentene, 3,4-dimethyl-2-nitro-	EtOH	258(3.96)	19-0351-73
sodium salt	EtOH	272(4.22)	19-0351-73
2-Propenal, 3-(dimethylamino)-3-ethoxy-	CH_2Cl_2	292(4.41)	33-0944-73
$C_7H_{13}NO_3$			
2-Propenoic acid, 3-(dimethylamino)-3-methoxy-, methyl ester	n.s.g.	275.5(4.28)	33-0944-73

Compound	Solvent	$\lambda_{max}(\log \epsilon)$	Ref.
$C_7H_{13}N_3O$			
1,2,4-Triazine, 2,5-dihydro-3-methoxy-5,5,6-trimethyl-	n.s.g.	218(3.65),255(3.89), 322(3.42)	22-2493-73
$C_7H_{13}N_3S$			
1,3,4-Thiadiazol-2-amine, 5-pentyl-	EtOH	257(3.68)	80-1777-73
	EtOH-HCl	247(3.76)	80-1777-73
1,2,4-Triazine, 2,5-dihydro-5,5,6-trimethyl-3-(methylthio)-	n.s.g.	214(3.90),271(3.30)	22-2493-73
1H-1,2,4-Triazolium, 4-butyl-3-mercapto-1-methyl-, hydroxide, inner salt	MeCN	250(4.16)	103-1048-73
$C_7H_{13}N_5O_2$			
1,3-Propanediol, 2-[(5,6-diamino-4-pyrimidinyl)amino]-	pH 1	384(4.01)	103-0117-73
	H_2O	386(4.02)	103-0117-73
	pH 13	385(3.95)	103-0117-73
$C_7H_{13}OPS$			
Phosphine oxide, diethyl[(methylthio)-ethynyl]-	hexane	218(3.32),228(3.30), 236(3.18)	54-0762-73
$C_7H_{13}S_4$			
2-Propenylium, 1,1,3,3-tetrakis(methylthio)-, perchlorate	MeCN	414(4.64)	88-3409-73
$C_7H_{14}B_7Co$			
Cobalt, (η^5-2,4-cyclopentadien-1-yl)-[η^5-nonahydrodicarbanonaborato(2-)]-	MeCN	254(4.02),308(3.57), 448(2.23)	35-4565-73
isomer	MeCN	250(4.01),274s(3.84), 350(3.56),460(2.32)	35-4565-73
$C_7H_{14}NO$			
2-Isoxazolium, 4,5-dihydro-2,3,5,5-tetramethyl-, perchlorate	EtOH	230(3.62)	22-1390-73
$C_7H_{14}NO_5P$			
Phosphonic acid, (1-methyl-2-nitroethenyl)-, diethyl ester	nonane	229(3.69),305s(2.08)	65-2164-73
$C_7H_{14}N_2O$			
3-Buten-2-one, 4-(dimethylamino)-3-(methylamino)-	CH_2Cl_2	323(4.21)	33-0944-73
3-Buten-2-one, 4-(dimethylamino)-4-(methylamino)-	CH_2Cl_2	234(3.81),304(4.31)	33-0944-73
2-Propenal, 2,3-bis(dimethylamino)-	EtOH	289(3.81)	73-1168-73
	CH_2Cl_2	288(4.44)	33-0944-73
2-Propenal, 3,3-bis(dimethylamino)-	CH_2Cl_2	252(3.81),304(4.39)	33-0944-73
$C_7H_{14}N_2OS_2$			
Carbamothioic acid, methyl[3-(methylamino)-3-thioxopropyl]-, O-methyl ester	n.s.g.	251(4.36)	128-0495-73
$C_7H_{14}N_2O_2$			
2-Propenoic acid, 3-(dimethylamino)-3-(methylamino)-, methyl ester	CH_2Cl_2	232(3.78),283(4.38)	33-0944-73
$C_7H_{14}N_2O_2S$			
Carbamic acid, N-methyl-N-[2-(methylthiocarbamoyl)ethyl]-, methyl ester	n.s.g.	203(3.93),265(4.11)	128-0495-73

Compound	Solvent	$\lambda_{max}(\log \epsilon)$	Ref.
Thiocarbamic acid, N-methyl-N-[2-(methylcarbamoyl)ethyl]-, methyl ester	n.s.g.	247(4.29)	128-0495-73
$C_7H_{14}N_2S_2$			
Methanedithiol, amino[(2-methylcyclopentylidene)amino]-	EtOH	222s(3.98),237s(3.60), 340(4.36)	39-1009-73C
$C_7H_{14}OSi$			
3-Buten-2-one, 3-(trimethylsilyl)-	C_6H_{12}	208(3.88),332(1.68), 341(1.65),355(1.46), 374(0.95)	23-2024-73
3-Buten-2-one, 4-(trimethylsilyl)-	C_6H_{12}	220(4.04),327(1.72), 337(1.73),351(1.69), 365(1.48),382(1.00)	23-2024-73
$C_7H_{14}S$			
Butane, 1-(ethenylthio)-2-methyl-	heptane	232(3.76),237s(3.74), 250s(3.65)	143-0019-73
$C_7H_{14}S_2$			
Propanedithioic acid, 2-methyl-, isopropyl ester	C_6H_{12}	307(3.94),460(2.08)	101-0121-73I
$C_7H_{15}NO_2$			
2-Pentanone, 4-methoxy-4-methyl-, oxime	EtOH	205(3.51)	22-1395-73
$C_7H_{16}GeS_2$			
Germane, trimethyl[(2-methyl-1-thioxopropyl)thio]-	C_6H_{12}	310(4.12),483(2.10)	101-0121-73I
	$CHCl_3$	313(4.03),478(2.32)	101-0121-73I
$C_7H_{16}IOP$			
Phosphonium, acetyldiethylmethyl-, iodide	CH_2Cl_2	326(2.47)	18-1803-73
	MeCN	205(4.38),240(4.15), 313(2.18)	18-1803-73
$C_7H_{16}N_2S$			
Thiourea, 1,1-dipropyl-	EtOH	247(4.16)	48-0144-73
$C_7H_{16}S_2Si$			
Propanedithioic acid, 2-methyl-, trimethylsilyl ester	C_6H_{12}	303(4.08),487(2.08)	101-0121-73I
	$CHCl_3$	306(3.98),483(2.33)	101-0121-73I
$C_7H_{16}S_2Sn$			
Stannane, trimethyl[(2-methyl-1-thioxopropyl)thio]-	C_6H_{12}	319(4.17),473(2.00)	101-0121-73I
	$CHCl_3$	321(4.05),470(2.34)	101-0121-73I

Compound	Solvent	$\lambda_{max}(\log \epsilon)$	Ref.
$C_8Br_2Cl_8$			
Bicyclo[4.2.0]octa-1,5-diene, 7,8-dibromo-2,3,3,4,4,5,7,8-octachloro-	heptane	228(4.6),255s(4.0), 285(3.0),293(3.1), 305(3.1)	5-2025-73
$C_8Br_4Cl_4$			
Bicyclo[4.2.0]octa-1,3,5-triene, 7,7,8,8-tetrabromo-2,3,4,5-tetrachloro-	heptane	236(4.6),260s(4.0), 290s(3.0),300(3.3), 312(3.3)	5-2025-73
$C_8F_{12}N_2$			
Pyridazine, 3,6-difluoro-4,5-bis(pentafluoroethyl)-	C_6H_{12}	277(3.70),286s(3.65)	39-1405-73C
$C_8HF_9N_2$			
7,8-Diazatricyclo[4.3.0.0^{2,5}]nona-3,8-diene, 1,2,3,4,5,6-hexafluoro-9-(trifluoromethyl)-	hexane	203(3.25),248(3.34)	39-1798-73C
$C_8H_2Br_4N_2O_2$			
1H-Isoindole-1,3(2H)-dione, 3-amino-4,5,6,7-tetrabromo-	EtOH	242(4.04),337(3.22)	115-0297-73
$C_8H_2Br_4O_5$			
2(5H)-Furanone, 5,5'-oxybis[3,4-dibromo-, α-	MeOH	245.0(4.33)	39-0107-73B
β-	MeOH	244(4.29)	39-0107-73B
$C_8H_2Cl_4N_2O_2$			
1H-Isoindole-1,3(2H)-dione, 2-amino-4,5,6,7-tetrachloro-	EtOH	236(4.42),335(3.05)	115-0297-73
$C_8H_2Cl_4O_5$			
2(5H)-Furanone, 5,5'-oxybis[3,4-dichloro-, α-	MeOH	231.5(4.33)	39-0107-73B
β-	MeOH	230.5(4.28)	39-0107-73B
$C_8H_3ClF_7NO$			
Pyridine, 4-(1-chloro-1,2,2,2-tetrafluoroethyl)-2,3,5-trifluoro-6-methoxy-	C_6H_{12}	301(3.63)	39-1411-73C
$C_8H_3Cl_3S_2$			
2,3'-Bithiophene, 2',3,5-trichloro-	MeOH	249(4.10),278(4.05)	18-3603-73
C_8H_4BrCl			
Benzene, 1-(bromoethynyl)-4-chloro-	hexane	251(4.36),262(4.35)	39-0063-73B
	MeOH	260(4.36)	35-1602-73
$C_8H_4BrClN_2$			
1,8-Naphthyridine, 2-bromo-3-chloro-	EtOH	208(5.24),222(4.88), 336(4.49)	56-2361-73
$C_8H_4BrNO_2$			
Benzene, 1-(bromoethynyl)-4-nitro-	MeOH	217(4.00),296(4.26)	39-0063-73B
$C_8H_4Br_2$			
Benzene, 1-bromo-4-(bromoethynyl)-	MeOH	262(4.32)	35-1602-73

Compound	Solvent	λ_{max}(log ε)	Ref.
$C_8H_4Br_2N_2$			
1,8-Naphthyridine, 2,3-dibromo-	EtOH	207(5.68),315(4.82)	56-2361-73
$C_8H_4Cl_2N_2$			
1,8-Naphthyridine, 2,3-dichloro-	EtOH	207(5.17),326(4.62)	56-2361-73
$C_8H_4Cl_2N_4S$			
Thiazolo[2,3-f]purine, 2,4-dichloro-6-methyl-	EtOH	252(4.40),293(3.85), 307s(--)	94-0256-73
$C_8H_4Cl_2O_5$			
2(5H)-Furanone, 5,5'-oxybis[4-chloro-, α-	MeOH	213(4.40)	39-0107-73B
β-	MeOH	212.5(4.44)	39-0107-73B
$C_8H_4Cl_2S_2$			
2,3'-Bithiophene, 2',5-dichloro-	MeOH	249(4.10),298(4.25)	18-3603-73
$C_8H_4O_3$			
Phthalic anhydride	EtOH	214(4.30),216s(4.29), 246s(3.55),286(3.22), 295s(3.15)	141-0001-73
	dioxan	221(3.94),251(3.66), 281s(3.20),289(3.32), 298(3.30)	141-0001-73
C_8H_5Br			
Benzene, (bromoethynyl)-	hexane	242(4.27),253(4.26)	39-0063-73B
	MeOH	253(4.06)	35-1602-73
Benzene, 1-bromo-4-ethynyl-	MeOH	254.5(4.28)	35-1602-73
$C_8H_5BrN_2$			
1,8-Naphthyridine, 3-bromo-	EtOH	219(4.97),223(4.96), 320(4.69)	56-2361-73
$C_8H_5BrN_2O$			
1,8-Naphthyridin-2-ol, 3-bromo-	EtOH	207(5.68),315(4.82)	56-2361-73
$C_8H_5Br_4Cl$			
Spiro[2.4]hepta-4,6-diene, 4,5,6,7-tetrabromo-1-(chloromethyl)-	hexane	249(3.85),290(3.54)	44-1340-73
C_8H_5Cl			
Benzene, (chloroethynyl)-	MeOH	250(3.99)	35-1602-73
	EtOH	239(4.26),251(4.23)	39-0063-73B
Benzene, 1-chloro-4-ethynyl-	MeOH	252(4.32)	35-1602-73
$C_8H_5ClN_2$			
1,8-Naphthyridine, 3-chloro-	EtOH	208(5.03),311(4.35), 320(4.35)	56-2361-73
$C_8H_5ClN_2O$			
1,8-Naphthyridin-2-ol, 3-chloro-	EtOH	206(5.48),313(4.63)	56-2361-73
1,3,4-Oxadiazole, 2-chloro-5-phenyl-	C_6H_{12}	253(4.30)	4-0989-73
$C_8H_5ClN_4S$			
Thiazolo[2,3-f]purine, 4-chloro-6-methyl-	EtOH	247(4.33),288(3.82)	94-0256-73
$C_8H_5ClS_2$			
[2,3'-Bithiophene], 2'-chloro-	MeOH	244(4.10),287(4.14)	18-3603-73

Compound	Solvent	λ_{max}(log ε)	Ref.
$C_8H_5Cl_2N_3O_2$			
1,2,4-Triazolidine-3,5-dione, 1-(2,5-dichlorophenyl)-	EtOH	291.5(3.34)	88-5123-73
1,2,4-Triazolidine-3,5-dione, 1-(3,4-dichlorophenyl)-	EtOH	297.0(3.26)	88-5123-73
$C_8H_5F_3N_2O_3$			
Acetamide, 2,2,2-trifluoro-N-(4-nitrophenyl)-	MeOH	220(4.05),298(4.15)	24-0355-73
$C_8H_5F_3O$			
Benzaldehyde, 4-(trifluoromethyl)-	EtOH	236(4.06),280(3.11), 287(3.08)	36-0910-73
C_8H_5NO			
Benzonitrile, 3-formyl-	1% EtOH	245(3.90)	39-0786-73B
Benzonitrile, 4-formyl-	1% EtOH	254(4.28)	39-0786-73B
$C_8H_5NO_2$			
Benzene, 1-ethynyl-4-nitro-	EtOH	286(4.15),350s(2.70)	65-2627-73
$C_8H_5N_2O_2$			
Benzeneacetonitrile, 4-nitro-, ion(1-), tetrabutylammonium salt	$CHCl_3$	264(3.96),462(3.66), 596(3.68)	1-0258-73
$C_8H_5N_3$			
1,3-Benzenedicarbonitrile, 4-amino-	EtOH	277(4.34),330(3.63)	104-2331-73
$C_8H_5N_3OS_2$			
4H-Thiazolo[3,2-a]-1,3,5-triazin-4-one, 2-(2-propynylthio)-	EtOH	225(3.93),265(3.93), 310(4.30),319s(--)	94-0074-73
$C_8H_5N_5$			
Pyrido[2,3-b]pyrazine-7-carbonitrile, 6-amino-	pH -0.6	230(4.35),266s(3.53), 361(4.13),376s(4.05)	39-1615-73C
	pH 7	213(4.43),235(4.37), 258s(3.94),383(4.01)	39-1615-73C
C_8H_6			
Benzene, ethynyl-	MeOH	244.5(3.96)	35-1602-73
$C_8H_6BrCl_2O_2P$			
Phosphonic dichloride, [2-(4-bromophenoxy)ethenyl]-	C_6H_{12}	198(4.43),240(4.18), 272s(3.40)	65-2164-73
$C_8H_6BrIO_3$			
2-Propenoic acid, 3-(4-bromo-5-iodo-2-furanyl)-, methyl ester	MeOH	322(4.37)	103-0802-73
$C_8H_6Br_2O_3$			
2-Propenoic acid, 3-(4,5-dibromo-2-furanyl)-, methyl ester	MeOH	312(4.39)	103-0802-73
$C_8H_6ClF_3$			
Benzene, 1-(chloromethyl)-4-(trifluoromethyl)-	EtOH	264(2.70),271(2.60)	36-0910-73
$C_8H_6ClNO_3$			
Ethanone, 1-(4-chloro-3-nitrophenyl)-	DMF	295s(3.11)	39-1430-73B

Compound	Solvent	$\lambda_{max}(\log \epsilon)$	Ref.
$C_8H_6ClNO_4$			
Benzoic acid, 4-chloro-3-nitro-, methyl ester	DMF	294(3.10)	39-1430-73B
$C_8H_6ClNS_2$			
Benzothiazole, 4-chloro-2-(methylthio)-	$CHCl_3$	244(4.16),288(4.17)	22-3044-73
Benzothiazole, 5-chloro-2-(methylthio)-	$CHCl_3$	244(4.23),280(4.09), 311(3.92)	22-3044-73
Benzothiazole, 6-chloro-2-(methylthio)-	$CHCl_3$	242(4.05),287(4.17), 308(4.03)	22-3044-73
Benzothiazole, 7-chloro-2-(methylthio)-	$CHCl_3$	247(4.11),287(4.12)	22-3044-73
$C_8H_6ClN_5S$			
Thiazolo[2,3-f]purin-4-amine, 2-chloro-6-methyl-	pH 1	248(4.37),278(4.10)	94-0256-73
Thiazolo[3,2-e]purin-4-amine, 2-chloro-8-methyl-	pH 1	240(4.05),246s(--), 279s(--),290(4.17), 300s(--)	94-0034-73
	pH 13	243(--),289(--), 300(--)	94-0034-73
$C_8H_6Cl_2NO_3P$			
Phosphonic dichloride, [2-(3-nitrophenyl)ethenyl]-	dioxan	249(4.28),270(3.95), 312(2.90)	65-2164-73
$C_8H_6Cl_2N_2$			
1-Cyclohexene-1,2-dicarbonitrile, 4,5-dichloro-, trans	MeOH	231(4.05),241s(3.87)	33-3004-73
$C_8H_6Cl_2OS$			
Benzo[c]thiophen-4(5H)-one, 1,3-dichloro-6,7-dihydro-	EtOH	222(4.10),258(3.91), 302(3.43)	22-0335-73
4H-Cyclopenta[c]thiophen-4-one, 1,3-dichloro-5,6-dihydro-5-methyl-	EtOH	218(4.11),264(4.09), 306(3.64)	22-0335-73
$C_8H_6F_3N_2O_5$			
1,3-Cyclohexadiene, 2-methoxy-1,5-dinitro-3-(trifluoromethyl)-, ion(1-)	DMSO	362(4.13),490(4.42)	39-0710-73B
1,5-Cyclohexadiene, 4-methoxy-3,5-dinitro-1-(trifluoromethyl)-, ion(1-)	DMSO	360(4.00),488(4.20), 555(4.18)	39-0710-73B
$C_8H_6F_6OS_2$			
1,3-Dithiole-2-acetaldehyde, α-methyl-4,5-bis(trifluoromethyl)-	isooctane	232s(3.35),290s(3.34), 310(3.37)	35-4379-73
2-Propanone, 1-[4,5-bis(trifluoromethyl)-1,3-dithiole-2-yl]-	isooctane	233(3.36),285s(3.34), 311(3.39)	35-4379-73
$C_8H_6N_2$			
Quinoxaline	pH 6.2	235(4.36),315(3.76)	103-0369-73
	7.1N H_2SO_4	242(4.40),332(3.88)	103-0369-73
$C_8H_6N_2OS$			
Thiocyanic acid, 4-acetyl-3-pyridinyl ester	EtOH	224(4.20),247(3.74), 320(3.66)	23-1741-73
$C_8H_6N_2O_4$			
2,4(1H,3H)-Pyrimidinedione, 1-(2,5-dihydro-5-oxo-2-furanyl)-	pH 3-7	255(3.99)	44-3878-73

Compound	Solvent	λ_{max}(log ε)	Ref.
$C_8H_6N_2S_3$			
1,3,4-Thiadiazolidine-2,5-dithione, 3-phenyl-	n.s.g.	269(4.02),346(3.97)	48-0915-73
$C_8H_6N_3O_5$			
1,3-Cyclohexadiene-1-carbonitrile, 6-methoxy-3,5-dinitro-, ion(1-)	DMSO	390(4.32),490(4.34)	39-0710-73B
$C_8H_6N_4O$			
1,2,4-Triazin-5(2H)-one, 3-(2-pyridinyl)-	MeOH	239(4.23),265(4.12)	40-1519-73
$C_8H_6N_4OS$			
Thiazolo[2,3-f]purin-4(1H)-one, 6-methyl-	EtOH	241(4.31),247s(--), 276(4.01)	94-0256-73
Thiazolo[3,2-e]purin-4(3H)-one, 8-methyl-	pH 13	227(4.23),283(4.17)	94-0034-73
$C_8H_6N_4O_2$			
1,2,4-Triazine-5,6-dione, 1,2-dihydro-3-(2-pyridinyl)-	MeOH	290(4.19),298(4.20), 310s(4.09)	40-1519-73
1H-1,2,3-Triazole, 4-(4-nitrophenyl)-	EtOH	304(4.20)	78-3271-73
	anion	350(4.23)	78-3271-73
$C_8H_6N_4O_2S$			
1,3,4-Thiadiazol-2-amine, 5-(3-nitrophenyl)-	EtOH	308(3.98)	80-1777-73
	EtOH-HCl	274(3.95),300(3.91)	80-1777-73
1,3,4-Thiadiazol-2-amine, 5-(4-nitrophenyl)-	EtOH	252(3.88),352(4.17)	80-1777-73
	EtOH-HCl	246(3.88),347(4.06)	80-1777-73
Thiazolo[2,3-f]xanthine, 6-methyl-	pH 13	232(4.39),282(4.12)	94-0256-73
$C_8H_6N_4O_3S$			
1,2,4-Oxadiazole, 5-methyl-3-[2-(2-nitro-5-thiazolyl)ethenyl]-, (E)-	EtOH	260(4.04),361(4.19)	39-2769-73C
$C_8H_6N_4O_4$			
2,4(1H,3H)-Pteridinedione, 1-acetoxy-	pH 5.0	229(4.05),323(3.90)	44-0703-73
$C_8H_6N_6$			
2H-1,2,3-Triazole-4-carbonitrile, 5-amino-2-(4-pyridinyl)-	pH 1	244(4.13),351(4.28)	39-1629-73C
	pH 7	225(4.21),319(4.22)	39-1629-73C
$C_8H_6N_6O$			
Pyrido[2,3-e][1,2,4]triazolo[3,4-c]-[1,2,4]triazine, 9-methyl-, 5-oxide	EtOH	328(3.96),338(3.96)	4-0575-73
C_8H_6O			
6-Octene-2,4-diynal, (E)-	ether	228(4.08),235(4.36), 253(3.60),269(3.74), 284(3.85),300(3.93), 318(3.90)	39-0140-73C
$C_8H_6O_2$			
1,3-Benzenedicarboxaldehyde	1% EtOH	250(4.11)	39-0786-73B
2(3H)-Benzofuranone	EtOH	271(3.09),277(3.08)	44-1993-73
1(3H)-Isobenzofuranone	EtOH	227(4.05),232s(3.98), 265s(3.11),273(3.30), 281(3.30)	141-0001-73
	dioxan	228(3.96),232s(3.92), 267s(3.15),273(3.30), 280(3.34)	141-0001-73

Compound	Solvent	$\lambda_{max}(\log \epsilon)$	Ref.
$C_8H_6O_2S$			
Thiophene-3-ol, 5-ethynyl-, acetate	ether	245(3.66),253(3.67), 270(3.62)	24-0497-73
$C_8H_6O_3$			
Benzaldehyde, 2,3-(methylenedioxy)-	EtOH	229(4.24),258(4.02), 293s(2.80),342(3.54)	141-0001-73
	dioxan	231(4.16),255(4.01), 338(3.58)	141-0001-73
Benzaldehyde, 3,4-(methylenedioxy)-	EtOH	231(4.24),273(3.89), 314(3.98)	141-0001-73
	dioxan	233(4.19),272(3.90), 310(3.96)	141-0001-73
1(3H)-Isobenzofuranone, 4-hydroxy-	EtOH	216(4.26),236(3.82), 296(3.52)	141-0001-73
	EtOH-NaOH	228(4.47),254(3.75), 328(3.58)	141-0001-73
	dioxan	230s(3.81),235(3.85), 238s(3.80),289(3.50), 294s(3.49)	141-0001-73
1(3H)-Isobenzofuranone, 5-hydroxy-	EtOH	252(4.03),275s(3.45), 286(3.11)	141-0001-73
	EtOH-NaOH	244(3.96),275(3.26), 285(3.20)	141-0001-73
	dioxan	254(4.09),275(3.43), 286(3.13)	141-0001-73
1(3H)-Isobenzofuranone, 7-hydroxy-	EtOH	212(4.41),232(3.94), 299(3.66)	141-0001-73
$C_8H_6O_4$			
1,2-Benzenedicarboxylic acid	EtOH	225(3.92),276s(3.15), 282(3.16),293s(2.81)	141-0001-73
	EtOH-NaOH	218(3.94),232s(3.80), 274(3.02),280s(2.94)	141-0001-73
	dioxan	227(3.90),274(3.20), 281s(3.14)	141-0001-73
Benzoic acid, 2,3-(methylenedioxy)-	EtOH	211(4.43),216s(4.40), 233s(3.95),315(3.64)	141-0001-73
Benzoic acid, 3,4-(methylenedioxy)-	EtOH	217(4.29),259(3.85), 295(3.81)	141-0001-73
	EtOH-NaOH	253(3.83),291(3.75)	141-0001-73
	dioxan	225(4.02),261(3.83), 296(3.79)	141-0001-73
1(3H)-Isobenzofuranone, 4,7-dihydroxy-	EtOH	216(4.55),255(4.18), 290(3.70)	141-0001-73
Pyrano[3,4-b]pyran-4,8-dione, 5,6-dihydro-	EtOH	268(3.82)	95-1183-73
$C_8H_6O_4S_2$			
Acetic acid, (2,3-dihydro-7-oxo-1,4-dithiino[2,3-c]furan-5(7H)-ylidene)-	MeOH	237(3.49),265(3.53), 319(3.39)	49-1224-73
$C_8H_6O_5$			
1,2-Benzenedicarboxylic acid, 4-hydroxy-	EtOH	215(4.23),256(4.00), 297s(3.33)	141-0001-73
	EtOH-NaOH	223(4.13),274(4.17)	141-0001-73
	dioxan	221(3.88),253(3.98), 293s(3.20)	141-0001-73

Compound	Solvent	$\lambda_{max}(\log \epsilon)$	Ref.
$C_8H_7BF_2O_2$			
Boron, difluoro[1-(2-hydroxyphenyl)ethanone-O,O']-(T-4)-	$C_2H_4Cl_2$	252(4.0),327(3.55)	24-2427-73
$C_8H_7BrN_2O$			
Ethanehydrazonoyl bromide, 2-oxo-N-phenyl-	MeCN	233(3.98),336(4.33)	24-1661-73
$C_8H_7BrO_3$			
2-Propenoic acid, 3-(3-bromo-2-furanyl)-, methyl ester	MeOH	305(4.01)	103-0802-73
$C_8H_7ClN_2O$			
Ethanehydrazonoyl chloride, 2-oxo-N-phenyl-	MeCN	233(4.02),335(4.38)	24-1661-73
C_8H_7ClO			
Bicyclo[3.2.1]octa-3,6-dien-2-one, 3-chloro-	C_6H_{12}	270(3.36),360(1.95)	88-3759-73
C_8H_7ClOS			
Benzo[c]thiophen-4(5H)-one, 1-chloro-6,7-dihydro-	EtOH	222(4.03),262(3.95), 286s(3.33)	22-0335-73
4H-Cyclopenta[c]thiophen-4-one, 1-chloro-5,6-dihydro-5-methyl-	EtOH	218(4.03),264(4.15), 284s(3.49)	22-0335-73
$C_8H_7ClO_2$			
Benzoic acid, 4-chloro-3-methyl-	EtOH	240(4.11),277(3.02), 286(2.92)	12-1337-73
2,4,6-Cycloheptatrien-1-one, 5-chloro-2-hydroxy-4-methyl-	EtOH	237(4.07),329(3.54), 360(3.37),376(3.28)	12-1337-73
	EtOH-KOH	245(4.13),343(3.86), 406(3.70)	12-1337-73
$C_8H_7Cl_2NO_2$			
1H-Pyrrole-3,4-dicarboxaldehyde, 2,5-dichloro-1-ethyl-	EtOH	245(4.2),297(4.0)	103-0467-73
$C_8H_7Cl_2N_3O$			
Cyclopentanone, 2-(4,6-dichloro-1,3,5-triazin-2-yl)-	C_6H_{12}	329(4.60)	22-2039-73
$C_8H_7Cl_2OP$			
Phosphonic dichloride, (2-phenylethenyl)-	dioxan	215(4.18),218s(4.13), 270(4.27)	65-2164-73
$C_8H_7Cl_2OPS$			
Phosphonothioic dichloride, (2-phenoxyethenyl)-	C_6H_{12}	191(4.48),238(4.10)	65-2164-73
$C_8H_7Cl_2P$			
Phosphonous dichloride, (2-phenylethenyl)-	C_6H_{12}	214(4.22),218s(--), 270(4.28)	65-2164-74
$C_8H_7Cl_2PS$			
Phosphonothioic dichloride, (2-phenylethenyl)-	C_6H_{12}	216s(4.19),272(4.26)	65-2164-73

Compound	Solvent	λ_{max}(log ε)	Ref.
$C_8H_7Cl_4N$			
Methanamine, N,N-dimethyl-1-(2,3,4,5-tetrachloro-2,4-cyclopentadien-1-ylidene)-	hexane	234(3.61),343(4.50)	88-5101-73
$C_8H_7D_3N_2OS_3$			
Rhodanine, 5-(N-methyl-d_3-2-thiazolidinylidene)-3-methyl-	EtOH	277(4.15),385(4.53)	94-1431-73
$C_8H_7FN_2O$			
Ethanehydrazonoyl fluoride, 2-oxo-N-phenyl-	MeCN	233(4.03),334(4.38)	24-1661-73
$C_8H_7F_2NO_2$			
2-Azabicyclo[3.2.0]hepta-1(5),3-diene-3-carboxylic acid, 7,7-difluoro-, methyl ester	MeOH	240s(--),266(4.19)	24-3544-73
$C_8H_7F_2N_3O_2$			
2-Propenoic acid, 3-(2-azido-3,3-difluoro-1-cyclobuten-1-yl)-, methyl ester, (E)-	MeOH	218(3.97),303(4.39)	24-3544-73
$C_8H_7F_3O$			
Benzenemethanol, 4-(trifluoromethyl)-	EtOH	257(2.51),262(2.52), 268(2.40)	36-0910-73
$C_8H_7F_3O_2$			
2-Propenoic acid, 3-(2,3,3-trifluoro-1-cyclobuten-1-yl)-, methyl ester, (E)-	MeOH	256(4.36)	24-3544-73
$C_8H_7IO_3$			
2-Propenoic acid, 3-(5-iodo-2-furanyl)-, methyl ester	MeOH	315(4.23)	103-0802-73
C_8H_7N			
2H-Azirine, 3-phenyl-	EtOH	246(4.13),280s(3.24)	33-2007-73
Indole	MeOH	222(4.28),272(3.84), 278(3.83),281s(3.83), 288(3.74)	102-0447-73
after ten minutes (changing)	H_2SO_4	235(3.67),241(3.69), 255s(3.73),261(3.76), 282(3.54),359(3.18)	102-0447-73
C_8H_7NO			
1H-Indol-5-ol	MeOH	223(4.17),272(3.89), 298(3.66),310s(3.53)	102-0447-73
after ten minutes (changing)	H_2SO_4	245(3.72),280s(3.59), 308(3.70)	102-0447-73
C_8H_7NOS			
Thiazolo[3,2-a]pyridinium, 3-hydroxy-2-methyl-, hydroxide, inner salt	pH 1	212(4.14),234(3.71), 245s(--),336(3.93)	1-1749-73
	pH 13	221(3.53),246(3.86), 263(3.85),353(3.98)	1-1749-73
$C_8H_7NO_2$			
Benzene, 1-ethenyl-3-nitro-	dioxan	241(4.36),275(3.70), 312(3.08)	65-2164-73
Benzene, 1-ethenyl-4-nitro-	EtOH	299(4.14)	39-1574-73C

Compound	Solvent	λ_{max}(log ε)	Ref.
1,2-Benzisoxazole, 5-methoxy-	H_2O	236(3.92),306(3.54)	44-2294-73
1,2-Benzisoxazole, 6-methoxy-	H_2O	219(3.97),251(3.88), 283(3.76),291(3.73)	44-2294-73
1,2-Benzisoxazol-4-ol, 3-methyl-	MeOH	213(4.42),242(3.39), 292(3.36)	39-2220-73C
Benzonitrile, 2-hydroxy-4-methoxy-	pH 2	250(4.21),291(3.72)	44-2294-73
	pH 10	252(4.01),313(3.85)	44-2294-73
Benzonitrile, 2-hydroxy-5-methoxy-	pH 2	233(3.92),319(3.67)	44-2294-73
	pH 10	241(3.82),347(3.77)	44-2294-73
Benzoxazole, 4-hydroxy-2-methyl-	MeOH	209(4.41),242(4.01), 274(3.25)	39-2220-73C
3-Cyclopentene-1-carbonitrile, 1,3-dimethyl-2,5-dioxo-	EtOH	232(3.97),302(2.71)	35-2603-73
1H-Isoindol-1-one, 2,3-dihydro-3-hydroxy-	H_2SO_4	231(3.90),237(3.85), 365(3.08)	24-1423-73
$C_8H_7NO_2S_2$			
Thieno[2,3-b]thiophene-3-carboxylic acid, 2-amino-, methyl ester	MeOH	251(3.94),293(3.92), 311(3.94)	48-0039-73
$C_8H_7NO_3$			
Benzeneacetaldehyde, 4-nitro-	MeOH	263(3.98)	104-2119-73
1,3-Benzodioxole-5-carboxaldehyde, oxime	EtOH	212(4.26),222s(4.15), 267(4.08),306(3.90), 318s(3.74)	141-0001-73
	dioxan	227(4.08),267(4.06), 306(3.89),317s(3.72)	141-0001-73
$C_8H_7NO_3S$			
Ethanethioic acid, S-(4-nitrophenyl) ester	C_6H_{12}	227(3.75),285(4.04)	44-1559-73
$C_8H_7NO_4$			
2,4-Pyridinedicarboxaldehyde, 3-hydroxy-5-(hydroxymethyl)-	pH 1	285(3.89),315s(2.00)	44-4295-73
	pH 7	255s(3.83),368(3.92)	44-4295-73
	pH 13	255s(3.81),368(3.95)	44-4295-73
$C_8H_7NO_5$			
1H-Pyrrole-3,4-dicarboxylic acid, 2-acetyl-	pH 1	398(4.20)	103-0925-73
	pH 13	363(4.50)	103-0925-73
Schiff's base with p-phenetidine	n.s.g.	418(4.38)	103-0925-73
$C_8H_7NS_2$			
Benzothiazole, 2-(methylthio)-	$CHCl_3$	245(3.92),281(4.10)	22-3044-73
Pyrrolo[2,1-b]thiazole-5-carbothioaldehyde, 6-methyl-	C_6H_{12}	222(4.21),328(3.89), 407s(4.42),417(4.51), 426(4.52),514(1.75), 539(1.78),579s(1.33)	39-0657-73C
C_8H_7NSe			
1,2-Benzisoselenazole, 3-methyl-	EtOH	202(4.35),229(4.34), 319(3.69)	4-0267-73
$C_8H_7N_3$			
1H-Benzotriazole, 1-ethenyl-	EtOH	220(4.18),262(3.82), 270(3.80)	103-1517-73
2:1 complex with $PhSnCl_3$	EtOH	215(4.62),262(4.09), 270(4.06)	103-1517-73
2-Quinoxalinamine	pH 7.05	247(4.26),300(3.38), 354(3.80)	103-0369-73

Compound	Solvent	$\lambda_{max}(\log \epsilon)$	Ref.
2-Quinoxalinamine (cont.)	0.1N H_2SO_4	232(4.23),256(4.05), 318(3.70),350(3.83)	103-0369-73
1,2,3-Triazole, 4-phenyl-	EtOH	246(4.19)	78-3271-73
	anion	261(4.22)	78-3271-73
$C_8H_7N_3O$			
Benzamide, 2-amino-3-cyano-	EtOH	263(3.71),352(3.79)	104-2331-73
1,2,3-Benzotriazine, 4-methyl-, 3-oxide	MeOH	302(3.91),310(3.83), 395(3.08)	35-2390-73
4(3H)-Quinazolinone, 6-amino-	MeOH	290(4.11)	4-0403-73
3H-1,2,4-Triazol-3-one, 2,4-dihydro-5-phenyl-	EtOH	264(4.03)	94-1342-73
	THF	274(3.95)	94-1342-73
$C_8H_7N_3OS_2$			
4H-Thiazolo[3,2-a]-1,3,5-triazin-4-one, 2-(2-propen-1-ylthio)-	EtOH	225(4.03),246(3.88), 269(3.95),310(4.32), 317(4.32)	94-0074-73
$C_8H_7N_3O_4$			
Benzeneacetaldehyde, α-(hydroxyimino)-4-nitro-, anti	n.s.g.	242(4.2)	104-1027-73
anti-amphi	n.s.g.	222(4.1),260(4.0), 305(3.9)	104-1027-73
Ethanediamide, (4-nitrophenyl)-	dioxan	277s(3.85),320(4.25)	30-0001-73
$(C_8H_7N_3O_5)_n$			
2,4(1H,3H)-Pyrimidinedione, 1-(2,5-dioxo-4-oxazolidinyl)methyl]-, homopolymer	H_2O	263(4.21)	126-0327-73G
	base	264(4.20)	126-0327-73G
$C_8H_7N_3O_6S$			
Benzene, 2-(ethylthio)-1,3,5-trinitro-, 2:1 Meisenheimer complex with EtSNa	DMSO	525(4.1)	77-0229-73
1:1 Meisenheimer complex with EtSNa	DMSO	464(4.0),545(4.2)	77-0229-73
$C_8H_7N_3S$			
1,3,4-Thiadiazol-2-amine, 5-phenyl-	EtOH	300(4.20)	80-1777-73
	EtOH-HCl	284(4.26)	80-1777-73
2-Thiazolamine, 5-(4-pyridinyl)-	EtOH	202(4.05),230(4.26), 302(3.75)	34-0099-73
3H-1,2,4-Triazole-3-thione, 1,2-dihydro-5-phenyl-	EtOH	226(4.17),256(4.27), 281s(3.99)	94-1342-73
	THF	225(4.09),251(4.21), 275s(4.04)	94-1342-73
$C_8H_7N_5O$			
Phenol, 4-(1H-1,2,4-triazol-3-ylazo)-	MeOH	353(4.3),445s(3.2+)	12-1585-73
Pyrido[2,3-b]pyrazine-7-carboxamide, 6-amino-	pH 1	225(4.21),260s(3.42), 356(3.98)	39-1615-73C
	pH 7	210s(4.29),234(4.13), 262s(3.71),378(3.87)	39-1615-73C
1,2,4-Triazin-5(2H)-one, 6-amino-3-(2-pyridinyl)-	MeOH	239(4.21),248(4.16), 272(4.16),310(3.95)	40-1519-73
$C_8H_7N_5S$			
Thiazolo[2,3-f]purin-4-amine, 1-methyl-, hydrochloride	pH 1	249(4.24),281(4.06)	94-0256-73
Thiazolo[3,2-e]purin-4-amine, 8-methyl-, hydrochloride	pH 1	249(4.38),293(4.14)	94-0034-73
	pH 13	242s(--),286(--), 298(--)	94-0034-73

Compound	Solvent	λ_{max}(log ϵ)	Ref.
C_8H_8			
Bicyclo[2.2.1]hepta-2,5-diene, 7-methylene-	C_6H_{12}	242(2.30)	44-1893-73
Styrene	C_6H_{12}	205(4.40),214s(4.10), 248(4.15),274(2.93), 282(2.93),291(2.74)	65-2164-73
$C_8H_8BrNO_2S$			
2,1-Benzisothiazole, 5-bromo-1,3-dihydro-1-methyl-, 2,2-dioxide	EtOH	242(4.11),298(3.18)	4-0249-73
$C_8H_8Br_2N_2O_3$			
4(5H)-Benzofurazanone, 5,5-dibromo-6,7-dihydro-6,6-dimethyl-, 1-oxide	MeOH	222(3.97),322(3.18)	39-0351-73C
4(5H)-Benzofurazanone, 5,5-dibromo-6,7-dihydro-6,6-dimethyl-, 3-oxide	MeOH	222(3.88),248(3.68), 296(3.67)	39-0351-73C
$C_8H_8Br_2O$			
2,5-Cyclohexadien-1-one, 4-(dibromomethyl)-4-methyl-	EtOH	234(4.0)	111-0290-73
$C_8H_8Br_4O_2$			
1,5-Cyclooctanedione, 2,4,6,8-tetrabromo-, cis-cis-trans	MeOH	322(2.07)	33-0723-73
	MeOH	322(2.25)	33-0723-73
cis-trans-cis	MeOH	330(2.53)	33-0723-73
$C_8H_8ClNO_3$			
Pyridoxal, 6-chloro-	pH 1	292(3.76)	87-0638-73
	pH 6.8	287(3.64)	87-0638-73
	pH 12.5	247(4.05),311(3.86)	87-0638-73
	M HCl	302(3.91)	87-0638-73
$C_8H_8ClN_3S$			
2(3H)-Benzothiazolone, 4-chloro-3-methyl-, hydrazone	$CHCl_3$	260(4.21),292(3.83), 320(3.76)	22-3044-73
2(3H)-Benzothiazolone, 5-chloro-3-methyl-, hydrazone	$CHCl_3$	244(4.18),276(3.81), 320(3.94)	22-3044-73
2(3H)-Benzothiazolone, 6-chloro-3-methyl-, hydrazone	$CHCl_3$	246(4.09),280(3.97), 323(3.81)	22-3044-73
2(3H)-Benzothiazolone, 7-chloro-3-methyl-, hydrazone	$CHCl_3$	244(4.29),315(4.22)	22-3044-73
$C_8H_8ClN_5O_2$			
Carbamic acid, (7-chloro-1H-1,2,3-triazolo[4,5-b]pyridin-5-yl)-, ethyl ester	pH 7	222(4.36),302(4.17)	44-1095-73
$C_8H_8Cl_2N_2O_3$			
4(5H)-Benzofurazanone, 5,5-dichloro-6,7-dihydro-6,6-dimethyl-, 1-oxide	MeOH	221(4.00),267(3.20), 318(3.08)	39-0351-73C
4(5H)-Benzofurazanone, 5,5-dichloro-6,7-dihydro-6,6-dimethyl-, 3-oxide	MeOH	222(3.90),249(3.53), 293(3.59)	39-0351-73C
$C_8H_8Cl_2O$			
2,5-Cyclohexadien-1-one, 4-(dichloromethyl)-4-methyl-	EtOH	232(4.2)	111-0290-73
$C_8H_8FNO_3$			
Pyridoxal, 6-fluoro-	pH 1	288(3.60)	87-0638-73
	pH 6.65	282(3.58)	87-0638-73
	pH 10.0	236(3.54),309(3.62)	87-0638-73
	M HCl	288(3.60)	87-0638-73

Compound	Solvent	λ_{max}(log ε)	Ref.
$C_8H_8FN_3$			
Pyrazolo[1,5-a]pyrimidine, 3-fluoro-5,7-dimethyl-	MeOH	232(4.45),280(3.26), 292(3.22),320(3.12)	88-3149-73
$C_8H_8HgN_2$			
Mercury, (diazophenylmethyl)methyl-	MeOH	260(3.87),273(3.89), 477(1.49)	44-3937-73
C_8H_8INO			
Acetamide, 2-iodo-N-phenyl-	H_2O	256(3.88)	63-1611-73
$C_8H_8INO_4S$			
Benzenesulfonic acid, 4-[(iodoacetyl)-amino]-	H_2O	261(4.05)	63-1611-73
$C_8H_8NO_7P$			
2,4-Pyridinedicarboxaldehyde, 3-hydroxy-5-[(phosphonooxy)methyl]-	pH 1	295(3.79),325s(3.36)	44-4295-73
	pH 7	255s(3.72),415(3.74)	44-4295-73
	pH 13	255s(3.73),410(3.77)	44-4295-73
$C_8H_8N_2$			
3H-Diazirine, 3-(4-methylphenyl)-	hexane	272(2.50),368(2.49)	35-5072-73
$C_8H_8N_2O$			
1H-Pyrrole-3-carbonitrile, 4-acetyl-5-methyl-	EtOH	204(4.05),216(3.95), 249(3.67),273(3.75)	12-1551-73
$C_8H_8N_2OS_2$			
Acetamide, N-(5-methylthieno[2,3-d]thiazol-2-yl)-	MeCN	261(3.77),269(3.78), 301(4.20)	48-0539-73
1H-Thieno[2,3-c]pyrazole-5-carboxaldehyde, 1,3-dimethyl-	EtOH	333(4.7)	104-2216-73
$C_8H_8N_2OSe$			
1H-Seleno[2,3-c]pyrazole-5-carboxaldehyde, 1,3-dimethyl-	EtOH	334(3.8)	104-2216-73
$C_8H_8N_2O_2$			
Benzenamine, 4-ethenyl-2-nitro-	hexane	206(4.42),250(4.75), 267(4.67),398s(4.00)	24-1116-73
Ethanediamide, phenyl-	dioxan	268(4.00)	30-0001-73
Formamide, N-[2-[(hydroxyimino)methyl]-phenyl]-	EtOH	235(4.45),272(4.05)	94-1943-73
$C_8H_8N_2O_2S$			
6H-Thiazolo[3,4-a]pyrimidine-2,4(1H,3H)-dione, 1-ethyl-, meso-ionic didehydro deriv.	H_2O	180(3.58),242(4.46), 248(4.44)	4-0487-73
$C_8H_8N_2O_2S_3$			
Rhodanine, 5-(N-acetyl-2-thiazolidinylidene)-	EtOH	284(4.03),390(4.45)	94-1431-73
$C_8H_8N_2O_2S_4$			
[5,5'-Bithiazolidine]-4,4'-dione, 3,3'-dimethyl-2,2'-dithioxo-	EtOH	258(4.25),295(4.38)	94-0279-73
$C_8H_8N_2O_3$			
1H-Pyrrolo[2,3-c]pyridine-2-carboxylic acid, 4,5,6,7-tetrahydro-5-oxo-	EtOH	270(4.18)	44-1824-73

Compound	Solvent	$\lambda_{max}(\log \epsilon)$	Ref.
$C_8H_8N_2O_3S_2$			
Thiazolidine, 3-acetyl-2-(2,4-dioxo-5-thiazolidinylidene)-	EtOH	263(3.79),340(4.20)	94-1431-73
$C_8H_8N_2O_4$			
2-Propenoic acid, 3-(1,2,3,4-tetrahydro-1-methyl-2,4-dioxo-5-pyrimidinyl)-	pH 1	270s(4.11),305(4.29)	44-0264-73
	pH 7.4	261(4.14),301(4.18)	44-0264-73
	pH 12.0	265(3.95),301(3.97)	44-0264-73
$C_8H_8N_2O_4S$			
2,1-Benzisothiazole, 1,3-dihydro-1-methyl-5-nitro-, 2,2-dioxide	EtOH	228(3.79),324(4.07)	4-0249-73
$C_8H_8N_2S_2$			
4H-Cyclopenta[4,5]thieno[2,3-c]isothiazol-3-amine, 5,6-dihydro-	MeOH	238(4.56),311(3.76)	48-0539-73
Propanedicarbonitrile, [(methylthio)-(2-propenylthio)methylene]-	EtOH	333(4.00)	78-2077-73
$C_8H_8N_4O$			
6H-Purin-6-one, 1,7-dihydro-7-(1-methylethenyl)-	pH 1	253(3.97)	94-0256-73
	pH 13	263(3.94)	94-0256-73
$C_8H_8N_4O_2$			
2,4(1H,3H)-Pteridinedione, 1,3-dimethyl-	pH 6.0	236(4.19),331(3.88)	24-3149-73
	MeOH	235(4.17),328(3.82)	24-1401-73
2,4(1H,3H)-Pteridinedione, 6,7-dimethyl-	pH 6.0	208(4.27),245(3.93),327(4.01)	24-3149-73
	pH 11.0	215(4.20),236(4.13),272(4.10),348(3.86),365s(3.79)	24-3149-73
1H-Pyrazolo[4,3-b]pyridine, 1,5-dimethyl-3-nitro-	EtOH	250(3.87),307(4.00)	39-2901-73C
$C_8H_8N_4O_2S$			
Acetamide, N-[5-(5-methyl-1,2,4-oxadiazol-3-yl)-2-thiazolyl]-	EtOH	291(4.21)	39-2769-73C
2-Quinoxalinesulfonamide, 3-amino-	EtOH	248(4.37),301(3.51),379(3.76)	18-1890-73
$C_8H_8N_4O_3$			
2,4(1H,3H)-Pteridinedione, 1,3-dimethyl-, 5-oxide	pH 5.0	242(4.42),289(3.90),349(3.71)	24-3149-73
2,4(1H,3H)-Pteridinedione, 6,7-dimethyl-, 8-oxide	pH 3.0	239(4.37),276s(3.67),342(3.86)	24-3149-73
	pH 9.0	240(4.13),267(4.14),285s(4.10),380(3.89)	24-3149-73
2,4,7(1H,3H,8H)-Pteridinetrione, 1,3-dimethyl-	pH 1.0	238(4.04),263(3.81),325(4.10)	24-3203-73
	pH 5.7	240s(3.86),277(3.96),329(4.23)	24-3203-73
$C_8H_8N_4O_4$			
4,5-Isoxazolinedione, 3-methyl-, 4-[(2,5-dihydro-3-methyl-5-oxo-4-isoxazolyl)hydrazone]	EtOH	213(3.98),278(3.95),500(3.57)	32-1045-73
2,4(1H,3H)-Pteridinedione, 6,7-dimethyl-, 5,8-dioxide	pH 3.0	237(4.21),263(4.37),312(3.97),386(3.75)	24-3149-73
	pH 8.0	250(4.28),268(4.33),317(3.91),407(3.84)	24-3149-73

Compound	Solvent	$\lambda_{max}(\log \epsilon)$	Ref.
2,4,6,7(1H,3H)-Pteridinetetrone, 5,8-dihydro-1,3-dimethyl-	pH 1.0	292(4.03),330(3.98)	24-3203-73
	pH 7.0	235(4.25),289(3.92), 334(4.17),348(4.19), 365s(3.95)	24-3203-73
2,4,7(1H,3H,8H)-Pteridinetrione, 1,3-dimethyl-, 5-oxide	pH 0.0	243(4.34),285(3.91), 339(4.01)	24-3203-73
	pH 6.0	230(4.40),257(4.24), 280s(3.78),342(4.12)	24-3203-73
$C_8H_8N_6$			
1H-Pyrazolo[3,4-d]pyrimidine-3-carbonitrile, 1-methyl-4-(methylamino)- (all spectra in ethanol)	pH 1	231s(--),250s(--), 270s(--),281(3.92), 299s(--),308(4.18), 318(4.13)	39-1903-73C
	pH 7	227(4.06),253(3.90), 266s(--),314(3.99)	39-1903-73C
	pH 12	235s(--),262(3.95), 280s(--),310(3.97)	39-1903-73C
$C_8H_8N_6O$			
1H-Tetrazol-5-amine, N-nitroso-N-(phenylmethyl)-	MeOH	265(3.62)	39-1357-73C
1H-Tetrazol-5-amine, N-nitroso-1-(phenylmethyl)-	pH 13	273(3.88)	39-1357-73C
	MeOH	245(3.67)	39-1357-73C
$C_8H_8N_6O_2$			
5,5'-Bi-1,2,4-triazine, 3,3'-dimethoxy-	n.s.g.	222(4.54),328(4.36)	22-2493-73
$C_8H_8N_6O_6$			
2,4,6(1H,3H,5H)-Pyrimidinetrione, 5,5'-hydrazobis-	EtOH	248(4.22)	103-0247-73
$C_8H_8N_6S_2$			
5,5'-Bi-1,2,4-triazine, 3,3'-bis(methylthio)-	n.s.g.	205(4.16),221s(4.14), 276(4.31),330s(3.48), 375(3.52)	22-2493-73
$C_8H_8N_8O_2$			
Carbamic acid, (7-azido-1H-1,2,3-triazolo[4,5-b]pyridin-5-yl)-, ethyl ester	pH 7	222(4.33),300(4.24)	44-1095-73
C_8H_8O			
Acetophenone	EtOH	242(4.10),280(3.08)	141-0001-73
	EtOH-NaOH	244(4.10),281(2.97)	141-0001-73
	dioxan	241(4.07),279(3.03), 288s(2.90)	141-0001-73
at -75°	FSO_3H	295(4.36),330s(<3.48)	59-0807-73
Benzaldehyde, 3-methyl-	1% EtOH	254(4.14)	39-0786-73B
Benzaldehyde, 4-methyl-	H_2O	261(4.23)	39-0786-73B
Benzene, (ethenyloxy)-	C_6H_{12}	196(4.42),225(4.15), 263s(3.03),269(3.14), 276(3.03)	65-2164-73
	nonane	226(4.12),270(3.09)	30-0941-73
Benzeneacetaldehyde	MeOH	209(3.88)	104-2119-73
$C_8H_8OS_2$			
4H-1,2-Benzodithiole-7-carboxaldehyde, 5,6-dihydro-	n.s.g.	418(4.14),437(4.17)	97-0026-73

Compound	Solvent	λ_{max}(log ϵ)	Ref.
$C_8H_8O_2$			
Acetophenone, 3'-hydroxy-	EtOH	219(4.28),251(3.94), 311(3.44)	141-0001-73
	EtOH-NaOH	238(4.37),263s(3.80), 357(3.40)	141-0001-73
	dioxan	220(4.16),247(3.94), 306(3.48)	141-0001-73
Benzaldehyde, 2-methoxy-	EtOH	215(4.20),254(3.99), 320(3.65)	141-0001-73
	dioxan	220(4.08),251(4.05), 315(3.72)	141-0001-73
Benzaldehyde, 3-methoxy-	EtOH	219(4.28),254(3.93), 313(3.44)	141-0001-73
	1% EtOH	255(3.95)	39-0786-73B
	dioxan	223(4.26),250(4.02), 310(3.54)	141-0001-73
Benzaldehyde, 4-methoxy-	EtOH	220(4.10),277(4.21), 283(4.21),290s(4.14)	141-0001-73
	1% EtOH	280(4.20)	39-0786-73B
	dioxan	220(4.10),271(4.23), 281s(4.16),289s(3.96)	141-0001-73
	FSO_3H	348(4.58)	59-0807-73
at -75°	FSO_3H	341(4.49)	59-0807-73
Benzoic acid, methyl ester	EtOH	228(4.11),273(3.00), 280(2.95)	141-0001-73
	dioxan	229(4.10),273(3.10), 280(3.05)	141-0001-73
Benzoic acid, 4-methyl-, anion	H_2O	234(3.99)	104-2111-73
1,2:3,4-Diepoxycycloocta-5,7-diene	hexane	222(3.40)	44-2421-73
1,2:5,6-Diepoxycycloocta-3,7-diene	hexane	198(3.63)	44-2421-73
stereoisomer	hexane	196(3.32)	44-2421-73
1,4:2,3-Diepoxycycloocta-5,7-diene	hexane	237s(2.83),245s(2.98), 253(3.08),262(3.09), 272(2.86)	44-2421-73
4,5-Heptadien-2-ynoic acid, 6-methyl-	n.s.g.	215(3.87),246(4.02), 260(3.80)	70-1029-73
4-Oxabicyclonona-2,5-diene, 8,9-epoxy-	hexane	206(3.57),218(3.53)	44-2421-73
$C_8H_8O_2S$			
Benzene, (ethenylsulfonyl)-	MeOH	225(4.10),267(3.02)	2-0882-73
9-Thiabicyclo[4.2.1]nona-2,4,7-triene, 9,9-dioxide	EtOH	279(3.37)	35-2230-73
$C_8H_8O_3$			
Acetophenone, 2',4'-dihydroxy-	EtOH	213(4.21),216s(4.20), 231(3.95),277(4.16), 315(3.86)	141-0001-73
	EtOH-NaOH	217(4.06),251(3.79), 335(4.47)	141-0001-73
	dioxan	217(4.20),229(4.00), 273(4.16),312(3.81)	141-0001-73
Acetophenone, 2',5'-dihydroxy-	EtOH	227(4.19),257(3.84), 367(3.60)	141-0001-73
	EtOH-NaOH	243(4.19),273s(3.67), 297s(3.44),407(3.26)	141-0001-73
	dioxan	226(4.20),255(3.85), 361(3.65)	141-0001-73
Acetophenone, 2',6'-dihydroxy-	EtOH	223(4.09),270(4.04), 344(3.52)	141-0001-73
	EtOH-NaOH	216(4.02),241(4.13), 286(3.96),392(3.75)	141-0001-73

Compound	Solvent	$\lambda_{max}(\log \epsilon)$	Ref.
Acetophenone, 2',6'-dihydroxy- (cont.)	dioxan	223(4.14),267(4.06), 338(3.54)	141-0001-73
Acetophenone, 3',4'-dihydroxy-	EtOH	230(4.30),276(4.00), 307(3.90)	141-0001-73
	EtOH-NaOH	262(4.00),314(3.95), 383(4.03)	141-0001-73
Acetophenone, 3',5'-dihydroxy-	EtOH	218(4.30),265(3.90), 321(3.60)	141-0001-73
Benzaldehyde, 2-hydroxy-3-methoxy-	EtOH	221(4.26),267(4.04), 344(3.53)	141-0001-73
	EtOH-NaOH	238(4.28),282(3.81), 396(3.83)	141-0001-73
	dioxan	225(4.24),264(4.01), 341(3.46)	141-0001-73
Benzaldehyde, 2-hydroxy-4-methoxy-	EtOH	213(4.17),229(4.09), 277(4.24),314(3.88)	141-0001-73
	EtOH-NaOH	227(4.16),243(4.22), 282(3.06),368(3.96)	141-0001-73
	dioxan	229(4.16),270(4.23), 313(3.92)	141-0001-73
Benzaldehyde, 2-hydroxy-5-methoxy-	EtOH	229(4.21),257(3.87), 360(3.62)	141-0001-73
	EtOH-NaOH	224(4.21),263s(3.87), 414(3.85)	141-0001-73
	dioxan	230(4.39),257(3.94), 362(3.72)	141-0001-73
Benzaldehyde, 3-hydroxy-4-methoxy-	EtOH	208(4.14),232(4.23), 276(4.04),314(3.93)	141-0001-73
	EtOH-NaOH	252(4.38),292(3.90), 365(3.77)	141-0001-73
	dioxan	230(4.27),272(4.07), 308(3.92)	141-0001-73
Benzaldehyde, 4-hydroxy-3-methoxy-	EtOH	208(4.14),232(4.20), 280(4.03),309(4.04)	141-0001-73
	EtOH-NaOH	252(3.98),294(3.46), 354(4.48)	141-0001-73
	dioxan	229(4.22),274(4.09), 303(3.98)	141-0001-73
Benzoic acid, 2-hydroxy-, methyl ester	EtOH	210(4.21),238(3.94), 305(3.63)	141-0001-73
	EtOH-NaOH	222(4.32),247(3.87), 339(3.76)	141-0001-73
	dioxan	238(3.96),305(3.67)	141-0001-73
Benzoic acid, 3-hydroxy-, methyl ester	EtOH	213(4.28),237(3.92), 298(3.52)	141-0001-73
	EtOH-NaOH	227(4.53),248(4.00), 333(3.58)	141-0001-73
	dioxan	235(3.88),295(3.50)	141-0001-73
Benzoic acid, 2-methoxy-	EtOH	232(3.83),291(3.48)	141-0001-73
	EtOH-NaOH	227(3.74),279(3.37)	141-0001-73
	dioxan	233(3.81),293(3.49)	141-0001-73
Benzoic acid, 3-methoxy-	EtOH	212(4.28),231(3.85), 294(3.41)	141-0001-73
	EtOH-NaOH	228(3.82),287(3.36)	141-0001-73
	dioxan	235(3.85),294(3.48)	141-0001-73
Benzoic acid, 4-methoxy-	EtOH	254(4.19),272s(3.77), 281s(3.18)	141-0001-73
	EtOH-NaOH	245(4.11),271s(3.26), 282(2.88)	141-0001-73
	dioxan	254(4.18),271s(3.73), 281s(3.04)	141-0001-73

Compound	Solvent	λ_{max}(log ε)	Ref.
Benzoic acid, 4-methoxy-, anion	H_2O	246(4.09)	104-2111-73
2H-Cyclopenta[b]furan-4-carboxaldehyde, 3,3a,6,6a-tetrahydro-2-oxo-	n.s.g.	230(3.77)	88-1319-73
1,2,4-Cyclopentanetrione, 3-(2-propenyl)-	EtOH	276(4.08)	94-2195-73
3,6,11-Trioxatetracyclo[8.1.0.0^{2,4}.0^{5,7}]-undec-8-ene (1α,2β,4β,5α,7α,10α)-	hexane	200(3.04)	44-2421-73
$C_8H_8O_4$			
Acetophenone, 2',3',4'-trihydroxy-	EtOH	237(3.93),296(4.10)	141-0001-73
	EtOH-NaOH	309(4.10)	141-0001-73
Acetophenone, 2',4',5'-trihydroxy-	EtOH	214(4.12),241(4.08), 280(4.03),349(3.85)	141-0001-73
Acetophenone, 2',4',6'-trihydroxy-	EtOH	211(4.04),227(4.10), 288(4.21),325s(3.47)	141-0001-73
	EtOH-NaOH	228(4.13),240s(4.02), 319(4.39),370s(3.50)	141-0001-73
	dioxan	229(4.18),282(4.21), 320s(3.45)	141-0001-73
Benzaldehyde, 3,5-dihydroxy-4-methoxy-	EtOH	220(4.35),285(4.00), 325s(3.55)	141-0001-73
	EtOH-NaOH	238(4.33),334(3.83)	141-0001-73
	dioxan	226(4.21),280(4.02), 320s(3.47)	141-0001-73
Benzaldehyde, 4,5-dihydroxy-3-methoxy-	EtOH	219(4.26),229s(4.19), 309(4.10),368s(3.17)	141-0001-73
	EtOH-NaOH	219(4.15),252(3.94), 364(4.18)	141-0001-73
	dioxan	231(4.22),295(4.12)	141-0001-73
Benzoic acid, 2,6-dihydroxy-, methyl	EtOH	212(4.23),219(4.21), 255(3.04),300(3.58), 323(3.36)	141-0001-73
	EtOH-NaOH	215(4.00),235(4.15), 277(3.82),306(3.03), 352(3.47)	141-0001-73
	dioxan	223(4.12),254(3.06), 300(3.54),323(3.35)	141-0001-73
Benzoic acid, 2-hydroxy-3-methoxy-	EtOH	242s(3.73),311(3.55)	141-0001-73
	EtOH-NaOH	221(4.23),230s(4.01), 304(3.74)	141-0001-73
	dioxan	221(4.28),249(3.80), 321(3.58)	141-0001-73
Benzoic acid, 2-hydroxy-4-methoxy-	EtOH	211(4.48),224s(4.06), 253(4.08),294(3.75)	141-0001-73
	EtOH-NaOH	218(4.22),248(4.05), 293(3.71)	141-0001-73
	dioxan	222s(4.15),259(4.21), 297(3.84)	141-0001-73
Benzoic acid, 2-hydroxy-5-methoxy-	EtOH	214(4.41),236(3.86), 331(3.66)	141-0001-73
	EtOH-NaOH	230s(3.90),320(3.68)	141-0001-73
	dioxan	221(4.19),238(3.87), 335(3.71)	141-0001-73
Benzoic acid, 2-hydroxy-6-methoxy-	EtOH	213(4.25),251(3.87), 311(3.54)	141-0001-73
	EtOH-NaOH	220(4.21),246(3.96), 300(3.71)	141-0001-73
	dioxan	217(4.18),252(3.87), 315(3.58)	141-0001-73
Benzoic acid, 3-hydroxy-4-methoxy-	EtOH	219(4.34),258(4.02), 295(3.75)	141-0001-73

Compound	Solvent	λmax(log ε)	Ref.
Benzoic acid, 3-hydroxy-4-methoxy- (cont.)	EtOH-NaOH	227(4.36),259(3.81), 311(3.70)	141-0001-73
	dioxan	223(4.17),257(4.03), 294(3.74)	141-0001-73
Benzoic acid, 3-hydroxy-5-methoxy-	EtOH	213(4.27),245(3.68), 298(3.36)	141-0001-73
	EtOH-NaOH	227(4.31),245s(3.94), 315(3.58)	141-0001-73
	dioxan	216(4.21),251(3.75), 306(3.46)	141-0001-73
Benzoic acid, 4-hydroxy-3-methoxy-	EtOH	218(4.26),260(4.02), 291(3.74)	141-0001-73
	EtOH-NaOH	225(4.20),286s(4.18), 297(4.20)	141-0001-73
	dioxan	221(4.26),259(4.09), 289(3.73),295s(3.71)	141-0001-73
	n.s.g.	220(3.66),260(3.83), 295(4.08)	105-0252-73
2,5-Cyclohexadiene-1,4-dione, 2,6-dimethoxy-	H_2O	289(4.16),396(2.82)	44-3226-73
	aq base	249(4.18)	44-3226-73
	$CHCl_3$	286(4.26),376(2.78)	44-3226-73
2H-Pyran-3-carboxylic acid, 2-oxo-, ethyl ester	MeOH	308(3.72)	23-3263-73
2H-Pyran-5-carboxylic acid, 2-oxo-, ethyl ester	EtOH	245(3.8),288(3.4)	23-3263-73
$C_8H_8O_5S$			
2,5-Thiophenedicarboxylic acid, 3-hydroxy-4-methyl-, 2-methyl ester	EtOH	279(3.99)	2-0313-73
$C_8H_8S_2$			
Thieno[2,3-b]thiophene, 2-ethyl-	EtOH	228(4.41),235(4.36), 263(3.62)	70-2017-73
$C_8H_8S_3$			
4H-1,2-Benzodithiole-7-carbothioaldehyde, 5,6-dihydro-	n.s.g.	487(3.97)	97-0026-73
C_8H_9			
Cycloheptatrienylium, methyl-, perchlorate	pH 1	287(3.68)	18-1785-73
	H_2SO_4	226(4.57),288(3.55)	33-2796-73
C_8H_9BrO			
Phenol, 2-bromo-4,6-dimethyl-	dioxan	288(3.41)	126-0039-73L
$C_8H_9BrO_2$			
Benzenemethanol, 3-bromo-2-hydroxy-5-methyl-	dioxan	285(3.46)	126-0039-73L
Phenol, 4-bromo-2-methoxy-5-methyl-	90% EtOH	231(3.74),289(3.53), 294s(3.49)	12-1069-73
$C_8H_9BrO_3$			
4H-Pyran-4-one, 3-bromo-2-ethoxy-6-methyl-	EtOH	264(3.95)	94-1047-73
$C_8H_9ClN_2O_2$			
1H-Pyrrole-3-carboxaldehyde, 2-chloro-4,5-dihydro-1-methyl-4-[(methylamino)methylene]-5-oxo-	C_6H_{12}	300(4.2),410(4.0)	103-0467-73
	EtOH	230(3.7),293(4.2), 400(4.2)	103-0467-73

Compound	Solvent	$\lambda_{max}(\log \epsilon)$	Ref.
$C_8H_9ClN_4$			
9H-Purine, 6-chloro-8-(1-methylethyl)-	pH 1	267(4.07)	39-1855-73C
	pH 11	278(4.06)	39-1855-73C
	MeOH	268(4.05)	39-1855-73C
$C_8H_9ClO_3$			
4H-Pyran-4-one, 3-chloro-2-ethoxy-6-methyl-	EtOH	262(3.96)	94-1047-73
$C_8H_9Cl_2N$			
Methanamine, 1-(2,4-dichloro-2,4-cyclopentadien-1-ylidene)-N,N-dimethyl-	hexane	224(3.73),323(4.50), 330(4.50)	88-5101-73
$C_8H_9F_2N_3O_2$			
1-Cyclobutene-1-carboxylic acid, 2-azido-3,3-difluoro-, 1-methylethyl ester	MeOH	273(4.01)	24-3544-73
$C_8H_9F_2N_3O_3$			
1-Cyclobutene-1-carboxylic acid, 2-azido-3,3-difluoro-, 2-methoxyethyl ester	MeOH	274(4.03)	24-3544-73
C_8H_9N			
4-Azabicyclo[5.2.0]nona-2,5,8-triene	hexane	219(3.37),265(3.20)	77-0601-73
1,3-Cyclohexadiene-1-carbonitrile, 5-methyl-	ether	282(3.65)	24-3779-73
Methanamine, N-(phenylmethylene)-	EtOH	244(4.12),277s(3.09), 284s(2.95)	35-4692-73
C_8H_9NO			
Acetanilide	C_6H_{12}	240(3.37)	95-1100-73
	EtOH	242(4.14)	95-1100-73
	$EtOH-H_2SO_4$	243.5(4.27)	95-1100-73
	95% H_2SO_4	245(4.03)	95-1100-73
Acetophenone, 4'-amino-	pH 1	239(3.95),280(3.07)	80-0677-73
	EtOH	233(3.88),318(4.43)	80-0677-73
at -75°	FSO_3H	278(4.30),320s(<3.48)	59-0807-73
Acetophenone, oxime	pH 6.61	240(4.10)	36-1381-73
	MeOH	242(4.052)	30-0394-73
2-Propenal, 2-methyl-3-(1H-pyrrol-2-yl)-	EtOH	345(4.48)	39-1416-73C
1H-Pyrrole-2-carboxaldehyde, 4-(1-propenyl)-	EtOH	242(4.28),250s(4.18), 325(3.99)	105-0223-73
$C_8H_9NO_2$			
Benzaldehyde, 3-methoxy-, oxime	EtOH	217(4.29),256(4.08), 299(3.52)	141-0001-73
	dioxan	227(4.12),256(4.08), 299(3.51),308s(3.37)	141-0001-73
Benzaldehyde, 4-methoxy-, oxime	EtOH	212(4.18),265(4.28), 293s(3.65),302s(3.36)	141-0001-73
	dioxan	263(4.29),284s(3.67), 293s(3.23)	141-0001-73
Ethanone, 1-(3-hydroxy-2-methyl-4-pyridinyl)-	pH 1	331(3.61)	70-1057-73
	pH 7	371(3.61)	70-1057-73
	pH 13	349(3.46)	70-1057-73
2-Propenoic acid, 3-(1H-pyrrol-2-yl)-, methyl ester	EtOH	331(4.41)	39-1416-73C
$C_8H_9NO_2S$			
Acetic acid, cyano(dihydro-3(2H)-thienylidene)-, methyl ester	MeOH	233(4.12)	48-0039-73

Compound	Solvent	$\lambda_{max}(\log \epsilon)$	Ref.
Sulfone, 2-aminoethenyl phenyl	MeOH	233(4.1),280(4.1)	2-0882-73
$C_8H_9NO_2S_2$			
Thieno[2,3-b]thiophene-3-carboxylic acid, 2-amino-4,5-dihydro-, methyl ester	MeOH	230(3.80),287(3.43)	48-0039-73
$C_8H_9NO_3$			
Acetophenone, 2',4'-dihydroxy-, oxime	EtOH	218(4.30),228s(4.12), 266(4.11),299(3.86)	141-0001-73
	EtOH-NaOH	232(4.22),262(3.95), 267s(3.94),311(4.12), 352(4.27)	141-0001-73
	dioxan	222(4.15),227s(4.12), 236s(4.01),266(4.10), 272s(4.06),300(3.85), 305s(3.84)	141-0001-73
Acetophenone, 2',6'-dihydroxy-, oxime	MeOH	218(4.27),262(3.86)	39-2220-73C
Phenol, 2,4-dimethyl-6-nitro-	acid	295(3.85),375(3.42)	49-1315-73
	anion	295(3.61),446(3.65)	49-1315-73
3-Pyridinecarboxylic acid, 1,2-dihydro-6-methyl-2-oxo-, methyl ester	EtOH	240(3.81),336(3.98)	70-2478-73
2(1H)-Pyridinone, 4-hydroxy-3-(1-oxopropyl)-	MeOH	209(4.03),227(4.05), 267(3.42),322(3.96)	88-2823-73
1H-Pyrrole-2-carboxaldehyde, 5-(acetoxymethyl)-	CHCl	250(3.69),290(4.30)	39-2281-73C
$C_8H_9NO_4$			
2-Furanbutanoic acid, α-amino-γ-oxo-, (L)-	n.s.g.	278(4.12)	88-0037-73
4-Pyridinecarboxaldehyde, 3-hydroxy-2,5-bis(hydroxymethyl)-	pH 1	288(3.90)	44-4295-73
	pH 7	315(3.86),390(2.00)	44-4295-73
	pH 13	305(3.73),390(2.85)	44-4295-73
Pyridoxal N-oxide	pH 1	258(3.70),291(3.90)	44-4295-73
	pH 7	310(3.75),393(3.38)	44-4295-73
	pH 13	312(3.79),387(3.26)	44-4295-73
1H-Pyrrole-3,4-dicarboxylic acid, dimethyl ester	EtOH	253(3.90)	23-1089-73
$C_8H_9NO_4S$			
Benzeneethanesulfonic acid, 2-amino-β-oxo-	MeOH	228(4.27),265(3.85), 363(3.68)	94-1080-73
C_8H_9NS			
Benzenecarbothioamide, N-methyl-	H_2O	275(4.25)	1-0209-73
	H_2SO_4	264(4.44)	1-0209-73
Benzenecarboximidothioic acid, methyl ester	H_2O	239(4.43)	1-0209-73
protonated	H_2O	258(4.25)	1-0209-73
hydriodide	MeOH	222(4.04)	80-0685-73
$C_8H_9NS_2$			
Carbamodithioic acid, methylphenyl-	pH 1	237(4.06),270(4.07)	94-0329-73
	pH 13	253(4.16),285(4.18)	94-0329-73
	15M KOH	249(4.23)	94-0329-73
	80% H_2SO_4	244(4.09)	94-0329-73
$C_8H_9N_2O_5S$			
1,3-Cyclohexadiene, 6-methoxy-1-(methylthio)-3,5-dinitro-, ion(1-)	DMSO	366(4.15),534(4.28)	39-0710-73B

Compound	Solvent	λ_{max}(log ε)	Ref.
$C_8H_9N_2O_7S$			
1,3-Cyclohexadiene, 6-methoxy-1-(methylsulfonyl)-3,5-dinitro-, ion(1-)-	DMSO	376(4.23),481(4.36)	39-0710-73B
1,3-Cyclohexadiene, 6-methoxy-3-(methylsulfonyl)-1,5-dinitro-, ion(1-)-	DMSO	372(4.11),485(4.34), 540(3.90)	39-0710-73B
$C_8H_9N_3OS_2$			
4H-Thiazolo[3,2-a]-1,3,5-triazin-4-one, 7-ethyl-2-(methylthio)-	EtOH	246(3.85),267(3.91), 314(4.30),322s(--)	94-0074-73
4H-Thiazolo[3,2-a]-1,3,5-triazin-4-one, 2-[(1-methylethyl)thio]-	EtOH	226(4.01),246(3.88), 270(3.95),310(4.32), 317(4.32)	94-0074-73
4H-Thiazolo[3,2-a]-1,3,5-triazin-4-one, 2-(propylthio)-	EtOH	226(4.00),246(3.86), 270(3.93),310(4.31), 317(4.31)	94-0074-73
$C_8H_9N_3O_2$			
Ethanediamide, (4-aminophenyl)-	dioxan	308(4.07)	30-0001-73
$C_8H_9N_3O_2S_2$			
Carbamic acid, (5-methyl-2H-thiazolo-[3,2-b][1,2,4]thiadiazol-2-ylidene)-, ethyl ester	EtOH	251(3.52),312(4.35)	94-2408-73
Carbamic acid, (6-methyl-2H-thiazolo-[3,2-b][1,2,4]thiadiazol-2-ylidene)-, ethyl ester	EtOH	254(3.40),311(4.35)	94-2408-73
Carbamic acid, (2H-thiazolo[3,2-b]-[1,2,4]thiadiazol-2-ylidene)-, 1-methylethyl ester	EtOH	251(3.46),308(4.36)	94-2408-73
Carbamic acid, (2H-thiazolo[3,2-b]-[1,2,4]thiadiazol-2-ylidene)-, propyl ester	EtOH	251(3.48),308(4.36)	94-2408-73
$C_8H_9N_3S$			
2(3H)-Benzothiazolone, 3-methyl-, hydrazone	$CHCl_3$	244(3.96),274(3.90), 312(3.77)	22-3044-73
$C_8H_9N_5$			
Guanidine, 1H-benzimidazol-2-yl-, MnCl complex (also other metal complexes)	BuOH	320(3.56),350(3.36), 400s(3.04),540s(2.51), 600s(2.38)	120-0096-73
$C_8H_9N_5O$			
2(1H)-Pteridinone, 4-(dimethylamino)-	pH 0.0	247(4.05),336(3.98)	33-1225-73
	pH 7.0	204(4.40),249(3.86), 307s(3.82),343(3.99)	33-1225-73
1H-Purin-2-amine, 6-(2-propenyloxy)-	pH 1	230s(3.78),285(4.04)	35-7174-74
	pH 7	239(3.90),281(3.92)	35-7174-73
	pH 13	245s(3.69),283(3.94)	35-7174-73
$C_8H_9N_5O_2$			
2,4(1H,3H)-Pteridinedione, 7-amino-1,3-dimethyl-	pH -3.0	227(4.50),261(4.07), 365(4.17)	24-3203-73
	pH 5.0	215(4.46),247(3.84), 275(3.98),336(4.23)	24-3203-73
4(1H)-Pteridinone, 2-amino-6,7-dimethyl-, 8-oxide	pH -2.0	250(4.33),280s(3.88), 343(3.79),390(3.19)	24-3175-73
	pH 3.0	212(4.14),244(4.09), 270(4.42),287s(4.02), 370(3.83)	24-3175-73

Compound	Solvent	$\lambda_{max}(\log \epsilon)$	Ref.
4(1H)-Pteridinone, 2-amino-6,7-dimethyl-, 8-oxide (cont.)	pH 10.0	210(4.17),259(4.49), 283s(3.83),378(3.93)	24-3175-73
4(3H)-Pteridinone, 2-amino-3,6-dimethyl-, 8-oxide	H_o -1.85	257(4.19),287s(3.99), 352(3.62)	35-6407-73
	pH 3.93	270(4.25),292s(3.98), 382(3.81)	35-6407-73
7(8H)-Pteridinone, 2-amino-4-methoxy-8-methyl-	pH -2.0	222(4.14),290(3.89), 331(4.24)	24-1952-73
	pH 4.0	232(4.03),279(3.66), 343(4.22)	24-1952-73
4(1H)-Pteridinone, 6-methyl-2-(methylamino)-, 8-oxide	pH 13	265(4.51),295s(3.90), 400(3.90)	35-6407-73
Pyrimido[5,4-e]-1,2,4-triazine, 3-ethoxy-5-methoxy-	C_6H_{12}	214(4.09),236(4.18), 262s(3.55),279s(2.97), 322s(3.45),328s(3.55), 336(3.68),344(3.74), 351(3.81),360(3.67), 367(3.69),482(2.46), 524s(2.08)	12-1689-73
$C_8H_9N_5O_3$			
5(3H)-Pteridinecarboxaldehyde, 2-amino-4,6,7,8-tetrahydro-8-methyl-4,7-dioxo-	pH 6	232(4.48),315(3.92)	24-1389-73
	pH 11	223(4.35),304(3.77)	24-1389-73
2,4(1H,3H)-Pteridinedione, 7-amino-1,3-dimethyl-, 5-oxide	pH -4.0	230(4.52),255(3.95), 353(4.18)	24-3203-73
	pH 5.5	237(4.42),261(4.32), 288s(3.84),354(4.18)	24-3203-73
2,4,6(3H)-Pteridinetrione, 7-amino-1,5-dihydro-1,3-dimethyl-	pH -5.5	224(4.19),283(3.92), 357(3.93),368s(3.92)	24-3203-73
	pH 3.15	243(4.20),250s(4.15), 280(3.88),342(4.09), 355(4.14),370s(3.97)	24-3203-73
	pH 11.0	238(4.30),285(3.85), 341s(4.11),353(4.19), 367s(4.06)	24-3203-73
4(1H)-Pteridinone, 2-amino-6,7-dimethyl-, 5,8-dioxide	pH -1.0	258(4.30),271(4.29), 310(3.84),355s(3.48), 394(3.76)	24-3175-73
	pH 3.0	272(4.39),317(3.85), 393(3.75),415s(3.67)	24-3175-73
	pH 10.0	262(4.42),280s(4.13), 320(3.85),396(3.85), 413s(3.75)	24-3175-73
Pyrimido[5,4-e]-1,2,4-triazine, 3,5,7-trimethoxy-	C_6H_{12}	233(4.29),255s(3.81), 275s(3.08),353s(3.62), 363s(3.71),370(3.79), 381(3.69),389(3.70), 476(2.47),488s(2.44)	12-1689-73
$C_8H_9N_6O$			
1H-Purinium, 2-amino-7-(cyanomethyl)-6,9-dihydro-9-methyl-6-oxo-, bromide	pH 1	253(4.04),284(3.82)	24-1389-73
chloride	pH 1	206(4.30),255(4.06), 285(3.83)	24-1389-73
C_8H_{10}			
Benzene, 1,3-dimethyl-	C_6H_{12}	215(3.88),265(2.49)	49-0644-73
Bicyclo[2.2.0]hexane, 2,3-bis(methylene)-	C_6H_{12}	243s(3.98),252(4.04), 260s(3.90)	89-0505B-73
Bicyclo[4.2.0]octa-1,5-diene	C_6H_{12}	271(3.71)	89-0505B-73

Compound	Solvent	$\lambda_{max}(\log \epsilon)$	Ref.
Cyclohexene, 3-ethenylidene-	n.s.g.	227(3.87)	88-4591-73
Spiro[3.4]octa-5,7-diene	EtOH	261(3.29)	35-8468-73
Tricyclo[3.2.1.0^{7,8}]oct-2-ene	hexane	210(3.59)(end abs.)	88-4403-73
$C_8H_{10}BF_4N_3$			
Benzenediazonium, 2-(dimethylamino)-, tetrafluoroborate	M HCl	274(3.79),434(3.77)	48-0725-73
$C_8H_{10}BrN$			
Methanamine, 1-(2-bromo-2,4-cyclopentadien-1-ylidene)-N,N-dimethyl-	hexane	222(3.71),321(4.48), 327(4.47)	88-5101-73
$C_8H_{10}BrNO_3$			
Pyridoxol, 6-bromo-	pH 1	300(3.68)	87-0638-73
	pH 6.7	293(3.58)	87-0638-73
	pH 10.7	254(3.72),319(3.88)	87-0638-73
	M HCl	304(3.80)	87-0638-73
$C_8H_{10}BrN_5O_2$			
1,2-Propanediol, 3-(6-amino-8-bromo-9H-purin-9-yl)-	H_2O	264(4.20)	121-1297-73
$C_8H_{10}ClN$			
Methanamine, 1-(2-chloro-2,4-cyclopentadien-1-ylidene)-N,N-dimethyl-	hexane	319(4.50)	88-5101-73
$C_8H_{10}ClNO_2$			
4-Pyridinol, 3-chloro-2-ethoxy-6-methyl-	EtOH	265(3.42)	94-1047-73
$C_8H_{10}ClNO_3$			
3,4-Pyridinedimethanol, 2-chloro-5-hydroxy-6-methyl-	pH 1	301(3.64)	87-0638-73
	pH 6.7	291(3.57)	87-0638-73
	pH 9.6	255(3.79),319(3.98)	87-0638-73
	M HCl	303(3.78)	87-0638-73
$C_8H_{10}ClN_2O_3P$			
Phosphonic acid, [(4-chlorophenyl)azo]-, dimethyl ester, (Z)-	MeOH	230(4.04),310(4.23), 496(1.98)	44-4402-73
$C_8H_{10}ClN_3$			
Imidazo[4,5-b]pyridinium, 1,3-dimethyl-, chloride	EtOH	242(3.61),274(3.95), 282(3.89)	103-0531-73
Imidazo[4,5-b]pyridinium, 1,4-dimethyl-, chloride	EtOH	292(4.11)	103-0531-73
$C_8H_{10}Cl_2N_2O_3S$			
Sulfonium, bis(2-chloroethyl)-, 1,3,4,6-tetrahydro-2,4,6-trioxo-5(2H)-pyrimidinylide	EtOH	231(4.38)	104-2213-73
$C_8H_{10}FNO_3$			
3,4-Pyridinedimethanol, 2-fluoro-5-hydroxy-6-methyl-	pH 1	288(3.57)	87-0638-73
	pH 6.8	287(3.40)	87-0638-73
	pH 10.3	243(3.64),317(3.64)	87-0638-73
	M HCl	282(3.58)	87-0638-73
$C_8H_{10}F_3NO$			
Ethanone, 2,2,2-trifluoro-1-(1,4,5,6-tetrahydro-1-methyl-3-pyridinyl)-	MeOH	318(4.45)	107-0073-73

Compound	Solvent	λ_{max}(log ϵ)	Ref.
$C_8H_{10}IN_3$			
1H-Imidazo[4,5-b]pyridinium, 1,4-dimethyl-, iodide	EtOH	295(4.21)	103-0531-73
$C_8H_{10}NO_6P$			
2-Pyridinecarboxaldehyde, 3-hydroxy-4-methyl-5-[(phosphonooxy)methyl]-	pH 1	285(3.85),310s(3.51)	44-4295-73
	pH 7	237(3.96),303(3.58), 378(3.72)	44-4295-73
	pH 13	237(4.06),308(3.49), 378(3.81)	44-4295-73
$C_8H_{10}N_2O$			
3(2H)-Cinnolinone, 5,6,7,8-tetrahydro-	EtOH	280(4.28)	22-0625-73
Formamide, N-(2-aminophenyl)-N-methyl-	EtOH	238(3.92),277s(--), 282s(--),290(3.38)	22-1285-73
$C_8H_{10}N_2OS$			
Ethanone, 1-[2-(2-propenylamino)-5-thiazolyl]-	pH 1	255(3.93)	80-0677-73
	EtOH	229(4.05),315(3.45)	80-0677-73
$C_8H_{10}N_2OS_3$			
Rhodanine, 5-(N-methyl-2-thiazolidinylidene)-3-methyl-	EtOH	283(4.00),393(4.54)	94-1431-73
$C_8H_{10}N_2O_2$			
Benzenamine, 4-ethyl-2-nitro-	hexane	226(4.75),247(4.26), 268s(4.11),384(4.08)	24-1116-73
4(5H)-Benzofurazanone, 6,7-dihydro-6,6-dimethyl-	MeOH	233(3.48)	39-0351-73C
Ethanone, 1-(3-hydroxy-2-methyl-4-pyrimidinyl)-, oxime	pH 13	280(3.91),350(3.71)	70-1057-73
5,8-Methano-2(1H)-azocinone, 5,6,7,8-tetrahydro-N-nitroso-	MeOH	245(3.84),269(3.83)	39-1661-73C
$C_8H_{10}N_2O_2S$			
Acetamide, N-(5-acetyl-4-methyl-2-thiazolyl)-	EtOH	229(3.95),305(4.14)	80-0677-73
	EtOH-HCl	229(3.79),303(4.16)	80-0677-73
5H-Thiazolo[3,2-a]pyrimidinium, 8-ethyl-2,3-dihydro-7-hydroxy-5-oxo-	H_2O	222(4.28),265(3.88), 284s(3.46)	4-0487-73
$C_8H_{10}N_2O_3$			
4(5H)-Benzofurazanone, 6,7-dihydro-6,6-dimethyl-, 1-oxide	MeOH	213(4.07),308(3.30)	39-0351-73C
4(5H)-Benzofurazanone, 6,7-dihydro-6,6-dimethyl-, 3-oxide	MeOH	215(4.07),250(3.54), 284(3.54)	39-0351-73C
2,5-Piperazinedione, 1-acetyl-3-ethylidene-	EtOH	222(4.15)	88-1135-73
$C_8H_{10}N_2O_3S_3$			
4-Thiazolidinone, 3-ethyl-5-[1-(methylthio)-2-nitroethylidene]-2-thioxo-	EtOH	290(3.91),387(4.46)	95-0612-73
$C_8H_{10}N_2O_4$			
Thymine, 1-(2-carboxyethyl)-	H_2O	269(3.94)	138-0967-73
$C_8H_{10}N_2O_6S_2$			
2H-Pyrrole-3-carboxylic acid, 5-[[(methylsulfonyl)oxy]amino]-4-(methylthio)-2-oxo-, methyl ester	EtOH	302(4.01),360(3.91)	94-1667-73

Compound	Solvent	$\lambda_{max}(\log \epsilon)$	Ref.
$C_8H_{10}N_2S$			
Thiourea, N-methyl-N-phenyl-	EtOH	247(3.56),267(3.60)	48-0144-73
$C_8H_{10}N_3$			
Benzenediazonium, 2-(dimethylamino)-	M HCl	274(3.79),434(3.77)	48-0725-73
Imidazo[4,5-b]pyridinium, 1,3-dimethyl-, chloride	EtOH	242(3.61),274(3.95), 282(3.89)	103-0531-73
Imidazo[4,5-b]pyridinium, 1,4-dimethyl-, chloride	EtOH	292(4.11)	103-0531-73
iodide	EtOH	295(4.21)	103-0531-73
$C_8H_{10}N_3O_2$			
Pyridinium, 2,4-bis[(hydroxyimino)meth-	0.05M HCl	300(4.08)	73-2788-73
yl]-1-methyl-, iodide	pH 13	360(4.31)	73-2788-73
Pyridinium, 2,5-bis[(hydroxyimino)meth-	0.05M HCl	322(4.24)	73-2788-73
yl]-1-methyl-, iodide	pH 8.6	363(4.37)	73-2788-73
	pH 13	372(4.38)	73-2788-73
$C_8H_{10}N_3O_5P$			
Phosphonic acid, [(4-nitrophenyl)azo]-, dimethyl ester, (Z)-	MeOH	257(4.34),510(2.03)	44-4402-73
$C_8H_{10}N_4$			
1H-Imidazo[4,5-b]pyrazine, 1,5,6-tri-	pH 1	285s(3.94),304(4.15)	39-0244-73C
methyl-	pH 11	295s(3.92),313(4.17)	39-0244-73C
	MeOH	260(3.35),298s(4.05), 309(4.11)	39-0244-73C
Propanedinitrile, (1,3-dimethyl-2-imid-	C_6H_{12}	225s(3.94),274(4.19)	1-0258-73
azolidinylidene)-	EtOH	240s(3.90),262(4.20)	1-0258-73
1H-Purine, 2,6,8-trimethyl-	pH 9.2	271(3.9)	95-1685-73
1H-Pyrazolo[3,4-b]pyridin-4-amine, N,N-dimethyl-	EtOH	237(4.17),243(4.10), 324(4.08)	104-1294-73
$C_8H_{10}N_4O$			
Pyrazinecarbonitrile, 3-amino-6-propyl-, 4-oxide	MeOH	229(3.83),252(4.05), 378(3.46)	35-6413-73
$C_8H_{10}N_4OS$			
9H-Purine-9-ethanol, 6-(methylthio)-	H_2O	287(4.21),292(4.21)	121-1297-73
2H-Purin-2-one, 1,3-dihydro-1,3-dimeth-	neutral	258(3.91),336(4.13)	39-2445-73C
yl-6-(methylthio)-	cation	267(4.02),338(4.06)	39-2445-73C
2H-Purin-2-one, 3,7-dihydro-3,7-dimeth-	neutral	272(4.07),319(4.20)	39-2445-73C
yl-6-(methylthio)-	cation	258(3.95),343(4.26)	39-2445-73C
6H-Purin-6-one, 3,7-dihydro-3,7-dimeth-	neutral	232(4.12),279(4.16)	39-2647-73C
yl-2-(methylthio)-	cation	228(4.06),272(4.10)	39-2647-73C
6H-Purin-6-one, 1,2,3,7-tetrahydro-1,3,7-trimethyl-2-thioxo-	MeOH	286(4.25)	39-2647-73C
$C_8H_{10}N_4OS_2$			
2H-Purin-2-one, 1,9-dihydro-9-methyl-	pH 1	248(4.41),357(4.30)	44-2066-73
6,8-bis(methylthio)-	pH 6	330(4.28)	44-2066-73
	pH 12	327(4.34)	44-2066-73
2H-Purin-2-one, 3,7-dihydro-3-methyl-	pH 1	279(4.04),370(4.59)	44-2066-73
6,8-bis(methylthio)-	pH 6	342(4.47)	44-2066-73
	pH 12	340(4.45)	44-2066-73
6H-Purin-6-one, 1,9-dihydro-1-methyl-	pH 1	225(4.40),283(4.47)	44-2066-73
2,8-bis(methylthio)-	pH 6	280(4.39)	44-2066-73
	neutral	280(4.39)	39-2647-73C
	pH 12	235(4.40),286(4.36)	44-2066-73
6H-Purin-6-one, 1,9-dihydro-9-methyl-	pH 1	283(4.20)	44-2066-73
2,8-bis(methylthio)-	cation	283(4.20)	39-2647-73C

Compound	Solvent	λ_{max}(log ϵ)	Ref.
6H-Purin-6-one, 1,9-dihydro-9-methyl-2,8-bis(methylthio)- (cont.)	pH 6	280(4.21)	44-2066-73
	pH 12	286(4.24)	44-2066-73
	anion	286(4.24)	39-2647-73C
6H-Purin-6-one, 3,7-dihydro-3-methyl-	pH 6	297.5(4.30)	44-3367-73
	neutral	297.5(4.30)	39-2647-73C
	pH 12	303(4.30)	44-3367-73
	cation	310(4.16)	39-2647-73C
8H-Purin-8-one, 7,9-dihydro-9-methyl-2,6-bis(methylthio)-	pH 1	255(4.25),316(4.06)	44-2066-73
	pH 6	256(4.19),315(4.09)	44-2066-73
	pH 12	286(4.04),324(4.02)	44-2066-73
$C_8H_{10}N_4O_2$			
Caffeine	n.s.g.	273(3.99)	105-0652-73
Oxazolo[4,5-d]pyrimidin-2(3H)-one, 5-amino-3-ethyl-7-methyl-	EtOH	304(3.97)	95-0817-73
Pyrazine, 2,6-diacetamido-	EtOH	217(4.43),244s(3.84), 313(4.11)	39-0606-73C
Xanthine, 7-isopropyl-	pH 1	263(3.87)	94-0256-73
	pH 13	290(3.93)	94-0256-73
$C_8H_{10}N_4O_2S$			
1H-Purine-2,6-dione, 3,7-dihydro-3,7-dimethyl-8-(methylthio)-	pH 1.0	294(4.23)	44-3367-73
	pH 6.0	295(4.23)	44-3367-73
	pH 12.0	295(4.12)	44-3367-73
1H-Purine-2,6-dione, 3,9-dihydro-1,9-dimethyl-8-(methylthio)-	pH 1.0	285(4.20)	44-3367-73
	pH 6.0	287(4.20)	44-3367-73
	pH 12	291(4.17)	44-3367-73
$C_8H_{10}N_4O_3$			
Pyrazine, 2,6-diacetamido-, N-oxide	EtOH	252(4.51),277s(4.01), 327(3.95)	39-0606-73C
$C_8H_{10}N_4S_3$			
6H-Purine-6-thione, 1,7-dihydro-1-methyl-2,8-bis(methylthio)-	MeOH	263(4.22),350(4.15)	39-2647-73C
$C_8H_{10}N_6$			
2,4-Pteridinediamine, 6,7-dimethyl-	pH 2.0	217s(4.20),242(4.17), 277(3.64),334(4.08), 344s(4.04)	24-3175-73
	pH 8.0	230(4.14),252(4.31), 272s(3.82),362(3.91)	24-3175-73
$C_8H_{10}N_6O$			
2,4-Pteridinediamine, 6,7-dimethyl-, 8-oxide	pH 0.0	247(4.53),282(3.93), 346(3.97),360(3.92)	24-3175-73
	pH 6.0	213(4.20),260(4.53), 286s(3.86),382(3.95)	24-3175-73
2,4-Pteridinediamine, 6-ethyl-, 8-oxide	pH 1	251(4.46),281(3.96), 357(3.91),376(3.88)	35-6413-73
Pyrimido[5,4-e]-1,2,4-triazin-3-amine, 5-methoxy-N,7-dimethyl-	MeOH	227s(4.05),266(4.02), 401(3.79)	12-1689-73
Pyrimido[5,4-e]-1,2,4-triazin-5-amine, 3-ethoxy-N-methyl-	MeOH	214(4.06),224(4.05), 268(3.95),295s(3.38), 403(3.78)	12-1689-73
Urea, N,N-dimethyl-N'-1H-purin-6-yl-	pH 1-2	280(4.33)	87-0139-73
	pH 5-7	277.5(4.27)	87-0139-73
	pH 12	278(4.17)	87-0139-73

Compound	Solvent	λ_{max}(log ε)	Ref.
$C_8H_{10}N_6O_2$			
Carbamic acid, (7-amino-1H-1,2,3-triazolo[4,5-b]pyridin-5-yl)-, ethyl ester	pH 7	281(4.23),302(4.35)	44-1095-73
Formamide, N-[2-amino-1,6-dihydro-4-(methylamino)-6-oxo-5-pyrimidinyl]-N-(cyanomethyl)-	pH -1	266(4.31)	24-1389-73
	pH 5	219(4.51),266(4.18)	24-1389-73
	pH 12	212(4.51),262(4.06)	24-1389-73
2,4-Pteridinediamine, 6,7-dimethyl-, 5,8-dioxide	pH -2.0	219(4.16),255(4.35), 379(3.90)	24-3175-73
	pH 6.0	265(4.58),375(3.94)	24-3175-73
$C_8H_{10}N_6S_2$			
1H-1,2,4-Triazole-1-propanenitrile, 4-amino-3-[(2-cyanoethyl)thio]-4,5-dihydro-5-thioxo-	EtOH	218(3.2),265(3.3)	103-0518-73
$C_8H_{10}N_{12}O_2$			
Urea, N,N"-[azinobis(methylidyne-1H-1,2,3-triazole-5,4-diyl)]bis-	MeOH-20% DMSO	347(4.28)	39-1625-73C
$C_8H_{10}N_{12}S_2$			
Thiourea, N,N"-[azinobis(methylidyne-1H-1,2,3-triazole-5,4-diyl)]bis-	MeOH-20% DMSO	267(4.69),364(4.31)	39-1625-73C
$C_8H_{10}O$			
Bicyclo[3.2.0]hept-3-en-2-one, 7-methyl-, endo	EtOH	232(3.91),326(1.89)	35-4346-73
exo	EtOH	227(3.76),325(1.86)	35-4346-73
Bicyclo[3.1.0]hex-2-ene-6-carboxaldehyde, 4-methyl-	C_6H_{12}	230(2.76),235(2.78)	44-4007-73
Bicyclo[3.1.0]hex-3-en-2-one, 6,6-dimethyl-	EtOH	284(2.11)	35-5086-73
Bicyclo[5.1.0]oct-2-en-4-one, cis	isooctane	237(3.89),322(1.70), 337s(1.60)	44-3250-73
Bicyclo[2.2.2]oct-3-en-2-one, (+)-	C_6H_{12}	288(2.00),296(2.09), 306(2.05),317(1.78)	22-2836-73
Bicyclo[3.2.1]oct-3-en-2-one	EtOH	230(4.00)	44-3829-73
2,4-Cycloheptadien-1-one, 2-methyl-	MeOH	300(3.95)	35-3289-73
2,4-Cycloheptadien-1-one, 7-methyl-	MeOH	295(3.8)	35-3289-73
2,6-Cycloheptadien-1-one, 2-methyl-	EtOH	240(3.89),275(3.40)	35-3289-73
3,5-Cycloheptadien-1-one, 2-methyl-	MeOH	228(3.64)	35-3289-73
at -50°	FSO_3H	315(3.3)	35-3289-73
2,5-Cyclohexadien-1-one, 4,4-dimethyl-	hexane	224(4.187)	39-0084-73B
	hexane	224(4.19)	39-0529-73C
	isooctane	225(4.182)	39-0084-73B
	H_2O	240(4.189)	39-0084-73B
cation	75% H_2SO_4	260(4.14),290(4.08)	39-0084-73B
2,4-Cyclooctadien-1-one	C_6H_{12}	268(3.76),346(1.71)	23-2207-73
	benzene	343(1.7)	23-2207-73
	EtOH	278(3.77)	23-2207-73
1(2H)-Pentalenone, 3,3a,4,6a-tetrahydro-, cis	isooctane	284s(1.65),293(1.78), 303(1.85),313(1.78), 323s(1.48)	44-3250-73
Phenol, 2,4-dimethyl-	acid	281(3.26)	49-1315-73
	anion	239(3.93),297(3.52)	49-1315-73
	dioxan	281(3.38)	126-0039-73L
Phenol, 2,6-dimethyl-	dioxan	273.5(3.26)	126-0039-73L
Spiro[3.4]oct-7-en-6-one	EtOH	229(4.07),315(1.71)	35-8468-73
Tricyclo[3.2.1.0^{2,7}]octan-3-one	C_6H_{12}	192(3.979)	33-1046-73
	EtOH	199(3.89)	33-1046-73
Tricyclo[3.2.1.0^{2,7}]octan-4-one	C_6H_{12}	190(3.19)(end abs.)	33-1046-73

Compound	Solvent	$\lambda_{max}(\log \epsilon)$	Ref.
$C_8H_{10}OS_2$			
[1,2]Dithiolo[1,5-b][1,2]oxathiole-7-S^{IV}, 2,3,4-trimethyl-	C_6H_{12}	205(3.98),224(4.20), 274(3.16),422(4.05), 436(4.02)	39-2351-73C
2H-Thiopyran-2-thione, 4-ethoxy-6-methyl-	MeOH	269(4.42),312(3.78), 405(3.89)	7-0269-73
$C_8H_{10}O_2$			
Benzene, 1,2-dimethoxy-	EtOH	225(3.86),275(3.44), 281s(3.35)	141-0001-73
	dioxan	228(3.83),275(3.44), 283s(3.35)	141-0001-73
Benzene, 1,3-dimethoxy-	EtOH	221(3.83),268s(3.22), 275(3.34),281(3.28)	141-0001-73
	dioxan	222(3.81),267s(3.15), 275(3.34),281(3.28)	141-0001-73
Benzene, 1,4-dimethoxy-	C_6H_{12}	226(3.99),291(3.51)	30-0941-73
	EtOH	226(3.97),290(3.48), 300s(3.30)	141-0001-73
	dioxan	228(3.94),292(3.50), 300s(3.37)	141-0001-73
1,2-Benzenediol, 3-ethyl-	MeOH	277(3.30)	69-1520-73
Benzenemethanol, 3-hydroxy-4-methyl-	H_2O	275(3.52)	70-1271-73
	pH 13	294(3.76)	70-1271-73
2,5-Cyclohexadien-1-one, 2-hydroxy-4,4-dimethyl-	EtOH	238(3.80),283(3.39)	44-4068-73
$C_8H_{10}O_2S$			
2H-Thiopyran-2-one, 4-ethoxy-6-methyl-	MeOH	228(4.40),255(3.70), 317(3.63)	7-0269-73
$C_8H_{10}O_3$			
1,3-Benzenedimethanol, 2-hydroxy-	H_2O	281(3.37)	70-1271-73
	pH 13	241(3.80),301(3.53)	70-1271-73
2(4H)-Benzofuranone, 5,6,7,7a-tetrahydro-7a-hydroxy-	EtOH	214(3.98)	22-0625-73
Bicyclo[2.1.0]pentane-2-carboxylic acid, 3-oxo-, ethyl ester	EtOH	249(1.88)	70-1042-73
3-Buten-2-one, 4,4'-oxybis-	dioxan	268(4.25)	24-0435-73
2-Butynoic acid, 4-[(2-methyl-1-propenyl)oxy]-	EtOH	205(3.77)	39-1349-73C
Ethanone, 1-(5,6-dihydroxy-1,3-cyclohexadien-1-yl)-	MeOH	295(3.94)	69-1520-73
2-Furancarboxylic acid, 5-methyl-, ethyl ester	heptane	258(--)	103-0546-73
	H_2O	265(--)	103-0546-73
	EtOH	262(--)	103-0546-73
	dioxan	261(4.31)	103-0546-73
3(2H)-Furanone, 4-acetyl-2,5-dimethyl-	hexane	223(3.97),266(4.00)	44-0123-73
2(3H)-Furanone, 3-ethenylidenedihydro-5-hydroxy-4,4-dimethyl-	EtOH	209(3.42),231(3.32), 260s(3.15)	39-1349-73C
4H-Pyran-4-one, 2-ethoxy-6-methyl-	EtOH	241(4.04)	94-1047-73
$C_8H_{10}O_4$			
Butanedioic acid, bis(methylene)-, dimethyl ester	MeOH	215(3.76)(end abs.)	33-3004-73
1-Cyclobutene-1,2-dicarboxylic acid, dimethyl ester	MeOH	233(4.03)	33-3004-73
2(5H)-Furanone, 5-methoxy-5-(2-oxopropyl)-	H_2O	194(3.87),273(2.80)	35-5700-73
2,4-Heptadienoic acid, 4-methoxy-6-oxo-, sodium salt	aq NaOH	203(3.56),293(4.05)	35-5700-73
	pH 2.63	195(3.57),280(3.75)	35-5700-73

Compound	Solvent	λ_{max}(log ϵ)	Ref.
$C_8H_{10}O_5$			
4-Hexenedioic acid, 3-oxo-, 1-ethyl ester, (E)-	EtOH	223(3.83),283(4.15)	78-4251-73
$C_8H_{10}O_5S$			
2-Propenoic acid, 3,3'-sulfinylbis-, dimethyl ester, trans-trans	heptane	222(4.12)	143-0205-73
$C_8H_{10}O_5S_2$			
1,3-Dithiole-4,5-dicarboxylic acid, 2-methoxy-, dimethyl ester	EtOH	218(3.50),238(3.58), 314(3.71)	35-4379-73
$C_8H_{10}S$			
Benzene, (ethylthio)-	C_6H_{12}	205(4.08),258(3.88), 283f(3.08)	39-1125-73B
	EtOH	205(4.03),255(3.90)	39-1125-73B
	5% EtOH	203(4.12),250(3.87)	39-1125-73B
Benzene, 1-methyl-2-(methylthio)-	C_6H_{12}	209(4.26),252(3.89), 281s(3.15)	39-1125-73B
	EtOH	209(4.34),250(3.98), 278(3.10)	39-1125-73B
	5% EtOH	206(4.32),247(3.96), 276(3.11)	39-1125-73B
Benzene, 1-methyl-3-(methylthio)-	C_6H_{12}	210s(4.20),257(3.93), 284s(2.97)	39-1125-73B
	EtOH	210(4.28),255(3.97), 284s(2.98)	39-1125-73B
	5% EtOH	208(4.23),252(3.92), 273s(3.06)	39-1125-73B
Benzene, 1-methyl-4-(methylthio)-	C_6H_{12}	210(4.08),258(3.96), 290s(2.93)	39-1125-73B
	EtOH	207(4.18),255(4.08), 289s(2.92)	39-1125-73B
	5% EtOH	205(4.32),253(4.01), 275(3.07)	39-1125-73B
$C_8H_{11}BrN_5O_5P$			
1,2-Propanediol, 3-(6-amino-8-bromo-9H-purin-9-yl)-, 1-(dihydrogen phosphate)	H_2O	264(4.18)	121-1297-73
$C_8H_{11}BrO$			
Bicyclo[4.2.0]octan-3-one, 4(a)-bromo-	EtOH	309(2.06)	78-1865-73
Bicyclo[4.2.0]octan-3-one, 4(e)-bromo-	EtOH	289(1.64)	78-1965-73
2-Cyclohexen-1-one, 6-bromo-4,4-dimethyl-	EtOH	228(4.01)	39-0529-73C
$C_8H_{11}BrO_2$			
2-Cyclobuten-1-one, 2-bromo-3-ethoxy-4,4-dimethyl-	EtOH	249(4.00)	44-1451-73
2,4-Hexadienoic acid, 6-bromo-, ethyl ester, (E,E)-	EtOH	263(4.29)	107-0025-73
$C_8H_{11}ClO$			
Bicyclo[4.2.0]octan-3-one, 4(a)-chloro-	EtOH	304(1.72)	78-1865-73
Bicyclo[4.2.0]octan-3-one, 4(e)-chloro-	EtOH	287(1.54)	78-1865-73
$C_8H_{11}Cl_3N_2O_2$			
1H-Pyrazole-3-carboxylic acid, 4,5-dihydro-4,4-dimethyl-, 2,2,2-trichloroethyl ester	n.s.g.	298(4.08)	39-1182-73C

Compound	Solvent	λ_{max}(log ε)	Ref.
$C_8H_{11}FO$			
Bicyclo[4.2.0]octan-3-one, 4(a)-fluoro-	EtOH	299(1.34)	78-1865-73
Bicyclo[4.2.0]octan-3-one, 4(e)-fluoro-	EtOH	292(1.54)	78-1865-73
$C_8H_{11}F_3O_2$			
Cyclohexanone, 2-(2,2,2-trifluoro-1-hydroxyethyl)-, erythro	EtOH	223(1.94),280(1.58)	23-3177-73
threo	EtOH	204(1.54),281(1.49)	23-3177-73
$C_8H_{11}IN_4O$			
1H-Purinium, 6,7-dihydro-1,7,9-trimethyl-6-oxo-, iodide	M HCl	253(4.02)	39-2647-73C
$C_8H_{11}N$			
Aniline, 2,4-dimethyl-	C_6H_{12}	235(3.83),292(3.28)	49-0644-73
$C_8H_{11}NO$			
2-Azabicyclo[4.2.1]non-4-en-3-one	MeOH	215(4.07)	39-1661-73C
Ethanone, 1-(2,4-dimethyl-1H-pyrrol-3-yl)-	H_2O	253(3.99),290(3.67)	103-1355-73
	16N H_2SO_4	276(4.20),335(3.41)	103-1355-73
Ethanone, 1-(3,5-dimethyl-1H-pyrrol-2-yl)-	H_2O	260(3.65),305(4.31)	103-1355-73
	20N H_2SO_4	319(4.34)	103-1355-73
Pyridine, 3-ethyl-4-methyl-, 1-oxide	H_2O	256(4.16)	59-1069-73
	cation	262(3.54)	59-1069-73
Pyridine, 5-ethyl-2-methyl-, 1-oxide	H_2O	252(3.95)	59-1069-73
	cation	271(3.64)	59-1069-73
Pyridine, 2,4,6-trimethyl-, 1-oxide, hydrochloride	H_2O	253(4.04)	59-0139-73
	6M HCl	267(3.81)	59-0139-73
2-Pyridinemethanol, α-ethyl-, (S)-	EtOH	257(3.30),262(3.32), 269(3.23)	35-0811-73
3-Pyridinemethanol, α-ethyl-, (S)-	MeOH	253s(3.30),257s(3.40), 260(3.48),266s(3.30)	35-0811-73
1H-Pyrrole-2-carboxaldehyde, 3,4,5-trimethyl-	H_2O	270(3.81),316(4.28)	103-1355-73
	14N H_2SO_4	293(4.20),330(3.94)	103-1355-73
$C_8H_{11}NO_2$			
1H-Azepine-1-carboxylic acid, 2,3-dihydro-, methyl ester	C_6H_{12}	277(5.23)	35-7320-73
2H-Azepin-2-one, 1,3-dihydro-4-methoxy-1-methyl-	EtOH	263(3.73)	39-1079-73C
1,3-Benzenediol, 5-(dimethylamino)-	EtOH	253(4.13),282s(3.27), 289(3.18),292s(3.11)	33-0510-73
3H-Cyclohept[c]isoxazol-3-one, 1,4,5,6,7,8-hexahydro-	EtOH	264(3.97)	1-2802-73
4-Pyridinol, 2-ethoxy-6-methyl-	EtOH	250(4.06)	94-1047-73
2(1H)-Pyridinone, 4-ethoxy-5-methyl-	pH 1.0	266(3.64)	87-0524-73
	pH 14.0	283(3.52)	87-0524-73
	MeOH	283(3.60)	87-0524-73
1H-Pyrrole-3-carboxylic acid, 2-methyl-, ethyl ester	EtOH	255(3.87)	5-0207-73
1H-Pyrrole-2,5-dione, 1-butyl-	CH_2Cl_2	300(2.9)	35-0137-73
$C_8H_{11}NO_3$			
2,5-Pyridinedimethanol, 3-hydroxy-4-methyl-	pH 1	282(3.92)	44-4295-73
	pH 7	252(3.59),313(3.87)	44-4295-73
	pH 13	244(3.84),303(3.82)	44-4295-73
3-Pyridinemethanol, 5-hydroxy-4,6-dimethyl-, 1-oxide	pH 1	258(3.61),285(3.81)	44-4295-73
	pH 7	317(3.77)	44-4295-73
	pH 13	317(3.86)	44-4295-73

Compound	Solvent	$\lambda_{max}(\log \epsilon)$	Ref.
$C_8H_{11}NO_3S$			
Acetic acid, (3-methyl-4-oxo-2-thiazolidinylidene)-, ethyl ester	EtOH	281(4.32)	1-1923-73
Carbamic acid, (4-ethylidene-1,3-oxathiolan-2-ylidene)-, ethyl ester	EtOH	266(3.81)	94-0062-73
$C_8H_{11}NO_4$			
4-Isoxazoleacetic acid, 4,5-dihydro-3-methyl-5-oxo-, ethyl ester	EtOH	259(4.01)	1-2802-73
4-Isoxazoleacetic acid, 3-hydroxy-5-methyl-, ethyl ester	EtOH	212(3.70)	1-2802-73
$C_8H_{11}NO_5$			
2,4,5-Pyridinetrimethanol, 3-hydroxy-, 1-oxide	pH 1	262(3.96),300(3.72)	44-4295-73
	pH 7	331(3.76)	44-4295-73
	pH 13	331(3.88)	44-4295-73
$C_8H_{11}NO_9P_2$			
Diphosphoric acid, P-ethyl-P'-(4-nitrophenyl) ester	H_2O	290(4.00)	18-3275-73
$C_8H_{11}NS_2$			
6H-[1,2]Dithiolo[5,1-e]isothiazole-7-S^{IV}, 2,5,6-trimethyl-	MeOH	214(4.05),237(4.24), 263s(3.89),414(3.95)	39-2351-73C
6H-[1,2]Dithiolo[5,1-e]isothiazole-7-S^{IV}, 3,4,6-trimethyl-	C_6H_{12}	209(4.21),238(4.35), 269s(3.71),436(4.04)	39-2351-73C
	MeOH	209(4.06),243(4.42), 268s(3.77),433(4.03)	39-2351-73C
$C_8H_{11}N_2O$			
Pyridinium, 3-acetyl-1-methyl-, oxime	pH 6.61	258(3.78)	36-1381-73
$C_8H_{11}N_2O_3P$			
Phosphonic acid, (phenylazo)-, dimethyl ester, (Z)-	MeOH	293(4.08),485(1.86)	44-4402-73
$C_8H_{11}N_3O$			
Cyclopentanecarbonitrile, 1-(acetylazo)-	C_6H_{12}	395(1.56)	23-1378-73
$C_8H_{11}N_3O_2S_2$			
Isothiourea, 1-carbomethoxy-2-methyl-3-(3-methyl-2-thiazolinylidene)-	dioxan	245(3.48),280(3.85), 331(4.35)	94-0074-73
$C_8H_{11}N_3O_3$			
Pyrazinecarboxylic acid, 3-amino-6-methyl-, ethyl ester, 4-oxide	H_2O	226(4.05),246(4.29), 378(3.94)	35-6407-73
$C_8H_{11}N_3O_4S_2$			
Carbamic acid, [5-[(ethoxycarbonyl)-amino]-3H-1,2,4-dithiazol-3-ylidene)-, ethyl ester	EtOH	269(4.17),302(3.97), 320s(3.93)	94-2396-73
$C_8H_{11}N_3O_5$			
2H-Pyrrole-3-carboxylic acid, 5-(hydroxyamino)-4-[(2-hydroxyethyl)-amino]-2-oxo-, methyl ester	EtOH	359(4.09)	94-1667-73
1,2,4-Triazin-3(4H)-one, 4-β-D-ribofuranosyl-	pH 1	227(3.81),255s(3.68), 346(3.33)	44-3277-73
	pH 11	234(3.78),347(3.46)	44-3277-73
	EtOH	226(3.84),255(3.69), 346(3.38)	44-3277-73

Compound	Solvent	$\lambda_{max}(\log \epsilon)$	Ref.
$C_8H_{11}N_3O_5S$			
1,2,4-Triazin-5(2H)-one, 3,4-dihydro-2-β-D-ribofuranosyl-3-thioxo-	H_2O	218(4.1),269(3.9)	24-3039-73
	pH 12	236(4.1),267(4.3)	24-3039-73
$C_8H_{11}N_3O_6$			
1,2,4-Triazin-3(4H)-one, 4-β-D-ribofuranosyl-, 1-oxide	pH 1	207(4.22),267(3.93), 343(3.88)	44-3277-73
	H_2O	207(4.22),267(3.93), 343(3.88)	44-3277-73
	pH 11	232(3.97),273(3.82), 340(2.87)	44-3277-73
$C_8H_{11}N_4O$			
1H-Purinium, 6,7-dihydro-1,7,9-trimethyl-6-oxo-, iodide	M HCl	253(4.02)	39-2647-73C
$C_8H_{11}N_4O_4PS$			
9H-Purine-9-ethanol, 6-(methylthio)-, dihydrogen phosphate	H_2O	287(4.24),292(4.24)	121-1297-73
$C_8H_{11}N_5$			
1H-Purin-6-amine, N-propyl-	pH 1	272(4.19)	94-2349-73
	pH 7	270(4.22)	94-2349-73
	pH 13	275(4.22),282s(4.11)	94-2349-73
9H-Purin-6-amine, 8-isopropyl-	pH 1	267(4.16)	39-1855-73C
	pH 11	267(4.12)	39-1855-73C
	MeOH	261(4.17)	39-1855-73C
9H-Purin-6-amine, 9-isopropyl-	0.05M HCl	260.5(4.15)	94-0034-73
	0.05M NaOH	263(--)	94-0034-73
$C_8H_{11}N_5O$			
Ethanol, 2-[(3-methyl-1H-pyrazolo-[4,3-d]pyrimidin-7-yl)amino]- (all spectra in ethanol)	pH 1	262(3.79),310(4.08)	102-0025-73
	pH 7	237(3.78),295(4.07), 306(3.97),319s(--)	102-0025-73
	pH 12	243(4.19),264s(--), 308(3.86)	102-0025-73
9H-Purin-6-amine, N-methoxy-7,9-dimethyl-	pH 1	220(4.36),276(4.20)	88-4873-73
	pH 7	220(4.41),276(4.24)	88-4873-73
	pH 13	276(4.23)	88-4873-73
	EtOH	277(4.22)	88-4873-73
9H-Purine-9-ethanol, 6-amino-α-methyl-	H_2O	261(4.11)	138-0967-73
$C_8H_{11}N_5O_2$			
Methanimidamide, N-hydroxy-N'-[3-(hydroxyimino)methyl]-5,6-dimethyl-pyrazinyl]-	EtOH	222(4.25),291(4.20), 350(4.02)	39-1974-73C
1,3-Propanediol, 2-(6-amino-9H-purin-9-yl)-	pH 1	260(4.16)	103-0117-73
	H_2O	261(4.16)	103-0117-73
	pH 13	261(4.17)	103-0117-73
$C_8H_{11}N_5O_3$			
1,2-Propanediol, 3-(6-amino-9H-purin-9-yl)-, N-oxide	H_2O	233(4.65)	126-0019-73J
$C_8H_{11}N_5O_4$			
Glycine, N-[2-amino-1,6-dihydro-4-(methylamino)-6-oxo-5-pyrimidinyl]-N-formyl-	pH -1	268(4.31)	24-1389-73
	pH 5	219(4.50),268(4.18)	24-1389-73
	pH 10	264(4.09)	24-1389-73

Compound	Solvent	$\lambda_{max}(\log \epsilon)$	Ref.
$C_8H_{11}N_6O_2$			
1H-Purinium, 2-amino-7-(2-amino-2-oxo-ethyl)-6,9-dihydro-9-methoxy-6-oxo-, bromide	pH 4	253(4.07),281(3.86)	24-1389-73
	pH 10	248(3.74),284(3.89)	24-1389-73
$C_8H_{11}N_7$			
Pyrimido[5,4-e]-1,2,4-triazine-3,5-di-amine, N,N',7-trimethyl-	pH 1.0	226(4.32),280(4.06), 290s(4.01),310s(3.79), 445(3.70)	12-1689-73
	pH 9.0	223(4.39),281(4.18), 450(3.69)	12-1689-73
$C_8H_{11}N_7O$			
Pyrimido[5,4-e]-1,2,4-triazine-3,5-di-amine, 7-propoxy-	MeOH	215s(4.10),220(4.17), 251s(4.25),254s(4.28), 261(4.31),310(3.23), 437(3.76)	12-1689-73
Urea, N-(2-aminoethyl)-N'-1H-purin-6-yl-	pH 1-2	276.5(4.30)	87-0139-73
	pH 5-7	269(4.27)	87-0139-73
	pH 12	277.5(4.24)	87-0139-73
$C_8H_{11}O$			
Cycloheptadienylium, 1-hydroxy-2-methyl-	FSO_3H	398(3.72)	35-3289-73
$C_8H_{11}O_2$			
Pyrylium, 4-methoxy-2,6-dimethyl-, perchlorate	MeCN	190(4.36),219(3.24), 245(4.16),258(4.10)	78-0795-73
C_8H_{12}			
1,3-Cyclohexadiene, 1,6-dimethyl-	n.s.g.	263(3.81)	78-3781-73
1,3-Cyclohexadiene, 5,6-dimethyl-, cis	n.s.g.	261(3.61)	78-3781-73
trans	n.s.g.	263(3.60)	78-3781-73
1,6-Heptadiene, 3-methylene-	EtOH	224(4.1)	35-8209-73
1,3,5-Hexatriene, 2,4-dimethyl-, (E)-	heptane	255(4.38),263(4.34), 272s(--)	78-1393-73
1,3,5-Hexatriene, 2,4-dimethyl-, (Z)-	heptane	255(4.38),262(4.34), 272s(--)	78-1393-73
1,3,5-Hexatriene, 2,5-dimethyl-, (E)-	heptane	250(4.50),260(4.64), 270(4.53)	78-1393-73
1,3,5-Hexatriene, 2,5-dimethyl-, (Z)-	heptane	237(4.09)	78-1393-73
1,3,5-Hexatriene, 3-ethyl-, 3-cis	isooctane	256(4.22),266(4.39), 275(4.27)	44-2478-73
1,3,5-Hexatriene, 3-ethyl-, trans	isooctane	248s(--),257(4.34), 266(4.47),277(4.35)	44-2478-73
1,3,5-Octatriene, 3-cis-5-cis	isooctane	257(4.06),266(4.16), 276(4.04)	44-2478-73
3-cis-5-trans	isooctane	254(4.46),264(4.54), 274(4.43)	44-2478-73
3-trans-5-cis	isooctane	255(4.42),265(4.56), 275(4.44)	44-2478-73
3-trans-5-trans	isooctane	241s(--),252(4.54), 262(4.64),273(4.50)	44-2478-73
2,4,6-Octatriene, (E,E,E)-	heptane	253(4.49),263(4.74), 274(4.65)	78-1393-73
2,4,6-Octatriene, (E,Z,E)-	n.s.g.	255(4.53),267(4.62), 277(4.48)	78-3781-73
2,4,6-Octatriene, (Z,Z,E)-	n.s.g.	257(4.51),265(4.59), 276(4.47)	78-3781-73
2,4,6-Octatriene, (Z,Z,Z)-	n.s.g.	262(4.42),270(4.51), 280(4.39)	78-3781-73

Compound	Solvent	λ_{max}(log ϵ)	Ref.
$C_8H_{12}BrN_3O_2S_2$			
Isothiourea, 3-(5-bromo-2-thiazolyl)-1-ethoxycarbonyl-2-methyl-	dioxan	246(3.79),324(4.38)	94-0074-73
$C_8H_{12}Br_3N_2O_2$			
1H-Imidazol-1-yloxy, 2,5-dihydro-2,2,5,5-tetramethyl-4-(tribromomethyl)-, 3-oxide	EtOH	204(3.75),240(3.68)	104-1990-73
$C_8H_{12}NO_6P$			
2,5-Pyridinedimethanol, 3-hydroxy-4-methyl-, 5-(dihydrogen phosphate)	pH 1	282(3.96)	44-4295-73
	pH 7	252(3.60),313(3.93)	44-4295-73
	pH 13	244(3.84),303(3.84)	44-4295-73
$C_8H_{12}NO_7P$			
3,4-Pyridinedimethanol, 5-hydroxy-6-methyl-, 3-(dihydrogen phosphate), 1-oxide	pH 1	260(3.68),293(3.71)	44-4295-73
	pH 7	258s(3.90),325(3.68)	44-4295-73
	pH 13	255s(3.85),325(3.83)	44-4295-73
$C_8H_{12}N_2$			
Acetonitrile, (1-methyl-2-piperidinylidene)-	EtOH	272(4.17)	103-0880-73
$C_8H_{12}N_2O$			
Acetamide, N-(2,4-dimethyl-1H-pyrrol-3-yl)-	EtOH	217(4.19)	70-1859-73
Acetamide, N-[(4-methyl-1H-pyrrol-2-yl)-methyl]-	EtOH	216(3.87)	70-2036-73
3-Pyridinol, 4-(1-aminoethyl)-2-methyl-, dihydrochloride	pH 1	314(3.80)	70-1057-73
	pH 7	312(3.79)	70-1057-73
	pH 13	302(3.76)	70-1057-73
$C_8H_{12}N_2OS$			
4(1H)-Pyrimidinone, 2-[(1,1-dimethylethyl)thio]-	MeOH	231(3.9),290(3.9)	24-3039-73
$C_8H_{12}N_2OS_2$			
Acetamide, N-[3,4-dimethyl-2-(methylthio)-5-thiazolidinylidene]-, mesoionic didehydro deriv.	EtOH	262(3.80),363(3.89)	18-0964-73
	THF	395(4.09)	18-0964-73
	pyridine	391(4.07)	18-0964-73
$C_8H_{12}N_2O_2$			
1H-1,2-Diazepine-1-carboxylic acid, 2,3-dihydro-, ethyl ester	MeOH	288(3.97)	22-2847-73
2,6-Piperidinedione, 3-(1-aminoethylidene)-4-methyl-	EtOH	311(4.19)	95-1437-73
2,6-Piperidinedione, 3-(1-aminoethylidene)-5-methyl-	EtOH	312(4.24)	95-1437-73
3-Pyridinecarboxamide, 1,4-dihydro-1-(methoxymethyl)-	EtOH	337(3.77)	64-0471-73B
$C_8H_{12}N_2O_2S$			
Carbamic acid, (3-ethyl-2(3H)-thiazolylidene)-, ethyl ester	EtOH	233(3.38),284(4.17)	94-0074-73
2-Propenoic acid, 2-cyano-3-(dimethylamino)-3-(methylthio)-, methyl ester	C_6H_{12}	265(3.75),319(4.16)	1-0258-73
	EtOH	265(3.62),318(4.06)	1-0258-73
Thiazole, N-ethoxycarbonyl-2-(ethylamino)-	EtOH	259(3.97)	94-0074-73
$C_8H_{12}N_2O_3$			
2-Propenal, 2-nitro-3-piperidino-	$CHCl_3$	294(4.00),357(4.19)	104-0477-73

Compound	Solvent	λ_{max}(log ε)	Ref.
1H-Pyrazole-3-carboxylic acid, 5-ethyl-4-hydroxy-, ethyl ester	pH 1	272(3.76)	4-0843-73
	pH 11	237(3.90),317(3.94)	4-0843-73
	MeOH	228(3.98),275(3.75)	4-0843-73
$C_8H_{12}N_2O_3S$			
Sulfonium, dimethyl-, hexahydro-1,3-dimethyl-2,4,6-trioxo-5-pyrimidinylide	EtOH	242(4.11)	104-2213-73
$C_8H_{12}N_2O_4$			
2,4-Pentadienoic acid, 5-(dimethylamino)-2-nitro-, methyl ester	EtOH	245(3.74),303(4.09), 417(4.62)	70-1959-73 +70-1963-73
Propanedioic acid, diazo-, 1,1-dimethylethyl methyl ester	EtOH	250(3.83)	22-2071-73
Propanedioic acid, diazo-, methyl 2-methylpropyl ester	EtOH	250(3.91)	22-2071-73
2,6(1H,3H)-Pyrazinedione, 5-ethoxy-3-hydroxy-1,3-dimethyl-	EtOH	218(4.08)	39-0404-73C
2,4(1H,3H)-Pyrimidinedione, 1-(2,3-dihydroxypropyl)-5-methyl-	H_2O	210(4.13),273(4.08)	18-1572-73
Sydnone, 3-(5-carboxypentyl)-	EtOH	203(3.71),293(3.83)	103-0441-73
$C_8H_{12}N_4$			
Propanedinitrile, [bis(dimethylamino)-methylene]-	C_6H_{12}	239(3.97),282(4.28)	1-0258-73
	EtOH	243(3.97),276(4.26)	1-0258-73
1-Propen-2-amine, N,N-dimethyl-1-(1,2,4-triazin-5-yl)-	MeOH	239(3.45),325(4.04), 385(4.51)	5-1963-73
$C_8H_{12}N_4O_2$			
Propanamide, N-(4-amino-1,6-dihydro-6-oxo-5-pyrimidinyl)-2-methyl-	pH 1	258(3.89)	39-1855-73C
	pH 11	255(3.71)	39-1855-73C
	MeOH	260(3.80)	39-1855-73C
$C_8H_{12}N_4O_3$			
Carbonic acid, 2,4-diamino-6-methyl-5-pyrimidinyl ethyl ester	EtOH	287.5(4.04)	95-0817-73
Pyrazinecarboxamide, 5-methoxy-N-methyl-3-(methylamino)-, 1-oxide	MeOH	226(4.11),258(4.40), 373(3.99)	24-3203-73
$C_8H_{12}N_4O_4S$			
Carbamic acid, 1,2,4-thiadiazole-3,5-diylbis-, diethyl ester	EtOH	256.5(3.60)	94-2396-73
1,2,4-Thiadiazole-2(3H)-carboxylic acid, 5-[(ethoxycarbonyl)amino]-3-imino-, ethyl ester	EtOH	262(4.18),271(4.18)	94-2396-73
$C_8H_{12}N_4O_6$			
1H-Imidazol-5-amine, 4-nitro-1-β-D-ribofuranosyl-	pH 1	222(4.08),366(4.17)	39-0244-73C
	pH 11	234(3.85),265s(3.69), 366(4.16)	39-0244-73C
	MeOH	223(4.00),360(4.15)	39-0244-73C
$C_8H_{12}N_5$			
3H-Purinium, 3,9-dimethyl-6-(methylamino)-, iodide	H_2O	285(4.25)	104-1308-73
7H-Purinium, 7,9-dimethyl-6-(methylamino)-, iodide or perchlorate	H_2O	279(4.16)	104-1308-73
9H-Purinium, 1,9-dimethyl-6-(methylamino)-, iodide	H_2O	263(4.10)	104-1308-73

Compound	Solvent	$\lambda_{max}(\log \epsilon)$	Ref.
$C_8H_{12}N_8$			
Pyrimido[5,4-e]-1,2,4-triazine-3,5,7-triamine, N,N',N"-trimethyl-	pH 1.0	221(4.42),263(4.41), 326(3.60),450(3.62)	12-1689-73
	pH 9.0	228s(4.22),277(4.46), 330(3.46),475(3.66)	12-1689-73
$C_8H_{12}O$			
Bicyclo[3.1.0]hexane, 1-acetyl-, cis	n.s.g.	219(3.47),280(1.78)	22-1800-73
Bicyclo[3.1.0]hexan-2-one, 1,5-dimethyl-	EtOH	204(3.71),280(1.83)	35-0468-73
Cyclobutanone, 2-(1-methylpropylidene)-, anti	hexane	347(1.86)	35-3947-73
	benzene	342(1.85)	35-3947-73
	MeOH	329(1.89)	35-3947-73
syn	hexane	347(1.82)	35-3947-73
	benzene	342(1.82)	35-3947-73
	MeOH	330(1.84)	35-3947-73
2-Cyclohexen-1-one, 2,4-dimethyl-	EtOH	236(3.99)	35-0468-73
2-Cyclohexen-1-one, 3,5-dimethyl-	CH_2Cl_2	233(4.14),323(1.56)	88-3251-73
BF complex	CH_2Cl_2	268.9(4.09)	88-3251-73
2-Cyclohexen-1-one, 4,4-dimethyl-	CH_2Cl_2	225(4.06),330(1.43)	88-3251-73
BF complex	CH_2Cl_2	252.7(3.97)	88-3251-73
2-Cyclohexen-1-one, 5,5-dimethyl-	CH_2Cl_2	226(3.97),330(1.46)	88-3251-73
BF complex	CH_2Cl_2	253.3(3.89)	88-3251-73
Ethanone, 1-(2-methyl-1-cyclopenten-1-yl)-	EtOH	253(3.98)	39-0374-73B
9-Oxabicyclo[3.3.1]non-1-ene	n.s.g.	190(3.79)	35-1342-73
$C_8H_{12}OS$			
Cyclohexanethione, 2-acetyl-	C_6H_{12}	293(3.55),377(2.59), 453s(0.39)	78-2449-73
	EtOH	297(3.53),367s(2.20), 441s(0.27)	78-2449-73
$C_8H_{12}O_2$			
Acetic acid, cyclohexylidene-	hexane	222.5(4.15)	94-1601-73
2-Cyclobuten-1-one, 3-ethoxy-4,4-dimethyl-	EtOH	233(4.10)	44-1451-73
3,5-Cyclohexadiene-1,2-diol, 3-ethyl-, (+)-cis	MeOH	265(3.76)	69-1520-73
Cyclohexanone, 2-acetyl-	EtOH	290(3.97)	44-0514-73
1,5-Cyclooctanedione	MeOH	292(1.38)	33-0723-73
1,3-Cyclopentanedione, 4-ethyl-2-methyl-	pH 1	254(4.22)	95-0566-73
	pH 10	272(4.33)	95-0566-73
	EtOH	250(4.24)	95-0566-73
3(2H)-Furanone, 2,4-diethyl-	EtOH	272(3.68)	35-4103-73
1-Oxaspiro[2.4]heptan-4-one, 2,2-dimethyl-	EtOH	209(3.36)	23-3173-73
1-Oxaspiro[2.5]octan-4-one, 2-methyl-	EtOH	207(2.78)	23-3173-73
2,4-Pentadienoic acid, 3-methyl-, ethyl ester	EtOH	251(4.32)	39-0584-73C
2,4-Pentadien-1-ol, 3-methyl-, acetate, (E)-	EtOH	228(4.36)	39-0584-73C
$C_8H_{12}O_2S$			
Cyclobutanone, 2,2,4,4-tetramethyl-3-sulfinyl-	hexane	273(3.87)	39-0073-73C
$C_8H_{12}O_2S_2$			
1,3-Cyclobutanedithione, 2,2,4,4-tetramethyl-, S,S'-dioxide, (E)-	hexane	271(4.23)	39-0073-73C
2,4-Pentanedione, 3-[bis(methylthio)-methylene]-	C_6H_{12}	309(3.87)	1-0258-73
	EtOH	223(3.76),317(3.91)	1-0258-73

Compound	Solvent	$\lambda_{max}(\log \epsilon)$	Ref.
$C_8H_{12}O_3$			
Acetic acid, (dihydro-2(3H)-furanylidene)-, ethyl ester	EtOH	245(4.13)	44-3428-73
3,5-Cyclohexadiene-1,2-diol, 3-(1-hydroxyethyl)-, cis	MeOH	265(3.75)	69-1520-73
$C_8H_{12}O_3S_2$			
Butanoic acid, 2-[bis(methylthio)methylene]-3-oxo-, methyl ester	EtOH	317(3.95)	1-0258-73
$C_8H_{12}O_4S$			
2-Propenoic acid, 3-[(2-carboxyethyl)thio]-, 1-ethyl ester, cis	H_2O	287(4.09)	44-3507-73
trans	H_2O	278(4.26)	44-3507-73
$C_8H_{12}O_4S_2$			
Propanedioic acid, [bis(methylthio)methylene]-, dimethyl ester	C_6H_{12}	307(3.99)	1-0258-73
	EtOH	311(4.01)	1-0258-73
$C_8H_{12}S$			
9-Thiabicyclo[3.3.1]non-1-ene	pentane	196(3.67),210(3.66)	35-6120-73
$C_8H_{13}ClN_2$			
1-Pyrazoline, 4-(chloromethylene)-3,3,5,5-tetramethyl-	n.s.g.	323(2.45)	89-0224-73
$C_8H_{13}ClO$			
3-Hexen-2-one, 4-chloro-3-ethyl-	EtOH	244(3.70)	78-4241-73
$C_8H_{13}ClSi_2$			
Silane, chloromethyl[4-(methylsilyl)phenyl]-	heptane	277.8(2.61)	70-1825-73
$C_8H_{13}F_3O_2$			
4-Heptanone, 1,1,1-trifluoro-2-hydroxy-6-methyl-	EtOH	212(2.60),269(2.26)	23-3177-73
$C_8H_{13}I$			
2,4-Hexadiene, 3-iodo-2,4-dimethyl-, (E)-	EtOH	212(4.19)	22-2506-73
(Z)-	EtOH	211(4.11)	22-2506-73
$C_8H_{13}IN_2OS_2$			
3H-Thiazol-1-ium, 5-(acetylamino)-3,4-dimethyl-2-(methylthio)-, iodide	EtOH	324(4.042)	18-0964-73
$C_8H_{13}NO$			
1,2-Benzisoxazole, 3a,4,5,6,7,7a-hexahydro-3-methyl-	EtOH	215(3.66)	22-1390-73
2,3-Hexadienamide, 4-ethyl-	EtOH	208(4.16)	88-0209-73
$C_8H_{13}NO_2$			
2,4-Pentanedione, 3-[(dimethylamino)methylene]-	EtOH	278(4.03),301(4.11)	70-1963-73
3-Piperidinone, 1-acetyl-6-methyl-, (S)-	isooctane	282(1.58)	35-3678-73
	MeOH	285(1.79)	35-3678-73
$C_8H_{13}NO_3$			
Butanoic acid, 2-[(dimethylamino)methylene]-3-oxo-, methyl ester	EtOH	251(3.96),312(4.19)	70-1963-73

Compound	Solvent	$\lambda_{max}(\log \epsilon)$	Ref.
$C_8H_{13}NO_4$			
Propanedioic acid, [(dimethylamino)methylene]-, dimethyl ester	EtOH	244(3.76),288(4.29)	70-1963-73
$C_8H_{13}NO_5$			
α-L-erythro-Hex-3-enopyranoside, 3,4,6-trideoxy-2-O-methyl-3-nitro-	$CHCl_3$	245(3.72)	136-0347-73F
$C_8H_{13}NO_6S_2$			
2H-1,4-Thiazine-6-carboxylic acid, 3,4-dihydro-3-[(methylsulfonyl)oxy]methyl-, methyl ester, 1-oxide, (1R-trans)	EtOH	270(4.14)	78-3023-73
$C_8H_{13}N_2OS$			
Pyrimidinium, 2-ethoxy-1-methyl-4-(methylthio)-, iodide	H_2O	228(4.27),258(3.68), 304(4.27)	94-1451-73
Pyrimidinium, 4-ethoxy-1-methyl-2-(methylthio)-, iodide	H_2O	228(4.49),251s(4.13), 275s(3.88)	94-1451-73
$C_8H_{13}N_2O_4$			
1H-Imidazol-1-yloxy, 4-carboxy-2,5-dihydro-2,2,5,5-tetramethyl-, 3-oxide	EtOH	244(3.99)	104-1990-73
$C_8H_{13}N_3O$			
4(1H)-Pyrimidinone, 2-(dimethylamino)-5,6-dimethyl-	EtOH	227(4.15),303(3.93)	54-0705-73
$C_8H_{13}N_3O_2$			
Pyrazole, 3-tert-butyl-5-methyl-4-nitro-	0.05M HCl	288(3.87)	4-1055-73
	0.05M NaOH	323(4.03)	4-1055-73
Sydnone imine, N-acetyl-3-butyl-	EtOH	236(3.82),312(4.16)	103-1327-73
$C_8H_{13}N_3O_3$			
Sydnone imine, 3-(5-carboxypentyl)-, hydrochloride	EtOH	200(3.91),296(3.91)	103-1327-73
$C_8H_{13}N_3O_5S$			
Thiourea, 1-ethoxycarbonyl-3-(N-ethoxycarbonylcarbamoyl)-	EtOH	222(3.42),281(3.23)	94-2396-73
$C_8H_{13}N_3O_6$			
Acetamide, 2-diazo-N-β-D-glucopyranosyl-	MeOH	252(4.20)	136-0101-73F
$C_8H_{13}N_5$			
7H-Purin-6-amine, 8,9-dihydro-N,7,9-trimethyl-	H_2O	230(4.24),290(3.98)	104-1308-73
$C_8H_{13}N_5O$			
Formamide, N-[4,6-bis(methylamino)-5-pyrimidinyl]-N-methyl-	EtOH	227(4.50),263(3.75)	104-1308-73
Formamide, N-(4,6-diamino-5-pyrimidinyl)-N-propyl-	pH 1	264(3.99)	39-1855-73C
	pH 11	257(3.61)	39-1855-73C
	MeOH	264(3.85)	39-1855-73C
1H-Imidazole-4-carboxamide, 5-[(1-methylpropylidene)hydrazino]-	H_2O	206(3.97),245(3.78), 278(4.07)	103-0083-73
$C_8H_{13}N_5OS_2$			
Thioimidodicarbonic diamide, N,N'-diethyl-N'-(1,3,4-thiadiazol-2-yl)-	EtOH	216(3.97),264(4.29)	44-3868-73

Compound	Solvent	$\lambda_{max}(\log \epsilon)$	Ref.
$C_8H_{13}N_5O_2S$			
Imidodicarbonic diamide, N,N'-diethyl-N-(1,3,4-thiadiazol-2-yl)-	EtOH	218(3.75),254(4.07)	44-3868-73
$C_8H_{13}N_5O_4$			
1,4-Butanediol, 2-[(6-amino-5-nitro-4-pyrimidinyl)amino]-	pH 1	340(3.87)	103-0117-73
	H_2O	339(3.98)	103-0117-73
	pH 13	339(3.90)	103-0117-73
$C_8H_{14}ClNiO_3P$			
Nickel, π-cyclopentadienyl-, trimethyl phosphite, chloride	MeOH	211(4.09),270(3.97), 301(3.6),468(2.86)	33-1620-73
$C_8H_{14}IN_3OS_2$			
1,3,4-Thiadiazolium, 3-methyl-2-(methylthio)-5-(4-morpholinyl)-, iodide	EtOH	318(3.98)	104-2631-73
$C_8H_{14}N_2$			
1H-Imidazole, 2,5-dimethyl-3-(1-methylethyl)-	MeOH	215(3.79)	78-2153-73
$C_8H_{14}N_2O$			
3-Buten-2-one, 4-(1-aziridinyl)-4-(dimethylamino)-	CH_2Cl_2	243(3.66),305(4.42)	33-0944-73
$C_8H_{14}N_2O_2$			
2-Propenoic acid, 3-(1-aziridinyl)-3-(dimethylamino)-, methyl ester	CH_2Cl_2	282(4.32)	33-0944-73
$C_8H_{14}N_2O_2S$			
Carbamic acid, (1-pyrrolidinylthioxomethyl)-, ethyl ester	EtOH	270(4.18),321(2.37)	48-0144-73
$C_8H_{14}N_2O_3$			
1H-1,2-Diazepine-1-carboxylic acid, 2,3,4,5-tetrahydro-4-hydroxy-, ethyl ester	MeOH	220(4.04)	22-2847-73
$C_8H_{14}N_2O_3S$			
Carbamic acid, (4-morpholinylthioxomethyl)-, ethyl ester	EtOH	280(4.18),342(2.49)	48-0144-73
4(1H)-Pyrimidinone, 5-(dimethoxymethyl)tetrahydro-6-methyl-2-thioxo-	H_2O	234(3.93),275(4.17)	44-1963-73
2H-1,2,6-Thiadiazin-3(6H)-one, 2-butyl-5-methyl-, 1,1-dioxide	EtOH	258(3.87)	4-0469-73
2H-1,2,6-Thiadiazin-3(6H)-one, 6-butyl-5-methyl-, 1,1-dioxide	EtOH	295(3.89)	4-0469-73
$C_8H_{14}N_2O_6$			
Heptanoic acid, 2,7-dinitro-, methyl ester	MeOH	265(2.26)	18-3462-73
	MeOH-NaOMe	183(3.89),305(3.61)	18-3462-73
Hexanoic acid, 2,6-dinitro-, ethyl ester	MeOH	261(2.55)	18-3462-73
	MeOH-NaOMe	306(4.10)	18-3462-73
Hexanoic acid, 4-methyl-2,6-dinitro-, methyl ester	MeOH	255(2.43)	18-3462-73
	MeOH-NaOMe	235(3.71),307(4.48)	18-3462-73
$C_8H_{14}N_2O_8S$			
Carbamic acid, [2-methyl-3-(sulfooxy)-1-propene-1,3-diyl]bis-, dimethyl ester	100% H_2SO_4	323(4.81)	104-0908-73

Compound	Solvent	$\lambda_{max}(\log \epsilon)$	Ref.
$C_8H_{14}N_3O_3$			
1H-Imidazol-1-yloxy, 2,5-dihydro-4-[(hydroxyimino)methyl]-2,2,5,5-tetramethyl-, 3-oxide	EtOH	239(3.89),288(4.09)	104-1990-73
$C_8H_{14}N_3O_6P$			
2,4(1H,3H)-Pyrimidinedione, 5-(ethylamino)-1-[2-(phosphonooxy)ethyl]-	H_2O	212(3.85),281(3.84)	18-1762-73
$C_8H_{14}N_6O_2S$			
Carbothioic acid, 2-[2-(aminocarbonyl)hydrazono]-, 2-(aminocarbonyl)hydrazide	EtOH	235(3.79),274(3.72)	39-1009-73C
$C_8H_{14}O$			
Cyclohexanone, 2,2-dimethyl-	C_6H_{12}	294(1.30)	22-2231-73
	heptane	294(1.32)	22-2231-73
	H_2O	284(--)	22-2231-73
	MeOH	289(1.40)	22-2231-73
	EtOH	290(1.38)	22-2231-73
	MeCN	292(1.34)	22-2231-73
	CCl_4	295(1.40)	22-2231-73
	$CHCl_3$	292(1.40)	22-2231-73
	CH_2Cl_2	293(1.30)	22-2231-73
Cyclohexanone, 2,5-dimethyl-	C_6H_{12}	294(1.23)	22-2231-73
	heptane	295(1.23)	22-2231-73
	H_2O	280(--)	22-2231-73
	MeOH	287(1.30)	22-2231-73
	EtOH	286(1.32)	22-2231-73
	MeCN	289(1.28)	22-2231-73
	CCl_4	294(1.36)	22-2231-73
	$CHCl_3$	289(1.34)	22-2231-73
	CH_2Cl_2	290(1.30)	22-2231-73
Cyclohexanone, 2,6-dimethyl-	hexane	291(1.28)	46-1830-73
	C_6H_{12}	292(1.26)	22-2231-73
	heptane	292(1.26)	22-2231-73
	H_2O	280(--)	22-2231-73
	MeOH	284(1.32)	22-2231-73
	EtOH	285(1.31)	22-2231-73
	MeCN	287(1.28)	22-2231-73
	CCl_4	292(1.36)	22-2231-73
	$CHCl_3$	288(1.36)	22-2231-73
	CH_2Cl_2	288(1.27)	22-2231-73
Cyclohexanone, 3,5-dimethyl-	hexane	290(1.18)	46-1830-73
Cyclohexanone, 4,4-dimethyl-	C_6H_{12}	291(1.11)	22-2231-73
	heptane	291(1.11)	22-2231-73
	H_2O	276(--)	22-2231-73
	MeOH	282(1.11)	22-2231-73
	EtOH	284(1.18)	22-2231-73
	MeCN	287(1.15)	22-2231-73
	CCl_4	292(1.26)	22-2231-73
	$CHCl_3$	287(1.28)	22-2231-73
	CH_2Cl_2	287(1.23)	22-2231-73
Cyclooctanone	hexane	290(1.23)	46-1830-73
Cyclopentanone, 2,2,5-trimethyl-	C_6H_{12}	298(1.34),307(1.28)	22-2231-73
	heptane	298(1.34),308(1.28)	22-2231-73
	H_2O	290(--)	22-2231-73
	MeOH	295(1.40)	22-2231-73
	EtOH	295(1.39)	22-2231-73
	MeCN	295(1.36)	22-2231-73

Compound	Solvent	λ_{max}(log ϵ)	Ref.
Cyclopentanone, 2,2,5-trimethyl- (cont.)	CCl_4	298(1.42)	22-2231-73
	$CHCl_3$	296(1.40)	22-2231-73
	CH_2Cl_2	296(1.38)	22-2231-73
Cyclopentanone, 2,4,4-trimethyl-	C_6H_{12}	291(1.28),300(1.32), 311(1.26)	22-2231-73
	heptane	291(1.28),300(1.32), 311(1.26)	22-2231-73
	H_2O	286(--)	22-2231-73
	MeOH	291(1.32)	22-2231-73
	EtOH	292(1.34)	22-2231-73
	MeCN	296(1.30),305(1.26)	22-2231-73
	CCl_4	299(1.40),309(1.32)	22-2231-73
	$CHCl_3$	295(1.36)	22-2231-73
	CH_2Cl_2	296(1.36)	22-2231-73
2-Cyclopenten-1-ol, 2,3,4-trimethyl-	n.s.g.	238(3.84)	70-0034-73
Ethanone, 1-(1-ethyl-2-methylcyclopropyl)-, cis	n.s.g.	204(3.64),285(1.64)	78-2821-73
trans	n.s.g.	204(3.46),290(1.61)	78-2821-73
Ethanone, 1-(2-ethyl-1-methylcyclopropyl)-, cis	n.s.g.	203(3.56),283(1.54)	78-2821-73
trans	n.s.g.	204(3.61),288(1.63)	78-2821-73
2-Hepten-4-one, 2-methyl-	C_6H_{12}	237(4.08),327(1.74)	22-2301-73
2-Hepten-4-one, 6-methyl-, cis	hexane	222(3.99)	35-7345-73
trans	hexane	217(4.14)	35-7345-73
4-Hexen-3-one, 2,2-dimethyl-, cis	hexane	222(3.93)	35-7345-73
trans	hexane	222(4.05)	35-7345-73
1-Octen-3-one	hexane	210(3.65)	20-0699-73
3-Octen-2-one, trans	n.s.g.	225(3.98)	39-2789-73C
$C_8H_{14}O_2$			
1,3-Butadiene, 2,3-bis(methoxymethyl)-	isooctane	224(4.17)	88-2361-73
1-Buten-2-ol, 3,3-dimethyl-, acetate	EtOH	210(2.93)(end abs.)	35-3310-73
1,2-Dioxaspiro[3.5]nonane, 3-methyl-	heptane	295(1.4)	23-0468-73
2,3-Octanedione	hexane	432(1.18)	28-0247-73B
$C_8H_{14}O_2Si$			
Cyclopropene-1-carboxylic acid, 2-(trimethylsilyl)-, methyl ester	MeOH	243(3.83)	22-2739-73
$C_8H_{14}O_5$			
2-Octenoic acid, 4,5,7-trihydroxy-	EtOH	211(3.99)	39-1487-73C
$C_8H_{14}S_4$			
Disulfide, bis(2-methyl-1-thioxopropyl)	C_6H_{12}	315(4.02),382(3.82)	143-0437-73
	$CHCl_3$	317(4.08),389(3.75)	143-0437-73
$C_8H_{15}IN_2$			
4H-Pyrazolium, 1,3,4,4,5-pentamethyl-, iodide	EtOH	221(4.25)	78-4159-73
$C_8H_{15}N$			
1-Pentanamine, N-allylidene-	EtOH	214(4.34)	78-4111-73
$C_8H_{15}NO$			
3-Piperidinone, 1-ethyl-6-methyl-, (6S)-	isooctane	290(1.53)	35-3678-73
	MeOH	290(1.51)	35-3678-73
$C_8H_{15}NOS_2$			
2H-1,3-Oxazine-2-thione, tetrahydro-6-[3-(methylthio)propyl]-	EtOH	252(4.17)	102-0929-73

Compound	Solvent	λmax(log ε)	Ref.
$C_8H_{15}NO_2$			
3-Buten-2-one, 4-ethoxy-4-(dimethyl-amino)-	CH_2Cl_2	296(4.31)	33-0944-73
$C_8H_{15}N_3O$			
Azoisopropane, 1-cyano-1'-methoxy-	C_6H_{12}	369(1.25)	108-0819-73
	EtOH	362(1.23)	108-0819-73
	MeCN	363(1.24)	108-0819-73
$C_8H_{15}N_3O_3$			
1H-Imidazole-4-carboxaldehyde, 2,5-di-hydro-1-hydroxy-2,2,5,5-tetramethyl-, oxime, 3-oxide	EtOH	240(3.77),290(4.14)	104-1990-73
$C_8H_{15}N_3O_4$			
3,6-Pyridazinedione, 5-aminotetrahydro-4,4-dimethoxy-1,2-dimethyl-	EtOH	225(3.53),249(3.66)	78-0529-73
$C_8H_{15}N_3S$			
1,3,4-Thiadiazol-2-amine, 5-hexyl-	EtOH	256(3.80)	80-1777-73
	EtOH-HCl	247(3.89)	80-1777-73
$C_8H_{15}N_5O_2$			
1,4-Butanediol, 2-[(5,6-diamino-4-pyri-midinyl)amino]-, sulfate (1:1)	pH 1	283(4.00)	103-0117-73
	H_2O	288(4.01)	103-0117-73
	pH 13	280(3.80)	103-0117-73
$C_8H_{16}N_2$			
1H-Imidazole, 4,5-dihydro-2-pentyl-	EtOH	220(3.64)	93-2424-73
Pyrazine, 5-ethyl-1,2,3,4-tetrahydro-	C_6H_{12}	238(3.81)	28-1319-73A
$C_8H_{16}N_2O$			
3-Buten-2-one, 3,4-bis(dimethylamino)-	CH_2Cl_2	298(4.24)	33-0944-73
3-Buten-2-one, 4,4-bis(dimethylamino)-	CH_2Cl_2	252(3.86),307(4.33)	33-0944-73
2-Propenal, 3-(dimethylamino)-2-[(1-methylethyl)amino]-	CH_2Cl_2	316(4.18)	33-0944-73
2-Propenal, 3-(dimethylamino)-3-[(1-methylethyl)amino]-	CH_2Cl_2	236(3.64),306(4.25)	33-0944-73
2-Propenamide, N,N-dimethyl-3-[(1-meth-ylethyl)amino]-	C_6H_{12}	283.5(4.31)	33-1318-73
$C_8H_{16}N_2O_2$			
Ethanediamide, N,N'-dipropyl- (also qualitative spectra in other solvents)	H_2O	215(4.08),270s(2.15)	82-0469-73C
	EtOH	213(4.02),273(1.98)	82-0469-73C
	MeCN	212(4.03),275(1.89), 280s(1.88),295s(1.54)	82-0469-73C
2-Propenoic acid, 3,3-bis(dimethyl-amino)-, methyl ester	CH_2Cl_2	246(3.85),286(4.30)	33-0944-73
$C_8H_{16}N_2O_3$			
1H-Pyrazole, 2,3-dihydro-2-hydroxy-1,3-dimethoxy-3,4,5-trimethyl-	EtOH	206(3.81)	39-0167-73C
$C_8H_{16}N_8$			
Methanimidic acid, N-[5-(dimethylhydra-zono)methyl]-1H-1,2,3-triazol-4-yl]-, 2,2-dimethylhydrazide	MeOH	231(4.01),243s(3.99), 292(4.16)	39-1625-73C
$C_8H_{16}O$			
2-Octanone	hexane	282(1.30)	28-0247-73B

Compound	Solvent	$\lambda_{max}(\log \epsilon)$	Ref.
$C_8H_{16}S$			
Pentane, 1-(ethenylthio)-3-methyl-	heptane	229(3.80),237s(3.79), 250s(3.61)	143-0019-73
$C_8H_{16}S_2$			
1,3-Dithietane, 2,2,4,4-tetramethyl-	C_6H_{12}	234(2.26),304(1.30)	18-2253-73
$C_8H_{16}N_4S_2$			
2-Imidazoline, 1-(2-imidazolin-2-yl)-2-(methylthio)-, methanethiol adduct, monohydriodide	EtOH	219(4.68)	44-1641-73
dihydriodide	EtOH	218(4.57)	44-1641-73
$C_8H_{17}OPS_2$			
Ethene, 1,2-bis(ethylthio)-1-(dimethylphosphinyl)-, P-oxide	hexane	268(3.85)	54-0762-73
$C_8H_{18}O$			
Dibutyl ether	MeOH or neat	none above 200 nm	8-0167-73
$C_8H_{20}SSi$			
Ethanethiol, 2-(triethylsilyl)-	hexane	198.5(3.09)	67-0061-73

Compound	Solvent	λ_{max}(log ε)	Ref.
$C_9BrF_{18}N_3$			
1,2-Propadiene-1,1,3-triamine, 3-bromo-N,N,N',N',N",N"-hexakis(trifluoromethyl)-	n.s.g.	211(4.12),255s(3.96)	39-1066-73C
$C_9F_{11}N$			
Pyridine, 2,3,5,6-tetrafluoro-4-(heptafluorocyclobutyl)-	C_6H_{12}	284(3.57)	39-1710-73C
$C_9F_{13}N$			
Pyridine, 2,3,5-trifluoro-4,6-bis(pentafluoro)-	C_6H_{12}	275.5(3.68)	39-1405-73C
$C_9HF_{18}N_3$			
1,2-Propadiene-1,1,3-triamine, N,N,N'-N',N",N"-hexakis(trifluoromethyl)-	n.s.g.	213(3.35),237s(2.90)	39-1066-73C
$C_9H_2Cl_4O_2S_2$			
Spiro[1,3-benzodioxole-2,2'-[1,3]dithiole], 4,5,6,7-tetrachloro-	benzene	297(3.23)	97-0465-73
$C_9H_3Br_3N_4$			
1,3,6,9b-Tetraazaphenalene, 4,7,9-tribromo-	EtOH	207(4.24),247(3.91), 288(3.89),348(3.94), 367s(3.72),386(3.67), 404(3.62),580(1.93), 630(2.12),688(2.30)	1-3264-73
$C_9H_4Br_2N_4$			
1,3,6,9b-Tetraazaphenalene, 4,7-dibromo-	EtOH	244(4.04),279(4.11), 342(4.10),360(3.82), 379(3.88),388s(3.77), 397(3.84)	1-3264-73
	acetone	566(1.92),616(2.13), 673(2.13)	1-3264-73
1,3,6,9b-Tetraazaphenalene, 4,9-dibromo-	EtOH	241(4.34),284(4.14), 343(4.24),349s(4.18), 360s(4.09),375(4.01), 392(3.94)	1-3264-73
	acetone	575(1.91),620(2.15), 677(2.21)	1-3264-73
C_9H_4ClN			
2-Propynenitrile, 3-(4-chlorophenyl)-	EtOH	267(4.42),282(4.34)	39-2241-73C
$C_9H_4Cl_2N_6S$			
3-Pyridazinamine, 6-chloro-N-(6-chloro-3H-[1,2,4]thiadiazolo[4,3-b]pyridazin-3-ylidene)-	n.s.g.	253(4.23),368(3.94), 425(3.96)	44-3087-73
$C_9H_4Cl_4O_2$			
Spiro[2.4]hepta-1,4,6-triene-1-carboxylic acid, 4,5,6,7-tetrachloro-, methyl ester	$CHCl_3$	239(3.88),286(3.64)	5-0214-73
$C_9H_4Cl_4O_2S_2$			
Spiro[1,3-benzodioxole-2,2'-[1,3]dithiolane], 4,5,6,7-tetrachloro-	benzene	303(3.63)	97-0465-73

Compound	Solvent	λ_{max}(log ε)	Ref.
$C_9H_4O_5$			
Phthalic anhydride, 3,4-(methylenedi-oxy)-	EtOH	220(4.25),246(4.09), 267(3.41),283(3.39), 308s(3.41),344(3.69)	141-0001-73
	dioxan	221(4.20),244(4.00), 278s(3.35),337(3.58)	141-0001-73
Phthalic anhydride, 4,5-(methylenedi-oxy)-	EtOH	219s(4.23),224(4.25), 238(4.18),241s(4.17), 267s(3.57),298(3.67), 325s(3.25)	141-0001-73
	dioxan	217(4.16),224(4.15), 244(4.38),302s(3.62), 306(3.62),330s(3.40)	141-0001-73
$C_9H_5BrN_4$			
1,3,6,9b-Tetraazaphenalene, 4-bromo-	EtOH	233(4.17),272(4.06), 336(4.09),351s(3.93), 369(3.93),378(3.83), 387(3.90)	1-3264-73
	acetone	560(2.10),605(2.27), 663(2.25)	1-3264-73
1,3,6,9b-Tetraazaphenalene, 7-bromo-	EtOH	234(4.23),266(4.25), 335(4.23),359(3.92), 376(4.06),387(3.99), 394(4.00),555(2.16), 597(2.34),651(2.26)	1-3264-73
1,3,6,9b-Tetraazaphenalene, 9-bromo-	EtOH	233(4.24),267(4.18), 334(4.21),357(3.89), 374(4.00),389(3.93), 550(2.22),598(2.34), 650(2.30)	1-3264-73
$C_9H_5BrOS_2$			
1,3-Dithiol-2-one, 4-(4-bromophenyl)-	EtOH	230(4.17),292(4.20)	143-0273-73
$C_9H_5Br_3O$			
Benzofuran, 5,7-dibromo-2-(bromomethyl)-	n.s.g.	262(3.83),283s(3.41)	33-1457-73
$C_9H_5ClINO_4S$			
8-Quinolinol, 5-chloro-7-iodo-, hydro-gen sulfate, sodium salt	M HCl	260(4.42)	94-0903-73
	H_2O	244(4.59)	94-0903-73
	M NaOH	244(4.58)	94-0903-73
$C_9H_5ClN_2O$			
2-Quinoxalinecarboxaldehyde, 3-chloro-	EtOH	242(4.52),322(3.95), 330(3.88)	103-0785-73
$C_9H_5Cl_2DO$			
Benzofuran-3-d, 7-chloro-2-(chlorometh-yl)-	n.s.g.	253(4.21),275s(3.49), 288(3.26)	33-1457-73
$C_9H_5Cl_2N_5S$			
1,3,6-Triazaphenothiazin-2-amine, 4,7-dichloro-	MeOH	234(4.21),318(4.07)	44-4386-73
$C_9H_5N_3OS$			
Benzothiazole, 2-(1,2,4-oxadiazol-3-yl)-	EtOH	245(3.92),286(4.15)	39-0047-73C
$C_9H_5N_3O_2$			
Benzoxazole, 2-(1,2,4-oxadiazol-3-yl)-	EtOH	280(4.16)	39-0047-73C

Compound	Solvent	$\lambda_{max}(\log \epsilon)$	Ref.
[1,2,4]Oxadiazolo[2,3-a]quinoxalin-2-one	MeOH	237s(4.32),257(4.29)	39-2707-73
$C_9H_6BF_4N_3$			
8-Quinolinediazonium tetrafluoroborate	M HCl	334(4.0)	48-0725-73
C_9H_6BrIO			
2-Propen-1-one, 1-(4-bromophenyl)-3-iodo-	dioxan	287(4.33)	24-0435-73
C_9H_6BrNOS			
3H-Indol-3-one, 6-bromo-2-(methylthio)-	hexane	217(3.94),242(4.40), 247(4.40),278(4.04), 318(3.72),333(3.70), 355(3.43),426(3.23), 447(3.23)	12-2153-73
$C_9H_6Br_2O$			
Benzofuran, 5,7-dibromo-2-methyl-	n.s.g.	255(4.11),283(3.50), 294(3.33)	33-1457-73
C_9H_6ClIO			
2-Propen-1-one, 1-(4-chlorophenyl)-3-iodo-	dioxan	274(4.26),287(4.28)	24-0435-73
C_9H_6ClN			
Benzeneacetonitrile, α-(chloromethylene)-, cis	EtOH	261(4.01)	22-0724-73
trans	EtOH	221(4.06),267(4.06)	22-0724-73
2-Propenenitrile, 3-(4-chlorophenyl)-, trans	EtOH	276(4.36)	39-2241-73C
C_9H_6ClNO			
Oxazole, 5-chloro-2-phenyl-	EtOH	211(4.11),270(4.29)	2-1203-73
2-Propynamide, 3-(2-chlorophenyl)-	EtOH	249(4.09)	4-0399-73
$C_9H_6ClNO_2S$			
4H-1,4-Benzothiazine-3-carboxylic acid, 6-chloro-	EtOH	208(4.33),255(4.24), 272(3.71),346(3.44), 416(2.78)	7-0045-73
$C_9H_6ClNO_4$			
2-Propenoic acid, 3-(2-chloro-5-nitrophenyl)-	EtOH	272(3.98)	12-1337-73
	EtOH-KOH	253(4.27)	12-1337-73
$C_9H_6ClNO_4S$			
4H,5H-Pyrano[3,4-e]-1,3-oxazine-4,5-dione, 7-chloro-2-(ethylthio)-	$CHCl_3$	280(4.17),344(4.20)	39-2432-73
$C_9H_6ClN_3O$			
1,2,4-Oxadiazol-3-amine, N-[(4-chlorophenyl)methylene]-	EtOH	282(4.34)	39-0047-73C
$C_9H_6ClN_3O_2$			
1,2,4-Oxadiazole-3-carboxamide, N-(4-chlorophenyl)-	EtOH	272(4.05)	39-0047-73C
$C_9H_6Cl_2N_2O_4$			
2(1H)-Pyrimidinone, 1-(3,4-dichloro-2,5-dihydro-5-oxo-2-furanyl)-4-methoxy-	pH 0	231(4.11)	44-3878-73
	50% EtOH	231(4.11),268(3.80)	44-3878-73

Compound	Solvent	$\lambda_{max}(\log \epsilon)$	Ref.
$C_9H_6Cl_2O$			
Benzene, 2,4-dichloro-1-(2-propynyl-oxy)-	n.s.g.	228(3.96),278s(3.17),282(3.31),290(3.62)	33-1457-73
Benzofuran, 7-chloro-2-(chloromethyl)-	n.s.g.	253(4.21),274s(3.50),287(3.27)	33-1457-73
Benzofuran, 5,7-dichloro-2-methyl-	n.s.g.	253(4.09),284(3.32),293(3.38)	33-1457-73
2H-1-Benzopyran, 3,8-dichloro-	n.s.g.	226(4.41),232s(4.30),271(3.94),282(3.87),310(3.54)	33-1457-73
2H-1-Benzopyran, 6,8-dichloro-	n.s.g.	225(4.27),256(3.54),265(3.54),271s(3.39),320(3.13)	33-1457-73
$C_9H_6Cl_4O_2$			
Spiro[2.4]hepta-4,6-diene-1-carboxylic acid, 4,5,6,7-tetrachloro-, methyl ester	$CHCl_3$	242(3.86),294(3.49)	5-0214-73
C_9H_6FIO			
2-Propen-1-one, 1-(4-fluorophenyl)-3-iodo-	dioxan	269(4.17),284(4.20)	24-0435-73
$C_9H_6F_3N$			
Benzeneacetonitrile, 4-(trifluorometh-yl)-	EtOH	256(2.51),262(2.58),267(2.51)	36-0910-73
$C_9H_6I_2O$			
2-Propen-1-one, 3-iodo-1-(4-iodophenyl)-	dioxan	296(4.38)	24-0435-73
C_9H_6NO			
Benzenepropanenitrile, β-oxo-, ion(1-), tetrabutylammonium salt	$CHCl_3$	242(3.78),251(3.64),317(3.86)	1-0258-73
$C_9H_6N_2O$			
Benzonitrile, 2-(cyanomethoxy)-	EtOH	231(4.04),237s(4.00),289(3.58),294(3.57)	48-0779-73
$C_9H_6N_2O_2$			
2-Quinoxalinecarboxylic acid	0.1N H_2SO_4	245(4.55),321(3.87)	103-0369-73
	15.3N H_2SO_4	255(4.53),342(4.01)	103-0369-73
$C_9H_6N_2O_3$			
2-Indolecarboxaldehyde, 5-nitro-	EtOH	288(4.58),318s(4.08)	78-0603-73
1,2,4-Oxadiazol-3(2H)-one, 5-benzoyl-	EtOH	261(4.10)	4-0357-73
1,2,4-Oxadiazol-5(2H)-one, 3-benzoyl-	EtOH	264(4.02),287s(--)	4-0357-73
4(1H)-Quinolinone, 8-nitro-	EtOH	220(4.27),258(4.10),382(3.81)	4-0459-73
$C_9H_6N_2O_4$			
2H-1-Benzopyran-2-one, 4-amino-3-nitro-	EtOH	248(4.18),330(4.08)	103-0816-73
$C_9H_6N_2S_2$			
[1]Benzothieno[2,3-d]thiazol-2-amine	MeOH	233(4.21),257s(4.17),264(4.24),310(4.23)	48-0539-73
Thiocyanic acid, 2-aminobenzo[b]thien-3-yl ester	MeOH	229(4.56),284(4.16)	48-0539-73
$C_9H_6N_3$			
8-Quinolinediazonium (tetrafluoroborate)	M HCl	334(4.0)	48-0725-73

Compound	Solvent	$\lambda_{max}(\log \epsilon)$	Ref.
$C_9H_6N_4$			
1,8-Naphthyridine-3-carbonitrile, 2-amino-	EtOH	213(4.50),240(4.62), 267s(3.86),375(3.90)	94-2643-73
Propanedinitrile, (3-cyano-5-methyl-1H-pyrrol-2-yl)-	EtOH	209(4.30),234(3.94), 311(3.99)	12-1551-73
$C_9H_6N_4O$			
1H-Benzimidazole, 2-(1,2,4-oxadiazol-3-yl)-	EtOH	294(4.24)	39-0047-73C
$C_9H_6N_4O_2S$			
2H-Thiadiazino[5,6-b]quinoxaline, 1,1-dioxide	EtOH	246(4.36),277(4.14), 363(3.92)	18-1890-73
$C_9H_6N_4O_4$			
Pyrazole, 3,4-dinitro-5-phenyl-	0.05M HCl	225(--),265s(--)	4-1055-73
(spectra in 2.5% methanol)	0.05M NaOH	230(--),340(3.78)	4-1055-73
Pyrazole, 3-nitro-5-(4-nitrophenyl)-	0.05M HCl	306(4.25)	4-1055-73
(spectra in 2.5% methanol)	0.05M NaOH	346(4.27)	4-1055-73
Pyrazole, 4-nitro-3-(4-nitrophenyl)-	0.05M HCl	277(4.0),300s(--)	4-1055-73
(spectra in 2.5% methanol)	0.05M NaOH	307(4.0),330s(--)	4-1055-73
$C_9H_6N_6$			
3,5-Pyridinedicarbonitrile, 2,4-diamino-6-(cyanomethyl)-	EtOH	240(4.55),249(4.44), 317(3.74)	12-2567-73
3,5-Pyridinedicarbonitrile, 2,6-diamino-4-(cyanomethyl)-	EtOH	227(4.32),278(4.12), 337(3.89)	12-2567-73
Triimidazo[1,2-a:1',2'-c:1",2"-e]-[1,3,5]triazine	EtOH	228(4.52),235(4.50), 255s(3.77)	35-8389-73
$C_9H_6N_6S$			
Pyrazinamine, N-3H-[1,2,4]thiadiazolo-[4,3-a]pyrazin-3-ylidene-	n.s.g.	242(4.08),253s(3.99), 278(4.00),358(4.19), 385s(3.82)	44-3087-73
C_9H_6OS			
4H-Cyclohepta[b]thiophen-4-one	n.s.g.	238(4.33),241(4.33), 324(3.94),346(3.89), 360(3.84)	35-6655-73
$C_9H_6OS_2$			
1,3-Dithiol-2-one, 4-phenyl-	EtOH	222(4.11),285(4.02)	143-0273-73
$C_9H_6O_2$			
4H-Cyclohepta[b]furan-4-one	EtOH	244s(--),259s(--), 270s(--),300(3.72), 311(3.79),341(3.83), 355(3.80),372s(--)	39-0968-73C
$C_9H_6O_3$			
Homophthalic acid anhydride	EtOH	228(3.83),277(2.98)	141-0001-73
	dioxan	232(3.89),278(3.07)	141-0001-73
$C_9H_6O_3S$			
2H-1-Benzopyran-2-one, 7-hydroxy-4-mercapto-	EtOH	233(3.90),280(4.12), 320(3.85)	95-0836-73
$C_9H_6O_4$			
2H-1-Benzopyran-2-one, 6,7-dihydroxy-	MeOH	227(4.27),253(3.79), 297(3.92),340(4.01)	83-0857-73

Compound	Solvent	λ_{max}(log ε)	Ref.
2H-1-Benzopyran-2-one, 6,7-dihydroxy- (cont.)	MeOH-KOH	220(3.99),269(4.07), 353(3.96)(changing)	83-0857-73
	n.s.g.	234(3.99),315(3.88), 345(3.82)	105-0465-73
1,3-Dioxolane-2,4-dione, 5-phenyl-	n.s.g.	238.0(4.396)	25-0695-73
Phthalic anhydride, 3-methoxy-	EtOH	214(4.27),241s(3.56), 298(3.46)	141-0001-73
	dioxan	229(4.10),240s(3.67), 255s(3.27),310s(3.40), 327(3.53)	141-0001-73
Phthalic anhydride, 4-methoxy-	EtOH	209(4.18),235(4.31), 260(3.71),272s(3.66), 311(3.50)	141-0001-73
	dioxan	234(4.26),276(3.71), 310(3.62)	141-0001-73
Phthalide, 4,5-(methylenedioxy)-	EtOH	224(4.45),269(3.79), 294(3.69)	141-0001-73
	dioxan	226(4.05),266(3.85), 280s(3.65),293(3.64)	141-0001-73
Phthalide, 5,6-(methylenedioxy)-	EtOH	220(4.34),256(3.73), 298(3.86)	141-0001-73
Phthalide, 6,7-(methylenedioxy)-	EtOH	221(4.39),234(3.90), 322(3.66)	141-0001-73
	dioxan	226(4.01),234s(3.85), 319(3.65)	141-0001-73
$C_9H_6O_6$			
Phthalic acid, 3,4-(methylenedioxy)-	EtOH	220(4.28),261(3.67), 305(3.68)	141-0001-73
	EtOH-NaOH	219(4.26),244s(3.66), 296(3.56)	141-0001-73
	dioxan	227(4.05),261(3.73), 303(3.78)	141-0001-73
Phthalic acid, 4,5-(methylenedioxy)-	EtOH	223(4.37),271(3.69), 293(3.73)	141-0001-73
	EtOH-NaOH	219(4.23),249s(3.71), 294(3.62)	141-0001-73
	dioxan	227(4.09),267(3.71), 295(3.73)	141-0001-73
Pyrano[3,4-b]pyran-2-carboxylic acid, 4,5,6,8-tetrahydro-4,8-dioxo-	EtOH	274(3.86)	95-1183-73
C_9H_7Br			
Benzene, 1-(bromoethynyl)-4-methyl-	MeOH	256(4.29)	35-1602-73
$C_9H_7BrN_2O_3$			
2-Propenal, 3-[(4-bromophenyl)amino]-2-nitro-	$CHCl_3$	298(3.73),365(3.99)	104-0477-73
C_9H_7BrO			
2-Propyn-1-ol, 3-(4-bromophenyl)-	EtOH	248(4.40),258(4.36), 278(3.06),285(2.79)	44-1051-73
C_9H_7Cl			
Benzene, 1-(chloroethynyl)-4-methyl-	MeOH	253.5(4.24)	35-1602-73
$C_9H_7ClN_2$			
Quinoxaline, 2-chloro-3-methyl-	EtOH	238(4.45),320(3.88), 328(3.81)	103-0785-73

Compound	Solvent	$\lambda_{max}(\log \epsilon)$	Ref.
$C_9H_7ClN_2O$			
3-Isoxazolamine, 5-(4-chlorophenyl)-	EtOH	265(4.34)	39-2241-73C
$C_9H_7ClN_2O_2$			
Indole, 5-chloro-3-methyl-2-nitro-	isoPrOH	246(3.94),346(4.22)	44-3077-73
$C_9H_7ClN_6S$			
1H-Pyrido[2,3-b]pyrimido[4,5-e][1,4]-thiazine-2,4-diamine, 7-chloro-	MeOH	254(4.47),290s(3.61), 353(3.64)	44-4386-73
C_9H_7ClO			
Benzofuran, 7-chloro-2-methyl-	n.s.g.	249(4.15),273(3.34), 276(3.35),283(3.35)	33-1457-73
	n.s.g.	249(4.23),272(3.35), 275(3.35),283(3.38)	33-1457-73
2H-1-Benzopyran, 8-chloro-	n.s.g.	225(4.34),231s(4.22), 267(3.66),273s(3.57), 310(3.38)	33-1457-73
p-Benzoquinone, 2-chloro-5-hydroxy-3,6-dimethyl-	isopentane	274(4.23),283(4.29), 410(2.57)	94-1547-73
$C_9H_7F_3$			
Benzene, 1-ethenyl-3-(trifluoromethyl)-	EtOH	214s(3.86),240s(3.80), 247(2.82),256s(3.61), 275(2.70),283(2.70), 294(2.52)	35-5288-73
Benzene, 1-ethenyl-4-(trifluoromethyl)-	EtOH	215s(4.04),238s(4.04), 250(4.10),260s(3.89), 280(3.02),285(3.02), 292(2.72)	35-5288-73
$C_9H_7F_3O$			
Ethanone, 1-[4-(trifluoromethyl)phenyl]-	EtOH	233(4.12),278(3.15)	36-0910-73
$C_9H_7F_3O_2$			
Benzeneacetic acid, 4-(trifluoromethyl)-	EtOH	202(2.48),257(2.45), 268(2.36)	36-0910-73
C_9H_7IO			
2-Propen-1-one, 3-iodo-1-phenyl-	dioxan	267(4.20),284(4.20)	24-0435-73
C_9H_7N			
Isoquinoline	$C_2H_4Cl_2$	268(3.55),318(3.45)	24-2427-73
C_9H_7NO			
2H-Azirine-2-carboxaldehyde, 3-phenyl-	C_6H_{12}	241(4.18)	77-0539-73
Benzeneacetonitrile, α-formyl-	10% EtOH-pH 12	197(4.27),221(4.03), 247(3.93),286(4.18)	22-3458-73
1H-Indole-3-carboxaldehyde	MeOH	243(4.15),260(4.09), 296(4.14)	102-0447-73
	H_2SO_4	235(4.26),241s(4.22), 261(4.33),267(4.41), 338(4.11)	102-0447-73
bisulfite compound	H_2SO_4	235(3.64),241(3.61), 288(3.65)(changing)	102-0447-73
Isoxazole, 3-phenyl-	C_6H_{12}	239(4.02)	77-0539-73
$C_9H_7NO_2$			
1H-Indole-2-carboxylic acid	MeOH	223(4.30),291(4.27)	102-0447-73
after 20 minutes	H_2SO_4	235(3.98),318(4.09)	102-0447-73

Compound	Solvent	λmax(log ε)	Ref.
1H-Indole-2-carboxylic acid (cont.) after 1560 minutes	H_2SO_4	242(4.25),246s(4.22), 307(4.16)	102-0447-73
1H-Indole-5-carboxylic acid	MeOH	236(3.60),275(3.81)	102-0447-73
	H_2SO_4	227(3.78),235s(3.72), 273(3.97)(changing)	102-0447-73
1H-Indole-2,3-dione, 5-methyl-	EtOH	248(4.31)	95-0008-73
2-Indolizinecarboxylic acid	EtOH	290(3.29),300(3.34), 342(3.33)	36-1897-73
$C_9H_7NO_2S$			
2,4-Thiazolidinedione, 5-phenyl-	EtOH	220(3.78)	132-0113-73
	EtOH-NaOH	235(3.58)	132-0113-73
$C_9H_7NO_3S$			
Benzothiophene, 2-methoxy-3-nitro-	MeOH	348(3.86)	32-0649-73
Benzothiophene, 3-methoxy-2-nitro-	MeOH	258(3.91),331(4.08)	32-0649-73
$C_9H_7NO_3S_2$			
5-Quinolinesulfonic acid, 8-mercapto- (cation)	1.02M $HClO_4$	241(4.33),311s(3.67), 318(3.74),340s(3.48)	18-2112-73
	30% EtOH-$HClO_4$	241(4.34),310s(3.68), 318(3.72),340s(3.48)	18-2112-73
	80% EtOH-$HClO_4$	241(4.34),310s(3.71), 319(3.72),340s(3.51)	18-2112-73
anion	NaOH	265(4.37),378(3.93)	18-2112-73
in 30% EtOH	NaOH	266(4.38),382(3.93)	18-2112-73
in 60% EtOH	NaOH	267(4.39),387(3.93)	18-2112-73
in 80% EtOH	NaOH	268(4.40),389(3.93)	18-2112-73
in 90% EtOH	NaOH	268(4.40),391(3.93)	18-2112-73
$C_9H_7NO_4S$			
3-Quinolinesulfonic acid, 4-hydroxy-	MeOH	236(4.39),292(3.77), 313(4.01),326(3.99)	94-1080-73
C_9H_7NS			
Thiazole, 2-phenyl-	n.s.g.	290(4.30)	124-0353-73
hydrochloride	n.s.g.	286.5(4.25)	124-0353-73
Thiazole, 4-phenyl-	n.s.g.	252(4.19)	124-0353-73
hydrochloride	n.s.g.	255(4.34)	124-0353-73
Thiazole, 5-phenyl-	n.s.g.	273.5(4.13)	124-0353-73
hydrochloride	n.s.g.	283(3.99)	124-0353-73
$C_9H_7N_3O$			
1,2,4-Oxadiazol-3-amine, N-(phenylmethylene)-	EtOH	272.5(3.88)	39-0047-73C
2-Quinoxalinecarboxamide	0.01N H_2SO_4	243(4.56),321(3.89)	103-0369-73
	14.1N H_2SO_4	254(4.53),340(3.98)	103-0369-73
1,2,4-Triazin-5(4H)-one, 6-phenyl-	EtOH	246(3.90),305(4.00)	22-2126-73
1,2,3-Triazole-4-carboxaldehyde, 5-phenyl-	EtOH	275(3.74)	78-3271-73
	anion	225(4.40),290(3.86)	78-3271-73
$C_9H_7N_3O_2$			
Methanone, (5-amino-1,2,4-oxadiazol-3-yl)phenyl-	MeOH	258(4.09)	4-0357-73
Pyrazole, 3-nitro-4-phenyl- (in 2.5% methanol)	0.05M HCl	225(--),268(3.69)	4-1055-73
	0.05M NaOH	230(--),325(3.83)	4-1055-73
Pyrazole, 3-nitro-5-phenyl- (in 2.5% methanol)	0.05M HCl	254(4.34),270s(--)	4-1055-73
	0.05M NaOH	258(4.23),315(3.91)	4-1055-73
Pyrazole, 4-nitro-3-phenyl- (in 2.5% methanol)	0.05M HCl	225(--),280(3.83)	4-1055-73
	0.05M NaOH	230(--),329(3.95)	4-1055-73

Compound	Solvent	λmax(log ε)	Ref.
$C_9H_7N_3O_2S$			
2-Thiazolamine, 5-(4-nitrophenyl)-	EtOH	203(4.06),218(3.98), 235(3.36),345(2.98)	34-0099-73
$C_9H_7N_3O_5$			
2-Propenal, 2-nitro-3-[(4-nitrophenyl)-amino]-	$CHCl_3$	292(4.20),374(4.48)	104-0477-73
$C_9H_7N_3O_5S$			
Benzoic acid, 2-[[(aminothioxomethyl)-amino]carbonyl]-6-nitro-	MeOH	212(4.46),271(4.30)	56-1275-73
	MeOH-base	265(--),399(--)	56-1275-73
$C_9H_7N_3S$			
1H-1,2,3-Triazine, 1-(phenylthioxomethyl)-	C_6H_{12}	305(4.02),334(4.04)	5-0636-73
	CH_2Cl_2	300s(4.00),330(4.06)	5-0636-73
1H-1,2,4-Triazole, 1-(phenylthioxomethyl)-	C_6H_{12}	295(4.08),325(4.01)	5-0636-73
	CH_2Cl_2	295(4.06),325(4.01)	5-0636-73
2H-1,2,3-Triazole, 2-(phenylthioxomethyl)-	C_6H_{12}	298(4.21),321s(4.09)	5-0636-73
	CH_2Cl_2	301(4.24),320s(4.13)	5-0636-73
[1,2,4]Triazolo[5,1-b]benzothiazole, 2-methyl-	MeOH	208(4.18),225(4.43), 280(3.45),288(3.50)	4-0947-73
$C_9H_7N_5$			
Pyrido[2,3-b]pyrazine-7-carbonitrile, 6-amino-8-methyl-	pH -0.2	231(4.38),343s(4.07), 356(4.17),371(4.10)	39-1974-73C
	pH 7.0	218(4.44),236(4.28), 257(3.97),379(3.92)	39-1974-73C
$C_9H_7N_5O$			
Ethanone, 2-azido-1-imidazo[1,5-a]pyridin-1-yl-	50% EtOH	224(4.18),228(4.17), 255(3.46),263(3.48), 307(3.93),346(4.17)	87-1272-73
$C_9H_7N_5O_2$			
Pyrrolo[1,2-f]pteridin-1(2H)-one, 3-amino-7-hydroxy-	pH 1	240(4.2),285(4.6), 340(3.7),350(3.7)	33-1819-73
	pH 13	240(4.3),290(4.5), 345(3.8),355(3.8)	33-1819-73
$C_9H_7S_2$			
1,2-Dithiol-1-ium, 3-phenyl-	MeOH	200(4.32),226(3.85), 243(3.79),283(3.53), 357(4.08)	78-3399-73
	MeCN	202(4.47),221(3.84), 243(3.68),282(3.59), 357(4.33)	78-3399-73
1,2-Dithiol-1-ium, 4-phenyl-	MeOH	200(3.33),233(4.00), 247(3.87),302(3.93), 352(3.17)	78-3399-73
	MeCN	202(3.80),243(3.69), 348(2.57)	78-3399-73
C_9H_8			
Benzene, 1-ethynyl-4-methyl-	MeOH	249.5(4.20)	35-1602-73
Spiro[4.4]nona-1,3,6,8-tetraene	isooctane	217(3.81),281(3.13)	35-7325-73
	EtOH	218(3.73),276(3.05)	35-7325-73
$C_9H_8BrIO_3$			
2-Propenoic acid, 3-(4-bromo-5-iodo-2-furanyl)-, ethyl ester	MeOH	321(4.01)	103-0802-73

Compound	Solvent	$\lambda_{max}(\log \epsilon)$	Ref.
C_9H_8BrNO			
Isoxazole, 3-(4-bromophenyl)-4,5-dihydro-	EtOH	215(4.05),271(4.23)	22-1390-73
$C_9H_8BrNO_2S_2$			
Benzene, 1-[(2-bromoethyl)sulfonyl]-4-isothiocyanato-	EtOH	229(4.44),285(4.33), 292(4.36)	73-0289-73
Benzene, 1-bromo-4-[(2-isothiocyanatoethyl)sulfonyl]-	EtOH	236(4.23),265s(3.13), 269s(3.03),277(2.98), 290s(2.65)	73-0620-73
$C_9H_8BrNO_3$			
Benzene, 1-(2-bromo-2-nitroethenyl)-4-methoxy-	n.s.g.	245(3.90),370(4.25)	135-1299-73
$C_9H_8BrNS_2$			
Benzene, 1-bromo-4-[(2-isothiocyanatoethyl)thio]-	EtOH	220s(4.04),261(4.09)	73-0620-73
$C_9H_8BrN_5O$			
Ethanone, 2-(5-amino-1H-tetrazol-1-yl)-1-(4-bromophenyl)-	EtOH	258f(4.07)	22-1854-73
$C_9H_8Br_2O$			
Benzene, 2-bromo-4-(2-bromoethenyl)-1-methoxy-, cis	EtOH	221(4.36),270(4.30)	39-2202-73C
trans	EtOH	221(4.36),270(4.30)	39-2202-73C
$C_9H_8Br_2O_2$			
4H-Cyclohepta[b]furan-4-one, 5,5-dibromo-5,6,7,8-tetrahydro-	EtOH	228s(--),290(3.72)	39-0968-73C
Ethanone, 2-bromo-1-(3-bromo-4-methoxyphenyl)-	EtOH	279(4.01)	39-2202-73C
$C_9H_8Br_2O_3$			
2-Propenoic acid, 3-(4,5-dibromo-2-furanyl)-, ethyl ester	MeOH	312(4.43)	103-0802-73
C_9H_8ClNO			
Isoxazole, 3-(4-chlorophenyl)-4,5-dihydro-	EtOH	214(4.02),270(4.19)	22-1390-73
$C_9H_8ClNO_2$			
2-Propenoic acid, 3-(5-amino-2-chlorophenyl)-	EtOH	258(4.25),354(3.32)	12-1337-73
	EtOH-HCl	265(4.13)	12-1337-73
	EtOH-KOH	238(4.61)	12-1337-73
$C_9H_8ClNO_2S_2$			
Benzene, 1-[(2-chloroethyl)sulfonyl]-4-isothiocyanato-	EtOH	230(4.41),286s(4.31), 293(4.35)	73-0289-73
Benzene, 1-chloro-4-[(2-isothiocyanatoethyl)sulfonyl]-	EtOH	230(4.19),264s(3.05), 268s(3.03),277s(2.98)	73-0620-73
$C_9H_8ClNS_2$			
Benzene, 1-[(2-chloroethyl)thio]-4-isothiocyanato-	EtOH	220s(4.58),289(4.38), 299s(4.4)	73-0289-73
Benzene, 1-chloro-4-[(2-isothiocyanatoethyl)thio]-	EtOH	220(4.03),260(4.03)	73-0620-73

Compound	Solvent	λmax(log ε)	Ref.
$C_9H_8ClN_3OS$			
3H-Pyrazol-3-one, 4-[(2-amino-4-chloro-phenyl)thio]-1,2-dihydro-	EtOH	214(4.40),250(4.01), 309(3.62)	7-0045-73
3H-Pyrazol-3-one, 4-[(2-amino-5-chloro-phenyl)thio]-1,2-dihydro-	EtOH	210(4.27),222(4.20), 250(3.98),313(3.43)	7-0045-73
$C_9H_8ClN_3O_2$			
2-Propenal, 1-nitro-, (4-chlorophenyl)-hydrazone	EtOH	336(3.53)	19-0881-73
$C_9H_8Cl_2N_4$			
1,3,5-Triazine, 2,4-dichloro-6-(1-ethyl-1H-pyrrol-2-yl)-	EtOH	235(3.76),347(4.38)	39-2075-73B
$C_9H_8Cl_2OS$			
4H-Cyclohepta[c]thiophen-4-one, 1,3-di-chloro-5,6,7,8-tetrahydro-	EtOH	228(4.13),252(3.96), 290(3.57)	22-0335-73
$C_9H_8Cl_4$			
Spiro[2.4]hepta-4,6-diene, 4,5,6,7-tetrachloro-1,2-dimethyl-	$CHCl_3$	245(3.99),287(3.70)	5-0214-73
$C_9H_8CuF_3O_3S$			
1,3,5,7-Cyclooctatetraenecopper(I) trifluoromethanesulfonate	n.s.g.	233(3.56),280(3.32)	35-1889-73
$C_9H_8F_2OS$			
4H-Cyclohepta[b]thiophen-4-one, 5,5-di-fluoro-5,6,7,8-tetrahydro-	n.s.g.	224(3.89),260(3.76)	35-6655-73
$C_9H_8F_6OS_2$			
2-Butanone, 3-[4,5-bis(trifluoromethyl)-1,3-dithiol-2-yl]-	isooctane	235s(3.33),285s(3.25), 314(3.43)	35-4379-73
$C_9H_8HgN_2O$			
Mercury, (1-diazo-2-oxopropyl)phenyl-	MeOH	288(3.92),366(1.90)	44-3937-73
$C_9H_8HgN_2O_2$			
Mercury, (1-diazo-2-methoxy-2-oxoethyl)-phenyl-	MeOH	268(4.01),377(1.77)	44-3937-73
$C_9H_8INO_2S_2$			
Benzene, 1-[(2-iodoethyl)sulfonyl]-4-isothiocyanato-	EtOH	229(4.45),285s(4.34), 293(4.38)	73-0289-73
$C_9H_8INO_3$			
Benzoic acid, 4-[(iodoacetyl)amino]-	H_2O	274(--)	63-1611-73
	50% MeOH	277(4.28)	63-1611-73
$C_9H_8INS_2$			
Benzene, 1-[(2-iodoethyl)thio]-4-iso-thiocyanato-	EtOH	220s(4.60),290(4.49), 299s(4.45)	73-0289-73
$C_9H_8NO_4P$			
3-Quinolinephosphonic acid, 4-hydroxy-	MeOH	241(4.24),292(3.85), 311(3.96),323(3.93)	94-1080-73
$C_9H_8N_2$			
1H-Benzimidazole, 1-ethenyl- (also spectra of tin complexes)	EtOH	226(3.98),232(3.99), 250(3.79),280(3.48), 288(3.41)	103-1517-73

Compound	Solvent	λ_{max}(log ε)	Ref.
2-Propenenitrile, 3-amino-3-phenyl-	MeCN	225(4.03),289(4.01)	44-2287-73
Quinoxaline, 2-methyl-	pH 4.50	236(4.34),321(3.76)	103-0369-73
	5.2N H_2SO_4	245(4.39),336(3.96)	103-0369-73
$C_9H_8N_2O$			
Indole, 2-methyl-3-nitroso-	aq $HClO_4$	249(4.18),263(4.17), 347(3.76)	39-0918-73B
2-Oxazolamine, 4-phenyl-	EtOH	268(3.85)	27-0099-73
	EtOH-HCl	253(4.03)	27-0099-73
3H-Pyrazol-3-one, 2,4-dihydro-2-phenyl-	MeOH	240(4.11),270(3.47)	48-0382-73
	50% MeOH	239(4.02),263(3.73)	48-0382-73
	10% MeOH	238(3.93),251(3.77)	48-0382-73
2H-Pyrido[1,2-a]pyrimidin-2-one, 4-methyl-	MeOH	225(4.54),245(4.30), 270(3.99),280s(3.93), 326(3.52)	4-0821-73
4H-Pyrido[1,2-a]pyrimidin-4-one, 2-methyl-	MeOH	200(4.40),210s(4.22), 235(3.98),244(4.01), 250(3.95),335(3.97)	4-0821-73
4(1H)-Quinolinone, 8-amino-	EtOH	231(4.18),275(3.85), 339(3.88)	4-0459-73
Quinoxaline, 2-methoxy-	0.001N H_2SO_4	223(4.17),244(4.25), 290(3.50),330(3.73)	103-0369-73
	11.4N H_2SO_4	221(4.07),251(4.25), 346(3.75)	103-0369-73
$C_9H_8N_2OS$			
6-Benzothiazolecarbonitrile, 4,5,6,7-tetrahydro-2-methyl-7-oxo-	EtOH	260(3.84),356(3.81)	32-0755-73
2-Thiazolidinimine, 4-oxo-5-phenyl-	EtOH	220(4.43),250(3.86)	132-0113-73
	EtOH-NaOH	230(4.32)	132-0113-73
Thiazolo[4,5-g]benzisoxazole, 4,5-dihydro-7-methyl-	EtOH	311(4.09)	32-0755-73
Thiazolo[5,4-d]benzisoxazole, 4,5-dihydro-7-methyl-	EtOH	284(4.23)	32-0755-73
$C_9H_8N_2O_2$			
Acetic acid, diazo-, phenylmethyl ester	EtOH	251(4.19)	78-3609-73
1H-Indole-2-carbonitrile, 4,5,6,7-tetrahydro-3-hydroxy-4-oxo-	EtOH	236(4.48),250s(4.25)	94-2571-73
4H-Pyrido[1,2-a]pyrimidin-4-one, 9-hydroxy-2-methyl-	EtOH	235(3.80),258(3.85), 264(3.89),300(3.83), 311(3.88),342(4.06), 357(4.14)	4-0143-73
4,5-Trimethylenepyridine-3-carbonitrile, 2,6-dihydroxy-	EtOH	261(4.13),329(4.31)	78-4103-73
$C_9H_8N_2O_2S$			
Thieno[2,3-b]pyridine, 5-ethyl-3-nitro-	EtOH	229(4.33),251(3.47), 318(3.64)	4-0871-73
$C_9H_8N_2O_2S_2$			
Acetamide, N-acetyl-N-thieno[2,3-c]isothiazol-3-yl-	MeOH	235(4.36),265s(3.67), 273(3.78),283(3.81), 312(4.14)	48-0539-73
Benzene, 1-[(2-isothiocyanatoethyl)thio]-4-nitro-	EtOH	220s(3.90),236s(3.84), 243s(3.76),330(4.12)	73-0620-73
$C_9H_8N_2O_3$			
Acetic acid, (4-diazirinophenoxy)-	hexane	269(3.21),378(2.48)	35-5072-73
2-Propenal, 2-nitro-3-(phenylamino)-	$CHCl_3$	298(3.94),362(4.33)	104-0477-73

Compound	Solvent	$\lambda_{max}(\log \epsilon)$	Ref.
1H-Pyrrole-2-carboxylic acid, 4-acetyl-3-cyano-5-methyl-	EtOH	218(4.24),227(4.18), 290(3.98)	12-1551-73
1H-Pyrrolo[2,3-c]pyridine-2-carboxylic acid, 5,6-dihydro-3-methyl-5-oxo-	EtOH	242(4.34),298(3.94), 302(3.88)	44-1824-73
4(1H)-Quinolinone, 2,3-dihydro-8-nitro-	EtOH	239(4.11),260(3.74), 429(3.78)	4-0459-73
$C_9H_8N_2O_3S$			
3-Quinolinesulfonamide, 4-hydroxy-	MeOH	242(4.27),292(3.83), 311(3.95),324(3.93)	94-1080-73
$C_9H_8N_2O_4$			
2,4(1H,3H)-Pyrimidinedione, 1-[5-(hydroxymethyl)-2-furanyl]-	EtOH	251(3.94),298s(3.64)	44-0990-73
$C_9H_8N_2O_4S_2$			
Benzene, 1-[(2-isothiocyanatoethyl)sulfonyl]-4-nitro-	EtOH	248(4.08),289s(3.77), 290(2.65)	73-0620-73
$C_9H_8N_2S$			
4H-Pyrido[1,2-a]pyrimidine-4-thione, 2-methyl-	MeOH	206(4.58),220(4.73), 271(4.36),280s(4.43), 380(4.42)	4-0821-73
2-Thiazolamine, 4-phenyl-	EtOH	229(4.34),255(3.85), 282(3.87)	27-0099-73
	EtOH-HCl	215(4.18),268(4.18)	27-0099-73
2-Thiazolamine, 5-phenyl-	EtOH	223(3.76),306(4.23)	27-0099-73
	EtOH-HCl	217(3.84),290(4.22)	27-0099-73
$C_9H_8N_2S_3$			
1,3,4-Thiadiazole-2-thione, 5-(methylthio)-3-phenyl-	n.s.g.	328(4.09)	48-0915-73
$C_9H_8N_4O$			
1,2,4-Triazin-5(2H)-one, 6-methyl-3-(2-pyridinyl)-	MeOH	237(4.20),266(4.13)	40-1519-73
$C_9H_8N_4O_2$			
Hydrazinecarboxamide, 2-(1,2-dihydro-2-oxo-3H-indol-3-ylidene)-, anti	EtOH	245(4.15),265(4.04), 315(4.19)	104-1565-73
syn	EtOH	204(4.17),251(4.09), 267(4.23),318(4.19)	104-1565-73
4,5-Isoxazoledione, 3-methyl-, 4-(3-pyridinylhydrazono)-	EtOH	248(3.94),385(4.31)	12-2723-73
$C_9H_8N_4O_4$			
2-Propenal, 1-nitro-, (4-nitrophenyl)-hydrazone	EtOH	392(3.80)	19-0881-73
2,4(1H,3H)-Pteridinedione, 6-acetoxy-1-methyl-	MeOH	242(4.10),339(3.82)	24-3149-73
1,2,4-Triazolidine-3,5-dione, 1-(4-methyl-2-nitrophenyl)-	EtOH	276.0(3.72)	88-5123-73
$C_9H_8N_4O_6$			
Methanol, [(2,4-dinitrophenyl)azo]-, acetate	MeOH	266(4.01),344(3.49)	25-1066-73
C_9H_8O			
Benzene, 1-ethynyl-2-methoxy-	EtOH	239(4.03),250(4.04), 292(3.60),301(3.60)	23-3620-73

Compound	Solvent	λ_{max}(log ϵ)	Ref.
1-Indanone	EtOH	244(4.16),286(3.48), 291(3.49)	141-0001-73
$C_9H_8O_2$			
2(3H)-Benzofuranone, 3-methyl-	90% EtOH	220s(3.54),264s(2.92), 270(3.04),277(2.99)	12-1079-73
2,4,6-Cycloheptatrien-1-one, 2-acetyl-	EtOH	231(4.18),306(3.73)	88-0877-73
1-Indanone, 4-hydroxy-	EtOH	225(4.40),257(4.94), 312(4.43)	141-0001-73
1-Indanone, 5-hydroxy-	MeOH	224(4.15),268(4.13), 290(4.05),295(4.05)	24-1303-73
	EtOH	270(3.90),292(3.90)	141-0001-73
1-Indanone, 7-hydroxy-	EtOH	255(4.00),315(3.50)	141-0001-73
	EtOH-NaOH	238(4.30),262(3.90), 368(3.80)	141-0001-73
2-Propenoic acid, 3-phenyl-, cis	EtOH	257(4.11)	141-0001-73
	EtOH-NaOH	254(4.08)	141-0001-73
2-Propenoic acid, 3-phenyl-, trans	EtOH	211s(4.13),216(4.20), 222(4.14),274(4.33), 296s(3.96)	141-0001-73
	EtOH-NaOH	217(4.17),221(4.20), 267(4.31),296(3.68)	141-0001-73
	dioxan	218(4.09),222(4.08), 274(4.31)	141-0001-73
$C_9H_8O_3$			
3(2H)-Benzofuranone, 6-methoxy-	MeOH	209(4.24),232(4.03), 267(4.10),316(3.98)	24-1182-73
1(3H)-Isobenzofuranone, 3-methoxy-	MeOH	228(3.98),272(2.93), 280(2.91)	44-3375-73
1(3H)-Isobenzofuranone, 4-methoxy-	EtOH	214(4.51),229(3.85), 292(3.46)	141-0001-73
	dioxan	226(3.89),239s(3.70), 288(3.49),295(3.48)	141-0001-73
1(3H)-Isobenzofuranone, 5-methoxy-	EtOH	210(4.20),215s(4.11), 256(4.07),276s(3.56), 287(3.22)	141-0001-73
	dioxan	254(4.08),275s(3.45), 286(3.12)	141-0001-73
1(3H)-Isobenzofuranone, 6-methoxy-	EtOH	211(4.50),226s(3.86), 298(3.56)	141-0001-73
	dioxan	231(3.86),296(3.58), 301s(3.56)	141-0001-73
1(3H)-Isobenzofuranone, 7-methoxy-	EtOH	209(4.52),234(3.91), 296(3.67)	141-0001-73
2-Propenoic acid, 3-(2-hydroxyphenyl)-, cis	EtOH-NaOH	228(4.11),254s(3.90), 330(3.77)	141-0001-73
2-Propenoic acid, 3-(2-hydroxyphenyl)-, trans	EtOH	216(4.16),226s(4.08), 274(4.22),326(3.96)	141-0001-73
	EtOH-NaOH	232(4.15),274(4.02), 365(3.86)	141-0001-73
	dioxan	218(4.11),224s(4.08), 274(4.22),324(3.96)	141-0001-73
2-Propenoic acid, 3-(3-hydroxyphenyl)-, trans	EtOH	216(4.20),234(4.11), 277(4.28),313s(3.71)	141-0001-73
	EtOH-NaOH	214(4.20),230(4.18), 252(4.30),277(4.18), 330s(3.40)	141-0001-73
	dioxan	219(4.10),233(4.08), 277(4.25),315(3.68)	141-0001-73

Compound	Solvent	λ_{max}(log ε)	Ref.
2-Propenoic acid, 3-(4-hydroxyphenyl)-, trans	EtOH	211(4.05),226(4.08), 292s(4.29),300s(4.31), 311(4.33)	141-0001-73
	EtOH-NaOH	313s(4.22),336(4.31)	141-0001-73
	dioxan	227(4.11),294(4.32), 299(4.32),311(4.32)	141-0001-73
$C_9H_8O_4$			
Benzoic acid, 4-formyl-2-hydroxy-, methyl ester	EtOH	250(4.03),258(4.08), 264s(4.05),340(3.51)	78-0857-73
Benzoic acid, 3,4-(methylenedioxy)-, methyl ester	EtOH	221(4.36),263(3.88), 298(3.84)	141-0001-73
	dioxan	225(4.01),263(3.85), 296(3.87)	141-0001-73
2-Propenoic acid, 3-(2,3-dihydroxyphenyl)-, trans	EtOH	224(4.20),288(4.27), 335s(3.53)	141-0001-73
	EtOH-NaOH	235(4.10),287(3.96), 442(3.39)	141-0001-73
	dioxan	224(4.20),285(4.27), 330s(3.66)	141-0001-73
2-Propenoic acid, 3-(2,4-dihydroxyphenyl)-, trans	EtOH	217(4.10),244s(3.80), 286(4.00),324(4.10)	141-0001-73
2-Propenoic acid, 3-(2,5-dihydroxyphenyl)-, trans	EtOH	216(4.11),250(3.99), 278(4.18),355(3.82)	141-0001-73
	EtOH-NaOH	216(4.09),305(3.88), 427(3.20)	141-0001-73
	dioxan	216(4.08),247(3.98), 275(4.16),355(3.83)	141-0001-73
2-Propenoic acid, 3-(3,4-dihydroxyphenyl)-, trans	EtOH	218(4.22),235(4.06), 243(4.06),299(4.17), 326(4.25)	141-0001-73
	EtOH-NaOH	215(4.26),245s(4.06), 302(3.96),348(4.20), 394s(3.79)	141-0001-73
	dioxan	220(4.15),236s(4.08), 241(4.08),296(4.17), 324(4.25)	141-0001-73
$C_9H_8O_5$			
1,2-Benzenedicarboxylic acid, 3-methoxy-	EtOH	215(4.25),238s(3.72), 297(3.54)	141-0001-73
	EtOH-NaOH	219(4.20),288(3.51)	141-0001-73
	dioxan	217(4.18),241s(3.64), 297(3.56)	141-0001-73
1,2-Benzenedicarboxylic acid, 4-methoxy-	EtOH	213(4.28),254(4.01), 285s(3.33)	141-0001-73
	EtOH-NaOH	245(3.92),274s(3.19), 284s(3.10)	141-0001-73
	dioxan	254(4.01),281s(3.34)	141-0001-73
C_9H_8S			
Benzene, [(methylthio)ethynyl]-	HOAc	248(4.04),260(4.02)	78-3819-73
2H-1-Benzothiopyran	EtOH	243(4.35)	2-0446-73
$C_9H_9AsN_2$			
2H-1,2,3-Diazarsole, 5-methyl-2-phenyl-	heptane	230(4.03),275(3.59), 337(3.74)	88-4503-73
C_9H_9BrO			
Benzene, 1-(1-bromoethenyl)-4-methoxy-	C_6H_{12}	266(4.16)	39-0301-73B

Compound	Solvent	$\lambda_{max}(\log \epsilon)$	Ref.
Benzene, 1-(1-bromoethenyl)-4-methoxy- (cont.)	HCOOH	262(4.16),485(1.60), 540s(1.48)	39-0301-73B
	HOAc	262(4.30)	39-0301-73B
	CF_3CH_2OH	257(4.2),550(3.0)	39-0301-73B
$C_9H_9BrO_2$			
Ethanone, 1-(4-bromo-3-methoxyphenyl)-	EtOH	231(4.22),275(4.12)	39-2202-73C
$C_9H_9BrO_3$			
2-Propenoic acid, 3-(5-bromo-2-furanyl)-, ethyl ester	MeOH	310(4.35)	103-0802-73
$C_9H_9ClN_2O$			
Cinnamamide oxime, p-chloro-	EtOH	273(4.24)	39-2241-73C
Pyrido[1,2-à]pyrimidin-1-ium, 1,4-dihydro-2-methyl-4-oxo-, chloride	MeOH	202(4.48),205s(4.44), 215s(4.24),245s(3.88), 252s(3.85),335(3.87)	4-0821-73
$C_9H_9ClN_2O_5$			
Pyrido[1,2-a]pyrimidin-1-ium, 1,4-dihydro-2-methyl-4-oxo-, perchlorate	MeOH	200(4.50),210s(4.11), 244s(3.92),252s(3.88), 335(3.95)	4-0821-73
$C_9H_9ClN_3O_3P$			
Pyrido[3,2-d]pyrimidine, 2-chloro-4-(dimethylphosphono)-	EtOH	324(4.38)	108-0723-73
$C_9H_9ClN_4OS$			
9H-Purine, 6-chloro-9-(1,4-oxathian-2-yl)-	pH 1	264(3.97)	136-0225-73E
	pH 12	264(3.97)	136-0225-73E
	EtOH	265(3.99)	136-0225-73E
9H-Purine, 6-chloro-9-(1,4-oxathian-3-yl)-	pH 1	265(3.90)	136-0225-73E
	pH 12	266(3.92)	136-0225-73E
	EtOH	265(3.90)	136-0225-73E
$C_9H_9ClN_6S$			
2(1H)-Pyridinethione, 6-chloro-3-[(2,6-diamino-4-pyrimidinyl)amino]-	MeOH	251(4.15),306(3.96), 345(3.72)	44-4386-73
C_9H_9ClOS			
4H-Cyclohepta[c]thiophen-4-one, 1-chloro-5,6,7,8-tetrahydro-	EtOH	224(4.01),256(3.93)	22-0335-73
$C_9H_9ClO_2$			
Benzoic acid, 4-chloro-3-ethyl-	EtOH	240(4.12),278(3.03), 286(2.96)	12-1337-73
2,4,6-Cycloheptatrien-1-one, 5-chloro-4-ethyl-2-hydroxy-	EtOH	242(3.97),330(3.36), 360(3.17),380(3.07)	12-1337-73
	EtOH-KOH	248(4.06),343(3.81), 408(3.63)	12-1337-73
2,4,6-Cycloheptatrien-1-one, 5-chloro-2-methoxy-6-methyl-	EtOH	238(4.21),247(4.18), 255(4.08),315(3.65), 328(3.72),353(3.51), 366(3.34)	12-1337-73
$C_9H_9Cl_2NO_2$			
1H-Pyrrole-3,4-dicarboxaldehyde, 2,5-dichloro-1-(1-methylethyl)-	EtOH	245(3.8),303(3.7)	103-0467-73

Compound	Solvent	$\lambda_{max}(\log \epsilon)$	Ref.
$C_9H_9Cl_2N_3$			
2-Imidazolidinimine, N-(2,6-dichloro-	pH 1	268(2.71),277(2.64)	111-0545-73
phenyl)-	MeOH	255s(2.7),290s(2.0)	111-0545-73
$C_9H_9Cl_2N_3O$			
Cyclohexanone, 2-(4,6-dichloro-1,3,5-triazin-2-yl)-	C_6H_{12}	330(4.49)	22-2039-73
$C_9H_9IN_2O$			
Pyrido[1,2-a]pyrimidin-1-ium, 1,4-dihydro-2-methyl-4-oxo-, iodide	MeOH	200(4.58),215(4.39), 243s(4.00),252s(3.91), 335(4.00)	4-0821-73
$C_9H_9IO_3$			
2-Propenoic acid, 3-(5-iodo-2-furanyl)-, ethyl ester	MeOH	317(4.46)	103-0802-73
C_9H_9N			
2H-Azirine, 3-(phenylmethyl)-	EtOH	266(3.53)	33-2007-73
Benzeneacetonitrile, α-methyl-	EtOH	208(3.86)	22-0724-73
Benzonitrile, 2,4-dimethyl-	C_6H_{12}	235(4.05),285(3.07)	49-0644-73
1H-Indole, 3-methyl-	MeOH	228(4.31),275s(3.79), 282(3.82),291(3.74)	102-0447-73
at 70° after ten minutes	H_2SO_4	235(3.66),240(3.63), 287(3.70)	102-0447-73
at 70° after ten hours	H_2SO_4	235(3.69),240(3.67), 283(3.65)	102-0447-73
Isoquinoline, 3,4-dihydro-	EtOH	254(3.86),280s(3.05)	35-4692-73
in 40% ethanol	pH 1	282(3.96),310s(3.18)	35-4692-73
C_9H_9NO			
Isoquinoline, 3,4-dihydro-, 2-oxide	EtOH	305(4.20)	35-4692-73
Isoxazole, 4,5-dihydro-3-phenyl-	EtOH	212s(--),265(3.94)	22-1390-73
C_9H_9NOS			
4-Thiazolol, 4,5-dihydro-2-phenyl-	MeOH	244(4.14)	80-0685-73
hydrochloride	MeOH	242(4.16)	80-0685-73
$C_9H_9NOS_2$			
Ethanol, 2-[(4-isothiocyanatophenyl)-thio]-	EtOH	220s(4.39),291(4.39), 300s(4.36)	73-0289-73
$C_9H_9NO_2$			
Benzaldoxime, O-acetyl-, syn	pH 6.61	257(3.76)	36-1381-73
Benzeneacetonitrile, 2-hydroxy-3-meth-	EtOH	205s(3.77),278(3.45)	39-2209-73C
oxy-	EtOH-base	247(3.91),294(3.65)	39-2209-73C
1H-Isoindol-1-one, 2,3-dihydro-3-hydroxy-2-methyl-	H_2SO_4	232(4.42),264(3.25), 361(3.54)	24-1423-73
1H-Isoindol-1-one, 2,3-dihydro-3-hydroxy-3-methyl-	H_2SO_4	233(4.28),331(3.75)	24-1423-73
$C_9H_9NO_2S$			
7(4H)-Benzothiazolone, 5,6-dihydro-6-(hydroxymethylene)-2-methyl-	EtOH	214(3.87),277(4.00), 322(3.78)	32-0755-73
Thiazolo[3,2-a]pyridinium, 3-carboxy-2,3-dihydro-2-methyl-, hydroxide,	pH 1	212(4.01),250(3.96), 325(3.84)	1-1749-73
inner salt, trans	pH 13	222(4.08),277(4.04), 353(3.95)	1-1749-73

Compound	Solvent	$\lambda_{max}(\log \epsilon)$	Ref.
$C_9H_9NO_2S_2$			
Benzene, [(2-isothiocyanatoethyl)sulfonyl]-	EtOH	219(3.95),246(3.26), 250(3.25),257(3.32), 266(3.17),273(3.06)	73-0620-73
$C_9H_9NO_3$			
Benzene, 1-methoxy-4-(2-nitroethenyl)-	n.s.g.	242(3.99),355(4.31)	135-1299-73
2H-1-Benzopyran, 3,4-dihydro-7-nitro-	EtOH	237(4.04),279(3.83), 332(3.43)	4-0623-73
Oxirane, 2-methyl-2-nitro-3-phenyl-, trans	EtOH	230(3.65),290(2.65)	18-3198-73
2H-Pyran-3-carbonitrile, 4-ethoxy-6-methyl-2-oxo-	EtOH	310(3.95)	94-1047-73
4H-Pyran-3-carbonitrile, 2-ethoxy-6-methyl-4-oxo-	EtOH	248(3.83)	94-1047-73
$C_9H_9NO_3S$			
1H-Indole-3-sulfonic acid, methyl ester	EtOH	276(3.89),283(3.76)	78-0669-73
Thiazolo[3,2-a]pyridinium, 3-carboxy-2,3-dihydro-8-hydroxy-2-methyl-, hydroxide, inner salt, trans	pH 13	224(3.86),250(3.99), 355(4.04)	1-1749-73
$C_9H_9NO_3S_2$			
Ethanol, 2-[(4-isothiocyanatophenyl)-sulfonyl]-	EtOH	227(4.46),283s(4.30), 290(4.31)	73-0289-73
$C_9H_9NO_4S$			
2,1-Benzisothiazole-5-carboxylic acid, 1,3-dihydro-1-methyl-, 2,2-dioxide	EtOH	268(4.17)	4-0249-73
C_9H_9NS			
1,2-Benzisothiazole, 3,5-dimethyl-	EtOH	233(4.19),312(3.52)	44-2809-73
$C_9H_9NS_2$			
Benzene, [(2-isothiocyanatoethyl)thio]-	EtOH	212s(4.12),253(3.90)	73-0620-73
Pyrrolo[2,1-b]thiazole-5-carbothioaldehyde, 2,6-dimethyl-	C_6H_{12}	224(4.21),335(3.91), 410s(4.42),420(4.49), 428(4.51),510(1.84), 536(1.84),578s(1.41)	39-0657-73C
Pyrrolo[2,1-b]thiazole-5-carbothioaldehyde, 3,6-dimethyl-	C_6H_{12}	204(4.09),225(4.11), 326(3.52),408s(4.62), 417(4.65),539(1.71), 615s(1.19)	39-0657-73C
Pyrrolo[2,1-b]thiazole-5-carbothioaldehyde, 6,7-dimethyl-	C_6H_{12}	220(4.27),331(3.93), 417s(4.41),428(4.49), 437(4.52),508(1.89), 536(1.89),573s(1.38)	39-0657-73C
Pyrrolo[2,1-b]thiazole-7-carbothioaldehyde, 3,6-dimethyl-	C_6H_{12}	227(4.32),254s(3.67), 284(3.74),397s(4.16), 405(4.36),416(4.31), 520(1.81)	39-0657-73C
Pyrrolo[2,1-b]thiazole-7-carbothioaldehyde, 5,6-dimethyl-	C_6H_{12}	228(4.39),297(3.73), 413(4.29),425(4.12), 515(1.81)	39-0657-73C
$C_9H_9N_2O$			
Pyrido[1,2-a]pyrimidin-1-ium, 1,4-dihydro-2-methyl-4-oxo-, chloride (also iodide and perchlorate spectra)	MeOH	202(4.48),205s(4.44), 215s(4.24),245s(3.88), 252s(3.85),335(3.87)	4-0821-73

Compound	Solvent	$\lambda_{max}(\log \epsilon)$	Ref.
$C_9H_9N_2O_7$			
Cyclohexadiene-1-carboxylic acid, 2-methoxy-3,5-dioxo-, methyl ester, ion(1-)	DMSO	392(4.27),496(4.34)	39-0710-73B
Cyclohexadiene-1-carboxylic acid, 4-methoxy-3,5-dioxo-, methyl ester, ion(1-)	DMSO	378(4.26),514(4.24), 550(4.24)	39-0710-73B
$C_9H_9N_3$			
2-Quinoxalinamine, N-methyl-	pH 1.0	237(4.29),256(4.06), 308(3.74),352(3.85)	103-0369-73
	pH 7.2	248(4.43),291(3.25), 363(3.79)	103-0369-73
1H-1,2,3-Triazole, 4-(4-methylphenyl)-	EtOH	252(4.16)	78-3271-73
	anion	263(4.22)	78-3271-73
$C_9H_9N_3O$			
Ethanone, 2-amino-1-imidazo[1,5-a]pyridin-1-yl-, hydrochloride	H_2O	245(3.40),263(3.39), 345(4.29),359(4.20)	87-1272-73
1(2H)-Isoquinolinone, 2,3-diamino-	EtOH	229(4.25),304(4.03), 376(3.43)	95-1581-73
1H-Pyrazolo[4,3-b]pyridine, 1-acetyl-5-methyl-	C_6H_{12}	234(4.31),285(3.46), 291(3.53),296(3.57), 303(3.49)	39-2901-73C
2H-Pyrazolo[4,3-b]pyridine, 2-acetyl-5-methyl-	C_6H_{12}	214(4.19),296(3.81)	39-2901-73C
1,2,4-Triazol-5-ol, 1-methyl-3-phenyl-	EtOH	268(4.05)	94-1342-73
	THF	279(4.10)	94-1342-73
1,2,4-Triazol-5-ol, 2-methyl-3-phenyl-	EtOH	253(3.96)	94-1342-73
	THF	257(3.97)	94-1342-73
1,2,4-Triazol-5-ol, 4-methyl-3-phenyl-	EtOH	254(3.92)	94-1342-73
	THF	267(3.98)	94-1342-73
$C_9H_9N_3OS$			
Acetamide, N-(3-amino-2(3H)-benzothiazolylidene)-	dioxan	234(4.01),255(3.60), 282s(3.81),307s(4.34), 313(4.36)	4-0947-73
Acetamide, N-(5-methylthiazolo[4,5-b]-pyridin-2-yl)-	MeOH	255(4.14),292(4.15)	44-4383-73
1,3,4-Thiadiazol-2-amine, 5-(4-methoxyphenyl)-	EtOH	246(3.49),305(4.26)	80-1777-73
	EtOH-HCl	300(4.25)	80-1777-73
$C_9H_9N_3O_2$			
2,4-Hexadienamide, 2,3-dicyano-5-methoxy-	EtOH	356(4.16)	12-1551-73
1,3(2H,4H)-Isoquinolinedione, dioxime	EtOH	238(4.22),269(3.86)	39-0606-73C
$C_9H_9N_3O_3$			
2-Propenimidamide, N-hydroxy-3-(4-nitrophenyl)-	EtOH	265.5(4.17)	39-2241-73C
1H-Pyrazol-4-ol, 4,5-dihydro-1-(4-nitrophenyl)-	n.s.g.	230(3.99),390(4.50)	22-3159-73
5H-Pyrrolo[3,2-c]pyridazine-6-carboxylic acid, ethyl ester, 2-oxide (all spectra in ethanol)	pH 1	215s(4.14),254(4.42), 348(4.12)	4-0807-73
	pH 7	255(4.43),348(4.10)	4-0807-73
	pH 11	263(4.48),345(4.15)	4-0807-73
$C_9H_9N_3O_4$			
Quinoline, 1,2,3,4-tetrahydro-5,7-dinitro-	EtOH	341(3.92),400(4.09)	103-0069-73

Compound	Solvent	λ_{max}(log ε)	Ref.
Quinoline, 1,2,3,4-tetrahydro-6,7-di-nitro-	EtOH	223(4.04),327(4.18)	103-0069-73
Quinoline, 1,2,3,4-tetrahydro-6,8-di-nitro-	EtOH	215(4.12),270(4.00), 360(4.20)	103-0069-73
Quinoline, 1,2,3,4-tetrahydro-7,8-di-nitro-	EtOH	234(4.20),358(3.62), 434(3.72)	103-0069-73
$C_9H_9N_3O_5$			
Methanimidic acid, N-(2,4-dinitrophen-yl)-, ethyl ester	MeCN	302(4.12)	35-1253-73
$C_9H_9N_3O_8$			
Bicyclo[3.3.1]non-2-en-7-one, 3-hydroxy-2,4,9-trinitro-, sodium salt	H_2O	268(3.64),422(4.30)	94-2168-73
2-Propanone, 1-(3-hydroxy-2,4,6-tri-nitrocyclohexadien-1-yl)-, disodium salt	H_2O	238(3.97),326(3.79), 420(4.27)	94-2168-73
$C_9H_9N_3S$			
2H-Pyrazolo[4,3-g]benzothiazole, 4,5-dihydro-7-methyl-	EtOH	216(3.81),296(4.24)	32-0755-73
1H-Pyrimido[2,3-b]thiazolo[5,4-b]pyri-dine, 2,3-dihydro-, hydrochloride	EtOH	213(4.23),260(3.86), 292(3.94)	2-0744-73
1,2,4-Triazolidine-3-thione, 1-methyl-4-phenyl-, meso-ionic didehydro deriv.	MeCN	236(4.02)	103-1048-73
3H-1,2,4-Triazoline-3-thione, 1-methyl-5-phenyl-	MeOH	242(4.25),306(3.44)	103-1216-73
	EtOH	242(4.22),310(3.33)	94-1342-73
	THF	236(4.25),278(3.52)	94-1342-73
3H-1,2,4-Triazoline-3-thione, 2-methyl-5-phenyl-	EtOH	227(4.21),255(4.28), 288s(3.99)	94-1342-73
3H-1,2,4-Triazoline-3-thione, 4-methyl-5-phenyl-	EtOH	217(4.11),254(4.34), 280s(3.93)	94-1342-73
	THF	218s(4.01),248(4.20)	94-1342-73
$C_9H_9N_4O_7$			
1-Oxa-4-azaspiro[4.5]decadiene, 4-meth-yl-6,8,10-trinitro-, ion(1-), K salt	H_2O	427(4.35)	44-2838-73
$C_9H_9N_5O$			
Ethanone, 2-(5-amino-1H-tetrazol-1-yl)-1-phenyl-	EtOH	249(4.07),280s(3.09)	22-1854-73
Ethanone, 2-(5-amino-2H-tetrazol-2-yl)-1-phenyl-	EtOH	247(4.07),291s(2.92)	22-1854-73
Phenol, 2-methyl-4-(1H-1,2,4-triazol-3-ylazo)-	MeOH	361(4.1),445s(3.2+)	12-1585-73
Phenol, 3-methyl-4-(1H-1,2,4-triazol-3-ylazo)-	MeOH	361(4.1),445s(3.2+)	12-1585-73
Phenol, 4-methyl-2-(1H-1,2,4-triazol-3-ylazo)-	MeOH	318(4.2),396(3.6)	12-1585-73
5-Pyrazolone, 3-methyl-4-(3-pyridyl-hydrazono)-	EtOH	228(3.85),354(4.13), 382(4.13)	12-2723-73
$C_9H_9N_5O_5S$			
Yellow compound I, bromine oxidation product	pH 1	234(3.99),270(4.07), 318(4.03)	18-0939-73
	pH 13	277(4.21),316(3.87), 372(4.06)	18-0939-73
$C_9H_9N_5O_6$			
Diazene, (2,4-dinitrophenyl)(1-methyl-1-nitroethyl)-	$CHCl_3$	403(2.52)	78-3929-73

Compound	Solvent	$\lambda_{max}(\log \epsilon)$	Ref.
Propanal, 1-nitro-, (2,4-dinitrophenyl)-hydrazone	$CHCl_3$	350(4.28),378s(--)	78-3929-73
$C_9H_9N_5S$			
Thiazolo[3,2-e]purin-4-amine, 7,8-di-methyl-	pH 1	253(4.39),293(4.10)	94-0034-73
	pH 13	241(--),289(--), 300s(--)	94-0034-73
Thiazolo[3,2-e]purin-4-amine, 8-ethyl-	pH 1	249(4.39),293(4.15)	94-0034-73
	pH 13	239(--),287(--), 297s(--)	94-0034-73
	EtOH	240(--),253(--), 288(--),298s(--)	94-0034-73
$C_9H_9N_5S_2$			
Thiazolo[3,2-e]purin-4-amine, 8-methyl-2-(methylthio)-	pH 1	257(4.22),298(4.19)	94-0034-73
	pH 13	248s(--),294(--), 305s(--)	94-0034-73
$C_9H_9N_7O_6S$			
Hydrazinecarbothioamide, 2,2-bis(hexa-hydro-2,4,6-trioxo-5-pyrimidinyl)-	EtOH	238(4.15),360(4.12)	103-0247-73
$C_9H_7N_7O_7$			
Hydrazinecarboxamide, 2,2-bis(hexahydro-2,4,6-trioxo-5-pyrimidinyl)-	EtOH	304(4.25)	103-0247-73
C_9H_{10}			
Spiro[2.4]hepta-1,4,6-triene, 1,2-di-methyl-	MeOH	239(3.11)	89-0577-73
Spiro[4.4]nona-1,3,7-triene	EtOH	254(3.44)	35-7325-73
$C_9H_{10}BrNO$			
2,4,6-Cycloheptatrien-1-one, 2-bromo-7-(dimethylamino)-	EtOH	266(4.19),359(4.05), 437(3.95)	39-1960-73C
$C_9H_{10}BrN_3S$			
Hydrazinecarbothioamide, 2-[1-(4-bromo-phenyl)ethylidene]-	$CHCl_3$	315(4.21)	7-0363-73
in 10% isopropanol	pH 7.0	302(4.2)	7-0363-73
in 10% isopropanol	pH 12.5	340(4.3)	7-0363-73
$C_9H_{10}Cl$			
Ethylium, 1-(4-chlorophenyl)-1-methyl-	FSO_3H at -75°	345(4.48)	59-0803-73
$C_9H_{10}ClNO$			
2H-1-Benzopyran-8-amine, 6-chloro-3,4-dihydro-	EtOH	237(3.84),297(3.49)	4-0623-73
Methanimidic acid, N-(4-chlorophenyl)-, ethyl ester	MeCN	248(4.03)	35-1253-73
$C_9H_{10}ClNO_2S$			
2,1-Benzisothiazole, 5-chloro-1,3-di-hydro-1,3-dimethyl-, 2,2-dioxide	EtOH	243(4.09),296(3.24)	4-0249-73
$C_9H_{10}ClN_2$			
Benzimidazolium, 2-chloro-1,3-dimethyl-, perchlorate	EtOH	273(3.91),281(3.84)	104-2622-73

Compound	Solvent	$\lambda_{max}(\log \epsilon)$	Ref.
$C_9H_{10}ClN_3S$			
Hydrazinocarbothioamide, 2-[1-(4-chloro-phenyl)ethylidene]-	$CHCl_3$	310(4.18)	7-0363-73
in 10% isopropanol	pH 7.0	300(4.20)	7-0363-73
in 10% isopropanol	pH 12.5	337(4.3)	7-0363-73
Thiazolo[5,4-b]pyridin-2-amine, N-(3-chloropropyl)-	EtOH	225(3.98),240(3.99), 280(3.85)	2-0744-73
$C_9H_{10}Cl_2$			
Bicyclo[4.2.1]nona-2,4-diene, 3,4-di-chloro-	EtOH	206(3.79),223(3.71), 271(3.88)	33-1083-73
$C_9H_{10}Cl_2OS$			
4H-Cyclohepta[c]thiophene-4-ol, 1,3-di-chloro-5,6,7,8-tetrahydro-	EtOH	241(3.82)	22-0335-73
$C_9H_{10}Cl_2O_2$			
2,5-Cyclohexadien-1-one, 4-(dichloro-methyl)-2-methoxy-4-methyl-	EtOH	238(3.94),287(3.38)	12-1337-73
$C_9H_{10}FNO_4$			
Tyrosine, 3-fluoro-5-hydroxy-, hydro-bromide	pH 1	276(2.82)	87-0416-73
$C_9H_{10}F_2N_2O_4$			
Uridine, 2',3'-dideoxy-3',5-difluoro-	pH 7	267.5(3.93)	48-0149-73
$C_9H_{10}N_2$			
1H-Indol-2-amine, N-methyl-, hydrochlor-ide	MeOH	244(4.02),250(4.02)	103-0598-73
1H-Indol-2-amine, 1-methyl-, hydrochlor-ide	MeOH	209(4.30),258(4.03)	103-0598-73
$C_9H_{10}N_2O$			
Acetic acid, (phenylmethylene)hydrazide	EtOH	283(4.4)	22-2029-73
Cyclopenta[c]pyrrol-1(2H)-one, 3-(di-methylamino)-	MeOH	218(4.39),252(4.14), 360(4.02),444(3.44)	89-0418-73
3H-Indol-3-ol, 2-amino-3-methyl-	MeOH	215(4.49),270(4.02), 306(3.49)	103-0471-73
Pyrazolin-4-ol, 1-phenyl-	n.s.g.	242(3.87),292(4.12), 305s(4.02)	22-3159-73
4(1H)-Quinolinone, 8-amino-2,3-dihydro-	EtOH	231(4.04),247(4.04), 289(3.57),392(3.54)	4-0459-73
$C_9H_{10}N_2O_2$			
Benzenamine, 4-ethenyl-N-methyl-2-nitro-	hexane	210(4.30),253s(4.66), 278(4.67),427(4.04)	24-1116-73
Benzenamine, 4-nitro-4-(2-propenyl)-	MeOH	232(3.86),384(4.33)	24-0355-73
Benzonitrile, 4-amino-2,5-dimethoxy-	EtOH	235(4.28),272(4.22), 315(4.18)	104-2542-73
Butanoic acid, 3-dicyanomethylene-, ethyl ester	EtOH	232(4.12),355(4.54)	78-4103-73
	EtOH-NaOH	229(4.14),355(4.62)	78-4103-73
Isoxazole, 5,5'-methylenebis[3-methyl-	n.s.g.	216.5(4.22)	32-0037-73
3-Pyridinecarbonitrile, 2-ethoxy-4-hy-droxy-6-methyl-	EtOH	245(3.87)	94-1047-73
$C_9H_{10}N_2O_2S$			
Diazoethane, 1-(p-toluenesulfonyl)-	n.s.g.	260(3.96),430(1.86)	27-0320-73
Thiazolo[5,4-d]benzisoxazol-3-ol, 3,3a,4,5-tetrahydro-7-methyl-	EtOH	286(4.00)	32-0755-73

Compound	Solvent	λ_{max}(log ε)	Ref.
$C_9H_{10}N_2O_2S_2$			
Thieno[2,3-d]thiazole-5-carboxylic acid, 2-amino-6-methyl-, ethyl ester	MeCN	263s(3.75),275(3.90), 284(3.91),332(4.34)	48-0539-73
2-Thiophenecarboxylic acid, 5-amino-3-methyl-4-thiocyanato-, ethyl ester	MeOH	231(4.12),320(4.21)	48-0539-73
$C_9H_{10}N_2O_2S_3$			
Rhodanine, 5-(N-acetyl-2-thiazolinylidene)-3-methyl-	EtOH	286(4.06),392(4.46)	94-1431-73
$C_9H_{10}N_2O_3$			
2H-1-Benzopyran-6-amine, 3,4-dihydro-5-nitro-, hydrochloride	EtOH	236(4.18),443(3.46)	4-0623-73
2H-1-Benzopyran-6-amine, 3,4-dihydro-7-nitro-	EtOH	236(4.28),269(3.83), 292(3.77),450(3.70)	4-0623-73
2H-1-Benzopyran-8-amine, 3,4-dihydro-5-nitro-	EtOH	267(3.80),392(4.05)	4-0623-73
2H-1-Benzopyran-8-amine, 3,4-dihydro-6-nitro-	EtOH	229(4.06),262(4.05), 318(3.73),370(3.59)	4-0623-73
Ethanediamide, (4-methoxyphenyl)-	dioxan	285(4.06)	30-0001-73
Methanimidic acid, N-(3-nitrophenyl)-, ethyl ester	MeCN	238(4.23),315s(3.36)	35-1253-73
Methanimidic acid, N-(4-nitrophenyl)-, ethyl ester	n.s.g.	309(4.15)	35-1253-73
1H-Pyrrole-3-carboxylic acid, 5-cyano-4-hydroxy-2-methyl-, ethyl ester	EtOH	224(4.50),242s(4.17)	94-2571-73
3,4-Pyrrolediol, 5-(2-furanyl)-2,5-dihydro-2-imino-1-methyl-	n.s.g.	220(4.01),305(3.78)	12-2221-73
1H-Pyrrolo[2,3-c]pyridine-2-carboxylic acid, 4,5,6,7-tetrahydro-3-methyl-5-oxo-	EtOH	272(4.07)	44-1824-73
$C_9H_{10}N_2O_4S$			
2,1-Benzisothiazole, 1,3-dihydro-1,3-dimethyl-5-nitro-, 2,2-dioxide	EtOH	229(3.79),322(4.06)	4-0249-73
$C_9H_{10}N_2O_5$			
2,2'-Anhydro-1-β-D-arabinofuranosyluracil	H_2O	224(3.90),251(3.88)	18-0550-73
	H_2O	223(3.92),250(3.91)	44-0593-73
2,2'-Anhydro-3-β-D-arabinofuranosyluracil	pH 2 and 7	271(3.84)	88-2939-73
	pH 12	272(3.83)	88-2939-73
2,2'-Anhydro-1-α-D-ribofuranosyluracil	H_2O	225(3.93),250(3.92)	44-0593-73
Benzenemethanol, α-(2,2-dinitroethyl)-	n.s.g.	378(4.18)	70-0212-73
2,4,6(1H,3H,5H)-Pyrimidinetrione, 5-(1,3-dioxobutyl)-1-methyl-	EtOH	243(3.78),277(4.09)	94-2639-73
$C_9H_{10}N_2O_5S$			
2H-Pyrrole-3-carboxylic acid, 5-[(acetyloxy)amino]-4-(methylthio)-2-oxo-, methyl ester	EtOH	310(4.04)	94-1667-73
$C_9H_{10}N_2S$			
Thiocyanic acid, 5-[(dimethylamino)methylene]-1,3-cyclopentadien-1-yl ester	dioxan	338(4.48)	88-5105-73
$C_9H_{10}N_2S_2$			
[1]Benzothieno[2,3-c]isothiazol-3-amine, 4,5,6,7-tetrahydro-	MeOH	238(4.56),310(3.76)	48-0539-73
[1]Benzothieno[2,3-d]thiazol-2-amine, 5,6,7,8-tetrahydro-	MeCN	251(3.80),291(4.00)	48-0539-73

Compound	Solvent	$\lambda_{max}(\log \epsilon)$	Ref.
$C_9H_{10}N_3O_3P$			
Phosphonic acid, [(4-cyanophenyl)azo]-, dimethyl ester	MeOH	235(4.04),286(4.20), 505(1.92)	44-4402-73
$C_9H_{10}N_4O_2$			
2,4(1H,3H)-Pteridinedione, 1,6,7-trimethyl-	pH 1.0	225s(4.28),250(3.97), 333(3.98)	24-1401-73
	pH 5.0	225s(4.28),250(3.97), 333(3.98)	24-3149-73
	pH 11.0	246(4.27),280(3.45), 340(4.05)	24-1401-73 +24-3149-73
2,4(1H,3H)-Pteridinedione, 3,6,7-trimethyl-	pH 5.0	232(4.21),328(4.03)	24-1401-73 +24-3149-73
	pH 11.0	245(4.25),271(4.06), 360(3.87)	24-1401-73 +24-3149-73
Pyrido[2,3-d]pyrimidine-2,4(1H,3H)-dione, 7-amino-1,3-dimethyl-	isoPrOH-DMF	244(3.79),271(3.94), 313(4.30),318(4.24), 326(4.26)	107-0397-73
$C_9H_{10}N_4O_2S$			
Hydrazinecarbothioamide, N-methyl-2-[(4-nitrophenyl)methylene]-	$CHCl_3$	345(4.01)	7-0363-73
	10% isoPrOH-pH 7.0	335(4.27)	7-0363-73
$C_9H_{10}N_4O_3$			
2,4(1H,3H)-Pteridinedione, 7-hydroxy-1,3,6-trimethyl-	pH 1.5	269(3.82),284(3.79), 327(4.09)	24-3203-73
2,4(1H,3H)-Pteridinedione, 7-methoxy-1,3-dimethyl-	pH 5.0	239(4.09),262(3.84), 322(4.13)	24-3203-73
2,4(1H,3H)-Pteridinedione, 1,6,7-trimethyl-, 5-oxide	pH 6.0	238(4.40),287(3.71), 349(3.84)	24-3149-73
	pH 11.0	244(4.38),289(3.83), 353(3.88)	24-3149-73
2,4(1H,3H)-Pteridinedione, 3,6,7-trimethyl-, 8-oxide	pH 3.0	238(4.44),281s(3.96), 343(3.88)	24-3149-73
	pH 9.0	239s(4.18),266(4.33), 382(3.90)	24-3149-73
7H-Purine-7-acetaldehyde, 1,2,3,6-tetrahydro-1,3-dimethyl-2,6-dioxo-	H_2O	231(--),273(3.95)	126-0327-73G
2,4,6(1H,3H,5H)-Pyrimidinetrione, 1-methyl-5-(5-methyl-1H-pyrazol-3-yl)-, 1:1 compound with hydrazine	EtOH	273(4.37)	94-2639-73
$C_9H_{10}N_4O_4$			
2,4(1H,3H)-Pteridinedione, 7-hydroxy-1,3,6-trimethyl-, 5-oxide	pH 0.0	250(4.25),284(3.76), 339(4.01)	24-3203-73
	pH 6.0	228(4.36),258(4.18), 337(4.13)	24-3203-73
2,4(1H,3H)-Pteridinedione, 7-methoxy-1,3-dimethyl-, 5-oxide	MeOH	250(4.39),287(3.84), 340(3.94)	24-3203-73
2,4(1H,3H)-Pteridinedione, 3,6,7-trimethyl-, 5,8-dioxide	pH 2.0	239(4.21),263(4.38), 312(4.01),385(3.77)	24-3149-73
	pH 8.0	258(4.30),280s(4.16), 320(3.91),409(3.80)	24-3149-73
$C_9H_{10}N_5O$			
1H-Purinium, 2-amino-6,9-dihydro-9-methyl-6-oxo-7-(2-propynyl)-, bromide	pH 4	253(4.05),281(3.83)	24-1389-73
	pH 10	220(4.28),248(3.73), 284(3.84)	24-1389-73

Compound	Solvent	λ_{max}(log ε)	Ref.
$C_9H_{10}N_5O_6P$			
D-Neopterin 2',3'-cyclophosphate	pH 1	251(4.1),320(4.0)	33-1819-73
	pH 6.8	238(4.1),275(4.2), 345(3.8)	33-1819-73
	pH 13	255(4.4),362(3.9)	33-1819-73
$C_9H_{10}N_6O_2S$			
2-Propenoic acid, 3-[5-[(aminothioxo-methyl)amino]-1H-1,2,3-triazol-4-yl]-2-cyano-, ethyl ester, K salt	pH 7	235(4.06),267(4.40), 364(3.56)	39-1620-73C
$C_9H_{10}N_6O_3$			
L-Alanine, N-[(1H-purin-6-ylamino)-carbonyl]-	pH 1-2	277(4.33)	87-0139-73
	pH 5-7	269(4.30)	87-0139-73
	pH 12	277(4.27)	87-0139-73
Glycine, N-(N-1H-purin-6-ylglycyl)-	pH 1	276(4.23)	94-2349-73
	pH 7	267(4.22)	94-2349-73
	pH 13	273(4.20),280s(4.07)	94-2349-73
Propanoic acid, 3-[[(1H-purin-6-yl-amino)carbonyl]amino]-	pH 1-2	278(4.28)	87-0139-73
	pH 5-7	270(4.24)	87-0139-73
	pH 12	278(4.20)	87-0139-73
$C_9H_{10}N_6O_4$			
L-Serine, N-[(1H-purin-6-ylamino)carbo-nyl]-	pH 1-2	277.5(4.26)	87-0139-73
	pH 5-7	269.5(4.23)	87-0139-73
	pH 12	278(4.23)	87-0139-73
$C_9H_{10}O$			
Benzene, (2-propenyloxy)-	heptane	263(3.12),271(3.22), 277(3.14)	110-1210-73
Benzeneacetaldehyde, α-methyl-	MeOH	209(3.81)	104-2119-73
1H-Inden-4-ol, 2,3-dihydro-	50% dioxan	275(2.79),285(1.53)	35-1673-73
1H-Inden-6-one, 2,4,5,6-tetrahydro-	EtOH	291(4.27)	22-2098-73
2-Propanone, 1-phenyl-	MeOH	209(3.88)	104-2119-73
$C_9H_{10}OS$			
Benzene, [2-(methylsulfinyl)ethenyl]-	MeOH	266(4.27)	78-3819-73
Benzo[b]thiophene, 6,7-dihydro-4-meth-oxy-	EtOH	225(4.17),288(3.26)	44-0146-73
Ethanethioic acid, S-(4-methylphenyl) ester	C_6H_{12}	233(4.08)	44-1559-73
6-Octene-2,4-diyn-1-ol, 7-(methylthio)-, cis	ether	238(4.02),291(4.35), 306(4.37)	24-3772-73
trans	ether	235(3.70),296(4.14), 311(4.20)	24-3772-73
Oxirane, [(phenylthio)methyl]-	heptane	254(3.83)	110-1210-73
Thiirane, (phenoxymethyl)-	heptane	220(3.88),270(3.20), 277(3.10)	110-1210-73
$C_9H_{10}OSe$			
Oxirane, [(phenylseleno)methyl]-	heptane	244(3.56),274(3.45)	110-1210-73
$C_9H_{10}O_2$			
Acetic acid, 4-methylphenyl ester	EtOH	256s(2.54),261(2.64), 264(2.69),270(2.65)	33-1266-73
Benzeneacetaldehyde, 4-methoxy-	MeOH	225(4.00)	104-2119-73
Benzoic acid, 2,4-dimethyl-	C_6H_{12}	238(4.06),278(3.05)	49-0644-73
2,4,6-Cycloheptatrien-1-one, 5-ethyl-2-hydroxy-	EtOH	234(4.28),249(4.12), 323(3.86),354(3.64), 368(3.61)	12-1337-73

Compound	Solvent	λ_{max}(log ε)	Ref.
2,4,6-Cycloheptatrien-1-one, 5-ethyl-2-hydroxy- (cont.)	EtOH-KOH	243(4.34),253(4.14), 262(3.84),336(4.11), 402(3.97)	12-1337-73
Ethanone, 1-(3-methoxyphenyl)-	EtOH	217(4.35),249(3.94), 306(3.39)	141-0001-73
	dioxan	214(4.40),244(3.93), 250s(3.79),298(3.45), 308s(3.32)	141-0001-73
Ethanone, 1-(4-methoxyphenyl)-	EtOH	271.5(4.22)	39-0301-73B
	FSO_3H	350(4.53)	59-0807-73
at -75°	FSO_3H	335(4.38)	59-0807-73
at -75°	FSO_3H-SbF_5	283(4.26)	59-0807-73
1,5-Methanopentalene-2,3-dione, hexahydro-	CH_2Cl_2	478(1.53)	88-1151-73
Oxirane, (phenoxymethyl)-	heptane	220(3.91),267(3.09), 271(3.19),277(3.10)	110-1210-73
1-Propanone, 1-(2-hydroxyphenyl)-	EtOH	213(4.26),251(3.94), 325(3.52)	141-0001-73
	EtOH-NaOH	230(4.27),260s(3.76), 365(3.72)	141-0001-73
	dioxan	220(4.04),251(3.90), 326(3.50)	141-0001-73
1-Propanone, 1-(4-hydroxyphenyl)-	EtOH	220(4.05),277(4.18)	141-0001-73
	EtOH-NaOH	237(3.82),329(4.39)	141-0001-73
	dioxan	219(4.05),265(4.21), 276s(4.08)	141-0001-73
$C_9H_{10}O_3$			
Benzaldehyde, 2,3-dimethoxy-	EtOH	220(4.26),260(3.94), 323(3.40)	141-0001-73
	dioxan	227(4.10),257(3.96), 319(3.47)	141-0001-73
Benzaldehyde, 2,4-dimethoxy-	EtOH	209(4.10),232(4.16), 274(4.14),314(4.00)	141-0001-73
	dioxan	232(4.20),271(4.15), 309(3.96)	141-0001-73
Benzaldehyde, 2,5-dimethoxy-	EtOH	225(4.27),257(3.98), 355(3.72)	141-0001-73
	dioxan	225(4.24),254(3.95), 350(3.72)	141-0001-73
Benzaldehyde, 3,4-dimethoxy-	EtOH	230(4.21),275(4.02), 309(3.94)	141-0001-73
	dioxan	231(4.25),274(4.07), 305(3.95)	141-0001-73
	n.s.g.	230(3.84),280(3.70), 310(3.69)	105-0252-73
Benzaldehyde, 3,5-dimethoxy-	EtOH	215(4.41),269(3.87), 325(3.44)	141-0001-73
	dioxan	221(4.21),267(3.86), 322(3.45)	141-0001-73
Benzaldehyde, 4-hydroxy-5-methoxy-2-methyl-	EtOH	235(4.23),283(4.02), 316(3.88)	12-1337-73
	EtOH-KOH	255(4.03),354(4.39)	12-1337-73
Benzoic acid, 2-methoxy-, methyl ester	EtOH	210(4.24),234(3.86), 295(3.55)	141-0001-73
	dioxan	232(3.82),292(3.51)	141-0001-73
Benzoic acid, 3-methoxy-, methyl ester	EtOH	213(4.27),235(3.78), 296(3.37)	141-0001-73
	dioxan	236(3.88),297(3.49)	141-0001-73
Benzoic acid, 4-methoxy-, methyl ester	EtOH	213s(4.08),256(4.22), 265s(4.10)	141-0001-73

Compound	Solvent	λ_{max}(log ε)	Ref.
Benzoic acid, 4-methoxy-, methyl ester (cont.)	dioxan	254(4.18),263s(3.98), 271s(3.68),281s(3.15)	141-0001-73
Ethanone, 1-(2-hydroxy-4-methoxyphenyl)-	EtOH	230(4.00),273(4.20), 314(3.90)	141-0001-73
Ethanone, 1-(2-hydroxy-5-methoxyphenyl)-	EtOH	227(4.60),255(3.95), 357(3.78)	141-0001-73
	dioxan	226(4.65),256(3.90), 360(3.70)	141-0001-73
Ethanone, 1-(2-hydroxy-6-methoxyphenyl)-	EtOH	207(4.09),217(4.09), 272(4.04),340(3.52)	141-0001-73
	EtOH-NaOH	227(4.00),275(3.74), 340(3.42)	141-0001-73
	dioxan	221(4.09),272(4.03), 335(3.54)	141-0001-73
Ethanone, 1-(3-hydroxy-4-methoxyphenyl)-	EtOH	231(4.60),274(4.20), 310(4.04)	141-0001-73
	dioxan	226(4.51),262(4.09), 298(3.77)	141-0001-73
Ethanone, 1-(4-hydroxy-2-methoxyphenyl)-	EtOH	229(4.20),276(4.03), 304(3.95)	141-0001-73
	EtOH-NaOH	250(3.96),348(4.38)	141-0001-73
Ethanone, 1-(4-hydroxy-3-methoxyphenyl)-	EtOH	207(4.10),230(4.18), 278(4.02),305(3.96)	141-0001-73
	EtOH-NaOH	250(3.96),295s(3.60), 348(4.39)	141-0001-73
	dioxan	228(4.20),271(4.09), 298(3.88)	141-0001-73
Ethanone, 1-(5-hydroxy-2-methoxyphenyl)-	EtOH	230(4.20),250(4.00), 340(3.85)	141-0001-73
$C_9H_{10}O_4$			
Benzaldehyde, 2-hydroxy-4,6-dimethoxy-	EtOH	212(4.22),224s(4.07), 294(4.32),335s(3.50)	141-0001-73
	EtOH-NaOH	219(4.29),235(4.25), 293(4.28),359(3.88)	141-0001-73
	dioxan	226(4.09),292(4.32), 331s(3.50)	141-0001-73
Benzaldehyde, 4-hydroxy-3,5-dimethoxy-	EtOH	217(4.24),232(4.20), 310(4.12),368s(2.90)	141-0001-73
	EtOH-NaOH	218(4.08),254(4.03), 294s(2.85),370(4.41)	141-0001-73
	dioxan	233(4.24),303(4.14)	141-0001-73
Benzoic acid, 3,6-dihydroxy-2,4-dimethyl-	MeOH	210(4.28),250(3.85), 300(3.54)	24-1182-73
Benzoic acid, 2,3-dimethoxy-	EtOH	212(4.26),235s(3.63), 294(3.32)	141-0001-73
	EtOH-NaOH	223(3.91),279(2.92)	141-0001-73
	dioxan	225(3.87),238s(3.60), 294(3.39)	141-0001-73
Benzoic acid, 2,4-dimethoxy-	EtOH	214(4.29),221s(4.24), 254(4.12),290(3.73)	141-0001-73
	EtOH-NaOH	245(3.94),282(3.56), 287s(3.55)	141-0001-73
	dioxan	221(4.20),253(4.13), 289(3.72)	141-0001-73
Benzoic acid, 2,5-dimethoxy-	EtOH	213(4.41),236(3.86), 331(3.66)	141-0001-73
	EtOH-NaOH	230s(3.91),320(3.67)	141-0001-73
	dioxan	221(4.18),238(3.85), 336(3.68)	141-0001-73

Compound	Solvent	$\lambda_{max}(\log \epsilon)$	Ref.
Benzoic acid, 2,6-dimethoxy-	EtOH	210(4.22),241s(3.38), 280(3.34)	141-0001-73
	EtOH-NaOH	227s(3.81),275s(3.15), 277(3.16)	141-0001-73
	dioxan	219(3.95),238s(3.42), 280(3.40)	141-0001-73
Benzoic acid, 3,4-dimethoxy-	EtOH	217(4.28),258(4.02), 290(3.71)	141-0001-73
	EtOH-NaOH	249(4.00),283(3.60), 287s(3.58)	141-0001-73
	dioxan	225(4.05),261(4.08), 290(3.79),293s(3.77)	141-0001-73
Benzoic acid, 3,5-dimethoxy-	EtOH	213(4.29),249(3.74), 301(3.45)	141-0001-73
	EtOH-NaOH	243(3.64),294(3.34)	141-0001-73
	dioxan	216(4.24),250(3.73), 304(3.47)	141-0001-73
Ethanone, 1-(2,4-dihydroxy-5-methoxyphenyl)-	EtOH	239(4.18),276(4.03), 350(3.86)	141-0001-73
Ethanone, 1-(2,4-dihydroxy-6-methoxyphenyl)-	EtOH	287(4.31)	141-0001-73
Ethanone, 1-(2,6-dihydroxy-4-methoxyphenyl)-	MeOH	226(4.27),248(4.33), 323(3.56)	83-0857-73
$C_9H_{10}O_4S$			
2H-Thiopyran-5-carboxylic acid, 4-hydroxy-6-methyl-2-oxo-, ethyl ester	MeOH	229(4.34),314(3.67)	7-0269-73
$C_9H_{10}O_5$			
Benzoic acid, 2,6-dihydroxy-4-methoxy-, methyl ester	EtOH	223(4.68),267(4.55), 305(3.80)	12-2459-73
	EtOH-KOH	213(4.80),235(4.65), 272(4.35),333(4.05)	12-2459-73
Benzoic acid, 3,4-dihydroxy-5-methoxy-, methyl ester	n.s.g.	219(4.45),276(4.08)	102-1427-73
Benzoic acid, 2-hydroxy-4,5-dimethoxy-	EtOH	222(4.30),256(4.03), 318(3.87)	141-0001-73
Benzoic acid, 2-hydroxy-4,6-dimethoxy-	EtOH	219(4.49),263(4.16), 295(3.52)	141-0001-73
	EtOH-NaOH	218(4.53),256(4.07), 292(3.46)	141-0001-73
	dioxan	224(4.20),264(4.21), 297(3.55)	141-0001-73
Benzoic acid, 4-hydroxy-3,5-dimethoxy-	EtOH	216(4.43),271(4.01)	141-0001-73
	EtOH-NaOH	223s(4.18),227(4.19), 301(4.21)	141-0001-73
	dioxan	226(4.21),275(4.09)	141-0001-73
4H-Pyran-4-one, 5-acetoxy-2-(methoxymethyl)-	EtOH	251(4.00)	23-0388-73
$C_9H_{10}O_5S$			
2,5-Thiophenedicarboxylic acid, 3-hydroxy-4-methyl-, dimethyl ester	EtOH	278(4.14)	2-0313-73
2,5-Thiophenedicarboxylic acid, 3-hydroxy-4-methyl-, 2-ethyl ester	EtOH	279(4.25)	2-0313-73
$C_9H_{10}O_5S_2$			
4H-Pyran, 4-(1,3-dithietan-2-ylidene)-2,6-dimethyl-, S,S,S',S'-tetraoxide	CH_2Cl_2	249(3.80),323s(4.24), 336(4.38),350(4.32)	83-0389-73

Compound	Solvent	λmax(log ε)	Ref.
$C_9H_{10}O_6$			
Carolinic acid, (RS)-	EtOH	235s(--),258(3.94)	78-4251-73
$C_9H_{10}S$			
Benzene, [2-(methylthio)ethenyl]-	HOAc	286(4.51)	78-3819-73
Benzene, (2-propenylthio)-	heptane	255(3.90)	110-1210-73
	HOAc	266(3.90)	78-3819-73
$C_9H_{10}SSe$			
Thiirane, [(phenylseleno)methyl]-	heptane	244(3.48),274(3.38)	110-1210-73
$C_9H_{10}S_2$			
Thiirane, [(phenylthio)methyl]-	heptane	253(3.82)	110-1210-73
$C_9H_{10}Se$			
Benzene, (2-propenylseleno)-	heptane	245(3.69),274(3.42)	110-1210-73
C_9H_{11}			
Cycloheptatrienylium, ethyl-	pH 1	292(3.69)	18-1785-73
Propylium, 2-phenyl- (at -75°)	FSO_3H	317(4.08),390s(3.3-)	59-0803-73
$C_9H_{11}BrN_2OS$			
Ethanone, 2-bromo-1-[4-methyl-2-(2-propenylamino)-5-thiazolyl]-	pH 1	303(4.13)	80-0677-73
	EtOH	262(3.47),345(3.80)	80-0677-73 +83-0152-73
$C_9H_{11}BrN_2O_2S$			
Acetone, (p-bromophenylsulfonyl)hydrazone	MeOH	235(4.15)	78-2645-73
$C_9H_{11}BrO_2$			
Phenol, 3-bromo-4-methoxy-2,6-dimethyl-	MeOH	210(4.20),225s(3.98), 292(3.61)	24-1198-73
$C_9H_{11}Br_3N_2OS$			
Ethanone, 2-bromo-1-[2-[(2,3-dibromopropyl)amino]-4-methyl-5-thiazolyl]-	pH 1	305(4.00)	80-0677-73
	EtOH	239(3.53),345(4.02)	80-0677-73 +83-0152-73
$C_9H_{11}Cl$			
Bicyclo[4.2.1]nona-2,4-diene, 3-chloro-	EtOH	204(3.37),223(3.39), 265(3.63)	33-1083-73
$C_9H_{11}ClN_2O_2$			
1H-Pyrrole-3-carboxaldehyde, 2-chloro-4-[(dimethylamino)methylene]-4,5-dihydro-1-methyl-5-oxo-	C_6H_{12}	300(4.1),410(3.9)	103-0467-73
	EtOH	232(3.9),294(4.4), 400(4.3)	103-0467-73
$C_9H_{11}ClN_2O_5$			
2,4(1H,3H)-Pyrimidinedione, 1-(3-chloro-3-deoxy-β-D-arabinosyl)-	MeOH	259(3.97)	117-0075-73
$C_9H_{11}ClN_4$			
9H-Purine, 8-tert-butyl-6-chloro-	pH 1	267(4.09)	39-1855-73C
	pH 11	263(4.07)	39-1855-73C
	MeOH	268(4.06)	39-1855-73C
$C_9H_{11}ClOS$			
4H-Cyclohepta[c]thiophene-4-ol, 1-chloro-5,6,7,8-tetrahydro-	EtOH	239(3.86)	22-0335-73

Compound	Solvent	λ max(log ε)	Ref.
$C_9H_{11}FN_2O_4$			
Uridine, 2',3'-dideoxy-3'-fluoro-	MeOH	260(3.92)	48-0895-73
$C_9H_{11}FN_2O_6$			
Uridine, 5-fluoro-	pH 7	269(3.95)	48-0149-73
$C_9H_{11}Li_2N_2O_8PS$			
2(1H)-Pyrimidinone, 3,4-dihydro-1-(3-O-phosphono-β-D-arabinofuranosyl)-4-thioxo-, dilithium salt	pH 1 and 7	330(4.25)	103-1056-73
	pH 13	316(4.26)	103-1056-73
$C_9H_{11}NO$			
Acetamide, N-methyl-N-phenyl-	C_6H_{12}	237.5(3.36)	95-1100-73
	EtOH	240(3.69)	95-1100-73
	EtOH-H_2SO_4	240(3.69)	95-1100-73
	95% H_2SO_4	238(3.76)	95-1100-73
Benzaldehyde, 4-(dimethylamino)-	CH_2Cl_2	338.5(4.52)	39-0514-73B
protonated	CH_2Cl_2	242(4.11),279(3.11), 290s(--)	39-0514-73B
diprotonated	CH_2Cl_2	279(3.94),325s(2.85)	39-0514-73B
at -75°	FSO_3H	284(4.15),320s(<3.3)	59-0807-73
BF_3 adduct (on nitrogen)	CH_2Cl_2	238(4.23),277(3.15), 287(3.08)	39-0514-73B
2H-1-Benzopyran-5-amine, 3,4-dihydro-	EtOH	285(3.24)	4-0623-73
2-Cyclohexene-1-acetonitrile, 1-methyl-4-oxo-	EtOH	223(4.00)	39-1989-73C
Methanimidic acid, N-phenyl-, ethyl ester	MeCN	246(3.81)	35-1253-73
1-Propanone, 1-(2-aminophenyl)-	EtOH	209s(4.06),227(4.43), 257(3.87),366(3.73)	78-1429-73
$C_9H_{11}NOS$			
Sulfilimine, N-acetyl-S-methyl-S-phenyl-	EtOH	217s(4.16)	44-4324-73
$C_9H_{11}NO_2$			
2H-Azepin-2-one, 4-acetyl-1,3-dihydro-1-methyl-	EtOH	220(4.19),322(3.79)	39-1079-73C
Benzeneacetic acid, 2-amino-, methyl ester, hydrochloride	EtOH	207(4.11),234(3.78), 290(3.11)	103-1152-73
Cyclohexanecarbonitrile, 4,4-dimethyl-2,6-dioxo-	EtOH	232(3.88),270(4.31)	70-0811-73
Ethanone, 1-(3-hydroxy-2,5-dimethyl-4-pyridinyl)-	pH 1	292(3.76)	70-1057-73
	pH 7	328(3.70)	70-1057-73
	pH 13	313(3.46)	70-1057-73
1,3-Oxazonine, 2-ethoxy-	MeOH	300(4.53)	89-0328-73
2-Propenoic acid, 2-methyl-3-(1H-pyrrol-2-yl)-, methyl ester, cis	EtOH	335(4.18)	39-1416-73C
trans	EtOH	325(4.41)	39-1416-73C
$C_9H_{11}NO_3$			
Benzaldehyde, 2,3-dimethoxy-, oxime	EtOH	222(4.43),260(4.11), 301(3.38)	141-0001-73
	dioxan	230(4.22),262(4.08), 300(3.34)	141-0001-73
Benzaldehyde, 3,4-dimethoxy-, oxime	EtOH	215(4.26),222s(4.21), 266(4.17),299(3.89), 310s(3.75)	141-0001-73
	dioxan	228(4.14),267(4.17), 291s(3.88),297s(3.89), 301(3.90),312s(3.71)	141-0001-73

Compound	Solvent	$\lambda_{max}(\log \epsilon)$	Ref.
Ethanone, 1-(4-hydroxy-3-methoxyphenyl)-, oxime	EtOH	216(4.26),263(4.11), 293(3.77)	141-0001-73
	EtOH-NaOH	219(4.21),233s(4.05), 294(4.17),312(4.19)	141-0001-73
	dioxan	222(4.10),263(4.12), 294(3.75)	141-0001-73
1-Propanone, 1-(2-hydroxyphenyl)-, oxime	EtOH	217(4.29),255(3.97), 263s(3.82),304(3.61)	141-0001-73
	EtOH-NaOH	231(4.25),279(3.97), 353(3.84)	141-0001-73
	dioxan	224(4.15),256(3.99), 263s(3.86),307(3.66)	141-0001-73
3-Pyridinecarboxylic acid, 1,2-dihydro-5,6-dimethyl-2-oxo-, methyl ester	EtOH	243(3.89),350(3.96)	70-2478-73
3-Pyridinecarboxylic acid, 1,2-dihydro-6-methyl-2-oxo-, ethyl ester	EtOH	241(3.91),338(4.01)	70-2478-73
3,4-Pyridinedimethanol, 6-ethenyl-5-hydroxy-, hydrochloride	pH 1	324(3.81)	87-1096-73
	pH 7	367(3.83)	87-1096-73
	pH 13	353(3.80)	87-1096-73
1H-Pyrrole-3-carboxylic acid, 4-(1-oxopropyl)-, methyl ester	EtOH	253(3.85)	23-1089-73
3H-Pyrrolizin-3-one, 2-acetyl-5,6,7,7a-tetrahydro-1-hydroxy-	EtOH	232s(3.74),253s(3.85), 279(4.04)	119-0132-73
	EtOH-HCl	226(3.83),279(4.03)	119-0132-73
	EtOH-NaOH	225s(3.81),247(4.07), 278(4.09)	119-0132-73
$C_9H_{11}NO_3S$			
1H-Pyrrole-3-carboxylic acid, 4-[(ethylthio)carbonyl]-, methyl ester	EtOH	255(3.98),272(3.89)	23-1089-73
$C_9H_{11}NO_4$			
2,5-Cyclohexadien-1-ol, 4-methyl-4-nitro-, acetate, cis	MeOH	198(2.97)	39-0237-73B
trans	MeOH	197(2.96)	39-0237-73B
2(1H)-Pyridinone, 4-hydroxy-3-(1-hydroxy-2-oxopropyl)-6-methyl-	EtOH	235(3.88),300(4.08)	107-0355-73
1H-Pyrrole-3,4-dicarboxylic acid, ethyl methyl ester	EtOH	252(3.93)	23-1089-73
$C_9H_{11}NO_6$			
2H-1,3-Oxazine-2,6(3H)-dione, 3-(2-deoxy-α-D-erythro-pentofuranosyl)-	EtOH	268(3.85)	88-3493-73
2H-1,3-Oxazine-2,6(3H)-dione, 3-(2-deoxy-β-D-erythro-pentofuranosyl)-	EtOH	269(3.85)	88-3493-73
$C_9H_{11}NS$			
Benzenecarbothioamide, N,N-dimethyl-	H_2O	271(3.81)	1-0209-73
	H_2SO_4	249(3.82)	1-0209-73
Benzenecarboximidothioic acid, N-methyl-, methyl ester	H_2O	226(4.32)	1-0209-73
protonated	H_2O	257(4.22)	1-0209-73
$C_9H_{11}NS_2$			
[1,2]Dithiolo[4,5,1-hi][1,2]benzisothiazole-8-S^{IV}, 2,4,5,7-tetrahydro-7-methyl-	C_6H_{12}	209s(4.17),229(4.29), 246s(4.18),274s(3.62), 438(3.99)	39-2351-73C
	MeOH	211(4.06),237(4.48), 270s(3.73),434(4.03)	39-2351-73C

Compound	Solvent	λ_{max}(log ϵ)	Ref.
$C_9H_{11}N_2$			
1H-Benzimidazolium, 1,3-dimethyl-, perchlorate	EtOH	270(4.03),277(3.97)	104-2622-73
$C_9H_{11}N_2O_7PS$			
Uridine, 4-thio-, cyclic 2',3'-(hydrogen phosphate)	pH 1	330(4.32)	103-0917-73
	pH 7	330(4.31)	103-0917-73
	pH 13	318(4.27)	103-0917-73
$C_9H_{11}N_3$			
Imidazo[1,2-a]pyridin-2-ethanamine, dihydrochloride	EtOH	275(3.85)	87-1272-73
Imidazo[1,5-a]pyridin-1-ethanamine, hydrochloride	H_2O	274(3.79),285(3.74), 331(3.43)	87-1272-73
Imidazo[1,5-a]pyridin-3-ethanamine, dihydrochloride	EtOH	272(3.88),282(3.85), 310(3.49)	87-1272-73
2H-Indazol-2-amine, N,N-dimethyl-	EtOH	275(4.02)	118-0363-73
Propanedinitrile, (1-methyl-2-piperidinylidene)-	EtOH	286(4.27)	103-0880-73
$C_9H_{11}N_3O$			
Imidazo[1,5-a]pyridine-1-methanol, α-(aminomethyl)-, dihydrochloride	EtOH	273(3.81),284(3.77), 328(3.47)	87-1272-73
$C_9H_{11}N_3OS$			
Acetophenone, p-hydroxy-, thiosemicarbazone	$CHCl_3$	315(4.24)	7-0363-73
	10% isoPrOH-pH 7.0	306(4.45)	7-0363-73
$C_9H_{11}N_3OS_2$			
4H-Thiazolo[3,2-a]-1,3,5-triazin-4-one, 2-(butylthio)-	EtOH	226(4.02),246(3.88), 270(3.95),311(4.34), 318(4.34)	94-0074-73
4H-Thiazolo[3,2-a]-1,3,5-triazin-4-one, 2-[(2-methylpropyl)thio]-	EtOH	226(4.00),246(3.85), 270(3.93),311(4.32), 317(4.32)	94-0074-73
4H-Thiazolo[3,2-a]-1,3,5-triazin-4-one, 2-(methylthio)-7-propyl-	EtOH	246(3.73),268(3.92), 313(4.32),322s(--)	94-0074-73
$C_9H_{11}N_3O_2$			
4-Quinazolinecarboxylic acid, 2-amino-5,6,7,8-tetrahydro-	pH -2.0	226(4.10),330(4.40)	39-2814-73C
	pH 2	223(4.24),315(3.75)	39-2814-73C
	pH 7	226(4.04),300(3.63)	39-2814-73C
	MeOH	227(3.81),305(3.35)	39-2814-73C
$C_9H_{11}N_3O_2S_2$			
Carbamic acid, (5-ethyl-2H-thiazolo[3,2-b][1,2,4]thiadiazol-2-ylidene)-, ethyl ester	EtOH	251(3.52),312(4.36)	94-2408-73
Carbamic acid, 2H-thiazolo[3,2-b]-[1,2,4]thiadiazol-2-ylidene-, butyl ester	EtOH	252(3.46),308(4.36)	94-2408-73
Carbamic acid, 2H-thiazolo[3,2-b]-[1,2,4]thiadiazol-2-ylidene-, 2-methylpropyl ester	EtOH	251(3.46),308(4.35)	94-2408-73
$C_9H_{11}N_3O_4$			
2,2'-Anhydro-1-β-D-ribofuranosylcytosine, acetate	H_2O	232(3.99),261(4.03)	44-0593-73
HF salt	H_2O	232(3.99),262(4.03)	44-0593-73

Compound	Solvent	$\lambda_{max}(\log \epsilon)$	Ref.
$C_9H_{11}N_3O_6S$			
4(1H)-Pyrimidinone, 1-(2-deoxy-α-D-erythro-pentofuranosyl)-2,3-dihydro-5-nitro-2-thioxo-	MeOH	216(4.2),248s(3.8), 269(4.0),343(4.2)	24-3039-73
$C_9H_{11}N_3S$			
Acetophenone, thiosemicarbazone	EtOH	302(4.37)	7-0363-73
	isoPrOH	295(4.36)	7-0363-73
	$CHCl_3$	310(4.48)	7-0363-73
in 10% isopropanol	pH 9.1	296(4.35)	7-0363-73
in 10% isopropanol	pH 13.5	316(4.17)	7-0363-73
$C_9H_{11}N_5O$			
4(1H)-Pteridinone, 2-amino-1,6,7-trimethyl-	pH 0.0	216(4.30),253(3.97), 320(4.02)	24-3175-73
	pH 5.0	241(4.26),328(4.06)	24-3175-73
$C_9H_{11}N_5O_2$			
4(1H)-Pteridinone, 2-amino-6-propyl-, 8-oxide	pH 13	217(4.01),248(3.90), 276(4.31),300s(3.99), 382(3.70)	35-6407-73
4(1H)-Pteridinone, 2-amino-1,6,7-trimethyl-, 5-oxide	pH 0.0	242(4.30),290(3.77), 337(3.80)	24-3175-73
	pH 5.0	242(4.38),291(3.90), 341(3.90)	24-3175-73
1H-Purine-8-butanoic acid, 6-amino-	pH 1	266.5(4.15)	35-4010-73
	H O	262.5(4.15)	35-4010-73
	pH 13	270.5(4.13)	35-4010-73
9H-Purine-9-butanoic acid, 6-amino-	pH 1	258.5(4.14)	35-4010-73
	H_2O	261.5(4.14)	35-4010-73
	pH 13	261(4.15)	35-4010-73
Pyrimido[5,4-e]-1,2,4-triazine, 3,5-diethoxy-	C_6H_{12}	213(4.14),237(4.19), 264s(3.51),281s(2.93), 322s(3.45),329s(3.57), 337(3.71),345(3.76), 352(3.84),361(3.70), 368(3.71),482(2.45), 512s(2.26),522s(2.11)	12-1689-73
Pyrimido[5,4-e]-1,2,4-triazine, 3-ethoxy-5-methoxy-7-methyl-	C_6H_{12}	216(4.11),237(4.19), 262s(3.60),280s(2.84), 341s(3.62),349s(3.68), 356(3.74),366s(3.62), 373(3.60),480(2.40), 502s(2.29),522s(2.06)	12-1689-73
$C_9H_{11}N_5O_3$			
4(1H)-Pteridinone, 2-amino-7,8-dihydro-6-(1,3-dihydroxypropyl)-	pH 1	246(3.05),324(3.93)	18-0939-73
	H_2O	236(4.12),275(4.17), 348(3.83)	18-0939-73
	pH 13	255(4.36),368(3.89)	18-0939-73
4(1H)-Pteridinone, 2-amino-7,8-dihydro-6-(3-hydroxy-1-oxopropyl)-	pH 1	282(4.07),408(3.90)	18-0939-73
	H_2O	267(4.26),417(4.02)	18-0939-73
	pH 13	269(4.24),440(4.09)	18-0939-73
Pyrimido[5,4-e]-1,2,4-triazine, 3-ethoxy-5,7-dimethoxy-	C_6H_{12}	210s(4.04),233(4.31), 260s(3.61),276s(3.03), 352s(3.61),362s(3.71), 370(3.79),381(3.69), 389(3.72),474(2.47), 502s(2.32),516s(2.21)	12-1689-73

Compound	Solvent	$\lambda_{max}(\log \epsilon)$	Ref.
$C_9H_{11}N_5O_4$			
4(1H)-Pteridinone, 2-amino-6-(2,3-dihydroxy-1-oxopropyl)-7,8-dihydro-	pH 1	273(4.11),416(3.92)	18-0939-73
	H_2O	268(4.25),424(4.01)	18-0939-73
	pH 13	270(4.24),446(4.11)	18-0939-73
$C_9H_{11}N_5O_5S$			
6-Pteridinepropanesulfonic acid, 2-amino-1,4,7,8-tetrahydro-γ,4-dioxo-	pH 1	248(3.24),406(4.15)	18-0939-73
	H_2O	267(4.25),418(4.05)	18-0939-73
	pH 13	268(3.24),438(4.15)	18-0939-73
$C_9H_{11}N_7O_2$			
2-Propenoic acid, 3-[5-[(aminoiminomethyl)amino]-1H-1,2,3-triazol-4-yl]-2-cyano-, ethyl ester	MeOH	219(4.22),237s(3.61), 313(3.74)	39-1620-73C
	MeOH-HCl	234(3.97)	39-1620-73C
C_9H_{12}			
Benzene, 1,2,4-trimethyl-	C_6H_{12}	220(3.88),266(2.88)	49-0644-73
Bicyclo[4.2.1]nona-2,4-diene	EtOH	204(3.18),259(3.72)	33-1083-73
Bicyclo[5.1.0]oct-2-ene, 4-methylene-, cis	isooctane	237(4.23)	44-3250-73
2,3-Heptadien-5-yne, 2,4-dimethyl-	EtOH	218(3.87)	35-3324-73
2,4-Heptadiyne, 6,6-dimethyl-	EtOH	213(2.45),223(2.54), 237(2.50),250(2.23)	35-3324-73
1H-Indene, 4,5,6,7-tetrahydro-	n.s.g.	255.5(3.44)	88-4591-73
Spiro[4.4]nona-1,3-diene	EtOH	254(3.35)	35-7325-73
	EtOH	254(3.44)	89-0577-73
Trispiro[2.0.2.0.2.0]nonane	C_6H_{12}	205s(1.48),213(1.53), 262(0.30)	89-0334-73
$C_9H_{12}BrNO_2$			
1,3-Propanediol, 2-amino-1-(4-bromophenyl)-	EtOH	223(4.17),260(2.65), 266(2.64),276(2.45)	104-2144-73
$C_9H_{12}BrNS$			
Thiazolo[3,2-a]pyridinium, 2,3-dihydro-2,3-dimethyl-, bromide	pH 1	210(4.13),252(3.88), 327(3.99)	1-1749-73
	pH 13	225s(--),252(3.88), 327(3.88)	1-1749-73
$C_9H_{12}BrN_3O_2S_2$			
Carbamic acid, [[(5-bromo-3-methyl-2(3H)-thiazolylidene)amino](methylthio)methylene]-, ethyl ester	dioxan	282(3.88),338(4.38)	94-0074-73
$C_9H_{12}Br_2N_2OS$			
Ethanone, 1-[2-[(2,3-dibromopropyl)-amino]-4-methyl-5-thiazolyl]-	pH 1	242(2.95),297(4.15)	80-0677-73
	EtOH	231(3.52),332(4.15)	80-0677-73 +83-0152-73
$C_9H_{12}ClNO$			
4H-1,3-Oxazine, 2-(chloroethynyl)-5,6-dihydro-4,4,6-trimethyl-	EtOH	222(4.00)	18-0540-73
$C_9H_{12}ClNO_2$			
1,3-Propanediol, 2-amino-1-(4-chlorophenyl)-	EtOH	222(4.16),260(2.64), 267(2.66),276(2.5)	104-2144-73
$C_9H_{12}ClNO_3$			
2(5H)-Furanone, 3-chloro-4-pyrrolidino-	MeOH	288(4.36)	73-1091-73

Compound	Solvent	$\lambda_{max}(\log \epsilon)$	Ref.
$C_9H_{12}CrINO_5$			
Tetramethylammonium (pentacarbonyl-chromium iodide)	CH_2Cl_2	258(4.20),430(3.26)	101-0077-73N
$C_9H_{12}FN_3O_3$			
Cytidine, 2',3'-dideoxy-3'-fluoro-	MeOH	233s(--),273(3.93)	48-0895-73
$C_9H_{12}FN_3O_4$			
Cytidine, 2'-deoxy-2'-fluoro-	pH 1	212(4.00),278(4.11)	44-0593-73
	pH 12	230(3.92),272(3.96)	44-0593-73
$C_9H_{12}F_3NO_4$			
Acetamide, 2,2,2-trifluoro-N-(tetra-hydro-2,2-dimethylfuro[2,3-d]-1,3-dioxol-6-yl)-	EtOH	206(3.47)	33-2689-73
$C_9H_{12}LiN$			
Lithium, [2-[(dimethylamino)methyl]-phenyl]-	DMSO	264(2.70),306(2.30)	101-0001-73H
$C_9H_{12}NOS$			
Thiazolo[3,2-a]pyridinium, 3-ethoxy-2,3-dihydro-, perchlorate	EtOH	245(3.91),314(3.84)	103-1138-73
$C_9H_{12}N_2O$			
2H-1-Benzopyran-6,8-diamine, 3,4-di-hydro-	EtOH	240(3.90),305(3.56)	4-0623-73
1-Cyclohexene-1-carbonitrile, 2-amino-4,4-dimethyl-6-oxo-	EtOH	226(3.82),276(4.34)	70-0811-73
4-Pyrazolidinol, 1-phenyl-	n.s.g.	242(4.00),285(3.83)	22-3159-73
$C_9H_{12}N_2OS$			
Ethanone, 1-[4-methyl-2-(2-propenyl-amino)-5-thiazolyl]-	pH 1	248(3.60),300(4.12)	80-0677-73
	EtOH	226(4.07),330(4.36)	80-0677-73
$C_9H_{12}N_2O_2$			
Carbamic acid, (4-cyano-1,3-pentadien-yl)-, ethyl ester, (Z,Z)-	$CHCl_3$	297(4.38)	22-0635-73
Carbamic acid, (3-methyl-2-pyridinyl)-, ethyl ester	EtOH	221(3.87),270(3.65)	22-0635-73
Carbamic acid, (5-methyl-2-pyridinyl)-, ethyl ester	EtOH	250(4.33),290(3.97)	22-0635-73
2,3-Diazabicyclo[3.2.0]hepta-3,6-diene-2-carboxylic acid, 5-methyl-, ethyl ester	EtOH	252(3.69),294(3.29)	22-0630-73
1H-1,2-Diazepine-1-carboxylic acid, 4-methyl-, ethyl ester	benzene	358(2.48)	22-0630-73
	MeOH	224(3.93),240s(3.78), 350s(2.42)	22-0630-73
1H-1,2-Diazepine-1-carboxylic acid, 6-methyl-, ethyl ester	benzene	365(2.32)	22-0630-73
	MeOH	224(3.90),250s(3.53), 330s(2.38)	22-0630-73
Ethanone, 1-(3-hydroxy-2,5-dimethyl-4-pyridinyl)-, oxime	pH 13	309(3.78)	70-1057-73
Isoxazole, 4,5-dihydro-3-methyl-5-[(3-methyl-5-isoxazolyl)methyl]-	n.s.g.	214.5(3.97)	32-0037-73
2,4-Pentadienoic acid, 2-cyano-5-(di-methylamino)-	EtOH	223(4.00),386(4.78)	70-1959-73
2,5-Piperazinedione, 1-acetyl-3-propyli-dene-	EtOH	222(4.16)	88-1135-73
1-Propanone, 3-(hydroxyamino)-1-phenyl-, oxime, hydrochloride	EtOH	245(4.07)	104-0793-73

Compound	Solvent	λ_{max}(log ε)	Ref.
3-Pyridinecarboxamide, 1,4,5,6-tetrahydro-1-methyl-, product with ethyl bromoacetate	H_2O or MeOH	226(3.82),341(4.73)	33-0374-73
	pH 1	318.5(4.58)	33-0374-73
Pyridinium, 1-[(ethoxycarbonyl)amino]-3-methyl-, hydroxide, inner salt	benzene	344(3.96)	22-0630-73
$C_9H_{12}N_2O_3$			
2,3-Diazabicyclo[3.2.0]hepta-3,6-diene-2-carboxylic acid, 5-methoxy-, ethyl ester	EtOH	255(3.65),300s(1.65)	22-0630-73
6H-Isoxazolo[3,4-d]azepin-3-one, 6-acetyl-1,3,4,5,7,8-hexahydro-	EtOH	263(3.93)	1-3251-73
Pyridinium, 1-[(ethoxycarbonyl)amino]-3-methoxy-, hydroxide, inner salt	benzene	344(4.00)	22-0630-73
$C_9H_{12}N_2O_3S$			
Cysteine, S-(3-hydroxy-6-methyl-2-pyridinyl)-	M HCl	237(3.59),318(3.97)	1-1059-73
	pH 1	237(3.59),318(3.97)	1-1390-73
	pH 13	248(3.90),326(4.00)	1-1390-73
5-Pyrimidineacetic acid, 1,6-dihydro-2-(methylthio)-6-oxo-, ethyl ester	MeOH	231(3.9),289(4.0)	24-3039-73
	MeOH-NaOH	246(4.0),281(3.9)	24-3039-73
$C_9H_{12}N_2O_4$			
4(1H)-Pyridazinone, 1-(2-deoxy-α-D-erythro-pentofuranosyl)-	n.s.g.	271(4.52)	106-0103-73
4(1H)-Pyridazinone, 1-(2-deoxy-β-D-erythro-pentofuranosyl)-	n.s.g.	271(4.54)	106-0103-73
Uracil, 5-(tetrahydropyran-2-yl)oxy-	pH 6.5	272(3.75)	39-1089-73C
	pH 9.80	275(3.62)	39-1089-73C
	pH 12.0	295(3.59)	39-1089-73C
$C_9H_{12}N_2O_4S$			
2(1H)-Pyrimidinethione, 1-β-D-ribofuranosyl-	pH 6	283(4.11),345(3.11)	73-1381-73
1H-Pyrrole-3-carboxylic acid, 2,3-dihydro-5-(methoxyimino)-1-methyl-4-(methylthio)-2-oxo-, methyl ester	EtOH	340(4.07)	94-1667-73
$C_9H_{12}N_2O_5$			
2(1H)-Pyrazinone, 1-(2-deoxy-α-D-erythro-pentofuranosyl)-, 4-oxide	EtOH	223(4.30),283(3.96), 335(3.67)	87-0183-73
2(1H)-Pyrazinone, 1-(2-deoxy-β-D-erythro-pentofuranosyl)-, 4-oxide	EtOH	223(4.34),283(3.97), 335(3.68)	87-0183-73
$C_9H_{12}N_2O_5S$			
2(1H)-Pyrimidinone, 1- -D-arabinofuranosyl-3,4-dihydro-4-thioxo-	pH 1	331(4.29)	103-1056-73
	pH 7	331(4.31)	103-1056-73
	pH 13	311(4.27)	103-1056-73
Uridine, 2-thio-	H_2O	218(4.2),275(4.1)	24-3039-73
	pH 12	239(4.3),271(4.1)	24-3039-73
Uridine, 4-thio-	pH 7	331(4.35)	103-0917-73
$C_9H_{12}N_2O_6$			
2,4(1H,3H)-Pyrimidinedione, 1-β-D-arabinofuranosyl-	pH 2	263(4.02)	44-0593-73
	pH 11	262.5(3.90)	44-0593-73
2(1H)-Pyrimidinone, 5-hydroxy-1-β-D-ribofuranosyl-	pH 2 and 6	272(3.65),326(3.72)	73-1381-73
Uridine	pH 2	262(4.00)	69-0194-73
	pH 12	262(3.86)	69-0194-73

Compound	Solvent	$\lambda_{max}(\log \epsilon)$	Ref.
$C_9H_{12}N_2S_2$			
Benzo[b]thiophene-3-carbothioamide, 2-amino-4,5,6,7-tetrahydro-	MeOH	254(4.16),293s(3.92), 373(3.74)	48-0539-73
$C_9H_{12}N_4$			
1H-Tetrazole, 4,5-dihydro-1,4-dimethyl-5-phenyl-	EtOH	281(3.06)	18-1250-73
1H-Tetrazole, 4,5-dihydro-1,5-dimethyl-4-phenyl-	EtOH	222(3.47),304(3.59)	18-1250-73
$C_9H_{12}N_4OS_2$			
6H-Purin-6-one, 1,9-dihydro-1,9-dimethyl-2,8-bis(methylthio)-	pH 1.0	283(4.42)	44-3367-73
	pH 6.0	279(4.32)	44-3367-73
	neutral	280(4.32)	39-2647-73C
6H-Purin-6-one, 3,7-dihydro-3,7-dimethyl-2,8-bis(methylthio)-	cation	310(4.18)	39-2647-73C
	pH 6.0	297.5(4.30)	44-3367-73
	neutral	297.5(4.30)	39-2647-73C
6H-Purin-6-one, 1,2,3,7-tetrahydro-1,3,7-trimethyl-8-(methylthio)-2-thioxo-	MeOH	241(4.08),301(4.26)	39-2647-73C
$C_9H_{12}N_4O_2$			
6H-Pyrimido[5,4-b][1,4]oxazin-7(8H)-one, 2-amino-8-ethyl-4-methyl-	EtOH	324(3.87)	95-0817-73
$C_9H_{12}N_4O_2S$			
1,2-Propanediol, 3-[6-(methylthio)-3H-purin-3-yl]-	H_2O	224(4.03),295(4.15), 302(4.11)	126-0019-73J
1,2-Propanediol, 3-[6-(methylthio)-9H-purin-9-yl]-	H_2O	211(3.99),287(4.15), 292(4.14)	126-0019-73J
$C_9H_{12}N_4O_3$			
Glycine, N-[N-(6-methyl-4-pyrimidinyl)-glycyl]-	pH 1	259(4.26)	94-2349-73
	pH 7	242(4.14),263s(3.76)	94-2349-73
	pH 12	241(4.16),265s(3.63)	94-2349-73
$C_9H_{12}N_4O_6$			
1H-Imidazole-5-carboxamide, 1-(2-deoxy-α-D-erythro-pentofuranosyl)-4-nitro-	pH 7	298(3.70)	5-1286-73
$C_9H_{12}N_4O_7$			
1H-Imidazole-4-carboxamide, 1-α-D-arabinofuranosyl-5-nitro-	pH 7	304(3.88)	5-1286-73
L-isomer	pH 7	305(3.64)	5-1286-73
1H-Imidazole-4-carboxamide, 5-nitro-1-β-D-ribofuranosyl-	pH 7	304(3.52)	5-1286-73
1H-Imidazole-4-carboxamide, 5-nitro-1-β-D-ribopyranosyl-	pH 7	296.5(3.57)	5-1286-73
1H-Imidazole-4-carboxamide, 5-nitro-1-β-D-xylofuranosyl-	pH 7	305(3.65)	5-1286-73
1H-Imidazole-4-carboxamide, 5-nitro-1-β-D-xylopyranosyl-	pH 7	297.5(3.54)	5-1286-73
1H-Imidazole-5-carboxamide, 1-α-D-arabinopyranosyl-4-nitro-	pH 7	294.5(3.65)	5-1286-73
L-isomer	pH 7	293.3(3.69)	5-1286-73
1H-Imidazole-5-carboxamide, 4-nitro-1-β-D-ribofuranosyl-	pH 7	295(3.56)	5-1286-73
1H-Imidazole-5-carboxamide, 4-nitro-1-β-D-ribopyranosyl-	pH 7	292.5(3.60)	5-1286-73
1H-Imidazole-5-carboxamide, 4-nitro-1-β-D-xylofuranosyl-	pH 7	299.3(3.63)	5-1286-73

Compound	Solvent	$\lambda_{max}(\log \epsilon)$	Ref.
1H-Imidazole-5-carboxamide, 4-nitro-1-β-D-xylopyranosyl-	pH 7	292.2(3.52)	5-1286-73
$C_9H_{12}N_5O_2$			
1H-Purinium, 2-amino-6,9-dihydro-9-methyl-6-oxo-7-(2-oxopropyl)-, bromide	pH 4	253(4.05),280(3.87)	24-1389-73
	pH 11	220(4.29),250(3.74), 286(3.88)	24-1389-73
$C_9H_{12}N_5O_7P$			
D-Neopterin 3'-phosphate	pH 1	251(4.1),320(4.0)	33-1819-73
	pH 6.8	238(4.1),275(4.2), 345(3.8)	33-1819-73
	pH 13	255(4.4),362(3.9)	33-1819-73
$C_9H_{12}N_5O_8P$			
5'-Uridylic acid, 2'-azido-2'-deoxy-, barium salt	pH 7.6	262(4.00)	69-3962-73
$C_9H_{12}N_6$			
2,4-Pteridinediamine, 6-propyl-	pH 1	243(4.22),278(3.75), 338(4.02),351(3.97)	35-6413-73
$C_9H_{12}N_6O$			
Acetamide, N-[2-(dimethylamino)-1H-purin-6-yl]-	pH 1	239(4.30),334(3.72)	69-4790-73
	pH 7	222(4.39),237(4.40), 336(3.66)	69-4790-73
	pH 13	232(4.46),324(3.72)	69-4790-73
2,4-Pteridinediamine, 6-isopropyl-, 8-oxide	pH 1	251(4.44),282(3.92), 357(3.89),370(3.84)	35-6413-73
2,4-Pteridinediamine, 6-propyl-, 8-oxide	0.12N HCl	251(4.40),282(3.89), 369(3.79)	35-6413-73
7(8H)-Pteridinone, 2-amino-4-(dimethylamino)-8-methyl-	pH 1.0	223(4.50),308(4.21), 344(4.25)	24-0317-73
	pH 5.0	208(4.54),235s(4.01), 274(4.22),364(4.17)	24-0317-73
	MeOH	214(4.54),235s(4.01), 279(4.23),362(4.18)	24-0317-73
Pyrimido[5,4-e]-1,2,4-triazin-5-amine, 3-ethoxy-N,7-dimethyl-	MeOH	227s(4.06),267(4.04), 402(3.78)	12-1689-73
Urea, 1-isopropyl-3-(1H-purin-6-yl)-	pH 1-2	278(4.29)	87-0139-73
	pH 5-7	269(4.23)	87-0139-73
	pH 12	277(4.19)	87-0139-73
Urea, 1-propyl-3-(1H-purin-6-yl)-	pH 1-2	278(4.32)	87-0139-73
	pH 5-7	269(4.27)	87-0139-73
	pH 12	278(4.23)	87-0139-73
$C_9H_{12}N_6O_2$			
3-Furanol, 4-amino-2-(6-amino-9H-purin-9-yl)tetrahydro-	H_2O	260(4.10)	33-2689-73
Urea, N-(2-hydroxypropyl)-N'-1H-purin-6-yl-	pH 1-2	277(4.33)	87-0139-73
	pH 5-7	269(4.27)	87-0139-73
	pH 12	277.5(4.23)	87-0139-73
Urea, N-(3-hydroxypropyl)-N'-1H-purin-6-yl-	pH 1-2	277.5(4.32)	87-0139-73
	pH 5-7	269.5(4.25)	87-0139-73
	pH 12	277.5(4.23)	87-0139-73
$C_9H_{12}O$			
Bicyclo[3.2.0]hept-3-en-2-one, 3,4-dimethyl-	EtOH	243(4.07),311(2.13)	35-4346-73
Bicyclo[3.1.0]hex-3-en-2-one, 4,6,6-trimethyl-	EtOH	228(3.68),253(3.58), 315(2.38)	35-5086-73

Compound	Solvent	λ_{max}(log ε)	Ref.
Bicyclo[3.3.0]oct-1(5)-en-2-one, 7-methyl-	EtOH	238(4.04)	39-2454-73C
1,3,5-Cycloheptatriene, 1-ethoxy-	EtOH	207(4.23),290(3.61)	39-2202-73C
2,5-Cyclohexadien-1-one, 2,4,4-tri-	isooctane	229.5(4.094)	39-0529-73C
methyl-	H_2O	242(4.19)	39-0529-73C
2,5-Cyclohexadien-1-one, 3,4,4-tri-	hexane	227(4.151)	39-0084-73B
methyl-	isooctane	227(4.151)	39-0529-73C
	H_2O	241(4.172)	39-0084-73B
cation	78% H_2SO_4	260(4.17),305(3.78)	39-0084-73B
2-Cyclopenten-1-one, 2-methyl-5-(1-methylethylidene)-	EtOH	257(4.13)	22-1454-73
1-Indanone, 3a,4,5,7a-tetrahydro-, cis	C_6H_{12}	260(3.70)	44-3257-73
1-Indanone, 4,5,6,7-tetrahydro-	EtOH	237(4.09)	88-2375-73
Phenol, 2,4,6-trimethyl-	dioxan	282(3.36)	126-0039-73L
Tricyclo[4.3.0.0^{3,8}]nonan-2-one, (-)-	MeOH	289(1.63)	18-0888-73
$C_9H_{12}O_2$			
Benzenemethanol, 2-hydroxy-3,5-dimethyl-	dioxan	281(3.40)	126-0039-73L
2H-1-Benzopyran-2-one, 3,4,5,6,7,8-hexahydro-	EtOH	274(4.00)	22-1409-73
1,3-Cyclohexadiene-1-carboxylic acid, 5-methyl-, methyl ester	ether	288(3.97)	24-3779-73
1,3-Cyclohexadiene-1-carboxylic acid, 6-methyl-, methyl ester	ether	289(3.96)	24-3779-73
2,5-Cyclohexadien-1-one, 2-methoxy-4,4-dimethyl-	EtOH	238(3.96),283(3.49)	44-4068-73
2-Cyclohexene-1,4-dione, 2,5,5-trimethyl-	EtOH	242(4.18)	44-4068-73
2H-Pyran-2-one, 3,4,5,6-tetramethyl-	96% H_2SO_4	226(3.56),306(4.27)	35-7914-73
$C_9H_{12}O_3$			
Benzene, 1,2,3-trimethoxy-	EtOH	210(4.22),223s(3.91), 268(2.95),276s(2.82)	141-0001-73
	dioxan	225s(3.87),268(2.93), 277s(2.78)	141-0001-73
Benzene, 1,2,4-trimethoxy-	EtOH	226(3.85),287(3.56)	141-0001-73
	dioxan	227s(3.85),231(3.86), 288(3.58)	141-0001-73
Benzene, 1,3,5-trimethoxy-	EtOH	211(4.26),225s(3.90), 266(2.79)	141-0001-73
	dioxan	225s(3.96),267(2.80)	141-0001-73
1,2-Benzenedimethanol, 3-hydroxy-	H_2O	281(3.45)	70-1271-73
4-methyl-	pH 13	241(3.87),301(3.75)	70-1271-73
1,2-Benzenedimethanol, 4-hydroxy-	H_2O	280(3.43)	70-1271-73
5-methyl-	pH 13	241(3.85),300(3.72)	70-1271-73
1,3,5-Cycloheptatrien-1-ol, 7,7-dimethoxy-, K salt	n.s.g.	367(3.8)	77-0523-73
1-Cyclohexene-1-carboxylic acid, 2-hy-	EtOH	270(3.78)	107-0129-73
droxy-3-methylene-, methyl ester	EtOH-NaOH	325(3.48)	107-0129-73
2,4-Pentadienoic acid, 2-acetyl-, ethyl ester	EtOH	262(3.94)	70-2301-73
4H-Pyran-4-one, 2-ethoxy-3,6-dimethyl-	EtOH	259(3.98)	94-1047-73
$C_9H_{12}O_4$			
D-erythro-Hex-1-en-3-ulose, 1,5-anhydro-2-deoxy-4,6-O-isopropylidene-	EtOH	260(3.91)	23-3950-73
Oxireno[4,5]cyclopenta[1,2-c]pyran-2,6-diol, 1a,1b,2,5a,6,6a-hexahydro-5-methyl- (mentzelol)	n.s.g.	203(3.56)	23-0760-73
2H-Pyran-2-one, 5,6-dihydro-3-hydroxy-4-(1-oxobutyl)-	EtOH	284(3.86)	95-1183-73

Compound	Solvent	λ max (log ε)	Ref.
$C_9H_{12}S$			
Benzene, 1-(ethylthio)-2-methyl-	C_6H_{12}	209f(4.19),254(3.82), 281(3.11)	39-1125-73B
	EtOH	209(4.20),251(3.91), 279(3.11)	39-1125-73B
	5% EtOH	205(4.30),247(3.90), 275(3.15)	39-1125-73B
Benzene, 1-(ethylthio)-3-methyl-	C_6H_{12}	210s(4.12),259(3.86), 284s(3.04)	39-1125-73B
	EtOH	210(4.20),259(3.90)	39-1125-73B
	5% EtOH	208(4.23),253(3.85)	39-1125-73B
Benzene, 1-(ethylthio)-4-methyl-	C_6H_{12}	210(4.11),259(3.84), 290s(2.86)	39-1125-73B
	EtOH	207(4.11),257(3.97)	39-1125-73B
	5% EtOH	205(4.15),253(3.91)	39-1125-73B
Benzene, [(1-methylethyl)thio]-	C_6H_{12}	205(4.32),258(3.78), 282s(3.11)	39-1125-73B
	EtOH	204(4.04),257(3.75)	39-1125-73B
	5% EtOH	202(4.18),252(3.77)	39-1125-73B
Benzenethiol, 2,4,6-trimethyl-	C_6H_{12}	209(4.47),240(3.89), 280s(2.86)	39-1125-73B
	EtOH	209(4.45),239(3.84), 279s(2.96)	39-1125-73B
	EtOH-base	215(4.42),267(4.06)	39-1125-73B
	5% EtOH	208(4.47),240(3.92), 270s(3.04)	39-1125-73B
	+ base	214(4.33),261(4.14)	39-1125-73B
$C_9H_{13}As$			
Arsenin, 4-(1,1-dimethylethyl)-	EtOH	221(4.19),275(4.18)	89-0931-73
$C_9H_{13}BO_6$			
Boron, bis(acetato-O)(2,4-pentanedion-ato-O,O')-, (T-4)-	CH_2Cl_2	295(4.25)	39-1796-73B
$C_9H_{13}BO_7$			
Boron, bis(acetato-O)(methyl 3-oxobut-anoato-$O^{1'}$,O^3)-, (T-4)-	CH_2Cl_2	270(4.47)	39-1796-73B
$C_9H_{13}DO_2$			
Acetic-2-d acid, cyclohexylidene-, methyl ester	EtOH	221(4.12)	22-2071-73
$C_9H_{13}IN_4OS$			
1H-Purinium, 6,7-dihydro-1,7,9-trimeth-yl-2-(methylthio)-, iodide	MeOH	275(4.20)	39-2647-73C
$C_9H_{13}N$			
2H-Pyrrole, 2,5-dimethyl-2-(2-propenyl)-	MeOH	207(3.57)	35-4356-73
$C_9H_{13}NO$			
1-Azatricyclo[3.3.1.$1^{3,7}$]decan-4-one	hexane	243(3.13),290s(1.52)	78-1691-73
2H-Azepin-2-one, 1,3-dihydro-1,4,6-tri-methyl-	EtOH	256(3.71)	39-1079-73C
Benzenemethanamine, 4-methoxy-α-methyl-, (-)-	EtOH	206(3.77),229(3.99), 280(3.18),286s(3.11)	33-1266-73
2-Cyclopenten-1-one, 2-(1-pyrrolidinyl)-	EtOH	316(3.53)	44-0551-73
Ethanone, 1-(2,4,5-trimethyl-1H-pyrrol-3-yl)-	H_2O	255(4.00),300(3.61)	103-1355-73
	23N H_2SO_4	278(4.27),360(3.47)	103-1355-73
Ethanone, 1-(3,4,5-trimethyl-1H-pyrrol-2-yl)-	H_2O	265(3.67),316(4.27)	103-1355-73
	26N H_2SO_4	302(4.14),330(4.03)	103-1355-73

Compound	Solvent	$\lambda_{max}(\log \epsilon)$	Ref.
Norephedrine, (-)-	pH 13	258(2.26)	133-0389-73
	MeOH	258(2.32)	133-0389-73
	dioxan	258(2.32)	133-0389-73
	CCl_4	259(2.51)	133-0389-73
	$CHCl_3$	259(2.36)	133-0389-73
Norpseudoephedrine, (+)-	pH 13	258(2.26)	133-0389-73
	MeOH	258(2.28)	133-0389-73
	dioxan	258(2.28)	133-0389-73
	CCl_4	259(2.42)	133-0389-73
	$CHCl_3$	259(2.30)	133-0389-73
4H-1,3-Oxazine, 2-ethynyl-5,6-dihydro-4,4,6-trimethyl-	EtOH	208(3.97)	18-0540-73
1H-Pyrrole-3-carboxaldehyde, 1-ethyl-2,5-dimethyl-	H_2O	263(4.08),295(3.88)	103-1355-73
	16N H_2SO_4	280(4.29),335(3.46)	103-1355-73
$C_9H_{13}NO_2$			
1,3-Propanediol, 2-amino-1-phenyl-	EtOH	240(1.96),280(1.42), 340(0.93)	104-2144-73
4-Pyridinol, 2-ethoxy-3,6-dimethyl-	EtOH	263(3.54)	94-1047-73
2(1H)-Pyridinone, 4-ethoxy-1,5-dimethyl-	pH 1.0	269(3.63)	87-0524-73
	pH 14	286(3.60)	87-0524-73
	MeOH	286(3.63)	87-0524-73
$C_9H_{13}NO_3S$			
2H-1,4-Thiazine-6-carboxylic acid, 3,4-dihydro-3-(1-methylethenyl)-, methyl ester, 1-oxide, (1R-trans)-	n.s.g.	274(4.22)	39-2460-73C
$C_9H_{13}NO_4$			
α-D-glycero-Pent-3-enodialdo-1,4-furanose, 1,2-O-isopropylidene-, 5-(N-methyloxime)	EtOH	278(4.58)	136-0159-73F
$C_9H_{13}NO_5S$			
2H-1,4-Thiazine-6-carboxylic acid, 3-(acetoxymethyl)-3,4-dihydro-, methyl ester, oxide, (1R-trans)-	EtOH	275(4.19)	78-3023-73
(1S-cis)-	EtOH	271(4.18)	78-3023-73
$C_9H_{13}NO_8$			
1,2,3-Propanetricarboxylic acid, 2-nitro-, trimethyl ester	MeOH	283(1.56)	18-0337-73
2-Propene-1,1,3-triol, 2-nitro-, triacetate	$CHCl_3$	278(2.51)	104-2245-73
$C_9H_{13}NO_9P_2$			
Diphosphoric acid, P-(4-nitrophenyl) P'-propyl ester	H_2O	290(4.00)	18-3275-73
$C_9H_{13}NS_2$			
2(3H)-Thiophenethione, 3-[(dimethylamino)methylene]-5-ethyl-	EtOH	285(4.43),315(3.94), 490(4.10)	70-2017-73
$C_9H_{13}N_2O_3P$			
Phosphonic acid, [(4-methylphenyl)azo]-, dimethyl ester	MeOH	304(4.17),490(2.03)	44-4402-73
$C_9H_{13}N_2O_4P$			
Phosphonic acid, [(4-methoxyphenyl)-azo]-, dimethyl ester	MeOH	242(4.10),345(4.30), 475(2.38)	44-4402-73

Compound	Solvent	$\lambda_{max}(\log \epsilon)$	Ref.
$C_9H_{13}N_2O_8PS$			
2(1H)-Pyrimidinone, 3,4-dihydro-1-(3-O-phosphono-β-D-arabinofuranosyl)-4-thioxo-, dilithium salt	pH 1 and 7	330(4.25)	103-1056-73
	pH 13	316(4.26)	103-1056-73
$C_9H_{13}N_3O$			
Acetamide, 2-cyano-2-(1-methyl-2-piperidinylidene)-	EtOH	302(4.20)	103-0880-73
$C_9H_{13}N_3O_2$			
Acetic acid, cyano(1,3-dimethyl-2-imidazolidinylidene)-, methyl ester	C_6H_{12}	229s(3.89),284(4.14)	1-0258-73
	EtOH	232s(4.02),276(4.15)	1-0258-73
Imidazo[1,2-a]pyrimidin-5(1H)-one, 2,3-dihydro-6-(2-hydroxyethyl)-7-methyl-	MeOH	230(3.96),290(3.86)	5-0103-73
$C_9H_{13}N_3O_2S_2$			
Carbamic acid, [(ethyl-2-thiazolylamino)thioxomethyl]-, ethyl ester	dioxan	264(3.88),315(4.27)	94-0074-73
Carbamic acid, [[(3-ethyl-2(3H)-thiazolylidene)amino]thioxomethyl]-, ethyl ester	EtOH	279(4.05),347(4.25)	94-0074-73
Carbamic acid, [(ethylthio)(2-thiazolylimino)methyl]-, ethyl ester	dioxan	242(3.58),315(4.31)	94-0074-73
Carbamic acid, [[(3-methyl-2(3H)-thiazolylidene)amino](methylthio)methylene]-, ethyl ester	dioxan	247(3.28),280(3.86), 332(4.36)	94-0074-73
Carbamic acid, [(4-methyl-2-thiazolyl)imino](methylthio)methyl]-, ethyl ester	dioxan	240(3.79),319(4.30)	94-0074-73
Carbamic acid, [(5-methyl-2-thiazolyl)imino](methylthio)methyl]-, ethyl ester	dioxan	242(3.81),319(4.32)	94-0074-73
Carbamic acid, [(methylthio)(2-thiazolimino)methyl]-, 1-methylethyl ester	dioxan	242(3.78),314(4.32)	94-0074-73
Carbamic acid, [(methylthio)(2-thiazolimino)methyl]-, propyl ester	dioxan	243(3.83),313(4.33)	94-0074-73
$C_9H_{13}N_3O_3$			
Imidazo[1,2-a]pyrimidine-6-carboxylic acid, 1,2,3,5,6,7-hexahydro-2-oxo-, ethyl ester	EtOH-NaOH	229(4.22)	44-1591-73
1,3,5-Triazine-2,4(1H,3H)-dione, 6-(2-oxohexyl)-	EtOH	297(4.21)	22-2039-73
$C_9H_{13}N_3O_3S$			
Carbamic acid, [(ethyl-2-thiazolylamino)carbonyl]-, ethyl ester	EtOH	267(4.10)	94-0074-73
Carbamic acid, [[(3-ethyl-2(3H)-thiazolylidene)amino]carbonyl]-, ethyl ester	EtOH	235(3.53),295(4.33)	94-0074-73
$C_9H_{13}N_3O_4S$			
Cytidine, 2-thio-	MeOH	210(3.8),247(4.3), 273(4.2)	24-3039-73
	MeOH-HCl	229(4.2),277(4.3), 311s(3.7)	24-3039-73
$C_9H_{13}N_3O_5$			
Cytidine	pH 2	280(4.13)	69-0194-73
	pH 12	271(3.96)	69-0194-73

Compound	Solvent	$\lambda_{max}(\log \epsilon)$	Ref.
2(1H)-Pyrimidinone, 4-amino-5-α-D-ribo-furanosyl-	pH 1	284(3.95)	136-0015-73D
	pH 5.5	273(3.71)	136-0015-73D
	pH 13	286(3.86)	136-0015-73D
2(1H)-Pyrimidinone, 4-amino-5-β-D-ribo-furanosyl-	pH 1	281(3.98)	136-0015-73D
	pH 5.5	271(3.77)	136-0015-73D
	pH 13	284(3.87)	136-0015-73D
$C_9H_{13}N_3O_5S$			
6-Azauridine, 5-methyl-2-thio-	MeOH	219(4.1),274(4.3)	24-3039-73
	MeOH-NaOH	240(4.1),267(4.4)	24-3039-73
$C_9H_{13}N_4OS$			
1H-Purinium, 6,7-dihydro-1,7,9-trimeth-yl-2-(methylthio)-, iodide	MeOH	275(4.20)	39-2647-73C
$C_9H_{13}N_5$			
9H-Adenine, 8-tert-butyl-	pH 1	267(4.13)	39-1855-73C
	pH 11	265(4.09)	39-1855-73C
	MeOH	261(4.13)	39-1855-73C
$C_9H_{13}N_5O_2$			
1,4-Butanediol, 2-(6-amino-9H-purin-9-yl)-	pH 1	260(4.10)	103-0117-73
	H_2O	261(4.06)	103-0117-73
	pH 13	262(4.12)	103-0117-73
C_9H_{14}			
1-Cyclohexene, 3-(1-methylethylidene)-	n.s.g.	236(4.27)	88-4595-73
1,3-Cyclopentadiene, 1,4,5,5-tetra-methyl-	heptane	258(3.60)	70-0346-73
1,3,5-Hexatriene, 3-(1-methylethyl)-, 3-cis	isooctane	258(4.27),266(4.33), 277(4.20)	44-2478-73
trans	isooctane	259(4.38),268(4.43), 279(4.34)	44-2478-73
1,3,5-Octatriene, 7-methyl-, cis-cis	isooctane	257(4.11),267(4.18), 277(4.07)	44-2478-73
3-cis-5-trans	isooctane	254(4.49),263(4.56), 274(4.45)	44-2478-73
3-trans-5-cis	isooctane	257(4.46),266(4.57), 277(4.48)	44-2478-73
trans-trans	isooctane	242s(--),253(4.47), 263(4.61),274(4.51)	44-2478-73
$C_9H_{14}ClNO_3$			
2(5H)-Furanone, 3-chloro-4-(diethyl-amino)-5-methoxy-	MeOH	284(4.37)	73-1091-73
$C_9H_{14}ClNO_4$			
Acetamide, 2-chloro-N-(tetrahydro-2,2-dimethylfuro[2,3-d]-1,3-dioxol-6-yl)-, [3aS-(3aα,6β,6aα)]-	EtOH	222(2.86)	33-2689-73
Pyridinium, 1,2,4,6-tetramethyl-, per-chlorate	EtOH	230(3.53),270(3.76)	103-0333-73
$C_9H_{14}ClNO_5$			
α-D-Xylofuranuronimidoyl chloride, N-hydroxy-3-O-methyl-1,2-O-(1-methylethylidene)-	EtOH	224(3.76)	136-0297-73D
$C_9H_{14}ClN_5O_2$			
Acetamide, N-[3-[(5-amino-6-chloro-4-pyrimidinyl)amino]-2-hydroxypropyl]-	pH 1	302(4.19)	87-0037-73
	pH 7	262(4.06),290(4.09)	87-0037-73

Compound	Solvent	λ_{max}(log ϵ)	Ref.
Acetamide, N-[3-[(5-amino-6-chloro-4-pyrimidinyl)amino]-2-hydroxypropyl]-	pH 13	262(4.06),290(4.09)	87-0037-73
$C_9H_{14}IN_5$			
Methanaminium, N-(3,9-dihydro-3,9-dimethyl-6H-purin-6-ylidene)-N-methyl-, iodide	H_2O	286(4.31)	104-1316-73
7H-Purinium, 6-(dimethylamino)-3,7-dimethyl-, iodide	H_2O	298(4.29)	104-1316-73
7H-Purinium, 6-(dimethylamino)-7,9-dimethyl-, iodide	H_2O	296(4.18)	104-1316-73
9H-Purinium, 6-(dimethylamino)-1,9-dimethyl-, iodide	H_2O	292(4.12)	104-1316-73
$C_9H_{14}NO_4$			
Pyridinium, 1,2,4,6-tetramethyl-, perchlorate	EtOH	230(3.53),270(3.76)	103-0333-73
$C_9H_{14}N_2O$			
3-Pyrazolol, 1-cyclohexyl-	MeOH	228(3.80),254(2.83)	48-0382-73
	50% MeOH	228(3.68),253(3.18)	48-0382-73
	10% MeOH	230(3.59),249(3.43)	48-0382-73
5-Pyrazolone, 1-cyclohexyl-	MeOH	219(3.50),246(3.50)	48-0382-73
	50% MeOH	244(3.78)	48-0382-73
	10% MeOH	242(3.84)	48-0382-73
$C_9H_{14}N_2OS_2$			
Acetamide, N-[3-(1-methylethyl)-2-(methylthio)-5-thiazolidinylidene]-, meso-ionic didehydro deriv.	EtOH	264(3.717)	18-0964-73
	THF	382(4.055)	18-0964-73
	pyridine	377(4.047)	18-0964-73
$C_9H_{14}N_2O_2$			
1H-1,2-Diazepine-1-carboxylic acid, 2,3-dihydro-5-methyl-, ethyl ester	MeOH	282(3.90)	22-2847-73
1,3-Propanediol, 2-amino-1-(4-aminophenyl)-	EtOH	241(4.2),289(3.3)	104-2144-73
2,4(1H,3H)-Pyrimidinedione, 1-butyl-5-methyl-	MeOH	272.0(3.94)	39-0391-73C
4(1H)-Pyrimidinone, 2-(2-ethoxyethyl)-6-methyl-	EtOH	225(4.82),269(4.64)	95-1437-73
$C_9H_{14}N_2O_2S$			
Pyridinium, 2,4,6-trimethyl-1-[(methylsulfonyl)amino]-, hydroxide, inner salt	EtOH	245(3.97),271(3.68), 295s(2.95)	44-3311-73
$C_9H_{14}N_2O_3$			
Imidazolidinetrione, dipropyl-	H_2O	221(--),268(--)	35-6928-73
	EtOH	220(4.00),263s(2.73), 315s(1.79)	35-6928-73
	ether	219(--),257(--), 316(1.76)	35-6928-73
	MeCN	220(--),263(--), 310s(1.91)	35-6928-73
2,4-Pentadienoic acid, 2-(aminocarbonyl)-5-(dimethylamino)-, methyl ester	EtOH	236(4.00),382(4.79)	70-1959-73
	EtOH	234(4.01),380(4.82)	70-1963-73
$C_9H_{14}N_2O_4$			
Propanedioic acid, diazo-, methyl 2-methylbutyl ester	EtOH	250(3.89)	22-2071-73

Compound	Solvent	λmax(log ε)	Ref.
2,4(1H,3H)-Pyrimidinedione, 5-(4,5-dihydroxypentyl)-, (S)-	H_2O	207(3.98),265(3.89)	35-4081-73
Sydnone, 3-(6-carboxyhexyl)-	EtOH	203(3.50),293(3.90)	103-0441-73
$C_9H_{14}N_4$			
1-Propen-2-amine, N,N-dimethyl-1-(3-methyl-1,2,4-triazin-5-yl)-	MeOH	241(3.44),316(3.93), 386(4.46)	5-1963-73
1-Propen-2-amine, N,N-dimethyl-1-(6-methyl-1,2,4-triazin-5-yl)-	MeOH	240(3.39),314(3.72), 384(4.30)	5-1963-73
$C_9H_{14}N_4O_2$			
Propanamide, N-(4-amino-1,6-dihydro-6-oxo-5-pyrimidinyl)-2,2-dimethyl-	pH 1	258(3.88)	39-1855-73C
	pH 11	255(3.70)	39-1855-73C
	MeOH	260(3.79)	39-1855-73C
$C_9H_{14}N_4O_4$			
1H-Imidazole-5-carboxamide, 4-amino-1-(2-deoxy-α-D-erythro-pentofuranosyl)-	pH 7	272.1(3.88)	5-1286-73
Sydnone imine, N-(aminocarbonyl)-3-(5-carboxypentyl)-	EtOH	198(3.34),235(3.87), 330(3.78)	103-1327-73
$C_9H_{14}N_5$			
7H-Purinium, 6-(dimethylamino)-3,7-dimethyl-, perchlorate	H_2O	298(4.29)	104-1316-73
$C_9H_{14}O$			
Bicyclo[3.1.0]hexan-2-one, 3,6,6-trimethyl-	EtOH	208(3.57),278s(1.58)	35-0468-73
Bicyclo[6.1.0]nonan-2-one	n.s.g.	217(3.25),285(1.70)	22-1800-73
Bicyclo[4.2.0]octan-3-one, 4(a)-methyl-	EtOH	275(1.79)	78-1865-73
Bicyclo[4.2.0]octan-3-one, 4(e)-methyl-	EtOH	282(1.49)	78-1865-73
2-Cyclohexen-1-one, 3,4,4-trimethyl-	EtOH	236(4.13)	39-0529-73C
2-Cyclohexen-1-one, 3,5,5-trimethyl-	CH_2Cl_2	234(4.11),324(1.54)	88-3251-73
BF_3 complex	CH_2Cl_2	271.2(4.07)	88-3251-73
2-Cyclohexen-1-one, 3,6,6-trimethyl-	EtOH	235(4.21)	39-0529-73C
2-Cyclohexen-1-one, 4,4,5-trimethyl-	EtOH	227(4.03),320(1.48)	39-0529-73C
Cyclopentanone, 2-(1-methylpropylidene)-, anti	benzene	338(1.73),350(1.75)	35-3947-73
syn	benzene	338(1.67),350(1.67)	35-3947-73
1-Propanone, 1-(2-methyl-1-cyclopenten-1-yl)-	EtOH	253(3.98)	39-0374-73B
$C_9H_{14}OSi$			
Silane, trimethylphenoxy-	C_6H_{12}	212(3.84),268(3.10)	30-0941-73
$C_9H_{14}O_2$			
Acetic acid, cyclohexylidene-, methyl ester	EtOH	221(4.24)	22-2071-73
1,2-Cyclopentanedione, 3-isopropyl-4-methyl-	EtOH	257(3.94)	22-1454-73
5,7-Octadienoic acid, 4-methyl-	hexane	227(4.43)	70-1624-73
1-Oxaspiro[2.3]hexan-5-one, 4,4,6,6-tetramethyl-	MeOH	313(1.34)	35-3947-73
$C_9H_{14}O_2S$			
Acetic acid, (dihydro-5-methyl-2(3H)-thienylidene)-, ethyl ester	EtOH	288(4.13)	44-3428-73
$C_9H_{14}O_3$			
Acetic acid, (dihydro-5-methyl-2(3H)-furanylidene)-, ethyl ester	EtOH	245(4.13)	44-3428-73

Compound	Solvent	$\lambda_{max}(\log \epsilon)$	Ref.
4-Oxepincarboxylic acid, 2,3,6,7-tetrahydro-, ethyl ester	EtOH	223(3.81)	44-1767-73
$C_9H_{14}O_4$			
2-Hexenedioic acid, 4-isopropyl-	EtOH	206(4.18)	39-2671-73C
$C_9H_{14}O_4S$			
Butanoic acid, 4-[(3-ethoxy-3-oxo-1-propenyl)thio]-, cis	H_2O	289(4.11)	44-3507-73
trans	MeOH	278(4.26)	44-3507-73
2-Propenoic acid, 3-[(3-methoxy-3-oxopropyl)thio]-, ethyl ester, cis	MeOH	284(4.11)	44-3507-73
trans	MeOH	275(4.23)	44-3507-73
$C_9H_{14}O_5$			
α-D-xylo-Pentodialdo-1,4-furanose, 1,2-O-isopropylidene-3-O-methyl-	EtOH	215(1.27)	33-1310-73
$C_9H_{15}ClO$			
4-Hepten-3-one, 5-chloro-4-ethyl-	EtOH	247(3.56)	78-4241-73
isomer	EtOH	243(3.53)	78-4241-73
$C_9H_{15}IN_2OS_2$			
3H-Thiazol-1-ium, 5-(acetylamino)-3-(1-methylethyl)-2-(methylthio)-, iodide	EtOH	319(4.036)	18-0964-73
$C_9H_{15}N$			
Cyclohexanamine, N-propenylidene-	EtOH	215(4.39)	78-4111-73
$C_9H_{15}NO$			
2,3-Hexadienamide, 4,5,5-trimethyl-	EtOH	209(4.11)	88-0209-73
Morpholine, 4-(1-cyclopenten-1-yl)-	heptane	212(3.70)	135-1154-73
	MeOH	205(3.57)	135-1154-73
	isoPrOH	195(3.38)	135-1154-73
	ether	213(3.95)	135-1154-73
	$C_2H_4Cl_2$	209(3.32)	135-1154-73
$C_9H_{15}NO_2S$			
2,4-Pentanedione, 3-[(methylamino)(methylthio)methylene]-	C_6H_{12}	246s(3.92),264(4.16), 333s(3.73),352(3.72)	1-0258-73
	EtOH	268(4.27),272s(4.26), 350(3.15)	1-0258-73
$C_9H_{15}NO_3S$			
Butanoic acid, 2-[(dimethylamino)methylthio)methylene]-, methyl ester	EtOH	257(4.36),345(3.45)	1-0258-73
$C_9H_{15}NO_4$			
D-Ribitol, 2,5-anhydro-1-deoxy-3,4-O-(1-methylethylidene)-1-(methylimino)-, N-oxide, (Z)-	EtOH	239(3.96)	136-0159-73F
$C_9H_{15}NO_4S$			
Propanedioic acid, [(dimethylamino)-(methylthio)methylene]-, dimethyl ester	C_6H_{12}	279s(3.68),313(4.04)	1-0258-73
	EtOH	241(4.08),265(3.85), 331(3.83)	1-0258-73
2H-1,4-Thiazine-6-carboxylic acid, 3,4-dihydro-3-(hydroxymethyl)-2,2-dimethyl-, methyl ester, 1-oxide	n.s.g.	275(4.13)	39-0022-73C

Compound	Solvent	$\lambda_{max}(\log \epsilon)$	Ref.
$C_9H_{15}NS_2$			
Cyclopentanecarbodithioic acid, 2-imino-3-isopropyl-	EtOH	304(3.93),392(4.32)	39-1009-73C
$C_9H_{15}N_2O_4$			
1H-Imidazol-1-yloxy, 2,5-dihydro-4-(methoxycarbonyl)-2,2,5,5-tetramethyl-, 3-oxide	EtOH	267(4.02)	104-1990-73
$C_9H_{15}N_2S$			
2H-1,2,3-Benzothiadiazinium, 5,6,7,8-tetrahydro-2,2-dimethyl-, perchlorate	MeOH	229(3.85),280(3.65)	118-0225-73
$C_9H_{15}N_3O_2$			
2-Propenoic acid, 2-cyano-3,3-bis(dimethylamino)-, methyl ester	C_6H_{12}	249(3.79),290(4.20)	1-0258-73
	EtOH	251(3.94),284(4.27)	1-0258-73
$C_9H_{15}N_3O_3$			
Glycine, N-(4,5-dihydro-1-methyl-4-oxo-1H-imidazol-2-yl)-N-methyl-, ethyl ester, hydrochloride	pH 12	229(4.33)	44-1591-73
Sydnone imine, 3-(6-carboxyhexyl)-	EtOH	204(4.61),225(4.10), 303(3.80)	103-1327-73
hydrochloride	EtOH	200(3.82),296(3.62)	103-1327-73
$C_9H_{15}N_3O_6$			
D-Ribitol, 1-C-(4-amino-1,2-dihydro-2-oxo-5-pyrimidinyl)-	pH 1.0	284(3.91)	136-0015-73D
	pH 5.5	274(3.70)	136-0015-73D
	pH 13	287(3.81)	136-0015-73D
$C_9H_{15}N_4O_4$			
Pyrimidinium, 2,4-diamino-1-β-D-ribofuranosyl-, perchlorate	H_2O	210(4.41),234s(3.11), 267(3.90)	94-1530-73
	aq base	231(4.32),276s(3.53), 305s(3.15)	94-1530-73
$C_9H_{15}N_5O$			
Propanamide, N-(4,6-diamino-5-pyrimidinyl)-2,2-dimethyl-	pH 1	266(4.21)	39-1855-73C
	pH 4.5	261(4.20)	39-1855-73C
	pH 11	266(4.16)	39-1855-73C
$C_9H_{15}S_3$			
Cyclopropenylium, 1,2,3-tris(ethylthio)-, perchlorate	MeCN	273(4.35)	88-3409-73
C_9H_{16}			
2,4-Hexadiene, 2,3,4-trimethyl-	EtOH	206(3.85)	22-2506-73
$C_9H_{16}BrN_2$			
1,4-Diazepinylium, 6-bromo-2,3,4,?-tetrahydro-2,2,5,7-tetramethyl-, perchlorate	MeOH	261(2.85),347(4.12)	39-1729-73B
$C_9H_{16}ClN_2$			
1,4-Diazepinylium, 6-chloro-2,3,4,?-tetrahydro-2,2,5,7-tetramethyl-, perchlorate	MeOH	344(4.07)	39-1729-73B
$C_9H_{16}IN_2$			
1,4-Diazepinylium, 2,3,4,?-tetrahydro-6-iodo-2,2,5,7-tetramethyl- $(ClO_4)^-$	MeOH	307(3.38),354(3.96)	39-1729-73B

Compound	Solvent	λ max (log ε)	Ref.
$C_9H_{16}NO$			
1,2-Benzisoxazolium, 3a,4,5,6,7,7a-hexahydro-2,3-dimethyl-, perchlorate	EtOH	230(3.49)	22-1390-73
$C_9H_{16}N_2O_2$			
2,3-Piperazinedione, 1-isopropyl-5,5-dimethyl-	H_2O	215s(3.98),222(4.01), 233s(3.88),240s(3.65)	82-0469-73C
	MeCN	223(3.93),232s(3.81), 240s(3.56)	82-0469-73C
$C_9H_{16}N_2O_2S$			
Carbamic acid, (1-piperidinothioxomethyl)-, ethyl ester	EtOH	278(4.20),331(2.49)	48-0144-73
$C_9H_{16}N_2O_3$			
1H-1,2-Diazepine-1-carboxylic acid, 2,3,4,5-tetrahydro-4-hydroxy-5-methyl-, ethyl ester	MeOH	222(3.99)	22-2847-73
$C_9H_{16}N_2O_6$			
Heptanoic acid, 2,7-dinitro-, ethyl ester	MeOH	265(2.47)	18-3462-73
	MeOH-NaOMe	232(3.99),300(3.92)	18-3462-73
Hexanoic acid, 2,6-dinitro-, propyl ester	MeOH	263(2.60)	18-3462-73
Hexanoic acid, 4-methyl-2,6-dinitro-, ethyl ester	MeOH	255(2.43)	18-3462-73
$C_9H_{16}N_2S_2$			
Cyclopenta[e]-1,3-thiazine-2(3H)-thione, 7a-aminohexahydro-4,4-dimethyl-	EtOH	244(3.88),289(4.22)	39-1009-73C
$C_9H_{16}N_3O_2$			
1,4-Diazepinylium, 2,3,4,?-tetrahydro-2,2,5,7-tetramethyl-6-nitro-, perchlorate	MeOH	323(4.10)	39-1729-73B
$C_9H_{16}N_5O_{14}P_2$			
Uridine, 2'-azido-2'-deoxy-, 5'-diphosphate (lithium salt)	H_2O	262(4.00)	69-3962-73
$C_9H_{16}O$			
Cyclohexanone, 2,2,6-trimethyl-	C_6H_{12}	295(1.40)	22-2231-73
	heptane	295(1.36)	22-2231-73
	H_2O	287(--)	22-2231-73
	MeOH	291(1.46)	22-2231-73
	EtOH	291(1.48)	22-2231-73
	MeCN	292(1.43)	22-2231-73
	CCl_4	295(1.46)	22-2231-73
	$CHCl_3$	292(1.45)	22-2231-73
	CH_2Cl_2	292(1.42)	22-2231-73
Cyclopentanone, 2,2,4,4-tetramethyl-	C_6H_{12}	299(1.36)	22-2231-73
	hexane	300(1.26)	46-1830-73
	heptane	300(1.34)	22-2231-73
	H_2O	289(--)	22-2231-73
	MeOH	294(1.42)	22-2231-73
	EtOH	294(1.40)	22-2231-73
	MeCN	296(1.40)	22-2231-73
	CCl_4	299(1.43)	22-2231-73
	$CHCl_3$	296(1.44)	22-2231-73
	CH_2Cl_2	296(1.40)	22-2231-73

Compound	Solvent	λmax(log ε)	Ref.
Cyclopentanone, 2,2,5,5-tetramethyl-	C_6H_{12}	297(1.18)	22-2231-73
	heptane	296(1.18)	22-2231-73
	H_2O	291(--)	22-2231-73
	MeOH	294(1.20)	22-2231-73
	EtOH	295(1.20)	22-2231-73
	MeCN	294(1.18)	22-2231-73
	CCl_4	298(1.28)	22-2231-73
	$CHCl_3$	295(1.18)	22-2231-73
	CH_2Cl_2	294(1.20)	22-2231-73
2-Cyclopenten-1-ol, 2,3,4,5-tetramethyl-	n.s.g.	262(3.53)	70-0034-73
Ethanone, 1-[1-methyl-2-(1-methylethyl)-cyclopropyl]-, cis	n.s.g.	204(3.52),285(1.48)	78-2821-73
trans	n.s.g.	205(3.58),289(1.62)	78-2821-73
2-Hepten-4-one, 6,6-dimethyl-, cis	hexane	224(3.99)	35-7345-73
trans	hexane	219(4.03)	35-7345-73
3-Hexenal, 2,3,4-trimethyl-, (E)-	pentane	308(2.11)	33-2961-73
3-Hexenal, 2,3,4-trimethyl-, (Z)-	pentane	305(2.06)	33-2961-73
2-Nonen-4-one	pentane	216(4.07)	33-2975-73
3-Nonen-5-one	pentane	218(4.07)	33-2975-73
$C_9H_{16}O_3$			
Ethanone, 1-[2-(1-methylethyl)-1,3-di-oxan-5-yl]-, cis	C_6H_{12}	274(1.42)	80-1379-73
trans	C_6H_{12}	280(1.36)	80-1379-73
2-Heptenoic acid, 5-hydroxy-2-methyl-, methyl ester	EtOH	217.5(4.48)	78-1227-73
$C_9H_{17}N$			
1-Hexanamine, N-propenylidene-	EtOH	215(4.29)	78-4111-73
$C_9H_{17}NO_2$			
2-Propenoic acid, 3-(dimethylamino)-3-ethoxy-, ethyl ester	CH_2Cl_2	276.5(4.34)	33-0944-73
$C_9H_{17}N_5$			
4(1H)-Pyrimidinone, 2-(dimethylamino)-5,6-dimethyl-, methylhydrazone	EtOH	238(4.09),297(3.88)	54-0705-73
$C_9H_{18}Cl_3O_3P$			
Phosphonic acid, (trichloromethyl)-, bis(2-methylpropyl) ester	hexane	253.7(0.3)	18-1009-73
$C_9H_{18}N_2$			
Diazene, (2,2-dimethyl-1-methylenepro-pyl)(1-methylethyl)-	hexane	226(3.53),255(3.32), 400(2.15)	103-0112-73
	MeCN	397(1.74)	103-0112-73
1H-Imidazole, 2-hexyl-4,5-dihydro-	EtOH	220(3.65)	93-2424-73
$C_9H_{18}N_2O$			
3-Buten-2-one, 4-(dimethylamino)-3-[(1-methylethyl)amino]-	CH_2Cl_2	331(4.12)	33-0944-73
3-Buten-2-one, 4-(dimethylamino)-4-[(1-methylethyl)amino]-	CH_2Cl_2	234(3.73),304(4.32)	33-0944-73
3-Penten-2-one, 4,5-bis(dimethylamino)-	EtOH	318(4.29)	70-1237-73
2-Propenal, 2-(diethylamino)-3-(dimeth-ylamino)-	CH_2Cl_2	288(4.46)	33-0944-73
2-Propenal, 3-(diethylamino)-3-(dimeth-ylamino)-	CH_2Cl_2	257(3.84),307(4.37)	33-0944-73

Compound	Solvent	λmax(log ε)	Ref.
$C_9H_{18}N_2O_2$			
2-Propenoic acid, 3-(dimethylamino)-3-[(1-methylethyl)amino]-, methyl ester	C_6H_{12}	237(3.66),278(4.32)	33-0944-73
$C_9H_{18}OSi$			
5-Hexen-2-one, 5-(trimethylsilyl)-	C_6H_{12}	281(1.43)	23-2024-73
$C_9H_{18}O_2S_2$			
1-Propene, 1,2-bis(propylsulfinyl)-	hexane	235(3.91),250s(3.77)	132-0233-73
$C_9H_{18}O_3S$			
Propanoic acid, 3-[(1,1-dimethylethyl)-sulfinyl]-, ethyl ester	heptane	217(3.18)	143-0205-73
$C_9H_{20}ClN_3O_4$			
Methanaminium, N-[2,3-bis(dimethyl-amino)-2-propenylidene]-N-methyl-, perchlorate	EtOH	306(4.45)	73-1168-73
$C_9H_{20}N_2O$			
Diazene, methyl(1-methylheptyl)-, 1-oxide	EtOH	223(3.85)	88-4701-73
$C_9H_{20}N_2S$			
Thiourea, N,N-dibutyl-	EtOH	248(4.17)	48-0144-73
$C_9H_{23}B_{16}Co$			
Cobalt, (η^5-2,4-cyclopentadien-1-yl)-[η^6-(1,10-dicarbadecaboran(10)-1-yl)nonahydrodicarbadecaborato(2-)]-	MeCN	235(4.29),274s(3.71), 358(3.78),448(2.66), 578(2.60)	35-4565-73

Compound	Solvent	$\lambda_{max}(\log \epsilon)$	Ref.
$C_{10}BrF_7O$			
1(4H)-Naphthalenone, 4-bromo-2,3,4,5,6,7,8-heptafluoro-	C_6H_{12}	220(3.94),244(3.95),308(3.45)	104-1246-73
2(1H)-Naphthalenone, 1-bromo-1,3,4,5,6,7,8-heptafluoro-	C_6H_{12}	215(4.74),238(4.16),334(3.81)	104-1246-73
$C_{10}ClF_7O$			
1(4H)-Naphthalenone, 4-chloro-2,3,4,5,6,7,8-heptafluoro-	C_6H_{12}	233(4.07),292(3.17),304(3.14),350(3.10)	104-1246-73
2(1H)-Naphthalenone, 1-chloro-1,3,4,5,6,7,8-heptafluoro-	C_6H_{12}	236(4.26),329(3.92)	104-1246-73
$C_{10}Cl_{10}Hg$			
Mercury, bis(1,2,3,4,5-pentachloro-2,4-cyclopentadien-1-yl)-	C_6H_{12}	223(4.2),298(4.2),350s(3.1)	35-8658-73
	glyme	226(4.2),301(4.3),342s(3.1)	35-8658-73
$C_{10}F_{12}S_4$			
1,3-Dithiole, 2-[4,5-bis(trifluoromethyl)-1,3-dithiol-2-ylidene]-4,5-bis-(trifluoromethyl)-	isooctane	222(4.10),310(4.13),412(3.18)	35-4379-73
$C_{10}F_{13}N$			
Pyridine, 2,3,5,6-tetrafluoro-4-(nonafluorocyclopentyl)-	C_6H_{12}	284(3.65)	39-1710-73C
$C_{10}F_{14}N_2$			
Pyridazine, 3,4,6-trifluoro-5-(undecafluorocyclohexyl)-	C_6H_{12}	230(3.87),272(3.84)	39-1710-73C
$C_{10}F_{15}N$			
Pyridine, 2,3,5-trifluoro-6-(pentafluoroethyl)-4-[1,2,2,2-tetrafluoro-1-(trifluoromethyl)ethyl]-	C_6H_{12}	274.5(3.68)	39-1405-73C
$C_{10}F_{16}N_2$			
Pyridazine, 3-fluoro-4,5,6-tris(pentafluoroethyl)-	C_6H_{12}	268(3.498)	39-1405-73C
$C_{10}H_2F_8O_3$			
1(2H)-Naphthalenone, 2,2,4,4,5,6,7,8-octafluoro-3,4-dihydro-3,3-dihydroxy-	heptane	201(3.26),240(2.89),248(2.90),291(2.29)	104-0578-73
$C_{10}H_3Br_3N_4O_2$			
Benzo[g]pteridine-2,4(1H,3H)-dione, 6,7,9-tribromo-	EtOH	350(3.90),395(3.77)	65-1578-73
$C_{10}H_3F_5N_2O$			
1,2,4-Oxadiazole, 3-[2-(pentafluorophenyl)ethenyl]-, (E)-	EtOH	278(4.45)	39-2241-73C
$C_{10}H_3F_5O_4$			
1,3-Dioxolane-2,4-dione, 5-methyl-5-(pentafluorophenyl)-	n.s.g.	233(4.76),268(4.94)	25-0695-73
$C_{10}H_3F_{12}NO$			
Pyridine, 2,5-difluoro-3-methoxy-4,6-bis(pentafluoroethyl)-	C_6H_{12}	286(3.70)	39-1405-73C

Compound	Solvent	λ_{max}(log ε)	Ref.
$C_{10}H_4Br_2N_4O_2$			
Benzo[g]pteridine-2,4(1H,3H)-dione, 7,9-dibromo-	EtOH	350(3.94),395(3.75)	65-1578-73
$C_{10}H_4Br_2O_5$			
2-Furancarboxylic acid, 5-bromo-, anhydride	heptane	277(--)	103-0546-73
	dioxan	279(4.55)	103-0546-73
$C_{10}H_4Br_2O_6$			
Peroxide, bis[(5-bromo-2-furanyl)carbonyl]	heptane	271(--)	103-0546-73
	EtOH	278(--)	103-0546-73
	dioxan	278(4.60)	103-0546-73
$C_{10}H_4Cl_2O_6$			
Peroxide, bis[(5-chloro-2-furanyl)carbonyl]	heptane	269(--)	103-0546-73
	EtOH	276(--)	103-0546-73
	dioxan	276(4.60)	103-0546-73
$C_{10}H_4I_2O_6$			
Peroxide, bis[(5-iodo-2-furanyl)carbonyl]	heptane	274(--)	103-0546-73
	EtOH	281(--)	103-0546-73
	dioxan	285(4.59)	103-0546-73
$C_{10}H_4N_2O_9$			
2-Furancarboxylic acid, 5-nitro-, anhydride	heptane	286(--)	103-0546-73
	dioxan	299(4.27)	103-0546-73
$C_{10}H_4N_2O_{10}$			
Peroxide, bis[(5-nitro-2-furanyl)carbonyl]	heptane	286(--)	103-0546-73
	EtOH	296(--)	103-0546-73
	dioxan	294(4.43)	103-0546-73
$C_{10}H_5BrN_4O_2$			
Benzo[g]pteridine-2,4(1H,3H)-dione, 9-bromo-	EtOH	332(4.06),385(4.24)	65-1578-73
$C_{10}H_5ClN_2O$			
1,2,4-Oxadiazole, 3-[(4-chlorophenyl)-ethynyl]-	EtOH	258(3.42),286(4.32)	39-2241-73C
$C_{10}H_5ClO_3$			
1H-2-Benzopyran-3-carboxaldehyde, 4-chloro-1-oxo-	EtOH	232(4.34),246(4.17), 261(3.94),270(3.99), 280(3.92),318(3.78)	22-2093-73
2H-1-Benzopyran-3-carboxaldehyde, 4-chloro-2-oxo-	EtOH	284(3.98),308s(3.86)	22-2093-73
$C_{10}H_5Cl_3N_3P$			
1,3,2-Diazaphosphorine-5-carbonitrile, 2,2,4-trichloro-2,2-dihydro-6-phenyl-	hexane	249(4.07),349(4.00)	112-0621-73
$C_{10}H_5N_3O_3$			
1,2,4-Oxadiazole, 3-[(4-nitrophenyl)-ethynyl]-	EtOH	284(4.35)	39-2241-73C
$C_{10}H_6$			
2,4,6,8-Decatetrayne	C_6H_{12}	236(5.50)	33-1752-73
	+2.5% CS_2	236(5.44)	33-1752-73

Compound	Solvent	$\lambda_{max}(\log \epsilon)$	Ref.
$C_{10}H_6BrClN_2O$			
1,2,4-Oxadiazole, 3-[2-bromo-2-(4-chlorophenyl)ethenyl]-, trans	EtOH	268(4.11)	39-2241-73C
$C_{10}H_6BrClS_2$			
Thiophene, 2-bromo-5-[2-(5-chloro-2-thienyl)ethenyl]-	DMF	355(4.50)	24-0655-73
$C_{10}H_6BrNOS$			
Thiocyanic acid, 3-(4-bromophenyl)-3-oxo-1-propenyl ester	dioxan	309(4.40)	24-0435-73
$C_{10}H_6BrNO_2S_2$			
Thiophene, 2-bromo-5-[2-(5-nitro-2-thienyl)ethenyl]-	DMF	296(3.96),430(4.41)	24-0655-73
Thiophene, 2-[(3-bromophenyl)thio]-3-nitro-	MeOH	364(3.84)	4-1007-73
Thiophene, 2-[(4-bromophenyl)thio]-3-nitro-	MeOH	364(3.86)	4-1007-73
Thiophene, 3-[(3-bromophenyl)thio]-2-nitro-	MeOH	370(4.04)	4-1007-73
Thiophene, 3-[(4-bromophenyl)thio]-2-nitro-	MeOH	370(4.05)	4-1007-73
$C_{10}H_6ClNO_2S_2$			
Thiophene, 2-[(3-chlorophenyl)thio]-3-nitro-	MeOH	362(3.83)	4-1007-73
Thiophene, 2-[(4-chlorophenyl)thio]-3-nitro-	MeOH	364(3.86)	4-1007-73
Thiophene, 3-[(3-chlorophenyl)thio]-2-nitro-	MeOH	368(4.03)	4-1007-73
Thiophene, 3-[(4-chlorophenyl)thio]-2-nitro-	MeOH	370(4.05)	4-1007-73
$C_{10}H_6ClN_5S$			
2-Pyridinamine, 5-chloro-N-3H-[1,2,4]-thiadiazolo[4,3-a]pyrimidin-3-ylidene-	n.s.g.	247(4.23),280(4.12), 330s(4.13),341(4.20), 400(3.68)	44-3087-73
$C_{10}H_6Cl_4O_2S_2$			
Spiro[1,3-benzodioxole-2,2'-[1,3]dithiane], 4,5,6,7-tetrachloro-	benzene	296(3.69)	97-0465-73
$C_{10}H_6FNOS$			
Thiocyanic acid, 3-(4-fluorophenyl)-3-oxo-1-propenyl ester	dioxan	304(4.31)	24-0435-73
$C_{10}H_6FNO_2S_2$			
Thiophene, 2-[(4-fluorophenyl)thio]-3-nitro-	MeOH	364(3.82)	4-1007-73
Thiophene, 3-[(4-fluorophenyl)thio]-2-nitro-	MeOH	370(4.01)	4-1007-73
$C_{10}H_6INOS$			
Thiocyanic acid, 3-(4-iodophenyl)-3-oxo-1-propenyl ester	dioxan	314(4.46)	24-0435-73
$C_{10}H_6IN_5S$			
2-Pyridinamine, 5-iodo-N-3H-[1,2,4]thiadiazolo[4,3-a]pyrimidin-3-ylidene-	n.s.g.	245(4.21),285(4.15), 333s(4.23),343(4.31), 398(3.77)	44-3087-73

Compound	Solvent	$\lambda_{max}(\log \epsilon)$	Ref.
$C_{10}H_6N_2O$			
1,2,4-Oxadiazole, 3-(phenylethynyl)-	EtOH	261(4.33),275(4.25)	39-2241-73C
$C_{10}H_6N_2OS$			
2H-Pyrimido[2,1-b]benzothiazol-2-one	EtOH	230(4.40),241(4.32), 263(4.11),301(4.15)	94-2019-73
$C_{10}H_6N_2O_2$			
1H-Indole-2-carboxylic acid, 3-cyano-, sodium salt	EtOH	297(3.78)	95-1433-73
2H-Pyrimido[2,1-b]benzoxazol-2-one	EtOH	243(4.18),292(4.30)	94-2019-73
$C_{10}H_6N_2O_4S_2$			
Thiophene, 2-nitro-3-[(3-nitrophenyl)-thio]-	MeOH	364(4.05)	4-1007-73
Thiophene, 2-nitro-3-[(4-nitrophenyl)-thio]-	MeOH	368(4.11)	4-1007-73
Thiophene, 3-nitro-2-[(3-nitrophenyl)-thio]-	MeOH	358(3.84)	4-1007-73
Thiophene, 3-nitro-2-[(4-nitrophenyl)-thio]-	MeOH	364(3.89)	4-1007-73
$C_{10}H_6N_2S$			
Thiocyanic acid, 4-(2-cyanoethenyl)-phenyl ester, (E)-	EtOH	290(4.43)	39-2241-73C
$C_{10}H_6N_4O_2$			
Pyridazino[4,5-b]quinoxaline-1,4-dione, 2,3-dihydro-	EtOH	245(4.6),294(3.8), 322(3.7)	103-0513-73
disodium deriv.	H_2O	246(4.9),310(4.2), 340(3.8)	103-1284-73
	EtOH	246(4.8),320(4.3)	103-1284-73
$C_{10}H_6N_6O_4$			
Pyridine, 2,2'-azobis[5-nitro-	EtOH	325(4.52)	104-2622-73
$C_{10}H_6OS$			
2-Propynal, 3-[5-(1-propynyl)-2-thien-yl]-	ether	275s(3.78),287s(3.80), 317s(4.19),334(4.34), 347(4.37)	24-0497-73
$C_{10}H_6O_2$			
1,2-Naphthalenedione	EtOH	250(4.4),345(3.4), 395(3.5)	136-0247-73A
1,4-Naphthalenedione	EtOH	246(4.28),256(4.13), 334(3.44)	136-0247-73A
$C_{10}H_6O_4$			
1,2-Dioxane-3,6-dione, 4-phenyl- (phenylmaleic peroxide)	CCl_4	312s(4.06)	44-1588-73
1,2-Indandione, 4,5-(methylenedioxy)-	EtOH	208(4.19),239(4.32), 265s(3.63),293(3.92), 312s(3.86),380s(3.16)	141-0001-73
	dioxan	256(4.08),335s(3.78), 345(3.79)	141-0001-73
1,2-Indandione, 5,6-(methylenedioxy)-	EtOH	234(4.17),272(3.83), 326(3.96),373s(3.28)	141-0001-73
	dioxan	223(4.01),239s(3.86), 250(3.83),293(3.75), 363(3.86)	141-0001-73

Compound	Solvent	λmax(log ε)	Ref.
1,2-Indandione, 6,7-(methylenedioxy)-	EtOH	233(4.28),260(4.08), 295(3.20),353(3.48)	141-0001-73
	dioxan	238(4.10),251s(4.03), 286(4.12),390(3.41)	141-0001-73
1,4-Naphthalenedione, 2,5-dihydroxy-	MeOH	283(4.08),408(3.61)	33-0619-73
	MeOH-NaOH	243(4.2),293(3.94), 433(3.77)	33-0619-73
1,4-Naphthalenedione, 2,8-dihydroxy-	MeOH	241(3.98),283(3.98), 410(3.59)	33-0619-73
	MeOH-NaOH	230(4.26),262(4.23), 375(3.50),472(3.59)	33-0619-73
$C_{10}H_6O_4S$			
Benzo[b]thiophene-2,3-dicarboxylic acid	pH 1	229(4.07),245(3.97), 289(3.94)	1-0595-73
Benzo[c]thiophene-1,3-dicarboxylic acid	aq NaOH	219(4.35),235(5.96), 326(3.93),373(4.01)	88-1871-73
$C_{10}H_6O_5$			
2H-1-Benzopyran-4-carboxylic acid, 7-hydroxy-2-oxo-	EtOH	221(4.05),337(3.97)	95-0836-73
2-Furancarboxylic acid anhydride	heptane	260(--)	103-0546-73
	dioxan	264(4.42)	103-0546-73
Homophthalic acid anhydride, 4,5-(methylenedioxy)-	EtOH	217(4.21),259(3.67), 293(3.64)	141-0001-73
	dioxan	226(4.11),258(3.69), 299(3.57),341(2.98)	141-0001-73
Peroxide, bis(2-furanylcarbonyl)	heptane	256(--)	103-0546-73
	EtOH	261(--)	103-0546-73
	dioxan	262(4.50)	103-0546-73
Phthalic anhydride, 3-methoxy-4,5-(methylenedioxy)-	EtOH	222(4.42),254(3.90), 269s(3.72),293s(3.44), 326s(3.92)	141-0001-73
$C_{10}H_7BrClNS$			
Thiazole, 2-(4-bromophenyl)-4-(chloromethyl)-	MeOH	220(4.11),295(4.20)	80-0685-73
$C_{10}H_7BrN_2OS$			
4-Imidazolidinone, 5-[(3-bromophenyl)-methylene]-2-thioxo-	pH 3-5	285(4.02),361(4.43)	104-2418-73
	pH 12-13	254(4.03),328(3.98), 390(4.24)	104-2418-73
	EtOH	249(4.08),290(3.86), 365(4.45)	104-2418-73
4-Imidazolidinone, 5-[(4-bromophenyl)-	pH 3-5	251(4.04),290(4.12), 368(4.49)	104-2418-73
	pH 12-13	254(4.03),320(4.02), 392(4.33)	104-2418-73
	EtOH	250(4.02),300(3.90), 370(4.53)	104-2418-73
$C_{10}H_7BrOS$			
4H-Cyclohepta[b]thiophen-4-one, 3-bromo-2-methyl-	EtOH	245(4.29),268s(--), 335(3.95)	39-0968-73C
	H_2SO_4	225(4.10),253(4.43), 283(4.34),356(4.76), 421(4.63)	39-0968-73C
$C_{10}H_7BrO_2$			
8H-Cyclohepta[b]furan-8-one, 7-bromo-2-methyl-	EtOH	238(4.06),244(4.05), 275(4.52),306s(3.79),	39-1960-73C

Compound	Solvent	$\lambda_{max}(\log \epsilon)$	Ref.
8H-Cyclohepta[b]furan-8-one, 7-bromo-2-methyl- (cont.)	EtOH	321(3.74),332s(3.60), 349(3.61),366(3.49)	39-1960-73C
2,4,6-Cycloheptatrien-1-one, 2-bromo-7-(2-propynyloxy)-	EtOH	256(4.42),327(3.92), 358(3.88),372s(3.72)	39-1960-73C
2,4,6-Cycloheptatrien-1-one, 3-bromo-2-(2-propynyloxy)-	EtOH	253(4.31),324(3.80)	39-1960-73C
$C_{10}H_7Br_2ClN_2O$			
1,2,4-Oxadiazole, 3-[1,2-dibromo-2-(4-chlorophenyl)ethyl]-	EtOH	236(3.95)	39-2241-73C
$C_{10}H_7Cl$			
1-Buten-3-yne, 1-(4-chlorophenyl)-	EtOH	283(4.59)	78-3797-73
$C_{10}H_7ClF_3N$			
Benzenepropanenitrile, α-chloro-4-(trifluoromethyl)-	EtOH	263(3.79)	39-2241-73C
$C_{10}H_7ClN_2O$			
1,2,4-Oxadiazole, 3-[2-(4-chlorophenyl)-ethenyl]-	EtOH	280(4.48)	39-2241-73C
cis	EtOH	276(4.24)	39-2241-73C
2-Propenoyl chloride, 3-amino-2-cyano-3-phenyl-	MeCN	243s(3.67),306(4.18)	44-2287-73
$C_{10}H_7ClN_2OS$			
4-Imidazolidinone, 5-[(3-chlorophenyl)-methylene]-2-thioxo-	pH 3-5	248(3.99),288(3.85), 362(4.44)	104-2418-73
	pH 12-13	257(3.99),328(3.97), 397(4.24)	104-2418-73
	EtOH	248(4.05),295(3.85), 366(4.47)	104-2418-73
$C_{10}H_7ClN_2S$			
Thiocyanic acid, 4-(2-chloro-2-cyano-ethyl)phenyl ester	EtOH	236(4.09)	39-2241-73C
$C_{10}H_7ClO_2$			
2H-1-Benzopyran-3-carboxaldehyde, 4-chloro-	EtOH	298(4.06),362(3.75)	22-2093-73
$C_{10}H_7ClS_2$			
Thiophene, 2-chloro-5-[2-(2-thienyl)-ethenyl]-, (E)-	n.s.g.	258(3.90),334s(4.43), 346(4.46),361s(4.34)	1-3133-73
$C_{10}H_7F$			
Naphthalene, 2-fluoro-	$C_2H_4Cl_2$	274(3.7),318(3.15)	24-2427-73
$C_{10}H_7F_6NO_2$			
7-Azabicyclo[2.2.1]hepta-2,5-diene-7-carboxylic acid, 2,3-bis(trifluoromethyl)-, methyl ester	EtOH	227(2.87),267s(2.18)	24-3824-73
1H-Azepine-1-carboxylic acid, 3,6-bis-(trifluoromethyl)-, methyl ester	EtOH	245(3.65),323(2.51)	24-3824-73
1H-Azepine-1-carboxylic acid, 4,5-bis-(trifluoromethyl)-, methyl ester	EtOH	244(3.32),325(2.63)	24-3824-73
$C_{10}H_7IN_2OS$			
4-Imidazolidinone, 5-[(4-iodophenyl)-methylene]-2-thioxo-	pH 3-5	248(3.92),298(3.85), 375(4.34)	104-2418-73

Compound	Solvent	λ_{max}(log ε)	Ref.
4-Imidazolidinone, 5-[(4-iodophenyl)-methylene]-2-thioxo- (cont.)	pH 12-13	248(4.03),320(4.03), 392(4.40)	104-2418-73
	EtOH	251(4.04),300(3.94), 375(4.58)	104-2418-73
$C_{10}H_7NO$			
9H-Cyclohepta[b]pyridin-9-one	EtOH	220(4.57),256s(--), 321s(--),338(4.20)	39-0968-73C
$C_{10}H_7NOS$			
Furo[2,3-d]thieno[2,3-b]pyridine, 2-methyl-	MeOH	242(4.48),305(3.49)	24-0368-73
Thiocyanic acid, 3-oxo-3-phenyl-1-propenyl ester, cis	dioxan	301(4.26)	24-0435-73
$C_{10}H_7NO_2$			
Azulene, 1-nitro-	MeOH	313(4.21),405(4.09)	78-0867-73
5H-Cyclopropa[g]quinoline-5,7(5aH)-dione, 6,6a-dihydro-	EtOH	219(4.08),238s(--)	39-0026-73C
2-Naphthalenol, 1-nitroso-	pH 3	217(4.13),260(4.19), 380(3.76)	48-0202-73
	pH 7	260(4.17),285(3.73), 380(3.79),420(3.56)	48-0202-73
	pH 11	265(4.05),290(3.97), 380(3.93),420(3.85)	48-0202-73
	EtOH	262(4.13),273s(--), 365(3.72)	48-0202-73
	acetone	375(3.73)	48-0202-73
	ether	273(4.12),373(3.76)	48-0202-73
	$CHCl_3$	274(4.14),378(3.77)	48-0202-73
$C_{10}H_7NO_3$			
1H-Indole-3-acetic acid, α-oxo-	MeOH	254(4.03),266(4.01), 273s(3.94),310(3.97)	102-0447-73
	H_2SO_4	243s(3.99),250(4.01), 275(4.14),390(4.01)	102-0447-73
$C_{10}H_7NO_4$			
1,2-Indandione, 4,5-(methylenedioxy)-, 2-oxime	EtOH	254(4.29),321s(3.88), 341(3.95)	141-0001-73
	dioxan	251(4.29),313s(3.88), 332(3.94)	141-0001-73
1,2-Indandione, 5,6-(methylenedioxy)-, 2-oxime	EtOH	240s(3.98),251(4.04), 290(3.97),352(4.03)	141-0001-73
	dioxan	233s(3.99),248(4.10), 285(3.95),347(4.02)	141-0001-73
1,2-Indandione, 6,7-(methylenedioxy)-, 2-oxime	EtOH	240(4.08),282(4.26), 379(3.41)	141-0001-73
	dioxan	242(4.15),248s(4.12), 277(4.23),369(3.47)	141-0001-73
1H-Pyrano[3,4-c]pyridine-3-carboxylic acid, 1-oxo-, methyl ester	MeOH	221(3.71),242(3.54), 250(3.51),272(3.36), 291(3.38),381(3.00)	44-4305-73
$C_{10}H_7NO_5$			
2-Butenoic acid, 4-(4-nitrophenyl)-4-oxo-	EtOH	225(3.95),268(4.24)	22-0625-73
$C_{10}H_7NO_8S_2$			
Nitroso R salt	pH 3	230(4.25),265(4.27), 370(3.80)	48-0202-73

Compound	Solvent	λ_{max}(log ε)	Ref.
Nitroso R salt (1-nitroso-2-naphthol-3,6-disulfonic acid disodium salt) (cont.)	pH 7	233(4.27),270(4.21), 290(3.92),370(3.80), 420(3.60)	48-0202-73
	pH 11	233(4.39),270(4.13), 290(4.08)	48-0202-73
$C_{10}H_7N_3$			
1H-Imidazo[4,5-f]quinoline	EtOH	250(4.38),254(4.41)	78-0221-73
1-Phthalazinecarbonitrile, 4-methyl-	EtOH	230(4.34),290(3.56)	95-0409-73
3-Quinolinecarbonitrile, 2-amino-	EtOH	217(4.56),248(4.64), 289(3.37),374(4.06)	94-1943-73
$C_{10}H_7N_3O$			
Benzenamine, 4-(1,2,4-oxadiazol-3-yl-ethynyl)-	EtOH	315(4.37)	39-2241-73C
Pyrimido[1,2-a]benzimidazol-2(1H)-one	pH 1	236(4.48),289(3.96)	4-0071-73
	pH 13	253(4.71),268s(4.06)	4-0071-73
	MeOH	211(4.05),237s(4.24), 248(4.03),263(4.66), 283(3.79)	39-1588-73C
	EtOH	239(4.47),248s(--), 264s(--),298(4.03)	4-0071-73
	EtOH	239(4.22),249(4.05)	94-2019-73
Pyrimido[1,2-a]benzimidazol-4(10H)-one	MeOH	228(4.33),250s(4.06), 321(4.02),331(4.05)	39-1588-73C
$C_{10}H_7N_3OS_2$			
4H-1,3,5-Triazino[2,1-b]benzothiazol-4-one, 2-(methylthio)-	EtOH	227(4.33),276(4.04), 316(4.36),326(4.39)	94-0074-73
$C_{10}H_7N_3O_3$			
2,3'-Bipyridine, 4-nitro-, 1-oxide	n.s.g.	276(4.24),332(4.18)	103-0352-73
1,2,4-Oxadiazole, 3-[2-(4-nitrophenyl)-ethenyl]-, (E)-	EtOH	308(4.32)	39-2241-73C
$C_{10}H_7N_3O_3S$			
4-Imidazolidinone, 5-[(3-nitrophenyl)-methylene]-2-thioxo-	pH 3-5	239(4.10),280(4.03), 358(5.39)	104-2418-73
	pH 12-13	251(4.14),320(3.95), 395(4.15)	104-2418-73
	EtOH	235(4.16),280(3.98), 360(4.37)	104-2418-73
4-Imidazolidinone, 5-[(4-nitrophenyl)-methylene]-2-thioxo-	pH 3-5	238(4.07),298(4.03), 381(5.41)	104-2418-73
	pH 12-13	258(3.96),316(4.00), 457(4.23)	104-2418-73
	EtOH	240(4.07),300(4.00), 381(4.41)	104-2418-73
	dioxan	300(4.00),381(4.40)	104-2418-73
$C_{10}H_7N_3S$			
Thiazolo[3,2-b][1,2,4]triazole, 2-phen-yl-	MeOH	210(4.20),256(4.33)	4-0947-73
$C_{10}H_7N_5OS$			
2H-Purin-2-one, 1,3,6,7-tetrahydro-8-(3-pyridinyl)-6-thioxo-	pH 8	247(4.29),366(4.45)	35-0739-73

Compound	Solvent	$\lambda_{max}(\log \epsilon)$	Ref.
$C_{10}H_7N_5O_2$			
1H-1,2,3-Triazole-4-carbonitrile, 5-amino-1-(4-hydroxy-5-oxo-1,3,6-cycloheptatrien-1-yl)-	n.s.g.	227(4.41),246(4.20), 346(3.88)	18-1212-73
$C_{10}H_7N_5S$			
6H-Purine-6-thione, 1,9-dihydro-8-(3-pyridinyl)-	pH 8	256(4.31),348(4.40)	39-2019-73C
2-Pyridinamine, N-3H-[1,2,4]thiadiazolo-[4,3-a]pyrimidin-4-ylidene-	n.s.g.	252(4.14),273(4.02), 324(4.10),337(4.16), 407(3.53),423(3.51)	44-3087-73
Thiazolo[5,4-e]-1,2,4-triazine, 6-methyl-3-(2-pyridinyl)-	MeOH	246(4.32),276(4.13), 287(4.14),307(4.07)	40-1519-73
$C_{10}H_8$			
Benzene, 1-buten-3-ynyl-	EtOH	282(4.48)	78-3797-73
Naphthalene	$C_2H_4Cl_2$	277(3.75),311(2.35)	24-2427-73
tetracyanoethylene complex	CH_2Cl_2	430(3.04),550(3.08)	39-0447-73B
$C_{10}H_8Br_2N_2$			
Benzo[1,2-b:4,5-b']dipyrrole, 4,8-dibromo-1,2,3,5-tetrahydro-	EtOH	224(4.53),280(3.97), 324(3.71)	39-0832-73C
	EtOH-acid	295(4.04)	39-0832-73C
Compound A, m. 155°	EtOH	303(4.10)	39-0832-73C
	EtOH-acid	282(4.04),295s(3.98)	39-0832-73C
$C_{10}H_8Br_2N_2O_2$			
2H-Pyrrol-2-one, 3,4-dibromo-1,5-dihydro-5-hydroxy-1-methyl-5-(3-pyridinyl)-	EtOH	225(4.12),262(3.65)	39-2046-73C
$C_{10}H_8ClIN_2O_2$			
Iodonium, phenyl(1,2,3,4-tetrahydro-2,4-dioxo-5-pyrimidinyl)-, chloride	pH 3	270(4.1)	103-0510-73
	pH 9	298(4.1)	103-0510-73
	pH 13	295(4.0)	103-0510-73
$C_{10}H_8ClNO$			
1H-Indole-2-carboxaldehyde, 5-chloro-3-methyl-	EtOH	240(4.28),315(4.39)	78-0603-73
	isoPrOH	238(4.27),314(4.37)	44-3077-73
$C_{10}H_8ClNS$			
2-Propenenitrile, 3-[(4-chlorophenyl)-thio]-2-methyl-	EtOH	240s(--),282(4.15)	94-1305-73
2(1H)-Quinolinethione, 6-chloro-4-methyl-	EtOH	230(4.20),285(3.96), 400(4.10)	103-0481-73
Thiazole, 4-(chloromethyl)-2-phenyl-	MeOH	218(3.95),290(4.05)	80-0685-73
$C_{10}H_8ClN_5S$			
1H-Pyrido[2,3-b]pyrimido[4,5-e][1,4]-thiazin-2-amine, 7-chloro-4-methyl-	MeOH	245(3.45),321(3.47)	44-4386-73
$C_{10}H_8Cl_3N_2P$			
1,3,2-Diazaphosphorine, 2,2,4-trichloro-2,2-dihydro-5-methyl-6-phenyl-	hexane	262(4.00),353(4.12)	112-0621-73
$C_{10}H_8Cl_5N$			
Quinoline, 2,5,6,7,8-pentachloro-5,6,7,8-tetrahydro-4-methyl-	EtOH	270(3.72),278(3.69)	95-0073-73
Quinoline, 5,6,7,8,8-pentachloro-5,6,7,8-tetrahydro-4-methyl-	EtOH	267(3.28),274(3.16)	95-0073-73

Compound	Solvent	λ_{max}(log ε)	Ref.
$C_{10}H_8FNO_3$			
1H-Pyrrole-2-carboxylic acid, 4-fluoro-5-(2-furanyl)-, methyl ester	MeOH	220(4.13),317(4.20)	24-3544-73
$C_{10}H_8F_3N_2O_4$			
2-Propanone, 1-[2,4-dinitro-6-(trifluoromethyl)-2,4-cyclohexadien-1-yl]-, ion(1-), K salt	acetone	373(--),533(4.40)	104-2106-73
2-Propanone, 1-[2,6-dinitro-4-(trifluoromethyl)-2,4-cyclohexadien-1-yl]-, ion(1-), K salt	acetone	373(--),639(4.26)	104-2106-73
$C_{10}H_8F_3N_3O$			
Pyrazolo[1,5-a]pyrimidine, 3-(trifluoroacetyl)-5,7-dimethyl-	MeOH	212(3.73),224(4.48), 317(4.01)	88-3149-73
$C_{10}H_8F_4OS$			
4H-Cyclopropa[e][1]benzothiophene, 6a-(difluoromethoxy)-6,6-difluoro-5,5a,6,6a-tetrahydro-	n.s.g.	236(3.75)	35-6655-73
$C_{10}H_8F_6O_2S_2$			
2,4-Pentanedione, 3-[4,5-bis(trifluoromethyl)-1,3-dithiol-2-yl]-	isooctane	235s(3.41),315(3.41)	35-4379-73
$C_{10}H_8IN_7$			
3H-1,2,3-Triazolo[4,5-d]pyrimidine-5,7-diamine, 3-(4-iodophenyl)-	EtOH	220(4.42),303(4.25)	42-0260-73
$C_{10}H_8N_2$			
Benzo[1,2-b:4,5-b']dipyrrole, 1,5-dihydro-	EtOH	302(4.22),324(3.96), 334(3.96)	39-0832-73C
1H-Indole-3-acetonitrile	MeOH	224(4.28),272(3.83), 278(3.83),288(3.75)	102-0447-73
after ten minutes	H_2SO_4	237(3.69),242(3.66), 295(3.70)(changing)	102-0447-73
4-Isoquinolinecarbonitrile, 1,2-dihydro-	EtOH	330(3.77)	94-1914-73
3-Quinolinecarbonitrile, 1,4-dihydro-	EtOH	325(4.06)	94-1914-73
$C_{10}H_8N_2O$			
2,3'-Bipyridine, 1-oxide	EtOH	243(4.4),270(4.1)	103-0349-73
2,3'-Bipyridine, 1'-oxide	EtOH	245(4.5),270(4.5)	103-0349-73
7-Oxabicyclo[2.2.1]hepta-2,5-diene-2,3-dicarbonitrile, 1,4-dimethyl-	EtOH	307(3.05)	88-4321-73
7-Oxabicyclo[4.3.0]nona-3,8-diene-3,4-dicarbonitrile	MeOH	236(3.98),239(3.97), 247(3.85)	33-3004-73
3(2H)-Pyridazinone, 6-phenyl-	EtOH	253(4.34)	22-0625-73
Pyridine, 2-(2-pyridinyloxy)-	50% EtOH	216(4.00),264(3.90)	32-0709-73
Pyridine, 2-(3-pyridinyloxy)-	50% EtOH	214(4.00),264(3.80)	32-0709-73
$C_{10}H_8N_2OS$			
4-Imidazolidinone, 5-(phenylmethylene)-2-thioxo-	pH 3-5	246(4.11),288(3.95), 364(4.52)	104-2418-73
	pH 12-13	246(4.02),325(4.00), 380(4.36)	104-2418-73
	EtOH	246(4.11),291(3.91), 364(4.53)	104-2418-73
	dioxan	291(3.93),364(4.53)	104-2418-73

Compound	Solvent	$\lambda_{max}(\log \epsilon)$	Ref.
$C_{10}H_8N_2O_2$			
2,3'-Bipyridine, 1,1'-dioxide	EtOH	240(4.5),260(4.3)	103-0349-73
1H-Indole, 3-(2-nitroethenyl)-	EtOH-pH 7	400(4.35)	104-1082-73
	EtOH-pH 8	480(4.58)	104-1082-73
1H-Indole-3-acetamide, α-oxo-	MeOH	255(4.09),267(4.03), 272(4.00),323(4.06)	102-0447-73
after 30 minutes	H_2SO_4	249(4.05),271(4.15), 376(3.96)(changing)	102-0447-73
1H-Indole-3-glyoxal, 1-oxime	EtOH	238(4.03),251(4.02), 270(3.96),276(3.93), 333(4.01)	78-3761-73
2,4(1H,3H)-Pyrimidinedione, 5-phenyl-	EtOH	240(4.03),279(3.93)	94-1090-73
1H-Pyrrole-2,5-dione, 3-amino-1-phenyl-	EtOH	233(4.31),258(4.03), 360(3.45)	44-4324-73
4(3H)-Quinazolinone, 2-acetyl-	EtOH	226(4.04),230(4.05), 250(3.66),261(3.53), 290(3.69),304(3.80), 320(3.92)	95-0619-73
$C_{10}H_8N_2O_2S$			
2(1H)-Quinolinethione, 4-methyl-6-nitro-	DMF	283(4.21),417(4.33)	103-0481-73
$C_{10}H_8N_2O_2S_2$			
Benzenamine, 4-[(2-nitro-3-thienyl)-thio]-	MeOH	368(4.03)	4-1007-73
Benzenamine, 4-[(3-nitro-2-thienyl)-thio]-	MeOH	362(3.83)	4-1007-73
$C_{10}H_8N_2O_2S_3$			
Benzene, 1-isothiocyanato-4-[(2-isothio-cyanatoethyl)sulfonyl]-	EtOH	229(4.42),285s(4.32), 293(4.36)	73-0289-73
Thiocyanic acid, 2-[(4-isothiocyanato-phenyl)sulfonyl]ethyl ester	EtOH	229(4.33),285s(4.26), 293(4.33)	73-0289-73
$C_{10}H_8N_2O_3$			
2,3,4(5H)-Furantrione, 3-(phenylhydra-zone)	EtOH	230(3.95),246(3.85), 255(3.80),389(4.28)	98-0676-73
1H-Indole-2-carboxaldehyde, 3-methyl-4-nitro-	EtOH	233(4.19),337(3.89)	78-0603-73
1H-Indole-2-carboxaldehyde, 3-methyl-5-nitro-	EtOH	296(4.59),335s(4.06)	78-0603-73
1H-Indole-2-carboxaldehyde, 3-methyl-6-nitro-	EtOH	240(4.04),255(4.02), 330(4.26),370s(3.64)	78-0603-73
1H-Indole-2-carboxaldehyde, 3-methyl-7-nitro-	EtOH	298(4.18),372(4.11)	78-0603-73
2,7-Naphthyridinium, 6-carboxy-7,8-di-hydro-2-methyl-8-oxo-, hydroxide, inner salt	H_2O	356(4.10)	88-1447-73
$C_{10}H_8N_2O_4$			
2H-1-Benzopyran-2-one, 4-(methylamino)-3-nitro-	EtOH	252(4.20),282(4.08), 352(3.33)	103-0816-73
$C_{10}H_8N_2S_3$			
Benzene, 1-isothiocyanato-4-[(2-isothio-cyanatoethyl)thio]-	EtOH	220s(4.42),290(4.37), 299s(4.33)	73-0289-73
$C_{10}H_8N_3O_5S$			
Thiocyanic acid, 2,4-dinitro-5-(2-oxo-propyl)-1,3-cyclohexadien-1-yl ester, ion(1-), K salt	acetone	380(4.19),560(4.36)	104-2106-73

Compound	Solvent	λ_{max}(log ε)	Ref.
Thiocyanic acid, 4,6-dinitro-5-(2-oxo-propyl)-1,3-cyclohexadien-1-yl ester, ion(1-), K salt	DMSO	342(4.27),660(4.21)	104-2106-73
$C_{10}H_8N_4$			
Pyridazine, 3,3'-(1,2-ethenediyl)bis-	EtOH	273(4.26)	94-0125-73
$C_{10}H_8N_4O_2$			
Pyridazine, 3,3'-(1,2-ethenediyl)bis-, 1,1'-dioxide	EtOH	263(3.43)	94-0125-73
Pyridazine, 3,3'-(1,2-ethenediyl)bis-, 2,2'-dioxide	EtOH	262(3.26),323(3.04)	94-0125-73
$C_{10}H_8N_4O_2S$			
2H-1,2,4-Thiadiazino[5,6-b]quinoxaline, 3-methyl-, 1,1-dioxide	EtOH	246(4.46),273(4.19), 362(3.98)	18-1890-73
$C_{10}H_8N_4O_3$			
1,2,4-Triazine-5,6-dione, 1-acetyl-1,2-dihydro-3-(2-pyridinyl)-	MeOH	288(4.16),298(4.16)	40-1519-73
$C_{10}H_8N_6O_2$			
Benzo[g]pteridine-2,4(1H,3H)-dione, 8,9-diamino-	EtOH-2% DMSO	320(4.55),398(3.99), 500(3.62)	65-2285-73
$C_{10}H_8N_6O_3$			
2,4,6(1H,3H,5H)-Pyrimidinetrione, 5-(1,4-dihydro-4-pteridinyl)-	pH 5.0	255(4.25),309(3.94)	39-1615-73C
	pH 10.0	258(4.25),301(3.70), 310(3.70),337(3.80)	39-1615-73C
$C_{10}H_8N_6O_7$			
2,4,6(1H,3H,5H)-Pyrimidinetrione, 5-[2-(2,4-dinitrophenyl)hydrazino]-	EtOH	395(4.40)	103-0247-73
$C_{10}H_8O$			
2-Naphthalenol	heptane	328(3.50)	2-0577-73
	C_6H_{12}	330(3.23)	2-0577-73
	THF	333(3.39)	2-0577-73
	pyridine	335(3.40)	2-0577-73
	$C_2H_2Cl_2$	330(3.53)	2-0577-73
$C_{10}H_8OS$			
2H-1-Benzothiopyran-2-one, 4-methyl-	EtOH	335(4.04)	40-0118-73
	$HClO_4$	358(3.86)	40-0118-73
4H-Cyclohepta[b]thiophen-4-one, 2-methyl-	EtOH	242(4.27),330(3.93), 350(3.90),365(3.88)	39-0968-73C
	H_2SO_4	247(4.02),275(4.03), 293s(--),325(3.33), 335(3.38),405(3.47)	39-0968-73C
$C_{10}H_8OS_2$			
1,3-Dithiol-2-one, 4-methyl-5-phenyl-	EtOH	225(3.67),261(3.83)	143-0273-73
$C_{10}H_8O_2$			
2H-1-Benzopyran-2-one, 4-methyl-	EtOH	274(4.08)	40-0118-73
2,4,6-Cycloheptatrien-1-one, 2-(2-propynyloxy)-	EtOH	237(4.38),319(3.93), 343s(3.83)	39-1960-73C
4H-Pyran, 4-(4H-pyran-4-ylidene)-	MeCN-Et_3N	305s(--),316(4.60), 332(4.71),375s(--), 395s(--),420s(--)	5-1036-73

Compound	Solvent	$\lambda_{max}(\log \epsilon)$	Ref.
$C_{10}H_8O_2S_2$			
1,3-Dithiol-2-one, 4-(4-methoxyphenyl)-	EtOH	230(3.83),288(4.10)	143-0273-73
$C_{10}H_8O_3$			
2-Benzofurancarboxaldehyde, 5-methoxy-	EtOH	220(4.11),293(4.30), 337s(3.76)	103-0552-73
3-Benzofurancarboxaldehyde, 2-methoxy-	90% EtOH	233(4.11),244(4.00), 283s(3.96),288(3.98)	12-1079-73
4-Benzofurancarboxylic acid, methyl ester	90% EtOH	267(3.96),272(3.96), 302(3.76)	12-1079-73
2(3H)-Benzofuranone, 3-(methoxymethyl-ene)-	90% EtOH	222(4.00),244(4.06), 248(4.06),252(4.05), 289s(3.95),294(3.97), 317(3.91)	12-1079-73
1H-2-Benzopyran-5-carboxaldehyde, 3,4-dihydro-1-oxo-	n.s.g.	223(4.84),290(3.54)	102-1191-73
2H-1-Benzopyran-2-one, 6-methoxy-	MeOH	225(4.39),275(4.04), 341(3.65)	24-0388-73
2,5-Etheno-5H-1,3,4-benzotrioxepin	ether	212(3.86),278(3.22), 285(3.18)	77-0344-73
Furo[2,3-b]benzofuran-2(3H)-one, 3a,8a-dihydro-	EtOH	274(3.42),281(3.34)	44-3874-73
1-Indanone, 4,5-(methylenedioxy)-	EtOH	236(4.37),286(3.80), 307s(3.69)	141-0001-73
	dioxan	231s(4.40),235(4.45), 282(3.92),291s(3.84), 302s(3.71)	141-0001-73
1-Indanone, 5,6-(methylenedioxy)-	EtOH	231(4.20),267(3.85), 316(3.95)	141-0001-73
	dioxan	226s(4.23),230(4.26), 263(3.88),313(3.96)	141-0001-73
1-Indanone, 6,7-(methylenedioxy)-	EtOH	232(4.30),247(4.01), 256(4.02),347(3.55)	141-0001-73
	dioxan	230(4.41),245(4.06), 254(4.02),338(3.62)	141-0001-73
1,3-Isobenzofurandione, 4,7-dimethyl-	ether	217(4.59),254(3.54), 308(3.58),320(3.59)	24-0674-73
$C_{10}H_8O_3S$			
2H-1-Benzopyran-2-one, 7-hydroxy-4-(methylthio)-	EtOH	254(3.83),294(4.39), 327(4.42)	95-0836-73
$C_{10}H_8O_4$			
Cinnamic acid, 2',3'-(methylenedioxy)-, trans	EtOH	232(4.18),275(4.28), 329(3.52)	141-0001-73
	dioxan	235(4.12),278(4.32), 336(3.54)	141-0001-73
Cinnamic acid, 3',4'-(methylenedioxy)-, trans	EtOH	215(4.19),234(4.08), 238s(4.06),289(4.07), 324(4.18)	141-0001-73
	EtOH-NaOH	218(4.21),229s(4.16), 279s(4.12),282(4.13), 314(4.13)	141-0001-73
	dioxan	218(4.12),235(4.08), 240s(4.05),290(4.09), 324(4.23)	141-0001-73
1,3-Dioxolane-2,4-dione, 5-methyl-5-phenyl-	n.s.g.	235.5(3.234)	25-0695-73
1-Indanone, 2-hydroxy-5,6-(methylene-dioxy)-	EtOH	233(4.22),270(3.88), 322(4.01)	141-0001-73

Compound	Solvent	$\lambda_{max}(\log \epsilon)$	Ref.
1-Indanone, 2-hydroxy-5,6-(methylene-dioxy)- (cont.)	dioxan	232(4.25),267(3.90), 319(4.01)	141-0001-73
$C_{10}H_8O_4S$			
2-Propynoic acid, 3-(4-acetoxy-2-thien-yl)-, methyl ester	ether	254(4.02),264(4.00), 290(4.09)	24-0497-73
$C_{10}H_8O_5$			
2H-1-Benzopyran-2-one, 5,6-dihydroxy-7-methoxy-	n.s.g.	277(3.45),350(3.80)	105-0465-73
Phthalic anhydride, 3,4-dimethoxy-	EtOH	214(4.24),242(4.16), 270s(3.60),334(3.46)	141-0001-73
	dioxan	232s(4.22),240(4.27), 275(3.63),331(3.72)	141-0001-73
Phthalic anhydride, 3,5-dimethoxy-	EtOH	209(4.44),219s(4.34), 240s(3.94),305(3.56), 342s(3.09)	141-0001-73
	dioxan	225(4.34),241(4.34), 283(3.60),333(3.80)	141-0001-73
Phthalic anhydride, 4,5-dimethoxy-	EtOH	220(4.19),246(4.36), 266s(3.69),293(3.61), 323(3.50)	141-0001-73
	dioxan	222s(4.06),244s(4.45), 247(4.47),268s(3.48), 303s(3.62),322(3.69)	141-0001-73
Phthalide, 4-methoxy-5,6-(methylene-dioxy)-	EtOH	222(4.42),273(3.85), 295s(3.62)	141-0001-73
Phthalide, 6-methoxy-4,5-(methylene-dioxy)-	EtOH	223(4.43),283(3.90)	141-0001-73
	dioxan	229(4.29),277(3.90)	141-0001-73
$C_{10}H_8O_6$			
Cyclopentaneacetic acid, α,2,3,5-tetra-oxo-4-(2-propenyl)-	H_2O	256(4.13),327(4.03)	94-2195-73
Homophthalic acid, 4,5-(methylenedioxy)-	EtOH	219(4.36),262(3.78), 297(3.68)	141-0001-73
	EtOH-NaOH	219(4.08),250(3.71), 293(3.62)	141-0001-73
	dioxan	226(4.20),263(3.81), 299(3.71)	141-0001-73
$C_{10}H_8O_8$			
1,2,3-Benzenetricarboxylic acid, 4,6-dihydroxy-5-methyl-	EtOH	239(4.46),314(3.56)	33-2287-73
$C_{10}H_8S_2$			
4H-Thiopyran, 4-(4H-thiopyran-4-ylid-ene)-	$MeCN-Et_3N$	350s(--),415s(--), 440(4.44),451(4.64), 666(3.90),726(4.17)	5-1036-73
$C_{10}H_9Br$			
Benzene, 1-bromo-3-(1-methylene-2-prop-enyl)-	hexane	218(4.36),223(4.21), 239(3.93)	104-2473-73
Benzene, 1-bromo-4-(1-methylene-2-prop-enyl)-	hexane	216(4.14),223(4.09), 243(3.84)	104-2473-73
$C_{10}H_9BrClNOS$			
4-Thiazolol, 2-(4-bromophenyl)-4-(chlo-romethyl)-4,5-dihydro-	MeOH	255(4.34)	80-0685-73
hydrochloride	MeOH	255(4.29)	80-0685-73

Compound	Solvent	λmax(log ε)	Ref.
$C_{10}H_9BrN_2O_2$			
2H-Pyrrol-2-one, 3-bromo-1,5-dihydro-5-hydroxy-1-methyl-5-(3-pyridinyl)-	EtOH	218(4.11),262(3.58)	39-2046-73C
2H-Pyrrol-2-one, 4-bromo-1,5-dihydro-5-hydroxy-1-methyl-5-(3-pyridinyl)-	EtOH	217(4.16),262(3.61)	39-2046-73C
$C_{10}H_9BrO$			
Benzofuran, 7-bromo-2,5-dimethyl-	n.s.g.	252(4.03),277(3.44),290(3.48)	33-1457-73
2-Propen-1-one, 1-(4-bromophenyl)-2-methyl-	MeOH	258(4.11)	44-4044-73
$C_{10}H_9BrOS$			
1-Benzothiepin-5(2H)-one, 4-bromo-3,4-dihydro-	EtOH	243(4.24),261(3.79),330(3.55)	44-2623-73
8H-Cyclohepta[b]thiophene, 5-bromo-4-methoxy-	EtOH	225(4.32),278(3.89),365(2.81)	44-0146-73
$C_{10}H_9BrO_2$			
2,4,6-Cycloheptatrien-1-one, 2-bromo-7-hydroxy-6-(2-propenyl)-	EtOH	260(4.55),328(3.83),374(3.81)	39-1960-73C
2,4,6-Cycloheptatrien-1-one, 2-bromo-7-(2-propenyloxy)-	C_6H_{12}	256(4.43),328(3.92),360(3.89),374s(3.77)	39-1960-73C
2,4,6-Cycloheptatrien-1-one, 3-bromo-2-(2-propenyloxy)-	C_6H_{12}	254(4.28),326(3.83)	39-1960-73C
$C_{10}H_9BrO_3S$			
1-Benzothiepin-5(2H)-one, 4-bromo-3,4-dihydro-, 1,1-dioxide	EtOH	224(3.59),242(3.56),270(3.29),308(2.64)	44-2623-73
$C_{10}H_9Br_2NO$			
9H-Cyclohepta[b]pyridin-9-one, 8,8-dibromo-6,7,8,9-tetrahydro-	EtOH	211(3.85),264(3.58),270s(--)	39-0968-73C
$C_{10}H_9Br_3OS$			
4H-Cyclohepta[b]thiophen-4-one, 3,5,5-tribromo-5,6,7,8-tetrahydro-2-methyl-	EtOH	232s(--),268(3.32)	39-0968-73C
$C_{10}H_9ClN_2O$			
1,2,4-Oxadiazole, 3-[2-(4-chlorophenyl)-ethenyl]-4,5-dihydro-, (E)-	EtOH	274(4.34)	39-2241-73C
2(1H)-Quinoxalinone, 6(or 7)-chloro-1,3-dimethyl-	EtOH	234(4.48),277(3.57),340(3.57)	22-1285-73
$C_{10}H_9ClN_2O_2S$			
1H-Pyrazole, 3-[(4-chlorophenyl)sulfonyl]-4,5-dihydro-4-methylene-	EtOH	237(4.35),325(3.86)	22-2746-73
$C_{10}H_9ClN_2S$			
2-Thiazolamine, 4-(chloromethyl)-N-phenyl-	MeOH	246s(--),290(4.29)	80-0685-73
hydrochloride	MeOH	292(4.45)	80-0685-73
$C_{10}H_9ClO$			
2-Propen-1-one, 3-chloro-1-phenyl-	EtOH	246(4.15)	78-4241-73
$C_{10}H_9ClOS$			
8H-Cyclohepta[b]thiophene, 5-chloro-4-methoxy-	EtOH	225(4.32),278(3.91),360(2.81)	44-0146-73

Compound	Solvent	λ max(log ε)	Ref.
$C_{10}H_9ClS$			
8H-Cyclohepta[b]thiophene, 5-chloro-4-methyl-	MeCN	225(4.30),280(3.88)	44-0146-73
$C_{10}H_9F_3$			
Benzene, 1-(1-propenyl)-3-(trifluoromethyl)-	EtOH	225(3.22),250(3.40)	35-5288-73
$C_{10}H_9IO$			
2-Propen-1-one, 3-iodo-1-(4-methylphenyl)-	dioxan	287(4.30)	24-0435-73
$C_{10}H_9N$			
Bicyclo[6.1.0]nona-2,4,6-triene-9-carbonitrile, anti	hexane	242.5(3.67)	88-3067-73
syn	hexane	242.5(3.52)	88-3067-73
1H-Indene-1-carbonitrile, 3a,7a-dihydro-	hexane	210(3.18),251s(3.52), 260(3.62),268(3.59), 278s(3.32)	88-3067-73
isomer	hexane	210s(3.32),252s(3.51), 260(3.61),269(3.59), 278s(3.36)	88-3067-73
1H-Indene-1-carbonitrile, 7,7a-dihydro-	hexane	295(4.02)	88-3067-73
1-Naphthalenamine	heptane	318(3.32)	2-0577-73
	THF	333(3.55)	2-0577-73
	pyridine	334(3.66)	2-0577-73
Quinoline, 8-methyl-	EtOH	233(4.51),235(4.51), 292(3.55),304(3.51), 316(3.39)	105-0191-73
$C_{10}H_9NO$			
Benzeneacetonitrile, α-acetyl-	10% EtOH-pH 12	197(4.26),223(3.94), 251(3.98),292(4.18)	22-3458-73
1H-Indole-2-carboxaldehyde, 3-methyl-	EtOH	237(4.09),314(4.32)	78-0603-73
	n.s.g.	240(4.33),316(4.53)	35-3400-73
2-Propenenitrile, 3-(4-methoxyphenyl)-	EtOH	228(4.15),308(4.39)	40-2347-73
2H-Pyrrol-2-one, 3,4-dihydro-5-phenyl-	EtOH	242(4.09),274s(3.08)	39-2523-73C
2(1H)-Quinolinone, 4-methyl-	DMF	331(3.83)	40-0118-73
$C_{10}H_9NOS$			
2-Propenenitrile, 3-[4-(methylsulfinyl)-phenyl]-, (E)-	EtOH	282(4.36)	39-2241-73C
$C_{10}H_9NO_2$			
3-Benzofurancarboxamide, 2-methyl-	EtOH	213(4.18),233(4.00), 261(4.06),294(4.01), 306(3.98)	103-0026-73
Benzonitrile, 2-(2-oxopropoxy)-	EtOH	231(4.05),237s(4.01), 293(3.67),299s(3.66)	48-0779-73
5H-Cyclohepta[b]pyridine-5,9(6H)-dione, 7,8-dihydro-	EtOH	212(4.08),236(3.80), 270s(--)	39-0026-73C
5H-Cyclohepta[c]pyridine-5,9(6H)-dione, 7,8-dihydro-	EtOH	209(4.02),228(3.69), 283(3.35)	39-0026-73C
Ethanone, 1-(3-amino-2-benzofuranyl)-	EtOH	235(4.18),255(4.05), 301s(4.05),308(4.12), 351(4.14)	48-0779-73
1H-Indole-3-acetic acid	MeOH	223(4.40),273(3.78), 280(3.80),289(3.72)	102-0447-73
after ten minutes at 70°	H_2SO_4	234(3.67),240s(3.60), 289(3.70)	102-0447-73

Compound	Solvent	λ_{max}(log ε)	Ref.
1H-Indole-3-acetic acid (cont.) after three hours at 70°	H_2SO_4	232(4.00),264(3.63), 285(3.63)	102-0447-73
2-Indolizinecarboxylic acid, methyl ester	EtOH	291(3.37),301(3.43), 342(3.41)	36-1897-73
5(2H)-Oxazolone, 4-benzyl-	EtOH	230(3.10)(end abs.)	33-2007-73
$C_{10}H_9NO_3$			
1,3-Benzodioxole-5-propanenitrile, β-hydroxy-	EtOH	238(3.51),287(3.53)	40-2347-73
1-Indanone, 5,6-(methylenedioxy)-, oxime	EtOH	212(4.44),225s(4.14), 262(4.09),314(4.04), 319s(4.02),326s(3.99)	141-0001-73
	dioxan	221(4.12),260(4.08), 316(4.02),321s(4.00)	141-0001-73
1H-Indole-3-acetic acid, 5-hydroxy-	MeOH	227(4.22),277(3.86), 299(3.72),312s(3.60)	102-0447-73
after ten minutes	H_2SO_4	248(3.71),318(3.71)	102-0447-73
$C_{10}H_9NO_3S$			
2-Propenal, 2-nitro-3-[(phenylmethyl)-thio]-	$CHCl_3$	273(3.91),350(4.25)	104-2245-73
$C_{10}H_9NO_3S_2$			
Thieno[2,3-b]thiophene-3-carboxylic acid, 2-(acetylamino)-, methyl ester	MeOH	249(4.16),319(3.97)	48-0039-73
$C_{10}H_9NO_4$			
2H-1,4-Benzoxazine-6,7-dione, 5-acetyl-3,4-dihydro-	EtOH	293(4.40),452(3.34)	78-2881-73
	CH_2Cl_2	290(4.34),447(3.33)	78-2881-73
$C_{10}H_9NO_4S$			
Thiazolo[3,2-a]pyridinium, 2,3-dicarboxy-2,3-dihydro-5-methyl-, hydroxide, inner salt, trans	pH 13	227(3.86),242(3.86), 337(3.80)	1-1749-73
	HCOOH	262(3.08),330(3.87)	1-1749-73
$C_{10}H_9NO_5$			
2H-1,4-Benzoxazine-5-carboxylic acid, 3,4,6,7-tetrahydro-6,7-dioxo-, methyl ester	EtOH	270(4.08),308(4.19), 452(3.49)	78-2881-73
	CH_2Cl_2	272(4.08),304(4.13), 444(3.36)	78-2881-73
$C_{10}H_9NS$			
2-Propenenitrile, 3-[4-(methylthio)-phenyl]-	EtOH	330(4.45)	39-2241-73C
trans	EtOH	238(4.07),329(4.43)	39-2241-73C
2(1H)-Quinolinethione, 4-methyl-	EtOH	220(4.48),280(4.32), 390(4.10)	103-0481-73
$C_{10}H_9N_3$			
[2,3'-Bipyridin]-4-amine	n.s.g.	238(4.55)	103-0352-73
Imidazo[2,1-b]quinazoline, 5,10-dihydro-	EtOH	230(3.70),237(3.61), 274(4.10)	87-0407-73
$C_{10}H_9N_3O$			
Acetamide, N-2-quinoxalinyl-	pH 4.02	227(4.01),255(4.51), 340(3.93)	103-0369-73
	8.6N H_2SO_4	236(4.09),262(4.41), 353(4.04)	103-0369-73
1,2,4-Oxadiazole, 3-(4-aminostyryl)-, trans	EtOH	281(4.32)	39-2241-73C
1-Phthalazinecarboxamide, 4-methyl-	EtOH	222(4.52),278(3.51)	95-0409-73

Compound	Solvent	λ_{max}(log ϵ)	Ref.
2-Propanone, 1-pyrido[2,3-d]pyrimidin-2-yl-	EtOH	228(4.17),244(4.04), 321(4.06)	94-2643-73
Pyrimido[1,2-a]benzimidazol-2(1H)-one, 3,4-dihydro-	pH 1	234(4.13),279(4.15), 287(4.18)	4-0071-73
	pH 13	263(3.89),272(3.87), 302(4.32)	4-0071-73
	EtOH	252(4.06),260s(--), 284(4.12),292(4.13)	4-0071-73
1,2,4-Triazine, 3-methoxy-5-phenyl-	n.s.g.	205(4.47),232(3.99), 269(4.06),309(4.36)	22-2493-73
1,2,4-Triazine, 5-methoxy-6-phenyl-	EtOH	252(3.89),294(3.90)	22-2126-73
1,2,4-Triazin-3(2H)-one, 2-methyl-5-phenyl-	EtOH	220(3.72),297(3.80)	22-2818-73
1,2,4-Triazin-5(2H)-one, 2-methyl-6-phenyl-	EtOH	256(3.93),307(4.04)	22-2126-73
1,2,4-Triazin-5(4H)-one, 4-methyl-6-phenyl-	EtOH	230(3.91),315(4.04)	22-2126-73
$C_{10}H_9N_3OS$			
Benzamide, N-(3-amino-2(3H)-thiazolylidene)-	dioxan	240(4.08),324(4.26)	4-0947-73
$C_{10}H_9N_3O_3$			
Carbamic acid, [[(2-cyanophenyl)amino]-carbonyl]-, methyl ester	MeOH	247(4.15)	39-2707-73C
Carbamic acid, (1-formyl-1H-benzimidazol-2-yl)-, methyl ester	MeCN	288s(4.17),294(4.21)	39-2707-73C
Carbamic acid, (2-quinoxalinyl)-, methyl ester, N-oxide	MeOH	256(4.74)	39-2707-73C
Sydnone imine, 3-[4-(carboxymethyl)-phenyl]-	EtOH	205(3.65),298(3.59)	103-1327-73
hydrochloride	EtOH	199(4.48),225(4.04), 285(3.85)	103-1327-73
$C_{10}H_9N_3O_4$			
Pyrido[2,3-b]pyrazine-7-carboxylic acid, 5,8-dihydro-3-methoxy-5-methyl-8-oxo-	MeOH or MeOH-acid	229(4.44),261s(4.25), 267(4.32),315s(3.91), 330(3.98)	111-0346-73
	MeOH-NaOH	225(4.32),267(4.33), 308(3.73),344(3.93)	111-0346-73
$C_{10}H_9N_3S$			
1,2,4-Triazine, 3-(methylthio)-5-phenyl-	n.s.g.	210(4.07),245s(4.01), 268(4.24),283s(4.20), 340(3.57)	22-2493-73
1,2,4-Triazine-3(2H)-thione, 2-methyl-5-phenyl-	EtOH	220(4.13),297(4.54)	22-2818-73
$C_{10}H_9N_5$			
Pyrido[2,3-b]pyrazine-7-carbonitrile, 6-amino-2,3-dimethyl-	pH -0.2	235(4.32),269(3.66), 277(3.43),368(4.18), 384(4.18)	39-1974-73C
	pH 7.0	217(4.51),237(4.34), 267s(3.95),385(4.06)	39-1974-73C
$C_{10}H_9N_5O$			
1H-1,2,3-Triazolo[4,5-b]pyridin-7-amine, N-(2-furanylmethyl)-	N HCl	219(4.30),259(3.90), 315(4.26)	102-2087-73
	N NaOH	224(4.20),265(3.90), 272(3.95),299(4.20)	102-2087-73

Compound	Solvent	$\lambda_{max}(\log \epsilon)$	Ref.
1H-1,2,3-Triazolo[4,5-b]pyridin-7-amine, N-(2-furanylmethyl)- (cont.)	EtOH	221(4.23),267(4.00), 310(4.23),318s(--)	102-2087-73
1H-1,2,3-Triazolo[4,5-c]pyridin-4-amine, N-(2-furanylmethyl)-	N HCl	217(4.08),280(4.08)	102-2087-73
	N NaOH	225(4.34),292(4.18)	102-2087-73
	EtOH	221(4.30),277(4.32)	102-2087-73
$C_{10}H_9N_5O_2$			
Acetamide, N-[2,5-dihydro-5-oxo-3-(2-pyridinyl)-1,2,4-triazin-6-yl]-	MeOH	238(3.21),246(4.18), 269(4.24),302(4.03)	40-1519-73
$C_{10}H_9N_5O_4$			
4-Pyridinecarboxylic acid, 2-(hexahydro-2,4,6-trioxo-5-pyrimidinyl)hydrazide	EtOH	246(4.17)	103-0247-73
$C_{10}H_9O_2$			
1,3-Butanedione, 1-phenyl-, ion(1-), tetrabutylammonium salt	$CHCl_3$	248(3.79),310(4.10)	1-0258-73
$C_{10}H_9P$			
Isophosphinoline, 3-methyl-	ether	252(4.46),304(3.82), 343(2.65),360(2.43)	88-2397-73
$C_{10}H_{10}$			
Bicyclo[3.2.2]nona-2,6,8-triene, 4-methylene-	C_6H_{12}	232(3.96),255s(3.74)	44-1893-73
Bicyclo[4.2.1]nona-2,4,7-triene, 9-methylene-	C_6H_{12}	254s(3.46),261(3.53), 270(3.53),280s(3.33)	44-1893-73
	C_6H_{12}	217(3.57),245s(3.52), 260(3.59),265(3.58), 275s(3.31)	89-0081-73
1,3-Butadiene, 1-phenyl-	MeOH	220(4.1),230(3.9), 270(4.4),280(4.5), 290(4.3),300(3.8)	32-0309-73
2,4,6,8-Cyclononatetraene, 1-methylene-	C_6H_{12}	233(3.93),260s(3.75)	88-3623-73
Naphthalene, 4a,8a-dihydro-, trans	MeCN	285(3.42)	89-0572-73
$C_{10}H_{10}BrN$			
Acetonitrile, [4-(bromomethylene)-5,5-dimethyl-2-cyclopenten-1-ylidene]-	EtOH	310(4.17)	88-0411-73
$C_{10}H_{10}BrNOS_2$			
3H-Indol-3-one, 6-bromo-1,2-dihydro-2,2-bis(methylthio)-	EtOH	225s(4.32),248(4.40), 270s(3.90),355s(3.20), 402(3.43)	12-2153-73
$C_{10}H_{10}BrN_4O_7P$			
Inosine, 8-bromo-, cyclic 3',5'-(hydrogen phosphate)	pH 1	253(4.15)	69-5310-73
	pH 11	258(4.10)	69-5310-73
$C_{10}H_{10}BrN_4O_8P$			
Xanthosine, 8-bromo-, cyclic 3',5'-(hydrogen phosphate)	pH 1	250(4.09),263(4.10)	69-5310-73
	pH 11	262(4.13),280s(4.10)	69-5310-73
$C_{10}H_{10}Br_2N_2$			
Imidazo[1,2,3-ij][1,8]naphthyridinediium, 1,2-dihydro-, dibromide	pH 1.0	259(3.63),314(3.68), 349(3.74)	39-2885-73C
	pH 5.6	257(3.68),351(3.78)	39-2885-73C
$C_{10}H_{10}Br_2OS$			
4H-Cyclohepta[b]thiophen-4-one, 5,5-dibromo-5,6,7,8-tetrahydro-2-methyl-	EtOH	230s(--),266(3.38)	39-0968-73C

Compound	Solvent	$\lambda_{max}(\log \epsilon)$	Ref.
$C_{10}H_{10}ClNO$			
10-Azabicyclo[7.2.0]undeca-2,5,7-trien-11-one, 4-chloro-, (1R*,4S*,9R*)-	EtOH	239(3.64)	35-4647-73
2-Buten-1-one, 3-amino-2-chloro-1-phenyl-	hexane	240(3.86),322(4.06)	40-2152-73
$C_{10}H_{10}ClNOS$			
2-Azetidinone, 4-[(4-chlorophenyl)thio]-3-methyl-, trans	EtOH	226(4.08),258(3.88)	94-1090-73
Benzenepropanenitrile, α-chloro-4-(methylsulfinyl)-	EtOH	227(4.05)	39-2241-73C
2-Propenamide, 3-[(4-chlorophenyl)thio]-2-methyl-	EtOH	260s(--),284(4.19)	94-1090-73
4-Thiazolol, 4-(chloromethyl)-4,5-dihydro-2-phenyl-	MeOH	242(4.32)	80-0685-73
hydrochloride	MeOH	244(4.88)	80-0685-73
$C_{10}H_{10}ClNO_2S$			
2-Azetidinone, 4-[(4-chlorophenyl)sulfinyl]-3-methyl-, trans	EtOH	249(3.92),295s(--)	94-1305-73
$C_{10}H_{10}ClNO_3S$			
2-Azetidinone, 4-[(4-chlorophenyl)sulfonyl]-3-methyl-, trans	EtOH	231.5(4.22)	94-1305-73
$C_{10}H_{10}ClNS$			
Benzenepropanenitrile, α-chloro-4-(methylthio)-	EtOH	260(4.18)	39-2241-73C
$C_{10}H_{10}ClN_2$			
Quinoxalinium, 6(or 7)-chloro-1,3-dimethyl-, perchlorate	H_2O	248s(--),251(4.74), 348(3.72)	22-1285-73
$C_{10}H_{10}ClN_2O_3P$			
Phosphonic acid, (2-chloro-4-quinoxalinyl)-, dimethyl ester	EtOH	238(4.56),274(3.43), 285(3.43),298(3.67), 326(3.38)	48-0649-73
	EtOH	240(4.56)	108-0723-73
$C_{10}H_{10}ClN_3$			
Acetonitrile, [[1-(2-amino-5-chlorophenyl)ethylidene]amino]-	EtOH	231(4.52),362(3.66)	95-1253-73
$C_{10}H_{10}ClN_3OS$			
3-Pyrazolin-5-one, 4-[(2-amino-4-chlorophenyl)thio]-3-methyl-	EtOH	214(4.37),244(4.05), 310(3.62)	7-0045-73
3-Pyrazolin-5-one, 4-[(2-amino-5-chlorophenyl)thio]-3-methyl-	EtOH	210(4.32),222(4.28), 250(4.08),314(3.49)	7-0045-73
$C_{10}H_{10}ClN_3O_2$			
2-Butenal, 1-nitro-, (4-chlorophenyl)-hydrazone	EtOH	293(3.51)	19-0881-73
Diazene, (4-chlorophenyl)(1-methyl-1-nitro-2-propenyl)-	EtOH	284(3.64)	19-0881-73
2-Propenal, 2-methyl-1-nitro-, (4-chlorophenyl)hydrazone	EtOH	294(3.66)	19-0881-73
$C_{10}H_{10}ClN_3O_3$			
1H-Pyrimido[5,4-b][1,4]oxazine-6-carboxylic acid, 4-chloro-7-methyl-, ethyl ester	EtOH	233(4.2),255(4.0), 330(3.6),390(3.6)	103-1532-73

Compound	Solvent	$\lambda_{max}(\log \epsilon)$	Ref.
$C_{10}H_{10}ClN_5S$			
2(1H)-Pyridinethione, 3-[(2-amino-6-methyl-4-pyrimidinyl)amino]-5-chloro-	MeOH	220(3.96),245(3.89), 280s(3.66),315(4.06)	44-4386-73
$C_{10}H_{10}Cl_2OS$			
4H-Cyclohepta[c]thiophen-4-one, 1,3-dichloro-5,6,7,8-tetrahydro-5-methyl-	EtOH	228(4.01),248(3.82), 288(3.13)	22-0335-73
$C_{10}H_{10}Cl_2O_4$			
2-Cyclopentene-1-carboxylic acid, 3,5-dichloro-1-hydroxy-4-oxo-2-(1-propenyl)-, methyl ester	EtOH	289(4.37)	35-3000-73
$C_{10}H_{10}FNO_3$			
DL-Propanoic acid, 2-amino-3-(4-fluorobenzoyl)-	M HCl	249(4.13)	7-0457-73
	pH 7.38	248(4.13)	7-0457-73
	pH 13	248(4.06)	7-0457-73
Propanoic acid, 3-amino-3-(4-fluorobenzoyl)-, hydrochloride	M HCl	252(4.07)	7-0457-73
	pH 7.38	251(4.06)	7-0457-73
	pH 13	249(3.95)	7-0457-73
$C_{10}H_{10}FNO_5$			
4-Pyridinone, 1-β-D-arabinofuranosyl-2-hydroxy-5-fluoro-, ($O^2 \rightarrow 2'$)-cyclonucleoside	pH 1.0	258(4.02),266s(4.02), 276s(3.89)	87-0524-73
	pH 14.0	258(4.24),266s(4.18), 276s(3.81)	87-0524-73
$C_{10}H_{10}F_5NO$			
Hydroxylamine, N-tert-butyl-N-(pentafluorophenyl)-	EtOH	254(3.45)	78-3833-73
$C_{10}H_{10}Fe$			
Ferrocene	EtOH	320(1.7),440(2.0)	18-1851-73
(also other solvents)	CH_2Cl_2	325(1.7)	18-1851-73
$C_{10}H_{10}FeI_3$			
Ferrocenium triiodide	CH_2Cl_2	250(3.66),295(3.88), 370(3.61),500(2.81), 620(2.06)	2-0134-73
$C_{10}H_{10}HgN_2O_2$			
Mercury, (1-diazo-2-methoxy-2-oxoethyl)-(phenylmethyl)-	MeOH	251(4.28),272s(3.96), 376(1.77)	44-3937-73
$C_{10}H_{10}I_2N_8O_{14}$			
Diazodimedon-iodotrinitromethane adduct	benzene	255(4.08)	104-0208-73
	EtOH	350(3.93)	104-0208-73
$C_{10}H_{10}NO_4P$			
Phosphonic acid, (1,4-dihydro-1-methyl-4-oxo-3-quinolinyl)-	MeOH	238(4.50),294(4.01), 320(4.09),330(4.05)	94-1080-73
$C_{10}H_{10}NS$			
Thiazolium, 3-methyl-2-phenyl-, perchlorate	n.s.g.	280(4.04)	124-0353-73
Thiazolium, 3-methyl-4-phenyl-, perchlorate	n.s.g.	265(3.60)	124-0353-73
Thiazolium, 3-methyl-5-phenyl-, methosulfate	n.s.g.	287(3.99)	124-0353-73

Compound	Solvent	λ_{max}(log ϵ)	Ref.
$C_{10}H_{10}N_2$			
Benzo[1,2-b:4,5-b']dipyrrole, 1,2,3,5-tetrahydro-	EtOH	278(3.78),315(3.70)	39-0832-73C
Benzo[1,2-b:4,5-b']dipyrrole, 2,3,6,7-tetrahydro-	EtOH	293(4.23)	39-0832-73C
2-Butenenitrile, 3-(phenylamino)-	MeCN	225s(3.92),287(4.21)	44-2287-73
Imidazo[1,2,3-ij][1,8]naphthyridinediium, 1,2-dihydro-, dibromide	pH 1	259(3.63),314(3.68), 349(3.74)	25-0275-73 +39-2285-73C
	pH 5.6	257(3.68),351(3.78)	25-0275-73
1H-Pyrrolo[1,2-a]benzimidazole, 2,3-dihydro-	pH 8.0	243(3.72),248(3.69), 266(3.58),271(3.71), 278(3.72)	18-3898-73
8-Quinolinecarbonitrile, 1,2,3,4-tetrahydro-`	EtOH	261(3.81),348(3.69)	94-1914-73
$C_{10}H_{10}N_2O$			
Ethanone, 2-diazo-1-(2,5-dimethylphenyl)-	EtOH	258(3.96),292(4.01)	22-2065-73
Ethanone, 1-(1-methyl-1H-benzimidazol-2-yl)-	EtOH	237(3.58),241(3.53), 303(3.98)	22-1285-73
Indole, 1,2-dimethyl-3-nitroso-	aq $HClO_4$	250(4.18),267(4.18), 345(3.77)	39-0918-73B
1H-Indole-3-acetamide	MeOH	225(4.30),274(3.82), 281(3.85),290(3.77)	102-0447-73
after ten minutes	H_2SO_4	236(3.68),241(3.66), 291(3.72)(changing)	102-0447-73
8-Indolizinecarbonitrile, 1,2,3,7-tetrahydro-5-methyl-7-oxo-	EtOH	259(4.12),287(3.65)	95-1084-73
	EtOH-HCl	246(3.89),260(3.73)	95-1084-73
1(2H)-Isoquinolinone, 3-amino-2-methyl-	EtOH	231(4.43),304(4.25), 370(3.66)	95-1581-73
3H-Pyrazol-3-one, 2,4-dihydro-2-methyl-5-phenyl-	EtOH	301(4.09)	23-0338-73
5-Pyrazolone, 1-benzyl-	MeOH	249(3.15)	48-0382-73
	50% MeOH	245(3.46)	48-0382-73
	10% MeOH	245(3.47)	48-0382-73
4H-Pyrido[1,2-a]pyrimidin-4-one, 2,8-dimethyl-	H_2O	233(4.05),239(4.07), 246(4.00),307s(3.91), 325s(4.05),334(4.10)	4-0123-73
2(1H)-Quinoxalinone, 1,3-dimethyl-	EtOH	230(4.35),279(3.60), 336(3.69)	22-1285-73
$C_{10}H_{10}N_2OS_2$			
[1]Benzothieno[2,3-d]pyrimidin-4(1H)-one, 2,3,5,6,7,8-hexahydro-2-thioxo-	EtOH	290(3.97),330(4.14)	103-0525-73
$C_{10}H_{10}N_2O_2$			
4(3H)-Quinazolinone, 2-(1-hydroxyethyl)-	EtOH	226(4.34),230(4.32), 238(4.11),265(3.86), 273(3.82),292(3.46), 305(3.59),316(3.51)	95-0619-73
	EtOH-NaOH	226(4.27),231(4.35), 238(4.13),274(3.83), 284(3.86),312(3.68), 324(3.55)	95-0619-73
$C_{10}H_{10}N_2O_2S$			
1,2,4-Oxadiazole, 3-[4-(methylsulfinyl)-styryl]-, cis	EtOH	278(4.18)	39-2241-73C
1H-Pyrazole, 4,5-dihydro-4-methylene-3-(phenylsulfonyl)-	EtOH	222(4.03),328(3.93)	22-2746-73
1H-Pyrazole, 3-[(phenylsulfonyl)methyl]-	EtOH	218(4.08)	22-2746-73

Compound	Solvent	$\lambda_{max}(\log \epsilon)$	Ref.
$C_{10}H_{10}N_2O_3$			
Acetamide, N-(4-ethenyl-2-nitrophenyl)-	hexane	256(4.83),273(4.70), 375s(3.95)	24-1116-73
Acetamide, N-[2-(4-nitrophenyl)ethenyl]-	MeOH	342(4.24)	104-2119-73
1H-Indole-2-methanol, 3-methyl-5-nitro-	EtOH	260s(4.27),275(4.31), 334(3.94)	78-0603-73
1H-Indole-2-methanol, 3-methyl-7-nitro-	EtOH	238(4.11),257(4.02), 371(3.86)	78-0603-73
2-Propenal, 3-[(4-methylphenyl)amino]-2-nitro-	$CHCl_3$	302(3.89),367(4.30)	104-0477-73
1H-Pyrrolo[2,3-c]pyridine-2-carboxylic acid, 3-ethyl-5,6-dihydro-5-oxo-	EtOH	235(4.34),298(3.98), 302(3.94)	44-1824-73
$C_{10}H_{10}N_2O_3S$			
1,2,4-Oxadiazole, 3-[4-(methylsulfonyl)-styryl]-, cis	EtOH	273(4.23),281s(4.19)	39-2241-73C
3-Quinolinesulfonamide, 1,4-dihydro-1-methyl-4-oxo-	MeOH	244(4.29),293(3.88), 317(4.06),328(4.05)	94-1080-73
$C_{10}H_{10}N_2O_4$			
2H-Pyrano[2,3-d]pyrimidine-2,4,5(1H,3H)-trione, 1,3,7-trimethyl-	EtOH	227(4.39),260(4.08)	94-2639-73
$C_{10}H_{10}N_2O_7$			
Orotic acid, 1-β-D-arabinofuranosyl-, 2',6-lactone	H_2O	290(3.89)	44-0593-73
Orotic acid, 1-α-D-ribofuranosyl-, 2',6-lactone	H_2O	291(3.88)	44-0593-73
$C_{10}H_{10}N_2O_8$			
Benzoic acid, 2-hydroxy-4-methoxy-6-methyl-3,5-dinitro-	n.s.g.	238s(4.45),306(3.45)	1-2710-73
$C_{10}H_{10}N_2S$			
2H-Pyrimido[2,1-b]benzothiazole, 3,4-dihydro-	EtOH	225(4.62),268(4.00), 298(3.73)	103-0546-73
$C_{10}H_{10}N_4$			
Pyridazine, 3,3'-(1,2-ethanediyl)bis-	EtOH	251(3.42),255(3.42), 315(2.87)	94-0125-73
$C_{10}H_{10}N_4O$			
Hydrazinecarboxamide, 2-(2-cyano-2-phenylethenyl)-	MeOH	284(4.09),305(3.97)	28-1457-73A
Hydrazinecarboxamide, 2-(2-cyano-1-phenylethylidene)-	MeOH	272(4.20)	28-1457-73A
$C_{10}H_{10}N_4OS$			
2H-Pyrazolo[4,3-g]benzothiazole-2-carboxamide, 4,5-dihydro-7-methyl-	EtOH	280s(4.23),302(4.66), 312(4.23)	32-1057-73
$C_{10}H_{10}N_4O_2$			
Hydrazinecarboxamide, 2-(1,2-dihydro-1-methyl-2-oxo-3H-indol-3-ylidene)-, anti	EtOH	251(4.07),273(4.03), 317(4.17)	104-1565-73
syn	EtOH	205(4.75),253(4.03), 270(4.28),275(4.28), 325(4.21)	104-1565-73
Hydrazinecarboxamide, 2-(1,2-dihydro-4-methyl-2-oxo-3H-indol-3-ylidene)-	EtOH	247(4.22),250(4.21), 255(4.10),264(4.15), 281(4.13),314(4.45),	104-1565-73

Compound	Solvent	$\lambda_{max}(\log \epsilon)$	Ref.
Hydrazinecarboxamide, 2-(1,2-dihydro-4-methyl-2-oxo-3H-indol-3-ylidene)- (cont.)	EtOH	338(4.23)	104-1565-73
Hydrazinecarboxamide, 2-(1,2-dihydro-2-oxo-3H-indol-3-ylidene)-2-methyl-	EtOH	256(4.16),356(3.96)	104-1565-73
Pyridazine, 3,3'-(1,2-ethanediyl)bis-, 1,1'-dioxide	EtOH	264(4.26),317(3.93)	94-0125-73
Pyridazine, 3,3'-(1,2-ethanediyl)bis-, 1,2'-dioxide	EtOH	262(3.90),316(3.59)	94-0125-73
Pyridazine, 3,3'-(1,2-ethanediyl)bis-, 2,2'-dioxide	EtOH	261(4.24),316(3.91)	94-0125-73
$C_{10}H_{10}N_4O_4$			
2-Butenal, 1-nitro-, (4-nitrophenyl)-hydrazone	EtOH	410(3.71)	19-0881-73
Diazene, (1-methyl-1-nitro-2-propenyl)-(4-nitrophenyl)-	EtOH	289(3.73)	19-0881-73
2-Propenal, 2-methyl-1-nitro-, (4-nitro-phenyl)hydrazone	EtOH	373(3.39)	19-0881-73
$C_{10}H_{10}N_4O_4S$			
Hypoxanthine, 8,2'-anhydro-8-mercapto-9-β-D-arabinofuranosyl-	pH 1	267(4.18)	94-1143-73
	pH 7	266.5(4.20)	94-1143-73
	pH 13	272(4.22)	94-1143-73
Hypoxanthine, 8,3'-anhydro-8-mercapto-9-β-D-xylofuranosyl-	pH 1	272.5(4.25)	94-1143-73
	pH 7	271(4.25)	94-1143-73
	pH 13	282(4.27)	94-1143-73
$C_{10}H_{10}N_4S_2$			
1,2,4-Thiadiazol-3(2H)-imine, 2-(imino-phenylmethyl)-5-(methylthio)-	H_2O	256(4.51)	138-0917-73
$C_{10}H_{10}N_6OS$			
1H-Pyrido[2,3-b]pyrimido[4,5-e][1,4]-thiazine-2,4-diamine, 7-methoxy-	MeOH	252(4.36),300(3.65), 335(3.79)	44-4386-73
$C_{10}H_{10}N_7O_7P$			
Inosine, 8-azido-, cyclic 3',5'-(hydro-gen phosphate)	pH 1	273(4.20)	69-5310-73
	pH 11	280(4.11)	69-5310-73
$C_{10}H_{10}N_8O_8$			
Ethanedioic acid, bis[2-(hexahydro-2,4,6-trioxo-5-pyrimidinyl)hydrazide]	EtOH	265(4.10)	103-0247-73
$C_{10}H_{10}O$			
Benzofuran, 2,3-dimethyl-	EtOH	247(4.02),275(3.46), 282(3.40)	103-0026-73
Benzofuran, 2,5-dimethyl-	n.s.g.	240(4.07),275(3.54), 282(3.49)	33-1457-73
Benzofuran, 3,5-dimethyl-	EtOH	250(3.84),272(3.18), 278(3.26),283(3.32), 289(3.34)	33-2961-73
2H-1-Benzopyran, 6-methyl-	n.s.g.	221(4.31),265(3.72), 315(3.33)	33-1457-73
6,7-Nonadiene-2,4-diyn-1-ol, 8-methyl-(8λ,7ε)	n.s.g.	208(4.58),212(4.67), 227(3.72),237(3.79), 252(3.81),266(4.01), 283(3.59),309(?)	70-1029-73
Tricyclo[3.3.2.0^{2,4}]deca-7,9-dien-6-one	MeOH	221(3.78),238s(3.40), 302(2.34),312(2.35), 344(2.11)	25-0041-73

Compound	Solvent	λ_{max}(log ϵ)	Ref.
$C_{10}H_{10}OS$			
1-Benzothiepin-5(2H)-one, 3,4-dihydro-	EtOH	241(4.26)	44-2623-73
Isothiochroman-4-one, 1-methyl-	EtOH	206(4.28),250(3.93), 291(3.23),347(2.38)	39-0410-73C
$C_{10}H_{10}OS_2$			
Thieno[2,3-b]thiophene, 2-acetyl- 5-ethyl-	EtOH	244(4.29),300(4.12)	70-2017-73
$C_{10}H_{10}O_2$			
Benzene, 3,4-(methylenedioxy)-1-prop- enyl-	EtOH	216(4.26),260(4.10), 264s(4.08),304(3.73), 320s(3.38)	141-0001-73
	dioxan	226(4.04),261(4.11), 266s(4.08),303(3.75), 320s(3.44)	141-0001-73
Benzenemethanol, α-methylene-, acetate	isooctane	243(4.09)	35-3310-73
2(3H)-Benzofuranone, 3,3-dimethyl-	EtOH	270(3.09),276(3.07)	44-1993-73
	90% EtOH	221s(3.60),263s(3.08), 269(3.15),276(3.11)	12-1079-73
2H-1-Benzopyran, 5-methoxy-	EtOH	232(4.23),282(3.83)	44-3832-73
2H-1-Benzopyran, 6-methoxy-	EtOH	241(4.00),269(3.31), 333(3.59)	44-3832-73
2H-1-Benzopyran. 7-methoxy-	EtOH	226(4.25),286(3.82), 306(3.76)	44-3832-73
2H-1-Benzopyran, 8-methoxy-	EtOH	228(4.20),273(3.70), 280(3.68),310(2.91)	44-3832-73
2H-1-Benzopyran-2-methanol	EtOH	267(3.67),309(3.55)	77-0344-73
4H-1-Benzopyran-4-one, 2,3-dihydro- 2-methyl-	MeOH	253(3.95),331(3.56)	20-0705-73
p-Coumaric acid, methyl ester, cis	EtOH	210(3.95),230(3.96), 316(4.30)	105-0512-73
2,4,6-Cycloheptatrien-1-one, 2-(2-prop- enyloxy)-	EtOH	238(4.37),320(3.94), 347(3.86)	39-1960-73C
Cyclopropane-1-carboxylic acid, 2-phen- yl-, (R-trans)-	sulfolane	223(4.11),260(2.70), 266(2.70),273(2.54)	44-0804-73
	$MeSO_3H$	240(3.88)	44-0804-73
1-Indanone, 5-methoxy-	MeOH	222(4.19),266(4.19), 287(4.06),294(4.05)	24-1303-73
	EtOH	266(3.33),287(3.19)	141-0001-73
1-Indanone, 6-methoxy-	EtOH	219(4.29),248(3.95), 320(3.61)	141-0001-73
	dioxan	222(4.15),235s(3.85), 243(3.95),247s(3.92), 316(3.65)	141-0001-73
1-Indanone, 7-methoxy-	EtOH	240(3.80),295(3.30)	141-0001-73
Pentacyclo[4.3.0.0^{2,4}.0^{3,8}.0^{5,7}]nonane- 4-carboxylic acid	EtOH	210(2.92)	24-1804-73
Tetracyclo[4.3.0.0^{2,4}.0^{3,7}]non-8-ene- 8-carboxylic acid	EtOH	234(3.84)	24-1804-73
Tricyclo[3.3.2.0^{2,4}]deca-7,9-dien-6-one, 5-hydroxy-	MeOH	223(3.72),335(2.03)	25-0041-73
$C_{10}H_{10}O_2S$			
Benzo[b]thiophene-4-ol, 6,7-dihydro-, acetate	n.s.g.	224(4.29),274(3.54)	35-6655-73
2-Propenoic acid, 2-methyl-3-(phenyl- thio)-	EtOH	280(4.21)	94-1090-73

Compound	Solvent	λ_{max}(log ϵ)	Ref.
$C_{10}H_{10}O_3$			
Benzenepropanoic acid, α-oxo-, methyl ester (enol form)	hexane	282(4.36),293(4.48), 307(4.38)	39-1221-73C
	MeOH-NaOH	335(4.38)	39-1221-73C
1(3H)-Isobenzofuranone, 3-ethyl-3-hydroxy-	M H_2SO_4	281(3.08),287(3.04)	44-3375-73
1(3H)-Isobenzofuranone, 3-methoxy-3-methyl-	MeOH	230(3.97),272(2.97), 281(2.95)	44-3375-73
1(2H)-Naphthalenone, 3,4-dihydro-4,8-dihydroxy-	EtOH	220(4.1),260(3.8), 332(3.5)	23-3299-73
	EtOH-base	223(4.2),230(4.1), 263(3.7),372(3.7)	23-3299-73
1-Propanone, 1-(3,4-methylenedioxyphenyl)-	EtOH	232(4.32),274(3.86), 308(3.91)	141-0001-73
2-Propenoic acid, 3-(4-hydroxyphenyl)-, methyl ester	EtOH	211(4.01),229(4.08), 298s(4.31),314(4.38), 390s(2.51)	141-0001-73
	EtOH-NaOH	244(3.88),300s(3.67), 312(3.84),368(4.47)	141-0001-73
2-Propenoic acid, 3-(2-methoxyphenyl)-, cis	EtOH	225(4.10),265(3.80), 308s(3.70)	141-0001-73
	EtOH-NaOH	254(3.90),295(3.62)	141-0001-73
trans	EtOH	223(4.10),275(4.20), 320(3.91)	141-0001-73
	EtOH-NaOH	269(4.16),312(3.83)	141-0001-73
2-Propenoic acid, 3-(3-methoxyphenyl)-, trans	EtOH	217(4.19),228s(4.15), 276(4.25),309s(3.68)	141-0001-73
	EtOH-NaOH	222(4.29),270(4.25), 305s(3.68)	141-0001-73
	dioxan	218(4.22),232(4.20), 276(4.26),312(3.70)	141-0001-73
2-Propenoic acid, 3-(4-methoxyphenyl)-, trans	EtOH	211(4.05),225(4.09), 293s(4.32),299(4.33), 308(4.33)	141-0001-73
	EtOH-NaOH	220(4.17),284(4.35), 300s(4.21)	141-0001-73
	dioxan	226(4.09),291(4.33), 299(4.33),308(4.33)	141-0001-73
Tropolone, 3-acetonyl-	EtOH	242(4.38),322(3.87), 355(3.83),367s(3.79)	39-1960-73C
$C_{10}H_{10}O_3S$			
Isothiochroman-4-one, 1-methyl-, 2,2-dioxide	EtOH	206(4.34),253(4.04), 291(3.23)	39-0410-73C
$C_{10}H_{10}O_4$			
Benzaldehyde, 5-acetyl-4-hydroxy-2-methoxy-	EtOH	253(4.56),283(4.17), 325(3.85)	78-2343-73
	EtOH-base	253(--),313(--), 352(--)	78-2343-73
1H-2-Benzopyran-1-one, 3,4-dihydro-6,8-dihydroxy-3-methyl-	EtOH	217(4.21),269(4.10), 305(3.78)	102-1881-73
1(2H)-Naphthalenone, 3,4-dihydro-3,6,8-trihydroxy-	EtOH	222(4.18),232(3.81), 284(4.11),322(3.83)	23-1617-73
	EtOH-base	210(4.33),253(3.73), 334(4.5)	23-1617-73
1(2H)-Naphthalenone, 3,4-dihydro-4,6,8-trihydroxy-	EtOH	210(4.19),221(4.16), 234(3.98),239(3.94), 284(4.17),313(3.84)	88-3537-73
Phthalide, 4,5-dimethoxy-	EtOH	221(4.42),260(4.04), 291s(3.18)	141-0001-73

Compound	Solvent	$\lambda_{max}(\log \epsilon)$	Ref.
Phthalide, 4,5-dimethoxy- (cont.)	dioxan	226(4.02),258(4.08), 287s(3.19)	141-0001-73
Phthalide, 5,6-dimethoxy-	EtOH	220(4.38),258(3.97), 294(3.86)	141-0001-73
Phthalide, 5,7-dimethoxy-	EtOH	216(4.58),256(4.20), 290(3.72)	141-0001-73
Phthalide, 6,7-dimethoxy-	EtOH	238s(3.90),310(3.60)	141-0001-73
	dioxan	226(3.96),230s(3.90), 307(3.52)	141-0001-73
2-Propenoic acid, 3-(2-hydroxy-3-methoxyphenyl)-, trans	EtOH	227(4.30),278(4.30), 325s(3.70)	141-0001-73
2-Propenoic acid, 3-(2-hydroxy-4-methoxyphenyl)-, trans	EtOH	219(4.11),239(4.01), 292(4.12),328(4.17)	141-0001-73
	EtOH-NaOH	228(4.16),250s(3.98), 279(3.89),345(3.87)	141-0001-73
	dioxan	218(4.11),238(4.08), 285s(4.18),291(4.21), 324(4.25)	141-0001-73
2-Propenoic acid, 3-(2-hydroxy-5-methoxyphenyl)-, trans	EtOH	218(4.13),246(4.02), 276(4.17),354(3.85)	141-0001-73
	EtOH-NaOH	231(4.14),275s(3.96), 385(3.82)	141-0001-73
	dioxan	218(4.12),246(4.00), 275(4.15),351(3.85)	141-0001-73
2-Propenoic acid, 3-(2-hydroxy-6-methoxyphenyl)-, trans	EtOH	220(4.18),297(4.27)	141-0001-73
	EtOH-NaOH	236(4.12),295(4.02), 354(3.75)	141-0001-73
	dioxan	223(4.21),293(4.31)	141-0001-73
2-Propenoic acid, 3-(3-hydroxy-4-methoxyphenyl)-, trans	EtOH	218(4.18),235s(4.05), 242(4.07),292(4.16), 322(4.18)	141-0001-73
	EtOH-NaOH	216(4.20),230s(4.15), 260(4.22),289(4.13), 346s(3.75)	141-0001-73
	dioxan	220(4.15),235s(4.06), 241(4.11),293(4.19), 320(4.21)	141-0001-73
2-Propenoic acid, 3-(4-hydroxy-3-methoxyphenyl)-, trans	EtOH	218(4.15),235(4.10), 296(4.16),323(4.28)	141-0001-73
	EtOH-NaOH	218(4.14),238s(4.02), 306(4.05),348(4.35)	141-0001-73
	dioxan	219(4.05),235(4.08), 296(4.13),322(4.26)	141-0001-73
Unidentified compd. VIII	EtOH	270(4.12),305(3.78)	88-3537-73
$C_{10}H_{10}O_5$			
Benzaldehyde, 3-acetyl-2,6-dihydroxy-4-methoxy-	MeOH	268(4.51),296(4.16), 330(3.60)	83-0857-73
	MeOH-KOH	215(4.06),283(4.35), 314(4.24)	83-0857-73
Benzenebutanoic acid, 2,4-dihydroxy-γ-oxo-	EtOH	213(4.18),231(3.81), 276(4.11),313(3.83)	23-1617-73
	EtOH-base	215(4.1),252(3.72), 334(4.41)	23-1617-73
1,3-Cyclopentadiene-1,2-dicarboxylic acid, 5-(hydroxymethylene)-, dimethyl ester	MeOH	241(3.93),317(4.27), 370(3.36)	24-3817-73
sodium salt	MeOH	257(4.04),331(4.32)	24-3817-73
2H-Cyclopenta[b]furan-4-carboxaldehyde, 6-acetoxy-3,3a,6,6a-tetrahydro-2-oxo-	n.s.g.	227(3.61)	77-0119-73

Compound	Solvent	$\lambda_{max}(\log \epsilon)$	Ref.
Ethanone, 1-(6-hydroxy-4-methoxy-1,3-benzodioxol-5-yl)-	EtOH	243(4.05),284(4.07),350(3.60)	78-2703-73
1(2H)-Naphthalenone, 3,4-dihydro-3,4,6,8-tetrahydroxy- (5λ,6ε)	EtOH	216(4.22),221(4.17),234(3.98),239(3.93),284(4.14),?(3.79)	88-3537-73
Unidentified compd. VII, m. 156°	EtOH	216(4.45),268(4.04),301(3.78)	88-3537-73
$C_{10}H_{10}O_6$			
1,3-Benzenedicarboxaldehyde, 4,6-dihydroxy-2,5-dimethoxy-	MeOH	258(4.48),325s(3.78)	78-2645-73
	MeOH-HCl	213(4.06),243s(3.83),268(4.36)	78-2645-73
	MeOH-NaOH	302(4.70),358(3.98)	78-2645-73
1,2-Benzenedicarboxylic acid, 3,4-dimethoxy-	EtOH	215(4.29),255(4.08),283s(3.52)	141-0001-73
	EtOH-NaOH	219(4.29),246(4.03),272s(3.36)	141-0001-73
	dioxan	225(3.93),256(4.10),277s(3.56),288(3.56)	141-0001-73
1,2-Benzenedicarboxylic acid, 4,5-dimethoxy-	EtOH	225(4.36),270(3.91)	141-0001-73
	EtOH-NaOH	220(4.27),253(3.92),284(3.54)	141-0001-73
	dioxan	229(4.16),267(3.92),284s(3.79)	141-0001-73
$C_{10}H_{11}$			
Methylium, cyclopropylphenyl- (at -75°)	FSO_3H	343(4.20)	59-0803-73
$C_{10}H_{11}AsN_2$			
2H-1,2,3-Diazarsole, 5-ethyl-2-phenyl-	heptane	229(4.15),279(3.62),337(3.85)	88-4503-73
$C_{10}H_{11}Br$			
Benzene, 1-bromo-4-(1-methylenepropyl)-	hexane	248(4.16)	104-2473-73
$C_{10}H_{11}BrCl_2O_4$			
2-Cyclopentene-1-carboxylic acid, 2-(1-bromopropyl)-3,5-dichloro-1-hydroxy-4-oxo-, methyl ester	EtOH	252(3.88)	35-3000-73
$C_{10}H_{11}BrNO$			
Isoxazolium, 3-(4-bromophenyl)-4,5-dihydro-2-methyl-	EtOH	220(3.90),275(3.67)	22-1390-73
$C_{10}H_{11}BrN_2$			
2-Indolamine, 5-bromo-1,3-dimethyl-, hydrochloride	MeOH	214(4.57),270(4.32)	103-0471-73
1H-Indole-3-ethanamine, 5-bromo-	EtOH	226(4.53),280s(3.85),286(3.83),297(3.67)	103-0196-73
1H-Indole-3-ethanamine, 7-bromo-	EtOH	222(4.36),277s(3.66),284(3.68),293(3.63)	103-0196-73
$C_{10}H_{11}BrN_2O_2$			
Benzenamine, 4-(2-bromo-2-nitroethenyl)-N,N-dimethyl-	n.s.g.	272(4.08),453(4.54)	135-1299-73
$C_{10}H_{11}BrN_5O_7P$			
Guanosine, 8-bromo-, cyclic 3',5'-(hydrogen phosphate)	pH 1	256s(4.29),259(4.33)	69-5310-73
	pH 11	260(4.28)	69-5310-73

Compound	Solvent	$\lambda_{max}(\log \epsilon)$	Ref.
$C_{10}H_{11}BrO_3$			
2-Oxahomoadamantanedione, 9-bromo-	MeOH	220(2.45),296(1.40)	78-4013-73
$C_{10}H_{11}ClNO$			
Isoxazolium, 3-(4-chlorophenyl)-4,5-dihydro-2-methyl-, perchlorate	EtOH	222(3.83),255(3.69), 270s(3.51)	22-1390-73
$C_{10}H_{11}ClN_2O_3$			
Butanamide, 4-chloro-N-(4-nitrophenyl)-	MeCN	317(4.17)	35-1253-73
$C_{10}H_{11}ClN_4O_3$			
9H-Purine, 6-chloro-, 9-(2-deoxy-β-D-erythro-pentofuranosyl)-	H_2O	264(4.02)	23-3161-73
$C_{10}H_{11}ClO$			
2-Buten-1-one, 3-chloro-2-methyl-1-phenyl-	EtOH	249(3.98)	78-4241-73
2,4-Cyclohexadien-1-one, 2-chloro-6-methyl-6-(2-propenyl)-	EtOH	317(3.65)	33-0014-73
$C_{10}H_{11}ClOS$			
4H-Cyclohepta[c]thiophen-4-one, 1-chloro-5,6,7,8-tetrahydro-5-methyl-	EtOH	224(4.17),256(3.98)	22-0335-73
$C_{10}H_{11}ClO_2$			
Benzoic acid, 4-chloro-3-propyl-	EtOH	240(4.11),277(3.02), 286(2.92)	12-1337-73
2,4,6-Cycloheptatrien-1-one, 5-chloro-6-ethyl-2-methoxy-	EtOH	239(4.33),330(3.90)	12-1337-73
$C_{10}H_{11}ClO_2S$			
Thiophene, 3-chlorotetrahydro-3-phenyl-, 1,1-dioxide	EtOH	218(3.85),259(2.48)	44-2156-73
$C_{10}H_{11}ClO_3$			
2-Oxahomoadamantanedione, 9-chloro-	MeOH	230(1.90),295(1.38)	78-4013-73
$C_{10}H_{11}ClS_2$			
Benzenecarbodithioic acid, 4-chloro-, 1-methylethyl ester	C_6H_{12}	306(4.16),511(2.12)	101-0121-73I
$C_{10}H_{11}Cl_2N_3$			
1H-Imidazol-2-amine, N-[(2,6-dichlorophenyl)methyl]-4,5-dihydro-	pH 1	268(2.84),276(2.80)	111-0545-73
1,3,5-Triazine, 2,4-dichloro-6-(1-heptynyl)-	EtOH	254(4.27)	22-2039-73
$C_{10}H_{11}FN_2O_3$			
Thymidine, 4',5'-didehydro-3',5'-dideoxy-3'-fluoro-	MeOH	262.5(3.96)	48-0895-73
$C_{10}H_{11}FN_4O_3$			
9H-Purine, 9-(2-deoxy-β-D-erythro-pentofuranosyl)-6-fluoro-	H_2O	249(3.85)	23-3161-73
$C_{10}H_{11}IO_3$			
2-Oxahomoadamantanedione, 9-iodo-	MeOH	220(3.02),263(2.75)	78-4013-73
$C_{10}H_{11}N$			
Isoquinoline, 3,4-dihydro-1-methyl-	EtOH	250(3.89),285s(3.13)	35-4692-73
in 40% ethanol	pH 1	274(4.03),310s(3.26)	35-4692-73

Compound	Solvent	λ max (log ε)	Ref.
2-Propen-1-amine, N-(phenylmethylene)-, cis	EtOH	217(4.14),223(4.12), 231(3.91),281(4.24)	78-4111-73
trans	EtOH	217(4.20),223(4.18), 229(3.96),281(4.31)	78-4111-73
$C_{10}H_{11}NO$			
Acetamide, N-(2-phenylethenyl)-, cis	MeOH	269(4.16)	104-2119-73
trans	MeOH	278(4.37)	104-2119-73
2-Azabicyclo[5.2.0]nona-3,5,8-triene, 2-acetyl-	hexane	214(3.78),282(3.63)	44-1959-73
10-Azabicyclo[7.2.0]undeca-2,5,7-trien-11-one, trans	EtOH	224(3.83)	35-4647-73
3-Azatricyclo[4.4.1.0^{2,5}]undeca-7,9-di-en-4-one	EtOH	248s(3.63),255(3.75), 265(3.74),276(3.47)	44-1886-73
Benzenamine, N-(dihydro-2(3H)-furanyli-dene)-	isooctane	238.4(3.53)	35-7731-73
3-Buten-2-one, 4-phenyl-, oxime	C_6H_{12}	212(4.14),218(4.16), 224(4.14),230(3.92), 275s(--),280(4.46), 290s(--),303(3.92)	32-0309-73
plus shoulders not listed	MeOH	218(4.15),224(4.13), 282(4.46)	32-0309-73
9H-Cyclohepta[b]pyridin-9-one, 5,6,7,8-tetrahydro-	EtOH	209(3.64),228(3.64), 274(3.51)	39-0968-73C
1H-Indole, 1-acetyl-7,7a-dihydro-	hexane	228(4.10),345(3.98)	44-1959-73
Isoquinoline, 3,4-dihydro-1-methyl-, 2-oxide	EtOH	218(4.05),296(4.13)	35-4692-73
Isoxazole, 4,5-dihydro-4-methyl-3-phen-yl-	EtOH	212(4.02),264(4.00)	22-1390-73
Isoxazole, 4,5-dihydro-5-methyl-3-phen-yl-	EtOH	263(4.07)	22-1390-73
5H-2-Pyrindine-5-carboxaldehyde, 6,7-dihydro-7-methyl- (pedicularidine)	n.s.g.	236(3.36),270(3.32)	105-0137-73
Tryptophol	MeOH	275s(3.81),282(3.85), 291(3.76)	102-0447-73
after ten minutes at 70°	H_2SO_4	235(3.67),240s(3.63), 289(3.66)(changing)	102-0447-73
$C_{10}H_{11}NOS$			
2-Propenamide, 2-methyl-3-(phenylthio)-	EtOH	280(4.21)	94-1090-73
$C_{10}H_{11}NO_2$			
Acetamide, N-(4-acetylphenyl)-	EtOH	287(4.40)	80-0677-73
	EtOH-HCl	287(4.41)	80-0677-73
Benzenepropanenitrile, β-hydroxy-4-meth-oxy-	EtOH	227(4.06),277(3.24), 283(3.18)	40-2347-73
Ethanone, 1-phenyl-, O-acetyloxime	pH 6.61	239(4.12)	36-1381-73
1H-Isoindol-1-one, 2,3-dihydro-3-hy-droxy-2,3-dimethyl-	H_2SO_4	231(4.50),336(3.57)	24-1423-73
2,4-Pentadienoic acid, 5-(1H-pyrrol-2-yl)-, methyl ester	EtOH	368(4.54)	39-1416-73C
Propanal, 3-[(phenylmethylene)amino]-, N-oxide	EtOH	295(4.14)	104-0793-73
2-Pyrrolidinone, 5-hydroxy-5-phenyl-	H_2SO_4	298(4.16)	24-1423-73
$C_{10}H_{11}NO_2S$			
7(4H)-Benzothiazolone, 5,6-dihydro-6-(methoxymethylene)-2-methyl-	EtOH	210(4.00),278s(3.94), 313(4.12)	32-0755-73
1H,5H-Isothiazole, 4-methoxy-1-phenyl-, 1-oxide	MeOH	225(4.05),259s(3.39), 266s(3.34),274s(3.20)	44-0020-73

Compound	Solvent	λ_{max}(log ϵ)	Ref.
1H,5H-Isothiazol-4-ol, 1-(4-methylphenyl)-, 1-oxide	MeOH	227(4.18),258s(3.83), 265s(3.72),275s(3.53)	44-0020-73
Thiazolo[3,2-a]pyridinium, 3-carboxy-2,3-dihydro-2,5-dimethyl-, hydroxide, inner salt, trans	pH 1	210(4.10),242(4.04), 329(4.08)	1-1749-73
	pH 13	222(3.88),275(3.81), 355(3.86)	1-1749-73
$C_{10}H_{11}NO_3$			
DL-Alanine, β-benzoyl-	M HCl	246(4.12),285s(--)	7-0457-73
	pH 7.38	246(4.12),285s(--)	7-0457-73
	pH 13	244(4.07),280s(--)	7-0457-73
β-Alanine, β-benzoyl-, hydrochloride	M HCl	248(4.07),290s(--)	7-0457-73
	pH 7.38	248(4.08),290s(--)	7-0457-73
	pH 13	246(4.06)	7-0457-73
$C_{10}H_{11}NO_3S$			
Ethanone, 1-(1,3-dihydro-1-methyl-2,1-benzisothiazol-5-yl)-, S,S-dioxide	EtOH	228(4.16),288(4.38)	4-0249-73
1H-Indole-2-sulfonic acid, 1-methyl-, methyl ester	EtOH	270s(3.98),274(4.01), 294s(3.61),306s(3.44)	78-0669-73
1H-Indole-3-sulfonic acid, 1-methyl-, methyl ester	EtOH	277(3.86),288s(3.62)	78-0669-73
2H-Pyrido[2,1-b][1,3]thiazinium, 4-carboxy-3,4-dihydro-9-hydroxy-6-methyl-, hydroxide, inner salt	M HCl	211(4.00),239(3.70), 342(4.06)	1-1059-73
	M NaOH	247(3.94),360(4.07)	1-1059-73
Thiazolo[3,2-a]pyridinium, 3-carboxy-2,3-dihydro-8-hydroxy-2,5-dimethyl-, hydroxide, inner salt, trans	pH 1	216(4.00),240(3.77), 346(3.93)	1-1749-73
	pH 13	224(3.92),250(4.00), 364(4.06)	1-1749-73
$C_{10}H_{11}NO_4$			
Acetamide, N-(4-ethoxy-3,6-dioxo-1,4-cyclohexadien-1-yl)-	n.s.g.	297(4.36),393(2.66)	87-0499-73
1,5-Naphthalenediol, 1,2,3,4-tetrahydro-6-nitro-	25% EtOH	215(4.13),295(3.93), 358(3.55)	87-0254-73
	+ NaOH	237(4.13),298(3.72), 435(3.80)	87-0254-73
1,5-Naphthalenediol, 1,2,3,4-tetrahydro-8-nitro-	25% EtOH	240(3.75),315(3.69)	87-0254-73
	+ NaOH	233(3.78),268(3.68), 418(4.28)	87-0254-73
$C_{10}H_{11}NO_4S$			
2-Butenedioic acid, 2-(2-thienylamino)-, dimethyl ester, (Z)-	MeOH	238(3.74),308(4.02)	24-0368-73
7-Thia-8-azabicyclo[4.2.2]deca-2,4,9-triene-8-carboxylic acid, methyl ester, 7,7-dioxide	EtOH	261(3.31)	44-1249-73
$C_{10}H_{11}NO_6$			
1H-1,3,4-Pyrroletricarboxylic acid, trimethyl ester	MeOH	247(3.90)	23-1089-73
$C_{10}H_{11}NS$			
Benzo[b]thiophen-2-amine, N,N-dimethyl-	EtOH	233(4.19),283(4.12)	78-0321-73
$C_{10}H_{11}NS_2$			
Pyrrolo[2,1-b]thiazole-5-carbothioaldehyde, 2,3,6-trimethyl-	C_6H_{12}	205(4.06),227(4.11), 336(3.99),410s(4.59), 418(4.62),535(1.74)	39-0657-73C

Compound	Solvent	λ_{max}(log ϵ)	Ref.
Pyrrolo[2,1-b]thiazole-7-carbothioalde-hyde, 3,5,6-trimethyl-	C_6H_{12}	229(4.34),260(3.71), 289(3.69),409s(4.21), 416(4.29),429(4.26)	39-0657-73C
$C_{10}H_{11}N_2$			
Pyrido[1,2-a]pyrimidin-5-ium, 2,4-di-methyl-, iodide	MeOH	212(4.68),227(4.81), 305(3.94),312(3.89), 317(4.01)	4-0821-73
perchlorate	MeOH	207(4.37),229(4.51), 305(3.79),312(3.72), 317(3.84)	4-0821-73
Quinoxalinium, 1,3-dimethyl-, perchlor-ate	H_2O	244(4.27),247(4.27), 337(3.62)	22-1285-73
$C_{10}H_{11}N_2O_5$			
2-Propanone, 1-(2-methyl-4,6-dinitro-2,4-cyclohexadien-1-yl)-, ion(1-), K salt	acetone	360(4.24),584(4.52)	104-2106-73
$C_{10}H_{11}N_2O_6$			
2-Propanone, 1-(2-methoxy-4,6-dinitro-2,4-cyclohexadien-1-yl)-, ion(1-), K salt	acetone	360(4.04),590(4.35)	104-2106-73
2-Propanone, 1-(3-methoxy-2,6-dinitro-2,4-cyclohexadien-1-yl)-, ion(1-), K salt	DMSO	338(4.54),625(4.32)	104-2106-73
2-Propanone, 1-(5-methoxy-2,4-dinitro-2,4-cyclohexadien-1-yl)-, ion(1-), K salt	acetone	354(4.08),562(4.35)	104-2106-73
$C_{10}H_{11}N_2S$			
Pyrido[1,2-a]pyrimidin-5-ium, 2-methyl-4-(methylthio)-, iodide	MeOH	206(4.68),223(4.77), 280(3.78),312(4.18), 325(4.30)	4-0821-73
$C_{10}H_{11}N_3$			
Butanenitrile, 3-(phenylhydrazono)-	MeOH	270(4.27),295s(3.81)	28-1457-73A
2-Quinoxalinamine, N,N-dimethyl-	pH 1.0	247(4.22),317(3.72), 368(3.93)	103-0369-73
	pH 7.2	254(4.40),300(3.17), 382(3.84)	103-0369-73
$C_{10}H_{11}N_3O$			
2-Pyrazoline, 1-acetyl-3-(2-pyridinyl)-	$CHCl_3$	306(4.56)	103-0055-73
2-Pyrazoline, 1-acetyl-3-(4-pyridinyl)-	$CHCl_3$	306(4.30)	103-0055-73
Pyrimido[1,2-b]indazol-2(1H)-one, 7,8,9,10-tetrahydro-	MeOH	244(4.24),284(3.85)	4-0261-73
1,2,4-Triazine, 4,5-dihydro-3-methoxy-5-phenyl-	n.s.g.	264(3.90),287(3.72)	22-2493-73
1,2,4-Triazole, 5-methoxy-1-methyl-3-phenyl-	EtOH	251(4.11)	94-1342-73
	THF	252(4.19)	94-1342-73
1,2,4-Triazole, 5-methoxy-2-methyl-3-phenyl-	EtOH	249(3.97)	94-1342-73
	THF	255(4.01)	94-1342-73
1,2,4-Triazole, 5-methoxy-4-methyl-3-phenyl-	EtOH	244(4.06)	94-1342-73
	THF	253(4.04)	94-1342-73
1,2,4-Triazolin-5-one, 1,2-dimethyl-3-phenyl-	EtOH	233(4.14),275s(3.69)	94-1342-73
	THF	234(4.06),280(3.43)	94-1342-73
1,2,4-Triazolin-5-one, 1,4-dimethyl-3-phenyl-	EtOH	260(3.99)	94-1342-73
	THF	271(3.91)	94-1342-73

Compound	Solvent	$\lambda_{max}(\log \epsilon)$	Ref.
$C_{10}H_{11}N_3O_2$			
2,4-Hexadienamide, 2,3-dicyano-5-ethoxy-	EtOH	358(4.19)	12-1551-73
Pyrimido[1,2-a]pyrimidin-5-ium, 1,4-dihydro-2-hydroxy-1,6,8-trimethyl-4-oxo-, hydroxide, inner salt	MeOH	228(3.91),240(3.95), 322(3.20)	44-3485-73
$C_{10}H_{11}N_3O_2S$			
Urea, [(4,7-dihydro-2-methyl-7-oxo-6(5H)-benzothiazolylidene)methyl]-	EtOH	282(3.82),337(4.14)	32-1063-73
$C_{10}H_{11}N_3O_2S_2$			
Carbamic acid, [(2-propynylthio)(2-thiazolylimino)methyl]-, ethyl ester	dioxan	238(3.84),313(4.31)	94-0074-73
$C_{10}H_{11}N_3O_3$			
Pyrido[2,3-d]pyrimidine-2,4,5(1H,3H,8H)-trione, 1,3,7-trimethyl-	EtOH	222(4.55),264(3.64), 300(3.72)	94-2014-73
$C_{10}H_{11}N_3O_5$			
Ethanimidic acid, N-(2,4-dinitrophenyl)-, ethyl ester	MeCN	306(4.12)	35-1253-73
$C_{10}H_{11}N_3S$			
2H-Imidazo[4,5-g]quinoline-2-thione, 1,3,5,6,7,8-hexahydro-	EtOH	325(3.81)	103-1028-73
4H-Imidazo[4,5,1-ij]quinoline-2(1H)-thione, 8-amino-5,6-dihydro-	EtOH	226(3.90),293(3.91), 322(3.86)	103-1028-73
1H-Pyrazolo[4,3-g]benzothiazole, 4,5-dihydro-1,7-dimethyl-	EtOH	308(3.95)	32-0755-73
2H-Pyrazolo[4,3-g]benzothiazole, 4,5-dihydro-2,7-dimethyl-	EtOH	301(4.11)	32-0755-73
Pyrrolo[2,3-f]benzimidazole-2(1H)-thione, 3,5,6,7-tetrahydro-6-methyl-	DMSO	325(3.95),341(3.98)	103-1028-73
1,2,4-Triazole, 4,5-dihydro-3-(methylthio)-5-phenyl-	n.s.g.	235(3.91),286s(3.78)	22-2493-73
1,2,4-Triazole, 1-methyl-5-(methylthio)-3-phenyl-	EtOH	223(4.20),252(4.16)	94-1342-73
	THF	227(4.14),242(4.13)	94-1342-73
1,2,4-Triazole, 2-methyl-5-(methylthio)-3-phenyl-	EtOH	220(4.18),261s(3.72)	94-1342-73
	THF	221(4.17),265s(3.59)	94-1342-73
1,2,4-Triazole, 4-methyl-5-(methylthio)-3-phenyl-	EtOH	253(4.13)	94-1342-73
	THF	247(4.09)	94-1342-73
1,2,4-Triazolidine-3-thione, 4-methyl-1-(phenylmethyl)-, meso-ionic didehydro deriv.	MeCN	250(4.24)	103-1048-73
1,2,4-Triazoline-5-thione, 1,2-dimethyl-3-phenyl-	EtOH	248(4.29),290(3.49)	94-1342-73
	THF	241(4.31),275s(3.67)	94-1342-73
1,2,4-Triazoline-5-thione, 1,4-dimethyl-3-phenyl-	EtOH	219(4.11),254(4.27), 280s(3.81)	94-1342-73
	THF	230s(4.04),247(4.21), 275s(3.73)	94-1342-73
$C_{10}H_{11}N_4O_7PS$			
8,2'-Anhydro-8-mercapto-9- -D-arabinofuranosylhypoxanthine-5'-phosphate, disodium salt	pH 1	267(4.15)	94-1143-73
Inosine, 7,8-dihydro-8-thioxo-, cyclic 3',5'-(hydrogen phosphate)	pH 1	291(4.13)	69-5310-73
	pH 11	288(4.24)	69-5310-73
$C_{10}H_{11}N_4O_8P$			
Inosine, 7,8-dihydro-8-oxo-, cyclic 3',5'-(hydrogen phosphate)	pH 1	253(4.04),283s(3.73)	69-5310-73
	pH 11	263(4.07)	69-5310-73

Compound	Solvent	λ max(log ε)	Ref.
Xanthosine, cyclic 3',5'-(hydrogen phosphate)	pH 1	234(3.93),260(4.00)	69-5310-73
	pH 11	247(4.04),276(3.99)	69-5310-73
$C_{10}H_{11}N_5$			
Benzo[1,2-d:3,4-d']diimidazol-2-amine, 3,6-dihydro-3,6-dimethyl-	MeOH	265(4.0),275(4.0), 297(4.0)	103-0740-73
$C_{10}H_{11}N_5O$			
Phenol, 2,4-dimethyl-6-(1H-1,2,4-triazol-3-ylazo)-	MeOH	329(4.0),388s(3.4)	12-1585-73
Phenol, 2,5-dimethyl-4-(1H-1,2,4-triazol-3-ylazo)-	MeOH	370(4.2),445s(3.2+)	12-1585-73
Phenol, 2,6-dimethyl-4-(1H-1,2,4-triazol-3-ylazo)-	MeOH	363(4.3),460(3.1)	12-1585-73
$C_{10}H_{11}N_5O_2$			
4(1H)-Pteridinone, 2-amino-6-methyl-7-(1-methylethenyl)-, 8-oxide	pH 13	262(4.53),290s(3.93), 385(4.02)	35-6407-73
7H-Purine-7-propanenitrile, 1,2,3,6-tetrahydro-1,3-dimethyl-2,6-dioxo-	n.s.g.	209(4.29),274(3.90)	73-1571-73
$C_{10}H_{11}N_5O_3$			
Adenosine, 2',3'-anhydro-	MeOH	258(4.17)	35-4025-73
Formycin, 2',3'-anhydro-	MeOH-acid	235(3.92),297(4.05)	44-3179-73
	MeOH-base	235(4.26),305(3.89)	44-3179-73
$C_{10}H_{11}N_5O_3S$			
1H-Tetrazol-5-amine, 1-[4-(methylsulfonyl)benzoyl]methyl-	EtOH	245(4.05),285(3.14)	22-1854-73
$C_{10}H_{11}N_5O_4$			
Acetamide, N-(1,2,3,4,5,6-hexahydro-1,3-dimethyl-2,4,6-trioxo-7-pteridinyl)-	50% MeOH	243(4.32),270(4.03), 377(4.12),395s(4.01)	24-3203-73
$C_{10}H_{12}$			
Bicyclo[6.1.0]nona-2,4,6-triene, 1-methyl-, cis	C_6H_{12}	243.5(3.51)	35-4647-73
Bicyclo[6.1.0]nona-2,4,6-triene, 3-methyl-, cis	C_6H_{12}	241(3.47)	35-4647-73
Bicyclo[6.1.0]nona-2,4,6-triene, 4-methyl-, cis	C_6H_{12}	245(3.61)	35-4647-73
$C_{10}H_{12}BF_4N_3$			
Benzenediazonium, 2-(1-pyrrolidinyl)-, tetrafluoroborate	M HCl	273(3.75),434(3.78)	48-0725-73
$C_{10}H_{12}BrNO$			
2,5-Cyclohexadien-1-one, 2-bromo-4-[(1,1-dimethylethyl)imino]-	EtOH	276(4.86)	39-0456-73C
$C_{10}H_{12}BrNO_2$			
2,5-Cyclohexadiene-1,4-dione, 2-bromo-5-[(1,1-dimethylethyl)amino]-	EtOH	296(4.03),500(3.41)	39-0456-73C
2,5-Cyclohexadien-1-one, 2-bromo-4-[(1,1-dimethylethyl)imino]-, N-oxide	EtOH	269(3.50),395(4.39)	39-0456-73C
$C_{10}H_{12}BrNO_3S$			
Butanoic acid, 2-bromo-4-[(3-hydroxy-6-methyl-2-pyridyl)thio]-, (R)-	M HCl	238(3.61),322(3.96)	1-1059-73

Compound	Solvent	$\lambda_{max}(\log \epsilon)$	Ref.
$C_{10}H_{12}BrN_5O_3$			
D-Arabinitol, 1-C-(7-amino-1H-pyrazolo-[4,3-d]pyrimidin-3-yl)-1,4-anhydro-2-bromo-2-deoxy-, (S)-	MeOH-acid	236(3.89),298(4.02)	44-3179-73
	MeOH-base	236(4.27),306(3.87)	44-3179-73
9H-Purin-6-amine, 9-(2-bromo-2-deoxy-β-D-arabinofuranosyl)-	MeOH	259(4.17)	35-4025-73
9H-Purin-6-amine, 9-(3-bromo-3-deoxy-β-D-xylofuranosyl)-	MeOH	259(4.16)	35-4025-73
D-Xylitol, 1-C-(7-amino-1H-pyrazolo-[4,3-d]pyrimidin-3-yl)-1,4-anhydro-3-bromo-3-deoxy-, (S)-	MeOH-acid	238(3.93),298(4.08)	44-3179-73
	MeOH-base	213(4.42),236(4.30), 305(3.91)	44-3179-73
$C_{10}H_{12}Br_2N_2O_2$			
2,5-Cyclohexadiene-1,4-dione, 2,5-bis-(2-aminoethyl)-3,6-dibromo-, dinitrate	pH 1	295(4.25)	39-0832-73C
$C_{10}H_{12}Br_2N_4S_2$			
[4,5'-Bithiazole]-2,2'-diamine, $N^{2'}$-(2,3-dibromopropyl)-4'-methyl-	EtOH	244(4.21),316(4.00)	83-0152-73
$C_{10}H_{12}Br_4N_2$			
Methanediamine, N,N,N',N'-tetramethyl-1-(2,3,4,5-tetrabromo-2,4-cyclopentadien-1-ylidene)-	dioxan	254(3.95),352(4.26)	88-5101-73
$C_{10}H_{12}ClNO$			
Acetamide, N-(4-chloro-3-ethylphenyl)-	EtOH	249(4.24)	12-1337-73
Benzenamine, N-(2-chloro-2-propenyl)-2-methoxy-	ether	243(4.05),287(3.50)	24-0355-73
2,5-Cyclohexadien-1-one, 2-chloro-4-[(1,1-dimethylethyl)imino]-	EtOH	273(4.47)	39-0456-73C
$C_{10}H_{12}ClNO_2$			
2,5-Cyclohexadiene-1,4-dione, 2-chloro-5-[(1,1-dimethylethyl)amino]-	EtOH	282(4.07),500(3.41)	39-0456-73C
2,5-Cyclohexadien-1-one, 2-chloro-4-[(1,1-dimethylethyl)imino]-, N-oxide	EtOH	380(4.51)	39-0456-73C
$C_{10}H_{12}ClNO_3$			
Carbamic acid, (3-chloro-4-hydroxyphenyl)-, 1-methylethyl ester	pH 13	253(4.19),307(3.54)	98-0792-73
	75% MeOH	240(4.20),293(3.40)	98-0792-73
Carbamic acid, (5-chloro-2-hydroxyphenyl)-, 1-methylethyl ester	pH 13	252(4.03),312(3.82)	98-0792-73
	75% MeOH	238(4.23),292(3.02)	98-0792-73
$C_{10}H_{12}ClN_3O_2$			
Cyclohexanone, 2-(4-chloro-6-methoxy-1,3,5-triazin-2-yl)-	C_6H_{12}	319(3.49)	22-2039-73
Hydrazinecarboxamide, N-(2-chloro-1-oxopropyl)-2-phenyl-	MeOH	233(4.21),287(3.46)	104-1200-73
$C_{10}H_{12}ClN_5O_2$			
Purine, 6-chloro-9-(3-acetamido-2-hydroxypropyl)-	pH 1	265(3.98)	87-0037-73
	pH 7 and 13	265(3.98)	87-0037-73
$C_{10}H_{12}ClN_5O_3$			
9H-Purin-6-amine, 9-(2-chloro-2-deoxy-β-D-arabinofuranosyl)-	MeOH	259(4.18)	35-4025-73
9H-Purin-6-amine, 9-(3-chloro-3-deoxy-β-D-xylofuranosyl)-	MeOH	259(4.18)	35-4025-73

Compound	Solvent	λ_{max}(log ϵ)	Ref.
$C_{10}H_{12}Cl_2O$			
2,5-Cyclohexadien-1-one, 4-(dichloro-methyl)-2,4,5-trimethyl-	H_2O	244(4.23)	39-0084-73B
cation	80% H_2SO_4	264(4.21),318(3.81)	39-0084-73B
$C_{10}H_{12}Cl_2O_2$			
2,5-Cyclohexadien-1-one, 4-(dichloro-methyl)-4-ethyl-2-methoxy-	EtOH	239(3.98),288(3.40)	12-1337-73
$C_{10}H_{12}Cl_2O_4$			
2-Cyclopentene-1-carboxylic acid, 3,5-dichloro-1-hydroxy-4-oxo-2-propyl-, methyl ester	EtOH	244(4.05)	35-3000-73
$C_{10}H_{12}Cl_4N_2$			
Methanediamine, N,N,N',N'-tetramethyl-1-(2,3,4,5-tetrachloro-2,4-cyclo-pentadien-1-ylidene)-	dioxan	260(3.89),345(4.31)	88-5101-73
$C_{10}H_{12}FIN_2O_3$			
Thymidine, 3',5'-dideoxy-3'-fluoro-5'-iodo-	MeOH	209(4.01),263(4.02)	48-0895-73
$C_{10}H_{12}FNO_5$			
2(1H)-Pyridinone, 1-(2-deoxy-α-D-ery-thro-pentofuranosyl)-5-fluoro-4-hydroxy-	pH 1.0	289(3.23)	87-0524-73
	pH 3.2	290(3.66)	87-0524-73
	pH 7.2	257(3.95),277s(3.73)	87-0524-73
	pH 14.0	257(3.97),277s(3.75)	87-0524-73
β-isomer	pH 1.0	289(3.31)	87-0524-73
	pH 3.2	290(3.58)	87-0524-73
	pH 7.2	257(3.88),277s(3.66)	87-0524-73
	pH 14.0	257(3.88),277s(3.65)	87-0524-73
2(1H)-Pyridinone, 5-fluoro-1-β-D-ribo-furanosyl-	MeOH	316(3.74)	4-0779-73
$C_{10}H_{12}FNO_6$			
2(1H)-Pyridinone, 5-fluoro-4-hydroxy-1-β-D-ribofuranosyl-	pH 1.0	288(3.30)	87-0524-73
	pH 3.2	290(3.52)	87-0524-73
	pH 7.2	257(3.97),275s(3.77)	87-0524-73
	pH 14.0	257(3.96),275s(3.73)	87-0524-73
$C_{10}H_{12}F_3NO_3$			
Acetamide, 2,2,2-trifluoro-N-(4,4-di-methyl-2,6-dioxo-1-cyclohexyl)-	MeOH	279(4.14)	5-0407-73
	MeOH-HCl	256(4.08)	5-0407-73
	MeOH-NaOH	279(4.31)	5-0407-73
$C_{10}H_{12}F_3NO_6$			
Acetamide, N-[4,5-bis(acetyloxy)tetra-hydro-3-furanyl]-2,2,2-trifluoro-	EtOH	213(3.24)	33-2689-73
$C_{10}H_{12}INO_4$			
1H-Pyrrole-3-acetic acid, 4-iodo-2-(methoxycarbonyl)-5-methyl-, methyl ester	MeOH	282(4.21)	39-1546-73C
$C_{10}H_{12}I_4N_2$			
Methanediamine, N,N,N',N'-tetramethyl-1-(2,3,4,5-tetraiodo-2,4-cyclopenta-dien-1-ylidene)-	dioxan	259(3.97),359(4.15)	88-5101-73

Compound	Solvent	$\lambda_{max}(\log \epsilon)$	Ref.
$C_{10}H_{12}NO$			
Isoxazolium, 4,5-dihydro-2-methyl-3-phenyl-, perchlorate	EtOH	210s(--),275(3.84)	22-1390-73
$C_{10}H_{12}N_2$			
Indol-2-amine, N,1-dimethyl-, hydro-chloride	MeOH	214(4.29),264(3.87)	103-0471-73
	MeOH	262(4.11)	103-0598-73
Indol-2-amine, 1,3-dimethyl-, hydro-chloride	MeOH	210(4.31),260(3.99)	103-0471-73
1H-Indole-3-ethanamine (tryptamine)	EtOH	222(4.42),272(3.93), 294(3.90)	102-0193-73
	EtOH	221(4.63),274s(3.77), 281(3.81),289(3.74)	103-0196-73
hydrochloride	MeOH	225(4.27),274(3.81), 281(3.83),290(3.75)	102-0447-73
after ten minutes at 70°	H_2SO_4	236(3.61),241(3.59), 291(3.65)(changing)	102-0447-73
$C_{10}H_{12}N_2O$			
1H-Pyrazol-4-ol, 4,5-dihydro-1-(4-meth-ylphenyl)-	n.s.g.	246(4.00),292(4.07), 312(3.93)	22-3159-73
1H-Pyrazol-4-ol, 4,5-dihydro-4-methyl-1-phenyl-	n.s.g.	241(3.93),286(4.21), 306(4.03)	22-3159-73
1H-Pyrazol-4-ol, 4,5-dihydro-5-methyl-1-phenyl-	n.s.g.	243(3.86),292(4.14), 307s(4.00)	22-3159-73
$C_{10}H_{12}N_2OS$			
Benzamide, N-[(dimethylamino)thioxo-methyl]-	EtOH	234(4.49),271(4.05), 336(2.82)	48-0144-73
2-Propenimidamide, N-hydroxy-3-[4-(meth-ylthio)phenyl]-	EtOH	230(4.10),311(4.44)	39-2241-73C
$C_{10}H_{12}N_2O_2$			
Benzenamine, N,N-dimethyl-4-(2-nitroeth-enyl)-	n.s.g.	264(4.06),437(4.46)	135-1299-73
Benzenamine, 4-ethenyl-N-ethyl-2-nitro-	hexane	210(4.48),253s(4.80), 278(4.81),428(4.20)	24-1116-73
2,5-Piperazinedione, 3-(2-butenylidene)-6-ethylidene-	EtOH	321(4.48)	18-3876-73
Propanal, 3-[(phenylmethylene)amino]-, oxime N-oxide	EtOH	296(4.32)	104-0793-73
$C_{10}H_{12}N_2O_2S$			
2-Propenimidamide, N-hydroxy-3-[4-(methylsulfinyl)phenyl]-, (E)-	EtOH	299(4.23)	39-2241-73C
Z-Glyt-NH_2	EtOH	265(4.14)	35-5677-73
hydrobromide	EtOH-HBr	264(4.06)	35-5677-73
$C_{10}H_{12}N_2O_2S_2$			
Carbamic acid, [[(2-mercaptophenyl)-amino]thioxomethyl]-, ethyl ester	EtOH	273(4.01)	95-0977-73
$C_{10}H_{12}N_2O_2S_4$			
[5,5'-Bithiazolidine]-4,4'-dione, 3,3'-diethyl-2,2'-dithioxo-	EtOH	260(4.25),296(4.39)	94-0279-73
$C_{10}H_{12}N_2O_3$			
Acetic acid, (4-acetylphenoxy)-, hydra-zide	EtOH	215(4.14),268(4.25)	111-0574-73
Carbamic acid, [(phenylamino)carbonyl]-, ethyl ester	EtOH	240.5(4.23)	94-2396-73

Compound	Solvent	λ_{max}(log ϵ)	Ref.
1H-Pyrrolo[2,3-c]pyridine-2-carboxylic acid, 3-ethyl-4,5,6,7-tetrahydro-5-oxo-	EtOH	274(4.20)	44-1824-73
$C_{10}H_{12}N_2O_3S$			
Carbamic acid, [[(2-hydroxyphenyl)amino]-thioxomethyl]-, ethyl ester	EtOH	253(4.06),280(3.94), 310(4.03)	95-0977-73
7H-Thiazolo[3,2-a]pyrimidine-6-acetic acid, 2,3-dihydro-7-oxo-, ethyl ester	MeOH	231(4.36),274(3.86)	39-2022-73C
1H-Thieno[3,4-d]imidazole-4-pentanoic acid, 2,3-dihydro-2-oxo-	EtOH	262(4.20),306(2.89)	70-1641-73
$C_{10}H_{12}N_2O_4$			
Butanamide, 4-hydroxy-N-(4-nitrophenyl)-	MeCN	319(4.14)	35-1253-73
2,5-Pyrazinedicarboxylic acid, 3,6-dimethyl-, dimethyl ester	EtOH	222(3.83),290(3.88)	107-0225-73
1H-Pyrazole-3-carboxylic acid, 1-[1-(methoxycarbonyl)cyclopropyl]-, methyl ester	MeOH	221(4.11)	88-2655-73
$C_{10}H_{12}N_2O_5$			
O^2,2'-Anhydrouridine, 6-methyl-	H_2O	251(4.00)	73-3912-73
	H_2O	250(4.00)	88-1147-73
O^2,2'-Anhydro-α-uridine, 6-methyl-	H_2O	250(4.00)	73-3912-73
2,4(1H,3H)-Pyrimidinedione, 1-(2,3-dideoxy-β-D-threo-hex-2-enopyranosyl)-	MeOH	259(4.06)	78-1801-73
2,4,6(1H,3H,5H)-Pyrimidinetrione, 5-(1,3-dioxobutyl)-1,3-dimethyl-	EtOH	277(4.03)	94-2639-73
Uracil, O^2,2'-anhydro-1-α-D-xylofuranosyl-6-methyl-	H_2O	250(4.00)	73-3912-73
$C_{10}H_{12}N_2O_6$			
Benzene, 1,5-diethoxy-2,4-dinitro-	hexane	221(4.25),256(4.17), 275s(4.02),312(3.81), 340s(3.28)	124-1265-73
	EtOH	225(4.14),266(4.15), 280s(4.08),322(3.88)	124-1265-73
	dioxan	227(4.16),266(4.13), 280s(4.05),321(3.86)	124-1265-73
$C_{10}H_{12}N_3$			
Benzenediazonium, 2-(1-pyrrolidinyl)-, tetrafluoroborate	M HCl	273(3.75),434(3.78)	48-0725-73
$C_{10}H_{12}N_4$			
3(2H)-Pyridazinone, 4,5-dihydro-6-phenyl-, hydrazone	CH_2Cl_2	228(3.95),310(4.25)	39-2532-73C
$C_{10}H_{12}N_4O$			
1H-1,2,3-Triazole-4-methanol, 5-amino-1-(phenylmethyl)-	pH -2	265(3.73)	39-1629-73C
	pH 4	246(3.74)	39-1629-73C
$C_{10}H_{12}N_4OS_2$			
1H-Pyrazolo[4,3-g]benzothiazole-1-carbothioamide, 3a,4,5,8b-tetrahydro-8b-hydroxy-7-methyl-	EtOH	277(4.36)	32-1057-73
$C_{10}H_{12}N_4O_2$			
2,4(1H,3H)-Pteridinedione, 1,3,6,7-tetramethyl-	MeOH	237(4.16),253s(3.92), 333(3.92)	24-1401-73 +24-3149-73

Compound	Solvent	$\lambda_{max}(\log \epsilon)$	Ref.
$C_{10}H_{12}N_4O_2S$			
1H-Pyrazolo[4,3-g]benzothiazole-1-carboxamide, 3a,4,5,8b-tetrahydro-8b-hydroxy-7-methyl-	EtOH	233(4.06),277(4.06)	32-1057-73
$C_{10}H_{12}N_4O_3$			
2,4(1H,3H)-Pteridinedione, 7-methoxy-1,3,6-trimethyl-	pH 5.0	235s(3.98),265(3.86), 324(4.07)	24-3203-73
2,4(1H,3H)-Pteridinedione, 1,3,6,7-tetramethyl-, 5-oxide	pH -4.9	247(4.22),353(3.85)	24-3149-73
	pH 7.0	241(4.45),287(3.87), 351(3.83)	24-3149-73
2,4,6(1H,3H,5H)-Pyrimidinetrione, 1,3-dimethyl-5-(5-methyl-1H-pyrazol-3-yl)-	pH 2	260(4.15),292(4.36)	94-2639-73
	EtOH	265s(4.20),286(4.30) (anom.)	94-2639-73
	EtOH-KOH	274(4.38)	94-2639-73
1:1 hydrazine adduct	EtOH	274(4.37)	94-2639-73
$C_{10}H_{12}N_4O_3S$			
Inosine, 2'-deoxy-6-thio-	pH 1	224(3.99),324(4.32)	23-3161-73
	pH 13	231(4.16),311(4.32)	23-3161-73
$C_{10}H_{12}N_4O_4$			
1H-Imidazo[4,5-b]pyrazine, 1-β-D-ribofuranosyl-	pH 1	252s(3.40),288(4.00), 303s(3.85)	39-0244-73C
	pH 1	247(3.36),288(3.94)	87-0643-73
	pH 11	250(3.58),289(4.03), 304s(3.88),312s(3.74)	39-0244-73C
	pH 13	245(3.78),325(3.70)	87-0643-73
	MeOH	259s(3.52),290(4.06)	39-0244-73C
	MeOH	255s(--),290(4.07)	87-0643-73
Inosine, 3'-deoxy-	pH 1	251(4.04)	94-1143-73
	pH 7	250.5(4.05)	94-1143-73
	pH 13	255.5(4.12)	94-1143-73
Isoxazole, 4,4'-azobis[5-methoxy-3-methyl-	EtOH	241(3.92),323s(4.13), 335(4.15),400s(3.20)	32-1045-73
4,5-Isoxazoledione, 3-methyl-, 4-[(2,5-dihydro-2,3-dimethyl-5-oxo-4-isoxazolyl)methylhydrazone]	EtOH	271(4.02),377(3.93)	32-1045-73
4,5-Isoxazoledione, 4-[(5-methoxy-3-methyl-4-isoxazolyl)methylhydrazone]	EtOH	230(3.82),376(4.02)	32-1045-73
5(2H)-Isoxazolone, 4,4'-azobis[2,3-dimethyl-	EtOH	284(3.80),340s(4.05), 353(4.10),410s(3.66)	32-1045-73
5(2H)-Isoxazolone, 4-[(5-methoxy-3-methyl-4-isoxazolyl)azo]-2,3-dimethyl-	EtOH	253(3.76),283(3.83), 330s(4.20),346(4.27), 400s(3.65)	32-1045-73
2,4(1H,3H)-Pteridinedione, 7-methoxy-1,3,6-trimethyl-, 5-oxide	MeOH	246(4.41),287s(3.72), 342(3.96)	24-3203-73
6H-Purin-6-one, 8-(2-deoxy-α-D-erythro-pentofuranosyl)-1,7-dihydro-	pH 1	252(4.12)	88-2971-73
	pH 13	267(4.15)	88-2971-73
7H-Pyrazolo[4,3-d]pyrimidin-7-one, 3-(2-deoxy-β-D-erythro-pentofuranosyl)-1,6-dihydro-	pH 1	220(4.10),277(3.81)	23-1313-73
	H O	218(4.11),278(3.82)	23-1313-73
	pH 13	228(4.15),292(3.85)	23-1313-73
7H-Pyrazolo[4,3-d]pyrimidin-7-one, 3-(3-deoxy-β-D-erythro-pentofuranosyl)-1,6-dihydro-	pH 1	220(4.14),277(3.87)	23-1313-73
	H O	219(4.16),279(3.87)	23-1313-73
	pH 13	228(4.20),292(3.91)	23-1313-73
2H-Pyrrole-3-carboxylic acid, 4-[(2-cyanoethyl)methylamino]-5-(hydroxyamino)-2-oxo-, methyl ester	EtOH	357(4.09)	94-1667-73
2H-1,2,3-Triazole-4-carboxylic acid, 2-(5-methoxy-3-methyl-4-isoxazolyl)-5-methyl-, methyl ester	EtOH	230(3.91),260(3.90)	32-1045-73

Compound	Solvent	λ_{max}(log ε)	Ref.
$C_{10}H_{12}N_4O_5$			
1H-Imidazo[4,5-b]pyrazine, 1-β-D-ribofuranosyl-, 4-oxide	pH 1	222(4.36),305(4.32)	87-0643-73
	pH 13	236(4.43),337(4.00)	87-0643-73
	MeOH	227(4.24),303(4.21)	87-0643-73
$C_{10}H_{12}N_4S$			
4-Isoquinolinecarbonitrile, 2,3-diamino-1,2,5,6,7,8-hexahydro-1-thioxo-	MeOH	271(3.80),293(3.87), 377(4.37)	48-0679-73
$C_{10}H_{12}N_4S_2$			
[4,5'-Bithiazole]-2,2'-diamine, 4'-methyl-N$^{2'}$-2-propenyl-	EtOH	268(3.90),320(3.96)	83-0152-73
$C_{10}H_{12}N_5O_7P$			
Inosine, 8-amino-, cyclic 3',5'-(hydrogen phosphate)	pH 1	253(4.13),283s(3.63)	69-5310-73
	pH 11	261(4.16)	69-5310-73
$C_{10}H_{12}N_5O_8P$			
Guanosine, 8-hydroxy-, cyclic 3',5'-(hydrogen phosphate), ammonium salt	pH 1	246(4.06),294(3.98)	69-5310-73
	pH 11	248(4.00),278(3.94)	69-5310-73
$C_{10}H_{12}N_6O$			
Urea, N-methyl-N-2-propenyl-N'-1H-purin-6-yl-	pH 1-2	276.5(4.26)	87-0139-73
	pH 5-7	276(4.20)	87-0139-73
	pH 12	281(4.14)	87-0139-73
$C_{10}H_{12}N_6OS$			
2(1H)-Pyridinethione, 3-[(2,6-diamino-4-pyrimidinyl)amino]-6-methoxy-	MeOH	249(3.87),311(3.88), 384(3.54)	44-4386-73
$C_{10}H_{12}N_6O_3$			
Glycine, N-[(1H-purin-6-ylamino)carbonyl]-, ethyl ester	pH 1-2	276(4.33)	87-0139-73
	pH 5-7	268.5(4.30)	87-0139-73
	pH 12	277.5(4.26)	87-0139-73
Propanoic acid, 2-methyl-3-[[(1H-purin-6-ylamino)carbonyl]amino]-	pH 1-2	277(4.28)	87-0139-73
	pH 5-7	269(4.24)	87-0139-73
	pH 12	278(4.20)	87-0139-73
$C_{10}H_{12}N_8$			
Pyrazolo[4,3-c]pyrazole, 3-[(3,5-dimethyl-1H-pyrazol-4-yl)azo]-1,5-dihydro-6-methyl-	EtOH	221(4.03),360(4.27)	88-1199-73
$C_{10}H_{12}O$			
Benzene, 1-methoxy-2-(2-propenyl)-	EtOH	272(3.36)	88-4841-73
Benzene, 1-methoxy-4-(2-propenyl)-	EtOH	229(4.26),281(3.60), 287(3.52)	88-4841-73
Benzene, 1-methoxy-4-propenyl-	EtOH	210(4.20),259(4.27), 289s(3.41),305s(3.15)	141-0001-73
	dioxan	214(4.09),261(4.17), 270s(4.09),286s(3.52), 309s(2.95)	141-0001-73
Bicyclo[5.1.0]octa-2,5-dien-4-one, 3,5-dimethyl-	EtOH	216(3.77),281(3.74)	138-0003-73
	H_2SO_4	207(4.08),250(4.25), 328(3.67)	138-0003-73
2-Butanone, 4-phenyl-	C_6H_{12}	280(1.53)	28-0407-73B
	MeOH	280(1.56)	28-0407-73B
5H-Inden-5-one, 1,6,7,7a-tetrahydro-2-methyl-	EtOH	291(4.32)	22-2098-73
5H-Inden-5-one, 2,3,6,7-tetrahydro-1-methyl-	EtOH	300(4.25)	22-2098-73

Compound	Solvent	$\lambda_{max}(\log \epsilon)$	Ref.
5H-Inden-5-one, 2,3,6,7-tetrahydro-2-methyl-	EtOH	290(4.23)	22-2098-73
2(1H)-Naphthalenone, 4a,5,8,8a-tetrahydro-, cis	MeOH	230.5(3.92)	12-0595-73
2(3H)-Naphthalenone, 4,6,7,8-tetrahydro-	EtOH	289(4.14)	22-2098-73
$C_{10}H_{12}OS$			
Benzeneethanethioic acid, O-ethyl ester	C_6H_{12}	243(3.95),377(1.65)	39-1571-73C
Benzo[b]thiophene, 4-ethoxy-6,7-dihydro-	EtOH	225(4.17),288(3.26)	44-0146-73
$C_{10}H_{12}O_2$			
1,8-Azulenedione, 2,3,4,5,6,7-hexahydro-	MeOH	234(3.92)	44-0095-73
2,4,6-Cycloheptatrien-1-one, 2-hydroxy-5-propyl-	EtOH	237(4.14),248(4.05), 310(3.57),324(3.63), 356(3.51),368(3.43)	12-1337-73
	EtOH-KOH	243(4.21),337(3.88), 398(3.76)	12-1337-73
1-Cyclohexene-1,4-dicarboxaldehyde, 4-ethenyl-	EtOH	230(4.16)	78-2715-73
2,4-Decadien-6-ynoic acid, (E,E)-	ether	284(4.57),296s(4.53)	24-1328-73
1H-Indene-1,5(6H)-dione, 2,3,7,7a-tetrahydro-7a-methyl-	EtOH	237(4.05)	22-0359-73
1,5-Naphthalenedione, 2,3,4,6,7,8-hexahydro-	EtOH	265(4.08)	44-4281-73
2(1H)-Naphthalenone, 4a,5,8,8a-tetrahydro-1-hydroxy-, cis	MeOH	227(3.86)	12-0595-73
Phenol, 2-methoxy-4-propenyl-	EtOH	215(4.25),260(4.10), 265s(4.09),292s(3.65), 313s(3.34)	141-0001-73
	EtOH-NaOH	220(4.20),286(4.17), 308s(4.00),360s(3.04)	141-0001-73
	dioxan	226(4.05),261(4.12), 265s(4.11),302s(3.63), 315s(3.33)	141-0001-73
1-Propanone, 1-(2-hydroxy-6-methylphenyl)-	C H	256(3.86),335(3.48)	22-3087-73
	EtOH	251(3.32),286(3.22)	22-3087-73
1-Propanone, 1-(2-methoxyphenyl)-	EtOH	212(4.21),249(3.87), 310(3.45)	141-0001-73
	dioxan	247(3.89),304(3.48), 330s(3.66)	141-0001-73
1-Propanone, 1-(4-methoxyphenyl)-	EtOH	217(4.03),271(4.18), 315s(2.50)	141-0001-73
	dioxan	267(4.19),275s(4.11)	141-0001-73
Spiro[4.5]dec-6-ene-1,8-dione	EtOH	222(3.78),247(3.74)	39-0393-73C
$C_{10}H_{12}O_2S$			
9-Thiabicyclo[4.2.1]nona-2,4,7-triene, 7,8-dimethyl-, 9,9-dioxide	EtOH	282(3.32)	35-2230-73
$C_{10}H_{12}O_3$			
Benzaldehyde, 2-ethyl-4-hydroxy-5-methoxy-	EtOH	236(4.26),283(4.00), 315(3.88)	12-1337-73
	EtOH-KOH	255(4.06),352(4.37)	12-1337-73
Bicyclo[3.3.1]non-2-en-9-one, 7-carboxy-, (1R)-	MeOH	292(1.38)	78-4013-73
Ethanone, 1-(2,3-dimethoxyphenyl)-	EtOH	218(4.26),251(3.79), 306(3.33)	141-0001-73
	dioxan	220(4.23),248(3.76), 303(3.33)	141-0001-73
Ethanone, 1-(2,4-dimethoxyphenyl)-	EtOH	212(4.16),227(4.16), 267(4.10),303(3.92)	141-0001-73

Compound	Solvent	$\lambda_{max}(\log \epsilon)$	Ref.
Ethanone, 1-(2,4-dimethoxyphenyl)- (cont.)	dioxan	224(4.18),229(4.18), 263(4.12),298(3.85)	141-0001-73
Ethanone, 1-(2,5-dimethoxyphenyl)-	EtOH	224(4.40),250(4.10), 336(3.95)	141-0001-73
	dioxan	223(4.70),234(4.20), 321(4.00)	141-0001-73
Ethanone, 1-(2,6-dimethoxyphenyl)-	EtOH	213s(4.08),259(3.44), 270s(3.40)	141-0001-73
	dioxan	220(3.85),244s(3.39), 279(3.27)	141-0001-73
Ethanone, 1-(3,4-dimethoxyphenyl)-	EtOH	228(4.21),272(4.02), 303(3.88)	141-0001-73
	dioxan	269(4.20),280(4.30), 298(3.81)	141-0001-73
Ethanone, 1-(3,5-dimethoxyphenyl)-	EtOH	218(4.42),263(4.00), 318(3.70)	141-0001-73
	dioxan	215(4.48),259(4.30), 312(3.90),351(1.70)	141-0001-73
Propanoic acid, 3-(4-hydroxyphenyl)-, methyl ester	EtOH	224(3.92),277(3.25), 283s(3.17)	33-1266-73
$C_{10}H_{12}O_4$			
Acetic acid, 2,2'-(1,2-cyclohexanediylidene)bis-, (Z,Z)-	EtOH	211(4.19)	64-0675-73C
Benzaldehyde, 2,4,5-trimethoxy-	EtOH	237(4.21),275(4.07), 344(3.96)	141-0001-73
	dioxan	235(4.26),273(4.10), 336(3.96)	141-0001-73
Benzaldehyde, 2,4,6-trimethoxy-	EtOH	211(4.19),227(4.22), 288(4.31)	141-0001-73
	dioxan	229(4.23),280(4.26), 311s(3.55)	141-0001-73
Benzaldehyde, 3,4,5-trimethoxy-	EtOH	218(4.38),288(4.01)	141-0001-73
	dioxan	226(4.20),288(4.02), 315s(3.66)	141-0001-73
7a(2H)-Benzofuranacetic acid, 4,5,6,7-tetrahydro-2-oxo-	EtOH	213(4.17)	64-0675-73C
Benzoic acid, 2,3-dimethoxy-, methyl ester	EtOH	213(4.28),240s(3.59), 295(3.36)	141-0001-73
	dioxan	217(4.18),243s(3.52), 292(3.40)	141-0001-73
Benzoic acid, 2,4-dimethoxy-, methyl ester	EtOH	215(4.27),255(4.12), 291(3.76)	141-0001-73
	dioxan	217(4.28),252(4.12), 289(3.73)	141-0001-73
Benzoic acid, 2,5-dimethoxy-, methyl ester	EtOH	215(4.27),235(3.87), 320(3.59)	141-0001-73
	dioxan	216(4.21),234(3.89), 316(3.56)	141-0001-73
Benzoic acid, 2,6-dimethoxy-, methyl ester	EtOH	209(4.18),246s(3.40), 281(3.42)	141-0001-73
	dioxan	222s(3.86),273s(3.34), 281(3.40)	141-0001-73
Benzoic acid, 3,4-dimethoxy-, methyl ester	EtOH	220(4.30),261(4.10), 292(3.80)	141-0001-73
	dioxan	226(4.04),262(4.03), 291(3.76),295s(3.73)	141-0001-73
1,3-Cyclopentanedione, 4-acetoxy-2-(2-propenyl)-	EtOH	250(4.16)	94-2195-73
Ethanone, 1-(2-hydroxy-4,5-dimethoxyphenyl)-	EtOH	237(4.21),275(4.07), 342(3.89)	141-0001-73

Compound	Solvent	$\lambda_{max}(\log \epsilon)$	Ref.
Ethanone, 1-(2-hydroxy-4,6-dimethoxy-phenyl)-	EtOH	228(4.20),288(4.24), 320s(3.60)	141-0001-73
	EtOH-NaOH	235(4.20),288(3.82), 338(3.62)	141-0001-73
	n.s.g.	213(4.05),225(3.99), 290(4.10)	105-0390-73
Tricyclo[3.1.0.0^{2,4}]hexane-1,2-dicarb-oxylic acid, dimethyl ester	heptane	227(1.92)	44-1697-73
$C_{10}H_{12}O_4S_2$			
1,3-Dithiole-4-carboxylic acid, 2-(1-acetyl-2-oxopropyl)-, methyl ester	EtOH	230(3.74),335(3.65)	35-4379-73
$C_{10}H_{12}O_5$			
Benzoic acid, 2-hydroxy-4,6-dimethoxy-, methyl ester	EtOH	221(4.89),226(4.76), 298(4.10)	12-2459-73
	EtOH-KOH	218(4.90),227s(4.83), 260(4.20),303(4.07)	12-2459-73
Benzoic acid, 2,4,5-trimethoxy-	EtOH	221(4.34),255(4.00), 307(3.82)	141-0001-73
	EtOH-NaOH	218(4.21),246(3.94), 297(3.74)	141-0001-73
	dioxan	227(4.24),255(4.05), 308(3.85)	141-0001-73
Benzoic acid, 2,4,6-trimethoxy-	EtOH	214(4.31),250s(3.67)	141-0001-73
	EtOH-NaOH	218(4.17),238s(3.80), 273s(3.00)	141-0001-73
	dioxan	221(4.09),250s(3.69)	141-0001-73
Benzoic acid, 3,4,5-trimethoxy-	EtOH	214(4.51),262(3.95), 295s(3.49)	141-0001-73
	EtOH-NaOH	219(4.23),251(4.02), 291(3.73)	141-0001-73
	dioxan	217(4.47),266(3.99), 290s(3.64)	141-0001-73
2-Cyclohexen-1-one, 4,5-diacetoxy-	EtOH	218(3.95)	35-7821-73
$C_{10}H_{12}O_6$			
Benzoic acid, 2,4-dihydroxy-3-(hydroxy-methyl)-6-methoxy-, methyl ester	EtOH	224(4.30),269(4.27), 300(3.43)	12-2459-73
	EtOH-KOH	213(4.46),243(3.96), 299(4.28)	12-2459-73
Benzoic acid, 2,6-dihydroxy-3-(hydroxy-methyl)-4-methoxy-, methyl ester	EtOH	226(4.39),268(4.18), 305(3.44)	12-2459-73
	EtOH-KOH	211(4.26),240(4.32), 273(4.02),334(3.76)	12-2459-73
$C_{10}H_{12}S_2$			
Benzenecarbodithioic acid, 1-methyl-ethyl ester	C_6H_{12}	296(4.12),509(2.08)	101-0121-73I
$C_{10}H_{13}$			
Cycloheptatrienylium, (1-methylethyl)-, perchlorate	pH 1	294(3.70)	18-1785-73
Cycloheptatrienylium, 1,2,4-trimethyl-, chloroplatinate	H_2SO_4	236(4.66),256s(3.73), 289(3.70),306(3.51)	33-2796-73
	MeCN	236(4.73),269(4.15), 300s(3.80)	33-2796-73
Ethylium, 1-methyl-1-(4-methylphenyl)-	FSO_3H at -75°	337(4.40)	59-0803-73

Compound	Solvent	$\lambda_{max}(\log \epsilon)$	Ref.
$C_{10}H_{13}BrCl_4O$			
p-Menthan-2-one, 3-bromo-1,6,8,9-tetra-chloro-, (1S,3R,4R,6S,8R)-	C_6H_{12}	229(2.38),300(1.71)	12-1283-73
$C_{10}H_{13}BrNO$			
Nitroxide, 2-bromophenyl 1,1-dimethyl-ethyl	EtOH	297(3.13),500(2.10)	39-0456-73C
$C_{10}H_{13}Br_2Cl_3O$			
p-Menthan-2-one, 8,9-dibromo-1,3,6-tri-chloro-, (1S,3R,4S,6S,8R)-	C_6H_{12}	227(2.72),299(1.76)	12-1283-73
(1S,3R,4S,6S,8S)-	C_6H_{12}	232(2.60),300(1.77)	12-1283-73
$C_{10}H_{13}Br_3Cl_2O$			
p-Menthan-2-one, 3,8,9-tribromo-1,6-di-chloro-, (1S,3R,4S,6S,8R)-	C_6H_{12}	231(2.82),300(1.73)	12-1283-73
(1S,3R,4S,6S,8S)-	C_6H_{12}	226(2.96),297(1.80)	12-1283-73
$C_{10}H_{13}Br_3O$			
p-Menth-8-en-2-one, 1,3,6-tribromo-, (1R,3S,4S,6S)-	C_6H_{12}	233(2.79),307(2.11)	12-1977-73
$C_{10}H_{13}Br_4ClO$			
p-Menthan-2-one, 1,6,8,9-tetrabromo-3-chloro-, (1R,3S,4R,6R,8S)-	C_6H_{12}	232(2.90),307(2.06)	12-1977-73
$C_{10}H_{13}Br_5O$			
p-Menthan-2-one, 1,3,6,8,9-pentabromo-, (1S,3R,4S,6S,8R)-	C_6H_{12}	233(3.03),306(2.00)	12-1283-73
(1S,3R,4S,6S,8S)-	C_6H_{12}	231(3.03),306(2.06)	12-1283-73
$C_{10}H_{13}ClGeOS$			
Germane, [(2-chlorobenzoyl)thio]tri-methyl-	C_6H_{12}	241(3.90),260(3.65)	18-0244-73
Germane, [(3-chlorobenzoyl)thio]tri-methyl-	C_6H_{12}	240(4.08),270(3.91)	18-0244-73
Germane, [(4-chlorobenzoyl)thio]tri-methyl-	C_6H_{12}	250(4.23),269(4.09)	18-0244-73
$C_{10}H_{13}ClGeS_2$			
Germane, [[(4-chlorophenyl)thioxometh-yl]thio]trimethyl-	C_6H_{12}	311(4.19),531(2.06)	101-0121-73I
$C_{10}H_{13}ClNO$			
Nitroxide, 2-chlorophenyl 1,1-dimethyl-ethyl	EtOH	296(3.14),495(1.79)	39-0456-73C
$C_{10}H_{13}ClN_6O_3$			
1,2-Cyclopentanediol, 3-(5-amino-7-chloro-3H-1,2,3-triazolo[4,5-d]-pyrimidin-3-yl)-5-(hydroxymethyl)-, (1α,2α,3β,5β)-(±)-	pH 1	226(4.33),253s(--), 316(3.88)	36-1432-73
	pH 7	226(4.34),253s(--), 316(3.88)	36-1432-73
	pH 13	246(3.67),286(4.00)	36-1432-73
$C_{10}H_{13}ClOSSi$			
Benzenecarbodithioic acid, 3-chloro-, O-(trimethylsilyl) ester	C_6H_{12}	250(3.84),292(3.98), 443(1.93)	18-0244-73
Benzenecarbodithioic acid, 4-chloro-, O-(trimethylsilyl) ester	C_6H_{12}	255(3.98),302(4.08), 439(1.97)	18-0244-73

Compound	Solvent	λmax(log ε)	Ref.
$C_{10}H_{13}ClOSSn$			
Stannane, [(2-chlorobenzoyl)thio]trimethyl-	C_6H_{12}	205(3.71),243(3.92)	18-0244-73
Stannane, [(3-chlorobenzoyl)thio]trimethyl-	C_6H_{12}	243(3.99),274(3.83)	18-0244-73
Stannane, [(4-chlorobenzoyl)thio]trimethyl-	C_6H_{12}	251(4.20),278(4.07)	18-0244-73
$C_{10}H_{13}ClS_2Si$			
Benzenecarbodithioic acid, 4-chloro-, trimethylsilyl ester	C_6H_{12}	308(4.12),534(2.14)	101-0121-73I
$C_{10}H_{13}ClS_2Sn$			
Stannane, [[(4-chlorophenyl)thioxomethyl]thio]trimethyl-	C_6H_{12}	314(4.16),525(1.99)	101-0121-73I
$C_{10}H_{13}FN_2O_3S$			
2(1H)-Pyrimidinone, 1-(2,3-dideoxy-3-fluoro-β-D-erythro-pentofuranosyl)-4-(methylthio)-	MeOH	223s(--),280s(--), 301(4.16)	48-0895-73
$C_{10}H_{13}F_3Si$			
Silane, trimethyl[3-(trifluoromethyl)-phenyl]-	EtOH	212(3.79),258(2.28), 264(2.58),272(2.58)	35-5288-73
Silane, trimethyl[4-(trifluoromethyl)-phenyl]-	EtOH	235(3.36),252(3.38), 257s(3.36),264s(3.26), 272s(3.11)	35-5288-73
$C_{10}H_{13}GeNO_3S$			
Germane, trimethyl[(2-nitrobenzoyl)-thio]-	C_6H_{12}	237(3.97)	18-0244-73
Germane, trimethyl[(3-nitrobenzoyl)-thio]-	C_6H_{12}	257(4.02),266(4.36)	18-0244-73
Germane, trimethyl[(4-nitrobenzoyl)-thio]-	C_6H_{12}	264(4.14),287(4.00)	18-0244-73
$C_{10}H_{13}NO$			
1H-Azepine, 1-acetyl-4,5-dihydro-4-methyl-5-methylene-	$CHCl_3$	272(4.19)	78-0391-73
Benzenamine, 2-methoxy-N-2-propenyl-	ether	249(4.05),292(3.54)	24-0355-73
2H-1,6-Benzoxazocine, 3,4,5,6-tetrahydro-	EtOH	255(4.02),303(3.37)	4-0689-73
	EtOH-HCl	260s(2.75),264(2.83), 270(2.79)	4-0689-73
5H-Cyclohepta[b]pyridine, 6,7,8,9-tetrahydro-, 1-oxide	EtOH	221(4.36),264(4.02)	39-0968-73C
5H-Cyclohepta[b]pyridin-9-ol, 6,7,8,9-tetrahydro-	EtOH	210(3.75),263(3.62), 290s(--)	39-0968-73C
Ethanone, 1-[4-(dimethylamino)phenyl]-	FSO_3H at -75°	280(4.34),320s(<3.48)	59-0807-73
1-Propanone, 1-(2-aminophenyl)-2-methyl-	EtOH	210s(4.08),228(4.47), 258(3.89),368(3.71)	78-1429-73
1-Propanone, 1-(3-aminophenyl)-2-methyl-	EtOH	208s(4.03),231(4.45), 261s(3.91),335(3.39)	78-1429-73
$C_{10}H_{13}NOS$			
Ethanethioic acid, S-[4-(dimethylamino)-phenyl] ester	C_6H_{12}	270(4.42)	44-1559-73
$C_{10}H_{13}NO_2$			
Benzoic acid, 2-(dimethylamino)-, methyl ester	EtOH	267(3.69),339(3.37)	5-1955-73

Compound	Solvent	$\lambda_{max}(\log \epsilon)$	Ref.
Benzoic acid, 4-(dimethylamino)-, methyl ester	MeOH	227(3.84),310(4.43)	5-1955-73
2,5-Cyclohexadien-1-one, 4-[(1,1-dimethylethyl)imino]-, N-oxide	EtOH	384(4.33)	39-0456-73C
1-Cyclohexene-1-carboxylic acid, 2-cyano-, ethyl ester	EtOH	233(3.96)	78-0683-73
2-Cyclohexene-1-carboxylic acid, 2-cyano-, ethyl ester	EtOH	211(4.03)	78-0683-73
Formimidic acid, N-(4-methoxyphenyl)-, ethyl ester	MeCN	258(4.04)	35-1253-73
Pyridine, 1,4-diacetyl-1,4-dihydro-4-methyl-	MeOH	254(4.23)	78-0391-73
2(1H)-Pyridinone, 3-acetyl-1-propyl-	EtOH	243(3.65),350(3.90)	103-0615-73
4(1H)-Pyridinone, 3-acetyl-1,2,6-trimethyl-	EtOH	263(4.17)	95-1084-73
	EtOH-HCl	242(3.98)	95-1084-73
$C_{10}H_{13}NO_2S_2$			
2-Propenoic acid, 3-(2-butenylthio)-2-cyano-3-(methylthio)-, methyl ester	EtOH	330(4.04)	78-2077-73
1H-Pyrrole-3,4-dicarbothioic acid, S,S-diethyl ester	EtOH	270(4.12)	23-1089-73
$C_{10}H_{13}NO_3$			
Acetophenone, 2',4'-dimethoxy-, oxime	EtOH	215(4.26),249(4.03), 285(3.58)	141-0001-73
	dioxan	220(4.06),247(4.06), 285(3.58)	141-0001-73
Benzoic acid, 4-(2-aminoethyl)-2-hydroxy-, methyl ester	EtOH	243(4.09),309(3.68)	78-0857-73
D-ribo-Hept-2-enonitrile, 4,7-anhydro-2,3-dideoxy-5,6-O-(1-methylethylidene)-, cis	EtOH	212(3.72)	33-1310-73
trans	EtOH	213(3.83)	33-1310-73
Propanenitrile, 3-(dihydro-2,2-dimethylfuro[3,4-d]-1,3-dioxol-4(3aH)-ylidene)-, (3aR-cis)-	EtOH	212(3.48)	33-1310-73
$C_{10}H_{13}NO_3S$			
2,1-Benzisothiazole-5-methanol, 1,3-dihydro-α,1-dimethyl-	EtOH	238(4.04),289(3.21)	4-0249-73
$C_{10}H_{13}NO_3SSn$			
Stannane, trimethyl[(2-nitrobenzoyl)-thio]-	C_6H_{12}	263(4.11),291(3.97)	18-0244-73
Stannane, trimethyl[(3-nitrobenzoyl)-thio]-	C_6H_{12}	226(4.40)	18-0244-73
$C_{10}H_{13}NO_4$			
DL-Phenylalanine, 3,4-dihydroxy-, methyl ester	pH 1	280(3.42)	36-0510-73
1H-Pyrrole-3-acetic acid, 2-(methoxycarbonyl)-5-methyl-, methyl ester	MeOH	278(4.24)	39-1546-73C
1H-Pyrrole-3,4-dicarboxylic acid, diethyl ester	EtOH	252(3.88)	23-1089-73
$C_{10}H_{13}NO_5S$			
1H,3H-Oxazolo[4,3-c][1,4]thiazine-6-carboxylic acid, 8,8a-dihydro-3,3-dimethyl-1-oxo-, methyl ester, 7-oxide	EtOH	280(4.16)	78-3023-73

Compound	Solvent	$\lambda_{max}(\log \epsilon)$	Ref.
$C_{10}H_{13}NO_6S$			
3H-Indole-3a-sulfonic acid, 1,2,3,4,5,6-hexahydro-3-methoxy-1-methyl-5,6-dioxo-, sodium salt	H_2O	245(3.87),349(4.19)	39-0509-73C
$C_{10}H_{13}N_2O_2$			
Pyridinium, 3-[1-[(acetyloxy)imino]ethyl]-1-methyl-, iodide	pH 6.61	254(3.71)	36-1381-73
$C_{10}H_{13}N_3$			
1H-Pyrazol-3-amine, 4,5-dihydro-5-methyl-1-phenyl-	EtOH	274(4.12)	104-1776-73
$C_{10}H_{13}N_3OS$			
Acetophenone, 4'-methoxy-, thiosemicarbazone	$CHCl_3$	315(4.15)	7-0363-73
in 10% isopropanol	pH 7.0	305(4.34)	7-0363-73
in 10% isopropanol	pH 13.5	335(4.13)	7-0363-73
$C_{10}H_{13}N_3OS_2$			
4H-Thiazolo[3,2-a]-1,3,5-triazin-4-one, 7-butyl-2-(methylthio)-	EtOH	246(3.85),267(3.91), 315(4.31),322s(--)	94-0074-73
$C_{10}H_{13}N_3O_2$			
Ethanediamide, [4-(dimethylamino)phenyl]-	dioxan	245(3.85),318(4.14)	30-0001-73
4-Quinazolinecarboxylic acid, 2-amino-5,6,7,8-tetrahydro-, methyl ester	pH 0.1	226(3.92),333(3.48)	39-2814-73C
	pH 7.0	231(4.04),319(3.44)	39-2814-73C
	MeOH	233(4.10),321(3.60)	39-2814-73C
$C_{10}H_{13}N_3O_2S$			
Carbamic acid, [[(2-aminophenyl)amino]-thioxomethyl]-, ethyl ester	EtOH	268(4.08)	95-0977-73
$C_{10}H_{13}N_3O_2S_2$			
Carbamic acid, [(2-propenylthio)(2-thiazolylimino)methyl]-, ethyl ester	dioxan	243(3.82),314(4.31)	94-0074-73
Carbamic acid, (5-propyl-2H-thiazolo-[3,2-b][1,2,4]thiadiazol-2-ylidene)-, ethyl ester	EtOH	251(3.54),312(4.38)	94-2408-73
$C_{10}H_{13}N_3O_4$			
2,4(1H,3H)-Pyrimidinedione, 5-(1,3-dioxobutyl)dihydro-6-imino-1,3-dimethyl-	EtOH	219(4.47),262(3.70), 304(4.04)	94-2014-73
$C_{10}H_{13}N_3O_6$			
2H-Pyrrole-3-carboxylic acid, 4-[(2-ethoxy-2-oxoethyl)amino]-5-(hydroxyamino)-2-oxo-, methyl ester	EtOH	356(4.17)	94-1667-73
$C_{10}H_{13}N_3S$			
1-Pyrazolidinecarbothioamide, 2-phenyl-	EtOH	250(4.30)	103-0456-73
$C_{10}H_{13}N_4O_4$			
1H-Purinium, 7-(2-ethoxy-2-oxoethyl)-2,3,6,9-tetrahydro-2,6-dioxo-, bromide	pH 0	238(3.73),263(3.95)	24-1389-73
	pH 6	251(3.92),289(3.89)	24-1389-73
$C_{10}H_{13}N_5$			
1H-1,2,3-Triazole-4-methanamine, 5-amino-1-(phenylmethyl)-	pH -2.8	266(3.65)	39-1634-73C
	pH 6.0	244(3.70)	39-1634-73C
	pH 11.0	244(3.70)	39-1634-73C

Compound	Solvent	λ_{max}(log ε)	Ref.
1H-1,2,3-Triazolo[4,5-b]pyridin-7-amine, N-(3-methyl-2-butenyl)-	M HCl	222(4.15),257(3.81), 318(4.26)	102-2087-73
	M NaOH	226(4.11),266(3.85), 273(3.90),304(4.18)	102-2087-73
	EtOH	223(4.08),269(3.90), 311(4.23),321s(--)	102-2087-73
1H-1,2,3-Triazolo[4,5-c]pyridin-7-amine, N-(3-methyl-2-butenyl)-	M HCl	213(4.18),281(4.15)	102-2087-73
	M NaOH	226(4.06),294(4.00)	102-2087-73
	EtOH	224(4.15),293(4.00)	102-2087-73
$C_{10}H_{13}N_5O$			
4(1H)-Pteridinone, 2-amino-7-(1,1-dimethylethyl)-	pH 0.0	215(4.32),245s(3.90), 312(4.02)	24-3175-73
	pH 5.0	215s(4.19),233s(4.15), 271(4.06),338(3.87)	24-3175-73
	pH 11.0	249(4.33),273s(3.72), 355(3.92)	24-3175-73
7(8H)-Pteridinone, 2-(dimethylamino)-8-ethyl-	MeOH	223(4.14),242s(3.95), 300(3.55),364(4.07)	24-0317-73
3H-Purine, 3-methyl-6-morpholino-	n.s.g.	297(4.28)	104-1316-73
6H-Purin-6-one, 2-amino-1,7-dihydro-8-(3-methyl-2-butenyl)-	pH 1	248(4.09)	35-7174-73
	H_2O	246(4.00),278(3.87)	35-7174-73
	pH 13	276(3.98)	35-7174-73
4H-Pyrazolo[3,4-d]pyrimidin-4-one, 1,5-dihydro-1-(1-pyrrolidinylmethyl)-	EtOH	253(3.92)	103-1280-73
$C_{10}H_{13}N_5O_2$			
Formycin, 2',3'-dideoxy-, hydrochloride	MeOH-acid	234(3.95),296(4.01)	44-3179-73
	MeOH-base	234(4.24),304(3.90)	44-3179-73
4(1H)-Pteridinone, 2-amino-7-(1,1-dimethylethyl)-, 5-oxide	pH -1.0	235s(4.32),244(4.33), 283(3.90),342(3.80), 393(3.21)	24-3175-73
	pH 5.0	228(4.30),250(4.24), 272(4.32),297s(3.75), 366(3.74)	24-3175-73
	pH 10.0	223(4.27),260(4.37), 300s(3.74),372(3.81)	24-3175-73
7(8H)-Pteridinone, 2-(dimethylamino)-4-methoxy-8-methyl-	MeOH	240(4.20),287(3.65), 360(4.26)	24-1952-73
7H-1,2,3-Triazolo[4,5-d]pyrimidin-7-one, 3,6-dihydro-3-[3-(hydroxymethyl)-cyclopentyl]-, cis-(±)-	pH 1	254(4.00),269s(--)	4-0601-73
	pH 7	255(3.97),268s(--), 280s(--)	4-0601-73
	pH 13	275(4.05)	4-0601-73
$C_{10}H_{13}N_5O_2S$			
Adenine, 9-(3-deoxy-4-thio-β-D-erythro-pentofuranosyl)- (4'-thiocordycepin)	MeOH	261(4.17)	77-0686-73
$C_{10}H_{13}N_5O_3$			
Adenosine, 2'-deoxy-	H_2O	259(4.15)	23-3161-73
Formycin, 2'-deoxy-, hydrochloride	pH 1	233(3.89),295(4.01)	23-1313-73
	pH 13	234(4.26),303(3.91)	23-1313-73
	MeOH-acid	233(3.95),295(4.03)	44-3179-73
	MeOH-base	234(4.22),304(3.86)	44-3179-73
Formycin, 3'-deoxy-, hydrochloride	pH 1	233(3.92),296(4.04)	23-1313-73
	pH 13	233(4.02),303(3.92)	23-1313-73
D-erythro-Pentitol, 1-C-(6-amino-1H-purin-8-yl-1,4-anhydro-2-deoxy-	pH 1	267(4.18)	88-2971-73
	pH 13	272(4.15)	88-2971-73
7H-1,2,3-Triazolo[4,5-d]pyrimidin-7-one, 3,6-dihydro-3-[2-hydroxy-4-(hydroxymethyl)cyclopentyl]-, (1α,2β,4α)-(±)-	pH 1	255(4.00),270s(--)	4-0601-73
	pH 7	256(3.95),268s(--), 280s(--)	4-0601-73

Compound	Solvent	$\lambda_{max}(\log \epsilon)$	Ref.
7H-1,2,3-Triazolo[4,5-d]pyrimidin-7-one, 3,6-dihydro-3-[2-hydroxy-4-(hydroxymethyl)cyclopentyl]-, (1α,2β,4α)-(±)-	pH 13	277(4.05)	4-0601-73
7H-1,2,3-Triazolo[4,5-d]pyrimidin-7-one, 3,6-dihydro-3-[3-hydroxy-4-(hydroxymethyl)cyclopentyl]-, (1α,3β,4α)-(±)-	pH 1	255(4.01),270s(--)	4-0601-73
	pH 7	256(3.97),268s(--), 280s(--)	4-0601-73
	pH 13	275(4.06)	4-0601-73
$C_{10}H_{13}N_5O_4$			
Adenine, 9-(2,3,4,5-tetrahydroxycyclopentyl-, 1,2,3/4,5 (DL)	pH 1	259(3.95)	18-2562-73
	pH 7	260(4.23)	18-2562-73
	pH 13	263(4.20)	18-2562-73
1,2,3,4,5/0 (all-cis)(meso)	pH 1	261(4.08)	18-2562-73
	pH 7	260(4.15)	18-2562-73
	pH 13	260(4.15)	18-2562-73
1,2,4/3,5 (DL)	pH 1	259(4.36)	18-2562-73
	pH 7	261(4.32)	18-2562-73
	pH 13	261(4.28)	18-2562-73
1,4/2,3,5 (meso)	pH 1	259(4.18)	18-2562-73
	pH 7	261(4.18)	18-2562-73
	pH 13	261(4.18)	18-2562-73
1,4,5/2,3 (meso)	pH 1	260(3.85)	18-2562-73
	pH 7	260(3.85)	18-2562-73
	pH 13	260(4.04)	18-2562-73
Adenosine	pH 1	257(4.19)	18-3858-73
	pH 7	258.5(4.19)	18-3858-73
	pH 12	260(4.20)	18-3858-73
Purine, 6-(hydroxyamino)-, 2'-deoxyriboside	MeOH	266(4.10)	23-3161-73
7H-Purine-7-propanoic acid, α-amino-1,2,3,6-tetrahydro-1,3-dimethyl-2,6-dioxo-, (±)-	H_2O	231(--)	126-0327-73G
	acid	283(3.90)	126-0327-73G
	base	273(3.83)	126-0327-73G
7H-1,2,3-Triazolo[4,5-d]pyrimidin-7-one, 3,6-dihydro-3-[2,3-dihydroxy-4-(hydroxymethyl)cyclopentyl]-, (1α,2β,3β,4α)-(±)-	pH 1	256(4.00),270s(--)	4-0601-73
	pH 7	256(3.98),268s(--), 282s(--)	4-0601-73
	pH 13	275(4.05)	4-0601-73
$C_{10}H_{13}N_5O_5$			
Guanine, 7-β-D-ribofuranosyl-	pH 1	251(3.95)	136-0149-73B
	H_2O	287(3.87)	136-0149-73B
	pH 13	283(3.80)	136-0149-73B
Guanine, 9-α-D-ribofuranosyl-	pH 1	256(4.08),275s(3.94)	136-0149-73B
	H_2O	253(4.14),276s(3.99)	136-0149-73B
	pH 13	263(4.03)	136-0149-73B
Guanine, 9-β-D-ribofuranosyl-	pH 1	257(4.10),276s(3.95)	136-0149-73B
	H_2O	254(4.15),270s(4.00)	136-0149-73B
	pH 13	263(4.05)	136-0149-73B
Guanine, 9-β-D-ribopyranosyl-	pH 1	257(4.11),280s(3.93)	136-0149-73B
	H_2O	253(4.14),270s(4.00)	136-0149-73B
	pH 13	263(4.06)	136-0149-73B
Guanine, 7-β-D-xylopyranosyl-	pH 1	255(3.89)	136-0149-73B
	H_2O	286(3.87)	136-0149-73B
	pH 13	283(3.79)	136-0149-73B
Guanine, 9-β-D-xylopyranosyl-	pH 1	258(4.08),275s(3.93)	136-0149-73B
	H_2O	253(4.13),270s(3.97)	136-0149-73B
	pH 13	263(4.03)	136-0149-73B
Isoguanine, 3-β-D-ribofuranosyl-	pH 1	286(4.21)	4-0687-73
	pH 11	288(4.16)	4-0687-73

Compound	Solvent	$\lambda_{max}(\log \epsilon)$	Ref.
$C_{10}H_{13}N_6O_5P$			
1,2-Cyclopentanediol, 3-(7-amino-3H-1,2,3-triazolo[4,5-d]pyrimidin-3-yl)-5-(hydroxymethyl)-, cyclic 1,5-(hydrogen phosphate)	pH 1	264(4.11),275s(--)	4-0601-73
	pH 7 and 13	279(4.10)	4-0601-73
$C_{10}H_{13}N_7O_3$			
Butanamide, 3-hydroxy-2-[[(1H-purin-6-ylamino)carbonyl]amino]-	pH 1-2	277(4.27)	87-0139-73
	pH 5-7	269(4.25)	87-0139-73
	pH 13	278(4.19)	87-0139-73
$C_{10}H_{14}$			
Bicyclo[5.2.0]non-2-ene, 4-methylene-, trans	isooctane	235(4.17),275(3.01)	44-3257-73
Cyclohexene, 1-(1,3-butadienyl)-	EtOH	259(4.27),264(4.32), 272(4.24)	78-3797-73
Cyclohexene, 1,2-diethenyl-	EtOH	260(4.40),269(4.48), 279(4.32)	78-3797-73
Cyclohexene, 3-methyl-1-(1-propynyl)-	n.s.g.	230(4.06)	88-4591-73
1,3-Cyclopentadiene, 5-(1-methyl-2-butenyl)-	EtOH	237(3.58)	104-2534-73
1,3-Cyclopentadiene, 5-(3-methyl-2-butenyl)-	EtOH	238(3.48)	104-2534-73
Naphthalene, 1,2,3,4,6,7-hexahydro-	EtOH	263(3.68)	78-3797-73
Naphthalene, 1,2,3,5,6,7-hexahydro-	EtOH	242(4.24)	78-3797-73
$C_{10}H_{14}BF_4N_3$			
Benzenediazonium, 2-(diethylamino)-, tetrafluoroborate	M HCl	274(3.72),436(3.74)	48-0725-73
$C_{10}H_{14}BrN$			
Benzenamine, 2-bromo-N-(1,1-dimethylethyl)-	EtOH	254(3.97),305(3.32)	39-0456-73C
Benzenamine, 3-bromo-N-(1,1-dimethylethyl)-	EtOH	257(4.04),308(3.29)	39-0456-73C
$C_{10}H_{14}BrNO_3$			
2(5H)-Furanone, 3-bromo-5-methoxy-4-(1-piperidinyl)-	MeOH	288(4.36)	73-1091-73
$C_{10}H_{14}Br_2Cl_2O$			
p-Menthan-2-one, 1,6-dibromo-3,8-dichloro-, (1R,3S,4R,6S)-	C_6H_{12}	231(2.64),308(2.09)	12-1977-73
p-Menthan-2-one, 3,8-dibromo-1,6-dichloro-, (1S,3R,4S,6S)-	C_6H_{12}	227(2.70),304(1.72)	12-1283-73
p-Menthan-2-one, 8,9-dibromo-1,6-dichloro-, (1S,4R,6S.8R)-	C_6H_{12}	230(2.75),305(1.71)	12-1283-73
$C_{10}H_{14}Br_2N_2O_2$			
1,4-Benzenediol, 2,5-bis(2-aminoethyl)-3,6-dibromo-, dihydrobromide	EtOH	303(3.76)	39-0832-73C
$C_{10}H_{14}Br_2N_4O_8$			
2,5-Cyclohexadiene-1,4-dione, 2,2-bis-(2-aminoethyl)-3,6-dibromo-, dinitrate	pH 1	295(4.25)	39-0832-73C
$C_{10}H_{14}Br_2O$			
p-Menth-8-en-2-one, 1,3-dibromo-, (1S,3S,4S)-	C_6H_{12}	229(2.86),306(2.11)	12-1977-73

Compound	Solvent	$\lambda_{max}(\log \epsilon)$	Ref.
$C_{10}H_{14}Br_2O_4$			
α-D-xylo-Hex-5-enofuranose, 6,6-dibromo-5,6-dideoxy-1,2-O-isopropylidene-3-O-methyl-	EtOH	215(3.81)	33-1310-73
$C_{10}H_{14}Br_3ClO$			
p-Menthan-2-one, 1,3,6-tribromo-8-chloro-, (1R,3S,4S,6R)-	C_6H_{12}	228(2.95),303(1.99)	12-1977-73
p-Menthan-2-one, 1,6,8-tribromo-3-chloro-, (1R,3S,4R,6S)-	C_6H_{12}	226(2.85),307(2.11)	12-1977-73
$C_{10}H_{14}Br_4O$			
β-Carvone tetrabromide	C_6H_{12}	229(2.96),310(2.04)	12-1283-73
p-Menthan-2-one, 1,3,6,8-tetrabromo-, (1R,3S,4R,6R)-	C_6H_{12}	232(2.99),308(1.94)	12-1977-73
p-Menthan-2-one, 1,3,6,8-tetrabromo-, (1R,3S,4R,6S)-	C_6H_{12}	233(2.94),317(1.91)	12-1977-73
$C_{10}H_{14}ClN$			
Benzenamine, 2-chloro-N-(1,1-dimethylethyl)-	EtOH	251(4.04),302(3.31)	39-0456-73C
Benzenamine, 3-chloro-N-(1,1-dimethylethyl)-	EtOH	257(4.08),306(3.26)	39-0456-73C
$C_{10}H_{14}ClNO_2$			
Acetamide, N-(2-chloro-5,5-dimethyl-3-oxo-1-cyclohexen-1-yl)-	EtOH	291(4.29)	94-1372-73
$C_{10}H_{14}ClNO_3$			
2(5H)-Furanone, 3-chloro-5-methoxy-4-(1-piperidinyl)-	MeOH	284(4.41)	73-1091-73
$C_{10}H_{14}Cl_2N_2O_3S$			
Sulfonium, bis(2-chloroethyl)-, hexahydro-1,3-dimethyl-2,4,6-trioxo-5-pyrimidinylide	EtOH	235(4.23)	104-2213-73
$C_{10}H_{14}Cl_4O$			
p-Menthan-2-one, 1,3,6,8-tetrachloro-, (1S,3R,4S,6S)-	C_6H_{12}	303(1.68)	12-1283-73
p-Menthan-2-one, 1,6,8,9-tetrachloro-, (1S,4R,6S,8R)-	C_6H_{12}	304(1.74)	12-1283-73
$C_{10}H_{14}FNO$			
Benzenamine, N-(1,1-dimethylethyl)-4-fluoro-N-hydroxy-	ether	250(3.60)	78-3833-73
$C_{10}H_{14}GeOS$			
Germane, (benzoylthio)trimethyl-	C_6H_{12}	240(4.11),267(3.91)	18-0244-73
$C_{10}H_{14}GeS_2$			
Germane, trimethyl[(phenylthioxomethyl)-thio]-	C_6H_{12}	303(4.12),528(2.04)	101-0121-73I
$C_{10}H_{14}I_2O_2$			
1,2-Cyclohexanedione, 3,6-bis(iodomethyl)-3,6-dimethyl-	$CHCl_3$	257(3.79),390(2.34)	24-2255-73
$C_{10}H_{14}LiN$			
Lithium, [[2-[(dimethylamino)methyl]-phenyl]methyl]-	DMSO	264(2.70),306(2.30)	101-0001-73H

Compound	Solvent	λ_{max}(log ε)	Ref.
$C_{10}H_{14}NOS$			
Thiazolo[3,2-a]pyridinium, 3-ethoxy-2,3-dihydro-5-methyl-, perchlorate	EtOH	245(3.85),317(3.89)	103-1138-73
Thiazolo[3,2-a]pyridinium, 3-ethoxy-2,3-dihydro-7-methyl-, perchlorate	EtOH	240(3.89),310(3.90)	103-1138-73
$C_{10}H_{14}N_2O$			
6-Phthalazinol, 1,2,3,4-tetrahydro-1,1-dimethyl-	EtOH	280(3.24)	39-0471-73C
2-Propanone, [(3-hydroxyphenyl)methyl]-hydrazone	EtOH	275(3.40)	39-0471-73C
4-Pyrazolidinol, 2-methyl-1-phenyl-	n.s.g.	253(4.10),290(3.50)	22-3159-73
Pyrimido[1,2-a]azepin-4(6H)-one, 7,8,9,10-tetrahydro-3-methyl-	EtOH	227(3.77),279(3.80), 300s(--)	94-1305-73
$C_{10}H_{14}N_2O_2$			
Acetamide, N-[(1-acetyl-4-methyl-1H-pyrrol-2-yl)methyl]-	EtOH	244(4.00)	70-2036-73
2-Azabicyclo[4.1.1]oct-4-en-3-one, 5,7,7-trimethyl-2-nitroso-	EtOH	275(3.95)	39-1661-73C
4-Azatricyclo[4.3.1.1^{3,8}]undecan-5-one, 4-nitroso-	EtOH	258(3.74)	39-1661-73C
2,5-Cyclohexadiene-1,4-dione, 2,5-bis-(2-aminoethyl)-, dihydrobromide	M HCl	252(4.22)	39-0832-73C
2,4-Pentadienoic acid, 2-cyano-5-(di-methylamino)-, ethyl ester	EtOH	221(3.90),378(4.81)	70-1959-73
Pyrrolo[1,2-a]pyrimidin-2(6H)-one, 7,8-dihydro-3-(2-hydroxyethyl)-4-methyl-	MeOH	247(4.0)	5-0103-73
Pyrrolo[1,2-a]pyrimidin-4(6H)-one, 7,8-dihydro-3-(2-hydroxyethyl)-2-methyl-	MeOH	233(3.74),271(3.72)	5-0103-73
$C_{10}H_{14}N_2O_2S_4$			
Acetamide, N-[2-[[(ethylthio)(4-oxo-2-thioxo-5-thiazolidinylidene)-methyl]thio]ethyl]-	EtOH	287(4.10),391(4.54)	94-1431-73
[2,5'-Bithiazolidin]-4'-one, 3-acetyl-2-(ethylthio)-2'-thioxo-	EtOH	261(3.94),306(4.28)	94-1431-73
$C_{10}H_{14}N_2O_3$			
2,5-Piperazinedione, 1-acetyl-3-butyli-dene-	EtOH	222(4.16)	88-1135-73
2,5-Piperazinedione, 1-acetyl-3-(2-meth-ylpropylidene)-	EtOH	222(4.15)	88-1135-73
$C_{10}H_{14}N_2O_3S$			
Homocysteine, S-(3-hydroxy-6-methyl-2-pyridinyl)-	M HCl	237(3.59),321(3.96)	1-1059-73
Propanenitrile, α-amino-, p-toluene-sulfonate	EtOH	253(2.24),258(2.36), 264(2.42),270(2.29)	78-3761-73
$C_{10}H_{14}N_2O_3S_3$			
[2,5'-Bithiazolidine]-2',4'-dione, 3-acetyl-2-(ethylthio)-	EtOH	none	94-1431-73
$C_{10}H_{14}N_2O_4$			
6H-Isoxazolo[3,4-d]azepine-6-carboxylic acid, 1,3,4,5,7,8-hexahydro-3-oxo-, ethyl ester	EtOH	263(3.92)	1-3251-73

Compound	Solvent	$\lambda_{max}(\log \epsilon)$	Ref.
Propanedioic acid, diazo-, cyclohexyl methyl ester	EtOH	250(3.91)	22-2071-73
2(1H)-Pyrimidinone, 1-(2-deoxy-β-D-erythro-pentofuranosyl)-5-methyl-	pH 2	322(3.73)	73-1381-73
	pH 7	315(3.72)	73-1781-73
$C_{10}H_{14}N_2O_4S$			
Thymidine, 2-thio-	MeOH	221(4.2),276(4.2)	24-3039-73
	MeOH-NaOH	242(4.4),264s(4.2)	24-3039-73
$C_{10}H_{14}N_2O_4S_2$			
Methanesulfonamide, N-(1,3-dihydro-1,3-dimethyl-2,1-benzisothiazol-5-yl)-, S,S-dioxide	EtOH	247(4.17),298(3.23)	4-0249-73
$C_{10}H_{14}N_2O_5$			
2,4(1H,3H)-Pyrimidinedione, 1-(2-deoxy-α-D-lyxofuranosyl)-6-methyl-	H_2O	262(4.08)	73-3912-73
2,4(1H,3H)-Pyrimidinedione, 1-(2-deoxy-α-D-ribofuranosyl)-6-methyl-	H_2O	262(4.08)	73-3912-73
2(1H)-Pyrimidinone, 5-methyl-1-β-D-ribofuranosyl-	pH 2	324(3.72)	73-1381-73
Uridine, 2'-deoxy-6-methyl-	H_2O	261(4.08)	73-3912-73
	H_2O	262(4.08)	88-1147-73
$C_{10}H_{14}N_2O_5S$			
D-Altritol, 2,5-anhydro-1-deoxy-1-(3,4-dihydro-2-oxo-4-thioxo-1(2H)-pyrimidinyl)-	pH 1	243(3.60)	136-0245-73F
	pH 11	314(4.29)	136-0245-73F
$C_{10}H_{14}N_2O_6$			
D-Altritol, 2,5-anhydro-1-deoxy-1-(3,4-dihydro-2,4-dioxo-1(2H)-pyrimidinyl)-	pH 1	264(3.92)	136-0245-73F
	pH 11	261(4.11)	136-0245-73F
2-Propenoic acid, 3-[tetrahydro-6-hydroxy-5-(hydroxymethyl)-2-iminofuro-[2,3-d]oxazol-3(2H)-yl]-, methyl ester, [3aR-(3α,5β,6α,6aα)]-	pH 1	248(4.26)	44-0593-73
	pH 12	264(4.26)	44-0593-73
2,4(1H,3H)-Pyrimidinedione, 1-β-D-arabinofuranosyl-6-methyl-	H_2O	263(4.08)	73-3912-73
2,4(1H,3H)-Pyrimidinedione, 6-methyl-1-α-D-ribofuranosyl-	H_2O	262(4.08)	73-3912-73
2,4(1H,3H)-Pyrimidinedione, 6-methyl-1-α-D-xylofuranosyl-	H_2O	262(4.08)	73-3912-73
α-D-Ribofuranoside, methyl 5-deoxy-5-(3,4-dihydro-2,4-dioxo-1(2H)-pyrimidinyl)-	pH 2	264(4.01)	18-3165-73
	H_2O	265(4.05)	18-3165-73
	pH 12	266(3.87)	18-3165-73
β-isomer	pH 2	266(4.12)	18-3165-73
	H_2O	265(4.05)	18-3165-73
	pH 12	265(3.99)	18-3165-73
Uridine, 2'-O-methyl-	pH 1	263(3.85)	78-2807-73
	pH 2	262(4.01)	69-0194-73
	pH 7	263(3.85)	78-2807-73
	pH 12	262(3.88)	69-0194-73
	pH 12	292(3.98)	78-2807-73
Uridine, 3'-O-methyl-	pH 2	262(3.99)	69-0194-73
	pH 12	262(3.85)	69-0194-73
Uridine, 5'-O-methyl-	pH 2	262(4.00)	69-0194-73
	pH 12	262(3.86)	69-0194-73
$C_{10}H_{14}N_2O_6S$			
Uridine, 5-methoxy-2-thio-	MeOH	227(4.0),285(4.1)	24-3039-73
	MeOH-NaOH	248(4.3),272s(4.1)	24-3039-73

Compound	Solvent	λ_{max}(log ε)	Ref.
$C_{10}H_{14}N_3$			
Benzenediazonium, 2-(diethylamino)-, tetrafluoroborate	M HCl	274(3.72),436(3.74)	48-0725-73
$C_{10}H_{14}N_4$			
Butanedinitrile, bis[(1-methylethyl)-imino]-	MeCN	230(1.25),306(2.56)	44-3302-73
$C_{10}H_{14}N_4O_2$			
2,5-Pyrazinedicarboxamide, N,N',3,6-tetramethyl-	EtOH	226(3.76),295(3.89)	107-0225-73
$C_{10}H_{14}N_5O_3$			
1H-Purinium, 2-amino-7-(2-ethoxy-2-oxo-ethyl)-6,9-dihydro-9-methyl-6-oxo-, bromide	pH 2	254(4.07),282(3.86)	24-1389-73
$C_{10}H_{14}N_6O$			
Cyclopentanemethanol, 3-(7-amino-3H-1,2,3-triazolo[4,5-d]pyrimidin-3-yl)-, cis-(±)-	pH 1	263(4.09),275s(--)	4-0601-73
	pH 7 and 13	278(4.08)	4-0601-73
2,4-Pteridinediamine, 6-(2-methyl-propyl)-, 8-oxide	pH 1	251(4.48),282(3.98), 357(3.91),372(3.88)	35-6413-73
Urea, N-(2-methylpropyl)-N'-1H-purin-6-yl-	pH 1-2	277.5(4.32)	87-0139-73
	pH 5-7	268.5(4.26)	87-0139-73
	pH 12	278(4.22)	87-0139-73
$C_{10}H_{14}N_6O_2$			
Cyclopentanemethanol, 3-(7-amino-3H-1,2,3-triazolo[4,5-d]pyrimidin-3-yl)-4-hydroxy-, (1α,3α,4β)-(±)-	pH 1	263(4.09),275s(--)	4-0601-73
	pH 7	279(4.09)	4-0601-73
	pH 13	279(4.08)	4-0601-73
Cyclopentanemethanol, 4-(7-amino-3H-1,2,3-triazolo[4,5-d]pyrimidin-3-yl)-2-hydroxy-, (1α,2β,4α)-(±)-	pH 1	264(4.10),275s(--)	4-0601-73
	pH 7	278(4.08)	4-0601-73
	pH 13	278(4.09)	4-0601-73
Pyrimido[5,4-e]-1,2,4-triazin-5-amine, 3-ethoxy-7-propoxy-	MeOH	216s(3.95),221(4.07), 256(4.25),307(3.29), 405(3.72)	12-1689-73
Urea, N-(2-ethoxyethyl)-N'-1H-purin-6-yl-	pH 1-2	277(4.28)	87-0139-73
	pH 5-7	269(4.24)	87-0139-73
	pH 12	277.5(4.19)	87-0139-73
Urea, N-(4-hydroxybutyl)-N'-1H-purin-6-yl-	pH 1-2	278(4.30)	87-0139-73
	pH 5-7	269.5(4.23)	87-0139-73
	pH 12	278(4.20)	87-0139-73
$C_{10}H_{14}N_6O_3$			
1,2-Cyclopentanediol, 3-(7-amino-3H-1,2,3-triazolo[4,5-d]pyrimidin-3-yl)-5-(hydroxymethyl)-	pH 1	263(4.10),275s(--)	4-0601-73
	pH 7	278(4.10)	4-0601-73
	pH 13	279(4.11)	4-0601-73
$C_{10}H_{14}N_6O_4$			
7H-1,2,3-Triazolo[4,5-d]pyrimidin-7-one, 5-amino-3,4-dihydro-3-[2,3-dihydroxy-4-(hydroxymethyl)cyclopentyl]-, (1α,2β,3β,4α)-(±)-	pH 1	253(4.07),270s(--)	36-1432-73
	pH 7	253(4.07),270(3.93)	36-1432-73
	pH 13	260s(--),279(4.04)	36-1432-73
$C_{10}H_{14}NiO_4$			
Nickel, acetylacetone chelate	CH_2Cl_2	265(4.37),300(3.93)	18-0166-73
$C_{10}H_{14}O$			
Adamantanone	hexane	290(1.28)	78-1691-73

Compound	Solvent	λ_{max}(log ε)	Ref.
Adamantanone (cont.)	EtOH	284(1.36)	107-0369-73
2,5-Cyclohexadien-1-one, 3-ethyl-4,4-dimethyl-	H_2O	242(4.182)	39-0084-73B
	H_2O	242(4.18)	39-0529-73C
	EtOH	238(4.175)	39-0084-73B
	71% H_2SO_4	260(4.17),305(3.78)	39-0084-73B
2,5-Cyclohexadien-1-one, 2,4,4,5-tetramethyl-	H_2O	246.5(4.177)	39-0084-73B
	H_2O	246.5(4.18)	39-0529-73C
	71% H_2SO_4	266(4.15),315(3.74)	39-0084-73B
2,5-Cyclohexadien-1-one, 3,4,4,5-tetramethyl-	hexane	230.5(4.222)	39-0084-73B
	isooctane	230.8(4.212)	39-0084-73B +39-0529-73C
	H_2O	246(4.251)	39-0084-73B
	75% H_2SO_4	261(4.24),314(3.88)	39-0084-73B
1-Cyclohexene-1-methanol, 2-ethynyl-α-methyl-	EtOH	230(4.03)	22-2331-73
3,5-Cyclooctadien-1-one, 7-ethyl-	MeOH	230(3.89)	78-3813-73
4,6,8-Decatrien-3-one	MeOH	216(3.73),313(4.37)	78-3813-73
1H-Inden-1-one, 2,3,3a,4,5,6-hexahydro-3-methyl-	EtOH	245(3.93)	22-1109-73
4H-Inden-4-one, 1,2,3,5,6,7-hexahydro-3-methyl-	EtOH	249(4.14),307(2.26)	88-3441-73
p-Mentha-1,8-dien-10-ol	MeOH	218(4.10),329(2.6)	105-0118-73
5,6-Octadien-3-yn-2-ol, 2,7-dimethyl-	n.s.g.	212(4.03),220(4.09), 228(4.02),273(2.90), 294(2.64)	70-1029-73
Phenol, 4-(1,1-dimethylethyl)-	CCl_4	276(3.258)	30-0394-73
	$C_2H_4Cl_2$	278(3.32),285(3.26)	116-0305-73
$C_{10}H_{14}OS$			
Adamantanethione S-oxide	hexane	270(3.98)	39-0073-73C
$C_{10}H_{14}OSSi$			
Benzenecarbothioic acid, O-(trimethylsilyl) ester	C_6H_{12}	247(3.90),298(3.98), 437(1.88)	18-0244-73
$C_{10}H_{14}OSSn$			
Stannane, (benzoylthio)trimethyl-	C_6H_{12}	242(4.07),271(3.91)	18-0244-73
$C_{10}H_{14}O_2$			
4H-1-Benzopyran-4-one, 2,3,5,6,7,8-hexahydro-2-methyl-	EtOH	271(4.05)	22-1409-73
Bicyclo[3.3.1]nonane-2,9-dione, 3-methyl-	EtOH	286(1.85)	22-1409-73
Bicyclo[3.3.1]nonane-2,9-dione, 4-methyl-	EtOH	287(2.28)	22-1409-73
1,3-Cyclohexadiene-1-carboxylic acid, 2-methyl-, ethyl ester	ether	278(3.85)	24-3779-73
1,3-Cyclohexadien-2-ol, 5,5-dimethyl-, acetate	EtOH	258(3.60)	39-0529-73C
11-Oxadispiro[4.0.4.1]undecan-1-one, (±)-	pentane	314(1.54)	33-0239-73
Phenol, 2-[(1-methylethoxy)methyl]-	EtOH	275(3.43)	44-1993-73
Spiro[4.5]decane-1,6-dione, (±)-	pentane	310(2.03)	33-0239-73
Spiro[3.4]oct-2-en-1-one, 3-ethoxy-	EtOH	234.5(4.05)	44-1451-73
$C_{10}H_{14}O_2S$			
Benzo[b]thiophene, 4,5,6,7-tetrahydro-4,4-dimethoxy-	EtOH	235(3.61)	44-0146-73

Compound	Solvent	$\lambda_{max}(\log \epsilon)$	Ref.
$C_{10}H_{14}O_2S_2$			
4H-Pyran, 3,3'-dithiobis[5,6-dihydro-	EtOH	245(3.72)	39-1187-73C
$C_{10}H_{14}O_3$			
2,3-Butadienoic acid, 2-(1,1-dimethyl-2-oxoethyl)-, ethyl ester	EtOH	206(3.79)	39-1349-73C
2-Butynoic acid, 4-[(2-methyl-1-propenyl)oxy]-, ethyl ester	EtOH	208(3.85)	39-1349-73C
2-Cyclohexene-1-carboxylic acid, 2-methyl-4-oxo-, ethyl ester	n.s.g.	233.0(4.08)	35-0240-73
1-Cyclohexene-1-propanoic acid, β-methyl-3-oxo-	EtOH	236(3.9)	118-0213-73
$C_{10}H_{14}O_4$			
1,4-Benzodioxan, 4a,8a-dihydro-4a,8a-dimethoxy-, trans	EtOH	225(3.46),265(3.45)	78-0279-73
1,4-Butanediol, 2,3-bis(methylene)-, diacetate	isooctane	223(4.19)	88-2361-73
Crotonic acid, β-crotonoyloxy-, ethyl ester	EtOH	216(4.32)	22-3416-73
Cyclohexaneacetic acid, 2-methyl-3,6-dioxo-, methyl ester	EtOH	280(1.78)	78-1227-73
1-Cyclohexene-1,2-dicarboxylic acid, dimethyl ester	EtOH	215(3.97)	78-0683-73
2-Cyclohexene-1,2-dicarboxylic acid, dimethyl ester	EtOH	205(3.43)	78-0683-73
2H-Pyran-5-carboxylic acid, 3,4-dihydro-4,6-dimethyl-2-oxo-, ethyl ester	EtOH	237(3.95)	22-3416-73
2H-Pyran-5-carboxylic acid, 5,6-dihydro-4,6-dimethyl-2-oxo-, ethyl ester	MeOH	212(4.10)	39-1374-73C
2H-Pyran-2-one, 5,6-dihydro-3-hydroxy-4-(3-methyl-1-oxobutyl)-	EtOH	283(3.90)	95-1183-73
$C_{10}H_{14}O_5$			
1,1-Cyclopropanedicarboxylic acid, 2-formyl-, diethyl ester	C_6H_{12}	207(3.29)	23-3263-73
2,2(3H)-Furandicarboxylic acid, diethyl ester	C_6H_{12}	203(3.2)	23-3263-73
	EtOH	203(3.45)	23-3263-73
$C_{10}H_{14}O_6$			
3,4-Hexanedione, 2,5-diacetoxy-, meso-	EtOH	291(1.72),430(1.15)	33-1882-73
α-D-erythro-Hex-1-enopyranos-3-ulose, 2-O-acetyl-1-deoxy-4,6-di-O-methyl-	EtOH	266(4.16)	23-0388-73
$C_{10}H_{14}S$			
Benzene, [(1,1-dimethylethyl)thio]-	C_6H_{12}	220(4.20),268(3.23)	39-1125-73B
	EtOH	219(4.11),265(3.18)	39-1125-73B
	5% EtOH	218(4.04),257(3.18)	39-1125-73B
Benzene, 1-methyl-2-[(1-methylethyl)-thio]-	C_6H_{12}	210s(4.26),253(3.75), 281s(3.20)	39-1125-73B
	EtOH	205(4.20),252(3.71), 280(3.15)	39-1125-73B
	5% EtOH	206(4.18),249(3.72), 278(3.11)	39-1125-73B
Benzene, 1-methyl-3-[(1-methylethyl)-thio]-	C_6H_{12}	213s(4.23),260(3.82), 282s(3.15)	39-1125-73B
	EtOH	210(4.11),257(3.78)	39-1125-73B
	5% EtOH	208(4.18),254(3.73)	39-1125-73B
Benzene, 1-methyl-4-[(1-methylethyl)-thio]-	C_6H_{12}	211(4.11),261(3.83), 290s(2.76)	39-1125-73B

Compound	Solvent	λmax(log ε)	Ref.
Benzene, 1-methyl-4-[(1-methylethyl)-thio]-	EtOH	222(3.98),257(3.80)	39-1125-73B
	5% EtOH	220(3.95),254(3.78)	39-1125-73B
Benzene, 1,3,5-trimethyl-2-(methylthio)-	C_6H_{12}	207(4.46),224(4.01), 268(3.34)	39-1125-73B
	EtOH	206(4.43),220(4.04), 265(3.34)	39-1125-73B
	5% EtOH	203(4.58),220(4.00), 261(3.36)	39-1125-73B
$C_{10}H_{14}S_2Si$			
Benzenecarbodithioic acid, trimethyl-silyl ester	C_6H_{12}	298(4.03),531(2.11)	101-0121-73I
$C_{10}H_{14}S_2Sn$			
Stannane, trimethyl[(phenylthioxometh-yl)thio]-	C_6H_{12}	307(4.17),520(1.99)	101-0121-73I
$C_{10}H_{15}BO_7$			
Boron, bis(acetato-O)(ethyl 3-oxobutan-oato-$O^{1'}$,O^3)-(T-4)-	CH_2Cl_2	272(4.19)	39-1796-73B
$C_{10}H_{15}BrCl_2O$			
p-Menthan-2-one, 1-bromo-3,8-dichloro-, (1S,3S,4R)-	C_6H_{12}	232(2.39),305(1.97)	12-1977-73
p-Menthan-2-one, 3-bromo-1,8-dichloro-, (1S,3S,4S)-	C_6H_{12}	327(1.69)	12-1977-73
p-Menthan-2-one, 8-bromo-1,3-dichloro-, (1S,3S,4R)-	C_6H_{12}	224(2.36),300(1.68)	12-1977-73
$C_{10}H_{15}Br_2ClO$			
p-Menthan-2-one, 1,3-dibromo-8-chloro-, (1S,3S,4S)-	C_6H_{12}	236(2.75),315(1.66)	12-1977-73
p-Menthan-2-one, 1,6-dibromo-3-chloro-, (1R,3S,4S,6S)-	C_6H_{12}	228(2.69),306(2.13)	12-1977-73
p-Menthan-2-one, 1,6-dibromo-8-chloro-, (1R,4S,6S)-	C_6H_{12}	230(2.64),309(2.06)	12-1977-73
p-Menthan-2-one, 1,8-dibromo-3-chloro-, (1S,3S,4R)-	C_6H_{12}	233(2.28),303(1.64)	12-1977-73
p-Menthan-2-one, 3,8-dibromo-1-chloro-, (1S,3S,4R)-	C_6H_{12}	230(2.64),328(1.74)	12-1977-73
$C_{10}H_{15}Br_3O$			
p-Menthane, 1,6,8-tribromo-2,3-epoxy-, (1R,2R,3R,4R,6S)-	C_6H_{12}	227(2.64)	12-1977-73
p-Menthan-2-one, 1,3,6-tribromo-, (1R,3S,4S,6S)-	C_6H_{12}	231(2.72),307(2.15)	12-1977-73
p-Menthan-2-one, 1,3,8-tribromo-, (1S,3S,4R)-	C_6H_{12}	234(2.85),313(1.67)	12-1977-73
$C_{10}H_{15}ClN_4O_3$			
1,2-Cyclopentanediol, 3-[(2-amino-6-chloro-4-pyrimidinyl)amino]-5-(hydroxymethyl)-	pH 1	214(4.30),240(4.10), 274(3.98),287s(--), 302s(--)	36-1432-73
	pH 7	237(4.06),286(4.01)	36-1432-73
	pH 13	238(4.05),287(4.01)	36-1432-73
$C_{10}H_{15}ClN_5O_{13}P_3$			
Adenosine 5'-(tetrahydrogen phosphate), 2'-chloro-, triammonium salt	pH 1	265(4.09)	87-1188-73

Compound	Solvent	$\lambda_{max}(\log \epsilon)$	Ref.
$C_{10}H_{15}Cl_3O$			
p-Menthan-2-one, 1,3,8-trichloro-, (1S,3S,4R)-	C_6H_{12}	301(1.66)	12-1977-73
$C_{10}H_{15}FO$			
2(1H)-Naphthalenone, 8a-fluorooctahydro-, trans	EtOH	301(1.73)	22-2320-73
$C_{10}H_{15}N$			
Benzenemethanamine, N,N,2-trimethyl-	isooctane	254(2.48),260(2.70), 268(2.60)	101-0001-73H
2H-Pyrrole, 2-(2-butenyl)-2,5-dimethyl-, cis	MeOH	219(3.53)	35-4356-73
trans	MeOH	219(3.52)	35-4356-73
2H-Pyrrole, 2,5-dimethyl-2-(1-methyl-2-propenyl)-	MeOH	211(3.57)	35-4356-73
$C_{10}H_{15}NO$			
2-Azabicyclo[4.1.1]oct-4-en-3-one, 5,7,7-trimethyl-	EtOH	236(4.10)	39-1661-73C
2-Cyclopenten-1-one, 2-piperidino-	EtOH	288(3.56)	44-0551-73
Ethanone, 1-(4-ethyl-3,5-dimethyl-1H-pyrrol-2-yl)-	H_2O	265(3.69),315(4.29)	103-1355-73
	26N H_2SO_4	302(4.15),330(4.16)	103-1355-73
Ethanone, 1-(5-ethyl-2,4-dimethyl-1H-pyrrol-3-yl)-	H_2O	254(3.98),300(3.59)	103-1355-73
	17N H_2SO_4	278(4.25),360(3.20)	103-1355-73
$C_{10}H_{15}NO_2$			
Benzeneethanamine, 3,4-dimethoxy-	EtOH	205(4.55),227(4.05), 284(3.59)	102-0193-73
2-Cyclohexen-1-one, 2-acetyl-3-amino-5,5-dimethyl-	EtOH	256(4.17),282(4.20)	94-1372-73
2,4-Pentanedione, 3-[3-(dimethylamino)-2-propenylidene]-	EtOH	240(3.56),289(3.84), 400(4.78)	70-1963-73
1H-Pyrrolizine-7-carboxylic acid, 2,3,5,6-tetrahydro-, ethyl ester	hexane	289(4.11)	1-0433-73
	EtOH	303(4.26)	1-0433-73
1H-Pyrrolizine-7-carboxylic acid, 2,3,5,7a-tetrahydro-, ethyl ester	EtOH	212(3.89)	1-0433-73
$C_{10}H_{15}NO_3$			
Acetamide, N-(2-hydroxy-4,4-dimethyl-6-oxo-1-cyclohexenyl)-	C_6H_{12}	284(--)	5-0407-73
	MeOH	280(4.18)	5-0407-73
	MeOH-HCl	257(3.93)	5-0407-73
	MeOH-NaOH	282(4.31)	5-0407-73
2-Cyclopenten-1-one, 2-hydroxy-3-(1-morpholinylmethyl)-	EtOH	261(4.08)	44-0551-73
2,4-Pentadienoic acid, 2-acetyl-5-(dimethylamino)-, methyl ester	EtOH	241(3.81),266(3.84), 400(4.76)	70-1963-73
2-Propenoic acid, 2-[(cyclohexylcarbonyl)amino]-	EtOH	242(3.81)	39-1134-73C
$C_{10}H_{15}NO_4$			
Propanedioic acid, [3-(dimethylamino)-2-propenylidene]-, dimethyl ester	EtOH	235(3.85),374(4.76)	70-1959-73 +70-1963-73
2,3-Pyridinedicarboxylic acid, 1,4,5,6-tetrahydro-1-methyl-, dimethyl ester	MeOH	298(4.37)	107-0073-73
$C_{10}H_{15}NO_4S$			
1H,3H-Oxazolo[4,3-c][1,4]thiazine-6-carboxylic acid, 8,8a-dihydro-3,3-dimethyl-, methyl ester, 7-oxide, (R)-	EtOH	285(4.19)	78-3023-73
(S)-	EtOH	235(3.60),298(4.15)	78-3023-73

Compound	Solvent	λmax(log ε)	Ref.
$C_{10}H_{15}NO_9P_2$			
Diphosphoric acid, P-butyl P'-(4-nitrophenyl) ester	H_2O	290(4.00)	18-3275-73
$C_{10}H_{15}NS_2$			
Benzoic acid, dithio-, trimethylamine salt	EtOH	286(3.95),360(3.88), 491(2.18)	143-0359-73
6H-[1,2]Dithiolo[5,1-e]isothiazole-7-S^{IV}, 2-(1,1-dimethylethyl)-6-methyl-	MeOH	213(4.06),233(4.28), 265s(3.74),414(4.09)	39-2351-73C
Thieno[2,3-b]thiophen-3-amine, 5-ethyl-2,3-dihydro-N,N-dimethyl-, hydrochloride	EtOH	215(4.05),280(3.81)	70-2017-73
$C_{10}H_{15}N_2O_8P$			
5'-Uridylic acid, 2'-deoxy-6-methyl-	H_2O	262(4.06)	73-3912-73
$C_{10}H_{15}N_3O$			
Cycloheptanecarbonitrile, 1-(acetylazo)-	C_6H_{12}	397(1.54)	23-1378-73
4H-1,3-Oxazine, 5,6-dihydro-4,4,6-trimethyl-2-(1H-pyrazol-3-yl)-	MeOH	224(4.08)	18-0540-73
4H-1,3-Oxazine, 5,6-dihydro-4,4,6-trimethyl-2-(1H-pyrazol-4-yl)-	EtOH	220(4.12)	18-0540-73
$C_{10}H_{15}N_3O_2$			
4H-Pyrimido[1,2-a]pyrimidin-4-one, 6,7,8,9-tetrahydro-3-(2-hydroxyethyl)-2-methyl-	MeOH	238(3.89),296(3.95)	5-0103-73
$C_{10}H_{15}N_3O_2S_2$			
Carbamic acid, [[(3,4-dimethyl-2(3H)-thiazolylidene)amino](methylthio)-methylene]-, ethyl ester	dioxan	279(3.85),335(4.34)	94-0074-73
Carbamic acid, [(3,5-dimethyl-2(3H)-thiazolylidene)amino](methylthio)-methylene]-, ethyl ester	dioxan	245(3.48),280(3.85), 331(4.35)	94-0074-73
Carbamic acid, [[(5-ethyl-2-thiazolyl)-imino](methylthio)methyl]-, ethyl ester	dioxan	242(3.84),330(4.34)	94-0074-73
Carbamic acid, [[(1-methylethyl)thio]-(2-thiazolylimino)methyl]-, ethyl ester	dioxan	243(3.79),325(4.31)	94-0074-73
Carbamic acid, [[(3-methyl-2(3H)-thiazolylidene)amino](methylthio)methylene]-, 1-methylethyl ester	dioxan	245(3.54),280(3.91), 330(4.40)	94-0074-73
Carbamic acid, [[(3-methyl-2(3H)-thiazolylidene)amino][methylthio)methylene]-, propyl ester	dioxan	245(3.32),280(3.85), 331(4.35)	94-0074-73
Carbamic acid, [(methylthio)(2-thiazolylimino)methyl]-, butyl ester	dioxan	242(3.81),314(4.32)	94-0074-73
Carbamic acid, [(methylthio)(2-thiazolylimino)methyl]-, 2-methylpropyl ester	EtOH	242(3.65),314(4.34)	94-0074-73
Carbamic acid, [(propylthio)(2-thiazolylimino)methyl]-, ethyl ester	dioxan	243(3.85),315(4.32)	94-0074-73
$C_{10}H_{15}N_3O_3$			
Imidazo[1,2-a]pyrimidine-6-carboxylic acid, 1,2,3,5,6,7-hexahydro-1-methyl-2-oxo-, ethyl ester	EtOH-NaOH	210(3.99)	44-1591-73

Compound	Solvent	$\lambda_{max}(\log \epsilon)$	Ref.
Imidazo[1,2-a]pyrimidine-6-carboxylic acid, 2,3,5,6,7,8-hexahydro-8-methyl-2-oxo-, ethyl ester	pH 12	223(4.30)	44-1591-73
Pyrazinecarboxylic acid, 3-amino-6-propyl-, ethyl ester, 4-oxide	EtOH	228(4.08),252(4.30), 380(3.91)	35-6407-73
2,4,6(1H,3H,5H)-Pyrimidinetrione, 5-[1-(ethylamino)ethylidene]-1,3-dimethyl-	MeOH	223(4.07),246(3.50), 302(4.38)	39-0823-73C
2H-Pyrimido[1,2-a]pyrimidine-7-carboxylic acid, 1,3,4,6,7,8-hexahydro-2-oxo-, ethyl ester	EtOH-NaOH	227(4.33)	44-1591-73
1,3,5-Triazine-2,4(1H,3H)-dione, 6-(2-oxoheptyl)-	EtOH	298(4.39)	22-2039-73
$C_{10}H_{15}N_3O_4$			
Sydnone imine, N-acetyl-3-(5-carboxypentyl)-	EtOH	198(3.52),243(3.65), 326(4.00)	103-1327-73
hydrochloride	EtOH	198(3.50),243(3.85), 330(4.06)	103-1327-73
$C_{10}H_{15}N_3O_4S_2$			
Carbamic acid, [5-[[(1-methylethoxycarbonyl)amino]-3H-1,2,4-dithiazol-3-ylidene]-, 1-methylethyl ester	EtOH	223(4.06),269(4.24), 304(4.10),324s(3.97)	94-2396-73
Carbamic acid, [5-[(propoxycarbonyl)-amino]-3H-1,2,4-dithiazol-3-ylidene]-, propyl ester	EtOH	223(4.05),269(4.26), 310(4.02)	94-2396-73
$C_{10}H_{15}N_3O_5$			
D-Altritol, 1-(4-amino-2-oxo-1(2H)-pyrimidinyl)-2,5-anhydro-1-deoxy-	pH 1	280(4.11)	136-0245-73F
	pH 7	272(3.93)	136-0245-73F
	pH 11	270(3.93)	136-0245-73F
Cytidine, 2'-O-methyl-	pH 2	280(4.13)	69-0194-73
	pH 12	271(3.97)	69-0194-73
Cytidine, 3'-O-methyl-	pH 2	280(4.11)	69-0194-73
	pH 12	271(3.95)	69-0194-73
Cytidine, 5'-O-methyl-	pH 2	280(4.11)	69-0194-73
	pH 12	271(3.94)	69-0194-73
α-D-Ribofuranoside, methyl 5-(4-amino-2-oxo-1(2H)-pyrimidinyl)-5-deoxy-	pH 2	283(3.90)	18-3165-73
	H_2O	273(3.70)	18-3165-73
	pH 12	275(3.72)	18-3165-73
β-isomer	pH 2	285(4.06)	18-3165-73
	H_2O	275(3.90)	18-3165-73
	pH 12	275(3.93)	18-3165-73
$C_{10}H_{15}N_4O_7P$			
Theophylline, 7-(2,3-dihydroxypropyl)-, 3'-phosphate	pH 1	274(3.95)	126-0007-73B
	H_2O	274(3.96)	126-0001-73B
	pH 13	274(3.98)	126-0007-73B
$C_{10}H_{15}N_5$			
1H-Pyrazolo[4,3-d]pyrimidin-7-amine, N-butyl-3-methyl- (all spectra in ethanol)	pH 1	261(3.77),310(4.09)	102-0025-73
	pH 7	236(3.77),295(4.07), 306(3.97),318s(--)	102-0025-73
	pH 12	244(4.17),264s(--), 308(3.88)	102-0025-73
1H-Pyrazolo[4,3-d]pyrimidin-7-amine, 3-methyl-N-(2-methylpropyl)- (all spectra in ethanol)	pH 1	263(3.78),311(4.10)	102-0025-73
	pH 7	236(3.78),295(4.08), 306(3.98),318s(--)	102-0025-73
	pH 12	243(4.17),264s(--), 308(3.88)	102-0025-73

Compound	Solvent	$\lambda_{max}(\log \epsilon)$	Ref.
1,3,5-Triazine-2,4-diamine, N,N,N',N'-tetramethyl-6-(1-propynyl)-	EtOH	232(3.68),296(2.56)	22-2039-73
$C_{10}H_{15}N_5O$			
4H-Pyrazolo[3,4-d]pyrimidin-4-one, 1-[(diethylamino)methyl]-1,5-dihydro-	EtOH	253(3.92)	103-1280-73
$C_{10}H_{15}N_5O_2$			
1H-Purine-2,6-dione, 7-(3-aminopropyl)-3,7-dihydro-1,3-dimethyl-, hydrochloride	n.s.g.	209(4.26),275(3.89)	73-1571-73
$C_{10}H_{15}N_6O_6P$			
1,2-Cyclopentanediol, 3-(7-amino-3H-1,2,3-triazolo[4,5-d]pyrimidin-3-yl)-5-[(phosphonooxy)methyl]-, (1α,2α,3β,5β)-(±)-	pH 1	264(4.09),275s(--)	4-0601-73
	pH 7	278(4.09)	4-0601-73
	pH 13	278(4.08)	4-0601-73
$C_{10}H_{15}N_7O$			
Pyrimido[5,4-e]-1,2,4-triazine-3,5-diamine, N,N'-dimethyl-7-propoxy-	MeOH	216s(4.17),221(4.27), 258s(4.18),260s(4.20), 268s(4.25),272(4.26), 320(3.26),457(3.71)	12-1689-73
Urea, N-[2-(dimethylamino)ethyl]-N'-1H-purin-6-yl-	pH 1-2	276(4.24)	87-0139-73
	pH 5-7	268.5(4.22)	87-0139-73
	pH 12	277(4.18)	87-0139-73
$C_{10}H_{16}$			
Bicyclo[3.1.0]hex-2-ene, 6-(1-methylethyl)-2-methyl-, endo	isooctane	208(3.02)	39-2671-73C
exo	isooctane	206(3.72)	39-2671-73C
1,3,5-Hexatriene, 3-(1,1-dimethylethyl)-, 3-cis	isooctane	241.0(4.16)	44-2478-73
2,4,6-Nonatriene, 6-methyl-, (E,E,E)-	heptane	250(4.97),260(4.96), 270(4.97)	70-1617-73
2,4,7-Nonatriene, 6-methyl-, (E,E,E)-	heptane	226(4.46),230(4.48)	70-1618-73
1,6-Octadiene, 7-methyl-3-methylene-	EtOH	225(4.13)	2-0104-73
1,7-Octadiene, 3-methyl-6-methylene-	EtOH	225(4.26)	18-0600-73
1,3,5-Octatriene, 7,7-dimethyl-, cis-cis	isooctane	258(4.09),267(4.15), 278(4.03)	44-2478-73
1,3,6-Octatriene, 2,6-dimethyl-	EtOH	230(4.38)	18-0600-73
1,3,6-Octatriene, 2,7-dimethyl-	EtOH	230(4.40)	18-0600-73
$C_{10}H_{16}BrClO$			
p-Menthan-2-one, 1-bromo-8-chloro-, (1S,4R)-	C_6H_{12}	228(2.49),310(2.05)	12-1977-73
p-Menthan-2-one, 8-bromo-1-chloro-, (1S,4R)-	C_6H_{12}	224(2.26),303(1.67)	12-1977-73
$C_{10}H_{16}Br_2Cl_2$			
p-Menthane, 1,2-dibromo-4,8-dichloro-	C_6H_{12}	230(2.64)	12-2235-73
p-Menthane, 1,7-dibromo-4,8-dichloro-	C_6H_{12}	227(2.72)	12-2235-73
p-Menthane, 4,8-dibromo-1,2-dichloro-, (1R,2R,4R)-(±)-	C_6H_{12}	234(2.61)	12-2235-73
(1R,2R,4S)-(±)-	C_6H_{12}	234(2.62)	12-2235-73
p-Menthane, 8,9-dibromo-1,2-dichloro-, (1R,2R,4S,8R)-(±)-	C_6H_{12}	227(2.69)	12-2235-73
$C_{10}H_{16}Br_2O$			
p-Menthane, 1,8-dibromo-2,3-epoxy-, (1S,2R,3R,4R)-	C_6H_{12}	325(2.58)	12-1977-73

Compound	Solvent	λ_{max}(log ε)	Ref.
p-Menthan-2-one, 1,3-dibromo-, (1S,3S,4S)-	C_6H_{12}	225(2.65),306(2.08)	12-1977-73
p-Menthan-2-one, 1,8-dibromo-, (1S,4R)-	C_6H_{12}	227(2.66),311(2.07)	12-1977-73
p-Menthan-3-one, 2,4-dibromo-, (R,S,R)-	C_6H_{12}	227(2.66),309(2.02)	12-1977-73
$C_{10}H_{16}Br_3Cl$			
Cyclohexane, 1-bromo-4-chloro-1-(1,2-dibromo-1-methylethyl)-4-methyl-, trans-(±)-	C_6H_{12}	224(2.81)	12-0571-73
$C_{10}H_{16}Br_4$			
p-Menthane, 1,4,7,8-tetrabromo-	C_6H_{12}	232(2.83)	12-2235-73
$C_{10}H_{16}ClN_4P$			
1,3,2-Diazaphosphorine, 2,2-bis(1-aziridinyl)-4-chloro-6-ethyl-2,2-dihydro-5-methyl-	hexane	346(3.82)	112-0621-73
$C_{10}H_{16}ClN_5O_3$			
1,2-Cyclopentanediol, 3-[(2,5-diamino-6-chloro-4-pyrimidinyl)amino]-5-(hydroxymethyl)-, (1α,2α,3β,5β)-(±)-	pH 1	210(4.21),237(4.19), 298(3.90)	36-1432-73
	pH 7	204(4.28),225s(--), 240s(--),303(3.95)	36-1432-73
	pH 13	225s(--),240s(--), 303(3.95)	36-1432-73
$C_{10}H_{16}Cl_2O$			
p-Menthan-2-one, 1,3-dichloro-, (1S,3S,4S)-	C_6H_{12}	299(1.76)	12-1977-73
p-Menthan-2-one, 1,8-dichloro-, (1S,4R)-	C_6H_{12}	302(1.67)	12-1977-73
p-Menthan-3-one, 2,4-dichloro-, (1R,2S,4R)-	C_6H_{12}	301(1.70)	12-1977-73
$C_{10}H_{16}Cl_2Si_2$			
Silane, 1,4-phenylenebis[chlorodimethyl-	heptane	276.3(2.59)	70-1825-73
$C_{10}H_{16}N_2$			
1-Pyrrolidinepropanenitrile, β-(1-methylethylidene)-	EtOH	204(3.64),245(3.72)	39-1108-73C
$C_{10}H_{16}N_2O_2$			
2-Azabicyclo[3.2.1]octan-3-one, 5,8,8-trimethyl-2-nitroso-	EtOH	259(3.80)	39-1661-73C
1,4-Benzenediol, 2,5-bis(2-aminoethyl)-, dihydrobromide	M HCl	291(3.92)	39-0832-73C
2,4-Pentanedione, 3-(1,3-dimethyl-2-imidazolidinylidene)-	C_6H_{12}	252s(3.95),270(4.12), 302s(3.48)	1-0258-73
	EtOH	253(4.09),277(4.33)	1-0258-73
4(1H)-Pyrimidinone, 2-(2-ethoxy-1-methylethyl)-6-methyl-	EtOH	226(4.84),270(4.68)	95-1437-73
4(1H)-Pyrimidinone, 2-(2-ethoxypropyl)-6-methyl-	EtOH	225(4.88),270(4.69)	95-1437-73
$C_{10}H_{16}N_2O_3$			
Butanoic acid, 2-(1,3-dimethyl-2-imidazolidinylidene)-3-oxo-, methyl ester	EtOH	252(4.39)	1-0258-73
2,4-Hexadienoic acid, 2-(aminocarbonyl)-5-(dimethylamino)-, methyl ester	EtOH	255(3.81),396(4.86)	70-2478-73

Compound	Solvent	$\lambda_{max}(\log \epsilon)$	Ref.
2,4-Pentadienoic acid, 2-(aminocarbonyl)-5-(dimethylamino)-, ethyl ester	EtOH	234(4.01),250(3.82), 380(4.82)	70-1959-73
$C_{10}H_{16}N_2O_4$			
Propanedioic acid, (1,3-dimethyl-2-imidazolidinylidene)-, dimethyl ester	EtOH	240(4.40),274(3.79)	1-0258-73
$C_{10}H_{16}N_2O_5$			
L-Glutamine, 4-hydroxy-N-[2-(hydroxymethyl)-1,3-butadienyl]-, (S)-	H_2O	262(4.38)	78-2715-73
$C_{10}H_{16}N_3O_4S$			
Pyrimidinium, 4-amino-2-(methylthio)-1-β-D-ribofuranosyl-, chloride	H_2O	247(4.45),275s(3.95)	94-1530-73
$C_{10}H_{16}N_4$			
1-Propen-2-amine, 1-(3,6-dimethyl-1,2,4-triazin-5-yl)-N,N-dimethyl-	MeOH	246(3.43),308(3.80), 385(4.44)	5-1963-73
4-^{15}N-	MeOH	244(3.43),307(3.80), 385(4.43)	5-1963-73
$C_{10}H_{16}N_4O_4S$			
Carbamic acid, (2,4-dimethyl-1,2,4-thiadiazolidine-3,5-diylidene)bis-, diethyl ester	EtOH	248(4.38),286(3.53)	94-2396-73
Carbamic acid, 1,2,4-thiadiazole-3,5-diylbis-, bis(1-methylethyl) ester	EtOH	257.5(3.61)	94-2396-73
Carbamic acid, 1,2,4-thiadiazole-3,5-diylbis-, dipropyl ester	EtOH	258(3.61)	94-2396-73
1,2,4-Thiadiazole-2(3H)-carboxylic acid, 3-imino-5-[[(1-methylethoxycarbonyl]-amino]-, 1-methylethyl ester	EtOH	261(4.29),273(4.29)	94-2396-73
1,2,4-Thiadiazole-2(3H)-carboxylic acid, 3-imino-5-[(propoxycarbonyl)amino]-, propyl ester	EtOH	261(4.32),272(4.32)	94-2396-73
$C_{10}H_{16}N_4O_6$			
D-Glucose, 2-[5-amino-4-(aminocarbonyl)-1H-imidazol-1-yl]-2-deoxy-	H_2O	265(4.00)	39-2345-73C
	acid	267(3.89)	39-2345-73C
	base	265(4.02)	39-2345-73C
$C_{10}H_{16}N_6O_2$			
5,5'-Bi-1,2,4-triazine, 2,2',5,5'-tetrahydro-3,3'-dimethoxy-5,5'-dimethyl-	n.s.g.	228(4.41),255(4.37)	22-2493-73
$C_{10}H_{16}N_6S$			
1,2':1',2"-Ter-1H-imidazole, 4,4',4"-5,5',5"-hexahydro-2-(methylthio)-, hydriodide	EtOH	217(4.61)	44-1641-73
$C_{10}H_{16}O$			
Bicyclo[7.1.0]decan-2-one	64.5% H_2SO_4	215(3.58)	30-0061-73
	79.5% H_2SO_4	240(3.78)	30-0061-73
Bicyclo[3.1.0]hexan-2-one, 3,3,6,6-tetramethyl-	EtOH	205(3.65),287s(1.68)	35-0468-73
Cyclohexanone, 5-methyl-2-(1-methylethenyl)-, (2S,5R)-(-)-	MeOH	297(1.47)	18-1546-73
Cyclohexene, 3,4-epoxy-3,4,5,5-tetramethyl-	EtOH	215(3.54)(end abs.)	39-2485-73C
3-Cyclohexen-1-ol, 1,6,6-trimethyl-2-methylene-	EtOH	230(4.15)	39-2485-73C

Compound	Solvent	λ max(log ε)	Ref.
2-Cyclohexen-1-one, 5-ethyl-4,4-dimethyl-	EtOH	227(4.04)	39-0529-73C
2-Cyclohexen-1-one, 3-methyl-6-(1-methylethyl)-	CH_2Cl_2	233(4.11),328(1.60)	88-3251-73
BF_3 complex	CH_2Cl_2	272.5(4.05)	88-3251-73
2-Cyclohexen-1-one, 3,4,4,5-tetramethyl-	EtOH	236(4.13)	39-0529-73C
3-Cyclohexen-1-one, 2,2,6,6-tetramethyl-	EtOH	215(2.3),295(1.41)	39-2485-73C
Propanal, 2-(2-methyl-1-cyclohexen-	EtOH	223(3.30)(end abs.)	33-2961-73
2-Propen-1-ol, 3-(4,4-dimethyl-1-cyclopenten-1-yl)-	EtOH	233(3.56)	44-2870-73
$C_{10}H_{16}OSi$			
Silane, (4-methoxyphenyl)trimethyl-	EtOH	228(4.16),273(3.15), 282(3.15)	35-5288-73
$C_{10}H_{16}O_2$			
1,2-Cyclohexanedione, 4-methyl-3-(1-methylethyl)-	EtOH	274(3.97)	22-1454-73
2-Cyclohexen-1-one, 4-hydroxy-3,4,5,5-tetramethyl-	MeOH	239(3.95),313(1.68)	39-2485-73C
2-Cyclohexen-1-one, 2-methoxy-3,5,5-trimethyl-	EtOH	247(3.98)	35-5086-73
2-Cyclohexen-1-one, 4-methoxy-3,6,6-trimethyl-	EtOH	232(4.00)	44-4068-73
1,3-Cyclooctadiene, 5,5-dimethoxy-	MeOH	239(3.87)	23-2215-73
trans-cis	MeOH	233(3.50)	23-2215-73
3,5-Heptadienoic acid, 3,6-dimethyl-, methyl ester	EtOH	244(4.33)	35-5086-73
p-Menth-1-en-3-one, 6-hydroxy-, (±)-	EtOH	235.5(3.95)	12-0845-73
p-Menth-1-en-3-one, 7-hydroxy-, (±)-	EtOH	236(4.11)	12-0845-73
p-Menth-1-en-3-one, 8-hydroxy-, (±)-	EtOH	235(3.92)	12-0845-73
7-Oxabicyclo[4.1.0]heptan-3-one, 2,2,4,4-tetramethyl-	C_6H_{12}	284(1.23)	77-0881-73
$C_{10}H_{16}O_2Se$			
1,2-Benzoxaseleninium, 2-hydroxyoctahydro-7-methyl-4-methylene-, hydroxide, inner salt	EtOH	209(3.59),241(3.27)	35-7917-73
$C_{10}H_{16}O_3$			
Acetic acid, (5-ethyldihydro-2(3H)-furanylidene)-, ethyl ester	EtOH	245(4.13)	44-3428-73
2-Heptenoic acid, 2-methyl-6-oxo-, ethyl ester	EtOH	219(4.09)	65-0409-73
5-Hepten-2-one, 6-formyl-, ethylene ketal	EtOH	230(4.14)	65-0409-73
4,5-Oxepindione, tetrahydro-3,3,6,6-tetramethyl-	EtOH	283(1.30),292(1.42), 326(1.42)	44-4087-73
$C_{10}H_{16}O_3S$			
D-ribo-Hex-1-enitol, 3,6-anhydro-2-deoxy-1-S-methyl-4,5-O-(1-methylethylidene)-1-thio-, cis	EtOH	233(3.53),244(2.62)	33-1310-73
trans	EtOH	228(3.81),239(3.77)	33-1310-73
4,5-Thiepanedione, 3,3,6,6-tetramethyl-, 1-oxide	EtOH	304(1.32),329(1.23)	78-2135-73
$C_{10}H_{16}O_4$			
Cyclohexanecarboxylic acid, 2,2-(ethylenedioxy)-4-methyl-	MeOH	212(1.88)	39-2113-73C

Compound	Solvent	$\lambda_{max}(\log \epsilon)$	Ref.
$C_{10}H_{16}O_4S$			
4,5-Thiepanedione, 3,3,6,6-tetramethyl-, 1,1-dioxide	EtOH	302(1.57),330(1.46)	78-2135-73
$C_{10}H_{16}O_5$			
2-Heptenedioic acid, 6-hydroxy-3,5,6-trimethyl-	EtOH	220(4.12)	73-2504-73
$C_{10}H_{16}Si$			
Silane, trimethyl(4-methylphenyl)-	EtOH	217(3.93),222(3.97), 226s(3.89),260(2.22)	35-5288-73
$C_{10}H_{17}BrCl_2$			
p-Menthane, 4-bromo-1,8-dichloro-	C_6H_{12}	224(2.88)	12-0571-73
p-Menthane, 8-bromo-1,2-dichloro-, (1R,2R,4R)-(+)-	C_6H_{12}	226(2.43)	12-2235-73
(1R,2S,4R)-	C_6H_{12}	224(2.43)	12-2235-73
(1R,2S,4S)-	C_6H_{12}	225(2.42)	12-2235-73
$C_{10}H_{17}FO$			
5-Octen-4-one, 5-fluoro-2,7-dimethyl-, cis	n.s.g.	234(3.61)	35-6655-73
trans	n.s.g.	232(4.00)	35-6655-73
$C_{10}H_{17}N$			
1-Cyclopentene, 1-piperidino-	heptane	220(3.89)	135-1154-73
	MeOH	198(4.03)	135-1154-73
	isoPrOH	196(3.66)	135-1154-73
	ether	218(3.95)	135-1154-73
	$C_2H_4Cl_2$	209(3.43)	135-1154-73
$C_{10}H_{17}NO$			
2,3-Hexadienamide, 5-methyl-4-(1-methylethyl)-	EtOH	210(4.18)	88-0209-73
Morpholine, 4-(1-cyclohexen-1-yl)-	heptane	219(3.95)	135-1154-73
	MeOH	195(3.89)	135-1154-73
	isoPrOH	192(3.78),214(3.63)	135-1154-73
	ether	200(4.29),231(4.32)	135-1154-73
	$C_2H_4Cl_2$	217(3.27)	135-1154-73
$C_{10}H_{17}NO_3S$			
2H-1,4-Thiazine-6-carboxylic acid, 3,4-dihydro-3-(hydroxymethyl)-4-(1-methylethyl)-, methyl ester	EtOH	221(3.83),256(3.30), 315(4.13)	78-3023-73
$C_{10}H_{17}NO_4S$			
2H-1,4-Thiazine-6-carboxylic acid, 3,4-dihydro-3-(hydroxymethyl)-4-(1-methylethyl)-, methyl ester, 1-oxide, (R)-	EtOH	283(4.33)	78-3023-73
$C_{10}H_{17}NO_5$			
α-D-xylo-Pentodialdo-1,4-furanose, 1,2-O-isopropylidene-3-O-methyl-, 5-(N-methyloxime)	EtOH	298(4.05)	136-0159-73F
$C_{10}H_{17}N_5O$			
2-Propanone, 1-[4,6-bis(dimethylamino)-1,3,5-triazin-2-yl]-	EtOH	232(4.48),274(4.15), 324(4.06)	22-2039-73

Compound	Solvent	$\lambda_{max}(\log \epsilon)$	Ref.
$C_{10}H_{17}N_5O_4$			
Carbamic acid, [5-[[(ethoxycarbonyl)-amino]methyl]-1-methyl-1H-1,2,3-triazol-4-yl]-, ethyl ester	pH 7.0	220(3.65)	39-1634-73C
$C_{10}H_{18}Ge_2$			
Germane, 1,3-butadiyne-1,4-diylbis[tri-methyl-	C_6H_{12}	246(2.60),259(2.66), 274(2.57)	47-1107-73
$C_{10}H_{18}N_2$			
2-Pentenenitrile, 3-(butylamino)-4-methyl-	EtOH	273(4.38)	39-1108-73C
2-Pentenenitrile, 3-(diethylamino)-4-methyl-	EtOH	277(4.27)	39-1108-73C
3-Pentenenitrile, 3-(butylamino)-4-methyl-	EtOH	222(3.83)	39-1108-73C
3-Pentenenitrile, 3-(diethylamino)-4-methyl-	EtOH	204(3.68),230(3.34)	39-1108-73C
Pyridazine, 3-butyl-3,4-dihydro-3,6-di-methyl-	C_6H_{12}	268(3.33),447(2.18)	23-1724-73
Quinoxaline, 1,2,3,4,5,6,7,8-octahydro-1,4-dimethyl-	C_6H_{12}	235(3.85)	28-1319-73A
$C_{10}H_{18}N_2O$			
Morpholine, 4-[(1-methyl-2-pyrrolidin-ylidene)methyl]-	C_6H_{12}	226(3.86)	28-0519-73A
2-Propenal, 3-(dimethylamino)-3-(1-pip-eridinyl)-	CH_2Cl_2	255(3.83),305(4.34)	33-0944-73
$C_{10}H_{18}N_2O_2$			
2,4-Pentanedione, 3-[bis(dimethylamino)-methylene]-	C_6H_{12}	254(4.20),264s(3.99), 315(3.92)	1-0258-73
	EtOH	257(4.24),275(4.21), 292s(4.07)	1-0258-73
$C_{10}H_{18}N_2O_2Si$			
3H-Pyrazole-4-carboxylic acid, 3,3-di-methyl-5-(trimethylsilyl)-, methyl ester	MeOH	258(3.68),382(--)	22-2739-73
$C_{10}H_{18}N_2O_3$			
Butanoic acid, 2-[bis(dimethylamino)-methylene]-3-oxo-, methyl ester	EtOH	247(4.28),299(3.88)	1-0258-73
$C_{10}H_{18}N_2O_4$			
Propanedioic acid, [bis(dimethylamino)-methylene]-, dimethyl ester	C_6H_{12}	247s(3.91),293(4.16)	1-0258-73
	EtOH	237(4.27),293(4.09)	1-0258-73
$(C_{10}H_{18}N_2O_4)_n$			
Poly(N^{ϵ}-acetoacetyl-L-lysine)	pH 3.47	256(2.69),330(2.17)	116-0571-73
	pH 10.06	280(3.85)	116-0571-73
	pH 13.00	272.5(4.14)	116-0571-73
$C_{10}H_{18}N_2O_6$			
Hexanoic acid, 2,6-dinitro-, butyl ester	MeOH	264(2.48)	18-3462-73
$C_{10}H_{18}N_2O_8S$			
Carbamic acid, [2-methyl-3-(sulfooxy)-1-propene-1,3-diyl]bis-, diethyl ester	100% H_2SO_4	326(4.85)	104-0908-73

Compound	Solvent	$\lambda_{max}(\log \epsilon)$	Ref.
$C_{10}H_{18}N_3O_6P$			
2,4(1H,3H)-Pyrimidinedione, 5-(diethyl-amino)-1-[2-(phosphonooxy)ethyl]-	H_2O	212(3.96),281(3.95)	18-1762-73
$C_{10}H_{18}N_4$			
Dipyrido[1,2-d:2',1'-f][1,2,3,4]tetra-zine, 1,2,3,4,9,10,11,12,12a,12b-decahydro-	MeOH	223(3.4),275(3.7)	89-0495-73
$C_{10}H_{18}N_4O$			
Dipyrido[1,2-d:2',1'-f][1,2,3,4]tetra-zine, 1,2,3,4,9,10,11,12,12a,12b-decahydro-, 6-oxide	MeOH	291(4.08)	89-0495-73
$C_{10}H_{18}N_4O_6$			
D-Glucitol, 2-[5-amino-4-(aminocarbo-nyl)-1H-imidazol-1-yl]-2-deoxy-	acid	245(3.91),268(4.01)	39-2345-73C
	neutral	268(4.02)	39-2345-73C
	base	267(4.12)	39-2345-73C
$C_{10}H_{18}O$			
Cyclohexanone, 4-(1,1-dimethylethyl)-	C_6H_{12}	292(1.18)	22-2231-73
	heptane	292(1.18)	22-2231-73
	H_2O	276(--)	22-2231-73
	MeOH	282(1.16)	22-2231-73
	EtOH	284(1.20)	22-2231-73
	MeCN	287(1.26)	22-2231-73
	CCl_4	293(1.32)	22-2231-73
	$CHCl_3$	287(1.30)	22-2231-73
	CH_2Cl_2	288(1.26)	22-2231-73
Cyclohexanone, 2,2,6,6-tetramethyl-	C_6H_{12}	303(1.38)	22-2231-73
	heptane	303(1.36)	22-2231-73
	H_2O	295(--)	22-2231-73
	MeOH	299(1.43)	22-2231-73
	EtOH	300(1.40)	22-2231-73
	MeCN	301(1.38)	22-2231-73
	CCl_4	304(1.45)	22-2231-73
	$CHCl_3$	302(1.40)	22-2231-73
	CH_2Cl_2	302(1.40)	22-2231-73
Cyclohexanone, 3,3,5,5-tetramethyl-	hexane	288(1.23)	46-1830-73
2-Heptenal, 2-propyl-	EtOH	231(4.2),314(--)	22-2429-73
2-Hepten-4-one, 5,6,6-trimethyl-, cis	hexane	225(4.00)	35-7345-73
trans	hexane	220(4.05)	35-7345-73
3-Hepten-2-one, 5-(1-methylethyl)-	EtOH	223(4.16)	102-2555-73
Myrcenol	EtOH	225(4.17)	42-0329-73
$C_{10}H_{18}O_2$			
2-Cyclohexene-1,4-diol, 1,2,6,6-tetra-methyl-, cis	EtOH	210(2.9)	39-2485-73C
trans	EtOH	210(3.0)	39-2485-73C
$C_{10}H_{18}O_2S_4Zn$			
Zinc butyl xanthate	ether	222(4.28),240s(3.77), 294(4.34)	47-0119-73
$C_{10}H_{18}O_3$			
4(5H)-Oxepinone, tetrahydro-5-hydroxy-3,3,6,6-tetramethyl-	EtOH	261(1.63)	44-4087-73
$C_{10}H_{18}O_4S$			
2-Pentanone, 5-(2-methyl-1,3-dioxolan-2-yl)-1-(methylsulfinyl)-	EtOH	282(2.10)	44-3244-73
	EtOH-KOMe	252(3.73)	44-3244-73

Compound	Solvent	λ_{max}(log ϵ)	Ref.
$C_{10}H_{18}Si_2$			
Silane, 1,4-phenylenebis[dimethyl-	heptane	277.0(2.59)	70-1825-73
$C_{10}H_{18}Sn_2$			
Stannane, 1,3-butadiyne-1,4-diylbis-[trimethyl-	C_6H_{12}	226(2.38),236(2.38), 247(2.49),261(2.49), 277(2.41)	47-1107-73
$C_{10}H_{19}ClN_2$			
Pyridazine, 3-butyl-6-chloro-3,4,5,6-tetrahydro-	C_6H_{12}	385(1.88)	23-1724-73
isomer B	C_6H_{12}	390(1.90)	23-1724-73
$C_{10}H_{19}N$			
Heptanamine, N-allylidene-	EtOH	214(4.38)	78-4111-73
$C_{10}H_{19}NO_2$			
Butanamide, N-hexyl-3-oxo-	pH 3.94	272(1.63)	116-0571-73
	pH 13.02	272(4.18)	116-0571-73
4-Hexen-2-one, 6-tert-butoxy-, oxime, cis	EtOH	229(4.29)	78-4111-73
trans	EtOH	233(4.28)	78-4111-73
$C_{10}H_{19}N_2$			
1,4-Diazepinylium, 2,3,4,?-tetrahydro-2,2,5,6,7-pentamethyl-, perchlorate	MeOH	340(4.13)	39-1729-73B
$C_{10}H_{19}N_2O$			
1,4-Diazepinylium, 1,2,3,4-tetrahydro-6-methoxy-2,2,5,7-tetramethyl-, perchlorate	MeOH	347(4.14)	39-1729-73B
$C_{10}H_{20}N_2$			
1H-Imidazole, 2-heptyl-4,5-dihydro-	EtOH	220(3.65)	93-2424-73
$C_{10}H_{20}N_2O$			
3-Buten-2-one, 4-(diethylamino)-4-(dimethylamino)-	CH_2Cl_2	254(3.83),309(4.31)	33-0944-73
$C_{10}H_{20}N_2O_2$			
Ethanediamide, tetraethyl-	C_6H_{12}	210(3.99),219s(--)	82-0469-73C
	heptane	216s(4.00)	82-0469-73C
	H_2O	202(4.14),220s(3.92)	82-0469-73C
	gas	212(--)	82-0469-73C
1-Propanol, 1-(tert-butylazo)-2-methyl-, acetate, trans	n.s.g.	357(1.28)	89-0224-73
2-Propenoic acid, 3-(diethylamino)-3-(dimethylamino)-, methyl ester	CH_2Cl_2	252(4.00),288(4.31)	33-0944-73
$C_{10}H_{20}NiO_6P_2$			
Nickel, (η^5-2,4-cyclopentadien-1-yl)-(dimethyl phosphito-P)(trimethyl phosphite-P)-	MeOH	250(4.35),295(3.83), 371(3.03),506(1.74)	33-1620-73
$C_{10}H_{21}ClN_4O_4$			
Methanaminium, N-[3-(dimethylamino)-2-[[(dimethylamino)methylene]amino]-2-propenylidene]-N-methyl-, perchlorate	H_2O	222(4.10),337(4.40)	73-2633-73

Compound	Solvent	$\lambda_{max}(\log \epsilon)$	Ref.
$C_{10}H_{22}Cl_2N_4O_8$			
Methanaminium, N-[3-(dimethylamino)-2-[[(dimethylamino)methylene]amino]-2-propenylidene]-N-methyl-, diperchlorate	H_2O	211(4.07),309(4.58)	73-2633-73
$C_{10}H_{22}N_2O$			
Diazene, ethyl(1-methylheptyl)-, 2-oxide, trans	n.s.g.	218(3.82),285(1.89)	35-3070-73
$C_{10}H_{22}SSi$			
Silane, [2-(ethenylthio)ethyl]triethyl-	hexane	229(3.79),238s(3.65)	67-0061-73

Compound	Solvent	$\lambda_{max}(\log \epsilon)$	Ref.
$C_{11}F_{15}N$			
Pyridine, 2,3,5,6-tetrafluoro-4-(undeca-fluorocyclohexyl)-	C_6H_{12}	284(3.68)	39-1710-73C
$C_{11}F_{17}N$			
Pyridine, 2,5-difluoro-3,4,6-tris(penta-fluoroethyl)-	C_6H_{12}	285(3.81)	39-1405-73C
$C_{11}HF_{18}N_3O_5$			
1,3,6-Trioxa-9-azaspiro[4.4]non-8-en-8-amine, N-nitro-2,2,4,4,7,7-hexa-kis(trifluoromethyl)-	EtOH	288(4.09)	44-1751-73
$C_{11}H_2Br_5N_5$			
1,3,6,9b-Tetraazaphenalene-4-carbo-nitrile, 7,9-dibromo-2-(tribromo-methyl)-	EtOH	227(4.47),242s(4.38), 293(4.37),354(4.34), 370s(4.26),385s(4.20), 398s(4.13),479(1.92), 512(2.35),575s(2.66), 614(2.84),660(2.69), 719(2.43)	1-2095-73
$C_{11}H_3Br_4N_5$			
1,3,6,9b-Tetraazaphenalene-4-carbo-nitrile, 7,9-dibromo-2-(dibromo-methyl)-	EtOH	231(4.34),243s(4.28), 292(4.32),353(4.35), 387(4.16),398s(4.09), 404(4.07),568s(2.20), 611(2.48),662(2.61), 720(2.19)	1-2095-73
$C_{11}H_3Cl_5O_4$			
2-Furancarboxylic acid, 5-chloro-, 2,3,4,5-tetrachloro-6-hydroxy-phenyl ester	MeOH	215(4.76),257(4.35), 300(3.46)	48-0419-73
$C_{11}H_4Br_3N_5$			
1,3,6,9b-Tetraazaphenalene-4-carbo-nitrile, 7-bromo-2-(bromomethyl)-	EtOH	222(4.30),241(4.26), 282(4.33),346(4.30), 378(4.10),388s(4.04), 397(4.01),474(1.65), 558s(2.41),595(2.60), 641(2.62),696s(2.31)	1-2095-73
1,3,6,9b-Tetraazaphenalene-4-carbo-nitrile, 9-bromo-2-(bromomethyl)-	EtOH	224(4.31),234(4.31), 285(4.19),345(4.17), 363(4.02),381(4.11), 398(4.06),554s(2.31), 596(2.53),645(2.53), 698s(2.15)	1-2095-73
$C_{11}H_4Cl_4O_3S$			
2-Thiophenecarboxylic acid, 2,3,4,5-tetrachloro-6-hydroxyphenyl ester	MeOH	215(4.82),250(4.26)	48-0419-73
$C_{11}H_4Cl_4O_4$			
2-Furancarboxylic acid, 2,3,4,5-tetra-chloro-6-hydroxyphenyl ester	MeOH	215(4.72),250(4.27), 300(3.40)	48-0419-73
$C_{11}H_5Br_2N_5$			
1,3,6,9b-Tetraazaphenalene-4-carbo-nitrile, 2-(dibromomethyl)-	EtOH	236(4.38),272(4.42), 338(4.29),355(4.15), 372(4.23),380(4.17),	1-2095-73

Compound	Solvent	$\lambda_{max}(\log \epsilon)$	Ref.
1,3,6,9b-Tetraazaphenalene-4-carbo- nitrile, 2-(dibromomethyl)- (cont.)	EtOH	389(4.19),455(1.94), 544s(2.47),578(2.61), 621(2.56),670s(2.16)	1-2095-73
$C_{11}H_5Br_4N_5O$			
1,3,6,9b-Tetraazaphenalene-4-carbox- amide, 7,9-dibromo-2-(dibromomethyl)-	EtOH	224(4.44),241(4.46), 285(4.36),346(4.38), 360s(4.29),382(4.27), 400(4.19),467(2.55), 497(2.53),600(2.70), 636(2.73),690s(2.43)	1-2095-73
$C_{11}H_5ClO_3$			
Benzo[1,2-b:4,3-b']difuran-2-carbox- aldehyde, 7-chloro-	n.s.g.	265s(3.77),274(4.31), 285(4.46),295s(4.32)	1-3133-73
$C_{11}H_5Cl_2N_3$			
1,3,5-Triazine, 2,4-dichloro-6-(phenyl- ethynyl)-	EtOH	207(4.35),228(4.23), 311(4.45)	22-2039-73
$C_{11}H_5Cl_4N_3O_2$			
2,4-Cyclopentadien-1-one, 2,3,4,5-tetra- chloro-, (3-nitrophenyl)hydrazone	EtOH	402(4.48)	39-1155-73B
	EtOH-KOH	460(--)	39-1155-73B
2,4-Cyclopentadien-1-one, 2,3,4,5-tetra- chloro-, (4-nitrophenyl)hydrazone	EtOH	418(4.65)	39-1155-73B
	EtOH-KOH	542(--)	39-1155-73B
$C_{11}H_5Cl_5Hg$			
Mercury, (1,2,3,4,5-pentachloro-2,4- cyclopentadien-1-yl)phenyl-	C_6H_{12}	223(4.3),285(4.0), 329s(3.1)	35-8658-73
$C_{11}H_5Cl_5N_2$			
2,4-Cyclopentadien-1-one, 2,3,4,5-tetra- chloro-, (3-chlorophenyl)hydrazone	EtOH	416(4.29)	39-1155-73B
	EtOH-KOH	458(--)	39-1155-73B
2,4-Cyclopentadien-1-one, 2,3,4,5-tetra- chloro-, (4-chlorophenyl)hydrazone	EtOH	416(4.50)	39-1155-73B
	EtOH-KOH	458(--)	39-1155-73B
$C_{11}H_5Cl_5N_3P$			
1,3,2-Diazaphosphorine-5-carbonitrile, 2,2,4-trichloro-6-(dichloromethyl- phenyl)-2,2-dihydro-	hexane	245(4.12),343(3.89)	112-0621-73
$C_{11}H_6BrNO_6$			
2-Furanacetic acid, 5-bromo-α-[(5-nitro- 2-furanyl)methylene]-, cis	MeOH	227(4.29),310(4.05), 404(4.08)	18-2498-73
trans	MeOH	305(4.21),406(4.40)	18-2498-73
$C_{11}H_6BrN_5$			
1,3,6,9b-Tetraazaphenalene-4-carbo- nitrile, 2-(bromomethyl)-	EtOH	216s(4.05),237(4.14), 271(4.13),335(4.04), 354s(3.87),371(3.96), 388(3.91),535s(2.28), 575(2.44),610(2.42), 662s(2.05)	1-2095-73
$C_{11}H_6Br_2N_4O_2$			
Benzo[g]pteridine-2,4(1H,3H)-dione, 6,8-dibromo-7-methyl-	EtOH	276(4.38),350(4.00), 400(3.76)	65-1578-73
$C_{11}H_6Cl_2N_4S$			
Benzenamine, 2,5-dichloro-N-3H-[1,2,4]- thiadiazolo[4.3-a]pyrimidin-3-ylidene-	n.s.g.	239(4.32),292(3.96), 335s(3.52),415(3.40)	44-3087-73

Compound	Solvent	λ_{max}(log ε)	Ref.
Benzenamine, 3,4-dichloro-N-3H-[1,2,4]-thiadiazolo[4,3-a]pyrimidin-3-ylidene-	n.s.g.	244(4.24),302(4.09), 332s(3.62),420(3.46)	44-3087-73
$C_{11}H_6Cl_4N_2$			
2,4-Cyclopentadien-1-one, 2,3,4,5-tetrachloro-, phenylhydrazone	EtOH	414(4.48)	39-1155-73B
	EtOH-KOH	450(--)	39-1155-73B
$C_{11}H_6Cl_4O_4$			
Spiro[2.4]hepta-1,4,6-triene-1,2-dicarboxylic acid, 4,5,6,7-tetrachloro-, dimethyl ester	$CHCl_3$	241(4.09),288(3.70)	5-0214-73
$C_{11}H_6F_6OS_2$			
Phenol, 4-[4,5-bis(trifluoromethyl)-1,3-dithiol-2-yl]-	isooctane	282(3.60),325(3.41)	35-4379-73
$C_{11}H_6N_4$			
Propanedinitrile, 4-quinazolinyl-	EtOH	216(4.57),253(3.71), 270(3.74),382(4.37), 401(4.31)	95-0094-73
$C_{11}H_6N_4O$			
Pyrimido[1,2-a]benzimidazole-3-carbonitrile, 1,4-dihydro-4-oxo-	EtOH	228s(4.34),244s(4.23), 264s(--),276s(--), 284s(--),296s(--), 322(4.24),345(4.23)	4-0071-73
$C_{11}H_6N_4S$			
Pyrido[3",2":4',5']imidazo[2',1':2,3]-thiazolo[5,4-b]pyridine, hydrochloride	EtOH	216(4.17),285(4.27), 320(4.30)	2-0744-73
$C_{11}H_6N_6O_2$			
Imidazo[4,5-i]alloxazine	EtOH-2%DMSO	268(4.54),373(4.23)	65-2285-73
Imidazo[4,5-j]alloxazine	EtOH-2%DMSO	279(4.52),368(4.05)	65-2285-73
$C_{11}H_6OS_2$			
4H-Cyclohepta[1,2-b:5,4-b']dithiophen-4-one	EtOH	205(3.91),254(4.49), 337(4.19),352(4.20), 373(4.10)	1-2485-73
4H-Cyclohepta[1,2-c:4,5-c']dithiophen-4-one	EtOH	205(3.36),250(4.00), 264(4.11),270(4.15), 295s(3.55),311(3.45), 380(2.65)	1-2485-73
9H-Cyclohepta[2,1-b:4,5-b']dithiophen-9-one	EtOH	204(3.86),250(4.40), 289(4.41),330(2.86), 350(2.84),362(2.81), 370(2.81)	1-2485-73
$C_{11}H_6O_2S$			
4H-Thieno[3',2':4,5]cyclohepta[1,2-b]-furan-4-one	EtOH	243(4.32),250s(4.26), 273(3.89),285s(3.76), 322s(3.94),337(4.08), 355(4.18),376(4.05)	1-2485-73
$C_{11}H_6O_3$			
Psoralen	EtOH	240(4.4),290(4.0), 342(3.9)	102-2071-73

Compound	Solvent	λ_{max}(log ϵ)	Ref.
$C_{11}H_6O_4S_2$			
Naphtho[1,8-bc]thiophene-6-sulfonic acid, 2-oxo-	H_2O	256(4.25),298(3.80), 342(3.82)	103-0588-73
Naphtho[1,8-bc]thiophene-7-sulfonic acid, 2-oxo-	H_2O	226(3.95),262(3.70), 304(3.21),342(3.31)	103-0588-73
$C_{11}H_6O_5$			
2-Naphthalenecarboxaldehyde, 1,4-dihydro-3,8-dihydroxy-1,4-dioxo-	CH_2Cl_2	275(4.30),374(3.89)	33-0619-73
$C_{11}H_7BrOS$			
2-Thiophenecarboxaldehyde, 5-(3-bromophenyl)-	MeOH	262(4.03),287(4.18)	73-1809-73
2-Thiophenecarboxaldehyde, 5-(4-bromophenyl)-	MeOH	231(4.42),238(3.98)	73-1809-73
$C_{11}H_7BrOS_2$			
2-Thiophenecarboxaldehyde, 5-[2-(5-bromo-2-thienyl)ethenyl]-	DMF	382(4.49)	24-0655-73
$C_{11}H_7BrO_3$			
2-Furancarboxylic acid, 5-bromo-, phenyl ester	heptane	267(--)	103-0546-73
	dioxan	267(4.60)	103-0546-73
$C_{11}H_7ClO_2$			
3-Furancarboxaldehyde, 2-chloro-5-phenyl-	EtOH	278(4.27)	103-0659-73
$C_{11}H_7ClO_3$			
2-Furancarboxaldehyde, 5-[2-(5-chloro-2-furanyl)ethenyl]-, (E)-	n.s.g.	273(3.93),366(4.54)	1-3133-73
2-Furancarboxylic acid, 5-chloro-, phenyl ester	heptane	264(--)	103-0546-73
	dioxan	263(4.58)	103-0546-73
2-Furancarboxylic acid, 5-(2-chlorophenyl)-	MeOH	216(4.05),227s(3.96), 235s(3.91),288s(4.35), 295(4.40),319s(4.22)	12-1147-73
2-Furancarboxylic acid, 5-(3-chlorophenyl)-	MeOH	217(3.94),228s(3.78), 234s(3.69),290s(4.17), 297(4.22),312s(4.09)	12-1147-73
2-Furancarboxylic acid, 5-(4-chlorophenyl)-	MeOH	218(3.82),300(4.20), 315s(4.09)	12-1147-73
$C_{11}H_7F_2N_3O_2$			
1-Cyclobutene-1-carboxylic acid, 2-azido-3,3-difluoro-, phenyl ester	MeOH	277(4.09)	24-3544-73
$C_{11}H_7IO_3$			
2-Furancarboxylic acid, 5-iodo-, phenyl ester	heptane	269(--)	103-0546-73
	dioxan	272(4.63)	103-0546-73
$C_{11}H_7N$			
1-Naphthalenecarbonitrile	EtOH	224(4.32),288(3.47), 296(3.49),309(3.33), 322(3.04)	95-0409-73
$C_{11}H_7NOS$			
Benzothiazole, 2-(2-furanyl)-	EtOH	320(4.43)	104-2596-73
cation	H_2O	355(4.40)	104-2596-73

Compound	Solvent	$\lambda_{max}(\log \epsilon)$	Ref.
$C_{11}H_7NO_3$			
2H-1-Benzopyran-3-carbonitrile, 6-methoxy-2-oxo-	MeOH	230(4.28),297(4.17), 375(3.70)	24-0388-73
$C_{11}H_7NO_3S$			
2H-1-Benzopyran-3-carbonitrile, 7-hydroxy-4-(methylthio)-2-oxo-	EtOH	255(3.71),320(4.07), 372(4.34)	95-0836-73
Methanone, (2-nitrophenyl)-2-thienyl-	EtOH	264(4.19),288s(4.07)	59-0161-73
Methanone, (3-nitrophenyl)-2-thienyl-	EtOH	264(4.14),294s(4.04)	59-0161-73
Methanone, (4-nitrophenyl)-2-thienyl-	EtOH	268(4.26),295s(4.08)	59-0161-73
Methanone, (3-nitro-2-thienyl)phenyl-	EtOH	259(4.16),290s(3.89)	59-0161-73
Methanone, (4-nitro-2-thienyl)phenyl-	EtOH	256(4.36),275s(4.24)	59-0161-73
Methanone, (5-nitro-2-thienyl)phenyl-	EtOH	226(3.81),313(4.13)	59-0161-73
2-Thiophenecarboxaldehyde, 5-(2-nitrophenyl)-	MeOH	278(4.20),298(4.25)	73-1809-73
2-Thiophenecarboxaldehyde, 5-(3-nitrophenyl)-	MeOH	223(4.27),284(4.22)	73-1809-73
2-Thiophenecarboxaldehyde, 5-(4-nitrophenyl)-	MeOH	276(3.97),311(4.16)	73-1809-73
$C_{11}H_7NO_4$			
2H-1-Benzopyran-3-carbonitrile, 7-hydroxy-4-methoxy-2-oxo-	EtOH	241(4.12),337(4.35)	95-0836-73
$C_{11}H_7NO_5$			
2-Furancarboxylic acid, 5-nitro-, phenyl ester	heptane	290(--)	103-0546-73
	EtOH	300(--)	103-0546-73
	dioxan	297(4.40)	103-0546-73
2-Furancarboxylic acid, 5-(2-nitrophenyl)-	MeOH	218(4.03),280(4.14)	12-1147-73
2-Furancarboxylic acid, 5-(3-nitrophenyl)-	MeOH	217(4.23),296(4.21), 308s(4.10)	12-1147-73
2-Quinolinecarboxylic acid, 5,8-dihydro-4-hydroxy-5,8-dioxo-, methyl ester	$CHCl_3$	360(3.30)	39-2374-73C
$C_{11}H_7NS_2$			
Benzothiazole, 2-(2-thienyl)-	EtOH	322(4.33)	104-2596-73
cation	H_2O	355(4.45)	104-2596-73
Naphtho[1,2-d]thiazole-2-thiol	$CHCl_3$	244s(--),254(4.48), 320(4.05),341(4.20), 355(4.32)	22-3044-73
Naphtho[2,1-d]thiazole-2-thiol	$CHCl_3$	241(4.29),267(4.23), 294(4.28),338(4.34), 352(4.45)	22-3044-73
$C_{11}H_7N_3O$			
Pyrimido[4,5-b]quinolin-4(3H)-one	MeCN	248(4.5),307(4.0), 345(3.6)	24-3533-73
$C_{11}H_7N_3OS$			
Thiocyanic acid, 4-[2-(1,2,4-oxadiazol-3-yl)ethenyl]phenyl ester, (E)-	EtOH	286(4.52)	39-2241-73C
$C_{11}H_7N_3OS_2$			
Thiazolo[4,5-d]pyridazin-7(6H)-one, 2,3-dihydro-6-phenyl-2-thioxo-	$CHCl_3$	263(4.16),310(4.20)	22-3324-73
$C_{11}H_7N_3O_3$			
Pyrimido[1,2-a]benzimidazole-3-carboxylic acid, 1,4-dihydro-4-oxo-	EtOH	228(4.42),248s(--), 256s(--),330(4.23), 342(4.21)	4-0071-73

Compound	Solvent	$\lambda_{max}(\log \epsilon)$	Ref.
$C_{11}H_7N_5O_2S$			
Benzenamine, 3-nitro-N-3H-[1,2,4]thiadiazolo[4,3-a]pyrimidin-3-ylidene-	n.s.g.	247(4.33),277s(4.13), 300s(4.04),405(3.49)	44-3087-73
Benzenamine, 4-nitro-N-3H-[1,2,4]thiadiazolo[4,3-a]pyrimidin-3-ylidene-	n.s.g.	247(4.33),285s(3.90), 360(4.16),413(3.99)	44-3087-73
$C_{11}H_7OS$			
4H-Thieno[3',2':4,5]cyclohepta[1,2-b]-furan-4-ylium, perchlorate	0.2M HCl	210(4.02),263s(4.11), 296(4.72),378(3.90), 404s(3.56)	1-2485-73
9H-Thieno[3',2':5,6]cyclohepta[1,2-b]-furan-9-ylium, perchlorate	H_2SO_4	220(4.11),275(4.22), 306(4.63),368(4.24), 414s(3.62)	1-2485-73
$C_{11}H_7S_2$			
4H-Cyclohepta[1,2-b:5,4-b']dithien-4-ylium, perchlorate	H_2SO_4	205(4.25),223(4.25), 230s(4.19),312(4.91), 374(3.78),411(3.89), 440s(3.46),470s(3.05)	1-2485-73
9H-Cyclohepta[2,1-b:4,5-b']dithien-9-ylium, perchlorate	H_2SO_4	208(4.24),235(4.16), 266(3.93),302(4.57), 331(4.66),375(3.86), 395(4.20),447(3.67), 461(3.70),471(3.67)	1-2485-73
$C_{11}H_8$			
1H-Cyclopropa[b]naphthalene	C_6H_{12}	221(4.76)	35-4099-73
$C_{11}H_8ClNO_5$			
2-Quinolinecarboxylic acid, 6-chloro-1,4-dihydro-5,8-dihydroxy-4-oxo-, methyl ester	MeOH	243(4.33),263(4.22), 290s(3.81),345(3.81), 397(3.52)	39-2374-73C
$C_{11}H_8ClN_3S$			
Pyridazino[4,5-b][1,4]benzothiazine, 1-chloro-3-methyl-	EtOH	278(4.19),380(3.58), 477(3.39)	7-0255-73
Pyridazino[4,5-b][1,4]benzothiazine, 1-chloro-10-methyl-	EtOH	227(4.15),271(4.30), 296s(3.65),382(3.00)	7-0255-73
$C_{11}H_8ClN_5S$			
2-Pyridinamine, N-(6-chloro-3H-[1,2,4]-thiadiazolo[4,3-b]pyridazin-3-ylidene)-5-methyl-	n.s.g.	263(4.36),270s(4.34), 315s(4.14),327(4.26), 336(4.17),338(4.19), 425(3.39)	44-3087-73
$C_{11}H_8Cl_4O_4$			
Spiro[2.4]hepta-4,6-diene-1,2-dicarboxylic acid, 4,5,6,7-tetrachloro-, dimethyl ester, cis	$CHCl_3$	243(3.89),305(3.38)	5-0214-73
trans	$CHCl_3$	242(3.71),300(3.40)	5-0214-73
$C_{11}H_8CrO_5$			
Chromium, tricarbonyl[(1,2,3,4,5,6-η)-2-methylbenzoic acid]	n.s.g.	319(4.14),383(3.46)	6-0397-73
Chromium, tricarbonyl[(1,2,3,4,5,6-η)-3-methylbenzoic acid]	n.s.g.	321(4.08),385(3.42)	6-0397-73
$C_{11}H_8CrO_6$			
Chromium, tricarbonyl[(1,2,3,4,5,6-η)-2-methoxybenzoic acid]	n.s.g.	317(3.95),375(3.52)	6-0397-73

Compound	Solvent	$\lambda_{max}(\log \epsilon)$	Ref.
Chromium, tricarbonyl[(1,2,3,4,5,6-η)-3-methoxybenzoic acid]	n.s.g.	318(3.94),380(3.18)	6-0397-73
$C_{11}H_8N_2$			
9H-Pyrido[3,4-b]indole (norharman)	MeOH	235(4.49),288(4.25),350(3.66)	95-0033-73
Tetracyclo[4.3.0.0^{2,4}.0^{3,7}]non-8-ene-8,9-dicarbonitrile	EtOH	252(3.89)	24-1804-73
$C_{11}H_8N_2OS$			
Acetonitrile, (1,2-dihydro-2-oxo-3H-indol-3-ylidene)(methylthio)-	EtOH	255(4.21),260(4.26),364(4.21)	95-1520-73
Benzothiazole, 2-(3-methyl-5-isoxazolyl)-	MeOH	222(3.75),238s(3.51),325(3.50)	103-0944-73
$C_{11}H_8N_2O_2$			
1H-Indole-2-carboxylic acid, 3-cyano-1-methyl-	EtOH	232(4.34),302(4.12)	95-1433-73
$C_{11}H_8N_2S_2$			
Thieno[2,3-d]thiazol-2-amine, 5-phenyl-	MeCN	229(3.94),263(3.80),336(4.45)	48-0539-73
Thiocyanic acid, 2-amino-5-phenyl-3-thienyl ester	MeOH	231(4.25),326(4.16)	48-0539-73
$C_{11}H_8N_4O$			
Propanedinitrile, (4-acetyl-3-cyano-5-methyl-1H-pyrrol-2-yl)-	EtOH	202(4.35),239(4.27),302(4.03),364(3.94)	12-1551-73
Pyrazinecarbonitrile, 3-amino-6-phenyl-, 4-oxide	MeOH	281s(4.41),391(3.78)	35-6413-73
$C_{11}H_8N_4OS$			
1,2,4-Triazino[5,6-d][3,1]benzoxazepine, 3-(methylthio)-	EtOH	205(4.37),217(4.34),258(4.46),300(4.12),388(4.08)	78-0639-73
$C_{11}H_8N_4O_2$			
Propanedinitrile, (4-acetyl-3-cyano-1,5-dihydro-5-hydroxy-5-methyl-2H-pyrrol-2-ylidene)-	EtOH	244(4.26),385(3.64)	12-1551-73
Pyridazino[4,5-b]quinoxaline-1,4-dione, 2,3-dihydro-2-methyl-	EtOH	246(4.6),305s(4.1),322(4.2)	103-0513-73
Pyridazino[4,5-b]quinoxalin-1(2H)-one, 4-methoxy-	EtOH	250(4.7),284s(4.1),296(4.1),322(4.0)	103-0513-73
$C_{11}H_8N_4O_4$			
4-Pyridinamine, 3,5-dinitro-N-phenyl-	95.5% DMSO	388(3.70)	22-1225-73
anion	95.5% DMSO	500(3.64)	22-1225-73
$C_{11}H_8O$			
1-Naphthalenecarboxaldehyde	H_2O	316(3.85),327s(3.82)	112-0007-73
	H_2SO_4	376s(3.70),417(3.93)	112-0007-73
2-Naphthalenecarboxaldehyde	H_2O	283(4.08),345(3.42)	112-0007-73
	H_2SO_4	346(4.40),446(3.61)	112-0007-73
$C_{11}H_8OS$			
Methanone, phenyl-2-thienyl-	hexane	245(4.1),275(4.1)	35-4599-73
	EtOH	260(4.1),290(4.1)	35-4599-73
	EtOH	263(4.06),293(4.06)	59-0161-73
Methanone, phenyl-3-thienyl-	hexane	212s(4.1),250(4.2)	35-4599-73

Compound	Solvent	λmax(log ε)	Ref.
Methanone, phenyl-3-thienyl- (cont.)	EtOH	220(4.0),262(4.1)	35-4599-73
$C_{11}H_8O_2$			
2-Naphthalenecarboxaldehyde, 1-hydroxy-	MeOH	218(4.43),254(4.59), 262(4.58),285(3.91), 296(3.95),307(3.71), 380(3.82)	39-1802-73C
$C_{11}H_8O_3$			
2-Furancarboxylic acid, phenyl ester	heptane	252(--)	103-0546-73
	H_2O	259(--)	103-0546-73
	EtOH	256(--)	103-0546-73
	dioxan	254(4.49)	103-0546-73
1,2-Naphthalenedione, 4-methoxy-	EtOH	250(4.07),339(3.26), 403(3.29)	136-0247-73A
$C_{11}H_8O_4$			
2,5-Furandione, 3-methoxy-4-phenyl-	EtOH	227(3.79),335(3.62)	39-1538-73C
$C_{11}H_8O_4S$			
Benzo[b]thiophene-2,3-dicarboxylic acid, 5-methyl-	EtOH-HCl	232(4.03),245s(3.87), 292(3.87)	1-0595-73
$C_{11}H_8O_5$			
2H-1-Benzopyran-6-carboxaldehyde, 7-hydroxy-5-methoxy-2-oxo-	MeOH	206(3.77),225s(3.43), 266(4.30),312(3.50), 340s(3.13)	78-2645-73
	MeOH-HCl	207(4.06),222s(3.76), 267(4.19),314(3.75)	78-2645-73
	MeOH-NaOH	206(4.27),238(4.14), 262(3.95),285s(3.62), 347(3.94),394(3.99)	78-2645-73
2H-1-Benzopyran-6-carboxylic acid, 7-hydroxy-2-oxo-, methyl ester	EtOH	218(4.30),224(4.28), 245(4.46),292s(3.99), 303(4.06),323(4.16), 332(4.15)	36-1879-73
2H-1-Benzopyran-2-one, 6-acetoxy-7-hydroxy-	n.s.g.	257(3.68),299(3.76), 345(4.03)	102-0726-73
$C_{11}H_9As$			
Arsenin, 4-phenyl-	EtOH	226(4.35),302(4.49)	89-0931-73
$C_{11}H_9BrCl_2$			
Benzene, 1-bromo-3-(2,2-dichloro-1-ethenylcyclopropyl)-	hexane	220(3.97),250(3.23), 269(2.85)	104-2473-73
Benzene, 1-bromo-4-(2,2-dichloro-1-ethenylcyclopropyl)-	hexane	228(4.10),253(3.41), 259(3.37),266(3.27), 268(3.22)	104-2473-73
$C_{11}H_9BrOS_2$			
Thiophene, 2-bromo-5-[2-(5-methoxy-2-thienyl)ethenyl]-	DMF	363(4.35)	24-0655-73
$C_{11}H_9BrS_2$			
Thiophene, 2-bromo-5-[2-(5-methyl-2-thienyl)ethenyl]-	DMF	357(4.39)	24-0655-73
$C_{11}H_9ClN_2O$			
2-Butenoyl chloride, 2-cyano-3-(phenylamino)-	MeCN	222(4.07),308(4.32)	44-2287-73

Compound	Solvent	λmax(log ε)	Ref.
$C_{11}H_9ClN_2O_2$			
5(4H)-Isoxazolone, 4-[[(2-chlorophenyl)-amino]methylene]-3-methyl-	EtOH	232(3.87),355(4.21)	12-0889-73
5(4H)-Isoxazolone, 4-[[(3-chlorophenyl)-amino]methylene]-3-methyl-	EtOH	236(3.77),348(4.10)	12-0889-73
5(4H)-Isoxazolone, 4-[[(4-chlorophenyl)-amino]methylene]-3-methyl-	EtOH	233(3.88),354(4.21)	12-0889-73
$C_{11}H_9ClN_2O_3$			
Ethanone, 1-(5-chloro-3-methyl-3-nitro-3H-indol-2-yl)-	isoPrOH	240(4.08),324(3.96)	44-3077-73
$C_{11}H_9ClN_2O_4$			
4H,5H-Pyrano[3,4-e][1,3]oxazine-4,5-dione, 7-chloro-2-pyrrolidino-	MeCN	299(3.88),341(4.10)	39-2432-73C
$C_{11}H_9ClN_2O_5$			
Pyrano[3,4-e][1,3]oxazine-4,5-dione, 7-chloro-2-morpholino-	MeCN	298(4.10),340(4.31)	39-2432-73C
$C_{11}H_9ClN_4$			
2H-Tetrazole, 2-(4-chlorophenyl)-5-(1,3-butadienyl)-, (Z)-	EtOH	253(4.31),283(4.25)	88-4295-73
$C_{11}H_9ClN_4O_2S$			
1H-Pyrido[2,3-b]pyrimido[4,5-e][1,4]-thiazine, 7-chloro-2,4-dimethoxy-	MeOH	224s(4.14),261(4.05), 308(4.19),343(3.89)	44-4386-73
$C_{11}H_9ClO$			
Furan, 2-(4-chlorophenyl)-5-methyl-	EtOH	293(4.35)	22-1760-73
$C_{11}H_9Cl_2N$			
Quinoline, 3-chloro-2-(chloromethyl)-4-methyl-	EtOH	215(4.15),235(4.76), 282(3.65),311(3.48), 325(3.40)	44-0927-73
$C_{11}H_9Cl_2N_3O_4S$			
10H-Pyridazino[4,5-b][1,4]benzothiazine, 1-chloro-3-methyl-, perchlorate	EtOH	275(4.45),284(4.45), 333(3.72),371(3.65), 473(3.20)	7-0255-73
$C_{11}H_9Cl_3$			
Benzene, 1-chloro-4-(2,2-dichloro-1-ethenylcyclopropyl)-	hexane	225(4.03),249(2.99), 253(2.97),258(2.94)	104-2473-73
$C_{11}H_9IN_6$			
9H-Purine-2,6-diamine, 9-(4-iodophenyl)-	EtOH	215(4.34),250(4.29)	42-0260-73
$C_{11}H_9NO$			
Isoxazole, 3-(2-phenylethenyl)-	C_6H_{12}	207(4.11),214(4.12), 219(4.17),226(4.07), 233s(--),279(4.36), 290s(--),300(4.08), 307s(--)	32-0309-73
	MeOH	206(4.16),213(4.15), 218(4.20),225(4.08), 276(4.41),290s(--), 300s(--)	32-0309-73
Isoxazole, 5-(2-phenylethenyl)- (plus shoulders)	C_6H_{12}	220(3.95),226(3.99), 233(3.84),298(4.46)	32-0309-73

Compound	Solvent	$\lambda_{max}(\log \epsilon)$	Ref.
Isoxazole, 5-(2-phenylethenyl)- (cont.)	MeOH	220s(--),226(3.99), 231(3.86),298(4.46), 305s(--)	32-0309-73
1,3-Oxazepine, 2-phenyl-	EtOH	238(4.16),323(3.66), 400(--)	88-1835-73
Pyridine, 2-phenoxy-	hexane	220(4.23),234s(3.86), 267(3.81),274s(3.80), 305s(3.00)	32-0709-73
	MeOH	220(4.03),233(3.80), 265(3.84),270s(3.83)	32-0709-73
Pyridine, 3-phenoxy-	MeOH	222s(4.11),266s(3.81), 272(3.82)	32-0709-73
Pyridine, 4-phenoxy-	MeOH	206(4.30),220s(4.14), 270(3.79)	32-0709-73
Pyridinium 2-formylcyclopentadienylide	MeOH	251(3.87),287(4.24), 440(3.83)	88-5105-73
1H-Pyrrole, 1-benzoyl-	hexane	220(4.1),250(4.1)	18-1437-73
$C_{11}H_9NOS$			
Ethanone, 1-(2-phenyl-5-thiazolyl)-	MeOH	227(4.07),312(4.36)	80-0685-73
$C_{11}H_9NO_2$			
2-Propenoic acid, 3-(1H-indol-3-yl)-	MeOH	226(4.31),274(4.08), 323(4.33)	102-0447-73
after ten minutes	H_2SO_4	253(4.10),260(4.11), 356(3.58)(changing)	102-0447-73
3-Pyridinol, 2-phenyl-, 1-oxide	M HCl	220(4.20),302(4.00)	99-0417-73
	H_2O	222(4.26),255(3.83), 302(3.56)	99-0417-73
	M NaOH	240(4.32),324(4.00)	99-0417-73
	EtOH	244(4.22),265(3.80), 310(3.50)	99-0417-73
2(1H)-Quinolinone, 3-acetyl-	EtOH	292(4.07),337(4.59), 370(3.88)	94-1943-73
$C_{11}H_9NO_2S$			
Spiro[2H-indene-2,2'-thiazolidine]-1,3-dione	MeOH	228(4.62),246s(4.08)	78-4271-73
Thiocyanic acid, 3-(4-methoxyphenyl)-3-oxo-1-propenyl ester, cis	dioxan	232(3.88),319(4.46)	24-0435-73
$C_{11}H_9NO_2S_2$			
1,3(2H,4H)-Isoquinolinedione, 4-[mercapto(methylthio)methylene]-	EtOH	313(2.95)	95-0322-73
Thiophene, 2-methyl-5-[2-(5-nitro-2-thienyl)ethenyl]-	DMF	297(3.81),446(4.23)	24-0655-73
Thiophene, 2-[(2-methylphenyl)thio]-3-nitro-	MeOH	368(3.85)	4-1007-73
Thiophene, 2-[(3-methylphenyl)thio]-3-nitro-	MeOH	368(3.84)	4-1007-73
Thiophene, 2-[(4-methylphenyl)thio]-3-nitro-	MeOH	368(3.85)	4-1007-73
Thiophene, 3-[(2-methylphenyl)thio]-2-nitro-	MeOH	372(4.04)	4-1007-73
Thiophene, 3-[(3-methylphenyl)thio]-2-nitro-	MeOH	374(4.03)	4-1007-73
Thiophene, 3-[(4-methylphenyl)thio]-, 2-nitro-	MeOH	374(4.03)	4-1007-73

Compound	Solvent	$\lambda_{max}(\log \epsilon)$	Ref.
$C_{11}H_9NO_2S_3$			
Thiophene, 2-[[4-(methylthio)phenyl]-thio]-3-nitro-	MeOH	368(3.91)	4-1007-73
Thiophene, 3-[[4-(methylthio)phenyl]-thio]-2-nitro-	MeOH	374(4.06)	4-1007-73
$C_{11}H_9NO_3$			
1H-Indole-3-propanoic acid, α-oxo-	MeOH	234(4.38),323(4.33)	102-0447-73
after ten minutes	H_2SO_4	225(3.73),258(3.40), 340(4.03)(changing)	102-0447-73
1H-Indole-3-propanoic acid, β-oxo-	EtOH	242(4.12),258(3.97), 298(4.12)	78-3761-73
6-Isoquinolinecarboxylic acid, 5-hy-droxy-, methyl ester	EtOH	254(4.40),275s(3.70), 351(3.75),365(3.72)	78-0857-73
6-Isoquinolinecarboxylic acid, 7-hy-droxy-, methyl ester	EtOH	235(4.71),270(3.76), 380(3.46)	78-0857-73
$C_{11}H_9NO_3S$			
Ethanone, 1-(2,4-dihydroxyphenyl)-2-(4-thiazolyl)-	n.s.g.	280(4.26)	104-2580-73
6H-Pyrano[3,4-b]thieno[3,2-e]pyridine-4,8-dione, 5,9-dihydro-6-methyl-	MeOH	249(4.35),283(3.65), 342(3.81)	24-0368-73
$C_{11}H_9NO_3S_2$			
Thiophene, 2-[(3-methoxyphenyl)thio]-3-nitro-	MeOH	368(3.85)	4-1007-73
Thiophene, 2-[(4-methoxyphenyl)thio]-3-nitro-	MeOH	368(3.87)	4-1007-73
Thiophene, 3-[(3-methoxyphenyl)thio]-2-nitro-	MeOH	372(4.03)	4-1007-73
Thiophene, 3-[(4-methoxyphenyl)thio]-2-nitro-	MeOH	374(4.03)	4-1007-73
$C_{11}H_9NO_4$			
Phthalimide, N-ethyl-3,4-(methylenedi-oxy)-	EtOH	226(4.52),235(4.41), 252(3.86),260s(3.81), 348(3.77)	141-0001-73
	dioxan	236(4.25),253(3.88), 259s(3.80),342(3.77)	141-0001-73
Phthalimide, N-ethyl-4,5-(methylenedi-oxy)-	EtOH	245(4.54),301(3.19), 312(3.18),344(2.94)	141-0001-73
	dioxan	243(4.24),296(3.11), 312(3.15),328s(2.90)	141-0001-73
$C_{11}H_9NO_4S$			
2H-1-Benzopyran-3-carboxamide, 7-hy-droxy-4-(methylthio)-2-oxo-	EtOH	337(4.23)	95-0836-73
$C_{11}H_9NO_5$			
2-Quinolinecarboxylic acid, 1,4-dihydro-5,8-dihydroxy-4-oxo-, methyl ester	EtOH	237(4.30),260(4.16), 290(3.79),340(3.72), 400(3.39)	39-2374-73C
$C_{11}H_9NO_5S$			
Furan, 2-nitro-5-[(phenylsulfonyl)meth-yl]-	EtOH	211s(4.45),219(4.38), 267(3.80),275(3.88), 318(4.35)	73-1705-73
$C_{11}H_9NS$			
3H-Pyrrolo[1,2-a]indole-3-thione, 1,2-dihydro-	EtOH	233(4.00),273(4.09), 310(4.00)	88-2401-73

Compound	Solvent	λmax(log ε)	Ref.
$C_{11}H_9N_3O$			
Pyrimido[1,2-a]benzimidazol-2(1H)-one, 1-methyl-	MeOH	212(4.32),227s(4.11), 248(4.36),262s(4.11), 290(3.96)	39-1588-73C
	EtOH	249(4.47),263(4.20), 290(3.95)	4-0071-73
Pyrimido[1,2-a]benzimidazol-2(10H)-one, 10-methyl-	MeOH	215(4.33),237(4.51), 303(4.09)	39-1588-73C
Pyrimido[1,2-a]benzimidazol-4(10H)-one, 10-methyl-	MeOH	228(4.36),250s(4.10), 324(4.11),337(4.15)	39-1588-73C
$C_{11}H_9N_3OS$			
1H-Pyridazino[4,5-b][1,4]benzothiazin-1-one, 2,10-dihydro-10-methyl-	EtOH	267(4.21),278(4.13), 306s(3.59),408(3.20)	7-0255-73
$C_{11}H_9N_3OS_4$			
4-Thiazolidinone, N-ethyl-5-[N-(2-thiazolyl)-2-thiazolinylidene]-2-thioxo-	EtOH	430(4.82)	103-0687-73
$C_{11}H_9N_3O_2$			
2-Pyridinamine, 3-nitro-N-phenyl-	86.4% DMSO	425(3.80)	22-1225-73
anion	86.4% DMSO	540(3.91)	22-1225-73
2-Pyridinamine, 5-nitro-N-phenyl-	86.4% DMSO	385(4.29)	22-1225-73
anion	86.4% DMSO	470(4.44)	22-1225-73
$C_{11}H_9N_3O_2S$			
Naphtho[1,2-d]thiazol-2-amine, 4,5-dihydro-8-nitro-	EtOH	201(4.02),223(4.25), 268(4.27)	34-0099-73
$C_{11}H_9N_3O_2S_2$			
Carbamic acid, 2H-[1,2,4]thiadiazolo-[3,2-b]benzothiazol-2-ylidene-, ethyl ester	EtOH	252s(3.85),262(4.10), 280s(3.56),290s(3.71), 322(4.43)	94-2408-73
$C_{11}H_9N_3O_3$			
1,3,5-Triazine-2,4(1H,3H)-dione, 6-(2-oxo-2-phenylethyl)-	EtOH	326(4.31)	22-2039-73
$C_{11}H_9N_3S$			
Benzothiazole, 2-(5-methyl-1H-pyrazol-3-yl)-	MeOH	225(4.16),265(3.73), 300(3.66)	103-0944-73
Naphtho[1,2-d]thiazol-2(1H)-one, hydrazone	$CHCl_3$	242s(--),262(4.66), 268(4.61),290s(3.86), 302(3.88),313(3.81)	22-3044-73
Naphtho[2,1-d]thiazol-2(1H)-one, hydrazone	$CHCl_3$	242(4.26),260(4.66), 266(4.67),292s(--), 302(3.90),314(3.86)	22-3044-73
10H-Pyridazino[4,5-b][1,4]benzothiazine, 10-methyl-	EtOH	221(4.18),261(4.49), 300(3.60),380(3.03)	7-0255-73
Sulfilimine, N-(2,2-dicyanoethenyl)-S-methyl-S-phenyl-	EtOH	218s(3.85),292(4.23)	44-4324-73
2-Thiazolamine, 5-(1H-indol-3-yl)-	EtOH	203(4.02),227(4.39), 383(3.52)	34-0099-73
Thiazolo[3,2-b][1,2,4]triazole, 5-methyl-2-phenyl-	MeOH	203(4.28),233(4.06), 258(4.34)	4-0947-73
$C_{11}H_9N_5O$			
6H-Purin-6-one, 3,7-dihydro-3-methyl-8-(3-pyridinyl)-	pH 8	225(4.21),311(4.34)	39-2019-73C

Compound	Solvent	λ max(log ε)	Ref.
1,3,6,9b-Tetraazaphenalene-4-carboxamide, 2-methyl-	EtOH	237(4.26),260(4.08), 332(4.16),352(3.88), 370(3.97),388(3.89), 545(2.54),586(2.60), 633(2.29)	1-3259-73
$C_{11}H_9N_5OS$			
2H-Purin-2-one, 1,3-dihydro-6-(methylthio)-8-(3-pyridinyl)-	pH 8	228(3.85),263(3.89), 351(4.12)	39-0739-73C
Thiazolo[4,5-d]pyridazine-2,7(3H,6H)-dione, 6-phenyl-, 2-hydrazone	$CHCl_3$	252(4.53),298(4.17)	22-3324-73
$C_{11}H_9N_5O_5$			
3-Pyridazinamine, 4,6-dinitro-N-(phenylmethyl)-, 1-oxide	MeOH	260(3.8),290(3.85), 450(3.7)	4-0835-73
$C_{11}H_9N_5S$			
6H-Purine-6-thione, 3,9-dihydro-3-methyl-8-(3-pyridinyl)-	pH 8	258(4.06),262(4.17)	39-2019-73C
3-Pyridinamine, 4-methyl-N-3H-[1,2,4]-thiadiazolo[4,3-a]pyrimidin-3-ylidene-	n.s.g.	247(3.81),270(3.75), 321(3.82),329(3.87), 376(3.29),396(3.34)	44-3087-73
$C_{11}H_{10}$			
Benzene, (2-cyclopropylideneethenyl)-	n.s.g.	215(4.26),263(4.20)	88-1349-73
$C_{11}H_{10}BrNO_3S$			
2-Buten-1-one, 1-(4-bromophenyl)-3-(methylthio)-4-nitro-	EtOH	272(4.07),332(4.31)	95-0612-73
$C_{11}H_{10}BrNO_4S$			
2-Cyclopentene-1-sulfonic acid, 3-[(4-bromophenyl)amino]-4-oxo-	EtOH	258(4.27),313(3.89)	12-0893-73
$C_{11}H_{10}BrN_3OS$			
3(2H)-Pyridazinone, 4-bromo-5-[(2-methylaminophenyl)thio]-	EtOH	222(4.06),268(4.21), 306s(3.49),408(3.19)	7-0255-73
$C_{11}H_{10}Br_2N_4S$			
1,2,4-Triazolo[3,4-b][1,3,4]thiadiazin-4-ium, 6-(4-bromophenyl)-1,7-dihydro-1-methyl-	MeOH	228(3.86),283(4.19), 315s(--)	48-1131-73
$C_{11}H_{10}Br_2O_4$			
Propanoic acid, 3-(2,4-dibromo-3,6-dioxo-1,4-cyclohexadien-1-yl)-, ethyl ester	MeOH	288(4.00)	35-8319-73
$C_{11}H_{10}ClNO$			
Ethanone, 1-(5-chloro-3-methyl-1H-indol-3-yl)-	isoPrOH	238(3.97),312(4.31)	44-3077-73
$C_{11}H_{10}ClNO_2S$			
4H-1,4-Benzothiazine-2-carboxylic acid, 6-chloro-, ethyl ester	EtOH	218(4.23),262(4.40), 278s(3.91),353(3.36), 433(3.25)	7-0045-73
4H-1,4-Benzothiazine-2-carboxylic acid, 7-chloro-, ethyl ester	EtOH	218(4.29),262(4.39), 280s(3.90),353(3.50), 435(3.33)	7-0045-73
4H-1,4-Benzothiazine-3-carboxylic acid, 6-chloro-, ethyl ester	EtOH	217(4.18),258(4.28), 280(3.72),340(3.33),	7-0045-73

Compound	Solvent	$\lambda_{max}(\log \epsilon)$	Ref.
4H-1,4-Benzothiazine-3-carboxylic acid, 6-chloro-, ethyl ester (cont.)	EtOH	410(2.78)	7-0045-73
$C_{11}H_{10}ClNO_3S$			
2-Buten-1-one, 1-(4-chlorophenyl)-3-(methylthio)-4-nitro-	EtOH	268(4.03),332(4.31)	95-0612-73
$C_{11}H_{10}ClNO_4S$			
2-Cyclopentene-1-sulfonic acid, 3-[(3-chlorophenyl)amino]-4-oxo-, Na salt	EtOH	255(4.23),311(3.88)	12-0893-73
2-Cyclopentene-1-sulfonic acid, 3-[(4-chlorophenyl)amino]-4-oxo-, Na salt	EtOH	257(4.27),313(3.86)	12-0893-73
$C_{11}H_{10}ClNS$			
Quinoline, 6-chloro-4-methyl-2-(methylthio)-	EtOH	227(4.31),300(4.02)	103-0481-73
Thiazole, 4-(chloromethyl)-2-(4-methylphenyl)-	MeOH	218(4.11),290(4.19)	80-0685-73
$C_{11}H_{10}ClN_3O_2$			
1H-1,2,3-Triazole-4-carboxylic acid, 5-(4-chlorophenyl)-, ethyl ester	EtOH	252(4.02)	78-3271-73
anion	EtOH	268(4.05)	78-3271-73
$C_{11}H_{10}ClN_3O_4$			
5H-Pyrrolo[3,2-c]pyridazine-7-acetic acid, 3-chloro-6-methyl-α-oxo-,	pH 1	234(4.56),353(4.01)	4-0807-73
ethyl ester, 1-oxide (all spectra	pH 7	236(4.54),298(3.87), 364(3.97)	4-0807-73
in ethanol)	pH 11	238(4.53),298(4.01), 323(3.93),376(4.05)	4-0807-73
$C_{11}H_{10}ClN_3S$			
Benzaldehyde, [4-(chloromethyl)-2-thiazolyl]hydrazone	MeOH	237(4.26),330(4.30)	80-0685-73
hydrochloride	MeOH	330(4.28)	80-0685-73
$C_{11}H_{10}Cl_4$			
Spiro[2.4]heptatriene, 4,5,6,7-tetrachloro-1,2-diethyl-	$CHCl_3$	239(3.76),284(3.53)	5-0214-73
$C_{11}H_{10}F_2O_2S$			
6aH-Cyclopropa[e][1]benzothiophen-6a-ol, 6,6-difluoro-4,5,5a,6-tetrahydro-	n.s.g.	236(3.80)	35-6655-73
$C_{11}H_{10}FeO_4$			
Iron, tricarbonyl[(2,3,4,5-)-3,5-dimethyl-2,4-cyclohexadien-1-one]-	EtOH	231(4.16)	39-1882-73C
$C_{11}H_{10}IN_5S$			
Pyridinium, 1-[(7,8-dihydro-8-oxo-1H-purin-6-yl)methyl]-, iodide	pH 8	225(4.47),266(4.29), 363(4.32)	39-2019-73C
$C_{11}H_{10}N_2$			
1H-Indene-5,6-dicarbonitrile, 3a,4,7,7a-tetrahydro-	MeOH	234(4.02)	33-3004-73
1H-Indole-3-carbonitrile, 1,2-dimethyl-	EtOH	282(3.79),289(3.74)	95-1433-73
2-Pyridinamine, N-phenyl-	pH 2	243(3.99),315(3.85)	39-2111-73B
	pH 10	266(4.16),310s(3.74)	39-2111-73B
2H-Pyrrole-3-carbonitrile, 3,4-dihydro-5-phenyl-	EtOH	245(4.09)	35-1945-73

Compound	Solvent	λ_{max}(log ϵ)	Ref.
$C_{11}H_{10}N_2O$			
2H-Azepin-2-one, 1,3-dihydro-5-(4-pyri-dinyl)-	EtOH	244(4.31)	39-1079-73C
Imidazole, 2-benzoyl-1-methyl-	EtOH	259(3.89),296(4.15)	12-0415-73
Imidazo[4,5,1-ij]quinolin-6-one, 4,5-dihydro-2-methyl-	EtOH	219(4.01),294(3.84), 322(3.81)	4-0459-73
Pyrimidine, 4-methoxy-5-phenyl-	EtOH	247(4.00),274(3.84)	22-3397-73
4(1H)-Pyrimidinone, 1-methyl-5-phenyl-	EtOH	260(3.98),288(3.94)	22-3397-73
4(3H)-Pyrimidinone, 3-methyl-5-phenyl-	EtOH	241(3.74),300(3.98)	22-3397-73
Pyrrolo[2,3-b]indole, 1,8-dihydro-1-hy-droxy-2-methyl-	EtOH	240(4.47),308(4.06)	142-0251-73
$C_{11}H_{10}N_2OS$			
Imidazole, 1-[(4-methoxyphenyl)thioxo-methyl]-	C_6H_{12}	287(3.99),337(4.22)	5-0636-73
4-Imidazolidinone, 1-methyl-5-(phenyl-methylene)-2-thioxo-	pH 3-5	284(4.26),360(4.55)	104-2418-73
	EtOH	285(4.13),365(4.62)	104-2418-73
	dioxan	285(4.13),365(4.62)	104-2418-73
4-Imidazolidinone, 3-methyl-5-(phenyl-methylene)-2-thioxo-	pH 3-5	245(4.06),294(3.93), 364(4.48)	104-2418-73
	EtOH	246(4.13),298(3.93), 375(4.50)	104-2418-73
4-Imidazolidinone, 5-[(4-methylphenyl)-methylene]-2-thioxo-	pH 3-5	251(4.01),290(3.86), 370(4.50)	104-2418-73
	pH 12-13	252(3.97),320(3.98), 386(4.38)	104-2418-73
	EtOH	250(4.00),296(3.76), 372(4.50)	104-2418-73
4-Imidazol-4-one, 3,5-dihydro-2-(methyl-thio)-5-(phenylmethylene)-	pH 3-5	241(3.92),266(3.91), 361(4.37)	104-2418-73
	EtOH	241(3.92),266(3.91), 360(4.37)	104-2418-73
	dioxan	240(3.93),267(3.91), 360(4.38)	104-2418-73
1,2,4-Oxadiazole, 3-[2-[4-(methylthio)-phenyl]ethenyl]-, (E)-	EtOH	237(4.05),322(4.39)	39-2241-73C
Thiocyanic acid, 2-amino-1-benzoyl-1-propenyl ester	EtOH	299(4.14)	40-2152-73
$C_{11}H_{10}N_2O_2$			
Furo[3,4-b]quinoxalin-1-ol, 1,3-dihydro-3-methyl-	EtOH	238(4.50),320(3.83)	33-1882-73
1H-Indole, 1-methyl-3-(2-nitroethenyl)-	EtOH-pH 7	400(4.32)	104-1082-73
5(4H)-Isoxazolone, 3-methyl-4-[(phenyl-amino)methylene]-	EtOH	232(3.81),351(4.12)	12-0889-73
2,4(1H,3H)-Pyrimidinedione, 3-(phenyl-methyl)-	EtOH	257(3.86)	44-0598-73
2-Quinoxalinecarboxylic acid, ethyl ester	0.01N H_2SO_4	245(4.65),322(3.95)	103-0369-73
	14.1N H_2SO_4	255(4.62),345(4.05)	103-0369-73
$C_{11}H_{10}N_2O_2S$			
4-Imidazolidinone, 5-[(3-methoxyphenyl)-methylene]-2-thioxo-	pH 3-5	248(3.99),290(3.88), 364(4.45)	104-2418-73
	pH 12-13	247(4.02),320(4.01), 385(4.30)	104-2418-73
	EtOH	246(4.10),295(3.93), 370(4.53)	104-2418-73
4-Imidazolidinone, 5-[(4-methoxyphenyl)-methylene]-2-thioxo-	pH 3-5	254(4.02),293(3.90), 385(4.51)	104-2418-73
	pH 12-13	245(3.97),305(3.98), 382(4.41)	104-2418-73

Compound	Solvent	$\lambda_{max}(\log \epsilon)$	Ref.
4-Imidazolidinone, 5-[(4-methoxyphenyl)-methylene]-2-thioxo-	EtOH	254(4.03),297(3.93), 381(4.54)	104-2418-73
	dioxan	254(4.04),297(3.94), 378(4.54)	104-2418-73
1,2,4-Oxadiazole, 3-[2-[4-(methylsulfin-yl)phenyl]ethenyl]-, (E)-	EtOH	287(4.46)	39-2241-73C
Pyridinium, 1-[(phenylsulfonyl)amino]-, hydroxide, inner salt	EtOH	244(4.06),312(3.30)	44-3311-73
1H-Pyrrole-2,5-dione, 3-(methylthio)-4-phenyl-, 2-oxime	EtOH	246(3.89),306(4.03)	94-1667-73
Quinoline, 4-methyl-2-(methylthio)-6-nitro-	DMF	266(4.41),356(4.47)	103-0481-73
$C_{11}H_{10}N_2O_2S_2$			
Benzeneacetonitrile, α-[bis(methylthio)-methylene]-4-nitro-	EtOH	258(4.00),292(3.95), 362(4.05)	1-0258-73
$C_{11}H_{10}N_2O_3$			
Butanoic acid, 2-diazo-3-oxo-, phenyl-methyl ester	EtOH	258(3.87)	78-3609-73
Ethanone, 1-(2-methyl-1H-indol-3-yl)-2-nitro-	EtOH	246(4.15),269(4.02), 310(4.07)	95-0612-73
1H-Indole-2-carboxaldehyde, 1,3-dimeth-yl-5-nitro-	EtOH	298(4.66),335s(4.08)	78-0603-73
$C_{11}H_{10}N_2O_3S$			
Benzo[b]thiophen-3(2H)-one, 2-(2-imida-zolidinylidene)-, 1,1-dioxide	EtOH	247(4.05),267(4.21)	95-0612-73
1H-Indole-2-carboxylic acid, 3-[(hy-droxyimino)(methylthio)methyl]-	EtOH	298(4.18)	95-1433-73
2H-Indol-2-one, 1,3-dihydro-3-[1-(meth-ylthio)-2-nitroethylidene]-	EtOH	248(4.21),256(4.24), 282(3.93),345(4.16)	95-0612-73
$C_{11}H_{10}N_2O_4$			
Propanedioic acid, methyl phenylmethyl ester	EtOH	252(3.74)	78-3609-73
Sydnone, 3-(1-carboxy-2-phenylethyl)-	EtOH	210(3.99),300(3.74)	103-0441-73
Sydnone, 3-(2-carboxy-2-phenylethyl)-	EtOH	204(3.88),270(3.55)	103-0441-73
$C_{11}H_{10}N_2O_5$			
Acetic acid, (2-cyano-4-nitrophenoxy)-, ethyl ester	EtOH	231s(4.17),292(4.11), 300s(4.07)	48-0779-73
2-Benzofurancarboxylic acid, 3-amino-5-nitro-, ethyl ester	EtOH	233(4.24),284(4.48), 322s(4.10)	48-0779-73
2-Furancarboxylic acid, 5-(3,4-dihydro-2,4-dioxo-1(2H)-pyrimidinyl)-, ethyl ester	EtOH	264(4.02),298(4.04)	44-0990-73
$C_{11}H_{10}N_2S$			
1H-Imidazole, 1-[(4-methylphenyl)-thioxomethyl]-	C_6H_{12}	283(4.04),315(4.13)	5-0636-73
$C_{11}H_{10}N_4O$			
1H-Imidazo[4,5-b]pyridin-7-amine, N-(2-furanylmethyl)-	M HCl	220(4.32),266(4.06)	102-2087-73
	M NaOH	225(4.32),279(4.23)	102-2087-73
	EtOH	220(4.40),267(4.18), 283(4.18)	102-2087-73
1H-Imidazo[4,5-c]pyridin-7-amine, N-(2-furanylmethyl)-	M HCl	216(4.18),272(4.04)	102-2087-73
	M NaOH	226(4.20),274(4.15)	102-2087-73
	EtOH	220(4.11),273(4.18)	102-2087-73

Compound	Solvent	$\lambda_{max}(\log \epsilon)$	Ref.
$C_{11}H_{10}N_4OS$			
1,2,4-Triazino[5,6-d][3,1]benzoxazepine, 6,7-dihydro-3-(methylthio)-	EtOH	200(4.2),238(4.41), 346(4.01),431(3.78)	78-0639-73
$C_{11}H_{10}N_4O_2$			
Imidazolecarbohydrazide, N-(2-hydroxy-benzylidene)-	n.s.g.	271(4.16),344(4.04)	140-0971-73
Pyrazinecarboxamide, 3-amino-6-phenyl-, 4-oxide	EtOH	245s(4.08),280(4.38), 390(3.81)	35-6407-73
$C_{11}H_{10}N_4O_4$			
1H-Pyrrole-3-carboxylic acid, 4-(di-cyanomethyl)-2,5-dihydro-5-(methoxy-imino)-1-methyl-2-oxo-, methyl ester	EtOH	322(3.80),433(4.33)	94-1667-73
1H-1,2,3-Triazole-4-carboxylic acid, 5-(3-nitrophenyl)-, ethyl ester	EtOH	249(4.22)	78-3271-73
anion	EtOH	266(4.28)	78-3271-73
1H-1,2,3-Triazole-4-carboxylic acid, 5-(4-nitrophenyl)-, ethyl ester	EtOH	290(4.09)	78-3271-73
anion	EtOH	326(4.11)	78-3271-73
$C_{11}H_{10}N_4O_6$			
2,3,4-Pentanetrione, 3-(2,4-dinitro-phenylhydrazone)	MeCN	243(4.00),383(4.38)	1-3632-73
$C_{11}H_{10}N_5$			
1H-[1,2,4]Triazolo[1,5-a]pyrimidin-8-ium, 2-amino-1-phenyl-, perchlorate	n.s.g.	258(3.88),315(4.16)	124-1036-73
$C_{11}H_{10}N_5S$			
Pyridinium, 1-[(7,8-dihydro-8-oxo-1H-purin-6-yl)methyl]-, iodide	pH 8	225(4.47),266(4.29), 363(4.32)	39-2019-73C
$C_{11}H_{10}N_6O_2$			
Benzo[g]pteridine-2,4(1H,3H)-dione, 8,9-diamino-7-methyl-	EtOH-2% DMSO	317(4.54),403(4.11), 495(3.61)	65-2285-73
Urea, N-(2-furanylmethyl)-N'-1H-purin-6-yl)-	pH 1-2	277.5(4.34)	87-0139-73
	pH 5-7	269.5(4.30)	87-0139-73
	pH 12	277.5(4.25)	87-0139-73
$C_{11}H_{10}O$			
Acetaldehyde, (2,3-dihydro-1H-inden-1-ylidene)-, (E)-	EtOH	301s(4.25),321(4.27)	39-0615-73C
5H-Benzocyclohepten-5-one, 6,7-dihydro-	EtOH	247(3.96),287(3.16), 328(1.95)	18-2504-73
Bicyclo[4.3.2]undeca-2,4,8,10-tetraen-7-one	isooctane	258(3.40),267(3.39), 335(2.05),347(2.14), 358(2.05)	88-1089-73
Furan, 2-methyl-5-phenyl-	EtOH	287(4.31)	22-1760-73
$C_{11}H_{10}OS$			
Benzenecarbothioic acid, O-3-butynyl ester	CH_2Cl_2	248(3.86),290(4.10), 420(2.26)	39-1574-73C
4H-Cyclohepta[b]thiophen-4-one, 2,6-di-methyl-	EtOH	245(4.87),332(4.38), 344s(--),360(4.31)	39-0968-73C
$C_{11}H_{10}O_2$			
Acetic acid, (2,3-dihydro-1H-inden-1-ylidene)-, (Z)-	EtOH	274(4.09),283(4.08), 306(4.05)	39-0615-73C

Compound	Solvent	λ_{max}(log ε)	Ref.
Cyclohepta[b]furan-8-one, 2,7-dimethyl-	EtOH	223(4.18),264(4.49), 270(4.49),300s(3.80), 324(3.69),337(3.68), 352(3.54)	39-1960-73C
2,4,6-Cycloheptatrien-1-one, 2-methyl-7-(2-propynyloxy)-	EtOH	237(4.45),320(3.92), 342s(3.87)	39-1960-73C
2,4,6-Cycloheptatrien-1-one, 3-methyl-2-(2-propynyloxy)-	EtOH	241(4.32),322(3.84)	39-1960-73C
Ethanone, 1-(2H-1-benzopyran-8-yl)-	EtOH	245(4.02),334(3.50)	44-3832-73
Ethanone, 1-(2-methyl-3-benzofuranyl)-	EtOH	228(4.18),256(3.94), 271(4.04)	103-0026-73
1H-Indene-3-acetic acid	EtOH	252(3.97)	39-0615-73C
	EtOH	254(2.97),280(2.3)	44-1439-73
1H-Indene-2-carboxylic acid, 7-methyl-	MeOH	227(4.03),235(3.98), 285(4.23)	44-0741-73
Indeno[1,7a-b]furan-2(1H)-one, 3a,5a-dihydro-, (3aα,5aβ,9aR*)-	C_6H_{12}	248s(3.46),256(3.58), 269(3.58),276s(3.29)	44-1893-73
12-Oxabicyclo[7.2.1]dodeca-5,6,9,11-tetraen-3-one	EtOH	227(3.48),251(3.18), 310(2.36),318(2.42), 330(2.26)	44-0864-73
Tricyclo[3.3.1.0^{2,8}]non-6-ene-3,4-dione, 2-methyl-9-methylene-	EtOH	268(2.89),275s(2.88), 429(1.85)	39-19-0-73C
Tricyclo[3.3.1.0^{2,8}]non-6-ene-3,4-dione, 5-methyl-9-methylene-	EtOH	260s(2.94),427(1.95)	39-1960-73C
$C_{11}H_{10}O_2S$			
Benzo[b]thiophene-2-propanoic acid	EtOH	228(4.49),260(3.95), 288(3.30),298(3.33)	2-0446-73
2H-1-Benzothiopyran-2-one, 7-methoxy-4-methyl-	EtOH	356(3.85)	40-0118-73
	$HClO_4$	381(4.11)	40-0118-73
2H-Thiopyran, 3-phenyl-, 1,1-dioxide	H_2O	226(3.87),311(3.97)	39-0050-73B
	aq base	256(4.29),367(3.81)	39-0050-73B
	MeOH	226(3.95),310(3.98)	39-0050-73B
anion	MeOH-NaOMe	255(4.12),371(3.79)	39-0050-73B
$C_{11}H_{10}O_3$			
3-Benzofurancarboxylic acid, 2-methyl-, methyl ester	90% EtOH	244(3.86),263(3.88), 275(3.78),282(3.70)	12-1079-73
4-Benzofurancarboxylic acid, 7-methyl-, methyl ester	90% EtOH	220(4.41),274(4.06), 297(3.75)	12-1059-73
2(3H)-Benzofuranone, 3-(1-methoxyethylidene)-	90% EtOH	221(4.03),247(4.05), 251(4.08),255s(4.04), 288s(3.92),297(4.01), 319(4.08)	12-1079-73
4H-1-Benzopyran-4-one, 7-hydroxy-2,5-dimethyl-	MeOH	220(4.57),242(4.54), 250(4.57),290(4.35)	94-0149-73
2H-1-Benzopyran-2-one, 7-methoxy-4-methyl-	EtOH	322(4.18)	40-0118-73
2-Butenoic acid, 4-oxo-4-phenyl-, methyl ester	EtOH	235(4.08),268(3.95)	22-0625-73
2,8-Decadiene-4,6-diynoic acid, 10-hydroxy-, monomethyl ester, (E,E)-	EtOH	235s(4.35),248(4.45), 260(4.36),293s(4.20), 313(4.32),333(4.24)	39-2642-73C
Ethanone, 1-(2-methoxy-3-benzofuranyl)-	90% EtOH	232(4.15),250(4.13), 278(4.11),284(4.11)	12-1079-73
2H-Pyran-2-one, 5,6-dihydro-4-hydroxy-6-phenyl-	EtOH	216(3.70),243(3.27)	28-1131-73A
	pH 11	217(3.72),271(3.62)	28-1131-73A
$C_{11}H_{10}O_3S$			
2H-1-Benzopyran-2-one, 7-methoxy-4-(methylthio)-	EtOH	252(3.64),296(4.15), 324(4.15)	95-0836-73

Compound	Solvent	λ_{max}(log ε)	Ref.
1,2-Oxathiin, 4-methyl-6-phenyl-, 2,2-dioxide	EtOH	219(4.02),307(4.18)	44-2257-73
$C_{11}H_{10}O_4$			
4H-1-Benzopyran-4-one, 5-hydroxy-7-methoxy-2-methyl- (eugenin)	EtOH	230(4.23),249(4.30), 256(4.30),290(3.88)	102-1881-73
1H-Cyclohepta[c]furan-3a(3H)-carboxylic acid, 3-oxo-, methyl ester	EtOH	273(3.60)	78-3609-73
1,2-Indandione, 4,5-dimethoxy-	EtOH	233(4.18),289(4.11), 340s(3.39)	141-0001-73
	dioxan	249(4.02),324(4.07)	141-0001-73
Pentacyclo[4.3.0.$0^{2,4}$.$0^{3,8}$.$0^{5,7}$]nonane-4,5-dicarboxylic acid	EtOH	210(3.04)	24-1804-73
Tetracyclo[4.3.0.$0^{2,4}$.$0^{3,7}$]non-8-ene-8,9-dicarboxylic acid	EtOH	251(3.77)	24-1804-73
$C_{11}H_{10}O_5$			
2H-1-Benzopyran-2-one, 6-hydroxy-5,7-dimethoxy- (fraxinol)	n.s.g.	234(3.99),315(3.88), 345(3.82)	105-0465-73
	n.s.g.	233(4.27),315(4.24), 340(3.96)	105-0586-73
2H-1-Benzopyran-2-one, 7-hydroxy-5,6-dimethoxy- (arscotin)	n.s.g.	258(3.63),312(3.95)	105-0402-73
	NaOAc	287(3.76),331(3.17)	105-0402-73
Homophthalic anhydride, 4,5-dimethoxy-	EtOH	220(4.38),259(3.97), 291(3.60)	141-0001-73
	dioxan	227(4.16),262(4.00), 294(3.66)	141-0001-73
Homophthalic anhydride, 5,6-dimethoxy-	EtOH	221(4.27),258(3.87), 282s(3.69),353(3.27)	141-0001-73
	dioxan	227(4.15),261(3.92), 288(3.62),347(2.95)	141-0001-73
2-Oxaspiro[4.5]deca-6,9-diene-4-carboxylic acid, 3,8-dioxo-, methyl ester	EtOH	235(4.16)	78-3609-73
$C_{11}H_{10}O_6$			
Phthalic anhydride, 3,4,5-trimethoxy-	EtOH	216(4.21),245(4.29), 310(3.58)	141-0001-73
Pyrano[3,4-b]pyran-2-carboxylic acid, 4,5,6,8-tetrahydro-4,8-dioxo-, ethyl ester	EtOH	275(3.89)	95-1183-73
$C_{11}H_{10}O_8$			
1,3-Cyclopentadiene-1,2,3-tricarboxylic acid, 4-hydroxy-5-oxo-, trimethyl ester, sodium salt	H_2O	220(4.2),300(4.4), 335s(2.7),570(3.4)	65-2718-73
	EtOH	220(4.2),300(4.4), 355(2.6),570(3.4)	65-2718-73
$C_{11}H_{10}S$			
Thiophene, 2-methyl-5-phenyl-	C_6H_{12}	290.5(4.23)	78-0413-73
$C_{11}H_{11}BrCl_2$			
Benzene, 1-bromo-4-(2,2-dichloro-1-ethylcyclopropyl)-	hexane	227(4.05),255(2.61), 261(2.56),267(2.49), 274(2.33)	104-2473-73
$C_{11}H_{11}BrN_2O_3$			
4H-Pyrido[1,2-a]pyrimidinium, 1-(carboxymethyl)-2-methyl-4-oxo-, bromide	MeOH	201(4.85),212s(4.61), 230s(4.34),245(4.30), 252(5.25),335(4.32)	4-0821-73

Compound	Solvent	λmax(log ε)	Ref.
$C_{11}H_{11}BrOS$			
8H-Cyclohepta[b]thiophene, 5-bromo-4-ethoxy-	EtOH	232(4.32),280(3.88), 365(2.83)	44-0146-73
$C_{11}H_{11}ClN_2O$			
4H-Pyrido[1,2-a]pyrimidin-4-one, 3-(2-chloroethyl)-2-methyl-	MeOH	246(4.0),342(4.0)	5-0103-73
$C_{11}H_{11}ClN_2O_2$			
1,4-Phthalazinedione, 2-(2-chloroethyl)-1,2,3,4-tetrahydro-3-methyl-	MeOH	297(3.76)	1-1891-73
1(2H)-Phthalazinone, 4-(2-chloroethoxy)-2-methyl-	MeOH	252(3.58),262(3.61), 297(3.78)	1-1891-73
4H-Pyrido[1,2-a]pyrimidin-4-one, 7-chloro-3-(2-hydroxyethyl)-2-methyl-	MeOH	257(4.01),344(3.98)	5-0103-73
$C_{11}H_{11}ClN_2O_4$			
Pyrano[3,4-e][1,3]oxazine-4,5-dione, 2-(butylamino)-7-chloro-	MeCN	294(4.14),337(4.23)	39-2432-73C
$C_{11}H_{11}ClN_2O_4S_2$			
1(2H)-Pyrimidinesulfonyl chloride, tetrahydro-5-methyl-2,4-dioxo-6-(phenylthio)-	EtOH	253.5(3.60)	94-1090-73
$C_{11}H_{11}ClN_4O_2S$			
2(1H)-Pyridinethione, 6-chloro-3-[(2,6-dimethoxy-4-pyrimidinyl)amino]-	MeOH	209(4.37),244(4.39), 295(3.72),348(3.67)	44-4386-73
$C_{11}H_{11}ClN_4O_4$			
9H-Purine, 6-chloro-9-(6-deoxy-β-L-lyxo-hexopyranos-2-ulos-1-yl)-	n.s.g.	265(3.79)	136-0192-73E
$C_{11}H_{11}ClO$			
Benzeneacetaldehyde, 4-chloro-α-propylidene-	n.s.g.	221(4.21),258(3.94)	22-1676-73
2-Buten-1-one, 3-chloro-2-methyl-1-phenyl-	EtOH	249(3.89)	78-4241-73
2-Penten-1-one, 3-chloro-1-phenyl-	EtOH	265(4.23)	78-4241-73
4-Penten-2-one, 5-(4-chlorophenyl)-, (E)-	n.s.g.	254(4.23),287(3.46), 298(3.33)	22-1676-73
$C_{11}H_{11}ClOS$			
8H-Cyclohepta[b]thiophene, 5-chloro-4-ethoxy-	EtOH	228(4.32),282(3.90), 362(2.84)	44-0146-73
$C_{11}H_{11}Cl_3$			
Benzene, 1-chloro-4-(2,2-dichloro-1-ethylcyclopropyl)-	hexane	224(4.10),255(2.41), 262(2.47),267(2.44), 276(2.23)	104-2473-73
$C_{11}H_{11}IN_2$			
Iodonium, (3,5-dimethyl-1H-pyrazol-4-yl)phenyl-, hydroxide, inner salt	50% EtOH-acid	235s(4.0)	103-0226-73
	+ KOH	285s(3.7)	103-0226-73
$C_{11}H_{11}IO$			
2-Propen-1-one, 1-(4-ethylphenyl)-3-iodo-	dioxan	287(4.32)	24-0435-73

Compound	Solvent	$\lambda_{max}(\log \epsilon)$	Ref.
$C_{11}H_{11}NO$			
1-Benzazocin-5-ol, 3,4-dihydro-	EtOH	227s(3.83),254(4.04), 302s(3.49),313(3.53)	18-2504-73
1,4-Ethenocyclohepta[c]pyrrol-3(2H)-one, 1,3a,4,8a-tetrahydro-	EtOH	243(3.70)	44-1886-73
1H-Indeno[1,7a-b]pyrrol-2(3H)-one, 3a,5a-dihydro-	EtOH	250s(3.46),259(3.59), 267(3.60),276s(3.35)	44-1893-73
1H-Indole-2-carboxaldehyde, 3,5-dimethyl-	EtOH	239(4.22),318(4.44)	78-0603-73
2H-Indol-2-one, 1,3-dihydro-3-(1-methylethylidene)-	EtOH	202(4.11),219(3.51), 250(4.33),254(4.33), 259(4.42),292(3.43)	103-1152-73
1,4-Methanocyclohepta[c]pyrrol-3(2H)-one, 1,3a,4,8a-tetrahydro-9-methylene-	EtOH	254(3.70)	44-1893-73
2-Propanone, 1-(1H-indol-3-yl)-	MeOH	225(4.26),274(3.83), 281(3.85),289(3.77)	102-0447-73
after two minutes (changing)	H_2SO_4	235(3.71),241(3.67), 288(3.72),348s(3.11)	102-0447-73
$C_{11}H_{11}NOS$			
Ethanol, 1-(3-methyl-2H-1,4-benzothiazin-2-ylidene)-	EtOH	440(3.10)	124-0922-73
	$CHCl_3$	422(3.09)	124-0922-73
2(1H)-Quinolinethione, 6-methoxy-4-methyl-	EtOH	225(4.57),295(4.33), 395(4.06)	103-0481-73
$C_{11}H_{11}NO_2$			
1H-Indole-1-propanoic acid	MeOH	227(4.25),273(3.83), 281(3.83),285s(3.81), 292(3.72)	102-0447-73
after ten minutes	H_2SO_4 at 70°	236(3.49),241(3.48), 284(3.68)	102-0447-73
1H-Indole-3-propanoic acid	MeOH	227(4.31),275s(3.80), 282(3.83),291(3.76)	102-0447-73
after ten minutes	H_2SO_4 at 70°	235(3.72),240(3.69), 288(3.72)	102-0447-73
2-Propenenitrile, 3-(2,4-dimethoxyphenyl)-	EtOH	215(4.06),239(4.12), 292(4.23),325(4.29)	40-2347-73
2(1H)-Quinolinone, 7-methoxy-4-methyl-	DMF	328(4.06)	40-0118-73
$C_{11}H_{11}NO_2S_2$			
Ethanethioic acid, S-[2-(2-oxo-3(2H)-benzothiazolyl)ethyl] ester	MeOH	215(4.60),283(3.43), 290(3.44)	4-1015-73
$C_{11}H_{11}NO_3$			
Acetic acid, (2-cyanophenoxy)-, ethyl ester	EtOH	231(4.08),237s(4.02), 291(3.68),296s(3.67)	48-0779-73
Benzamide, N-(1,3-dioxobutyl)-	EtOH	237(4.2),278(3.6)	104-2034-73
	EtOH-NaOH	240(4.3),313(4.0)	104-2034-73
2-Benzofurancarboxylic acid, 3-amino-, ethyl ester	EtOH	246(4.09),251s(4.07), 293s(4.06),300(4.12), 321(4.07)	48-0779-73
Cinnamamide, β-carbomethoxy-, cis	MeOH	278s(3.72)	44-1841-73
1H-Indole-3-propanoic acid, -hydroxy-	MeOH	227(4.27),275(3.79), 282(3.81),290(3.74)	102-0447-73
after ten minutes at 70°	H_2SO_4	234(3.67),240s(3.63), 287(3.60)(changing)	102-0447-73
$C_{11}H_{11}NO_3S$			
2-Buten-1-one, 3-(methylthio)-4-nitro-1-phenyl-	EtOH	260(3.86),325(4.23)	95-0612-73

Compound	Solvent	$\lambda_{max}(\log \epsilon)$	Ref.
$C_{11}H_{11}NO_4$			
2H-1,4-Benzoxazine-6,7-dione, 5-acetyl-3,4-dihydro-2-methyl-	EtOH	292(4.33),450(3.29)	78-2881-73
2H-1,4-Benzoxazine-6,7-dione, 5-acetyl-3,4-dihydro-3-methyl-	EtOH	293(4.32),450(3.25)	78-2881-73
	CH_2Cl_2	293(4.32),450(3.25)	78-2881-73
1,2-Indandione, 4,5-dimethoxy-, 2-oxime	EtOH	248(4.20),319(4.20)	141-0001-73
	dioxan	246(4.24),312(4.20)	141-0001-73
2(1H)-Quinolinone, 4-hydroxy-6,8-dimethoxy-	MeOH	248(4.54),276(3.94), 287(3.92),339(3.54), 350s(3.44)	78-1215-73
	base	245(4.53),290(4.02), 325s(3.55),340s(3.40)	78-1215-73
2(1H)-Quinolinone, 4-hydroxy-7,8-dimethoxy-	MeOH	242(4.31),250s(4.11), 280s(3.87),288(3.94), 309(3.94),320(3.79)	78-1721-73
	MeOH-acid	243(4.61),314(3.98)	78-1721-73
	MeOH-base	239s(4.45),297(4.08), 311s(4.02)	78-1721-73
$C_{11}H_{11}NO_4S$			
2-Cyclopentene-1-sulfonic acid, 4-oxo-3-(phenylamino)-, sodium salt	EtOH	250(4.25),321(3.79)	12-0893-73
$C_{11}H_{11}NO_5$			
2H-1,4-Benzoxazine-5-carboxylic acid, 3,4,6,7-tetrahydro-2-methyl-6,7-dioxo-, methyl ester	EtOH	271(4.07),277s(4.06), 308(4.18),457(3.27)	78-2881-73
	CH_2Cl_2	272(4.07),305(4.14), 447(3.30)	78-2881-73
1H-Pyrano[3,4-b]pyridine-2-carboxylic acid, 1-ethyl-4,5,6,8-tetrahydro-4,8-dioxo-	EtOH	230(4.14),304(3.88)	95-1183-73
$C_{11}H_{11}NS$			
Quinoline, 4-methyl-2-(methylthio)-	EtOH	215(4.62),255(4.45), 340(3.76)	103-0481-73
2(1H)-Quinolinethione, 1,4-dimethyl-	EtOH	220(4.43),285(4.05), 405(4.29)	103-0481-73
$C_{11}H_{11}NS_2$			
Benzeneacetonitrile, α-[bis(methylthio)-methyl]-	EtOH	234(3.91),322(4.04)	1-0258-73
$C_{11}H_{11}N_2O_3$			
4H-Pyrido[1,2-a]pyrimidinium, 1-(carboxymethyl)-2-methyl-4-oxo-, bromide	MeOH	201(4.85),212s(4.61), 230s(4.34),245(4.30), 252(5.25),335(4.32)	4-0821-73
$C_{11}H_{11}N_2O_7$			
1,3-Cyclohexadiene-1-carboxylic acid, 2,4-dinitro-5-(2-oxopropyl)-, methyl ester, ion(1-), K salt	acetone	376(4.01),560(4.42)	104-2106-73
1,3-Cyclohexadiene-1-carboxylic acid, 4,6-dinitro-5-(2-oxopropyl)-, methyl ester, ion(1-), K salt	acetone	357(4.62),686(4.24)	104-2106-73
$C_{11}H_{11}N_3$			
Imidazo[2,1-b]quinazoline, 5,10-dihydro-10-methyl-	EtOH	230(3.81),239(3.72), 278(4.06)	87-0407-73
4-Pyridinemethanamine, α-4-pyridinyl-	EtOH	265(3.46),278(3.35)	94-1927-73
4(1H)-Pyrimidinimine, 1-methyl-5-phenyl-	EtOH	270(3.97)	22-3397-73

Compound	Solvent	λ_{max}(log ε)	Ref.
$C_{11}H_{11}N_3O$			
Pyrazinamine, 3-methyl-5-phenyl-, 1-oxide	EtOH	261(4.40),287(4.17), 351(3.80)	78-3761-73
Pyrazinamine, 3-methyl-6-phenyl-, 1-oxide	EtOH	242(4.28),293s(3.63), 343(3.97)	78-3761-73
Pyrimido[1,2-a]benzimidazol-2(1H)-one, 3,4-dihydro-3-methyl-	pH 1	234(4.14),279(4.16), 287(4.19)	4-0071-73
	pH 13	263(4.00),272(3.97), 302(4.35)	4-0071-73
	EtOH	251(4.05),258s(--), 284(4.13),291(4.13)	4-0071-73
Pyrimido[1,2-a]benzimidazol-2(1H)-one, 3,4-dihydro-4-methyl-	pH 1	234(4.14),279(4.16), 287(4.19)	4-0071-73
	pH 13	262(4.10),272(4.07), 303(4.37)	4-0071-73
	EtOH	252(4.06),260s(--), 285(4.13),292(4.14)	4-0071-73
1,2,4-Triazine, 3,5-dimethyl-6-phenyl-, 4-oxide	EtOH	278(3.9)	103-0123-73
$C_{11}H_{11}N_3OS$			
2H-Pyrazolo[4,3-g]benzothiazole, 2-acetyl-4,5-dihydro-7-methyl-	EtOH	307(4.35),318(4.28)	32-0755-73
1,3,4-Thiadiazolium, 3-methyl-5-[(methylcarbonyl)amino]-2-phenyl-	MeOH	254(4.02),318(4.25)	103-1216-73
$C_{11}H_{11}N_3O_2$			
Acetamide, N-(3-amino-1-oxo-2(1H)-isoquinolinyl)-	EtOH	230(4.32),300(4.14), 373(3.54)	95-1581-73
1H-Indole-2,3-dicarboxamide, 1-methyl-	EtOH	245(4.17),304(4.09)	95-1433-73
1(2H)-Isoquinolinone, 4-acetyl-2,3-diamino-	EtOH	243(4.44),286(4.06), 363(3.98)	95-1581-73
1,8-Naphthyridine-3-carboxylic acid, 2-amino-, ethyl ester	EtOH	214(4.42),241(4.47), 270s(3.94),379(3.77)	94-2643-73
3-Penten-2-one, 4-(2H-benzotriazol-2-yl)-, N-oxide, (E)-	EtOH	275s(3.98),319(4.17), 360s(3.65)	88-0891-73
(Z)-	EtOH	305(3.86),342s(3.62)	88-0891-73
2-Propenenitrile, 3-[4-(dimethylamino)-phenyl]-2-nitro-	n.s.g.	280(3.92),485(4.67)	135-1299-73
Pyridinium, 1-[(2-cyano-3-ethoxy-3-oxo-2-propenyl)amino]-, hydroxide, inner salt	EtOH	218(4.06),277(4.16), 394(4.18)	39-2580-73C
2H-1,2,3-Triazole-4-carboxylic acid, 5-phenyl-, ethyl ester	EtOH	240(3.99)	78-3271-73
anion	EtOH	262(4.00)	78-3271-73
$C_{11}H_{11}N_3O_2S$			
Acetamide, N-[3-(acetylamino)-2(3H)-benzothiazolylidene]-	dioxan	234(4.30),276(3.73), 305s(4.30),310(4.34)	4-0947-73
$C_{11}H_{11}N_3O_3$			
Carbamic acid, 2-quinoxalinyl-, ethyl ester, 1-oxide	MeOH	256(4.78)	39-2707-73C
Carbamic acid, 2-quinoxalinyl-, ethyl ester, 4-oxide	MeOH	256(--)	39-2707-73C
$C_{11}H_{11}N_3O_4$			
2,3,4-Pentanetrione, 3-[(2-nitrophenyl)-hydrazone]	MeCN	390(4.48)	1-3632-73
2,3,4-Pentanetrione, 3-[(3-nitrophenyl)-hydrazone]	MeCN	237(3.97),375(4.49)	1-3632-73

Compound	Solvent	$\lambda_{max}(\log \epsilon)$	Ref.
$C_{11}H_{11}N_3O_5$			
Pyrido[2,3-d]pyrimidine-5-carboxylic acid, 1,2,3,4,7,8-hexahydro-1,3-dimethyl-2,4,7-trioxo-, methyl ester	EtOH	234(3.99),264(3.63), 314(3.96)	94-2014-73
Pyrido[2,3-d]pyrimidine-7-carboxylic acid, 1,2,3,4,5,8-hexahydro-1,3-dimethyl-2,4,5-trioxo-, methyl ester	EtOH	268(4.40)	94-2014-73
$C_{11}H_{11}N_3O_6$			
Acetamide, N-(3,4-dihydro-7,8-dinitro-2H-1-benzopyran-6-yl)-	EtOH	234(4.26),353(3.42)	4-0623-73
Fumaric acid, (3-diazo-5-methyl-2,4-dioxo-1-pyrrolidinyl)-, dimethyl ester	EtOH	240(4.8),297(3.7)	39-2024-73C
Maleic acid, (3-diazo-5-methyl-2,4-dioxo-1-pyrrolidinyl)-, dimethyl ester	EtOH	251(4.0),282(4.2)	39-2024-73C
$C_{11}H_{11}N_3S$			
1,2,4-Triazine, 5-methyl-3-(methylthio)-6-phenyl-	n.s.g.	216(4.00),226(4.33), 345(3.42)	22-2493-73
1,2,4-Triazine, 6-methyl-3-(methylthio)-5-phenyl-	n.s.g.	212(4.12),280(4.29), 340(3.63)	22-2493-73
$C_{11}H_{11}N_3S_2$			
3(2H)-Thiazolecarbothioamide, 2-[(phenylmethyl)imino]-	EtOH	217(4.03),293(4.29)	44-3868-73
$C_{11}H_{11}N_5OS$			
1H-Pyrido[2,3-b]pyrimido[4,5-e][1,4]thiazin-2-amine, 7-methoxy-4-methyl-	MeOH	232(4.07),308(3.91)	44-4386-73
$C_{11}H_{11}N_5O_2$			
1H-Imidazole-4-carboxamide, 5-[[(2-hydroxyphenyl)methylene]hydrazino]-	H_2O	202(3.84),280(3.23), 348(3.80)	103-0083-73
$C_{11}H_{11}N_5O_3$			
2-Furancarboxylic acid, 5-(6-amino-9H-purin-9-yl)-4,5-dihydro-, methyl ester, (R)-	EtOH	257(4.17)	44-0990-73
$C_{11}H_{11}N_5O_6$			
Diazene, (1-cyclopropyl-1-nitroethyl)-(2,4-dinitrophenyl)-	$CHCl_3$	403(2.62)	78-3929-73
$C_{11}H_{11}N_5S$			
Benzothiazolo[3,2-e]purin-4-amine, 7,8,9,10-tetrahydro-	pH 1	254(4.24),294(3.86)	94-0034-73
	pH 13	245s(--),285(--)	94-0034-73
$C_{11}H_{11}N_7$			
8-Azapurine-2,6-diamine, 9-(4-methylphenyl)-	EtOH	225(4.54),298(4.21)	42-0260-73
$C_{11}H_{11}N_7O$			
8-Azapurine-2,6-diamine, 9-(4-methoxyphenyl)-	EtOH	230(4.47),293(4.13)	42-0260-73
$C_{11}H_{12}$			
Benzene, (1-cyclopropylethenyl)-	EtOH	248(3.99),255(3.92), 268(3.61)	78-1169-73
5H-Benzocycloheptene, 6,7-dihydro-	C_6H_{12}	253(4.08)	118-0149-73

Compound	Solvent	$\lambda_{max}(\log \epsilon)$	Ref.
$C_{11}H_{12}BrClO_3$			
Propanoic acid, 3-chloro-, 4-bromo-2-methoxy-5-methylphenyl ester	90% EtOH	222(3.54),278s(3.51), 283(3.52),288(3.51)	12-1069-73
$C_{11}H_{12}BrNO$			
3-Penten-2-one, 3-bromo-4-(phenylamino)-	hexane	233(3.70),338(4.22)	40-2152-73
$C_{11}H_{12}BrNOS$			
Pyrido[2,1-b]benzothiazolium, 5a,6,7,8-9,9a-hexahydro-9-oxo-, bromide, cis	pH 1	213(3.85),240(3.92), 330(3.74)	39-2049-73C
$C_{11}H_{12}Br_2N_2$			
1H-Indole-3-ethanamine, 5,6-dibromo-N-methyl-	MeOH	232(4.47),297(3.57), 307(3.52)	88-0299-73
$C_{11}H_{12}Br_2OS$			
4H-Cyclohepta[b]thiophen-4-one, 5,5-dibromo-5,6,7,8-tetrahydro-2,6-dimethyl-	EtOH	229s(--),265(2.84), 305s(--)	39-0968-73C
$C_{11}H_{12}Br_4$			
Spiro[2.4]hepta-4,6-diene, 4,5,6,7-tetrabromo-1-(1,1-dimethylethyl)-	hexane	253(3.90),286(3.55)	44-1340-73
$C_{11}H_{12}Cl$			
Ethylium, 1-(4-chlorophenyl)-1-cyclopropyl-	FSO_3H at -75°	360(4.51),420s(<3.3)	59-0803-73
$C_{11}H_{12}ClNO$			
2-Buten-1-one, 2-chloro-3-(methylamino)-1-phenyl-	hexane	242(3.85),347(4.17)	40-2152-73
3-Penten-2-one, 3-chloro-4-(phenylamino)-	hexane	227(3.90),338(4.23)	40-2152-73
$C_{11}H_{12}ClNOS$			
4-Thiazolol, 4-(chloromethyl)-4,5-dihydro-2-(4-methylphenyl)-	MeOH	255(3.97)	80-0685-73
hydrochloride	MeOH	253(4.30)	80-0685-73
$C_{11}H_{12}ClN_3O_2$			
2-Butenal, 3-methyl-1-nitro-, (4-chlorophenyl)hydrazone	EtOH	292(3.62)	19-0881-73
Diazene, (4-chlorophenyl)(1,2-dimethyl-1-nitro-2-propenyl)-	EtOH	281(3.70)	19-0881-73
Diazene, (4-chlorophenyl)(1-ethyl-1-nitro-2-propenyl)-	EtOH	286(3.71)	19-0881-73
Diazene, (4-chlorophenyl)(1-methyl-1-nitro-2-butenyl)-	EtOH	282(3.71)	19-0881-73
$C_{11}H_{12}ClN_3O_3$			
1H-Pyrimido[4,5-b][1,4]oxazine-6-carboxylic acid, 4-chloro-2,7-dimethyl-, ethyl ester	EtOH	236(4.2),253(3.9), 328(3.5),390(3.5)	103-1532-73
$C_{11}H_{12}ClN_3O_4$			
1H-Pyrazolo[3,4-b]pyridine, 4-chloro-1-β-D-ribofuranosyl-	EtOH	216(4.47),272(3.72), 297(3.84)	104-1294-73
$C_{11}H_{12}Cl_2N_2O_2$			
Propanoic acid, 2-[(2,6-dichlorophenyl)-hydrazono]-, ethyl ester, (E)-	EtOH	289(4.23)	94-1481-73

Compound	Solvent	$\lambda_{max}(\log \epsilon)$	Ref.
Propanoic acid, 2-[(2,6-dichlorophenyl)-hydrazono]-, ethyl ester, (Z)-	EtOH	322(4.14)	94-1481-73
Propanoic acid, 2-[(3,4-dichlorophenyl)-hydrazono]-, ethyl ester, (E)-	EtOH	328(4.36)	94-1481-73
(Z)-	EtOH	343.5(4.30)	94-1481-73
$C_{11}H_{12}F_2N_2O_2$			
Morpholine, 4-[(7,7-difluoro-2-aza-bicyclo[3.2.0]hepta-1(5),3-dien-3-yl)carbonyl]-	MeOH	230(3.9),268(4.08)	24-3544-73
$C_{11}H_{12}F_2N_4O_2$			
Morpholine, 4-[3-(2-azido-3,3-difluoro-1-cyclobuten-1-yl)-1-oxo-2-propenyl]-, (E)-	MeOH	222(3.92),305(4.45)	24-3544-73
$C_{11}H_{12}F_3NO_2$			
Morpholine, 4-[1-oxo-3-(2,3,3-trifluoro-1-cyclobutenyl)-2-propenyl]-, (E)-	MeOH	259(4.28)	24-3544-73
$C_{11}H_{12}NO$			
2H-Pyrroline, 3,4-dihydro-1-methyl-2-oxo-5-phenyl-, hexachloroantimonate	MeCN	222(3.92),273(4.05)	24-1423-73
	H_2SO_4	201(3.76),244(3.24), 320(3.51)	24-1423-73
$C_{11}H_{12}NOS$			
Pyrido[2,1-b]benzothiazolium, 5a,6,7,8-9,9a-hexahydro-9-oxo-, bromide, cis	pH 1	213(3.85),240(3.92), 330(3.74)	39-2049-73C
$C_{11}H_{12}N_2$			
2-Butenenitrile, 3-[(phenylmethyl)-amino]-	MeCN	205(3.87),258(4.30)	44-2287-73
1H-Indene-5,6-dicarbonitrile, 2,3,3a,4,7,7a-hexahydro-	MeOH	234(4.00),245s(3.82)	33-3004-73
2-Propenenitrile, 3-[4-(dimethylamino)-phenyl]-	EtOH	246(4.01),363(4.55)	40-2347-73
Pyrimido[1,2-a]indole, 1,2,3,4-tetra-hydro-, hydrochloride	MeOH	213(4.31),262(4.12)	103-0598-73
Quinazoline, 4-ethyl-2-methyl-	EtOH	261(3.51),268(3.51), 309(3.51)	39-0453-73C
2(1H)-Quinolinimine, N,1-dimethyl-, perchlorate	EtOH	236(4.25),255(3.98), 290(3.70),340(3.84)	104-2622-73
$C_{11}H_{12}N_2O$			
Ethanone, 1-(2,7-dimethylpyrazolo[1,5-a]pyridin-3-yl)-	MeOH	225(4.40),253s(3.58), 259(3.67),308(3.96)	4-0821-73
2H-Indol-2-one, 1,3-dihydro-3-[1-(meth-ylamino)ethylidene]-	MeOH	210(4.42),221s(4.34), 273(4.36),339(4.35)	24-2070-73
2-Indolizinecarboxamide, N-ethyl-	EtOH	288(3.15),300(3.16), 341(3.13)	36-1897-73
2(1H)-Quinoxalinone, 1,3,6(or 7)-tri-methyl-	EtOH	232(4.29),290(3.56), 340(3.69)	22-1285-73
$C_{11}H_{12}N_2OS$			
Acetamide, N-(5-ethylthieno[2,3-b]pyri-din-3-yl)-	EtOH	233f(4.11),246(4.25), 305(3.30)	4-0871-73
$C_{11}H_{12}N_2O_2$			
2-Benzofurancarboximidic acid, 3-amino-, ethyl ester	EtOH	248(4.01),293s(4.03), 301(4.08),311(4.06)	48-0779-73

Compound	Solvent	λ_{max}(log ϵ)	Ref.
Cyclopentanecarboxylic acid, 2-(dicyano-methylene)-, ethyl ester	EtOH	228(4.14),356(4.29)	78-4103-73
	EtOH-NaOH	224(4.39),356(4.55)	78-4103-73
3H-Indazole-3-carboxylic acid, 3-methyl-, ethyl ester	EtOH	220(4.00),266(3.81), 345(2.48)	78-1833-73
Indole, 2-ethyl-3-methyl-4-nitro-	n.s.g.	218(4.11),252(3.88), 390(3.26)	103-0031-73
Indole, 2-ethyl-3-methyl-6-nitro-	n.s.g.	217(4.20),251(3.72), 402(3.30)	103-0031-73
3H-Indole, 2,3,3-trimethyl-6-nitro-	n.s.g.	215(4.23),243(4.30)	103-0031-73
Pyrazolo[1,5-a]pyridine-3-carboxylic acid, 5-methyl-, ethyl ester	EtOH	220(4.59),224(4.67), 242(4.03),248(4.01), 292(4.08),308s(3.98)	39-2580-73C
Pyridinium, 1-[(2-acetyl-3-oxo-1-buten-yl)amino]-, hydroxide, inner salt	EtOH	257s(3.98),279(4.24), 391(4.14)	39-2580-73C
4H-Pyrido[1,2-a]pyrimidin-4-one, 3-(2-hydroxyethyl)-2-methyl-	MeOH	246(4.01),338(4.00)	5-0103-73
1H-Pyrrole-3,4-diol, 2,5-dihydro-2-imino-1-methyl-5-phenyl-	n.s.g.	219(4.16),307(3.91)	12-2221-73
Pyrrolo[2,3-b]indol-3a(3H)-ol, 8,8a-dihydro-2-methyl-, 1-oxide	EtOH	230(4.28),295(3.27)	142-0251-73
2,3-Quinoxalinedimethanol, α-methyl-	EtOH	237(4.49),319(3.83)	33-1882-73
Tetracyclo[4.3.0.0^{2,4}.0^{3,7}]non-8-ene-8,9-dicarboxamide	EtOH	237(3.92)	24-1804-73
Tryptophan	MeOH	227(4.17),274s(3.80), 280(3.81),289(3.74)	102-0447-73
after ten minutes	H_2SO_4	236(3.69),241(3.66), 290(3.70)(changing)	102-0447-73
$C_{11}H_{12}N_2O_2S$			
1H-Pyrrole, 4,5-dihydro-4-methylene-3-[(4-methylphenyl)sulfonyl]-	EtOH	232(4.16),325(4.10)	22-2746-73
$C_{11}H_{12}N_2O_3$			
1,4-Phthalazinedione, 2,3-dihydro-2-(2-hydroxyethyl)-3-methyl-	MeOH	303(3.63)	1-1891-73
1(2H)-Phthalazinone, 4-(2-hydroxyeth-oxy)-2-methyl-	MeOH	253(3.52),262(3.58), 298(3.77)	1-1891-73
Tryptophan, 5-hydroxy-	MeOH	225(4.21),276(3.79), 300(3.67),312s(3.57)	102-0447-73
after ten minutes	H_2SO_4	249(3.73),320(3.70), (changing)	102-0447-73
$C_{11}H_{12}N_2O_3S$			
1H-Pyrazole, 4,5-dihydro-3-[(4-methoxy-phenyl)sulfonyl]-4-methylene-	EtOH	250(4.08),325(3.86)	22-2746-73
2H-1,2,6-Thiadiazin-3(6H)-one, 2-benzyl-5-methyl-, 1,1-dioxide	EtOH	255(3.95)	4-0469-73
2H-1,2,6-Thiadiazin-3(6H)-one, 6-benzyl-5-methyl-, 1,1-dioxide	EtOH	293(3.90)	4-0469-73
$C_{11}H_{12}N_2O_3S_2$			
Thieno[2,3-d]thiazole-5-carboxylic acid, 2-(acetylamino)-6-methyl-, ethyl ester	MeCN	269(3.68),282s(4.11), 292(4.22),322(4.47), 330s(4.42)	48-0539-73
$C_{11}H_{12}N_2O_4$			
Acetamide, N-(3,4-dihydro-5-nitro-2H-1-benzopyran-6-yl)-	EtOH	233(4.11),330(3.10)	4-0623-73
Acetamide, N-(3,4-dihydro-5-nitro-2H-1-benzopyran-8-yl)-	EtOH	230(4.02),251(3.89), 309(3.85)	4-0623-73

Compound	Solvent	$\lambda_{max}(\log \epsilon)$	Ref.
Acetamide, N-(3,4-dihydro-6-nitro-2H-1-benzopyran-8-yl)-	EtOH	234(4.03),259(4.21), 310(3.88)	4-0623-73
Acetamide, N-(3,4-dihydro-7-nitro-2H-1-benzopyran-6-yl)-	EtOH	240(4.22),366(3.34)	4-0623-73
Acetamide, N-(3,4-dihydro-8-nitro-2H-1-benzopyran-6-yl)-	EtOH	247(4.31),360(3.36)	4-0623-73
Carbamic acid, (4-ethenyl-2-nitrophenyl)-, ethyl ester	hexane	204(4.34),252(4.79), 256(4.79),270(4.64), 372(3.90)	24-1116-73
2-Propenal, 3-[(4-ethoxyphenyl)amino]-2-nitro-	$CHCl_3$	307(3.92),378(4.30)	104-0477-73
8H-Pyrano[3,4-b]pyridine-2-carboxamide, 1,4,5,6-tetrahydro-N,1-dimethyl-4,8-dioxo-	EtOH	230(4.14),303(3.89)	95-1183-73
2,4(1H,3H)-Pyrimidinedione, 1-(3-ethyl-2,5-dihydro-4-methyl-5-oxo-2-furanyl)-	pH 3-7	255(3.99)	44-3878-73
$C_{11}H_{12}N_2O_5$			
7-Azabicyclo[2.2.1]hepta-2,5-diene-2,3-dicarboxylic acid, 7-(aminocarbonyl)-, dimethyl ester	EtOH	293(3.02)	24-3824-73
Pyrazolo[1,5-a]pyridine-2,3-dicarboxylic acid, 4,5,6,7-tetrahydro-7-oxo-, dimethyl ester	EtOH	240(3.91)	44-0825-73
$C_{11}H_{12}N_2O_6$			
6H-Furo[2',3':4,5]oxazolo[3,2-a]pyrimidin-6-one, 3-acetoxy-2,3,3a,9a-tetrahydro-2-(hydroxymethyl)-, [2R-(2α,3β,3aβ,9aβ)]-	MeOH	224(3.97),250(3.91)	35-4016-73
hydrochloride	MeOH	223(3.94),251(3.89)	35-4016-73
$C_{11}H_{12}N_2O_7$			
2,2'-Anhydro-1-α-D-ribofuranosylorotic acid, methyl ester	H_2O	267(3.84)	44-0593-73
2,2'-Anhydro-1-β-D-arabinofuranosylorotic acid, methyl ester	pH 1.5	276(3.85)	44-0593-73
	pH 13	267(3.85)	44-0593-73
$C_{11}H_{12}N_2S$			
2H-Pyrimido[2,1-b]benzothiazole, 3,4-dihydro-3-methyl-	EtOH	225(4.61),268(4.05), 297(3.79)	103-0546-73
$C_{11}H_{12}N_3O$			
Quinolinium, 4-(hydrazinocarbonyl)-1-methyl-, iodide	M HCl	324(3.92)	35-1323-73
	pH 2.8	322(3.93)	35-1323-73
	pH 6.2	322(3.93)	35-1323-73
changing	pH 10.8	318(3.88),408(3.30)	35-1323-73
$C_{11}H_{12}N_3S$			
1H-1,2,4-Triazolium, 4-ethyl-1-(phenylthioxomethyl)-, tetrafluoroborate	CH_2Cl_2	343(4.05),540(2.43)	5-0636-73
$C_{11}H_{12}N_4O$			
Hydrazinecarboxamide, 2-(2-cyano-1-methyl-2-phenylethylidene)-	MeOH	232(4.20)	28-1457-73A
$C_{11}H_{12}N_4O_2$			
Hydrazinecarboxamide, 2-(1,2-dihydro-1-methyl-2-oxo-3H-indol-3-ylidene)-1-methyl-	EtOH	255(4.14),279(3.80), 354(4.01)	104-1565-73

Compound	Solvent	$\lambda_{max}(\log \epsilon)$	Ref.
$C_{11}H_{12}N_4O_3$			
7H-Pyrrolo[2,3-d]pyrimidin-4-amine, 7-(2,3-anhydro-β-D-ribofuranosyl)-	acid	228(4.36),272(4.05)	44-3179-73
	base	270(4.09)	44-3179-73
$C_{11}H_{12}N_4O_4$			
2-Butenal, 3-methyl-1-nitro-, (4-nitrophenyl)hydrazone	EtOH	355(3.67)	19-0881-73
Diazene, (1,2-dimethyl-1-nitro-2-propenyl)(4-nitrophenyl)-	EtOH	270(3.54)	19-0881-73
Diazene, (1-ethyl-1-nitro-2-propenyl)-(4-nitrophenyl)-	EtOH	293(3.75)	19-0881-73
Diazene, (1-methyl-1-nitro-2-butenyl)-(4-nitrophenyl)-	EtOH	291(3.72)	19-0881-73
2,4(1H,3H)-Pteridinedione, 7-(acetoxymethyl)-3,6-dimethyl-	MeOH	233(4.15),332(3.94)	24-3149-73
1H-Pyrazole, 1-acetyl-3-(hexahydro-1-methyl-2,4,6-trioxo-5-pyrimidinyl)-5-methyl-	EtOH	262(4.27),293(4.30)	94-2639-73
1,1'-Trimethylenebisuracil	pH 1	219s(3.73)	35-2320-73
	H_2O	220s(3.73)	35-2320-73
	pH 13	241(3.99)	35-2320-73
$C_{11}H_{12}N_4O_5$			
2,4(1H,3H)-Pteridinedione, 7-(acetoxymethyl)-3,6-dimethyl-, 5-oxide	pH 4.0	237(4.43),287(3.85), 352(3.84)	24-3149-73
	pH 10.0	254(4.20),295s(3.64), 384(3.78)	24-3149-73
2,4(1H,3H)-Pteridinedione, 1-(2-deoxy-D-erythro-pentofuranosyl)-	pH 3.0	228(4.11),315(3.86)	24-1401-73
	pH 11.0	237(4.16),277(3.60), 323(3.86)	24-1401-73
$C_{11}H_{12}N_4O_6$			
2,4(1H,3H)-Pteridinedione, 1-β-D-ribofuranosyl-	pH 3.0	228(4.11),315(3.86)	24-1401-73
	pH 11.0	237(4.16),277(3.59), 323(3.86)	24-1401-73
$C_{11}H_{12}N_4S_2$			
1,2,4-Thiadiazol-3(2H)-imine, 2-[imino-(4-methylphenyl)methyl]-5-(methylthio)-	H_2O	263(4.54)	138-0917-73
1,2,4-Thiadiazol-3(2H)-imine, 2-(1-imino-2-phenylethyl)-5-(methylthio)-	H_2O	247(4.45)	138-0917-73
$C_{11}H_{12}O$			
Benzeneacetaldehyde, α-propylidene-	n.s.g.	221(4.11),247(3.88), 281(3.86)	22-1676-73
Benzofuran, 3-ethyl-2-methyl-	EtOH	247(3.94),276(3.40), 282(3.36)	103-0026-73
1,3-Butadiene, 2-(3-methoxyphenyl)-	hexane	215(4.96),224(4.43)	104-2473-73
2,4-Cyclohexadien-1-one, 5,6-dimethyl-6-(2-propynyl)-	MeOH	315(3.71)	33-0075-73
3-Penten-2-one, 5-phenyl-	n.s.g.	230(4.04),283(2.88), 292(2.78)	22-1676-73
4-Penten-2-one, 5-phenyl-	n.s.g.	250(4.32),283(3.65), 292(3.55)	22-1676-73
Spiro[naphthalene-1(2H),2'-oxirane], 3,4-dihydro-	EtOH	251(3.24),267s(2.99), 276(2.85),283s(2.54)	25-1111-73
$C_{11}H_{12}OS$			
Benzenecarbothioic acid, O-3-butenyl ester	CH_2Cl_2	248(3.86),287(4.07)	39-1574-73C

Compound	Solvent	λ_{max}(log ϵ)	Ref.
$C_{11}H_{12}O_2$			
3-Benzofuranethanol, 2-methyl-	EtOH	246(4.10),275(3.45), 281(3.36)	103-0026-73
2H-1-Benzopyran, 6-methoxy-2-methyl-	EtOH	238(3.80),265(3.27), 332(3.41)	44-3832-73
2H-1-Benzopyran, 6-methoxy-4-methyl-	EtOH	224(3.60),242(3.81), 266(3.15),331(3.54)	44-3832-73
2H-1-Benzopyran, 8-methoxy-4-methyl-	EtOH	236(3.90),276(3.69), 316(3.23)	44-3832-73
4H-1-Benzopyran-4-one, 2,3-dihydro-2,6-dimethyl-	MeOH	254(3.95),331(3.56)	20-0705-73
Bicyclo[3.3.1]nona-3,6-diene-2,8-dione, 4,6-dimethyl-	EtOH	220(4.28),271s(3.28)	94-1213-73
Bicyclo[3.3.1]nona-3,7-diene-2,6-dione, 4,8-dimethyl-	EtOH	238(4.21),266s(3.19), 279s(2.81),348(2.95)	94-1213-73
2-Butenoic acid, 3-phenyl-, methyl ester	EtOH	265(4.21)	78-3609-73
2-Buten-1-one, 1-(2-hydroxy-5-methyl-phenyl)-	MeOH	272(4.23),355(3.67)	20-0299-73
2,5-Cyclohexadiene-1,4-dione, 2-(3-meth-yl-2-butenyl)-	EtOH	248(4.2),320(2.8)	1-3211-73
Pentacyclo[4.3.0.0^{2,4}.0^{3,8}.0^{5,7}]nonane-4-carboxylic acid, methyl ester	EtOH	210(3.00)	24-1804-73
Spiro[bicyclo[2.2.1]hepta-2,5-diene-7,1'-cyclopropane]-2-carboxylic acid, methyl ester	EtOH	232(3.48),269(3.15)	24-1822-73
Tetracyclo[4.3.0.0^{2,4}.0^{3,7}]non-8-ene-8-carboxylic acid, methyl ester	EtOH	235(3.82)	24-1804-73
$C_{11}H_{12}O_2S$			
1H-2-Benzothiopyran, 1,4-dimethyl-, 2,2-dioxide	EtOH	208(4.19),214(4.18), 219(4.19),273(3.88)	39-0410-73C
2-Propenoic acid, 2-methyl-3-[(4-methyl-phenyl)thio]-	EtOH	255s(--),282(4.29)	94-1090-73
$C_{11}H_{12}O_3$			
Benzene, 3-methoxy-4,5-(methylenedioxy)-1-propenyl-	EtOH	220(4.46),273(4.09), 294s(3.73),304s(3.48)	141-0001-73
	dioxan	231(4.23),275(4.08), 298s(3.71),309s(3.42)	141-0001-73
2H-1-Benzopyran-6-carboxylic acid, 3,4-dihydro-8-methyl-	EtOH	262(4.13)	4-0623-73
1-Indanone, 4,5-dimethoxy-	EtOH	230(4.36),281(4.14)	141-0001-73
	dioxan	229(4.41),272(4.16), 280s(4.09)	141-0001-73
1-Indanone, 5,6-dimethoxy-	EtOH	210(4.22),229(4.25), 268(4.05),312(4.00)	141-0001-73
	dioxan	226s(4.28),231(4.32), 266(4.12),307(4.00), 314s(3.98)	141-0001-73
1-Indanone, 5,7-dimethoxy-	EtOH	226(4.35),275(4.27), 298(3.81)	141-0001-73
	dioxan	225(4.45),229s(4.40), 269(4.26),288s(3.70), 298(3.68)	141-0001-73
1(3H)-Isobenzofuranone, 3-ethyl-3-meth-oxy-	MeOH	227(4.02),273(3.02), 280(2.99)	44-3375-73
1(3H)-Isobenzofuranone, 3-hydroxy-3-(1-methylethyl)-	M H_2SO_4	233(3.98),276(3.10), 283(3.08)	44-3375-73
1,4-Naphthalenediol, 5,8-dihydro-2-meth-oxy-	MeOH	291.5(3.59)	12-0595-73

Compound	Solvent	λ_{max}(log ε)	Ref.
1,4-Naphthalenedione, 4a,5,8,8a-tetra-hydro-2-methoxy-, cis	$CHCl_3$	270(4.00),330(2.30)	12-0595-73
1(2H)-Naphthalenone, 3,4-dihydro-4,8-dihydroxy-3-methyl- (isoshinanolone)	EtOH	261(3.96),334(3.64)	102-0175-73
diastereoisomer racemate	EtOH	260(4.03),334(3.56)	102-0175-73
2-Propen-1-one, 1-(2-hydroxy-3-methoxy-6-methylphenyl)-	90% EtOH	232(3.81),278(3.57), 329s(2.93)	12-1069-73
$C_{11}H_{12}O_4$			
3-Benzofurancarboxylic acid, 2,3-di-hydro-2-methoxy-, methyl ester, (E)-	90% EtOH	213(3.72),276(3.43), 283(3.36)	12-1079-73
(Z)-	90% EtOH	214(3.72),275(3.40), 280(3.35)	12-1079-73
1H-2-Benzopyran-1-one, 3,4-dihydro-8-hydroxy-6-methoxy-3-methyl-, (R)-	EtOH	217(4.31),267(4.15), 302(3.74)	102-1881-73
1(2H)-Naphthalenone, 3,4-dihydro-3,8-di-hydroxy-6-methoxy-	EtOH	222(3.82),231(3.77), 237(3.69),281(3.84), 316(3.43)	23-1617-73
	EtOH-base	218(3.91),238(3.93), 281(3.58),347(3.33)	23-1617-73
1-Propanone, 1-(7-methoxy-1,3-benzodiox-ol-5-yl)-	n.s.g.	225(4.16),346(4.10), 301(3.80)	105-0095-73
2-Propenoic acid, 3-(2,3-dimethoxyphen-yl)-, cis	EtOH	220(4.25),264(3.94)	141-0001-73
	EtOH-NaOH	222(4.28),259(4.01), 300s(3.20)	141-0001-73
	dioxan	221(4.25),270(3.96)	141-0001-73
trans	EtOH	226(4.29),279(4.29), 320s(3.45)	141-0001-73
	EtOH-NaOH	226(4.35),273(4.25), 311s(3.33)	141-0001-73
	dioxan	228(4.27),280(4.29), 330s(3.35)	141-0001-73
2-Propenoic acid, 3-(2,4-dimethoxyphen-yl)-, cis	EtOH	210(4.13),230s(4.00), 275(3.90),315(3.98)	141-0001-73
	EtOH-NaOH	220(4.17),267(4.08), 303(3.91)	141-0001-73
	dioxan	215(4.08),238(4.03), 282s(3.99),293(4.01), 322(4.11)	141-0001-73
trans	EtOH	216(4.07),237(4.05), 290(4.13),324(4.19)	141-0001-73
	EtOH-NaOH	220(4.09),273(4.07), 285s(4.00),309(3.97)	141-0001-73
	dioxan	237(4.10),285s(4.15), 291(4.18),324(4.23)	141-0001-73
2-Propenoic acid, 3-(2,5-dimethoxyphen-yl)-, cis	EtOH	218(4.12),237s(3.98), 272(3.93),335(3.66)	141-0001-73
	EtOH-NaOH	261(3.97),323(3.69)	141-0001-73
	dioxan	221(4.11),238s(3.99), 275(4.00),345(3.73)	141-0001-73
trans	EtOH	218(4.13),240s(4.03), 275(4.16),346(3.80)	141-0001-73
	EtOH-NaOH	219(4.14),235s(4.02), 265(4.03),328(3.72)	141-0001-73
	dioxan	221(4.13),228s(4.10), 241(4.05),275(4.20), 351(3.86)	141-0001-73
2-Propenoic acid, 3-(2,6-dimethoxyphen-yl)-, cis	EtOH	211(4.23),285(3.90)	141-0001-73
	EtOH-NaOH	221(4.23),273(3.91)	141-0001-73
	dioxan	217(4.26),284(3.93)	141-0001-73

Compound	Solvent	$\lambda_{max}(\log \epsilon)$	Ref.
2-Propenoic acid, 3-(3,4-dimethoxyphen-yl)-, trans	EtOH	208(4.11),218s(4.03), 233(4.03),287(3.93), 318(3.95)	141-0001-73
	EtOH-NaOH	219(4.08),230(4.10), 283(4.01),309(3.92)	141-0001-73
	dioxan	235(4.08),289(3.94), 323(4.00)	141-0001-73
$C_{11}H_{12}O_4S$			
Benzoic acid, 2-[1-(carboxymethyl)thio]-ethyl-	EtOH	277(2.94)	39-0410-73C
$C_{11}H_{12}O_5$			
Phthalide, 4,5,6-trimethoxy-	EtOH	216(4.57),259(3.89), 298(3.57)	141-0001-73
	dioxan	224(4.07),256(3.91), 292(3.56),299(3.56)	141-0001-73
2-Propenoic acid, 3-(4-hydroxy-3,5-di-methoxyphenyl)- (sinapic acid)	EtOH	218(4.09),240(4.07), 320(4.06)	105-0718-73
2-Propenoic acid, 3-(5-hydroxy-2,4-di-methoxyphenyl)-	EtOH	250(3.87),288(3.12), 350(3.93)	95-0624-73
$C_{11}H_{12}O_6$			
Butanedioic acid, 2-hydroxy-2-[(4-hy-droxyphenyl)methyl]-	EtOH	228(3.98),276(3.40), 282(3.40),320(2.92)	44-4457-73
2,3-Furandicarboxylic acid, 4-acetyl-5-methyl-, dimethyl ester	$CHCl_3$	275(4.25)	103-1307-73
Homophthalic acid, 4,5-dimethoxy-	EtOH	220(4.37),259(4.01), 291(3.63)	141-0001-73
	EtOH-NaOH	220(4.11),247(3.88), 285(3.44)	141-0001-73
	dioxan	227(4.24),262(4.06), 294(3.72)	141-0001-73
Homophthalic acid, 5,6-dimethoxy-	EtOH	211(4.26),228s(3.94), 286(3.30)	141-0001-73
	EtOH-NaOH	221(4.05),281(3.28)	141-0001-73
	dioxan	221(3.99),284(3.42)	141-0001-73
$C_{11}H_{12}O_6S$			
2-Thiabicyclo[2.2.2]octa-5,7-diene-5,6-dicarboxylic acid, dimethyl ester, 2,2-dioxide	MeOH	239(3.59)	44-3073-73
$C_{11}H_{12}S$			
1H-2-Benzothiopyran, 1,3-dimethyl-	EtOH	207(4.39),236(3.82), 242(3.80),303(3.70), 313(3.72)	39-0410-73C
1H-2-Benzothiopyran, 1,4-dimethyl-	EtOH	209(4.31),239(3.87), 248(3.78),318(3.77)	39-0410-73C
$C_{11}H_{13}$			
Ethylium, 1-cyclopropyl-1-phenyl-	FSO_3H at -75°	340(4.34)	59-0803-73
Methylium, cyclopropyl(4-methylphenyl)-	FSO_3H at -75°	366(4.51)	59-0803-73
$C_{11}H_{13}BrN_2$			
Isoquinolinium. 2-(2-aminoethyl)-, bro-mide hydrobromide	MeOH	232(4.68),278(3.47), 338(3.64)	44-0437-73
Quinazoline, 6-bromo-4-ethyl-1,4-di-hydro-2-methyl-	EtOH	293(3.99)	39-0453-73C

Compound	Solvent	λ_{max}(log ε)	Ref.
Quinazoline, 8-bromo-4-ethyl-1,4-dihydro-2-methyl-	EtOH	294(3.86)	39-0453-73C
$C_{11}H_{13}BrN_2O$			
Isoquinolinium, 2-(acetylamino)-3,4-dihydro-, bromide	EtOH	267(3.05),273(3.14), 302(3.32)	95-0648-73
$C_{11}H_{13}BrN_2O_6$			
Uracil-1-malonic acid, 5-bromo-, diethyl ester	neutral	281(3.91)	46-0482-73
	pH 11	257(4.37)	46-0482-73
$C_{11}H_{13}BrN_4O_3$			
7H-Pyrrolo[2,3-d]pyrimidin-4-amine, 7-(3-bromo-3-deoxy-β-D-xylofuranosyl)-	MeOH-acid	228(4.40),272(4.06)	44-3179-73
	MeOH-base	270(4.09)	44-3179-73
$C_{11}H_{13}ClN_2$			
Quinazoline, 6-chloro-4-ethyl-1,4-dihydro-2-methyl-	EtOH	293(3.98)	39-0453-73C
$C_{11}H_{13}ClN_2O_2$			
Propanoic acid, 2-[(2-chlorophenyl)-hydrazono]-, ethyl ester, (E)-	EtOH	316(4.29)	94-1481-73
(Z)-	EtOH	343(4.23)	94-1481-73
$C_{11}H_{13}ClN_2O_6$			
Uridine, 2'-chloro-2'-deoxy-, 3'-acetate	MeOH	258(4.00)	35-4016-73
$C_{11}H_{13}ClN_4O_3$			
1,2-Cyclopentanediol, 3-(6-chloro-9H-purin-9-yl)-5-(hydroxymethyl)-, (1α,2α,3β,5β)-(±)-	pH 1 and 7	265(3.97)	36-1252-73
7H-Pyrrolo[2,3-d]pyrimidin-4-amine, 7-(3-chloro-3-deoxy-β-D-xylofuranosyl)-	MeOH-acid	228(4.39),272(4.05)	44-3179-73
	MeOH-base	270(4.09)	44-3179-73
$C_{11}H_{13}ClN_4O_4$			
Purine, 6-chloro-9-(6-deoxy-β-L-galactopyranosyl)-	n.s.g.	265(3.88)	136-0192-73E
$C_{11}H_{13}ClO$			
1-Pentanone, 1-(2-chlorophenyl)-	heptane	234(3.68)	35-5604-73
1-Pentanone, 1-(3-chlorophenyl)-	heptane	239(4.00)	35-5604-73
1-Pentanone, 1-(4-chlorophenyl)-	heptane	249(4.27)	35-5604-73
$C_{11}H_{13}ClOS$			
2H-Pyran, 2-[(4-chlorophenyl)thio]tetrahydro-	40% dioxan	254(4.03)	35-8407-73
$C_{11}H_{13}ClO_2$			
2,4,6-Cycloheptatrien-1-one, 5-chloro-2-methoxy-6-propyl-	EtOH	240(4.32),330(3.88)	12-1337-73
$C_{11}H_{13}ClO_3$			
Propanoic acid, 3-chloro-, 2-methoxy-5-methylphenyl ester	90% EtOH	227(3.56),276s(3.36), 278(3.45),283s(3.30)	12-1069-73
1-Propanone, 3-chloro-1-(2-hydroxy-3-methoxy-6-methylphenyl)-	90% EtOH	228(3.83),262(3.53), 288s(3.30),303s(3.18)	12-1069-73
1-Propanone, 3-chloro-1-(4-hydroxy-5-methoxy-2-methylphenyl)-	90% EtOH	233(4.21),277(3.95), 309(3.82)	12-1069-73

Compound	Solvent	λmax(log ε)	Ref.
$C_{11}H_{13}Cl_2N_3$			
Benzenamine, 2,6-dichloro-N-(1,3-dimethyl-2-imidazolidinylidene)-	pH 1	270(2.61),277(2.50)	111-0545-73
	MeOH	260(2.9)	111-0545-73
1H-Imidazol-2-amine, N-(2,6-dichlorophenyl)-4,5-dihydro-N,1-dimethyl-	pH 1	270(2.74),277(2.65)	111-0545-73
$C_{11}H_{13}FN_2O_4S$			
Uridine, 2',3'-dideoxy-3'-fluoro-4-thio-, 5'-acetate	MeOH	229(4.29),247(3.69)	48-0895-73
$C_{11}H_{13}FO$			
1-Pentanone, 1-(2-fluorophenyl)-	heptane	233(4.04)	35-5604-73
1-Pentanone, 1-(3-fluorophenyl)-	heptane	236(4.04)	35-5604-73
1-Pentanone, 1-(4-fluorophenyl)-	heptane	240(4.04)	35-5604-73
$C_{11}H_{13}FO_2S$			
Benzo[b]thiophene, 6-fluoro-2,3-dihydro-2-propyl-, 1,1-dioxide	EtOH	266(2.15),273(2.20), 281(2.26)	2-0628-73
$C_{11}H_{13}N$			
1H-Indole, 1,4,5-trimethyl-	EtOH	277(3.70),294(3.60), 298(3.54),305(3.53)	28-1327-73A
$C_{11}H_{13}NO$			
Acetamide, N-(1-methyl-2-phenylethenyl)-, cis	MeOH	268(4.21)	104-2119-73
trans	MeOH	257(4.12)	104-2119-73
Acetamide, N-(2-phenyl-1-propenyl)-, (E)-	MeOH	274(4.28)	104-2119-73
10-Azabicyclo[4.3.2]undeca-2,4,7-trien-11-one, 7-methyl-	EtOH	215s(3.63),254(3.55)	35-4647-73
10-Azabicyclo[7.2.0]undeca-2,5,7-trien-11-one, 2-methyl-, trans	EtOH	224(3.62)	35-4647-73
10-Azabicyclo[7.2.0]undeca-2,5,7-trien-11-one, 3-methyl-, trans	EtOH	225(3.56)	35-4647-73
10-Azabicyclo[7.2.0]undeca-2,5,7-trien-11-one, 4-methyl-	EtOH	240(3.63)	35-4647-73
10-Azabicyclo[7.2.0]undeca-2,5,7-trien-11-one, 8-methyl-, trans	EtOH	228(3.67)	35-4647-73
1-Benzazocin-6(1H)-one, 2,3,4,5-tetrahydro-	EtOH	230(3.88),269(2.84), 275(2.76)	18-2504-73
4H-3,1-Benzoxazine, 2,4,4-trimethyl-	EtOH	262(3.84)	88-0903-73
3H-Indol-5-ol, 2,3,3-trimethyl-	EtOH	277(3.99)	88-0903-73
	EtOH-base	307(3.93)	88-0903-73
Isoxazole, 4,5-dihydro-5,5-dimethyl-3-phenyl-	EtOH	215(--),265(4.30)	22-1390-73
Methylamine, N-(2-benzylidenepropylidene)-, N-oxide	EtOH	235(4.1),330(4.3)	22-1390-73
$C_{11}H_{13}NOS$			
2-Azetidinone, 3-methyl-4-[(4-methylphenyl)thio]-, trans	EtOH	214(4.05),254(3.72)	94-1090-73
2-Propenamide, 2-methyl-3-[(4-methylphenyl)thio]-	EtOH	253s(--),281(4.22)	94-1090-73
$C_{11}H_{13}NOS_2$			
Benzene, 1-ethoxy-4-[(2-isothiocyanatoethyl)thio]-	EtOH	229(4.09),254(3.98), 283s(3.27)	73-0620-73

Compound	Solvent	$\lambda_{max}(\log \epsilon)$	Ref.
$C_{11}H_{13}NO_2$			
Acetamide, N-(3,4-dihydro-2H-1-benzo-pyran-8-yl)-	EtOH	248(4.03),284(3.64), 290(3.63)	4-0623-73
Acetamide, N-(2,3-dihydro-2-methyl-4-benzofuranyl)-	EtOH	237(3.94),283(3.41)	44-0831-73
Acetamide, N-(2,3-dihydro-2-methyl-6-benzofuranyl)-	EtOH	249(4.01),291(3.76)	44-0831-73
Acetamide, N-[3-hydroxy-2-(2-propenyl)-phenyl]-	EtOH	278(3.39)	44-0831-73
Acetamide, N-[3-hydroxy-4-(2-propenyl)-phenyl]-	EtOH	247(4.13),285(3.66)	44-0831-73
Acetamide, N-[2-(4-methoxyphenyl)ethen-yl]-, (E)-	MeOH	284(4.47)	104-2119-73
2-Butanone, 4-[(phenylmethylene)amino]-, N-oxide	EtOH	296(4.23)	104-0793-73
7(1H)-Indolizinone, 8-acetyl-2,3-di-hydro-5-methyl-	EtOH	257(4.06),262(4.09), 302(3.61)	95-1084-73
	EtOH-HCl	242(3.95)	95-1084-73
Pedicularine	n.s.g.	265(3.12),272(3.15)	105-0137-73
2,4-Pentadienoic acid, 4-methyl-5-(1H-pyrrol-2-yl)-, methyl ester	EtOH	368(4.53)	39-1416-73C
2,3-trans	EtOH	364(4.53)	39-1416-73C
2-Pyrrolidinone, 5-hydroxy-1-methyl-	H_2SO_4	303(4.29)	24-1423-73
$C_{11}H_{13}NO_2S$			
Spiro[indane-2,2'-thiazolidine]-1,3-diol	MeOH	215(3.98)	78-4271-73
$C_{11}H_{13}NO_3$			
Benzenebutanoic acid, β-amino-p-methyl-γ-oxo-, hydrochloride	M HCl	261(4.18)	7-0457-73
	pH 7.38	261(4.16),287s(--)	7-0457-73
	pH 13	257(4.17)	7-0457-73
Benzenepropanenitrile, β-hydroxy-2,4-dimethoxy-	EtOH	229(3.85),277(3.38), 282(3.33)	40-2347-73
Benzoic acid, 4-[(N-formyl)methylamino]-, ethyl ester	pH 7.5	265(4.24)	35-8414-73
1-Indanone, 5,6-dimethoxy-, oxime	EtOH	216(4.26),261(4.18), 297s(3.85),308(4.03), 314s(3.99),321(3.99)	141-0001-73
	dioxan	224(4.16),260(4.20), 296s(3.83),303s(3.95), 308(4.00),314(3.99), 320(4.00)	141-0001-73
DL-Propanoic acid, 2-amino-3-(4-methyl-benzoyl)-	M HCl	259(4.24)	7-0457-73
	pH 7.38	257(4.23)	7-0457-73
	pH 13	256(4.22)	7-0457-73
Pyrrolo[3,2,1-hi]indole-2,6-dione, 1,4,5,5a,8a,8b-hexahydro-8a-methoxy-	H_2O	198(4.15)	88-3009-73
	EtOH	333(1.63)	88-3009-73
	CH_2Cl_2	340(1.56)	88-3009-73
Pyrrolo[3,2,1-hi]indole-2,7(1H,8H)-di-one, 4,5,8,8a-tetrahydro-8b-methoxy-	C_6H_{12}	240(3.71)	88-3009-73
	EtOH	324(1.59)	88-3009-73
$C_{11}H_{13}NO_3S$			
1H-Indole-2-sulfonic acid, 1,3-dimeth-yl-, methyl ester	EtOH	275s(3.98),280(4.02), 304(3.72),314s(3.56)	78-0669-73
1H-Indole-3-sulfonic acid, 1,2-dimeth-yl-, methyl ester	EtOH	273(3.90),277(3.94), 285(3.89)	78-0669-73
2H-Pyran, tetrahydro-2-[(4-nitrophenyl)-thio]-	40% dioxan	330(4.00)	35-8407-73

Compound	Solvent	$\lambda_{max}(\log \epsilon)$	Ref.
$C_{11}H_{13}NO_3S_2$			
Benzene, 1-ethoxy-4-[(2-isothiocyanato-ethyl)sulfonyl]-	EtOH	242(4.26),268(3.37), 277(2.99)	73-0620-73
$C_{11}H_{13}NO_4$			
1-Cyclohexene-1,3-dicarboxylic acid, 2-cyano-, dimethyl ester	EtOH	233(3.96)	78-0683-73
$C_{11}H_{13}NO_5$			
Glycine, N-(2,6-dimethoxybenzoyl)-	EtOH	280(3.19)	4-0935-73
Propanoic acid, 3-[(2,3-dimethoxyphen-yl)amino]-3-oxo-	MeOH	247(4.04)	78-1721-73
Propanoic acid, 3-nitro-, 2-methoxy-5-methylphenyl ester	90% EtOH	227(3.58),276s(3.34), 278(3.40),283s(3.30)	12-1069-73
1H-Pyrrole-3-acetic acid, 4-formyl-2-(methoxycarbonyl)-5-methyl-, methyl ester	MeOH	238(4.28),289(4.04)	39-1546-73C
$C_{11}H_{13}NO_6$			
1H-Pyrrole-3-acetic acid, 4-carboxy-2-(methoxycarbonyl)-5-methyl-, α-methyl ester	MeOH	276(4.21)	39-1546-73C
$C_{11}H_{13}NO_6S$			
7-Azabicyclo[2.2.1]hepta-2,5-diene-2,3-dicarboxylic acid, 7-(methyl-sulfonyl)-, dimethyl ester	EtOH	291(3.01)	24-3824-73
1H-Azepine-4,5-dicarboxylic acid, 1-(methylsulfonyl)-, dimethyl ester	EtOH	348(2.90)	24-3824-73
$C_{11}H_{13}NS_2$			
Pyrrolo[2,1-b]thiazole-7-carbothioalde-hyde, 2,3,5,6-tetramethyl-	EtOH	230(4.28),263(3.78), 283(3.66),410s(4.17), 418(4.27),431(4.24)	39-0657-73C
$C_{11}H_{13}N_2$			
Isoquinolinium, 2-(2-aminoethyl)-, bromide hydrobromide	MeOH	232(4.68),278(3.47), 338(3.64)	44-0437-73
Quinoxalinium, 1,3,6(7)-trimethyl-, perchlorate	H_2O	248s(--),251(4.15), 348(3.54)	22-1285-73
$C_{11}H_{13}N_2O$			
Isoquinolinium, 2-(acetylamino)-3,4-di-hydro-, bromide	EtOH	267(3.05),273(3.14), 302(3.32)	95-0648-73
$C_{11}H_{13}N_2O_5S$			
2-Propanone, 1-[3-(ethylthio)-2,6-di-nitro-2,4-cyclohexadien-1-yl)-, ion(1-), potassium salt	acetone	362(4.45),658(4.48)	104-2106-73
2-Propanone, 1-[5-(ethylthio)-2,4-di-nitro-2,4-cyclohexadien-1-yl)-, ion(1-), potassium salt	acetone	396(4.52),578(4.35)	104-2106-73
$C_{11}H_{13}N_3$			
Benzeneacetonitrile, α-[(2,2-dimethyl-hydrazino)methylene]-	MeOH	290(4.17),307(4.13)	28-1457-73A
5-Cinnolinamine, 3,6,7-trimethyl-	M HCl	245(4.42),281(3.82), 360(3.28),472(2.65)	77-0926-73
1H-Imidazo[2,1-b][1,3]benzodiazepine, 2,3,5,6-tetrahydro-	EtOH-NaOH	294(4.97)	87-0407-73

Compound	Solvent	$\lambda_{max}(\log \epsilon)$	Ref.
3,5-Pyridinedicarbonitrile, 1,4-dihydro-2,4,4,6-tetramethyl-	EtOH	217(4.14),338(3.60)	103-0994-73
$C_{11}H_{13}N_3O$			
2-Pyrazoline, 1-acetyl-3-(2-methyl-5-pyridinyl)-	$CHCl_3$	304(4.34)	103-0055-73
2-Pyrazoline, 1-acetyl-4-methyl-3-(2-pyridinyl)-	$CHCl_3$	306(4.43)	103-0055-73
Pyridine, 2-(1-hydroxy-4,5-dimethyl-1H-imidazol-1-yl)-6-methyl-	n.s.g.	280(3.91),314(4.23)	46-2160-73
4H-Pyrido[1,2-a]pyrimidin-4-one, 3-(2-aminoethyl)-2-methyl-	MeOH	245(4.0),340(4.0)	5-0103-73
Pyrimido[1,2-b]indazol-2(1H)-one, 7,8,9,10-tetrahydro-4-methyl-	MeOH	243(4.24),282(3.87)	4-0261-73
Pyrimido[1,2-b]indazol-2(1H)-one, 7,8,9,10-tetrahydro-7-methyl-	MeOH	245(4.38),283(3.92)	4-0261-73
Pyrimido[1,2-b]indazol-4(1H)-one, 7,8,9,10-tetrahydro-2-methyl-	MeOH	254s(4.00),264(4.00), 300(3.80)	4-0261-73
1,2,4-Triazine, 2,5-dihydro-3-methoxy-5-methyl-5-phenyl-	n.s.g.	225(3.92),266(3.76)	22-2493-73
$C_{11}H_{13}N_3O_2S$			
Pentanoic acid, 5-(1H-pyrrolo[2,3-d]-pyrimidin-4-ylthio)-	pH 1	220(4.33),258(3.98), 312(4.05)	73-1438-73
	pH 13	221(4.31),248(3.93), 292(4.13)	73-1438-73
$C_{11}H_{13}N_3O_3$			
4-Morpholineacetamide, α-oxo-N-3-pyridinyl-	EtOH	247(4.2)	103-0621-73
2-Propenal, 3-[[4-(dimethylamino)phenyl]amino]-2-nitro-	$CHCl_3$	320(3.93),426(4.30)	104-0477-73
Pyrido[2,3-d]pyrimidine-2,4,5(1H,3H,8H)-trione, 1,3,7,8-tetramethyl-	EtOH	245(4.50),264(4.02)	94-2014-73
$C_{11}H_{13}N_3O_3S$			
1,8-Naphthyridine-3-sulfonamide, 1-ethyl-1,4-dihydro-7-methyl-4-oxo-	MeOH	253(4.35),322(4.04), 332(4.07)	94-1080-73
$C_{11}H_{13}N_3O_4$			
1H-Pyrazolo[3,4-b]pyridine, 1-β-D-ribofuranosyl-	EtOH	213(4.10),262(3.38), 296(3.51),306s(3.32)	104-1294-73
$C_{11}H_{13}N_3O_8$			
Uracil-1-malonic acid, 5-nitro-, diethyl ester	neutral	237(3.90),298(4.05)	46-0482-73
	pH 11	255(4.45)	46-0482-73
$C_{11}H_{13}N_3S$			
4-Isoquinolinecarbonitrile, 3-amino-1,2,5,6,7,8-hexahydro-2-methyl-1-thioxo-	MeOH	295(3.86),381(4.38)	48-0679-73
1,2,4-Triazine, 4,5-dihydro-5-methyl-3-(methylthio)-5-phenyl-	n.s.g.	216(4.00),265(3.40)	22-2493-73
1,2,4-Triazine, 4,5-dihydro-6-methyl-3-(methylthio)-5-phenyl-	n.s.g.	227(3.96),268(4.08), 335s(3.30)	22-2493-73
$C_{11}H_{13}N_4O_7PS$			
Inosine, 8-(methylthio)-, cyclic 3',5'-(hydrogen phosphate)	pH 1	268(4.09)	69-5310-73
	pH 11	275(4.08)	69-5310-73

Compound	Solvent	λ_{max}(log ε)	Ref.
$C_{11}H_{13}N_5$			
Benzo[1,2-d:3,4-d']diimidazol-2-amine, 3,6,7-trimethyl-	MeOH	267s(4.2),275(4.3), 292(4.2)	103-0740-73
$C_{11}H_{13}N_5O_2$			
7H-Purine-7-propanenitrile, 1,2,3,6-tetrahydro-1,3,8-trimethyl-2,6-dioxo-	n.s.g.	209(4.33),275(3.98)	73-1571-73
$C_{11}H_{13}N_5O_2S$			
1H-Purine-2,6-dione, 3,7-dihydro-7-(3-isothiocyanatopropyl)-1,3-dimethyl-	n.s.g.	209(4.28),274(3.89)	73-1571-73
$C_{11}H_{13}N_5O_4$			
Methyl 2'-deoxyadenosine uronate	EtOH	259(3.96)	44-0990-73
2(1H)-Pteridinone, 4-amino-1-(2-deoxy-D-erythro-pentofuranosyl)-	pH 0.0	236(4.14),332(3.91)	33-1225-73
	pH 7.0	242(4.12),285(3.70), 333(3.89)	33-1225-73
$C_{11}H_{13}N_5O_5$			
2(1H)-Pteridinone, 4-amino-1-β-D-ribofuranosyl-	pH 0.0	204(4.30),236(4.22), 328(3.95)	33-1225-73
	pH 7.0	241(4.17),284(3.74), 332(3.93)	33-1225-73
$C_{11}H_{13}N_5O_6$			
7(8H)-Pteridinone, 2-amino-4-hydroxy-8-β-D-ribofuranosyl-	pH 4.0	214(4.44),290(3.92), 347(4.14)	24-1952-73
	pH 11.0	260(4.03),284s(3.53), 360(4.13)	24-1952-73
$C_{11}H_{13}N_5S$			
Thiazolo[3,2-e]purin-4-amine, 8-(1,1-dimethylethyl)-	pH 1	250(4.36),293(4.14)	94-0034-73
	pH 13	238(--),287(--), 296s(--)	94-0034-73
$C_{11}H_{13}N_7O_4$			
Glycine, N-[N-(N-1H-purin-6-ylglycyl)-glycyl]-	pH 1	276(4.24)	94-2349-73
	pH 7	267(4.22)	94-2349-73
	pH 13	273(4.29),279s(4.08)	94-2349-73
$C_{11}H_{14}$			
Benzene, (1,2-dimethyl-1-propenyl)-	EtOH	238(4.04)	22-0249-73
Spiro[2.4]hepta-1,4,6-triene, 1,2-diethyl-	isooctane	242(3.46)	89-0577-73
	MeOH	241(3.39)	89-0577-73
Tetracyclo[6.3.0.0^{2,11}.0^{3,7}]undec-9-ene, 3,7-endo	pentane	220(3.36)	35-8250-73
exo	pentane	210s(3.65)	35-8250-73
$C_{11}H_{14}BF_4N_3$			
Benzenediazonium, 2-(1-piperidinyl)-, tetrafluoroborate	M HCl	275(3.77),446(3.70)	48-0725-73
$C_{11}H_{14}BrN$			
Piperidine, 1-[(2-bromo-2,4-cyclopentadien-1-ylidene)methyl]-	hexane	225(3.70),323(4.43)	88-5105-73
$C_{11}H_{14}BrN_5O_4$			
9H-Purin-6-amine, 9-(1-bromo-1-deoxy-β-D-psicofuranosyl)-	H_2O	208(4.16),261(4.07)	73-3181-73

Compound	Solvent	λ_{max}(log ε)	Ref.
$C_{11}H_{14}Cl$			
Propylium, (4-chlorophenyl)-1,2-dimethyl-	FSO_3H at -75°	353(4.38)	59-0803-73
$C_{11}H_{14}ClN$			
Piperidine, 1-[(2-chloro-2,4-cyclopentadien-1-ylidene)methyl]-	hexane	218(3.77),329(4.53)	88-5105-73
$C_{11}H_{14}ClN_3O_2$			
Hydrazinecarboxamide, N-(4-chloro-1-oxobutyl)-2-phenyl-	MeOH	238(3.68)	104-1200-73
$C_{11}H_{14}FNO_6$			
2(1H)-Pyridinone, 5-fluoro-4-methoxy-1-β-D-ribofuranosyl-	pH 1.0	288(3.67)	4-0779-73
	pH 14	291(3.68)	4-0779-73
	MeOH	293(3.66)	4-0779-73
$C_{11}H_{14}F_3NO_8$			
D-glycero-D-galacto-Non-2-enonic acid, 2,6-anhydro-3,5-dideoxy-5-(trifluoroacetyl)amino]-	n.s.g.	240(3.85)	49-0402-73
$C_{11}H_{14}IN_5O_4$			
9H-Purin-6-amine, 9-(6-deoxy-6-iodo-β-D-glucopyranosyl)-	pH 1	256(4.18)	136-0378-73C
	pH 7	258(4.15)	136-0378-73C
	pH 13	258(4.12)	136-0378-73C
$C_{11}H_{14}NO$			
Isoxazolium, 4,5-dihydro-2,3-dimethyl-5-phenyl-, perchlorate	EtOH	210(3.99),230s(--)	22-1390-73
Isoxazolium, 4,5-dihydro-2,4-dimethyl-3-phenyl-, perchlorate	EtOH	273(3.75)	22-1390-73
Isoxazolium, 4,5-dihydro-2,5-dimethyl-3-phenyl-, perchlorate	EtOH	274(3.77)	22-1390-73
$C_{11}H_{14}N_2$			
2-Indolamine, 3-ethyl-1-methyl-, hydrochloride	MeOH	212(4.26),261(3.89)	103-0471-73
1H-Indole-3-ethanamine, 1-methyl-	EtOH	225(4.56),279s(3.72), 287(3.75)	103-0196-73
1H-Indole-3-ethanamine, 5-methyl-	EtOH	223(4.48),277s(3.69), 284(3.67),295s(3.52)	103-0196-73
1H-Indole-3-ethanamine, 7-methyl-	EtOH	221(4.48),274s(3.79), 279(3.71),287s(3.61)	103-0196-73
2-Indolizinemethanamine, N-ethyl-	EtOH	288(3.15),300(3.16), 341(3.13)	36-1897-73
Quinazoline, 4-ethyl-3,4-dihydro-2-methyl-	EtOH	284(3.84)	39-0453-73C
Spiro[3H-1,5-benzodiazepine-3,1'-cyclopropane], 1,2,4,5-tetrahydro-	EtOH	242s(3.70),298(3.40)	78-2337-73
$C_{11}H_{14}N_2O$			
2H-1,2-Benzodiazepine, 2-acetyl-6,7,8,9-tetrahydro-	MeOH	262(3.79),333(2.68)	28-0959-73A
1-Cyclohexene-1-carbonitrile, 6-oxo-2-(1-pyrrolidinyl)-	EtOH	236(3.76),298(4.42)	70-0811-73
1H-Indole-3-ethanamine, 5-methoxy-	EtOH	223(4.41),276(3.84), 281s(3.83),283(3.78)	103-0196-73
1H-Indole-3-ethanamine, 7-methoxy-	EtOH	219(4.70),268(3.84), 277s(3.81),289(3.71)	103-0196-73

Compound	Solvent	λmax(log ε)	Ref.
1,8-Naphthyridin-4(1H)-one, 1-ethyl-3,4-dihydro-7-methyl-	EtOH	224(4.28),269(4.07), 383(4.49)	88-3187-73
$C_{11}H_{14}N_2OS_3$			
4-Thiazolidinone, 3-ethyl-2-thioxo-5-(3,4,5-trimethyl-2(3H)-thiazol-inylidene)- (2λ,1ε)	EtOH	418(?),432(4.62)	103-1078-73
$C_{11}H_{14}N_2O_2$			
Acetamide, N-(6-amino-3,4-dihydro-2H-1-benzopyran-8-yl)-	EtOH	245(4.05),313(3.68)	4-0623-73
Benzenamine, N,N-dimethyl-4-(2-nitro-1-propenyl)-	n.s.g.	265(--),430(4.34)	135-1299-73
2-Butanone, 4-[(phenylmethylene)amino]-, oxime, N-oxide	EtOH	294(4.34)	104-0793-73
Pyrrolo[2,3-b]indol-3a(1H)-ol, 2,3,8,8a-tetrahydro-1-hydroxy-2-methyl-	EtOH	241(4.20),297(3.37)	142-0251-73
"invertomer"	EtOH	240(3.94),297(3.42)	142-0251-73
$C_{11}H_{14}N_2O_2S$			
Acetamide, N-(5-acetyl-4-methyl-2-thia-zolyl)-N-2-propenyl-	EtOH	229(4.11),304(4.23)	80-0677-73
	EtOH-HCl	230(3.99),307(4.29)	80-0677-73
Benzene, 1-[(1-diazo-2-methylpropyl)-sulfonyl]-4-methyl-	n.s.g.	260(3.98),414(1.92)	27-0320-73
Carbamic acid, [(methylphenylamino)-thioxomethyl]-, ethyl ester	EtOH	286(4.22),353(2.34)	48-0144-73
$C_{11}H_{14}N_2O_3$			
1,7-Naphthyridin-2(1H)-one, 4-ethyl-3,4-dihydro-6-methoxy-3-oxo-	EtOH	246(4.25),298(3.79)	44-1824-73
$C_{11}H_{14}N_2O_3S$			
Acetamide, N-(1,3-dihydro-1,3-dimethyl-2,1-benzisothiazol-5-yl)-, S,S-dioxide	EtOH	260(4.25),298(3.31)	4-0249-73
1H-Thieno[3,4-d]imidazole-4-pentanoic acid, 2,3-dihydro-1-methyl-2-oxo-	EtOH	240(4.21),300(2.83)	70-1641-73
$C_{11}H_{14}N_2O_4$			
1H-1,2-Diazepine-1,4-dicarboxylic acid, diethyl ester	MeOH	214s(3.92),222(3.99),	22-0630-73
Pyridinium, 3-(ethoxycarbonyl)-1-(eth-oxycarbonyl)amino]-, hydroxide, inner salt	benzene	345(4.10)	22-0630-73
	MeOH	250s(--),324(3.69)	22-0630-73
$C_{11}H_{14}N_2O_4S$			
Homocysteine, N-formyl-S-(3-hydroxy-6-methyl-2-pyridinyl)-	M HCl	238(3.47),323(3.83)	1-1059-73
$C_{11}H_{14}N_2O_5$			
Acetamide, N-[2-hydroxy-1-(hydroxymeth-yl)-2-(4-nitrophenyl)ethyl]-	EtOH	273(4.1)	104-2144-73
$C_{11}H_{14}N_2O_6$			
Uracil-1-malonic acid, diethyl ester	neutral	260(4.00)	46-0482-73
	pH 10	253(4.22)	46-0482-73
$C_{11}H_{14}N_2O_6S$			
2H-Pyrrole-3-carboxylic acid, 5-[(2-eth-oxy-2-oxoethoxy)amino]-4-(methylthio)-2-oxo-, methyl ester	EtOH	360(4.12)	94-1667-73

Compound	Solvent	λ_{max}(log ε)	Ref.
Uridine, 4-thio-, 5'-acetate	MeOH	332(4.28)	103-0917-73
$C_{11}H_{14}N_3$			
Benzenediazonium, 2-(1-piperidinyl)-, tetrafluoroborate	M HCl	275(3.77),446(3.70)	48-0725-73
$C_{11}H_{14}N_4$			
1H-Imidazo[4,5-b]pyridin-7-amine, N-(3-methyl-2-butenyl)-	M HCl	224(4.15),266(3.95), 293(4.32)	102-2087-73
	M NaOH	226(4.30),282(4.30)	102-2087-73
	EtOH	225(4.04),267(4.08), 284(4.11)	102-2087-73
1H-Imidazo[4,5-c]pyridin-4-amine, N-(3-methyl-2-butenyl)-	M HCl	209(4.28),270(4.08)	102-2087-73
	M NaOH	227(4.22),279(4.02)	102-2087-73
	EtOH	216(4.18),269(4.24)	102-2087-73
$C_{11}H_{14}N_4O_2$			
2-Furanmethanol, 5-(4-amino-7H-pyrrolo-[2,3-d]pyrimidin-7-yl)tetrahydro-	MeOH-acid	219(4.28),275(3.92)	44-3179-73
	MeOH-base	272(3.95)	44-3179-73
2,4(1H,3H)-Pteridinedione, 7-(1,1-dimethylethyl)-3-methyl-	pH 5.0	228(4.16),323(4.02)	24-3149-73
	pH 11.0	244(4.29),270(3.95), 358(3.88)	24-3149-73
$C_{11}H_{14}N_4O_3$			
2,4(1H,3H)-Pteridinedione, 7-(1,1-dimethylethyl)-3-methyl-, 5-oxide	pH 4.0	235(4.41),286(3.93), 342(3.86)	24-3149-73
	pH 10.0	224(4.28),253(4.40), 270s(4.24),295s(3.76), 376(3.75)	24-3149-73
7H-Pyrrolo[2,3-d]pyrimidin-4-amine, 7-(3-deoxy-β-D-erythro-pentofuranosyl)-	pH 1	227(4.39),270(4.04)	23-1313-73
	pH 11	268(4.09)	23-1313-73
	MeOH	269(4.07)	23-1313-73
	MeOH-acid	230(4.38),273(4.05)	44-3179-73
	MeOH-base	271(4.05)	44-3179-73
$C_{11}H_{14}N_4O_3S$			
9H-Purine, 9-(2-deoxy-β-D-erythro-pentofuranosyl)-6-(methylthio)-	H_2O	282(4.35),290s(4.32)	23-3161-73
$C_{11}H_{14}N_4O_4$			
1H-Imidazo[4,5-b]pyrazine, 5(6)-methyl-1-β-D-ribofuranosyl-	pH 1	301(4.04),310s(4.02)	39-0244-73C
	pH 11	297s(4.04),305(4.06), 319s(3.90)	39-0244-73C
	MeOH	260s(3.43),295(4.07), 309(3.96)	39-0244-73C
9H-Purine, 2-methyl-9-β-D-ribofuranosyl-	pH 1	269(3.86)	94-0692-73
	pH 6	246(3.57),270(3.91)	94-0692-73
	pH 13	270(3.92)	94-0692-73
1H-Pyrazolo[3,4-b]pyridin-4-amine, 1-β-D-ribofuranosyl-	EtOH	218(3.72),232(3.69), 309(3.56)	104-1294-73
$C_{11}H_{14}N_4O_4S$			
Inosine, 2-methyl-6-thio-	pH 1	230(4.06),330(4.34)	94-0692-73
	pH 6	230(4.02),328(4.41)	94-0692-73
	pH 13	239s(--),315(4.29)	94-0692-73
$C_{11}H_{14}N_4O_4S_2$			
Inosine, 2-(methylthio)-6-thio-	pH 1	224(4.00),266(4.00), 337(4.13)	94-0692-73
	pH 6	228(4.08),264(4.05), 333(4.23)	94-0692-73

Compound	Solvent	λ_{max}(log ε)	Ref.
Inosine, 2-(methylthio)-6-thio- (cont.)	pH 13	267(4.21),321(4.17)	94-0692-73
$C_{11}H_{14}N_4O_5$			
D-Altritol, 2,5-anhydro-1-deoxy-1-(1,6-dihydro-6-oxo-9H-purin-9-yl)-	pH 1	249(4.04)	136-0245-73F
	H O	250(4.09)	136-0245-73F
	pH 11	253(4.13)	136-0245-73F
$C_{11}H_{14}N_5O_5P$			
1,2-Cyclopentanediol, 3-(6-amino-9H-purin-9-yl)-5-(hydroxymethyl)-, cyclic 1,5-(hydrogen phosphate)	pH 1	211(4.31),258(4.13)	36-1252-73
	pH 7	205(4.31),261(4.15)	36-1252-73
$C_{11}H_{14}N_5O_6P$			
Adenosine, 2'-O-methyl-, 3',5'-cyclic (hydrogen phosphate)	pH 1	256(4.17)	69-1010-73
	pH 11	258(4.18)	69-1010-73
$C_{11}H_{15}N_5O_7PS$			
Guanosine, 8-(methylthio)-, cyclic 3',5'-(hydrogen phosphate)	pH 1	273(4.25)	69-5310-73
	pH 11	283(4.17)	69-5310-73
$C_{11}H_{14}N_6O$			
Urea, N-ethyl-N-2-propenyl-N'-1H-purin-6-yl-	pH 1-2	280(4.31)	87-0139-73
	pH 5-7	277.5(4.24)	87-0139-73
	pH 12	279(4.16)	87-0139-73
$C_{11}H_{14}N_6O_3$			
Glycine, N-(N-1H-purin-6-yl)glycyl-, ethyl ester	pH 1	276(4.24)	94-2349-73
	pH 7	266(4.23)	94-2349-73
	pH 13	273(4.21),280s(4.08)	94-2349-73
L-Valine, N-(1H-purin-6-ylamino)carbonyl]-	pH 1-2	277.5(4.30)	87-0139-73
	pH 5-7	270(4.28)	87-0139-73
	pH 12	278(4.24)	87-0139-73
$C_{11}H_{14}N_6O_3S$			
L-Methionine, N-[(1H-purin-6-ylamino)-carbonyl]-	pH 1-2	277.5(4.31)	87-0139-73
	pH 5-7	270(4.27)	87-0139-73
	pH 12	278(4.24)	87-0139-73
$C_{11}H_{14}N_6O_4$			
DL-Threonine, N-[(1H-purin-6-ylamino)-carbonyl]-, methyl ester	pH 1-2	277(4.29)	87-0139-73
	pH 5-7	268(4.26)	87-0139-73
	pH 12	277(4.21)	87-0139-73
$C_{11}H_{14}N_6O_5$			
Adenosine, N-methyl-N-nitroso-	pH 1	221(4.09),265(3.76), 295(3.99)	87-0365-73
	pH 7	224(4.11),265(3.76), 295(3.99)	87-0365-73
	pH 13	227(4.11),265(3.76), 295(3.99)	87-0365-73
$C_{11}H_{14}N_6O_6$			
Adenosine, 5'-C-(nitromethyl)-	pH 1	256(4.16)	136-0225-73B
	pH 7	259(4.18)	136-0225-73B
	pH 13	253(4.32)	136-0225-73B
$C_{11}H_{14}O$			
2(1H)-Azulenone, 4,5,6,7,8,8aα-hexahydro-8-methylene-	EtOH	230(4.09)	44-0967-73
2(1H)-Azulenone, 4,5,6,7-tetrahydro-8-methyl-	EtOH	300(4.04)	44-0967-73

Compound	Solvent	$\lambda_{max}(\log \epsilon)$	Ref.
Benzene, 1-methoxy-4-(1-methyl-1-propenyl)-	hexane	254(4.13)	104-2473-73
5H-Benzocyclohepten-2-ol, 6,7,8,9-tetrahydro-	MeOH	218(3.77),224(3.76), 276(3.29)	73-2989-73
2-Butanone, 3-methyl-1-phenyl-	C_6H_{12}	290(1.13)	28-0407-73B
	MeOH	290(1.10)	28-0407-73B
3-Buten-2-ol, 2-(4-methylphenyl)-	hexane	218(3.93),258(2.60), 263(2.63),258(2.54), 272(2.51)[sic]	104-2473-73
2,4-Cyclohexadien-1-one, 2,6-dimethyl-6-(2-propenyl)-	EtOH	309(3.70)	33-0014-73
Cyclopent[cd]inden-1-one, 2,2a,3,4,4a-5,6,7-octahydro-	EtOH	241(4.08)	44-3829-73
3a,6-Ethano-3aH-inden-3(2H)-one, 1,6,7,7a-tetrahydro-, endo	EtOH	290(2.20)	35-5662-73
exo	EtOH	295(2.09)	35-5662-73
5H-Inden-5-one, 2,3,6,7-tetrahydro-1,2-dimethyl-	EtOH	303(4.29)	22-2098-73
1H-3a,6-Methanoazulen-7(4H)-one, 2,3,5,6-tetrahydro-	EtOH	242(4.07)	44-2125-73
2(3H)-Naphthalenone, 4,6,7,8-tetrahydro-5-methyl-	EtOH	300(4.21)	22-2098-73
2(3H)-Naphthalenone, 4,6,7,8-tetrahydro-6-methyl-	n.s.g.	287(4.05)	39-1757-73C
3-Pentanone, 1-phenyl-	C_6H_{12}	280(1.78)	28-0407-73B
	MeOH	280(1.83)	28-0407-73B
4-Penten-1-one, 1-(1,3-cyclohexadien-1-yl)-	EtOH	300(4.05)	35-5662-73
Phenol, 2,6-dimethyl-4-(1-propenyl)-, cis	EtOH	257(4.18)	49-1008-73
Spiro[4.5]deca-3,6-dien-2-one, 6-methyl-	EtOH	218(3.96)	44-0967-73
Tricyclo[7.2.0.0^{4,9}]undec-3-en-2-one	EtOH	236(4.12)	44-2125-73
Valerophenone	heptane	238(4.15)	35-5604-73
$C_{11}H_{14}OS$			
1H-2-Benzothiopyran-4-ol, 3,4-dihydro-1,4-dimethyl-	EtOH	205(4.03),262(2.32), 268(2.19),272(2.17)	39-0410-73C
4H-Cyclohepta[b]thiophen-4-one, 5,6,7,8-tetrahydro-2,6-dimethyl-	EtOH	226(4.12),256(4.08), 283s(--)	39-0968-73C
2H-Pyran, tetrahydro-2-(phenylthio)-	40% dioxan	250(3.85)	35-8407-73
$C_{11}H_{14}OSi$			
2,3-Octadiene-5,7-diyn-1-ol, 8-(trimethylsilyl)-, (E)-	n.s.g.	214(4.53),220(4.60), 233s(3.48),246(3.56), 259(3.83),274(4.11), 291(4.03)	88-1019-73
$C_{11}H_{14}O_2$			
1,8-Azulenedione, 2,3,4,5,6,7-hexahydro-4-methyl-	MeOH	233(4.12)	44-0095-73
Benzene, 1,2-dimethoxy-4-propenyl-	EtOH	260(4.22),293s(3.72)	141-0001-73
Benzeneacetaldehyde, 2-methoxy-α,5-dimethyl-	EtOH	280(3.36)	33-2961-73
Benzenepentanoic acid	EtOH	238(1.86),244(1.98), 249(2.13),254(2.26), 256(2.26),260(2.33), 262(2.33),265(2.22), 269(2.23)	18-2504-73
1-Butanone, 1-(2-hydroxy-4-methylphenyl)-	90% EtOH	219(3.91),262(3.94), 325(3.44)	12-1069-73

Compound	Solvent	$\lambda_{max}(\log \epsilon)$	Ref.
3-Buten-2-ol, 2-(3-methoxyphenyl)-	hexane	217(3.94),272(3.39), 280(3.35)	104-2473-73
5H-Inden-5-one, 1,2,3,7a-tetrahydro-4-methoxy-7a-methyl-	EtOH	242(3.74),276(3.14)	44-3663-73
1,5-Naphthalenedione, 2,3,4,6,7,8-hexahydro-4-methyl-	EtOH	264(4.08)	44-4281-73
1,6(2H,7H)-Naphthalenedione, 3,4,8,8a-tetrahydro-8a-methyl-	EtOH	244(4.08)	22-0359-73
1(4H)-Naphthalenone, 4a,5,8,8a-tetrahydro-3-methoxy-, cis	MeOH	251(4.09)	12-0595-73
12-Oxatricyclo[4.4.1.1^{2,5}]dodec-3-en-11-one	hexane	260(1.28),271(1.35), 281(1.41),290(1.50), 300(1.54),310(1.47), 321(1.17)	88-1737-73
Spiro[5.5]undec-7-ene-1,9-dione	EtOH	226(3.89)	39-0393-73C
$C_{11}H_{14}O_2S$			
Benzenecarbothioic acid, O-(2-ethoxyethyl) ester	EtOH	258(3.86),287(4.04), 418(2.15)	39-1574-73C
Benzo[b]thiophene, 2,3-dihydro-2-propyl-, 1,1-dioxide	EtOH	261(2.83),267(2.82), 275(2.02)	2-0628-73
1H-2-Benzothiopyran, 3,4-dihydro-1,3-dimethyl-, 2,2-dioxide, cis	EtOH	211(3.91),258(2.35), 263(2.40),272(2.28)	39-0410-73C
1H-2-Benzothiopyran, 3,4-dihydro-1,4-dimethyl-, 2,2-dioxide, cis	EtOH	211(3.87),258(2.32), 267(2.25),271(2.17)	39-0410-73C
$C_{11}H_{14}O_3$			
Benzaldehyde, 4-hydroxy-5-methoxy-2-propyl-	EtOH	236(4.26),283(4.00), 316(3.88)	12-1337-73
	EtOH-KOH	256(4.06),352(4.36)	12-1337-73
1(4H)-Naphthalenone, 4a,5,8,8a-tetrahydro-4-hydroxy-3-methoxy-	MeOH	251.5(4.11)	12-0595-73
Pentanoic acid, 3-hydroxy-5-phenyl-	EtOH	221(2.72),260(2.43)	28-1131-73A
$C_{11}H_{14}O_3S$			
2-Thiophenepentanoic acid, β,5-dimethyl-δ-oxo-	EtOH	264(3.90),296(3.99)	39-0968-73C
$C_{11}H_{14}O_4$			
1,7-Dioxa-2H-cyclopent[cd]indene-5-carboxylic acid, 2a,3,4,4a,7a,7b-hexahydro-, methyl ester, [2aR-(2aα,4aα,7aα,7bα)]-	MeOH	236.5(4.05)	94-0497-73
Ethanone, 1-(2,4,5-trimethoxyphenyl)-	EtOH	233(4.21),269(3.99), 329(3.91)	141-0001-73
	dioxan	231(4.23),266(3.99), 323(3.85)	141-0001-73
Ethanone, 1-(2,4,6-trimethoxyphenyl)-	EtOH	223(4.06),274(3.75)	141-0001-73
	dioxan	225(4.09),262(3.68)	141-0001-73
1-Propanone, 1-(2,6-dihydroxy-4-methoxyphenyl)-2-methyl-	MeOH	228(3.4),286(4.2), 324s(3.4)	12-2065-73
	MeOH-base	224(4.2),295(4.2), 375(3.55)	12-2065-73
$C_{11}H_{14}O_5$			
Benzoic acid, 2-hydroxy-5,6-dimethoxy-3-methyl-, methyl ester	EtOH	222(4.60),269(3.50), 308(3.35)	12-2459-73
Cyclopenta[c]pyran-4-carboxylic acid, 1,4a,5,6,7,7a-hexahydro-1-methoxy-6-oxo-, methyl ester	EtOH	236(4.01)	35-0540-73

Compound	Solvent	λ_{max}(log ε)	Ref.
Cyclopenta[c]pyran-4-carboxylic acid, 1,4a,5,7a-tetrahydro-1-hydroxy-7-(hydroxymethyl)-, methyl ester	EtOH	240(4.01)	94-2684-73
$C_{11}H_{14}O_6$			
Benzoic acid, 2-hydroxy-3-(hydroxymethyl)-4,6-dimethoxy-, methyl ester	EtOH	225(4.48),269(4.25), 303(3.59)	12-2459-73
	EtOH-KOH	217(4.46),267(3.61), 298(3.50)	12-2459-73
Benzoic acid, 6-hydroxy-3-(hydroxymethyl)-2,4-dimethoxy-, methyl ester	EtOH	222(4.70),263(4.55), 299(3.92)	12-2459-73
	EtOH-KOH	231s(4.58),256(4.26), 300(3.92)	12-2459-73
$C_{11}H_{14}O_7$			
2-Furancarboxaldehyde, 5-[(β-D-xylopyranosyloxy)methyl]-	n.s.g.	282(3.2)	23-1359-73
$C_{11}H_{14}S$			
1H-2-Benzothiopyran, 3,4-dihydro-1,4-dimethyl-, cis	EtOH	209(4.03),258(2.56), 263(2.57),270(2.43)	39-0410-73C
$C_{11}H_{14}S_2$			
Benzenecarbodithioic acid, 4-methyl-, 1-methylethyl ester	C_6H_{12}	309(4.10),509(2.10)	101-0121-73I
Thieno[3,2-b]thiophen, 2-ethyl-3,5,6-trimethyl-	C_6H_{12}	270(4.05),276(4.06), 287s(3.97)	49-0312-73
$C_{11}H_{15}$			
Cycloheptatrienylium, (1,1-dimethylethyl)-, perchlorate	pH 1	293(3.69)	18-1785-73
Cycloheptatrienylium, 1,2,3,4-tetramethyl-, trifluoroacetate	H_2SO_4	242(4.33),295(3.35), 301s(3.31)	33-2796-73
chloroplatinate	H_2SO_4	243(4.72),295(3.78)	33-2796-73
	MeCN	244(4.68),268(4.14), 297s(3.91)	33-2796-73
Cycloheptatrienylium, 1,2,4,6-tetramethyl-, trifluoroacetate	H_2SO_4	240(4.54),297(3.57), 307(3.44)	33-2796-73
chloroplatinate	H_2SO_4	240(4.95),292(4.07), 297s(4.00),307(3.84)	33-2796-73
	MeCN	241(4.84),269(4.24), 295s(4.14),308(3.89)	33-2796-73
Propylium, 1,2-dimethyl-1-phenyl-	FSO_3H at -75°	332(4.40),390s(<3.3)	59-0803-73
Propylium, 2-methyl-1-(4-methylphenyl)-	FSO_3H at -75°	337(4.32)	59-0803-73
$C_{11}H_{15}As$			
Arsenin, 4-cyclohexyl-	EtOH	223(4.12),288(4.20)	89-0931-73
$C_{11}H_{15}BrN_2S_2$			
Dithiobenzoic acid, 4-bromo-, piperazine salt	EtOH	298(4.18),360(3.89), 500(2.20)	143-0359-73
$C_{11}H_{15}BrO$			
2H-Inden-2-one, 7a-(2-bromoethyl)-1,4,5,6,7,7a-hexahydro-	EtOH	233(4.12)	44-2125-73
$C_{11}H_{15}BrO_3$			
Bicyclo[4.1.0]heptane-3-carboxylic acid, (cont.)	EtOH	212(3.58)	44-1726-73

Compound	Solvent	$\lambda_{max}(\log \epsilon)$	Ref.
4-bromo-7,7-dimethyl-5-oxo-, methyl ester, (1α,3β,4α,6α)-(±)-			
$C_{11}H_{15}Cl_2N$			
2H-Pyrrole, 5-(2,2-dichloroethenyl)-3,4-dihydro-2,2-dimethyl-4-(1-methylethylidene)-	MeOH	223s(--),231s(--), 252(3.95)	18-0540-73
$C_{11}H_{15}Cl_2NO_2$			
2,5-Cyclohexadien-1-one, 4-(dichloromethyl)-2-methoxy-4-propyl-, oxime	EtOH	243(4.37),274(4.18)	12-1337-73
$C_{11}H_{15}FN_2O_6S$			
Thymidine, 3'-deoxy-3'-fluoro-, 5'-methanesulfonate	MeOH	263.5(3.96)	48-0895-73
$C_{11}H_{15}F_2NO_8$			
D-glycero-D-galacto-Non-2-enonic acid, 2,6-anhydro-3,5-dideoxy-5-[(difluoroacetyl)amino]-	n.s.g.	240(3.83)	49-0402-73
$C_{11}H_{15}N$			
1-Benzazocine, 1,2,3,4,5,6-hexahydro-	EtOH	230(3.31),261(2.98), 304(2.26)	18-2504-73
1-Pentalenamine, 1,5-dihydro-N,N,2-trimethyl-	hexane	312(4.39),317(4.39)	89-0335-73
2-Propanamine, 2-methyl-N-(phenylmethylene)-	EtOH	244(4.19),277s(3.08), 284s(2.90)	35-4692-73
5H-2-Pyrindine, 6,7-dihydro-4,6,6-trimethyl-	EtOH	261(3.51),269(3.47)	1-1573-73
2H-Pyrrole, 5-ethynyl-3,4-dihydro-2,2-dimethyl-4-(1-methylethylidene)-	MeOH	208(3.79),223(3.84), 267(4.04)	18-0540-73
$C_{11}H_{15}NO$			
Benzaldehyde, 4-(diethylamino)-	CH_2Cl_2	343.0(4.55)	39-0514-73B
protonated	CH_2Cl_2	243(4.20),279(3.22), 290s(--)	39-0514-73B
diprotonated	CH_2Cl_2	280(4.09),325s(3.06)	39-0514-73B
1:1 BF_3 adduct to nitrogen	CH_2Cl_2	240(4.32),278(3.28), 288(3.23)	39-0514-73B
1:1 BF_3 adduct to carbonyl	CH_2Cl_2	392(--),404(--)	39-0514-73B
2:1 BF_3 adduct	CH_2Cl_2	268(4.04),315s(--)	39-0514-73B
2,4,6-Cycloheptatrien-1-one, 2-(butylamino)-	EtOH	337(3.95),406(3.93)	35-7101-73
2,4,6-Cycloheptatrien-1-one, 2-(diethylamino)-	EtOH	354(3.94),415(3.83)	35-7101-73
Ethanone, 1-[4-(1,1-dimethylethyl)-2-pyridinyl]-	MeOH	234(3.79),270(3.45)	78-0391-73
$C_{11}H_{15}NOS$			
Benzenamine, N,N-dimethyl-4-[2-(methylsulfinyl)ethenyl]-	EtOH	238(4.00),345(4.42)	118-0164-73
$C_{11}H_{15}NOS_2$			
Morpholinium dithiobenzoate	EtOH	284(4.08),360(3.79), 455(2.20)	143-0359-73
$C_{11}H_{15}NO_2$			
Acetamide, N-[2-(1-hydroxy-1-methylethyl)phenyl]-	EtOH	246(4.10)	88-0903-73

Compound	Solvent	$\lambda_{max}(\log \epsilon)$	Ref.
Acetamide, N-(3-hydroxy-2-propylphenyl)-	EtOH	278(3.36)	44-0831-73
Acetamide, N-(3-hydroxy-4-propylphenyl)-	EtOH	248(4.11),285(3.66)	44-0831-73
2,4,6-Cycloheptatrien-1-one, 2-methoxy-x-propyl-, oxime	EtOH	230(4.20),249(4.10), 320(3.94),352(3.54)	12-1337-73
1-Cyclohexene-1-carbonitrile, 2-ethoxy-4,4-dimethyl-6-oxo-	EtOH	270(4.20)	70-0811-73
Pyridine, 1,4-diacetyl-1,4-dihydro-3,4-dimethyl-	MeOH	256(4.20)	78-0391-73
Pyridine, 1,4-diacetyl-4-ethyl-1,4-dihydro-	MeOH	254(4.19)	78-0391-73
2(1H)-Pyridinone, 3-acetyl-1-butyl-	EtOH	242(3.88),349(4.16)	103-0615-73
$C_{11}H_{15}NO_2S$			
Benzo[b]thiophene-3-carboxylic acid, 2-amino-4,5,6,7-tetrahydro-, ethyl ester	EtOH	230(4.31),308(3.70)	103-0300-73
$C_{11}H_{15}NO_2Se$			
Benzo[b]selenophene-3-carboxylic acid, 2-amino-4,5,6,7-tetrahydro-, ethyl ester	EtOH	235(4.21),320(3.55)	103-0300-73
$C_{11}H_{15}NO_3S$			
2,1-Benzisothiazole, 1,3-dihydro-5-(1-methoxyethyl)-1-methyl-, 2,2-dioxide	EtOH	241(4.14),289(3.24)	4-0249-73
$C_{11}H_{15}NO_4$			
Acetophenone, 2',4',5'-trimethoxy-, oxime	EtOH	215(4.26),253(3.94), 298(3.75)	141-0001-73
	dioxan	222(4.10),252(3.97), 299(3.76)	141-0001-73
Glutaconic acid, 1-cyano-2-methyl-, diethyl ester	EtOH	236(4.17),355(3.86)	78-4103-73
	EtOH-NaOH	246(4.18),355(4.59)	78-4103-73
$C_{11}H_{15}NO_4S$			
3-Cyclohexen-1-one, 3-hydroxy-5,5-dimethyl-2-[1-(methylthio)-2-nitroethylidene]-	EtOH	263(4.12),355(4.02)	95-0612-73
$C_{11}H_{15}NO_5$			
Isoxazole, 3-(tetrahydro-6-methoxy-2,2-dimethylfuro[2,3-d]-1,3-dioxol-5-yl)-	EtOH	220(3.62)	136-0311-73D
2(1H)-Pyridinone, 1-(2-deoxy-α-D-erythro-pentofuranosyl)-4-hydroxy-5-methyl-	MeOH	286(3.58)	88-3079-73
	MeOH	285(3.68)	87-0524-73
	pH 1	271(3.62)	87-0524-73
	pH 14	258(3.94)	87-0524-73
β-anomer	MeOH	288(3.65)	88-3079-73
	MeOH	286(3.69)	87-0524-73
	pH 1	273(3.63)	87-0524-73
	pH 14	258(3.99)	87-0524-73
1H-Pyrrole-3,4-dicarboxylic acid, 1-(hydroxymethyl)-, diethyl ester	EtOH	250(3.83)	23-1089-73
$C_{11}H_{15}NO_6S$			
3aH-Indole-3a-sulfonic acid, 1,2,3,4,5-6-hexahydro-3-hydroxy-1-(1-methylethyl)-5,6-dioxo-, sodium salt	H_2O	247(3.86),352(4.21)	39-0509-73C
$C_{11}H_{15}NS_2$			
Cyclopentanecarbodithioic acid, 3-cyclopentylidene-2-imino-	EtOH	260(3.57),306(3.67), 322(3.69),436(4.11)	39-1009-73C

Compound	Solvent	$\lambda_{max}(\log \epsilon)$	Ref.
$C_{11}H_{15}N_2O$			
Cyclopenta[c]pyrrol-1-ylium, 3-(dimethylamino)-1-ethoxy-1,2-dihydro-	CH_2Cl_2	260(4.00),267(4.01), 272(3.87),372(4.08), 381(4.11),522(3.24)	89-0418-73
$C_{11}H_{15}N_3$			
Imidazo[1,2-a]pyridine-2-ethanamine, N,N-dimethyl-, dihydrobromide	H_2O	275(3.90)	87-1272-73
Imidazo[1,5-a]pyridine-1-ethanamine, N,N-dimethyl-, dihydrochloride	H_2O	274(3.80),284(3.76), 318(3.44)	87-1272-73
$C_{11}H_{15}N_3O$			
1,2,4-Triazin-4-ol, 2,3,4,5-tetrahydro-3,5-dimethyl-6-phenyl-	EtOH	286(4.04)	103-0123-73
$C_{11}H_{15}N_3O_2S_2$			
Carbamic acid, (5-butyl-2H-thiazolo-[3,2-b][1,2,4]thiadiazol-2-ylidene)-, ethyl ester	EtOH	251(3.62),314(4.37)	94-2408-73
$C_{11}H_{15}N_3O_3$			
Pyrazinecarboxylic acid, 3-amino-6-methyl-5-(1-methylethenyl)-, ethyl ester, 4-oxide	EtOH	233(4.17),253(4.25), 287s(3.55),378(3.94)	35-6407-73
$C_{11}H_{15}N_3O_5S$			
4H-Pyrrolo[2,3-d]pyrimidin-4-one, 2-(β-D-ribofuranosylthio)-3,5,6,7-tetrahydro-	EtOH	232(4.09),274(3.66)	104-1995-73
$C_{11}H_{15}N_3O_6$			
Cytidine, 2'-acetate	pH 2	278.5(4.06)	44-0593-73
	pH 10	270(3.89)	44-0593-73
Cytosine, 2,2'-anhydro-1-β-D-arabinofuranosyl-, acetic acid salt	H_2O	232(3.99),263(4.03)	44-0593-73
$C_{11}H_{15}N_3O_6S$			
Uridine, 5-(2-amino-2-oxoethyl)-2-thio-	MeOH	221(4.1),276(4.1)	24-3039-73
	MeOH-NaOH	242(4.3),272(4.2)	24-3039-73
$C_{11}H_{15}N_5$			
1H-Pyrazolo[4,3-d]pyrimidin-7-amine, N-cyclopentyl-3-methyl- (all spectra in ethanol)	pH 1	263(3.82),312(4.15)	102-0025-73
	pH 7	239(3.79),295(4.13), 308(4.02),320s(--)	102-0025-73
	pH 12	246(4.18),266s(--), 310(3.93)	102-0025-73
$C_{11}H_{15}N_5O_2$			
9H-Purine-9-butanoic acid, 6-amino-, ethyl ester	pH 1	258.5(4.11)	35-4010-73
	H_2O	261.5(4.15)	35-4010-73
	pH 13	261(4.16)	35-4010-73
$C_{11}H_{15}N_5O_3$			
9H-Purin-6-amine, 9-(3-deoxy-3-methyl-α-D-xylofuranosyl)-	H_2O	260(4.13)	136-0071-73A
β-anomer	H_2O	260(4.15)	136-0071-73A
Pyrimido[5,4-e]-1,2,4-triazine, 3-ethoxy-5-methoxy-7-propoxy-	C_6H_{12}	235(4.31),255s(3.86), 275s(3.02),355s(3.58), 364s(3.67),372(3.75), 383(3.66),391(3.67), 471(2.45)	12-1689-73

Compound	Solvent	λmax(log ε)	Ref.
Pyrimido[5,4-e]-1,2,4-triazine, 3,5,7-triethoxy-	C_6H_{12}	236(4.33),255s(3.86), 278s(2.98),355s(3.61), 365s(3.71),373(3.78), 384(3.69),391(3.70), 474(2.44)	12-1689-73
$C_{11}H_{15}N_5O_4$			
D-Altritol, 1-(6-amino-9H-purin-9-yl)-	pH 1	259(4.15)	136-0245-73F
2,5-anhydro-1-deoxy-	H_2O	260(4.15)	136-0245-73F
1,2-Cyclopentanediol, 3-[6-(hydroxy-	pH 1	266(4.22)	36-1252-73
amino)-9H-purin-9-yl]-5-(hydroxy-	pH 7	267(4.14)	36-1252-73
methyl)-, (1α,2α,3β,5β)-(±)-			
D-Glucitol, 6-(6-amino-9H-purin-9-yl)-	H_2O	260(4.23)	136-0243-73B
1,4-anhydro-6-deoxy-			
hydrochloride	pH 1	258(4.15)	136-0243-73B
	H_2O	260(4.25)	136-0243-73B
	pH 13	260(4.06)	136-0243-73B
Guanine, 9-[2,3-dihydroxy-4-(hydroxy-	pH 1	255(4.08),278(3.90)	36-1432-73
methyl)cyclopentyl]-	pH 7	253(4.11),268s(--)	36-1432-73
	pH 13	257s(4.02),268(4.05)	36-1432-73
Guanine, 7-β-D-glucopyranosyl-	pH 1	256(3.90)	136-0149-73B
	H_2O	287(3.88)	136-0149-73B
	pH 13	284(3.80)	136-0149-73B
Guanine, 9-β-D-glucopyranosyl-	pH 1	257(4.11),275s(3.95)	136-0149-73B
	H_2O	253(4.14),270s(3.99)	136-0149-73B
	pH 13	263(4.05)	136-0149-73B
D-Mannitol, 1-(6-amino-9H-purin-9-yl)-	pH 1	258(4.18)	136-0243-73B
3,6-anhydro-1-deoxy-, hydrochloride	H_2O	260(4.24)	136-0243-73B
	pH 13	260(4.26)	136-0243-73B
9H-Purin-6-amine, 9-(6-deoxy-L-manno-	pH 1	257(4.17)	44-3704-73
furanosyl)-	H_2O	260(4.17)	44-3704-73
	pH 13	260(4.18)	44-3704-73
α-D-Ribofuranoside, methyl 5-(6-amino-	pH 2	260(4.10)	18-3165-73
purin-9-yl)-5-deoxy-	H_2O	262(4.09)	18-3165-73
	pH 12	261(4.11)	18-3165-73
β-anomer	pH 2	260(4.19)	18-3165-73
	H_2O	261(4.18)	18-3165-73
	pH 12	261(4.18)	18-3165-73
$C_{11}H_{15}N_5O_5$			
Adenosine, N-methoxy-	pH 1	266(4.20)	94-1676-73
	pH 7	268(4.16)	94-1676-73
	pH 13	283(4.07)	94-1676-73
	EtOH	267(4.13)	94-1676-73
$C_{11}H_{15}N_6O_7P$			
Guanosine, 8-(methylamino)-, cyclic	pH 1	253(4.21),290(3.95)	69-5310-73
3',5'-(hydrogen phosphate)	pH 7	258(4.18),297(3.89)	69-5310-73
	pH 11	260(4.17)	69-5310-73
$C_{11}H_{15}OP$			
Phosphine, benzoyldiethyl-	C_6H_{12}	256(4.10),286s(--), 380(2.43)	18-1803-73
	MeCN	202(4.16),242(4.02), 276(3.54),376(2.78)	18-1803-73
	CH_2Cl_2	382(2.84)	18-1803-73
$C_{11}H_{15}OPS$			
Phosphine sulfide, benzoyldiethyl-	C_6H_{12}	255(4.04),287s(--), 407(2.61)	18-1803-73

Compound	Solvent	$\lambda_{max}(\log \epsilon)$	Ref.
Phosphine sulfide, benzoyldiethyl- (cont.)	MeCN	212(4.04),225(3.70), 255(4.13),286s(--), 395(2.83)	18-1803-73
	CH_2Cl_2	398(2.79)	18-1803-73
$C_{11}H_{15}P$			
Phosphorin, 4-cyclohexyl-	EtOH	210(4.34),225(4.16), 294(2.85),300(2.75)	89-0931-73
$C_{11}H_{16}$			
Bicyclo[5.3.1]undeca-7,9-diene	C_6H_{12}	273(3.67)	35-5088-73
1,3-Cyclohexadiene, 1-(4-pentenyl)-	hexane	263(3.80)	35-5662-73
1,3-Cyclohexadiene, 5-(4-pentenyl)-	hexane	259.5(3.63)	35-5662-73
1-Cyclohexene, 1-(1,3-pentadienyl)-, (Z,E)-	n.s.g.	250(4.22),269(4.35), 287(4.27)	78-3797-73
(Z,Z)-	n.s.g.	270(4.23)	78-3797-73
Naphthalene, 1,2,3,4,8,8a-hexahydro- 8-methyl-	n.s.g.	270(3.65)	78-3797-73
$C_{11}H_{16}ClNO_8$			
D-glycero-D-galacto-Non-2-enonic acid, 2,6-anhydro-5-[(chloroacetyl)amino]- 3,5-dideoxy-	n.s.g.	240(3.82)	49-0402-73
$C_{11}H_{16}ClN_3O$			
4H-1,3-Oxazine, 2-(4-chloro-1-methyl-1H- pyrazol-3-yl)-5,6-dihydro-4,4,6-tri- methyl-	EtOH	224(4.01)	18-0540-73
$C_{11}H_{16}FNO_8$			
D-glycero-D-galacto-Non-2-enonic acid, 2,6-anhydro-3,5-dideoxy-5-[(fluoro- acetyl)amino]-	n.s.g.	240(3.69)	49-0402-73
$C_{11}H_{16}GeOS$			
Germane, trimethyl[(2-methylbenzoyl)- thio]-	C_6H_{12}	240(4.05),267(3.88)	18-0244-73
Germane, trimethyl[(3-methylbenzoyl)- thio]-	C_6H_{12}	243(4.06),267(3.93)	18-0244-73
Germane, trimethyl[(4-methylbenzoyl)- thio]-	C_6H_{12}	249(4.15),267(4.09)	18-0244-73
$C_{11}H_{16}GeO_2S$			
Germane, [(2-methoxybenzoyl)thio]tri- methyl-	C_6H_{12}	246(3.98)	18-0244-73
Germane, [(4-methoxybenzoyl)thio]tri- methyl-	C_6H_{12}	222(4.12),279(4.28)	18-0244-73
$C_{11}H_{16}GeS_2$			
Germane, trimethyl[[(4-methylphenyl)- thioxomethyl]thio-	C_6H_{12}	314(4.16),530(2.17)	101-0121-73I
$C_{11}H_{16}INO_8$			
D-glycero-D-galacto-Non-2-enonic acid, 2,6-anhydro-3,5-dideoxy-5-[(iodoacet- yl)amino]-	n.s.g.	239(3.94)	49-0402-73
$C_{11}H_{16}NO_5P$			
Pyridine, 3-acetyl-1-(4-phosphonooxy- butyl)-, hydrochloride	pH 9.5	267(3.58)	5-0961-73

Compound	Solvent	λmax(log ε)	Ref.
$C_{11}H_{16}NO_6P$			
Phosphoric acid, butyl methyl 4-nitrophenyl ester	MeCN	212(3.91),273(3.98)	35-3019-73
$C_{11}H_{16}N_2$			
Benzenecarboximidamide, N,N-diethyl-	EtOH	205(4.15)	36-1899-73
Hydrazine, 2-(1-buten-3-yl)-1-methyl-1-phenyl-	MeCN	252(4.11),292(3.28)	22-3487-73
Methanimidamide, N'-(2,6-dimethylphenyl)-N,N-dimethyl-	C_6H_{12}	241(4.06)	78-4205-73
Pyrazole, 3-(3-buten-1-yl)-5-methyl-4-(2-propenyl)-	EtOH	223(3.73)	78-4159-73
$C_{11}H_{16}N_2O$			
1,8-Naphthyridin-4-ol, 1-ethyl-1,2,3,4-tetrahydro-7-methyl-	EtOH	256(4.25),319(3.85)	88-3187-73
6-Phthalazinol, 1-ethyl-1,2,3,4-tetrahydro-1-methyl-, hydrochloride	EtOH	280(3.18)	39-0471-73C
$C_{11}H_{16}N_2O_2S_4$			
Acetamide, N-[2-[[(ethylthio)(3-methyl-4-oxo-2-thioxo-5-thiazolidinylidene)methyl]thio]ethyl]-	EtOH	294(3.84),399(4.26)	94-1431-73
[2,5'-Bithiazolidin]-4'-one, 3-acetyl-2-(ethylthio)-3'-methyl-2'-thioxo-	EtOH	267(4.06),297(4.22)	94-1431-73
$C_{11}H_{16}N_2O_3$			
Acetamide, N-[2-(4-aminophenyl)-2-hydroxy-1-(hydroxymethyl)ethyl]-	EtOH	240(4.1),287(3.2)	104-2144-73
$C_{11}H_{16}N_2O_4S$			
Uridine, 2-deoxy-5-ethyl-2-thio-, α-anomer	MeOH	221(4.1),274(4.3)	24-3039-73
	MeOH-NaOH	240(4.3),264s(4.1)	24-3039-73
β-anomer	H_2O	220(4.2),278(4.2)	24-3039-73
	pH 12	242(4.4),265s(4.2)	24-3039-73
$C_{11}H_{16}N_2O_6$			
2,4(1H,3H)-Pyrimidinedione, 5-ethyl-1-β-D-xylopyranosyl-	acid	265.5(3.98)	94-1382-73
	pH 7	265.5(3.98)	94-1382-73
	base	265.5(3.85)	94-1382-73
Uridine, 2',3'-di-O-methyl-	pH 2	262(4.01)	69-0194-73
	pH 12	262(3.90)	69-0194-73
Uridine, 5'-O-ethyl-	pH 2	262(3.98)	69-0194-73
	pH 12	262(3.84)	69-0194-73
$C_{11}H_{16}N_2O_7$			
α-D-Glucopyranoside, methyl 6-deoxy-6-(3,4-dihydro-2,4-dioxo-1(2H)-pyrimidinyl)-	pH 2	266(4.08)	18-3165-73
	H_2O	266(4.08)	18-3165-73
	pH 12	265(3.95)	18-3165-73
$C_{11}H_{16}N_5O$			
Morpholinium, 4-(3,9-dihydro-3,9-dimethyl-6H-purin-6-ylidene)-, iodide	H_2O	292(4.34)	104-1316-73
perchlorate	H_2O	292(4.34)	104-1316-73
7H-Purinium, 3,7-dimethyl-6-morpholino-, iodide	H_2O	307(4.31)	104-1316-73
7H-Purinium, 7,9-dimethyl-6-morpholino-, iodide	H_2O	300(4.13)	104-1316-73
perchlorate	H_2O	300(4.13)	104-1316-73

Compound	Solvent	$\lambda_{max}(\log \epsilon)$	Ref.
$C_{11}H_{16}N_5O_3$			
1H-Purinium, 2-amino-7-(2-ethoxy-1-methyl-2-oxoethyl)-6,9-dihydro-9-methyl-6-oxo-, bromide	pH 5	255(4.08),281(3.89)	24-1389-73
	pH 10	220(4.43),251(3.77), 284(3.91)	24-1389-73
1H-Purinium, 2-amino-7-(2-ethoxy-2-oxoethyl)-6,9-dihydro-1,9-dimethyl-6-oxo-	pH 4	256(4.01),285(3.89)	24-1389-73
1H-Purinium, 2-amino-7-(2-ethoxy-2-oxoethyl)-6,9-dihydro-8,9-dimethyl-6-oxo-	pH 5	253(4.10),281(3.92)	24-1389-73
	pH 10	254(3.83),281(3.97)	24-1389-73
1H-Purinium, 2-amino-7-(3-ethoxy-3-oxopropyl)-6,9-dihydro-9-methyl-6-oxo-	pH 4	254(4.06),281(3.85)	24-1389-73
	pH 10	219(4.30),250(3.76), 283(3.88)	24-1389-73
$C_{11}H_{16}N_5O_6P$			
1,2-Cyclopentanediol, 3-(6-amino-9H-purin-9-yl)-5-[(phosphonooxy)methyl]-, (1α,2α,3β,5β)-(±)-	pH 1	212(4.32),258(4.16)	36-1252-73
	pH 7	204(4.34),261(4.18)	36-1252-73
$C_{11}H_{16}N_5O_8P$			
9H-Purin-6-amine, 9-(5-O-phosphono-α-D-mannofuranosyl)-	pH 2	256.5(4.18)	136-0133-73E
	pH 7	259(4.18)	136-0133-73E
9H-Purin-6-amine, 9-(6-O-phosphono-α-D-mannofuranosyl)-	pH 2	257(4.16)	136-0133-73E
	pH 7	259(4.19)	136-0133-73E
$C_{11}H_{16}N_6O$			
2,4-Pteridinediamine, 6-pentyl-, 8-oxide	pH 1	250(4.37),283(3.85), 357(3.79),372(3.76)	35-6413-73
Urea, N-(2,2-dimethylpropyl)-N'-1H-purin-6-yl-	pH 1-2	278(4.38)	87-0139-73
	pH 5-7	269(4.32)	87-0139-73
	pH 12	277(4.27)	87-0139-73
Urea, N-(3-methylbutyl)-N'-1H-purin-6-yl-	pH 1-2	277(4.33)	87-0139-73
	pH 5-7	269.5(4.28)	87-0139-73
	pH 12	277.5(4.24)	87-0139-73
Urea, N-pentyl-N'-1H-purin-6-yl-	pH 1-2	278.5(4.29)	87-0139-73
	pH 5-7	269(4.25)	87-0139-73
	pH 12	278(4.20)	87-0139-73
$C_{11}H_{16}N_6O_2$			
Pyrimido[5,4-e]-1,2,4-triazin-5-amine, 3-ethoxy-N-methyl-7-propoxy-	MeOH	216(4.29),261(4.15), 312(3.27),412(3.80)	12-1689-73
$C_{11}H_{16}O$			
2H-Benzocyclohepten-2-one, 3,4,4a,5,6,7,8,9-octahydro-	EtOH	242(4.14)	39-0393-73C
2,6-Cycloheptadien-1-one, 4-butyl-	pentane	224(3.87)	77-0937-73
Cyclopentanone, 2-(1-cyclopenten-1-yl)-2-methyl-	isooctane	258(2.53),287(2.02), 302(2.11),311(2.08), 313(2.08),323(1.80)	77-0501-73
3a,7a-Ethano-1H-inden-4(5H)-one, tetrahydro-	EtOH	293(1.42)	44-1222-73
4-Homoadamantanone	EtOH	284(1.48)	107-0369-73
2H-Inden-2-one, 1,3,3a,4,7,7a-hexahydro-3a,7a-dimethyl-, cis (or dehydro)	isooctane	255s(3.40),263(3.54), 272(3.49)	35-2230-73
2H-Inden-2-one, 1,4,5,6,7,7a-hexahydro-4,7a-dimethyl-	EtOH	233(4.16)	88-4869-73
1(2H)-Pentalenone, 3,3a,6,6a-tetrahydro-3,3,6a-trimethyl-, cis	EtOH	286(1.60)	44-3250-73
4-Pentyn-2-ol, 5-(1-cyclohexen-1-yl)-	n.s.g.	225(4.12)	78-3797-73
Phenol, 2-(1,1-dimethylethyl)-5-methyl-	C_6H_{12}	275(3.30),281(3.32)	22-3087-73
	EtOH	277(3.34),283(3.32)	22-3087-73
Tricyclo[4.1.1.0^{2,4}]octane-2-carboxaldehyde, 7,7-dimethyl-	C_6H_{12}	284(1.48)	22-1351-73

Compound	Solvent	λ_{max}(log ε)	Ref.
$C_{11}H_{16}OSSi$			
Benzenecarbothioic acid, 2-methyl-, O-(trimethylsilyl) ester	C_6H_{12}	242(3.95),288(3.86), 427(2.36)	18-0244-73
Benzenecarbothioic acid, 3-methyl-, O-(trimethylsilyl) ester	C_6H_{12}	252(3.85),300(4.06), 437(1.99)	18-0244-73
Benzenecarbothioic acid, 4-methyl-, O-(trimethylsilyl) ester	C_6H_{12}	253(3.91),303(4.13), 436(2.06)	18-0244-73
$C_{11}H_{16}OSSn$			
Stannane, trimethyl[(2-methylbenzoyl)-thio]-	C_6H_{12}	245(3.98),270(3.85)	18-0244-73
Stannane, trimethyl[(3-methylbenzoyl)-thio]-	C_6H_{12}	245(4.04),279(3.93)	18-0244-73
Stannane, trimethyl[(4-methylbenzoyl)-thio]-	C_6H_{12}	250(4.10),275(4.05)	18-0244-73
$C_{11}H_{16}O_2$			
2(1H)-Azulenone, 4,5,6,7,8,8a-hexahydro-8-hydroxy-8-methyl-	EtOH	237(4.11)	44-0967-73
2(4H)-Benzofuranone, 5,6,7,7a-tetra-hydro-4,4,7a-trimethyl-	EtOH	216(4.11)	33-1948-73
	n.s.g.	212(4.14)	88-5153-73
4H-1-Benzopyran-4-one, 2-ethyl-2,3,5,6,7,8-hexahydro-	EtOH	275(4.02)	22-1409-73
4H-1-Benzopyran-4-one, 2,3,5,6,7,8-hexa-hydro-2,2-dimethyl-	EtOH	279(4.10)	22-1409-73
Bicyclo[3.3.1]nonane-2,9-dione, 3,4-di-methyl-	EtOH	270(2.33)	22-1409-73
1,3-Cyclohexadiene-1-carboxylic acid, 2,5-dimethyl-, ethyl ester	ether	278(3.86)	24-3779-73
1,3-Cyclohexadiene-1-carboxylic acid, 4,6-dimethyl-, ethyl ester	ether	296(4.03)	24-3779-73
1,3-Cyclohexadiene-1-carboxylic acid, 6-propyl-, methyl ester	ether	290(3.97)	24-3779-73
2,4-Cyclohexadiene-1-carboxylic acid, 2,6-dimethyl-, ethyl ester	EtOH	262(4.44)	35-5824-73
5H-Inden-5-one, 1,2,3,6,7,7a-hexahydro-4-methoxy-7a-methyl-	EtOH	254(3.92)	44-3663-73
9-Oxatricyclo[4.3.3.0]dodecan-3-one	EtOH	239(1.88),288(1.42)	44-1215-73
2-Propenoic acid, 3-(4,4-dimethyl-1-cyclopenten-1-yl)-, methyl ester, (E)-	EtOH	270(4.40)	44-2870-73
Spiro[3.5]non-2-en-1-one, 3-ethoxy-	n.s.g.	236(3.95)	44-1451-73
3,8-Undecadiene-2,5-dione, 3E,8Z-	EtOH	230(4.13)	12-2671-73
$C_{11}H_{16}O_2S$			
2-Thiophenepentanoic acid, β,5-dimethyl-	EtOH	233(2.87)	39-0968-73C
$C_{11}H_{16}O_2SSi$			
Benzenecarbothioic acid, 2-methoxy-, O-(trimethylsilyl) ester	C_6H_{12}	246(3.96),304(3.71), 426(2.22)	18-0244-73
Benzenecarbothioic acid, 4-methoxy-, O-(trimethylsilyl) ester	C_6H_{12}	267(3.89),321(4.25), 429(2.18)	18-0244-73
$C_{11}H_{16}O_2SSn$			
Stannane, [(2-methoxybenzoyl)thio]tri-methyl-	C_6H_{12}	248(3.95),303(3.74)	18-0244-73
Stannane, [(4-methoxybenzoyl)thio]tri-methyl-	C_6H_{12}	283(4.32)	18-0244-73
$C_{11}H_{16}O_3$			
1-Cyclohexenepropanoic acid, β,4-di-methyl-3-oxo-	EtOH	238(3.98)	118-0213-73

Compound	Solvent	$\lambda_{max}(\log \epsilon)$	Ref.
3-Cyclohexene-1-propanoic acid, 4-methyl-2-oxo-, methyl ester	n.s.g.	233(4.08)	39-1757-73C
2-Cyclohexen-1-one, 4-acetoxy-3,6,6-trimethyl-	EtOH	229(4.14)	44-4068-73
2,4-Hexadienoic acid, 2-acetyl-5-methyl-, ethyl ester, cis (in equilibrium with cyclic form)	EtOH	236(3.83),294(3.80)	70-2301-73
trans	EtOH	217(3.65),295(4.23)	70-2301-73
2-Hexen-4-yn-1-ol, 6-[(tetrahydro-2H-pyran-2-yl)oxy]-	EtOH	227(4.13),236(4.04)	39-0720-73C
Norcarane-4-carboxylic acid, 7,7-dimethyl-2-oxo-, methyl ester, cis	EtOH	208(3.72)	44-1726-73
trans	EtOH	208(3.67)	44-1726-73
$C_{11}H_{16}O_4$			
2-Butenoic acid, 2-methyl-, 3-ethoxy-1-methyl-3-oxo-1-propenyl ester	EtOH	225(4.30)	22-3416-73
2-Butenoic acid, 3-methyl-, 3-ethoxy-1-methyl-3-oxo-1-propenyl ester	EtOH	225(4.29)	22-3416-73
Cyclohexanone, 4-acetoxy-2-(1-oxopropyl)-	EtOH	208(3.22),288(4.00)	70-0155-73
$C_{11}H_{16}O_5$			
Cyclopenta[c]pyran-4-carboxylic acid, 1,4a,5,6,7,7a-hexahydro-6-hydroxy-1-methoxy-, methyl ester	EtOH	238(4.03)	35-0540-73
$C_{11}H_{16}S$			
Benzene, 1-[(1,1-dimethylethyl)thio]-2-methyl-	C_6H_{12}	224(4.11),271(3.20), 277s(3.15)	39-1125-73B
	EtOH	223(4.04),271(3.18), 277s(3.08)	39-1125-73B
	5% EtOH	218(3.96),263(3.20), 277(3.04)	39-1125-73B
Benzene, 1-[(1,1-dimethylethyl)thio]-3-methyl-	C_6H_{12}	223(4.04),271(3.23), 277s(3.15)	39-1125-73B
	EtOH	218(4.08),267(3.23), 277s(3.08)	39-1125-73B
	5% EtOH	215(4.08),263(3.20), 270(3.18)	39-1125-73B
Benzene, 1-[(1,1-dimethylethyl)thio]-4-methyl-	C_6H_{12}	225(4.15),267(3.26)	39-1125-73B
	EtOH	224(4.18),263(3.26)	39-1125-73B
	5% EtOH	223(4.30),258(3.34)	39-1125-73B
Benzene, 2-(ethylthio)-1,3,5-trimethyl-	C_6H_{12}	206(4.64),225s(4.12), 267(3.38)	39-1125-73B
	EtOH	205(4.60),220(4.05), 265(3.33)	39-1125-73B
	5% EtOH	205(4.65),220(4.08), 262(3.34)	39-1125-73B
$C_{11}H_{16}S_2Si$			
Benzenecarbodithioic acid, 4-methyl-, trimethylsilyl ester	C_6H_{12}	310(4.04),533(2.18)	101-0121-73I
$C_{11}H_{16}S_2Sn$			
Stannane, trimethyl[[(4-methylphenyl)-thioxomethyl]thio]-	C_6H_{12}	318(4.24),527(2.18)	101-0121-73I
$C_{11}H_{17}ClN_5O_{12}P_3$			
5'-Adenylic acid, 2-chloro-, monoanhydride with methylenebis[phosphonic acid, triammonium salt	pH 1	264(4.09)	87-1188-73

Compound	Solvent	$\lambda_{max}(\log \epsilon)$	Ref.
$C_{11}H_{17}I$			
Cyclohexane, (1-iodo-2-methyl-2-buten-ylidene)-	EtOH	212(4.11)	22-2506-73
$C_{11}H_{17}N$			
3-Azabicyclo[5.3.1]undeca-7(11),9-diene, 3-methyl-	EtOH	209(3.61),260s(2.40)	77-0330-73
1-Cyclohexene-1-carbonitrile, 4-(1,1-dimethylethyl)-	EtOH	210(4.03)	44-3893-73
Pyridine, 2-methyl-5-(3-methylbutyl)-	MeOH	267(3.63)	103-1507-73
1H-Pyrrole, 1-(2-butenyl)-2-ethyl-5-methyl-, cis	MeOH	223(3.79)	35-4356-73
trans	MeOH	225(3.81)	35-4356-73
1H-Pyrrole, 3-(2-butenyl)-2-ethyl-5-methyl-, cis	MeOH	212(3.81)	35-4356-73
trans	MeOH	212(3.84)	35-4356-73
1H-Pyrrole, 2-ethyl-5-methyl-1-(1-methyl-2-propenyl)-	MeOH	210(3.71)	35-4356-73
2H-Pyrrole, 2-(2-butenyl)-2-ethyl-5-methyl-, cis	MeOH	221(3.52)	35-4356-73
trans	MeOH	220(3.38)	35-4356-73
2H-Pyrrole, 2-(2-butenyl)-5-ethyl-2-methyl-, trans	MeOH	220(3.55)	35-4356-73
2H-Pyrrole, 2-ethyl-5-methyl-2-(1-methyl-2-propenyl)-	MeOH	217(3.68)	35-4356-73
2H-Pyrrole, 5-ethyl-2-methyl-2-(1-methyl-2-propenyl)-	MeOH	211(3.61)	35-4356-73
Pyrrolidine, 2-(1,3,5-heptatrienyl)-, (E,E,E)-	EtOH	268(4.70),278(4.61)	54-0237-73
hydrochloride	EtOH	260(4.56),268(4.70), 279(4.60)	54-0237-73
$C_{11}H_{17}NO$			
3-Azabicyclo[4.2.1]non-4-en-2-one, 6,9,9-trimethyl-	EtOH	218.5(4.03)	39-1653-73C
Benzenemethanamine, N-ethyl-4-methoxy-α-methyl-, (S)-	EtOH	207(3.76),228(3.88), 277(3.26),285s(3.16)	33-1266-73
$C_{11}H_{17}NOS$			
Benzenamine, N-(1,1-dimethylethyl)-N-hydroxy-3-(methylthio)-	ether	269(4.04)	78-3833-73
$C_{11}H_{17}NOS_2$			
Dithiobenzoic acid, p-methoxy-, trimethylamine salt	EtOH	320(4.00),360(3.87), 500(2.13)	143-0359-73
$C_{11}H_{17}NO_2$			
Acetamide, N-(5,5-dimethyl-3-oxo-1-cyclohexen-1-yl)-N-methyl-	EtOH	284(4.05)	94-1372-73
2-Cyclohexen-1-one, 2-acetyl-5,5-dimethyl-3-(methylamino)-	EtOH	263(4.10),292(4.11)	94-1372-73
$C_{11}H_{17}NO_3$			
Benzenemethanol, 3,4-dimethoxy-α-[(methylamino)methyl]-	EtOH	208(4.45),230s(4.08), 285(3.95)	102-0193-73
2,4-Hexadienoic acid, 2-acetyl-5-(dimethylamino)-, methyl ester	EtOH	244(3.83),273(3.85), 417(4.72)	70-1963-73
$C_{11}H_{17}NO_4$			
2-Pyrrolidinecarboxylic acid, 1-(acetoacetyl)-, ethyl ester	EtOH	219(3.43),225(3.52)	119-0132-73

Compound	Solvent	λ_{max}(log ε)	Ref.
$C_{11}H_{17}NO_8$			
D-glycero-D-galacto-Non-2-enonic acid, 2,6-anhydro-3,5-dideoxy-5-(formylamino)-, methyl ester	n.s.g.	244(3.70)	49-0402-73
$C_{11}H_{17}NO_8S$			
D-glycero-D-galacto-Non-2-enonic acid, 2,6-anhydro-3,5-dideoxy-5-[(mercaptoacetyl)amino]-	n.s.g.	240(3.79)	49-0402-73
$C_{11}H_{17}NO_9P_2$			
Diphosphoric acid, P-(3-methylbutyl) P'-(4-nitrophenyl) ester	H_2O	290(4.00)	18-3275-73
$C_{11}H_{17}NS_2$			
Dithiobenzoic acid, p-methyl-, trimethylamine salt	EtOH	300(3.99),361(3.80), 495(2.15)	143-0359-73
$C_{11}H_{17}N_3O_2S_2$			
Carbamic acid, [(butylthio)(2-thiazolylimino)methyl]-, ethyl ester	dioxan	243(3.85),315(4.31)	94-0074-73
Carbamic acid, [[(5-ethyl-3-methyl-2(3H)-thiazolylidene)amino][methylthio)methylene]-, ethyl ester	dioxan	245(3.59),278(3.86), 337(4.38)	94-0074-73
Carbamic acid, [[(3-ethyl-2(3H)-thiazolylidene)amino](ethylthio)methyl]-, ethyl ester	dioxan	280(3.85),331(4.36)	94-0074-73
Carbamic acid, [[(2-methylpropyl)thio]-(2-thiazolylimino)methyl]-, ethyl ester	dioxan	243(3.86),315(4.33)	94-0074-73
Carbamic acid, [[(3-methyl-2(3H)-thiazolylidene)amino](methylthio)methylene]-, butyl ester	dioxan	245(3.32),279(3.88), 331(4.37)	94-0074-73
Carbamic acid, [[(3-methyl-2(3H)-thiazolylidene)amino](methylthio)methylene]-, 2-methylpropyl ester	dioxan	245(3.54),280(3.90), 330(4.39)	94-0074-73
Carbamic acid, [(methylthio)[(5-propyl-2-thiazolyl)imino]methyl]-, ethyl ester	dioxan	240(3.90),319(4.36)	94-0074-73
$C_{11}H_{17}N_3O_5$			
Cytidine, 2',3'-di-O-methyl-	pH 2	280(4.11)	69-0194-73
	pH 12	271(3.94)	69-0194-73
Cytidine, 5'-O-ethyl-	pH 2	280(4.11)	69-0194-73
	pH 12	271(3.95)	69-0194-73
$C_{11}H_{17}N_3O_6$			
α-D-Glucopyranoside, methyl 6-(4-amino-2-oxo-1(2H)-pyrimidinyl)-6-deoxy-	pH 2	282(4.08)	18-3165-73
	H_2O	274(3.95)	18-3165-73
	pH 12	277(3.82)	18-3165-73
1H-Imidazole-4-carboxylic acid, 5-amino-1-(α-D-ribofuranosyl)-, ethyl ester	MeOH	271(4.04)	39-1720-73C
β-anomer	MeOH	269(4.05)	39-1720-73C
$C_{11}H_{17}N_3O_7S$			
Glutathione, S-formyl-	pH 7.40	235(3.58)	69-3938-73
$C_{11}H_{17}N_5$			
1H-Pyrazolo[4,3-d]pyrimidin-7-amine, 3-methyl-N-pentyl-	EtOH-pH 1	263(3.82),311(4.12)	102-0025-73
	EtOH-pH 7	238(3.79),296(4.10), 307(4.00),319s(--)	102-0025-73

Compound	Solvent	$\lambda_{max}(\log \epsilon)$	Ref.
1H-Pyrazolo[4,3-d]pyrimidin-7-amine, 3-methyl-N-pentyl-	EtOH-pH 12	245(4.19),265s(--), 308(3.91)	102-0025-73
$C_{11}H_{17}N_5O_2$			
1H-Purine-2,6-dione, 7-(3-aminopropyl)-3,7-dihydro-1,3,8-trimethyl-, hydrochloride	n.s.g.	210(4.30),276(3.97)	73-1571-73
$C_{11}H_{17}N_5O_5$			
Carbonohydrazonic acid, (2-ethoxy-5-nitro-4-pyrimidinyl)-, diethyl ester	C_6H_{12}	233(3.81),271(4.05), 285s(3.93),297s(3.64), 381(3.44)	12-1689-73
$C_{11}H_{17}N_7O$			
Urea, N-[3-(dimethylamino)propyl]-N'-1H-purin-6-yl-	pH 1-2	278(4.25)	87-0139-73
	pH 5-7	269(4.20)	87-0139-73
	pH 12	277(4.16)	87-0139-73
$C_{11}H_{18}$			
1,3,5-Undecatriene, all-trans	MeOH	256(4.37),265(4.49), 275(4.39)	2-0207-73
$C_{11}H_{18}ClNO_3$			
Cyclopropanecarboxylic acid, 2-chloro-3-nitroso-2,3-dipropyl-, methyl ester (dimer)	benzene	666(1.01)	104-0732-73
$C_{11}H_{18}ClN_5O_4$			
3H-Purinium, 6-(diethylamino)-3,9-dimethyl-, perchlorate	H_2O	290(4.30)	104-1316-73
7H-Purinium, 6-(diethylamino)-7,9-dimethyl-, perchlorate	H_2O	300(4.11)	104-1316-73
$C_{11}H_{18}NO_3P$			
Phosphonic acid, (2,6-dimethyl-4-pyridinyl)-, diethyl ester	n.s.g.	279(3.51)	44-1306-73
$C_{11}H_{18}N_2$			
2-Hexenenitrile, 4-methyl-3-(1-pyrrolidinyl)-	EtOH	274(4.36)	39-1108-73C
3-Hexenenitrile, 4-methyl-3-(1-pyrrolidinyl)-	EtOH	204(3.68),244(3.76)	39-1108-73C
2-Pentenenitrile, 4-methyl-3-(1-piperidinyl)-	EtOH	277(4.35)	39-1108-73C
3-Pentenenitrile, 4-methyl-3-(1-piperidinyl)-	EtOH	204(3.62),236(3.49)	39-1108-73C
1H-Pyrazole, 1-(1-cyclopenten-1-yl)-4,5-dihydro-3,5,5-trimethyl-	heptane	226(3.32),281(3.45)	135-1154-73
	MeOH	225(3.66),275(3.04)	135-1154-73
	isoPrOH	223(3.85),278(3.93)	135-1154-73
	ether	225(3.85),280(4.05)	135-1154-73
	$C_2H_4Cl_2$	230(3.84),275(3.21)	135-1154-73
Pyrazole, 2-(2,2-dimethyl-3-butenyl)-3,4-dimethyl-	EtOH	225(3.75)	78-4159-73
1H-Pyrazole, 4-(2,2-dimethyl-3-butenyl)-3,5-dimethyl-	EtOH	229(3.78)	78-4159-73
$C_{11}H_{18}N_2O_2$			
1,3-Propanediol, 2-amino-1-[4-(dimethylamino)phenyl]-	EtOH	257(4.20),297(3.4)	104-2144-73

Compound	Solvent	λ_{max}(log ε)	Ref.
$C_{11}H_{18}N_2O_3$			
Decanoic acid, 10-diazo-9-oxo-, methyl ester	MeOH	245(4.18),270(4.11)	13-0139-73B
2,4-Hexadienoic acid, 2-(aminocarbonyl)-5-(dimethylamino)-, ethyl ester	EtOH	298(4.00),394(4.77)	70-2478-73
2,4,6(1H,3H,5H)-Pyrimidinetrione, 5-ethyl-5-(1-methylbutyl)-	50% MeOH	211(3.9)	35-8512-73
	+ HCl	212(3.87)	35-8512-73
	MeCN	208s(3.9)	35-8512-73
$C_{11}H_{18}N_2O_8$			
D-glycero-D-galacto-Non-2-enonic acid, 5-[(aminoacetyl)amino]-2,6-anhydro-3,5-dideoxy-	n.s.g.	232(3.74)	49-0402-73
D-glycero-D-galacto-Non-2-enonic acid, 5-[(aminocarbonyl)amino]-2,6-anhydro-3,5-dideoxy-, methyl ester	n.s.g.	231(3.77)	49-0402-73
$C_{11}H_{18}N_4$			
1-Buten-2-amine, 1-(3,6-dimethyl-1,2,4-triazin-5-yl)-N,N-dimethyl-	MeOH	245(2.66),307(3.67), 385(4.37)	5-1963-73
$C_{11}H_{18}N_4OS_2$			
Spiro[furo[2,3-d]thiazole-2(3H),4'-imidazolidine]-2'-thione, tetrahydro-5'-imino-1',3,3',3a-tetramethyl-	EtOH	271(4.02)	94-1300-73
$C_{11}H_{18}N_4O_6$			
α-D-Glucofuranoside, methyl 2-[5-amino-4-(aminocarbonyl)-1H-imidazol-1-yl)-2-deoxy-	acid	266(3.91)	39-2345-73C
	neutral	266(4.00)	39-2345-73C
	base	266(4.03)	39-2345-73C
α-D-Glucopyranoside, methyl 2-[5-amino-4-(aminocarbonyl)-1H-imidazol-1-yl)-2-deoxy-	acid	266(3.97)	39-2345-73C
	neutral	266(4.05)	39-2345-73C
	base	266(4.06)	39-2345-73C
β-anomer	acid	240(4.00),266(3.98)	39-2345-73C
	neutral	266(4.06)	39-2345-73C
	base	266(4.08)	39-2345-73C
$C_{11}H_{18}N_5$			
3H-Purinium, 6-(diethylamino)-3,9-dimethyl-, perchlorate	H_2O	290(4.30)	104-1316-73
7H-Purinium, 6-(diethylamino)-7,9-dimethyl-, perchlorate	H_2O	300(4.11)	104-1316-73
$C_{11}H_{18}N_5O_{13}P_3S$			
Adenosine 5'-(trihydrogen phosphate), 2-(methylthio)-, triammonium salt	pH 1	268(4.16)	87-1188-73
$C_{11}H_{18}O$			
Cyclohexanone, 2-(1-methylethenyl)-2,5-dimethyl-, (2S-cis)-	MeOH	294(1.71)	18-1546-73
Ethanone, 1-bicyclo[6.1.0]non-1-yl	n.s.g.	219.5(3.32)	22-1800-73
Ethanone, 1-[2-(1,1-dimethylethyl)-3,3-dimethyl-1-cyclopropen-1-yl]-	n.s.g.	252(3.77)	88-2875-73
1-Penten-4-ol, 1-cyclohexen-1-yl-, (Z)-	n.s.g.	228(4.09)	78-3797-73
$C_{11}H_{18}O_2$			
1-Cyclohexene-1-carboxylic acid, 4-(1,1-dimethylethyl)-	EtOH	213.5(4.10)	44-3893-73
2-Cyclohexen-1-one, 4-(1,1-dimethylethyl)-3-methoxy-	EtOH	255(4.18)	95-1406-73

Compound	Solvent	$\lambda_{max}(\log \epsilon)$	Ref.
2-Cyclohexen-1-one, 6-(1,1-dimethyleth-yl)-3-methoxy-	EtOH	250(4.16)	95-1406-73
2-Cyclopenten-1-one, 4-(1,1-dimethyleth-yl)-3-methoxy-2-methyl-	EtOH	253(4.19)	95-1406-73
2-Cyclopenten-1-one, 5-(1,1-dimethyleth-yl)-3-methoxy-2-methyl-	EtOH	255(4.33)	95-1406-73
Menthone, hydroxymethylene-, (+)-	isooctane	292(3.99),345s(2.14)	104-2149-73
	EtOH	292(2.96)	104-2149-73
3-Undecene-2,5-dione, (E)-	EtOH	228(4.05)	12-2671-73
$C_{11}H_{18}O_2S$			
Sulfoxonium, dimethyl-, (5,5-dimethyl-3-oxo-1-cyclohexen-1-yl)methylide	EtOH	355(4.67)	88-2351-73
$C_{11}H_{18}O_3$			
Cyclopropaneacetic acid, 2-acetyl-3-(1-methylethyl)-, methyl ester	MeOH	205(3.72),215(3.34) (end absorptions)	39-2671-73C
Ethanone, 1-(10-methyl-1,4-dioxaspiro-[4.5]dec-7-yl)-	MeOH	280(1.53)	39-2113-73C
2-Heptenoic acid, 4-(1-methylethyl)-6-oxo-, methyl ester	isooctane	205(4.12),215(4.05), 225(3.76)(end abs.)	39-2671-73C
2H-Pyran-5-carboxylic acid, 3,4-dihydro-2,2,6-trimethyl-, ethyl ester	EtOH	249(4.05)	70-2301-73
$C_{11}H_{18}O_4$			
2-Butenoic acid, 3-(2,2-dimethyl-1-oxo-propoxy)-, ethyl ester	EtOH	214(4.03)	22-3416-73
2-Hexenedioic acid, 4-(1-methylethyl)-, dimethyl ester	isooctane	207(4.14)	39-2671-73C
$C_{11}H_{18}O_4S$			
α-D-xylo-Hex-5-enofuranose, 5-deoxy-1,2-O-isopropylidene-3-O-methyl-6-S-methyl-6-thio-, cis	EtOH	240(3.30)	33-1310-73
trans	EtOH	235(3.75)	33-1310-73
$C_{11}H_{18}O_5$			
2H-Pyran-2-one, 6-(1,2-dihydroxypentyl)-5,6-dihydro-4-methoxy-, [6S-[6R*(1R*,2S*)]]-	MeOH	234(4.14)	44-3542-73
$C_{11}H_{19}N$			
Piperidine, 1-(1-cyclohexen-1-yl)-	heptane	222(4.05)	135-1154-73
	MeOH	199(3.50)	135-1154-73
	isoPrOH	203(3.84)	135-1154-73
	ether	195(4.13),220(4.19)	135-1154-73
	$C_2H_4Cl_2$	210(3.63)	135-1154-73
$C_{11}H_{19}NO$			
2,3-Heptadienamide, N-(1,1-dimethyl-ethyl)-	EtOH	212(4.30)	88-0209-73
2,3-Hexadienamide, N-(1,1-dimethyleth-yl)-4-methyl-	EtOH	213(4.17)	88-0209-73
$C_{11}H_{19}NO_3$			
Butanoic acid, 2-[(butylamino)methyl-ene]-3-oxo-, ethyl ester	EtOH	238(4.15),297(4.17)	70-2478-73
$C_{11}H_{19}N_3O_2$			
1H-Pyrazole, 3,5-bis(1,1-dimethylethyl)-4-nitro-	0.05M HCl	278(3.73)	4-1055-73
	0.05M NaOH	327(4.06)	4-1055-73

Compound	Solvent	$\lambda_{max}(\log \epsilon)$	Ref.
$C_{11}H_{19}N_4O_8P$			
5'-Cytidylic acid, 5-(dimethylamino)-	pH 1	218(3.95),312(3.68)	88-5077-73
	pH 7	224(4.23),294(3.78)	88-5077-73
	pH 12	224(4.30),294(3.85)	88-5077-73
$C_{11}H_{19}N_7O$			
6H-Purin-6-one, 2-amino-7-[2-[(3-amino-propyl)methylamino]ethyl]-1,7-dihydro-	pH 1	249(4.03),270s(--)	103-0377-73
	pH 7	248(3.95),283(3.96)	103-0377-73
	pH 13	280(3.98)	103-0377-73
$C_{11}H_{20}Cl_3N_4$			
Ethanaminium, N-[chloro[[chloro[[chloro-(diethylamino)methylene]amino]methyl-ene]amino]methylene]-N-ethyl-, chloride	$CHCl_3$	247(4.25),316(4.32)	114-0081-73A
$C_{11}H_{20}N_2$			
2-Hexenenitrile, 3-(butylamino)-4-meth-yl-	EtOH	262(4.31)	39-1108-73C
2-Hexenenitrile, 3-(diethylamino)-4-methyl-	EtOH	206(3.86),247(3.28)	39-1108-73C
3-Hexenenitrile, 3-(butylamino)-4-meth-yl-	EtOH	218(3.71),230(3.67)	39-1108-73C
3-Hexenenitrile, 3-(diethylamino)-4-methyl-	EtOH	277(4.30)	39-1108-73C
$C_{11}H_{20}N_2O$			
3-Buten-2-one, 4-(dimethylamino)-4-pip-eridino-	CH_2Cl_2	254(3.77),308(4.35)	33-0944-73
Morpholine, 4-[(1-methyl-2-piperidinyl-idene)methyl]-	C_6H_{12}	230(3.69)	28-0519-73A
$C_{11}H_{20}N_2O_2$			
2-Propenoic acid, 3-(dimethylamino)-3-piperidino-, methyl ester	CH_2Cl_2	250(3.99),286(4.32)	33-0944-73
$C_{11}H_{20}N_2O_6$			
Heptanoic acid, 2,7-dinitro-, butyl ester	MeOH	265(2.55)	18-3462-73
	MeOH-NaOMe	235(4.01),305(4.97)	18-3462-73
Hexanoic acid, 2,6-dinitro-, pentyl ester	MeOH	265(2.47)	18-3462-73
$C_{11}H_{20}N_4O_{11}P_2$			
Cytidine-5'-diphosphate, 5-(dimethyl-amino)-, trisodium salt	pH 1	312(3.70)	88-5077-73
	pH 7	294(3.78)	88-5077-73
	pH 12	294(3.79)	88-5077-73
$C_{11}H_{20}O$			
Cyclohexanone, 2,5-dimethyl-2-(1-meth-ylethyl)-, (2S,5R)-(-)-	MeOH	291(1.58)	18-1546-73
Cyclopentanone, 2,2,3,3,5,5-hexamethyl-	C_6H_{12}	305(1.36)	22-2231-73
	heptane	305(1.32)	22-2231-73
	MeOH	298(1.39)	22-2231-73
	EtOH	299(1.39)	22-2231-73
	MeCN	302(1.30)	22-2231-73
	CCl_4	304(1.44)	22-2231-73
	$CHCl_3$	302(1.42)	22-2231-73
	CH_2Cl_2	303(1.30)	22-2231-73
2-Hepten-4-one, 5,5,6,6-tetramethyl-, cis	hexane	226(4.01)	35-7345-73

Compound	Solvent	$\lambda_{max}(\log \epsilon)$	Ref.
2-Hepten-4-one, 5,5,6,6-tetramethyl-, trans	hexane	226(4.06)	35-7345-73
$C_{11}H_{20}OS$			
3-Hepten-2-one, 4-(methylthio)-3-propyl-	C_6H_{12}	301(4.02)	78-2449-73
	EtOH	314(4.04)	78-2449-73
$C_{11}H_{20}O_2$			
Cyclohexanone, 2-methoxy-3,3,5,5-tetramethyl-	EtOH	268(1.34)	44-3893-73
$C_{11}H_{21}N_7O_2$			
Formamide, N-[2-[(3-aminopropyl)methylamino]ethyl]-N-(2,4-diamino-1,6-dihydro-6-oxo-5-pyrimidinyl)-	pH 1	263(4.26)	103-0377-73
	pH 7	262(4.03)	103-0377-73
	pH 13	260(3.91)	103-0377-73
$C_{11}H_{21}S_4$			
2-Propenylium, 1,1,3,3-tetrakis(ethylthio)-, perchlorate	MeCN	420(3.96)	88-3409-73
$C_{11}H_{22}N_2O$			
Diazene, (1-methylheptyl)-1-propenyl-, 2-oxide	EtOH	232(3.88)	88-4701-73
Diazene, (1-methylheptyl)-2-propenyl-, 2-oxide	EtOH	224(3.84)	88-4701-73
2-Pentenamide, N-propyl-3-(propylamino)-	EtOH	225(3.63),293(4.09)	70-1033-73
$C_{11}H_{22}O_2$			
3-Heptanone, 5-hydroxy-2,2,6,6-tetramethyl-	EtOH	287(1.56)	35-3310-73
$C_{11}H_{24}Cl_2N_4O_8$			
1-Propen-2-aminium, 1-(dimethylamino)-N-[(dimethylamino)methylene]-3-(dimethylimino)-N-methyl-, diperchlorate	H_2O	216(4.08),307(4.57)	73-2633-73
$C_{11}H_{24}N_2O$			
Diazene, (1-methylheptyl)propyl-, 2-oxide	EtOH	223(3.81)	88-4701-73

Compound	Solvent	$\lambda_{max}(\log \epsilon)$	Ref.
$C_{12}F_{10}O$			
2,5-Cyclohexadien-1-one, 2,3,4,4,5-pentafluoro-6-(pentafluorophenyl)-	heptane	215(4.07),250(3.44)	104-0578-73
2,5-Cyclohexadien-1-one, 2,3,4,4,6-pentafluoro-5-(pentafluorophenyl)-	heptane	218(4.24),260(3.45)	104-0578-73
$C_{12}F_{10}O_2$			
[Bi-1,4-cyclohexadien-1-yl]-6,6'-dione, 2,2',3,3,3',3',4,4',5,5'-decafluoro-	heptane	222(3.16)	104-0578-73
$C_{12}F_{12}N_2$			
Pyridine, 4,4'-(tetrafluoroethylidene)-bis[2,3,5,6-tetrafluoro-	C_6H_{12}	280.5(3.92)	39-1411-73C
$C_{12}F_{12}S_{10}$			
1,2,3,5,6,7-Hexathiocane, 4,8-bis[4,5-bis(trifluoromethyl)-1,3-dithiol-2-ylidene]-	isooctane	213(4.54),322(3.99), 405(4.32)	35-4379-73
$C_{12}F_{19}N$			
Pyridine, 2,5-difluoro-3,6-bis(pentafluoroethyl)-4-[1,2,2,2-tetrafluoro-1-(trifluoromethyl)ethyl]-	C_6H_{12}	285s(3.79)	39-1405-73C
Pyridine, 2,5-difluoro-4,6-bis(pentafluoroethyl)-3-[1,2,2,2-tetrafluoro-1-(trifluoromethyl)ethyl]-	C_6H_{12}	286s(3.80)	39-1405-73C
Pyridine, 3,5-difluoro-2,4-bis(pentafluoroethyl)-6-[1,2,2,2-tetrafluoro-1-(trifluoromethyl)ethyl]-	C_6H_{12}	274s(3.63)	39-1405-73C
$C_{12}F_{20}N_2$			
Pyridazine, 3,4,5,6-tetrakis(pentafluoroethyl)-	C_6H_{12}	260s(2.87),356s(3.30)	39-1411-73C
$C_{12}H_2Cl_7NO_2$			
1,1'-Biphenyl, 2,2',3,4,4',5,6'-heptachloro-3'-nitro-	EtOH	285(3.05),294(3.04)	1-1109-73
$C_{12}H_2Cl_8$			
1,1'-Biphenyl, 2,2',3,3',4,4',5,6'-octachloro-	EtOH	285(2.98),294(2.97)	1-1109-73
$C_{12}H_3F_{14}NO$			
Pyridine, 2,3,5-trifluoro-6-methoxy-4-(undecafluorocyclohexyl)-	C_6H_{12}	303(3.74)	39-1710-73C
$C_{12}H_4Cl_4O$			
Dibenzofuran, 2,3,7,8-tetrachloro-	EtOH	223s(4.67),229(4.70), 240s(4.42),251(4.24), 260(4.46),299s(4.39), 304(4.45),314(4.37)	1-3121-73
$C_{12}H_4Cl_6$			
Biphenyl, 2,2',4,4',5,5'-hexachloro-	EtOH	281(3.31),290(3.27)	1-3121-73
$C_{12}H_5ClO_6$			
2,3,5(4H)-Furantrione, 4-(1,3-benzodioxol-5-ylchloromethylene)-	$CHCl_3$	274s(3.85),288(3.91), 364(3.72),425s(3.94), 473(4.11)	77-0265-73

Compound	Solvent	λ_{max}(log ϵ)	Ref.
$C_{12}H_5Cl_4NO_5$			
Furo[2,3-b][1,4]benzodioxin, 5,6,7,8-tetrachloro-2-(2-nitroethenyl)-	MeOH	215(4.81),235s(4.22), 304(3.97)	48-0419-73
$C_{12}H_5Cl_5$			
Biphenyl, 2,2',3',4,5-pentachloro-	EtOH	272(2.64),281(2.70), 290(2.62)	1-0600-73
Biphenyl, 2,2',4,5,5'-pentachloro-	EtOH	276s(3.11),281(3.24), 289(3.12)	1-0600-73
Biphenyl, 2,3',4,4',5-pentachloro-	EtOH	251.5(4.21)	1-0600-73
$C_{12}H_5Cl_5N_2$			
2,3-Diazabicyclo[3.2.0]hepta-1(5),3-diene, 4,7,7-trichloro-6-(dichloromethylene)-2-phenyl-	n.s.g.	240(3.79),420(3.72)	44-1470-73
$C_{12}H_5F_4I$			
Biphenyl, 2,3,5,6-tetrafluoro-4-iodo-	hexane	248(4.27)	39-1121-73C
$C_{12}H_6$			
2,4,6,8,10-Dodecapentayne	C_6H_{12}	238(--),249(--), 262(5.55)	33-1752-73
(and other mixtures of these solvents)	1:1 C_6H_{12}-CS_2	273(5.28)	33-1752-73
$C_{12}H_6Cl_4$			
Biphenyl, 2,2',3,3'-tetrachloro-	EtOH	272(2.88),280s(2.80)	1-0600-73
Biphenyl, 2,2',3,4'-tetrachloro-	EtOH	273(2.95),281(2.81)	1-0600-73
Biphenyl, 2,2',3,5'-tetrachloro-	EtOH	267s(2.97),276(3.07), 283(3.00)	1-0600-73
Biphenyl, 2,2',3,6'-tetrachloro-	EtOH	268(2.89),275(2.85)	1-0600-73
Biphenyl, 2,2',4,5'-tetrachloro-	EtOH	274(3.08),282(2.99)	1-0600-73
Biphenyl, 2,2',5,5'-tetrachloro-	EtOH	268s(3.06),276(3.21), 284(3.16)	1-0600-73
Biphenyl, 2,2',5,6'-tetrachloro-	EtOH	268s(2.91),276(3.00), 284(2.91)	1-0600-73
Biphenyl, 2,3,3',4'-tetrachloro-	EtOH	251(4.18)	1-0600-73
Biphenyl, 2,3,3',5'-tetrachloro-	EtOH	244(4.00),280s(3.09)	1-0600-73
Biphenyl, 2,3',4,4'-tetrachloro-	EtOH	251(4.22)	1-0600-73
Biphenyl, 2,3',4',5-tetrachloro-	EtOH	247(4.21),285s(3.40)	1-0600-73
Biphenyl, 2,3',5,5'-tetrachloro-	EtOH	245s(3.98),284s(3.25)	1-0600-73
Biphenyl, 2,3',4',6-tetrachloro-	EtOH	273s(3.10),281s(2.98)	1-0600-73
Biphenyl, 2',3,4,6'-tetrachloro-	EtOH	273s(3.10),281s(2.98)	1-0600-73
Biphenyl, 3,3',4,4'-tetrachloro-	EtOH	261(4.17)	1-0600-73
Biphenyl, 3,3',4,5'-tetrachloro-	EtOH	258.5(4.26)	1-0600-73
$C_{12}H_6F_4O$			
[1,1'-Biphenyl]-4-ol, 2,3,5,6-tetrafluoro-	hexane	242(4.18)	39-1121-73C
$C_{12}H_6N_6$			
1,3-Azulenedicarbonitrile, 2-amino-5-azido-	n.s.g.	238(4.23),326s(4.45), 336(4.56),403(4.37)	18-1212-73
$C_{12}H_6N_6S$			
Thiocyanic acid, 4-cyano-2-methyl-1,3,6,9b-tetraazaphenalenyl ester	EtOH	239(4.28),287(3.83), 293(3.84),346(4.23), 363s(4.07),387(3.90), 402s(3.88),580s(2.95), 614(3.07),665(2.84)	1-2095-73

Compound	Solvent	$\lambda_{max}(\log \epsilon)$	Ref.
Thiocyanic acid, (4-cyano-1,3,6,9b-tetraazaphenalen-2-yl)methyl ester	EtOH	234(4.21),269(4.02), 333(3.97),356(3.83), 372(3.90),390(3.88), 526s(2.95),572(3.38), 602(3.38),642(3.15)	1-2095-73
$C_{12}H_7Br$			
Acenaphthylene, 5-bromo-	C_6H_{12}	243(4.15),329(4.04), 344(3.77),351(3.81), 380(2.67)	35-6709-73
$C_{12}H_7BrClO_2P$			
10H-Phenoxaphosphine, 7-bromo-2-chloro-, 10-oxide	EtOH	224(4.59),240s(4.52), 252s(4.32),269s(3.36), 293s(3.59),303(3.66)	39-1972-73C
$C_{12}H_7BrFO_3P$			
10H-Phenoxaphosphine, 7-bromo-2-fluoro-10-hydroxy-, 10-oxide	EtOH	220(4.52),238s(4.32), 246s(4.09),268(3.30), 278s(3.37),292(3.61), 300(3.67)	39-1972-73C
$C_{12}H_7BrN_2O$			
Quinoxaline, 2-(5-bromo-2-furanyl)-	EtOH	220(4.58),268(4.46), 288(4.57),370(4.49)	103-0374-73
$C_{12}H_7BrN_2O_2$			
2(1H)-Quinoxalinone, 3-(5-bromo-2-furanyl)-	EtOH-2% DMF	380(4.64),400(4.50)	103-0374-73
$C_{12}H_7BrO_3$			
2-Furanacetaldehyde, 5-(4-bromophenyl)-α-oxo-	EtOH	226(4.13),330(4.47)	103-0403-73
$C_{12}H_7ClN_4O_6$			
Benzenamine, N-(3-chlorophenyl)-2,4,6-trinitro-	95.5% DMSO	385(4.16)	22-1225-73
anion	95.5% DMSO	445(4.41)	22-1225-73
Benzenamine, N-(4-chlorophenyl)-2,4,6-trinitro-	95.5% DMSO	385(4.12)	22-1225-73
anion	95.5% DMSO	445(4.36)	22-1225-73
$C_{12}H_7ClO_3$			
2-Furanacetaldehyde, 5-(4-chlorophenyl)-α-oxo-	EtOH	228(4.14),330(4.41)	103-0403-73
$C_{12}H_7Cl_2NO_2$			
1H-Pyrrole-3,4-dicarboxaldehyde, 2,5-dichloro-1-phenyl-	EtOH	220(4.2),300(3.8)	103-0467-73
$C_{12}H_7NOS$			
Benzonitrile, 4-(2-thienylcarbonyl)-	hexane	250(4.2),295(4.0)	35-4599-73
Benzonitrile, 4-(3-thienylcarbonyl)-	hexane	250(4.1)	35-4599-73
3H-Phenothiazin-3-one	MeCN	236(4.31),274(4.23), 362(3.96),495(3.90)	39-0264-73B
$C_{12}H_7NO_3$			
1,3-Dioxolo[4,5-g]furo[2,3-b]quinoline	EtOH	236(4.63),302(3.95), 308(3.99),328(4.06)	64-0196-73B

Compound	Solvent	$\lambda_{max}(\log \epsilon)$	Ref.
Naphtho[1,8-bc]pyran, 6-nitro-	EtOH	230(3.92),268(3.81), 292(3.87),354(3.17), 372(3.28),439(3.63)	107-0219-73
Naphtho[1,8-bc]pyran, 7-nitro-	EtOH	236(4.03),274s(--), 282(4.01),312(3.71), 324(3.71),432(3.75)	107-0219-73
$C_{12}H_7NO_5$			
2-Furanacetaldehyde, 5-(4-nitrophenyl)- α-oxo-	EtOH	222(4.22),352(4.58)	103-0403-73
$C_{12}H_7N_3OS$			
4H-Quinolizine-1,3-dicarbonitrile, 2-(methylthio)-4-oxo-	EtOH	269(4.29),288(4.09), 313(4.09),357(3.81), 416(4.31)	94-0921-73
$C_{12}H_8BrN_3$			
1,2,4-Triazolo[4,3-a]pyridine, 3-bromo- 7-phenyl-	EtOH	251(4.46),305(3.89)	95-0642-73
$C_{12}H_8Br_2N_4O_2$			
Benzo[g]pteridine-2,4(1H,3H)-dione, 6,9-dibromo-7,8-dimethyl-	EtOH-5% DMF	276(3.38),360(4.08)	65-1578-73
$C_{12}H_8ClNO_2S$			
Thiophene, 2-[2-(4-chlorophenyl)ethen- yl]-3-nitro-, (E)-	EtOH	278(4.17),375(3.96)	118-0313B-73
Thiophene, 3-[2-(4-chlorophenyl)ethen- yl]-2-nitro-, (E)-	EtOH	270(4.18),370(4.05)	118-0313B-73
$C_{12}H_8ClN_3O_2$			
5-Pyrimidinecarbonitrile, 3-[(4-chloro- phenyl)methyl]-1,2,3,4-tetrahydro- 2,4-dioxo-	MeOH-HCl	273(3.88)	39-1720-73C
	MeOH-NaOH	296(4.01)	39-1720-73C
$C_{12}H_8ClN_3O_4$			
Benzenamine, N-(3-chlorophenyl)-2,4-di- nitro-	41.4% DMSO	370(4.26)	22-1225-73
anion	41.4% DMSO	420(4.28)	22-1225-73
Benzenamine, N-(4-chlorophenyl)-2,4-di- nitro-	41.4% DMSO	370(4.26)	22-1225-73
anion	41.4% DMSO	425(4.29)	22-1225-73
Benzoic acid, 2-chloro-5-[(5-nitro- 2-pyridinyl)amino]-, anion	31.7% DMSO	383(4.28)	22-1553-73
dianion	31.7% DMSO	470(4.42)	22-1553-73
Benzoic acid, 4-chloro-2-[(5-nitro- 2-pyridinyl)amino]-, anion	70.5% DMSO	398(4.36)	22-1553-73
dianion	70.5% DMSO	465(4.44)	22-1553-73
Benzoic acid, 5-chloro-2-[(5-nitro- 2-pyridinyl)amino]-, anion	80% DMSO	394(4.34)	22-1553-73
dianion	80% DMSO	465(4.43)	22-1553-73
$C_{12}H_8Cl_2N_2O_2$			
1H-Isoindole-1,3(2H)-dione, 2-(2,3-di- chloro-5-azabicyclo[2.1.0]pent-5-yl)-	MeCN	231(3.40),295(2.15), 305(2.11)	78-2973-73
$C_{12}H_8Cl_2N_2S$			
Sulfur diimide, bis(4-chlorophenyl)-	C_6H_{12}	225(4.21),255s(4.04), 367s(3.86),428(4.00)	143-0285-73

Compound	Solvent	$\lambda_{max}(\log \epsilon)$	Ref.
$C_{12}H_8Cl_2N_6O$			
Urea, N-(2,5-dichlorophenyl)-N'-1H-purin-6-yl-	pH 1-2	280(4.17)	87-0139-73
	pH 5-7	287(4.37)	87-0139-73
	pH 12	295(4.31)	87-0139-73
$C_{12}H_8Cl_2O_2S_2$			
Benzenesulfonothioic acid, 4-chloro-, S-(4-chlorophenyl) ester	EtOH	239.5(4.32)	94-1305-73
$C_{12}H_8Cl_4$			
1H-Indene, 4,5,6,7-tetrachloro-2-(1-methylethenyl)-	C_6H_{12}	230(4.19),238(4.21), 246(4.25),255(4.13), 299(4.34),307(4.37), 319(4.18)	39-2569-73C
$C_{12}H_8Cl_4N_2$			
2,4-Cyclopentadien-1-one, 2,3,4,5-tetra-chloro-, (4-methylphenyl)hydrazone	EtOH	425(4.50)	39-1155-73B
	EtOH-KOH	451(--)	39-1155-73B
$C_{12}H_8Cl_4N_2O$			
2,4-Cyclopentadien-1-one, 2,3,4,5-tetra-chloro-, (4-methoxyphenyl)hydrazone	EtOH	440(4.46)	39-1155-73B
	EtOH-KOH	453(--)	39-1155-73B
$C_{12}H_8F_2N_6O$			
Urea, N-(2,4-difluorophenyl)-N'-1H-purin-6-yl-	pH 1-2	279(4.46)	87-0139-73
	pH 5-7	277.5(4.47)	87-0139-73
	pH 12	285(4.47)	87-0139-73
$C_{12}H_8I_2N_4O_2$			
Benzo[g]pteridine-2,4(1H,3H)-dione, 6,9-diiodo-7,8-dimethyl-	EtOH-5% DMF	282(4.36),370(4.38), 400(3.92)	65-1578-73
$C_{12}H_8NS$			
Phenothiazin-5-ium	MeCN	281(4.75),419(4.10)	39-0264-73B
10H-Phenothiazin-10-yl	MeCN	268(--),344(3.75), 381(4.00)	39-0264-73B
$C_{12}H_8N_2$			
Benzo[c]cinnoline	EtOH	304s(4.0),318(4.1), 362f(3.0)	61-0281-73
2,10-Diazaphenanthrene	EtOH	244(4.67)	78-0419-73
3,10-Diazaphenanthrene	EtOH	246(4.68)	78-0419-73
4,10-Diazaphenanthrene	EtOH	238(4.70)	78-0419-73
$C_{12}H_8N_2OS$			
Thiazolo[3,2-a]pyrimidin-4-ium, 3-hy-droxy-2-phenyl-, hydroxide, inner salt	50% dioxan-HCl	238(4.0),288(3.9), 475(3.9)	1-1763-73
	50% dioxan-NaOH	222(--),300(--), 347(--),449(--)	1-1763-73
$C_{12}H_8N_2O_2$			
Benzo[b][1,8]naphthyridin-2(1H)-one, 4-hydroxy-	DMSO	258(4.6),332(4.3), 361(4.2)	24-3533-73
Ethanedione, di-3-pyridinyl-	EtOH	242(4.06),270(4.00)	12-2027-73
$C_{12}H_8N_2O_2S$			
Acetonitrile, (2,3-dihydro-1,3-dioxo-4(1H)-isoquinolinylidene)(methylthio)-	EtOH	385(3.2)	95-0322-73

Compound	Solvent	$\lambda_{max}(\log \epsilon)$	Ref.
$C_{12}H_8N_2O_3S$			
2H-Pyrimido[2,1-b]benzothiazole-4-carboxylic acid, 2-oxo-, methyl ester	EtOH	229(4.24),250(4.09), 265(4.05),300(3.98)	94-2019-73
$C_{12}H_8N_2O_4$			
2H-Pyrimido[2,1-b]benzoxazole-4-carboxylic acid, 2-oxo-, methyl ester	EtOH	243(4.04),310(3.84)	94-2019-73
$C_{12}H_8N_2O_4S$			
Thiophene, 2-nitro-5-[2-(2-nitrophenyl)-ethenyl]-, trans	EtOH	260(4.10),382(4.23)	59-1601-73
Thiophene, 2-nitro-5-[2-(3-nitrophenyl)-ethenyl]-, trans	EtOH	267(4.18),385(4.21)	59-1601-73
Thiophene, 2-nitro-5-[2-(4-nitrophenyl)-ethenyl]-, trans	EtOH	236(3.95),275s(3.84), 396(4.40)	59-1601-73
Thiophene, 4-nitro-2-[2-(2-nitrophenyl)-ethenyl]-, trans	EtOH	220(4.17),269(4.45), 304s(4.20),335s(3.95)	59-1601-73
Thiophene, 4-nitro-2-[2-(3-nitrophenyl)-ethenyl]-, trans	EtOH	223(4.04),272(4.36), 310(4.25)	59-1601-73
Thiophene, 4-nitro-2-[2-(4-nitrophenyl)-ethenyl]-, trans	EtOH	262(4.31),338(4.05)	59-1601-73
$C_{12}H_8N_2S$			
Quinoxaline, 2-(2-thienyl)-	EtOH	218(4.36),273(--), 353(--)	34-0102-73
$C_{12}H_8N_4$			
1-Cyclohexene-1,2,4-tricarbonitrile, 4-(1-cyanoethenyl)-	MeOH	230(4.11)	88-0999-73
	MeOH	230(4.11)	33-3004-73
Pyrimido[4,5-d]pyrimidine, 2-phenyl-	MeCN	250(4.29),274(4.12), 312(4.08)	24-3743-73
$C_{12}H_8N_4O$			
6H-Pyrido[1,2-a]pyrimidine-8,9-dicarbonitrile, 2,4-dimethyl-6-oxo-	MeOH	239(4.34),274(3.80), 399(4.02),418(4.03)	44-3485-73
$C_{12}H_8N_4O_2$			
2,4(1H,3H)-Pteridinedione, 6-phenyl-	pH 5.0	272(4.35),356(4.00)	24-3149-73
	pH 11.0	293(4.37),373(3.93)	24-3149-73
2,4(1H,3H)-Pteridinedione, 7-phenyl-	pH 5.0	222(4.33),270s(3.82), 349(4.32)	24-3149-73
	pH 11.0	230(4.30),273(4.23), 365(4.09)	24-3149-73
4(3H)-Pteridinone, 6-phenyl-, 8-oxide	H_2O	225(4.23),295(4.44), 320s(4.16),370(3.87)	35-6407-73
$C_{12}H_8N_4O_3$			
2,4(1H,3H)-Pteridinedione, 6-phenyl-, 8-oxide	pH 2.0	250s(4.27),282(4.46), 370(3.83)	24-3149-73
	H_2O	248(3.88),295(4.14), 400(3.36)	35-6407-73
	pH 8.0	245(4.16),295(4.49), 405(3.88)	24-3149-73
2,4(1H,3H)-Pteridinedione, 7-phenyl-, 5-oxide	pH 4.0	229(4.26),253(4.41), 296(4.07),370(4.20)	24-3149-73
	pH 10.0	256(4.45),274(4.47), 300s(4.07),385(3.93)	24-3149-73
$C_{12}H_8N_4O_4$			
Diazene, (2,4-dinitrophenyl)phenyl-	MeCN	231(4.06),331(4.34), 444(2.89)	1-3632-73

Compound	Solvent	λ_{max}(log ϵ)	Ref.
2,4(1H,3H)-Pteridinedione, 7-phenyl-, 5,8-dioxide	pH 2.0	241(4.22),287(4.40), 340s(3.82),395(3.70)	24-3149-73
	pH 7.0	265(4.28),293(4.42), 330s(3.89),418(3.82)	24-3149-73
$C_{12}H_8N_4O_5$			
Phenol, 4-[(2,4-dinitrophenyl)azo]- (spectra in 50% DMSO)	acid	387(4.33)	1-3641-73
	KOH	553(4.59)	1-3641-73
$C_{12}H_8N_4O_6$			
Benzenamine, 2,4,6-trinitro-N-phenyl-	95.5% DMSO	390(4.12)	22-1225-73
anion	95.5% DMSO	455(4.35)	22-1225-73
$C_{12}H_8N_6$			
1,2,4,5-Tetrazine, 3,6-di-2-pyridinyl-	90% EtOH	257(4.04),296(4.36)	12-0389-73
$C_{12}H_8N_6OS$			
Thiocyanic acid, 4-(aminocarbonyl)-2-methyl-1,3,6,9b-tetraazaphenalenyl ester	EtOH	228(4.15),277s(3.70), 283(3.72),327(3.76), 342(3.64),383(3.60), 483s(2.89),519(3.08), 550(3.12)	1-2095-73
$C_{12}H_8N_6O_2$			
1H-Benzimidazo[5,4-g]pteridine-7,9(8H,10H)-dione, 4-methyl-	EtOH-2% DMSO	273(4.52),371(4.11)	65-2285-73
$C_{12}H_8OS$			
Thieno[2,3-b]furan, 2-phenyl-	EtOH	297(4.37)	103-0659-73
$C_{12}H_8OSe$			
Selenolo[2,3-b]furan, 2-phenyl-	EtOH	299(4.50)	103-0659-73
$C_{12}H_8O_2$			
Dibenzo[b,e][1,4]dioxin, cation radical	CH_2Cl_2-TFA	682(4.31)	39-1594-73B
1H,3H-Naphtho[1,8-cd]pyran-1-one	EtOH	213(4.62),241(4.36), 314(3.85)	44-1944-73
$C_{12}H_8O_3$			
3-Benzoxepin-2,4-dicarboxaldehyde	EtOH	258(4.40),276s(4.26)	78-0533-73
$C_{12}H_8O_4$			
Xanthotoxin	EtOH	219(4.48),245s(4.44), 249(4.45),262s(4.23), 301(4.16)	102-2071-73
$C_{12}H_8O_5$			
7H-Furo[3,2-g][1]benzopyran-7-one, 4-hydroxy-9-methoxy-	EtOH	225(4.22),275(4.20), 315(3.81)	4-0443-73
	EtOH-base	230(4.20),295(4.15), 328(3.61)	4-0443-73
$C_{12}H_9BrClNOS$			
Ethanone, 1-[2-(4-bromophenyl)-4-(chloromethyl)-5-thiazolyl]-	MeOH	247(4.51),316(4.41)	80-0685-73
$C_{12}H_9BrN_2O$			
Phenol, 4-[(4-bromophenyl)azo]-	C_6H_{12}	347(4.45)	62-0289-73
	EtOH	242(4.08),357(4.45)	62-0289-73
	ether	240(4.09),355(4.50)	62-0289-73

Compound	Solvent	λ_{max}(log ε)	Ref.
Phenol, 4-[(4-bromophenyl)azo]- (cont.)	$CHCl_3$	350(4.37)	62-0289-73
	CCl_4	350(4.48)	
$C_{12}H_9BrN_4O_2$			
Benzo[g]pteridine-2,4(1H,3H)-dione, 9-bromo-7,8-dimethyl-	EtOH-5% DMF	350(4.05),395(3.87)	65-1574-73
	EtOH-5% DMF	350(4.12),395(3.91)	65-1578-73
	40% H_2SO_4	400(4.24)	65-1574-73
$C_{12}H_9BrO_3$			
Methanone, (5-bromo-2-furanyl)(4-methoxyphenyl)-	n.s.g.	309(4.29)	39-2327-73C
$C_{12}H_9BrO_4$			
1,4-Naphthalenedione, 2-acetyl-3-bromo-2,3-dihydro-2-hydroxy-, trans-(±)-	n.s.g.	232(4.44),256(3.91), 303(3.37)	39-0368-73C
$C_{12}H_9ClN_2$			
Benzenamine, 2-chloro-N-(2-pyridinylmethylene)-	EtOH	242(4.12),275(3.88), 325(3.46)	12-1031-73
Benzenamine, 2-chloro-N-(3-pyridinylmethylene)-	EtOH	243(4.20),276s(4.00), 325(3.69)	12-1031-73
Benzenamine, 2-chloro-N-(4-pyridinylmethylene)-	EtOH	238(4.20),265(4.03), 335(3.61)	12-1031-73
Benzenamine, 3-chloro-N-(2-pyridinylmethylene)-	EtOH	242(4.10),282(3.99), 325(3.75)	12-1031-73
Benzenamine, 3-chloro-N-(3-pyridinylmethylene)-	EtOH	242(4.14),280(3.98), 325(3.76)	12-1031-73
Benzenamine, 3-chloro-N-(4-pyridinylmethylene)-	EtOH	233(4.20),241(4.18), 263(3.08),325(3.77)	12-1031-73
Benzenamine, 4-chloro-N-(2-pyridinylmethylene)-	EtOH	230(4.23),235(4.24), 253(4.22),282(4.23), 320(4.10)	12-1031-73
Benzenamine, 4-chloro-N-(3-pyridinylmethylene)-	EtOH	238(4.22),253s(4.17), 270(4.15),318(4.02)	12-1031-73
Benzenamine, 4-chloro-N-(4-pyridinylmethylene)-	EtOH	232(4.24),271(4.10), 325(3.93)	12-1031-73
$C_{12}H_9ClN_2O$			
Phenol, 4-chloro-2-[(2-pyridinylmethylene)amino]-, Co(II) chelate	pH 8.8	505(4.32)	18-2421-73
Cu chelate	pH 8.7	530(4.15)	18-2421-73
Mn chelate	pH 8.8	512(4.36)	18-2421-73
Zn chelate (also other metal chelates)	pH 8.7	513(4.36)	18-2421-73
Phenol, 4-[(2-chlorophenyl)azo]-	C_6H_{12}	352(4.37)	62-0289-73
	EtOH	235(4.24),355(4.33)	62-0289-73
	ether	237(4.30),352(4.38)	62-0289-73
	$CHCl_3$	352(3.73)	62-0289-73
	CCl_4	352(4.03)	62-0289-73
Phenol, 4-[(4-chlorophenyl)azo]-	C_6H_{12}	345(4.42)	62-0289-73
	EtOH	240(4.11),355(4.44)	62-0289-73
	ether	243(4.44),353(4.48)	62-0289-73
	$CHCl_3$	350(4.24)	62-0289-73
	CCl_4	350(4.50)	62-0289-73
$C_{12}H_9ClN_2O_3$			
Isoxazole, 5-[2-(4-chlorophenyl)ethenyl]-3-methyl-4-nitro-	EtOH	214(4.13),241(3.84), 341(4.07)	2-1074-73
isomer	EtOH	218(4.19),242(4.04), 347(4.20)	2-1074-73

Compound	Solvent	$\lambda_{max}(\log \epsilon)$	Ref.
$C_{12}H_9ClN_6O$			
Urea, N-(2-chlorophenyl)-N'-1H-purin-6-yl-	pH 1-2	282.5(4.35)	87-0139-73
	pH 5-7	278(4.34)	87-0139-73
	pH 12	284(4.36)	87-0139-73
Urea, N-(3-chlorophenyl)-N'-1H-purin-6-yl-	pH 1-2	286(4.41)	87-0139-73
	pH 5-7	279(4.44)	87-0139-73
	pH 12	284(4.40)	87-0139-73
Urea, N-(4-chlorophenyl)-N'-1H-purin-6-yl-	pH 1-2	288(4.22)	87-0139-73
	pH 5-7	281(4.37)	87-0139-73
	pH 12	286(4.40)	87-0139-73
$C_{12}H_9ClO_3$			
2-Furancarboxylic acid, 5-(2-chlorophenyl)-, methyl ester	MeOH	217(4.31),226s(4.12), 234s(3.99),297(4.57)	12-1147-73
2-Furancarboxylic acid, 5-(3-chlorophenyl)-, methyl ester	MeOH	216(4.16),228s(3.87), 233s(3.84),298(4.34), 312s(4.25)	12-1147-73
2-Furancarboxylic acid, 5-(4-chlorophenyl)-, methyl ester	MeOH	218(3.89),304(4.18)	12-1147-73
$C_{12}H_9ClO_4S$			
Benzo[b]thiophene-2,5-dicarboxylic acid, 5-chloro-, dimethyl ester	EtOH-HCl	233(4.18),245s(4.06), 292(3.96)	1-0595-73
$C_{12}H_9ClS$			
Thiophene, 2-[2-(4-chlorophenyl)ethenyl]-, cis	EtOH	240(4.12),292(4.02)	4-0643-73
trans	EtOH	234(3.95),240(3.96), 328(4.27)	4-0643-73
$C_{12}H_9FN_6O$			
Urea, N-(2-fluorophenyl)-N'-1H-purin-6-yl-	pH 1-2	283(3.40)	87-0139-73
	pH 5-7	278(4.41)	87-0139-73
	pH 12	284(4.36)	87-0139-73
$C_{12}H_9IN_2O$			
Phenol, 4-[(4-iodophenyl)azo]-	EtOH	242(4.09),360(4.43)	62-0289-73
	ether	244(4.18),358(4.56)	62-0289-73
	$CHCl_3$	355(4.30)	62-0289-73
	CCl_4	355(4.45)	62-0289-73
$C_{12}H_9IN_4O_2$			
Benzo[g]pteridine-2,4(1H,3H)-dione, 9-iodo-7,8-dimethyl-	EtOH-5% DMF	350(4.16),393(3.98)	65-1578-73
$C_{12}H_9N$			
2H-Azirine, 3-(2-naphthalenyl)-	C_6H_{12}	240(4.71),248(4.74), 275(3.96),284(4.05), 293(3.97),296(3.98), 322(3.08),339(3.15)	35-1945-73
$C_{12}H_9NO$			
Furo[2,3-b]quinoline, 4-methyl-	EtOH	239(4.67),309(3.92)	49-0633-73
$C_{12}H_9NOS$			
2,5-Cyclohexadiene-1,4-dione, 1-(S-phenylthiooxime)	CH_2Cl_2	278(4.13),440(4.30)	39-1031-73C
3,5-Cyclohexadiene-1,2-dione, 1-(S-phenylthiooxime)	CH_2Cl_2	260(3.79),460(4.08)	39-1031-73C
10H-Phenothiazine, 5-oxide	MeCN	269(4.14),298(3.86), 339(3.72)	39-0264-73B

Compound	Solvent	λ_{max}(log ϵ)	Ref.
$C_{12}H_9NO_2$			
9H-Pyrrolo[1,2-a]indol-9-one, 8-hydroxy-6-methyl-	EtOH	212(3.69),251(3.83), 286(3.29),297(3.70), 360(3.25)	44-3487-73
$C_{12}H_9NO_2S$			
Thiophene, 2-nitro-3-(2-phenylethenyl)-	EtOH	270(4.20),376(4.13)	118-0313-73B
Thiophene, 2-nitro-5-(2-phenylethenyl)-, trans	EtOH	220(4.10),276(4.15), 310s(3.91),405(4.46)	59-1601-73
	EtOH	276(4.15),405(4.46)	4-0191-73
Thiophene, 2-(2-nitro-2-phenylethenyl)-	EtOH	260s(3.60),357(4.12)	4-0191-73
Thiophene, 2-[2-(2-nitrophenyl)ethenyl]-, trans	EtOH	281(4.09),315(4.23), 365s(3.87)	59-1601-73
Thiophene, 2-[2-(3-nitrophenyl)ethenyl]-, trans	EtOH	216(4.07),279(4.06), 324(4.43)	59-1601-73
Thiophene, 2-[2-(4-nitrophenyl)ethenyl]-, cis	EtOH	269(4.20),354(3.88)	4-0643-73
trans	EtOH	272(4.09),372(4.21)	4-0643-73 +59-1601-73
Thiophene, 3-nitro-2-(2-phenylethenyl)-, trans	EtOH	277(4.11),376(3.83)	4-0191-73
Thiophene, 4-nitro-2-(2-phenylethenyl)-, trans	EtOH	228(4.19),272(4.42), 305(4.37),317(4.38), 330s(4.21)	59-1601-73
$C_{12}H_9NO_3$			
Furan, 2-ethenyl-5-(4-nitrophenyl)-	90% EtOH	223(4.05),278(3.95), 381(4.34)	12-1059-73
Furan, 2-nitro-5-(2-phenylethenyl)-	EtOH	210(4.47),239(4.24), 244(4.23),279(4.41), 395(4.69)	73-1705-73
Furo[2,3-b]quinolin-8-ol, 4-methoxy- (robustine)	EtOH	246(4.67),300s(3.57), 315(3.69),330(3.70)	2-1088-73
Pyrrolo[1,2-b]isoquinoline-1,5-dione, 2,3-dihydro-10-hydroxy-	EtOH	217(4.45),260(3.79), 356(3.83)	78-0213-73
$C_{12}H_9NO_3S$			
2H-1-Benzopyran-3-carbonitrile, 7-methoxy-4-(methylthio)-2-oxo-	EtOH	255(3.79),352(4.31)	95-0836-73
Furo[2,3-d]thieno[2,3-b]pyridine-4-carboxylic acid, 2-methyl-, methyl ester	MeOH	250(4.45),302(4.08), 338(3.78)	24-0368-73
$C_{12}H_9NO_3S_2$			
Ethanone, 1-[4-[(2-nitro-3-thienyl)-thio]phenyl]-	MeOH	372(4.06)	4-1007-73
Ethanone, 1-[4-[(3-nitro-2-thienyl)-thio]phenyl]-	MeOH	366(3.88)	4-1007-73
$C_{12}H_9NO_4S$			
Spiro[2H-indene-2,2'-thiazolidine]-4'-carboxylic acid, 1,3-dihydro-1,3-dioxo-, (R)-	MeOH	231(4.43),246s(4.01)	78-4271-73
$C_{12}H_9NO_5$			
2-Furancarboxylic acid, 5-(2-nitrophenyl)-, methyl ester	MeOH	215(4.02),278(4.08)	12-1147-73
2-Furancarboxylic acid, 5-(3-nitrophenyl)-, methyl ester	MeOH	213(4.34),296(4.54)	12-1147-73

Compound	Solvent	$\lambda_{max}(\log \epsilon)$	Ref.
$C_{12}H_9NO_6$			
2-Quinolinecarboxylic acid, 1,4,5,6-tetrahydro-8-methoxy-4,5,6-trioxo-, methyl ester	EtOH	260(4.33),360(3.48)	39-2374-73C
$C_{12}H_9NS$			
10H-Phenothiazine	MeCN	254(4.73),320(3.71)	39-0264-73B
Phenothiazine, radical cation	MeCN	271(4.73),437(3.64), 516(3.84)	39-0264-73B
4H-Thieno[3,2-b]pyrrole, 5-phenyl-	EtOH	226(4.02),313(4.43)	118-0313B-73
$C_{12}H_9NS_2$			
Naphtho[1,2-d]thiazole, 2-(methylthio)-	$CHCl_3$	247(4.61),298(4.05), 310(4.15),333(4.03)	22-3044-73
Naphtho[2,1-d]thiazole, 2-(methylthio)-	$CHCl_3$	242(4.17),265(4.56), 274(4.59),312(4.03)	22-3044-73
$C_{12}H_9N_3$			
Azuleno[2,1-d]pyrimidin-2-amine	MeOH	250(4.09),324(4.82), 336(4.78),391(3.50), 418(3.16),514(3.62), 550(2.43),610(2.06)	18-3161-73
Benzo[c]cinnolinium, 5-amino-, hydroxide, inner salt	EtOH	248(4.65),296(3.97), 308(3.90),322(3.87), 383(4.02),400s(3.98), 423s(3.74)	24-1589-73
2H-Benzotriazole, 2-phenyl-	MeOH	217(4.20),306(4.40)	73-0224-73
	$CHCl_3$	308(4.39)	73-0224-73
1H-Pyrrole-3,4-dicarbonitrile, 2,3-dihydro-5-phenyl-	EtOH	229(4.10),315(3.84)	35-1945-73
1,2,4-Triazolo[4,3-a]pyridine, 7-phenyl-	EtOH	248(4.13),302(3.93)	95-0642-73
$C_{12}H_9N_3O$			
Benzo[f]quinazolin-1(2H)-one, 3-amino-	EtOH-pH 1	212(4.51),225s(4.34), 233s(4.34),255(4.59), 263(4.62),300s(3.66), 313(3.78),333(3.61), 374(3.53)	4-0059-73
6H-Imidazo[1,2-c]pyrimidin-5-one, 2-phenyl-	MeOH	237(4.44),285(4.16), 308s(3.86)	7-0619-73
8H-Imidazo[1,2-a]pyrimidin-5-one, 2-phenyl-	MeOH	239(4.43),270s(3.84), 314(4.10)	7-0619-73
8H-Imidazo[1,2-a]pyrimidin-7-one, 2-phenyl-	MeOH	220s(4.39),263(4.08), 308(4.05)	7-0619-73
Phenol, 2-(2H-benzotriazol-2-yl)-	heptane	295(4.16)	73-0224-73
	0.05M HCl	296(4.26),325(4.28)	73-0224-73
	0.05M NaOH	277(4.19),344(3.78)	73-0224-73
	MeOH	212(4.33),236(4.01), 327(4.24)	73-0224-73
	EtOH	296(4.10)	73-0224-73
	dioxan	298(4.22),331(4.36)	73-0224-73
	50% dioxan	296(4.22)	73-0224-73
	$CHCl_3$	299s(4.02),334(4.25)	73-0224-73
Phenol, 3-(2H-benzotriazol-2-yl)-	MeOH	217(4.21),230s(4.16), 308(4.32)	73-0224-73
Phenol, 4-(2H-benzotriazol-2-yl)-	0.05M HCl	312.5(4.47)	73-0224-73
	0.05M NaOH	360(4.35)	73-0224-73
	MeOH	251(3.75),319(4.42)	73-0224-73
	dioxan	325(4.41)	73-0224-73
	$CHCl_3$	320(4.38)	73-0224-73

Compound	Solvent	λmax(log ε)	Ref.
1,2,4-Triazolo[4,3-a]pyridin-3(2H)-one, 7-phenyl-	EtOH	258(4.43),345(3.59)	95-0642-73
$C_{12}H_9N_3OS$			
Pyrimido[4,5-b]quinolin-4(1H)-one, 2,3-dihydro-3-methyl-2-thioxo-	MeCN	285(4.6),312(3.9), 368(3.9)	24-3533-73
$C_{12}H_9N_3OS_2$			
Thiazolo[4,5-d]pyridazin-7(6H)-one, 2-(methylthio)-6-phenyl-	$CHCl_3$	241s(4.21),273(4.40), 308s(4.21)	22-3324-73
4H-Thiazolo[3,2-a]-1,3,5-triazin-4-one, 2-(methylthio)-6-phenyl-	EtOH	260(4.25),323(4.26)	94-0074-73
4H-Thiazolo[3,2-a]-1,3,5-triazin-4-one, 2-(methylthio)-7-phenyl-	EtOH	279(4.04),296(3.93), 332(4.47)	94-0074-73
4H-Thiazolo[3,2-a]-1,3,5-triazin-4-one, 2-[(phenylmethyl)thio]-	EtOH	270(3.94),311(4.34),	94-0074-73
2H-Thiazolo[3,2-a]-1,3,5-triazin-2-one, 1,3,4,8a-tetrahydro-1-(phenylmethyl)-4-thioxo-, meso-ionic didehydro deriv.	H_2O	229(4.05),275(3.96), 320(4.10)	44-3868-73
4H-Thiazolo[3,2-a]-1,3,5-triazin-4-one, 1,2,3,8a-tetrahydro-1-(phenylmethyl)-2-thioxo-, meso-ionic didehydro deriv.	H_2O	217(4.57),256(3.93), 302(3.63)	44-3868-73
$C_{12}H_9N_3O_2$			
Diazene, (2-nitrophenyl)phenyl-	MeCN	229(4.05),316(4.25), 435(2.78)	1-3632-73
7,10-Methanopyridazino[1,2-a]pyrido-[2,3-d]pyridazine-5,12-dione, 7,10-dihydro-	EtOH	208(4.38),230s(--), 266(3.68),317(3.61)	39-0026-73C
7,10-Methanopyridazino[1,2-a]pyrido-[3,4-d]pyridazine-5,12-dione, 7,10-dihydro-	EtOH	205(4.38),224s(--), 270(3.63),320(3.66)	39-0026-73C
Pyrimido[4,5-b]quinoline-2,4(1H,3H)-dione, 3-methyl-	MeCN	237(4.6),248(4.6), 300(3.9),352(3.7)	24-3533-73
$C_{12}H_9N_3O_2S$			
Pyridinium, 4-cyano-1-[(phenylsulfonyl)-amino]-, hydroxide, inner salt	EtOH	273(3.93),350(3.89)	44-3311-73
2H-Thiazolo[3,2-a]-1,3,5-triazine-2,4(3H)-dione, 1,8a-dihydro-1-(phenylmethyl)-, meso-ionic didehydro deriv.	H_2O	215(4.33),272(3.75)	44-3868-73
$C_{12}H_9N_3O_3$			
Phenol, 4-[(2-nitrophenyl)azo]-	EtOH	232(4.12),250(--), 362(4.26)	62-0289-73
Phenol, 4-[(3-nitrophenyl)azo]-	EtOH	230(4.18),252(--), 360(4.22)	62-0289-73
Phenol, 4-[(4-nitrophenyl)azo]-	EtOH	257(3.88),380(4.30)	62-0289-73
Pyrimido[1,2-a]benzimidazole-4-carboxylic acid, 1,2-dihydro-2-oxo-, methyl ester	EtOH	213(4.35),239(4.42)	94-2019-73
$C_{12}H_9N_3O_4$			
Benzenamine, 2,4-dinitro-N-phenyl-	61.2% DMSO	367(4.26)	22-1225-73
anion	61.2% DMSO	425(4.29)	22-1225-73
Benzenamine, 4-nitro-N-(4-nitrophenyl)-	80.4% DMSO	418(4.58)	22-1225-73
anion	80.4% DMSO	587(4.80)	22-1225-73
Benzoic acid, 3-[(5-nitro-2-pyridinyl)-amino]-, anion	95.5% DMSO	400(4.32)	22-1553-73
dianion	95.5% DMSO	480(4.45)	22-1553-73

Compound	Solvent	$\lambda_{max}(\log \epsilon)$	Ref.
Benzoic acid, 4-[(3-nitro-2-pyridinyl)-amino]-, anion	80.4% DMSO	430(3.85)	22-1553-73
dianion	80.4% DMSO	540(3.92)	22-1553-73
Benzoic acid, 4-[(5-nitro-2-pyridinyl)-amino]-, anion	95.5% DMSO	397(4.33)	22-1553-73
dianion	95.5% DMSO	483(4.45)	22-1553-73
$C_{12}H_9N_3O_4S_2$			
Cyclopentanimine, 2-(4,6-dinitro-1,3-benzodithiol-2-ylidene)-	EtOH	262(4.09),318(4.33), 470(3.83)	39-1009-73C
$C_{12}H_9N_3O_5$			
Isoxazole, 3-methyl-4-nitro-5-[2-(4-nitrophenyl)ethenyl]-, (E)-	EtOH	216(4.02),334(4.49)	2-1074-73
$C_{12}H_9N_3O_7$			
Pyridinium 3,5-dinitrosalicylate	EtOH	340(4.09)	39-2949-73C
$C_{12}H_9N_3S$			
1,2,4-Triazolo[4,3-a]pyridine-3(2H)-thione, 7-phenyl-	EtOH	278(4.34),357(3.49)	95-0642-73
$C_{12}H_9N_5O$			
4(1H)-Pteridinone, 2-amino-6-phenyl-	pH 0.1	275(4.35),350(4.02)	24-3175-73
	pH 5.4	293(4.38),367(3.96)	24-3175-73
	pH 11.3	271(4.41),295s(4.16), 379(4.05)	24-3175-73
4(1H)-Pteridinone, 2-amino-7-phenyl-	pH 0.1	225(4.41),255s(3.91), 348(4.36)	24-3175-73
	pH 5.4	275(4.24),362(4.16)	24-3175-73
	pH 10.4	237(4.32),264(4.32), 373(4.13)	24-3175-73
$C_{12}H_9N_5O_2$			
Imidazo[1,2-a]pyrimidin-7(1H)-one, 5-hydroxy-6-(phenylazo)-	pH 1	244(4.07),391(4.34)	4-1021-73
	pH 11	235(4.21),371(4.33)	4-1021-73
4(1H)-Pteridinone, 2-amino-7-phenyl-, 5-oxide	pH -1.0	226(4.38),255s(4.04), 277s(3.88),348(4.32), 395s(3.12)	24-3175-73
	pH 3.0	238(4.34),272(4.30), 365(4.13)	24-3175-73
	pH 8.0	220(4.41),275(4.42), 365(4.20)	24-3175-73
4(3H)-Pteridinone, 2-amino-6-phenyl-, 8-oxide	pH -3.0	213s(4.13),248(4.23), 287(4.44),366(3.82)	24-3175-73
	pH 4.0	243(4.14),297(4.51), 393(3.89)	24-3175-73
	pH 10.0	282(4.52),402(3.99)	24-3175-73
	pH 13	283(4.73),320s(4.29), 397(4.15)	35-6407-73
$C_{12}H_{10}$			
Acenaphthylene, 1,5-dihydro-	C_6H_{12}	213(4.26),229(4.15), 257(4.08),261s(--), 292(3.28),304(3.20)	88-0159-73
Biphenyl	EtOH	249(4.23)	22-1517-73
$C_{12}H_{10}BrIN_2$			
Pyridinium, 1-[[(4-bromophenyl)methylene]amino]-, iodide	EtOH	213(4.42),261(4.21), 290(3.97)	103-1108-73

Compound	Solvent	λ_{max}(log ε)	Ref.
Pyridinium, 1-[[(4-bromophenyl)methylene]amino]-, iodide	acetone	260(4.62),290(4.64)	103-1108-73
	HOAc	297.5(4.35)	103-1108-73
	H_2SO_4	219(4.00),256(3.84), 278(4.21),330(4.41)	103-1108-73
	MeCN	247(4.29),298(4.40)	103-1108-73
	DMSO	296(4.35),420(0.84)	103-1108-73
$C_{12}H_{10}ClIN_2$			
Pyridinium, 1-[[(3-chlorophenyl)methylene]amino]-, iodide	EtOH	208(4.59),275(4.10)	103-1108-73
$C_{12}H_{10}ClNOS$			
Ethanone, 1-[4-(chloromethyl)-2-phenyl-5-thiazolyl]-	MeOH	238(4.44),316(4.57)	80-0685-73
$C_{12}H_{10}ClNO_3$			
1H-Indole-2-carboxylic acid, 3-chloro-1-formyl-, ethyl ester	EtOH	241(4.15),283s(4.20), 293(4.26),311s(4.00)	94-1481-73
1H-Indole-2,3-dione, 1-(4-chloro-1-oxobutyl)-	EtOH	237(4.36),264(3.94), 335(3.58)	39-0998-73C
$C_{12}H_{10}ClNO_3S$			
Thieno[2,3-b]pyridine-6-carboxylic acid, 5-(2-chloro-2-propenyl)-4,7-dihydro-4-oxo-, methyl ester	MeOH	241(4.25),322(3.65)	24-0368-73
$C_{12}H_{10}FNO_2$			
1H-Pyrrole-2-carboxylic acid, 4-fluoro-5-phenyl-, methyl ester	MeOH	220(4.11),294(4.0)	24-3544-73
$C_{12}H_{10}FN_3$			
Propanedinitrile, [[4-(dimethylamino)-phenyl]fluoromethylene]-	MeCN	240s(3.73),263(3.85), 315(3.13),424(4.71)	39-0616-73B
$C_{12}H_{10}IN_3O_2$			
Pyridinium, 1-[[(3-nitrophenyl)methylene]amino]-, iodide	EtOH	220(4.32),255(4.08)	103-1108-73
Pyridinium, 1-[[(4-nitrophenyl)methylene]amino]-, iodide	EtOH	216(4.42),269(4.30)	103-1108-73
	acetone	258(4.43),280(4.37)	103-1108-73
	HOAc	287(4.47),362(3.72)	103-1108-73
	MeCN	248(4.31),285(4.42)	103-1108-73
$C_{12}H_{10}IO_2P$			
Phosphinic acid, (2-iodophenyl)phenyl-	10% EtOH	218(4.32),266(3.16), 273(3.17),283(3.06)	139-0277-73B
Phosphinic acid, (4-iodophenyl)phenyl-	10% EtOH	243(4.31)	139-0277-73B
$C_{12}H_{10}IO_3P$			
1,2,3-Benziodoxaphosphole, 1,3-dihydro-1-hydroxy-3-phenyl-, 3-oxide	10% EtOH	225(4.23),268(3.21)	139-0277-73B
$C_{12}H_{10}NOS$			
Benzothiazolium, 2-(2-furanyl)-3-methyl-, perchlorate	H_2O	412(4.12)	104-2596-73
$C_{12}H_{10}NS_2$			
Benzothiazolium, 3-methyl-2-thienyl-, perchlorate	H_2O	355(4.37)	104-2596-73

Compound	Solvent	$\lambda_{max}(\log \epsilon)$	Ref.
$C_{12}H_{10}N_2$			
Benzenamine, N-(2-pyridinylmethylene)-	EtOH	235(4.06),250(4.04), 280(4.06),320s(3.85)	12-1031-73
Benzenamine, N-(3-pyridinylmethylene)-	EtOH	236(4.15),255s(4.07), 280s(4.00),320s(3.82)	12-1031-73
Benzenamine, N-(4-pyridinylmethylene)-	EtOH	230(4.23),265(4.12), 285s(4.03),320s(3.86)	12-1031-73
Diazene, diphenyl-	MeCN	228(4.07),230s(--), 280(3.83),318(4.22), 340s(--),445(2.85)	12-1251-73
anion	MeCN	226(4.06),290(3.98), 320s(3.74),417(4.45)	12-1251-73
dianion	MeCN	248(4.54),290(4.34), 420(3.20)	12-1251-73
Harman	MeOH	234(4.57),287(4.25), 347(3.66)	95-0033-73
$C_{12}H_{10}N_2O$			
Phenol, 2-(phenylazo)-	C_6H_{12}	203(4.32),219s(4.10), 237(3.92),244(3.93), 325(4.27),384s(3.98)	131-0255-73
	EtOH	203(4.28),217s(4.10), 236(4.00),243(4.01), 327(4.29),378s(4.01)	131-0255-73
Phenol, 3-(phenylazo)-	C_6H_{12}	207(4.18),232(4.00), 237s(3.96),317(4.14), 442(2.73)	131-0255-73
	EtOH	207(4.22),232s(4.01), 237s(3.98),317(4.14), 433(2.99)	131-0255-73
Phenol, 4-(phenylazo)-	C_6H_{12}	201(4.27),235(4.16), 243s(4.09),251s(3.90), 340(3.90),439(3.81)	131-0255-73
	EtOH	237(4.14),350(4.14)	62-0289-73
	EtOH	200(4.37),237(4.13), 350(4.46),430(3.20)	131-0255-73
	ether	235(4.44),348(4.53)	62-0289-73
	$CHCl_3$	340(3.95)	62-0289-73
	CCl_4	340(4.48)	62-0289-73
Phenol, 2-[(2-pyridinylmethylene)-amino]-, Cd chelate	pH 8.9	500(4.40)	18-2421-73
Co chelate	pH 8.9	493(4.23)	18-2421-73
Cu chelate	pH 8.9	515(4.11)	18-2421-73
Mn chelate	pH 8.9	500(4.34)	18-2421-73
Ni chelate	pH 8.9	520(4.34)	18-2421-73
Pb chelate	pH 8.9	475(3.83)	18-2421-73
Zn chelate	pH 8.9	500(4.42)	18-2421-73
4-Pyridinecarboxamide, N-phenyl-	EtOH	273(3.89)	12-2027-73
9H-Pyrido[3,4-b]indole-1-methanol	EtOH	213(4.40),235(4.58), 240s(4.56),250s(4.40), 282s(4.07),289(4.24), 338(3.71),347(3.70)	94-0837-73
$C_{12}H_{10}N_2OS$			
Thiazolo[3,2-a]pyrimidin-5-one, 2,3-dihydro-2-phenyl-	MeOH	213(4.30),293(3.93)	39-2022-73C
Thiazolo[3,2-a]pyrimidin-7-one, 2,3-dihydro-2-phenyl-	MeOH	234(4.48),275s(3.81)	39-2022-73C
5H-Thiazolo[3,2-c]pyrimidin-5-one, 2,3-dihydro-2-phenyl-	MeOH	212(4.13),323(4.15)	39-2022-73C

Compound	Solvent	λ_{max}(log ε)	Ref.
1H-Thieno[2,3-c]pyrazol-4(5H)-one, 3-methyl-1-phenyl-	C_6H_{12}	245(4.36)	104-2429-73
	H_2O	245(4.36)	104-2429-73
	EtOH	245(4.36)	104-2429-73
$C_{12}H_{10}N_2OS_3$			
4-Thiazolidinone, 3-phenyl-5-(2-thiazolidinylidene)-2-thioxo-	EtOH	284(4.08),395(4.50)	94-1431-73
$C_{12}H_{10}N_2O_2$			
Benzenamine, 2-nitro-N-phenyl-	95.5% DMSO	434(3.77)	22-1225-73
anion	95.5% DMSO	545(3.94)	22-1225-73
Benzenamine, 4-nitro-N-phenyl-	95.5% DMSO	407(4.29)	22-1225-73
anion	95.5% DMSO	505(4.52)	22-1225-73
1H-Isoindole-1,3(2H)-dione, 2-(5-azabicyclo[2.1.0]pent-5-yl)-	EtOH	234(4.57),295(3.08), 304(3.04),330s(2.57)	78-2973-73
Phenol, 2,2'-azobis-	C_6H_{12}	212(4.34),252(4.03), 325(4.23),403(4.05), 424(4.10)	131-0255-73
	EtOH	200(4.57),249(4.07), 321(4.24),397(4.24)	131-0255-73
Phenol, 4,4'-azobis-	C_6H_{12}	203(4.43),239(4.11), 243(4.13),350(4.43), 427(3.22)	131-0255-73
	EtOH	202(4.27),244(4.19), 359(4.45)	131-0255-73
	EtOH	246(4.26),360(4.60)	62-0289-73
	ether	243(4.61),358(3.93)	62-0289-73
$C_{12}H_{10}N_2O_2S_3$			
1,3-Thiazine-5-carboxamide, 6-(methylthio)-2-phenyl-, 1-oxide	EtOH	225(4.14),268(4.29), 329(3.78),370(4.48)	44-0802-73
$C_{12}H_{10}N_2O_3$			
1,3(2H,4H)-Isoquinolinedione, 4-(2-oxazolidinylidene)-	EtOH	232(4.40),287(3.20), 368(3.02)	95-0322-73
Isoxazole, 3-methyl-4-nitro-5-(2-phenylethenyl)-	EtOH	217(4.20),255(4.05), 350(4.20)	2-1074-73
dibromide	EtOH	217(4.32),255(4.05)	2-1074-73
$C_{12}H_{10}N_2O_4S$			
Benzenesulfonic acid, 4-[(4-hydroxyphenyl)azo]-	EtOH	240(4.00),355(4.37)	62-0289-73
$C_{12}H_{10}N_2O_7$			
2-Quinolinecarboxylic acid, 1,4-dihydro-5-hydroxy-8-methoxy-6-nitro-4-oxo-, methyl ester	$CHCl_3$	249(4.31),295s(3.70), 368(3.94)	39-2374-73C
$C_{12}H_{10}N_3O_2$			
Pyridinium, 1-[[(3-nitrophenyl)methylene]amino]-, iodide	EtOH	220(4.32),255(4.08)	103-1108-73
Pyridinium, 1-[[(4-nitrophenyl)methylene]amino]-, iodide	EtOH	216(4.42),269(4.30)	103-1108-73
	acetone	258(4.43),280(4.37)	103-1108-73
	HOAc	287(4.47),362(3.72)	103-1108-73
	MeCN	248(4.31),285(4.42)	103-1108-73
$C_{12}H_{10}N_4$			
1,2,4-Triazolo[4,3-a]pyridin-3-amine, 7-phenyl-	EtOH	252(4.43),343(3.43)	95-0642-73

Compound	Solvent	λ_{max}(log ε)	Ref.
$C_{12}H_{10}N_4OS$			
1,2,4-Triazino[5,6-d][3,1]benzoxazepine, 6-methyl-3-(methylthio)-	EtOH	205(4.37),216(4.28), 261(4.53),296(4.10), 386(4.11)	78-0639-73
$C_{12}H_{10}N_4O_2$			
Benzenamine, 4-[(4-nitrophenyl)azo]-	n.s.g.	425(4.31)	40-1738-73
Benzo[g]pteridine-2,4(1H,3H)-dione, 7,8-dimethyl-	EtOH	256(5.1),298(4.5), 325(4.5)	103-0513-73
Propanedinitrile, (4-acetyl-3-cyano-1,5-dihydro-5-methoxy-5-methyl-2H-pyrrol-2-ylidene)-	EtOH	245(4.11),392(3.51)	12-1551-73
Pyridazino[4,5-b]quinoxaline-1,4-dione, 2,3-dihydro-2,3-dimethyl-	EtOH	254(4.7),330(4.1)	103-0513-73
Pyridazino[4,5-b]quinoxalin-1(2H)-one, 4-methoxy-2-methyl-	EtOH	250(4.6),283s(3.8), 293(3.8),325(3.7)	103-0513-73
$C_{12}H_{10}N_6$			
2,4-Pteridinediamine, 6-phenyl-	pH 1	265(4.80),363(4.17)	35-6413-73
	pH 2.0	266(4.48),364(4.11)	24-3175-73
	pH 8.0	216(4.19),234s(4.02), 276(4.44),302s(4.22), 388(4.04)	24-3175-73
2,4-Pteridinediamine, 7-phenyl-	pH 2.0	227s(4.32),252(4.05), 280(3.90),356(4.38), 365s(4.36)	24-3175-73
	pH 9.0	221(4.33),238(4.31), 265(4.32),305s(3.81), 380(4.14)	24-3175-73
Pyrimido[5,4-e]-1,2,4-triazin-5-amine, 3-methyl-7-phenyl-	EtOH	251(3.73),290(3.93), 382(2.96)	44-2238-73
$C_{12}H_{10}N_6O$			
2,4-Pteridinediamine, 6-phenyl-, 8-oxide	pH 0.0	274(4.46),374(3.93)	24-3175-73
	0.12M HCl	275(4.49),375(3.92)	35-6413-73
	pH 5.0	283(4.48),407(3.94)	24-3175-73
2,4-Pteridinediamine, 7-phenyl-, 5-oxide	pH 0.0	221(4.38),235s(4.34), 275(4.21),305s(3.94), 380(4.24)	24-3175-73
	pH 5.0	224(4.47),271(4.43), 375(4.28)	24-3175-73
$C_{12}H_{10}N_6O_2$			
2,4-Pteridinediamine, 6-phenyl-, 5,8-dioxide	pH 0.0	273(4.41),294s(4.35), 385(3.84),420s(3.44)	24-3175-73
	pH 5.0	291(4.52),406(3.95)	24-3175-73
2,4-Pteridinediamine, 7-phenyl-, 5,8-dioxide	MeOH	225s(4.27),288(4.60), 370s(3.97),380(4.02), 396s(3.99)	24-3175-73
2-Pyridineacetic acid, 4,6-diamino-α,3,5-tricyano-, ethyl ester	EtOH	226(4.35),258(3.91), 348(4.42)	12-2567-73
$C_{12}H_{10}N_6O_8$			
2,4,6(1H,3H,5H)-Pyrimidinetrione, 5-acetoxy-, 2-(2,4-dinitrophenylhydrazone)	EtOH	386(4.52)	103-0247-73
$C_{12}H_{10}O$			
Benzo[a]cyclopropa[cd]pentalen-1(2H)-one, 2a,2b,6b,6c-tetrahydro-	EtOH	209(4.24),235s(4.52), 285(4.08)	35-4592-73

Compound	Solvent	$\lambda_{max}(\log \epsilon)$	Ref.
Diphenyl ether	C_6H_{12}	226(4.05),273(3.31)	32-0709-73
	H_2O	220s(3.94),270(3.17)	32-0709-73
	EtOH	225s(4.01),271(3.31)	32-0709-73
Ethanone, 1-(1-naphthalenyl)-	H_2O	307(3.73),325s(3.57)	112-0007-73
	H_2SO_4	388s(3.79),422(3.97)	112-0007-73
Ethanone, 1-(2-naphthalenyl)-	H_2O	282(4.01),344(3.29)	112-0007-73
	H_2SO_4	345(4.41),439(3.59)	112-0007-73
$C_{12}H_{10}OS$			
2-Thiophenecarboxaldehyde, 5-(4-methyl-phenyl)-	MeOH	236(3.92),336(4.35)	73-1809-73
3-Thiophenecarboxaldehyde, 2-methyl-5-phenyl-	EtOH	253(4.43),285(4.06)	78-0413-73
3-Thiophenecarboxaldehyde, 5-methyl-2-phenyl-	EtOH	239(4.23),263(3.97), 309(3.79)	78-0413-73
$C_{12}H_{10}O_2$			
4-Azuleneacetic acid	CH_2Cl_2	280(4.68),286(4.67), 329(3.54),343(3.68), 356(3.14),575(2.60), 617(2.52),677(2.08)	44-1106-73
2,3-Benzotropone, 11-methoxy-	n.s.g.	234(4.36),284(3.81)	35-6655-73
4-Cyclopentene-1,3-dione, 4-methyl-5-phenyl-	MeOH	224(4.00),286(3.89)	44-2945-73
1(2H)-Dibenzofuranone, 3,4-dihydro-	EtOH	226(4.3),262(3.9)	103-0137-73
1-Naphthalenecarboxylic acid, 7-methyl-	MeOH	223(4.67),296(3.75), 325s(3.46)	24-1341-73
Naphtho[2,3-d][1,2]dioxin, 1,4-dihydro-	EtOH	225(5.02),253s(3.32), 261(3.51),270(3.65), 280(3.68),291(3.49), 306(2.57),319(2.28)	88-3181-73
$C_{12}H_{10}O_2S$			
5,10-Epithiobenzocyclooctene, 5,10-di-hydro-, 11,11-dioxide	EtOH	267s(3.36),273(3.39), 278s(3.36)	35-2230-73
Methanone, (4-methoxyphenyl)-2-thienyl-	hexane	225(4.0),292(4.3)	35-4599-73
Methanone, (4-methoxyphenyl)-3-thienyl-	hexane	220(4.3),270(4.2)	35-4599-73
2-Thiophenecarboxaldehyde, 5-(4-methoxy-phenyl)-	MeOH	242(4.00),349(4.39)	73-1809-73
$C_{12}H_{10}O_2S_3$			
Sulfide, bis(6-methyl-2-thioxobenzo-pyran-4-yl)	MeOH	293(4.44),408(4.28)	7-0269-73
$C_{12}H_{10}O_2S_4$			
Disulfide, bis(6-methyl-2-thioxobenzo-pyran-4-yl)	MeOH	263(4.55),325(4.24)	7-0269-73
$C_{12}H_{10}O_3$			
5H-Benzocyclohepten-5-one, 6,9-di-hydroxy-7-methyl-	EtOH	233(4.45),255s(4.12), 316(3.89),356(4.00), 370s(3.94)	39-1223-73C
2-Furancarboxylic acid, 5-methyl-, phenyl ester	heptane	262(--)	103-0546-73
	H_2O	270(--)	103-0546-73
	EtOH	268(--)	103-0546-73
	dioxan	266(4.62)	103-0546-73
$C_{12}H_{10}O_4$			
2H-1-Benzopyran-3-carboxylic acid, 2-oxo-, ethyl ester	MeOH	292(4.15),330(3.87)	24-0388-73

Compound	Solvent	λ_{max}(log ε)	Ref.
1(2H)-Naphthalenone, 2-acetyl-2,3-epoxy-3,4-dihydro-4-hydroxy-	n.s.g.	218(3.80),258(4.02), 292(3.14)	39-0235-73C
1(2H)-Naphthalenone, 3-acetyl-2,3-epoxy-3,4-dihydro-4-hydroxy-	n.s.g.	217(3.86),256(4.04), 292(3.17)	39-0235-73C
Propanedioic acid, (3-phenyl-2-propenylidene)-	EtOH	236(3.59),330(4.17)	18-2504-73
$C_{12}H_{10}O_4S$			
2H-1-Benzopyran-2-one, 7-acetoxy-4-(methylthio)-	EtOH	232s(4.09),275s(4.17), 300(4.25),316s(4.14)	95-0836-73
Benzo[b]thiophene-2,3-dicarboxylic acid, dimethyl ester	EtOH-HCl	234(4.18),245s(4.06), 295(4.17)	1-0595-73
Benzo[c]thiophene-1,3-dicarboxylic acid, dimethyl ester	MeOH	218(4.25),248(4.48), 340(3.84),382(4.06)	88-1871-73
Propanedioic acid, (benzo[b]thien-2-ylmethyl)-	EtOH	229(4.41),260(3.87), 287(3.33),298(3.34)	2-0446-73
$C_{12}H_{10}O_4S_2$			
Disulfide, bis(6-methyl-2-oxo-4-pyranyl)	MeOH	220(4.49),262(4.21), 307(4.08)	7-0269-73
$C_{12}H_{10}O_5$			
4,5-Benzofurandicarboxylic acid, dimethyl ester	90% EtOH	225(4.52),255(3.75), 302(3.51)	12-1059-73
2-Furancarboxylic acid, 5-methyl-, anhydride	heptane	276(--)	103-0546-73
	dioxan	279(4.47)	103-0546-73
2,5-Furandione, 3-methoxy-4-(3-methoxyphenyl)-	EtOH	234s(3.85),263(3.60), 333(3.74)	39-1538-73C
2,5-Furandione, 3-methoxy-4-(4-methoxyphenyl)-	EtOH	240(4.03),368(3.93)	39-1538-73C
$C_{12}H_{10}O_6$			
2H-1-Benzopyran-6-carboxaldehyde, 7-hydroxy-5,8-dimethoxy-2-oxo-	MeOH	275(4.43)	78-2645-73
	MeOH-HCl	208(4.46),226s(4.19), 263(4.11),320(4.19)	78-2645-73
	MeOH-NaOH	238(4.28),269(4.22), 299(4.11),360(4.15)	78-2645-73
Peroxide, bis[(5-methyl-2-furanyl)carbonyl]	heptane	271(--)	103-0546-73
	EtOH	276(--)	103-0546-73
	dioxan	278(4.66)	103-0546-73
$C_{12}H_{10}O_6S$			
2H,5H-Pyrano[4,3-b]thiopyran-2,5-dione, 8-carbethoxy-4-hydroxy-7-methyl-	MeOH	240(4.36),286(4.00), 360(3.79)	7-0269-73
$C_{12}H_{10}O_8$			
4,5-Benzofurandicarboxylic acid, 2,3-dihydro-2,6-dihydroxy-2,7-dimethyl-3-oxo-	EtOH	241(4.43),300(3.87), 300(3.94)	33-2287-73
$C_{12}H_{10}S$			
Thiophene, 2-(2-phenylethenyl)-, cis	EtOH	233(4.01),290(3.99)	4-0643-73
Thiophene, 2-(2-phenylethenyl)-, trans	EtOH	230(3.98),270s(3.71), 325(4.42)	4-0643-73
$C_{12}H_{11}BrO_4$			
1(2H)-Naphthalenone, 4-acetoxy-2-bromo-	n.s.g.	248(4.06),290(3.22)	39-0368-73C
$C_{12}H_{11}Cl$			
Benzene, 1-chloro-4-(2,4-cyclohexadien-1-yl)-	n.s.g.	252(3.69)	78-3797-73

Compound	Solvent	λ_{max}(log ε)	Ref.
Benzene, 1-chloro-4-(1,3,5-hexatrien-yl)-, (E,Z)-	n.s.g.	217(4.72)	78-3797-73
$C_{12}H_{11}ClN_2O$			
Aziridine, 1-[(5-chloro-3-methyl-1H-indol-2-yl)carbonyl]-	isoPrOH	235(4.33),310(4.32)	44-3077-73
2-Butenoyl chloride, 2-cyano-3-[(phenylmethyl)amino]-	MeCN	301(4.31)	44-2287-73
$C_{12}H_{11}ClN_4$			
2H-Tetrazole, 2-(4-chlorophenyl)-5-(1-methyl-1,3-butadienyl)-, cis	EtOH	262(4.52),285s(--)	88-4295-73
2H-Tetrazole, 2-(4-chlorophenyl)-5-(2-methyl-1,3-butadienyl)-, cis	EtOH	255(4.38),286(4.36)	88-4295-73
2H-Tetrazole, 2-(4-chlorophenyl)-5-(3-methyl-1,3-butadienyl)-, cis	EtOH	263(4.42),290(4.11)	88-4295-73
2H-Tetrazole, 2-(4-chlorophenyl)-5-(1,3-pentadienyl)-, cis	EtOH	264(4.42),288(4.22)	88-4295-73
$C_{12}H_{11}ClO$			
5-Hexen-3-yn-1-ol, 6-(4-chlorophenyl)-, (E)-	n.s.g.	285(4.48)	78-3797-73
$C_{12}H_{11}ClO_4S$			
2-Butenedioic acid, 2-[(4-chlorophenyl)-thio]-, dimethyl ester	EtOH-HCl	223(4.20),263(4.06)	1-0595-73
$C_{12}H_{11}FO_2$			
5H-Benzocyclohepten-5-one, 6-fluoro-8,9-dihydro-2-methoxy-	n.s.g.	240(4.10),312(3.96)	35-6655-73
$C_{12}H_{11}IN_2$			
Pyridinium, 1-[(phenylmethylene)amino]-, iodide	EtOH	215(4.43),283(4.22)	103-1108-73
	acetone	247(4.19),298(3.90)	103-1108-73
	HOAc	222(4.05),286(4.32), 363(3.38)	103-1108-73
	H_2SO_4	263(3.66),298(4.29), 352(3.36)	103-1108-73
	MeCN	247(4.34),280(4.24)	103-1108-73
	DMSO	242(4.17),278(4.24), 438(2.15),570(2.58)	103-1108-73
$C_{12}H_{11}IN_2O$			
Pyridinium, 1-[(3-hydroxyphenyl)methylene]amino]-, iodide	EtOH	290(4.33),345s(3.83)	103-1108-73
$C_{12}H_{11}N$			
Pyridine, 2-(phenylmethyl)-	pH 2	265(3.86)	39-2111-73B
	pH 10	262(3.65),269s(3.53)	39-2111-73B
$C_{12}H_{11}NO$			
2H-Azepin-2-one, 1,3-dihydro-5-phenyl-	EtOH	240(4.35)	39-1079-73C
6H-Cyclopent[d]isoxazole, 3a,6a-dihydro-3-phenyl-	EtOH	267(4.06)	32-0047-73
9H-Cyclopenta[b]quinolin-9-one, 1,2,3,4-tetrahydro-	n.s.g.	238(4.48),317(4.09), 331(4.13)	4-0225-73
Ethanone, 1-(2-methyl-3-quinolinyl)-	EtOH	241(4.60),283(3.83)	94-1943-73
1H-Indene-1-propanenitrile, 2,3-dihydro-2-oxo-	EtOH	225s(3.62),257(2.95), 263(3.07),269(3.20), 276(3.23),302(2.84)	22-0691-73

Compound	Solvent	$\lambda_{max}(\log \epsilon)$	Ref.
1H-Indene-2-propanenitrile, 2,3-dihydro-1-oxo-	EtOH	246(4.06),292(3.39)	22-0691-73
Isoxazole, 3-methyl-5-(2-phenylethenyl)-	C_6H_{12}	221(3.98),226(4.01),234(3.89),292s(--),298(4.46),309(4.43),320s(--)	32-0309-73
	MeOH	220(3.96),226(4.01),233(3.89),300(4.49),305s(--),320s(--)	32-0309-73
	EtOH	222(3.95),227(4.00),234(3.88),301(4.48)	18-3533-73
Isoxazole, 5-methyl-3-(2-phenylethenyl)-	C_6H_{12}	204(4.25),213(4.20),219(4.22),226(4.08),275(4.41),290s(--),300(3.91)	32-0309-73
	MeOH	202(4.28),213(4.20),220(4.24),226(4.12),278(4.43),290s(--),300s(--)	32-0309-73
Pyridine, 4-(phenylmethyl)-, 1-oxide	H_2O	260(4.24)	59-1069-73
cation	H_2O	252(3.68)	59-1069-73
$C_{12}H_{11}NOS$			
2(3H)-Furanthione, 3-[(methylamino)methylene]-5-phenyl-	EtOH	432(4.10)	103-0659-73
3-Pyridinemethanol, 2-(phenylthio)-	MeOH	245(3.98),287(2.26)	73-1693-73
Thiocyanic acid, 3-(4-ethylphenyl)-3-oxo-1-propenyl ester	dioxan	306(4.40)	24-0435-73
$C_{12}H_{11}NOS_2$			
Benzenepropanenitrile, α-[bis(methylthio)methylene]-β-oxo-	EtOH	263(3.99),349(4.05)	1-0258-73
$C_{12}H_{11}NOSe$			
2(3H)-Furanselone, 3-[(methylamino)methylene]-5-phenyl-	EtOH	452(4.01)	103-0659-73
$C_{12}H_{11}NO_2$			
4H-Cyclopent[d]isoxazol-4-one, 3a,5,6,6a-tetrahydro-3-phenyl-	EtOH	269(4.08),277(4.05)	39-1148-73C
6H-Cyclopent[d]isoxazol-6-one, 3a,4,5,6a-tetrahydro-3-phenyl-	EtOH	264(4.11)	39-1148-73C
1(2H)-Isoquinolinone, 4-acetyl-2-methyl-	EtOH	222(4.49),260(3.96),304(4.06),312(4.03),325(3.96),339(3.75)	94-2585-73
1(2H)-Isoquinolinone, 7-acetyl-2-methyl-	EtOH	213(4.52),223(4.49),266(3.77),317(4.03),332(4.12),343(4.07)	94-2585-73
2-Propenoic acid, 3-(1H-indol-3-yl)-, methyl ester, cis	EtOH	226(4.37),271(3.88),342(4.21)	104-1275-73
trans	EtOH	225(4.33),276(4.02),331(4.37)	104-1275-73
$C_{12}H_{11}NO_2S_2$			
1,3(2H,4H)-Isoquinolinedione, 4-[bis(methylthio)methylene]-	EtOH	263(3.00),330(2.59)	95-0322-73
1,3(2H,4H)-Isoquinolinedione, 4-[mercapto(methylthio)methylene]-2-methyl-	EtOH	313(3.00)	95-0322-73

Compound	Solvent	λmax(log ε)	Ref.
$C_{12}H_{11}NO_3$			
Benzeneacetic acid, 2-(3-cyano-1-oxo-propyl)-	EtOH	243(3.92),284(3.11)	22-0691-73
1H-Indol-3-ol, 1-acetyl-, acetate	MeOH	237(4.30),262(4.00), 271s(3.95),291(3.93), 300(3.96)	102-0447-73
	H_2SO_4	238(4.46),243s(4.44), 264(4.24),317(3.70)	102-0447-73
$C_{12}H_{11}NO_3S$			
Ethanone, 1-(2,4-dihydroxy-6-methyl-phenyl)-2-(4-thiazolyl)-	n.s.g.	282(4.06)	104-2580-73
Ethanone, 1-(2,6-dihydroxy-4-methyl-phenyl)-2-(4-thiazolyl)-	n.s.g.	278(4.05)	104-2580-73
Ethanone, 1-(2,4-dihydroxyphenyl)-2-(2-methyl-4-thiazolyl)-	n.s.g.	282(4.03)	104-2580-73
Furo[2,3-d]thieno[2,3-b]pyridine-4-carboxylic acid, 2,3-dihydro-2-methyl-, methyl ester	MeOH	247(4.37),284(3.92), 327(3.80),338(3.79)	24-0368-73
Thieno[2,3-b]pyridine-6-carboxylic acid, 4,7-dihydro-4-oxo-5-(2-propenyl)-, methyl ester	MeOH	240(4.26),320(3.68)	24-0368-73
$C_{12}H_{11}NO_4$			
Benzeneacetic acid, α-oxo-2-(2-oxo-1-pyrrolidinyl)-	EtOH	233(4.07),293(3.18)	39-0998-73C
1,3-Butadien-1-ol, 3-methyl-, 4-nitro-benzoate	EtOH	231(4.37),256s(4.17), 286s(3.97)	33-0875-73
1H-Indole-1-butanoic acid, 2,3-dihydro-2,3-dioxo-	EtOH	210(4.24),246(4.36), 301(3.41)	39-0998-73C
1H-Indole-2-carboxylic acid, 3-formyl-5-hydroxy-, ethyl ester	n.s.g.	220(4.26),250(4.21), 330(4.10),370s(--)	22-2046-73
	base	262(3.98),278(4.00), 365(4.15),420s(3.89)	22-2046-73
1H-Indole-2-carboxylic acid, 4-formyl-5-hydroxy-, ethyl ester	n.s.g.	216(4.00),258(3.68), 350(3.88)	22-2046-73
	base	214(4.16),238(3.96), 330(3.79),422(3.76)	22-2046-73
$C_{12}H_{11}NO_5$			
2-Quinolinecarboxylic acid, 1,4-dihydro-5-hydroxy-8-methoxy-4-oxo-, methyl ester	pH 1	236(4.27),259(4.17), 281(3.72),290s(3.43), 327s(3.38),334(3.59), 388(3.40)	39-2374-73C
	$CHCl_3$	262(4.28),300(3.51), 339(3.48)	39-2374-73C
$C_{12}H_{11}NO_6S$			
2-Butenedioic acid, 2-[(4-nitrophenyl)-thio]-, dimethyl ester	EtOH-HCl	223(4.20),331(4.10)	1-0595-73
$C_{12}H_{11}NS_2$			
6H-[1,2]Dithiolo[5,1-e]isothiazole-7-S^{IV}, 2-(methylthio)-6-phenyl-	MeOH	234(4.50),289s(4.02), 435(4.19)	39-2351-73C
$C_{12}H_{11}N_2O_2$			
Pyrylium, 2-amino-3-(aminocarbonyl)-6-phenyl-, perchlorate	HOAc	260(4.13),291s(3.23), 384(4.30)	97-0132-73

Compound	Solvent	$\lambda_{max}(\log \epsilon)$	Ref.
$C_{12}H_{11}N_3O$			
1H-Indole-2-carboxamide, 3-cyano-N,N-dimethyl-	EtOH	293(4.11)	95-1433-73
Isoxazole-4-carbonitrile, 5-(dimethylamino)-3-phenyl-	MeOH	204(4.20),242(4.34)	7-0613-73
Phenol, 2-methyl-4-(2-pyridinylazo)-	pH 3.5	410(4.40)	140-0005-73
	pH 4-7	360(4.29)	140-0005-73
	pH 10+	460(4.45)	140-0005-73
Phenol, 2-methyl-6-(2-pyridinylazo)-	pH 2	365(4.26)	140-0005-73
	pH 4-8	335(4.23)	140-0005-73
	pH 9+	340(4.08),490(3.99)	140-0005-73
Phenol, 3-methyl-4-(2-pyridinylazo)-	pH 3	410(4.40)	140-0005-73
	pH 4-7	360(4.28)	140-0005-73
	pH 10+	430(4.46)	140-0005-73
Phenol, 4-methyl-2-(2-pyridinylazo)-	pH 2.5	355(4.23),460(3.90)	140-0005-73
	pH 4-8	330(4.20)	140-0005-73
	pH 9+	330(4.08),500(4.00)	140-0005-73
Pyrimido[1,2-a]benzimidazol-4(1H)-one,	pH 1	229(4.12),244s(3.94), 306(3.51)	4-0071-73
	pH 13	231s(4.21),250s(3.96), 318(3.44)	4-0071-73
	EtOH	233(4.22),248s(3.99), 316(3.45)	4-0071-73
$C_{12}H_{11}N_3OS_3$			
2-Pyrrolidinone, 3-([2,3'(2'H)-bithiazol]-2'-ylidene)-1-ethyl-5-thioxo-	EtOH	430(4.83)	103-0687-73
$C_{12}H_{11}N_3O_2$			
1,4-Diazepino[6,5-b]indole-2,5-dione, 1,3,4,6-tetrahydro-6-methyl-	isoPrOH	237(4.50),290s(3.96), 300(4.07),326(3.85)	4-0051-73
1,3(2H,4H)-Isoquinolinedione, 4-(2-imidazolidinylidene)-	EtOH	235(4.45),288(3.24), 368(3.03)	95-0322-73
7,10-Methanopyridazino[1,2-a]pyrido-[2,3-d]pyridazine-5,12-dione, 7,8,9,10-tetrahydro-	EtOH	205(4.34),229s(--), 258(3.77),315(3.66)	39-0026-73C
3-Pyridinol, 2-methoxy-6-(phenylazo)-	12M HCl	488(4.60)	103-0207-73
	0.45M HCl	260s(3.90),365(4.04), 488(4.24)	103-0207-73
	0.1M HCl	282(3.90),370(4.26), 480(3.95)	103-0207-73
	0.05M HCl	237(4.06),280(3.83), 365(4.24),485(4.03)	103-0207-73
	0.01M HCl	277(3.94),365(4.27), 480(3.91)	103-0207-73
	0.001M HCl	285(3.86),365(4.28), 480(3.91)	103-0207-73
	0.001M NaOH	260(3.96),450(4.46)	103-0207-73
	0.01M NaOH	255(3.13),450(4.45)	103-0207-73
	0.05M NaOH	282(3.32),451(4.42)	103-0207-73
	0.1M NaOH	260s(3.13),448(4.44)	103-0207-73
	0.45M NaOH	255(3.89),280s(3.68), 451(4.42)	103-0207-73
	EtOH	280(3.87),370(4.22), 472(3.90)	103-0207-73
	5% EtOH	270(3.83),280s(3.78), 375(4.10),483(3.18)	103-0207-73
	$CHCl_3$	275(3.98),285s(3.91), 356(3.69),478(4.52)	103-0207-73
	CCl_4	275(3.89),360(4.05), 470(3.99)	103-0207-73

Compound	Solvent	λ_{max}(log ε)	Ref.
$C_{12}H_{11}N_3O_4$			
3-Isoxazoleacetic acid, 2,5-dihydro-5-oxo-4-(phenylazo)-, methyl ester	EtOH	249(4.08),378(4.37)	70-2006-73
3-Isoxazoleacetic acid, 4,5-dihydro-5-oxo-α-(phenylhydrazono)-	EtOH	277(4.30)	70-2006-73
$C_{12}H_{11}N_3O_7$			
1H-Indole-3-carboxylic acid, 5-hydroxy-2-methyl-4,6-dinitro-, ethyl ester	MeOH or $CHCl_3$	265(4.21),366(4.18)	103-1490-73
$C_{12}H_{11}N_3S$			
Naphtho[1,2-d]thiazol-2(1H)-one, 1-methyl-, hydrazone	$CHCl_3$	243s(--),265(4.49), 350(3.85)	22-3044-73
Naphtho[2,1-d]thiazol-2(3H)-one, 3-methyl-, hydrazone	$CHCl_3$	244s(--),278(4.59), 308s(--),321(3.84), 365(3.11)	22-3044-73
10H-Pyridazino[4,5-b][1,4]benzothiazine, 2,10-dimethyl-, perchlorate	EtOH	222(4.28),245(4.26), 285(4.28),293(4.33), 321(3.91),360s(3.46), 470(3.13)	7-0255-73
10H-Pyridazino[4,5-b][1,4]benzothiazine, 3,10-dimethyl-, perchlorate	EtOH	223(4.17),240(3.96), 276(4.28),284(4.36), 316(3.73),355s(3.32), 453(3.27)	7-0255-73
1H-Thieno[2,3-c]pyrazol-4-amine, 3-methyl-1-phenyl-	C_6H_{12}	295(3.98)	104-2429-73
$C_{12}H_{11}N_3S_3$			
3a,6a-Epithio-4H-imidazo[4,5-d]thiazole-5(6H)-thione, 4,6-dimethyl-2-phenyl-	EtOH	274(3.99)	94-1300-73
$C_{12}H_{11}N_5O$			
9H-Purin-6-amine, N-hydroxy-9-(phenylmethyl)-	pH 1	266(4.23)	94-1835-73
	pH 7	267(4.11)	94-1835-73
	pH 13	257(3.93),306(3.79)	94-1835-73
	EtOH	268(4.11)	94-1835-73
$C_{12}H_{11}N_5OS$			
2H-Purin-2-one, 3,7-dihydro-3-methyl-6-(methylthio)-8-(3-pyridinyl)-	pH 8	229(4.19),263(4.19), 351(4.44)	39-0739-73C
Thiazolo[4,5-d]pyridazine-2,7(3H,6H)-dione, 3-methyl-6-phenyl-, 2-hydrazone	$CHCl_3$	262(4.37),313(3.80)	22-3324-73
$C_{12}H_{11}N_5O_2$			
6H-Purin-6-one, 2-amino-1,7-dihydro-1-(phenylmethoxy)	pH 1	249(4.06),278(3.87)	44-3046-73
	pH 13	257(3.89),278(3.92)	44-3046-73
$C_{12}H_{11}N_5O_5$			
4-Pyridinecarboxylic acid, 2-(5-acetoxy-1,4,5,6-tetrahydro-4,6-dioxo-2-pyrimidinyl)hydrazide	EtOH	220(4.10)	103-0247-73
$C_{12}H_{11}N_5S$			
3H-Purine, 3-methyl-6-(methylthio)-8-(3-pyridinyl)-	pH 8	246(4.28),337(4.52)	39-2019-73C
2-Pyridinamine, 4,6-dimethyl-N-3H-[1,2,4]thiadiazolo[4,3-a]pyrimidin-3-ylidene-	n.s.g.	250(4.11),272(4.00), 308(3.90),321s(4.15), 333(4.16),415(3.49)	44-3087-73

Compound	Solvent	λ_{max}(log ε)	Ref.
$C_{12}H_{11}N_7$			
2,4,7-Pteridinetriamine, 6-phenyl-	pH -4.0	222(4.19),243s(4.14), 304(4.13),363(4.27)	24-3175-73
	pH 4.0	215(4.53),253(4.21), 280s(3.88),356(4.34)	24-3175-73
	pH 9.0	230(4.62),268(4.16), 366(4.28)	24-3175-73
$C_{12}H_{11}N_7O_2$			
2,4,7-Pteridinetriamine, 6-phenyl-, 5,8-dioxide	pH -3.0	231(4.50),270s(4.04), 305(4.07),373(4.30)	24-3175-73
	pH 5.0	208(4.38),274(4.66), 376(4.28)	24-3175-73
$C_{12}H_{12}$			
Benzene, 2,4-cyclohexadien-1-yl-	C_6H_{12}	260(3.60)	78-3797-73
Benzene, 1,3,5-hexatrienyl-, (E,Z)-	C_6H_{12}	308(4.72)	78-3797-73
1H-Indene, 2-(1-methylethenyl)-	C_6H_{12}	212(4.14),226(4.12), 233(4.15),241(4.06), 288(4.23),294(4.26), 314(3.97)	39-2569-73C
1,2,3-Metheno-1H-cyclobuta[g]cycloprop-[cd]indene, 2,2a,2b,3,3a,5a,5b,5c-octahydro-	EtOH	285(3.41),295s(3.36)	77-0409-73
$C_{12}H_{12}BrNO_3$			
1H-Indole-2-carboxylic acid, 4-bromo-5-methoxy-, ethyl ester	n.s.g.	226(4.35),300(4.28)	22-2046-73
$C_{12}H_{12}ClNO_2S$			
4H-1,4-Benzothiazine-2-carboxylic acid, 6-chloro-3-methyl-, ethyl ester	EtOH	219(4.27),262(4.37), 278s(4.01),345(3.58), 413(3.21)	7-0045-73
4H-1,4-Benzothiazine-2-carboxylic acid, 7-chloro-3-methyl-, ethyl ester	EtOH	219(4.28),263(4.37), 273s(4.07),347(3.49), 418(3.25)	7-0045-73
$C_{12}H_{12}ClNO_3$			
2-Benzofuranpropanoic acid, α-amino-7-chloro-3-methyl-	n.s.g.	254(4.05),284(3.25)	56-1281-73
1H-Indole-3-carboxylic acid, 5-chloro-2,3-dihydro-3-methyl-2-oxo-, ethyl ester	isoPrOH	254(4.11),294(3.19)	44-3077-73
$C_{12}H_{12}ClNO_3S$			
2-Azetidinone, 1-acetyl-4-[(4-chlorophenyl)sulfinyl]-3-methyl-	EtOH	248(3.64)	94-1305-73
$C_{12}H_{12}ClNO_4$			
Benzeneacetic acid, 2-[(4-chloro-1-oxobutyl)amino]-α-oxo-	EtOH	230(4.38),263(4.03), 270(3.99),327(3.64)	39-0998-73C
$C_{12}H_{12}ClN_3OS$			
1H-Pyridazin-4-one, 3-chloro-1-methyl-5-[(2-methylaminophenyl)thio]-	EtOH	234(4.25),315(4.14)	7-0255-73
$C_{12}H_{12}Cl_2$			
Benzene, 1-(2,2-dichloro-1-ethenylcyclopropyl)-4-methyl-	hexane	223(--),258(3.18), 265(3.14)	104-2473-73

Compound	Solvent	$\lambda_{max}(\log \epsilon)$	Ref.
$C_{12}H_{12}Cl_2O$			
Benzene, 1-(2,2-dichloro-1-ethenylcyclopropyl)-3-methoxy-	hexane	224(3.73),276(3.11), 283(3.11)	104-2473-73
Benzene, 1-(2,2-dichloro-1-ethenylcyclopropyl)-4-methoxy-	hexane	232(3.96),269(3.13), 275(3.17),282(3.07)	104-2473-73
Tricyclo[4.4.1.1^{2,5}]dodeca-7,9-dien-11-one, 3,4-dichloro-, trans	EtOH	223(3.39),243s(3.32), 252(3.49),260(3.63), 270(3.61)	44-3145-73
$C_{12}H_{12}F_2O_2$			
5H-Benzocyclohepten-5-one, 6,6-difluoro-6,7,8,9-tetrahydro-1-methoxy-	n.s.g.	260(3.73),314(3.18)	35-6655-73
5H-Benzocyclohepten-5-one, 6,6-difluoro-6,7,8,9-tetrahydro-2-methoxy-	n.s.g.	230(3.98),286(4.03)	35-6655-73
$C_{12}H_{12}FeO_3$			
Iron, tricarbonyl[(1,2,3,4-η)-1,3-dimethyl-5-methylene-1,3-cyclohexadiene]	EtOH	204(4.44),244s(--), 294s(--)	101-0239-73H
$C_{12}H_{12}NOP$			
Phosphinic amide, P,P-diphenyl-	n.s.g.	225(4.23),260(2.86), 266(3.11),273(3.00)	35-8073-73
$C_{12}H_{12}N_2$			
Benzo[1,2-b:4,5-b']dipyrrole, 1,5-dimethyl-	EtOH	299(4.09),305(4.21), 338(3.97),348(4.12)	39-0832-73C
Hydrazine, 1,2-diphenyl-	MeCN	245(4.30),287(3.60), 320s(--)	12-1251-73
2-Pyridinamine, 3-methyl-N-phenyl-	EtOH	270(4.27),310(3.92)	117-0095-73
2-Pyridinamine, 5-methyl-N-phenyl-	EtOH	276(4.37),320(3.85)	117-0095-73
Pyridine, 2-methyl-6-(2-pyridinylmethyl)-	EtOH	258s(3.82),264(3.93), 269(3.94),273s(3.79)	12-1239-73
Pyrido[2,3-g]quinoline, 1,2,3,4-tetrahydro-	pH 2	215(4.49),274(4.39), 423(3.58)	39-0832-73C
	pH 12	215(4.26),252(4.34), 354(3.50)	39-0832-73C
	EtOH	213(4.50),260(4.53), 380(3.71)	39-0832-73C
2H-Pyrrole-3-carbonitrile, 3,4-dihydro-2-methyl-5-phenyl-, cis	C_6H_{12}	243(4.22)	35-1945-73
trans	C_6H_{12}	245(4.21)	35-1945-73
2H-Pyrrole-3-carbonitrile, 3,4-dihydro-3-methyl-5-phenyl-	EtOH	245(4.13)	35-1945-73
$C_{12}H_{12}N_2O$			
Benzo[1,2-b:4,5-b']dipyrrole, 1-acetyl-1,2,3,5-tetrahydro-	EtOH	247(4.43),305(3.85), 311(3.84),318(3.90)	39-0832-73C
1,2-Diazepine, 1-benzoyl-2,3-dihydro-	MeOH	295(3.92)	22-2847-73
4-Isoxazolamine, 3-methyl-5-(2-phenylethenyl)-, (E)-	EtOH	220(4.15),300(4.40)	2-1074-73
Isoxazole, 3-methyl-5-(2-aminostyryl)-	EtOH	230(3.98),331(4.27)	18-3533-73
Propanedinitrile, (4,4-dimethyl-2-methylene-6-oxocyclohexylidene)-	C_6H_{12}	290(4.48)	88-4335-73
	MeOH	297(4.31)	88-4335-73
1H-Pyrrolo[2,3-b]quinolin-4-ol, 2,3-dihydro-1-methyl-	EtOH	222(4.47),243(4.34), 319(4.17)	44-2614-73
$C_{12}H_{12}N_2OS$			
4-Imidazolidinone, 1,3-dimethyl-5-(phenylmethylene)-2-thioxo-	pH 3-5	245(4.06),292(3.96), 368(4.39)	104-2418-73

Compound	Solvent	λ_{max}(log ϵ)	Ref.
4-Imidazolidinone, 1,3-dimethyl-5-(phenylmethylene)-2-thioxo- (cont.)	EtOH	235(4.10),290(3.91), 375(4.48)	104-2418-73
4H-Imidazol-4-one, 3,5-dihydro-3-methyl-2-(methylthio)-5-(phenylmethylene)-	pH 3-5	241(3.95),266(3.95), 361(4.36)	104-2418-73
	EtOH	241(3.97),270(3.90), 366(4.35)	104-2418-73
	dioxan	240(3.96),270(3.95), 363(4.36)	104-2418-73
1,2,4-Oxadiazole, 3-[2-[4-(ethylthio)-phenyl]ethenyl]-, trans	EtOH	321(4.38)	39-2241-73C
Thiocyanic acid, 1-acetyl-2-(phenylamino)-1-propenyl ester	hexane	230(3.94),307(4.19)	40-2152-73
$C_{12}H_{12}N_2O_2$			
Acetamide, N-(1,2-dihydro-2-methyl-1-oxo-3-isoquinolinyl)-	EtOH	227(4.39),290(4.10), 326(3.77)	95-1581-73
Isoquinolinium, 2-[(ethoxycarbonyl)-amino]-, hydroxide, inner salt	EtOH	225(4.51),335(4.00)	78-2359-73
1(2H)-Isoquinolinone, 4-acetyl-3-amino-2-methyl-	EtOH	240(4.39),286(4.03), 364(3.96)	95-1581-73
1,8-Naphthyridine-3-carboxylic acid, 2-methyl-, ethyl ester	EtOH	221(4.75),259(3.75), 309(3.78),320(3.77)	94-2643-73
5(4H)-Oxazolone, 4-[1-(aminomethyl)-ethylidene]-2-phenyl-	EtOH	235(4.12),350(4.64)	70-2505-73
5(4H)-Oxazolone, 4-[(dimethylamino)-methylene]-2-phenyl-	EtOH	240(4.06),355(4.55)	70-2505-73
4(1H)-Pyrimidinone, 5-(methoxymethyl)-2-phenyl-	MeOH	242(4.18),296(3.04)	18-0580-73
	MeOH-HCl	242(--),281(--)	18-0580-73
	MeOH-NaOH	237(--),282(--), 295(--)	18-0580-73
Quinolinium, 1-[(ethoxycarbonyl)amino]-, hydroxide, inner salt	EtOH	240(4.49),325(3.70)	78-2359-73
$C_{12}H_{12}N_2O_2S$			
Pyridinium, 1-[[(4-methylphenyl)sulfonyl]amino]-, hydroxide, inner salt	EtOH	237(4.11),313(3.32)	44-3311-73
Pyridinium, 2-methyl-1-[(phenylsulfonyl)amino]-, hydroxide, inner salt	EtOH	244(4.03),311(3.18)	44-3311-73
$C_{12}H_{12}N_2O_2S_2$			
Benzenamine, N,N-dimethyl-4-[(2-nitro-3-thienyl)thio]-	MeOH	368(4.02)	4-1007-73
Benzenamine, N,N-dimethyl-4-[(3-nitro-2-thienyl)thio]-	MeOH	366(3.84)	4-1007-73
$C_{12}H_{12}N_2O_3$			
2H-Indol-2-one, 1,3-dihydro-1-methyl-3-(1-methylethylidene)-5-nitro-	EtOH	254(4.30),297(4.06), 350(3.98)	103-1152-73
2,4(1H,3H)-Pyrimidinedione, 1-[(2-hydroxy-3-methylphenyl)methyl]-	pH 2-7	267.5(4.07)	56-1645-73
	pH 13	267(3.95)	56-1645-73
$C_{12}H_{12}N_2O_3S$			
2H-Indol-2-one, 1,3-dihydro-1-methyl-3-[1-(methylthio)-2-nitroethylidene]-	EtOH	250(4.20),258(4.23), 293(3.63),345(4.23)	95-0612-73
$C_{12}H_{12}N_2O_4$			
Propanedioic acid, diazo-, methyl 1-phenylethyl ester	EtOH	250(3.95)	78-3609-73

Compound	Solvent	$\lambda_{max}(\log \epsilon)$	Ref.
$C_{12}H_{12}N_2O_5$			
Dehydro-L-ascorbic acid, 2-(phenylhydrazono)-	EtOH	233(3.95),246(3.88), 255(3.83),390(4.29)	98-0676-73
2,3,4(5H)-Furantrione, 5-(1,2-dihydroxyethyl)-, 3-(phenylhydrazone)-, [R-(R*,R*)]-	EtOH	235(3.73),247s(3.63), 255s(3.55),387(4.01)	95-0304-73
Propanedioic acid, diazo-, (4-methoxyphenyl)methyl methyl ester	EtOH	225(4.29),248s(3.95)	78-3609-73
$C_{12}H_{12}N_2O_6$			
Benzene, 1,4-dimethoxy-2,5-bis(2-nitroethenyl)-	EtOH	258(3.76),335(4.22), 445(4.10)	39-0832-73C
$C_{12}H_{12}N_2S$			
2-Thiazolamine, 5-(2,3-dihydro-1H-inden-5-yl)-	EtOH	205(4.43),233(4.22), 275(3.92)	34-0099-73
$C_{12}H_{12}N_3O_7$			
Cyclohexanone, 2-(2,4,6-trinitro-2,4-cyclohexadien-1-yl)-, ion(1-), Na salt	H_2O	245(4.36),475(4.05), 550(3.74)	94-0118-73
Tricyclo[5.3.1.1 ,]dodec-3-en-11-one, 3,5,12-trinitro-, ion(1-), Na salt	H_2O	262(3.78),480(4.14)	94-0118-73
$C_{12}H_{12}N_4OS$			
1,2,4-Triazino[5,6-d][3,1]benzoxazepine, 6,7-dihydro-6-methyl-3-(methylthio)-	EtOH	205(4.32),238(4.42), 346(4.02),440(3.77)	78-0639-73
$C_{12}H_{12}N_4O_2$			
Pyridazine, 3,3'-(1,2-ethenediyl)bis[6-methoxy-	EtOH	230(4.07),287(4.58)	94-0125-73
$C_{12}H_{12}N_4O_2S$			
2-Thiophenamine, N,N-dimethyl-5-[(4-nitrophenyl)azo]-	EtOH	554(4.70)	103-0850-73
	EtOH-HCl	464(4.70)	103-0850-73
$C_{12}H_{12}N_4O_3$			
3-Pentenamide, 3-acetyl-2-cyano-2-(dicyanomethyl)-4-methoxy-	EtOH	248(4.10)	12-1551-73
$C_{12}H_{12}N_4O_3S$			
1H-Pyrido[2,3-b]pyrimido[4,5-e][1,4]-thiazine, 2,4,7-trimethoxy-	MeOH	250(4.00),308(4.21)	44-4386-73
$C_{12}H_{12}N_4O_4$			
Diazene, (2,4-dinitrophenyl)(2,3-dimethyl-1,3-butadienyl)-	MeCN	231(4.07),270(3.63), 405(4.23)	1-3632-73
3-Pyridazinamine, 6-methoxy-5-nitro-N-(phenylmethyl)-, 2-oxide	MeOH	225(4.3),257(3.6), 305(3.58),430(3.47)	4-0835-73
2,4(1H,3H)-Pyrimidinedione, 5-[3-(1,2,3,4-tetrahydro-2,4-dioxo-5-pyrimidinyl)-1-butenyl]-, (E)-	pH 1	246(3.98),270s(--)	78-1611-73
2,4,6(1H,3H,5H)-Pyrimidinetrione, 5-acetoxy-, 2-(phenylhydrazone)	EtOH	262(4.33)	103-0247-73
$C_{12}H_{12}N_6O$			
9H-Purine-2,6-diamine, 9-(4-methoxyphenyl)-	EtOH	220(4.51),280(4.16)	42-0260-73

Compound	Solvent	$\lambda_{max}(\log \epsilon)$	Ref.
$C_{12}H_{12}N_6O_8$			
2,4,6(1H,3H,5H)-Pyrimidinetrione, 5-acetoxy-2-[(5-acetoxytetrahydro-4,6-dioxo-2(1H)-pyrimidinylidene)-hydrazone]	EtOH	220(4.25)	103-0247-73
$C_{12}H_{12}O$			
4-Azuleneethanol	CCl_4	281(4.62),331(3.69), 344(3.79),356(3.50), 569(2.61),588(2.59), 615(2.55),667(2.14)	44-1106-73
6-Azuleneethanol	CH_2Cl_2	280(4.80),286(4.79), 329(3.57),336(3.55), 344(3.74),565(2.50), 610(2.42),672(1.98)	44-1106-73
Benzofuran, 2-isopropenyl-3-methyl-	90% EtOH	215(3.99),223(3.98), 226(3.99),276s(4.11), 285(4.16),292(4.15), 296(4.12),310(4.04)	12-1093-73
2-Cyclohexen-1-one, 3-phenyl-	EtOH	221(3.72),284(4.13)	104-2172-73
Furan, 2-methyl-5-(4-methylphenyl)-	EtOH	285(4.32)	22-1760-73
5-Hexen-3-yn-1-ol, 6-phenyl-	EtOH	284(4.48)	78-3797-73
1-Naphthalenol, 3,5-dimethyl-	EtOH	225(4.87),298(4.14), 313s(4.00),326s(3.76)	42-0620-73
12-Oxatetracyclo[$4.4.3.0^{1,6}.0^{2,5}$]trideca-3,7,9-triene	MeOH	264(3.40)	118-0667-73
Tricyclo[$4.4.1.1^{2,5}$]dodeca-3,7,9-trien-11-one, (1α,2β,5β,6α)-	EtOH	216(3.55),240(3.44), 249(3.53),258(3.66), 267(3.69)	44-3145-73
$C_{12}H_{12}OS$			
1-Benzothiepin-5(2H)-one, 4-ethylidene-3,4-dihydro-	EtOH	251(4.16)	44-2629-73
$C_{12}H_{12}OS_2$			
Thiophene, 2-methoxy-5-[2-(5-methyl-2-thienyl)ethenyl]-	DMF	359(4.34)	24-0655-73
$C_{12}H_{12}O_2$			
Cyclobuta[b]naphthalene-3,8-dione, 2a,3a,4,7,7a,8a-hexahydro-	EtOH	298(2.23)	104-2389-73
3,4,9,10-Cyclododecatetraene-1,7-dione, (±)-	EtOH	227s(3.11),295(2.38)	35-4582-73
meso-	EtOH	230s(3.14),296(2.53)	35-4582-73
2-Cyclopenten-1-one, 3-(3-methoxyphenyl)-	EtOH	252(4.13),283(4.48)	95-1371-73
Cyclopent[a]inden-2(1H)-one, 3,3a,8,8a-tetrahydro-6-hydroxy-	EtOH	216(3.75),225s(3.66), 282(3.48),287s(3.43)	35-4582-73
Furan, 2-(4-methoxyphenyl)-5-methyl-	EtOH	288.5(4.36)	22-1760-73
1H-Indene-2-carboxylic acid, 7-methyl-, methyl ester	EtOH	231(4.00),237(3.95), 292(4.26)	44-0741-73
2-Naphthaleneacetic acid, 3,4-dihydro-	EtOH	265(4.12)	2-0131-73
4-Oxatetracyclo[$5.4.1.1^{2,6}.0^{3,5}$]trideca-8,10-dien-12-one	EtOH	222(3.55),239s(3.45), 248(3.61),256(3.78), 266(3.78)	44-3145-73
Resorcinol, dihydro-5-phenyl-	EtOH	257(4.40),280s(3.60)	104-2377-73
$C_{12}H_{12}O_2S$			
1H-2-Benzothiopyran-4-ol, 1-methyl-, acetate	EtOH	208(4.34),239(3.91), 319(3.77)	39-0410-73C
2H-Thiopyran, 6-methyl-3-phenyl-, 1,1-dioxide	H_2O	227(3.71),312(4.02)	39-0050-73B
	MeOH	230(3.89),312(4.15)	39-0050-73B

Compound	Solvent	$\lambda_{max}(\log \epsilon)$	Ref.
2H-Thiopyran, 6-methyl-3-phenyl-, 1,1-dioxide, anion	1.5M NaOH	257(4.16),373(3.74)	39-0050-73B
	MeOH-NaOMe	259(4.18),377(3.88)	39-0050-73B
$C_{12}H_{12}O_3$			
3-Benzofurancarboxylic acid, 2-ethyl-, methyl ester	90% EtOH	244(3.90),259(3.94), 275(3.87),283(3.78)	12-1079-73
3-Benzofurancarboxylic acid, 2-methyl-, ethyl ester	EtOH	216(4.11),220(4.11), 245(3.80),255(3.81), 274(3.67),282(3.62), 310(3.03)	103-0026-73
2(3H)-Benzofuranone, 3-(1-methoxypropylidene)-	90% EtOH	223(3.98),248(4.03), 251(4.03),256(4.00), 288s(3.85),299(3.95), 321(4.01)	12-1079-73
4H-1-Benzopyran-4-one, 7-methoxy-2,5-dimethyl-	MeOH	225(4.24),242(4.20), 250(4.21),285(3.98)	94-0149-73
4H-1-Benzopyran-4-one, 8-methoxy-2,5-dimethyl-	EtOH	227(4.39),252(4.16), 318(3.72)	95-0896-73
3-Benzoxepin-2,4-dimethanol	EtOH	238(4.57),285(3.08)	78-0533-73
Ethanone, 1-(6-methoxy-3-methyl-6-benzofuranyl)-	90% EtOH	249(3.72),325(4.26)	12-1093-73
1-Propanone, 1-(2-methoxy-3-benzofuranyl)-	90% EtOH	212(4.14),230(4.18), 251(4.12),277(4.06), 284s(4.05)	12-1079-73
2H-Pyran-2-one, 5,6-dihydro-4-methoxy-6-phenyl-	EtOH	217(3.89),239(3.78)	28-1131-73A
$C_{12}H_{12}O_4$			
1H-2-Benzopyran-1-one, 6,8-dihydroxy-3-propyl-	MeOH	201(4.04),238s(4.43), 245(4.51),258(3.90), 280(3.65),328(3.60)	102-2993-73
4H-1-Benzopyran-4-one, 3-hydroxy-8-methoxy-2,5-dimethyl-	EtOH	243(4.49),335(3.91)	95-0896-73
1,4-Naphthalenediol, 2-acetyl-2,3-epoxy-1,2,3,4-tetrahydro-	n.s.g.	222(3.04),261(2.32)	39-0235-73C
1(2H)-Naphthalenone, 3-acetyl-3,4-dihydro-3,4-dihydroxy-, trans-(±)-	n.s.g.	245(4.12),285(3.20)	39-0368-73C
$C_{12}H_{12}O_5$			
1H-Cyclohepta[c]furan-3a(3H)-carboxylic acid, 6-methoxy-3-oxo-, methyl ester	EtOH	273(3.60)	78-3609-73
$C_{12}H_{12}O_6$			
2H-1-Benzopyran-2-one, 6-hydroxy-5,7,8-trimethoxy-	MeOH	208(4.39),308(4.01)	78-2645-73
	MeOH-HCl	209(4.35),308(4.00)	78-2645-73
	MeOH-NaOH	248(4.53),317(4.33)	78-2645-73
Phthalic anhydride, 3-ethoxy-4,5-dimethoxy-	EtOH	215(4.48),247(3.98), 293(3.40),323s(2.91)	141-0001-73
Phthalic anhydride, 4-ethoxy-3,5-dimethoxy-	EtOH	215(4.43),246(4.13), 299(3.45),319s(3.30)	141-0001-73
Phthalic anhydride, 5-ethoxy-3,4-dimethoxy-	EtOH	218(4.30),247(4.26), 303(3.55),318s(3.50)	141-0001-73
$C_{12}H_{12}S_2$			
Thiophene, 2,2'-(1,2-ethenediyl)bis[5-methyl-	DMF	353(4.45)	24-0655-73
$C_{12}H_{13}BrN_2$			
1H-Pyrido[4,3-b]indole, 8-bromo-2,3,4,5-tetrahydro-2-methyl-	MeOH	228(4.8),306(4.0), 352(0.74)	103-0974-73

Compound	Solvent	$\lambda_{max}(\log \epsilon)$	Ref.
Pyrimido[1,2-a]indole, 8-bromo-1,2,3,4-tetrahydro-3-methyl-, hydrochloride	MeOH	212(4.52),267(4.20)	103-0598-73
$C_{12}H_{13}BrN_2O_5$			
2,4'-Anhydro-1-(5-deoxy-5-bromo-2,3-O-isopropylidene-α-L-lyxosyl)uracil	MeOH	229(4.12),245s(3.95)	88-2731-73
$C_{12}H_{13}Br_2N$			
Isoquinolinium, 2-(3-bromopropyl)-, bromide	MeOH	232(4.72),277(3.48), 337(3.62)	44-0437-73
$C_{12}H_{13}ClNO_2S$			
4H-1,4-Benzothiazinium, 6-chloro-2-(ethoxycarbonyl)-1-methyl-, perchlorate	EtOH	212(4.38),232(4.35), 321(3.72),372(4.03)	7-0045-73
4H-1,4-Benzothiazinium, 7-chloro-2-(ethoxycarbonyl)-1-methyl-, perchlorate	EtOH	210(4.33),260(3.53), 321(3.79),377(4.03)	7-0045-73
$C_{12}H_{13}ClN_2O$			
1,7-Methano-2H-1,7-benzodiazonin-12-one, 9-chloro-3,4,5,6-tetrahydro-	MeOH	219(4.35),289(3.50)	39-0702-73C
$C_{12}H_{13}ClN_4S$			
1,2,4-Triazolo[3,4-b][1,3,4]thiadiazin-4-ium, 1,7-dihydro-6-methyl-1-(phenylmethyl)-, chloride	MeOH	240(3.87),281(4.03)	48-1131-73
$C_{12}H_{13}ClO_3$			
2H-1-Benzopyran-2-one, 6-chloro-3,4-dihydro-7-methoxy-4,4-dimethyl-	EtOH	237(3.66),284(3.40), 290(3.38)	2-1099-73
Bicyclo[3.2.2]nona-2,8-diene-6-carboxylic acid, 5-chloro-6-methyl-4-oxo-, methyl ester, endo-methyl	MeOH	225(3.91),330(2.30)	18-2915-73
exo-methyl	MeOH	225(3.90),330(2.26)	18-2915-73
Bicyclo[3.2.2]nona-3,8-diene-6-carboxylic acid, 3-chloro-6-methyl-2-oxo-, methyl ester, endo-methyl	MeOH	241(3.78),262s(--), 323(2.00)	18-2915-73
exo-methyl	MeOH	241(3.78),262s(--), 320(2.00)	18-2915-73
$C_{12}H_{13}FO_2$			
5H-Benzocyclohepten-5-one, 6-fluoro-6,7,8,9-tetrahydro-2-methoxy-	n.s.g.	216(4.23),254(3.79), 310(3.35)	35-6655-73
$C_{12}H_{13}F_3O$			
1-Pentanone, 1-[2-(trifluoromethyl)-phenyl]-	heptane	218s(3.64)	35-5604-73
1-Pentanone, 1-[3-(trifluoromethyl)-phenyl]-	heptane	234(3.98)	35-5604-73
1-Pentanone, 1-[4-(trifluoromethyl)-phenyl]-	heptane	234(4.11)	35-5604-73
$C_{12}H_{13}N$			
Benzenamine, 4-methyl-N-(2-methyl-1,3-butadienylidene)-	C_6H_{12}	256(4.57)	35-5417-73
Pyridine, 2-(1,3,5-heptatrienyl)-, (E,E,E)-	EtOH	324(4.60)	54-0683-73
Pyrrolidine, 3,4-bis(methylene)-1-phenyl-	isooctane	246(4.30),300(3.52), 310(3.43),330s(3.03)	88-2361-73

Compound	Solvent	$\lambda_{max}(\log \epsilon)$	Ref.
$C_{12}H_{13}NO$			
4aH-Carbazol-4a-ol, 1,2,3,4-tetrahydro-	EtOH	257(3.58)	117-0017-73
2-Cyclohexen-1-one, 3-(phenylamino)-	EtOH	225(3.82),309(4.27)	18-2504-73
1,4-Ethenocyclohepta[c]pyrrol-3(2H)-one, 1,3a,4,8a-tetrahydro-4-methyl-	EtOH	245(3.67)	44-1886-73
1,4-Ethenocyclohepta[c]pyrrol-3(2H)-one, 1,3a,4,8a-tetrahydro-8a-methyl-	EtOH	244(3.71),248(3.73), 258(3.56)	44-1886-73
3,5-Hexadien-2-one, 6-phenyl-, oxime (plus shoulders not listed)	C_6H_{12}	198(4.04),229(4.10), 235(4.13),242(4.00), 298(4.63),311(4.72), 325(4.60)	32-0309-73
	MeOH	198(4.07),235(4.11), 242(3.90),311(4.74), 325(4.64)	32-0309-73
2H-Indol-2-one, 1,3-dihydro-1-methyl-3-(1-methylethylidene)-	EtOH	201(4.72),256(4.72), 262(4.80),294(4.02)	103-1152-73
13-Oxa-14-azatricyclo[8.2.1.1^{4,7}]tetradeca-4,6,10,12-tetraene	EtOH	222(4.00)	88-4017-73
$C_{12}H_{13}NOS$			
Morpholine, 4-benzo[b]thien-2-yl-	EtOH	227(4.54),284(4.33)	78-0321-73
Quinoline, 6-methoxy-4-methyl-2-(methylthio)-	EtOH	220(4.50),260(4.36), 345(3.77)	103-0481-73
$C_{12}H_{13}NO_2$			
1,4-Ethenocyclohepta[c]pyrrol-3(2H)-one, 1,3a,4,8a-tetrahydro-4-methoxy-	EtOH	245(3.62)	44-1886-73
1,4-Ethenocyclohepta[c]pyrrol-3(2H)-one, 1,3a,4,8a-tetrahydro-8a-methoxy-	EtOH	246(3.70),252(3.70), 261s(3.51)	44-1886-73
2(3H)-Furanone, dihydro-3,3-dimethyl-5-(phenylimino)-	MeCN	253(3.62)	35-6792-73
2,4,6-Heptatrienoic acid, 7-(1H-pyrrol-2-yl)-, methyl ester	EtOH	394(4.63)	39-1416-73C
1H-Indole-3-butanoic acid,	MeOH	229(4.18),276s(3.79), 282(3.82),291(3.74)	102-0447-73
after ten minutes	H_2SO_4	236(3.68),241(3.66), 290(3.72),354(2.30) (changing)	102-0447-73
1-Indolizinecarboxylic acid, 2-methyl-, ethyl ester	EtOH	230s(4.42),236(4.43), 260(3.94),269(3.97), 296s(3.85),309(4.05), 334(3.91),346s(3.90)	94-1139-73
2H-Pyrrole-3-carboxylic acid, 3,4-dihydro-5-phenyl-, methyl ester	EtOH	243(4.15)	35-1945-73
2,5-Pyrrolidinedione, 3,3-dimethyl-1-phenyl-	MeCN	253s(2.58)	35-6792-73
2H-Pyrrol-2-one, 4-ethyl-1,5-dihydro-3-hydroxy-5-phenyl-	EtOH	213(3.21),241(2.74)	88-2615-73
3-Quinolinecarboxylic acid, 1,4-dihydro-, ethyl ester	EtOH	338(4.13)	94-1914-73
$C_{12}H_{13}NO_2S$			
Acetic acid, [[1-(2-cyanophenyl)ethyl]thio]-, methyl ester	EtOH	202(4.49),226(4.00), 280(3.12),286(3.12)	39-0410-73C
$C_{12}H_{13}NO_3$			
2-Benzofuranpropanoic acid, α-amino-3-methyl-	n.s.g.	253(4.11),285(3.53)	56-1281-73
2H-1-Benzopyran-2-one, 3-amino-8-ethyl-4-hydroxy-6-methyl-, hydrochloride	MeOH	222(4.25),290(4.09)	2-0433-73

Compound	Solvent	$\lambda_{max}(\log \epsilon)$	Ref.
Isoquinoline, 5,6,7-trimethoxy-	EtOH	240(4.73),320(3.72), 335s(3.66)	44-0060-73
$C_{12}H_{13}NO_3S$			
4H-Thieno[3,2-b]pyrrole-6-carboxylic acid, 2-acetyl-5-methyl-, ethyl ester	EtOH	250(3.74),346(4.00)	103-1473-73
$C_{12}H_{13}NO_4$			
4-Isoquinolinol, 5,6,7-trimethoxy-	EtOH	248(4.53),287(3.77), 298(3.74),330(3.74), 343(3.77)	44-0060-73
Phthalimide, N-ethyl-3,4-dimethoxy-	EtOH	234(4.53),244s(4.20), 253s(4.15),338(3.64)	141-0001-73
	dioxan	237(4.28),245s(4.17), 252s(4.11),333(3.65)	141-0001-73
Phthalimide, N-ethyl-4,5-dimethoxy-	EtOH	247(4.71),296(3.26), 348(3.26)	141-0001-73
	dioxan	241(3.26),254s(4.24), 291s(3.27),296(3.32), 301s(3.19),344(3.30)	141-0001-73
2(1H)-Quinolinone, 4-hydroxy-6,8-dimethoxy-1-methyl-	MeOH	230(4.39),249(4.38), 267s(3.68),278(3.71), 289(3.74),329s(3.28), 343(3.41),358(3.24)	78-1215-73
	base	228(4.42),241s(4.39), 249s(4.35),297(3.83), 330s(3.49),345s(3.38)	78-1215-73
2(1H)-Quinolinone, 4,6,8-trimethoxy-	MeOH	249(4.43),262s(3.98), 272(3.76),281(3.67), 321s(3.31),338(3.49), 350s(3.40)	78-1215-73
$C_{12}H_{13}NO_4S$			
2-Buten-1-one, 1-(4-methoxyphenyl)-3-(methylthio)-4-nitro-	EtOH	332(4.27)	95-0612-73
2-Cyclopentene-1-sulfonic acid, 3-[(4-methylphenyl)amino]-4-oxo-, Na salt	EtOH	251(4.28),309s(3.70), 325(3.76)	12-0893-73
$C_{12}H_{13}NO_5$			
7-Azabicyclo[2.2.1]hepta-2,5-diene-2,3-dicarboxylic acid, 7-acetyl-, dimethyl ester	EtOH	290(3.08)	24-3824-73
1H-Azepine-4,5-dicarboxylic acid, 1-acetyl-, dimethyl ester	MeCN	226(4.30),355(2.89)	24-3824-73
1,2-Benzenedicarboxylic acid, 4-(acetylamino)-, dimethyl ester	EtOH	223(3.34),270(3.37), 279s(3.31),285s(3.24)	24-3824-73
Glycine, N-[3-(4-hydroxy-3-methoxyphenyl)-1-oxo-2-propenyl]-	MeOH	240(4.06),290(4.06), 319(4.23)	20-0243-73
	MeOH-KOH	240(4.08),305(3.83), 360(4.45)	20-0243-73
Phthalimide, 3,4,5-trimethoxy-N-methyl-	EtOH	231s(4.35),245(4.54), 326(3.55)	141-0001-73
$C_{12}H_{13}NO_5S$			
2-Cyclopentene-1-sulfonic acid, 3-[(4-methoxyphenyl)amino]-4-oxo-, Na salt	EtOH	250(4.30),315(3.72),	12-0893-73
$C_{12}H_{13}NO_6$			
7-Azabicyclo[2.2.1]hepta-2,5-diene-2,3,7-tricarboxylic acid, trimethyl ester	EtOH	291(3.03)	24-3824-73

Compound	Solvent	$\lambda_{max}(\log \epsilon)$	Ref.
$C_{12}H_{13}NS_2$			
1H-Indole-3-carbodithioic acid, 1,2-dimethyl-, methyl ester	EtOH	280(4.1),320(4.0), 380(4.5)	94-2770-73
$C_{12}H_{13}N_2$			
Pyridinium, 1-methyl-2-(phenylamino)-, iodide	pH 7	315(3.94)	39-2111-73B
	pH 12	273(3.97),348(3.80)	39-2111-73B
$C_{12}H_{13}N_2O_7$			
1,3-Cyclohexadiene-1-carboxylic acid, 3,5-dinitro-6-(2-oxopropyl)-, ethyl ester, ion(1-), K salt	acetone	424(4.39),558(4.48)	104-2106-73
1,5-Cyclohexadiene-1-carboxylic acid, 3,5-dinitro-4-(2-oxopropyl)-, ethyl ester, ion(1-), K salt	acetone	408(4.62),628(4.41)	104-2106-73
$C_{12}H_{13}N_3$			
Propanedinitrile, 1-azatricyclo-[3.3.1.1^{3,7}]dec-4-ylidene-	hexane	228(3.92),317(3.65)	78-1691-73
$C_{12}H_{13}N_3O$			
4-Pyrimidinamine, 5-(methoxymethyl)-2-phenyl-	MeCN	238(4.33),258s(4.17), 281(3.94),286s(3.93), 297(3.92)	18-0253-73
$C_{12}H_{13}N_3OS$			
4-Imidazolidinone, 5-[[4-(dimethylamino)phenyl]methylene]-2-thioxo-	pH 3-5	272(4.03),310(3.89), 455(4.41)	104-2418-73
	pH 12-13	314(3.92),425(4.17)	104-2418-73
	EtOH	272(4.05),315(3.92), 438(4.48)	104-2418-73
	dioxan	265(3.86),314(3.79), 429(4.48)	104-2418-73
2H-Imidazo[4,5-g]quinoline-2-thione, 5-acetyl-1,3,5,6,7,8-hexahydro-	EtOH	320(4.34),415(2.72)	103-1028-73
	DMSO	267(4.18),289(4.18), 322(4.17)	103-1028-73
1H-Pyridazin-4-one, 1-methyl-5-[2-(methylamino)phenylthio]-	EtOH	232(4.32),249(4.21), 314(4.23)	7-0255-73
Pyrrolo[2,3-f]benzimidazole-2(1H)-thione, 5-acetyl-3,5,6,7-tetrahydro-6-methyl-	EtOH	223(4.15),262(3.85), 335(4.28)	103-1028-73
$C_{12}H_{13}N_3O_2$			
Acetamide, N-(3,4-dihydro-2,4-dimethyl-3-oxo-6-quinoxalinyl)-	EtOH	229(4.47),347(3.91)	22-1285-73
Butanedinitrile, (aminoethoxymethylene)-(2-oxocyclopentylidene)-	EtOH	203(4.00),260(3.82), 340(3.70)	12-1551-73
4-Isoxazolecarboxamide, 5-(dimethylamino)-3-phenyl-	MeOH	205(4.23),232(4.24), 268(3.99)	7-0613-73
2-Propenamide, 2,3-dicyano-3-(2-ethoxy-1-cyclopenten-1-yl)-	EtOH	390(4.10)	12-1551-73
$C_{12}H_{13}N_3O_2S$			
Benzeneacetonitrile, α-[(dimethylamino)-(methylthio)methylene]-4-nitro-	EtOH	260(3.92),287(3.94), 401(4.23)	1-0258-73
Benzenesulfonamide, 4-methyl-N-(4-methyl-2-pyrimidinyl)-	EtOH	218(3.19),232(3.19), 264(3.61)	44-1591-73
$C_{12}H_{13}N_3O_2S_2$			
Carbamic acid, [(2-benzothiazolylimino)-(methylthio)methyl]-, ethyl ester	dioxan	228(4.26),254(4.08), 263(3.98),326(4.44),	94-0074-73

Compound	Solvent	$\lambda_{max}(\log \epsilon)$	Ref.
Carbamic acid, [(2-benzothiazolylimino)-(methylthio)methyl]-, ethyl ester (cont.)	dioxan	338s(--)	94-0074-73
$C_{12}H_{13}N_3O_3$			
1H-Pyrazole-3-carboxylic acid, 1-acetyl-4,5-dihydro-4-(2-pyridinyl)-, methyl ester	$CHCl_3$	286(4.40)	103-0055-73
$C_{12}H_{13}N_3O_4$			
Pyrido[2,3-b]pyrazine-7-carboxylic acid, 3-ethoxy-5-ethyl-5,8-dihydro-8-oxo-	MeOH or MeOH-acid	229(4.48),261s(4.27), 267(4.34),315s(3.93), 330(4.00)	111-0346-73
	MeOH-NaOH	227(4.34),248(4.43), 255(4.43),264(4.50), 320s(4.02),326(4.04)	111-0346-73
$C_{12}H_{13}N_3O_5$			
Pyrido[2,3-d]pyrimidine-7-carboxylic acid, 1,2,3,4,5,8-hexahydro-1,3,8-trimethyl-2,4,5-trioxo-, methyl ester	EtOH	259(4.04),281s(3.81)	94-2014-73
$C_{12}H_{13}N_3S$			
2-Thiophenamine, N,N-dimethyl-5-(phenylazo)-	EtOH	482(4.70)	103-0850-73
	EtOH-HCl	474(4.70)	103-0850-73
$C_{12}H_{13}N_4S$			
1,2,4-Triazolo[3,4-b][1,3,4]thiadiazin-4-ium, 1,7-dihydro-6-methyl-1-(phenylmethyl)-, chloride	MeOH	240(3.87),281(4.03)	48-1131-73
$C_{12}H_{13}N_5OS$			
Thiazolo[2,3-f]purine, 6-methyl-4-morpholino-	EtOH	227(4.21),263(4.18), 290(4.12)	94-0256-73
$C_{12}H_{13}N_5O_5$			
β-D-ribo-Hept-5-enofuranuronic acid, 1-(6-amino-9H-purin-9-yl)-1,5,6-trideoxy-	pH 1	257(4.17)	136-0225-73B
	pH 7	259(4.18)	136-0225-73B
	pH 13	259(4.18)	136-0225-73B
$C_{12}H_{13}N_5O_5S$			
N^2-Acetyl-8,2'-thioanhydroguanosine	EtOH	269(4.37),295(4.16)	23-2397-73
$C_{12}H_{13}N_5O_6$			
Diazene, (2,4-dinitrophenyl)(1-nitrocyclohexyl)-	$CHCl_3$	410(2.54)	78-3929-73
$C_{12}H_{14}$			
Benzene, (2,3,3-trimethyl-1-cyclopropen-1-yl)-	hexane	265(4.10)	118-0611-73
Bicyclo[6.4.0]dodeca-1,3,5,7-tetraene	isooctane	280s(2.46)	35-2230-73
1,7-Ethanonaphthalene, 5,6,7,8-tetrahydro-	n.s.g.	260(2.51),266(2.70), 273(2.78)	70-2593-73
Tricyclo[3.2.1.0^{2,7}]oct-3-ene, 1,5-dimethyl-6,8-dimethylene-	EtOH	226(3.82)	33-0681-73
$C_{12}H_{14}BrNOS$			
Pyrido[2,1-b]benzothiazolium, 5a,6,7,8-9,9a-hexahydro-1-methyl-9-oxo-, bromide, cis	pH 1	211(3.88),240(3.88), 331(3.81)	39-2049-73C

Compound	Solvent	$\lambda_{max}(\log \epsilon)$	Ref.
$C_{12}H_{14}BrNO_2S$			
Pyrido[2,1-b]benzothiazolium, 5a,6,7,8-9,9a-hexahydro-4-hydroxy-1-methyl-9-oxo-, bromide	pH 1	216(4.11),241(3.92), 348(4.00)	39-2049-73C
$C_{12}H_{14}BrNO_3$			
2,4,6-Cycloheptatrien-1-one, 3-bromo-2-hydroxy-7-(morpholinomethyl)-	EtOH	257(4.27),335s(3.59), 383(3.52),419(3.49)	39-1960-73C
$C_{12}H_{14}BrN_5O_4$			
9H-Purin-6-amine, 9-(2-O-acetyl-3-bromo-3-deoxy-β-D-xylofuranosyl)-	MeOH	260(4.20)	35-4025-73
$C_{12}H_{14}ClN_3O_2$			
Diazene, (4-chlorophenyl)(1-ethyl-1-nitro-2-butenyl)-	EtOH	284(3.67)	19-0881-73
$C_{12}H_{14}ClN_3O_3$			
4(3H)-Quinolinone, 6-chloro-3-(2-hydroxyethyl)-8-[(2-hydroxyethyl)amino]-	MeOH	279(3.98),300(3.81)	4-0403-73
$C_{12}H_{14}ClN_3O_5$			
1H-Imidazo[4,5-c]pyridine, 4-chloro-1-β-D-glucopyranosyl-	pH 1	272(3.74)	124-0703-73
	pH 13	245(3.63),272(3.73)	124-0703-73
	MeOH	249(3.62),272(3.70)	124-0703-73
1H-Pyrazolo[3,4-b]pyridine, 4-chloro-1-β-D-glucopyranosyl-	EtOH	214(4.38),270(3.42), 296(3.72),304s(3.60)	104-1294-73
$C_{12}H_{14}ClN_5O_4$			
9H-Purin-6-amine, 9-(2-O-acetyl-3-chloro-3-deoxy-β-D-xylofuranosyl)-	MeOH	258(4.20)	35-4025-73
$C_{12}H_{14}Cl_2$			
Benzene, 1-(2,2-dichloro-1-ethylcyclopropyl)-4-methyl-	hexane	221(3.94),252(2.40), 258(2.46),264(2.51), 273(2.35)	104-2473-73
$C_{12}H_{14}Cl_2O$			
Benzene, 1-(2,2-dichloro-1,3-dimethylcyclopropyl)-4-methoxy-	hexane	227(4.44),260(3.17), 267(3.27),274(3.30), 280(3.21)	104-2473-73
Benzene, 1-(2,2-dichloro-1-ethylcyclopropyl)-3-methoxy-	hexane	218(4.02),274(3.43), 282(3.43)	104-2473-73
Benzene, 1-(2,2-dichloro-1-ethylcyclopropyl)-4-methoxy-	hexane	230(4.06),277(3.21), 284(3.15)	104-2473-73
$C_{12}H_{14}FeO_3$			
Iron, tricarbonyl[(1,2,3,4-η)-1,3,5-trimethyl-1,3-cyclohexadiene]-	heptane	214(4.33),230s(--), 295s(--)	70-2027-73
$C_{12}H_{14}NO_2$			
Isoquinolinium, 6,7-dimethoxy-2-methyl-, perchlorate	MeOH	254(4.87),314(4.12)	83-0784-73
$C_{12}H_{14}N_2$			
Benzo[1,2-b:4,5-b']dipyrrole, 1,2,3,5-tetrahydro-1,5-dimethyl-	EtOH	283(3.80),324(3.65)	39-0832-73C
[2,2'-Bipyridinium], 1,1'-dimethyl-	MeCN	264s(4.10),269(4.16)	5-0324-73
[3,3'-Bipyridinium], 1,1'-dimethyl-	MeCN	242(3.95),271(4.04)	5-0324-73
[3,4'-Bipyridinium], 1,1'-dimethyl-	MeCN	258(4.22),268(4.21)	5-0324-73

Compound	Solvent	λ_{max}(log ε)	Ref.
[4,4'-Bipyridinium], 1,1'-dimethyl-	MeCN	258(4.33)	5-0324-73
Cyclobutanecarbonitrile, 3-(cyanomethylene)-2,2-dimethyl-4-(1-methylethylidene)-, anti	EtOH	282(4.06)	39-0885-73B
syn	EtOH	282(4.05)	39-0885-73B
Pyridiniumyl, 1,4-dihydro-1-methyl-4-(1-methyl-4(1H)-pyridinylidene)-, tetrafluoroborate	MeCN	248(3.64),311(3.80), 369(4.27),385(4.51), 396(4.66),576(4.10), 604(4.20),663(3.88), 735(3.48)	5-1036-73
1H-Pyrido[3,4-b]indole, 2,3,4,9-tetrahydro-2-methyl-	MeOH	225(4.7),280(4.0)	103-0974-73
Pyrimido[1,2-a]indole, 1,2,3,4-tetrahydro-3-methyl-, hydrochloride	MeOH	212(4.41),262(4.16)	103-0598-73
2H-Pyrimido[2,1-a]isoquinoline, 1,3,4,11b-tetrahydro-, bis(cyclohexylsulfamate)	MeOH	231(4.67),277(3.48), 335(3.62)	44-0437-73
Pyrrolo[3,2,1-hi]indole-1-ethanamine, 4,5-dihydro-	EtOH	227(4.27),285s(3.60), 295(3.64),304s(3.57)	103-0196-73
Quinazoline, 4-ethyl-2,6-dimethyl-	EtOH	260(3.54),316(3.54), 316(3.54)	39-0453-73C
Quinazoline, 4-ethyl-2,8-dimethyl-	EtOH	275(3.44),315(3.44)	39-0453-73C
$C_{12}H_{14}N_2O$			
Acetamide, N-(1,3-dimethyl-1H-indol-2-yl)-	MeOH	225(4.49),286(3.98)	103-0471-73
1,4-Ethano-4a,8a-(methanoxymethano)-phthalazine, 1,4-dihydro-, anti	MeCN	240(3.38),245s(3.37), 265s(3.34),270(3.32), 368(1.93),381(2.15)	78-2373-73
syn	MeCN	242(3.57),250(3.58), 260s(3.47),270s(3.26), 370s(2.02),380(2.15)	78-2373-73
1,4-Hexadien-3-one, 1,5-diamino-1-phenyl-	EtOH	240(4.01),265(3.79), 375(4.29)	18-3533-73
1H-Indole-2-carboxamide, N,N,1-trimethyl-	MeOH	287(4.07)	23-0792-73
1,7-Methano-2H-1,7-benzodiazonin-12-one, 3,4,5,6-tetrahydro-	MeOH	215(4.24),281(3.45)	39-0702-73C
Pyrazolidinium, 5,5-dimethyl-3-oxo-1-(phenylmethylene)-, hydroxide, inner salt	MeOH	346(4.2)	48-0711-73
3H-Pyrrolo[1,2-a]imidazole, 5,6,7,7a-tetrahydro-2-phenyl-, 1-oxide	MeOH	222(3.97),289(4.23)	24-1172-73
4H-Pyrrolo[1,2-e]-1,2,5-oxadiazine, 6,7,8,8a-tetrahydro-3-phenyl-	MeOH	245(4.09)	24-1172-73
4(3H)-Quinazolinone, 2-methyl-3-(1-methylethyl)-	MeOH	207(4.46),226(4.42), 267(3.92),305(3.54), 317(3.43)	78-2153-73
$C_{12}H_{14}N_2O_2$			
Cyclohexanecarboxylic acid, 2-(dicyanomethylene)-, ethyl ester	EtOH	240(4.12),356(1.81)	78-4103-73
	EtOH-NaOH	236(4.19),356(4.11)	78-4103-73
3H-Imidazo[2,1-c][1,4]oxazine, 5,6,8,8a-tetrahydro-2-phenyl-, 1-oxide	MeOH	222(3.91),289(4.20)	24-1172-73
4H-1,4-Oxazino[4,3-e]-1,2,5-oxadiazine, 6,7,9,9a-tetrahydro-3-phenyl-	MeOH	244(3.92)	24-1172-73
1H-Pyrazole, 1-methoxy-3,4-dimethyl-5-phenyl-, 2-oxide	MeOH	229(4.08),300(3.99)	39-0167-73C
3H-Pyrazole, 3-methoxy-3,4-dimethyl-5-phenyl-, 1-oxide	MeOH	228(4.15),255(3.62), 285(3.38)	39-0167-73C

Compound	Solvent	$\lambda_{max}(\log \epsilon)$	Ref.
3,5-Pyrazolidinedione, 1,2-dimethyl-4-(phenylmethyl)-	EtOH	258(4.04)	103-0717-73
Pyrazolo[1,5-a]pyridine-3-carboxylic acid, 2,7-dimethyl-, ethyl ester	MeOH	200(4.18),222(4.65), 243(4.08),308(4.18)	4-0821-73
Pyridinium, 1-[(2-acetyl-3-oxo-1-buten-yl)amino]-2-methyl-, hydroxide, inner salt	EtOH	261s(4.08),279(4.28), 383(4.10)	39-2580-73C
4H-Pyrido[1,2-a]pyrimidin-4-one, 3-(2-hydroxyethyl)-2,8-dimethyl-	MeOH	243(4.0),338(4.0)	5-0103-73
2,3-Quinoxalinedimethanol, α,α'-dimeth-yl-	EtOH	237(4.49),319(3.85)	33-1882-73
epimer	EtOH	237(4.48),319(3.82)	33-1882-73
$C_{12}H_{14}N_2O_2S$			
Acetamide, N-(4-morpholinylthioxometh-yl)-	EtOH	236(4.36),283(4.00), 341(2.75)	48-0144-73
1H-Pyrazole, 4,5-dihydro-4-(1-methyleth-ylidene)-3-(phenylsulfonyl)-	EtOH	222(4.20),322(3.79)	22-2746-73
$C_{12}H_{14}N_2O_2S_2$			
2-Propanoic acid, 2-cyano-3-mercapto-3-(methylthio)-, ethyl ester, pyri-dine salt	EtOH	224(4.73),289(4.57), 344(5.06)	18-0699-73
$C_{12}H_{14}N_2O_3$			
Acetamide, N-[2-(4-cyanophenyl)-2-hy-droxy-1-(hydroxymethyl)ethyl]-	EtOH	234(4.18),267(3.08), 278(2.91),293(2.29)	104-2144-73
2-Propenal, 2-nitro-3-[(2,4,6-trimethyl-phenyl)amino]-	$CHCl_3$	290(4.09),340(4.21)	104-0477-73
1H-Pyrrolo[2,3-c]pyridine-2-carboxylic acid, 5-methoxy-3-methyl-, ethyl ester	EtOH	285(4.00),293(4.07), 346(3.79)	44-1824-73
$C_{12}H_{14}N_2O_3S$			
L-Cysteinamide, N-acetyl-S-benzoyl-	3% MeCN	241(4.09),266(4.06)	44-0270-73
$C_{12}H_{14}N_2O_4$			
Acetamide, N-(3,4-dihydro-8-methyl-7-nitro-2H-1-benzopyran-6-yl)-	EtOH	236(4.08),338(3.15)	4-0623-73
2(5H)-Furanone, 5-(1,2-dihydro-2-oxo-4-methoxypyrimidin-1-yl)-4-ethyl-3-methyl-	50% EtOH	275(3.79)	44-3878-73
$C_{12}H_{14}N_2O_5$			
Ethyl 2,3'-anhydrothymidine uronate	EtOH	244(3.79)	44-0990-73
$C_{12}H_{14}N_2O_6$			
4-Pyridinepropanoic acid, 2-methoxy-β-methyl-5-nitro-α-oxo-, ethyl ester	EtOH	282(4.10)	44-1824-73
$C_{12}H_{14}N_2S$			
Benzeneacetonitrile, α-[(dimethylamino)-(methylthio)methylene]-	EtOH	230(3.98),261(3.91), 326(4.16)	1-0258-73
$C_{12}H_{14}N_2S_2$			
Propanedinitrile, [bis(2-butenylthio)-methylene]-	EtOH	330(4.04)	78-2077-73
$C_{12}H_{14}N_4O_2$			
Benzo[g]pteridine-2,4(3H,7H)-dione, 6,8,9,10-tetrahydro-7,8-dimethyl-	pH 0	240s(--),349(3.85)	33-1908-73
	pH 6	335(3.90)	33-1908-73

Compound	Solvent	$\lambda_{max}(\log \epsilon)$	Ref.
Benzo[g]pteridine-2,4(3H,7H)-dione, 6,8,9,10-tetrahydro-7,8-dimethyl- (cont.)	pH 13	264(4.24),375(3.86)	33-1908-73
Pyridazine, 3,3'-(1,2-ethanediyl)bis[6-methoxy-	EtOH	272(3.52)	94-0125-73
5H-Tetrazol-5-one, 1,4-dihydro-1-(1-oxo-2,4-hexadienyl)-4-(1,3-pentadienyl)-	heptane	285(4.4)	44-2982-73
	+ base	265(4.5)	44-2982-73
$C_{12}H_{14}N_4O_3$			
Furo[2,3-g]pteridine-8-carboxylic acid, 1,5,5a,8a-tetrahydro-7-methyl-, ethyl ester	EtOH	245(4.22),306(3.93)	39-1615-73C
$C_{12}H_{14}N_4O_4$			
Diazene, (1-ethyl-1-nitro-2-butenyl)-(4-nitrophenyl)-	EtOH	294(3.70)	19-0881-73
1H-Pyrazole, 1-acetyl-3-(hexahydro-1,3-dimethyl-2,4,6-trioxo-5-pyrimidinyl)-5-methyl-	EtOH	268s(4.26),285(4.33)	94-2639-73
2,4(1H,3H)-Pyrimidinedione, 1-[3-(3,4-dihydro-2,4-dioxo-1(2H)-pyrimidinyl)-propyl]-6-methyl-	H_2O	270.0(4.31)	56-1943-73
$C_{12}H_{14}N_4O_7$			
2,4(1H,3H)-Pteridinedione, 1-β-D-glucopyranosyl-	pH 4.0	227(4.13),314(3.85)	24-2982-73
	pH 12.0	237(4.16),280s(3.62), 317(3.87)	24-2982-73
	MeOH	238(4.34),290(3.84), 332(4.04)	24-2982-73
$C_{12}H_{14}N_4O_8$			
α-D-Mannopyranoside, 4-azido-2-nitrophenyl	H_2O	355(3.28)	136-0101-73F
$C_{12}H_{14}N_6$			
1H-Pyrazolo[3,4-d]pyrimidine-3-carbonitrile, 1-methyl-4-[(3-methyl-2-butenyl)amino]- (all spectra in ethanol)	pH 1	249(3.56),271s(--), 283s(--),311(4.00), 322(3.95)	39-1903-73C
	pH 7	229(3.89),254(3.72), 317(3.82)	39-1903-73C
	pH 12	262(3.82),314(3.85)	39-1903-73C
$C_{12}H_{14}O$			
Benzeneacetaldehyde, 4-methyl-α-propylidene-	n.s.g.	221(4.19),259(3.57), 272(3.44)	22-1676-73
5H-Benzocyclohepten-5-one, 6,7,8,9-tetrahydro-1-methyl-	EtOH	248(3.92)	22-3493-73
5H-Benzocyclohepten-5-one, 6,7,8,9-tetrahydro-4-methyl-	EtOH	247(3.63)	22-3493-73
Benzofuran, 2,3,4,6-tetramethyl-	n.s.g.	254(4.11),279(3.34), 289(3.23)	33-1457-73
Cyclopentanone, 2-methyl-5-phenyl-, trans	EtOH	244(2.00),250(2.20), 256(2.30),260(2.36), 265(2.30),269(2.24)	104-0835-73
7,8-Decadiene-3,5-diyn-2-ol, 2,9-dimethyl-	n.s.g.	208(4.61),212(4.72), 226(3.84),235(3.90), 252(3.89),266(4.05), 282(4.02),290(3.75), 300(3.61),308(3.62), 350(2.46)	70-1029-73

Compound	Solvent	$\lambda_{max}(\log \epsilon)$	Ref.
3,5-Hexadien-1-ol, 6-phenyl-, (Z,E)-	EtOH	280(4.36)	78-3797-73
3-Penten-2-one, 5-(4-methylphenyl)-	n.s.g.	220(4.18),284(3.24), 295(3.08)	22-1676-73
4-Penten-2-one, 5-(4-methylphenyl)-	n.s.g.	254(4.20),285(3.38), 296(3.24)	22-1676-73
Tricyclo[4.2.1.0^{2,5}]non-7-en-3-one, 4-(1-methylethylidene)-	C_6H_{12}	256(3.70),357(1.78), 375(1.78)	35-0274-73
$C_{12}H_{14}OS$			
Benzenecarbothioic acid, O-(2-cyclopropylethyl) ester	CH_2Cl_2	248(3.86),287(4.10), 420(2.20)	39-1574-73C
$C_{12}H_{14}OS_2$			
3-Buten-2-one, 4,4-bis(methylthio)-3-phenyl-	EtOH	220s(3.97),294(3.80)	1-0258-73
$C_{12}H_{14}O_2$			
Benzene, 1-methoxy-3-(3,4-pentadienyloxy)-	EtOH	222(3.90),274(3.37), 280(3.33)	78-0715-73
Benzeneacetaldehyde, 4-methoxy-α-propylidene-, (E)-	n.s.g.	223(4.31),275(3.68), 282(3.64)	22-1676-73
4H-1-Benzopyran-4-one, 2-ethyl-2,3-dihydro-6-methyl-	MeOH	254(3.95),331(3.56)	20-0705-73
Bicyclo[3.3.1]nona-3,6-diene-2,8-dione, 4,6,9-trimethyl-	EtOH	219(4.27),239s(3.98), 272s(3.21)	94-1213-73
Bicyclo[3.3.1]nona-3,7-diene-2,6-dione, 4,8,9-trimethyl-	EtOH	238(4.19),268s(3.1[illegible]), 279s(2.80),348s(2.92)	94-1213-73
2,4,6-Cycloheptatrien-1-one, 2-hydroxy-5-(3-methyl-2-butenyl)-	EtOH	234(4.45),325(4.04), 354s(3.86)	39-1958-73C
2,4,6-Cycloheptatrien-1-one, 2-[(3-methyl-2-butenyl)oxy]-	EtOH	236(4.38),320(3.94), 348(3.86),364s(3.68)	39-1958-73C
Ethanone, 1-(3,4-dihydro-8-methyl-2H-1-benzopyran-6-yl)-	EtOH	229(4.13),285(4.17)	4-0623-73
1-Naphthalenecarboxaldehyde, 2,4a,5,6,7-8-hexahydro-4a-methyl-2-oxo-	EtOH	242(4.08)	44-0967-73
2-Naphthalenecarboxaldehyde, 3,5,6,7,8-8a-hexahydro-8a-methyl-3-oxo-	EtOH	220(4.08),244(4.04)	44-0967-73
	EtOH-NaOH	242(4.08),347(3.98)	44-0967-73
2-Penten-1-one, 1-(2-hydroxy-5-methylphenyl)-	MeOH	272(4.23),355(3.67)	20-0299-73
Tricyclo[6.2.1.0^{2,6}]undec-2(6)-ene-6,11-dione, 1-methyl-	EtOH	227(3.91),247(3.95), 300(2.48)	39-2404-73C
$C_{12}H_{14}O_2S$			
5,10-Epithiobenzocyclooctene, 1,2,3,4-5,10-hexahydro-, 11,11-dioxide	EtOH	282(3.32)	35-2230-73
$C_{12}H_{14}O_3$			
2H-Azuleno[8,1-bc]furan-2,3(2aH)-dione, 5,6,7,8,8a,8b-hexahydro-8a-methyl-	EtOH	246(4.00),271(3.87)	44-0967-73
4H-1-Benzopyran-4-one, 2,3-dihydro-8-methoxy-2,5-dimethyl-	EtOH	217(4.25),266(3.94), 340(3.53)	95-0896-73
3H,7H-Cyclopenta[c]benzofuran-3,4(3aH)-dione, 5a,6,8,9-tetrahydro-5a-methyl-	EtOH	223(3.92)	44-0967-73
1-Indanone, 7-ethoxy-6-methoxy-	EtOH	219(4.36),255(3.98), 325(3.55)	141-0001-73
	dioxan	226(4.20),253(3.94), 320(3.55)	141-0001-73
1(3H)-Isobenzofuranone, 3-methoxy-3-(1-methylethyl)-	MeOH	229(3.97),274(3.08), 281(3.04)	44-3375-73

Compound	Solvent	λ_{max}(log ε)	Ref.
1-Naphthalenecarboxylic acid, 2,4a,5,6-7,8-hexahydro-4a-methyl-2-oxo-	EtOH	240(4.14)	44-0967-73
1-Naphthalenecarboxylic acid, 3,4,4a,5-8,8a-hexahydro-3-oxo-, methyl ester	MeOH	231(3.86)	18-0880-73
2(1H)-Naphthalenone, 1-acetoxy-4a,5,8,8a-tetrahydro-, cis	MeOH	228.5(3.96)	12-0595-73
13-Oxabicyclo[8.2.1]trideca-10,12-diene-4,7-dione	EtOH	222(3.56),292s(1.94)	88-4017-73
2-Propenoic acid, 9-oxobicyclo[3.3.1]-non-2-en-2-yl ester	EtOH	205(4.00)	22-1409-73
$C_{12}H_{14}O_4$			
Benzeneacetaldehyde, α-(2-hydroxyethyl-idene)-3,4-dimethoxy-, (Z)-	EtOH	224s(4.18),284(3.53)	39-2359-73C
Butanedioic acid, bis(methylene)-, di-2-propenyl ester	MeOH	218(3.40)(end abs.)	33-3004-73
3-Butenoic acid, 4-(3,5-dimethoxyphen-yl)-, (E)-	EtOH	227(4.58),260(4.35), 298(3.78)	23-3299-73
1-Cyclobutene-1,2-dicarboxylic acid, di-2-propenyl ester	MeOH	233(3.98)	33-3004-73
$C_{12}H_{14}O_5$			
Benzenebutanoic acid, 2-hydroxy-4-meth-oxy-γ-oxo-, methyl ester	EtOH	217(4.29),229(4.10), 236s(4.04),275(4.25), 315(4.00)	23-1617-73
	EtOH-base	218(4.22),230(4.23), 242(4.20),275(3.94), 350(4.04)	23-1617-73
2,5-Cyclohexadien-1-one, 4-acetoxy-4-(2-acetoxyethyl)-	EtOH	239(3.85)	1-0367-73
1,3-Cyclopentadiene-1,2-dicarboxylic acid, 5-(1-hydroxyethylidene)-3-methyl-, dimethyl ester	hexane	235(4.74),325(4.64), 382(4.28)	88-4325-73
	MeOH	235(4.13),323(4.08), 380(3.69)	24-3817-73
sodium salt	MeOH	249(4.26),330(4.30)	24-3817-73
7-Oxabicyclo[2.2.1]hepta-2,5-diene-2,3-dicarboxylic acid, 1,4-dimethyl-, dimethyl ester	MeOH	284(3.05)	24-0674-73
Propanedioic acid, (4-methoxyphenyl)-methyl methyl ester	EtOH	225(4.12),274(3.19), 280(3.12)	78-3609-73
2-Propenoic acid, 3-(5-hydroxy-2,4-di-methoxyphenyl)-, methyl ester, (E)-	EtOH	218(4.07),252(4.03), 292(4.13),357(4.17)	95-0624-73
$C_{12}H_{14}O_6$			
1,3-Benzenedicarboxaldehyde, 2,4,5,6-tetramethoxy-	MeOH	214(4.15),257(4.17), 314(3.44)	78-2645-73
1,4-Benzenedicarboxylic acid, 2,5-di-hydroxy-, diethyl ester	EtOH	220(4.25),251(3.99), 376(3.56)	33-2760-73
$C_{12}H_{14}O_8$			
α-D-erythro-Hex-2-en-3-ulose, 1,5-anhy-dro-, triacetate	EtOH	260(4.14)	23-0394-73
$C_{12}H_{14}S$			
Benzothiophene, 3-ethyl-5,6-dimethyl-	C_6H_{12}	227(4.44),262(3.97), 270(4.0),294(3.52), 305(3.62)	49-0312-73
$C_{12}H_{14}S_2$			
Thiophene, 2-ethyl-5-[(5-methyl-2-thien-yl)methyl]-	n.s.g.	238(3.88)	49-0312-73

Compound	Solvent	λ_{max}(log ϵ)	Ref.
$C_{12}H_{15}$			
Ethylium, 1-cyclopropyl-1-(4-methyl-phenyl)-	FSO_3H at -75°	368(4.49)	59-0803-73
$C_{12}H_{15}BrN_2$			
Isoquinolinium, 2-(3-aminopropyl)-, bromide, hydrobromide	MeOH	233(4.70),278(3.47), 337(3.63)	44-0437-73
$C_{12}H_{15}ClN_2O_3$			
Propanoic acid, 2-[(5-chloro-2-methoxy-phenyl)hydrazono]-, ethyl ester, (E)-	EtOH	333(4.29)	94-1481-73
(Z)-	EtOH	357.5(4.25)	94-1481-73
$C_{12}H_{15}FN_2O_5$			
Thymidine, 3'-deoxy-3'-fluoro-, 5'-acet-ate	MeOH	264.5(3.98)	48-0895-73
$C_{12}H_{15}F_3N_2$			
Benzenecarboximidamide, N,N-diethyl-3-(trifluoromethyl)-	EtOH	205(4.16)	36-1899-73
Benzenecarboximidamide, N,N-diethyl-4-(trifluoromethyl)-	EtOH	208(4.14)	36-1899-73
$C_{12}H_{15}NO$			
Aziridinone, 1-(1,1-dimethylethyl)-3-phenyl-	pentane	226(4.0)	35-3415-73
3H-Indole, 5-methoxy-2,3,3-trimethyl-	EtOH	213(4.16),273(3.93)	88-0903-73
6-Oxa-1-azabicyclo[3.1.0]hexane, 2,2-dimethyl-3-phenyl-, cis	EtOH	243(2.27),249(2.29), 254(2.34),260(2.38), 266(2.26),269(2.09)	12-2159-73
Oxazole, 2,5-dihydro-4-phenyl-5-propyl-	EtOH	243(4.33)	33-2611-73
$C_{12}H_{15}NO_2$			
Acetamide, N-(3,4-dihydro-8-methyl-2H-1-benzopyran-6-yl)-	EtOH	254.5(4.13)	4-0623-73
5H-Cyclohepta[b]pyridin-9-ol, 6,7,8,9-tetrahydro-, acetate	EtOH	207(3.85),249(3.64), 290(3.46)	39-0968-73C
2-Pentanone, 4-[(phenylmethylene)amino]-, N-oxide	EtOH	294(4.29)	104-0793-73
1H-Pyrrolo[2,1-c][1,4]thiazine-3-carbox-ylic acid, 1,1,6-trimethyl-, methyl ester	EtOH	249(3.84),334(4.00)	39-1985-73C
$C_{12}H_{15}NO_2S_2$			
4-Pentenoic acid, 2-cyano-2-[(2-propen-ylthio)thioxomethyl]-, ethyl ester	EtOH	318(3.96)	78-2077-73
$C_{12}H_{15}NO_3$			
8-Indolizinecarboxylic acid, 1,2,3,7-tetrahydro-5-methyl-7-oxo-, ethyl ester	EtOH	259(4.15),291(3.57)	95-1084-73
	EtOH-HCl	236(3.93)	95-1084-73
2H-Pyran-2-one, 3-acetyl-6-methyl-4-pyrrolidino-	EtOH	246(4.25),283(3.76), 325(3.89)	78-1083-73
$C_{12}H_{15}NO_3S$			
Thiazolo[3,2-a]pyridinium, 3-carboxy-8-ethoxy-2,3-dihydro-2,5-dimethyl-, hydroxide, inner salt, trans	pH 1	215(3.89),243(3.81), 346(3.90)	1-1749-73
	pH 13	220(3.73),242(3.72), 357(3.86)	1-1749-73

Compound	Solvent	λ max (log ε)	Ref.
$C_{12}H_{15}NO_4$			
2H-Pyran-2-one, 3-acetyl-6-methyl-4-morpholino-	EtOH	247(4.28),290(3.86), 339(3.92)	78-1083-73
1H-Pyrrole-2-carboxylic acid, 4-(3-methoxy-3-oxo-1-propenyl)-3,5-dimethyl-, methyl ester	MeOH	261(4.25),320(4.30)	39-1546-73C
$C_{12}H_{15}NO_5$			
Benzene, 1,2,3-trimethoxy-5-(2-nitro-1-propenyl)-	EtOH	215(4.30),343(4.04)	39-2388-73C
Butanedioic acid, (1,5-dihydro-3,4-dimethyl-5-oxo-2H-pyrrol-2-ylidene)-, dimethyl ester	MeOH	285(4.23)	24-0812-73
geometric isomer	MeOH	293(4.27)	24-0812-73
3,4-Pyridinedicarboxylic acid, 2-hydroxy-6-methyl-, diethyl ester	EtOH	263(4.22),330(4.47)	70-2478-73
$C_{12}H_{15}NO_6$			
2,4,5-Pyrroletricarboxylic acid, 1,3-dimethyl-, trimethyl ester	MeOH	224(4.31),269(4.07)	39-0881-73C
$C_{12}H_{15}NS_2$			
Pyrrolo[2,1-b]thiazole-5-thiocarboxaldehyde, 6-(1,1-dimethylethyl)-3-methyl-	EtOH	204(4.16),224(4.16), 326(3.79),420(4.46), 530(2.20),546(2.18)	39-0657-73C
Pyrrolo[2,1-b]thiazole-7-thiocarboxaldehyde, 6-(1,1-dimethylethyl)-3-methyl-	EtOH	226(4.34),261(3.83), 281(3.80),397s(4.22), 405(4.34),416(4.31), 506(1.78),513(1.84), 531(1.81),564s(1.14)	39-0657-73C
$C_{12}H_{15}N_2$			
Isoquinolinium, 2-(3-aminopropyl)-, bromide hydrobromide	MeOH	233(4.70),278(3.47), 337(3.63)	44-0437-73
$C_{12}H_{15}N_3$			
3,5-Pyridinedicarbonitrile, 4-ethyl-1,4-dihydro-2,4,6-trimethyl-	EtOH	217(4.4),343(3.9)	103-0994-73
$C_{12}H_{15}N_3O$			
Pyrimido[1,2-b]indazol-4(1H)-one, 7,8,9,10-tetrahydro-2,3-dimethyl-	MeOH	256s(3.90),264(4.00), 304(3.80)	4-0261-73
Pyrimido[1,2-b]indazol-4(1H)-one, 7,8,9,10-tetrahydro-2,7-dimethyl-	MeOH	258s(3.83),265(3.99), 305(3.69)	4-0261-73
1,2,4-Triazine, 2,5-dihydro-3-methoxy-5,6-dimethyl-5-phenyl-	n.s.g.	220(3.91),283(3.79)	22-2493-73
$C_{12}H_{15}N_3O_2$			
Butanedinitrile, (aminoethoxymethylene)-(1-methyl-2-oxobutylidene)-, (E,E)-	EtOH	204(4.11),253(4.10) 330(3.81)	12-1551-73
Pyrazine, 1,4,5,6-tetrahydro-1,4-dimethyl-2-(4-nitrophenyl)-	C_6H_{12}	470(4.14)	28-1319-73A
$C_{12}H_{15}N_3O_2S$			
Pentanoic acid, 5-(1H-pyrrolo[2,3-d]pyrimidin-4-ylthio)-, methyl ester	pH 1	220(4.30),258(3.89), 311(3.97)	73-1438-73
	pH 13	222(4.28),249(3.90), 294(4.05)	73-1438-73

Compound	Solvent	$\lambda_{max}(\log \epsilon)$	Ref.
$C_{12}H_{15}N_3O_3$			
4(3H)-Quinazolinone, 3-(2-hydroxyethyl)-8-(2-hydroxyethylamino)-	MeOH	274.5(4.07)	4-0403-73
$C_{12}H_{15}N_3O_4S$			
1H-Pyrazolo[3,4-b]pyridine, 4-(methylthio)-1-β-D-ribofuranosyl-	EtOH	238(3.52),314(3.68), 322(3.64)	104-1294-73
$C_{12}H_{15}N_3S$			
1,2,4-Triazine, 4,5-dihydro-5,5-dimethyl-3-(methylthio)-6-phenyl-	n.s.g.	226(4.11),275(3.74)	22-2493-73
1,2,4-Triazine, 4,5-dihydro-5,6-dimethyl-3-(methylthio)-5-phenyl-	n.s.g.	224(4.16),281(3.74)	22-2493-73
$C_{12}H_{15}N_4O_7PS$			
Inosine, 8-(ethylthio)-, cyclic 3',5'-(hydrogen phosphate)	pH 1	270(4.19)	69-5310-73
	pH 11	277(4.19)	69-5310-73
$C_{12}H_{15}N_5O$			
Acetamide, N-[[5-amino-1-(phenylmethyl)-1H-1,2,3-triazol-4-yl]methyl]-	pH 7.0	216s(3.86),245(3.76)	39-1634-73C
$C_{12}H_{15}N_5O_2$			
7H-Purine-7-propanenitrile, 8-ethyl-1,2,3,6-tetrahydro-1,3-dimethyl-2,6-dioxo-	n.s.g.	210(4.32),276(4.00)	73-1571-73
$C_{12}H_{15}N_5O_2S$			
1H-Purine-2,6-dione, 3,7-dihydro-7-(3-isothiocyanatopropyl)-1,3,8-trimethyl-	n.s.g.	210(4.33),276(3.98)	73-1571-73
$C_{12}H_{15}N_5O_3$			
2,4(1H,3H)-Pyrimidinedione, 1-[3-(4-amino-2-oxo-1(2H)-pyrimidinyl)propyl]-6-methyl-	H_2O	271.0(4.24)	56-1943-73
$C_{12}H_{15}N_5O_4$			
9H-Purin-6-amine, 9-(5,6-dideoxy-β-D-ribo-hept-5-enofuranosyl)-	pH 1	257(4.16)	136-0225-73B
	pH 7	259(4.17)	136-0225-73B
	pH 13	259(4.17)	136-0225-73B
$C_{12}H_{15}N_5O_5$			
2-Aza-α-inosine	pH 1	286(3.66)	4-0417-73
	pH 11	292(3.76)	4-0417-73
β-D-ribo-Heptofuranuronic acid, 1-(6-amino-9H-purin-9-yl)-1,5,6-trideoxy-	pH 1	257(4.16)	136-0225-73B
	pH 7	259(4.17)	136-0225-73B
	pH 13	259(4.17)	136-0225-73B
2(1H)-Pteridinone, 4-(methylamino)-1-β-D-ribofuranosyl-	pH 0.0	242(4.14),332(3.91)	33-1225-73
	pH 7.0	245(4.05),300(3.74), 339(3.91)	33-1225-73
$C_{12}H_{15}N_5O_6$			
2(1H)-Pteridinone, 4-amino-1-β-D-glucopyranosyl-	pH 0.0	236(4.14),328(3.86)	24-2982-73
	pH 7.0	240(4.53),285(3.70), 332(3.91)	24-2982-73
7(8H)-Pteridinone, 2-amino-4-methoxy-8-β-D-ribofuranosyl-	pH -2.0	217(4.24),300s(4.01), 329(4.20)	24-1952-73
	pH 4.0	230(4.08),281(3.69), 350(4.13)	24-1952-73
	MeOH	211(4.48),232(4.02), 280(3.55),348(4.11)	24-1952-73

Compound	Solvent	λ max (log ε)	Ref.
$C_{12}H_{15}N_6O_6P$			
Adenosine, 5'-deoxy-5'-(dihydroxyphos-	pH 2	257(4.17)	35-4404-73
phinyl)cyanomethyl-	pH 12	259(4.18)	35-4404-73
$C_{12}H_{15}N_6O_7P$			
Adenosine, N-[(methylamino)carbonyl]-,	pH 1	276(4.36),285s(4.24)	87-1075-73
cyclic 3',5'-(hydrogen phosphate)	pH 7	267(4.35),275s(4.28)	87-1075-73
	pH 11	267(4.34),275s(4.27)	87-1075-73
$C_{12}H_{16}$			
Benzene, 1-cyclohexyl-	EtOH	248(2.20),254(2.32), 255(2.32),259(2.39), 261(2.40),264(2.28), 268(2.31)	22-1517-73
Tetracyclo[5.3.0.0^{2,10}.0^{3,6}]dec-8-ene, 3,6-dimethyl-	pentane	221(3.48)	35-6197-73
3,6-exo	pentane	223(3.46)	35-6197-73
Tetracyclo[6.3.0.0^{2,11}.0^{3,7}]undec-9-ene, 1-methyl-	pentane	220(3.32)	35-6197-73
Tricyclo[3.1.0.0^{2,8}]hexane, 1,2,5,6-tetramethyl-3,4-bis(methylene)-	EtOH	204(3.95),250(3.78)	88-3747-73
$C_{12}H_{16}BrClO$			
Furan, 3-(3-bromo-4-chloro-4-methyl-cyclohexyl)-2-methyl-	EtOH	228(3.89)	88-3625-73
$C_{12}H_{16}BrClO_3$			
2(5H)-Furanone, 4-(3-bromo-4-chloro-4-methylcyclohexyl)-5-hydroxy-5-methyl-	EtOH	216(4.26)	88-3625-73
$C_{12}H_{16}ClNO_2$			
Benzoic acid, 4-chloro-, 3-(dimethyl-amino)propyl ester	H_2O	238(4.23)	104-2111-73
$C_{12}H_{16}ClNO_4Si$			
Silicon, (4-chloropheolato)[[2,2',2"-nitrilotris[ethanolato](3-)-N,O,O',O"]-	H_2O	225(4.08),280(3.23)	30-0941-73
$C_{12}H_{16}ClNS_2$			
Dithiobenzoic acid, 4-chloro-, piperi-dine salt	EtOH	298(4.11),365(3.91), 492(2.27)	143-0359-73
$C_{12}H_{16}CrO_6Si$			
Chromium, pentacarbonyl[1-ethoxy-2-(tri-methylsilyl)ethylidene]-, (OC-6-21)-	hexane	250(4.52),373(3.71)	101-0077-73N
$C_{12}H_{16}DNO_2$			
Ethanone, 1-[5-(1,1-dimethylethyl)-2-(hydroxy-d)phenyl]-, oxime	CCl_4	315(3.618)	30-0394-73
$C_{12}H_{16}F_3NO_8$			
D-glycero-D-galacto-Non-2-enonic acid, 2,6-anhydro-3,5-dideoxy-5-[(trifluoro-acetyl)amino]-, methyl ester	n.s.g.	243(3.92)	49-0402-73
$C_{12}H_{16}NO$			
Isoxazolium, 4,5-dihydro-2,5,5-trimeth-yl-3-phenyl-, perchlorate	EtOH	215s(--),275(4.05)	22-1390-73

Compound	Solvent	$\lambda_{max}(\log \epsilon)$	Ref.
$C_{12}H_{16}NO_4$			
7-Azoniabicyclo[2.2.1]hepta-2,5-diene-2,3-dicarboxylic acid, 7,7-dimethyl-, tetrafluoroborate	MeCN	279(2.98)	24-3824-73
$C_{12}H_{16}N_2$			
3H-1,3-Benzodiazepine, 4,5-dihydro-2,5,9-trimethyl-	EtOH	265(3.98)	39-0453-73C
Phenazine, 1,2,3,4,6,7,8,9-octahydro-	dioxan	215(3.70),290(4.01), 310(3.45)	56-0943-73
hydrochloride hydrate	EtOH	214(3.76),291(3.90), 310(3.93)	18-1816-73
Pyrazine, 1,4,5,6-tetrahydro-1,4-dimethyl-2-phenyl-	C_6H_{12}	314(4.05)	28-1319-73A
Quinazoline, 4-ethyl-3,4-dihydro-2,6-dimethyl-	EtOH	285(3.92)	39-0453-73C
Quinazoline, 4-ethyl-3,4-dihydro-2,8-dimethyl-	EtOH	267(3.91)	39-0453-73C
$C_{12}H_{16}N_2O$			
1-Cyclohexene-1-carbonitrile, 2-(1-azetidinyl)-4,4-dimethyl-6-oxo-	EtOH	237(3.74),298(4.35)	70-0811-73
1-Cyclohexene-1,2-dicarbonitrile, 4-butoxy-	MeOH	235(4.04)	33-3004-73
1,4-Ethanofuro[3,4-d]pyridazine, 4a,7a-diethenyl-1,4,4a,5,7,7a-hexahydro-, (1α,4α,4aα,7aα)-	MeCN	246s(3.10),249s(3.10), 251s(3.11),254(3.14), 367(1.93),370(2.00)	78-2373-73
(1α,4α,4aβ,7aβ)-	MeCN	228(3.89),233(3.88), 268s(2.06),368s(1.88), 376(1.95)	78-2373-73
4H-Imidazole, 2,2,4-trimethyl-5-phenyl-, 1-oxide	EtOH	252(3.60)	103-1008-73
1H-Indol-3-ol, 2-(ethylimino)-2,3-dihydro-1,3-dimethyl-	MeOH	273(4.12),298(3.21)	103-0471-73
Pyrazolidine, 2-acetyl-3-methyl-1-phenyl-	EtOH	238(4.12),287(3.13)	103-0503-73
$C_{12}H_{16}N_2O_2$			
1H-Imidazol-5-ol, 4,5-dihydro-2,4,4-trimethyl-5-phenyl-, 3-oxide	EtOH	258(3.79)	103-1008-73
Isoxazole, 5-[[3-(1,1-dimethylethyl)-5-isoxazolyl]methyl]-3-methyl-	n.s.g.	216(4.09)	32-0037-73
5-Isoxazolone, 3,4-dimethyl-, benzylammonium salt	n.s.g.	258(3.93)	1-2802-73
2-Pentanone, 4-[(phenylmethylene)amino]-, oxime N-oxide	EtOH	294(4.23)	104-0793-73
2,5-Piperazinedione, 6-butylidene-3-(2-butenylidene)-	EtOH	325(4.49)	18-3876-73
Propanediamide, N,N'-dimethyl-2-(phenylmethyl)-	EtOH	245(4.11)	103-0717-73
$C_{12}H_{16}N_2O_3$			
Benzoic acid, 4-[[(methoxyimino)methyl]methylamino]-, ethyl ester	pH 7.5	305(4.41)	35-8414-73
1H-Imidazole-1,5-diol, 4,5-dihydro-2,4,4-trimethyl-5-phenyl-, 3-oxide	EtOH	263(3.95)	103-1008-73
Propanoic acid, 2-[(2-methoxyphenyl)hydrazono]-, ethyl ester, (E)-	EtOH	331.5(4.29)	94-1481-73
(Z)-	EtOH	360(4.24)	94-1481-73

Compound	Solvent	$\lambda_{max}(\log \epsilon)$	Ref.
$C_{12}H_{16}N_2O_4$			
Benzoic acid, 3-nitro-, 3-(dimethyl-amino)propyl ester	H_2O	261(3.80)	104-2111-73
Benzoic acid, 4-nitro-, 3-(dimethyl-amino)propyl ester	H_2O	264(4.10)	104-2111-73
$C_{12}H_{16}N_2O_5$			
1,3-Diazatricyclo[3.3.1.1^{3,7}]decane-5,7-dicarboxylic acid, 6-oxo-, dimethyl ester	EtOH	255(3.14)	44-1648-73
	EtOH-HCl	227(3.08)	44-1648-73
	DMCS-HCl	224(2.82),285(2.22)	44-1648-73
2-Furancarboxylic acid, 5-(3,4-dihydro-5-methyl-2,4-dioxo-1(2H)-pyrimidinyl)-tetrahydro-, ethyl ester, (2S-cis)-	EtOH	237(3.28),268(3.95)	44-0990-73
$C_{12}H_{16}N_2O_5S$			
Uridine, 2',3'-O-isopropylidene-4-thio-	pH 7	330(4.32)	103-0917-73
$C_{12}H_{16}N_2O_6$			
Benzene, 1,4-dimethoxy-2,5-bis(2-nitro-ethyl)-	EtOH	225(4.00),297(3.67)	39-0832-73C
Uracil-1-malonic acid, 5-methyl-, di-ethyl ester	neutral	267(4.01)	46-0482-73
	pH 10	259(4.23)	46-0482-73
$C_{12}H_{16}N_2O_7S$			
5-Pyrimidineacetic acid, 1,2,3,4-tetra-hydro-4-oxo-1-β-D-ribofuranosyl-2-thioxo-, methyl ester	H_2O	220(4.12),278(4.2)	24-3039-73
	pH 12	242(4.4),270(4.2)	24-3039-73
$C_{12}H_{16}N_2O_8$			
D-glycero-D-galacto-Non-2-enonic acid, 2,6-anhydro-5-[(cyanoacetyl)amino]-3,5-dideoxy-	n.s.g.	240(3.81)	49-0402-73
$C_{12}H_{16}N_3O_6$			
1,3-Cyclohexadiene-1-carboxamide, N,N-diethyl-6-methoxy-3,5-dinitro-, ion(1-)	DMSO	370(4.20),510(4.43)	39-0710-73B
1,5-Cyclohexadiene-1-carboxamide, N,N-diethyl-4-methoxy-3,5-dinitro-, ion(1-)	DMSO	370(4.18),520(4.26), 580(4.20)	39-0710-73B
$C_{12}H_{16}N_4$			
1H-Imidazole-1,2-diamine, 4-phenyl-5-propyl-	EtOH	282(4.26)	103-1082-73
$C_{12}H_{16}N_4O$			
1,4:5,8-Diethano-4a,8a-(methanoxymeth-ano)pyridazino[4,5-d]pyridazine, 1,4,5,8-tetrahydro-, syn-anti	MeCN	243(3.16),247(3.16), 250(3.16),361s(2.27), 371(2.28),382(1.95)	78-2373-73
syn-syn	MeCN	258(2.61),360s(1.78), 369(2.02),409(1.93)	78-2373-73
$C_{12}H_{16}N_4O_2$			
1H-1,2,3-Triazol-5-amine, 4-(dimethoxy-methyl)-1-(phenylmethyl)-	n.s.g.	248(3.75)	39-2037-73C
$C_{12}H_{16}N_4O_4$			
1,2-Cyclopentanediol, 3-(hydroxymethyl)-5-(6-methoxy-9H-purin-9-yl)-, (±)-	pH 1	252(4.03),262s(--)	36-1252-73
	pH 7 and 13	252(4.06),262s(--)	36-1252-73

Compound	Solvent	λ max (log ε)	Ref.
1H-Imidazo[4,5-b]pyrazine, 5,6-dimethyl-1-β-D-ribofuranosyl-	pH 1	290s(4.00),306(4.12)	39-0244-73C
	pH 11	246(3.54),295s(3.99), 312(4.13)	39-0244-73C
	MeOH	258(3.42),295s(4.03), 309(4.09)	39-0244-73C
$C_{12}H_{16}N_4O_4S$			
Inosine, 2-ethyl-6-thio-	pH 1	229(3.91),326(4.28)	94-0692-73
	pH 13	313(4.27)	94-0692-73
Purine, 2-methyl-6-(methylthio)-9-β-D-ribofuranosyl-	pH 1	227(4.12),305(4.14)	94-0692-73
	pH 6	225(4.13),294(4.25)	94-0692-73
	pH 13	294(4.29)	94-0692-73
$C_{12}H_{16}N_6$			
1H-Pyrazolo[3,4-d]pyrimidine-3-carbonitrile, 1-methyl-4-[(3-methylbutyl)-amino]-	EtOH-pH 1	233s(--),259(3.82), 272s(--),281(3.94), 311(4.25)	39-1903-73C
	EtOH-pH 7	230(4.11),255(3.92), 320(4.03)	39-1903-73C
	EtOH-pH 12	263(4.02),314(4.05)	39-1903-73C
$C_{12}H_{16}N_6O_3$			
L-Isoleucine, N-[(1H-purin-6-ylamino)-carbonyl]-	pH 1-2	277(4.31)	87-0139-73
	pH 5-7	270(4.29)	87-0139-73
	pH 12	278(4.26)	87-0139-73
L-Leucine, N-[(1H-purin-6-ylamino)carbonyl]-	pH 1-2	277(4.30)	87-0139-73
	pH 5-7	269.5(4.27)	87-0139-73
	pH 12	278(4.22)	87-0139-73
$C_{12}H_{16}N_6O_5$			
Adenosine, N-[(methylamino)carbonyl]-	pH 1-2	270s(--),277(4.40)	87-0139-73
	pH 5-7	269(4.38),277s(--)	87-0139-73
	pH 12	278(4.26),298(4.27)	87-0139-73
$C_{12}H_{16}O$			
Bicyclo[2.2.2]oct-5-en-2-one, 3-methyl-7-(1-methylethenyl)-, (+)-	C_6H_{12}	288(2.03),297(2.11), 308(2.11),319(1.89)	22-2836-73
2-Butanone, 3,3-dimethyl-1-phenyl-	C_6H_{12}	290(2.04)	28-0407-73B
	MeOH	280(2.02)	28-0407-73B
2,4-Cyclohexadien-1-one, 6-(2-butenyl)-2,6-dimethyl-	EtOH	309(3.66)	33-0014-73
Cyclohexanone, 2-(2,4-cyclohexadien-1-yl)-	C_6H_{12}	261(3.63)	39-1882-73C
Cyclopent[a]inden-6(1H)-one, 2,3,3a,3b-4,5,8,8a-octahydro-, cis	EtOH	232(4.1)	39-2454-73C
3,4a-Ethanonaphthalen-2(3H)-one, 4,4a,5,6,7,8-hexahydro-	EtOH	244(4.08)	44-2125-73
1-Oxaspiro[4.5]deca-6,8-diene, 4-(1-methylethylidene)-	hexane	221(3.30),253(3.39)	35-3947-73
8-Oxatricyclo[4.3.0.0^{2,5}]nonane, 1,6-diethenyl-, (1α,2β,5β,6α)-	MeCN	225(3.61)	78-2373-73
1-Pentanone, 1-(3-methylphenyl)-	heptane	242(4.04)	35-5604-73
1-Pentanone, 1-(4-methylphenyl)-	heptane	247(4.19)	35-5604-73
2-Pentanone, 3-methyl-1-phenyl-	C_6H_{12}	290(2.20)	28-0407-73B
	MeOH	290(2.22)	28-0407-73B
2-Pentanone, 4-methyl-1-phenyl-	C_6H_{12}	288(2.53)	28-0407-73B
	MeOH	288(2.53)	28-0407-73B
Tricyclo[7.2.1.0^{5,12}]dodec-9(12)-en-10-one	EtOH	241(4.13)	44-3829-73

Compound	Solvent	$\lambda_{max}(\log \epsilon)$	Ref.
$C_{12}H_{16}OS$			
Benzo[b]thiophen-7(4H)-one, 2-(1,1-dimethylethyl)-5,6-dihydro-	n.s.g.	288(4.12)	22-0343-73
4H-Cyclopenta[c]thiophen-4-one, 3-(1,1-dimethylethyl)-5,6-dihydro-5-methyl-	n.s.g.	225(4.21),245(3.90), 267(3.59)	22-0343-73
1-Pentanone, 1-[4-(methylthio)phenyl]-	heptane	304(4.36)	35-5604-73
2H-Pyran, tetrahydro-2-[(4-methylphenyl)thio]-	40% dioxan	242(3.99)	35-8407-73
$C_{12}H_{16}OS_2$			
1-Propanone, 1-(3-ethyl-5,6-dihydro-4H-1,2-benzodithiol-7-yl)-	C_6H_{12}	228(4.25),245s(3.99), 265s(3.42),280s(3.08), 375s(3.46),395s(3.87), 414(4.12),434(4.12)	33-0597-73
	EtOH	226(4.22),242s(4.01), 265s(3.46),280s(3.23), 375s(3.40),394s(3.84), 417(4.15),436(4.18)	33-0597-73
$C_{12}H_{16}O_2$			
4H-1-Benzopyran, 2,3-dihydro-2,2-dimethyl-7-methoxy-	n.s.g.	282(3.33),288(3.29)	2-0091-73
3,9-Cyclododecadiene-1,7-dione, cis-cis	EtOH	210(3.19),291(2.13)	35-4582-73
cis-trans	EtOH	211(3.26),291(2.34)	35-4582-73
3,10-Cyclododecadiene-1,7-dione, cis-cis	EtOH	212(3.23),287(2.11)	35-4582-73
cis-trans	EtOH	212(3.28),290(2.18)	35-4582-73
1H-Indene-4-carboxylic acid, 2,3,3a,7a-tetrahydro-, ethyl ester	ether	295(3.98)	24-3779-73
2(3H)-Naphthalenone, 4,4a,5,6,7,8-hexahydro-3-(hydroxymethylene)-4a-methyl-	EtOH	250(4.02),306(3.75)	44-0967-73
	EtOH-NaOH	240(4.07),360(3.90)	44-0967-73
1-Pentanone, 1-(2-methoxyphenyl)-	heptane	243(3.89)	35-5604-73
1-Pentanone, 1-(3-methoxyphenyl)-	heptane	246(3.89)	35-5604-73
1-Pentanone, 1-(4-methoxyphenyl)-	heptane	264(4.23)	35-5604-73
Spiro[cycloheptane-1,1'-cyclohex-2'-ene]-2,4'-dione	EtOH	227(3.88)	39-0393-73C
Tricyclo[4.3.3.0]dodecane-2,7-dione	EtOH	292(1.62)	44-4281-73
Tricyclo[4.4.2.0]dodecane-2,7-dione	EtOH	296(1.77)	44-4281-73
$C_{12}H_{16}O_2S$			
2H-Pyran, tetrahydro-2-[(4-methoxyphenyl)thio]-	40% dioxan	241(4.00)	35-8407-73
$C_{12}H_{16}O_2S_2$			
3(2H)-Thiophenone, 2-(dihydro-4,4-dimethyl-3-oxo-2(3H)-thienylidene)dihydro-4,4-dimethyl-, cis	benzene	397(4.13)	46-0831-73
trans	benzene	452(4.10)	46-0831-73
$C_{12}H_{16}O_3$			
Benzeneacetic acid, 2-methoxy-α,α-dimethyl-, methyl ester	90% EtOH	215(3.89),272(3.26), 278(3.26)	12-1079-73
Butanoic acid, 2-methoxy-5-methylphenyl ester	90% EtOH	228(3.58),276s(3.34), 278(3.34),282(3.29)	12-1069-73
1-Butanone, 1-(2-hydroxy-3-methoxy-6-methylphenyl)-	90% EtOH	232(3.72),255(3.46), 289(3.26),301s(3.23)	12-1069-73
1-Butanone, 1-(4-hydroxy-5-methoxy-2-methylphenyl)-	90% EtOH	234(3.68),275(3.55), 307(3.40)	12-1069-73
2,5-Cyclohexadiene-1,4-dione, 2-methoxy-3-pentyl-	EtOH	254(4.0),275(2.9)	1-3211-73

Compound	Solvent	λ_{max}(log ε)	Ref.
2,5-Cyclohexadiene-1,4-dione, 2-methoxy-5-pentyl-	EtOH	266(4.2),360(2.9)	1-3211-73
2,5-Cyclohexadiene-1,4-dione, 2-methoxy-6-pentyl-	EtOH	269(4.1),366(2.8)	1-3211-73
2-Pentalenecarboxylic acid, 1,2,3,4,5,6-hexahydro-2-methyl-4-oxo-, ethyl ester	EtOH	240(4.04)	39-2454-73C
2-Pentanone, 5-(3-methoxyphenoxy)-	EtOH	222(3.76),274(3.29), 280(3.26)	78-0715-73
Spiro[1,3-dioxolane-2,1'-[1H]inden-5'(6'H)-one, 2',3',7',7'a-tetrahydro-7'a-methyl-	EtOH	242(3.15)	78-4225-73
$C_{12}H_{16}O_4$			
Acetic acid, 2,2'-(1,2-cyclohexanediylidene)bis-, dimethyl ester	EtOH	209(4.34)	64-0675-73C
Acetic acid, hydroxy(4,7,7-trimethyl-3-oxobicyclo[2.2.1]hept-2-ylidene)-, (1S)-	isooctane	285(4.19)	65-0923-73
	benzene	288(4.19)	65-0923-73
	MeOH	292(4.14)	65-0923-73
	MeOH-HCl	293(4.16)	65-0923-73
	MeOH-NaOH	308(4.28)	65-0923-73
	$CHCl_3$	287(4.18)	65-0923-73
	DMF	296(4.15)	65-0923-73
3,5-Cyclohexadiene-1,2-diol, 3-ethyl-, diacetate, cis-(+)-	MeOH	263(3.78)	69-1520-73
$C_{12}H_{16}O_5$			
Cyclopenta[c]pyran-4-carboxylic acid, 1,4a,5,6,7,7a-hexahydro-1-methoxy-7-methyl-6-oxo-, methyl ester, (1α,4aα,7α,7aα)-	EtOH	234(4.05)	35-0540-73
(1α,4aα,7β,7aα)-	EtOH	238(4.11)	35-0540-73
$C_{12}H_{16}O_6$			
Benzoic acid, 3-(hydroxymethyl)-2,4,6-trimethoxy-, methyl ester	EtOH	213(4.8),280(3.86)	12-2459-73
	EtOH-KOH	219(4.82),280(3.87)	12-2459-73
1,4-Cyclohexadiene-1,4-dicarboxylic acid, 2,5-dihydroxy-, diethyl ester	EtOH	241(4.30)	33-2760-73
1-Cyclohexene-1,2,3-tricarboxylic acid, trimethyl ester	EtOH	216(3.87)	78-0683-73
$C_{12}H_{17}$			
Cycloheptatrienylium, 1,2,3,5,6-pentamethyl-, trifluoroacetate	H_2SO_4	242(4.54),300(3.34), 310(3.31)	33-2796-73
chloroplatinate	H_2SO_4	243(4.89),300(3.84), 310s(3.70)	33-2796-73
	MeCN	244(4.83),269(4.12), 301s(3.93),312(3.83)	33-2796-73
Propylium, 1,2-dimethyl-1-(4-methylphenyl)-	FSO_3H at -75°	343(4.45)	59-0803-73
$C_{12}H_{17}BrO$			
2(3H)-Naphthalenone, 4a-(2-bromoethyl)-4,4a,5,6,7,8-hexahydro-	EtOH	241(4.15)	44-2125-73
$C_{12}H_{17}ClN_2O$			
Methanimidamide, N-(4-chlorophenyl)-N-ethyl-N'-(2-methoxyethyl)-	EtOH	267(4.45)	35-8414-73

Compound	Solvent	$\lambda_{max}(\log \epsilon)$	Ref.
$C_{12}H_{17}ClN_2O_4$			
3H-Azepinium, 4-chloro-2-(diethyl-amino)-, oxalate	EtOH	280(3.82)	39-1079-73C
	EtOH-NaOH	300(3.93)	39-1079-73C
3H-Azepinium, 6-chloro-2-(diethyl-amino)-, oxalate	EtOH	270(3.86)	39-1079-73C
	EtOH-NaOH	269(3.84),309(3.89)	39-1079-73C
$C_{12}H_{17}F_2NO_8$			
D-glycero-D-galacto-Non-2-enonic acid, 2,6-anhydro-3,5-dideoxy-5-[(difluoro-acetyl)amino]-, methyl ester	n.s.g.	244(3.83)	49-0402-73
$C_{12}H_{17}N$			
1-Pentalenamine, 1,2-dihydro-N,N,1,3-tetramethyl-	hexane	264(4.14),270(4.12), 377(2.84)	89-0335-73
Pyridine, 4-butyl-2-ethenyl-5-methyl-	EtOH	250(3.45),265(3.46)	103-0323-73
$C_{12}H_{17}NO$			
Cyclobutanecarbonitrile, 1-(1,1-dimeth-ylethyl)-3-ethylidene-2-methyl-4-oxo-, isomer 10	CCl_4	248(4.01),353(2.20)	88-4391-73
isomer 11	CCl_4	245(4.09),347(2.06)	88-4391-73
isomer 12	CCl_4	250(3.89),353(2.02)	88-4391-73
isomer 13	CCl_4	247(3.99)	88-4391-73
$C_{12}H_{17}NO_2$			
Benzoic acid, 3-(dimethylamino)propyl ester	H_2O	231(4.09),274(2.99)	104-2111-73
1-Butanone, 4-ethoxy-1-(3-methyl-2-pyri-dinyl)-	EtOH	220(3.82),272(3.48)	2-0621-73
Ethanone, 1-[5-(1,1-dimethylethyl)-2-hydroxyphenyl]-, oxime	MeOH	256(3.903)	30-0394-73
	CCl_4	316(3.569)	30-0394-73
Isoquinoline, 1,2,3,4-tetrahydro-6,7-dimethoxy-1-methyl- (salsolidine)	EtOH	212(4.08),232(3.99), 285(3.84)	102-0193-73
2-Propanamine, N-[(4-methoxyphenyl)-methylene]-2-methyl-, N-oxide	benzene	308(4.29)	35-4687-73
	EtOH	305(4.31)	35-4687-73
Pyridine, 1,4-diacetyl-1,4-dihydro-4-propyl-	MeOH	254(4.22)	78-0391-73
Pyridine, 1,4-dihydro-4-methyl-1,4-bis-(1-oxopropyl)-	MeOH	254(4.20)	78-0391-73
$C_{12}H_{17}NO_3$			
2(4H)-Benzofuranone, 5,6,7,7a-tetra-hydro-7a-morpholino-	EtOH	215(4.15)	22-0625-73
$C_{12}H_{17}NO_4$			
4-Isoquinolinol, 1,2,3,4-tetrahydro-5,6,7-trimethoxy-	EtOH	290(2.95)	44-0060-73
Phenylalanine, 3,4-dihydroxy-, 1-methyl-ethyl ester	pH 1	280(3.45)	36-0510-73
Phenylalanine, 3,4-dihydroxy-, propyl ester	pH 1	280(3.46)	36-0510-73
$C_{12}H_{17}NO_4S$			
1H,3H-Oxazolo[4,3-c][1,4]thiazine-6-car-boxylic acid, 8,8a-dihydro-3,3,8,8-tetramethyl-1-oxo-, methyl ester, (S)-	n.s.g.	268(3.53),321(3.99)	39-0022-73C
$C_{12}H_{17}NO_4Si$			
Silicon, [[2,2',2"-nitrilotris(ethanol-ato][(3-)-N,O,O',O"]phenoxy-	H_2O	212(3.79),270(3.11)	30-0941-73

Compound	Solvent	λ_{max}(log ϵ)	Ref.
$C_{12}H_{17}NO_7$			
Ethenetricarboxylic acid, 4-morpholino-, trimethyl ester	EtOH	230(3.94),320(4.06)	95-1008-73
$C_{12}H_{17}NS_2$			
Piperidinium dithiobenzoate	EtOH	286(3.97),362(3.91), 502(2.70)	143-0359-73
$C_{12}H_{17}N_3$			
1H-Pyrazole, 3-[3,4-dihydro-2,2-dimethyl-4-(1-methylethylidene)-2H-pyrrol-5-yl]-	MeOH	252(4.00)	18-0540-73
$C_{12}H_{17}N_3O_4$			
3-Isoxazoleacetic acid, α-(cyclohexylhydrazono)-4,5-dihydro-5-oxo-, methyl ester	EtOH	238(3.96)	70-2006-73
2,6-Pyridinedicarboxamide, 1,4-dihydro-3-(2-hydroxyethyl)-N,N',1-trimethyl-	EtOH	277(4.11)	95-1183-73
$C_{12}H_{17}N_3O_6$			
1H-Imidazole-4-carboxylic acid, 5-amino-1-[2,3-O-(1-methylethylidene)-β-D-ribofuranosyl]-	pH 1	244(3.92),266(4.03)	39-1720-73C
	MeOH	248(4.05)	39-1720-73C
$C_{12}H_{17}N_3O_6S$			
4H-Pyrrolo[2,3-d]pyrimidin-4-one, 2-(β-D-glucopyranosylthio)-3,5,6,7-tetrahydro-	EtOH	235(4.18),273(3.75)	104-1995-73
$C_{12}H_{17}N_3O_7$			
Carbamic acid, (1,2-dihydro-1-oxo-1-β-D-ribofuranosyl-4-pyrimidinyl)-, ethyl ester	pH 1	211(4.15),227s(3.98), 302(4.15)	35-2677-73
	H_2O	212(4.26),240(4.16), 291(3.94)	35-2677-73
$C_{12}H_{17}N_4O_8P$			
1H-Purine-2,6-dione, 7-[2-acetoxy-3-(phosphonooxy)propyl]-3,4-dihydro-1,3-dimethyl-	H_2O	255(3.89),264(3.93), 274(3.90)	18-1563-73
$C_{12}H_{17}N_5$			
1H-Pyrazolo[4,3-d]pyrimidin-7-amine, N-cyclohexyl-3-methyl-	EtOH-pH 1	262(3.79),311(4.11)	102-0025-73
	EtOH-pH 7	238(3.76),296(4.09), 307(3.98),319s(--)	102-0025-73
	EtOH-pH 12	245(4.16),264s(--), 308(3.90)	102-0025-73
$C_{12}H_{17}N_5O$			
4(1H)-Pteridinone, 2-amino-6-hexyl-	pH 13	253(4.31),363(3.77)	44-2073-73
4(1H)-Pteridinone, 2-amino-7-hexyl-	pH 13	251(4.30),355(3.93)	44-2073-73
$C_{12}H_{17}N_5O_3$			
1,2-Cyclopentanediol, 3-(hydroxymethyl)-5-[6-(methylamino)-9H-purin-9-yl]-, (1α,2α,3β,5β)-(±)-	pH 1	263(4.24)	36-1252-73
	pH 7 and 13	267(4.23)	36-1252-73
$C_{12}H_{17}N_5O_4$			
9H-Purin-6-amine, 9-(5,6-dideoxy-β-D-riboheptofuranosyl)-	pH 1	257(4.16)	136-0225-73B
	pH 7	259(4.17)	136-0225-73B
	pH 13	259(4.17)	136-0225-73B

Compound	Solvent	$\lambda_{max}(\log \epsilon)$	Ref.
$C_{12}H_{17}N_5O_5$			
Adenosine, N-ethoxy-	pH 1	267(4.22)	94-1676-73
	pH 7	268(4.16)	94-1676-73
	pH 13	283(4.05)	94-1676-73
	EtOH	267(4.15)	94-1676-73
α-D-Glucopyranoside, methyl 6-(6-amino-9H-purin-9-yl)-5-deoxy-	pH 2	260(4.14)	18-3165-73
	H_2O	260(4.14)	18-3165-73
	pH 12	260(4.15)	18-3165-73
$C_{12}H_{17}N_6O_7P$			
Guanosine, 8-(dimethylamino)-, cyclic 3',5'-(hydrogen phosphate)	pH 1	262(4.26),290s(4.08)	69-5310-73
	pH 11	265(4.21)	69-5310-73
$C_{12}H_{17}N_7$			
Propanedinitrile, (dicyanomethylhydrazone)-, triethylamine salt	H_2O	280(4.24)	22-3442-73
$C_{12}H_{17}OP$			
Phosphine oxide, diethyl(2-phenylethenyl)-	dioxan	212(4.30),216s(4.08), 260(4.31),286(3.56), 294(3.28)	65-2164-73
$C_{12}H_{17}O_3P$			
Phosphonic acid, (2-phenylethenyl)-, diethyl ester	nonane	217s(4.13),259(4.27), 284(3.40),294(3.15)	65-2164-73
$C_{12}H_{17}O_4P$			
Phosphonic acid, (2-phenoxyethenyl)-, diethyl ester	nonane	195(4.44),229(4.24), 262s(3.00),266(3.03), 272(2.95)	65-2164-73
	EtOH	193(4.42),228(4.18), 255(3.00)	65-2164-73
	dioxan	229(4.26),265(3.06), 272s(2.98)	65-2164-73
	MeCN	227(4.25),264(3.04)	65-2164-73
$C_{12}H_{17}P$			
Phosphine, diethyl(2-phenylethenyl)-	C_6H_{12}	255(4.16),284(3.89), 294(3.86)	65-2164-73
$C_{12}H_{17}PS$			
Phosphine sulfide, diethyl(2-phenylethenyl)-	nonane	216s(4.27),258(4.33), 285s(3.74),295(3.48)	65-2164-73
$C_{12}H_{18}$			
Bicyclo[5.1.0]oct-2-ene, 4,4,7-trimethyl-6-methylene-, cis	EtOH	272(2.15)	44-3250-73
Bicyclo[5.3.1]undeca-1(10),8-diene, 8-methyl-	C_6H_{12}	275(3.76)	35-5088-73
1,3,5-Cyclodecatriene, 1,6-dimethyl-, cis-cis-trans	heptane	212(4.02),262(3.81)	35-3932-73
trans-cis-cis	heptane	212(3.94),278(3.15)	35-3932-73
trans-cis-trans	heptane	214(3.91),262(3.15)	35-3932-73
1-Hepten-4-yne, 2,6-dimethyl-3-(1-methylethylidene)-	C_6H_{12}	250(3.97)	88-2031-73
Naphthalene, 1,2,3,4,4a,8a-hexahydro-4a,8a-dimethyl-, cis	heptane	262(3.51)	35-3932-73
trans	n.s.g.	264(3.43)	35-3932-73
3,5-Octadiyne, 2,2,7,7-tetramethyl-	heptane	215(2.18),226(2.39), 238(2.45),252(2.27)	44-3893-73

Compound	Solvent	λ_{max}(log ϵ)	Ref.
Tricyclo[5.3.0.0^{2,10}]dec-8-ene, 2,7-dimethyl-	heptane	212(3.57)	35-3932-73
$C_{12}H_{18}BN$			
Boranamine, 1-(2-butenyl)-N,N-dimethyl-1-phenyl-	C_6H_{12}	262(2.53),269(2.58), 276(2.47)	35-3425-73
Boranamine, N,N-dimethyl-1-(1-methyl-2-propenyl)-1-phenyl-	C_6H_{12}	262(2.57),269(2.58), 276(2.42)	35-3425-73
$C_{12}H_{18}ClNO_8$			
D-glycero-D-galacto-Non-2-enonic acid, 2,6-anhydro-5-[(chloroacetyl)amino]-3,5-dideoxy-, methyl ester	n.s.g.	244(3.82)	49-0402-73
$C_{12}H_{18}Cl_4N_3$			
Methanaminium, N-[[3,3-dichloro-4-(dichloromethylene)-2-(dimethylamino)-1-cyclobuten-1-yl](dimethylamino)-methylene]-N-methyl-, chloride	n.s.g.	273(4.40),372(3.79)	44-1470-73
$C_{12}H_{18}FNO_8$			
D-glycero-D-galacto-Non-2-enonic acid, 2,6-anhydro-3,5-dideoxy-5-[(fluoro-acetyl)amino]-, methyl ester	n.s.g.	244(3.83)	49-0402-73
$C_{12}H_{18}INO_8$			
D-glycero-D-galacto-Non-2-enonic acid, 2,6-anhydro-5-[(iodoacetyl)amino]-3,5-dideoxy-, methyl ester	n.s.g.	245(3.96)	49-0402-73
$C_{12}H_{18}IOP$			
Phosphonium, benzoyldiethylmethyl-, iodide	CH_2Cl_2	379(2.57)	18-1803-73
	MeCN	207(4.17),242(4.22), 267(4.08),365(2.04)	18-1803-73
$C_{12}H_{18}N_2$			
1H-Indole-3-ethanamine, 2,3-dihydro-N,N-dimethyl-	MeOH	242(3.77),293(3.36)	44-1504-73
$C_{12}H_{18}N_2O$			
6-Phthalazinol, 1,1-diethyl-1,2,3,4-tetrahydro-, monohydrochloride	EtOH	280(3.27)	39-0471-73C
$C_{12}H_{18}N_2O_2$			
1H-Azepine-3-carboxamide, N,N-diethyl-6,7-dihydro-1-methyl-7-oxo-	EtOH	274(3.73)	39-1079-73C
1H-Azepine-4-carboxamide, N,N-diethyl-2,3-dihydro-1-methyl-2-oxo-	EtOH	284(3.72)	39-1079-73C
Benzoic acid, 4-amino-, 3-(dimethyl-amino)propyl ester	H_2O	285(4.13)	104-2111-73
2,5-Cyclohexadiene-1,4-dione, 2,5-bis-[2-(methylamino)ethyl]-, dihydrochloride	pH 1	253(4.23)	39-0832-73C
Isoxazole, 3-(1,1-dimethylethyl)-4,5-dihydro-5-[(3-methyl-5-isoxazolyl)-methyl]-	n.s.g.	214.5(4.04)	32-0037-73
$C_{12}H_{18}N_2O_6$			
Uridine, 5-(1-methylethyl)-	pH 1	267(4.01)	56-1205-73
	pH 13	265(3.90)	56-1205-73

Compound	Solvent	λmax(log ε)	Ref.
Uridine, 2',3',5'-tri-O-methyl-	pH 2	262(4.00)	69-0194-73
	pH 12	262(3.87)	69-0194-73
$C_{12}H_{18}N_2O_7$			
2,4(1H,3H)-Pyrimidinedione, 5-ethyl-1-β-D-galactopyranosyl-	acid	265.5(3.99)	94-1382-73
	pH 7	265(3.99)	94-1382-73
	base	265.5(3.86)	94-1382-73
$C_{12}H_{18}N_2O_8S_2$			
1,5-Naphthyridinediium, 1,5-dimethyl-, dimethosulfate	pH 0.8	270(3.79),311(3.91), 323(4.11)	39-2885-73C
	pH 8.0	270(4.06),377(3.83)	39-2885-73
$C_{12}H_{18}N_4O_2$			
2,5-Pyrazinedicarboxamide, N,N,N',N'-3,6-hexamethyl-	EtOH	286(3.93)	107-0225-73
$C_{12}H_{18}N_4O_3$			
Propanamide, N,N'-(1,6-dihydro-6-oxo-4,5-pyrimidinediyl)bis[2-methyl-	pH 1	280(3.79)	39-1855-73C
	pH 11	275(3.68)	39-1855-73C
	MeOH	285(3.76)	39-1855-73C
$C_{12}H_{18}N_4O_5$			
1H-Imidazole-4-carboxamide, 5-amino-1-[2,3-O-(1-methylethylidene)-α-D-ribofuranosyl]-	MeOH	267(4.07)	39-1720-73
anomer	MeOH	267(4.10)	39-1720-73C
$C_{12}H_{18}N_5O_3$			
1H-Purinium, 2-amino-7-[2-(1,1-dimethylethoxy)-2-oxoethyl]-6,9-dihydro-9-methyl-6-oxo-, bromide	pH 4	253(4.09),283(3.89)	24-1389-73
	pH 10	220(4.31),248(3.76), 284(3.91)	24-1389-73
$C_{12}H_{18}N_6O$			
2-Butenenitrile, 3-[[4,6-bis(dimethylamino)-1,3,5-triazin-2-yl]oxy]-2-methyl-	EtOH	227(4.69)	22-2039-73
geometric isomer	EtOH	228(4.69)	22-2039-73
$C_{12}H_{18}N_6O_2$			
Acetamide, N-[3-[6-(dimethylamino)-9H-purin-9-yl]-2-hydroxypropyl]-	pH 1	269(4.23)	87-0037-73
	pH 7	276(4.24)	87-0037-73
	pH 13	278(4.24)	87-0037-73
$C_{12}H_{18}N_6O_3$			
Pentanamide, 2-amino-5-[(aminoiminomethyl)amino]-N-(4-nitrophenyl)-, (S)-	0.05M NaCl	304(4.06)	18-0572-73
$C_{12}H_{18}N_6O_4$			
Adenosine, 2-(dimethylamino)-	pH 1	218(4.33),261(4.21), 305(3.94)	69-4790-73
	pH 7	228(4.33),262(4.11), 295(3.92)	69-4790-73
	pH 13	227(4.42),262(4.10), 295(3.92)	69-4790-73
$C_{12}H_{18}N_6O_5$			
α-D-Glucopyranoside, methyl 6-deoxy-6-(2,6-diamino-9H-purin-9-yl)-	pH 2	253(4.00),291(4.00)	18-3165-73
	H_2O	255(3.92),280(4.01)	18-3165-73
	pH 12	256(3.94),281(4.02)	18-3165-73

Compound	Solvent	$\lambda_{max}(\log \epsilon)$	Ref.
$C_{12}H_{18}O$			
2,5-Cyclohexadien-1-one, 3,5-diethyl-4,4-dimethyl-	H_2O	247(4.26)	39-0529-73C
4a,8a-Ethanonaphthalen-1(2H)-one, hexahydro-	EtOH	292(1.15)	44-1218-73
2(1H)-Naphthalenone, 4a,5,6,7,8,8a-hexahydro-4a,8a-dimethyl-, cis	MeOH	234(3.85)	35-3932-73
trans	hexane	226(3.96)	35-3932-73
3a,7a-Propano-1H-inden-1-one, hexahydro-	EtOH	292(1.48)	44-1218-73
1-Propanone, 1-(6,6-dimethylbicyclo-[3.1.0]hept-2-en-2-yl)-, (-)-	C_6H_{12}	242(3.94),316(1.67)	22-1351-73
2-Propenal, 3-(3,3-dimethylbicyclo-[2.2.1]hept-2-yl)-	EtOH	233.0(4.20)	22-3071-73
Spiro[2.5]octan-4-one, 1-(2-methyl-1-propenyl)-	MeOH	237(3.74)	88-4425-73
$C_{12}H_{18}OP$			
Phosphonium, benzoyldiethylmethyl-,	CH_2Cl_2	379(2.57)	18-1803-73
iodide	MeCN	207(4.17),242(4.22), 267(4.08),365(2.04)	18-1803-73
$C_{12}H_{18}O_2$			
2(1H)-Azulenone, 4,5,6,7,8,8a-hexahydro-8-methoxy-8-methyl-	EtOH	238(4.10)	44-0967-73
4H-1-Benzopyran-4-one, 2,3,5,6,7,8-hexahydro-2-(1-methylethyl)-	EtOH	276(4.04)	22-1409-73
2-Cyclopenten-1-one, 5-acetyl-2,3,4,4,5-pentamethyl-	C_6H_{12}	233(4.17)	44-3418-73
2-Heptanone, 6-(2-furanyl)-6-methyl-	EtOH	217(3.92),276(1.48)	33-2151-73
7-Oxabicyclo[4.1.0]hept-3-en-2-one, 1,3,4,5,5,6-hexamethyl-	C_6H_{12}	246(3.92),323(1.94)	44-3418-73
2-Propenal, 3-(2,2,6-trimethyl-7-oxa-bicyclo[4.1.0]hept-1-yl)-, cis	EtOH	235(3.92)	33-2151-73
trans	EtOH	233(4.10),322(1.85)	33-2151-73
$C_{12}H_{18}O_2S$			
Benzo[b]thiophene, 4,4-diethoxy-4,5,6,7-tetrahydro-	EtOH	236(3.61)	44-0146-73
$C_{12}H_{18}O_3$			
Butanoic acid, 3-(4-methyl-3-oxocyclo-hexen-1-yl)-, methyl ester	EtOH	233(4.12)	118-0213-73
1-Cyclodecene-1-carboxylic acid, 9-oxo-, cis	MeOH	215(3.99)	39-1366-73C
trans	MeOH	218(4.02)	39-1366-73C
4,8-Dioxatricyclo[5.1.0.0^{3,5}]octan-2-one, 1,3,5,6,6,7-hexamethyl-, (1α,3α,5α,7α)-	C_6H_{12}	217(3.29),240(2.78)	44-3418-73
2-Hepten-4-yn-1-ol, 7-[(tetrahydro-2H-pyran-2-yl)oxy]-	EtOH	227(4.16),236s(4.09)	39-0720-73C
p-Menth-1-en-3-one, 6-acetoxy-, trans, (±)-	EtOH	235(3.98)	12-0845-73
p-Menth-1-en-3-one, 7-acetoxy-, (±)-	EtOH	236(4.11)	12-0845-73
2,6-Nonadienoic acid, 7-formyl-3-meth-yl-, methyl ester	EtOH	225(4.33)	33-2961-73
$C_{12}H_{18}O_4$			
Cyclohexaneacetic acid, α-oxo-2-(2-oxo-propyl)-, methyl ester	MeOH	232(3.94)	18-0880-73

Compound	Solvent	λ_{max}(log ε)	Ref.
$C_{12}H_{18}O_4S_2$			
Propanedioic acid, [(methylthio)thioxomethyl]-2-propenyl-, diethyl ester	EtOH	317(3.97)	78-2077-73
$C_{12}H_{18}O_5$			
Cyclopenta[c]pyran-4-carboxylic acid, 1,4a,5,6,7,7a-hexahydro-6-hydroxy-1-methoxy-7-methyl-, methyl ester, (1α,4aα,6α,7α,7aα)-	EtOH	237(4.08)	35-0540-73
(1α,4aα,6β,7β,7aα)-	EtOH	240(4.06)	35-0532-73
Loganin aglycone O-methyl ether	EtOH	238(4.08)	35-0532-73
isomer	EtOH	238(3.95)	35-0532-73
2H-Pyran-3-acetic acid, 4-(ethoxycarbonyl)-5,6-dihydro-, ethyl ester	EtOH	223(3.87)	44-1767-73
$C_{12}H_{18}S$			
Benzene, 1,3,5-trimethyl-2-[(1-methylethyl)thio]-	C_6H_{12}	207(4.67),225s(4.18), 268(3.46)	39-1125-73B
	EtOH	206(4.61),222(4.11), 266(3.40)	39-1125-73B
	5% EtOH	203(4.62),220(4.09), 262(3.43)	39-1125-73B
$C_{12}H_{19}ClN_2$			
1,2-Benzenediamine, 3-chloro-N^1,N^1-diethyl-N^2,N^2-dimethyl-, hydrochloride	EtOH	253(2.83)	39-1079-73C
$C_{12}H_{19}ClO$			
Bicyclo[2.2.1]heptan-2-one, 7-(3-chloropropyl)-1,7-dimethyl-	MeOH	285(1.64)	39-2113-73C
Cyclohexanone, 5-(4-chloro-1-methyl-1-butenyl)-2-methyl-	MeOH	284(1.51)	39-2113-73C
2-Cyclohexen-1-one, 3-(4-chloro-1-methylbutyl)-6-methyl-	MeOH	234(4.18),339(1.76)	39-2113-73C
$C_{12}H_{19}N$			
4,5-Heptadien-2-yn-1-amine, N,N-diethyl-6-methyl-	n.s.g.	217(3.92),240(4.00), 270(3.76)	70-1029-73
$C_{12}H_{19}NO_2$			
7-Azabicyclo[4.2.2]dec-9-ene-7-carboxylic acid, ethyl ester	EtOH	227(3.95)	44-3094-73
Benzeneethanamine, 3,4-dimethoxy-N,N-dimethyl-	EtOH	205(4.56),231(4.15), 285(3.95)	102-0193-73
5H-3,1-Benzoxazin-5-one, 1,2,4,6,7,8-hexahydro-2,4,7,7-tetramethyl-	EtOH	295(4.40)	103-0942-73
$C_{12}H_{19}NO_3S$			
1H,3H-Oxazolo[4,3-c][1,4]thiazine-6-carboxylic acid, 8,8a-dihydro-3,3,8,8-tetramethyl-, methyl ester, (S)-	n.s.g.	324(4.06)	39-1985-73C
$C_{12}H_{19}NO_4$			
Propanedioic acid, [3-(dimethylamino)-2-propenylidene]-, diethyl ester	EtOH	235(3.81),374(4.78)	70-1959-73
$C_{12}H_{19}NO_4S$			
1H,3H-Oxazolo[4,3-c][1,4]thiazine-6-carboxylic acid, 8,8a-dihydro-1-hydroxy-3,3,8,8-tetramethyl-, methyl ester	n.s.g.	221(4.01),255(3.59), 322(4.32)	39-0022-73C

Compound	Solvent	$\lambda_{max}(\log \epsilon)$	Ref.
$C_{12}H_{19}NO_5S$			
1H,3H-Oxazolo[4,3-c][1,4]thiazine-6-carboxylic acid, 8,8a-dihydro-1-hydroxy-3,3,8,8-tetramethyl-, methyl ester, 7-oxide	n.s.g.	286(4.03)	39-0022-73C
$C_{12}H_{19}NS_2$			
Dithiobenzoic acid, 4-methyl-, diethylamine salt	EtOH	298(4.10),361(3.93), 490(2.36)	143-0359-73
$C_{12}H_{19}N_3O_2S$			
4,6(1H,5H)-Pyrimidinedione, 1,3-diethyl-5-[1-(ethylamino)ethylidene]dihydro-2-thioxo-	MeOH	229(4.13),267(3.68), 326s(4.57),330(4.61)	39-0823-73C
$C_{12}H_{19}N_3O_2S_2$			
Carbamic acid, [[(5-butyl-2-thiazolyl)imino](methylthio)methyl]-, ethyl ester	dioxan	242(3.77),320(4.34)	94-0074-73
Carbamic acid, [[(3-methyl-5-propyl-2(3H)-thiazolylidene)amino](methylthio)methylene]-, ethyl ester	dioxan	245(3.60),279(3.87), 338(4.39)	94-0074-73
$C_{12}H_{19}N_3O_4S_2$			
Carbamic acid, (1,2,4-dithiazolidine-3,5-diylidene)bis-, dibutyl ester	EtOH	224(4.07),269(4.22), 301(4.21),324s(3.95)	94-2396-73
Carbamic acid, [5-[[(2-methylpropoxy)carbonyl]amino]-3H-1,2,4-dithiazol-3-ylidene]-, 2-methylpropyl ester	EtOH	224(4.07),269(4.23), 301(4.16),320s(4.02)	94-2396-73
$C_{12}H_{19}N_3O_5$			
Cytidine, 2',3',5'-tri-O-methyl-	pH 2	280(4.12)	69-0194-73
	pH 12	271(3.95)	69-0194-73
$C_{12}H_{19}N_3O_7S$			
Glutathione, S-acetyl-	pH 7.40	230(3.65)	69-3938-73
$C_{12}H_{19}N_3O_8S$			
Glutathione, S-glycolyl-	pH 7.40	233(3.66)	69-3938-73
$C_{12}H_{19}N_5$			
1H-Pyrazolo[4,3-d]pyrimidin-7-amine, N-hexyl-3-methyl-	EtOH-pH 1	262(3.74),310(4.07)	102-0025-73
	EtOH-pH 7	237(3.71),295(4.05), 307(3.95),318s(--)	102-0025-73
	EtOH-pH 12	244(4.14),263s(--), 308(3.86)	102-0025-73
$C_{12}H_{19}N_5O_2$			
1H-Purine-2,6-dione, 7-(3-aminopropyl)-8-ethyl-3,7-dihydro-1,3-dimethyl-, hydrochloride	n.s.g.	210(4.32),277(3.99)	73-1571-73
$C_{12}H_{19}N_5O_7$			
Carbamic acid, [2-amino-4-hydroxy-6-(β-D-ribofuranosylamino)-5-pyrimidinyl]-, ethyl ester	pH 1	215(4.30),272(4.23)	35-2677-73
	H_2O	216(4.49),273(4.20)	35-2677-73
	pH 13	266(4.07)	35-2677-73
$C_{12}H_{19}N_6O_2$			
1H-Purinium, 2-amino-7-[2-(diethylamino)-2-oxoethyl]-6,9-dihydro-9-methyl-6-oxo-	pH 4	254(4.07),283(3.86)	24-1389-73
	pH 10	249s(3.73),285(3.90)	24-1389-73

Compound	Solvent	λ_{max}(log ϵ)	Ref.
$C_{12}H_{20}$			
Cyclohexane, (1,2-dimethyl-2-butenylidene)-	EtOH	204(3.60)	22-2506-73
$C_{12}H_{20}GeN_2$			
Diazene, phenyl(triethylgermyl)-	n.s.g.	255(4.74),573(2.29)	22-0549-73
$C_{12}H_{20}LiNSi$			
Lithium, [2-[(dimethylamino)methyl]-3-(trimethylsilyl)phenyl]-	DMSO	265(3.00),295(2.00), 325(2.85)	101-0001-73H
$C_{12}H_{20}N_2$			
3H-Azepin-2-amine, N,N-diethyl-4,6-dimethyl-	EtOH	285(3.93)	39-1079-73C
Dicyclohexylidenazine	MeOH	210(4.41),231(3.82)	18-3467-73
2-Hexenenitrile, 4-ethyl-3-(1-pyrrolidinyl)-	EtOH	274(4.37)	39-1108-73C
2-Hexenenitrile, 4-methyl-3-(1-piperidinyl)-	EtOH	277(4.27)	39-1108-73C
3-Hexenenitrile, 4-ethyl-3-(1-pyrrolidinyl)-	EtOH	206(3.84),245(3.54)	39-1108-73C
1-Piperidinepropanenitrile, β-(1-methylpropylidene)-	EtOH	205(3.50),232(3.36)	39-1108-73C
1H-Pyrazole, 1-(1-cyclohexen-1-yl)-4,5-dihydro-3,5,5-trimethyl-	heptane	237(3.46),270(3.57)	135-1154-73
	MeOH	225(3.67),275(3.12)	135-1154-73
	isoPrOH	235(3.60),270(3.72)	135-1154-73
	ether	220(3.81),270(3.94)	135-1154-73
	$C_2H_4Cl_2$	208(4.36),235(4.47)	135-1154-73
Pyrazole, 3,5-dimethyl-4-(1,2,2-trimethyl-3-butenyl)-	EtOH	228(3.84)	78-4159-73
Pyrazole, 4-ethyl-5-methyl-3-(2,2-dimethyl-3-butenyl)-	EtOH	225(3.76)	78-4159-73
$C_{12}H_{20}N_2O_6Si$			
Uridine, 5-(trimethylsilyl)-	H_2O	265(4.00)	22-2715-73
	0.1M NH_3	263(--)	22-2715-73
$C_{12}H_{20}N_2O_7$			
Pyrazine, 2-(D-arabino-tetrahydroxybutyl)-5-(D-erythro-trihydroxybutyl)-	H_2O	275.7(3.92)	132-0153-73
Pyrazine, 2-(L-xylo-tetrahydroxybutyl)-6-(L-threo-2,3,4-trihydroxybutyl)-	H_2O	267(4.07)	136-0377-73A
$C_{12}H_{20}N_2O_8$			
D-glycero-D-galacto-Non-2-enonic acid, 5-[(3-amino-1-oxopropyl)amino]-2,6-anhydro-3,5-dideoxy-	n.s.g.	235(3.79)	49-0402-73
Pyrazine, 2,5-bis(D-arabino-tetrahydroxybutyl)-	H_2O	274.3(3.97)	132-0153-73
Pyrazine, 2,5-bis(L-xylo-tetrahydroxybutyl)-	H_2O	273.8(3.90)	136-0377-73A
$C_{12}H_{20}N_4O$			
Pyrazolidine, 1-acetyl-3,3,5-trimethyl-2-(5-methyl-1H-pyrazol-3-yl)-	EtOH	220(4.00)	103-0503-73
$C_{12}H_{20}N_4O_4S$			
Carbamic acid, 1,2,4-thiadiazole-3,5-diylbis-, bis(2-methylpropyl) ester	EtOH	258(3.62)	94-2396-73
Carbamic acid, 1,2,4-thiadiazole-3,5-diylbis-, dibutyl ester	EtOH	258(3.60)	94-2396-73

Compound	Solvent	$\lambda_{max}(\log \epsilon)$	Ref.
1,2,4-Thiadiazole-2(3H)-carboxylic acid, 3-imino-5-[(butoxycarbonyl)amino]-, butyl ester	EtOH	262(4.32),271(4.32)	94-2396-73
1,2,4-Thiadiazole-2(3H)-carboxylic acid, 3-imino-5-[[(2-methylpropoxy)carbonyl]amino]-, 2-methylpropyl ester	EtOH	261(4.34),271(4.34)	94-2396-73
$C_{12}H_{20}O$			
3-Cyclododecen-1-one, cis	EtOH	289(1.77)	88-1041-73
3-Cyclododecen-1-one, trans	EtOH	294(2.75)	88-1041-73
Ethanone, 1-[4-(1,1-dimethylethyl)-1-cyclohexen-1-yl]-	EtOH	232(3.96)	44-3893-73
$C_{12}H_{20}O_2$			
1-Cyclohexene-1-carboxylic acid, 4-(1,1-dimethylethyl)-, methyl ester	EtOH	216(4.09)	44-3893-73
4-Octene-3,6-dione, 2,2,7,7-tetramethyl-, (E)-	EtOH	235(3.99)	78-2065-73
$C_{12}H_{20}O_4$			
4(5H)-Oxepinone, 5-acetoxytetrahydro-3,3,6,6-tetramethyl-	EtOH	273(1.60)	44-4087-73
$C_{12}H_{20}O_5$			
1,3-Dioxolane-2-hexanoic acid, 2-methyl-β-oxo-, ethyl ester	EtOH	244(3.02)	44-3244-73
$C_{12}H_{21}IN_2O$			
3H-Azepinium, 2-(diethylamino)-4-methoxy-1-methyl-, iodide	EtOH	227(4.37),309(3.84)	39-1079-73C
$C_{12}H_{21}NO$			
2,3-Heptadienamide, 6-methyl-4-(2-methylpropyl)-	EtOH	211(4.01)	88-0209-73
2,3-Hexadienamide, 4-(1,1-dimethylethyl)-5,5-dimethyl-	EtOH	208(3.91)	88-0209-73
2,3-Hexadienamide, N-(1,1-dimethylethyl)-4-ethyl-	EtOH	214(4.16)	88-0209-73
$C_{12}H_{21}NO_3$			
2-Propenoic acid, 3-[2,2-dimethyl-4-(1-methylethyl)-3-oxazolidinyl]-, methyl ester, [E-(E)]-	EtOH	281(4.31)	39-1985-73C
$C_{12}H_{21}NO_5$			
Aldehydo-D-arabinose, 2,3:4,5-di-O-isopropylidene-, 1-(N-methyloxime)	EtOH	242(3.98)	136-0159-73F
$C_{12}H_{21}NSi$			
Benzenemethanamine, N,N-dimethyl-2-(trimethylsilyl)-	isooctane	262(2.30),265(2.30), 273(2.30)	101-0001-73H
$C_{12}H_{22}$			
2,4-Heptadiene, 3,4,5,6,6-pentamethyl-	EtOH	205(3.79)	22-2506-73
$C_{12}H_{22}N_2$			
2-Hexenenitrile, 3-(butylamino)-4-ethyl-	EtOH	264(4.31)	39-1108-73C
2-Hexenenitrile, 3-(diethylamino)-4-ethyl-	EtOH	277(4.32)	39-1108-73C
3-Hexenenitrile, 3-(butylamino)-4-ethyl-	EtOH	215(3.62),228(3.72)	39-1108-73C

Compound	Solvent	λ_{max}(log ε)	Ref.
3-Hexenenitrile, 3-(diethylamino)-4-ethyl-	EtOH	204(3.88),250(3.04)	39-1108-73C
$C_{12}H_{22}N_2O$			
Morpholine, 4-[[1-(1,1-dimethylethyl)-2-azetidinylidene]methyl]-	C_6H_{12}	235(3.72)	28-0519-73A
Oxazolidin-2-imine, 5-ethyl-N,3-diiso-propyl-4-methylene-	EtOH	238(4.12),288(3.53)	44-1051-73
$C_{12}H_{22}N_2O_2$			
2-Cyclohexen-1-one, 3,6-bis[(dimethyl-amino)methyl]-2-hydroxy-, dihydro-chloride	EtOH	274(3.79)	88-4059-73
$C_{12}H_{22}N_2O_4$			
Cyclohexanol, 2,2'-azobis-, N,N'-dioxide	MeOH	296(3.88)	23-1812-73
$C_{12}H_{22}N_2O_{10}$			
β-D-Xylopyranoside, 3,3'-azobis[methyl 3-deoxy-, N,N'-dioxide, (E)-	H_2O	300(3.85)	23-1812-73
$C_{12}H_{22}O$			
Isomenthone, 2,4-dimethyl-, (+)-	dioxan	298(1.74)	22-1049-73
Isomenthone, 4-ethyl-, (1R,4R)-(+)-	dioxan	300(1.60)	22-1049-73
$C_{12}H_{22}O_2$			
6,7-Dodecanedione	hexane	437(1.11)	28-0247-73B
$C_{12}H_{22}O_{10}$			
Erycordinobiose phenylosazone	EtOH	230s(4.39),257(4.49),311(4.26),327s(4.25),395(4.48)	105-0043-73
$C_{12}H_{22}Si_2$			
Silane, 1,4-phenylenebis[ethylmethyl-	heptane	277.0(2.60)	70-1825-73
Silane, 1,4-phenylenebis[trimethyl-	heptane	276.0(2.51)	70-1825-73
$C_{12}H_{24}N_2$			
1H-Imidazole, 4,5-dihydro-2-nonyl-	EtOH	220(3.64)	93-2424-73
$C_{12}H_{26}BNO_2$			
Hexane, 2,4-dimethyl-3-aci-nitro-, O-(diethylboryl) deriv.	hexane	235(4.01)	65-1118-73
$C_{12}H_{26}N_2O_2$			
Diazene, (2-methoxypropyl)(1-methylhep-tyl)-, 1-oxide	EtOH	223(3.82)	88-4701-73
$C_{12}H_{26}OSi_2$			
5-Hexen-2-one, 3,5-bis(trimethylsilyl)-	C_6H_{12}	285(1.96)	23-2024-73
$C_{12}H_{36}Cl_8N_4Si_4Ti_4$			
1,3,5,7,2,4,6,8-Tetraazatetratitanocine, 2,2,4,4,6,6,8,8-octachloro-1,3,5,7-tetrakis(trimethylsilyl)-	C_6H_{12}	219(3.61),226s(--),245s(--),299s(--),392(3.00)	101-0C19-73H

Compound	Solvent	$\lambda_{max}(\log \epsilon)$	Ref.
$C_{13}F_{21}N$			
Pyridine, 2,5-difluoro-4-(pentafluoroethyl)-3,6-bis[1,2,2,2-tetrafluoro-1-(trifluoromethyl)ethyl]-	C_6H_{12}	286s(3.83)	39-1405-73C
Pyridine, 3,5-difluoro-4-(pentafluoroethyl)-2,6-bis[1,2,2,2-tetrafluoro-1-(trifluoromethyl)ethyl]-	C_6H_{12}	274(3.66)	39-1405-73C
$C_{13}H_6BrClO_2$			
9H-Xanthen-9-one, 6-bromo-2-chloro-	EtOH	243(4.49),248s(4.48), 267(4.11),288s(3.79), 296(3.95),344(3.75)	39-1972-73C
$C_{13}H_6BrFO_2$			
9H-Xanthen-9-one, 6-bromo-2-fluoro-	EtOH	228(4.52),234(4.49), 267(4.26),286s(3.93), 295(4.15),345(3.98)	39-1972-73C
$C_{13}H_6ClNO_4S$			
4H,5H-Pyrano[3,4-e]-1,3-oxazine-4,5-dione, 7-chloro-2-(phenylthio)-	$CHCl_3$	280(4.03),347(4.17)	39-2432-73C
$C_{13}H_6F_2O_2$			
9H-Xanthen-9-one, 2,7-difluoro-	EtOH	230(4.60),257s(4.17), 294(3.74),355(3.96)	44-0841-73
$C_{13}H_6OS_2$			
2-Propynal, 3-[5-(2-thienylethynyl)-2-thienyl]-	ether	359(4.44),385(4.34)	24-2755-73
$C_{13}H_7ClN_2O_4$			
4H,5H-Pyrano[3,4-e]-1,3-oxazine-4,5-dione, 7-chloro-2-(phenylamino)-	MeCN	296(3.89),347(4.10)	39-2432-73C
$C_{13}H_7ClOS$			
9H-Thioxanthen-9-one, 1-chloro-	EtOH	221(4.19),258(4.62), 293(3.70),303(3.72), 380(3.75)	44-1743-73
$C_{13}H_7NO_4$			
6H-Dibenzo[b,d]pyran-6-one, 4-nitro-	n.s.g.	317(3.60)	39-2818-73C
$C_{13}H_7N_3OS$			
6H-Pyrido[3',2':4,5]thiazolo[2,3-b]quinazolin-6-one	EtOH	220(4.33),236(4.25), 303(4.18),334(4.35)	2-0744-73
$C_{13}H_8BrNO_2S$			
2(3H)-Thiazolone, 4-[5-(4-bromophenyl)-2-furanyl]-	EtOH	261(4.19),333(4.46)	103-0403-73
$C_{13}H_8BrN_3OS$			
2-Naphthalenol, 1-[(5-bromo-2-thiazolyl)azo]- (also Co complex spectra)	30% acetone	500(4.33)	140-1973-73
$C_{13}H_8Br_2N_2O_5$			
Benzene, 1,3-dibromo-2-(2,4-dinitrophenoxy)-5-methyl-	EtOH	281(4.12)	39-2949-73C
$C_{13}H_8ClFN_2S$			
3H-Pyrido[2,3-b][1,4]thiazine, 6-chloro-2-(2-fluorophenyl)-	EtOH	266(4.44),364(3.72)	103-1145-73

Compound	Solvent	$\lambda_{max}(\log \epsilon)$	Ref.
$C_{13}H_8ClN$			
1-Naphthaleneacetonitrile, α-(chloro-methylene)-, cis	EtOH	221(4.70),285(3.68), 294(3.71)	22-0724-73
trans	EtOH	221(4.79),283(3.72), 293(3.73)	22-0724-73
2-Naphthaleneacetonitrile, α-(chloro-methylene)-, cis	EtOH	218(4.51),253(4.16), 290(3.81),301(3.75)	22-0724-73
trans	EtOH	218(4.55),234(4.37), 240(4.37),256(4.36), 263(4.36),289(4.16), 301(4.22)	22-0724-73
$C_{13}H_8ClNOS$			
[1]Benzothiepino[2,3-b]pyridin-6(5H)-one, 8-chloro-	MeOH	239(4.28),256s(4.03), 276(3.87),336(3.62)	73-2778-73
$C_{13}H_8ClNO_2$			
Phenol, 2-(2-benzoxazolyl)-4-chloro-	EtOH	267s(4.03),277(4.11), 284(4.17),289s(4.12), 297(4.22),329(4.14), 340s(4.16)	2-1047B-73
$C_{13}H_8ClNO_2S$			
2(3H)-Thiazolone, 4-[5-(4-chlorophenyl)-2-furanyl]-	EtOH	256(4.11),330(4.42)	103-0403-73
$C_{13}H_8ClNS$			
[1]Benzothiepino[2,3-b]pyridine, 8-chloro-	MeOH	212(4.21),263(4.04), 279(3.43)	73-2778-73
$C_{13}H_8ClN_3O_6$			
Benzoic acid, 2-chloro-4-[(2,4-dinitro-phenyl)amino]-, anion	51.2% DMSO	367(4.26)	22-1553-73
dianion	51.2% DMSO	427(4.25)	22-1553-73
Benzoic acid, 2-chloro-5-[(2,4-dinitro-phenyl)amino]-, anion	51.2% DMSO	370(4.26)	22-1553-73
dianion	51.2% DMSO	425(4.30)	22-1553-73
Benzoic acid, 4-chloro-2-[(2,4-dinitro-phenyl)amino]-, anion	51.2% DMSO	390(4.25)	22-1553-73
dianion	51.2% DMSO	420(4.30),515(4.09)	22-1553-73
Benzoic acid, 5-chloro-2-[(2,4-dinitro-phenyl)amino]-, anion	51.2% DMSO	395(4.40)	22-1553-73
dianion	51.2% DMSO	425(4.41),515(4.16)	22-1553-73
$C_{13}H_8Cl_2N_4$			
1,3,5-Triazine, 2,4-dichloro-6-(1-phen-yl-1H-pyrazol-2-yl)-	EtOH	225(3.83),340(4.43)	39-2075-73B
$C_{13}H_8Cl_4N_2O$			
2,4-Cyclopentadien-1-one, 2,3,4,5-tetra-chloro-, (4-acetylphenyl)hydrazone	EtOH	415(4.60)	39-1155-73B
	EtOH-KOH	499(--)	39-1155-73B
$C_{13}H_8Cl_4O_2$			
1,4-Methanodibenzo[b,e][1,4]dioxin, 6,7,8,9-tetrachloro-1,4,4a,10a-tetrahydro-	C_6H_{12}	230s(4.35),290s(3.33), 298(3.42)	88-2059-73
isomeric compound	C_6H_{12}	231s(4.28),293s(3.29), 301(3.41)	88-2059-73

Compound	Solvent	$\lambda_{max}(\log \epsilon)$	Ref.
$C_{13}H_8Cl_4O_2S_2$			
Spiro[1,3-benzodioxole-2,2'-[1,3]benzodithiole], 4,5,6,7-tetrachloro-4',5',6',7'-tetrahydro-	benzene	297(3.40)	97-0465-73
$C_{13}H_8F_2N_2O$			
2H-Benzimidazol-2-one, 6-fluoro-1-(4-fluorophenyl)-1,3-dihydro-	THF	250(3.78),293(3.90)	44-1316-73
$C_{13}H_8F_4O$			
1,1'-Biphenyl, 2,3,5,6-tetrafluoro-4-methoxy-	hexane	243(4.22)	39-1121-73C
$C_{13}H_8F_6OS_2$			
Ethanone, 2-[4,5-bis(trifluoromethyl)-1,3-dithiol-2-yl]-1-phenyl-	isooctane	243(4.09),283(3.46), 292(3.47),315(3.47)	35-4379-73
$C_{13}H_8Li_2O$			
Benzophenone, dilithium deriv.	n.s.g.	494(4.40)	35-8118-73
$C_{13}H_8N_2O_2S$			
Pyrano[3,2-b]indole-3-carbonitrile, 2,5-dihydro-4-(methylthio)-2-oxo-	EtOH	256(3.97),325(4.10), 385(4.22)	94-1658-73
3H-Pyrrolo[1,2-a]indole-2-carbonitrile, 9-hydroxy-1-(methylthio)-3-oxo-	EtOH	253(4.26),342(3.96)	94-1658-73
$C_{13}H_8N_2O_3S$			
Thiazolo[3,2-a]pyridinium, 3-hydroxy-2-(4-nitrophenyl)-, hydroxide, inner salt	50% dioxan-HCl	227(4.0),253(3.8), 290s(3.9),472(4.1)	1-1763-73
	50% dioxan-NaOH	227(4.0),250s(3.9), 290(3.8),472(4.1)	1-1763-73
Thiazolo[3,2-a]pyridinium, 3-hydroxy-6-nitro-2-phenyl-, hydroxide, inner salt	50% dioxan-HCl	254(3.9),285(4.1), 455(4.0)	1-1763-73
	50% dioxan-NaOH	232(4.0),296(3.8), 357(3.9),428(--), 455(3.9),532s(3.7)	1-1763-73
Thiazolo[3,2-a]pyridinium, 3-hydroxy-8-nitro-2-phenyl-, hydroxide, inner salt	50% dioxan-HCl	248(3.8),338(3.8), 436(3.9)	1-1763-73
	50% dioxan-NaOH	230(3.9),255s(3.7), 305s(3.8),328(3.9), 382(3.8),494(3.9)	1-1763-73
$C_{13}H_8N_2O_4S_2$			
Benzenecarbodithioic acid, 2,4-dinitrophenyl ester	C_6H_{12}	228(4.00),310(4.00)	39-1571-73C
$C_{13}H_8N_4O_7$			
Benzoic acid, 5-[(2,4-dinitrophenyl)-azo]-2-hydroxy-	EtOH	227(4.43),270(4.18), 405(4.26)	62-0289-73
$C_{13}H_8OS_2$			
2-Propyn-1-ol, 3-[5-(2-thienylethynyl)-2-thienyl]-	ether	321s(4.44),330s(4.47), 335(4.49),342s(4.43),	24-2755-73
3-Thietanone 2-[3-[5-(1-propynyl)-	ether	352s(4.34),359(4.34)	
3-Thietanone, 2-[3-[5-(1-propynyl)-2-thienyl]-2-propynylidene]-	ether	294(4.06),307(4.13), 393(4.42),418(4.50)	24-0497-73
3(2H)-Thiophenone, 5-[[5-(1-propynyl)-2-thienyl]ethynyl]-	ether	302s(3.96),319s(4.05), 343s(4.15),350(4.13), 362s(4.07)	24-0497-73

Compound	Solvent	λ_{max}(log ε)	Ref.
$C_{13}H_8O_2$			
2H-Naphtho[1,2-b]pyran-2-one	EtOH	358(3.70)	40-0118-73
3H-Naphtho[2,1-b]pyran-3-one	EtOH	364(3.90)	40-0118-73
9H-Xanthen-9-one	EtOH	238(4.62),260(4.11), 285(3.85),332(3.82)	103-0911-73
$C_{13}H_8O_2S_3$			
5-Oxa-9,9a,10-trithia(9a-S^{IV})pentaleno-[2,1-a]naphthalen-6-one, 8-methyl-	EtOH	266(4.67),313(4.23), 356(3.87),467(3.97)	39-1022-73C
$C_{13}H_8O_3S$			
Thieno[3,2-b]furan-5-carboxylic acid, 2-phenyl-	EtOH	315(4.27)	103-0659-73
$C_{13}H_8O_3S_2$			
5,10-Dioxa-9,9a-dithia(9a-S^{IV})pentaleno-[2,1-a]naphthalen-6-one, 8-methyl-	EtOH	232(4.42),264(4.11), 418(4.54)	39-1022-73C
$C_{13}H_8O_4$			
9H-Xanthen-9-one, 2,6-dihydroxy-	MeOH	204(4.09),244(4.54), 267s(3.98),314(4.13), 353s(3.79)	24-1182-73
	EtOH	238(4.57),265s(3.99), 314(4.16)	35-7752-73
$C_{13}H_8O_6$			
9H-Xanthen-9-one, 1,3,5,8-tetrahydroxy-	EtOH	239(4.28),267(4.52), 332(4.10),390(3.88)	36-0929-73
$C_{13}H_8S_2$			
Thiophene, 2-(1-propynyl)-5-(2-thienyl-ethynyl)-	ether	321s(4.44),330s(4.47), 335(4.49),342s(4.43), 352s(4.33),358(4.33)	24-2755-73
$C_{13}H_9BrN_2OS$			
2-Thiazolamine, 4-[5-(4-bromophenyl)-2-furanyl]-	EtOH	272(4.27),335(4.41)	103-0403-73
$C_{13}H_9BrO$			
Naphthalene, 1-bromo-2-(2-propynyloxy)-	n.s.g.	230(4.86),281(3.66), 293(3.61)	33-1457-73
Naphtho[2,1-b]furan, 2-(bromomethyl)-	n.s.g.	223(4.61),227s(4.59), 230s(4.53),291(4.17), 309(4.00),315(3.98), 323(4.00),328(3.98)	33-1457-73
$C_{13}H_9ClN_2OS$			
2-Thiazolamine, 4-[5-(4-chlorophenyl)-2-furanyl]-	EtOH	272(4.41),334(4.49)	103-0403-73
$C_{13}H_9ClN_2O_3$			
Benzoic acid, 2-[(2-chloro-6-hydroxy-phenyl)azo]-	EtOH	252(4.01),329(4.15), 380(4.05)	39-1682-73C
Benzoic acid, 2-[(4-chloro-2-hydroxy-phenyl)azo]-	EtOH	251(4.05),328(4.16),	39-1682-73C
Benzoic acid, 2-[(2-chlorophenyl)-NNO-azoxy]-	EtOH	231(4.07),316(4.16)	39-1682-73C
Benzoic acid, 2-[(4-chlorophenyl)-NNO-azoxy]-	EtOH	232(4.04),315(4.12)	39-1682-73C
Benzoic acid, 5-[(2-chlorophenyl)azo]-2-hydroxy-	EtOH	257(4.14),365(4.38)	62-0289-73

Compound	Solvent	$\lambda_{max}(\log \epsilon)$	Ref.
Benzoic acid, 5-[(2-chlorophenyl)azo]-2-hydroxy- (cont.)	ether	232(4.15),255(--), 352(4.40)	62-0289-73
	CCl_4	350(4.15)	62-0289-73
Benzoic acid, 5-[(4-chlorophenyl)azo]-2-hydroxy-	EtOH	260(3.90),362(4.26)	62-0289-73
$C_{13}H_9ClN_2O_4$			
Benzoic acid, 2-chloro-4-[(4-nitrophenyl)amino]-, anion	70.5% DMSO	407(4.32)	22-1553-73
dianion	70.5% DMSO	510(4.52)	22-1553-73
Benzoic acid, 2-chloro-5-[(4-nitrophenyl)amino]-, anion	70.5% DMSO	410(4.35)	22-1553-73
dianion	70.5% DMSO	510(4.51)	22-1553-73
Benzoic acid, 4-chloro-2-[(4-nitrophenyl)amino]-, anion	91.0% DMSO	415(4.31)	22-1553-73
Benzoic acid, 5-chloro-2-[(4-nitrophenyl)amino]-, anion	91.0% DMSO	420(4.39)	22-1553-73
dianion	91.0% DMSO	500(4.23)	22-1553-73
$C_{13}H_9ClN_2S$			
3-Pyridineacetonitrile, 2-[(4-chlorophenyl)thio]-	MeOH	220(4.20),245(4.07), 259s(3.97),285s(3.77)	73-2778-73
$C_{13}H_9ClN_4S$			
1,2,4-Triazolo[3',4':2,3]thiazolo[5,4-b]pyridinium, 2-phenyl-, chloride	EtOH	216(4.33),290(4.19), 315(4.36)	2-0744-73
$C_{13}H_9ClO$			
Naphthalene, 1-chloro-2-(2-propynyloxy)-	n.s.g.	229(4.57),280(3.33), 292(3.26)	33-1457-73
Naphtho[2,1-b]furan, 2-(chloromethyl)-	n.s.g.	224(4.57),232(4.55), 240(4.50),293(4.05), 311(3.86),318(3.68), 325(3.96)	33-1457-73
3-Tridecene-5,7,9,11-tetrayn-2-ol, 1-chloro-, (E)-	ether	229(4.88),239(4.91), 255(5.03),272(5.17), 283(3.86),303(4.00), 323(4.19),347(4.26), 374(4.04)	24-2140-73
$C_{13}H_9ClO_2S$			
Benzeneacetic acid, 4-chloro-α-(2-thienylmethylene)-, cis	EtOH	222(4.07),270s(3.94), 305(4.19)	7-0055-73
trans	EtOH	241(3.89),321(4.41), 340s(4.25)	7-0055-73
$C_{13}H_9ClO_3$			
2-Propenoic acid, 2-(4-chlorophenyl)-3-(2-furanyl)-, (E)-	EtOH	235(3.97),307(4.27)	7-0779-73
(Z)-	EtOH	235(3.93),242s(3.90), 320(4.59)	7-0779-73
$C_{13}H_9D_3N_2OS_3$			
Rhodanine, 5-(N-methyl-d_3-2-thiazolidinylidene)-3-phenyl-	EtOH	280(4.05),394(4.51)	94-1431-73
$C_{13}H_9F_3$			
1,1'-Biphenyl, 3-(trifluoromethyl)-	EtOH	248(4.17)	35-5288-73
1,1'-Biphenyl, 4-(trifluoromethyl)-	EtOH	253(4.18)	35-5288-73

Compound	Solvent	$\lambda_{max}(\log \epsilon)$	Ref.
$C_{13}H_9K$			
Potassium, 9H-fluoren-9-yl-	DMSO	374(4.24),480f(3.6)	10-0240-73F
$C_{13}H_9N$			
Benzoxazole, 2-phenyl-	MeOH	234(3.90),298(4.38)	73-0224-73
	$CHCl_3$	300(4.38)	73-0224-73
1-Naphthaleneacetonitrile, α-formyl-	10%EtOH-pH 12	253(4.06),314(3.72)	22-3458-73
2-Naphthaleneacetonitrile, α-formyl-	10%EtOH-pH 12	263(4.36),273(4.30), 311(4.27)	22-3458-73
$C_{13}H_9NOS$			
Benzothiazole, 2-[2-(2-furanyl)ethenyl]-	EtOH	350(4.21)	104-2596-73
conjugate acid	H_2O	410(4.35)	104-2596-73
[1]Benzothiepino[2,3-b]pyridin-6(5H)-one	MeOH	237(4.24),255s(3.97), 279s(3.68),324(3.52)	73-1693-73
Phenol, 2-(2-benzothiazolyl)-	heptane	288(4.21)	73-0224-73
	0.05M HCl	291s(3.83),329(4.29)	73-0224-73
	0.05M NaOH	293(4.19),380(4.33)	73-0224-73
	MeOH	215(4.46),248(3.85), 256(3.87),287(4.18), 332(4.26)	73-0224-73
	EtOH	287(4.14)	73-0224-73
	dioxan	288(4.25),334(4.31)	73-0224-73
	$CHCl_3$	290(4.18),334(4.23)	73-0224-73
	50% dioxan	287(4.24)	73-0224-73
Phenol, 3-(2-benzothiazolyl)-	MeOH	221(4.41),248s(3.88), 258s(3.82),299(4.24)	73-0224-73
Phenol, 4-(2-benzothiazolyl)-	0.05M HCl	320(4.44)	73-0224-73
	0.05M NaOH	353(4.64)	73-0224-73
	MeOH	213(4.34),250(3.71), 257s(3.69),316(4.50)	73-0224-73
	dioxan	317,5(4.49)	73-0224-73
	$CHCl_3$	315(4.41)	73-0224-73
Thiazolo[3,2-a]pyridinium, 3-hydroxy-2-phenyl-, hydroxide, inner salt	50% dioxan-HCl	235(4.1),283(3.8), 432(4.1)	1-1763-73
	50% dioxan-NaOH	238(4.1),283(3.9), 436(4.2)	1-1763-73
$C_{13}H_9NO_2$			
Phenol, 2-(2-benzoxazolyl)-	heptane	292(4.41)	73-0224-73
	0.05M HCl	293(4.19),318(4.31)	73-0224-73
	0.05M NaOH	286(4.20),361(4.20)	73-0224-73
	MeOH	292(4.35),318(4.22)	73-0224-73
	EtOH	260s(4.06),272(4.11), 280(4.16),285(4.16), 293(4.28),318(4.23), 330s(4.17)	2-1047B-73
	dioxan	293(4.35),319(4.29)	73-0224-73
	$CHCl_3$	294(4.30),320(4.27)	73-0224-73
	50% dioxan	292.5(4.35)	73-0224-73
Phenol, 3-(2-benzoxazolyl)-	MeOH	298(4.26)	73-0224-73
Phenol, 4-(2-benzoxazolyl)-	0.05M HCl	306(4.46)	73-0224-73
	0.05M NaOH	336(4.66)	73-0224-73
	MeOH	305(4.46)	73-0224-73
	dioxan	305.5(4.57)	73-0224-73
	$CHCl_3$	307(4.46)	73-0224-73
$C_{13}H_9NO_3S$			
4H-1-Benzopyran-4-one, 7-hydroxy-2-methyl-3-(4-thiazolyl)-	n.s.g.	298(3.98)	104-2580-73

Compound	Solvent	$\lambda_{max}(\log \epsilon)$	Ref.
$C_{13}H_9NO_4S$			
Benzeneacetic acid, 4-nitro-α-(2-thienylmethylene)-, cis	EtOH	289(4.32)	7-0055-73
trans	EtOH	225s(3.93),280(4.00), 380(4.26)	7-0055-73
2H-1-Benzopyran-3-carbonitrile, 7-acetoxy-4-(methylthio)-2-oxo-	EtOH	235s(3.89),325(4.18), 340s(4.15)	95-0836-73
$C_{13}H_9NO_5$			
2-Propenoic acid, 3-(2-furanyl)-2-(4-nitrophenyl)-, (E)-	EtOH	285(4.39)	7-0779-73
(Z)-	EtOH	275(4.09),372(4.32)	7-0779-73
$C_{13}H_9NO_7$			
Acetic acid, (8-carboxy-4-nitro-1-naphthalenyloxy)-	EtOH	214(4.43),249(4.20), 360s(3.70),411(3.98)	107-0219-73
$C_{13}H_9NS$			
Benzothiazole, 2-phenyl-	MeOH	224(4.21),248(3.83), 255(3.83),296(4.29)	73-0224-73
Benzothiepino[2,3-b]pyridine	MeOH	245s(4.12),263(4.24), 297(3.80)	73-1693-73
$C_{13}H_9NS_2$			
Benzothiazole, 2-[2-(2-thienyl)ethenyl]-	EtOH	355(4.23)	104-2596-73
conjugate acid	H_2O	406(4.20)	104-2596-73
$C_{13}H_9NSe$			
1,2-Benzisoselenazole, 3-phenyl-	EtOH	203(4.35),226(4.48), 325(3.88)	4-0267-73
$C_{13}H_9N_3$			
Quinoxaline, 2-(2-pyridinyl)-	EtOH	211(4.08),251(--), 275(--),333(--)	34-0102-73
$C_{13}H_9N_3O$			
Benzaldehyde, 2-[1,2,3]triazolo[1,5-a]-pyridin-3-yl)-	EtOH	246(4.55),288(4.51), 318(4.51)	44-4167-73
Benzo[c]cinnolinium, 5-(formylamino)-, hydroxide, inner salt	EtOH	249(4.45),298(3.76), 425(3.98)	24-1589-73
1,2,3-Benzotriazine, 4-phenyl-, 3-oxide	MeOH	306(3.85),407(3.23)	35-2390-73
1H-Imidazo[4,5-c]pyridine, 2-benzoyl-	MeOH	238(3.83),292(4.00)	87-1296-73
7H-Indolo[5,4,3-def]cinnolin-7-one, 1,6-dihydro-3-methyl-	EtOH	254(3.43),343(3.70), 426(3.15)	104-1091-73
$C_{13}H_9N_3OS$			
2-Naphthalenol, 1-(2-thiazolylazo)- (also Co complex spectra)	30% acetone	490(4.30)	140-1973-73
$C_{13}H_9N_3O_3S$			
2-Thiazolamine, 4-[5-(4-nitrophenyl)-2-furanyl]-	EtOH	256(4.13),300(4.12), 406(4.30)	103-0403-73
$C_{13}H_9N_3O_4$			
Benzaldehyde, 2-hydroxy-5-[(4-nitrophenyl)azo]-	EtOH-NaOH	245(4.48),275s(4.18), 416s(4.34),470(4.52)	103-1463-73
	$CHCl_3$	272(4.07),360(4.45), 445s(3.18)	103-1463-73

Compound	Solvent	λ_{max}(log ε)	Ref.
$C_{13}H_9N_3O_5$			
Benzoic acid, 2-hydroxy-5-[(2-nitrophenyl)azo]-	EtOH	230(4.23),267(4.07), 370(4.29)	62-0289-73
Benzoic acid, 2-hydroxy-5-[(4-nitrophenyl)azo]-	EtOH	230(4.26),272(4.18), 390(4.51)	62-0289-73
	ether	222(4.40),265(4.30), 380(4.83)	62-0289-73
$C_{13}H_9N_3O_6$			
Benzoic acid, 2-[(2,4-dinitrophenyl)amino]-, anion	86.4% DMSO	398(4.29)	22-1553-73
dianion	86.4% DMSO	420(4.33),530(4.07)	22-1553-73
Benzoic acid, 3-[(2,4-dinitrophenyl)amino]-, anion	51.2% DMSO	370(4.28)	22-1553-73
dianion	51.2% DMSO	427(4.33)	22-1553-73
Benzoic acid, 4-[(2,4-dinitrophenyl)amino]-, anion	51.2% DMSO	373(4.26)	22-1553-73
dianion	51.2% DMSO	430(4.29)	22-1553-73
$C_{13}H_9N_3S$			
1H-Benzotriazole, 1-(phenylthioxomethyl)-	C_6H_{12}	330(4.01),345s(3.96)	5-0636-73
	CH_2Cl_2	335(3.98)	5-0636-73
$C_{13}H_9N_4S$			
1,2,4-Triazolo[3',4':2,3]thiazolo[5,4-b]pyridinium, 2-phenyl-, chloride	EtOH	216(4.33),290(4.19), 315(4.36)	2-0744-73
$C_{13}H_9N_5O_6$			
Benzaldehyde, α-nitro-, 2,4-dinitrophenylhydrazone	$CHCl_3$	356(4.30),386s(--)	78-3929-73
$C_{13}H_9N_5S$			
Thiazolo[3,2-e]purin-4-amine, 8-phenyl-	pH 1	253(4.34),297(4.17)	94-0034-73
	pH 13	244(--),290(--), 300s(--)	94-0034-73
$C_{13}H_{10}$			
Benzo[7,8]bicyclo[4.2.1]nonane	EtOH	208(4.20),253(3.50), 261(3.65),270(3.70), 282(3.51)	88-2149-73
$C_{13}H_{10}BF_2NO$			
Boron, difluoro(N-hydroxy-N-phenylbenzamidato-O,O')-, (T-4)-	$C_2H_4Cl_2$	298(4.15),368(3.9)	24-2427-73
$C_{13}H_{10}BrClN_2OS$			
Ethanone, 2-[(3-amino-6-chloro-2-pyridinyl)thio]-1-(2-bromophenyl)-	EtOH	258(4.12),334(3.63)	103-1145-73
1H-Pyrido[2,3-b][1,4]thiazin-2-ol, 2-(2-bromophenyl)-6-chloro-2,3-dihydro-	EtOH	236(4.24),260(4.12), 326(3.86)	103-1145-73
$C_{13}H_{10}BrN_3O_2$			
2,4(1H,3H)-Pyrimidinedione, 5-bromo-1-(1H-indol-3-ylmethyl)- (spectra in 45% ethanol)	pH 6.5	217(4.66),281(4.16), 288(4.14)	19-0257-73
	pH 13	281(4.11),288(4.06)	19-0237-73
$C_{13}H_{10}ClFN_2OS$			
Ethanone, 2-[(3-amino-6-chloro-2-pyridinyl)thio]-1-(2-fluorophenyl)-	EtOH	240(4.09),333(3.83)	103-1145-73
1H-Pyrido[2,3-b][1,4]thiazin-2-ol, 6-chloro-2-(2-fluorophenyl)-2,3-dihydro-	EtOH	240(4.0),270(4.03), 336(3.87)	103-1145-73

Compound	Solvent	λ_{max}(log ε)	Ref.
$C_{13}H_{10}ClNO_2S$			
Benzene, 4-chloro-1-[(4-methylphenyl)-thio]-2-nitro-	DMF	385(3.661)	39-1430-73B
3-Pyridineacetic acid, 2-[(4-chlorophenyl)thio]-	MeOH	247(4.02),287s(3.76)	73-2778-73
$C_{13}H_{10}ClN_3$			
2H-Indazol-2-amine, N-(4-chlorophenyl)-	EtOH	237(4.24),279(3.95)	118-0363-73
2H-Indazol-2-amine, 5-chloro-N-phenyl-	EtOH	280(3.88),300(3.78)	118-0363-73
$C_{13}H_{10}Cl_2O_5S$			
1,3-Dithiole-4,5-dicarboxylic acid, 2-(2,5-dichloro-4-hydroxyphenyl)-, dimethyl ester	EtOH	286(3.81),350(3.61)	35-4379-73
$C_{13}H_{10}Cl_4O_2$			
1,4-Methanodibenzo[b,e][1,4]dioxin, 6,7,8,9-tetrachloro-1,2,3,4,4a,10a-hexahydro-	C_6H_{12}	230s(4.25),290s(3.20), 298(3.28)	88-2059-73
$C_{13}H_{10}FNO_2$			
Benzamide, 2-fluoro-N-hydroxy-N-phenyl-	EtOH	267(4.00)	112-0547-73
$C_{13}H_{10}FN_3O_2$			
2,4(1H,3H)-Pyrimidinedione, 5-fluoro-1-(1H-indol-3-ylmethyl)-, (spectra in 45% ethanol)	pH 6.5	217(4.65),277(4.16), 287s(4.05)	19-0257-73
	pH 13	277(4.10),288(3.99)	19-0257-73
$C_{13}H_{10}INO_2$			
Benzamide, N-hydroxy-2-iodo-N-phenyl-	EtOH	233(4.12),260(3.98)	112-0547-73
$C_{13}H_{10}N_2$			
5-Azaindole, 1-phenyl-	MeOH	220(4.5),250(4.4), 280(3.9)	103-1119-73
1H-Benzimidazole, 2-phenyl-	MeOH	240(4.11),302(4.38)	73-0224-73
	EtOH	242(4.07),297(4.32), 304(4.36),317(4.12)	39-0469-73C
2H-Indazole, 2-phenyl-	MeOH	235(4.36),294(4.24)	73-0224-73
	$CHCl_3$	298(4.19)	73-0224-73
1H-Indole, 2-(2-pyridinyl)-	EtOH	206(3.09),255(2.89), 348(2.85)	34-0109-73
1H-Indole, 2-(3-pyridinyl)-	EtOH	207(4.13),225(4.09), 300(3.94),342(4.31)	34-0109-73
1H-Indole, 2-(4-pyridinyl)-	EtOH	206(4.00),230(3.88), 330(4.22)	34-0109-73
1,4-Methanonaphthalene-6,7-dicarbonitrile, 1,2,3,4-tetrahydro-	MeOH	257(3.93),283(3.20), 289(3.00),295(3.00)	33-3004-73
$C_{13}H_{10}N_2O$			
1H-Benzimidazole, 2-phenoxy-	EtOH	237s(3.94),275(3.92), 281(3.89)	39-0469-73C
Phenol, 2-(1H-benzimidazol-2-yl)-	heptane	293(4.00)	73-0224-73
	0.05M HCl	297(4.13),325(4.33)	73-0224-73
	pH 7	314(4.44)	73-0224-73
	0.05M NaOH	296(4.39),353(4.32)	73-0224-73
	MeOH	211(4.56),234s(4.09), 291(4.21),315(4.37)	73-0224-73
	EtOH	234(4.06),240(4.05), 248(3.84),263s(3.80), 274(3.93),286(4.05), (cont.)	39-0469-73C

Compound	Solvent	$\lambda_{max}(\log \epsilon)$	Ref.
Phenol, 2-(1H-benzimidazol-2-yl)- (cont.)	EtOH	292(4.13),318(4.32), 332(4.29)	39-0469-73C
	EtOH	290(4.12)	73-0224-73
	dioxan	292(4.18),318(4.39)	73-0224-73
	$CHCl_3$	294(4.16),320(4.32)	73-0224-73
	50% dioxan	291.5(4.27)	73-0224-73
Phenol, 3-(1H-benzimidazol-2-yl)-	MeOH	216(4.36),236s(4.06), 301(4.34)	73-0224-73
Phenol, 4-(1H-benzimidazol-2-yl)-	0.05M HCl	312(4.40)	73-0224-73
	pH 7	305(4.61)	73-0224-73
	0.05M NaOH	323(4.66)	73-0224-73
	MeOH	250(4.19),304(4.51)	73-0224-73
	dioxan	306(4.62)	73-0224-73
	$CHCl_3$	309(4.36)	73-0224-73
Phenol, 2-(2H-indazol-2-yl)-	heptane	288.5(4.06)	73-0224-73
	0.05M HCl	287s(3.48),310(4.15)	73-0224-73
	0.05M NaOH	288(3.99),324(4.03)	73-0224-73
	MeOH	214(4.40),231s(4.19), 288s(4.12),306(4.15)	73-0224-73
	EtOH	287.5s(4.11)	73-0224-73
	dioxan	288(4.16),313(4.34)	73-0224-73
	$CHCl_3$	290(4.00),318(4.30)	73-0224-73
	50% dioxan	287s(4.18)	73-0224-73
Phenol, 3-(2H-indazol-2-yl)-	MeOH	216(4.46),230s(4.42), 298(4.25)	73-0224-73
Phenol, 4-(2H-indazol-2-yl)-	0.05M HCl	305(4.27)	73-0224-73
	0.05M NaOH	324.5(4.33)	73-0224-73
	MeOH	245(3.98),299(4.14)	73-0224-73
	dioxan	303(4.39)	73-0224-73
	$CHCl_3$	307(4.32)	73-0224-73
3-Pyridinecarbonitrile, 1,2-dihydro-6-(4-methylphenyl)-2-oxo-	HOAc	261(3.96),360(4.34)	97-0132-73
8-Quinolinecarbonitrile, 4-(2-oxopropyl)-	EtOH	251(4.48),307(3.35), 400(2.44)	94-1943-73
$C_{13}H_{10}N_2OS$			
3-Pyridinecarbonitrile, 1,2-dihydro-6-(methylthio)-2-oxo-4-phenyl-	MeOH	251(4.39),368(4.24)	48-0679-73
$C_{13}H_{10}N_2O_2$			
Benzaldehyde, 2-hydroxy-5-(phenylazo)-	EtOH-NaOH	242(3.96),390(4.36)	103-1463-73
	$CHCl_3$	264(4.01),335(4.38), 435(2.97)	103-1463-73
2(10H)-Phenazinone, 3-hydroxy-10-methyl-	EtOH	245(4.11),278(4.13), 392(3.89),475(3.63)	22-1289-73
9H-Pyrido[3,4-b]indole-1-carboxylic acid, methyl ester	EtOH	246(4.26),258(4.26), 275(4.31),301(4.07), 350(3.83)	94-0837-73
9H-Pyrido[3,4-b]indole-3-carboxylic acid, 1-methyl-	n.s.g.	215(4.15),244(4.04), 275(4.26),367(3.60)	22-2058-73
$C_{13}H_{10}N_2O_2S$			
4H-Quinolizine-1-carbonitrile, 3-acetyl-2-(methylthio)-4-oxo-	EtOH	274(4.19),303(4.00), 397(4.17)	94-0921-73
$C_{13}H_{10}N_2O_3$			
Benzoic acid, 2-hydroxy-5-(phenylazo)-	EtOH	230(3.97),260(3.82), 352(4.18)	62-0289-73
	ether	227(4.20),255(4.00), 345(4.34)	62-0289-73

Compound	Solvent	$\lambda_{max}(\log \epsilon)$	Ref.
Benzoic acid, 2-hydroxy-5-(phenylazo)-	$CHCl_3$	340(4.18)	62-0289-73
(cont.)	CCl_4	335(4.32)	62-0289-73
Benzoic acid, 2-[(2-hydroxyphenyl)azo]-	EtOH	248(4.02),325(4.16), 386(3.89)	39-1682-73C
Benzoic acid, 4-[(4-hydroxyphenyl)azo]-	EtOH	240(3.78),253(3.85), 362(4.24)	62-0289-73
	ether	235(3.90),253(4.00), 360(4.42)	62-0289-73
Benzoic acid, 2-(phenyl-NNO-azoxy)-	EtOH	229(4.06),309(4.04)	39-1682-73C
$C_{13}H_{10}N_2O_3S$			
4H-Pyrimido[2,1-b]benzothiazole-3-carboxylic acid, 4-oxo-, ethyl ester	EtOH	237(4.19),245(4.19), 280(3.55),345(4.42), 358(4.43)	94-2019-73
4H-Quinolizine-3-carboxylic acid, 1-cyano-2-(methylthio)-4-oxo-, methyl ester	EtOH	273(4.25),300(4.02), 395(4.25)	94-0921-73
$C_{13}H_{10}N_2O_3S_2$			
4-Thiazolecarboxylic acid, 2-(6-hydroxy-2-benzothiazolyl)-, ethyl ester	MeOH	277(3.93),353(4.33)	69-1845-73
$C_{13}H_{10}N_2O_3S_3$			
[5,5'-Bithiazolidine]-2,4,4'-trione, 3'-(phenylmethyl)-2'-thioxo-	EtOH	262(4.03),295(4.19)	94-1132-73
$C_{13}H_{10}N_2O_4$			
Benzoic acid, 4-[(4-nitrophenyl)amino]-, anion	61.2% DMSO	410(4.32)	22-1553-73
dianion	61.2% DMSO	510(4.46)	22-1553-73
4H-Pyrimido[2,1-b]benzoxazole-3-carboxylic acid, 4-oxo-, ethyl ester	EtOH	234(4.27),323(4.33)	94-2019-73
$C_{13}H_{10}N_2O_4S$			
Benzene, 2,4-dinitro-1-[(4-methylphenyl)thio]-	DMF	342(4.045)	39-1430-73B
$C_{13}H_{10}N_2O_5$			
Benzene, 1-(2-methylphenoxy)-2,4-dinitro-	EtOH	290(4.06)	39-2949-73C
Isoxazole, 5-[2-(1,3-benzodioxol-5-yl)-ethenyl]-3-methyl-4-nitro-, (E)-	EtOH	214(4.35),255(4.08), 280(4.03),392(4.35)	2-1074-73
$C_{13}H_{10}N_4$			
Ethenetricarbonitrile, [4-(dimethylamino)phenyl]-	MeCN	514(4.61)	39-0616-73B
$C_{13}H_{10}N_4O$			
Pyrazinecarbonitrile, 3-amino-6-(2-phenylethenyl)-, 4-oxide	MeOH	297(4.40),313(4.43), 383(4.10)	35-6413-73
$C_{13}H_{10}N_4O$			
1H-Tetrazolium, 5-hydroxy-1,3-diphenyl-, hydroxide, inner salt	benzene	341.5(4.06)	2-0611-73
	MeOH	322(4.10)	2-0611-73
	EtOH	323(4.09)	2-0611-73
	BuOH	327(4.19)	2-0611-73
	CH_2Cl_2	332(4.05)	2-0611-73
	$CHCl_3$	332(4.16)	2-0611-73
	MeCN	326(4.16)	2-0611-73
2H-Tetrazolium, 5-hydroxy-2,3-diphenyl-, hydroxide, inner salt	benzene	345(--)	2-0611-73

Compound	Solvent	λ_{max}(log ϵ)	Ref.
2H-Tetrazolium, 5-hydroxy-2,3-diphenyl-, hydroxide, inner salt (cont.)	MeOH	326(3.79)	2-0611-73
	EtOH	328(3.74)	2-0611-73
	BuOH	335(3.71)	2-0611-73
	CH_2Cl_2	357(3.68)	2-0611-73
	$CHCl_3$	350(3.68)	2-0611-73
	acetone	350(3.67)	2-0611-73
	MeCN	347(3.70)	2-0611-73
$C_{13}H_{10}N_4O_2$			
4,5-Isoxazoledione, 3-methyl-, 4-(3-quinolinylhydrazone)	EtOH	229(4.21),260(3.74), 296(3.46),400(4.22)	12-2723-73
2,4(1H,3H)-Pteridinedione, 3-methyl-6-phenyl-	pH 5.0	245s(4.17),273(4.32), 354(4.01)	24-3149-73
	pH 11.0	252(4.14),294(4.38), 383(3.96)	24-3149-73
2,4(1H,3H)-Pteridinedione, 3-methyl-7-phenyl-	pH 5.0	223(4.37),272s(3.85), 349(4.32)	24-3149-73
	pH 11.0	233(4.34),272(4.28), 376(4.07)	24-3149-73
$C_{13}H_{10}N_4O_3$			
2,4(1H,3H)-Pteridinedione, 3-methyl-6-phenyl-, 8-oxide	pH 2.0	253s(4.37),280(4.47), 367(3.88)	24-3149-73
	pH 9.0	254(4.25),294(4.47), 403(3.92)	24-3149-73
2,4(1H,3H)-Pteridinedione, 3-methyl-7-phenyl-, 5-oxide	pH 4.0	228(4.26),252(4.38), 296(4.04),363(4.19)	24-3149-73
	pH 10.0	256(4.44),273(4.49), 300s(4.01),390(3.96)	24-3149-73
2,4(1H,3H)-Pteridinedione, 1-(phenylmethoxy)-	pH 5.0	232(4.11),245s(4.00), 282(3.53),329(3.82)	44-0703-73
$C_{13}H_{10}N_4O_4$			
Benzaldehyde, 2,4-dinitrophenylhydrazone (spectra in 50% DMSO)	acid	402(4.45)	1-3641-73
	KOH	472(4.51)	1-3641-73
4,5-Isoxazoledione, 3-methyl-, 4-[(5-hydroxy-3-phenyl-4-isoxazolyl)hydrazone]	EtOH	242(4.20),282(3.94), 515(3.79)	32-1045-73
2,4(1H,3H)-Pteridinedione, 3-methyl-7-phenyl-, 5,8-dioxide	pH 2.0	242(4.21),288(4.47), 340s(3.84),395(3.77)	24-3149-73
	pH 9.0	263(4.34),295(4.43), 330s(3.93),422(3.86)	24-3149-73
$C_{13}H_{10}N_4O_5$			
Phenol, 4-[(2,4-dinitrophenyl)azo]-2-methyl-	C_2Cl_4	393(4.42),429(4.41)	1-3632-73
	50% DMSO-acid	400(4.30)	1-3641-73
	+ KOH	580(4.69)	1-3641-73
Phenol, 4-[(2,4-dinitrophenyl)azo]-3-methyl-	C_2Cl_4	392(4.32)	1-3632-73
	50% DMSO-acid	402(4.29)	1-3641-73
	+ KOH	575(4.62)	1-3641-73
$C_{13}H_{10}N_4O_5S$			
2,4(1H,3H)-Pteridinedione, 1-[[(4-methylphenyl)sulfonyl]oxy]-	pH 5.0	234(4.34),315(3.79)	44-0703-73
$C_{13}H_{10}N_4S$			
2-Pyridinecarboxaldehyde, 2-benzothiazolylhydrazone, (E)-	EtOH	221(4.36),252(4.14), 345(4.41)	40-1314-73
(Z)-	EtOH	219(4.37),259(4.11), 355(4.33)	40-1314-73

Compound	Solvent	λ_{max}(log ε)	Ref.
$C_{13}H_{10}O$			
Benzophenone	C_6H_{12}	346(2.07)	59-0981-73
	benzene	342(2.12)	59-0981-73
	benzene	342(2.11)	70-2717-73
also other mixtures of these solvents	1:1 C_6H_{12}-benzene	345(2.10)	59-0981-73
	CCl_4	344(2.12)	59-0981-73
	+10% DMSO	342(2.14)	59-0981-73
also other mixtures of these solvents	+50% DMSO	340(2.17)	59-0981-73
	DMSO	341(2.18)	59-0981-73
	$CHCl_3$	337(2.20)	59-0891-73
	1:1 $CHCl_3$-CCl_4	338(2.19)	59-0981-73
	pyridine	342(2.17)	59-0981-73
	FSO_3H at -75°	292(4.04),344(4.38)	59-0807-73
2 $AlBr_3$ complex	benzene	335(4.20),440s(1.78)	70-2717-73
Naphthalene, 2-(1,2-propadienyloxy)-	n.s.g.	229(4.80),262(3.85), 272(3.82)	33-1457-73
Naphthalene, 2-(2-propynyloxy)-	n.s.g.	225(4.88),260(3.74), 268(3.73),280(3.61)	33-1457-73
Naphtho[2,1-b]furan, 2-methyl-	n.s.g.	223(4.51),230(4.49), 241(4.49),258s(3.72), 295(3.88),301s(3.71), 310(3.79),317(3.65), 324(3.79)	33-1457-73
	n.s.g.	223(4.55),230(4.50), 241(4.51),295(3.86), 310(3.77),314s(3.58), 324(3.78)	33-1457-73
3H-Naphtho[2,1-b]pyran	n.s.g.	241(4.59),256s(3.65), 300(3.63),313(3.65), 347(3.60)	33-1457-73
$C_{13}H_{10}OS_2$			
3-Thietanol, 2-[3-[5-(1-propynyl)-2-thienyl]-2-propynylidene]-	ether	274(3.78),321s(4.15), 341(4.22),346s(4.21), 362(4.14)	24-0497-73
$C_{13}H_{10}O_2$			
Benzoic acid, phenyl ester	C_6H_{12}	231(4.21)	22-1442-73
	EtOH	233(4.21)	22-1442-73
Methanone, (4-hydroxyphenyl)phenyl-	EtOH	295(4.18)	22-1442-73
$C_{13}H_{10}O_2S$			
Benzeneacetic acid, α-(2-thienylmethylene)-, cis	EtOH	230(3.89),270s(3.94), 304(4.18)	7-0055-73
trans	EtOH	232(3.91),317(4.35), 340s(4.12)	7-0055-73
$C_{13}H_{10}O_3$			
1-Azulenecarboxylic acid, 4-formyl-, methyl ester	ether	225(4.24),259(4.12), 303(4.46),324(4.33), 605(2.43)	24-1337-73
Benzeneacetic acid, α-(2-furanylmethylene)-, (E)-	EtOH	229(3.88),307(4.27)	7-0779-73
(Z)-	EtOH	233(4.00),242s(3.90), 314(4.41)	7-0779-73
1,4-Naphthalenedione, 2-acetyl-3-methyl-	n.s.g.	220(3.98),254(4.31), 337(3.46)	39-0235-73C

Compound	Solvent	λmax(log ε)	Ref.
$C_{13}H_{10}O_4$			
Methanone, (2,4-dihydroxyphenyl)(3-hydroxyphenyl)-	EtOH	218(4.33),239(4.01), 292(4.12),322(4.07)	35-7752-73
Naphth[2,3-b]oxirene-2,7-dione, 1a-acetyl-1a,2a-dihydro-2a-methyl-, cis	n.s.g.	234(4.23),262(3.76), 308(3.34)	39-0235-73C
$C_{13}H_{10}O_4S$			
Acetic acid, [(3-formyl-5-phenyl-2-furanyl)thio]-	EtOH	296(4.53)	103-0659-73
$C_{13}H_{10}O_4Se$			
Acetic acid, [(3-formyl-5-phenyl-2-furanyl)seleno]-	EtOH	296(4.09)	103-0659-73
$C_{13}H_{10}O_5$			
7H-Furo[3,2-g][1]benzopyran-7-one, 4,9-dimethoxy- (isopimpinellin)	EtOH	241(4.17),248(4.18), 272(4.29),314(4.10)	64-0260-73C
Iriflophenone	EtOH	215s(4.32),290s(4.12), 319(4.27)	94-2323-73
$C_{13}H_{10}O_7$			
2H-1-Benzopyran-3,4-dicarboxylic acid, 7-hydroxy-2-oxo-, dimethyl ester	EtOH	230(4.05),361(4.28)	95-0836-73
$C_{13}H_{10}Se$			
Benzo[f]selenochromene	EtOH	222(4.55),245s(4.35), 280s(3.63),355(3.73)	7-0319-73
1H-Benzo[h]selenochromene	EtOH	242s(4.37),294(3.95), 335s(3.45),345(3.57), 358(3.60)	7-0319-73
2H-Benzo[h]selenochromene	EtOH	233s(4.24),262(4.29), 280(4.21),330(3.45), 340s(3.42),360(3.40)	7-0319-73
3H-Naphtho[2,1-b]selenin	EtOH	231(4.52),253(4.34), 290(4.04),318s(3.67), 332s(3.59),360(3.40)	7-0319-73
$C_{13}H_{11}$			
Cycloheptatrienylium, phenyl-, tetrafluoroborate	pH 1	226(4.58),271(4.17), 368(4.21)	18-1785-73
$C_{13}H_{11}BrN_2O_3$			
2,4(1H,3H)-Pyrimidinedione, 5-bromo-1-(3-oxo-3-phenylpropyl)- (spectra in 45% ethanol)	pH 6.5	247(4.15),282(4.05)	19-0257-73
	pH 13	244(4.20),283(3.89)	19-0257-73
$C_{13}H_{11}BrO_4$			
1,4-Naphthalenedione, 2-acetyl-3-bromo-2,3-dihydro-2-hydroxy-3-methyl-	n.s.g.	235(4.28),256(3.91), 305(3.32)	39-0368-73C
$C_{13}H_{11}Cl$			
5,10-Methanobenzocyclooctene, 7-chloro-5,10-dihydro-	EtOH	213(3.92),257s(3.49), 267(3.59),276(3.57), 289(3.34)	88-2149-73
$C_{13}H_{11}ClN_2O_2$			
1H-Pyrrole-3-carboxaldehyde, 2-chloro-4,5-dihydro-1-methyl-5-oxo-4-[(phenylamino)methylene]-	C_6H_{12}	335(4.3),430(4.4)	103-0467-73
	EtOH	250(3.8),330(3.9), 430(4.2)	103-0467-73

Compound	Solvent	$\lambda_{max}(\log \epsilon)$	Ref.
$C_{13}H_{11}ClN_2O_3$			
1,2,4-Oxadiazole-5-carboxylic acid, 3-[2-(4-chlorophenyl)ethenyl]-, ethyl ester, (E)-	EtOH	228(4.11),285(4.50)	39-2241-73C
$C_{13}H_{11}ClN_2O_4$			
Benzo[b]quinolizinium, 11-amino-, perchlorate	EtOH	245(4.90),418(4.71)	44-4167-73
$C_{13}H_{11}ClN_4O$			
1H-1,2,4-Triazolo[4,3-b]pyridazin-4-ium, 1-[(3-chlorophenyl)methyl]-8-hydroxy-6-methyl-, hydroxide, inner salt	n.s.g.	225(3.71),280(3.79), 308(4.00)	48-0097-73
$C_{13}H_{11}ClN_4O_4$			
2H-Pyran-3(6H)-one, 4-acetoxy-2-(6-chloro-9H-purin-9-yl)-6-methyl-	n.s.g.	265(3.97)	136-0192-73E
$C_{13}H_{11}ClN_6O$			
Urea, N-(2-chloro-4-methylphenyl)-N'-1H-purin-6-yl-	pH 1-2	281(4.47)	87-0139-73
	pH 5-7	280.5(4.50)	87-0139-73
	pH 12	286(4.52)	87-0139-73
Urea, N-(2-chlorophenyl)methyl-N'-1H-purin-6-yl-	pH 1-2	278(4.29)	87-0139-73
	pH 5-7	269(4.25)	87-0139-73
	pH 12	278(4.20)	87-0139-73
$C_{13}H_{11}ClO_2$			
Ethanone, 1-[2-(4-chlorophenyl)-5-methyl-3-furanyl]-	EtOH	223(4.20),238s(3.98), 320(4.06)	22-1760-73
Ethanone, 1-[5-(4-chlorophenyl)-2-methyl-3-furanyl]-	EtOH	221s(4.29),287(4.33)	22-1760-73
$C_{13}H_{11}ClO_4$			
Benzo[1,2-b:4,3-b']difuran, 2-chloro-7-(dimethoxymethyl)-	n.s.g.	266s(3.95),273(4.30), 284(4.45),294s(3.79)	1-3133-73
$C_{13}H_{11}ClO_6$			
Benzofuro[3,2-c]pyrylium, 1,3-dimethyl-, perchlorate	n.s.g.	255(4.25),266(4.23), 320(3.69)	103-0416-73
$C_{13}H_{11}FN_2O_3$			
2,4(1H,3H)-Pyrimidinedione, 5-fluoro-1-(3-oxo-3-phenylpropyl)- (spectra in 45% ethanol)	pH 6.5	250(4.18),271s(4.04)	19-0257-73
	pH 13	246(4.19),273s(3.88)	19-0257-73
$C_{13}H_{11}FN_6O$			
Urea, N-(2-fluoro-4-methylphenyl)-N'-1H-purin-6-yl-	pH 1-2	285(4.42)	87-0139-73
	pH 5-7	283(4.52)	87-0139-73
	pH 12	287.5(4.56)	87-0139-73
$C_{13}H_{11}N$			
Benzenamine, N-(phenylmethylene)-	$CHCl_3$	260(4.23),316(3.92)	78-0057-73
4H-Cyclopenta[b]quinoline, 4-methyl-	ether	525(2.5)	44-0431-73
1-Naphthaleneacetonitrile, α-methyl-	EtOH	224(4.82),271(3.75), 281(3.81),288(3.65), 291(3.65)	22-0724-73
2-Naphthaleneacetonitrile, α-methyl-	EtOH	224(5.43),270(3.88), 275(3.89),286(3.79), 318(3.69)	22-0724-73

Compound	Solvent	$\lambda_{max}(\log \epsilon)$	Ref.
$C_{13}H_{11}NO$			
1-Acenaphthenylcarboxamide, 1,2-dihydro-	EtOH	228(4.79),288(3.76), 320(2.90)	44-3122-73
Benzofuro[3,2-c]pyridine, 1,3-dimethyl-	n.s.g.	255(4.17),282(4.14), 289(4.04),300(4.08)	103-0416-73
Benzophenone, 4-amino-	FSO_3H at -75°	285(4.08),332(4.43)	59-0807-73
Cyclobuta[a]naphthalene-2-carboxamide, 1,2-dihydro-	EtOH	226(4.95)	23-2578-73
2,4,6-Cycloheptatrien-1-one, 2-(phenylamino)-	EtOH	347(4.02),404(4.63)	35-7101-73
Cyclohept[b]indol-6(5H)-one, 7,8-dihydro-	EtOH	232(4.39),247(4.40), 322(4.12),360(3.81)	44-2882-73
Cyclopropa[b]carbazol-2(1H)-one, 1a,3,8,8a-tetrahydro-	EtOH	235(3.18),307(3.28)	44-2882-73
Phenol, 2-[(phenylimino)methyl]-	$C_2H_4Cl_2$	270(4.1)	24-2427-73
$C_{13}H_{11}NOS$			
[1]Benzothiepino[2,3-b]pyridin-6-ol, 5,6-dihydro-	MeOH	250(3.80),274(3.88), 290(3.77)	73-1693-73
$C_{13}H_{11}NO_2$			
Furo[2,3-b]quinoline, 7-methoxy-4-methyl-	EtOH	248(4.64),317(4.88)	49-0633-73
Furo[2,3-b]quinoline, 8-methoxy-4-methyl-	EtOH	244(4.72),332(4.12), 341(4.13)	49-0633-73
Nordictamnine, O-ethyl-	MeOH	236(4.73),242(4.70), 300s(3.87),308(3.92), 316(3.91),326s(3.79), 330(3.88)	78-1217-73
	acid	241(4.82),299s(3.79), 311(3.91),328(3.90), 341s(3.70)	78-1217-73
$C_{13}H_{11}NO_2S$			
Benzene, 1-[(4-methylphenyl)thio]-2-nitro-	DMF	375(3.667)	39-1430-73B
Benzene, 1-[(4-methylphenyl)thio]-4-nitro-	DMF	345(4.12)	32-0723-73
$C_{13}H_{11}NO_2S_2$			
4H-Thieno[3,2-b]indole-3-carboxylic acid, 2-(methylthio)-, methyl ester	EtOH	236(4.57),280(4.09), 326(4.03),356(4.04)	94-2344-73
$C_{13}H_{11}NO_3$			
γ-Fagarine	EtOH	245(4.68),311(3.76), 326(3.71),338(3.66)	95-0619-73
Furo[2,3-b]quinoline, 4,6-dimethoxy-	EtOH	237(4.69),249(4.59), 268(3.70),285s(3.83), 294(3.97),307(4.02), 332(3.75),348(3.72)	18-0577-73
Furo[2,3-b]quinoline, 4,7-dimethoxy-	EtOH	246(4.79),255s(4.29), 289s(3.76),299s(3.89), 307(3.98),318(3.96), 332(3.88)	18-0577-73
Furo[2,3-b]quinoline, 4,8-dimethoxy-	EtOH	223(4.21),240s(4.53), 246(4.64),253s(4.54), 270s(3.87),310(3.26), 323(3.22)	18-0577-73
Furo[2,3-b]quinoline, 6,7-dimethoxy-	EtOH	238(4.64),327(3.12)	64-0196-73B

Compound	Solvent	$\lambda_{max}(\log \epsilon)$	Ref.
Furo[2,3-b]quinoline, 7,8-dimethoxy-	EtOH	251(4.63),327(3.85)	64-0196-73B
$C_{13}H_{11}NO_3S$			
Thiophene, 3-[2-(4-methoxyphenyl)ethenyl]-2-nitro-	EtOH	284(4.26),410(4.23)	118-0313B-73
$C_{13}H_{11}NO_4$			
Furo[2,3-b]quinolin-7-ol, 4,8-dimethoxy-	EtOH	249(4.84),300s(3.68), 317(3.85),330(3.84)	2-1088-73
$C_{13}H_{11}NO_4S$			
Spiro[2H-indene-2,2'-thiazolidine]-4'-carboxylic acid, 1,3-dihydro-1,3-dioxo-, methyl ester, (R)-	EtOH	229(4.46),246s(4.11)	78-4271-73
$C_{13}H_{11}NS$			
6H-Thieno[2,3-b]pyrrole, 6-methyl-5-phenyl-	EtOH	295(4.04)	103-0521-73
$C_{13}H_{11}NS_3$			
Cyclopenta[d][1,3]thiazine-2,4-dithione, 1,5,6,7-tetrahydro-1-phenyl-	EtOH	242(2.87),308(3.66), 320s(3.57),412(3.38), 425s(3.31)	39-1009-73C
$C_{13}H_{11}NSe$			
Selenobenzamide, N-phenyl-	benzene	355(3.96),496(2.50)	143-0519-73
	EtOH	248(4.06),348(3.95), 453(2.49)	143-0519-73
6H-Selenopheno[2,3-b]pyrrole, 6-methyl-5-phenyl-	EtOH	299(4.16)	103-0521-73
$C_{13}H_{11}N_2$			
Benzo[b]quinolizinium, 11-amino-, perchlorate	EtOH	245(4.90),418(4.71)	44-4167-73
$C_{13}H_{11}N_2O$			
Pyrylium, 2-amino-3-cyano-6-(4-methylphenyl)-, perchlorate	HOAc	269(4.01),293s(3.21), 399(4.40)	97-0132-73
$C_{13}H_{11}N_2S$			
Thiopyrylium, 2-amino-3-cyano-6-(4-methylphenyl)-, perchlorate	HOAc	288(3.81),319s(3.59), 422(4.24)	97-0342-73
$C_{13}H_{11}N_3$			
Benzo[c]cinnolinium, 5-(methylamino)-, hydroxide, inner salt	EtOH	251(4.65),294(4.02), 304(4.05),318(3.84), 366(4.06),383(4.07), 400(3.86)	24-1589-73
1-Cyclohexene-1,2-dicarbonitrile, 4-(2-pyridinyl)-	MeOH	233(4.17),262(3.70), 268(3.56)	33-3004-73
1H-Imidazo[4,5-c]pyridine, 2-(phenylmethyl)-	MeOH	246(3.83),264(3.88)	87-1296-73
2H-Indazol-2-amine, N-phenyl-	EtOH	277(3.99)	118-0363-73
$C_{13}H_{11}N_3O$			
Benzenamine, 2-(benzoylazo)-	EtOH	313(4.02),485(3.76)	24-2530-73
	dioxan	295(4.06),435(3.75)	24-2530-73
2H-Benzotriazole, 2-(2-methoxyphenyl)-	MeOH	212(4.31),287(4.17)	73-0224-73
1H-Imidazo[4,5-c]pyridine-2-methanol, α-phenyl-	MeOH	243(3.74),249(3.75), 264(3.79)	87-1296-73

Compound	Solvent	$\lambda_{max}(\log \epsilon)$	Ref.
Pyrido[3,4-b]pyrazin-2(1H)-one, 3,4-dihydro-3-phenyl-	MeOH	225(4.63),317(3.58)	87-1296-73
1,3,10-Triazaphenanthrene, 6-methoxy-9-methyl-	EtOH	232(4.50),263(4.21), 275(4.16),322(3.75)	95-0330-73
$C_{13}H_{11}N_3OS_3$			
4-Thiazolidinone, 3-ethyl-5-(5H-thiazolidinethylidene)-2-thioxo-	n.s.g.	523(4.78),546(4.79)	124-1151-73
$C_{13}H_{11}N_3O_2$			
1H-Azuleno[1,2-d]triazole-9-carboxylic acid, ethyl ester	MeOH	244(4.35),302(4.68), 316(4.71),360s(3.78), 380(3.95),402(4.06), 480(2.50)	18-3161-73
2,4(1H,3H)-Pyrimidinedione, 1-(1H-indol-3-ylmethyl)- (spectra in 35% ethanol)	pH 6.5	217(4.61),270(4.19), 287s(3.94)	19-0257-73
	pH 13	270(4.12),287s(3.83)	19-0257-73
$C_{13}H_{11}N_3O_2S$			
Propanenitrile, 3-[(4-methyl-6-nitro-2-quinolinyl)thio]-	EtOH	225(4.29),255(4.44), 300(4.07)	103-0481-73
$C_{13}H_{11}N_3O_2S_2$			
Carbamic acid, (6-phenyl-2H-thiazolo-[3,2-b][1,2,4]thiadiazol-2-ylidene)-, ethyl ester	EtOH	258(4.01),316(4.31)	94-2408-73
$C_{13}H_{11}N_3O_3$			
2,5-Cyclohexadiene-1,4-dione, mono[methyl(4-nitrophenyl)hydrazone]	MeCN	443(4.50)	1-3632-73
Pyrimido[1,2-a]benzimidazole-3-carboxylic acid, 1,4-dihydro-4-oxo-, ethyl ester	EtOH	231s(--),247s(--), 276s(--),331(4.26), 341(4.26),358s(--)	4-0071-73
10H-Pyrimido[1,2-a]benzimidazole-3-carboxylic acid, 4,10-dihydro-4-oxo-, ethyl ester	MeOH	220(4.38),243s(4.21), 264(3.87),275s(3.73), 331(4.27),342(4.26)	39-1588-73C
	EtOH	248(4.31),273(4.11), 291(4.01)	94-2019-73
$C_{13}H_{11}N_3O_5$			
2,5-Piperazinedione, 1-acetyl-3-[(4-nitrophenyl)methylene]-	EtOH	229(4.12),331(4.19)	88-1135-73
$C_{13}H_{11}N_3O_7$			
Pyridinium, 1-methyl-, 3,5-dinitrosalicylate	EtOH	258(3.97),340(4.09)	39-2949-73C
$C_{13}H_{11}N_3S$			
1,2,4-Triazolo[4,3-a]pyridine, 3-(methylthio)-7-phenyl-	EtOH	255(4.41),310(3.76)	95-0642-73
$C_{13}H_{11}N_5O$			
Benzamide, N-(9-methyl-9H-purin-6-yl)-	MeOH	230s(4.16),280(4.26)	18-3228-73
Benzamide, 4-methyl-N-1H-purin-6-yl-	MeOH	252(4.21),287(4.37)	18-3228-73
1H-Pyrazole-4,5-dione, 3-methyl-, 4-(3-quinolinylhydrazone)	EtOH	231(4.17),292(3.56), 307(3.48),354(3.96), 410(4.16)	12-2723-73
$C_{13}H_{11}N_5O_8S$			
2-Propenimidamide, N-hydroxy-3-(2-thienyl)-, picrate	EtOH	343(4.23)	39-2241-73C

Compound	Solvent	$\lambda_{max}(\log \epsilon)$	Ref.
2-Propenimidamide, N-hydroxy-3-(2-thienyl)-, picrate, trans	EtOH	325(4.47)	39-2241-73C
2-Propenimidamide, N-hydroxy-3-(3-thienyl)-, picrate	EtOH	299(4.01),355(4.14)	39-2241-73C
$C_{13}H_{11}O_2$			
Benzofuro[3,2-c]pyrylium, 1,3-dimethyl-, perchlorate	n.s.g.	255(4.25),266(4.23), 320(3.69)	103-0416-73
$C_{13}H_{11}O_4P$			
Phosphonic acid, 9H-xanthen-9-yl-	EtOH	245(3.703)	65-0087-73
$C_{13}H_{11}O_4PS_2$			
Phosphonic acid, (2,6-dithienyl-4H-pyran-4-yl)-	EtOH	260(4.164)	65-0087-73
$C_{13}H_{12}$			
Azulene, 1-(1-propenyl)-	C_6H_{12}	286(4.57),371(3.85), 391(3.80),618s(2.38), 640(2.41),676s(2.32), 700s(2.24),753(2.86), 798(1.70)	5-0166-73
Benzocyclononatetraene	hexane	240s(3.47)	88-3103-73
1,1'-Biphenyl, 2-methyl-	EtOH	235(4.02)	22-1517-73
$C_{13}H_{12}AsNO_5$			
Benzoic acid, 2-[(4-aminophenyl)amino]-	EtOH	300(4.2),340(4.1)	140-0008-73
$C_{13}H_{12}BrN$			
Benzenemethanamine, 2-bromo-N-phenyl-	EtOH	244(4.11),293(3.39)	18-3316-73
$C_{13}H_{12}BrN_3$			
1H-Pyrrolo[1,2-b][1,2,4]triazole, 6-(4-bromophenyl)-1,2-dimethyl-	MeOH	220(3.96),271(4.27)	118-0414-73
$C_{13}H_{12}Br_2O_5$			
2H-Benzopyran-2,6-dione, 3,4,6,8a-tetrahydro-4,4-dimethyl-8a-acetoxy-5,7-dibromo-	MeOH	259(3.77)	35-8319-73
$C_{13}H_{12}ClN$			
Benzenemethanamine, 2-chloro-N-phenyl-	EtOH	246(4.32),296(3.04)	18-3316-73
2,5-Cyclohexadien-1-imine, 4-chloro-4-methyl-N-phenyl-	MeOH	260(4.46),360(3.75)	2-1187-73
$C_{13}H_{12}ClNO$			
7-Oxa-8-azabicyclo[4.2.1]nona-2,4-diene, 8-(4-chlorophenyl)-	MeOH	246(4.25)	18-3517-73
$C_{13}H_{12}ClNOS$			
Ethanone, 1-[4-(chloromethyl)-2-(3-methylphenyl)-5-thiazolyl]-	MeOH	238(4.19),318(4.29)	80-0685-73
Ethanone, 1-[4-(chloromethyl)-2-(4-methylphenyl)-5-thiazolyl]-	MeOH	241(4.13),318(4.26)	80-0685-73
$C_{13}H_{12}Cl_3N_5O$			
Acetamide, N-[2-[2-[(2,4,6-trichlorophenyl)azo]-1H-imidazol-4-yl]ethyl]-	EtOH	365(4.33)	44-1971-73
Acetamide, N-[2-[5-[(2,4,6-trichlorophenyl)azo]-1H-imidazol-4-yl]ethyl]-	EtOH	327(4.27)	44-1971-73

Compound	Solvent	$\lambda_{max}(\log \epsilon)$	Ref.
$C_{13}H_{12}FNO_3$			
Pyridine, 5-fluoro-2-methoxy-4-(phenylmethoxy)-, 1-oxide	MeOH	260(4.15),290(3.59)	4-0779-73
$C_{13}H_{12}F_4O_2$			
1H-Cyclopropa[a]naphthalene, 7b-(difluoromethoxy)-1,1-difluoro-1a,2,3,7b-tetrahydro-4-methoxy-	n.s.g.	246(3.82),276(3.40), 283(3.43),304(2.94), 348(2.88),364(2.85)	35-6655-73
1H-Cyclopropa[a]naphthalene, 7b-(difluoromethoxy)-1,1-difluoro-1a,2,3,7b-tetrahydro-5-methoxy-	n.s.g.	232(4.10),277(3.26), 284(3.23)	35-6655-73
$C_{13}H_{12}F_5N_2O_2$			
1H-Imidazol-1-yloxy, 4,5-dihydro-4,4,5,5-tetramethyl-2-(pentafluorophenyl)-, 3-oxide	EtOH	206s(3.95),249(3.79), 293(3.71),346(3.92), 547(2.51)	78-3833-73
$C_{13}H_{12}INO_2$			
1H-Carbazol-1-one, 2,3,4,9-tetrahydro-6-iodo-7-methoxy-	EtOH	216(4.37),245(4.28), 260(4.24),335(4.37)	39-0872-73B
$C_{13}H_{12}N$			
6H-Pyrido[2,1-a]isoindolium, 1-methyl-, chloride	H_2O	250s(3.08),254(4.12), 317(4.09)	44-2351-73
6H-Pyrido[2,1-a]isoindolium, 2-methyl-, chloride	H_2O	223s(4.16),250(4.04), 257(4.07),308(4.03)	44-2351-73
$C_{13}H_{12}NO$			
9H-Pyrano[2,3-b]indol-1-ium, 2,4-dimethyl-, chloride	EtOH	204(4.28),255(4.31), 260(4.35),335(3.96)	103-1152-73
$C_{13}H_{12}N_2$			
1H-Benzocycloheptene-2,3-dicarbonitrile, 4,4a,5,9a-tetrahydro-	MeOH	242(4.00),260s(3.67)	33-3004-73
1,4-Methanonaphthalene-6,7-dicarbonitrile, 1,4,4a,5,8,8a-hexahydro-	MeOH	234(3.95)	33-3004-73
4-Pyridinamine, 3-ethenyl-N-phenyl-	MeOH	225(4.7),282(4.7)	103-1119-73
9H-Pyrido[2,3-b]indole, 2,4-dimethyl-	MeOH	218(4.45),239(4.26), 261(4.02),296(4.13), 322(3.60)	103-0968-73 +103-1154-73
1H-Pyrrolo[3,2-c]pyridine, 2,3-dihydro-1-phenyl-	MeOH	300(4.3)	103-1119-73
$C_{13}H_{12}N_2O$			
Benzenamine, 2-methoxy-N-(2-pyridinylmethylene)-	EtOH	242(4.08),281(3.90), 343(3.61)	12-1031-73
Benzenamine, 2-methoxy-N-(3-pyridinylmethylene)-	EtOH	245(4.19),277s(3.95), 344(3.77)	12-1031-73
Benzenamine, 2-methoxy-N-(4-pyridinylmethylene)-	EtOH	236(4.12),245s(4.12), 270(3.92),355(3.72)	12-1031-73
Benzenamine, 3-methoxy-N-(2-pyridinylmethylene)-	EtOH	248(4.12),281(3.98), 323(3.74)	12-1031-73
Benzenamine, 3-methoxy-N-(3-pyridinylmethylene)-	EtOH	248(4.14),278(3.91), 325(3.70)	12-1031-73
Benzenamine, 3-methoxy-N-(4-pyridinylmethylene)-	EtOH	251(4.28),274(4.06), 335(3.84)	12-1031-73
Benzenamine, 4-methoxy-N-(2-pyridinylmethylene)-	EtOH	238(4.10),245s(4.07), 288(4.00),343(4.08)	12-1031-73
Benzenamine, 4-methoxy-N-(3-pyridinylmethylene)-	EtOH	233(4.18),283(3.92), 345(4.04)	12-1031-73

Compound	Solvent	λ_{max}(log ε)	Ref.
Benzenamine, 4-methoxy-N-(4-pyridinyl-methylene)-	EtOH	233(4.18),283(3.92), 345(4.04)	12-1031-73
Methanone, bis(4-aminophenyl)-	FSO_3H at -75°	284(4.08),322(4.36)	59-0807-73
Phenol, 4-[(2-methylphenyl)azo]-	C_6H_{12}	345(4.44)	62-0289-73
	EtOH	240(4.04),357(4.52)	62-0289-73
	ether	237(4.66),353(4.98)	62-0289-73
	$CHCl_3$	345(4.33)	62-0289-73
	CCl_4	345(4.38)	62-0289-73
Phenol, 4-[(3-methylphenyl)azo]-	EtOH	240(4.22),352(4.54)	62-0289-73
	ether	240(4.18),350(4.58)	62-0289-73
	$CHCl_3$	340(3.95)	62-0289-73
Phenol, 4-[(4-methylphenyl)azo]-	EtOH	240(4.18),352(4.51)	62-0289-73
	ether	240(4.34),347(4.66)	62-0289-73
	$CHCl_3$	345(3.95)	62-0289-73
	CCl_4	345(4.53)	62-0289-73
Phenol, 4-methyl-2-[(2-pyridinylmethyl-ene)amino]-, copper chelate	pH 9.9	535(4.08)	18-2421-73
manganese chelate	pH 9.0	520(4.28)	18-2421-73
nickel chelate	pH 9.2	540(4.30)	18-2421-73
zinc chelate	pH 7.2	518(4.34)	18-2421-73
$C_{13}H_{12}N_2OS$			
2H-Thiopyran-3-carboxamide, 2-imino-6-(4-methylphenyl)-	CH_2Cl_2	289(3.92),302s(3.87), 411(3.95)	97-0342-73
$C_{13}H_{12}N_2OS_3$			
4-Thiazolidinone, 5-(3-methyl-2-thiazol-idinylidene)-3-phenyl-2-thioxo-	EtOH	281(4.04),395(4.40)	94-1431-73
4-Thiazolidinone, 5-[3-(phenylmethyl)-2-thiazolidinylidene]-2-thioxo-	EtOH	284(4.15),395(4.57)	94-1431-73
$C_{13}H_{12}N_2O_2$			
2H-[1,2,4]Oxadiazolo[2,3-a]pyridin-2-one, 1,8a-dihydro-6-methyl-1-phenyl-	EtOH	234.5(4.09)	117-0095-73
2H-[1,2,4]Oxadiazolo[2,3-a]pyridin-2-one, 1,8a-dihydro-8-methyl-1-phenyl-	EtOH	234(4.11)	117-0095-73
Pyridine, 1,4-dihydro-1-methyl-4-[(4-nitrophenyl)methylene]- (also other solvents)	dioxan	235(3.90),324(3.91), 522(4.52)	48-0901-73
4-Pyridinecarboxamide, N-(4-methoxyphen-yl)-	EtOH	228(4.07),285(3.89)	12-2027-73
3H-Pyrido[3,4-b]indole-3-carboxylic acid, 4,9-dihydro-1-methyl-	n.s.g.	215(--),245(--), 355(4.17)	22-2058-73
	base	235(--),318(4.08)	22-2058-73
hydrochloride	n.s.g.	245(--),355(4.20)	22-2058-73
9H-Pyrrolo[3,4-b]quinolin-9-one, 2-acet-yl-1,2,3,4-tetrahydro-	n.s.g.	240(4.49),315(4.09), 328(4.14)	4-0225-73
$C_{13}H_{12}N_2O_2S$			
5-Thia-2,7-diazabicyclo[4.2.0]oct-3-en-8-one, 2-(phenylacetyl)-, (1R-cis)-	EtOH	275(3.88)	39-1187-73C
$C_{13}H_{12}N_2O_3$			
1H-Indole-2-carboxylic acid, 4-cyano-5-methoxy-	n.s.g.	220(4.36),345(4.17)	22-2046-73
7-Oxa-8-azabicyclo[4.2.1]nona-2,4-diene, 8-(4-nitrophenyl)-	MeOH	237(3.98),352(4.04)	18-3517-73
2,5-Piperazinedione, 1-acetyl-, 3-(phen-ylmethylene)-	EtOH	229(4.16),316(4.19)	88-1135-73

Compound	Solvent	$\lambda_{max}(\log \epsilon)$	Ref.
2,4(1H,3H)-Pyrimidinedione, 1-(3-oxo-3-phenylpropyl)- (in 10% ethanol)	pH 6.5	252(4.23)	19-0257-73
	pH 13	249(4.21)	19-0257-73
$C_{13}H_{12}N_2O_3S$			
Pyridinium 3-indolesulfonate	EtOH	258(3.90),265(3.90), 277(3.76),287(3.69)	78-0669-73
$C_{13}H_{12}N_2O_4$			
Isoxazole, 5-[2-(4-methoxyphenyl)ethenyl]-3-methyl-4-nitro-	EtOH	247(4.12),279(4.10), 383(4.40)	2-1074-73
2-Propenoic acid, 3-(1H-indol-3-yl)-2-nitro-, ethyl ester	EtOH-pH 7	350(3.99),410(4.03)	104-1082-73
	EtOH-pH 8	480(4.34)	104-1082-73
$C_{13}H_{12}N_2O_5$			
2H-1-Benzopyran-2-one, 4-morpholino-3-nitro-	EtOH	272(4.19),312(4.11), 385s(3.25)	103-0816-73
Pyridine, 2-methoxy-4-nitro-5-(phenylmethoxy)-, 1-oxide	MeOH	265(3.81),308(3.67), 369(3.80)	4-0779-73
$C_{13}H_{12}N_2O_7$			
2-Quinolinecarboxylic acid, 1,4-dihydro-5,8-dimethoxy-6-nitro-4-oxo-, methyl ester	$CHCl_3$	342(4.03),376(3.94)	39-2374-73C
$C_{13}H_{12}N_2S$			
Propanenitrile, 3-[(4-methyl-2-quinolinyl)thio]-	EtOH	215(4.56),255(4.49), 355(3.75)	103-0481-73
Thiourea, N,N'-diphenyl-, Te(IV) complex	benzene	385s(4.16),480(3.77)	140-0087-73
$C_{13}H_{12}N_3O_5$			
Spiro[naphthalene-1(2H),2'-oxazolidine], 3'-methyl-2,4-dinitro-, ion(1-),	DMSO	362(4.23),518(4.45)	44-2838-73
K salt	2% DMSO	338(4.08),497(4.11)	44-2838-73
Na salt	MeOH	344(4.15),502(4.29)	18-0693-73
$C_{13}H_{12}N_4$			
Benzenamine, 2-[(iminophenylmethyl)azo]-	EtOH	312(4.12),462(3.82)	24-2530-73
	dioxan	300(4.04),430(3.78)	24-2530-73
$C_{13}H_{12}N_4O$			
Pyrazinamine, 5-(1H-indol-3-yl)-3-methyl-, oxide	EtOH	276(4.22),298(4.19), 372(3.66)	78-3761-73
1H-1,2,4-Triazolo[4,3-b]pyridazin-4-ium, 8-hydroxy-6-methyl-1-(phenylmethyl)-, hydroxide, inner salt	n.s.g.	225(3.73),275(3.79), 308(4.00)	48-0097-73
	hexane	325(--)	48-0097-73
	H_2O	303(--)	48-0097-73
	MeOH	307(--)	48-0097-73
	dioxan	317(--)	48-0097-73
$C_{13}H_{12}N_4O_2$			
Benzamide, (2-nitrophenyl)hydrazone	MeOH	243(4.28),305(4.02), 470(3.79)	24-2530-73
Pyrimido[1,2-a]benzimidazole-3-carboxylic acid, 4-amino-, ethyl ester	EtOH	236s(--),247(4.50), 256(4.48),263s(--), 310(4.11),370s(--)	4-0071-73
$C_{13}H_{12}N_4O_2S$			
1,2,4-Triazino[5,6-d][3,1]benzoxazepine, 7-acetyl-6,7-dihydro-3-(methylthio)-	EtOH	237(4.37),376(4.16)	78-0639-73

Compound	Solvent	λ_{max}(log ε)	Ref.
$C_{13}H_{12}N_4O_4S$			
2H-1,2,3-Benzothiadiazine, 2-(2,4-dinitrophenyl)-5,6,7,8-tetrahydro-, perchlorate	MeOH	222(4.17),239(4.17), 262(4.11),290(4.10), 410(3.78)	118-0225-73
$C_{13}H_{12}N_4O_5$			
Benzoic acid, 2-(5-acetoxy-1,4,5,6-tetrahydro-4,6-dioxo-2-pyrimidinyl)-hydrazide	EtOH	220(4.38)	103-0247-73
$C_{13}H_{12}N_4S_2$			
Benzenamine, N,N-dimethyl-4-(thieno-[2,3-c]isothiazol-2-ylazo)-	MeCN	255(3.89),286(3.91), 327(3.63),339s(3.60), 354s(3.54),529(4.59)	48-0539-73
$C_{13}H_{12}N_6O$			
Urea, N-(2-methylphenyl)-N'-1H-purin-6-yl-	pH 1-2	280(4.38)	87-0139-73
	pH 5-7	279(4.42)	87-0139-73
	pH 12	286(4.47)	87-0139-73
Urea, N-(phenylmethyl)-N'-1H-purin-6-yl-	pH 1-2	277(4.33)	87-0139-73
	pH 5-7	269(4.29)	87-0139-73
	pH 12	278(4.24)	87-0139-73
$C_{13}H_{12}N_6O_2$			
2,4-Pteridinediamine, 6-(2-methoxyphenyl)-, 8-oxide	pH 1	259(4.30),276s(4.26), 294(4.14),383(3.81)	35-6413-73
$C_{13}H_{12}O$			
Bicyclo[3.1.0]hex-2-ene-6-carboxaldehyde, 4-phenyl-, endo-exo-	C_6H_{12}	232(3.30),252(2.83), 258(2.77)	44-4007-73
1,1'-Biphenyl, 4-methoxy-	EtOH	252(4.22)	35-5288-73
[1,1'-Biphenyl]-3-ol, 5-methyl-	EtOH	204(4.51),218(4.28), 254(4.07)	104-2172-73
[1,1'-Biphenyl]-3-ol, 6-methyl-	EtOH	218s(4.30),244s(3.80), 286(3.47)	104-2172-73
[1,1'-Biphenyl]-4-ol, 3-methyl-	EtOH	262(4.24)	104-2172-73
Ethanone, 1-(7-methyl-1-naphthalenyl)-	heptane	215(4.57),220s(4.54), 240s(4.28),305(3.73)	24-1341-73
1H-Fluoren-1-one, 2,3,4,9-tetrahydro-	C_6H_{12}	225(3.88),232(4.07), 238(4.07),290s(4.29), 296(4.30),307s(4.16)	44-1439-73
Furan, tetrahydro-2-(1-nonene-3,5,7-triynyl)-, trans	ether	231(4.86),241(5.01), 273(3.81),290(4.05), 308(4.17),330(4.00)	24-3775-73
5,10-Methanobenzocycloocten-11-one, 4a,5,10,10a-tetrahydro-	EtOH	240(3.71),258(3.81), 310s(2.97)	44-1893-73
$C_{13}H_{12}OS$			
Ethanone, 1-(2-methyl-5-phenyl-3-thienyl)-	EtOH	251(4.44),285(4.06)	78-0413-73
Ethanone, 1-(5-methyl-2-phenyl-3-thienyl)-	EtOH	227(4.14),257(3.97), 299(3.72)	78-0413-73
$C_{13}H_{12}O_2$			
6-Azuleneacetic acid, methyl ester	C_6H_{12}	279(4.86),285(4.86), 330(3.65),337(3.62), 344(3.80),573(2.49), 591(2.45),620(2.42), 684(1.98)	44-1106-73

Compound	Solvent	$\lambda_{max}(\log \epsilon)$	Ref.
5H-Benzocyclohepten-5-one, 6-hydroxy-7,8-dimethyl-	EtOH	262(4.47),270(4.73), 297(3.81),375(3.58)	39-1223-73C
3-Dodecene-6,8,10-triynoic acid, methyl ester, 12-^{14}C, (Z)-	ether	210(5.18)	24-2745-73
Ethanone, 1-(2-methyl-5-phenyl-3-furanyl)-	C_6H_{12}	224s(4.20),281(4.34)	22-1760-73
Ethanone, 1-(5-methyl-2-phenyl-3-furanyl)-	C_6H_{12}	306.5(3.98)	22-1760-73
2H-Pyran-2-one, 4,5-dimethyl-6-phenyl- 335(4.11)	96% H_2SO_4	219(4.12),243(3.82), 335(4.11)	35-7914-73
4H-Pyran-4-one, 2,6-dimethyl-3-phenyl-	96% H_2SO_4	227(4.14),257(3.97)	35-7914-73
$C_{13}H_{12}O_3$			
1-Azulenecarboxylic acid, 4-(hydroxymethyl)-, methyl ester	pet ether	233(4.30),289(4.54), 293(4.54),303(4.58), 338(3.71),349(3.72), 367(3.85),532(2.74), 571(2.69),623(2.28)	24-1337-73
5H-Benzocyclohepten-5-one, 6,9-dihydroxy-7,8-dimethyl-	EtOH	232(4.52),256s(4.03), 325(3.97),350(4.03)	39-1223-73C
2-Cyclohexen-1-one, 2-(3,4-methylenedioxyphenyl)-	EtOH	238(3.99),294(3.62)	23-2338-73
Ethanone, 1-(1,4-dihydroxy-3-methyl-2-naphthalenyl)-	n.s.g.	215(4.56),242(4.17), 275(4.17),396(3.49)	39-0235-73C
2-Furanpropanoic acid, 5-phenyl-	EtOH	283(4.16)	2-0301-73
2-Naphthaleneacetic acid, 6-hydroxy-α-methyl-	MeOH	225(5.10),256(3.49), 265(3.62),274(3.65), 322(3.18),334(3.24)	36-0937-73
$C_{13}H_{12}O_4$			
4H-1-Benzopyran-4-one, 7-acetoxy-2,5-dimethyl-	MeOH	226(4.03),241(3.81), 248(3.78),266s(--), 299(3.50)	94-0149-73
1,2,4-Naphthalenetriol, 3-methyl-, 1-acetate	n.s.g.	244(4.00),294(3.73)	39-0368-73C
Naphtho[2,3-b]oxiren-2(1aH)-one, 1a-acetyl-7,7a-dihydro-7-hydroxy-7a-methyl-, (1aα,7β,7aα)-	n.s.g.	218(3.83),257(4.01), 293(3.17)	39-0235-73C
Naphtho[2,3-b]oxiren-2(1aH)-one, 7a-acetyl-7,7a-dihydro-7-hydroxy-1a-methyl-	n.s.g.	216(3.89),254(4.01), 291(3.17)	39-0235-73C
2H-Pyran-2-one, 5,6-dihydro-3-hydroxy-4-(phenylacetyl)-	EtOH	283(3.91)	95-1183-73
$C_{13}H_{12}O_4S$			
Benzo[b]thiophene-6-carboxylic acid, 4-acetoxy-7-methyl-, methyl ester	EtOH	218(4.45),241(4.57), 280(4.20),324(3.95)	48-0300-73
Benzo[b]thiophene-2,3-dicarboxylic acid, 5-methyl-, dimethyl ester	EtOH-HCl	234(4.18),245s(4.06), 295(4.17)	1-0595-73
$C_{13}H_{12}O_5$			
Acetic acid, (4,7-dihydroxy-5-methyl-2H-1-benzopyran-2-ylidene)-, methyl ester	MeOH	250(3.72),286(3.81), 310(3.87)	94-0149-73
Acetic acid, (4-hydroxy-7-methoxy-5-methyl-2H-1-benzopyran-2-ylidene)-	MeOH	285s(--),304(3.77)	94-0149-73
4,5-Benzofurandicarboxylic acid, 7-methyl-, dimethyl ester	90% EtOH	228(4.41),262(3.75), 303(3.51)	12-1059-73
2H-1-Benzopyran-3-carboxylic acid, 6-methoxy-2-oxo-, ethyl ester	MeOH	230(4.29),293(4.16), 367(3.73)	24-0388-73

Compound	Solvent	λ_{max}(log ε)	Ref.
$C_{13}H_{12}O_6$			
2H-1-Benzopyran-6-carboxaldehyde, 5,7,8-trimethoxy-2-oxo-	MeOH	206(4.31),267(4.16), 300s(4.01)	78-2645-73
2,5-Furandione, 3-(3,4-dimethoxyphenyl)-4-methoxy-	EtOH	244(3.91),270s(3.68), 329s(3.53),382(3.75)	39-1538-73C
$C_{13}H_{12}S$			
Benzene, [(phenylmethyl)thio]-	n.s.g.	255.4(-0.48)	80-0263-73
Thiophene, 2-[2-(4-methylphenyl)ethenyl]-, cis	EtOH	237(4.08),294(3.99)	4-0643-73
trans	EtOH	232(3.99),327(4.45)	4-0643-73
$C_{13}H_{13}BrO_4$			
1(2H)-Naphthalenone, 2-acetyl-3-bromo-3,4-dihydro-2,4-dihydroxy-3-methyl-, (2α,3β,4α)-	n.s.g.	217(3.97),256(4.05), 296(3.08)	39-0235-73C
$C_{13}H_{13}Br_2N$			
1H-Cyclopenta[b]quinolinium, 3-bromo-2,3-dihydro-4-methyl-, bromide	EtOH	248(4.42),334(4.01)	103-1253-73
$C_{13}H_{13}ClO$			
Cyclohexanone, 2-[(2-chlorophenyl)methylene]-, (E)-	EtOH	278(4.04)	23-1458-73
Cyclohexanone, 2-[(3-chlorophenyl)methylene]-, (E)-	EtOH	284(4.11)	23-1458-73
Cyclohexanone, 2-[(4-chlorophenyl)methylene]-, (E)-	EtOH	293(4.21)	23-1458-73
Methanone, (2-chloro-1-cyclohexen-1-yl)-phenyl-	EtOH	249(4.07)	78-4241-73
$C_{13}H_{13}Cl_2N$			
Pyridinium, 1-[(2-chlorophenyl)methyl]-3-methyl-, chloride	H_2O	267(3.65),275s(3.52)	44-2351-73
Pyridinium, 1-[(2-chlorophenyl)methyl]-4-methyl-, chloride	H_2O	256(3.58),275s(2.76)	44-2351-73
$C_{13}H_{13}F_3$			
Cyclohexene, 1-[3-(trifluoromethyl)-phenyl-	EtOH	223(3.91),251(3.96)	35-5288-73
Cyclohexene, 1-[4-(trifluoromethyl)-phenyl-	EtOH	216(4.07),223(3.98), 257(4.11)	35-5288-73
$C_{13}H_{13}F_3N_2O_3$			
1H-Indole-3-acetamide, α-hydroxy-5-methoxy-2-methyl-4-(trifluoromethyl)-	MeOH	215(4.46),305(4.04)	44-1504-73
$C_{13}H_{13}IN_2$			
Pyridinium, 1-[[(3-methylphenyl)methylene]amino]-, iodide	EtOH	207(4.54),290(4.22)	103-1108-73
	MeCN	248(4.29),298(4.36)	103-1108-73
	DMSO	299(4.32)	103-1108-73
Pyridinium, 1-[[(4-methylphenyl)methylene]amino]-, iodide	EtOH	213(4.43),275(4.09), 302(4.28)	103-1108-73
	HOAc	290(4.30),360(3.35)	103-1108-73
	DMSO	240(4.18),285(4.28)	103-1108-73
Pyridinium, 2-methyl-1-[(phenylmethylene)amino]-, iodide	MeOH	199(4.69),220(4.39), 276(4.30)	4-0821-73
$C_{13}H_{13}IN_2O$			
Pyridinium, 1-[[(3-methoxyphenyl)methylene]amino]-, iodide	EtOH	270(4.56),290(4.16)	103-1108-73

Compound	Solvent	$\lambda_{max}(\log \epsilon)$	Ref.
Pyridinium, 1-[[(4-methoxyphenyl)methylene]amino]-, iodide	EtOH	219(4.46),265(3.93), 320(4.39)	103-1108-73
$C_{13}H_{13}IN_2O_2$			
Pyridinium, 1-methyl-4-[(4-nitrophenyl)-methyl]-, iodide	H_2O	226(4.41),259s(4.14), 265(4.16),274(4.11)	48-0901-73
$C_{13}H_{13}IN_2O_3$			
1H-Pyrazole-3-carboxylic acid, 5-(hydroxymethyl)-1-(4-iodophenyl)-, ethyl ester	C_6H_{12}	214(4.14),261(4.29)	4-0015-73
$C_{13}H_{13}N$			
3-Azatricyclo[3.2.1.0^{2,4}]oct-6-ene, 3-phenyl-, exo	EtOH	238(4.02),278(2.89)	12-0619-73
Benzenamine, N-(phenylmethyl)-, BF_3 complex	MeOH	207(4.16),250(2.48)	138-1111-73
1H-Indole, 2-(2,3-butadienyl)-3-methyl-	EtOH	227(4.54),278s(3.92), 285(3.95),292(3.91)	39-1913-73C
3H-Indole, 2,3-dimethyl-3-(2-propynyl)-	EtOH	209s(4.21),212(4.26), 218(4.26),224s(4.10), 258(3.73)	39-1913-73C
Pyridine, 2,5-dimethyl-4-phenyl-	n.s.g.	250(4.3),260s(4.0)	103-0212-73
$C_{13}H_{13}NO$			
2-Azabicyclo[3.2.0]hept-6-en-3-one, 2-methyl-5-phenyl-	EtOH	260(2.34)	39-1079-73C
2-Azabicyclo[3.2.0]hept-6-en-3-one, 2-methyl-6-phenyl-	EtOH	217(4.06),257(4.20), 291(3.65)	39-1079-73C
2H-Azepin-2-one, 1,3-dihydro-1-methyl-4-phenyl-	EtOH	228(4.15),301(4.04)	39-1079-73C
2H-Azepin-2-one, 1,3-dihydro-1-methyl-5-phenyl-	EtOH	242(4.36)	39-1079-73C
2H-Azepin-2-one, 1,3-dihydro-1-methyl-6-phenyl-	EtOH	282(3.98)	39-1079-73C
Benzo[f]quinoline, 1,2,3,4-tetrahydro-	EtOH	229(4.05),250(3.60), 259(3.53),308(4.18)	22-0691-73
2-Naphthalenepropanenitrile, 1,2,3,4-tetrahydro-1-oxo-	EtOH	249(4.11),293(3.28)	22-0691-73
7-Oxa-8-azabicyclo[4.2.1]nona-2,4-diene, 8-phenyl-	MeOH	238(4.09),264(3.80)	18-3517-73
$C_{13}H_{13}NO_2$			
1H-Carbazol-1-one, 2,3,4,9-tetrahydro-3-(hydroxymethyl)-	EtOH	237(3.15),304(3.34)	44-2882-73
1H-Carbazol-1-one, 2,3,4,9-tetrahydro-5-methoxy-	EtOH	243s(4.15),248(4.17), 307(4.14),343(3.74)	39-0878-73B
1H-Carbazol-1-one, 2,3,4,9-tetrahydro-7-methoxy-	EtOH	235(3.76),257(3.65), 332(4.08)	39-0878-73B
9H-Cyclopenta[b]quinolin-9-one, 1,2,3,4-tetrahydro-6-methoxy-	EtOH	227(3.18),247(3.81), 254(3.88),298s(3.25), 310(3.38),322(3.34)	39-0872-73B
Furo[3,2-c]quinoline, 2,3-dihydro-6-methoxy-2-methyl-	MeOH	231(4.73),302(3.84), 314(3.85),327(3.75)	24-0355-73
1H-Indole-2-acetic acid, 1-methyl-α-methylene-, methyl ester	MeOH	223(4.44),275(3.72), 283(3.70),295(3.70)	35-7146-73
1(2H)-Isoquinolinone, 2-methyl-4-(1-oxo-propyl)-	EtOH	222(4.49),258(3.95), 304(4.08),312(4.04), 325(3.99),339(3.80)	94-2585-73
1(2H)-Isoquinolinone, 2-methyl-5-(1-oxo-propyl)-	EtOH	215(4.54),253(3.96), 309(3.88),342(3.64)	94-2585-73

Compound	Solvent	$\lambda_{max}(\log \epsilon)$	Ref.
1(2H)-Isoquinolinone, 2-methyl-7-(1-oxo-propyl)-	EtOH	213(4.51),225(4.49), 266(3.81),317(4.04), 332(4.11),343(4.04)	94-2585-73
2-Propenoic acid, 3-(1H-indol-3-yl)-2-methyl-, methyl ester	EtOH	229(4.45),280(3.93), 331(4.35)	104-1275-73
2(1H)-Pyridinone, 5-methyl-4-(phenyl-methoxy)-	MeOH	283(3.67)	88-3079-73
3-Quinolinecarboxylic acid, 2-methyl-, ethyl ester	EtOH	238(4.66),282(3.75)	94-1943-73
4(1H)-Quinolinone, 8-methoxy-3-(2-prop-enyl)-	MeOH	231(4.58),299(3.89), 326(4.14),339(4.09)	24-0355-73
$C_{13}H_{13}NO_2S_2$			
1,3(2H,4H)-Isoquinolinedione, 4-[bis-(methylthio)methylene]-2-methyl-	EtOH	265(3.08)	95-0322-73
Thiophene, 2-nitro-3-[(2,4,6-trimethyl-phenyl)thio]-	MeOH	378(4.06)	4-1007-73
Thiophene, 3-nitro-2-[(2,4,6-trimethyl-phenyl)thio]-	MeOH	370(3.89)	4-1007-73
$C_{13}H_{13}NO_3$			
3-Azatricyclo[4.4.2.0^{2,5}]dodeca-7,9,11-trien-4-one, 2-acetoxy-	EtOH	246s(3.57),254(3.69), 263(3.71),273(3.50)	44-1886-73
Benzenepropanoic acid, 2-(3-cyano-1-oxo-propyl)-	EtOH	244(3.95),287(3.11)	22-0691-73
1H-Carbazol-1-one, 2,3,4,9-tetrahydro-7-hydroxy-6-(hydroxymethyl)-	EtOH	230(4.40),280(4.16)	44-2728-73
1,3-Dioxolo[4,5-g]pyrrolo[1,2-b]isoquin-olin-9(5H)-one, 7,8,9a,10-tetrahydro-	EtOH	292(3.63)	78-0213-73
1,4-Ethenocyclohepta[c]pyrrol-3(2H)-one, 4-acetoxy-1,3a,4,8a-tetrahydro-	EtOH	242.5(3.67)	44-1886-73
1,4-Ethenocyclohepta[c]pyrrol-3(2H)-one, 8a-acetoxy-1,3a,4,8a-tetrahydro-	EtOH	246(3.73),251(3.73), 263s(3.52)	44-1886-73
Furo[2,3-b]quinoline, 2,3-dihydro-4,6-dimethoxy-	EtOH	230(4.66),261(3.77), 269(3.77),279s(3.62), 311s(3.42),325(3.71), 339(3.72)	18-0577-73
Furo[2,3-b]quinoline, 2,3-dihydro-4,7-dimethoxy-	EtOH	226(4.72),243s(4.20), 251s(3.88),276(3.64), 287(3.71),300s(3.78), 306s(3.92),314(4.05), 320(4.05),327(4.02)	18-0577-73
2,4-Hexadienoic acid, 6-oxo-6-(phenyl-amino)-, methyl ester, (E,E)-	EtOH	270(4.26),308(4.02)	104-2527-73
1H-Pyrrole-2-acetic acid, 2,5-dihydro-5-oxo-1-phenyl-, methyl ester	EtOH	262(4.37)	104-2527-73
1H-Pyrrole-2-acetic acid, 4,5-dihydro-5-oxo-1-phenyl-, methyl ester	EtOH	263(4.64)	104-2527-73
$C_{13}H_{13}NO_3S$			
Carbamic acid, [4-(phenylmethylene)-1,3-oxathiolan-2-ylidene]-, ethyl ester	EtOH	271(4.18)	94-0062-73
Ethanone, 1-(2,4-dihydroxy-6-methyl-phenyl)-2-(2-methyl-4-thiazolyl)-	n.s.g.	280(3.98)	104-2580-73
Ethanone, 1-(2,6-dihydroxy-4-methyl-phenyl)-2-(2-methyl-4-thiazolyl)-	n.s.g.	277(4.15)	104-2580-73
Thioimidodicarbonic acid, O-ethyl O'-(3-phenyl-2-propynyl) ester	dioxan	246(4.31),256(4.32)	94-0062-73

Compound	Solvent	λ_{max}(log ε)	Ref.
$C_{13}H_{13}NO_4$			
1H-Indole-2-carboxylic acid, 5-acetoxy-, ethyl ester	n.s.g.	225(4.23),294(4.22)	22-2046-73
1H-Indole-2-carboxylic acid, 3-acetyl-5-hydroxy-, ethyl ester	n.s.g.	224(3.95),250(3.64), 320(3.67)	22-2046-73
	base	225(--),275(3.70), 340(3.60),410s(--)	22-2046-73
1H-Indole-2-carboxylic acid, 4-acetyl-5-hydroxy-, ethyl ester	n.s.g.	215(4.27),255(3.90), 342(4.15),360s(4.08)	22-2046-73
	base	215(4.51),235(4.27), 335(4.17),410(4.06)	22-2046-73
4-Isoquinolinecarboxaldehyde, 1,2-dihydro-6,7-dimethoxy-2-methyl-1-oxo-	EtOH	246(4.37),261(4.23), 324(3.73),337(3.72)	78-3881-73
1,3-Pentadien-2-ol, 4-methyl-, 4-nitrobenzoate	EtOH	235(4.28),254s(4.17), 298s(3.45)	33-0875-73
2,4-Pentadien-2-ol, 4-methyl-, 4-nitrobenzoate	EtOH	229(4.34),255s(4.18), 298s(3.47)	33-0875-73
3-Quinolinecarboxylic acid, 1-ethyl-1,4-dihydro-7-methoxy-4-oxo-	MeOH	221s(4.14),255(4.60), 266s(4.46),310(4.00), 315s(4.00)	111-0346-73
$C_{13}H_{13}NS$			
2H-Azepine-2-thione, 1,3-dihydro-1-methyl-5-phenyl-	EtOH	242(4.11),266(4.20), 313(3.99)	39-1079-73C
$C_{13}H_{13}NS_2$			
Dithiobenzoic acid, 3-methylpyridine salt	EtOH	286(4.08),362(4.03), 500(2.21)	143-0359-73
	ether	290(3.97),360(3.70), 506(2.07)	143-0359-73
	CH_2Cl_2	294(5.15),365(3.98), 490(2.33)	143-0359-73
6H-[1,2]Dithiolo[5,1-e]isothiazole-7-S^{IV}, 4,6-dimethyl-2-phenyl-	MeOH	236(4.52),284s(4.02), 442(4.19)	39-2351-73C
$C_{13}H_{13}N_2$			
Pyridinium, 1-[[(3-methylphenyl)methylene]amino]-, iodide	EtOH	207(4.54),290(4.22)	103-1108-73
	MeCN	248(4.29),298(4.36)	103-1108-73
	DMSO	299(4.32)	103-1108-73
Pyridinium, 1-[[(4-methylphenyl)methylene]amino]-, iodide	EtOH	213(4.43),275(4.09), 302(4.28)	103-1108-73
	HOAc	290(4.30),360(3.35)	103-1108-73
	DMSO	240(4.18),285(4.28)	103-1108-73
Pyridinium, 2-methyl-1-[(phenylmethylene)amino]-, iodide	MeOH	199(4.69),220(4.39), 276(4.30)	4-0821-73
$C_{13}H_{13}N_2O$			
Pyridinium, N-(α-acetyl-2-pyridinylmethyl)-, perchlorate	EtOH	256s(3.81),261(3.86), 266s(3.76)	94-0712-73
Pyridinium, 3-(1-hydroxyimino-2-phenylethyl)-	pH 6.61	252(4.04)	36-1381-73
Pyridinium, 1-[[(3-methoxyphenyl)methylene]amino]-, iodide	EtOH	270(4.56),290(4.16)	103-1108-73
Pyridinium, 1-[[(4-methoxyphenyl)methylene]amino]-, iodide	EtOH	219(4.46),265(3.93), 320(4.39)	103-1108-73
$C_{13}H_{13}N_2OS$			
Thiopyrylium, 2-amino-3-(aminocarbonyl)-6-(4-methylphenyl)-, perchlorate	HOAc	287(3.78),311s(3.56), 410(4.16)	97-0342-73

Compound	Solvent	$\lambda_{max}(\log \epsilon)$	Ref.
$C_{13}H_{13}N_2O_2$			
Pyridinium, N-methyl-4-(4-nitrobenzyl)-, perchlorate	H_2O	214(4.15),259s(4.11), 265(4.14),274(4.08)	48-0901-73
Pyrylium, 2-amino-3-(aminocarbonyl)-6-(4-methylphenyl)-, perchlorate	HOAc	266(4.08),293s(3.27), 391(4.37)	97-0132-73
$C_{13}H_{13}N_3$			
Benzenamine, N-methyl-3-(phenylazo)-	EtOH	228(4.46),319(4.58), 445(2.79)	7-0727-73
hydrochloride	EtOH	230(4.11),319(4.18), 433(3.23)	7-0727-73
Benzenamine, N-methyl-4-(phenylazo)-	EtOH	252(4.06),404(4.54)	7-0727-73
hydrochloride	EtOH	218(4.12),258(3.98), 300s(3.98),312(4.12), 500(4.75)	7-0727-73
Pyridine, 2-acetyl-, phenylhydrazone, (E)-	EtOH	241(3.88),343(4.22)	40-1314-73
(Z)-	EtOH	251(4.05),374(4.15)	40-1314-73
Pyridine, 3-acetyl-, phenylhydrazone	n.s.g.	340(3.72)	70-1057-73
Pyridine, 4-acetyl-, phenylhydrazone	n.s.g.	407(4.29)	70-1057-73
3,4,5-Triazatricyclo[5.2.1.$0^{2,6}$]deca-4,8-diene, exo	EtOH	287(3.73),304(3.77)	12-0619-73
$C_{13}H_{13}N_3O$			
Cyclopentanecarbonitrile, 1-(benzoylazo)-	C_6H_{12}	244(3.93),289s(3.23), 323s(2.39),408(1.66)	23-1378-73
$C_{13}H_{13}N_3OS_2$			
5H-Imidazo[4,5-d]thiazole-5-thione, 4,6-dihydro-2-(4-methoxyphenyl)-4,6-dimethyl-	EtOH	281(4.12),374(4.32)	94-1300-73
$C_{13}H_{13}N_3OS_4$			
4-Thiazolidinone, 5-[3-(2-thiazolyl)-4,5-dimethyl-2-thiazolinylidene]-3-ethyl-2-thioxo-	EtOH	437(4.90)	103-0687-73
$C_{13}H_{13}N_3O_2$			
4,4'-Bipyridinium, 1-[(ethoxycarbonyl)-amino]-, hydroxidem inner salt	EtOH	244(4.05),274(4.05), 351(4.09)	4-0447-73
1,4-Diazepino[6,5-b]indole-2,5-dione, 1,3,4,6-tetrahydro-4,6-dimethyl-	isoPrOH	210(4.22),239(4.52), 290s(4.00),300(4.10), 323(3.86)	4-0051-73
1,3(2H,4H)-Isoquinolinedione, 4-(2-imidazolidinylidene)-2-methyl-	EtOH	239(4.48),294(3.18), 368(3.05)	95-0322-73
$C_{13}H_{13}N_3O_2S_2$			
Carbamic acid, [[[3-(2-propynyl)-2(3H)-thiazolylidene]amino](2-propynylthio)-methylene]-, ethyl ester	dioxan	243(3.60),276(3.88), 333(4.37)	94-0074-73
$C_{13}H_{13}N_3O_3$			
Acetamide, N-(4-acetyl-3-amino-1-oxo-2(1H)-isoquinolinyl)-	EtOH	239(4.38),285(4.16), 361(3.98)	95-1581-73
Acetamide, N,N'-(1-oxo-2,3(1H)-isoquinolinediyl)bis-	EtOH	231(4.37),290(4.07), 325s(3.76)	95-1581-73
Pyrazinecarboxylic acid, 3-amino-6-phenyl-, ethyl ester, 4-oxide	EtOH	245s(4.09),278(4.41), 392(3.23)	35-6407-73

Compound	Solvent	$\lambda_{max}(\log \epsilon)$	Ref.
$C_{13}H_{13}N_3O_4$			
1H-Indazole-3-carbonitrile, 1-β-D-ribo-furanosyl-	EtOH	262s(3.77),270(3.84), 294(3.89)	104-0882-73
3-Isoxazoleacetic acid, 2,5-dihydro-5-oxo-4-(phenylazo)-, ethyl ester	EtOH	249(4.03),400(4.42)	70-2006-73
3-Isoxazoleacetic acid, 4,5-dihydro-5-oxo-α-(phenylhydrazono)-	EtOH	280(4.30)	70-2006-73
2H-Pyrrole-3-carboxylic acid, 5-hydroxy-amino-2-oxo-4-[(phenylmethyl)amino]-, methyl ester	EtOH	365(4.31)	94-1667-73
$C_{13}H_{13}N_3O_4S$			
4-Pyrimidinecarboxylic acid, 2-[[(4-methylphenyl)sulfonyl]amino]-, methyl ester	EtOH	222(4.19),235(4.25), 275(3.32),297(3.47)	44-1591-73
$C_{13}H_{13}N_3O_5$			
Ethanol, 2-[(2,4-dinitro-1-naphthalen-yl)methylamino]-	2% DMSO	420(3.88)	44-2838-73
Propanoic acid, 2-diazo-3-[(4-methoxy-5-oxo-1,3,5-cycloheptatrien-1-yl)-amino]-3-oxo-, ethyl ester	n.s.g.	225(4.41),244s(4.33), 340(4.16)	18-1212-73
$C_{13}H_{13}N_3O_7$			
1H-Indole-3-carboxylic acid, 5-hydroxy-1,3-dimethyl-4,6-dinitro-, ethyl ester	MeOH or $CHCl_3$	270(4.59),365(4.45)	103-1490-73
$C_{13}H_{13}N_5O$			
4(1H)-Pteridinone, 2-amino-7,8-dihydro-6-(phenylmethyl)-	pH 1	254(4.20),335(3.68), 370(3.59)	87-0869-73
9H-Purine-9-ethanol, 6-amino-α-phenyl-	H_2O	261(4.15)	138-0967-73
$C_{13}H_{14}$			
7H-Benzocyclononene, 4a,11a-dihydro-	hexane	255s(3.52),264(3.59), 273(3.58),283s(3.34)	88-3103-73
7H-Benzocyclononene, 8,9-dihydro-	hexane	260s(2.98)	88-3103-73
4a,8a-Methanonaphthalene, 9,9-dimethyl-	C_6H_{12}	385(1.59)	89-0570-73
$C_{13}H_{14}BrNO_3$			
1H-Indole-3-carboxylic acid, 6-bromo-5-hydroxy-1,2-dimethyl-, ethyl ester	EtOH	218(4.73),251(4.54), 295(4.20),304(4.22)	103-0306-73
$C_{13}H_{14}BrN_5O$			
Acetamide, N-[2-[2-[(4-bromophenyl)azo]-1H-imidazol-4-yl]ethyl]-	EtOH	388(4.46)	44-1971-73
Acetamide, N-[2-[5-[(4-bromophenyl)azo]-1H-imidazol-4-yl]ethyl]-	EtOH	353(4.37)	44-1971-73
$C_{13}H_{14}Br_2O_4$			
2H-1-Benzopyran-2-one, 5,7-dibromo-8a-ethoxy-3,4,6,8a-tetrahydro-4,4-di-methyl-	MeOH	256(3.95)	35-8319-73
$C_{13}H_{14}ClNO$			
1-Benzazocin-5-ol, 7-chloro-3,4-dihydro-3,3-dimethyl-	EtOH	257(4.20),306(3.85)	18-2504-73
$C_{13}H_{14}ClNO_4S$			
2-Butenedioic acid, 2-[(2-chloro-2-prop-enyl)thien-2-ylamino]-, dimethyl ester	MeOH	283(4.24)	24-0368-73

Compound	Solvent	$\lambda_{max}(\log \epsilon)$	Ref.
$C_{13}H_{14}ClNS$			
Cyclohexanethione, 2-[[(4-chlorophenyl)-amino]methylene]-	EtOH	450(4.34)	104-1739-73
$C_{13}H_{14}Cl_2N_4$			
1,3,5-Triazine, 2,4-dichloro-6-[4-(diethylamino)phenyl]-	EtOH	237(3.94),263(3.54), 403(4.71)	39-2075-73B
$C_{13}H_{14}FNO_4$			
1H-Indole, 5-fluoro-1-β-D-ribopyranosyl-	EtOH	221(4.19),268(3.75), 294(3.51)	104-0611-73
1H-Indole, 6-fluoro-1-β-D-ribopyranosyl-	EtOH	218(4.51),267(3.64), 288(3.44)	104-0611-73
$C_{13}H_{14}F_3NO$			
Aziridinone, 1-(1,1-dimethylethyl)-3-[4-(trifluoromethyl)phenyl]-	pentane	237(4.0)	35-3415-73
$C_{13}H_{14}F_3NOS$			
Ethanethione, 2-morpholino-1-[4-(trifluoromethyl)phenyl]-	EtOH	282(4.16)	36-0910-73
$C_{13}H_{14}F_6N_2$			
Benzenecarboximidamide, N,N-diethyl-3,5-bis(trifluoromethyl)-	EtOH	208(4.18)	36-1899-73
$C_{13}H_{14}INO_2$			
Isoquinolinium, 3-(ethoxycarbonyl)-2-methyl-, iodide	EtOH	241(4.75),277(3.52), 341(3.87)	78-0213-73
$C_{13}H_{14}INO_3$			
1H-1-Benzazonine-2,7-dione, 3,4,5,6-tetrahydro-9-iodo-10-methoxy-	EtOH	244(4.44),270(4.23)	39-0872-73B
$C_{13}H_{14}IN_5OS$			
Pyridinium, 3-[3,7-dihydro-3-methyl-6-(methylthio)-2-oxo-2H-purin-8-yl]-1-methyl-, iodide	pH 8	225(4.48),272(4.18), 365(4.39)	39-0739-73C
Pyridinium, 1-methyl-3-(2,3,6,7-tetrahydro-1,3-dimethyl-2-oxo-6-thien-1H-purin-8-yl)-, iodide	pH 8	227(4.35),271(4.16), 384(4.27)	39-0739-73C
$C_{13}H_{14}IN_5S$			
Pyridinium, 1-methyl-3-[3-methyl-6-(methylthio)-3H-purin-8-yl]-, iodide	pH 8	224(4.50),347(4.49)	39-2019-73C
$C_{13}H_{14}N$			
Methanaminium, N-(1-azulenylmethylene)-N-methyl-, tetrafluoroborate	n.s.g.	490(3.00),642(2.06)	5-0166-73
Pyridinium, 1-methyl-2-(phenylmethyl)-, iodide	neutral	350(4.41)	39-2111-73B
	pH 12	267(3.85)	39-2111-73B
$C_{13}H_{14}NO$			
Pyrylium, 4-[4-(dimethylamino)phenyl]-, perchlorate	MeCN	420(4.49)	78-0795-73
$C_{13}H_{14}NOP$			
Phosphinic amide, N-methyl-P,P-diphenyl-	n.s.g.	225(4.20),260(3.08), 266(3.18),273(3.23)	35-8073-73

Compound	Solvent	$\lambda_{max}(\log \epsilon)$	Ref.
$C_{13}H_{14}N_2$			
1H-Cyclopenta[b]quinolin-9-amine, 2,3-dihydro-N-methyl-	EtOH	222(4.27),248(4.30), 332(3.98)	103-0490-73
1,4-Methanonaphthalene-6,7-dicarbonitrile, 1,2,3,4,4a,5,8,8a-tetrahydro-	MeOH	238(4.05)	33-3004-73
Propanedinitrile, tricyclo[3.3.1.1^{3,7}]-dec-2-ylidene-	hexane	242(4.08)	78-1691-73
2H-Pyrrole-3-carbonitrile, 3,4-dihydro-2,2-dimethyl-5-phenyl-	C_6H_{12}	244(4.23)	35-1945-73
$C_{13}H_{14}N_2O$			
Benzamide, N-(2,4-dimethyl-1H-pyrrol-3-yl)-	EtOH	224(4.16)	70-1859-73
2-Pyridinamine, N-(1-phenylethyl)-, 1-oxide, (S)-	MeOH	232(4.42),252(3.91), 325(3.71)	32-1083-73
Pyrimido[1,2-a]indole, 1-acetyl-1,2,3,4-tetrahydro-	MeOH	222(4.46),297(4.23)	103-0598-73
$C_{13}H_{14}N_2OS$			
Acetamide, N-(3,4-dimethyl-2-phenyl-5-thiazolidinylidene)-, meso-ionic didehydro deriv.	EtOH	250(3.98),365(3.93)	18-0964-73
Benzenepropanenitrile, α-[(dimethylamino)(methylthio)methylene]-β-oxo-	EtOH	252(4.08),346(4.13)	1-0258-73
4-Imidazolidinone, 5-(1-methylpropylidene)-3-phenyl-2-thioxo-	EtOH	242(3.61),331(4.37)	63-1307-73
4-Imidazolidinone, 5-(2-methylpropylidene)-3-phenyl-2-thioxo-	EtOH	236(3.92),325(4.47)	63-1307-73
$C_{13}H_{14}N_2OSSe$			
[1]Benzoselenopheno[2,3-d]pyrimidin-4(1H)-one, 2,3,5,6,7,8-hexahydro-3-(2-propenyl)-2-thioxo-, K salt	EtOH	260(4.05),295(4.00), 340(4.18)	103-0300-73
$C_{13}H_{14}N_2OS_2$			
Acetamide, N-[3-methyl-2-(methylthio)-4-phenyl-5-thiazolidinylidene]-, meso-ionic didehydro deriv.	EtOH	234(3.91),305(3.92), 362(3.97)	18-0964-73
	THF	326(3.97),392(4.03)	18-0964-73
	pyridine	327(3.93),387(4.03)	18-0964-73
[1]Benzothieno[2,3-d]pyrimidin-4(1H)-one, 2,3,5,6,7,8-hexahydro-3-(2-propenyl)-2-thioxo-, K salt	EtOH	285(4.42),305(4.02), 330(4.32),350(4.41)	103-0300-73
$C_{13}H_{14}N_2O_2$			
Acetamide, N-(1-acetyl-3-methyl-1H-indol-2-yl)-	EtOH	242(4.15),265s(4.05), 292(3.86),301(3.85)	35-3400-73
2-Cyclohexene-1-carboxylic acid, 4-(dicyanomethylene)-2-methyl-, ethyl ester	EtOH	300(4.45),430(3.65)	78-4103-73
	EtOH-NaOH	236(4.06),430(4.48)	78-4103-73
$C_{13}H_{14}N_2O_2S$			
Pyridinium, 3,5-dimethyl-1-[(phenylsulfonyl)amino]-, hydroxide, inner salt	EtOH	243(4.13),310(3.38)	44-3311-73
Sulfilimine, N-(2-cyano-3-ethoxy-3-oxo-1-propenyl)-S-methyl-S-phenyl-	EtOH	215s(4.20),296(4.48)	44-4324-73
$C_{13}H_{14}N_2O_3$			
2-Propenoic acid, 3-(5-oxo-2-phenyl-3-pyrazolidinyl)-, methyl ester	EtOH	244(4.09),280s(--)	104-2527-73

Compound	Solvent	λ_{max}(log ε)	Ref.
1H-Pyrazole-3-carboxylic acid, 5-(hydroxymethyl)-1-phenyl-	C_6H_{12} or EtOH	220(4.50),250(4.65)	4-0015-73
2,4(1H,3H)-Pyrimidinedione, 3-[(2-hydroxy-3-methylphenyl)methyl]-5-methyl-	pH 2-7	269(3.92)	56-1645-73
	pH 13	291(4.15)	56-1645-73
$C_{13}H_{14}N_2O_4$			
2H-1-Benzopyran-2-one, 4-(butylamino)-3-nitro-	EtOH	256(3.98),281(3.99), 346(3.37)	103-0816-73
2H-1-Benzopyran-2-one, 4-(diethylamino)-3-nitro-	EtOH	277(3.94),314(3.89), 380s(3.30)	103-0816-73
2H-1-Benzopyran-2-one, 4-[(1,1-dimethylethyl)amino]-3-nitro-	EtOH	265(4.11),353(3.75)	103-0816-73
Propanedioic acid, diazo-, methyl 1-methyl-1-phenylethyl ester	EtOH	250(3.93)	22-2071-73
Propanedioic acid, diazo-, methyl 2-phenylpropyl ester	EtOH	250(3.87)	78-3609-73
Pyrazolo[1,5-a]pyridine-3,5-dicarboxylic acid, diethyl ester	EtOH	224s(4.21),230(4.28), 242(4.07),249(4.02), 286s(3.37),333(3.71)	39-2580-73C
$C_{13}H_{14}N_2O_4S$			
3H-Pyrazole-3-carboxylic acid, 4-methyl-5-(phenylsulfonyl)-, ethyl ester	EtOH	225(4.32)	22-2739-73
3H-Pyrazole-3-carboxylic acid, 5-methyl-4-(phenylsulfonyl)-, ethyl ester	EtOH	230(4.10)	22-2739-73
$C_{13}H_{14}N_2O_5$			
Pentanedioic acid, 3-oxo-2-(phenylazo)-, dimethyl ester	EtOH	243(4.18),360(4.40)	70-2006-73
1H-Pyrrolo[2,3-c]pyridine-2,3-dicarboxylic acid, 4,5-dihydro-5-oxo-, diethyl ester	EtOH	227(4.40),257(4.19), 366(3.84)	44-1824-73
2-Quinolinecarboxylic acid, 6-amino-1,4-dihydro-5,8-dimethoxy-4-oxo-, methyl ester	$CHCl_3$	269(4.42),347(3.80), 395(3.66)	39-2374-73C
$C_{13}H_{14}N_2O_8$			
Oxalacetic acid, 3-(2-hydroxy-5-nitro-4-pyridinyl)-, diethyl ester	EtOH	237(4.21)	44-1824-73
$C_{13}H_{14}N_2S$			
2H-1,2,3-Benzothiadiazine, 5,6,7,8-tetrahydro-2-phenyl-, perchlorate	MeOH	212(3.96),224(3.96), 248(3.92),340(3.36)	118-0225-73
$C_{13}H_{14}N_3O$			
Pyridinium, 3-(hydrazinocarbonyl)-1-(phenylmethyl)-	pH 2.8	260(3.74)	35-1323-73
	pH 6.2	260(3.74)	35-1323-73
	pH 10.8	256(3.79),306(3.63)	35-1323-73
Pyridinium, 4-(hydrazinocarbonyl)-1-(phenylmethyl)-	pH 2.8	267(3.80)	35-1323-73
	pH 6.2	263(3.80)	35-1323-73
	pH 10.8	255(3.76),380(3.76)	35-1323-73
$C_{13}H_{14}N_4O$			
Acetamide, N-[(4-amino-2-phenyl-5-pyrimidinyl)methyl]-	MeOH	242(4.32),290(3.88)	18-0253-73
	MeOH-HCl	255(--)	18-0253-73
Benzamide, N-[(4-amino-2-methyl-5-pyrimidinyl)methyl]-	EtOH	231(4.34),275(3.83)	18-0253-73
	EtOH-HCl	237(--)	18-0253-73
$C_{13}H_{14}N_4OS$			
1,2,4-Triazino[5,6-d][3,1]benzoxazepine, 6,7-dihydro-6,6-dimethyl-3-(methylthio)-	EtOH	208(4.28),238(4.41), 350(4.00),446(3.76)	78-0639-73

Compound	Solvent	λ_{max}(log ε)	Ref.
$C_{13}H_{14}N_4O_2$			
Benzeneacetonitrile, α-(1,3-dimethyl-2-imidazolidinylidene)-4-nitro-	EtOH	233(4.17),294(3.89)	1-0258-73
$C_{13}H_{14}N_4O_3$			
Benzo[g]pteridine-2,4(3H,7H)-dione, 6,10-dihydro-7-hydroxy-7,8,10-trimethyl-	H_2O	237(4.20),298(4.16), 446(4.26)	78-0879-73
Benzo[g]pteridine-2,4,8(1H,3H,9H)-tri-one, 9a,10-dihydro-7,9a,10-trimethyl-	pH 1	264(4.28),436(4.08)	78-0879-73
	pH 13	226(4.33),272(4.25), 456(4.20)	78-0879-73
$C_{13}H_{14}N_4O_3S$			
Purine, 9-(4-O-acetyl-2,3-dideoxy-α-D-glycero-pent-2-enopyranosyl)-6-(methylthio)-	EtOH	283(4.26),290s(4.24)	87-1056-73
β-anomer	EtOH	283(4.28),290s(4.25)	87-1056-73
Purine, 9-(4-O-acetyl-1,2,3-trideoxy-D-threo-pent-1-enopyranos-3-yl)-6-(methylthio)-	EtOH	284(4.25),291s(4.23)	87-1056-73
1,2,4-Triazino[5,6-d][3.1]benzoxazepine, 6,6(7H)-dimethanol, 3-(methylthio)-	EtOH	208(4.32),238(4.44), 350(4.06),459(3.76)	78-0639-73
$C_{13}H_{14}N_4O_6$			
2,4(1H,3H)-Pteridinedione, 6,7-bis(acetoxymethyl)-3-methyl-	MeOH	235(4.07),333(3.85)	24-3149-73
$C_{13}H_{14}N_4O_8S$			
1H-Imidazole-4-carbothioamide, 5-(formylamino)-1-(2,3,5-tri-O-formyl-β-D-ribofuranosyl)-	EtOH	289(4.01),338(3.72)	94-0692-73
$C_{13}H_{14}N_5$			
1H-[1,2,4]Triazolo[1,5-a]pyrimidin-8-ium, 2-amino-5,7-dimethyl-1-phenyl-, perchlorate	n.s.g.	255(4.20),310(3.81)	124-1036-73
$C_{13}H_{14}N_5OS$			
Pyridinium, 3-[3,7-dihydro-3-methyl-6-(methylthio)-2-oxo-2H-purin-8-yl]-1-methyl-, iodide	pH 8	225(4.48),272(4.18), 365(4.39)	39-0739-73C
Pyridinium, 1-methyl-3-(2,3,6,7-tetrahydro-1,3-dimethyl-2-oxo-6-thien-1H-purin-8-yl)-, iodide	pH 8	227(4.35),271(4.16), 384(4.27)	39-0739-73C
$C_{13}H_{14}N_6S$			
4-Pyrimidinamine, N-(5,7-dimethyl-3H-[1,2,4]thiadiazolo[4,3-c]pyrimidin-3-ylidene)-2,6-dimethyl-	n.s.g.	226(4.36),255s(3.96), 317(4.13),328(4.16), 370(4.17)	44-3087-73
$C_{13}H_{14}N_{10}$			
1H-Purin-6-amine, 8-[3-(6-amino-9H-purin-9-yl)propyl]-	pH 1	261(4.39)	35-4010-73
	H_2O	259(4.34)	35-4010-73
	pH 13	264(4.34)	35-4010-73
1H-Purin-6-amine, 8,8'-(1,3-propanediyl)-bis-	pH 1	264.5(4.41)	35-4010-73
	H_2O	260(4.33)	35-4010-73
	pH 13	271(4.46)	35-4010-73
7H-Purin-6-amine, 7-[3-(6-amino-9H-purin-9-yl)propyl]-	pH 1	266(4.33)	35-4010-73
	H_2O	265(4.24)	35-4010-73
	pH 13	265.5(4.24)	35-4010-73

Compound	Solvent	λmax(log ε)	Ref.
9H-Purine-9-propanamine, 6-amino-N-1H-purin-6-yl- (hydrate)	pH 1	262(4.41)	35-4010-73
	H_2O	260(4.40)	35-4010-73
	pH 13	264(4.37),271s(4.30), 280s(4.12)	35-4010-73
$C_{13}H_{14}O$			
6H-Benz[cd]azulen-6-one, 1,2,7,8,9,9a-hexahydro-	C_6H_{12}	243(4.03),291(3.77), 322s(1.95)	44-1439-73
Cyclohexanone, 2-(phenylmethylene)-, (E)-	EtOH	290(4.17)	23-1458-73
(Z)-	EtOH	222(3.90),272(3.75)	23-1458-73
2-Cyclohexen-1-one, 2-methyl-4-phenyl-	EtOH	235(4.08)	104-2172-73
2-Cyclohexen-1-one, 3-methyl-5-phenyl-	EtOH	235(4.10)	104-2172-73
2-Cyclohexen-1-one, 4-methyl-3-phenyl-	EtOH	222(4.04),280(4.30)	104-2172-73
2-Cyclohexen-1-one, 4-methyl-4-phenyl-	EtOH	198(4.31),305(2.77)	104-2172-73
Ethanone, 1-(3,3-dimethyl-2-phenyl-1-cyclopropen-1-yl)-	n.s.g.	304(3.86)	88-2875-73
Ethanone, 1-(1,2,3,4-tetrahydro-1,4-methanonaphthalen-2-yl)-, endo	C_6H_{12}	258(2.73),264(2.93), 272(2.98),293(1.45)	44-0639-73
exo	C_6H_{12}	259(2.84),266(3.02), 272(3.04),293(1.89)	44-0639-73
$C_{13}H_{14}O_2$			
Acetaldehyde, (3,4-dihydro-6-methoxy-1(2H)-naphthalenylidene)-, (E)-	EtOH	235s(4.01),240(4.29), 325(4.18)	39-0615-73C
Acetic acid, (2,3-dihydro-1H-inden-1-ylidene)-, ethyl ester, cis	EtOH	288(4.08),304(4.05)	39-0615-73C
trans	EtOH	224(4.17),235(4.17), 256(4.15),264s(4.09)	39-0615-73C
Benzofuran, 6-methoxy-3-methyl-2-(1-methylethenyl)-	90% EtOH	233(3.91),281(4.06), 293(4.08),306(4.21), 310s(4.20),317(4.18)	12-1093-73
7-Benzofuranacetaldehyde, α,3,5-trimethyl-	EtOH	252(3.95),282(3.38), 291(3.38)	33-2961-73
8H-Cyclohepta[b]furan-8-one, 2-methyl-7-propyl-	EtOH	226(4.13),266(4.47), 271(4.47),339(3.64), 354(3.48)	39-1960-73C
2,4,6-Cycloheptatrien-1-one, 2-propyl-7-(2-propynyloxy)-	EtOH	238(4.48),322(3.96)	39-1960-73C
2,4,6-Cycloheptatrien-1-one, 3-propyl-2-(2-propynyloxy)-	EtOH	243(4.37),321(3.86)	39-1960-73C
Cyclopentanone, 2-[(3-methoxyphenyl)-methylene]-	EtOH	245(3.6),300(4.2)	39-2454-73C
1,4-Ethenocyclopenta[c]pyran-3(1H)-one, 4,4a,7,7a-tetrahydro-7-(1-methylethylidene)-	EtOH	246(4.28)	44-3836-73
1H-Indene-3-acetic acid, ethyl ester	EtOH	252(3.94)	39-0615-73C
2-Naphthaleneacetic acid, 3,4-dihydro-, methyl ester	EtOH	264(4.1)	2-0131-73
2-Naphthaleneacetic acid, 3,4-dihydro-α-methyl-	EtOH	265(4.15)	2-0131-73
Tricyclo[3.3.1.0^{2,8}]non-6-ene-3,4-dione, 9-methylene-2-propyl-	C_6H_{12}	272(2.87),430(1.97)	39-1960-73C
$C_{13}H_{14}O_2S$			
1H-2-Benzothiopyran-4-ol, 1,3-dimethyl-, acetate	EtOH	208(4.61),238(3.93), 313(3.82)	39-0410-73C
$C_{13}H_{14}O_2S_2$			
1,3-Butanedione, 2-[bis(methylthio)methylene]-1-phenyl-	EtOH	253(4.06),318(3.94)	1-0258-73

Compound	Solvent	λ_{max}(log ε)	Ref.
$C_{13}H_{14}O_3$			
Acetic acid, (3,4-dihydro-6-methoxy-1(2H)-naphthalenylidene)-, (E)-	EtOH	297(4.21),312(4.23)	39-0615-73C
(Z)-	EtOH	296(4.02)	39-0615-73C
Cyclobuta[b]naphthalene-3,8-dione, 2a,3a,4,7,7a,8a-hexahydro-1-(hydroxymethyl)-	EtOH	300(2.33)	104-2389-73
5,8-Epoxy-7H-benzocyclohepten-7-one, 5,6,8,9-tetrahydro-9-hydroxy-6,8-dimethyl-	n.s.g.	258(2.47),266(2.49), 274(2.40)	39-0235-73C
1,3,5-Hexanetrione, 2-methyl-1-phenyl-	EtOH	249(4.08),281(4.06)	44-0896-73
1,3,5-Hexanetrione, 4-methyl-1-phenyl-	EtOH	222(3.79),247(3.73), 310(4.20)	44-0896-73
Naphthalene, 1,3,8-trimethoxy-	EtOH	235(4.69),285(3.73), 296(3.73),320(3.4), 335(3.6)	23-3299-73
1-Naphthaleneacetic acid, 3,4-dihydro-	EtOH	271(4.11)	39-0615-73C
1-Naphthalenol, 3,4-dihydro-5-methoxy-, acetate	n.s.g.	264(3.94)	35-6655-73
1-Naphthalenol, 3,4-dihydro-6-methoxy-, acetate	n.s.g.	272(4.15)	35-6655-73
$C_{13}H_{14}O_4$			
2-Benzofurancarboxylic acid, 4-hydroxy-3,7-dimethyl-, ethyl ester	EtOH	236(4.32),283(4.25), 315(3.81)	12-0201-73
1H-2-Benzopyran-1-one, 8-hydroxy-6-methoxy-3-propyl- (glomellin)	MeOH	201(4.08),238s(4.51), 245(4.58),258s(3.93), 280(3.74),330(3.69)	102-2993-73
Ethanone, 1-(7,7a-dihydro-2,7-dihydroxy-7a-methylnaphth[2,3-b]oxiren-1a(2H)-yl)-, (1aα,2α,7β,7aα)-	n.s.g.	242(2.48),254(2.53), 271(2.40)	39-0235-73C
(1aα,2β,7β,7aα)-	n.s.g.	211(3.73)	39-0235-73C
Ethanone, 1-(7,8-dihydroxy-2,2-dimethyl-2H-1-benzopyran-6-yl)-	MeOH	263(4.63),300(3.95)	2-0100-73
Ethanone, 1-(4,6-dimethoxy-3-methyl-2-benzofuranyl)-	90% EtOH	226s(4.14),250(3.89), 290(4.23),326(4.12)	12-1093-73
1H-Indene-2-acetic acid, 2,3-dihydro-5-methoxy-1-oxo-, methyl ester	EtOH	233(4.24),266(4.27), 286(4.16)	39-2454-73C
1(2H)-Naphthalenone, 3-acetyl-3,4-dihydro-3,4-dihydroxy-2-methyl-, (2α,3α,4α)-	n.s.g.	249(4.00),290(3.17)	39-0235-73C
(2α,3β,4α)-	n.s.g.	251(3.94),290(3.10)	39-0368-73C
9-Oxabicyclo[5.3.0]deca-2,4,6-triene-1-carboxylic acid, 8,8-dimethyl-10-oxo-, methyl ester	EtOH	269(3.56)	78-3609-73
Pentacyclo[4.3.0.0^{2,4}.0^{3,8}.0^{5,7}]nonane-4,5-dicarboxylic acid, dimethyl ester	EtOH	210(2.80)	24-1804-73
Tetracyclo[4.3.0.0^{2,4}.0^{3,7}]non-8-ene-8,9-dicarboxylic acid, dimethyl ester	EtOH	243(3.76)	24-1804-73
$C_{13}H_{14}O_4S$			
2(3H)-Furanone, 5-(acetoxymethyl)dihydro-4-(phenylthio)-, (4S-trans)-	EtOH	215s(4.32),253(3.72)	44-0187-73
$C_{13}H_{14}O_5$			
Benzeneacetic acid, 3-hydroxy-4-methoxy-2-(1-oxo-2-propenyl)-, methyl ester	90% EtOH	227(3.71),265(3.26), 280s(3.16),316s(2.91)	12-1069-73
$C_{13}H_{14}O_6$			
Acetophenone, 2,6-diacetoxy-4-methoxy-	MeOH	215(4.26),262(4.06), 317(3.00)	83-0857-73

Compound	Solvent	λmax(log ε)	Ref.
3-Furancarboxylic acid, tetrahydro-3-hydroxy-2-(4-methoxyphenyl)-5-oxo-, methyl ester	EtOH	228(4.07),274(3.14), 282(4.07)	44-4457-73
$C_{13}H_{14}S$			
1H-Cyclopenta[b][1]benzothiophene, 5(or 8)-ethyl-2,3-dihydro-	n.s.g.	234(4.48),242s(4.3), 265(3.8),273(3.78), 294(3.57),304(3.66)	49-0312-73
Thiophene, 2-(1-methylethyl)-5-phenyl-	n.s.g.	292(4.16)	49-0312-73
$C_{13}H_{15}$			
Methylium, dicyclopropylphenyl-	FSO_3H at -75°	339(4.28),400s(<3.3)	59-0803-73
$C_{13}H_{15}BrN_2$			
Pyridinium, 1-[5-[(dimethylamino)methylene]-1,3-cyclopentadien-1-yl]-, bromide	CH_2Cl_2	248(--),320(--), 413(--)	88-5105-73
$C_{13}H_{15}BrO$			
Naphthalene, 1-(2-bromoethyl)-3,4-dihydro-6-methoxy-	EtOH	271(4.05)	39-0615-73C
$C_{13}H_{15}BrO_4$			
Ethanone, 1-(3-bromo-1,2,3,4-tetrahydro-1,2,4-trihydroxy-3-methyl-2-naphthalenyl)-, (1α,2α,3β,4α)-	n.s.g.	218(3.86)	39-0235-73C
$C_{13}H_{15}Br_2N_5O_2$			
1H-Pyrrole-2-carboxamide, N-[3-[2-(acetylamino)-1H-imidazol-4-yl)propyl]-4,5-dibromo-	MeOH	237s(4.11),268(4.28)	77-0078-73
$C_{13}H_{15}ClN_2O$			
1,8-Methano-1,8-benzodiazecin-13-one, 10-chloro-2,3,4,5,6,7-hexahydro-	MeOH	221(4.33),293(3.72)	39-0702-73C
$C_{13}H_{15}ClN_2O_7$			
Uridine, 2'-chloro-2'-deoxy-, 3',5'-diacetate	MeOH	257(4.00)	35-4016-73
$C_{13}H_{15}ClN_4O_3S$			
1-Pyrrolidineacetamide, N-[2-[(2-amino-2-oxoethyl)thio]-6-chloro-3-pyridinyl]-α-oxo-	EtOH	232(4.2),306(3.8)	103-0621-73
$C_{13}H_{15}ClO$			
Naphthalene, 1-(2-chloroethyl)-3,4-dihydro-6-methoxy-	EtOH	271(4.01)	39-0615-73C
$C_{13}H_{15}ClO_5$			
Benzeneacetic acid, 3-(3-chloro-1-oxopropoxy)-4-methoxy-, methyl ester	90% EtOH	227(3.71),275(3.30), 281s(3.23)	12-1069-73
Benzeneacetic acid, 2-(3-chloro-1-oxopropyl)-5-hydroxy-4-methoxy-, methyl ester	90% EtOH	230(4.07),276(3.69), 306(3.56)	12-1069-73
$C_{13}H_{15}Cl_2NO_6S$			
4H-1,4-Benzothiazinium, 6-chloro-2-(ethoxycarbonyl)-1,3-dimethyl-, perchlorate	EtOH	214(4.50),230(4.36), 321(3.76),367(4.03)	7-0045-73

Compound	Solvent	λ max(log ε)	Ref.
4H-1,4-Benzothiazinium, 7-chloro-2-(ethoxycarbonyl)-1,3-dimethyl-, perchlorate	EtOH	212(4.40),228(4.20), 304(3.75),358(3.88)	7-0045-73
$C_{13}H_{15}F_3O$			
Cyclohexanol, 1-[3-(trifluoromethyl)-phenyl]-	EtOH	252s(3.81),257(3.88), 263(3.94),271(3.86)	35-5288-73
Cyclohexanol, 1-[4-(trifluoromethyl)-phenyl]-	EtOH	217(3.79),256(3.00)	35-5288-73
$C_{13}H_{15}F_5N_2O_2$			
Imidazolidine, 1,3-dihydroxy-4,4,5,5-tetramethyl-2-(pentafluorophenyl)-	EtOH	255(2.92)	78-3833-73
$C_{13}H_{15}FeN_3S$			
Ferrocene, [[1-(aminothioxomethyl)hydrazono]ethyl]-	EtOH	239(4.10),273(4.09), 308(4.43),455(2.98)	18-2896-73
$C_{13}H_{15}IN_2$			
Pyrido[1,2-a]quinazolin-11-ium, 7,8,9,10-tetrahydro-6-methyl-, iodide	MeOH	217(4.58),236(4.70), 242s(4.65),308(3.74), 322(3.90)	4-0821-73
$C_{13}H_{15}IN_2OS_2$			
3H-Thiazol-1-ium, 5-(acetylamino)-3-methyl-2-(methylthio)-4-phenyl-, iodide	EtOH	264(3.85),322(4.06)	18-0964-73
$C_{13}H_{15}N$			
1H-Carbazole, 2,3,4,4a-tetrahydro-4a-methyl-	EtOH	256(3.83)	33-2628-73
	EtOH-HCl	231(3.83),274(3.78)	33-2628-73
1H-Indole, 2-(3-butenyl)-3-methyl-	EtOH	228(4.52),277s(3.82), 284(3.86),292(3.82)	39-1913-73C
Spiro[cyclopentane-1,3'-[3H]indole], 2'-methyl-	EtOH	236(3.51),258(3.80)	39-0548-73B
$C_{13}H_{15}NO$			
2-Azabicyclo[3.2.0]heptan-3-one, 2-methyl-6-phenyl-	EtOH	260(2.32)	39-1079-73C
1-Benzazocin-5-ol, 3,4-dihydro-3,3-dimethyl-	EtOH	229s(4.02),253(4.21), 306s(3.68),315(3.71)	18-2504-73
1,2-Benzisoxazole, 3a,4,5,6,7,7a-hexahydro-3-phenyl-	EtOH	210(4.08),265(4.07)	22-1390-73
Carbazole, 1,2,3,4-tetrahydro-5-methoxy-	EtOH	227(4.32),273(3.69), 282s(3.67),294(3.68)	39-0878-73B
Carbazole, 1,2,3,4-tetrahydro-7-methoxy-	EtOH	230(4.51),270(3.68), 300(3.73)	39-0872-73B
Pyridine, 2-(1,3,5-heptatrienyl)-4-methoxy-, (E,E,E)-	EtOH	235(4.10),320(4.69)	54-0683-73
$C_{13}H_{15}NO_2$			
1,4-Ethenocyclohepta[c]pyrrol-3(2H)-one, 1,3a,4.8a-tetrahydro-4-methoxy-3a-methyl-	EtOH	244(3.63)	44-1886-73
1,4-Ethenocyclohepta[c]pyrrol-3(2H)-one, 1,3a,4,8a-tetrahydro-8a-methoxy-3a-methyl-	EtOH	247(3.69),253(3.69), 262s(3.51)	44-1886-73
2,4,6-Heptatrienoic acid, 6-methyl-7-(1H-pyrrol-2-yl)-, methyl ester	EtOH	393(4.62)	39-1416-73C

Compound	Solvent	$\lambda_{max}(\log \epsilon)$	Ref.
1-Indolizinecarboxylic acid, 2,5-dimethyl-, ethyl ester	EtOH	230s(4.30),234(4.32), 257(3.76),266(3.73), 296s(3.61),310(3.82), 325s(3.86),338(3.92), 354s(3.71)	94-1139-73
1-Indolizinecarboxylic acid, 2,7-dimethyl-, ethyl ester	EtOH	235s(4.45),238(4.47), 261(3.89),270(3.88), 299s(3.87),312(4.05), 331(3.89),345s(3.84)	94-1139-73
1-Indolizinecarboxylic acid, 2,8-dimethyl-, ethyl ester	EtOH	232s(4.33),237(4.34), 260(3.74),269(3.71), 297s(3.71),312(3.89), 329(3.85),343s(3.82)	94-1139-73
2H-Pyrrole-3-carboxylic acid, 3,4-dihydro-3-methyl-5-phenyl-, methyl ester	EtOH	245(4.11)	35-1945-73
2H-Pyrrole-4-carboxylic acid, 3,4-dihydro-4-methyl-5-phenyl-, methyl ester	EtOH	245(4.15)	35-1945-73
Spiro[cyclopentane-1,2'-[2H]indol]-3'(1'H)-one, 6'-methoxy-	EtOH	237(4.20),250s(4.16), 281(4.00),364(3.50)	39-0878-73B
$C_{13}H_{15}NO_3$			
Acetamide, N-[3-acetoxy-4-(2-propenyl)-phenyl]-	EtOH	246(4.27)	44-0831-73
1H-1-Benzazonine-2,7-dione, 3,4,5,6-tetrahydro-10-methoxy-	EtOH	218s(4.33),238(4.35), 270(4.19)	39-0872-73B
2-Benzofuranpropanoic acid, α-amino-3,5-dimethyl-	n.s.g.	256(4.28),287(3.49)	56-1281-73
2-Benzofuranpropanoic acid, α-amino-3,7-dimethyl-	n.s.g.	255(4.09),290(3.56)	56-1281-73
7H-Benzo[de]quinolin-7-one, 1,2,3,8,9-9a-hexahydro-5,6-dihydroxy-1-methyl-	EtOH	225(4.11),275(3.94), 363(3.51)	33-0759-73
2(3H)-Furanone, dihydro-5-[(4-methoxyphenyl)imino]-3,3-dimethyl-	MeCN	261(3.88)	35-6792-73
1H-Indole-3-butanoic acid, 6-methoxy-	EtOH	229(4.31),272(3.74), 290(3.72)	39-0872-73B
4-Isoquinolinecarboxaldehyde, 1,2-dihydro-6,7-dimethoxy-2-methyl-	EtOH	254(4.22),287(4.12)	78-3881-73
4-Isoquinolinecarboxaldehyde, 1,2-dihydro-7,8-dimethoxy-2-methyl-	EtOH	247(4.17),285(4.10)	78-3881-73
2,5-Pyrrolidinedione, 1-(4-methoxyphenyl)-3,3-dimethyl-	MeCN	273(3.11)	35-6792-73
Pyrrolo[2,1-a]isoquinolin-3(2H)-one, 1,5,6,10b-tetrahydro-6,8-dihydroxy-10b-methyl-	EtOH	282(3.29)	95-0925-73
$C_{13}H_{15}NO_4$			
Isoquinoline, 4,5,6,7-tetramethoxy-	EtOH	246(4.61),285(3.87), 325(3.79),338(3.83)	44-0060-73
Morpholine, 4-[(4-formylphenoxy)acetyl]-	EtOH	215(4.29),270(4.30)	111-0574-73
Phthalimide, 4-ethoxy-N-ethyl-3-methoxy-	EtOH	234(4.50),247s(4.24), 254s(4.17),340(3.65)	141-0001-73
	dioxan	233(4.55),246s(4.24), 253s(4.18),333(3.68)	141-0001-73
2(1H)-Quinolinone, 4,7,8-trimethoxy-1-methyl-	C_6H_{12}	239(4.67),254s(3.99), 282(3.78),288(3.77), 321(3.63),330s(3.57)	78-1721-73
	MeOH	228s(4.57),235(4.60), 252(4.26),289(3.96), 313(3.85),323(3.76)	78-1721-73

Compound	Solvent	λ max (log ε)	Ref.
2(1H)-Quinolinone, 4,7,8-trimethoxy-1-methyl- (cont.)	MeOH-acid	226(4.51),235(4.53), 245s(4.42),294(3.86), 315(3.90)	78-1721-73
$C_{13}H_{15}NO_4S$			
2-Butenedioic acid, 2-(2-propenyl)-2-(thienylamino)-, dimethyl ester, (E)-	MeOH	285(4.27)	24-0368-73
4H-Thieno[3,2-b]pyrrole-2,6-dicarboxylic acid, 5-methyl-, diethyl ester	EtOH	250(4.05),323(4.35)	103-1473-73
$C_{13}H_{15}NO_5$			
DL-Alanine, N-[3-(4-hydroxy-3-methoxyphenyl)-1-oxo-2-propenyl]-	MeOH	293(4.22),319(4.33)	20-0243-73
	MeOH-KOH	305s(3.85),359(4.47)	20-0243-73
Phthalimide, 5-ethoxy-3,4-dimethoxy-N-methyl-	EtOH	231s(4.36),245(4.57), 328(3.55)	141-0001-73
$C_{13}H_{15}NO_6$			
1-Cyclohexene-1-carbonitrile, 3,4,5-triacetoxy-, (3R,4R,5R)-	EtOH	207(4.12)	35-7821-73
(3R,4S,5R)-	EtOH	207(4.15)	35-7821-73
1,3-Dioxolan-4-one, 2,5,5-trimethyl-2-[(4-nitrophenyl)methoxy]-	MeOH	247(4.05)	35-4016-73
Propanoic acid, 2-acetoxy-2-methyl-, (4-nitrophenyl)methyl ester	MeOH	265(4.03)	35-4016-73
1H-Pyrrole-3-acetic acid, 4-(2-carboxyethenyl)-2-(methoxycarbonyl)-5-methyl-, methyl ester	MeOH	250(4.23),314(4.28)	39-1546-73C
$C_{13}H_{15}NO_7$			
Benzeneacetic acid, 4-methoxy-3-(3-nitro-1-oxopropoxy)-, methyl ester	90% EtOH	231(3.58),275(3.30), 281s(3.26)	12-1069-73
$C_{13}H_{15}NS$			
Cyclohexanethione, 2-[(phenylamino)methylene]-	EtOH	446(4.33)	104-1739-73
Piperidine, 1-benzo[b]thiophen-2-yl-	EtOH	232(4.03),292(4.91)	78-0321-73
$C_{13}H_{15}N_2$			
Pyrido[1,2-a]quinazolin-11-ium, 7,8,9-10-tetrahydro-6-methyl-, iodide	MeOH	217(4.58),236(4.70), 242s(4.65),308(3.74), 322(3.90)	4-0821-73
$C_{13}H_{15}N_3$			
Benzeneacetonitrile, α-(1,3-dimethyl-2-imidazolidinylidene)-	EtOH	229(4.10),277s(3.92), 317(4.22)	1-0258-73
$C_{13}H_{15}N_3OS$			
2-Thiophenamine, 5-[(4-methoxyphenyl)-azo]-N,N-dimethyl-	EtOH	483(4.70)	103-0850-73
	EtOH-HCl	503(4.70)	103-0850-73
$C_{13}H_{15}N_3O_2$			
Butanedinitrile, (aminoethoxymethylene)-(2-oxocyclohexylidene)-, (E,E)-	EtOH	204(4.19),253(4.10), 330(3.85)	12-1551-73
4-Pyrimidinamine, 5-(dimethoxymethyl)-2-phenyl-	MeCN	240(4.47),260s(--), 282(4.08),296(4.04)	18-0253-73
	MeCN-HCl	252(--)	18-0253-73
$C_{13}H_{15}N_3O_2S$			
Benzenesulfonamide, N,4-dimethyl-N-(4-methyl-2-pyrimidinyl)-	EtOH	223(4.30),264(3.69)	44-1591-73

Compound	Solvent	λ_{max}(log ϵ)	Ref.
Benzenesulfonamide, 4-methyl-N-(1,2-dihydro-1,4-dimethylpyrimidin-2-ylidene)-	EtOH	223(4.10),252(4.32), 318(3.64)	44-1591-73
1H-Pyrazole-4-carboxylic acid, 5-amino-3-(methylthio)-1-phenyl-	EtOH	248(4.78)	18-0699-73
$C_{13}H_{15}N_3O_2S_2$			
Carbamic acid, [[(3-methyl-2(3H)-benzothiazolylidene)amino](methylthio)-methylene]-, ethyl ester	dioxan	224(4.00),237s(--), 279(3.97),294(3.95), 338(4.54)	94-0074-73
$C_{13}H_{15}N_3O_4S_2$			
β-D-erythro-Hex-2-enopyranuronic acid, 1,2,3,4-tetradeoxy-1-(3,4-dihydro-2-oxo-4-thioxo-1(2H)-pyrimidinyl)-4-[(1-thioxoethyl)amino]-	MeOH	268(4.23),328(4.33)	78-1801-73
$C_{13}H_{15}N_3O_6$			
1H-Pyrrole-3-acetic acid, α-cyano-2,5-dihydro-4-(methoxycarbonyl)-2-(methoxyimino)-1-methyl-5-oxo-, ethyl ester	EtOH	322(3.73),440(4.09)	94-1667-73
$C_{13}H_{15}N_5S$			
Thiazolo[2,3-f]purine, 6-methyl-4-piperidino)-	EtOH	225(4.19),267(4.19), 291(4.14)	94-0256-73
$C_{13}H_{15}O_3Rh$			
Rhodium, [(2,3,6,7-η)-9-oxabicyclo-[6.1.0]nona-2,4,6-triene](2,4-pentanedionato-O,O')-	hexane	205(4.35),240(3.99), 302(3.70)	78-3903-73
$C_{13}H_{16}$			
Bicyclo[2.2.1]heptane, 2-phenyl-, endo	EtOH	211(3.83),216(3.80), 261(2.36)	35-4611-73
1H-Cycloheptacyclooctene, 2,3,4,5-tetrahydro-	isooctane	285s(2.09)	35-2230-73
1-Propyne, 3-(1,3,5-trimethyl-4-methylene-2,5-cyclohexadien-1-yl)-	EtOH	247(4.25)	33-0681-73
$C_{13}H_{16}Br_2N_4S_2$			
[4,5'-Bithiazole]-2,2'-diamine, $N^{2'}$-(2,3-dibromopropyl)-4'-methyl-N^2-2-propenyl-	EtOH	268(4.20),318(4.07)	83-0152-73
$C_{13}H_{16}ClN_5O_3$			
Oxazolidine, 3-acetyl-5-[(6-chloro-9H-purin-9-yl)methyl]-2-ethoxy-	pH 1	265(3.97)	87-0037-73
	pH 7	265(3.98)	87-0037-73
	pH 13	265(3.98)	87-0037-73
$C_{13}H_{16}FN_2O_2$			
1H-Imidazol-1-yloxy, 2-(2-fluorophenyl)-4,5-dihydro-4,4,5,5-tetramethyl-, 3-oxide	EtOH	215s(3.85),250(3.87), 341(3.96),553(2.86)	78-3833-73
1H-Imidazol-1-yloxy, 2-(3-fluorophenyl)-4,5-dihydro-4,4,5,5-tetramethyl-, 3-oxide	EtOH	224(3.95),262(4.04), 358(4.11),580(2.42)	78-3833-73
1H-Imidazol-1-yloxy, 2-(4-fluorophenyl)-4,5-dihydro-4,4,5,5-tetramethyl-, 3-oxide	EtOH	236(4.20),259(4.26), 354(4.29),590(2.86)	78-3833-73

Compound	Solvent	λmax(log ε)	Ref.
$C_{13}H_{16}FeO_3$			
Iron, tricarbonyl[(1,2,3,4-η)-1,3,5,5-tetramethyl-1,3-cyclohexadiene]-	heptane	217(4.30),228s(--), 290s(--)	70-2027-73
$C_{13}H_{16}INO_6$			
1H-Pyrrole-3-propanoic acid, 2-iodo-5-(methoxycarbonyl)-4-(2-methoxy-2-oxoethyl)-, methyl ester	MeOH	279(4.21)	39-1546-73C
$C_{13}H_{16}NO_4P$			
Phosphonic acid, (4-hydroxy-3-quinolinyl)-, diethyl ester	MeOH	242(4.29),292(3.92), 311(4.00),323(3.97)	94-1080-73
$C_{13}H_{16}N_2$			
2-Hexenenitrile, 6-(methylamino)-3-phenyl-	EtOH	256.5(4.21)	94-1601-73
1H-Pyrido[4,3-b]indole, 2,3,4,5-tetrahydro-1,1-dimethyl-	EtOH	225(4.55),274(3.78), 279(3.80),289(3.71)	44-4342-73
1H-Pyrido[4,3-b]indole, 2,3,4,5-tetrahydro-2,8-dimethyl-	MeOH	227(4.7),285(4.0), 360(1.20)	103-0974-73
4H-Pyrrolo[3,2,1-ij]quinoline-1-ethanamine, 5,6-dihydro-	EtOH	224(4.66),279s(3.84), 290(3.89),298s(3.84)	103-0196-73
$C_{13}H_{16}N_2O$			
Benzamide, 2-(cyclopentylideneamino)-N-methyl-	EtOH	225(4.67),340(3.68)	103-0490-73
1,2-Diazocin-3(2H)-one, 4,5,6,7-tetrahydro-2-methyl-8-phenyl-	EtOH	248(4.03)	22-2029-73
Imidazo[1,2-a]pyridine, 3,5,6,7,8,8a-hexahydro-2-phenyl-, 1-oxide	MeOH	222(3.93),290(4.19)	24-1172-73
1H-Pyrido[4,3-b]indole, 2,3,4,9-tetrahydro-8-methoxy-2-methyl-	MeOH	227(4.7),287(4.0), 350(1.80)	103-0974-73
3H-Pyrrol-3-one, 2-(3,4-dimethyl-1H-pyrrol-2-ylmethylene)-1,2-dihydro-4,5-dimethyl-	CH_2Cl_2	391(4.32),461(4.21)	5-0146-73
4(3H)-Quinazolinone, 3-(1,1-dimethylethyl)-2-methyl-	MeOH	206(4.37),228(4.40), 274(3.81),310(3.48)	78-2153-73
4(3H)-Quinazolinone, 2-ethyl-3-(1-methylethyl)-	MeOH	206(4.46),225(4.39), 265(3.91),305(3.51), 318(3.38)	78-2153-73
4(1H)-Quinolinone, 2-[(1,1-dimethylethyl)amino]-	MeOH	225(4.53),235(4.52), 245(4.52),300(4.23)	78-2153-73
$C_{13}H_{16}N_2O_2$			
Acetic acid, (1-phenyl-2-imidazolidinylidene)-, ethyl ester	EtOH	248(3.94),284(4.17)	39-1314-73C
Cyclohexanecarboxylic acid, 2-(dicyanomethylene)-1-methyl-, ethyl ester	EtOH	241(3.87)	78-4103-73
9H-6,12b-Methano-2H-furo[2,3-d]pyrido[1,2-b][1,2]diazocin-2-one, 6,7,10,11,12,12a-hexahydro-, [6S-(6α,12aα,12bα)]-	EtOH	218(4.06)	78-1063-73
2-Piperidinone, 1-[2-(hydroxyimino)-2-phenylethyl]-, (Z)-	MeOH	240(3.99)	24-1172-73
7H-4,10b-Propeno-2H-furo[2,3-d]pyrido[1,2-b]pyridazin-2-one, 4,5,8,9,10,10a-hexahydro-, [4S-(4α,10aβ,10bα)]-	EtOH	256(4.14)	78-1063-73
Pyridinium, 1-[(2-acetyl-3-oxo-1-butenyl)amino]-2,6-dimethyl-, hydroxide, inner salt	EtOH	278(4.34),297(4.31), 354(3.67)	39-2580-73C

Compound	Solvent	λ max (log ε)	Ref.
$C_{13}H_{16}N_2O_3$			
Acetamide, N,N'-(3,4-dihydro-2H-1-benzopyran-5,6-diyl)bis-	EtOH	295(3.37)	4-0623-73
Acetamide, N,N'-(3,4-dihydro-2H-1-benzopyran-6,7-diyl)bis-	EtOH	292(3.51)	4-0623-73
Acetamide, N,N'-(3,4-dihydro-2H-1-benzopyran-6,8-diyl)bis-	EtOH	239(4.35),298(3.61)	4-0623-73
1,2-Cyclohexanedione, mono[[4-(hydroxymethyl)-3-hydroxyphenyl]hydrazone]	EtOH	250(4.44),332(2.89), 380(4.46)	44-2728-73
1H-Pyrrolo[2,3-c]pyridine-2-carboxylic acid, 3-ethyl-5-methoxy-, ethyl ester	EtOH	285(4.05),294(4.11), 358(3.54)	44-1824-73
$C_{13}H_{16}N_2O_4$			
Morpholine, 4-[[4-(hydroxyimino)methyl]-phenoxy]acetyl]-	EtOH	213(4.32),263(4.33)	111-0574-73
1H-Pyrano[3,4-b]pyridine-2-carboxamide, 4,5,6,8-tetrahydro-4,8-dioxo-	EtOH	230(4.15),302(3.89)	95-1183-73
Pyridinium, 1-[[2-(ethoxycarbonyl)-3-oxo-1-butenyl]amino]-2-methyl-, hydroxide, inner salt	EtOH	238(4.22),278(4.21), 395(4.23)	39-2580-73C
$C_{13}H_{16}N_2O_4S$			
1H-Pyrrole-3-carboxylic acid, 2-amino-4,5-dihydro-1-[(4-methylphenyl)sulfonyl]-, methyl ester	MeOH	228(4.07),298(4.12)	118-0546-73
6H-Thieno[2,3-b]pyrrole-3,4-dicarboxylic acid, 5-amino-2-methyl-, diethyl ester	EtOH	266(4.06),300(3.90)	103-1473-73
$C_{13}H_{16}N_2O_5$			
1,7-Naphthyridine-4-acetic acid, 1,2,3,4-tetrahydro-3-hydroxy-6-methoxy-2-oxo-, ethyl ester	EtOH	248(4.18)	44-1824-73
$C_{13}H_{16}N_4O_2$			
Benzeneacetonitrile, α-[bis(dimethylamino)methylene]-4-nitro-	EtOH	231(4.20),290(4.03), 418(4.34)	1-0258-73
$C_{13}H_{16}N_4O_3S$			
Glycine, N-[1-oxo-5-(1H-pyrrolo[2,3-d]-pyrimidin-4-ylthio)pentyl]-	pH 1	218(4.37),257(4.03), 310(4.05)	73-1438-73
	pH 13	220(4.37),246(3.99), 292(4.16)	73-1438-73
$C_{13}H_{16}N_4O_4$			
Propanedioic acid, (3,4-dihydro-4-pteridinyl)-, diethyl ester	$CHCl_3$	329(3.95)	39-1615-73C
2,4(3H,8H)-Pteridinedione, 6-(2-hydroxy-2-methyl-3-oxobutyl)-7,8-dimethyl-	H_2O	258(4.16),276(4.04), 403(4.06)	78-0879-73
2,4(1H,3H)-Pyrimidinedione, 1-[3-(3,4-dihydro-2,4-dioxo-1(2H)-pyrimidinyl)-propyl]-5-ethyl-	H_2O	269.5(4.25)	56-1943-73
2,4(1H,3H)-Pyrimidinedione, 1-[3-(3,4-dihydro-6-methyl-2,4-dioxo-1(2H)-pyrimidinyl)propyl]-5-methyl-	H_2O	271.0(4.29)	56-1943-73
2,4(1H,3H)-Pyrimidinedione, 1,1'-(1,3-propanediyl)bis[5-methyl-	H_2O	269(4.23)	56-1943-73
2,4(1H,3H)-Pyrimidinedione, 1,1'-(1,3-propanediyl)bis[6-methyl-	H_2O	269.5(4.32)	56-1943-73

Compound	Solvent	λ max (log ε)	Ref.
$C_{13}H_{16}N_4O_5$			
Inosine, 2',3'-O-(1-methylethylidene)-	pH 1	249(4.10)	4-0417-73
	pH 11	253(4.11)	4-0417-73
2,4(1H,3H)-Pteridinedione, 1-(2-deoxy-D-ribofuranosyl)-6,7-dimethyl-	pH 3.0	245s(3.97),323(3.97)	24-1401-73
	pH 11.0	240(4.20),270(3.47), 330(4.00)	24-1401-73
$C_{13}H_{16}N_4O_5S$			
Inosine, 7,8-dihydro-2',3'-O-(1-methylethylidene)-8-thioxo-	pH 1	216(4.11),294(4.30)	94-1143-73
	pH 7	216(3.99),294(4.20)	94-1143-73
	pH 13	291.5(4.27)	94-1143-73
$C_{13}H_{16}N_4O_6$			
2,4(1H,3H)-Pteridinedione, 6,7-dimethyl-1-β-D-ribofuranosyl-	pH 3.0	245s(3.99),323(3.99)	24-1401-73
	pH 11.0	240(4.20),272(3.51), 330(4.01)	24-1401-73
1H-Purine-2,6-dione, 7-(3,6-anhydro-α-D-mannopyranosyl)-3,7-dihydro-1,3-dimethyl-	pH 7	276(3.91)	136-0378-73C
$C_{13}H_{16}N_4S_2$			
[4,5'-Bithiazole]-2,2'-diamine, 4'-methyl-N,N'-di-2-propenyl-	pH 1	269(3.96)	80-0677-73
	EtOH	268(3.89),320(3.91)	80-0677-73
	EtOH	264(3.97),322(3.91)	83-0152-73
$C_{13}H_{16}N_5O_8P$			
Carbamic acid, [9-(3,5-O-phosphinico-β-D-ribofuranosyl)-9H-purin-6-yl]-, ethyl ester, Na salt	pH 1	275(4.31)	87-1075-73
	pH 7	267(4.28)	87-1075-73
	pH 11	268(4.16),275s(4.14), 289(3.98)	87-1075-73
	pH 12	289(4.38)	87-1075-73
$C_{13}H_{16}N_6$			
3H-Cyclohepta[1,2-d:4,5-d']diimidazole-2,6-diamine, N^6,N^6,3,4-tetramethyl- (zoanthoxanthin)	MeOH	293(4.52),427(4.35)	77-0099-73
$C_{13}H_{16}O$			
Benzene, 1-(1-cyclohexen-1-yl)-4-methoxy-	EtOH	254(4.27),290s(2.94)	35-5288-73
Benzene, 1-(4,5-hexadienyl)-3-methoxy-	EtOH	222(4.00),272(3.45), 279(3.42)	78-0715-73
Benzeneacetaldehyde, α,4-dimethyl-α-(1-propenyl)-, (E)-	n.s.g.	249(3.45),271(3.14)	22-1676-73
5(6H)-Benzocyclooctanone, 7,8,9,10-tetrahydro-1-methyl-	EtOH	245(3.49)	22-3493-73
5(6H)-Benzocyclooctanone, 7,8,9,10-tetrahydro-8-methyl-	EtOH	248(3.81)	78-1843-73
4a(2H)-Biphenylenol, 1,3,4,8b-tetrahydro-8-methyl-	EtOH	260(2.75),266(2.86), 273(2.84)	22-3493-73
3-Hepten-2-one, 3-phenyl-	EtOH	215(4.11)	35-3310-73
3-Hexen-2-one, 3-(4-methylphenyl)-	n.s.g.	220(4.16),244(3.63), 270(3.35)	22-1676-73
4-Hexen-2-one, 3-(4-methylphenyl)-	n.s.g.	248(3.66),271(3.40)	22-1676-73
1H-Indene, 3-(3-methoxypropyl)-	EtOH	252(4.02),280(2.94), 290(1.70)	44-1439-73
1(2H)-Naphthalenone, 3,4-dihydro-2,5,8-trimethyl-	EtOH	213(4.7),254(4.2), 300(3.6)	8-0175-73
1(2H)-Naphthalenone, 3,4-dihydro-3,5,8-trimethyl-	EtOH	213(--),254(--), 306(--)	8-0176-73

Compound	Solvent	λ_{max}(log ε)	Ref.
2(3H)-Naphthalenone, 5-ethenyl-4,4a,7,8-tetrahydro-4a-methyl-	MeOH	236(4.35)	24-3636-73
4a,8a-Propanonaphthalen-10-one, 1,2,3,4-tetrahydro-	isooctane	257s(3.26),266(3.40),277(3.36),294s(2.71),304(2.45),315(2.11)	35-2230-73
$C_{13}H_{16}O_2$			
Benzeneacetaldehyde, 4-methoxy-α-methyl-α-1-propenyl-	n.s.g.	223(3.89),276(3.17),282(3.12)	22-1676-73
Benzenemethanol, 2,4,6-trimethyl-α-methylene-, acetate	isooctane	235s(3.88)	35-3310-73
4H-1-Benzopyran-4-one, 2,3-dihydro-6-methyl-2-(1-methylethyl)-	MeOH	254(3.95),331(3.56)	20-0705-73
4H-1-Benzopyran-4-one, 2,3-dihydro-6-methyl-2-propyl-	MeOH	254(3.95),332(3.56)	20-0705-73
Cyclohexanone, 2-(hydroxyphenylmethyl)-, eythro-	n.s.g.	255f(2.3),290(1.90)	35-3310-73
threo-	n.s.g.	255f(2.3),288(1.79)	35-3310-73
Ethanol, 2-(3,4-dihydro-6-methoxy-1(2H)-naphthalenylidene)-, (E)-	EtOH	269(4.05)	39-0615-73C
(Z)-	EtOH	261(4.04)	39-0615-73C
2-Hexen-1-one, 1-(2-hydroxy-5-methylphenyl)-	MeOH	272(4.23),355(3.67)	20-0299-73
3-Hexen-2-one, 3-(4-methoxyphenyl)-	n.s.g.	224(4.17),255(3.58),284(3.53)	22-1676-73
1H-Indene-1-butanoic acid, 2,3-dihydro-	EtOH	260(2.88),266(3.08),273(3.14)	44-1439-73
2-Naphthalenecarboxaldehyde, 3,5,6,7,8-8a-hexahydro-8,8a-dimethyl-3-oxo-, cis	MeOH	245(4.10)	23-2166-73
1,4-Naphthalenedione, 4a,5,8,8a-tetrahydro-2,8,8a-trimethyl-, (4aα,8β,8aα)-	EtOH	242(4.06)	23-3989-73
1-Naphthaleneethanol, 3,4-dihydro-6-methoxy-	EtOH	270(4.06)	39-0615-73C
1(2H)-Naphthalenone, 8-ethynyl-3,4,5,6-7,8-hexahydro-8-hydroxy-4-methyl-	EtOH	245(4.07)	88-0991-73
2(1H)-Naphthalenone, 5-ethynyl-4,4a,5,6-7,8-hexahydro-5-hydroxy-4a-methyl-, cis	MeOH	240(4.16)	24-3636-73
2-Penten-1-one, 1-(2-hydroxy-5-methylphenyl)-4-methyl-, (E)-	MeOH	272(4.23),355(3.67)	20-0299-73
$C_{13}H_{16}O_3$			
2H-1-Benzopyran-4-ol, 4-ethenyl-3,4-dihydro-7-methoxy-2-methyl-	EtOH	280(3.39),286(3.35)	2-0847-73
Butanoic acid, 2-methyl-4-(2,5-dimethylphenyl)-4-oxo-	EtOH	245(--),293(--)	8-0177-73
Butanoic acid, 3-methyl-4-(2,5-dimethylphenyl)-4-oxo-	EtOH	245(--),290(--)	8-0178-73
Ethanone, 1-(3,4-dihydro-5-hydroxy-2,2-dimethyl-2H-1-benzopyran-6-yl)-	MeOH	276(4.07),308(3.89)	2-0100-73
	MeOH	233(3.86),240s(3.80),287(4.13),322s(3.83)	32-0779-73
Ethanone, 1-(3,4-dihydro-5-hydroxy-2,2-dimethyl-2H-1-benzopyran-8-yl)-	MeOH	231(4.05),275(3.98),308(3.80)	32-0779-73
Ethanone, 1-(3,4-dihydro-7-hydroxy-2,2-dimethyl-2H-1-benzopyran-6-yl)-	MeOH	236(3.95),242s(3.92),282(4.16),325(3.80)	32-0779-73
Ethanone, 1-[2,4-dihydroxy-3-(3-methyl-2-butenyl)phenyl]-	MeOH	234s(3.88),282(4.15),323s(3.74)	32-0771-73
Ethanone, 1-(1,2,3,4-tetrahydro-1,2-dihydroxy-3-methyl-2-naphthalenyl)-, c-2	n.s.g.	251(2.57),264(2.61),272(2.58)	39-0235-73C

Compound	Solvent	λ_{max}(log ε)	Ref.
Ethanone, 1-(1,2,3,4-tetrahydro-1,2-dihydroxy-3-methyl-2-naphthalenyl)-, t-2	n.s.g.	264(2.66),271(2.59)	39-0235-73C
1-Naphthalenecarboxylic acid, 2,4a,5,6-7,8-hexahydro-4a-methyl-2-oxo-, methyl ester	EtOH	241(4.19)	44-0967-73
1-Naphthalenecarboxylic acid, 4a,5,6,7-8,8a-hexahydro-4a-methyl-7-oxo-, methyl ester	MeOH	214(3.58),291(3.78)	35-2303-73
2-Naphthalenecarboxylic acid, 3,5,6,7-8,8a-hexahydro-8,8a-dimethyl-3-oxo-, cis-(±)-	MeOH	253(3.99)	23-2166-73
$C_{13}H_{16}O_4$			
2-Benzofurancarboxylic acid, 4,5,6,7-tetrahydro-3,5-dimethyl-4-oxo-, ethyl ester	EtOH	217(4.14),252(4.14)	12-0201-73
2-Benzofurancarboxylic acid, 4,5,6,7-tetrahydro-3,7-dimethyl-4-oxo-, ethyl ester	EtOH	218(4.01),254(3.97)	12-0201-73
Butanedioic acid, (2-methylphenyl)-, dimethyl ester	EtOH	265(2.76),272(2.78)	44-0741-73
Ethanone, 1-(3,4-dihydro-5,7-dihydroxy-	EtOH	291(4.36)	2-0100-73
2,2-dimethyl-2H-1-benzopyran-6-yl)-	EtOH	291(4.28)	39-0419-73C
Ethanone, 1-(3,4-dihydro-5,7-dihydroxy-	EtOH	292(4.34)	2-0100-73
2,2-dimethyl-2H-1-benzopyran-8-yl)-	EtOH	292(4.21)	39-0419-73C
Ethanone, 1-(1,2,3,4-tetrahydro-1,2,4-trihydroxy-3-methyl-2-naphthalenyl)-	n.s.g.	255(2.35),262(2.42), 267(2.31),272(2.13)	39-0235-73C
Ethanone, 1-[2,4,6-trihydroxy-3-(3-methyl-2-butenyl)phenyl]-	MeOH	290(4.32)	2-0100-73
1(4H)-Naphthalenone, 4-acetoxy-4a,5,8-8a-tetrahydro-3-methoxy-	MeOH	249(4.17)	12-0595-73
$C_{13}H_{16}O_4S$			
2-Butenoic acid, 3-methyl-4-(phenylsulfonyl)-, ethyl ester, cis	EtOH	220(4.08)	22-0743-73
trans	EtOH	223(4.15)	22-0743-73
$C_{13}H_{16}O_5$			
4H-1-Benzopyran-4-one, 2,3-dihydro-5-hydroxy-6-(2-hydroxyethyl)-7-methoxy-	EtOH	240(4.07),288(4.21), 325(3.70)	94-2286-73
2-methyl-	EtOH-KOH	253(3.86),328(4.34)	94-2286-73
2(3H)-Furanone, dihydro-5-(2-hydroxy-3,4-dimethoxyphenyl)-3-methyl-	EtOH	274(3.20)	39-2388-73C
2-Propenoic acid, 3-(4-hydroxy-3,5-dimethoxyphenyl)-, ethyl ester, (E)-	EtOH	240(4.26),330(4.30)	102-0893-73
$C_{13}H_{16}O_6$			
2-Propenal, 3-(3-hydroxy-2,4,5,6-tetramethoxyphenyl)-, (E)-	EtOH	227(4.12),315(4.36)	102-2501-73
$C_{13}H_{16}O_7$			
2-Propenoic acid, 3-(3-hydroxy-2,4,5,6-tetramethoxyphenyl)-, (E)-	EtOH	225(4.04),298(4.15)	102-2501-73
$C_{13}H_{16}Si$			
Silane, trimethyl-1-naphthalenyl-, tetracyanoethylene complex	CH_2Cl_2	436(3.05),571(3.09)	39-0447-73B
Silane, trimethyl-2-naphthalenyl-, tetracyanoethylene complex	CH_2Cl_2	442(2.37),562(2.60)	39-0447-73B

Compound	Solvent	$\lambda_{max}(\log \epsilon)$	Ref.
$C_{13}H_{17}BrN_2O_6$			
Uracil, 1-[2,3-O-isopropylidene-4-methoxy-4-(bromomethylene)-3-D-erythrofuranosyl]-	MeOH	262(3.85)	88-2731-73
$C_{13}H_{17}BrO$			
Benzene, 1-(1-bromo-3,3-dimethyl-1-butenyl)-4-methoxy-, cis	EtOH	243(4.04)	88-2015-73
trans	EtOH	262(4.10)	88-2015-73
$C_{13}H_{17}ClO_2$			
1-Propanone, 1-[3-chloro-5-(1,1-dimethylethyl)-2-hydroxyphenyl]-	C_6H_{12}	259(3.97),265(3.94), 344(3.61)	22-1442-73
	EtOH	259(3.96),340(3.57)	22-1442-73
$C_{13}H_{17}N$			
1H-Carbazole, 2,3,4,4a,9,9a-hexahydro-4a-methyl-	EtOH	245(3.84),292(3.42)	33-2628-73
Cyclohexanamine, N-(phenylmethylene)-	EtOH	247(4.20),278s(3.16), 285s(2.96)	35-4692-73
Piperidine, 1-(1,2-dihydro-1-pentalenyl)-	hexane	257(3.98),260(3.97), 264(3.94),275(3.65), 340(3.08)	89-0337-73
$C_{13}H_{17}NO$			
Cycloheptanone, 3-(phenylamino)-	MeOH	249(4.16),296(3.40)	18-3517-73
2,4,6-Cycloheptatrien-1-one, 2-(2-methyl-1-piperidinyl)-	EtOH	360(3.91),410(3.87)	35-7101-73
7-Oxa-8-azabicyclo[4.2.1]nonane, 8-phenyl-	MeOH	239(3.97)	18-3517-73
Oxazole, 2,5-dihydro-5-ethyl-2,2-dimethyl-4-phenyl-	EtOH	241(4.11)	33-2611-73
2-Propenamide, N-butyl-3-phenyl-	n.s.g.	215(4.27),221(4.18), 272(4.40)	33-0474-73
$C_{13}H_{17}NOS$			
Benzenecarbothioic acid, O-[2-(1-pyrrolidinyl)ethyl] ester	C_6H_{12}	247(3.89),288(4.08)	39-1574-73C
3-Buten-2-one, 4-(dimethylamino)-4-(methylthio)-3-phenyl-	EtOH	227(3.86),274(3.97), 357(3.94)	1-0258-73
$C_{13}H_{17}NO_2$			
1H-Indole-3-butanol, 6-methoxy-	EtOH	227(4.42),270(3.83), 290(3.79)	39-0872-73B
2,6-Methano-2H-1,5-benzoxazocin-7-ol, 3,4,5,6-tetrahydro-2,5-dimethyl-	EtOH	280(3.30)	88-1623-73
$C_{13}H_{17}NO_3$			
2H-Pyran-2-one, 3-acetyl-6-methyl-4-(1-piperidinyl)-	EtOH	247(4.29),288(3.89), 333(3.88)	78-1083-73
$C_{13}H_{17}NO_4$			
Cyclopentanecarboxylic acid, 2-(1-cyano-2-ethoxy-2-oxoethylidene)-, ethyl ester	EtOH	238(4.07),356(2.43)	78-4103-73
	EtOH-NaOH	248(3.97),356(4.11)	78-4103-73
L-Tyrosine, N-acetyl-, ethyl ester	H_2O	274.6(3.14)	69-2011-73
	MeOH	277.4(3.22)	69-2011-73
	PrOH	277.8(3.23)	69-2011-73
	isoPrOH	277.7(3.24)	69-2011-73
	BuOH	278.0(3.24)	69-2011-73

Compound	Solvent	$\lambda_{max}(\log \epsilon)$	Ref.
L-Tyrosine, N-acetyl-, ethyl ester (cont.) (also solvent mixtures)	EtOAc	277.9(3.26)	69-2011-73
	$HOCH_2CH_2OH$	277.4(3.23)	69-2011-73
	$HCONH_2$	277.6(3.22)	69-2011-73
$C_{13}H_{17}NO_5$			
Benzoic acid, 4-[[(2,2-dimethoxyethyl)-imino]methyl]-2-hydroxy-	EtOH	265(4.36),272s(4.30), 334(3.66)	78-0857-73
Propanoic acid, 3-[(2,3-dimethoxyphen-yl)amino]-3-oxo-, ethyl ester	MeOH	247(4.02),279s(3.21), 287s(2.99)	78-1721-73
$C_{13}H_{17}NO_6$			
1H-Pyrrole-3-propanoic acid, 5-(methoxy-carbonyl)-4-(2-methoxy-2-oxoethyl)-, methyl ester	MeOH	273(4.16)	39-1546-73C
$C_{13}H_{17}NS_2$			
Dithiobenzoic acid, diethylamine salt	EtOH	285(4.09),361(4.04), 500(2.21)	143-0359-73
$C_{13}H_{17}N_3$			
Benzeneacetonitrile, α-[bis(dimethyl-amino)methylene]-	EtOH	235(4.13),247(4.18), 257s(4.07),318(4.24)	1-0258-73
3,5-Pyridinedicarbonitrile, 4,4-diethyl-1,4-dihydro-2,6-dimethyl-	EtOH	215(4.3),341(3.6)	103-0994-73
3,5-Pyridinedicarbonitrile, 1,4-dihydro-2,4,6-trimethyl-4-propyl-	EtOH	216(4.7),344(3.4)	103-0994-73
$C_{13}H_{17}N_3O$			
Pyrimido[1,2-b]indazol-4(1H)-one, 7,8,9,10-tetrahydro-2,3,7-trimethyl-	MeOH	260s(3.88),268(3.95), 312(3.75)	4-0261-73
$C_{13}H_{17}N_3O_2$			
1,2,4-Oxadiazole-3-carboxamide, N-(tri-cyclo[3.3.1.1^{3,7}]dec-1-yl-	EtOH	230(3.59)	39-0047-73C
4-Pyrimidinamine, 5,6-dihydro-5-(dimeth-oxymethyl)-2-phenyl-	EtOH	243(4.11),269(3.85)	18-0253-73
	EtOH-HCl	265(--),286s(--)	18-0253-73
$C_{13}H_{17}N_3O_2S$			
Pentanoic acid, 5-(1H-pyrrolo[2,3-d]-pyrimidin-4-ylthio)-, ethyl ester	pH 1	220(4.30),258(3.89), 311(3.98)	73-1438-73
	pH 13	222(4.31),249(3.91), 294(4.06)	73-1438-73
$C_{13}H_{17}N_3O_2S_2$			
Carbamic acid, [[[3-(2-propenyl)-2(3H)-thiazolylidene]amino](2-propenylthio)-methylene]-	dioxan	245(3.49),280(3.89), 333(4.36)	94-0074-73
$C_{13}H_{17}N_3O_4$			
3-Isoxazolidineacetic acid, 5-oxo-4-(2-phenylhydrazino)-, ethyl ester	EtOH	220(3.99),296(4.04), 327(4.30)	70-2006-73
$C_{13}H_{17}N_3O_5S$			
Quinoxalinium, 6-acetamido-2,4-dimeth-yl-, methyl sulfate	H_2O	267(4.55),338(3.20)	22-1285-73
$C_{13}H_{17}N_3S$			
1,2,4-Triazolidine-3-thione, 4-butyl-1-(phenylmethyl)-, meso-ionic didehydro deriv.	MeCN	251(4.49)	103-1048-73

Compound	Solvent	$\lambda_{max}(\log \epsilon)$	Ref.
$C_{13}H_{17}N_5$			
Benzo[1,2-d:3,4-d']diimidazol-2-amine, 4,6-dihydro-N,N,3,6,7-pentamethyl-	MeOH	270s(4.5),278(4.6), 295(4.5)	103-0740-73
$C_{13}H_{17}N_5O$			
4(1H)-Pteridinone, 2-amino-6-(cyclohexylmethyl)-	pH 13	252(4.38),363(3.83)	44-2073-73
$C_{13}H_{17}N_5O_2$			
7H-Purine-7-propanenitrile, 1,2,3,6-tetrahydro-1,3-dimethyl-2,6-dioxo-8-propyl-	n.s.g.	210(4.36),277(4.02)	73-1571-73
$C_{13}H_{17}N_5O_2S$			
1H-Purine-2,6-dione, 8-ethyl-3,7-dihydro-7-(3-isothiocyanatopropyl)-1,3-dimethyl-	n.s.g.	210(4.35),277(4.01)	73-1571-73
$C_{13}H_{17}N_5O_4$			
7(8H)-Pteridinone, 8-(2-deoxy- -D-ribofuranosyl)-2-(dimethylamino)-	MeOH	220(4.29),246(4.15), 310s(3.74),363(4.22)	24-0317-73
$C_{13}H_{17}N_5O_5$			
Adenosine, 2',3'-O-(1-methylethylidene)-, 1-oxide	pH 1	258(4.08)	94-0209-73
	pH 7	233(4.61),262(3.90), 296(3.32)	94-0209-73
	pH 13	232(4.35),269(3.92), 310(3.61)	94-0209-73
	EtOH	235(4.61),264(3.89), 301(3.36)	94-0209-73
2(1H)-Pteridinone, 4-(dimethylamino)-1-β-D-ribofuranosyl-	pH 0.0	248(4.13),330(3.99)	33-1225-73
	pH 7.0	207(4.41),249(3.99), 337(3.97)	33-1225-73
7(8H)-Pteridinone, 2-(dimethylamino)-8-β-D-ribofuranosyl-	MeOH	220(4.29),246(4.17), 310s(3.68),365(4.22)	24-0317-73
$C_{13}H_{17}N_6O_{10}P$			
Glycine, N-[(9-β-D-ribofuranosyl-9H-purin-6-yl)amino]carbonyl]-, 5'-(dihydrogen phosphate)	pH 1	277(4.36)	87-0956-73
	H_2O	269(4.37),276(4.30)	87-0956-73
	pH 13	270(4.25),278(4.24), 295(3.98)	87-0956-73
$C_{13}H_{17}N_7O_4$			
Glycine, N-[N-(N-1H-purin-6-ylglycyl)-glycyl]-, ethyl ester	pH 1	276(4.21)	94-2349-73
	pH 7	266(4.20)	94-2349-73
	pH 13	273(4.17),280s(4.05)	94-2349-73
$C_{13}H_{17}N_7O_6$			
Adenosine, N-[[(2-amino-2-oxoethyl)-amino]carbonyl]-	pH 1-2	270s(--),276(4.30)	87-0139-73
	pH 5-7	269(4.33),277s(--)	87-0139-73
	pH 12	270(4.02),297(4.29)	87-0139-73
$C_{13}H_{17}O_2Rh$			
Rhodium, [(2,3,6,7-η)-bicyclo[3.2.1]-octa-2,6-diene](2,4-pentanedionato-O,O')-	hexane	218(4.19),270(3.95), 300(3.67),386(3.15)	78-3903-73
Rhodium, [(1,2,5,6-η)-1,3,5-cyclooctatriene](2,4-pentanedionato-O,O']-	hexane	207(4.39),256(4.06), 300(3.70)	78-3903-73
Rhodium, [(2,3,5,6-η)-2-methylbicyclo-[2.2.1]hepta-2,5-diene](2,4-pentanedionato)-	EtOH	211s(4.17),249(3.88), 272(3.92),307s(3.67), 382(3.20)	78-3903-73

Compound	Solvent	λmax(log ε)	Ref.
$C_{13}H_{18}$			
Benzene, 1-cyclohexyl-2-methyl-	EtOH	257(2.48),263(2.55), 271(2.52)	22-1517-73
Benzene, (4,4-dimethyl-1-pentenyl)-, cis	EtOH	240(4.24)	44-2756-73
trans	EtOH	248(4.48)	44-2756-73
Benzene, 1-(2-methylcyclohexyl)-, cis	EtOH	248(2.33),254(2.44), 256s(2.42),259(2.50), 261(2.46),265(2.36), 269(2.34)	22-1517-73
trans	EtOH	248(2.16),254(2.29), 255(2.28),259(2.35), 262(2.35),265(2.23), 268(2.26)	22-1517-73
Bicyclo[6.1.0]nona-2,4,6-triene, 9-(1,1-dimethylethyl)-	hexane	252(3.57)	35-2379-73
isomer	hexane	248(3.54)	35-2379-73
Bicyclo[6.1.0]nona-2,4,6-triene, 1,3,5,7-tetramethyl-, cis	C_6H_{12}	242(3.57)	35-4647-73
1H-Indene, 1-(1,1-dimethylethyl)-3a,4-dihydro-	hexane	268.5(3.73)	35-2379-73
1H-Indene, 1-(1,1-dimethylethyl)-3a,7a-dihydro-	hexane	261(3.53)	35-2379-73
1H-Indene, 1-(1,1-dimethylethyl)-7,7a-dihydro-	hexane	299(3.99)	35-2379-73
Tetracyclo[5.3.0.0^{2,10}.0^{3,6}]dec-8-ene, 1,3,6-trimethyl-	pentane	223(3.72)	35-6197-73
Tetracyclo[5.3.0.0^{2,10}.0^{3,6}]dec-8-ene, 1,4,5-trimethyl-	pentane	235s(3.23)	35-6197-73
Tetracyclo[6.3.0.0^{2,11}.0^{3,7}]undec-9-ene, 1,2-dimethyl-	pentane	225(3.27)	35-6197-73
Tetracyclo[6.3.0.0^{2,11}.0^{3,7}]undec-9-ene, 1,8-dimethyl-	pentane	223(3.44)	35-6197-73
Tetracyclo[6.3.0.0^{2,11}.0^{3,7}]undec-9-ene, 1,9-dimethyl-	pentane	225s(3.55)	35-6197-73
Tetracyclo[6.3.0.0^{2,11}.0^{3,7}]undec-9-ene, 1,10-dimethyl-	pentane	222(3.37)	35-6197-73
Tetracyclo[6.3.0.0^{2,11}.0^{3,7}]undec-9-ene, 1,11-dimethyl-	pentane	230s(3.23)	35-6197-73
$C_{13}H_{18}Br_2O_5$			
α-D-Ribohexofuranose, 3-deoxy-3-(dibromomethylene)-1,2:5,6-bis-O-(1-methylethylidene)-	EtOH	292(1.46)	136-0129-73C
$C_{13}H_{18}ClN_3$			
1H-Pyrazole, 4-chloro-3-[3,4-dihydro-2,2-dimethyl-4-(1-methylethylidene)-2H-pyrrol-5-yl]-1-methyl-	MeOH	250(3.83)	18-0540-73
$C_{13}H_{18}Cl_2O_5$			
α-D-Ribohexofuranose, 3-deoxy-3-(dichloromethylene)-1,2:5,6-bis-O-(1-methylethylidene)-	EtOH	217(3.71)	136-0129-73C
$C_{13}H_{18}CuF_3O_3S$			
Copper, [(1,2,5,6,9,10-η)-1,5,9-cyclododecatriene](trifluoromethanesulfonato-O)-	n.s.g.	240(3.40),280(3.18)	35-1889-73

Compound	Solvent	λ_{max}(log ε)	Ref.
$C_{13}H_{18}DNO_2$			
Ethanone, 1-[5-(1,1-dimethylethyl)-2-(hydroxy-d)phenyl]-, O-methyloxime	CCl_4	320(3.63)	30-0394-73
Ethanone, 1-[5-(1,1-dimethylethyl)-2-methoxyphenyl]-, oxime-d	CCl_4	279(3.69)	30-0394-73
$C_{13}H_{18}NO_3P$			
Phosphonic acid, (1H-indol-2-ylmethyl)-, diethyl ester	MeOH	275(3.93),282(3.92), 291(3.82)	23-0792-73
$C_{13}H_{18}N_2$			
1,2-Diazocine, 1,4,5,6,7,8-hexahydro-1-methyl-3-phenyl-	EtOH	235(4.02),325(2.88)	22-2029-73
1H-Indole-3-ethanamine, 1-(1-methylethyl)-	EtOH	225(4.58),279s(3.69), 288(3.74),297(3.66)	103-0196-73
1H-Indole-3-ethanamine, N,N,1-trimethyl-, compd. with borane	MeOH	223(4.55),288(3.74)	44-1504-73
Pyrimido[1,2-a]indole, 1,2,3,4,10,10a-hexahydro-10,10-dimethyl- (maleate)	EtOH	243(4.05),293(3.42)	78-4049-73
$C_{13}H_{18}N_2O$			
1-Cyclohexene-1-carbonitrile, 4,4-dimethyl-6-oxo-2-(1-pyrrolidinyl)-	EtOH	237(3.74),302(4.33)	70-0811-73
1H-Indole-5-ethanamine, 5-methoxy-N,N-dimethyl-, borane adduct	MeOH	222(4.36),278(3.76), 298(3.67),308(3.53)	44-1504-73
Piperazine, 1,4,5,6-tetrahydro-2-(4-methoxyphenyl)-1,4-dimethyl-	C_6H_{12}	300(4.11)	28-1319-73A
Spiro[cyclohexane-1,1'(2'H)-phthalazin]-6'-ol, 3',4'-dihydro-, hydrochloride	EtOH	280(3.13)	39-0471-73C
$C_{13}H_{18}N_2O_2$			
Isoxazolin-5-one, 3-ethyl-4-methyl-, benzylammonium salt	EtOH	258(3.96)	1-2802-73
$C_{13}H_{18}N_2O_2S_2$			
Ethanamine, N,N-diethyl-2-[(4-isothiocyanatophenyl)sulfonyl]-	EtOH	229(4.36),283s(4.25), 292(4.30)	73-0289-73
$C_{13}H_{18}N_2O_4$			
Acetamide, N-[4-[2-(acetylamino)-1,3-dihydroxypropyl]phenyl]-, [S-(R*,R*)]-	EtOH	248(4.03)	104-2144-73
Propanoic acid, 2-[(2,5-dimethoxyphenyl)hydrazono]-, ethyl ester, (E)-	EtOH	340.5(4.26)	94-1481-73
(Z)-	EtOH	367(4.22)	94-1481-73
$C_{13}H_{18}N_2O_5$			
3,6-Diazatricyclo[4.3.1.1^{3,8}]undecane-1,8-dicarboxylic acid, 9-oxo-, dimethyl ester	EtOH	259(3.22)(end abs.)	44-1648-73
	EtOH-HCl	259(3.00)	44-1648-73
$C_{13}H_{18}N_2O_6$			
D-Ribofuranoside, methyl 5-deoxy-5-(3,4-dihydro-2,4-dioxo-1(2H)-pyrimidinyl)-2,3-O-(1-methylethylidene)-	MeOH	266(4.00)	18-3165-73
$C_{13}H_{18}N_2O_8$			
D-glycero-D-galacto-Non-2-enonic acid, 2,6-anhydro-5-[(cyanoacetyl)amino]-3,5-dideoxy-, methyl ester	n.s.g.	245(3.85)	49-0402-73

Compound	Solvent	$\lambda_{max}(\log \epsilon)$	Ref.
$C_{13}H_{18}N_2S$			
3-Butene-2-thione, 4-[[4-(dimethyl-amino)phenyl]amino]-3-methyl-	EtOH	445(4.38)	104-1739-73
$C_{13}H_{18}N_2S_2$			
Ethanamine, N,N-diethyl-2-[(4-isothio-cyanatophenyl)thio]-	EtOH	220s(4.36),269s(4.35), 291(4.32)	73-0289-73
$C_{13}H_{18}N_4O_2$			
Benzo[g]pteridine-2,4(1H,3H)-dione, 6,7,8,9,9a,10-hexahydro-7,8,10-trimethyl-	pH 1	236(4.20),274(4.33), 351(3.85)	33-1908-73
	pH 5	280(4.45),313(4.03)	33-1908-73
	pH 13	231(4.51),283(4.36), 320(4.05)	33-1908-73
2,4(1H,3H)-Pteridinedione, 1-methyl-6,7-bis(1-methylethyl)-	pH 6.0	230s(4.24),252(4.05), 331(3.99)	24-3149-73
	pH 11.0	242(4.18),338(4.03)	24-3149-73
$C_{13}H_{18}N_4O_3$			
Benzo[g]pteridine-5(1H)-carboxaldehyde, 2,3,4,5a,6,7,8,9,9a,10-decahydro-7,8-dimethyl-2,4-dioxo-	pH 5	285(4.26)	33-1908-73
2,4(1H,3H)-Pteridinedione, 1-methyl-6,7-bis(1-methylethyl)-, 5-oxide	pH 6.0	240(4.44),292(3.76), 353(3.84)	24-3149-73
	pH 11.0	245(4.42),292(3.78), 355(3.88)	24-3149-73
	MeOH	243(4.45),296(3.82), 359(3.78)	24-3149-73
$C_{13}H_{18}N_4O_4$			
1H-Pyrazolo[3,4-b]pyridin-4-amine, N,N-dimethyl-1-β-D-ribofuranosyl-	EtOH	219(3.76),242(3.73), 323(3.70)	104-1294-73
$C_{13}H_{18}N_4O_5$			
Tubercidin, 5'-deoxy-, acetic acid solvate	MeOH	270(4.10)	18-0618-73
$C_{13}H_{18}N_4O_7$			
1H-Purine-2,6-dione, 7-β-D-galactopyranosyl-3,7-dihydro-1,3-dimethyl-	H_2O	275(3.94)	136-0378-73C
1H-Purine-2,6-dione, 7-β-D-glucopyranosyl-3,7-dihydro-1,3-dimethyl-	H_2O	275(3.93)	136-0378-73C
1H-Purine-2,6-dione, 7-β-D-mannopyranosyl-3,7-dihydro-1,3-dimethyl-	H_2O	275(3.89)	136-0378-73C
$C_{13}H_{18}N_5O_5$			
1H-Purinium, 2-amino-7,9-bis(2-ethoxy-2-oxoethyl)-6,9-dihydro-6-oxo-, bromide	pH 4	256(4.08),284(3.89)	24-1389-73
	pH 10	219(4.27),249(3.69), 286(3.91)	24-1389-73
$C_{13}H_{18}N_6$			
1H-Pyrazolo[3,4-d]pyrimidine-3-carbonitrile, 4-(hexylamino)-1-methyl-	EtOH-pH 1	232s(--),249(3.77), 272s(--),281(3.89), 302s(--),311(4.19), 322(4.12)	39-1903-73C
	EtOH-pH 7	228(4.06),254(3.90), 317(3.98)	39-1903-73C
	EtOH-pH 12	262(3.96),312(3.97)	39-1903-73C

Compound	Solvent	$\lambda_{max}(\log \epsilon)$	Ref.
$C_{13}H_{18}N_6O_3$			
4H-Cyclopenta-1,3-dioxole-4-methanol, 6-(7-amino-3H-1,2,3-triazolo[4,5-d]-pyrimidin-3-yl)tetrahydro-2,2-dimethyl-, (3aα,4α,6α,6aα)-(±)-	pH 1	263(4.10),275s(--)	4-0601-73
	pH 7	279(4.09)	4-0601-73
	pH 13	278(4.08)	4-0601-73
$C_{13}H_{18}N_6O_5$			
7(8H)-Pteridinone, 2-amino-4-(dimethylamino)-8-α-D-ribofuranosyl-	pH 1.0	222(4.42),312(4.16), 348(4.15)	24-0317-73
	pH 5.0	208(4.50),237(4.00), 277(4.20),305s(3.79), 371(4.15)	24-0317-73
	MeOH	209(4.45),235s(3.95), 277(4.16),369(4.10)	24-0317-73
7(8H)-Pteridinone, 2-amino-4-(dimethylamino)-8-β-D-ribofuranosyl-	pH 1.0	222(4.47),312(4.20), 349(4.15)	24-0317-73
	pH 5.0	207(4.51),240(3.98), 277(4.18),305s(3.75), 372(4.13)	24-0317-73
	MeOH	208(4.46),236s(3.94), 277(4.14),370(4.08)	24-0317-73
$C_{13}H_{18}O$			
1-Naphthalenol, 1,2,3,4-tetrahydro-3,5,8-trimethyl-	EtOH	217s(4.0),270(2.8), 274s(2.8),279(2.8)	8-0179-73
1-Oxaspiro[4.5]deca-3,6-diene, 6,10,10-trimethyl-2-methylene-	pentane	267(3.86)	33-1956-73
Tricyclo[6.4.0.0^{2,7}]dodeca-2,4,6-trien-1-ol, 10-methyl-	EtOH	260(3.06),266(3.20), 272(3.15)	78-1843-73
Tricyclo[4.3.2.0]undecan-2-one, 10-methyl-11-methylene-	EtOH	295(1.79)	44-1222-73
$C_{13}H_{18}OS$			
8H-Cyclohepta[b]thiophen-8-one, 2-(1,1-dimethylethyl)-4,5,6,7-tetrahydro-	n.s.g.	290(4.20)	22-0343-73
$C_{13}H_{18}O_2$			
3H-2-Benzopyran-3-one, 1,5,6,7,8,8a-hexahydro-5,5,8a-trimethyl-1-methylene-	n.s.g.	226(4.05)	88-5153-73
Butanoic acid, 2-methyl-4-(2,5-dimethylphenyl)-	EtOH	215(4.1),263s(2.7), 267(2.8),270s(2.8), 276(2.8)	8-0180-73
Butanoic acid, 3-methyl-4-(2,5-dimethylphenyl)-	EtOH	215(4.1),263s(3.1), 268(2.8),277(2.8)	8-0181-73
2-Cyclohexen-1-one, 4-hydroxy-3,5,5-trimethyl-4-(3-oxo-1-butenyl)-	EtOH	237(4.30)	138-0245-73
3-Cyclohexen-1-one, 2,2,4-trimethyl-3-(1-oxo-2-butenyl)-	n.s.g.	227(4.11)	33-2028-73
4a,8a-Ethenonaphthalene-1,5(2H,6H)-dione, tetrahydro-4-methyl-, (4α,4aβ-8aβ)-	n.s.g.	296(1.74)	44-4281-73
1,3(2H,5H)-Naphthalenedione, 6,7,8,8a-tetrahydro-5,5,8a-trimethyl-	n.s.g.	242(4.00),291(3.71)	88-5153-73
1(2H)-Naphthalenone, 8-ethenyl-3,4,5,6-7,8-hexahydro-8-hydroxy-4-methyl-	EtOH	241(3.99)	88-0991-73
2(3H)-Naphthalenone, 5-ethenyl-4,4a,5,6-7,8-hexahydro-5-hydroxy-4a-methyl-	MeOH	243(4.15)	24-3636-73
2(3H)-Naphthalenone, 4,4a,5,6,7,8-hexahydro-1-(1-oxopropyl)-	C_6H_{12}	235(4.06)	28-0803-73A

Compound	Solvent	λ_{max}(log ε)	Ref.
3-Pentanone, 1-hydroxy-4,4-dimethyl-1-phenyl-	EtOH	255f(2),291(1.93)	35-3310-73
$C_{13}H_{18}O_3$			
5-Azulenecarboxylic acid, 1,2,3,4,5,6,7-8-octahydro-8-methyl-3-oxo-, methyl ester	EtOH	237(4.08)	39-2404-73C
1H-2-Benzopyran-3-one, 3,5,6,7,8,8a-hexahydro-1,5,5,8a-tetramethyl-	n.s.g.	227(4.06)	88-5153-73
2-Cyclohexen-1-one, 4-hydroxy-3,5,5-trimethyl-4-(3-oxo-1-butenyl)-	MeOH	234(4.33)	35-0239-73
	EtOH	238(4.29)	77-0566-73
2(3H)-Furanone, 5-(1,6-dimethyl-2-oxo-3-cyclohexen-1-yl)-4-methyl-	EtOH	228(4.05)	23-3989-73
5H-Inden-5-one, 7a-(2-acetoxyethyl)-1,2,3,6,7,7a-hexahydro-	EtOH	242(4.05)	44-1215-73
2-Naphthalenecarboxylic acid, 1,2,3,4-4a,7,8,8a-octahydro-4a,8-dimethyl-7-oxo-, (2α,4aα,8β,8aβ)-	MeOH	227(3.94)	44-0728-73
1,4,5(4aH)-Naphthalenetrione, hexahydro-3,4a,8-trimethyl-, (3α,4aβ,8α,8aα)-	EtOH	218(2.83),290(2.05)	23-3989-73
$C_{13}H_{18}O_4$			
1-Azulenecarboxylic acid, 1,2,4,5,6,7-8,8a-octahydro-8-hydroxy-8-methyl-2-oxo-, methyl ester, (1α,8α,8aα)-	EtOH	240(4.05)	44-0967-73
5-Heptenoic acid, 7-(3-hydroxy-5-oxo-1-cyclopenten-1-yl)-, methyl ester	MeOH	220(3.90)	88-2313-73
2H-Inden-2-one, 7-acetoxy-1,4,5,6,7,7a-hexahydro-3-methoxy-7-methyl-, cis-(±)-	EtOH	252(4.05)	44-3663-73
$C_{13}H_{18}O_5$			
1-Cyclopentene-1-heptanoic acid, 2-carboxy-5-oxo-	MeOH	245(4.10)	44-4412-73
5-Heptenoic acid, 7-(3-hydroxy-2,5-dioxocyclopentyl)-, methyl ester, [3R-[1(Z),3α]]-	MeOH	272(4.32)	88-2313-73
$C_{13}H_{18}O_6$			
Cyclopenta[c]pyran-4-carboxylic acid, 6α-acetoxy-1-hydroxy-7α-methyl-1,4aα,5,6,7,7aα-hexahydro-	EtOH-NaOH	274(4.03)	35-0540-73
Loganin aglucone 6-acetate	EtOH	236(4.02)	35-0532-73
$C_{13}H_{18}O_7$			
Salicin	n.s.g.	269(2.12)	105-0127-73
$C_{13}H_{19}BrN_4O_3$			
Sydnone imine, 4-bromo-N-(cyclohexylcarbonyl)-3-morpholino-, hydrochloride	EtOH	250(3.95),348(3.98)	87-0671-73
$C_{13}H_{19}BrO_5$			
α-D-ribo-Hexofuranose, 3-(bromomethylene)-3-deoxy-1,2:5,6-bis-O-(1-methylethylidene)-, cis	EtOH	236(2.53),275s(--)	136-0395-73E
trans	EtOH	227(3.61),258s(--)	136-0395-73E
$C_{13}H_{19}ClN_4O_3$			
Sydnone imine, 4-chloro-N-(cyclohexylcarbonyl)-3-morpholino-, hydrochloride	EtOH	254(4.00),348(4.02)	87-0671-73

Compound	Solvent	λ_{max}(log ε)	Ref.
$C_{13}H_{19}ClO_5$			
α-D-ribo-Hexofuranose, 3-(chloromethyl-ene)-3-deoxy-1,2:5,6-bis-O-(1-methyl-ethylidene)-, cis	EtOH	230(1.90),255s(--)	136-0395-73E
trans	EtOH	224(3.43),250s(--)	136-0395-73E
$C_{13}H_{19}FN_2O_2$			
Imidazolidine, 2-(2-fluorophenyl)-1,3-dihydroxy-4,4,5,5-tetramethyl-	EtOH	258(3.03)	78-3833-73
Imidazolidine, 2-(3-fluorophenyl)-1,3-dihydroxy-4,4,5,5-tetramethyl-	EtOH	259(2.99)	78-3833-73
Imidazolidine, 2-(4-fluorophenyl)-1,3-dihydroxy-4,4,5,5-tetramethyl-	EtOH	259(2.88)	78-3833-73
$C_{13}H_{19}IN_2$			
1H-Indole-2-methanaminium, N,N,N,1-tetramethyl-, iodide	MeOH	278(4.00),288s(3.87), 300s(3.59)	23-0792-73
$C_{13}H_{19}IN_4O_3$			
Sydnone imine, N-(cyclohexylcarbonyl)-4-iodo-3-morpholino-, hydrochloride	EtOH	253(3.89),350(3.78)	87-0671-73
$C_{13}H_{19}IO_5$			
α-D-ribo-Hexofuranose, 3-deoxy-3-(iodo-methylene)-1,2:5,6-bis-O-(1-methyl-ethylidene)-, cis	EtOH	234(3.50)	136-0395-73E
trans	EtOH	231.5(3.73)	136-0395-73E
$C_{13}H_{19}N$			
2H-1-Pyrindine, 5-(1-butenyl)-3,4,6,7-tetrahydro-3-methyl-, (E)-(+)-(pyrindicin)	MeOH	310(4.76)	94-2048-73
$C_{13}H_{19}NO$			
2-Cyclobutene-1-carbonitrile, 1,2-bis-(1,1-dimethylethyl)-4-oxo-	EtOH	228(3.75)	88-0009-73
1,3-Cyclohexadiene-1-carboxylic acid, 5-methyl-, piperidide	ether	273(3.81)	24-3779-73
$C_{13}H_{19}NOS_2$			
Dithiobenzoic acid, 4-methoxy-, piperi-dine salt	EtOH	286(3.96),352(3.78), 450(2.16)	143-0359-73
$C_{13}H_{19}NO_2$			
Acetic acid, 1-azatricyclo[3.3.1.1^{3,7}]-dec-4-ylidene-, ethyl ester	hexane	207(4.10),275(3.65)	78-1691-73
Benzoic acid, 4-methyl-, 3-(dimethyl-amino)propyl ester	H_2O	241(4.07)	104-2111-73
Bicyclo[2.2.2]oct-5-en-2-one, 5-methyl-1-(4-morpholinyl)-	n.s.g.	292(2.37)	39-1757-73C
Ethanone, 1-[5-(1,1-dimethylethyl)-2-hydroxyphenyl]-, O-methyloxime	MeOH	260(4.022)	30-0394-73
	CCl_4	319(3.648)	30-0394-73
Ethanone, 1-[5-(1,1-dimethylethyl)-2-methoxyphenyl]-, oxime	CCl_4	292(3.542)	30-0394-73
Pyridine, 1,4-diacetyl-4-(1,1-dimethyl-ethyl)-1,4-dihydro-	MeOH	256(4.22)	78-0391-73
$C_{13}H_{19}NO_3$			
Benzoic acid, 4-methoxy-, 3-(dimethyl-amino)propyl ester	H_2O	259(4.21)	104-2111-73

Compound	Solvent	λ_{max}(log ε)	Ref.
2-Propenoic acid, 3-methoxy-2-methyl-, 8-methyl-8-azabicyclo[3.2.1]oct-2-en-3-yl ester	n.s.g.	243(3.44)	88-5099-73
$C_{13}H_{19}NO_4$			
Phenylalanine, 3,4-dihydroxy-, butyl ester	pH 1	280(3.46)	36-0510-73
Phenylalanine, 3,4-dihydroxy-, isobutyl ester	pH 1	280(3.45)	36-0510-73
Propanedioic acid, (3-piperidino-2-propenylidene)-, dimethyl ester	EtOH	238(3.86),379(4.61)	70-1959-73
$C_{13}H_{19}NO_4S_2$			
Pyridine, 1-butyl-4-(1,3-dithietan-2-ylidene)-1,4-dihydro-2,6-dimethyl-, S,S,S',S'-tetraoxide	CH_2Cl_2	244(3.82),288(3.11), 340s(4.41),352(4.56), 360s(4.41)	83-0389-73
$C_{13}H_{19}NO_4Si$			
Silicon, (4-methylphenolato)[2,2',2"-nitrilotris[ethanolato](3-)-N,O,O',O"]-	H_2O	213(3.91),270(3.15)	30-0941-73
$C_{13}H_{19}NO_5Si$			
Silicon, (4-methoxyphenolato)[2,2',2"-nitrilotris[ethanolato](3-)]-	H_2O	223(3.93),288(3.46)	30-0941-73
$C_{13}H_{19}NO_{10}$			
D-glycero-D-galacto-Non-2-enonic acid, 2,6-anhydro-5-[(3-carboxy-1-oxopropyl)amino]-3,5-dideoxy-	n.s.g.	241(3.69)	49-0402-73
$C_{13}H_{19}NS_2$			
Dithiobenzoic acid, 4-methyl-, piperidine salt	EtOH	297(3.92),361(3.73), 491(2.25)	143-0359-73
$C_{13}H_{19}N_2$			
1H-Indole-2-methanaminium, N,N,N,1-tetramethyl-, iodide	MeOH	278(4.00),288s(3.87), 300s(3.59)	23-0792-73
$C_{13}H_{19}N_3O$			
Spiro[phthalazine-1(2H),4'-piperidin]-6-ol, 3,4-dihydro-1'-methyl-, dihydrochloride	EtOH	280(3.13)	39-0471-73C
$C_{13}H_{19}N_3O_2$			
Spiro[cycloheptane-1,1'-cyclohex-2'-ene]-2,4'-dione, monosemicarbazone	EtOH	270(4.31)	39-0393-73C
$C_{13}H_{19}N_3O_6$			
1H-Imidazole-4-carboxylic acid, 5-amino-1-[2,3-O-(1-methylethylidene)-α-D-ribofuranosyl]-, methyl ester	MeOH	268(4.06)	39-1720-73C
β-	MeOH	275(3.99)	39-1720-73C
$C_{13}H_{19}N_3O_7S$			
5-Pyrimidinecarboxylic acid, 4-amino-1-β-D-glucopyranosyl-1,2-dihydro-2-thioxo-, ethyl ester	MeOH	225(4.2),240(4.1), 260(4.1),305(4.1)	24-3039-73
	MeOH-HCl	244(4.4)	24-3039-73
	MeOH-NaOH	240(4.1),290(3.9)	24-3039-73
Uridine, 5'-S-(3-amino-3-carboxypropyl)-5'-thio-, (S)-	H_2O	260(3.90)	88-2811-73

Compound	Solvent	λmax(log ε)	Ref.
$C_{13}H_{19}N_3O_8S$			
Uridine, 5'-[(3-amino-3-carboxypropyl)-sulfinyl]-5'-deoxy-, (S)-	H_2O	260(3.88)	88-2811-73
$C_{13}H_{19}N_5O$			
4(1H)-Pteridinone, 2-amino-6-heptyl-	pH 13	253(4.34),363(3.80)	44-2073-73
$C_{13}H_{19}N_5O_3$			
1,2-Cyclopentanediol, 3-[6-(dimethyl-amino)-9H-purin-9-yl]-5-(hydroxy-methyl)-, (1α,2α,3β,5β)-(±)-	pH 1	268(4.25)	36-1252-73
	pH 7	277(4.26)	36-1252-73
	pH 13	277(4.26)	36-1252-73
$C_{13}H_{19}N_5O_5$			
Adenosine, 2'-O-(1-methoxyethyl)-	pH 7	259(4.16)	69-3956-73
$C_{13}H_{19}O_4P$			
Xanthene-9-phosphonic acid, 1,2,3,4,5,6-7,8-octahydro-	EtOH	227(3.547)	65-0087-73
$C_{13}H_{20}$			
1H-Benzocycloheptene, 2,3,4,5,6,7-hexa-hydro-1,1-dimethyl-	C_6H_{12}	243(3.63)	22-3187-73
1H-Benzocycloheptene, 2,3,4,7,8,9-hexa-hydro-1,1-dimethyl-	C_6H_{12}	246(3.75)	22-3187-73
1H-Benzocycloheptene, 2,3,5,6,7,8-hexa-hydro-1,1-dimethyl-	C_6H_{12}	242(4.20)	22-3187-73
Cyclohexene, 6-(1,3-butadienyl)-1,5,5-trimethyl-	C_6H_{12}	277.5(4.42)	22-3187-73
Cyclohexene, 6-(2-butenylidene)-1,5,5-trimethyl-	C_6H_{12}	274(4.15)	22-3187-73
$C_{13}H_{20}ClNS_2$			
Dithiobenzoic acid, 4-chloro-, triethyl-amine salt	EtOH	284(3.95),365(3.56), 486(2.16)	143-0359-73
$C_{13}H_{20}ClN_3O_4$			
Benzimidazolium, 2-(1,1-dimethylethyl)-1,3-dimethyl-, perchlorate	EtOH	281(4.17),286(4.14)	104-2622-73
$C_{13}H_{20}ClN_5O_3$			
9H-Purin-6-aminium, 9-(2-deoxy-β-D-ery-thro-pentofuranosyl)-N,N,N-trimethyl-, chloride	MeOH	266(3.95)	23-3161-73
$C_{13}H_{20}Cl_2N_2$			
Pyrimidine, 4,6-dichloro-5,5-diethyl-2-(1-ethylpropylidene)-2,5-dihydro-	C_6H_{12}	262(4.25)	18-0299-73
$C_{13}H_{20}N_2$			
1H-Indole-3-ethanamine, 2,3-dihydro-N,N,1-trimethyl-, compd. with bornane	MeOH	250(4.10),295(3.79)	44-1504-73
$C_{13}H_{20}N_2O$			
1-Cyclohexene-1-carbonitrile, 2-(butyl-amino)-4,4-dimethyl-6-oxo-	EtOH	228(3.77),288(4.39)	70-0811-73
$C_{13}H_{20}N_2O_3$			
Acetamide, N-[2-[4-(dimethylamino)phen-yl]-2-hydroxy-1-(hydroxymethyl)ethyl]-	EtOH	258(4.20),298(3.38)	104-2144-73

Compound	Solvent	λ_{max}(log ε)	Ref.
Furo[3,4-c]pyridazine-5,7-dione, 3-(1,1-dimethylethyl)-1,4,4a,7a-tetrahydro-1-(1-methylethyl)-, cis	hexane	250(3.70)	103-0112-73
1H-Pyrrole-2-carboxylic acid, 4-[2-(diethylamino)ethyl]-5-formyl-3-methyl-	H_2O	227(4.12),312(4.31)	103-0186-73
SO_3 mol. compd.	H_2O	230(3.90),277(4.04), 307(4.05)	103-0186-73
$C_{13}H_{20}N_2O_4$			
3H-Azepinium, 2-(diethylamino)-6-methyl-, oxalate	EtOH	266(3.94)	39-1079-73C
	EtOH-NaOH	296(3.86)	39-1079-73C
1H-Imidazole-4-hexanoic acid, 2,3-dihydro-1,5-dimethyl- ,2-dioxo-, ethyl ester	EtOH	215(3.64),302(4.13)	70-1380-73
$C_{13}H_{20}N_2O_5$			
3H-Azepinium, 2-(diethylamino)-4-methoxy-, oxalate	EtOH	257(3.69),289(3.69)	39-1079-73C
	EtOH-NaOH	288(3.96)	39-1079-73C
1H-Imidazole-4,5-dicarboxylic acid, 1-(1-butoxyethyl)-, dimethyl ester	EtOH	214s(3.97),247(4.01)	95-0893-73
$C_{13}H_{20}N_2O_6$			
4(1H)-Pyrimidinone, 5,6-dihydro-2-methoxy-1-[2,3-O-(1-methylethylidene)-β-D-ribofuranosyl]-	n.s.g.	244(4.05)	77-0495-73
Uridine, 5-(1,1-dimethylethyl)-	pH 1	265(3.97)	56-1205-73
	pH 13	263(3.91)	56-1205-73
Uridine, 2',3'-di-O-ethyl-	pH 2	262(4.01)	69-0194-73
	pH 12	262(3.88)	69-0194-73
$C_{13}H_{20}N_2O_9$			
D-glycero-D-galacto-Non-2-enonic acid, 5-[[(acetylamino)acetyl]amino]-2,6-anhydro-3,5-dideoxy-	n.s.g.	241(3.78)	49-0402-73
$C_{13}H_{20}N_2S$			
Ethanimidamide, N'-(2,6-dimethylphenyl)-N,N-dimethyl-2-(methylthio)-	C_6H_{12}	246(4.19)	78-4205-73
$C_{13}H_{20}N_3$			
Benzimidazolium, 2-(1,1-dimethylethyl)-1,3-dimethyl-, perchlorate	EtOH	281(4.17),286(4.14)	104-2622-73
$C_{13}H_{20}N_4O_3$			
Sydnone imine, N-(cyclohexylcarbonyl)-3-morpholino-, hydrochloride	EtOH	243(3.96),325(4.06)	87-0671-73
$C_{13}H_{20}N_4O_4$			
1H-Purine-2,6-dione, 7-(2,2-diethoxyethyl)-3,7-dihydro-1,3-dimethyl-	n.s.g.	231(--),273(4.38)	126-0327-73G
$C_{13}H_{20}N_4O_6S$			
L-Homocysteine, S-cytidyl-	H_2O	270(3.79)	88-2811-73
$C_{13}H_{20}N_4O_7$			
D-Mannitol, 1-deoxy-1-(1,2,3,6-tetrahydro-1,3-dimethyl-2,6-dioxo-7H-purin-7-yl)-	H_2O	273(3.46)	136-0154-73F

Compound	Solvent	λmax(log ε)	Ref.
$C_{13}H_{20}N_4O_7S$			
L-Homocysteine, S-cytidyl-, S-oxide	H_2O	270(3.50)	88-2811-73
$C_{13}H_{20}N_5O_3$			
9H-Purin-6-aminium, 9-(2-deoxy-β-D-erythro-pentofuranosyl)-N,N,N-trimethyl-, chloride	MeOH	266(3.95)	23-3161-73
$C_{13}H_{20}N_6O_4$			
9H-Purin-6-amine, 9-[3-(2-aminoethyl)-3-deoxy-β-D-allofuranosyl]-	H_2O	261(4.18)	44-0193-73
$C_{13}H_{20}O$			
6H-Benzocyclohepten-6-one, 1,2,3,4,7,8-9,9a-octahydro-7,9a-dimethyl-	EtOH	243(3.88)	44-2821-73
2H-1-Benzopyran, 4a,5,6,7,8,8a-hexahydro-5,5,8a-trimethyl-2-methylene-	pentane	248(4.08)	33-1956-73
β-Ionone, dehydrodihydro-	pentane	264(3.82)	33-1062-73
1-Propanone, 1-(6,6-dimethylbicyclo-[3.1.1]hept-2-en-2-yl)-2-methyl-	C_6H_{12}	239(3.88),324(1.70)	22-1351-73
2-Propenal, 3-(1,3,3-trimethylbicyclo-[2.2.1]hept-2-yl)-	EtOH	233.0(4.12)	22-3071-73
$C_{13}H_{20}O_2$			
3-Buten-2-one, 4-(5-methyl-2-(1-methylethyl)-6-oxobicyclo[3.1.0]hex-1-yl]-	EtOH	245(4.03),312(1.85)	33-2151-73
3-Buten-2-one, 4-[1-methyl-5-(1-methylethyl)-2-oxocyclopentyl]-, cis	EtOH	230(3.72),284s(2.95)	33-2151-73
trans	EtOH	240(4.01),286(2.32)	33-2151-73
2-Cyclohexen-1-one, 3-(3-hydroxy-1-butynyl)-3,5,5-trimethyl-	EtOH	235(3.95)	1-2107-73
3,7a-Etheno-7aH-1,2-benzodioxole, 3,3a,4,5,6,7-hexahydro-3,3a,7,7-tetramethyl-	EtOH	224s(2.53),246s(2.31)	33-2151-73
2-Heptanone, 6-methyl-5-(4-methyl-2-furanyl)-	EtOH	220(3.93)	33-0265-73
2-Heptanone, 6-methyl-5-(5-methyl-2-furanyl)-	EtOH	220(3.95),294(2.04)	33-2151-73
2-Heptanone, 6-methyl-6-(5-methyl-2-furanyl)-	EtOH	231(3.72)	33-1948-73
	EtOH	220(3.98),276(1.45)	33-2151-73
β-Ionone, 5,6-epoxide, trans	EtOH	235(4.04),315(1.74)	33-2151-73
1(2H)-Naphthalenone, 3,4,4a,7,8,8a-hexahydro-4-hydroxy-3,4a,8-trimethyl-	EtOH	215(2.54)	23-3989-73
2(1H)-Naphthalenone, octahydro-1-propionyl-, cis	C_6H_{12}	292(3.64)	28-0803-73A
trans	C_6H_{12}	293(1.77)	28-0803-73A
3,4-Undecadiene-2,10-dione, 6,6-dimethyl-	EtOH	229(4.11)	33-1948-73
$C_{13}H_{20}O_3$			
3-Buten-2-one, 4-(1,4-dihydroxy-2,6,6-trimethyl-2-cyclohexen-1-yl)-	MeOH	227(4.19)	35-0239-73
2-Cyclohexen-1-one, 4-hydroxy-4-(3-hydroxy-1-butenyl)-3,5,5-trimethyl-(vomifoliol)	MeOH	237(4.14)	138-0245-73
3-Undecene-2,5,10-trione, 6,6-dimethyl-	EtOH	233(4.10),345(1.90)	33-2025-73
$C_{13}H_{20}O_4$			
Cyclohexanecarboxylic acid, 3-ethoxy-1-methyl-3-oxo-1-propenyl ester	EtOH	215(4.05)	22-3416-73

Compound	Solvent	λmax(log ε)	Ref.
1-Cyclopentene-1-heptanoic acid, 3-hydroxy-5-oxo-, methyl ester	MeOH	222(3.91)	35-1676-73
Propanedioic acid, (3-methyl-2-methylene-3-butenyl)-, diethyl ester	EtOH	232(4.27)	44-1483-73
$C_{13}H_{20}O_5$			
Cyclopentaneheptanoic acid, 3-hydroxy-2,5-dioxo-, methyl ester	MeOH	272(4.37)	35-1676-73
D-allo-Heptitol, 1,1,2,2-tetradehydro-1,2-dideoxy-4,5:6,7-bis-O-(1-methylethylidene)-	EtOH	258.6(2.58)	94-2051-73
D-altro-Heptitol, 1,1,2,2-tetradehydro-1,2-dideoxy-4,5:6,7-bis-O-(1-methylethylidene)-	EtOH	260(2.62)	94-2051-73
$C_{13}H_{20}O_8$			
1,2,3,4-Pentanetetracarboxylic acid, tetramethyl ester, erythro-erythro-	EtOH	209(1.91)	104-0686-73
erythro-threo-	EtOH	214(2.61)	104-0686-73
threo-erythro-	EtOH	215(2.60)	104-0686-73
threo-threo-	EtOH	214(2.24)	104-0686-73
$C_{13}H_{20}S$			
Benzene, 2-[(1,1-dimethylethyl)thio]-1,3,5-trimethyl-	C_6H_{12}	210(4.69),230(4.06), 274(3.01)	39-1125-73B
	EtOH	207(4.70),231(4.08), 275(3.05)	39-1125-73B
	5% EtOH	207(4.72),235(4.04), 280(3.04)	39-1125-73B
Thiophene, 2-(1-propylidenehexyl)-, cis	EtOH	248(3.83),263(3.85)	88-2487-73
trans	EtOH	265(3.88),279(3.89)	88-2487-73
$C_{13}H_{21}IN_2O$			
3H-Azepinium, 4-acetyl-2-(diethylamino)-1-methyl-, iodide	n.s.g.	237(4.28),368(3.83)	39-1079-73C
$C_{13}H_{21}NO_3S_2$			
1H,3H-Oxazolo[4,3-c][1,4]thiazine-6-carboxylic acid, 8,8a-dihydro-3,3,8,8-tetramethyl-1-(methylthio)-, methyl ester	EtOH	221(3.85),255(3.45), 321(4.11)	39-1985-73
$C_{13}H_{21}NO_4$			
Propanedioic acid, (1-methyl-2-piperidinylidene)-, diethyl ester	EtOH	251(4.24),310(4.10)	103-0880-73
$C_{13}H_{21}NO_4S$			
1H,3H-Oxazolo[4,3-c][1,4]thiazine-6-carboxylic acid, 8,8a-dihydro-1-methoxy-3,3,8,8-tetramethyl-, methyl ester	EtOH	255(3.42),320(4.10)	39-1985-73C
$C_{13}H_{21}NO_4S_2$			
1H,3H-Oxazolo[4,3-c][1,4]thiazine-6-carboxylic acid, 8,8a-dihydro-3,3,8,8-tetramethyl-1-(methylthio)-, methyl ester, 7-oxide	EtOH	286(4.18)	39-1985-73C
$C_{13}H_{21}NO_6$			
α-D-Galactopyranose, 6-deoxy-1,2:3,4-bis-O-(1-methylethylidene)-6-(methylimino)-, N-oxide	EtOH	246(3.90)	136-0159-73F

Compound	Solvent	$\lambda_{max}(\log \epsilon)$	Ref.
α-D-Ribohexofuranos-3-ulose, 1,2:5,6-bis-O-(1-methylethylidene)-, 3-[trans-(O-C-2)-N-methyloxime]	EtOH	251(3.94)	136-0159-73F
$C_{13}H_{21}NS_2$			
Dithiobenzoic acid, triethylamine salt	EtOH	286(4.05),362(3.96), 507(2.14)	143-0359-73
$C_{13}H_{21}N_3O_2S_2$			
Carbamic acid, [[(5-butyl-3-methyl-2(3H)-thiazolylidene)amino](methylthio)methylene]-, ethyl ester	dioxan	245(3.63),279(3.85), 337(4.35)	94-0074-73
Carbamic acid, [[[3-(1-methylethyl)-2(3H)-thiazolylidene]amino][(1-methylethyl)thio]methylene]-, ethyl ester	dioxan	244(3.56),280(3.88), 331(4.36)	94-0074-73
$C_{13}H_{21}N_3O_5$			
Cytidine, 2',3'-di-O-ethyl-	pH 2	280(4.12)	69-0194-73
	pH 12	271(3.95)	69-0194-73
$C_{13}H_{21}N_3O_7S$			
Glutathione, S-propionyl-	pH 7.40	231(3.66)	69-3938-73
$C_{13}H_{21}N_3O_8S$			
Glutathione, S-lactyl-	pH 7.40	233(3.60)	69-3938-73
$C_{13}H_{21}N_3O_9S$			
Glutathione, S-glyceryl-	pH 7.40	235(3.61)	69-3938-73
$C_{13}H_{21}N_5$			
1H-Pyrazolo[4,3-d]pyrimidin-7-amine, N-heptyl-3-methyl- (all spectra in ethanol)	pH 1	262(3.76),311(4.11)	102-0025-73
	pH 7	237(3.76),296(4.08), 306(3.99),318s(--)	102-0025-73
	pH 12	224(4.21),263s(--), 309(3.93)	102-0025-73
$C_{13}H_{21}N_5O_2$			
1H-Purine-2,6-dione, 7-(3-aminopropyl)-3,7-dihydro-1,3-dimethyl-, hydrochloride	n.s.g.	210(4.35),277(4.02)	73-1571-73
$C_{13}H_{21}N_7O$			
Urea, N-[3-(diethylamino)propyl]-N'-1H-purin-6-yl-	pH 1-2	277(4.30)	87-0139-73
	pH 5-7	269(4.25)	87-0139-73
	pH 12	277.5(4.21)	87-0139-73
$C_{13}H_{22}$			
1,3-Cyclohexadiene, 1-butyl-2,6,6-trimethyl-	C_6H_{12}	264(3.72)	22-3187-73
Cyclohexene, 1-(1-butenyl)-2,6,6-trimethyl-	C_6H_{12}	227(3.78)	22-3187-73
1,3-Cyclopentadiene, 1,2(and 3)-bis(1-methylpropyl)-	heptane	252(3.58)	70-0357-73
1,3-Cyclopentadiene, 1,3(and 4)-bis(1-methylpropyl)-	heptane	253(3.56)	70-0357-73
$C_{13}H_{22}N_2$			
2-Hexenenitrile, 4-ethyl-3-piperidino-	EtOH	277(4.37)	39-1108-73C
1-Piperidinepropanenitrile, β-(1-ethylpropylidene)-	EtOH	206(3.70),236(3.49)	39-1108-73C

Compound	Solvent	$\lambda_{max}(\log \epsilon)$	Ref.
$C_{13}H_{22}N_2O$			
1H-Pyrrole-2-carboxaldehyde, 4-[2-(diethylamino)ethyl]-3,5-dimethyl-	EtOH	260(3.78),309(4.37)	103-0186-73
$C_{13}H_{22}N_2O_3$			
3-Penten-2-one, 4,5-dimorpholino-	EtOH	319(4.34)	70-1237-73
$C_{13}H_{22}N_2O_8$			
D-glycero-D-galacto-Non-2-enonic acid, 2,6-anhydro-3,5-dideoxy-5-[(dimethylamino)acetyl]amino]-	n.s.g.	234(3.72)	49-0402-73
$C_{13}H_{22}O$			
Isomenthone, 4-allyl-, (1R,4S)-(+)-	dioxan	300(1.56)	22-1049-73
1-Propanone, 1-(3,6,6-trimethylbicyclo-[3.1.1]hept-2-yl)-	C_6H_{12}	290(1.58)	22-1351-73
2-Propenal, 3-[5-methyl-2-(1-methylethyl)cyclohexyl]-	EtOH	229.0(4.06)	22-3071-73
$C_{13}H_{22}O_2$			
3-Buten-2-one, 4-(2-hydroxy-2,6,6-trimethyl-1-cyclohexyl)-, trans	EtOH	232(4.18)	33-1956-73
1-Cyclohexen-1-ol, 5-(1,1-dimethylethyl)-2-methyl-, acetate	EtOH	210(3.15)(end abs.)	44-1000-73
$C_{13}H_{22}O_3$			
3-Buten-2-one, 4-(1,2-dihydroxy-2,6,6-trimethylcyclohexyl)-, trans	EtOH	234(4.09)	33-1956-73
1(2H)-Naphthalenone, octahydro-4,8-dihydroxy-2,5,8a-trimethyl-, (2α,4β,4aα,5α,8α,8aβ)-	EtOH	210(2.47)	23-3989-73
2,5,10-Undecanetrione, 6,6-dimethyl-	EtOH	266(2.08)	33-2025-73
$C_{13}H_{23}NO$			
2,3-Hexadienamide, N-(1,1-dimethylethyl)-4,5,5-trimethyl-	EtOH	214(4.14)	88-0209-73
$C_{13}H_{23}N_5O$			
1-Hexen-2-ol, 1-[4,6-bis(dimethylamino)-1,3,5-triazin-2-yl]-	EtOH	231(4.29),277(4.00), 326(3.79)	22-2039-73
$C_{13}H_{24}N_2O$			
Ethanone, 1-[6-(1,1-dimethylethyl)-2,3,4,5-tetrahydro-2-(1-methylethyl)-3-pyridazinyl]-	hexane	240(3.91)	103-0112-73
Ethanone, 1-[6-(1,1-dimethylethyl)-2,3,4,5-tetrahydro-2-(1-methylethyl)-4-pyridazinyl]-	hexane	240(3.86)	103-0112-73
2H-Pyran-4,6-diamine, 2,2-dimethyl-N,N'-dipropyl-	EtOH	246(4.21)	70-1033-73
$C_{13}H_{24}N_2O_2Sn$			
3H-Pyrazole-4-carboxylic acid, 3,3-dimethyl-5-(triethylstannyl)-, methyl ester	MeOH	244(3.72),382(--)	22-2739-73
3H-Pyrazole-5-carboxylic acid, 3,3-dimethyl-4-(triethylstannyl)-, methyl ester	MeOH	265(4.04),335(1.76)	22-2739-73

Compound	Solvent	λ max(log ε)	Ref.
$C_{13}H_{24}N_4$			
1H-Pyrazole, 1,1'-methylenebis[4,5-dihydro-3,5,5-trimethyl-	heptane	205(3.41),249(3.91)	135-1154-73
	MeOH	193(3.76),233(4.00)	135-1154-73
	isoPrOH	198(3.95),238(4.05)	135-1154-73
	ether	210(3.83),248(4.24)	135-1154-73
	$C_2H_4Cl_2$	245(3.99)	135-1154-73
$C_{13}H_{24}O$			
Isomenthone, 2,2,4-trimethyl-, (1R,4R)-(+)-	hexane	308(1.38)	22-1049-73
	MeOH	303(1.49)	22-1049-73
$C_{13}H_{24}O_2Sn$			
Stannane, (2-carbomethoxy-3,3-dimethyl-1-cyclopropen-1-yl)triethyl-	MeOH	247.5(3.80)	22-2739-73
$C_{13}H_{24}Si_2$			
Silane, 1,6-heptadiyne-1,7-diylbis[trimethyl-	n.s.g.	292(2.53)	39-0599-73B
$C_{13}H_{25}N_3O_3S$			
Glycinamide, N-[(1,1-dimethylethoxy)-carbonyl]-L-leucylthio-	EtOH	266(4.15)	35-5677-73
$C_{13}H_{26}N_2$			
1H-Imidazole, 2-decyl-4,5-dihydro-	EtOH	220(3.66)	93-2424-73
Pyrazine, 1,4-diethyl-1,4,5,6-tetrahydro-2-pentyl-	C_6H_{12}	237(3.81)	28-1319-73A
$C_{13}H_{26}N_2O$			
3-Penten-2-one, 4,5-bis(diethylamino)-	EtOH	321(4.35)	70-1237-73
$C_{13}H_{26}N_2O_2$			
2-Hexenamide, 5-hydroxy-5-methyl-N-propyl-3-(propylamino)-	EtOH	225(3.91),290(4.41)	70-1033-73
$C_{13}H_{28}SSi$			
Silane, [2-(ethenylthio)ethyl]tripropyl-	hexane	229(3.75),238s(3.64)	67-0061-73

Compound	Solvent	λ max(log ε)	Ref.
$C_{14}F_{21}N$			
Pyridine, 2,3,5-trifluoro-4-[1,2,2,2-tetrafluoro-1-(trifluoromethyl)ethyl]-6-(undecafluorocyclohexyl)-	C_6H_{12}	274(3.74)	39-1710-73C
$C_{14}H_4F_4O_2$			
9,10-Anthracenedione, 1,4,5,8-tetrafluoro-	EtOH	238(4.42),344(3.79), 440s(3.36),467s(3.51), 496(3.52),513s(3.42), 529s(3.34),589(2.90)	108-0791-73
$C_{14}H_5ClF_4$			
Compound 1A from 1-(phenylethynyl)-4-chlorotetrafluorobenzene and PdCl	n.s.g.	218(3.00),260(3.90), 325(3.60)	101-0423-73A
Compound 1B	n.s.g.	262(3.85),328(3.51)	101-0423-73A
Compound 2	n.s.g.	250(3.95),331(3.54)	101-0423-73A
$C_{14}H_6Br_2O_2$			
9,10-Anthracenedione, 1,8-dibromo-	EtOH	213(4.46),255(4.53), 351(3.65),416s(2.89)	44-1167-73
$C_{14}H_6F_2O_2$			
9,10-Anthracenedione, 1,4-difluoro-	EtOH	212(4.28),249(4.44), 256s(4.33),263s(4.18), 337(3.79),350s(3.68), 403(2.56),423(2.56), 452(2.54),465(2.54), 477(2.56),497s(2.40), 510(2.32)	108-0791-73
$C_{14}H_6N_2O_6$			
9,10-Anthracenedione, 1,8-dinitro-	EtOH	255(--),265(--), 320(4.53)	115-0067-73A
	ether	252(4.54),275(4.30), 315(4.13)	115-0067-73A
	acetone	330(4.06)	115-0067-73A
	$CHCl_3$	320(4.35)	115-0067-73A
$C_{14}H_7ClF_2O$			
9H-Xanthene, 9-(chloromethylene)-2,7-difluoro-	EtOH	240s(4.04),258s(3.71), 290s(3.51),338(3.92)	44-0841-73
$C_{14}H_7Cl_2NO_4S$			
4H,5H-Pyrano[3,4-e][1,3]oxazine-4,5-dione, 7-chloro-2-[[(4-chlorophenyl)methyl]thio]-	$CHCl_3$	279(4.18),342(4.23)	39-2432-73C
$C_{14}H_7FO_2$			
9,10-Anthracenedione, 1-fluoro-	EtOH	211(4.30),243s(4.42), 250(4.51),261s(4.21), 269(4.13),313(3.57), 330(3.76),351s(3.38), 396s(2.20),417s(2.00)	108-0791-73
9,10-Anthracenedione, 2-fluoro-	EtOH	244s(4.50),248s(4.58), 253(4.68),263s(4.30), 273(4.19),321(3.61), 393(2.18),417(1.85)	108-0791-73

Compound	Solvent	λ_{max}(log ε)	Ref.
$C_{14}H_7NOS$			
4H-Naphtho[1,2-b]thiopyran-3-carbonitrile, 4-oxo-	EtOH	222(4.36),236(4.48), 255(4.29),281(4.27), 297s(4.08),333(4.00)	32-1073-73
$C_{14}H_7N_3O_2$			
1-Oxa-4,6-diazafluoranthene-3-carbonitrile, 2,4-dihydro-2-oxo-	EtOH	245(4.59),322(4.36), 340(4.28),357(4.42)	95-0964-73
$C_{14}H_7N_5$			
2H-Pyrrole-3,3,4,4-tetracarbonitrile, 5-phenyl-	EtOH	242(4.26)	35-1945-73
$C_{14}H_8BrNOS$			
Methanone, (4-bromophenyl)(4-isothiocyanatophenyl)-	MeOH	297(4.37)	73-1609-73
$C_{14}H_8BrN_3O$			
1H-Imidazo[4,5-f]quinoline, 2-(5-bromo-2-furanyl)-	MeOH	242(4.05),294(4.31), 335(4.05)	103-0406-73
Pyrido[1',2':2,3]pyrazolo[5,4-c]quinolin-6(5H)-one, 2-bromo-	EtOH-DMF	247(4.60),257s(4.42), 265s(4.33),318s(4.13), 330(4.24),347s(4.09), 363s(3.90)	44-3995-73
$C_{14}H_8BrN_5O$			
2(1H)-Quinolinone, 3-azido-6-bromo-4-(2-pyridinyl)-	EtOH	215(4.38),240(4.52), 294(4.03),304(4.08), 345(4.05),360(3.95)	44-3995-73
$C_{14}H_8ClNO_4S$			
4H,5H-Pyrano[3,4-e][1,3]oxazine-4,5-dione, 7-chloro-2-[(phenylmethyl)thio]-	$CHCl_3$	280(3.99),346(4.14)	39-2432-73C
$C_{14}H_8Cl_2$			
Anthracene, 1,8-dichloro-	EtOH	218(4.10),252(5.05), 256(5.05),319s(3.13), 333(3.47),350(3.74), 368(3.91),388(3.87)	44-1667-73
$C_{14}H_8Cl_2OS$			
Dibenzo[b,f]thiepin-10(11H)-one, 6,8-dichloro-	MeOH	249(4.26),269(3.98), 276(3.93),340(3.56)	73-3321-73
Dibenzo[b,f]thiepin-10(11H)-one, 6,9-dichloro-	MeOH	240s(4.08),272s(3.60), 330(3.13)	73-3321-73
9H-Thioxanthene-9-carboxaldehyde, 1,4-dichloro-	MeOH	224(4.27),310(3.94)	73-3321-73
$C_{14}H_8Cl_2O_2S$			
9H-Thioxanthene-9-carboxylic acid, 1,4-dichloro-	MeOH	233(4.36),281(3.95)	73-3321-73
$C_{14}H_8Cl_2S$			
Dibenzo[b,f]thiepin, 1,4-dichloro-	MeOH	269(4.24),295s(3.72)	73-3321-73
Dibenzo[b,f]thiepin, 2,4-dichloro-	MeOH	267(4.31),296(3.73)	73-3321-73
$C_{14}H_8Cl_2S_4$			
Disulfide, bis[(4-chlorophenyl)thioxomethyl]	$CHCl_3$	324(4.15),522(2.53)	143-0437-73

Compound	Solvent	$\lambda_{max}(\log \epsilon)$	Ref.
$C_{14}H_8FNO_2$			
Anthracene, 9-fluoro-10-nitro-	$CHCl_3$	256(4.95),354(3.52), 372(3.61),392(3.59)	22-1305-73
$C_{14}H_8F_6$			
1,1'-Biphenyl, 3,3'-bis(trifluoromethyl)-	EtOH	235(4.24),237s(4.20), 284(3.20),322(2.41)	35-5288-73
1,1'-Biphenyl, 4,4'-bis(trifluoromethyl)-	EtOH	253(4.26)	35-5288-73
$C_{14}H_8INO_2$			
Anthracene, 9-iodo-10-nitro-	$CHCl_3$	262(5.07),340s(3.47), 360(3.73),378(3.91), 400(3.91)	22-1305-73
$C_{14}H_8N_2$			
2,7-Diazapyrene	MeOH	229(4.62),243(4.25), 291s(3.67),302(4.04), 315(4.41),330(4.57), 346(3.50),365(3.78), 381s(3.74),386(4.04)	5-0339-73
$C_{14}H_8N_2O$			
4a,8a-Epoxy-1,4-ethenonaphthalene-2,3-dicarbonitrile, 1,4-dihydro-	dioxan	250(3.86)	89-0840-73
5,8-Etheno-1aH-naphth[1,8a-b]oxirene-6,7-dicarbonitrile, 5,8-dihydro-	dioxan	253(3.91)	89-0840-73
Indeno[1,2,3-de]phthalazin-3(2H)-one	HOAc	248(4.34),255(4.45), 278(3.92),328(4.02)	115-0145-73A
$C_{14}H_8N_2O_2$			
Propanedinitrile, (1,4-dihydro-3-methyl-1,4-dioxo-2-naphthalenyl)-	EtOH	322(3.74)	83-0257-73
	EtOH-KOH	590(3.85)	83-0257-73
$C_{14}H_8N_2O_3S$			
Methanone, (4-isothiocyanatophenyl)(4-nitrophenyl)-	MeOH	276(4.59)	73-1609-73
$C_{14}H_8N_2O_4$			
4H-3,1-Benzoxazin-4-one, 6-nitro-2-phenyl-	EtOH	226(4.40),245s(4.28), 337(4.46)	78-0603-73
1H-Inden-1-one, 3-hydroxy-6-nitro-2-(2-pyridinyl)-	pH 1	282(4.14),382(4.21)	65-2301-73
	M NaOH	276(4.24),302(4.21), 360(3.98),480(3.27)	65-2301-73
$C_{14}H_8N_4O_2$			
Anthracene, 9-azido-10-nitro-	ether	255(4.94),360s(3.83), 395(3.83)	22-1305-73
$C_{14}H_8O_2$			
9,10-Anthracenedione	EtOH	236s(4.32),245s(4.48), 253(4.65),263s(4.24), 273(4.16),324(4.49), 375s(--),394s(--), 404s(--),416s(2.00)	108-0791-73
	EtOH	234(3.90),250(4.25), 270(3.74),320(3.30), 410(3.60)	115-0067-73A

Compound	Solvent	λ_{max}(log ε)	Ref.
$C_{14}H_8O_3$			
9,10-Anthracenedione, 1-hydroxy-	EtOH	248(4.61),276(4.24), 324(3.63),399(3.90)	115-0067-73A
	ether	245(4.66),280(4.29), 310(3.85),395(3.99)	115-0067-73A
	acetone	397(3.70)	115-0067-73A
	$CHCl_3$	310(3.30),390(3.70)	115-0067-73A
9,10-Anthracenedione, 2-hydroxy-	EtOH	240(3.88),270(4.20), 325(3.18),375(3.15)	115-0067-73A
	ether	230(3.88),280(3.42), 322(3.42),367(3.51)	115-0067-73
	acetone	330(3.49),372(3.61)	115-0067-73A
	$CHCl_3$	322(3.79),370(3.69)	115-0067-73A
$C_{14}H_8O_4$			
9,10-Anthracenedione, 1,2-dihydroxy- (alizarin)	EtOH	245(4.65),275(4.42), 340(3.70),438(3.93)	115-0067-73A
	ether	295(4.36),325(4.12), 425(4.29)	115-0067-73A
	acetone	325(3.72),425(4.05)	115-0067-73A
	$CHCl_3$	330(4.02),418(4.24)	115-0067-73A
	CCl_4	319(3.62),416(3.78)	115-0067-73A
9,10-Anthracenedione, 2,3-dihydroxy-	EtOH	208(4.29),239(4.11), 289(4.56)	56-1949-73
9,10-Anthracenedione, 1,4-dihydroxy- (quinizarin)	EtOH	252(4.43),280(3.90), 326(3.90),477(3.90)	115-0067-73A
	ether	250(4.51),275(4.26), 322(3.52),475(3.86)	115-0067-73A
	$CHCl_3$	475(3.70)	115-0067-73A
	CCl_4	473(3.79)	115-0067-73A
9,10-Anthracenedione, 1,5-dihydroxy-	EtOH	250(3.83),278(3.60), 325(3.00),425(3.60)	115-0067-73A
	ether	245(4.38),276(4.10), 322(2.85),420(3.60)	115-0067-73A
9,10-Anthracenedione, 1,8-dihydroxy-	EtOH	225(4.32),280(3.70), 322(2.85),425(3.78)	115-0067-73A
	ether	222(4.45),285(3.98), 305(3.34),423(3.90)	115-0067-73A
	acetone	423(3.48)	115-0067-73A
	$CHCl_3$	423(3.31)	115-0067-73A
	CCl_4	422(3.31)	115-0067-73A
$C_{14}H_8O_5$			
9,10-Anthracenedione, 1,2,4-trihydroxy- (purpurin)	EtOH	252(4.77),280(4.49), 335(4.08),480(4.18), 550(3.78)	115-0067-73A
	ether	250(4.67),280(4.35), 330(3.88),475(4.10)	115-0067-73A
	acetone	470(4.09)	115-0067-73A
	$CHCl_3$	470(3.93)	115-0067-73A
	CCl_4	470(3.62)	115-0067-73A
$C_{14}H_8O_5S$			
2-Anthracenesulfonic acid, 9,10-dihydro-9,10-dioxo-	EtOH	265(4.46),276(3.90), 320(3.48),475(4.32)	115-0067-73A
	ether	254(4.26),280(3.81), 300(3.53),470(3.95)	115-0067-73A
$C_{14}H_8O_6$			
9,10-Anthracenedione, 1,2,5,8-tetrahydroxy- (quinalizarin)	acetone	334(3.30),487(3.94)	115-0067-73A

Compound	Solvent	λ max (log ε)	Ref.
9,10-Anthracenedione, 1,2,5,8-tetrahydroxy- (cont.)	EtOH	238(4.20),295(3.98), 350(3.54),506(4.00), 550(3.88)	115-0067-73A
	ether	235(4.42),290(3.86), 315(3.40),480(4.14)	115-0067-73A
$C_{14}H_8O_7S$			
2-Anthracenesulfonic acid, 9,10-dihydro-3,4-dihydroxy-9,10-dioxo-	EtOH	250(4.63),285(4.32), 325(3.70),432(3.95)	115-0067-73A
	ether	247(4.32),290(4.26), 308(3.11),419(3.00)	115-0067-73A
	$CHCl_3$	415(2.48)	115-0067-73A
$C_{14}H_8S_4$			
1,3-Benzodithiole, 3-(1,3-benzodithiol-2-ylidene)-	MeCN	253(4.31),256(4.25), 286(4.26),308(4.32), 340s(--),428(2.47)	5-0310-73
cation tetrafluoroborate	MeCN	315(3.55),402s(--), 423(4.12),442s(--), 483s(--),597s(--), 630(3.98)	5-0310-73
$C_{14}H_9BFNO_3$			
N-Salicylideneanthranilic acid BF_3 chelate	$C_2H_4Cl_2$	319(4.2),391(4.05)	24-2427-73
$C_{14}H_9BrN_8$			
2H-Tetrazolium, 2-(4-bromophenyl)-5-phenyl-3-(1H-tetrazol-5-yl)-, hydroxide, inner salt	n.s.g.	245(4.71),320s(--)	103-1423-73
$C_{14}H_9ClFNO$			
2H-Indol-2-one, 5-chloro-3-(2-fluorophenyl)-	isoPrOH	256(4.15),293(3.22)	44-0449-73
$C_{14}H_9ClN_2$			
Cinnoline, 6-chloro-4-phenyl-	n.s.g.	232(4.52),305(3.89), 320(3.86)	2-0631-73
Quinoxaline, 6-chloro-2-phenyl-	n.s.g.	254(4.33),340(4.00)	2-0631-73
$C_{14}H_9ClN_2O_2$			
1H-Indole, 5-chloro-2-nitro-3-phenyl-	isoPrOH	235(4.26),253s(4.11), 350(3.15)	44-3077-73
$C_{14}H_9ClN_2O_4$			
4H,5H-Pyrano[3,4-e][1,3]oxazine-4,5-dione, 7-chloro-2-[(phenylmethyl)amino]-	MeCN	293(4.19),338(4.27)	39-2432-73C
$C_{14}H_9ClN_8$			
2H-Tetrazolium, 2-(4-chlorophenyl)-5-phenyl-3-(1H-tetrazol-5-yl)-, hydroxide, inner salt	n.s.g.	247(4.21),320s(--)	103-1423-73
$C_{14}H_9ClO_3$			
Benzoic acid, 2-(4-chlorobenzoyl)-	H_2O	262(4.24)	44-3383-73
$C_{14}H_9Cl_2N$			
1H-Indole, 2,5-dichloro-3-phenyl-	isoPrOH	230(4.50),270(4.06), 283s(4.03),290s(3.97), 301(3.86)	44-3077-73

Compound	Solvent	$\lambda_{max}(\log \epsilon)$	Ref.
$C_{14}H_9CrNO_5$			
Chromium, (1-aziridinylphenylmethylene)-pentacarbonyl-, (OC-6-21)-	n.s.g.	243(4.58),390(3.86)	101-0111-73I
$C_{14}H_9I$			
Anthracene, 1-iodo-	EtOH	217(4.10),252(5.11), 317s(3.13),331(3.48), 347(3.76),365(3.91), 385(3.89)	44-1167-73
$C_{14}H_9IN_8$			
2H-Tetrazolium, 2-(4-iodophenyl)-5-phenyl-3-(1H-tetrazol-5-yl)-, hydroxide, inner salt	n.s.g.	245(4.50),310(3.93)	103-1423-73
$C_{14}H_9IOS$			
Dibenzo[b,f]thiepin-10(11H)-one, 8-iodo-	MeOH	231(4.35),244(4.31), 268s(4.07),342(3.56)	73-2484-73
$C_{14}H_9IS$			
Dibenzo[b,f]thiepin, 2-iodo-	MeOH	235s(4.41),244(4.45), 266(4.50),295s(3.82)	73-2484-73
$C_{14}H_9NOS$			
Benzo[h]thiochromano[3,4-d]isoxazole	EtOH	211(4.37),231(4.38), 278(4.46),288(4.54)	32-1073-73
Benzo[h]thiochromano[4,3-c]isoxazole	EtOH	233(4.62),269(4.44), 275s(4.40)	32-1073-73
Methanone, (4-isothiocyanatophenyl)-phenyl-	MeOH	299(4.44)	73-1609-73
$C_{14}H_9NO_2$			
Anthracene, 9-nitro-	EtOH	217(4.16),245s(5.01), 250(5.08),333s(3.40), 347(3.58),364(3.67), 383(3.60),402s(3.34)	44-1167-73
9,10-Anthracenedione, 1-amino-	C_6H_{12}	450(3.10)	115-0067-73A
	EtOH	241(4.33),274(3.78), 325(3.50),468(3.79)	115-0067-73A
	ether	240(3.98),280(3.63), 320(3.48),462(3.81)	115-0067-73A
	acetone	462(3.80)	115-0067-73A
	$CHCl_3$	455(3.92)	115-0067-73A
	CCl_4	452(3.78)	115-0067-73A
	n.s.g.	474(3.84)	40-1738-73
9,10-Anthracenedione, 2-amino-	EtOH	240(4.24),270(3.86), 330(4.08),442(3.70)	115-0067-73A
	ether	240(4.08),280(3.80), 320(4.16),420(3.95)	115-0067-73A
	acetone	330(4.02),430(3.89)	115-0067-73A
	$CHCl_3$	330(3.78),420(3.65)	115-0067-73A
	n.s.g.	435(3.65)	40-1738-73
1H-Inden-1-one, 3-hydroxy-2-(2-pyridinyl)-	pH 1	255(4.06),284(4.39), 373(4.41)	65-2301-73
	M NaOH	278(4.28),330(4.09), 440(3.26)	65-2301-73
$C_{14}H_9NO_3$			
9,10-Anthracenedione, 1-amino-4-hydroxy-	n.s.g.	525(3.96)	40-1738-73

Compound	Solvent	λmax(log ε)	Ref.
$C_{14}H_9NO_4$			
Isoxazolium, 2-(2-furanylmethylene)-2,5-dihydro-3-hydroxy-5-oxo-4-phenyl-, hydroxide, inner salt	dioxan	484(3.63)	44-1782-73
$C_{14}H_9NO_5$			
Benzoic acid, 2-benzoyl-5-nitro-	H_2O	263(4.52)	44-3383-73
Naphtho[1,8-bc]pyran-3-ol, 6-nitro-, acetate	EtOH	236(4.30),325(3.61), 430(3.95)	107-0219-73
Naphtho[1,8-bc]pyran-3-ol, 7-nitro-, acetate	EtOH	242(4.11),274(4.05), 316(3.76),330(3.78), 425(3.76)	107-0219-73
$C_{14}H_9N_3O$			
Pyrido[1',2':2,3]pyrazolo[5,4-c]quinolin-6(5H)-one	isoPrOH	253(4.47),263s(4.25), 304s(3.92),318s(4.08), 329(4.14),350s(3.92), 368s(3.67)	44-3995-73
$C_{14}H_9N_3O_2$			
Quinoxaline, 2-(4-nitrophenyl)-	EtOH	203(4.49),239(--), 273(--),323(--)	44-3995-73
$C_{14}H_9N_3O_3$			
Quinoxaline, 2-(4-nitrophenyl)-, 4-oxide	EtOH	202(--),236(--), 282(4.24),324(--)	34-0102-73
$C_{14}H_9N_3S$			
[1,2,4]Triazolo[5,1-b]benzothiazole, 2-phenyl-	MeOH	213(4.47),240(4.38), 267(4.33),284s(4.16), 296(4.02)	4-0947-73
$C_{14}H_9N_5O$			
2(1H)-Quinolinone, 3-azido-4-(2-pyridinyl)-	EtOH	230(4.48),304(4.10), 326(4.01),339(4.10), 354(3.97)	44-3995-73
$C_{14}H_9N_9O_2$			
2H-Tetrazolium, 2-(3-nitrophenyl)-5-phenyl-3-(1H-tetrazol-5-yl)-, hydroxide, inner salt	n.s.g.	251(4.86),320s(--)	103-1423-73
2H-Tetrazolium, 2-(4-nitrophenyl)-5-phenyl-3-(1H-tetrazol-5-yl)-, hydroxide, inner salt	n.s.g.	255(4.18),320s(--)	103-1423-73
$C_{14}H_{10}$			
1,2,3-Metheno-1H-phenalene, 2,3-dihydro-	C_6H_{12}	217(4.51),234(4.47), 284(3.84),295(3.91), 304(3.76),310(3.71), 319(3.07),323(2.97)	88-0047-73
$C_{14}H_{10}BrCl_2N$			
Aziridine, 1-(3-bromophenyl)-2,2-dichloro-3-phenyl-	heptane	240(4.20),276(3.08), 284(3.04)	104-2360-73
$C_{14}H_{10}BrN$			
1H-Indole, 3-(4-bromophenyl)-	EtOH	225(4.48),284(4.24)	94-2786-73
$C_{14}H_{10}BrNO$			
9(10H)-Acridinone, 2-bromo-10-methyl-	EtOH	254(4.64),262(4.64),	94-0742-73

Compound	Solvent	λ_{max}(log ε)	Ref.
9(10H)-Acridinone, 2-bromo-10-methyl- (cont.)	EtOH	270s(--),279(4.47), 300(3.58),311(3.34), 392(3.93),411(3.89)	94-0742-73
$C_{14}H_{10}BrNOS$			
Thiazole, 4-[5-(4-bromophenyl)-2-furan-yl]-2-methyl-	EtOH	233(4.11),328(4.54)	103-0403-73
$C_{14}H_{10}BrNO_2$			
Benzamide, 2-(4-bromobenzoyl)-	EtOH	226(4.29)	39-1160-73B
$C_{14}H_{10}BrN_5O_2$			
Pyridine, 2-(2-azidoacetamido-5-bromo-benzoyl)-	EtOH	239(4.44),343(3.44)	44-3995-73
$C_{14}H_{10}ClNO$			
9(10H)-Acridinone, 2-chloro-10-methyl-	EtOH	253(4.67),261(4.66), 269(4.51),276(4.44), 299(3.52),311(3.26), 392(3.91),411(3.96)	94-0742-73
1H-Isoindol-1-one, 3-chloro-2,3-dihydro-3-phenyl-	MeCN	223(4.32)	24-1423-73
	$MeNO_2-SbCl_5$	239(3.95),402(4.03)	24-1423-73
$C_{14}H_{10}ClNOS$			
Thiazole, 4-[5-(4-chlorophenyl)-2-furan-yl]-2-methyl-	EtOH	230(4.23),324(4.54)	103-0403-73
$C_{14}H_{10}ClNO_2$			
Benzamide, 2-(4-chlorobenzoyl)-	EtOH	226(4.29)	39-1160-73B
$C_{14}H_{10}ClNO_3$			
1H-Pyrano[3,4-b]quinolin-1-one, 5-chlo-ro-9-methoxy-3-methyl-	MeOH	263(4.56),297(4.29), 307(4.32)	24-0355-73
$C_{14}H_{10}Cl_2N_4$			
1H-1,2,4-Triazol-5-amine, 1,3-bis(4-chlorophenyl)-	EtOH	234(4.25),277(4.24)	22-2843-73
$C_{14}H_{10}Cl_2OS$			
Dibenzo[b,f]thiepin-10-ol, 6,9-dichloro-10,11-dihydro-	MeOH	259(3.93)	73-3321-73
9H-Thioxanthene-9-methanol, 1,4-di-chloro-	MeOH	276.5(4.26)	73-3321-73
$C_{14}H_{10}Cl_2O_2S$			
Dibenzo[b,f]thiepin, 2,11-dichloro-10,11-dihydro-, 5,5-dioxide	MeOH	270(3.37),278(3.33), 285(3.07)	73-0599-73
$C_{14}H_{10}Cl_2S$			
Thiophene, 2-[4-(2,6-dichlorophenyl)-1,3-butadienyl]-, (E,E)-	EtOH	335(4.53)	35-2058-73
$C_{14}H_{10}Cl_3N$			
Aziridine, 2,2-dichloro-3-(3-chlorophen-yl)-1-phenyl-	heptane	219(4.28),270(3.18), 278(3.04)	104-2360-73
$C_{14}H_{10}Cl_3NO_3$			
Acetamide, N-hydroxy-N-phenyl-2-(2,4,5-trichlorophenoxy)-	EtOH	241(4.13),252(4.11), 290s(3.54),300s(3.30)	112-0547-73

Compound	Solvent	λ_{max}(log ϵ)	Ref.
$C_{14}H_{10}Cl_4O_2S_2$			
Spiro[1,3-benzodioxole-2,2'-[4H]cyclohepta[1,3]dithiole], 4,5,6,7-tetrachloro-5',6',7',8'-tetrahydro-	benzene	297(3.43)	97-0465-73
$C_{14}H_{10}F_3NO_3$			
Benzoic acid, 2-[[4-hydroxy-3-(trifluoromethyl)phenyl]amino]-	EtOH-HCl	212(4.40),219(4.39), 236s(3.97),283(4.10), 350(3.84)	39-0001-73C
Benzoic acid, 5-hydroxy-2-[[3-(trifluoromethyl)phenyl]amino]-	EtOH-HCl	222(3.82),289(3.45), 370(3.75)	39-0001-73C
$C_{14}H_{10}NO$			
1H-Isoindolium, 1-oxo-3-phenyl-, hexachloroantimonate	MeCN	228(4.09),274(4.09), 337(3.64)	24-1423-73
	H_2SO_4	240(4.20),348(4.25), 393(4.19)	24-1423-73
$C_{14}H_{10}N_2$			
Cinnoline, 4-phenyl-	n.s.g.	227(4.55),298(3.79), 325(3.74)	2-0631-73
Quinoxaline, 2-phenyl-	C_6H_{12}	258(4.45),333(4.08)	33-2227-73
	benzene	336(4.07)	33-2227-73
	EtOH	259(4.41),334(4.07)	33-2227-73
	n.s.g.	262(4.45),335(4.08)	2-0631-73
$C_{14}H_{10}N_2O$			
1H-Indole, 3-nitroso-3-phenyl-	aq $HClO_4$	272(4.49)	39-0918-73B
Phenol, 4-(2-quinoxalinyl)-	EtOH	213(4.34),245(--), 260(--),283(--), 355(--)	34-0102-73
2(1H)-Quinazolinone, 4-phenyl-	EtOH	210(0.2),230(1.0), 270(0.4),360(0.8)	30-0828-73
$C_{14}H_{10}N_2OS$			
Naphtho[2',1':5,6]thiopyrano[4,3-c]pyrazol-1(2H)-one, 3,11-dihydro-	EtOH	211(4.42),231(4.37), 278(4.47),324(3.85)	32-1073-73
$C_{14}H_{10}N_2O_2$			
9,10-Anthracenedione, 1,4-diamino-	n.s.g.	588(4.19)	40-1738-73
1H-Indole, 2-nitro-3-phenyl-	isoPrOH	238(4.17),352(4.12)	44-3077-73
1H-Indole, 3-(4-nitrophenyl)-	EtOH	220(4.49),281(3.91), 286s(3.89),391(4.17)	94-2786-73
Phenol, 4-(2-quinoxalinyl)-, N-oxide	EtOH	210(--),301(4.97), 354(--)	34-0102-73
$C_{14}H_{10}N_2O_2S$			
3H-Pyrrolo[1,2-a]indole-2-carbonitrile, 9-methoxy-1-(methylthio)-3-oxo-	EtOH	235(4.35),308(4.20), 319(4.23),358(4.20)	94-1658-73
$C_{14}H_{10}N_2O_3S$			
Thiazole, 2-methyl-4-[5-(4-nitrophenyl)-2-furanyl]-	EtOH	272(4.08),386(4.37)	103-0403-73
Thiazolo[3,2-a]pyridinium, 3-hydroxy-5-methyl-2-(4-nitrophenyl)-, hydroxide, inner salt	50% dioxan-HCl	230s(--),256(--), 302(--),494(--)	1-1763-73
	50% dioxan-NaOH	227(4.1),256(4.1), 303(3.7),494(4.4)	1-1763-73
$C_{14}H_{10}N_2O_4$			
Benzamide, 2-benzoyl-3-nitro-	EtOH	224(4.15),250(3.80)	39-1160-73B

Compound	Solvent	λ_{max}(log ε)	Ref.
Benzamide, 2-benzoyl-4-nitro-	EtOH	226(4.15),252(4.07)	39-1160-73B
Benzamide, 2-benzoyl-5-nitro-	EtOH	226(4.15),250(4.14)	39-1160-73B
Benzamide, 2-benzoyl-6-nitro- (cyclic)	EtOH	226(4.16)	39-1160-73B
Benzamide, 2-(4-nitrobenzoyl)- (cyclic)	EtOH	226(4.29)	39-1160-73B
$C_{14}H_{10}N_2O_4S$			
Benzoic acid, 2-(2H-1,2,4-benzothiadiazin-3-yl)-, S,S-dioxide	EtOH	275(3.94)	7-0635-73
$C_{14}H_{10}N_2O_5$			
1H-Pyrrole-3-carboxylic acid, 4-(1,2-dihydro-2-oxo-3H-indol-3-ylidene)-4,5-dihydro-2-hydroxy-5-oxo-, methyl ester	EtOH	260(4.44),330(4.07)	95-1520-73
$C_{14}H_{10}N_2S$			
Acridinium thiocyanate	EtOH	211(4.2),218s(4.1), 250(5.0),325s(3.0), 340(3.3),349(3.8), 355(3.9),367s(--), 380(3.2),408s(2.6), 429(3.2),455s(2.9), 479s(--)	97-0072-73
$C_{14}H_{10}N_4$			
1,2,4,5-Tetrazine, 3,6-diphenyl-	EtOH	268(4.13),297(4.57)	12-0389-73
$C_{14}H_{10}N_4O$			
1,2,4-Triazin-5(2H)-one, 6-phenyl-3-(2-pyridinyl)-	MeOH	234(4.24),274(4.25), 312(4.10)	40-1519-73
$C_{14}H_{10}N_4O_2$			
1-Phthalazineacetic acid, α,4-dicyano-, ethyl ester	EtOH	229(4.49),288(3.96), 297(4.11),377(4.35), 390(4.32)	95-0409-73
$C_{14}H_{10}N_4O_6$			
Ethanediamide, N,N'-bis(4-nitrophenyl)-	dioxan	280s(4.07),325(4.53)	30-0001-73
$C_{14}H_{10}N_8$			
2H-Tetrazolium, 2,5-diphenyl-3(1H-tetrazol-5-yl)-, hydroxide, inner salt	n.s.g.	245(4.39),320s(--)	103-1423-73
$C_{14}H_{10}O$			
Cycloprop[a]phenalen-7(7aH)-one, 8,8a-dihydro-	C_6H_{12}	212(4.56),248(4.35), 319(3.75),334(3.74), 350s(3.45),365s(3.18), 383s(2.65)	88-1591-73
	EtOH	212(4.53),249(4.29), 323(3.69),335(3.74), 355s(3.62)	88-1591-73
	CF_3COOH	240(4.03),295(3.40), 364(3.71),440s(3.14)	88-1591-73
Methanol, 9H-fluoren-9-ylidene-	EtOH	282(4.23),293(4.27), 316(3.99),325s(3.95)	23-1995-73
Naphth[1,8-de]oxocin	n.s.g.	237s(4.60),241(4.61), 307s(3.90),319(3.97), 338(3.85)	35-1874-73
Spiro[9H-fluorene-9,2'-oxirane]	EtOH	230(4.46),237(4.48), 241s(3.95),278(4.09), 286s(4.03)	25-1111-73

Compound	Solvent	λ_{max}(log ε)	Ref.
$C_{14}H_{10}OS$			
Dibenzo[b,f]thiepin-2-ol	MeOH	222(4.51),240(4.26), 263(4.38),290(3.76)	73-1579-73
2H-Naphtho[1,2-b]thiopyran-2-one, 4-methyl-	EtOH	360(3.88)	40-0118-73
	EtOH-HClO$_4$	393(3.64)	40-0118-73
2H-Naphtho[2,1-b]thiopyran-3-one, 1-methyl-	EtOH	356(3.72)	40-0118-73
$C_{14}H_{10}O_2$			
9(10H)-Anthracenone, 10-hydroxy-	EtOH	272(4.23),303s(3.57), 350(2.04),363(1.95), 378(1.48)	3-1794-73
$C_{14}H_{10}O_2S$			
Dibenzo[b,f]thiepin-10(11H)-one, 8-hydroxy-	MeOH	239(4.34),256s(3.98), 356(3.52)	73-1579-73
$C_{14}H_{10}O_3$			
Benzaldehyde, 5-benzoyl-2-hydroxy-	CHCl$_3$	282(4.14),330(3.49)	103-1463-73
Furo[2,3-b]naphtho[2,3-d]furan-2(3H)-one, 3a,10a-dihydro=	EtOH	264(3.65),274(3.70), 285(3.54),316(3.30), 329(3.48)	44-3874-73
10,16,17-Trioxatricyclo[11.2.1.1^{4,7}]heptadeca-2,4,6,8,11,13,15-heptaene	EtOH	228(4.39),254(4.70), 278(4.59),465(3.28)	78-0809-73
9H-Xanthen-9-one, 2-methoxy-	MeOH	252(4.50),292s(3.65), 300(3.74),361(3.80)	39-1329-73C
$C_{14}H_{10}O_3S_2$			
2-Propen-1-one, 3,3'-oxybis[1-(2-thienyl)-	dioxan	319(4.91)	24-0435-73
$C_{14}H_{10}O_4$			
1H-Phenalen-1-one, 3,9-dihydroxy-4-methoxy-	EtOH	212(4.53),254(4.10), 276(4.01),286(3.91), 372(4.07),416(4.07), 431(3.90)	39-2159-73C
4H,5H-Pyrano[3,2-c][1]benzopyran-4,5-dione, 2,9-dimethyl-	EtOH	242(4.16),279(4.08), 289s(4.03),327(4.79)	39-1022-73C
9H-Xanthene-2,9(4aH)-dione, 6-hydroxy-4a-methyl-	MeOH	205(4.46),241(4.21), 362(3.83)	24-1182-73
9H-Xanthen-9-one, 2,6-dihydroxy-4-methyl-	MeOH	204(4.18),244(4.52), 269s(4.04),314(4.12), 359s(3.72)	24-1182-73
9H-Xanthen-9-one, 3-hydroxy-2-methoxy-	MeOH	230(4.50),265(3.86), 308(4.08),348(3.96)	39-1329-73C
$C_{14}H_{10}O_5$			
9H-Xanthen-9-one, 1,7-dihydroxy-6-methoxy-	MeOH	251(4.43),260s(4.19), 269(4.01),311s(3.80), 311?(3.80),360(3.97)	39-1329-73C
9H-Xanthen-9-one, 3,4-dihydroxy-2-methoxy-	MeOH	240(4.48),258(4.45), 286(3.79),337(4.11)	39-1329-73C
$C_{14}H_{10}O_6$			
Altenuisol	EtOH	216(3.95),256(4.04), 278s(3.54)	88-0945-73
	EtOH-NaOH	208(4.44),264(3.97)	88-0945-73
Bellidifolin	EtOH	252(4.25),278(4.10), 332(3.9),400(3.72)	102-2542-73

Compound	Solvent	λ_{max}(log ε)	Ref.
9H-Xanthen-9-one, 1,3,8-trihydroxy-5-methoxy-	EtOH	220(4.20),252(4.32),276(4.18),308s(3.73),339(4.08)	36-0929-73
9H-Xanthen-9-one, 1,5,8-trihydroxy-3-methoxy-	EtOH	220(4.28),240(4.15),255(4.20),277(4.10),308s(3.71),329(3.92)	36-0926-73
9H-Xanthen-9-one, 3,5,6-trihydroxy-1-methoxy-	MeOH	244(4.68),288s(4.12),317(4.46),342(4.00)	39-1329-73C
$C_{14}H_{10}S_4$			
Disulfide, bis(phenylthioxomethyl)	$CHCl_3$	306(4.23),525(2.42)	143-0437-73
$C_{14}H_{11}AsN_2$			
2H-1,2,3-Diazarsole, 2,5-diphenyl-	heptane	239(4.16),263(4.36),352(3.80)	88-4503-73
$C_{14}H_{11}BrNO$			
Pyridinium, 1-[3-(4-bromophenyl)-3-oxo-1-propenyl]-, diphenyl phosphate	H_2O	272(4.32),276(4.32)	24-0435-73
$C_{14}H_{11}BrN_8$			
Formazan, 5-(4-bromophenyl)-3-phenyl-1-(1H-tetrazol-5-yl)-	pH 13	498(4.69)	103-1423-73
	EtOH	480(4.32)	103-1423-73
Co complex	EtOH	640(--)	103-1423-73
Cu complex	EtOH	616(--)	103-1423-73
Ni complex	EtOH	580(--)	103-1423-73
$C_{14}H_{11}ClNO$			
Pyridinium, 1-[3-(4-chlorophenyl)-3-oxo-1-propenyl]-, diphenyl phosphate	H_2O	271(4.31),276(4.31)	24-0435-73
$C_{14}H_{11}ClN_2$			
1H-Indol-1-amine, 5-chloro-3-phenyl-	isoPrOH	226(4.45),235s(4.43),268(4.23),308s(3.86)	4-0883-73
$C_{14}H_{11}ClN_2O_2$			
1,2-Diazabicyclo[5.2.0]nona-3,5-dien-9-one, 2-benzoyl-8-chloro-, cis	CH_2Cl_2	293(3.95)	88-4163-73
1H-Indol-3-ol, 5-chloro-2,3-dihydro-1-nitroso-3-phenyl-	isoPrOH	225s(4.13),280(4.04),291(4.01),309(4.02)	4-0883-73
Methanone, [5-chloro-2-(methylnitrosoamino)phenyl]phenyl-	isoPrOH	249(4.34),285s(3.86)	4-0883-73
$C_{14}H_{11}ClN_4$			
1H-1,2,4-Triazol-5-amine, 1-(4-chlorophenyl)-3-phenyl-	EtOH	294(4.11)	42-0589-73
$C_{14}H_{11}ClN_8$			
Formazan, 5-(4-chlorophenyl)-3-phenyl-1-(1H-tetrazol-5-yl)-	pH 13	490(4.57)	103-1423-73
	EtOH	470(3.78)	103-1423-73
Co complex	EtOH	640(--)	103-1423-73
Cu complex	EtOH	616(--)	103-1423-73
Ni complex	EtOH	580(--)	103-1423-73
$C_{14}H_{11}ClOS$			
Ethanone, 1-[2-[(4-chlorophenyl)thio]-phenyl]-	MeOH	258(3.94),277(3.67),303(3.59)	73-0115-73
$C_{14}H_{11}ClO_3S$			
Benzenesulfonic acid, 4-(1-chloro-2-phenylethenyl)-	EtOH	287(4.42)	104-1511-73

Compound	Solvent	λ_{max}(log ε)	Ref.
$C_{14}H_{11}ClO_4S$			
Benzeneacetic acid, 2-[(4-chlorophenyl)-sulfonyl]-	MeOH	240(4.22),270s(3.34)	73-0599-73
$C_{14}H_{11}Cl_2$			
Ethylium, 1,1-bis(4-chlorophenyl)-	FSO_3H at -75°	330(4.08),456(3.86)	59-0803-73
$C_{14}H_{11}FNO$			
Pyridinium, 1-[3-(4-fluorophenyl)-3-oxo-1-propenyl]-, diphenyl phosphate	H_2O	271(4.36),275s(4.31)	24-0435-73
$C_{14}H_{11}INO$			
Pyridinium, 1-[3-(4-iodophenyl)-3-oxo-1-propenyl]-, diphenyl phosphate	H_2O	267(4.33),311(4.15)	24-0435-73
$C_{14}H_{11}IN_8$			
Formazan, 5-(4-iodophenyl)-3-phenyl-1-(1H-tetrazol-5-yl)-	pH 13	494(4.66)	103-1423-73
	EtOH	460(3.96)	103-1423-73
Co complex	EtOH	650(--)	103-1423-73
Cu complex	EtOH	620(--)	103-1423-73
Ni complex	EtOH	590(--)	103-1423-73
$C_{14}H_{11}IOS$			
Dibenzo[b,f]thiepin-10-ol, 10,11-dihydro-8-iodo-	MeOH	232s(4.13),271(4.06)	73-2484-73
$C_{14}H_{11}N$			
1H-Benz[f]indene-4-carbonitrile, 2,3-dihydro-	EtOH	220(4.77),240(4.48), 290(3.76),302(3.91), 315(3.85),329(3.76)	95-0409-73
1H-Indole, 2-phenyl-	MeOH	237(4.27),308(4.42)	73-0224-73
$C_{14}H_{11}NO$			
Benzo[f]quinolin-3(4H)-one, 1-methyl-	DMF	356(3.88)	40-0118-73
Benzo[h]quinolin-2(1H)-one, 4-methyl-	DMF	358(3.88)	40-0118-73
1H-Isoindol-1-one, 2,3-dihydro-3-phenyl-	EtOH	223(4.09)	39-1160-73B
Isoquinoline, 1-(2-furanylmethyl)-	MeOH	218(4.80),271(3.72), 309(3.51),322(3.60)	83-0592-73
1-Naphthaleneacetonitrile, α-acetyl-	10% EtOH-pH 12	263(4.12),310(3.57)	22-3458-73
2-Naphthaleneacetonitrile, α-acetyl-	10% EtOH-pH 12	267(4.30),277(4.29), 319(4.17)	22-3458-73
4H-Oxepino[3,4,5,6-def]carbazole, 8,10-dihydro-	MeOH	243(4.53),252(4.51), 296(4.10),327(3.67), 340(3.67)	39-2818-73C
Phenol, 2-(1H-indol-2-yl)-	heptane	301s(4.17)	73-0224-73
	0.05M HCl	297s(3.93),320(4.36)	73-0224-73
	0.05M NaOH	295(4.06),351(4.38)	73-0224-73
	MeOH	214(4.52),244(4.26), 297s(4.18),319(4.37)	73-0224-73
	EtOH	298s(4.12)	73-0224-73
	$CHCl_3$	302s(4.11),321(4.28)	73-0224-73
	dioxan	300s(4.16),324(4.37)	73-0224-73
	50% dioxan	297.5s(4.10)	73-0224-73
Phenol, 3-(1H-indol-2-yl)-	MeOH	222(4.32),245(4.16), 317(4.36)	73-0224-73
Phenol, 4-(1H-indol-2-yl)-	0.05M HCl	309(4.42)	73-0224-73
	0.05M NaOH	326(4.60)	73-0224-73
	MeOH	246(4.26),309(4.45)	73-0224-73

Compound	Solvent	$\lambda_{max}(\log \epsilon)$	Ref.
Phenol, 4-(1H-indol-2-yl)- (cont.)	$CHCl_3$	312(4.46)	73-0224-73
	dioxan	308(4.54)	73-0224-73
$C_{14}H_{11}NOS$			
Benzothiazole, 2-(2-methoxyphenyl)-	MeOH	214(4.40),248(3.89), 258(3.89),331(4.24)	73-0224-73
Thiazolo[3,2-a]pyridinium, 3-hydroxy-5-methyl-2-phenyl-, hydroxide, inner salt	50% dioxan-HCl	448(--)	1-1763-73
	50% dioxan-NaOH	237(4.1),290(3.9), 455(4.1)	1-1763-73
Thiazolo[3,2-a]pyridinium, 3-hydroxy-6-methyl-2-phenyl-, hydroxide, inner salt	50% dioxan-HCl	233(4.1),283(3.8), 432(4.1)	1-1763-73
	50% dioxan-NaOH	235(4.1),283(3.9), 432(4.1)	1-1763-73
$C_{14}H_{11}NO_2$			
Benzamide, 2-benzoyl-	EtOH	224(4.16)	39-1160-73B
Benzoxazole, 2-(2-methoxyphenyl)-	MeOH	215(4.21),318(4.22)	73-0224-73
1,1'-Biphenyl, 2-isocyanato-2'-methoxy-	hexane	277(3.61)	44-1157-73
1,1'-Biphenyl, 2-isocyanato-3'-methoxy-	hexane	251(3.85),281(3.59)	44-1157-73
1,1'-Biphenyl, 2-isocyanato-4-methoxy-	ether	228(4.26),257(4.08)	44-1157-73
1,1'-Biphenyl, 2-isocyanato-4'-methoxy-	ether	228(4.32),258(4.08)	44-1157-73
1,1'-Biphenyl, 2-isocyanato-5-methoxy-	ether	226(4.42),295(3.51)	44-1157-73
1H-Isoindol-1-one, 2,3-dihydro-3-hydroxy-2-phenyl-	H_2SO_4	245(4.32),366(3.59), 432(3.56)	24-1423-73
1H-Isoindol-1-one, 2,3-dihydro-3-hydroxy-3-phenyl-	H_2SO_4	240(4.15),345(4.25), 285(4.21)	24-1423-73
Murrayanine	EtOH	238(4.45),274(4.30), 287(4.55),335(4.15)	102-1831B-73
6(5H)-Phenanthridinone, 2-methoxy-	ether	227(4.63),233(4.58), 242(4.34),264(4.10), 273(4.02),343(3.93), 357(3.84)	44-1157-73
6(5H)-Phenanthridinone, 3-methoxy-	ether	228(4.72),237s(4.60), 246s(4.36),263(4.18), 278(4.10),312(4.06), 325(4.13),339(3.99)	44-1157-73
6(5H)-Phenanthridinone, 8-methoxy-	ether	228(4.66),233s(4.64), 242s(4.30),264(4.26), 272s(4.11),280s(4.00), 312(4.02),328(3.98), 343(3.88)	44-1157-73
6(5H)-Phenanthridinone, 9-methoxy-	ether	242(4.67),266(4.20), 309(3.66),320(3.77), 334(3.76)	44-1157-73
6(5H)-Phenanthridinone, 10-methoxy-	ether	233(4.71),253(4.08), 262(4.04),269(3.99), 278(3.87),291(3.61), 302(3.69),318(3.86), 331(4.10),347(4.07)	44-1157-73
$C_{14}H_{11}NO_2S$			
Dibenzo[c,e]thiepin, 5,7-dihydro-1-nitro-	MeOH	234(4.11),244(4.08)	39-2818-73C
1H-Indole, 1-(phenylsulfonyl)-	EtOH	252(4.17),275s(3.60), 285s(3.51),292s(3.48)	44-3324-73
Thiazolo[3,2-a]pyridinium, 3-hydroxy-2-(4-methoxyphenyl)-, hydroxide, inner salt	50% dioxan-HCl	242(4.1),275s(3.9), 285(3.9),355s(3.6), 443(4.1)	1-1763-73
	50% dioxan-NaOH	242(4.2),275(3.9), 285(3.9),444(4.2)	1-1763-73

Compound	Solvent	$\lambda_{max}(\log \epsilon)$	Ref.
6H-Thieno[2,3-b]pyrrole-2-carboxylic acid, 6-methyl-5-phenyl-	EtOH	315(4.49)	103-0521-73
4H-Thiepino[3,4,5,6-def]carbazole, 8,10-dihydro-, 9,9-dioxide	MeCN	246(4.50),253(4.51), 298(4.12),329(3.71), 343(3.71)	39-2818-73C
$C_{14}H_{11}NO_2S_2$			
Dibenzo[d,f][1,2]dithiocin, 5,8-dihydro-1-nitro-	MeOH	254s(3.81)	39-2818-73C
$C_{14}H_{11}NO_2Se$			
Selenolo[2,3-b]pyrrole-2-carboxylic acid, 6-methyl-5-phenyl-	EtOH	330(4.15)	103-0521-73
$C_{14}H_{11}NO_3$			
Benzoic acid, 2-[[(2-hydroxyphenyl)methylene]amino]-	$C_2H_4Cl_2$	274(3.9)	24-2427-73
Tricyclo[6.2.1.0^{2,7}]undeca-2,4,6-triene-5,6-dicarboximide, N-methyl-11-oxo-, endo	90% EtOH	215(3.68),257(2.64), 264(2.75),272(2.69)	12-1725-73
exo	90% EtOH	215(3.81),258(3.73), 265(3.86),272(2.90)	12-1725-73
$C_{14}H_{11}NO_3S$			
4H-1-Benzopyran-4-one, 7-hydroxy-2-methyl-3-(2-methyl-4-thiazolyl)-	n.s.g.	297(3.97)	104-2580-73
4H-1-Benzopyran-4-one, 7-methoxy-2-methyl-3-(4-thiazolyl)-	n.s.g.	295(3.88)	104-2580-73
$C_{14}H_{11}NO_4$			
Benzoic acid, 2,2'-iminobis-	EtOH	300(4.1),360(4.1)	140-0008-73
Naphtho[2,1-b]furan-6,9-dione, 7-amino-5-hydroxy-2,4-dimethyl-	EtOH	262(4.42),325(4.08), 490(3.81)	33-2323-73
1H-Pyrano[3,4-b]quinoline-1,5(10H)-dione, 9-methoxy-3-methyl-	MeOH	228(4.42),277(4.20), 285(4.21),320(3.92), 335(4.04),397(3.95)	24-0355-73
$C_{14}H_{11}NO_4S$			
Pyrano[3,2-b]indole-3-carboxylic acid, 2,5-dihydro-4-(methylthio)-2-oxo-, methyl ester	EtOH	255(4.18),380(4.26)	94-1658-73
2-Thiophenecarboxylic acid, 4-nitro-5-(2-phenylethenyl)-, methyl ester, (E)-	EtOH	243(4.22),367(3.89)	118-0313B-73
$C_{14}H_{11}NO_6$			
Naphtho[2,1-b]furan-1,6,9(2H)-trione, 7-amino-2,5-dihydroxy-2,4-dimethyl-	EtOH	228(4.42),273(4.26), 311(4.04),350(4.05)	33-2287-73
	EtOH-HCl	225(4.43),270(4.30), 313(4.03),347(4.08), 410s(--)	33-2323-73
$C_{14}H_{11}NS$			
Benzo[b]thiophen-2-amine, N-phenyl-	EtOH	231(4.62),311(4.47)	78-0321-73
Isoquinoline, 1-(2-thienylmethyl)-	MeOH	218(4.77),272(3.74), 310(3.54),323(3.62)	83-0592-73
4H-Thiepino[3,4,5,6-def]carbazole, 8,10-dihydro-	MeOH	246(4.49),253(4.47), 298(4.06),330(3.67), 344(3.70)	39-2818-73C

Compound	Solvent	$\lambda_{max}(\log \epsilon)$	Ref.
$C_{14}H_{11}N_2P$			
2H-1,2,3-Diazaphosphole, 2,5-diphenyl-	heptane	229(4.39),251(4.44), 280s(3.96),321(3.99)	88-4503-73
$C_{14}H_{11}N_3$			
Benzeneacetonitrile, α-(phenylhydrazono)-	MeOH	240(4.30),290(3.53), 370(4.38)	80-0723-73
$C_{14}H_{11}N_3O$			
Benzamide, N-2H-indazol-2-yl-	EtOH	277(3.98)	118-0363-73
Benzo[c]cinnolinium, 5-(acetylamino)-, hydroxide, inner salt	EtOH	250(4.59),345(3.92), 414(3.87)	24-1589-73
1H-Pyrazolo[4,3-b]pyridine, 1-benzoyl-5-methyl-	C_6H_{12}	256(4.39),303(3.61)	39-2901-73C
2H-Pyrazolo[4,3-b]pyridine, 2-benzoyl-5-methyl-	C_6H_{12}	254(4.80),302(4.07)	39-2901-73C
4-Pyridineacetonitrile, α-[(4-methoxyphenyl)imino]-	EtOH	240(4.00),290(3.76), 398(4.01)	12-2027-73
2(1H)-Quinazolinone, 4-(4-aminophenyl)-	EtOH	210(1.14),213(1.10), 382(0.50)	30-0828-73
$C_{14}H_{11}N_3O_2$			
Benzaldehyde, 5-methoxy-2-([1,2,3]triazolo[1,5-a]pyridin-3-yl)-	EtOH	241(4.70),293(4.67), 333(4.67)	44-4167-73
$C_{14}H_{11}N_3O_3$			
1H-Benzimidazole, 1-methoxy-2-(4-nitrophenyl)-	EtOH	240(4.07),339(4.23)	39-1310-73C
$C_{14}H_{11}N_3O_4$			
Ethanediamide, N-(4-nitrophenyl)-N'-phenyl-	dioxan	275s(4.09),315(4.36)	30-0001-73
$C_{14}H_{11}N_3O_5$			
Benzaldehyde, 2-hydroxy-3-methoxy-5-[(4-nitrophenyl)azo]-	EtOH-NaOH	245s(4.01),265(4.08), 410s(4.06),495(4.44)	103-1463-73
	$CHCl_3$	275(4.36),310(4.21), 390(4.51),450s(--)	103-1463-73
$C_{14}H_{11}N_3O_6$			
Benzamide, N-hydroxy-N-(3-methylphenyl)-3,5-dinitro-	EtOH	235s(4.35)	112-0547-73
Benzamide, N-hydroxy-N-(4-methylphenyl)-3,5-dinitro-	EtOH	235s(4.38)	112-0547-73
$C_{14}H_{11}N_3S$			
Naphth[2',1':5,6]thiopyrano[4,3-c]pyrazol-1-amine, 3,11-dihydro-	EtOH	211(4.52),262s(4.48), 278(4.60),333(3.93)	32-1073-73
$C_{14}H_{11}N_5O$			
Phenol, 4-[[4-(1H-triazol-1-yl)phenyl]azo]-	MeOH	360(4.2),450(3.1)	12-1585-73
Phenol, 4-[[4-(4H-1,2,4-triazol-4-yl)phenyl]azo]-	MeOH	356(4.3),450(3.2)	12-1585-73
$C_{14}H_{11}N_5O_2$			
4(1H)-Pteridinone, 2-amino-6-(2-phenylethenyl)-, 8-oxide	pH 13	245(4.03),280s(4.27), 320(4.53),415(4.04)	35-6407-73

Compound	Solvent	λ_{max}(log ϵ)	Ref.
$C_{14}H_{11}N_5O_6$			
Diazene, (2,4-dinitrophenyl)(1-nitro-1-phenylethyl)-	$CHCl_3$	418(2.64)	78-3929-73
$C_{14}H_{11}N_5O_8$			
1H-Pyrrole-3,4-dicarboxylic acid, 2-acetyl-, 2,4-dinitrophenylhydrazone	EtOH	432(4.20)	103-0925-73
$C_{14}H_{11}N_9O_2$			
Formazan, 5-(3-nitrophenyl)-3-phenyl-	pH 13	496(4.60)	103-1423-73
1-(1H-tetrazol-5-yl)-	EtOH	460(3.79)	103-1423-73
Co complex	EtOH	654(--)	103-1423-73
Cu complex	EtOH	614(--)	103-1423-73
Ni complex	EtOH	596(--)	103-1423-73
Formazan, 5-(4-nitrophenyl)-3-phenyl-	pH 13	568(4.55)	103-1423-73
1-(1H-tetrazol-5-yl)-	EtOH	480(4.02)	103-1423-73
Co complex	EtOH	670(--)	103-1423-73
Cu complex	EtOH	644(--)	103-1423-73
Ni complex	EtOH	630(--)	103-1423-73
$C_{14}H_{12}$			
Anthracene, 9,10-dihydro-	C_6H_{12}	255(2.83),259(2.87), 265(3.03),271(3.03)	78-1379-73
Benzene, 1,1'-(1,2-ethenediyl)bis-, trans	$C_2H_4Cl_2$	299(4.45)	24-2427-73
carbonium ion	81.5% H_2SO_4	295(2.9),385(2.7)	48-0810-73
	96% H_2SO_4	440(3.42)	48-0810-73
	33% SO_3	450(3.11)	48-0810-73
Biquadricyclanylidene	MeCN	210(4.40)	89-0991-73
Bis(norbornadienylidene)	hexane	243s(2.52),250s(2.40), 269s(2.18),276(2.20), 286s(2.08)	89-0991-73
Cyclohepta[de]naphthalene, 7,8-dihydro-	EtOH	231s(4.57),235(4.59), 246(4.14),255(4.00), 297(3.97),309(4.11), 324(3.97)	44-3592-73
Cyclohepta[de]naphthalene, 7,10-dihydro-	EtOH	225(4.73),269s(3.60), 277(3.79),287(3.89), 298(3.76),306(3.43), 316(2.97),321(2.97)	44-3592-73
1,3,5-Cycloheptatriene, 7-(2,4,6-cycloheptatrien-1-ylidene)-	EtOH	234(4.34),362(4.32)	35-0826-73
5,10-Methanobenzocyclooctene, 5,10-dihydro-11-methylene-	C_6H_{12}	242s(3.47),254(3.51), 262(3.64),273(3.67), 284(3.47)	44-1893-73
$C_{14}H_{12}BF_2NO$			
Boron, difluoro[2-[1-(phenylimino)ethyl]phenolato-N,O]-, (T-4)-	$C_2H_4Cl_2$	270(4.2),349(3.75)	24-2427-73
$C_{14}H_{12}BF_3O_6$			
Boron, bis(acetato-O)(4,4,4-trifluoro-1-phenyl-1,3-butanedionato-O,O')-, (T-4)-	CH_2Cl_2	332(4.61)	39-1796-73B
$C_{14}H_{12}Br$			
Ethylium, 2-bromo-1,1-diphenyl-	n.s.g.	358(3.82),463(4.46)	30-0932-73
$C_{14}H_{12}BrNO_2$			
Benzamide, 2-bromo-N-hydroxy-N-(3-methylphenyl)-	EtOH	260(4.05)	112-0547-73

Compound	Solvent	$\lambda_{max}(\log \epsilon)$	Ref.
Benzamide, 3-bromo-N-hydroxy-N-(3-methylphenyl)-	EtOH	272(4.00)	112-0547-73
Benzamide, 4-bromo-N-hydroxy-N-(3-methylphenyl)-	EtOH	230(4.10),272(4.00)	112-0547-73
$C_{14}H_{12}Cl$			
Ethylium, 2-chloro-1,1-diphenyl-	n.s.g.	332(3.54),460(4.15)	30-0932-73
Ethylium, 1-(4-chlorophenyl)-1-phenyl-	FSO_3H at -75°	321(4.11),440(4.73)	59-0803-73
$C_{14}H_{12}ClNO_2$			
Benzamide, 4-chloro-N-hydroxy-N-(3-methylphenyl)-	EtOH	274(3.99)	112-0547-73
$C_{14}H_{12}ClNO_2S$			
Benzenesulfonamide, 4-(2-chloro-2-phenylethenyl)-	EtOH	237(4.18)	104-1511-73
$C_{14}H_{12}ClN_3$			
2H-Indazol-2-amine, 5-chloro-N-(3-methylphenyl)-	EtOH	279(3.97),300(3.87)	118-0363-73
2H-Indazol-2-amine, N-(4-chlorophenyl)-3-methyl-	EtOH	236(4.26),290(3.89)	118-0363-73
$C_{14}H_{12}ClN_3O$			
Carbamic chloride, methyl[4-(phenylazo)-phenyl]-	MeOH	323(4.35)	69-3023-73
$C_{14}H_{12}ClN_3O_2$			
Quinolinium, 1-[(1,2,3,4-tetrahydro-2,4-dioxo-5-pyrimidinyl)methyl]-, chloride	H_2O	218(3.84),262(3.85)	69-2879-73
$C_{14}H_{12}Cl_4$			
Cyclopent[a]indene, 4,5,6,7-tetrachloro-1,2,3,8-tetrahydro-1,1-dimethyl-	C_6H_{12}	209(4.22),221(4.28), 228(4.33),235(4.35), 243(4.28),277(4.22), 287(4.20)	39-2569-73C
$C_{14}H_{12}FNO_2$			
Benzamide, 2-fluoro-N-hydroxy-N-(3-methylphenyl)-	EtOH	265(4.06)	112-0547-73
Benzamide, 2-fluoro-N-hydroxy-N-(4-methylphenyl)-	EtOH	267(4.04)	112-0547-73
Benzamide, 4-fluoro-N-hydroxy-N-(3-methylphenyl)-	EtOH	269(4.02)	112-0547-73
$C_{14}H_{12}F_4$			
Cyclopent[a]indene, 4,5,6,7-tetrafluoro-1,2,3,8-tetrahydro-1,1-dimethyl-	C_6H_{12}	209(4.2),217(4.18), 257(4.06),266(4.0), 280(3.46),296(3.23)	39-2569-73C
$C_{14}H_{12}I$			
Ethylium, 2-iodo-1,1-diphenyl-	n.s.g.	319(3.60),331(3.60), 433(4.23)	30-0932-73
$C_{14}H_{12}NO$			
Pyridinium, 1-(3-oxo-3-phenyl-1-propenyl)-, diphenyl phosphate	H_2O	271(4.31),378(3.43)	24-0435-73

Compound	Solvent	$\lambda_{max}(\log \epsilon)$	Ref.
$C_{14}H_{12}NOS$			
Benzothiazolium, 2-[2-(2-furanyl)ethen-yl]-3-methyl-, bromide	H_2O	412(4.12)	104-2596-73
$C_{14}H_{12}NS_2$			
Benzothiazolium, 3-methyl-2-[2-(2-thien-yl)ethenyl]-	H_2O	412(4.21)	104-2596-73
$C_{14}H_{12}N_2$			
Azuleno[1,2-b]pyrazine, 2,3-dimethyl-	MeOH	470(2.00),505(2.11), 550(2.24),595(2.28), 650(2.16)	18-3161-73
Benzenamine, 4-(1H-indol-3-yl)-	EtOH	231(4.33),270(4.21)	94-2786-73
1H-Benzimidazole, 1-methyl-2-phenyl-	MeOH	233(4.16),287(4.21)	73-0224-73
	$CHCl_3$	290.5(4.23)	73-0224-73
5,6-Diazacyclopenta[cd]phenalene, 1,2-dihydro-7-methyl-	EtOH	262(3.33),338(3.33), 355(3.29),374(3.33)	104-1091-73
1H-Indazole, 1-methyl-3-phenyl-	MeOH	215(4.51),245s(3.95), 274(3.75),309(4.09)	24-3432-73
3H-Indol-2-amine, 3-phenyl-, hydrochlor-ide	MeOH	210(4.39),261(3.94)	103-0471-73
Pyrazino[1,2,3,4-lmn][1,10]phenanthro-linediium, 5,6-dihydro-, bis(tetra-	MeCN	210(3.61),225s(4.32), 308(4.07),321(3.78), 381(4.59)	5-0339-73
Quinoxaline, 1,2-dihydro-3-phenyl-	benzene	395(3.64)	33-2227-73
	EtOH	258(4.37),350s(3.82), 394(3.64)	33-2227-73
$C_{14}H_{12}N_2O$			
1H-Benzimidazole, 2-(2-methoxyphenyl)-	MeOH	212(4.25),241(4.05), 312(4.36)	73-0224-73
1H-Carbazole-3-acetonitrile, 2,3,4,9-tetrahydro-1-oxo-	EtOH	236(3.18),308(3.30)	44-2882-73
2H-Indazole, 2-(2-methoxyphenyl)-	MeOH	216(4.33),236s(4.09), 296(4.16)	73-0224-73
1H-Indazol-4-ol, 1-methyl-3-phenyl-	MeOH	216(4.55),240(4.15), 279(3.83),310(4.04)	24-3432-73
Phenol, 2-(1-methyl-1H-benzimidazol-2-yl)-	heptane	291(4.15)	73-0224-73
	0.05M HCl	283(4.06),304(3.94)	73-0224-73
	pH 7	318(3.58)	73-0224-73
	0.05M NaOH	286(3.77),320(3.94)	73-0224-73
	MeOH	215(4.59),234(3.85), 288(4.10),319s(3.52)	73-0224-73
	dioxan	292(4.16),320(4.25)	73-0224-73
	50% dioxan	292(3.91)	73-0224-73
	$CHCl_3$	293(4.18),320(4.32)	73-0224-73
Phenol, 4-(1-methyl-1H-benzimidazol-2-yl)-	0.05M HCl	302(4.37)	73-0224-73
	pH 7	295(4.21)	73-0224-73
	0.05M NaOH	316(4.44)	73-0224-73
	MeOH	247(4.09),292(4.32)	73-0224-73
	dioxan	297(4.38)	73-0224-73
	$CHCl_3$	295(4.26)	73-0224-73
1H-Pyrazino[3,2,1-kl]phenoxazine, 2,3-dihydro-	EtOH	246(4.22),319(3.59)	95-0020-73
$C_{14}H_{12}N_2O_2$			
1H-Azuleno[1,2-d]imidazole-9-carboxylic acid, ethyl ester	MeOH	244(4.28),305(4.70), 317(4.72),332s(4.1), 370(3.73),386(3.84), 405(3.92),475s(2.27), 515(2.36),550s(2.32)	18-3161-73

Compound	Solvent	λ max(log ε)	Ref.
Benzamide, 2-(4-aminobenzoyl)-	EtOH	224(4.28),242(3.93), 334(3.21)	39-1160-73B
Benzoic acid, [(2-hydroxyphenyl)methylene]hydrazide	n.s.g.	235(4.21),285(4.34), 329(4.19)	140-0971-73
Ti complex	n.s.g.	253(4.65),305(4.53)	140-0971-73
Ethanediamide, N,N'-diphenyl-	dioxan	278(4.27)	30-0001-73
Isoxazole, 5-[(3-methyl-5-isoxazolyl)-methyl]-3-phenyl-	n.s.g.	207(4.39),240(4.20)	32-0037-73
9H-Pyrido[3,4-b]indole-3-carboxylic acid, 1-methyl-, methyl ester	n.s.g.	236(4.44),272(4.60), 305(3.95),332(--), 346(--)	22-2058-73
$C_{14}H_{12}N_2O_2S_3$			
Thiazolidinone, 3-acetyl-2-(4-oxo-3-phenyl-2-thioxo-5-thiazolidinylidene)-	EtOH	288(4.04),393(4.48)	94-1431-73
$C_{14}H_{12}N_2O_3$			
Benzaldehyde, 2-hydroxy-3-methoxy-5-(phenylazo)-	$CHCl_3$	275(4.11),345(4.18), 440s(3.03)	103-1463-73
	EtOH-NaOH	255(3.90),270s(3.86), 405(4.31)	103-1463-73
Benzoic acid, 2-hydroxy-, [(2-hydroxyphenyl)methylene]hydrazide	n.s.g.	294(4.42)	140-0971-73
Ti complex	n.s.g.	260(3.66)	140-0971-73
Benzoic acid, 2-[(2-hydroxy-4-methylphenyl)azo]-	EtOH	252(3.99),327(4.19), 402(3.81)	39-1682-73C
Benzoic acid, 2-[(2-hydroxy-6-methylphenyl)azo]-	EtOH	246(3.85),341(4.20), 394s(3.82)	39-1682-73C
1,4-Benzoquinone, 2-acetyl-3-amino-6-anilino-	EtOH	247(3.91),285(3.92), 317(3.98),437(3.10)	39-0493-73C
$C_{14}H_{12}N_2O_3S$			
3H-Pyrazolo[1,2-a]indole-2-carboxylic acid, 9-hydroxy-3-imino-1-(methylthio)-, methyl ester	EtOH	259(4.60),420(4.10)	94-1658-73
4H-Quinolizine-3-carboxylic acid, 1-cyano-2-(methylthio)-4-oxo-, ethyl ester	EtOH	273(4.19),300(3.94), 396(4.07)	94-0921-73
$C_{14}H_{12}N_2O_4$			
Benzamide, N-hydroxy-N-(3-methylphenyl)-2-nitro-	EtOH	255(4.19)	112-0547-73
Benzamide, N-hydroxy-N-(3-methylphenyl)-3-nitro-	EtOH	265(4.20)	112-0547-73
Benzamide, N-hydroxy-N-(3-methylphenyl)-4-nitro-	EtOH	255(4.15)	112-0547-73
Benzamide, N-hydroxy-N-(4-methylphenyl)-2-nitro-	EtOH	255(4.27)	112-0547-73
Benzene, 1,1'-(1,2-ethanediyl)bis[2-nitro-	MeOH	257(3.94)	6-0329-73
$C_{14}H_{12}N_2O_4S$			
Benzenesulfonic acid, 4-methyl-, 1,3-benzodioxol-2-ylidenehydrazide, sodium salt	MeOH	273.5(3.87)	24-1678-73
1,2,4-Benzothiadiazine, 3-(2-carboxyphenyl)-3,4-dihydro-, 1,1-dioxide	EtOH	276(3.44),315(3.48)	7-0635-73
$C_{14}H_{12}N_2O_5$			
2,3,4(5H)-Furantrione, 5-(2-acetoxyethylidene)-, 3-phenylhydrazone	EtOH	225(3.84),234s(3.80), 240s(3.78),248s(3.72),	95-0304-73

Compound	Solvent	λmax(log ε)	Ref.
2,3,4(5H)-Furantrione, 5-(2-acetoxy-ethylidene)-, 3-phenylhydrazone (cont.)	EtOH	255s(3.60),270s(3.44), 390s(4.07),403(4.09)	95-0304-73
$C_{14}H_{12}N_2O_5S$			
Benzenesulfonamide, 2-(2-carboxybenz-oyl)amino-	EtOH	272(3.91),302(3.83)	7-0635-73
$C_{14}H_{12}N_2O_6$			
1H-Isoindole-1,3(2H)-dione, 2-(2-acetyl-3-oxobutyl)-5-nitro-	EtOH	205(4.28),276(3.97)	87-0512-73
Phenol, 2-[(5-hydroxy-2-methylphenyl)-methyl]-4,6-dinitro-	neutral	273(4.19)	49-1315-73
	anion	275(3.85),370(4.16)	49-1315-73
	dianion	296(3.92),374(4.16)	49-1315-73
$C_{14}H_{12}N_3OS$			
Benzothiazolium, 3-amino-2-(-hydroxy-benzylidene)amino-, inner salt	dioxan	242(4.28),266s(3.74), 275s(3.66),286s(3.63), 334(4.46)	4-0947-73
$C_{14}H_{12}N_3O_2$			
Quinolinium, 1-[(1,2,3,4-tetrahydro-2,4-dioxo-5-pyrimidinyl)methyl]-, chloride	H_2O	218(3.84),262(3.85)	69-2879-73
$C_{14}H_{12}N_4$			
1H-1,2,3-Triazol-4-amine, 1,5-diphenyl-	EtOH	288(3.90)	42-0589-73
$C_{14}H_{12}N_4O$			
6H-Pyrimido[1',2':1,2]pyrimido[4,5-b]-quinolin-6-one, 1,2,3,4-tetrahydro-	DMSO	285(4.6),400(3.8)	24-3533-73
$C_{14}H_{12}N_4O_2$			
9,10-Anthracenedione, 1,4,5,8-tetra-amino-	n.s.g.	615(4.26)	40-1738-73
2,4(1H,3H)-Pteridinedione, 1,3-dimethyl-6-phenyl-	MeOH	252s(4.16),278(4.33), 357(3.94)	24-3149-73
2,4(1H,3H)-Pteridinedione, 1,3-dimethyl-7-phenyl-	MeOH	229(4.33),255s(3.95), 278(3.92),353(4.24)	24-3149-73
$C_{14}H_{12}N_4O_3$			
2,4(1H,3H)-Pteridinedione, 1,3-dimethyl-6-phenyl-, 5-oxide	MeOH	252(4.40),274(4.37), 367(3.87)	24-3149-73
2,4(1H,3H)-Pteridinedione, 1,3-dimethyl-7-phenyl-, 5-oxide	MeOH	205(4.39),243s(4.26), 259(4.43),300(4.08), 370(4.07)	24-3149-73
2,4,7(1H,3H,8H)-Pteridinetrione, 3,6-di-methyl-1-phenyl-	pH 1.0	280(4.03),325(4.11)	24-3203-73
	pH 6.0	278(4.01),328(4.24)	24-3203-73
$C_{14}H_{12}N_4O_4$			
1H-Isoindole-1,3(2H)-dione, 2-[(3,5-di-methyl-7H-pyrazol-4-yl)methyl]-5-nitro-	EtOH	208(4.46),238(4.31)	87-0512-73
2,4,7(1H,3H,8H)-Pteridinetrione, 3,6-di-methyl-1-phenyl-, 5-oxide	pH 0.0	252(4.26),285s(3.83), 334(3.98)	24-3203-73
	pH 6.0	229(4.33),260(4.24), 337(4.12)	24-3203-73
$C_{14}H_{12}N_4O_5$			
Phenol, 4-[(2,4-dinitrophenyl)azo]-2,3-dimethyl- (spectra in 50% DMSO)	acid	412(4.31)	1-3641-73
	KOH	603(4.74)	1-3641-73
Phenol, 4-[(2,4-dinitrophenyl)azo]-2,5-dimethyl- (spectra in 50% DMSO)	acid	417(4.31)	1-3641-73
	KOH	599(4.74)	1-3641-73

Compound	Solvent	$\lambda_{max}(\log \epsilon)$	Ref.
Phenol, 4-[(2,4-dinitrophenyl)azo]-2,6-	acid	443(4.14)	1-3641-73
dimethyl- (spectra in 50% DMSO)	KOH	604(4.63)	1-3641-73
Phenol, 4-[(2,4-dinitrophenyl)azo]-	acid	402(4.33)	1-3641-73
2-ethyl- (spectra in 50% DMSO)-	KOH	590(4.71)	1-3641-73
Phenol, 4-[(2,4-dinitrophenyl)azo]-	acid	402(4.31)	1-3641-73
3-ethyl- (spectra in 50% DMSO)	KOH	577(4.69)	1-3641-73
	C_2Cl_4	391(4.32)	1-3632-73
$C_{14}H_{12}N_4S$			
Ethanone, 1-(2-pyridinyl)-, 2-benzothia-zolylhydrazone, (E)-	EtOH	224(4.36),249(4.15), 335(4.37)	40-1314-73
(Z)-	EtOH	221(4.37),260(4.17), 355(4.30)	40-1314-73
$C_{14}H_{12}N_6$			
2,4-Pteridinediamine, 6-(2-phenylethen-yl)-	pH 1	244(4.06),306s(4.38), 386(4.10)	35-6413-73
$C_{14}H_{12}N_6O$			
2,4-Pteridinediamine, 6-(2-phenylethen-yl)-	0.12N HCl	280(4.19),323(4.49)	35-6413-73
$C_{14}H_{12}N_6O_6$			
2,4,6(1H,3H,5H)-Pyrimidinetrione, 5,5'-(phenylhydrazono)bis-	EtOH	280(3.72),370(3.77)	103-0247-73
$C_{14}H_{12}N_8$			
Formazan, 3,5-diphenyl-1-(1H-tetrazol-	pH 13	486(4.48)	103-1423-73
5-yl)- (also metal chelates)	EtOH	442(3.82)	103-1423-73
$C_{14}H_{12}O$			
Benzeneacetaldehyde, α-phenyl-	MeOH	254(3.80)	104-2119-73
Ethanone, 1,2-diphenyl-	MeOH	245(4.06)	104-2119-73
Naphthalene, 1-methyl-2-(2-propynyloxy)-	n.s.g.	230(4.24),297(4.02)	33-2981-73
Phenol, 2-(1-phenylethenyl)-	EtOH	281(3.53)	44-1993-73
Phenol, 2-(2-phenylethenyl)-, cis	MeOH	277(3.95),305(3.85)	35-4426-73
trans	MeOH	286(4.14),297(4.12), 317(4.10)	35-4426-73
$C_{14}H_{12}O_2$			
5-Acenaphthenecarboxylic acid, methyl ester	MeOH	239(4.47),316(3.90)	88-1803-73
1-Acenaphthylenecarboxylic acid, 1,2-dihydro-, methyl ester	EtOH	227(4.85),288(3.83)	44-3122-73
Benzaldehyde, 3-(hydroxyphenylmethyl)-	EtOH	213(4.40),251(4.09), 291(3.42)	23-3756-73
Benzaldehyde, 4-(hydroxyphenylmethyl)-	EtOH	213(4.23),259(4.21)	23-3756-73
2(3H)-Benzofuranone, 3-phenyl-	EtOH	272(3.18),279(3.15), 318(2.00)	44-1993-73
Ethanone, 1,1'-(1,6-naphthalenediyl)bis-	n.s.g.	227s(4.46),235(4.47), 260s(4.38),267(4.42), 291(3.72),343s(3.1)	39-1181-73C
Methanone, (4-methoxyphenyl)phenyl-	FSO_3H	295(3.90),380(4.54)	59-0807-73
at -75°	FSO_3H	295(4.00),370(4.52)	59-0807-73
at -75°	+ SbF_5	285(3.95),335(4.36)	59-0807-73
2-Propenoic acid, 2-methyl-, 2-naphtha-lenyl ester	dioxan	258(--),265(3.82), 274(--)	126-0025-73B
$C_{14}H_{12}O_2S$			
Benzeneacetic acid, 4-methyl-α-(2-thien-ylmethylene)-, cis	EtOH	240(3.81),270s(3.91), 305(4.16)	7-0055-73

Compound	Solvent	λ_{max}(log ϵ)	Ref.
Benzeneacetic acid, 4-methyl-α-(2-thienylmethylene)-, trans	EtOH	241(3.88),320(4.40), 340s(4.20)	7-0055-73
$C_{14}H_{12}O_3$			
Benzeneacetic acid, α-(2-furanylmethylene)-4-methyl-, (E)-	EtOH	230(3.91),305(4.26)	7-0779-73
(Z)-	EtOH	235(3.93),242(3.84), 316(4.36)	7-0779-73
2H-Furo[2,3-h]-1-benzopyran-2-one, 8,9-dihydro-8-(1-methylethenyl)-	EtOH	253(3.4),262(3.52), 328(4.15)	102-3010-73
as-Indaceno[4,5-c]furan-1,3-dione, 4,5,6,7,8,9-hexahydro-	MeCN	231(4.46),282(3.56), 326(3.58)	22-2121-73
Methanone, (2-hydroxy-4-methoxyphenyl)-phenyl-	MeOH	244(4.03),290(4.18), 329(3.98)	18-1498-73
Methanone, (4-hydroxy-3-methoxyphenyl)-phenyl-	EtOH	211(4.13),246(4.10), 286(3.89),318(3.97)	56-1949-73
$C_{14}H_{12}O_4$			
Butanedioic acid, 2-naphthalenyl-	EtOH	226(5.08),268(3.77), 276(3.78)	2-0131-73
7H-Furo[3,2-g][1]benzopyran-7-one, 6-ethyl-7-methoxy-	EtOH	238(4.34),245(4.32), 294(4.03),321(4.07)	40-0137-73
Methanone, (2,5-dihydroxy-4-methoxyphenyl)phenyl-	MeOH	255(4.18),292(4.00), 370(3.89)	18-1498-73
Methanone, (2,4-dihydroxyphenyl)(5-hydroxy-2-methylphenyl)-	MeOH	218(4.33),240s(3.99), 287(4.18),323(4.03)	24-1182-73
1H,3H-Naphtho[1,8-cd]pyran-1-one, 4,9-dimethoxy-	EtOH	218(4.52),232(4.72), 255(4.21),344(4.08)	44-1944-73
$C_{14}H_{12}O_5$			
1,3-Butanedione, 1-(4-hydroxy-6-methyl-2-oxo-2H-1-benzopyran-3-yl)-	EtOH	227(4.09),306(4.10), 332s(4.11),350(4.16), 360s(4.10)	39-1022-73C
Psoralen, 5-(2-hydroxyethyl)-8-methoxy-	MeOH	220(4.39),245s(4.27), 251(4.32),265(4.24), 306(4.10)	78-2645-73
$C_{14}H_{12}O_6$			
2H-Naphtho[2,3-b]pyran-5,10-dione, 3,4-dihydro-3,4,6-trihydroxy-2-methyl-	MeOH	240(4.08),287(4.00), 408(3.65)	33-0619-73
(cryptosporin)	MeOH-NaOH	225(4.43),290(4.02), 382(3.14)	33-0619-73
$C_{14}H_{12}O_6S$			
2,3-Furandicarboxylic acid, 4-acetyl-5-(2-thienyl)-, dimethyl ester	$CHCl_3$	285(4.15),320(4.38)	103-1307-73
$C_{14}H_{12}O_6Se$			
2,3-Furandicarboxylic acid, 4-acetyl-5-(selenophene-2ylcarbonyl)-, dimethyl ester	$CHCl_3$	286s(4.06),320(4.17)	103-1307-73
$C_{14}H_{12}O_8$			
4-Cyclopentene-1,3-dione, 2-(3,4-dimethoxy-2,5-dioxo-3-cyclopentne-1-ylidene)-4,5-dimethoxy-1,3-dioxo-	CH_2Cl_2	270(4.16),321s(3.92), 403(4.03)	78-0253-73
$C_{14}H_{12}S$			
Benzene, [(2-phenylethenyl)thio]-	HOAc	290(4.63)	78-3819-73
Methanethione, (2-methylphenyl)phenyl-	EtOH	319(--),600(2.07)	143-0427-73

Compound	Solvent	λmax(log ε)	Ref.
$C_{14}H_{13}$			
Ethylium, 1,1-diphenyl-	H_2SO_4	313(3.95),427(4.53)	59-0807-73
	FSO_3H at -75°	312(4.00),422(4.53)	59-0803-73 +59-0807-73
	+ SbF_5	312(4.04),422(4.57)	59-0807-73
	n.s.g.	315(3.88),427(4.57)	30-0932-73
$C_{14}H_{13}BrN_2O$			
Phenol, 4-bromo-2-[[[1-(4-pyridinyl)ethyl]imino]methyl]-, (S)-	MeOH	224(4.57),256(4.16), 328(3.61)	35-0811-73
$C_{14}H_{13}BrN_2O_2S$			
Thiazolo[3,2-a]pyridinium, 2,3-dihydro-5-methyl-2-(4-nitrophenyl)-, bromide	pH 1	208(4.33),253(4.19), 270s(--),328(4.08)	1-1749-73
	pH 13	223(4.13),270(4.02), 322(4.18),460(3.41)	1-1749-73
$C_{14}H_{13}BrN_2O_3$			
1H-Pyrazole-3-carboxylic acid, 5-acetyl-1-(4-bromophenyl)-, ethyl ester	C_6H_{12} or EtOH	236(4.43),266(4.21)	4-0015-73
$C_{14}H_{13}BrO_2$			
Methanone, (3-bromo-2,4,6-trimethylphenyl)(2-furanyl)-	n.s.g.	278(3.72)	39-2327-73C
$C_{14}H_{13}ClN_2O$			
4H-Indazol-4-one, 3-(4-chlorophenyl)-1,5,6,7-tetrahydro-1-methyl-	MeOH	231(4.38),265(4.08)	24-0450-73
$C_{14}H_{13}ClN_2OS$			
Ethanone, 2-[(3-amino-6-chloro-2-pyridinyl)thio]-1-(2-methylphenyl)-	EtOH	252(4.17),325(3.79)	103-1145-73
1H-Pyrido[2,3-b][1,4]thiazin-2-ol, 6-chloro-2,3-dihydro-2-(2-methylphenyl)-	EtOH	235(4.14),268(4.13), 322(3.63)	103-1145-73
$C_{14}H_{13}ClN_2O_2$			
Benzenemethanol, α-[[(4-chlorophenyl)-nitrosoamino]methyl]-	isoPrOH	217s(4.22),276(3.89), 301s(3.72)	4-0883-73
1H-Pyrrole-3-carboxaldehyde, 2-chloro-4,5-dihydro-1-methyl-4-[(methylphenylamino)methylene]-5-oxo-	C_6H_{12}	315(4.0),430(3.9)	103-0467-73
	EtOH	230(4.2),278(4.1), 385(4.3)	103-0467-73
$C_{14}H_{13}ClN_2O_3$			
1H-Pyrrole-3-carboxylic acid, 5-acetyl-1-(4-chlorophenyl)-, ethyl ester	C_6H_{12} or EtOH	226(4.34),268(3.93)	4-0015-73
$C_{14}H_{13}ClN_2O_5$			
Benzo[h]quinolizinium, 11-amino-8-methoxy-, perchlorate	EtOH	250(4.77),266(4.76), 305s(--),342s(--), 420(4.75)	44-4167-73
$C_{14}H_{13}ClO_3S$			
3-Thiophenecarboxylic acid, 5-[(2-chlorophenyl)methylene]tetrahydro-4-oxo-, ethyl ester	EtOH	214(4.10),236(3.90), 351(4.41)	133-0157-73
3-Thiophenecarboxylic acid, 5-[(4-chlorophenyl)methylene]tetrahydro-4-oxo-, ethyl ester	EtOH	211(4.05),239(4.04), 351(4.46),368(4.44)	133-0157-73

Compound	Solvent	$\lambda_{max}(\log \epsilon)$	Ref.
$C_{14}H_{13}ClO_6$			
Benzofuro[3,2-c]pyrylium, 1-ethyl-3-methyl-, perchlorate	n.s.g.	254(4.25),265(4.22), 313(3.65)	103-0416-73
$C_{14}H_{13}Cl_2NO_2$			
2-Propenoic acid, 2-chloro-3-(5-chloro-3-methyl-1H-indol-2-yl)-, ethyl ester	isoPrOH	262(3.99),356(4.52)	44-3077-73
2-Propenoic acid, 3-(3,5-dichloro-3-methyl-3H-indol-2-yl)-, ethyl ester, (E)-	isoPrOH	271(4.11)	44-3077-73
$C_{14}H_{13}Cl_2N_5O_2S$			
1H-Benzimidazolium, 2-[[chloro(5-nitro-2-pyridinyl)amino]thio]-1,3-dimethyl-, chloride	98% H_2SO_4	301(4.28)	104-2622-73
$C_{14}H_{13}FN_2$			
1H-Pyrrole-2-carbonitrile, 4-fluoro-5-(2,4,6-trimethylphenyl)-	MeOH	250(3.86)	24-3544-73
$C_{14}H_{13}N$			
3H-Benz[e]indole, 2,3-dimethyl-	EtOH	231(4.50),258(4.45), 266(4.34),316(3.90), 322(3.92),335(3.79)	33-0478-73
9H-Carbazole, 4,5-dimethyl-	EtOH	221(4.29),245(4.51), 253(4.38),293(4.07), 330(3.45),343(3.51)	39-2818-73C
$C_{14}H_{13}NO$			
3H-3-Benzazonine, 3-acetyl-	hexane	230(4.17),275s(3.80)	88-3805-73
Benzofuro[3,2-c]pyridine, 1-ethyl-3-methyl-	n.s.g.	255(4.60),280(4.44), 289(4.38),302(4.43)	103-0416-73
Benzophenone oxime, N-methyl deriv.	n.s.g.	307(4.13)	32-0681-73
3-Buten-2-one, 4-(1-naphthalenyl)-, oxime	MeOH	315(4.2)	83-0813-73
isomer	MeOH	319(4.3)	83-0813-73
3-Buten-2-one, 4-(2-naphthalenyl)-, oxime	MeOH	265(4.3),270(4.3), 302(4.3),315(4.3)	83-0813-73
isomer	MeOH	265(4.3),275(4.3), 310(4.3)	83-0813-73
6H-Dibenz[b,f][1,4]oxazocine, 11,12-dihydro-	EtOH	267(3.16),273(3.16), 283s(2.77)	95-0982-73
Phenol, 2-[1-(phenylimino)ethyl]-, BF_2 chelate	$C_2H_4Cl_2$	253(4.1)	24-2427-73
$C_{14}H_{13}NOS$			
2,5-Cyclohexadiene-1,4-dione, 2,6-dimethyl-, 4-(S-phenylthiooxime)	$CHCl_3$	280(4.08),345(3.45), 443(4.30)	39-1031-73C
3,5-Cyclohexadiene-1,2-dione, 3,5-dimethyl-, 1-(S-phenylthiooxime)	CH_2Cl_2	270(3.77),410(3.96), 465(4.06)	39-1031-73C
Sulfilimine, N-acetyl-S,S-diphenyl-	EtOH	226s(4.23)	44-4324-73
Sulfilimine, N-benzoyl-S-methyl-S-phenyl-	EtOH	229(4.11),253(3.99)	44-4324-73
$C_{14}H_{13}NO_2$			
1H-Isoindole-1,3(2H)-dione, 3a,4,7,7a-tetrahydro-2-phenyl-, (1R,2R,3R)-	EtOH	217(3.96)	104-2317-73
(1R,2S,3S)-	EtOH	218(3.96)	104-2317-73
2(1H)-Pyrimidinone, 3-acetyl-1-(phenylmethyl)-	EtOH	242(3.65),353(3.88)	103-0615-73

Compound	Solvent	λ_{max}(log ε)	Ref.
$C_{14}H_{13}NO_2S$			
Benzene, 1-methyl-2-[(4-methylphenyl)-thio]-5-nitro-	DMF	347(4.07)	32-0723-73
Benzene, 1-methyl-3-[(4-methylphenyl)-thio]-6-nitro-	DMF	340(4.02)	32-0723-73
Benzene, 4-methyl-1-[(4-methylphenyl)-thio]-2-nitro-	DMF	385(3.653)	39-1430-73B
5H-Dibenz[b,g][1,5]thiazocine, 6,7-di-hydro-, 12,12-dioxide	EtOH	247(4.16),273(3.38), 281(3.34)	95-0997-73
$C_{14}H_{13}NO_3$			
Benzamide, N-hydroxy-3-methoxy-N-phenyl-	EtOH	275(3.99)	112-0547-73
Furo[2,3-b]quinoline, 6,7-dimethoxy-4-methyl-	EtOH	246(4.74),330(4.26), 345(4.24)	49-0633-73
Furo[2,3-b]quinoline, 7,8-dimethoxy-4-methyl-	EtOH	223(4.48),251(4.79), 340(4.03)	49-0633-73
Furo[3,2-c]quinoline-4-carboxaldehyde, 2,3-dihydro-6-methoxy-2-methyl-	ether	259(4.60),303(3.63), 315(3.46),367(3.74), 385(3.66)	24-0355-73
1H-Indene-2-pentanenitrile, 2,3-dihydro-5-hydroxy-γ,1-dioxo-	MeOH	225(4.12),270(4.12), 292s(4.07),296(4.07)	24-1303-73
Nor-γ-fagarine, O-ethyl-	MeOH	243(4.64),260(3.70), 270(3.44),298(3.55), 311(3.64),325(3.61), 338(3.58)	78-1217-73
	acid	249(4.64),270s(3.44), 280s(3.34),300(3.34), 315(3.47),342(3.60)	78-1217-73
Spiro[1,3-dioxolane-2,1'(5'H)-pyrrolo-[1,2-b]isoquinolin]-5'-one, 2',3'-dihydro-	EtOH	226(4.25),249(3.86), 291(3.98),325(3.68), 338s(3.54)	78-0213-73
$C_{14}H_{13}NO_3S$			
Benzene, 1-methoxy-4-[(4-methylphenyl)-thio]-3-nitro-	DMF	406(3.606)	39-1430-73B
$C_{14}H_{13}NO_4$			
Furo[2,3-b]quinoline, 4,6,8-trimethoxy-	EtOH	247(4.76),283s(3.78), 293(3.83),305(3.72), 337(3.43),353(3.42)	18-0577-73
Isomaculosidine	MeOH	249(4.29),262s(4.07), 290(3.36),330s(3.50), 345(3.69),360(3.69)	78-1217-73
	MeOH-acid	256(4.37),306s(3.42), 317(3.52),347s(3.46), 360(3.42)	78-1217-73
Phenol, 2-[(2-hydroxy-5-methylphenyl)-methyl]-4-nitro-	neutral	280(3.75),325(3.95)	49-1315-73
	anion	277(3.72),402(4.18)	49-1315-73
	dianion	297(3.71),416(4.26)	49-1315-73
1H-Pyrano[3,4-b]quinoline-1,5(3H)-dione, 4,10-dihydro-9-methoxy-3-methyl-	MeOH	256(4.48),364(3.93)	24-0355-73
1H-Pyrrole-3-carboxylic acid, 4-(4-meth-oxybenzoyl)-, methyl ester	EtOH	218(3.93),283(3.95)	23-1089-73
$C_{14}H_{13}NO_4S$			
Spiro[2H-indene-2,2'-thiazolidine]-4'-carboxylic acid, 1,3-dihydro-5,5'-di-methyl-1,3-dioxo-	MeOH	232(4.48),246s(4.18)	78-4271-73
Spiro[2H-indene-2,2'-thiazolidine]-4'-carboxylic acid, 1,3-dihydro-3'-meth-yl-1,3-dioxo-, methyl ester	MeOH	235(4.76),250s(4.44), 287(3.68)	78-4271-73

Compound	Solvent	λ max(log ε)	Ref.
$C_{14}H_{13}NO_5$			
1H-Pyrrole-3,4-dicarboxylic acid, 1-[(phenylmethoxy)methyl]-	EtOH	257(3.87)	23-1089-73
$C_{14}H_{13}NO_6$			
7H-Cyclohepta[b]pyridine-6,8-dicarboxylic acid, 5,9-dihydroxy-, dimethyl ester	EtOH	203(4.20),233s(--), 238(4.17),280(4.36), 322s(--)	39-0026-73C
$C_{14}H_{13}NO_6S$			
Acridizinium, 11-hydroxy-8-methoxy-, bisulfate	EtOH	245(4.82),262s(--), 286(4.79),302(4.78), 334(4.76),418(4.80)	44-4167-73
$C_{14}H_{13}NS$			
Benzothiazole, 2-(1,3,5-heptatrienyl)-, (E,E,E)-	CH_2Cl_2	352(4.71)	54-0683-73
$C_{14}H_{13}N_2O$			
Benzo[h]quinolizinium, 11-amino-8-methoxy-, perchlorate	EtOH	250(4.77),266(4.76), 305s(--),342s(--), 420(4.75)	44-4167-73
$C_{14}H_{13}N_2O_2S$			
Thiazolo[3,2-a]pyridinium, 2,3-dihydro-5-methyl-2-(4-nitrophenyl)-, bromide	pH 1	208(4.33),253(4.19), 270s(--),328(4.08)	1-1749-73
	pH 13	223(4.13),270(4.02), 322(4.18),460(3.41)	1-1749-73
$C_{14}H_{13}N_3$			
2H-Indazol-2-amine, N-(3-methylphenyl)-	EtOH	278(4.01)	118-0363-73
2H-Indazol-2-amine, N-(4-methylphenyl)-	EtOH	278(3.92)	118-0363-73
Propanedinitrile, [3-(methylamino)-3-(4-methylphenyl)-2-propenylidene]-	CH_2Cl_2	262(4.15),322s(3.28), 409(3.92)	97-0342-73
$C_{14}H_{13}N_3OS$			
Acetamide, N-(3-methyl-1-phenyl-1H-thieno[2,3-c]pyrazol-4-yl)-	EtOH	290(4.24)	104-2429-73
$C_{14}H_{13}N_3OS_3$			
4-Thiazolidinone, 3-ethyl-5-[(7-methyl-5H-thiazolo[3,2-a]pyrimidin-5-ylidene)ethylidene]-2-thioxo-	n.s.g.	520(4.81),544(4.94)	124-1151-73
$C_{14}H_{13}N_3O_2$			
Ethanediamide, N-(4-aminophenyl)-N'-phenyl-	dioxan	250(3.97),302(4.14)	30-0001-73
Ethanediamide, N-(phenylmethyl)-N'-(3-pyridinyl)-	EtOH	255(4.1)	103-0621-73
Hydrazinecarboxamide, N-benzoyl-2-phenyl-	MeOH	234(4.53),278(3.93)	104-1200-73
2,4(1H,3H)-Pyrimidinedione, 1-(1H-indol-3-ylmethyl)-5-phenyl- (in 35% ethanol)	pH 6.5	217(4.62),275(4.18), 287s(4.05)	19-0257-73
	pH 13	273(4.12),287s(3.96)	19-0257-73
2,4(1H,3H)-Pyrimidinedione, 5-(1(2H)-quinolinylmethyl)-	EtOH	231(4.49),262(3.89), 351(3.40)	69-2879-73
Pyrimido[4,5-c]isoquinoline, 7,9-dimethoxy-6-methyl-	EtOH	240(4.48),271(4.17), 285s(--),328(3.63)	95-0330-73

Compound	Solvent	$\lambda_{max}(\log \epsilon)$	Ref.
$C_{14}H_{13}N_3O_3$			
Phenol, 3-ethyl-4-[(2-nitrophenyl)azo]-	C_2Cl_4	364(4.33),444(3.56)	1-3632-73
Phenol, 3-ethyl-4-[(4-nitrophenyl)azo]-	C_2Cl_4	378(4.60)	1-3632-73
Pyrimido[1,2-a]benzimidazole-3-carboxylic acid, 1,4-dihydro-1-methyl-4-oxo-, ethyl ester	MeOH	228(4.40),240(4.37), 329(4.00)	39-1588-73C
Pyrimido[1,2-a]benzimidazole-3-carboxylic acid, 4,10-dihydro-10-methyl-4-oxo-, ethyl ester	MeOH	217(4.45),240(4.19), 267(3.68),276(3.64), 326(4.33),343(4.31)	39-1588-73C
$C_{14}H_{13}N_3O_5$			
1H-Pyrazole-3-carboxylic acid, 5-acetyl-1-(4-nitrophenyl)-	C_6H_{12} or EtOH	215(3.79),285(3.44)	4-0015-73
$C_{14}H_{13}N_3O_6Si$			
Methane, [(methyldiphenylsilyl)-aci-nitro]dinitro-	CH_2Cl_2	305(3.57)(changing)	70-0212-73
$C_{14}H_{13}N_3O_7$			
Pyridinium, 1-ethyl-, 3,5-dinitrosalicylate	EtOH	258(4.04),340(4.10)	39-2949-73C
$C_{14}H_{13}N_3O_8$			
1H-Indole-3-carboxylic acid, 5-acetoxy-2-methyl-4,6-dinitro-, ethyl ester	MeOH or $CHCl_3$	263(4.10),340(3.81)	103-1490-73
$C_{14}H_{13}N_5O$			
Benzamide, 4-methyl-N-(9-methyl-9H-purin-6-yl)-	MeOH	282(4.19)	18-3228-73
4(1H)-Pteridinone, 2-amino-6-(2-phenylethyl)-	pH 13	254(4.36),363(3.81)	44-2073-73
4(1H)-Pteridinone, 2-amino-7-(2-phenylethyl)-	pH 13	252(4.32),357(3.94)	44-2073-73
$C_{14}H_{13}OP$			
1H-Isophosphindole, 2,3-dihydro-2-phenyl-, 2-oxide	EtOH	222(3.66),266(2.81)	139-0225-73B
$C_{14}H_{13}O_2$			
Benzofuro[3,2-c]pyrylium, 1-ethyl-3-methyl-, perchlorate	n.s.g.	254(4.25),265(4.22), 313(3.65)	103-0416-73
$C_{14}H_{14}$			
Azulene, 1-(1-butenyl)-	n.s.g.	235(4.28),284(4.60), 371(3.87),391(3.86), 620s(2.46),640(2.48), 661s(2.41),700s(2.30), 796(1.74)	5-0166-73
Azulene, 1-(2-methyl-1-propenyl)-	C_6H_{12}	626(2.31)	5-0166-73
1,1'-Biphenyl, 4,4'-dimethyl-	heptane	254.8(4.33)	101-0353-73C
1,1'-Biphenyl, 2-ethyl-	EtOH	233(4.02)	22-1517-73
	EtOH	227(3.91)	35-5288-73
2,3,9,10-Dodecatetraene-5,7-diyne, 2,11-dimethyl-	n.s.g.	223(4.63),276(4.07), 290(4.18),313(4.03)	70-1029-73
4,6,8,10-Tetradecatetraene-2,12-diyne, (3E,5Z,7Z,9E)-	hexane	310s(4.45),324(4.77), 340(4.99),359(4.95)	5-1339-73
all trans	hexane	313(4.40),327(4.76), 343(5.00),362(5.05)	5-1339-73

Compound	Solvent	λmax(log ε)	Ref.
$C_{14}H_{14}BBrO_6$			
Boron, bis(acetato-O)[1-(4-bromophenyl)-1,3-butanedionato-O,O']-, (T-4)-	CH_2Cl_2	340(4.96)	39-1796-73B
$C_{14}H_{14}BNO_8$			
Boron, bis(acetato-O)[1-(4-nitrophenyl)-1,3-butanedionato]-, (T-4)-	CH_2Cl_2	330(4.22)	39-1796-73B
$C_{14}H_{14}BrNS$			
Thiazolo[3,2-a]pyridinium, 2,3-dihydro-5-methyl-2-phenyl-, bromide	pH 1	209(4.30),249(3.97), 330(3.90)	1-1749-73
	pH 13	224(3.74),249(4.08), 330(3.99)	1-1749-73
$C_{14}H_{14}BrN_3$			
Benzenamine, 2-bromo-3,4-dimethyl-6-(phenylazo)-	EtOH	328(4.01),450(3.74)	65-1574-73
$C_{14}H_{14}ClNO_2$			
Morpholine, 4-[5-(4-chlorophenyl)-2-furanyl]-	EtOH	224(4.04),330(4.34)	39-2523-73C
2-Propenoic acid, 3-(5-chloro-3-methyl-1H-indol-2-yl)-, ethyl ester, trans	isoPrOH	239(4.09),254(4.05), 345(4.52)	44-3077-73
Unknown compd. 11b	EtOH	274(4.30)	18-2504-73
$C_{14}H_{14}ClN_3$			
Benzenamine, 4-[(4-chlorophenyl)azo]-N,N-dimethyl-	C_6H_{12}	410(4.53)	18-0194-73
	50% EtOH-acid	325(4.11),520(4.52)	18-0194-73 +18-3139-73
$C_{14}H_{14}ClN_3O$			
Cyclohexanecarbonitrile, 1-[(4-chlorobenzoyl)azo]-	C_6H_{12}	259(4.11),415(1.76)	23-1378-73
3-Pyridinecarboxamide, 6-(4-chlorophenyl)-1-ethyl-1,2-dihydro-2-imino-	CH_2Cl_2	250(3.85),380(4.10)	97-0342-73
$C_{14}H_{14}FNO_4$			
1H-Pyrrole-2-carboxylic acid, 5-(2,4-dimethoxyphenyl)-4-fluoro-, methyl ester	MeOH	223s(--),298(3.97)	24-3544-73
1H-Pyrrole-2-carboxylic acid, 5-(2,5-dimethoxyphenyl)-4-fluoro-, methyl ester	MeOH	223s(--),285(3.83), 310(3.86)	24-3544-73
$C_{14}H_{14}F_2O_3$			
7bH-Cyclopropa[a]naphthalen-7b-ol, 1,1-difluoro-1,1a,2,3-tetrahydro-4-methoxy-, acetate	n.s.g.	274(3.27)	35-6655-73
7bH-Cyclopropa[a]naphthalen-7b-ol, 1,1-difluoro-1,1a,2,3-tetrahydro-5-methoxy-, acetate	n.s.g.	232(4.05),278(3.27)	35-6655-73
$C_{14}H_{14}N$			
6H-Pyrido[2,1-a]isoindolium, 1,3-dimethyl-, chloride	H_2O	253(4.04),257(4.08), 310(4.15)	44-2351-73
$C_{14}H_{14}NO_3$			
Pyrylium, 2-amino-3-(ethoxycarbonyl)-6-phenyl-, perchlorate	HOAc	260(4.08),383(4.30)	97-0132-73

Compound	Solvent	λmax(log ε)	Ref.
$C_{14}H_{14}N_2$			
Acetophenone, phenylhydrazone	MeOH	232(4.11),302(4.14), 330(4.30)	80-0723-73
Benzaldehyde, (phenylmethylhydrazone)	EtOH	250(4.26),310(3.86), 345(4.44)	118-0159B-73
1H-Indazole, 6,7-dihydro-1-methyl-	MeOH	205(4.54),245(4.17), 264(4.16)	24-3432-73
2,7-Phenanthrolinium, N,N'-dimethyl-, bis(tetrafluoroborate)	MeCN	214(4.45),240(4.57), 280(4.01),300(3.92), 318(3.83),333(4.16), 350(4.28)	5-0339-73
2,8-Phenanthrolinium, N,N'-dimethyl-, bis(tetrafluoroborate)	MeCN	222(4.25),245(4.34), 253s(4.39),262(4.48), 276(4.14),310(4.11), 342(3.81),350(3.39)	5-0339-73
2,9-Phenanthrolinium, N,N'-dimethyl-, bis(tetrafluoroborate)	MeCN	230(4.53),248(4.72), 303(4.15),312(4.19), 327(3.78),343(3.39)	5-0339-73
3,7-Phenanthrolinium, N,N'-dimethyl-, bis(tetrafluoroborate)	MeCN	215(4.41),258(4.20), 312(4.66)	5-0339-73
3,8-Phenanthrolinium, N,N'-dimethyl-, bis(tetrafluoroborate)	MeCN	214(4.21),248(4.80), 270(4.06),286(3.98), 353s(3.85),368(3.71), 387(3.79)	5-0339-73
4,7-Phenanthrolinium, N,N'-dimethyl-, bis(tetrafluoroborate)	MeCN	228(4.47),237(4.33), 287(4.33),306)4.18), 318(4.18)	5-0339-73
$C_{14}H_{14}N_2O$			
4H-Indazol-4-one, 1,5,6,7-tetrahydro-1-methyl-3-phenyl-	MeOH	226(4.33),259(4.01)	24-0450-73
Phenol, 3-methyl-2-[(2-methylphenyl)-azo]-	EtOH	240(3.93),335(4.32), 395s(4.00)	23-3827-73
Phenol, 2-[[[1-(2-pyridinyl)ethyl]-imino]methyl]-, (S)-	MeOH	214(4.88),256(4.69), 319(4.08)	35-0811-73
$C_{14}H_{14}N_2OS$			
Propanenitrile, 3-(6-methoxy-4-methyl-quinolin-2-yl)thio-	EtOH	215(4.48),260(4.34), 350(3.67)	103-0481-73
$C_{14}H_{14}N_2OS_3$			
4-Thiazolidinone, 3-methyl-5-[3-(phenyl-methyl)-2-thiazolidinylidene)-2-thioxo-	EtOH	279(4.19),395(4.55)	94-1431-73
$C_{14}H_{14}N_2O_2$			
Acetamide, N,N'-1,2-azulenylenebis-	MeOH	242(4.25),297(4.81), 345s(3.63),360(3.79), 380(3.81),395s(3.32), 560(2.50)	18-3266-73
1H-1,4-Benzodiazepine-5-carboxaldehyde, 2,3-dihydro-1-methyl-2-oxo-3-(2-prop-enyl)-	isoPrOH	234(4.30),275s(3.45), 324(3.07)	44-3502-73
Isoxazole, 4,5-dihydro-5-[(3-methyl-5-isoxazolyl)methyl]-3-phenyl-	n.s.g.	213(4.37),262(4.17)	32-0037-73
Isoxazole, 4,5-dihydro-3-methyl-5-[(3-phenyl-5-isoxazolyl)methyl]-	n.s.g.	208(4.30),241(4.23)	32-0037-73
Pyridine, 1,4-dihydro-1-methyl-4-[1-(4-nitrophenyl)ethylidene]-	dioxan	273(4.06)	48-0901-73
perchlorate	dioxan	214(4.14),259s(4.11), 265(4.13),274(4.08)	48-0901-73

Compound	Solvent	$\lambda_{max}(\log \epsilon)$	Ref.
Pyridine, 1-ethyl-1,4-dihydro-4-[(4-nitrophenyl)methylene]-	dioxan	238(3.92),281(3.81), 324(3.91),524(4.54)	48-0901-73
3-Pyridinecarboxylic acid, 2-amino-4-phenyl-, ethyl ester	MeOH	246(4.23),334(3.67)	48-0679-73
Pyrimido[2,1-a]isoindol-2(6H)-one, 3-(2-hydroxyethyl)-4-methyl-	MeOH	245(4.57),277(3.96), 287(3.94)	5-0103-73
Pyrimido[2,1-a]isoindol-4(6H)-one, 3-(2-hydroxyethyl)-2-methyl-	MeOH	243(4.06),300(4.13)	5-0103-73
$C_{14}H_{14}N_2O_2S$			
Benzeneacetamide, N-(8-oxo-5-thia-1-azabicyclo[4.2.0]oct-2-en-7-yl)-, (6R-trans)-	EtOH	255(3.88)	39-1187-73C
$C_{14}H_{14}N_2O_3$			
1-Azulenecarboxylic acid, 2-amino-3-(formylamino)-, ethyl ester	MeOH	242(3.94),316(4.46), 355(3.62)	18-3161-73
Glycine, N-(N-1-naphthalenylglycyl)-	EtOH	246(4.29),329(3.85)	94-2349-73
2,4(1H,3H)-Pyrimidinedione, 5-methyl-3-(3-oxo-3-phenylpropyl)- (spectra in 10% ethanol)	pH 6.5	252(4.18),270s(4.07)	19-0257-73
	pH 13	249(4.16)	19-0257-73
$C_{14}H_{14}N_2O_3S$			
1,3(2H,4H)-Isoquinolinedione, 4-(mercapto-4-morpholinylmethylene)-	EtOH	224(3.35),290(3.29), 358(2.58)	95-0322-73
Pyridinium, 2-methyl-, 3-indolesulfonate	EtOH	258(3.85),264(3.88), 280(3.81),287(3.74)	78-0669-73
$C_{14}H_{14}N_2O_4$			
2H-1-Benzopyran-2-one, 3-nitro-4-piperidino-	EtOH	280(4.15),312(3.96), 380s(3.30)	103-0816-73
1-Isoquinolinecarbonitrile, 4,5,6,7-tetramethoxy-	EtOH	260(4.57),303(3.73), 314(3.75),353(3.85)	44-0060-73
2,5-Piperazinedione, 1-acetyl-3-[(4-methoxyphenyl)methylene]-	EtOH	230(4.20),334(4.32)	88-1135-73
2-Propenoic acid, 3-(1-methyl-1H-indol-3-yl)-2-nitro-, ethyl ester	EtOH-pH 7	360(4.06),410(4.11)	104-1082-73
Pyridine, 2-[(4-methoxyphenyl)methoxy]-4-methyl-5-nitro-	EtOH	282(3.99)	44-1824-73
$C_{14}H_{14}N_2O_4S$			
Benzeneacetamide, N-(8-oxo-5-thia-1-azabicyclo[4.2.0]oct-2-en-7-yl)-, S,S-dioxide, (6R-trans)-	EtOH	241(3.91)	39-1187-73C
2H-Pyrrole-3-carboxylic acid, 4-(methylthio)-2-oxo-5-[(phenylmethoxy)amino]-, methyl ester	EtOH	364(4.23)	94-1667-73
$C_{14}H_{14}N_2O_5$			
6H-Pyrido[1,2-a]pyrimidine-8,9-dicarboxylic acid, 2,4-dimethyl-6-oxo-, dimethyl ester	MeOH	237(4.16),268s(4.08), 407(3.82)	44-3485-73
$C_{14}H_{14}N_3$			
Pyridinium, 2-amino-3-cyano-1-methyl-6-(4-methylphenyl)-, perchlorate	HOAc	253(4.02),279(3.50), 347(4.23)	97-0342-73
$C_{14}H_{14}N_4$			
1,2,3,4-Tetrazine, 1,4,5,6-tetrahydro-1,4-diphenyl-	CH_2Cl_2	249(3.92),324(4.33)	24-3097-73

Compound	Solvent	$\lambda_{max}(\log \epsilon)$	Ref.
$C_{14}H_{14}N_4O_2$			
Benzenamine, N,N-dimethyl-4-[(4-nitrophenyl)azo]-	EtOH	480(4.52)	103-0850-73
	EtOH-HCl	510(4.81)	103-0850-73
Benzenecarboximidic acid, N-methyl-, 2-(2-nitrophenyl)hydrazide	MeOH	259(4.36),288s(4.03), 500(3.81)	24-2530-73
Ethanediamide, N,N'-bis(4-aminophenyl)-	dioxan	237s(4.09),317(4.35)	30-0001-73
1H-Isoindole-1,3(2H)-dione, 4-amino-2-[(3,5-dimethyl-1H-pyrazol-4-yl)-methyl]-	EtOH	250s(4.29),259(4.33), 306(3.68),378(3.60)	87-0512-73
$C_{14}H_{14}N_4O_2S$			
[1,2,4]Triazino[5,6-d][3,1]benzoxazepine, 7-acetyl-6,7-dihydro-6-methyl-3-(methylthio)-	EtOH	221(4.26),238(4.36), 376(4.10)	78-0639-73
[1,2,4]Triazino[5,6-d][3,1]benzoxazepine-7(6H)-carboxaldehyde, 6,6-dimethyl-3-(methylthio)-	dioxan	237(4.40),250s(4.08), 380(4.20)	78-0639-73
$C_{14}H_{14}N_4O_3S$			
[1,2,4]Triazino[5,6-d][3,1]benzoxazepine-6-carboxylic acid, 6,7-dihydro-6-methyl-3-(methylthio)-, methyl ester	EtOH	238(4.40),351(3.98), 434(3.86)	78-0639-73
$C_{14}H_{14}N_4O_6$			
Benzoic acid, 3-methoxy-, (5-acetoxy-tetrahydro-4,6-dioxo-2(1H)-pyrimidinylidene)hydrazide	EtOH	225(4.19)	103-0247-73
$C_{14}H_{14}N_4S$			
1H-Thieno[2,3-c]pyrazole-5-carboxaldehyde, 1,3-dimethyl-, phenylhydrazone	EtOH	259(4.0),302(3.8), 363(4.4)	104-2216-73
$C_{14}H_{14}N_5O_2$			
1H-Purinium, 2-amino-6,9-dihydro-9-methyl-6-oxo-7-(2-oxo-2-phenylethyl)-, chloride	pH 4	251(4.41),281(3.99)	24-1389-73
	pH 10	221(4.30),248(4.33), 282(3.95)	24-1389-73
$C_{14}H_{14}N_6O$			
Urea, N-(2-phenylethyl)-N'-1H-purin-6-yl)-	pH 1-2	277(4.30)	87-0139-73
	pH 5-7	268(4.25)	87-0139-73
	pH 12	277(4.26)	87-0139-73
$C_{14}H_{14}N_6O_3$			
1,2-Ethanediol, 1-(2,4-diamino-6-pteridinyl)-2-phenyl-, N-oxide, (R*,S*)-(±)-	pH 1	255(4.49),280(4.06), 357(3.90),370(3.84)	35-6413-73
$C_{14}H_{14}N_8O_{10}$			
Ethanedioic acid, bis[2-(5-acetoxy-1,4,5,6-tetrahydro-4,6-dioxo-2-pyrimidinyl)hydrazide]	EtOH	248(4.50)	103-0247-73
$C_{14}H_{14}O$			
[1,1'-Biphenyl]-3-ol, 2,6-dimethyl-	EtOH	284(3.45)	104-2172-73
1H-Cyclopenta[2,3]cyclopropa[1,2-a]naphthalen-1-one, 2,3,4,5,9b,9c-hexahydro-	EtOH	235(4.07)	78-0309-73
1,4-Methano-1H-cyclopropa[a]heptalen-10-one, 1a,4,4a,5,9a,9b-hexahydro-	MeOH	237(3.64),293(2.40)	88-2737-73
isomer VII	MeOH	255(3.40),297(1.93)	88-2737-73
isomer VIII	MeOH	231(3.80),250s(3.64), 330(2.11)	88-2737-73

Compound	Solvent	$\lambda_{max}(\log \epsilon)$	Ref.
1,4-Methano-1H-cyclopropa[a]heptalen-10-one, 1a,4,4a,5,9a,9b-hexahydro-, isomer IXa	MeOH	232(4.00),255(3.69),265(3.59),290(3.26),340(2.11)	88-2737-73
isomer X	MeOH	280(1.78)	88-2737-73
2(1H)-Naphthalenone, 1-methyl-1-(2-propenyl)-	EtOH	245(4.08),307(4.00)	33-0014-73
Naphth[1,8-de]oxocin, 1,2,4,5-tetrahydro-	n.s.g.	224s(4.78),228(3.93),245s(3.15),265s(3.59),273(3.78),288(3.82),291(3.71),296(3.71),304(4.04),309(2.75),314(2.75),318(2.66)	35-2940-73
Phenol, 2-(1-phenylethyl)-	EtOH	275.5(3.43)	44-1993-73
$C_{14}H_{14}O_2$			
4-Azuleneethanol, acetate	C_6H_{12}	242(3.76),279(4.04),284(4.03),330(3.90),342(4.02),350(3.53),555(2.45),573(2.57),594(2.53),622(2.53),684(2.30)	44-1106-73
1H-Benz[e]indene-3,5(2H,4H)-dione, 3a,9b-dihydro-3a-methyl-, trans	EtOH	253(3.54),298(3.38)	104-0835-73
2-Butenoic acid, 4-(2,3-dihydro-1H-inden-1-ylidene)-, methyl ester	EtOH	243(3.95),250(3.92),338(4.04)	44-1439-73
Ethanone, 1-[2-methyl-5-(4-methylphenyl)-3-furanyl]-	EtOH	221s(4.25),281(4.35)	22-1760-73
Ethanone, 1-[5-methyl-2-(4-methylphenyl)-3-furanyl]-	EtOH	223(4.19),254s(3.99),317(3.96)	22-1760-73
1,4-Ethenocyclonona[c]pyran-3(1H)-one, 4,4a,9,11a-tetrahydro-	hexane	218s(3.70)	88-3103-73
1,8-Nonadiene-4,6-diyn-3-one, 9-(tetrahydro-2H-pyran-2-yl)-, (E)-	n.s.g.	206(4.38),238(4.36),251(4.28),267(3.83),284(3.87),303(3.94),320(3.90)	39-0145-73C
$C_{14}H_{14}O_2S$			
1,3,5,7-Tridecatetraene-9,11-diyne, 7-(methylsulfonyl)-	ether	253(4.02),265(4.16),278(4.17),354(4.10)	24-3621-73
$C_{14}H_{14}O_3$			
Benzene, 1,1'-[oxybis(methyleneoxy]bis-	C_6H_{12}	261(3.23),268(3.45),275(3.36)	80-0883-73
Ethanone, 1-[2-(4-methoxyphenyl)-5-methyl-3-furanyl]-	EtOH	223(4.14),240(3.94),327(3.99)	22-1760-73
Ethanone, 1-[5-(4-methoxyphenyl)-2-methyl-3-furanyl]-	EtOH	284(4.34)	22-1760-73
2-Furanpropanoic acid, 5-(4-methylphenyl)-	EtOH	288(4.25)	2-0301-73
as-Indaceno[4,5-c]furan-1,3-dione, 3b,4,5,6,7,8,9,9a-octahydro-	MeOH	255(3.42)	22-2121-73
5,8-Methano-9H-benzocyclohepten-9-one, 5,8-dihydro-1,4-dimethoxy-	C_6H_{12}	216(4.27),263(3.35),340(3.62),350(3.56)	39-1840-73C
5,9-Methano-6H-benzocyclohepten-6-one, 5,9-dihydro-1,4-dimethoxy- (data include non-maxima)	C_6H_{12}	230(4.12),240(3.37),250(3.06),260(2.96),270(2.84),280(2.69),290(2.98),300(3.26),315(3.45),320(3.43),330(3.29),340(2.98),350(2.63),356(2.69),	39-1840-73C

Compound	Solvent	λmax(log ε)	Ref.
5,9-Methano-6H-benzocyclohepten-6-one, 5,9-dihydro-1,4-dimethoxy- (cont.)	C_6H_{12}	366(2.47),372(2.51), 380(2.29)	39-1840-73C
	EtOH	265s(3.2),325(3.4)	39-1840-73C
4H-Pyran-4-one, 2-ethoxy-6-methyl-3-phenyl-	EtOH	260(4.00)	94-1047-73
$C_{14}H_{14}O_3S$			
3-Thiophenecarboxylic acid, tetrahydro-4-oxo-5-(phenylmethylene)-, ethyl ester	EtOH	211(4.17),234(4.04), 347(4.46),364(4.43)	133-0157-73
$C_{14}H_{14}O_4$			
Benzaldehyde, 4-hydroxy-2-methoxy-5-(1-oxo-2,4-hexadienyl)-, (E,E)-	EtOH	256(4.33),265s(4.32), 309(4.39),345s(4.16)	78-2343-73
Butanedioic acid, (3,4-dihydro-2-naphthalenyl)-	EtOH	266(4.15)	2-0131-73
as-Indacene-4,5-dicarboxylic acid, 1,2,3,6,7,8-hexahydro-	MeCN	293(3.33)	22-2121-73
1H-Indene-1,2-dicarboxylic acid, 5-methyl-, dimethyl ester	EtOH	233(4.27),239(4.28), 292(4.17)	44-0741-73
Marmesin, (+)-	EtOH	224(4.02),247(3.61), 260(3.55),335(4.23)	100-0333-73
2,4-Pentadienoic acid, 3-acetoxy-5-phenyl-, methyl ester, (E,E)-	EtOH	232(4.03),239(3.98), 313(4.56)	5-0650-73
(Z,E)-	EtOH	233(4.21),315(4.46)	5-0650-73
$C_{14}H_{14}O_4S$			
3-Thiophenecarboxylic acid, tetrahydro-5-[(4-hydroxyphenyl)methylene]-, ethyl ester	EtOH	250(3.78),361(4.25), 373(4.26)	133-0157-73
$C_{14}H_{14}O_5$			
Acetic acid, (4,7-dimethoxy-5-methyl-2H-1-benzopyran-2-ylidene)-, methyl ester	MeOH	286s(--),300(3.82)	94-0149-73
Acetic acid, (4-hydroxy-7-methoxy-5-methyl-2H-benzopyran-2-ylidene)-, methyl ester	MeOH	306(3.92)	94-0149-73
7H-Furo[2,3-g][1]benzopyran-7-one, 2,3-dihydro-3-hydroxy-2-(1-hydroxy-1-methylethyl)- (xanthoarnol)	EtOH	223(4.15),249(3.58), 260(3.52),331(4.27)	94-2346-73
$C_{14}H_{14}O_9$			
1,3-Cyclopentadiene-1,2,3,4-tetracarboxylic acid, 5-(hydroxymethylene)-, tetramethyl ester	MeOH	260(4.23),333(4.26)	24-3817-73
Na deriv.	MeOH	272(4.57),330(4.16)	24-3817-73
$C_{14}H_{14}O_{10}$			
Unknown acid, m. 106-109°	MeOH	287(4.6),330(4.3)	24-1758-73
$C_{14}H_{14}S$			
Benzene, 1-methyl-4-[(phenylmethyl)thio]-	n.s.g.	257(-0.62)	80-0263-73
1,3,5,7-Tridecatetraene-9,11-diyne, 7-(methylthio)-, (Z,E,E,E)-	ether	269(4.18),347(4.56), 366(4.59)	24-3621-73
isomer	ether	283(4.40),345(4.35)	24-3621-73
$C_{14}H_{15}BO_6$			
Boron, bis(acetato-O)(1-phenyl-1,3-butanedionato-O,O')-, (T-4)-	CH_2Cl_2	335(4.30)	39-1796-73B

Compound	Solvent	$\lambda_{max}(\log \epsilon)$	Ref.
$C_{14}H_{15}BrN_2O$			
Pyrimido[1,2-a]indole, 1-acetyl-8-bromo-1,2,3,4-tetrahydro-3-methyl-	MeOH	226(4.54),307(4.25)	103-0598-73
$C_{14}H_{15}ClN_2O$			
Benzaldehyde, 4-chloro-, methyl(3-oxo-1-cyclohexen-1-yl)hydrazone	MeOH	235(3.91),254(3.97), 347(4.77),358(4.77)	24-0450-73
$C_{14}H_{15}ClN_2O_5$			
Pyridinium, 1-[1-(4-methyl-2-pyridinyl)-2-oxopropyl]-, perchlorate	EtOH	260(3.90),265s(3.84)	94-0712-73
$C_{14}H_{15}ClN_3O$			
Pyridinium, 2-amino-3-(aminocarbonyl)-6-(4-chlorophenyl)-1-ethyl-, perchlorate	HOAc	252(3.99),338(4.04)	97-0342-73
$C_{14}H_{15}ClN_4O_4$			
9H-Purine, 6-chloro-9-[(6-deoxy-3,4-O-(1-methylethylidene)-β-L-lyxohexo-pyranos-2-ulos-1-yl]-	n.s.g.	265(3.79)	136-0192-73E
$C_{14}H_{15}ClO$			
Spiro[cyclopentane-1,2'(1'H)-naphthalen]-3-one, 1'-chloro-3',4'-dihydro-	$CHCl_3$	268(2.89)	78-0309-73
$C_{14}H_{15}ClO_2$			
Cyclopentaneacetyl chloride, 1-methyl-2-oxo-5-phenyl-, trans	EtOH	249(2.62),253(2.66), 259(2.65),264(2.48)	104-0835-73
$C_{14}H_{15}Cl_2N$			
Pyridinium, 1-[(2-chlorophenyl)methyl]-2,4-dimethyl-, chloride	H_2O	262(3.74)	44-2351-73
Pyridinium, 1-[(2-chlorophenyl)methyl]-3,4-dimethyl-, chloride	H_2O	262(3.67)	44-2351-73
Pyridinium, 1-[(2-chlorophenyl)methyl]-3,5-dimethyl-, chloride	H_2O	273(3.80)	44-2351-73
$C_{14}H_{15}Cl_2NO_4$			
Pyridinium, 1-(4-chlorophenyl)-2,4,6-trimethyl-, perchlorate	EtOH	224(3.88),270(3.90)	103-0333-73
$C_{14}H_{15}N$			
15-Azatricyclo[8.2.2.1^{4,7}]pentadeca-4,6,10,12,13-pentaene	EtOH	219(4.3),269s(2.98), 286s(2.79)	88-4017-73
1H-Indole, 2-(2,3-butadienyl)-1,3-dimethyl-	EtOH	231(4.52),282s(3.83), 288(3.87),294(3.86), 325s(3.20)	39-1913-73C
3H-Indole, 2-ethyl-3-methyl-3-(2-propynyl)-	EtOH	210s(4.15),212(4.19), 218(4.19),224(4.04), 260(3.68)	39-1913-73C
$C_{14}H_{15}NO$			
3H-3-Benzazonine, 3-acetyl-7a,11a-dihydro-	hexane	262(3.90)	88-3805-73
5H-Benzocycloheptene-6-propanenitrile, 6,7,8,9-tetrahydro-5-oxo-	EtOH	247(3.88),288(3.04)	22-0691-73
5H-Benzocycloheptene-7-propanenitrile, 6,7,8,9-tetrahydro-6-oxo-	EtOH	247(3.13),289(2.74)	22-0691-73
7-Oxa-8-azabicyclo[4.2.1]nona-2,4-diene, 8-(4-methylphenyl)-	MeOH	238(4.12),265(3.92)	18-3517-73

Compound	Solvent	λ$_{max}$(log ε)	Ref.
1H-Pyrrole, 1-(2,4,6-trimethylbenzoyl)-	hexane	244(4.1),248(4.1)	18-1437-73
Pyrrolidine, 1-(5-phenyl-2-furanyl)-	EtOH	222(4.00),340(4.29)	39-2523-73C
2-Pyrrolidinone, 4-methylene-3-(1-methylethylidene)-5-phenyl-	EtOH	263.5(4.00)	44-1015-73
2-Pyrrolidinone, 3-(1-methylethylidene)-4-(phenylmethylene)-	EtOH	297.5(3.86)	44-1015-73
2H-Pyrrol-2-one, 1,3-dihydro-4-methyl-3-(1-methylethylidene)-5-phenyl-	EtOH	372.5(3.71)	44-1015-73
$C_{14}H_{15}NOS_2$			
Dithiobenzoic acid, 4-methoxy-, 3-methylpyridine salt	EtOH	304(3.93),360(3.78), 510(2.22)	143-0359-73
$C_{14}H_{15}NO_2$			
2(3H)-Benzofuranone, 3-(4,4-dimethyl-2-pyrrolidinylidene)-	EtOH	250(4.14),321(4.2)	103-0137-73
4H-Cyclohept[d]isoxazol-4-one, 3a,5,6-7,8,8a-hexahydro-3-phenyl-, cis	EtOH	269(4.09)	39-1148-73C
8H-Cyclohept[d]isoxazol-8-one, 3a,4,5-6,7,8a-hexahydro-3-phenyl-, cis	EtOH	262(4.06)	39-1148-73C
2,4,6-Heptatrienoic acid, 7-(2-pyridinyl)-, ethyl ester, (E,E,E)-	dioxan	326(4.64),338(4.78), 356(4.69)	54-0683-73
1(2H)-Isoquinolinone, 2-methyl-5-(1-oxobutyl)-	EtOH	215(4.56),256(3.98), 310(3.92),342(3.70)	94-2585-73
1(2H)-Isoquinolinone, 2-methyl-7-(1-oxobutyl)-	EtOH	215(4.54),225(4.50), 267(3.93),318(4.07), 334(4.14),346(4.09)	94-2585-73
Morpholine, 4-(5-phenyl-2-furanyl)-	EtOH	217(3.96),230s(3.85), 318(4.24)	39-2523-73C
2-Propenoic acid, 3-(2-methyl-1H-indol-3-yl)-, ethyl ester, cis	EtOH	226(4.16),267(3.60), 281(3.63),342(3.73)	104-1275-73
trans	EtOH	226(4.33),266(3.92), 271(4.00),340(4.33)	104-1275-73
4-Pyridinol, 2-ethoxy-6-methyl-3-phenyl-	EtOH	255(4.02)	94-1047-73
$C_{14}H_{15}NO_3$			
2,4-Hexadienoic acid, 6-[(3-methylphenyl)amino]-6-oxo-, methyl ester	EtOH	268(4.64),313(4.39)	104-2527-73
1H-Indole-3-butanoic acid, 1-methyl-γ-oxo-, methyl ester	EtOH	215(3.89),250(3.83), 275(3.81),290s(3.80)	39-0548-73B
1H-Indole-3-butanoic acid, 2-methyl-γ-oxo-, methyl ester	EtOH	223(4.14),244(4.17), 268(4.10),299(4.06)	39-0548-73B
5,9-Methano-6H-benzocyclohepten-6-one, 5,9-dihydro-1,4-dimethoxy-, oxime	EtOH	215(4.15),245(3.95), 303(3.60)	39-1840-73C
1H-Pyrrole-2-acetic acid, 4,5-dihydro-1-(3-methylphenyl)-5-oxo-, methyl ester	EtOH	262(4.59)	104-2527-73
$C_{14}H_{15}NO_4$			
Acetamide, N-(8-ethyl-4-hydroxy-6-methyl-2-oxo-2H-1-benzopyran-3-yl)-	MeOH	215(4.45),290(4.03)	2-0433-73
Furo[2,3-b]quinoline, 2,3-dihydro-4,6,8-trimethoxy-	EtOH	220(4.44),247(4.56), 266(3.80),276(3.40), 326(3.63),342(3.64)	18-0577-73
4,6-Isoquinolinediol, 1,2,3,4-tetrahydro-1-[5-(hydroxymethyl)-2-furanyl]-	EtOH	282(3.33)	95-0925-73
1(2H)-Isoquinolinone, 4-acetyl-6,7-dimethoxy-2-methyl-	EtOH	247(4.40),261(4.23)	78-3881-73

Compound	Solvent	$\lambda_{max}(\log \epsilon)$	Ref.
$C_{14}H_{15}NO_5$			
1H-Indole-3-butanoic acid, 2-carboxy-6-methoxy-	EtOH	225(4.28),250(4.11), 258s(4.01),310(4.25), 320s(4.25)	39-0872-73B
5(4H)-Oxazolone, 2-(2,6-dimethoxyphenyl)-4-(ethoxymethylene)-	EtOH	292(4.29)	4-0935-73
2-Quinolinecarboxylic acid, 4,5,8-trimethoxy-, methyl ester	$CHCl_3$	257(4.46),336(3.64), 370(3.57)	39-2374-73C
$C_{14}H_{15}NS_2$			
Dithiobenzoic acid, 4-methyl-, 3-methylpyridine salt	EtOH	325(4.18),355(3.76), 515(2.16)	143-0359-73
$C_{14}H_{15}N_2O$			
Pyridinium, 3-acetyl-1-(phenylmethyl)-, oxime	pH 6.61	254(3.95)	36-1381-73
Pyridinium, 1-[1-(4-methyl-2-pyridinyl)-2-oxopropyl]-, perchlorate	EtOH	260(3.90),265s(3.84)	94-0712-73
$C_{14}H_{15}N_2O_2$			
Pyridinium, 1-ethyl-4-[(4-nitrophenyl)-methyl]-, perchlorate	H_2O	214(4.15),259s(4.10), 265(4.13),274(4.07)	48-0901-73
$C_{14}H_{15}N_3$			
Benzenamine, N,N-dimethyl-3-(phenylazo)-	EtOH	230(4.17),317(4.11), 424(3.31)	7-0727-73
hydrochloride	EtOH	230(3.87),250(3.83), 317(3.91),435(3.01)	7-0727-73
Benzenamine, N,N-dimethyl-4-(phenylazo)-	C_6H_{12}	400(4.48)	18-3139-73
	EtOH	412(4.44)	103-0850-73
	EtOH-HCl	520(4.53)	103-0850-73
	50%EtOH-HCl	320(4.00),516(4.53)	18-0194-73
ammonium ion	H_2O	320(4.00)	18-3139-73
azonium ion	H_2O	516(4.53)	18-3139-73
$C_{14}H_{15}N_3O$			
Benzenepropanenitrile, α-(1,3-dimethyl-2-imidazolidinylidene)-β-oxo-	EtOH	251s(3.98),310(4.08)	1-0258-73
1-Phthalazinecarbonitrile, 3,4-dihydro-4-(1-methyl-2-oxobutyl)-	EtOH	221(4.16),242(4.00), 335(3.84)	95-0409-73
Propanedinitrile, [[4-(dimethylamino)-phenyl]ethoxymethylene]-	MeCN	377(4.40)	39-0616-73B
Pyridine, 4-acetyl-3-hydroxy-2-methyl-, phenylhydrazone	n.s.g.	391(4.22)	70-1057-73
Pyridine, 5-acetyl-3-hydroxy-2-methyl-, phenylhydrazone	n.s.g.	335(3.42)	70-1057-73
$C_{14}H_{15}N_3O_2$			
2,4(1H,3H)-Pyrimidinedione, 5-[(3,4-dihydro-1(2H)-quinolinyl)methyl]-	EtOH	259(4.25),303(3.42)	69-2879-73
$C_{14}H_{15}N_3O_2S$			
3-Pyridinecarboxylic acid, 1,2-diamino-1,6-dihydro-4-phenyl-6-thioxo-, ethyl ester	MeOH	270(4.01),287s(3.93), 383(4.35)	48-0679-73
$C_{14}H_{15}N_3O_2S_2$			
Carbamic acid, [(methylthio)[(4-phenyl-2-thiazolyl)imino]methyl]-, ethyl ester	dioxan	222(4.26),262(4.26), 288(4.10),333(4.23)	94-0074-73

Compound	Solvent	$\lambda_{max}(\log \epsilon)$	Ref.
Carbamic acid, [(methylthio)[(5-phenyl-2-thiazolyl)imino]methyl]-, ethyl ester	dioxan	345(4.32)	94-0074-73
Carbamic acid, [(phenylmethyl)thio]-2-thiazolyliminomethyl-, ethyl ester	dioxan	245(3.86),315(4.31)	94-0074-73
$C_{14}H_{15}N_3O_3$			
Benzaldehyde, 4-nitro-, methyl(2-methyl-3-oxo-1-cyclopenten-1-yl)hydrazone	MeOH	259(4.13),291(4.25), 385(4.42)	24-0450-73
Benzaldehyde, 4-nitro-, methyl(3-oxo-1-cyclohexen-1-yl)hydrazone	MeOH	258(3.88),298(4.12), 382(4.56)	24-0450-73
$C_{14}H_{15}N_3O_4$			
3-Isoxazoleacetic acid, 2,5-dihydro-5-oxo-4-(phenylazo)-, 1-methylethyl ester	EtOH	249(3.99),396(4.28)	70-2006-73
$C_{14}H_{15}N_3O_5$			
1H-1,2,3-Triazole-4-carboxylic acid, 5-methoxy-1-(4-methoxy-5-oxo-1,3,6-cycloheptatrien-1-yl)-, ethyl ester	n.s.g.	224(4.41),246(4.41), 334(4.17)	18-1212-73
$C_{14}H_{15}N_5$			
9H-Purin-6-amine, 9-methyl-N-[(4-methyl-phenyl)methyl]-	MeOH	270(4.26)	18-3228-73
$C_{14}H_{15}N_5O$			
6H-Purin-6-one, 1,9-dihydro-9-(phenyl-methyl)-, (O-ethyloxime)	pH 1	268(4.22)	94-1676-73
	pH 7	269(4.19)	94-1676-73
	pH 13	285(4.06)	94-1676-73
	EtOH	268(4.15)	94-1676-73
6H-Purin-6-one, 9-ethyl-1,9-dihydro-, O-(phenylmethyl)oxime	pH 1	272(4.14)	94-1676-73
	pH 7	270(4.20)	94-1676-73
	pH 13	286(4.09)	94-1676-73
	EtOH	270(4.18)	94-1676-73
$C_{14}H_{15}N_5O_4$			
3,6-Pyridazinedicarboxylic acid, 4-(3,6-dimethyl-1,2,4-triazin-5-yl)-5-meth-yl-, methyl ester	MeOH	266(3.80)	5-1963-73
$C_{14}H_{15}N_5O_6$			
L-Arabinitol, 1-deoxy-1-(3,4-dihydro-2,4-dioxopyrido[3,2-g]pteridin-10(2H)-yl)-	H_2O	238s(--),254(4.30), 258(4.30),300(3.61), 385(3.89),424(3.91)	4-0209-73
D-Ribitol, 1-deoxy-1-(3,4-dihydro-2,4-dioxopyrido[3,2-g]pteridin-10(2H)-yl)-	H_2O	237s(--),254(4.32), 258(4.32),297(3.60), 385(3.92),424(3.74)	4-0209-73
$C_{14}H_{16}$			
Benzene, (2-cyclopropyl-2-cyclopropen-ylideneethyl)-	hexane	205(4.15),255(4.12)	44-1703-73
Benzene, [2-ethylidene-3-(1-methyleth-ylidene)-1-cyclopropyl]-	EtOH	249(4.25)	39-0278-73B
isomer	EtOH	248(4.27)	39-0278-73B
Benzene, [1-methyl-2-methylene-3-(1-methylethylidene)cyclopropyl]-	EtOH	246.0(4.27)	39-0278-73B
2-Butyne, 1-(1,3,5-trimethyl-4-methyl-ene-2,5-cyclohexadien-1-yl)-	EtOH	248(4.38)	33-0681-73
1H-Indene, 1,2-dimethyl-3-(1-methyleth-enyl)-	EtOH	262(4.03)	39-0278-73B

Compound	Solvent	λmax(log ε)	Ref.
1H-Indene, 1,3-dimethyl-2-(1-methylethenyl)-	EtOH	276.5(4.15)	39-0278-73B
1H-Indene, 2,3-dimethyl-1-(1-methylethenyl)-	EtOH	261.5(4.03)	39-0278-73B
Naphthalene, 1-(1,1-dimethylethyl)-, tetracyanoethylene complex	CH_2Cl_2	438(2.57),592(2.85)	39-0447-73B
$C_{14}H_{16}BrNO_3$			
1H-Indole-3-carboxylic acid, 4-bromo-5-hydroxy-1,2,6-trimethyl-, ethyl ester	isooctane	221(4.36),308(4.08)	103-0306-73
1H-Indole-3-carboxylic acid, 6-bromo-5-methoxy-1,2-dimethyl-, methyl ester	isooctane	218(4.59),242(4.43), 288(4.09),300(4.11), 313(3.98)	103-0306-73
$C_{14}H_{16}BrNO_4$			
Morpholine, 4-[[4-(bromoacetyl)phenoxy]-acetyl]-	EtOH	214(4.34),266(4.16)	111-0574-73
$C_{14}H_{16}BrN_7NaO_8P$			
Adenosine, 8-bromo-N-[(methylamino)carbonyl]-, cyclic 3',5'-(hydrogen phosphate) 2'-(methylcarbonate), Na salt	pH 1	281(4.34),291s(4.19)	87-1075-73
	pH 7	277(4.35),280(4.28)	87-1075-73
	pH 11	277(4.35),280(4.28)	87-1075-73
	pH 13	299(4.33)	87-1075-73
$C_{14}H_{16}ClNO_4$			
Pyridinium, 1,2,4-trimethyl-6-phenyl-, perchlorate	EtOH	286(3.93)	103-0333-73
Pyridinium, 2,4,6-trimethyl-1-phenyl-, perchlorate	EtOH	224(4.06),270(3.87)	103-0333-73
$C_{14}H_{16}ClNS$			
Benzenamine, 4-chloro-N-[[2-(methylthio)-1-cyclohexen-1-yl]methylene]-	EtOH	334(4.17)	104-1739-73
$C_{14}H_{16}ClN_5O_5$			
9H-Purin-6-amine, 9-(3,5-di-O-acetyl-2-chloro-2-deoxy-β-D-arabinofuranosyl)-	MeOH	259(4.18)	35-4025-73
$C_{14}H_{16}GeS_2$			
Germane, trimethyl[(1-naphthalenylthioxomethyl)thio]-	C_6H_{12}	316(4.32),520(2.43)	101-0121-73I
$C_{14}H_{16}IN$			
3H-Indolium, 1,2,3-trimethyl-3-(2-propynyl)-, iodide	EtOH	206s(4.23),210(4.21), 221(4.23),238s(3.86), 278(3.81)	39-1913-73C
$C_{14}H_{16}IN_3$			
Pyridinium, 1-[[[4-(dimethylamino)phenyl]methylene]amino]-, iodide	EtOH	219(4.38),255(4.01), 301(3.82),406(4.04)	103-1108-73
	acetone	216(4.02),251(3.93), 320(3.42),402(4.02)	103-1108-73
	H_2SO_4	255(4.12)	103-1108-73
	MeCN	247(4.45),295(3.90), 402(4.35)	103-1108-73
	DMSO	258(4.04),290(3.88), 401(4.22)	103-1108-73

Compound	Solvent	λ_{max}(log ε)	Ref.
$C_{14}H_{16}NOP$			
Phosphinic amide, N,N-dimethyl-P,P-diphenyl-	n.s.g.	225(4.23),261(3.17), 267(3.24),274(3.12)	35-8073-73
$C_{14}H_{16}N_2$			
Benzeneacetonitrile, α-(1-methyl-2-piperidinylidene)-	EtOH	270s(3.83),309(4.16)	103-0880-73
1H-Cyclopenta[b]quinolin-9-amine, N-ethyl-2,3-dihydro-	EtOH	222(4.44),248(4.46), 328(4.12)	103-0490-73
1H-Indazole, 4,5,6,7-tetrahydro-1-methyl-3-phenyl-	MeOH	255(4.18)	24-3432-73
1H-Indole, 2-(4-piperidinylidenemethyl)-	MeOH	240(4.28),307(4.34), 313(4.30)	23-0792-73
1,5-Methano-1H-azocino[3,4-b]indole, 2,3,4,5,6,11-hexahydro-	EtOH	226(4.52),276(3.84), 283(3.86),291(3.79)	44-2882-73
Pyridinium, 2,2'-(1,2-ethenediyl)bis[1-methyl-	MeCN	208(4.05),312(4.36)	5-0324-73
Pyridinium, 3,3'-(1,2-ethenediyl)bis[1-methyl-	MeCN	233(4.17),238(4.11), 282(4.35),308s(4.27)	5-0324-73
Pyridinium, 4,4'-(1,2-ethenediyl)bis[1-methyl-	MeCN	228(3.88),307s(4.55), 318(4.62),332(4.45)	5-0324-73
Pyridinium, 1-methyl-2-[2-(1-methylpyridinium-3-yl)ethenyl]-	MeCN	215s(4.17),257(3.92), 312(4.41)	5-0324-73
Pyridinium, 1-methyl-2-[2-(1-methylpyridinium-4-yl)ethenyl]-	MeCN	220(3.97),272s(3.94), 315(4.46),343s(4.10)	5-0324-73
Pyridinium, 1-methyl-3-[2-(1-methylpyridinium-4-yl)ethenyl]-	MeCN	222(4.13),303s(4.48), 312(4.49)	5-0324-73
$C_{14}H_{16}N_2O$			
Benzaldehyde, methyl(2-methyl-3-oxo-1-cyclopenten-1-yl)hydrazone	MeOH	242(4.04),249(4.05), 262(3.91),342(4.64)	24-0450-73
Benzaldehyde, methyl(3-oxo-1-cyclohexen-1-yl)hydrazone	MeOH	228(4.01),252(3.93), 344(4.71),355(4.72)	24-0450-73
1H-Indazol-4-ol, 4,5,6,7-tetrahydro-1-methyl-3-phenyl-	MeOH	250(4.19)	24-3432-73
2-Pyridinamine, N-(1-methyl-2-phenylethyl)-, 1-oxide	MeOH	233(4.46),252(3.95), 328(3.73)	32-1083-73
2-Pyridinamine, N-methyl-N-(1-phenylethyl)-, 1-oxide, (S)-	MeOH	246(4.26),273(3.79), 328(3.59)	32-1083-73
Pyrimido[1,2-a]indole, 1-acetyl-1,2,3,4-tetrahydro-3-methyl-	MeOH	212(4.42),297(4.35)	103-0598-73
Pyrrolidine, 1-[(3-methyl-1H-indol-2-yl)carbonyl]-	isoPrOH	222(4.51),242s(4.08), 293(4.16)	44-3077-73
$C_{14}H_{16}N_2O_2$			
2H-1,4-Benzodiazepin-2-one, 1,3-dihydro-5-(hydroxymethyl)-1-methyl-3-(2-propenyl)-	isoPrOH	225(4.54),250s(3.79), 297(3.24)	44-3502-73
3,6-Ethano-1,8-benzodiazecin-4(1H)-one, 2,3,7,8-tetrahydro-5-hydroxy-	MeOH	263(4.01)	88-4059-73
Isoxazolin-5-one, 3-methyl-4-(2-propynyl)-, benzylammonium salt	EtOH	255(3.95)	1-2802-73
3H-Isoxazolo[3,4-d]azepine, 1,4,5,6,7,8-hexahydro-3-oxo-6-(phenylmethyl)-, hydrochloride	EtOH	259(3.86)	1-3251-73
4H-Isoxazolo[3,4-d]azepin-3-ol, 5,6,7,8-tetrahydro-6-(phenylmethyl)-, zwitterion	EtOH	254(3.90)	1-3251-73
Pyrrolidine, 1-(3-methyloxindole-3-carbonyl)-	isoPrOH	251(3.91),282(3.19)	44-3077-73

Compound	Solvent	λmax(log ε)	Ref.
$C_{14}H_{16}N_2O_2S$			
Pyridinium, 2,4,6-trimethyl-1-[(phenylsulfonyl)amino]-, hydroxide, inner salt	EtOH	246(4.11),295s(3.04)	44-3311-73
$C_{14}H_{16}N_2O_3$			
Ethanone, 2-(1-methyl-2-piperidinylidene)-1-(3-nitrophenyl)-	EtOH	227(4.23),250s(4.05), 340(4.33)	103-0880-73
Ethanone, 2-(1-methyl-2-piperidinylidene)-1-(4-nitrophenyl)-	EtOH	291(4.23),372(4.15)	103-0880-73
1H-Pyrazole-3-carboxylic acid, 5-(hydroxymethyl)-1-(4-methylphenyl)-, ethyl ester	C_6H_{12} or EtOH	217(4.11),255(4.01)	4-0015-73
1H-Pyrido[3,4-b]indole-3-carboxylic acid, 2,3,4,9-tetrahydro-6-methoxy-1-methyl-, hydrochloride	n.s.g.	368(4.34)	22-2058-73
	base	326(4.21)	22-2058-73
2,4(1H,3H)-Pyrimidinedione, 5-ethyl-1-[(2-hydroxy-3-methylphenyl)methyl]-	pH 2-7	273(4.06)	56-1645-73
	pH 13	275(3.96)	56-1645-73
1H-Pyrrolizin-3-one, 1-(hexahydro-1,3-dioxopyrrolizin-2-yl)hexahydro-	EtOH	249(4.06),287s(--), 305(3.98),333(3.89)	119-0132-73
	EtOH-HCl	250(4.19),298(4.12)	119-0132-73
	EtOH-NaOH	240(3.78),277(3.95), 337(4.30)	119-0132-73
$C_{14}H_{16}N_2O_3S_2$			
2,3-Dithia-5,7-diazabicyclo[2.2.2]octane-6,8-dione, 1-(hydroxymethyl)-5,7-dimethyl-4-(phenylmethyl)- (hyalodendrin)	EtOH	260s(3.00)	39-2600-73C
$C_{14}H_{16}N_2O_4$			
1,2-Cyclopentanedicarboxylic acid, 3-(dicyanomethylene)-, diethyl ester	EtOH	229(3.90),355(4.04)	78-4103-73
	EtOH-NaOH	224(4.21),356(4.33)	78-4103-73
1H-Indole-2-propanoic acid, 2-cyano-2,3,4,5,6,7-hexahydro-3,4-dioxo-, ethyl ester	EtOH	255(4.19),291(3.94)	94-2571-73
2,4-Pentadienoic acid, 5-(dimethylamino)-2-nitro-5-phenyl-, methyl ester	EtOH	255(3.85),310(3.94),	70-1963-73
1H-Pyrrole-2,5-dione, 1,1'-(1,6-hexanediyl)bis-	CH_2Cl_2	302(3.1)	35-0137-73
$C_{14}H_{16}N_2O_4S$			
1-Naphthalenesulfonic acid, 5-[[2-(acetylamino)ethyl]amino]-	pH 7.0	262(--),337(3.79)	69-4154-73
	H_2O	336.0(3.79)	69-4154-73
	EtOH	340.0(3.84)	69-4154-73
	80% EtOH	339.0(3.83)	69-4154-73
	20% EtOH	337.0(3.80)	69-4154-73
	dioxan	339.0(3.87)	69-4154-73
	DMF	341.0(3.91)	69-4154-73
1-Naphthalenesulfonic acid, 8-[[2-(acetylamino)ethyl]amino]-	H_2O	342.5(3.80)	69-4154-73
	EtOH	349.0(3.87)	69-4154-73
	20% EtOH	345.5(3.83)	69-4154-73
	DMF	352.0(3.88)	69-4154-73
$C_{14}H_{16}N_2O_5$			
1H-Indole-3-carboxylic acid, 5-methoxy-1,2-dimethyl-4-nitro-, ethyl ester	MeOH or $CHCl_3$	217(4.67),242(4.40), 287(3.50)	103-1490-73
1H-Indole-3-carboxylic acid, 5-methoxy-1,2-dimethyl-6-nitro-, ethyl ester	MeOH	213(4.30),273(4.16), 349(3.72)	103-1490-73

Compound	Solvent	λ_{max}(log ε)	Ref.
1H-Pyrrolo[2,3-c]pyridine-2,3-dicarboxylic acid, 5-methoxy-, diethyl ester	EtOH	242(4.11),263(4.05), 316(3.75)	44-1824-73
$C_{14}H_{16}N_2O_7$			
2,4(1H,3H)-Pyrimidinedione, 1-(4,6-di-O-acetyl-2,3-dideoxy-α-D-threo-hex-2-enopyranosyl)-	MeOH	260(4.02)	78-1801-73
	MeOH-NaOH	260(3.90)	78-1801-73
$C_{14}H_{16}N_2O_8$			
Butanedioic acid, 2-(2-methoxy-5-nitro-4-pyridinyl)-3-oxo-, diethyl ester	EtOH	245(4.53),304s(--)	44-1824-73
2-Butenoic acid, 2-[(2,5-dimethoxy-4-nitrophenyl)amino]-, dimethyl ester, (Z)-	$CHCl_3$	262(3.82),328(3.97), 395(4.28)	39-2374-73C
$C_{14}H_{16}N_3O$			
Pyridinium, 2-amino-3-(aminocarbonyl)-1-methyl-6-(4-methylphenyl)-, perchlorate	HOAc	252(3.98),278(3.37), 343(4.14)	97-0342-73
$C_{14}H_{16}N_4OS$			
1,2,4-Triazino[5,6-d][3,1]benzoxazepine, 6-ethyl-6,7-dihydro-6-methyl-3-(methylthio)-	EtOH	204(4.32),238(4.43), 348(4.02),448(3.78)	78-0639-73
$C_{14}H_{16}N_4OS_2$			
Biuret, 1-benzyl-1-(2-thiazolyl)-5-ethyl-2-thio-	EtOH	220(4.14),269(4.35)	44-3868-73
3(2H)-Thiazolecarbothioamide, N-[(ethylamino)carbonyl]-2-[(phenylmethyl)-imino]-	EtOH	216(3.93),305(4.27)	44-3868-73
$C_{14}H_{16}N_4O_2$			
1,3-Cyclohexanedione, 2-(1,4-dihydro-4-pteridinyl)-5,5-dimethyl-	pH 5.0	279(4.31),314(4.01)	39-1615-73C
	pH 9.5	282(4.34),340(3.92)	39-1615-73C
$C_{14}H_{16}N_4O_2S$			
Biuret, 1-benzyl-1-(2-thiazolyl)-5-ethyl-	EtOH	218(3.95),267(4.11)	44-3868-73
$C_{14}H_{16}N_4O_4$			
3-Pyridinecarboxamide, 1-[[[5-(aminocarbonyl)-1(2H)-pyridinyl]methoxy]-methyl]-1,6-dihydro-6-oxo-	H_2O	260(4.13),305(3.70), 345(3.63)	5-1237-73
$C_{14}H_{16}N_5$			
1H-[1,2,4]Triazolo[1,5-a]pyrimidin-8-ium, 2-amino-5,6,7-trimethyl-1-phenyl-	n.s.g.	255(4.20),312(3.74)	124-1036-73
$C_{14}H_{16}O$			
2-Cyclohexen-1-one, 2,4-dimethyl-3-phenyl-	EtOH	259(4.04)	104-2172-73
Methanone, (1,2-dimethyl-2-cyclopenten-1-yl)phenyl-	isooctane	238(4.02),330(2.09)	33-1741-73
Methanone, (2,3-dimethyl-2-cyclopenten-1-yl)phenyl-	isooctane	237(4.08)	33-1741-73
Spiro[cyclopentane-1,2'(1'H)-naphthalen]-3-one, 3',4'-dihydro-	EtOH	250(2.78),266(2.85), 274(2.85)	78-0309-73

Compound	Solvent	$\lambda_{max}(\log \epsilon)$	Ref.
$C_{14}H_{16}O_2$			
Benz[e]indene-3,7(5H)-dione, 1,2,3a,4-8,9-hexahydro-3a-methyl-	MeOH	297(4.20)	78-3631-73
4,4'-Bipyrylium, 2,2',6,6'-tetramethyl-, diperchlorate	MeCN	261(4.11),322(4.14)	5-1036-73
semiquinone	MeCN	235(3.91),328s(4.18), 342(4.28),385s(3.99), 508s(3.85),544(4.12), 595(4.20)	5-1036-73
3,4,10,11-Cyclotetradecatetraene-1,8-dione, (±)-	EtOH	223s(2.85),276(2.28)	35-4582-73
meso-	EtOH	224s(2.92),284(2.52)	35-4582-73
2H-Inden-2-one, 1-acetyl-1,3-dihydro-1,3,3-trimethyl-	C_6H_{12}	262(2.84),263s(2.84), 268(3.05),275(3.02)	23-1598-73
2H-Inden-2-one, 5(6)-acetyl-1,3-dihydro-1,1,3-trimethyl-	C_6H_{12}	248(4.22),274s(3.27), 283(3.38),293(3.29)	23-1598-73
2-Naphthaleneacetic acid, 3,4-dihydro-α-methyl-, methyl ester	EtOH	265(4.1)	2-0131-73
2-Naphthalenepropanoic acid, 3,4-dihydro-1-methyl-	EtOH	265(4.15)	78-0309-73
1,8-Nonadiene-4,6-diyn-3-ol, 9-(tetrahydro-2H-pyran-2-yl)-, trans	n.s.g.	215(4.45),241(3.83), 254(4.13),264(4.30), 284(4.20)	39-0145-73C
8-Nonene-4,6-diyn-3-one, 9-(tetrahydro-2H-pyran-2-yl)-	n.s.g.	227(4.45),250s(--), 265(3.85),279(3.93), 294(3.98),313(3.91)	39-0145-73C
$C_{14}H_{16}O_2S$			
2-Propenoic acid, 3-(methylthio)-, 8-decene-4,6-diynyl ester, (Z,E)-	n.s.g.	228(3.46),240(3.57), 252(4.12),266(4.39), 282(4.52)	105-0283-73
$C_{14}H_{16}O_3$			
Benzofuran, 4,6-dimethoxy-3-methyl-2-(1-methylethenyl)-	90% EtOH	221s(4.07),231s(4.02), 299(4.18),312s(4.04)	12-1093-73
Cyclobuta[b]naphthalene-3,8-dione, 1-ethoxy-2a,3a,4,7,7a,8a-hexahydro-	EtOH	231s(3.22),302(2.49)	104-2389-73
Cyclopentaneacetic acid, 1-methyl-2-oxo-5-phenyl-, trans	EtOH	248(2.20),254(2.31), 259(2.40),265(2.29), 268(2.18)	104-0835-73
Drupacin	n.s.g.	217(3.99),234(3.95), 316(4.17)	105-0672-73
1,3,5-Heptanetrione, 2-methyl-1-phenyl-	EtOH	249(4.05),282(4.04)	44-0896-73
1,3,5-Heptanetrione, 4-methyl-1-phenyl-	EtOH	222(3.76),248(3.74), 314(4.19)	44-0896-73
1,3,5-Hexanetrione, 2,4-dimethyl-1-phenyl-	EtOH	220(3.91),290(3.98)	44-0896-73
1,3,5-Hexanetrione, 4,4-dimethyl-1-phenyl-	EtOH	223(3.85),229s(3.81), 244(3.74),306(4.20)	44-0896-73
5,9-Methano-5H-benzocyclohepten-6-ol, 6,9-dihydro-1,4-dimethoxy-	C_6H_{12}	290(3.52),298(3.50)	39-1840-73C
5,9-Methanobenzocyclohepten-6-one, 5,7,8,9-tetrahydro-1,4-dimethoxy-	C_6H_{12}	292(3.56)	39-1840-73C
$C_{14}H_{16}O_4$			
Benzaldehyde, 4-hydroxy-2-methoxy-5-(1-oxo-4-hexenyl)-, (E)-	EtOH	255(4.39),282(4.01), 321(3.82)	78-2343-73
Cyclobuta[1,2-b:4,3-b']dipyran-4,5-dione, 4a,4b,8a,8b-tetrahydro-2,7,8a,8b-tetramethyl-	EtOH	267(4.29)	23-1267-73

Compound	Solvent	λ_{max}(log ε)	Ref.
4H,8H-Cyclobuta[1,2-b:3m4-b']dipyran-4,8-dione, 4a,4b,8a,8b-tetrahydro-2,4b,6,8b-tetramethyl-	EtOH	266(4.34)	23-1267-73
1,4-Cyclopentadiene-1,3-dicarboxylic acid, 3-(3-methyl-1-butynyl)-, dimethyl ester	EtOH	218(--),238(--), 244(--),271(--), 276(4.5),322(3.8), 346(3.7)	35-8380-73
2,4-Cyclopentadiene-1,2-dicarboxylic acid, 1-(3-methyl-1,2-butadienyl)-, dimethyl ester	EtOH	253(3.6),283(3.6)	35-8380-73
Ethanone, 1-(7-hydroxy-5-methoxy-2,2-dimethyl-2H-1-benzopyran-8-yl)- (alloevodionol)	MeOH	220(4.20),277(4.49), 354(3.44)	83-0857-73
2H-Pyran-2-one, 5,6-dihydro-5-hydroxy-4-methoxy-6-(2-phenylethyl)-, (+)-	EtOH	231(4.11),261(2.85)	24-0570-73
racemic	EtOH	231(4.09)	24-0570-73
Tricyclo[3.2.0.0^{2,7}]hept-3-ene-1,5-dicarboxylic acid, 6-(1-methylethylidene)-, dimethyl ester	EtOH	223(4.2),290s(3.3)	35-8380-73
$C_{14}H_{16}O_5$			
Butanedioic acid, 2-[(3-methylphenyl)-methyl]-3-oxo-, dimethyl ester	EtOH	217(3.70),260(3.26), 273s(3.22)	44-0741-73
$C_{14}H_{16}O_6$			
1,4-Benzenediol, 2-[2-(acetyloxy)ethyl]-, diacetate	EtOH	217(3.74),268(2.76), 273(2.74)	1-0367-73
Furo[2,3-b]benzofuran-5-carboxylic acid, 2,3,3a,8a-tetrahydro-3,4-dihydroxy-2,2-dimethyl-, methyl ester, (3α,3aα,8aα)-	MeOH	231(4.07),265(4.09), 297(3.69)	78-3099-73
(3α,3aβ,8aβ)-	MeOH	215(4.43),226(4.29), 264(4.20),296(3.68)	78-3099-73
$C_{14}H_{16}S_2$			
4,4'-Bithiopyrylium, 2,2',6,6'-tetramethyl-, diperchlorate	MeCN-$HClO_4$	214(4.63),233s(--), 297(4.32),324s(--)	5-1036-73
semiquinone	MeCN-iso-PrOH	265s(--),322s(--), 383(4.03),414s(--), 452(4.25),600s(--), 663(3.82),725(4.00)	5-1036-73
$C_{14}H_{16}S_2Sn$			
Stannane, trimethyl[(1-naphthalenylthioxomethyl)thio]-	C_6H_{12}	325(4.21),490(2.39)	101-0121-73I
$C_{14}H_{16}S_4$			
1,3-Benzodithiole, 4,5,6,7-tetrahydro-2-(4,5,6,7-tetrahydro-1,3-benzodithiol-2-ylidene)-	MeCN	300(4.18),323(4.15), 470(2.46)	5-0310-73
cation perchlorate	MeCN	267(3.09),343(3.59), 409s(--),433(4.05), 458(4.20),508(3.61), 662(3.87)	5-0310-73
$C_{14}H_{17}$			
Methylium, dicyclopropyl(4-methylphenyl)-	FSO_3H at -75°	354(4.40)	59-0803-73

Compound	Solvent	λ max (log ε)	Ref.
$C_{14}H_{17}BrN_2$			
Pyrido[2,3-g]quinolinium, 1,2,3,4-tetrahydro-1,6-dimethyl-, bromide	H_2O	219(4.38),285(4.34), 447(3.69)	39-0832-73C
$C_{14}H_{17}BrN_2O_4$			
Morpholine, 4-[[4-[2-bromo-1-(hydroxyimino)ethyl]phenoxy]acetyl]-	EtOH	215(4.46),259(4.21)	111-0574-73
$C_{14}H_{17}ClN_2O_2$			
1H-Isoindole-1,3(2H)-dione, 2-[3-[(2-chloroethyl)methylamino]propyl]-, hydrochloride	pH 1	300(3.18)	103-0383-73
	pH 7	300(--)	103-0383-73
	pH 13	270s(--)	103-0383-73
$C_{14}H_{17}ClN_4O_4$			
9H-Purine, 6-chloro-9-[6-deoxy-3,4-O-(1-methylethylidene)-β-L-galactopyranosyl]-	n.s.g.	265(3.73)	136-0192-73E
$C_{14}H_{17}N$			
2-Azabicyclo[3.2.0]heptane, 3-ethenyl-2-phenyl-	EtOH	246(4.82),285(3.87)	78-2973-73
1-Azulenemethanamine, N,N,α-trimethyl-	EtOH	277(3.62),281(3.58), 340(2.77),592(2.31), 640(2.25),710s(1.86)	5-0166-73
1H-Indole, 2-(3-butenyl)-1,3-dimethyl-	EtOH	230(4.52),281s(3.81), 287(3.86),293(3.84)	39-1913-73C
1H-Indole, 3-methyl-2-(1-methyl-3-butenyl)-	EtOH	209(4.36),231(4.23), 248(4.05),286(3.66), 293(3.65)	39-1913-73C
3H-Indole, 2-ethyl-3-methyl-3-(2-propenyl)-	EtOH	210s(4.23),212(4.26), 218(4.24),224s(4.10), 257(3.78)	39-1913-73C
$C_{14}H_{17}NO$			
1H-Carbazole, 2,3,4,4a-tetrahydro-8-methoxy-4a-methyl-	EtOH	256(3.80),300(3.64)	33-2628-73
	EtOH-HCl	244(3.57),281(3.66), 318(3.67)	33-2628-73
9H-Carbazole-9-carboxaldehyde, 1,2,3,4-4a,9a-hexahydro-4a-methyl-	EtOH	253(4.10),282(3.72)	33-2628-73
Ethanone, 2-(1-methyl-2-piperidinylidene)-1-phenyl-	EtOH	245(4.00),338(4.41)	103-0880-73
Pyrrolidine, 2-methyl-1-(1-oxo-3-phenyl-2-propenyl)-, [R-(Z)]-	MeOH	252.5(4.11)	1-1982-73
$C_{14}H_{17}NOS$			
Cyclohexanethione, 2-[[(4-methoxyphenyl)amino]methylene]-	EtOH	452(4.33)	104-1739-73
$C_{14}H_{17}NO_2$			
1-Benzazocin-5-ol, 3,4-dihydro-7-methoxy-3,3-dimethyl-	EtOH	215(4.28),252(4.03), 300(3.57)	18-2504-73
1-Benzazocin-5-ol, 3,4-dihydro-8-methoxy-3,3-dimethyl-	EtOH	252(4.07),316(3.46)	18-2504-73
2H-1-Benzopyran-2-one, 7-(diethylamino)-4-methyl-	EtOH	376(4.42)	40-0118-73
Carbazole, 1,2,3,4-tetrahydro-6,7-dimethoxy-	EtOH	229(4.45),280s(3.72), 303(3.95)	44-0215-73
2-Cyclohexen-1-one, 3-[(3-hydroxyphenyl)amino]-5,5-dimethyl-	EtOH	314(4.41)	18-2504-73
	EtOH-acid	301(4.25)	18-2504-73

Compound	Solvent	λ_{max}(log ε)	Ref.
2-Cyclohexen-1-one, 3-[(4-hydroxyphenyl)amino]-5,5-dimethyl-	EtOH	304(4.23)	18-2504-73
Cyclopentaneacetamide, 1-methyl-2-oxo-5-phenyl-, trans	EtOH	243(2.00),250(2.11), 255(2.26),260(2.34), 266(2.23),269(2.08)	104-0835-73
2H-Pyrrole-3-carboxylic acid, 3,4-dihydro-2,2-dimethyl-5-phenyl-, methyl ester	C_6H_{12}	243(4.25)	35-1945-73
$C_{14}H_{17}NO_2S$			
1,3-Butanedione, 2-[(dimethylamino)-(methylthio)methylene]-1-phenyl-	EtOH	233(4.05),271s(4.08), 287(4.11),345(3.58)	1-0258-73
$C_{14}H_{17}NO_3$			
7H-Benzo[de]quinolin-7-one, 1,2,3,8,9-9a-hexahydro-6-hydroxy-5-methoxy-1-methyl-	EtOH	227(4.22),271(3.92), 361(3.57)	33-0759-73
Butanoic acid, 3-oxo-2-[[(phenylmethyl)-amino]methylene]-, ethyl ester	EtOH	236(4.20),299(4.24)	70-2478-73
Piperidine, 1-[(4-formylphenoxy)acetyl]-	EtOH	215(4.28),273(4.28)	111-0574-73
Pyrrolidine, 1-[(4-acetylphenoxy)acetyl]-	EtOH	212(4.14),268(4.12)	111-0574-73
$C_{14}H_{17}NO_3S$			
2-Propenoic acid, 3-[[3-oxo-3-(phenylamino)propyl]thio]-, ethyl ester, (Z)-	MeOH	245(4.20),285(4.20)	44-3507-73
$C_{14}H_{17}NO_4$			
2-Hexenedioic acid, 4-(phenylamino)-, dimethyl ester	EtOH	245(4.31),290(3.62)	104-2527-73
1(2H)-Isoquinolinone, 4-(1-hydroxyethyl)-6,7-dimethoxy-2-methyl-	EtOH	247(4.67),262(4.53), 324(4.00),338(3.99)	78-3881-73
Morpholine, 4-[(4-acetylphenoxy)acetyl]-	EtOH	213(4.29)	111-0574-73
4(1H)-Quinolinone, 2-(hydroxymethyl)-3-(2-hydroxypropyl)-8-methoxy-	MeOH	233(4.58),321(4.07), 333(4.03)	24-0355-73
$C_{14}H_{17}NO_4S$			
6H-Thieno[2,3-b]pyrrole-3,4-dicarboxylic acid, 2,5-dimethyl-, diethyl ester	EtOH	266(4.15)	103-1473-73
$C_{14}H_{17}NO_5$			
DL-Alanine, N-[3-(4-hydroxy-3-methoxyphenyl)-1-oxo-2-propenyl]-, methyl ester	MeOH	293(4.06),320(4.16)	20-0243-73
	MeOH-KOH	304(3.83),365(4.40)	20-0243-73
Glycine, N-[3-(4-hydroxy-3-methoxyphenyl)-1-oxo-2-propenyl]-, ethyl ester	EtOH	295(4.17),320(4.28)	20-0243-73
	MeOH-KOH	310(3.76),366(4.44)	20-0243-73
Spiro[1,3-dioxolane-2,1'(5'H)-indolizine]-6'-carboxylic acid, 2',3'-dihydro-7'-methyl-5'-oxo-, ethyl ester	EtOH	232s(3.47),310(3.73)	78-1949-73
$C_{14}H_{17}NO_6$			
2-Butenedioic acid, 2-[(2,5-dimethoxyphenyl)amino]-, dimethyl ester, (Z)-	$CHCl_3$	279(3.73),301(3.67),	39-2374-73C
Indoxyl β-D-glucoside	MeOH	230(4.08),272s(3.60), 282(3.66),289(3.62)	102-0447-73
after ten minutes	H_2SO_4	250(3.98),285s(3.26), 396(3.30)(changing)	102-0447-73
Phenylpenaldic acid, 2,6-dimethoxy-, ethyl ester	EtOH	274(3.76)	4-0935-73

Compound	Solvent	λ_{max}(log ϵ)	Ref.
$C_{14}H_{17}NO_7$			
Holocalin	EtOH	222(3.52),280(3.34)	102-0457-73
	EtOH-pH 12	246(3.55),304(3.41)	102-0457-73
2,3,4-Pyridinetricarboxylic acid, 1,6-dihydro-1,5-dimethyl-6-oxo-, 2-ethyl 3,4-dimethyl ester	EtOH	270(4.08),306(3.81)	39-0404-73C
1H-Pyrrole-3-propanoic acid, 2-formyl-5-(methoxycarbonyl)-4-(2-methoxy-2-oxoethyl)-, methyl ester	MeOH	233(4.14),301(4.30)	39-1546-73C
$C_{14}H_{17}NS$			
Cyclohexanethione, 2-[[(4-methylphenyl)-amino]methylene]-	EtOH	447(4.43)	104-1739-73
$C_{14}H_{17}N_2$			
Pyrido[2,3-g]quinolinium, 1,2,3,4-tetra-hydro-1,6-dimethyl-, bromide	H_2O	219(4.38),285(4.34), 447(3.69)	39-0832-73C
$C_{14}H_{17}N_2O_4PS$			
Phosphorothioic acid, O,O-diethyl S-[4-[2-(1,2,4-oxadiazol-3-yl)ethenyl]-phenyl] ester, (E)-	EtOH	288(4.45)	39-2241-73C
$C_{14}H_{17}N_3$			
3-Azaspiro[5.5]undeca-1,4-diene-1,5-di-carbonitrile, 2,4-dimethyl-	EtOH	216(4.3),342(3.4)	103-0994-73
$C_{14}H_{17}N_3O$			
Benzenepropanenitrile, α-[bis(dimethyl-amino)methylene]-β-oxo-	EtOH	253s(4.09),320(4.09)	1-0258-73
$C_{14}H_{17}N_3OS$			
4-Imidazolidinone, 5-[[4-(diethylamino)-phenyl]methylene]-2-thioxo-	pH 3-5	278(4.08),320(3.94), 468(4.55)	104-2418-73
	pH 12-13	285(4.00),320(3.98), 445(4.57)	104-2418-73
	EtOH	274(4.07),315(3.96), 447(4.64)	104-2418-73
	dioxan	270(4.03),313(3.99), 435(4.66)	104-2418-73
$C_{14}H_{17}N_3O_4$			
2-Propenal, 3-(2,2-dimethyl-1,3-dioxol-an-4-yl)-, (4-nitrophenyl)hydrazone	EtOH	215(4.00),249(3.78), 294(3.85),323(3.60), 399(4.48)	136-0201-73C
$C_{14}H_{17}N_3O_7$			
Acetamide, 2-diazo-N-[4-(α-D-manno-pyranosyloxy)phenyl]-	MeOH	275(4.18)	136-0101-73F
$C_{14}H_{17}N_5O_3$			
Benzo[g]pteridine-2,4,9(3H)-trione, 6,7,8,10-tetrahydro-3,7,8,10-tetra-methyl-, 9-oxime	pH 0.0	262(3.87),404(4.15)	33-1908-73
	pH 6	215(4.14),270(4.10), 310s(--),440(4.03)	33-1908-73
	pH 13	255(4.12),360s(--), 470(4.21)	33-1908-73
$C_{14}H_{17}N_5O_4$			
Adenosine, 3'-(carboxymethyl)-3'-deoxy-N,N-dimethyl-, γ-lactone	MeOH	274(4.16)	44-0198-73

Compound	Solvent	λ max (log ε)	Ref.
$C_{14}H_{17}N_5O_5$			
β-D-ribo-Hept-5-enofuranuronic acid, 1-(6-amino-9H-purin-9-yl)-1,5,6-trideoxy-, ethyl ester, (E)-	pH 1	257(4.18)	136-0225-73B
	pH 7	259(4.18)	136-0225-73B
	pH 13	259(4.19)	136-0225-73B
$C_{14}H_{17}N_7NaO_8P$			
Adenosine, N-[(methylamino)carbonyl]-, cyclic 3',5'-(hydrogen phosphate) 2'-(methylcarbamate), Na salt	pH 1	276(4.36),285s(4.25)	87-1075-73
	pH 7	267(4.35),275s(4.33)	87-1075-73
	pH 11	267(4.34),275s(4.27)	87-1075-73
$C_{14}H_{17}N_7NaO_8PS$			
Adenosine, 7,8-dihydro-N-[(methylamino)-carbonyl]-8-thioxo-, cyclic 3',5'-(hydrogen phosphate) 2'-(methyl-carbamate), Na salt	pH 1	244(4.30),313(4.53)	87-1075-73
	pH 7	233(4.25),312(4.49)	87-1075-73
	pH 11	233(4.24),311(4.47)	87-1075-73
$C_{14}H_{17}OP$			
9-Phosphatricyclo[4.2.1.0^{2,5}]nonane, 9-phenyl-, 9-oxide	EtOH	218(4.11),253(2.55), 258(2.72),265(2.88), 272(2.82)	35-4292-73
$C_{14}H_{17}O_2Rh$			
Rhodium, [(2,3,6,7-η)bicyclo[6.1.0]nona-2,4,6-triene](2,4-pentanedionato-O,O')-	hexane	205(4.31),302(3.69), 361s(3.05)	78-3903-73
$C_{14}H_{18}$			
Cycloheptane, benzylidene-	hexane	250(4.18)	35-8114-73
$C_{14}H_{18}BrNO_2S$			
Pyrido[2,1-b]benzothiazolium, 4-ethoxy-5a,6,7,8,9,9a-hexahydro-1-methyl-9-oxo-, bromide, cis	pH 1	218(3.94),243(3.91), 349(3.95)	39-2049-73C
$C_{14}H_{18}BrN_5O_4$			
Adenine, 9-[4-(bromomethylene)-4-meth-oxy-2,3-O-(1-methylethylidene)-β-D-erythrofuranosyl]-	EtOH	258(4.12)	35-1350-73
$C_{14}H_{18}Br_2O_4$			
Cyclobuta[1,2-b:4,3-b']dipyran-4,5-di-one, 3,6-dibromooctahydro-2,7,8a,8b-tetramethyl-	EtOH	304(2.20)	23-1267-73
$C_{14}H_{18}NO$			
1,2-Benzisoxazolium, 3a,4,5,6,7,7a-hexa-hydro-2-methyl-3-phenyl-, perchlorate	EtOH	276(4.00)	22-1390-73
$C_{14}H_{18}NO_4P$			
Phosphonic acid, (1,4-dihydro-1-methyl-4-oxo-3-quinolinyl)-, diethyl ester	MeOH	242(4.32),293(3.98), 316(4.12),328(4.11)	94-1080-73
$C_{14}H_{18}N_2$			
Cyclobutanecarbonitrile, 3-(cyanomethyl-ene)-2-ethyl-2-methyl-4-(1-methylprop-ylidene)-	EtOH	282(4.30)	39-0885-73B
Cyclopent[b]indole-4(1H)-propanamine, 2,3-dihydro-, maleate	EtOH	214(4.51),231(4.55), 279(3.82),284(3.86), 292(3.81)	78-4045-73
Indole, 2-(4-piperidinylmethyl)-	MeOH	275(3.89),281(3.89), 291(3.77)	23-0792-73

Compound	Solvent	$\lambda_{max}(\log \epsilon)$	Ref.
4H-Pyrrolo[3,2,1-ij]quinolin-1-ethan-amine, 5,6-dihydro-4-methyl-	EtOH	224(4.57),279s(3.77), 288(3.81),297(3.75)	103-0196-73
$C_{14}H_{18}N_2O$			
1H-Azepino[5,4,3-cd]indole, 3,4,5,6-tetrahydro-7-methoxy-2,5-dimethyl-	MeOH	230(4.44),288(3.93), 300(3.91)	44-1504-73
Benzamide, 2-(cyclopentylidenamino)-N-ethyl-	EtOH	225(4.69),340(3.44)	103-0490-73
3H-Imidazo[1,2-a]azepine, 5,6,7,8,9,9a-hexahydro-2-phenyl-, 1-oxide	MeOH	224(3.95),289(4.18)	24-1172-73
2-Propanone, 1-(1,3-dimethyl-2-imidazol-idinylidene)-1-phenyl-	EtOH	235(3.82),292(4.10), 318s(3.96)	1-0258-73
$C_{14}H_{18}N_2OS_3$			
4-Thiazolidinone, 3-ethyl-5-[(3-ethyl-4,5-dimethylthiazol-2-ylidene)ethyl-idene]-2-thioxo-	EtOH	544(5.26)	103-0687-73
4-Thiazolidinone, 3-ethyl-5-[1-methyl-2-(3,4,5-trimethyl-2(3H)-thiazolyli-dene)ethylidene]-2-thioxo-	EtOH	539(5.02)	103-1078-73
$C_{14}H_{18}N_2O_2$			
Acetic acid, 1-azatricyclo[3.3.1.1^{3,7}]-dec-4-ylidenecyano-, ethyl ester	hexane	229(3.94),316(3.69)	78-1691-73
2H-Azepin-2-one, hexahydro-1-[2-(hy-droxyimino)-2-phenylethyl]-, (Z)-	MeOH	243(3.91)	24-1172-73
3,4-Tetramethyleneisoxazolin-5-one, benzylammonium salt	EtOH	261(3.96)	1-2802-73
$C_{14}H_{18}N_2O_3$			
2H-1,2-Benzodiazepine-2-carboxylic acid, 3-ethoxy-1,3-dihydro-, ethyl ester	EtOH	225(4.59),259(3.90), 308(3.27)	78-2359-73
1H-Indole-3-carboxylic acid, 4-amino-5-methoxy-1,2-dimethyl-, ethyl ester	MeOH	224(4.51),251(4.24), 313(3.99)	103-1490-73
1H-Isoindole-1,3(2H)-dione, 2-[3-[(2-hy-droxyethyl)methylamino]propyl]-	pH 1	300(3.28)	103-0383-73
	pH 7	300(--)	103-0383-73
	pH 13	270s(--)	103-0383-73
Piperidine, 1-[[4-(hydroxyimino)methyl]-phenoxy]acetyl]-	EtOH	210(4.42),264(4.37)	111-0574-73
Pyrrolidine, 1-[[4-(1-hydroxyimino)eth-yl]phenoxy]acetyl]-	EtOH	210(4.32),257(4.27)	111-0574-73
$C_{14}H_{18}N_2O_4$			
DL-Alanine, N-acetyl-3-[(phenylmethyl-ene)amino]-, ethyl ester, N^3-oxide	EtOH	224(3.92),229(3.86), 296(4.30)	87-0289-73
1,6-Diazabicyclo[6.2.1]undec-3-ene-2,5,7,10-tetrone, 3(or 4)-ethyl-4(or 3),9,11-trimethyl-	dioxan	228(4.29),280(2.50)	24-0803-73
Morpholine, 4-[[4-[1-(hydroxyimino)eth-yl]phenoxy]acetyl]-	EtOH	209(4.38),257(4.24)	111-0574-73
Pyridinium, 1-[[3-ethoxy-2-(ethoxycarbo-nyl)-3-oxo-1-propenyl]amino]-2-methyl-, hydroxide, inner salt	EtOH	239(4.15),280(4.20), 386(4.04)	39-2580-73C
Pyridinium, 1-[[3-ethoxy-2-(ethoxycarbo-nyl)-3-oxo-1-propenyl]amino]-4-methyl-, hydroxide, inner salt	EtOH	250(4.18),278(4.16), 385(4.17)	39-2580-73C
$C_{14}H_{18}N_2O_4S$			
1H-Pyrazole-3-carboxylic acid, 2-amino-4,5-dihydro-1-[(4-methylphenyl)sulfon-yl]-	MeOH	228(4.10),297(4.15)	118-0546-73

Compound	Solvent	λ_{max}(log ε)	Ref.
$C_{14}H_{18}N_2O_4S_5$			
2-Propenoic acid, 2-(aminothioxomethyl)-3-[[2-cyano-3-ethoxy-1-(methylthio)-3-oxo-1-propenyl]dithio]-3-(methylthio)-, ethyl ester, (E,E)-	EtOH	224(4.25),240s(4.16), 294s(4.14),334(4.53)	18-0699-73
$C_{14}H_{18}N_2O_5$			
1H-Pyrrole-2-propanoic acid, 2-cyano-4-(ethoxycarbonyl)-2,3-dihydro-5-methyl-3-oxo-, ethyl ester	EtOH	236(4.13),299(3.93)	94-2571-73
$C_{14}H_{18}N_2O_6$			
2,5-Diazabicyclo[2.2.2]octa-2,7-diene-7,8-dicarboxylic acid, 3-ethoxy-1,5-dimethyl-6-oxo-, dimethyl ester	EtOH	264.5(3.38)	39-0404-73C
4-Pyridinepropanoic acid, 2-methoxy-5-nitro-α-oxo-β-propyl-, ethyl ester	EtOH	236(4.23),299(3.63)	44-1824-73
$C_{14}H_{18}N_2O_6S$			
Uridine, 2',3'-O-(1-methylethylidene)-4-thio-, 5'-acetate	pH 7	329(4.27)	103-0917-73
$C_{14}H_{18}N_2O_7$			
1H-Pyrrole-3-acetic acid, α-acetyl-2,5-dihydro-4-(methoxycarbonyl)-2-(methoxyimino)-1-methyl-5-oxo-, ethyl ester	EtOH	258(4.10),330(4.05)	94-1667-73
$C_{14}H_{18}N_4O_3$			
3-Pyridinecarboxamide, 1,1'-[oxybis-(methylene)]bis[1,6-dihydro-	H_2O	258(3.79),345(3.68)	5-1237-73
7H-Pyrrolo[2,3-d]pyrimidin-4-amine, 7-[5-deoxy-2,3-O-(1-methylethylidene)-β-D-ribofuranosyl]-	MeOH	268(4.08)	18-0618-73
$C_{14}H_{18}N_4O_4$			
2,4(1H,3H)-Pyrimidinedione, 1-[3-(3,4-dihydro-5-methyl-2,4-dioxo-1(2H)-pyrimidinyl)propyl]-5-ethyl-	H_2O	271.5(4.22)	56-1943-73
2,4(1H,3H)-Pyrimidinedione, 1-[3-(3,4-dihydro-6-methyl-2,4-dioxo-1(2H)-pyrimidinyl)propyl]-5-ethyl-	H_2O	270.5(4.30)	56-1943-73
2,4(1H,3H)-Pyrimidinedione, 1-[3-(3,4-dihydro-2,4-dioxo-1(2H)-pyrimidinyl)-propyl]-5-methyl-	H_2O	271.0(4.29)	56-1943-73
1H-Pyrimido[5,4-b][1,4]oxazine-6-carboxylic acid, 7-methyl-4-(4-morpholinyl)-, ethyl ester	EtOH	241(4.3),274(4.0), 380(3.3)	103-1532-73
$C_{14}H_{18}N_6O_3$			
Adenosine, 3'-(cyanomethyl)-3'-deoxy-N,N-dimethyl-	H_2O	275(4.20)	44-0198-73
$C_{14}H_{18}N_6O_5$			
Adenosine, N-[(2-propenylamino)carbonyl]-	pH 1-2	270s(--),277(4.36)	87-0139-73
	pH 5-7	269(4.35),277s(--)	87-0139-73
	pH 12	278(4.18),298(4.12)	87-0139-73
β-D-Allofuranuronamide, 1-(6-amino-9H-purin-9-yl)-1-deoxy-2,3-O-(1-methylethylidene)-	pH 2	256(4.18)	69-3328-73
	pH 7+	259(4.18)	69-3328-73

Compound	Solvent	λ max(log ε)	Ref.
α-L-Talofuranuronamide, 1-(6-amino-9H-purin-9-yl)-1-deoxy-2,3-O-(1-methylethylidene)-	pH 2	256(4.18)	69-3328-73
	pH 7+	258(4.19)	69-3328-73
$C_{14}H_{18}N_6O_7$			
L-Alanine, N-[[(9-β-D-ribofuranosyl-9H-purin-6-yl)amino]carbonyl]-	pH 1-2	270s(--),277(4.36)	87-0139-73
	pH 5-7	270(4.37),277s(--)	87-0139-73
	pH 12	270(4.25),300(3.96)	87-0139-73
β-Alanine, N-[[(9-β-D-ribofuranosyl-9H-purin-6-yl)amino]carbonyl]-	pH 1-2	270s(--),277(4.35)	87-0139-73
	pH 5-7	269(4.34),277s(--)	87-0139-73
$C_{14}H_{18}N_6O_8$			
L-Serine, N-[[(9-β-D-ribofuranosyl-9H-purin-6-yl)amino]carbonyl]-	pH 1-2	270s(--),276(4.30)	87-0139-73
	pH 5-7	269(4.31),277s(--)	87-0139-73
	pH 12	271(4.16),295(4.03)	87-0139-73
$C_{14}H_{18}N_8O_8$			
Hexanedioic acid, bis[2-(hexahydro-2,4,6-trioxo-5-pyrimidinyl)hydrazide]	EtOH	243(4.25)	103-0247-73
$C_{14}H_{18}O$			
4bH-Benzo[3,4]cyclobuta[1,2]cyclohepten-4b-ol, 5,6,7,8,9,9a-hexahydro-1-methyl-	EtOH	260(2.76),266(2.89), 273(2.86)	22-3493-73
5H-Benzocyclononen-5-one, 6,7,8,9,10,11-hexahydro-1-methyl-	EtOH	241(3.49)	22-3493-73
5(6H)-Benzocyclooctenone, 7,8,9,10-tetrahydro-8,8-dimethyl-	EtOH	238.5(3.72)	78-1857-73
Bicyclo[2.2.1]heptane, 2-methoxy-2-phenyl-, exo	EtOH	212(3.64),216(3.64), 259(2.66)	35-4611-73
Ethanone, 1-(2,3-dihydro-1,3,3-trimethyl-1H-inden-1-yl)-	C_6H_{12}	261s(2.88),266(3.02), 273(3.04)	23-1598-73
3H-Fluoren-3-one, 1,2,6,7,8,8a,9,9a-octahydro-5-methyl-	EtOH	307(4.29)	22-1109-73
1(2H)-Naphthalenone, 3,4-dihydro-2,2,4-4-tetramethyl-	C_6H_{12}	225(4.07),241(3.97), 286(3.21)	23-1598-73
Tricyclo[6.4.0.0^{2,7}]dodeca-2,4,6-trien-1-ol, 10,10-dimethyl-	EtOH	261(3.04),267(3.18), 274(3.12)	78-1843-73
$C_{14}H_{18}O_2$			
7H-Benz[e]inden-7-one, 1,2,3,3a,4,5,8,9-octahydro-3-hydroxy-3a-methyl-, (3S-cis)	MeOH	307(4.34)	78-3631-73
1,8(2H,5H)-Benzocyclooctenedione, 3,6,7,10a-tetrahydro-4,10a-dimethyl-	EtOH	224(3.52)	88-0991-73
4H-1-Benzopyran-4-one, 2-butyl-2,3-dihydro-6-methyl-	MeOH	254(3.95),331(3.54)	20-0705-73
4H-1-Benzopyran-4-one, 2,3-dihydro-6-methyl-2-(2-methylpropyl)-	MeOH	254(3.95),332(3.54)	20-0705-73
2-Hepten-1-one, 1-(2-hydroxy-5-methylphenyl)-	MeOH	272(4.23),354(3.68)	20-0299-73
2-Hexen-1-one, 1-(2-hydroxy-5-methylphenyl)-5-methyl-, (E)-	MeOH	272(4.23),358(3.68)	20-0299-73
8-Nonene-4,6-diyn-3-ol, 9-(tetrahydro-2H-pyran-2-yl)-, trans	n.s.g.	230(4.38),242(3.78), 255(4.08),269(4.24), 285(4.15)	39-0145-73C
1H-Phenalen-5(7H)-one, 2,3,8,9,9a,9b-hexahydro-9b-hydroxy-9a-methyl-	EtOH	245(4.15)	118-0308-73
2-Propenal, 3-(3a,4,5,7a-tetrahydro-3,3a,6-trimethyl-2-benzofuranyl)-	EtOH	237(3.78),340(4.00)	39-1989-73C

Compound	Solvent	λ_{max}(log ϵ)	Ref.
Tricyclo[4.3.3.0]dodec-8-ene-2,7-dione, 8,9-dimethyl-	EtOH	247(4.01),296(2.68)	44-4281-73
Tricyclo[4.4.2.0]dodec-11-ene-2,7-dione, 11,12-dimethyl-	EtOH	230(3.56),299(2.67)	44-4281-73
Tricyclo[7.3.0.0^{4,9}]dodec-3-ene-2,8-dione, 1,3-dimethyl-	EtOH	221(3.65),251(3.90), 315(2.48)	44-4281-73
$C_{14}H_{18}O_3$			
1-Butanone, 1-(5-acetyl-2-methoxyphenyl)-3-methyl- (espeleton)	ether	237(4.27),262(4.06), 300(3.26)	24-3035-73
1,4-Cyclohexadiene-1-propanal, β,β,2,4-5-pentamethyl-3,6-dioxo-	MeOH	257(4.18)	35-8313-73
5,9-Methano-5H-benzocyclohepten-6-ol, 6,7,8,9-tetrahydro-1,4-dimethoxy-	EtOH	286(3.47)	39-1840-73C
2-Naphthalenecarboxylic acid, 5,6,7,8-tetrahydro-8,8a-dimethyl-3-oxo-, methyl ester	MeOH	245(4.02)	23-2166-73
2H-Naphtho[1,8-bc]furan-2,6(2aH)-dione, 3,4,5,5a,8a,8b-hexahydro-2a,5a,7-trimethyl-	EtOH	228(3.81)	32-1271-73
2-Propenoic acid, 2-methyl-, 3-methyl-9-oxobicyclo[3.3.1]non-2-en-2-yl ester	EtOH	208(4.09)	22-1409-73
Spiro[1,3-dioxolane-2,2'(1'H)-naphthalen]-5'(3'H)-one, 4',4'a,8',8'a-tetrahydro-4'a-methyl-8'-methylene-, cis	MeOH	275(4.14)	35-2303-73
4,12-Tetradecadiene-8,10-diyne-1,6,7-triol, trans-trans	MeOH	215(4.56),241(3.63), 254(3.91),268(4.06), 284(3.92)	39-0140-73C
6,12-Tetradecadiene-8,10-diyne-1,5,14-triol, trans-trans	n.s.g.	233(4.51),237(4.52), 247s(--),262(3.92), 276(4.21),294(4.39), 313(4.30)	39-0145-73C
6,13-Tetradecadiene-8,10-diyne-1,5,12-triol, trans	n.s.g.	213(4.20),241(3.87), 254(4.17),269(4.30), 284(4.22)	39-0145-73C
$C_{14}H_{18}O_4$			
Benzenebutanoic acid, 2-hydroxy-γ-oxo-4-propyl-, methyl ester	MeOH	260(4.20),325(3.63)	33-0075-73
Benzenebutanoic acid, 4-hydroxy-γ-oxo-2-propyl-, methyl ester	MeOH	276(4.10)	33-0075-73
2-Benzoxepin-6,9-dione, 1,3,4,5-tetrahydro-3-hydroxy-5,5,7,8-tetramethyl-	MeOH	261(4.16)	35-8313-73
1,5-Heptadiene-3,4-diol, 1-[3-hydroxy-2-(hydroxymethyl)phenyl]-	EtOH	219(4.47),254(3.97), 293(3.52)	88-3537-73
4-Hexene-2,3-diol, 1-(1,3-dihydro-4-hydroxy-1-isobenzofuranyl)-	EtOH	270(3.42),278(3.37)	88-3537-73
2-Naphthaleneacetic acid, 1,2,3,4,4a,5-8,8a-octahydro-1,4-dioxo-, ethyl ester	EtOH	277(1.76)	104-2389-73
$C_{14}H_{18}O_5$			
Ethanone, 1-[2,3-dihydro-6-hydroxy-2-(1-hydroxy-1-methylethyl)-4-methoxy-7-benzofuranyl]-	MeOH	218(4.09),229(4.10), 284(4.23),337(3.44)	83-0857-73
$C_{14}H_{18}O_6$			
Benzenebutanoic acid, 2-hydroxy-3,4-dimethoxy-α-methyl-γ-oxo-, methyl ester	EtOH	219(4.15),232s(4.01), 284(4.26)	39-2388-73C

Compound	Solvent	$\lambda_{max}(\log \epsilon)$	Ref.
Benzoic acid, 2-hydroxy-3-(3-hydroxy-3-methyl-2-oxobutyl)-4-methoxy-	MeOH	215(4.34),263(4.20), 301(3.70)	78-3099-73
Butanedioic acid, 2-hydroxy-2-[(4-methoxyphenyl)methyl]-, dimethyl ester	MeOH	225(4.01),276(3.23), 283(3.18)	44-4457-73
1,3-Cyclohexadiene-1-methanol, 5,6-diacetoxy-α-methyl-, acetate, cis	MeOH	258(3.62)	69-1520-73
$C_{14}H_{18}O_8$			
1,3-Benzenediol, 2,4,5,6-tetramethoxy-, diacetate	MeOH	203(4.60),272(4.00)	78-2645-73
1-Cyclohexene-1-carboxylic acid, 3,4,5-triacetoxy-, methyl ester	EtOH	210(4.12)	35-7821-73
isomer	EtOH	211(4.08)	35-7821-73
1,5-Hexadiene-1,2,5,6-tetracarboxylic acid, tetramethyl ester	EtOH	221(4.31)	39-2016-73C
1,5-Hexadiene-2,3,4,5-tetracarboxylic acid, tetramethyl ester	EtOH	212.5(3.89)	39-2016-73C
$C_{14}H_{19}BrO_3$			
2H-Naphtho[1,8-bc]furan-2,6(2aH)-dione, 7-bromooctahydro-2a,5a,7-trimethyl-	EtOH	310(1.90)	32-1271-73
$C_{14}H_{19}IN_2O$			
2-Pyrrolidinone, 5-[[3,4-dihydro-2-(iodomethylene)-3,3-dimethyl-2H-pyrrol-5-yl]methylene]-4,4-dimethyl-	EtOH	228(3.95),237(4.01), 345(4.12)	89-0912-73
$C_{14}H_{19}N$			
6,7-Nonadiene-2,4-diyn-1-amine, N,N-diethyl-8-methyl-	n.s.g.	209(4.36),213(4.45), 227(4.03),238(4.00), 252(4.05),267(4.08), 283(4.03),303(3.45), 310(3.43)	70-1029-73
Piperidine, 1-(2,3-dihydro-3-methyl-1-pentalenyl)-	hexane	315(4.46),321(4.47)	89-0335-73
$C_{14}H_{19}NO$			
13-Azabicyclo[7.3.1]trideca-1(13),9,11-trien-2-one, 3,3-dimethyl-	hexane	235(3.79),272(3.50)	18-1579-73
1H-Carbazole, 2,3,4,4a,9,9a-hexahydro-8-methoxy-4a-methyl-	EtOH	245(3.86),287(3.36)	33-2628-73
Oxazole, 2,5-dihydro-2,2-dimethyl-5-(1-methylethyl)-4-phenyl-	EtOH	239(4.10)	33-2611-73
$C_{14}H_{19}NO_2$			
2-Butenoic acid, 2-methyl-3-[(phenylmethyl)amino]-, ethyl ester	EtOH	301(4.18)	1-2802-73
2,5-Cyclohexadiene-1,4-dione, 3-amino-5-(1,1-dimethylethyl)-2-(2-methyl-2-propenyl)-	EtOH	216(4.16),274(3.89), 494(3.66)	39-0268-73C
$C_{14}H_{19}NO_2S_2$			
4-Hexenoic acid, 2-[(2-butenylthio)thioxomethyl]-2-cyano-, ethyl ester	EtOH	318(3.88)	78-2077-73
$C_{14}H_{19}NO_3$			
1H,10bH-Benzo[ij]quinolizine-10b-carboxylic acid, 2,3,5,6,7,7a,8,10a-octahydro-8-oxo-, methyl ester, (7aα,10aα-10bα)-	MeOH	226(3.89)	35-8427-73

Compound	Solvent	$\lambda_{max}(\log \epsilon)$	Ref.
1H,10bH-Benzo[ij]quinolizine-10b-carboxylic acid, 2,3,5,6,7,7a,8,10a-octahydro-8-oxo-, methyl ester, (7aα,10aα,10bβ)-	MeOH	233(3.76)	35-8427-73
(7aα,10aβ,10bβ)-	MeOH	225(3.89)	35-8427-73
$C_{14}H_{19}NO_4$			
1H-Indole-3-ethanol, 1-acetyl-2,3-dihydro-5,6-dimethoxy-	MeOH	216(4.28),261(4.19), 303(3.91)	44-3350-73
$C_{14}H_{19}NO_5$			
Butanedioic acid, (5-ethoxy-3,4-dimethyl-2H-pyrrol-2-ylidene)-, dimethyl ester	MeOH	277(4.05),384(3.90)	24-0812-73
2-Butenedioic acid, 2-(5-ethoxy-3,4-dimethyl-1H-pyrrol-2-yl)-, dimethyl ester, (Z)-	MeOH	221(4.03),423(4.27)	24-0812-73
Spiro[1,3-dioxolane-2,1'(5'H)-indolizine]-6'-carboxylic acid, 2',3',8',9'-tetrahydro-7'-methyl-5'-oxo-, ethyl ester	EtOH	260(3.08)	78-1949-73
$C_{14}H_{19}NO_6$			
1H-Pyrrole-3-propanoic acid, 5-(methoxycarbonyl)-4-(2-methoxy-2-oxoethyl)-2-methyl-, methyl ester	MeOH	283(3.95)	39-1546-73C
$C_{14}H_{19}NO_9S$			
Benzoic acid, 2-[(β-D-glucopyranosylamino)sulfonyl]-, methyl ester	MeOH	275(3.14)	5-1943-73
$C_{14}H_{19}N_3$			
3,5-Pyridinedicarbonitrile, 4-butyl-1,4-dihydro-2,4,6-trimethyl-	EtOH	216(4.3),342(3.8)	103-0994-73
$C_{14}H_{19}N_3O_3$			
2-Butenedinitrile, 2-(aminoethoxymethyl)-3-(1-ethoxy-2-oxocyclopentyl)-, (Z)-	EtOH	215(4.27)	12-1551-73
$C_{14}H_{19}N_3S$			
2H-Imidazol[4,5-g]quinoline-2-thione, 3-butyl-1,3,5,6,7,8-hexahydro-	EtOH	260(3.94)	103-1028-73
$C_{14}H_{19}N_5O_2$			
7H-Purine-7-propanenitrile, 8-butyl-1,2,3,6-tetrahydro-1,3-dimethyl-2,6-dioxo-	n.s.g.	210(4.37),277(4.04)	73-1571-73
$C_{14}H_{19}N_5O_2S$			
1H-Purine-2,6-dione, 3,7-dihydro-7-(3-isothiocyanatopropyl)-1,3-dimethyl-8-propyl-	n.s.g.	210(4.37),277(4.02)	73-1571-73
$C_{14}H_{19}N_5O_4$			
D-Mannitol, 1-(6-amino-9H-purin-9-yl)-3,6-anhydro-1-deoxy-4,5-O-(1-methylethylidene)-	90% EtOH	260(4.22)	136-0243-73B
4H-Pyrazolo[3,4-b]pyridin-4-one, 1,7-dihydro-1-β-D-ribofuranosyl-, (1-methylethylidene)hydrazone	EtOH	207(4.02),255(4.01), 273s(3.73),324(4.03)	104-1294-73

Compound	Solvent	λ_{max}(log ε)	Ref.
$C_{14}H_{19}N_5O_5$			
Adenosine, N-methoxy-2',3'-O-(1-methyl-ethylidene)-	pH 1	267(4.21)	94-1676-73
	pH 7	268(4.17)	94-1676-73
	pH 13	284(4.07)	94-1676-73
	EtOH	268(4.15)	94-1676-73
Adenosine, 1-methoxy-2',3'-O-(1-methyl-ethylidene)-, hydroiodide	pH 1	259(4.10)	94-1676-73
	pH 7	259(4.11)	94-1676-73
	pH 13	257(4.06)	94-1676-73
	EtOH	260(4.09)	94-1676-73
β-D-ribo-Heptofuranuronic acid, 1-(6-amino-9H-purin-9-yl)-1,5,6-trideoxy-, ethyl ester	pH 1	257(4.17)	136-0225-73B
	pH 7	259(4.18)	136-0225-73B
	pH 13	259(4.18)	136-0225-73B
7(8H)-Pteridinone, 2-(dimethylamino)-6-methyl-8-β-D-ribofuranosyl-	MeOH	219(4.26),247(4.21), 315s(3.82),363(4.20)	24-0317-73
$C_{14}H_{19}N_5O_6$			
7(8H)-Pteridinone, 2-amino-4-(1-methyl-ethoxy)-8-β-D-ribofuranosyl-	pH -2.0	222(4.22),285s(3.95), 330(4.17)	24-1952-73
	pH 4.0	232(4.07),281(3.66), 350(4.18)	24-1952-73
	MeOH	211(4.54),232(4.11), 280(3.67),349(4.19)	24-1952-73
7(8H)-Pteridinone, 2-(dimethylamino)-8-β-D-glucopyranosyl-	MeOH	220(4.20),244(4.09), 310s(3.73),363(4.14)	24-0317-73
7(8H)-Pteridinone, 2-(dimethylamino)-4-methoxy-8-β-D-ribofuranosyl-	MeOH	243(4.23),290(3.64), 371(4.22)	24-1952-73
$C_{14}H_{19}N_5O_6S$			
Inosine, 5'-S-(3-amino-3-carboxypropyl)-5'-thio-, (S)-	H_2O	249(4.09)	88-2811-73
$C_{14}H_{19}N_5O_7S$			
Inosine, 5'-[(3-amino-3-carboxypropyl)-sulfinyl]-5'-deoxy-, (S)-	H_2O	249(4.05)	88-2811-73
$C_{14}H_{19}N_6O_7P$			
Adenosine, N-[(propylamino)carbonyl]-, cyclic 3',5'-(hydrogen phosphate)	pH 1	277(4.38),285s(4.27)	87-1075-73
	pH 7	268(4.36),276s(4.28)	87-1075-73
	pH 11	268(4.35),276s(4.28)	87-1075-73
	pH 12.65	269s(4.22),277(4.17), 296(4.14)	87-1075-73
$C_{14}H_{19}N_6O_8P$			
5'-Adenylic acid, N-[(2-propenylamino)-carbonyl]-	pH 1	277(4.35)	87-0956-73
	H_2O	269(4.34),275(4.27)	87-0956-73
	pH 13	269(4.22),277(4.21), 297(4.00)	87-0956-73
$C_{14}H_{19}OP$			
9-Phosphabicyclo[4.2.1]nonane, 9-phen-yl-, P-oxide	EtOH	220(4.01),254s(2.50), 265(2.84),272(2.77)	35-4292-73
$C_{14}H_{19}P$			
9-Phosphabicyclo[4.2.1]nonane, 9-phenyl-	EtOH	260(3.88)	35-4292-73
$C_{14}H_{20}$			
Benzene, 1-cyclohexyl-3,5-dimethyl-	EtOH	258(2.38),264(2.43), 271(2.37)	78-0085-73
Benzene, 1-cyclohexyl-2-ethyl-	EtOH	257(2.39),263(2.47), 271(2.40)	22-1517-73

Compound	Solvent	λ max(log ε)	Ref.
Benzene, (2-ethylcyclohexyl)-, cis	EtOH	248(2.28),255(2.34), 260(2.37),262s(2.33), 265(2.26),269(2.20)	22-1517-73
trans	EtOH	249(2.51),254(2.58), 256(2.56),259(2.60), 262(2.60),265(2.53), 268(2.51)	22-1517-73
Benzene, 1-octenyl-, cis	MeOH	243.5(4.18)	24-1612-73
Cyclobuta[1,2:3,4]dicycloheptene, 1,2,3,4,7,8,9,10,10a,10b-decahydro-	isooctane	251s(--),259(4.02), 269s(--)	78-1975-73
Tetracyclo[6.3.0.0^{2,11}.0^{3,7}]undec-9-ene, 1,9,11-trimethyl-	pentane	241(3.74)	35-6197-73
Tetracyclo[6.3.0.0^{2,11}.0^{3,7}]undec-9-ene, 2,8,10-trimethyl-	pentane	238s(3.43)	35-6197-73
$C_{14}H_{20}BrIO$			
2,4-Cyclohexadien-1-one, 5-(bromomethyl)-6-(5-iodo-3-methylpentyl)-6-methyl-	EtOH	317(3.86)	39-1843-73C
$C_{14}H_{20}F_7N_2P$			
Phosphine, difluoro(pentafluorophenyl)-, bis(diethylamino)deriv.	n.s.g.	208(3.59),265(2.84)	104-1729-73
$C_{14}H_{20}N_2$			
Pyrazine, 1,4-diethyl-1,4,5,6-tetrahydro-2-phenyl-	C_6H_{12}	318(4.07)	28-1319-73A
$C_{14}H_{20}N_2O$			
3-Buten-2-one, 4,4-bis(dimethylamino)-3-phenyl-	EtOH	225(3.89),270(4.13), 340(4.14)	1-0258-73
1-Cyclohexene-1-carbonitrile, 4,4-dimethyl-6-oxo-2-piperidino-	EtOH	237(3.71),306(4.43)	70-0811-73
$C_{14}H_{20}N_2O_2$			
Benzoic acid, 2-[[1-[(1,1-dimethylethyl)imino]ethyl]amino]-	MeOH	215(4.45),308(3.57)	78-2153-73
$C_{14}H_{20}N_2O_3$			
Benzoic acid, 4-[[[(2-methoxyethyl)-imino]methyl]methylamino]-, ethyl ester, hydrochloride	pH 7.5	261(4.27)	35-8414-73
	pH 10.5	303(4.45)	35-8414-73
$C_{14}H_{20}N_2O_4$			
Acetamide, N,N'-(2,5-dihydroxy-1,4-phenylene)di-2,1-ethanediyl]bis-	EtOH	275(3.83)	39-0832-73C
Benzoic acid, 2-[[[3-[(2-hydroxyethyl)-methylamino]propyl]amino]carbonyl]-	pH 1	275(3.10)	103-0383-73
$C_{14}H_{20}N_2O_5$			
3H-Azepinium, 4-acetyl-2-(diethylamino)-, oxalate	EtOH-HCl	227(4.35),320(3.77)	39-1079-73C
	EtOH-NaOH	241(4.90),398(3.89)	39-1079-73C
$C_{14}H_{20}N_2O_6$			
Butanedioic acid, 2-(5-amino-2-methoxy-4-pyridinyl)-3-hydroxy-, diethyl ester	EtOH	232(4.44),285(3.60)	44-1824-73
$C_{14}H_{20}N_3O_3P$			
Phosphonic acid, [2-(butylamino)-4-quinazolinyl]-, dimethyl ester	EtOH	260(3.76),320(3.14), 369(2.86)	48-0649-73

Compound	Solvent	$\lambda_{max}(\log \epsilon)$	Ref.
$C_{14}H_{20}N_4O_2$			
2,4(1H,3H)-Pteridinedione, 1,3-dimethyl-6,7-bis(1-methylethyl)-	MeOH	238(4.20),332(3.98)	24-3149-73
$C_{14}H_{20}N_4O_3$			
Benzo[g]pteridine-5(1H)-carboxaldehyde, 2,3,4,5a,6,7,8,9,9a,10-decahydro-7,8,10-trimethyl-2,4-dioxo-	pH 5	294(4.29)	33-1908-73
2,4(1H,3H)-Pteridinedione, 1,3-dimethyl-6,7-bis(1-methylethyl)-, 5-oxide	MeOH	243(4.45),296(3.82), 359(3.78)	24-3149-73
1H-Pyrimido[5,4-b][1,4]oxazine-6-carboxylic acid, 4-(diethylamino)-7-methyl-, ethyl ester	EtOH	241(4.3),282(4.1), 384(2.9)	103-1532-73
$C_{14}H_{20}N_6$			
1,3,5-Triazine-2,4,6-triamine, N,N,N',N'-tetramethyl-N''-(phenylmethyl)-	MeOH	228(4.61)	114-0419-73C
$C_{14}H_{20}N_6O_4$			
Adenosine, 3'-(2-amino-2-oxoethyl)-3'-deoxy-N,N-dimethyl-	H_2O	275(4.15)	44-0198-73
D-Arginine, N^2-acetyl-, 4-nitroanilide	aq NaCl	316(4.06)	18-0572-73
$C_{14}H_{20}N_6O_5$			
Adenosine, N-[[(1-methylethyl)amino]-carbonyl]-	pH 1-2	270s(--),277(4.37)	87-0139-73
	pH 5-7	270(4.39),277s(--)	87-0139-73
	pH 12	278(4.18),298(4.15)	87-0139-73
$C_{14}H_{20}N_6O_5S$			
Adenosine, 5'-S-(3-amino-3-carboxypropyl)-5'-thio-, (S)-	H_2O	260(4.17)	88-2811-73
$C_{14}H_{20}N_6O_6$			
Adenosine, N-[[(2-hydroxypropyl)amino]-carbonyl]-	pH 1-2	270s(--),277(4.36)	87-0139-73
	pH 5-7	269(4.39),277s(--)	87-0139-73
	pH 12	278(4.20),297(4.18)	87-0139-73
Adenosine, N-[[(3-hydroxypropyl)amino]-carbonyl]-	pH 1-2	270s(--),277(4.38)	87-0139-73
	pH 5-7	269(4.37),277s(--)	87-0139-73
	pH 12	277(4.22),298(3.97)	87-0139-73
$C_{14}H_{20}N_6O_6S$			
Adenosine, 5'-[(3-amino-3-carboxypropyl)sulfinyl]-5'-deoxy-, (R)-(±)-	H_2O	260(4.05)	88-2811-73
Guanosine, 5'-S-(3-amino-3-carboxypropyl)-5'-thio-, (S)-	H_2O	252(4.10)	88-2811-73
$C_{14}H_{20}N_6O_7S$			
Guanosine, 5'-[(3-amino-3-carboxypropyl)sulfinyl]-5'-deoxy-, (S)-	H_2O	252(4.06)	88-2811-73
$C_{14}H_{20}O$			
2,4-Cyclohexadien-1-one, 2-(1,1-dimethylethyl)-6-methyl-6-(2-propenyl)-	EtOH	306(3.73)	33-0014-73
2,4-Cyclohexadien-1-one, 4-(1,1-dimethylethyl)-6-methyl-6-(2-propenyl)-	EtOH	301(3.65)	33-0014-73
6H-3a,7-Methanoazulen-6-one, 1,2,3,7,8-8a-hexahydro-3,8,8-trimethyl-, [3S-(3α,3aα,7α,8aα)]-	EtOH	240(3.93)	88-0017-73
Norcedrenone	EtOH	230(4.03)	78-2087-73

Compound	Solvent	$\lambda_{max}(\log \epsilon)$	Ref.
$C_{14}H_{20}OS$			
8H-Cyclohepta[b]thiophen-8-one, 2-(1,1-dimethylethyl)-4,5,6,7-tetrahydro-7-methyl-	n.s.g.	293(4.10)	22-0343-73
$C_{14}H_{20}OSi$			
5,6-Undecadiene-8,10-diyn-1-ol, 11-(trimethylsilyl)-	n.s.g.	214(4.62),220(4.61), 233s(3.76),246(3.86), 259(4.03),274(4.15), 291(4.05)	88-1019-73
$C_{14}H_{20}O_2$			
Acetic acid, tricyclo[3.3.1.1^{3,7}]dec-2-ylidene-, ethyl ester	hexane	224(4.26)	78-1691-73
Eremophilenolide, 11-demethyl-, (±)-	MeOH	216(4.17)	23-2166-73
5H-Inden-5-one, 1,2,3,7a-tetrahydro-4-methoxy-7a-methyl-3-(1-methylethyl)-, (3α)-	EtOH	243(3.83),283(3.56)	44-3663-73
(3β)-	EtOH	243(3.62),283(3.05)	44-3663-73
Ligularenolide, 11-demethyl-, (±)-	MeOH	216(4.17)	23-2166-73
Phenol, 2-(1,1-dimethylethyl)-5-methyl-, propanoate	C_6H_{12}	267(2.62),274(2.60)	22-3087-73
	EtOH	265(2.64),273(2.62)	22-3087-73
1-Propanone, 1-[3-(1,1-dimethylethyl)-4-hydroxy-6-methylphenyl]-	EtOH	229(4.19),279(4.12)	22-3087-73
1-Propanone, 1-[3-(1,1-dimethylethyl)-6-hydroxy-2-methylphenyl]-	C_6H_{12}	266(3.93),342(3.57)	22-3087-73
	EtOH	266(3.80),340(3.42)	22-3087-73
1-Propanone, 1-[3-(1,1-dimethylethyl)-6-hydroxy-5-methylphenyl]-	C_6H_{12}	259(4.02),265(4.00), 343(3.59)	22-1442-73
	EtOH	261(4.02),342(3.56)	22-1442-73
Spiro[4.5]dec-7-ene-2-carboxylic acid, 10-methyl-6-methylene-, methyl ester	MeOH	232(4.14)	88-4967-73
$C_{14}H_{20}O_3$			
Benzenepropanol, 4-[(4-hydroxy-3-methyl-2-butenyl)oxy]- (cuspidiol)	EtOH	279(3.42),286(3.35)	88-4189-73
2H-1-Benzopyran-5-methanol, 3,4-dihydro-6-hydroxy-4,4,7,8-tetramethyl-	MeOH	290(3.22)	35-8308-73
2H-1-Benzopyran-6(8aH)-one, 3,4-dihydro-8a-hydroxy-4,4,5,7,8-pentamethyl-	MeOH	239(4.05)	35-8308-73
2-Naphthaleneacetic acid, 1,2,3,5,6,7,8-8a-octahydro-8,8a-dimethyl-3-oxo-	MeOH	238(4.17)	23-2166-73
2-Naphthalenecarboxylic acid, 1,2,3,5,6-7,8,8a-octahydro-8,8a-dimethyl-3-oxo-, methyl ester	MeOH	240(4.17)	23-2166-73
1-Oxaspiro[4.5]dec-7-ene-6,9-dione, 4,4,7,8,10-pentamethyl-	MeOH	249(4.08)	35-8308-73
Spiro[4.5]dec-6-ene-1-carboxylic acid, 4-methyl-8-oxo-, ethyl ester	MeOH	230(4.05),317(1.48)	33-1812-73
6-Tetradecene-8,10-diyne-1,5,12-triol, trans	n.s.g.	217(4.18),230(3.51), 241(3.81),254(4.10), 268(4.27),284(4.17)	39-0145-73C
$C_{14}H_{20}O_4$			
2H-1-Benzopyran-5,8-dione, 3,4,4a,8a-tetrahydro-2-hydroxy-4,4,6,7,8a-pentamethyl-	MeOH	252(4.08)	35-8313-73
Cyclobuta[1,2-b:4,3-b']dipyran-4,5-dione, octahydro-2,7,8a,8b-tetramethyl-	EtOH	285(1.93)	23-1267-73
isomer B	EtOH	281(1.99)	23-1267-73
isomer C	EtOH	281(1.99)	23-1267-73

Compound	Solvent	λmax(log ε)	Ref.
1-Naphthalenecarboxylic acid, decahydro-1,4a-dimethyl-5,7-dioxo-	hexane	280(1.70)	78-1237-73
	pH 1	252.5(4.18)	78-1237-73
	pH 13	283(4.36)	78-1237-73
	EtOH	282.5(4.27)	78-1237-73
Spiro[5.5]undecane-2-carboxylic acid, 7-methyl-3,11-dioxo-, methyl ester	EtOH	255(3.72)	77-0526-73
	EtOH-base	285(3.94)	77-0526-73
$C_{14}H_{20}O_4S_2$			
Propanedioic acid, 2-propenyl[(2-propenylthio)thioxomethyl]-, diethyl ester	EtOH	320(4.07)	78-2077-73
$C_{14}H_{20}O_6$			
Benzenebutanoic acid, 2-hydroxy-γ,3,4-trimethoxy-α-methyl-	EtOH	226s(3.91),275(3.11)	39-2388-73C
Cyclopenta[c]pyran-4-carboxylic acid, 6-acetoxy-1,4a,5,6,7,7a-hexahydro-1-methoxy-7-methyl-, methyl ester	EtOH	236(4.05)	35-0540-73
α-D-Galacto-oct-6-enodialdo-1,5-pyranose, 6,7-dideoxy-1,2:3,4-bis-O-(1-methylethylidene)-, (E)-	EtOH	241(4.23)	136-0201-73C
$C_{14}H_{20}O_8$			
2,5-Cyclohexadien-1-one, 4-[2-(β-D-glucopyranosyloxy)ethyl]-4-hydroxy-	EtOH	227(3.97)	1-0367-73
$C_{14}H_{20}O_9$			
Koaburaside	EtOH	280(3.52)	95-0223-73
	EtOH-NaOH	250(--),295(--)	95-0223-73
$C_{14}H_{21}ClN_2O_2$			
Piperidine, 1-[3-chloro-1,4-dioxo-2-(1-piperidinyl)-2-butenyl]-	MeOH	254(1.71),319(4.31)	73-1091-73
$C_{14}H_{21}ClO$			
Phenol, 4-(2-chloropropyl)-2-(1,1-dimethylethyl)-6-methyl-	EtOH	276(3.21)	33-0014-73
$C_{14}H_{21}MoN_7$			
Molybdenum(2+), heptakis(isocyanomethane)-, diiodide	MeOH	221(4.62),243(4.52), 275(4.26),402(3.03)	77-0202-73
$C_{14}H_{21}N$			
13-Azabicyclo[7.3.1]trideca-1(13),9,11-triene, 3,3-dimethyl-	hexane	214(3.94),270(3.34)	18-1579-73
Benzenamine, 4-cyclohexyl-2,6-dimethyl-	EtOH	235(3.85),288(3.15)	78-0085-73
Pyridine, 5-(2-cyclohexylethyl)-2-methyl-	MeOH	267(3.59)	103-1507-73
Pyrrolidine, 1-(2,6,7,7a-tetrahydro-1-methyl-1H-inden-3-yl)-	hexane	296(4.26)	22-1109-73
Pyrrolidine, 1-(5,6,7,7a-tetrahydro-4-methyl-1H-inden-3-yl)-	hexane	282(3.34),295s(--)	22-1109-73
$C_{14}H_{21}NO$			
2(3H)-Naphthalenone, 1-[1-(dimethylamino)ethenyl]-4,4a,5,6,7,8-hexahydro-	C_6H_{12}	237(4.22)	28-0803-73A
$C_{14}H_{21}NO_2$			
2,5-Cyclohexadiene-1,4-dione, 2-amino-3,6-bis(1,1-dimethylethyl)-	$CHCl_3$	273(4.13),465(3.21)	39-0268-73C

Compound	Solvent	λ_{max}(log ε)	Ref.
2,5-Cyclohexadiene-1,4-dione, 2-(1,1-dimethylethyl)-5-[(1,1-dimethylethyl)amino]-	EtOH	275(4.07),480(3.38)	39-0268-73C
2,5-Cyclohexadiene-1,4-dione, 2-(1,1-dimethylethyl)-6-[(1,1-dimethylethyl)amino]-	EtOH	278(4.24),486(3.47)	39-0268-73C
Ethanone, 1-[5-(1,1-dimethylethyl)-2-methoxyphenyl]-, O-methyloxime	CCl_4	286(3.482)	30-0394-73
Pyridine, 1,4-dihydro-4-methyl-1,4-bis-(1-oxobutyl)-	MeOH	255(4.21)	78-0391-73
$C_{14}H_{21}NO_3$			
7-Oxabicyclo[4.1.0]hept-3-ene-2,5-dione, 3-amino-1,4-bis(1,1-dimethylethyl)-	EtOH	211(3.93),254(3.71), 372(3.70)	39-0268-73C
L-Proline, 1-(5-methyl-3-oxo-1-cyclohexen-1-yl)-, ethyl ester	n.s.g.	310(4.17)	44-3487-73
$C_{14}H_{21}NO_4$			
Phenylalanine, 3,4-dihydroxy-, isopentyl ester	pH 1	280(3.45)	36-0510-73
Phenylalanine, 3,4-dihydroxy-, pentyl ester	pH 1	280(3.45)	36-0510-73
$C_{14}H_{21}NO_6$			
1-Cyclopentene-1-heptanoic acid, 2-carboxy-3-hydroxy-5-(methoxyimino)-	MeOH	269(4.17)	44-4412-73
Tyramine O-glucoside	pH 6.5	270(3.0),277(2.9)	102-2243-73
	pH 13	270(3.0),276(2.9)	102-2243-73
$C_{14}H_{21}NO_7$			
Dopamine 3-O-glucoside	pH 6.5	277(3.2)	102-2243-73
	pH 13	294(3.3)	102-2243-73
Dopamine 4-O-glucoside	pH 6.5	277(3.3)	102-2243-73
	pH 13	294(3.5)	102-2243-73
$C_{14}H_{21}N_3O_3$			
Carbamic acid, [[5-[bis(dimethylamino)-methylene]-1,3-cyclopentadien-1-yl]-carbonyl]-, ethyl ester	dioxan	258(4.25),335(3.93), 369(4.13)	89-0418-73
$C_{14}H_{21}N_3O_6$			
1H-Imidazole-4-carboxylic acid, 5-amino-1-[2,3-O-(1-methylethylidene)-D-ribofuranosyl]-, ethyl ester	MeOH	267(4.04)	39-1720-73C
epimer	MeOH	267(4.11)	39-1720-73C
$C_{14}H_{21}N_5O_6$			
Adenosine, N,N-bis(2-hydroxyethyl)-	pH 1	274(4.26)	87-0358-73
	H_2O	279(4.30)	87-0358-73
	pH 13	279(4.31)	87-0358-73
$C_{14}H_{21}N_6O_8P$			
5'-Adenylic acid, N-[[(1-methylethyl)-amino]carbonyl]-	pH 1	277(4.42)	87-0956-73
	H_2O	269(4.40),275(4.33)	87-0956-73
	pH 13	270(4.27),277(4.26), 297(4.06)	87-0956-73
$C_{14}H_{21}PS$			
Phosphine sulfide, bis(1-methylethyl)-(2-phenylethenyl)-	nonane	218s(4.20),260(4.33), 285s(3.72),295(3.49)	65-2164-73

Compound	Solvent	$\lambda_{max}(\log \epsilon)$	Ref.
$C_{14}H_{22}$			
1H-Benzocycloheptene, 2,3,4,5,6,7-hexahydro-1,1,7-trimethyl-	C_6H_{12}	241(3.78)	22-3187-73
1H-Benzocycloheptene, 2,3,4,6,7,8-hexahydro-1,1,7-trimethyl-	C_6H_{12}	228(3.78)	22-3187-73
1H-Benzocycloheptene, 2,3,5,6,7,8-hexahydro-1,1,7-trimethyl-	C_6H_{12}	241(4.34)	22-3187-73
1H-Benzocycloheptene, 2,5,6,7,8,9-hexahydro-1,1,7-trimethyl-	C_6H_{12}	267(3.48)	22-3187-73
Cyclohexene, 1,5,5-trimethyl-6-(3-methyl-2-butenylidene)-	C_6H_{12}	284(4.60)	22-3187-73
$C_{14}H_{22}N_2O$			
Acetamidine, 2-ethoxy-N,N-dimethyl-N'-(2,6-dimethylphenyl)-	C_6H_{12}	245(4.19)	78-4205-73
2-Pyridinamine, N-(2-cyclohexyl-1-methylethyl)-, 1-oxide, (S)-	MeOH	233(4.47),253(3.93), 330(3.78)	32-1083-73
$C_{14}H_{22}N_2O_2$			
3-Pyridinecarboxamide, N,1-dibutyl-1,2-dihydro-2-oxo-	EtOH	236(3.75),330(3.94)	70-1959-73
$C_{14}H_{22}N_2O_4$			
3H-Azepinium, 2-(diethylamino)-3,5-dimethyl-, oxalate	EtOH	281(3.82)	39-1079-73C
	EtOH-NaOH	303(3.88)	39-1079-73C
3H-Azepinium, 2-(diethylamino)-5,7-dimethyl-, oxalate	EtOH	263(3.87)	39-1079-73C
	EtOH-NaOH	294(3.87)	39-1079-73C
$C_{14}H_{22}N_2O_4S$			
1H-Imidazole-4-hexanoic acid, ε-(acetylthio)-2,3-dihydro-5-methyl-2-oxo-, ethyl ester	EtOH	220(4.03)	70-2566-73
1H-Imidazole-4-hexanoic acid, 5-[(acetylthio)methyl]-2,3-dihydro-2-oxo-, ethyl ester	EtOH	220(3.70)	70-2566-73
$C_{14}H_{22}N_2O_6$			
5-Pyrimidinepropanoic acid, α-(dimethoxymethyl)-1,4-dihydro-α-(methoxymethyl)-2-methyl-4-oxo-, methyl ester	MeOH	278(3.78)	18-0580-73
$C_{14}H_{22}N_2O_9$			
D-glycero-D-galacto-Non-2-enonic acid, 5-[[3-(acetylamino)-1-oxopropyl]amino]-2,6-anhydro-3,5-dideoxy-	n.s.g.	240(3.72)	49-0402-73
$C_{14}H_{22}N_4O_2$			
1H-Pyrazole, 1-acetyl-3-(2-acetyl-3,5,5-trimethyl-1-pyrazolidinyl)-5-methyl-	EtOH	233(3.93),265(3.99)	103-0503-73
$C_{14}H_{22}N_4O_3$			
Propanamide, N,N'-(1,6-dihydro-6-oxo-4,5-pyrimidinediyl)bis[2,2-dimethyl-	pH 1	279(3.87)	39-1855-73C
	pH 11	279(3.79)	39-1855-73C
	MeOH	288(3.87)	39-1855-73C
$C_{14}H_{22}N_6O_6$			
Adenosine, 2-amino-N,N-bis(2-hydroxyethyl)-	pH 1.0	232(4.09),238(4.11), 259(4.13)	87-0358-73
	H_2O	232(4.28),288(4.21)	87-0358-73
	pH 13	230(4.31),288(4.22)	87-0358-73

Compound	Solvent	$\lambda_{max}(\log \epsilon)$	Ref.
$C_{14}H_{22}O$			
2-Cyclohexen-1-one, 4-(1-butenyl)-3-methyl-5-propyl-	EtOH	235(4.17),280s(3.46)	6-0217-73
2-Cyclohexen-1-one, 3-(1-pentenyl)-5-propyl-	EtOH	238(3.70),278(4.23)	6-0217-73
Ethanone, 1-(5-ethyl-2-methyl-4-propyl-1,5-cyclohexadien-1-yl)-	EtOH	235(4.29)	6-0217-73
Ethanone, 1-(5-ethyl-2-methyl-6-propyl-1,3-cyclohexadien-1-yl)-	EtOH	231(4.17)	6-0217-63
Isonordrimenone	EtOH	237(3.79)	102-2555-73
1-Propanone, 1-(6,6-dimethylbicyclo-[3.1.1]hept-2-en-2-yl)-2,2-dimethyl-	C_6H_{12}	243(4.02),316(1.89)	22-1351-73
1-Propanone, 1-(7,7-dimethyltricyclo-[4.1.1.0^{2,4}]oct-2-yl)-2-methyl-, (1α,2β,4β,6α)-	C_6H_{12}	294(1.70)	22-1351-73
Spiro[4.5]dec-6-en-8-one, 1-methyl-4-(1-methylethyl)-	EtOH	211(4.18)	88-3153-73
$C_{14}H_{22}O_2$			
2,4-Cyclopentadiene-1-methanol, acetate	hexane	261(3.48)	24-0857-73
2-Heptanone, 6-(4,5-dimethyl-2-furanyl)-6-methyl-	EtOH	223(3.95),277(1.51)	33-2151-73
5H-Inden-5-one, 1,2,3,6,7,7a-hexahydro-4-methoxy-7a-methyl-3-(1-methylethyl)-	EtOH	259(3.90)	44-3663-73
β-Ionone, 8-methyl-, 5,6-epoxide, trans	EtOH	232(4.10),313(1.78)	33-2151-73
$C_{14}H_{22}O_3$			
1-Cyclopentene-1-heptanoic acid, 5-oxo-, ethyl ester	EtOH	228(4.00)	32-0031-73
1-Naphthalenecarboxylic acid, decahydro-4a,5-dimethyl-2-oxo-, methyl ester, (1α,4aβ,5β,8aα)-	EtOH	258(2.11)	138-0929-73
$C_{14}H_{22}O_4$			
1-Cyclooctene-1,4-dicarboxylic acid, diethyl ester	EtOH	223(4.02)	39-0051-73C
$C_{14}H_{22}S$			
1,3-Pentadiene, 4,4'-thiobis[2,3-dimethyl-	EtOH	227(4.34)	35-1285-73
$C_{14}H_{23}N$			
Pyridine, 2-methyl-5-(3,4,4-trimethyl-pentyl)-	MeOH	267(3.66)	103-1507-73
$C_{14}H_{23}NOS_2$			
Dithiobenzoic acid, 4-methoxy-, triethylamine salt	EtOH	321(4.19),360(4.01), 492(2.33)	143-0359-73
$C_{14}H_{23}NO_2$			
1,3-Benzenediol, 4-amino-3,6-bis(1,1-dimethylethyl)-	EtOH	291(3.85)	39-0268-73C
$C_{14}H_{23}NO_5$			
1,3-Dioxane-4,6-dione, 2,2-dimethyl-5-[2-methyl-1-(4-morpholinyl)propyl]-	MeOH	260(4.09)	49-0447-73
$C_{14}H_{23}NO_7$			
α-D-Glucofuranose, 1,2:5,6-bis-O-(1-methylethylidene)-3-C-[(methylimino)-methyl]-, N-oxide, (Z)-	EtOH	245(3.64)	136-0159-73F

Compound	Solvent	$\lambda_{max}(\log \epsilon)$	Ref.
$C_{14}H_{23}NS_2$			
Dithiobenzoic acid, 4-methyl-, triethylamine salt	EtOH	300(4.10),362(3.98), 480(2.38)	143-0359-73
$C_{14}H_{23}N_5$			
1H-Pyrazolo[4,3-d]pyrimidin-7-amine, N,N-dibutyl-3-methyl- (spectra in ethanol)	pH 1	265(3.71),323(4.21), 335s(--)	102-0025-73
	pH 7	245(3.54),305s(--), 316(4.20),330(4.03)	102-0025-73
	pH 12	252(4.04),317(4.00)	102-0025-73
$C_{14}H_{23}N_5O_2$			
1H-Purine-2,6-dione, 7-(3-aminopropyl)-8-butyl-3,7-dihydro-1,3-dimethyl-, hydrochloride	n.s.g.	210(4.37),277(4.03)	73-1571-73
$C_{14}H_{24}$			
Cyclobutane, 1-(1,1-dimethylethyl)-3-(2,2-dimethylpropylidene)-2-methylene-, anti	EtOH	256(4.23)	35-7925-73
1,3-Cyclohexadiene, 2,6,6-trimethyl-1-(3-methylbutyl)-	C_6H_{12}	262(3.63)	22-3187-73
Cyclohexene, 1,3,3-trimethyl-2-(3-methyl-2-butenyl)-	C_6H_{12}	228(3.78)	22-3187-73
$C_{14}H_{24}Cl_2Si_2$			
Silane, 1,4-phenylenebis[chlorodiethyl-	heptane	278.2(2.81)	70-1825-73
$C_{14}H_{24}N_2$			
2,4-Hexadiyne-1,6-diamine, N,N'-bis-(1,1-dimethylethyl)-	EtOH	243(3.85),257(2.63)	78-4111-73
2-Propenamine, N,N'-2,4-hexadiene-1,6-diylidenebis[2-methyl-	EtOH	280(4.69),290(4.80), 302(4.69)	78-4111-73
$C_{14}H_{24}N_2O_2$			
1,4-Benzenediol, 2,5-bis[3-(methylamino)propyl]-, dihydrobromide	H_2O	291(3.57)	39-0832-73C
1,4-Benzenedipropanamine, 2,5-dimethoxy-	$CHCl_3$	295(3.61)	39-0832-73C
$C_{14}H_{24}N_4O_4$			
1,2,8,9-Tetraaza-1,8-cyclotetradecadiene-3,10-diol, diacetate	n.s.g.	357(1.78)	89-0224-73
$C_{14}H_{24}O$			
3-Buten-2-one, 4-[5-methyl-2-(1-methylethyl)cyclohexyl]-	EtOH	231.0(4.16)	22-3071-73
1-Propanone, 1-(7,7-dimethylbicyclo-[4.1.1]oct-2-yl)-2-methyl-	C_6H_{12}	287(1.54),294(1.54)	22-1351-73
$C_{14}H_{24}O_2$			
Cyclohexanone, 4-acetyl-3,5-dipropyl-	EtOH	260(3.17),275(2.95)	6-0217-73
$C_{14}H_{25}NO_2$			
3(2H)-Furanone, 5-[3-(methylamino)propyl]-2,4-bis(1-methylethyl)-	EtOH	274(4.04)	35-4103-73
$C_{14}H_{25}N_5O$			
1-Hepten-2-ol, 1-[4,6-bis(dimethylamino)-1,3,5-triazin-2-yl]-	C_6H_{12}	229(4.48),278(4.20)	22-2039-73

Compound	Solvent	$\lambda_{max}(\log \epsilon)$	Ref.
$C_{14}H_{26}ClN_2O_2P$			
1,3,2-Diazaphosphorine, 2,2-dibutoxy-4-chloro-6-ethyl-2,2-dihydro-5-methyl-	hexane	329(3.93)	112-0621-73
$C_{14}H_{26}N_2O_{10}$			
α-D-Glucopyranoside, 3,3'-azobis[methyl-3,6-dideoxy-, N,N-dioxide, (E)-	H_2O	298(3.88)	23-1812-73
$C_{14}H_{26}N_4$			
1,2,3,4-Tetrazine, 1,4-dicyclohexyl-1,4,5,6-tetrahydro-	MeOH	223(3.4),275(3.7)	89-0495-73
	CH_2Cl_2	235(3.64),272(3.41)	24-3097-73
$C_{14}H_{26}N_4O$			
1,2,3,4-Tetrazine, 1,4-dicyclohexyl-1,4,5,6-tetrahydro-, 2-oxide	MeOH	291(4.08)	89-0495-73
$C_{14}H_{26}O$			
Isomenthone, 2,4-diethyl-, (1R,2S,4R)-(+)-	dioxan	288(1.68)	22-1049-73
(1R,2R,4R)-(-)-	dioxan	283(2.00)	22-1049-73
2-Nonenal, 2-pentyl-	EtOH	231(4.2),314(--)	22-2429-73
$C_{14}H_{26}Si_2$			
Silane, (1,2-di-1-propenylidene-1,2-ethanediyl)bis[trimethyl-	n.s.g.	246(3.76),259(3.93), 273(4.07),287(4.03)	39-0599-73B
Silane, 1,4-phenylenebis[diethyl-	heptane	277.6(2.64)	70-1825-73
$C_{14}H_{28}N_2$			
1H-Imidazole, 4,5-dihydro-2-undecyl-	EtOH	220(3.69)	93-2424-73
$C_{14}H_{29}N_3$			
1,3-Pentadiene-1,1,3-triamine, N,N',N"-tripropyl-, hydrobromide	EtOH	225(3.91),300(4.32)	70-1033-73
1-Pentene-1,1-diamine, N,N'-dipropyl-3-(propylimino)-	EtOH	222(4.23)	70-1033-73
hydrobromide	EtOH	235(3.82),294(4.37)	70-1033-73
$C_{14}H_{29}O_4P$			
Phosphonic acid, (2-butoxyethenyl)-, dibutyl ester	nonane	206(4.12),227s(3.18)	65-2164-73
$C_{14}H_{30}O_2Si$			
3-Heptanone, 2,2,6,6-tetramethyl-5-[(trimethylsilyl)oxy]-	EtOH	285(1.51)	35-3310-73

Compound	Solvent	$\lambda_{max}(\log \epsilon)$	Ref.
$C_{15}D_{10}O$			
2-Cyclopropen-1-one, 2,3-di(phenyl-d_5)-	C_6H_{12}	222(4.24),229(4.23), 284s(4.20),291(4.27), 300(4.32),316(4.10), 363(3.00)	44-3064-73
$C_{15}F_{25}N$			
Pyridine, pentakis(pentafluorophenyl)-	hexane	210(3.93),269(3.13)	39-1542-73C
$C_{15}H_5BrCl_4O_2S_2$			
Spiro[1,3-benzodioxole-2,2'-[1,3]dithiole], 4'-(4-bromophenyl)-4,5,6,7-tetrachloro-	benzene	299(4.38)	97-0465-73
$C_{15}H_5Cl_5O_2S_2$			
Spiro[1,3-benzodioxole-2,2'-[1,3]dithiole], 4,5,6,7-tetrachloro-4'-(4-chlorophenyl)-	benzene	294(4.28)	97-0465-73
$C_{15}H_6Br_2N_2O$			
7H-Benzo[e]perimidin-7-one, 4,6-dibromo-	EtOH	320(3.84),361(3.92), 381(4.08),390(3.98), 403(4.11)	104-1523-73
$C_{15}H_6Cl_2N_2O$			
7H-Benzo[e]perimidin-7-one, 4,6-dichloro-	EtOH	286(3.68),288(3.67), 317(3.82),358(3.90), 376(4.09),398(4.12)	104-1523-73
$C_{15}H_6Cl_4O_2S_2$			
Spiro[1,3-benzodioxole-2,2'-[1,3]dithiole], 4,5,6,7-tetrachloro-4'-phenyl-	benzene	293(3.80)	97-0465-73
$C_{15}H_6Cl_8$			
4,7-Methano-1H-indene, 2,3,3a,7a-tetrachloro-3a,4,7,7a-tetrahydro-1-(2,3,4-5-tetrachloro-2,4-cyclopentadien-1-ylidene)-, (3aα,4α,7α,7aα)-	C_6H_{12}	384(4.40),534(2.41)	77-0910-73
$C_{15}H_7BrN_2O$			
7H-Benzo[e]perimidin-7-one, 4-bromo-	EtOH	317(3.66),356(3.90), 374(4.06),394(4.04)	104-1523-73
$C_{15}H_7BrO_5$			
6H-Benzofuro[3,2-c][1]benzopyran-6-one, 2-bromo-8,9-dihydroxy-	n.s.g.	247(4.1),285(3.8), 358(4.2)	2-0115-73
$C_{15}H_7Br_2NO_3$			
Formamide, N-(2,4-dibromo-9,10-dihydro-9,10-dioxo-1-anthracenyl)-	EtOH	260(4.65),340(3.46)	104-1523-73
$C_{15}H_7ClO_5$			
6H-Benzofuro[3,2-c][1]benzopyran-6-one, 2-chloro-8,9-dihydroxy-	n.s.g.	248(4.2),285(3.8), 362(4.3)	2-0115-73
6H-Benzofuro[3,2-c][1]benzopyran-6-one, 3-chloro-8,9-dihydroxy-	n.s.g.	247(4.2),285(3.8), 348(4.3)	2-0115-73
6H-Benzofuro[3,2-c][1]benzopyran-6-one, 4-chloro-8,9-dihydroxy-	n.s.g.	245(3.9),280(3.8), 346(4.0)	2-0115-73

Compound	Solvent	λmax(log ε)	Ref.
$C_{15}H_8BrNO_3$			
Formamide, N-(2-bromo-9,10-dihydro-9,10-dioxo-1-anthracenyl)-	EtOH	260(4.66),330(3.66)	104-1523-73
Formamide, N-(4-bromo-9,10-dihydro-9,10-dioxo-1-anthracenyl)-	EtOH	265(4.29),405(3.67)	104-1523-73
$C_{15}H_8Br_2O_2$			
4H-1-Benzopyran-4-one, 6,8-dibromo-2-phenyl-	$CHCl_3$	261(4.24),304(4.21), 329(4.14)	78-1037-73
$C_{15}H_8ClNO_3$			
Formamide, N-(2-chloro-9,10-dihydro-9,10-dioxo-1-anthracenyl)-	EtOH	255(4.56),325(3.72)	104-1523-73
Formamide, N-(4-chloro-9,10-dihydro-9,10-dioxo-1-anthracenyl)-	EtOH	275(4.25),400(3.79)	104-1523-73
$C_{15}H_8ClN_3O_2$			
5H-1,3,4-Oxadiazolo[2,3-b]quinazolin-5-one, 2-(2-chlorophenyl)-	n.s.g.	225(4.39),254(4.04), 283(4.14),315(4.01)	48-0185-73
$C_{15}H_8Cl_2O$			
2-Propyn-1-one, 3-(3,4-dichlorophenyl)-1-phenyl-	EtOH	233(4.17),287(4.35), 307(4.29)	44-2544-73
$C_{15}H_8Cl_4O_2S_2$			
Spiro[1,3-benzodioxole-2,2'-[1,3]benzodithiole], 4,5,6,7-tetrachloro-5',6'-dimethyl-	benzene	299(3.72)	97-0465-73
$C_{15}H_8Fe_2O_6$			
Iron, hexacarbonyl[μ(1,2,3,4-η:6,7,8,9-η)spiro[4.4]nona-1,3,6,8-tetraene]]di-	isooctane	228(4.65),288(3.91)	35-7325-73
$C_{15}H_8N_2$			
9H-Fluorene-2,3-dicarbonitrile	MeOH	223(4.45),241s(4.38), 247(4.44),298(4.34)	33-3004-73
$C_{15}H_8N_2O$			
7H-Benzo[e]perimidin-7-one	EtOH	287(3.62),311(3.79), 349(3.83),356(3.96), 380(3.94)	104-1523-73
$C_{15}H_8N_6O_4$			
2H-1,2,3-Triazolo[4,5-f]quinoline, 2-(2,4-dinitrophenyl)-	EtOH	255(4.25),295(4.36), 345(4.31)	78-0221-73
2H-1,2,3-Triazolo[4,5-f]quinoline, 3-(2,4-dinitrophenyl)-	EtOH	250(4.87),294s(4.33), 330(4.27)	78-0221-73
$C_{15}H_8N_8$			
1,3-Azulenedicarbonitrile, 2-amino-5-(5-amino-4-cyano-1H-1,2,3-triazol-1-yl)-	n.s.g.	230(4.23),238(4.50), 315(4.27),410(3.61), 426(4.80)	18-1212-73
$C_{15}H_8O$			
4H-Cyclopenta[cd]phenalen-4-one	C_6H_{12}	215(4.57),268(3.99), 300(4.05),405(3.70), 410s(3.67),430(3.77), 490(2.96)	138-0413-73
	MeOH	213(4.61),250s(4.23), 302(4.07),415s(3.66), 425(3.67),490(2.98)	138-0413-73

Compound	Solvent	$\lambda_{max}(\log \epsilon)$	Ref.
$C_{15}H_9BrN_2O$			
1H-Perimidine, 2-(5-bromo-2-furanyl)-	MeOH	268(4.42),330(4.17), 344(4.22)	103-0922-73
$C_{15}H_9BrO$			
2-Propyn-1-one, 3-(4-bromophenyl)-	EtOH	226(4.34),267(4.45), 293(4.53),309(4.56)	44-2544-73
$C_{15}H_9Br_2NO$			
4H-Quinolizin-4-one, 1,3-dibromo-2-phenyl-	$CHCl_3$	265(4.28),395(3.83)	4-0139-73
$C_{15}H_9ClF_2O$			
9H-Xanthene, 9-(1-chloroethylidene)-2,7-difluoro-	EtOH	238s(4.00),253s(3.95), 288(3.51),322(3.96)	44-0841-73
$C_{15}H_9ClN_2$			
1H-Benzimidazole, 2-[(2-chlorophenyl)-ethynyl]-	EtOH	243s(4.02),248(4.03), 256(4.15),305s(4.42), 312(4.45),320s(4.43), 333(4.35)	4-0399-73
$C_{15}H_9ClO$			
2-Propyn-1-one, 3-(4-chlorophenyl)-1-phenyl-	EtOH	228(4.16),273(4.20), 292(4.33),308(4.36)	44-2544-73
$C_{15}H_9ClO_2$			
4H-1-Benzopyran-4-one, 6-chloro-3-phenyl-	EtOH	243(4.45),315(3.83)	114-0093-73B
$C_{15}H_9Cl_2FN_2O$			
3H-Indole-2-carboxamide, 3,5-dichloro-3-(2-fluorophenyl)-	isoPrOH	242(4.27),318(3.81)	44-3077-73
$C_{15}H_9D_3O_2$			
2(3H)-Benzofuranone, 3-(methyl-d_3)-3-phenyl-	EtOH	271(3.10),277(3.08)	44-1993-73
$C_{15}H_9FO$			
2-Propyn-1-one, 3-(4-fluorophenyl)-1-phenyl-	EtOH	221(4.27),270(4.27), 288(4.19),302(4.19)	44-2544-73
$C_{15}H_9NO_3$			
Formamide, N-(9,10-dihydro-9,10-dioxo-1-anthracenyl)-	EtOH	265(4.45),335(3.60)	104-1523-73
2-Propyn-1-one, 3-(4-nitrophenyl)-1-phenyl-	EtOH	296(4.43)	44-2544-73
$C_{15}H_9N_3O$			
4H-Quinolizine-1-carbonitrile, 4-oxo-3-(2-pyridinyl)-	EtOH	261(4.35),415(4.33)	94-0921-73
$C_{15}H_9N_3O_2$			
5H-1,3,4-Oxadiazolo[2,3-b]quinazolin-5-one, 2-phenyl-	n.s.g.	231(4.65),242(4.63), 253(4.76),261s(4.77), 273(4.84),282(4.90), 312(5.17),324(5.12), 338s(5.28)	48-0185-73

Compound	Solvent	λ_{max}(log ε)	Ref.
$C_{15}H_9N_3O_5$			
4H-Quinolizin-4-one, 1,3-dinitro-2-phenyl-	$CHCl_3$	386(4.45)	4-0139-73
$C_{15}H_9N_5O_2$			
1H-Pyrazolo[3,4-b]quinoxaline, 1-(4-nitrophenyl)-	H_2O	267(4.60),335(4.04), 397(3.72)	48-0517-73
2H-1,2,3-Triazolo[4,5-f]quinoline, 2-(4-nitrophenyl)-	EtOH	262s(4.04),294(4.40), 300(4.39),343(4.44)	78-0221-73
$C_{15}H_{10}$			
2H-Cyclopenta[jk]fluorene	hexane	247(4.62),256(4.80), 278(3.90),306(3.87), 321(3.86)	88-0865-73
	DMSO-NaOEt	333(4.36),361(4.02), 500(3.58)	88-0865-73
$C_{15}H_{10}BrNO_2$			
Benzonitrile, 2-[2-(4-bromophenyl)-2-oxoethoxy]-	EtOH	233s(4.18),239(4.19), 260(4.28),289s(3.90)	48-0779-73
Methanone, (3-amino-2-benzofuranyl)-(4-bromophenyl)-	EtOH	259(4.20),317(3.97), 387(4.22)	48-0779-73
$C_{15}H_{10}BrN_3O$			
3H-Imidazo[4,5-f]quinoline, 2-(5-bromo-2-furanyl)-3-methyl-	MeOH	244(4.05),291(4.22), 340(4.05)	103-0406-73
2-Naphthalenol, 1-[(5-bromo-2-pyridinyl)azo]- (also Co complexes)	30% acetone	480(4.29)	140-1973-73
$C_{15}H_{10}BrN_3O_3S$			
Phenol, 4-bromo-2-[[(6-methyl-2-benzothiazolyl)imino]methyl]-6-nitro-	benzene	280(4.02),301(3.87), 398(3.99)	80-1781-73
	EtOH	225(--),263(--), 301(--),372(--)	80-1781-73
	ether	230(4.60),263(4.24), 303(3.86),391(3.98)	80-1781-73
	CH_2Cl_2	237(4.35),261(4.28), 300(3.88),393(4.04)	80-1781-73
$C_{15}H_{10}BrN_3O_4S$			
Phenol, 4-bromo-2-[[(6-methoxy-2-benzothiazolyl)imino]methyl]-6-nitro-	benzene	280(4.21),287(4.18), 335(3.96),400(4.11), 413(4.09)	80-1781-73
	EtOH	223(--),266(--), 305(--),372(--)	80-1781-73
	ether	228(4.42),274(4.28), 395(4.17)	80-1781-73
	CH_2Cl_2	236(4.28),275(4.31), 335(4.02),400(4.16)	80-1781-73
$C_{15}H_{10}ClFN_2O_2$			
1H-Indole-3-carboxamide, 5-chloro-3-(2-fluorophenyl)-2,3-dihydro-2-oxo-	isoPrOH	260(4.04),270s(3.92), 295(3.28)	44-3077-73
$C_{15}H_{10}ClN$			
Quinoline, 2-chloro-8-phenyl-	EtOH	217(4.44),240(4.53), 303(4.11),320s(3.99)	12-2213-73
$C_{15}H_{10}ClNO$			
1H-Indole-2-carboxaldehyde, 5-chloro-3-phenyl-	EtOH	249(4.42),318(4.31)	78-0603-73

Compound	Solvent	λ_{max}(log ε)	Ref.
1H-Indole-3-carboxaldehyde, 5-chloro-2-phenyl-	EtOH	225(4.41),259(4.56), 312(4.28)	78-0603-73
$C_{15}H_{10}ClNO_2$			
3(2H)-Benzofuranone, 2-[[(4-chlorophenyl)amino]methylene]-	MeOH	270(4.16),330(4.03), 418(4.51)	103-0141-73
2(1H)-Quinolinone, 6-chloro-3-hydroxy-4-phenyl-	isoPrOH	232(4.68),287(3.89), 313s(3.85),325(4.01), 338(3.91)	44-0449-73
$C_{15}H_{10}ClN_3O$			
2-Naphthalenol, 1-[(5-chloro-2-pyridinyl)azo]- (also Co complexes)	30% acetone	470(4.26)	140-1973-73
$C_{15}H_{10}ClN_3O_2S$			
1H-Benzimidazole-1-carboxamide, N-(4-chlorobenzoyl)-2,3-dihydro-2-thioxo-	MeOH	246(4.56),304(4.48)	103-0639-73
$C_{15}H_{10}Cl_2N_4$			
1,3,5-Triazin-2-amine, 4,6-dichloro-N,N-diphenyl-	EtOH	265(3.38),290(3.36), 408(4.07)	39-2075-73B
$C_{15}H_{10}Cl_3NO_2$			
Benzenepropanamide, α,2-dichloro-N-(2-chlorophenyl)-β-oxo-	pH 13	315(4.25)	39-0808-73B
$C_{15}H_{10}Cl_3N_2P$			
1,3,2-Diazaphosphorine, 2,2,4-trichloro-2,2-dihydro-5,6-diphenyl-	hexane	246(4.08),361(3.79)	112-0621-73
$C_{15}H_{10}N_2$			
6H-Pyrido[4,3-b]carbazole	EtOH	223(4.54),271(4.80), 282(4.89),291(4.90)	78-3357-73
	EtOH-HCl	236(4.51),304(4.85)	78-3357-73
6H-Pyrido[2,3,4-gh]phenanthridine	EtOH	224(4.71),261(4.12), 276(4.01),286(3.92), 323(3.88),358(3.99), 391(4.05),412(3.97)	12-2213-73
	EtOH-HCl	221(4.71),270(4.26), 333(4.02),363(4.02), 384(4.26),406(4.26)	12-2213-73
$C_{15}H_{10}N_2O_3$			
1H-Indole-2-carboxaldehyde, 5-nitro-3-phenyl-	EtOH	237(4.19),245s(4.19), 299(4.50),331s(4.04)	78-0603-73
1H-Indole-2-carboxaldehyde, 6-nitro-3-phenyl-	EtOH	234(4.29),244s(4.24), 300(4.28),329(4.30)	78-0603-73
1H-Indole-2-carboxaldehyde, 7-nitro-3-phenyl-	EtOH	242(4.61),270s(4.07), 306(4.04),376(4.17)	78-0603-73
1H-Indole-3-carboxaldehyde, 5-nitro-2-phenyl-	EtOH	263(5.46),285s(4.33), 326s(4.41)	78-0603-73
1H-Indole-3-carboxaldehyde, 6-nitro-2-phenyl-	EtOH	285(4.39),326(4.17)	78-0603-73
1H-Indole-3-carboxaldehyde, 7-nitro-2-phenyl-	EtOH	242(4.42),288s(3.90), 346(4.10)	78-0603-73
$C_{15}H_{10}N_2O_4$			
Methanone, (3-amino-5-nitro-2-benzofuranyl)phenyl-	EtOH	244(4.22),266s(4.07), 300(4.29),376(4.18)	48-0779-73

Compound	Solvent	λ_{max}(log ε)	Ref.
$C_{15}H_{10}N_4$			
Isoquinoline, 1-(1H-benzotriazol-1-yl)-	EtOH	223(4.62),257(4.01), 325(3.93)	12-2213-73
1H-Pyrazolo[3,4-b]quinoxaline, 1-phenyl-	H_2O	267(4.60),335(4.00), 410(3.57)	48-0517-73
Tetrazolo[1,5-a]quinoline, 9-phenyl-	EtOH	238(4.39),280(4.05), 290(3.96),317(3.31)	12-2213-73
2H-1,2,3-Triazolo[4,5-f]quinoline, 2-phenyl-	EtOH	225(4.39),285(4.58), 326(4.20),336(4.18)	78-0221-73
3H-1,2,3-Triazolo[4,5-f]quinoline, 3-phenyl-	EtOH	262s(4.04),294(4.40), 300(4.39),343(4.44)	78-0221-73
$C_{15}H_{10}N_4O$			
1H-Pyrazolo[3,4-b]quinoxaline, 1-(3-hydroxyphenyl)-	pH 2.5	257(4.53),335(4.01), 404(3.58)	48-0517-73
	pH 10.2	248(4.61),304(3.83), 335(4.02),404(3.57)	48-0517-73
$C_{15}H_{10}N_4O_3$			
3H-Imidazo[4,5-f]quinoline, 3-methyl-2-(5-nitro-2-furanyl)-	MeOH	235(4.26),273(4.23), 377(4.10)	103-0406-73
$C_{15}H_{10}O$			
2-Propen-1-one, 1,3-diphenyl-	EtOH	221(4.15),271(4.20), 287(4.25),300(4.25)	44-2544-73
$C_{15}H_{10}OS_2$			
1,3-Dithiol-2-one, 4-[1,1'-biphenyl]-4-yl-	EtOH	232(3.71),303(4.29)	143-0273-73
$C_{15}H_{10}OSe$			
Benzo[b]selenophen-3(2H)-one, 2-(phenylmethylene)-	EtOH	230s(3.95),256(4.21), 314(4.27),438(3.84)	28-1035-73A
$C_{15}H_{10}OTe$			
Benzo[b]tellurophen-3(2H)-one, 2-(phenylmethylene)-	EtOH	228(4.17),260(4.29), 314(4.26),472(3.65)	28-1035-73A
$C_{15}H_{10}O_2$			
6,12-Epoxy=9H-benzocycloundecen-9-one	MeOH	238(4.00),269(4.52), 289(4.45)	78-0533-73
	85% H_2SO_4	243(4.19),265(4.20), 345(4.65),480(4.16)	78-0533-73
$C_{15}H_{10}O_2S_2$			
2-Propyn-1-ol, 3-[5-(2-thienylethynyl)-2-thienyl]-, acetate	ether	321s(4.44),330s(4.47), 335(4.49),342s(4.43), 352s(4.34),358(4.33)	24-2755-73
Thiophene-3-ol, 5-[[5-(1-propynyl)-2-thienyl]ethynyl]-, acetate	ether	316s(4.37),322(4.41), 331s(4.44),336(4.47), 344s(4.41),354(4.32), 359(4.32)	24-0497-73
$C_{15}H_{10}O_3$			
Phenanthro[4,5-bcd]furan-3-ol, 7-methoxy-	EtOH	242(4.75),265(4.37), 313(4.05),327(4.20), 351(3.91),370(4.17)	18-1772-73
$C_{15}H_{10}O_3S$			
Dibenzo[b,f]thiepin-10,11-dione, 2-methoxy-	MeOH	217(4.25),236(4.24), 246(4.25),266(4.13),	73-1579-73

Compound	Solvent	λ_{max}(log ε)	Ref.
Dibenzo[b,f]thiepin-10,11-dione, 2-methoxy- (cont.)	MeOH	275(4.09),296(3.60), 364(3.65)	73-1579-73
1,3-Propanedione, 1-(2-benzofuranyl)-3-(2-thienyl)-	MeOH	279(4.14),380(4.24)	56-1053-73
1,3-Propanedione, 1-benzo[b]thien-2-yl-3-(2-furanyl)-	MeOH	225(4.24),255(3.89), 300(4.01),380(4.46)	56-1053-73
1,3-Propanedione, 1-benzo[b]thien-3-yl-3-(2-furanyl)-	MeOH	218(4.45),267(4.10), 365(4.40)	56-1053-73
$C_{15}H_{10}O_4$			
9,10-Anthracenedione, 1,8-dihydroxy-2-methyl-	EtOH	255(4.32),266s(4.27), 287(4.10),294s(4.08), 447(3.79)	64-0436-73C
9,10-Anthracenedione, 1-hydroxy-2-(hydroxymethyl)-	MeOH	222(4.24),253(4.47), 328(3.35),407(3.68)	102-2389-73
9,10-Anthracenedione, 2-hydroxy-3-methoxy-	EtOH	208(4.17),272(3.95), 286(4.44)	56-1949-73
1,3-Dioxolane-2,4-dione, 5,5-diphenyl-	n.s.g.	240.5(5.221)	25-0695-73
1,3-Propanedione, 1-(2-benzofuranyl)-3-(2-furanyl)-	MeOH	225(3.92),305(4.03),	56-1053-73
$C_{15}H_{10}O_5$			
Apigenin	EtOH	270(4.10),338(4.16)	95-1231-73
	EtOH-NaOAc	280(--),308(--), 345(--)	95-1231-73
4H-1-Benzopyran-4-one, 7-hydroxy-3-(3,4-dihydroxyphenyl)- (daidzein)	MeOH	209(4.51),249(4.65), 300s(--)	39-1737-73C
	MeOH-NaOAc	253(4.7),335(4.09)	39-1737-73C
$C_{15}H_{10}O_6$			
9,10-Anthracenedione, 1,4,5,8-tetrahydroxy-2-methyl- (cynodontin)	$CHCl_3$	295(3.99),490(4.07), 514(4.25),524(4.32), 550(4.30),564(4.37)	94-2286-73
Luteolin	EtOH	257(4.46),268(4.37), 353(4.79)	95-1231-73
	EtOH-NaOAc	270(--),362(--)	95-1231-73
	EtOH-$AlCl_3$	276(--),409(--)	95-1231-73
9H-Xanthene-1-carboxylic acid, 2-hydroxy-6-methoxy-9-oxo-	MeOH	205(4.23),243(4.49), 275s(4.09),311(4.14), 356(3.78)	24-1182-73
$C_{15}H_{10}O_9$			
Esculetin, 7-O-β-D-glucopyranosyl-	n.s.g.	228(4.1),292(3.77), 348(3.85)	105-0586-73
$C_{15}H_{11}BrN_2O$			
1H-Perimidine, 2-(5-bromo-2-furanyl)-2,3-dihydro-	MeOH	270(3.64),332(4.17), 344(4.18)	103-0922-73
$C_{15}H_{11}BrN_2OS$			
Phenol, 4-bromo-2-[[(6-methyl-2-benzothiazolyl)imino]methyl- (and other qualitative spectra)	benzene	278(4.03),394(4.28)	80-1781-73
	EtOH	226(--),274(--), 389(--)	80-1781-73
$C_{15}H_{11}BrN_2O_2$			
Benzenamine, 4-bromo-N-[3-(2-nitrophenyl)-2-propen-1-ylidene]-	MeOH	210(4.23),284(4.32), 340(4.22)	42-0277-73
$C_{15}H_{11}BrN_2O_2S$			
Phenol, 4-bromo-2-[[(6-methoxy-2-benzothiazolyl)imino]methyl]-	benzene	279(4.22),320(4.22), 381(4.33)	80-1781-73

Compound	Solvent	$\lambda_{max}(\log \epsilon)$	Ref.
Phenol, 4-bromo-2-[[(6-methoxy-2-benzothiazolyl)imino]methyl]- (cont.)	EtOH	225(--),273(--), 302(--),376(--)	80-1781-73
	ether	223(4.43),270(4.43), 274(4.40),317(4.30), 376(4.41)	80-1781-73
	CH_2Cl_2	237(4.36),270(4.38), 275(4.40),319(4.32), 379(4.44)	80-1781-73
$C_{15}H_{11}BrO_2S$			
Dibenzo[b,f]thiepin-10(11H)-one, 11-bromo-8-methoxy-	MeOH	239(4.36),265(4.02), 354(3.60)	73-1579-73
$C_{15}H_{11}BrS$			
8H-Cyclohepta[b]thiophene, 5-bromo-4-phenyl-	MeCN	230(4.35),275(3.93)	44-0146-73
$C_{15}H_{11}Br_2ClN_2$			
Pyridinium, 2-bromo-1-[(2-chloro-3-quinolinyl)methyl]-, bromide	H_2O	237(4.75),274(4.09), 307(3.58),321(3.57)	44-2355-73
$C_{15}H_{11}Br_2NO_5$			
Benzoic acid, 2-(2,4-dibromo-6-methylphenoxy)-5-nitro-, methyl ester	EtOH	293(3.93)	39-2949-73C
$C_{15}H_{11}ClN_2$			
1H-Pyrazole, 3-(4-chlorophenyl)-5-phenyl-	EtOH	258.0(4.59)	42-0589-73
$C_{15}H_{11}ClN_2O$			
1H-Perimidine, 2-(5-chloro-2-furanyl)-2,3-dihydro-	MeOH	270(3.03),332(4.17), 344(4.18)	103-0922-73
$C_{15}H_{11}ClN_2O_2$			
Benzenamine, 3-chloro-N-[3-(2-nitrophenyl)-2-propen-1-ylidene]-	MeOH	211(3.38),281(3.36), 330(3.15)	42-0277-73
Benzenamine, 4-chloro-N-[4-(2-nitrophenyl)-2-propen-1-ylidene]-	MeOH	212(4.21),281(4.37), 336(4.21)	42-0277-73
$C_{15}H_{11}ClN_2O_3$			
Benzenamine, 4-chloro-N-[3-(2-nitrophenyl)-2-propenylidene]-, N-oxide	MeOH	224(4.24),363(4.38)	2-0884-73
$C_{15}H_{11}ClN_4$			
2-Quinoxalinecarboxaldehyde, 3-chloro-, phenylhydrazone	EtOH	240(4.43),318(3.98), 450(4.33)	103-0785-73
$C_{15}H_{11}ClO_2$			
Benzoic acid, 4-(2-chloro-2-phenylethenyl)-	EtOH	242(4.14)	104-1511-73
2-Propen-1-one, 3-(4-chlorophenyl)-1-(2-hydroxyphenyl)-	isooctane	315(4.48),355s(--)	65-0638-73
	benzene	324(4.45),355s(--)	65-0638-73
	EtOH	318(4.45),355s(--)	65-0638-73
3-Tridecene-5,7,9,11-tetrayn-2-ol, 1-chloro-, acetate, (E)-	ether	229(4.88),239(4.91), 255(5.03),272(5.17), 283(3.86),303(4.00), 323(4.18),347(4.26), 375(4.04)	24-2140-73

Compound	Solvent	$\lambda_{max}(\log \epsilon)$	Ref.
$C_{15}H_{11}ClO_3$			
1(3H)-Isobenzofuranone, 3-(4-chlorophenyl)-3-methoxy-	H_2O	224(4.37)	44-3383-73
2-Propen-1-one, 3-(2-chlorophenyl)-1-(2,4-dihydroxyphenyl)-	EtOH	210(4.42),234s(3.89),272s(3.70),352(4.17)	42-0129-73
2-Propen-1-one, 3-(3-chlorophenyl)-1-(2,4-dihydroxyphenyl)-	EtOH	207(4.54),220s(4.37),232s(4.24),269s(4.21),298(4.32),359(4.23)	42-0129-73
2-Propen-1-one, 3-(4-chlorophenyl)-1-(2,4-dihydroxyphenyl)-	EtOH	209(4.37),222(4.21),269s(3.87),360(4.27)	42-0129-73
$C_{15}H_{11}ClS$			
8H-Cyclohepta[b]thiophene, 5-chloro-4-phenyl-	MeCN	230(4.34),270(3.94)	44-0146-73
$C_{15}H_{11}Cl_2NO$			
1H-Indole, 6,7-dichloro-2-methoxy-3-phenyl-	isoPrOH	234(4.36),278(4.16)	44-3077-73
$C_{15}H_{11}Cl_2NO_2$			
Benzenepropanamide, 2-chloro-N-(2-chlorophenyl)-β-oxo-	pH 13	309(4.35)	39-0808-73B
$C_{15}H_{11}F_6NO_2S$			
7-Azabicyclo[2.2.1]hepta-2,5-diene, 7-[(4-methylphenyl)sulfonyl]-2,3-bis-(trifluoromethyl)-	EtOH	227(4.11),255s(3.02),263(2.94),269s(2.88),274s(2.76)	24-3824-73
3-Azatetracyclo[3.2.0.0^{2,7}.0^{4,6}]heptane, 3-[(4-methylphenyl)sulfonyl]-1,5-bis-(trifluoromethyl)-	MeOH	230(4.13),255s(2.98),257s(2.95),263(2.95),265s(2.90),268s(2.87),274(2.81)	24-3824-73
1H-Azepine, 1-[(4-methylphenyl)sulfonyl]-3,6-bis(trifluoromethyl)-	EtOH	226(4.06),239s(3.95),244s(3.88),254s(3.79),263s(3.72),273s(3.57),329s(2.49),344s(2.41)	24-3824-73
1H-Azepine, 1-[(4-methylphenyl)sulfonyl]-4,5-bis(trifluoromethyl)-	EtOH	230s(4.06),240s(3.96),245s(3.88),255s(3.74),260s(3.68),272s(3.49),316(2.73),330s(2.70),345s(2.64)	24-3824-73
$C_{15}H_{11}IN_2O$			
1H-Perimidine, 2,3-dihydro-2-(5-iodo-2-furanyl)-	MeOH	270(3.83),332(4.09),342(4.08)	103-0922-73
$C_{15}H_{11}IO$			
2-Propen-1-one, 1-[1,1'-biphenyl]-4-yl-3-iodo-, trans	dioxan	305(4.42)	24-0435-73
$C_{15}H_{11}N$			
Quinoline, 2-phenyl-	EtOH	254(4.61)	33-2588-73
	EtOH	256(4.60)	94-1943-73
$C_{15}H_{11}NO$			
1H-Indole-2-carboxaldehyde, 3-phenyl-	EtOH	228(4.28),249(4.42),319(4.38)	78-0603-73
1H-Indole-3-carboxaldehyde, 2-phenyl-	EtOH	257(4.46),314(4.15)	78-0603-73
4H-Quinolizin-4-one, 2-phenyl-	EtOH	265(4.44),405(4.19)	4-0139-73

Compound	Solvent	λ_{max}(log ε)	Ref.
$C_{15}H_{11}NOS$			
Methanone, (4-isothiocyanatophenyl)-(4-methylphenyl)-	MeOH	294(4.50)	73-1609-73
$C_{15}H_{11}NO_2$			
3(2H)-Benzofuranone, 2-[(phenylamino)-methylene]-	MeOH	270(3.99),330(3.97), 417(4.49)	103-0141-73
Benzonitrile, 2-(2-oxo-2-phenylethoxy)-	EtOH	234s(4.46),238(4.47), 246s(4.35),291(3.74)	48-0779-73
2H-Indol-2-one, 1,3-dihydro-3-[(2-hydroxyphenyl)methylene]-	EtOH	246(4.30)	103-0034-73
Methanone, (3-amino-2-benzofuranyl)-phenyl-	EtOH	226(3.98),253(4.24), 313(4.02),380(4.26)	48-0779-73
$C_{15}H_{11}NO_2S$			
Benzene, 1-methyl-4-[[(4-nitrophenyl)-ethynyl]thio]-	MeOH	220s(4.16),249(4.22), 284(4.02),360(4.18)	39-0063-73B
Methanone, (4-isothiocyanatophenyl)-(4-methoxyphenyl)-	MeOH	276(4.74)	73-1609-73
2,4-Thiazolidinedione, 5,5-diphenyl-	EtOH	215(4.15)	132-0113-73
	EtOH-NaOH	245(3.71)	132-0113-73
$C_{15}H_{11}NO_3$			
2-Propen-1-one, 1-(4-nitrophenyl)-3-phenyl-	MeOH	313(4.50)	139-0037-73B
	EtOH	315(4.51)	
	PrOH	316(4.51)	
	isoPrOH	311(4.52)	
	BuOH	312(4.41)	
	isoBuOH	313(4.49)	
	sec-BuOH	309(4.43)	
	tert-BuOH	312(4.45)	
	$C_5H_{11}OH$	308(4.40)	
	isoAmOH	315(4.52)	
	sec-AmOH	307(4.40)	
	tert-AmOH	305(4.31)	
(and other solvents)	$C_6H_{13}OH$	316(4.36)	
$C_{15}H_{11}NO_3S$			
Thiazolo[3,2-a]pyridinium, 8-acetoxy-3-hydroxy-2-phenyl-, hydroxide,	50% dioxan-HCl	238(4.1),283(3.7), 432(4.0)	1-1763-73
inner salt	50% dioxan-NaOH	258(4.1),283s(3.7), 302s(3.7),410(4.2)	1-1763-73
$C_{15}H_{11}NO_4$			
2-Propen-1-one, 1-(2-hydroxyphenyl)-3-(3-nitrophenyl)-	EtOH	210(4.30),218(4.24), 278s(4.17),306(4.29)	42-0129-73
2-Propen-1-one, 1-(2-hydroxyphenyl)-3-(4-nitrophenyl)-	isooctane	310(4.54),365(4.01)	65-0638-73
	benzene	322(4.41),365s(--)	65-0638-73
	EtOH	320(4.48),365s(--)	65-0638-73
$C_{15}H_{11}NO_4S$			
4H-1-Benzopyran-4-one, 7-acetoxy-2-methyl-3-(4-thiazolyl)-	n.s.g.	299(3.86)	104-2580-73
$C_{15}H_{11}NO_5$			
Benzoic acid, 2-benzoyl-3-nitro-, methyl ester	n.s.g.	224(4.17),248(4.26)	39-1160-73B
Benzoic acid, 2-benzoyl-4-nitro-, methyl ester	n.s.g.	224(4.16),250(4.28)	39-1160-73B
Benzoic acid, 2-benzoyl-5-nitro-, methyl ester	n.s.g.	224(4.16),250(4.27)	39-1160-73B

Compound	Solvent	$\lambda_{max}(\log \epsilon)$	Ref.
Benzoic acid, 2-benzoyl-6-nitro-, methyl ester	n.s.g.	224(4.16),250(4.26)	39-1160-73B
1(3H)-Isobenzofuranone, 3-methoxy-6-nitro-3-phenyl-	H_2O	260(4.16)	44-3383-73
2-Propen-1-one, 1-(2,4-dihydroxyphenyl)-3-(3-nitrophenyl)-	EtOH	208(4.44),220s(4.13), 255s(3.87),275(4.07), 303(4.13)	42-0129-73
$C_{15}H_{11}NO_5S$			
4H-1-Benzopyran-2-carboxylic acid, 7-hydroxy-4-oxo-3-(4-thiazolyl)-	n.s.g.	310(3.98)	104-2580-73
$C_{15}H_{11}NS_3$			
2,4-Thiazolidinedithione, 5,5-diphenyl-	EtOH	250(3.98),337(4.35), 470s(3.83)	78-2781-73
$C_{15}H_{11}N_3$			
1,2,4-Triazine, 3,6-diphenyl-	EtOH	285(4.45)	103-0123-73
$C_{15}H_{11}N_3O$			
Ethanone, 1-phenyl-2-(2-pyrido[2,3-d]-pyrimidin-2-yl)-	EtOH	234(4.17),262(4.05), 333(4.25)	94-2643-73
1-Naphthalenol, 2-(2-pyridinylazo)-	30% acetone	480(4.23)	140-1973-73
Co(II) complex	$CHCl_3$	550(4.59)	140-1973-73
Co(II) complex	Bu_2O	540(4.62)	140-1973-73
1-Naphthalenol, 4-(2-pyridinylazo)-	30% acetone	480(4.26)	140-1973-73
2-Naphthalenol, 1-(2-pyridinylazo)-	30% acetone	470(4.22)	140-1973-73
Co(II) complex	$CHCl_3$	525(4.48)	140-1973-73
Co(II) complex	CCl_4	500(4.43)	140-1973-73
1,2,4-Triazine, 3,6-diphenyl-, 4-oxide	EtOH	286(4.57)	103-0123-73
$C_{15}H_{11}N_3OS$			
Spiro[benzothiazole-2(3H),3'-[3H]pyrazol]-4'(2'H)-one, 2'-phenyl-	EtOH	230s(4.13),257(4.05), 313(3.98),431(4.39)	94-0241-73
$C_{15}H_{11}N_3O_2S$			
1H-Benzimidazole-1-carboxamide, N-benzoyl-2,3-dihydro-2-thioxo-	MeOH	250(4.54),305(4.40)	103-0639-73
$C_{15}H_{11}N_3O_3$			
1H-Perimidine, 2,3-dihydro-2-(5-nitro-2-furanyl)-	MeOH	264(3.78),319(4.35), 380(3.47)	103-0922-73
$C_{15}H_{11}N_3O_3S$			
Phenol, 2-[[(6-methyl-2-benzothiazolyl)-imino]methyl]-4-nitro-	benzene	278(4.20),318(4.20), 374(4.10)	80-1781-73
	EtOH	222(--),274(--), 394(--)	80-1781-73
	ether	229(4.38),241(4.30), 278(4.17),284(4.14), 397(4.31)	80-1781-73
	CH_2Cl_2	242(4.21),278(4.10), 284(4.07),410(4.25)	80-1781-73
Phenol, 2-[[(6-methyl-2-benzothiazolyl)-imino]methyl]-6-nitro-	benzene	279(4.00),335(4.05), 388(4.23)	80-1781-73
	EtOH	225(--),271(--), 302(--),354(--), 472(--)	80-1781-73
	ether	226(4.32),262(4.30), 275(4.20),385(4.30)	80-1781-73

Compound	Solvent	λ_{max}(log ε)	Ref.
Phenol, 2-[[(6-methyl-2-benzothiazolyl)-imino]methyl]-6-nitro-	CH_2Cl_2	236(4.22),264(4.30), 275(4.22),385(4.33)	80-1781-73
$C_{15}H_{11}N_3O_4$			
Benzenamine, 4-nitro-N-[3-(2-nitrophenyl)-2-propen-1-ylidene]-	MeOH	213(4.57),230(4.53), 375(4.63)	42-0277-73
1H-Benzimidazole, 1-acetoxy-2-(4-nitrophenyl)-	EtOH	368(4.26)	39-1310-73C
$C_{15}H_{11}N_3O_4S$			
Phenol, 2-[[(6-methoxy-2-benzothiazolyl)imino]methyl]-4-nitro-	benzene	281(4.31),286(4.30), 322(4.11),394(4.34)	80-1781-73
	EtOH	224(--),276(--), 310(--),386(--)	80-1781-73
	ether	224(4.40),275(4.41), 316(4.15),388(4.31)	80-1781-73
	CH_2Cl_2	239(4.21),274(4.38), 320(4.14),392(4.36), 408(4.34)	80-1781-73
Phenol, 2-[[(6-methoxy-2-benzothiazolyl)imino]methyl]-6-nitro-	benzene	281(4.23),286(4.21), 325(4.04),394(4.30)	80-1781-73
	EtOH	222(--),275(--), 312(--),374(--)	80-1781-73
	ether	226(4.36),273(4.36), 320(4.12),390(4.35)	80-1781-73
	CH_2Cl_2	237(4.25),272(4.40), 324(4.13),394(4.40)	80-1781-73
$C_{15}H_{11}N_3O_5$			
Isoxazole, 4,5-dihydro-3,5-bis(4-nitrophenyl)-	EtOH	302(4.33)	39-1574-73C
$C_{15}H_{11}N_5$			
1H-Pyrazolo[3,4-b]quinoxaline, 1-(3-aminophenyl)-	pH 2.5	267(4.56),335(4.03), 400(3.68)	48-0517-73
	pH 10.2	247(4.53),290s(--), 333(4.03),405(3.58)	48-0517-73
$C_{15}H_{11}N_5O_4$			
Benzeneacetonitrile, α-[[2-(2,4-dinitrophenyl)hydrazino]methylene]-	MeOH	268(4.18),333(4.24)	28-1457-73A
$C_{15}H_{11}O$			
1-Benzopyrylium, 2-phenyl-, perchlorate	HOAc	397(4.54)	33-0983-73
$C_{15}H_{11}O_2$			
16,17-Dioxatricyclo[11.2.1.1^{4,7}]heptadecaheptaenylium tetrafluoroborate	30% H_2SO_4	231(4.33),331(5.04), 345(5.03),418(3.92), 503(3.93)	88-5065-73
$C_{15}H_{12}$			
9H-Cycloocta[de]naphthalene	n.s.g.	243(4.41),325(3.84)	35-1874-73
$C_{15}H_{12}BrN$			
1H-Indole, 3-(4-bromophenyl)-1-methyl-	EtOH	228(4.48),298(4.22)	94-2786-73
$C_{15}H_{12}BrNO$			
2,4,6-Cycloheptatrien-1-one, 2-amino-4-[2-(4-bromophenyl)ethenyl]-	MeOH	238(4.11),327(4.60), 432(3.95)	18-0199-73
2,4,6-Cycloheptatrien-1-one, 2-amino-6-[2-(4-bromophenyl)ethenyl]-	MeOH	246(4.11),326(4.64), 432(4.00)	18-0199-73

Compound	Solvent	$\lambda_{max}(\log \epsilon)$	Ref.
2-Propen-1-one, 3-amino-2-bromo-1,3-diphenyl-	hexane	231(3.92),336(4.00)	40-2152-73
$C_{15}H_{12}BrNOS$			
11H-Indeno[2',1':4,5]thiazolo[3,2-a]pyridinium, 4b,10a-dihydro-9-methyl-11-oxo-, bromide	pH 1	245s(4.0),330(3.50)	39-2049-73C
$C_{15}H_{12}BrNO_2$			
Benzenepropanamide, N-(2-bromophenyl)-β-oxo-	pH 13	332(4.36)	39-0808-73B
$C_{15}H_{12}ClN$			
1H-Indole, 5-chloro-2-methyl-3-phenyl-	EtOH	229(4.59),274(4.23),299s(4.00)	78-0603-73
1H-Indole, 5-chloro-3-methyl-2-phenyl-	EtOH	235(4.44),313(4.33)	78-0603-73
$C_{15}H_{12}ClNO$			
2,4,6-Cycloheptatrien-1-one, 4-[2-(3-chlorophenyl)ethenyl]-	MeOH	236(4.13),320(4.60),432(3.98)	18-0199-73
2,4,6-Cycloheptatrien-1-one, 4-[2-(4-chlorophenyl)ethenyl]-	MeOH	238(4.06),327(4.63),432(4.03)	18-0199-73
2,4,6-Cycloheptatrien-1-one, 6-[2-(3-chlorophenyl)ethenyl]-	MeOH	240(4.12),320(4.62),431(3.96)	18-0199-73
2,4,6-Cycloheptatrien-1-one, 6-[2-(4-chlorophenyl)ethenyl]-	MeOH	240(4.15),324(4.67),432(4.01)	18-0199-73
3H-Indol-3-ol, 5-chloro-3-methyl-2-phenyl-	EtOH	233s(4.21),241(4.22),248s(4.17),320(4.24)	78-0603-73
2-Propen-1-one, 3-amino-2-chloro-1,3-diphenyl-	EtOH	234(3.97),349(4.13)	40-2152-73
$C_{15}H_{12}ClNO_2$			
Benzenepropanamide, α-chloro-β-oxo-N-phenyl-	pH 13	317(4.34)	39-0808-73B
Benzenepropanamide, N-(2-chlorophenyl)-β-oxo-	pH 13	332(4.35)	39-0808-73B
2-Propen-1-one, 3-(4-aminophenyl)-1-(5-chloro-2-hydroxyphenyl)-	dioxan	257(4.12),413(4.54)	83-0299-73
$C_{15}H_{12}ClN_3$			
3H-1,5-Benzodiazepin-2-amine, 4-(2-chlorophenyl)-	EtOH	245(4.40),320(3.59)	4-0399-73
hydrochloride	EtOH	268(4.42),305s(3.44),397(3.06)	4-0399-73
2-Propynimidamide, 3-(2-chlorophenyl)-N-(2-aminophenyl)-	EtOH	247(4.37),333s(3.65)	4-0399-73
$C_{15}H_{12}ClN_3O$			
3H-1,4-Benzodiazepin-2-amine, 7-chloro-5-phenyl-, 4-oxide, anti	EtOH	233(4.41),370(3.75)	95-1253-73
syn	EtOH	249(4.39)	95-1253-73
2-Quinazolinemethanamine, 6-chloro-4-phenyl-, 3-oxide	EtOH	231(4.43),264(4.45)	94-2366-73
$C_{15}H_{12}ClN_3OS$			
3H-Pyrazol-3-one, 4-[(2-amino-4-chlorophenyl)thio]-1,2-dihydro-5-phenyl-	EtOH	209(4.52),246(4.23),308(3.75)	7-0045-73
3H-Pyrazol-3-one, 4-[(2-amino-5-chlorophenyl)thio]-1,2-dihydro-5-phenyl-	EtOH	207(4.46),223(4.35),253(4.22),308(4.54)	7-0045-73

Compound	Solvent	λ_{max}(log ε)	Ref.
$C_{15}H_{12}ClN_5O$			
1H-1,2,3-Triazole-4-carboxylic acid, 5-(4-chlorophenyl)-1-phenyl-, hydrazide	EtOH	251(4.24)	42-0589-73
1H-1,2,3-Triazole-5-carboxylic acid, 4-(4-chlorophenyl)-1-phenyl-, hydrazide	EtOH	249(4.31)	42-0589-73
$C_{15}H_{12}Cl_2N_2$			
Quinazoline, 2,6-dichloro-3,4-dihydro-3-methyl-4-phenyl-	n.s.g.	235(4.15),302(3.90)	40-1944-73
$C_{15}H_{12}Cl_3NO_2$			
2,4(1H,3H)-Quinolinedione, 3,3,8-trichloro-5,6,7,8-tetrahydro-1-phenyl-	EtOH	225(3.68),344(4.00)	5-1545-73
$C_{15}H_{12}Cl_3NO_3$			
Acetamide, N-hydroxy-N-(3-methylphenyl)-2-(2,4,5-trichlorophenoxy)-	EtOH	241(4.13),252(4.11), 290s(3.54),300s(3.30)	112-0547-73
Acetamide, N-hydroxy-N-(4-methylphenyl)-2-(2,4,5-trichlorophenoxy)-	EtOH	241(4.13),252(4.11), 290s(3.54),300s(3.30)	112-0547-73
$C_{15}H_{12}NO$			
1H-Isoindolium, 2-methyl-1-oxo-3-phenyl-, hexachloroantimonate	MeCN	224(4.04),267(3.99), 330(3.40)	24-1423-73
	H_2SO_4	240(4.20),347(3.89)	24-1423-73
1H-Isoindolium, 3-methyl-1-oxo-2-phenyl-, hexachloroantimonate	MeCN	227(4.18),262(4.19), 306(3.88),343(3.35)	24-1423-73
	H_2SO_4	240(4.19),320(3.92)	24-1423-73
$C_{15}H_{12}NOS$			
11H-Indeno[2',1':4,5]thiazolo[3,2-a]pyridinium, 4b,10a-dihydro-9-methyl-11-oxo-, bromide	pH 1	245s(4.0),330(3.50)	39-2049-73C
$C_{15}H_{12}NO_2$			
Benzo[b]quinolizinium, 11-acetoxy-, perchlorate	EtOH	250(4.87),371(4.67), 388(4.68),411(4.67)	44-4167-73
$C_{15}H_{12}N_2$			
9H-Acenaphtho[1',2':3,4]cyclobuta[1,2-c]pyrazole, 6b,6c,9a,9b-tetrahydro-	n.s.g.	224(4.90),229(5.19), 271s(3.77),282(3.98), 293(4.04),302(3.87), 307(3.78),317(3.38), 321(3.41),330s(2.82)	35-1874-73
Cinnoline, 6-methyl-4-phenyl-	n.s.g.	233(4.54),305(3.80), 325(3.72)	2-0631-73
1H-Fluorene-2,3-dicarbonitrile, 4,4a,9,9a-tetrahydro-	MeOH	216(4.10),234(4.00), 261(3.16),267(3.11), 274(3.07)	33-3004-73
1H-Indole, 2-[2-(2-pyridinyl)ethenyl]-, cis	MeOH	269(4.02),285(3.85), 298(3.92),373(4.37)	23-0792-73
trans	MeOH	263(4.02),359(4.56)	23-0792-73
1H-Indole, 2-[2-(4-pyridinyl)ethenyl]-, cis	MeOH	265(4.05),357(4.22)	23-0792-73
trans	MeOH	259(3.98),364(4.51)	23-0792-73
1H-Pyrazole, 3,5-diphenyl-	EtOH	253.5(4.52)	42-0589-73
2H-Pyrrole-3-carbonitrile, 5-(2-naphthyl)-	C_6H_{12}	243(4.74),251(4.76), 273(4.00),282(4.11), 293(4.04),305(3.32),	35-1945-73

Compound	Solvent	λ_{max}(log ε)	Ref.
2H-Pyrrole-3-carbonitrile, 5-(2-naphthyl)- (cont.)	C_6H_{12}	323(3.04),331(3.92), 339(3.08)	35-1945-73
Quinoxaline, 6-methyl-2-phenyl-	n.s.g.	258(4.43),340(4.09)	2-0631-73
$C_{15}H_{12}N_2O$			
6H-Indolo[2,3-a]quinolizin-5-ium, 7,12-dihydro-1-hydroxy-, hydroxide, inner salt	EtOH	220(3.8),304(3.4), 435(3.2)	24-2943-73
Phenol, 2-(5-phenyl-1H-pyrazol-3-yl)-	EtOH	208(4.52),255(4.52)	103-0038-73
3H-Pyrazol-3-one, 2,4-dihydro-4,5-diphenyl-	EtOH	241s(4.09),265s(4.03)	23-0338-73
$C_{15}H_{12}N_2OS$			
Naphtho[2',1':5,6]thiopyrano[4,3-c]pyrazol-1(2H)-one, 11,11a-dihydro-11a-methyl-	EtOH	213(4.17),231(4.46), 283(4.47),292(4.51)	32-1073-73
Phenol, 2-[[(6-methyl-2-benzothiazolyl)-imino]methyl]-	benzene	279(4.05),301(3.70), 384(4.10)	80-1781-73
	EtOH	223(--),268(--), 300(--),381(--)	80-1781-73
	ether	229(4.44),272(4.18), 305(3.78),381(4.11)	80-1781-73
	CH_2Cl_2	237(4.33),270(4.23), 275(4.22),301(3.83), 382(4.19)	80-1781-73
4(5H)-Thiazolone, 2-amino-5,5-diphenyl-	EtOH	224(4.40),255(3.82)	132-0113-73
	EtOH-NaOH	228(4.11)	132-0113-73
$C_{15}H_{12}N_2O_2$			
Azuleno[2,1-b]pyrazine-10-carboxylic acid, ethyl ester	MeOH	224(4.32),251(4.36), 318(4.63),330(4.64), 369(3.79),391(3.96), 417(4.03),468(2.39), 505(2.46),540(2.47), 585(2.33)	18-3161-73
Benzenamine, N-[3-(2-nitrophenyl)-2-propenylidene]-	MeOH	213(4.09),235(4.23), 281(4.59),335(4.33)	42-0277-73
Indole, 1-methyl-3-(4-nitrophenyl)-	EtOH	226(4.46),288s(3.85), 395(4.18)	94-2786-73
2H,4H-Oxazolo[5,4,3-ij]pyrido[3,2-g]-quinolin-4-one, 6,8-dimethyl-	EtOH	265s(4.78),275(4.86), 335(4.11)	35-5003-73
3,5-Pyrazolidinedione, 1,4-diphenyl-	EtOH	270(4.5)	103-0717-73
	EtOH-HCl	245(4.4)	103-0717-73
3H-Pyrazol-3-one, 2,4-dihydro-4-hydroxy-4,5-diphenyl-	EtOH	216(4.17),297(4.14)	23-0338-73
$C_{15}H_{12}N_2O_2S$			
Phenol, 2-[[(6-methoxy-2-benzothiazolyl)imino]methyl]-	benzene	281(4.15),286(4.15), 393(4.31)	80-1781-73
	EtOH	219(4.45),278(4.15), 390(4.25)	80-1781-73
	ether	226(4.31),277(4.12), 283(4.09),389(4.22)	80-1781-73
	CH_2Cl_2	237(4.23),279(4.25), 285(4.23),391(4.38)	80-1781-73
	MeCN	226(--),276(--), 385(--)	80-1781-73

Compound	Solvent	λ_{max}(log ε)	Ref.
$C_{15}H_{12}N_2O_3$			
Benzenamine, N-[3-(2-nitrophenyl)-2-propenylidene]-, N-oxide	MeOH	227(4.17),358(4.33)	2-0884-73
2,4,6-Cycloheptatrien-1-one, 2-amino-4-[2-(3-nitrophenyl)ethenyl]-	MeOH	231(4.14),314(4.59), 435(3.95)	18-0199-73
2,4,6-Cycloheptatrien-1-one, 2-amino-4-[2-(4-nitrophenyl)ethenyl]-	MeOH	222(4.06),282(4.11), 337(4.53),444(3.95)	18-0199-73
Ethanone, 1-[5-hydroxy-6-(phenylamino)-4-benzoxazolyl]-	EtOH	276(4.14),410(2.61)	39-0493-73C
1H-Indole-2-methanol, 7-nitro-3-phenyl-	EtOH	258(4.19),365(3.96)	78-0603-73
1H-Indole-3-methanol, 7-nitro-2-phenyl-	EtOH	273s(4.14),410(2.61)	78-0603-73
Isoxazole, 4,5-dihydro-3-(4-nitrophenyl)-5-phenyl-	EtOH	310(4.21)	39-1574-73C
2H,4H-Oxazolo[5,4,3-ij]pyrido[3,2-g]-quinoline-4,8(11H)-dione, 6,10-dimethyl-	EtOH	258(4.58),287(4.54), 300(4.70),355(4.11)	35-5003-73
Phenol, 2-[[3-(2-nitrophenyl)-2-propen-1-ylidene]amino]-	MeOH	210(4.54),240(4.33), 280(4.79),369(3.84)	42-0277-73
Phenol, 4-[[3-(2-nitrophenyl)-2-propen-1-ylidene]amino]-	MeOH	209(4.25),251(4.24), 285(4.32),365(4.26)	42-0277-73
$C_{15}H_{12}N_2O_3S$			
7H-Isoindolo[2,1-b][1,2,4]benzothiadiazin-7-one, 11b,12-dihydro-12-methyl-, 5,5-dioxide	EtOH	277(3.59)	7-0635-73
$C_{15}H_{12}N_2O_4$			
Benzamide, 2-benzoyl-N-methyl-3-nitro-	EtOH	224(4.17),250(3.73)	39-1160-73B
Benzamide, 2-benzoyl-N-methyl-4-nitro-	EtOH	226(4.17),250(3.96)	39-1160-73B
Benzamide, 2-benzoyl-N-methyl-5-nitro-	EtOH	226(4.17),252(4.10)	39-1160-73B
Benzamide, 2-benzoyl-N-methyl-6-nitro-, cyclic	EtOH	226(4.16)	39-1160-73B
Benzenepropanamide, N-(3-nitrophenyl)-β-oxo-	pH 13	329(4.37)	39-0808-73B
Benzo[b][1,8]naphthyridine-3-carboxylic acid, 1,2-dihydro-4-hydroxy-2-oxo-, ethyl ester	DMSO	258(4.6),332(4.3), 344(4.1)	24-3533-73
$C_{15}H_{12}N_2O_4S$			
Benzenesulfonamide, 2-(1,3-dihydro-1,3-dioxo-2H-isoindol-2-yl)-N-methyl-	EtOH	218(4.24),234(4.29), 267(3.37),275(3.38), 295(3.35)	7-0635-73
Benzoic acid, 2-(2-methyl-2H-1,2,4-benzothiadiazin-3-yl)-, S,S-dioxide	EtOH	216(4.35),270(3.92), 300(3.90)	7-0635-73
Benzoic acid, 2-(4-methyl-4H-1,2,4-benzothiadiazin-3-yl)-, S,S-dioxide	EtOH	278(3.95)	7-0635-73
$C_{15}H_{12}N_4O_2$			
Acetonitrile, [[(2-amino-5-nitrophenyl)-phenylmethylene]amino]-, anti	EtOH	230(4.30),360(4.25)	95-1253-73
$C_{15}H_{12}N_4O_7$			
Benzoic acid hydrazide, N-acetoxy-N-(2,4-dinitrophenyl)-	MeOH	237(4.21)	25-1066-73
$C_{15}H_{12}N_6O_7$			
Benzoic acid, 2,2'-bis(hexahydro-2,4,6-trioxo-5-pyrimidinyl)hydrazide	EtOH	224(4.22)	103-0247-73

Compound	Solvent	$\lambda_{max}(\log \epsilon)$	Ref.
$C_{15}H_{12}N_8$			
2H-Tetrazolium, 2-(4-methylphenyl)-5-phenyl-3-(1H-tetrazol-5-yl)-, hydroxide, inner salt	n.s.g.	250(4.38),320s(--)	103-1423-73
$C_{15}H_{12}O$			
Benzaldehyde, 3-(2-phenylethenyl)-	benzene	300(4.42)	23-3756-73
Benzaldehyde, 4-(2-phenylethenyl)-	benzene	335(4.52)	23-3756-73
Benzofuran, 2-methyl-3-phenyl-	EtOH	251(4.04),275(3.73), 283(3.60)	103-0026-73
2,4,6-Cycloheptatrien-1-one, 2-(2-phenylethenyl)-	EtOH	225(4.17),244(4.18), 265s(4.11),350s(4.02), 386(4.16)	88-0877-73
2-Propenal, 3-([1,1'-biphenyl]-4-yl)-	MeOH	318(4.52)	44-2254-73
2-Propen-1-one, 1,3-diphenyl-, (E)-	C_6H_{12}	226(4.23),300(4.30)	44-2629-73
	MeOH	227(--),305(4.40)	44-2629-73
$C_{15}H_{12}OS$			
2H-1-Benzothiopyran-2-ol, 3-phenyl-	EtOH	259(4.30),302(4.23), 335s(3.80)	7-0527-73
Dibenzo[b,f]thiepin, 3-methoxy-	MeOH	230(4.35),267(4.36), 297(3.71)	73-2301-73
$C_{15}H_{12}OS_2$			
1,3-Dithiol-2-one, 4,5-diphenyl-	EtOH	233(4.17),283(3.90), 307s(3.75)	143-0273-73
$C_{15}H_{12}OS_2$			
Thieno[2,3-b]thiophene, 2-benzoyl-5-ethyl-	EtOH	244(4.08),257(4.05)	70-2017-73
$C_{15}H_{12}OS_4$			
3(2H)-Thiophenethione, 2-[5-(4-methoxyphenyl)-3H-1,2-dithiol-3-ylidene]-5-methyl-	dioxan	270(4.79),355(4.48), 515(4.20)	22-1659-73
$C_{15}H_{12}O_2$			
2(3H)-Benzofuranone, 3-methyl-3-phenyl-	EtOH	271(3.13),277(3.09)	44-1993-73
Benzoic acid, (2-phenylethenyl) ester	EtOH	272(4.45)	118-0542-73
4,7:10,13-Diepoxycyclopenta-2,4,6,8,10-12,14-heptaene	EtOH	227(4.60),272s(4.62), 280(4.74),383(4.01)	78-0809-73
tetrafluoroborate	30% H_2SO_4	231(4.33),290(4.10), 331(5.04),345(5.03), 481(3.92),503(3.92)	78-0809-73
6,12-Epoxy-9H-benzocycloundecen-9-ol	EtOH	262(4.95)	78-0533-73
	70% $HClO_4$	245(4.12),289(4.46), 353(4.81),450(3.62), 476(3.75),570(3.43), 582(3.42),595(3.47), 610(3.54)	78-0533-73
2-Propen-1-one, 1-(2-hydroxyphenyl)-3-phenyl-	isooctane	220(4.03),310(4.41), 350(4.0)	65-0638-73
	benzene	320(4.35),350s(--)	65-0638-73
	EtOH	207(4.30),218(4.26), 255(3.80),332(3.76), 362s(3.66)	42-0129-73
	EtOH	220(4.00),316(4.32), 350s(--)	65-0638-73

Compound	Solvent	λ_{max}(log ε)	Ref.
$C_{15}H_{12}O_2S$			
Benzenecarbothioic acid, S-(2-oxo-2-phenylethyl) ester	EtOH	241(4.47),269(4.12)	48-0497-73
Dibenzo[b,e]thiepin-11(6H)-one, 3-methoxy-	MeOH	235s(3.70),244s(4.23), 254(4.30),293(4.09)	73-1596-73
Dibenzo[b,f]thiepin-10(11H)-one, 7-methoxy-	MeOH	259(4.33),280s(4.03), 313(3.48)	73-2301-73
$C_{15}H_{12}O_3$			
9(10H)-Anthracenone, 2-hydroxy-3-methoxy-	EtOH	212(4.51),256(4.28), 292(4.06)	56-1949-73
Benzoic acid, 2-(4-methylbenzoyl)-	H_2O	264(4.30)	44-3383-73
α-Lapachone, dehydroiso-	EtOH	253(4.45),295(3.86), 342(3.18)	102-0942-73
1,3-Propanedione, 1-(2-hydroxyphenyl)-3-phenyl-	pH 13	363(4.21)	39-0808-73B
2-Propen-1-one, 1,3-bis(2-hydroxyphenyl)-	EtOH	208(4.50),258(4.18), 368(4.23)	42-0129-73
2-Propen-1-one, 1-(2,4-dihydroxyphenyl)-3-phenyl-	EtOH	207(4.47),221(4.34), 266s(4.18),275s(4.22), 358(4.01)	42-0129-73
2-Propen-1-one, 1-(2-hydroxyphenyl)-3-(3-hydroxyphenyl)-	EtOH	211(3.40),256(3.91), 352(4.15)	42-0129-73
2-Propen-1-one, 1-(2-hydroxyphenyl)-3-(4-hydroxyphenyl)-	EtOH	209(4.26),222s(4.06), 244(4.06),256s(4.00), 276(3.80),370(4.42)	42-0129-73
$C_{15}H_{12}O_3S$			
Dibenzo[b,e]thiepin-11(6H)-one, 3-methoxy-, 5-oxide	MeOH	230s(4.18),263(3.97), 301(4.09)	73-1596-73
$C_{15}H_{12}O_4$			
1,9,10(2H)-Anthracenetrione, 3,4-dihydro-8-hydroxy-6-methyl-	dioxan	425(3.52)	78-3721-73
dimer	dioxan	270(4.53),306(4.00), 315(4.00),330(3.91), 372(3.98),417(3.87), 434s(3.83)	78-3721-73
Benzoic acid, 2-benzoyl-5-methoxy-	H_2O	253(4.17)	44-3383-73
Benzoic acid, 2-(4-methoxybenzoyl)-	H_2O	290(4.16)	44-3383-73
4H-1-Benzopyran-4-one, 2,3-dihydro-2,5-dihydroxy-2-phenyl-	EtOH	270(3.80),350s(--)	22-1784-73
	EtOH-NaOH	277(--),385(--)	22-1784-73
	EtOH-$AlCl_3$	290(--),380(--)	22-1784-73
4H-1-Benzopyran-4-one, 2,3-dihydro-5,7-dihydroxy-2-phenyl- (pinocembrin)	MeOH	210(4.56),230s(--), 290(4.31),325s(--)	39-1737-73C
	MeOH-NaOMe	250(3.84),330(4.53)	39-1737-73C
4H-1-Benzopyran-4-one, 2,3-dihydro-7-hydroxy-2-(4-hydroxyphenyl)- (liquiritigenin)	NeOH	213(4.4),230(4.3), 275(4.17),313(3.87)	39-1737-73C
	MeOH-NaOMe	248(4.32),310s(--), 336(4.36)	39-1737-73C
2-Propen-1-one, 1-(2,4-dihydroxyphenyl)-3-(2-hydroxyphenyl)-	EtOH	210(4.42),254(3.84), 311(4.13),373(4.37)	42-0129-73
2-Propen-1-one, 1-(2,4-dihydroxyphenyl)-3-(3-hydroxyphenyl)-	EtOH	211(4.57),256(3.95), 314(4.26),360(4.32)	42-0129-73
9H-Xanthen-9-one, 2,8-dihydroxy-1,3-dimethyl-	MeOH	208(4.21),238(4.35), 248(4.34),260(4.39), 267(4.34),291(3.99), 315s(3.59),382(3.75)	24-1198-73
9H-Xanthen-9-one, 2,3-dimethoxy-	MeOH	242(4.64),267(4.05), 305(4.20),346(4.08)	39-1329-73C

Compound	Solvent	λ max (log ε)	Ref.
9H-Xanthen-9-one, 2,6-dimethoxy-	MeOH	204(4.27),241(4.58), 266s(4.08),312(4.20), 347(3.81)	24-1182-73
9H-Xanthen-9-one, 3,6-dimethoxy-	MeOH	243(4.65),269(4.03), 313(4.38),320(4.42)	18-1498-73
$C_{15}H_{12}O_4S$			
Dibenzo[b,e]thiepin-11(6H)-one, 3-methoxy-, 5,5-dioxide	MeOH	232(4.07),296(4.05)	73-1596-73
$C_{15}H_{12}O_5$			
Benzoic acid, 2-(4-hydroxy-3-methoxybenzoyl)-	EtOH	235(4.34),286(4.02), 316(4.03)	56-1949-73
4H-1-Benzopyran-4-one, 2,3-dihydro-5,7-dihydroxy-2-(4-hydroxyphenyl)- (naringenin)	MeOH	203(4.45),211(4.46), 224(4.43),289(4.25), 327(3.9)	39-1737-73C
	MeOH-NaOMe	245s(--),325(4.46)	39-1737-73C
	MeOH-AlCl3	224(4.65),313(4.44), 380(3.68)	39-1737-73C
4H-1-Benzopyran-4-one, 2,3-dihydro-2,5,7-trihydroxy-2-phenyl-	EtOH	290(4.3),330s(--)	22-1784-73
	EtOH-NaOH	327(--),390(--)	22-1784-73
	EtOH-AlCl3	308(--),375(--)	22-1784-73
2,5-Cyclohexadiene-1,4-dione, 2-(2,4-dihydroxybenzoyl)-3,5-dimethyl-	MeOH	212(4.28),242(4.25), 256(4.26),286(4.17), 316s(4.01)	24-1182-73
1H-Naphtho[2,3-c]pyran-1-one, 9,10-dihydroxy-7-methoxy-3-methyl- (toralactone)	EtOH	268(4.60),278(4.78), 392(3.39)	95-0261-73
9H-Xanthene-4,9(4aH)-dione, 1,6-dihydroxy-3,4a-dimethyl-	MeOH	209(4.17),239(4.15), 306(3.86),423(3.73)	24-1182-73
9H-Xanthene-4,9(4aH)-dione, 1,8-dihydroxy-3,4a-dimethyl-	MeOH	218(4.26),290(4.03), 357(3.84)	24-1198-73
9H-Xanthen-9-one, 1-hydroxy-3,7-dimethoxy-	CHCl3	245(4.33),262(4.63), 308(4.16),372(3.88)	39-1329-73C
9H-Xanthen-9-one, 1-hydroxy-5,6-dimethoxy-	MeOH	249(4.54),269s(3.92), 311(4.16),361(3.72)	39-1329-73C
9H-Xanthen-9-one, 1-hydroxy-6,7-dimethoxy-	MeOH	251(4.54),258s(4.34), 269(4.27),288(4.10), 308s(3.91),369(4.08)	39-1329-73C
9H-Xanthen-9-one, 3-hydroxy-2,4-dimethoxy-	MeOH	240(4.57),280(3.83), 313(4.13),350(3.97), 380s(3.20)	39-1329-73C
9H-Xanthen-9-one, 4-hydroxy-2,3-dimethoxy-	MeOH	237(4.42),256(4.52), 290s(3.96),307(4.00), 354(3.77)	39-1329-73C
$C_{15}H_{12}O_6$			
Benzoic acid, 3-(4-carboxyphenoxy)-4-methoxy-	EtOH	251(4.41)	33-1266-73
4H-1-Benzopyran-4-one, 2,3-dihydro-5,6,7-trihydroxy-2-(4-hydroxyphenyl)-	EtOH	300(4.13),368(3.18)	138-0917-73
4H-1-Benzopyran-4-one, 2,3-dihydro-5,7,8-trihydroxy-2-(4-hydroxyphenyl)-	EtOH	299(4.17),370(3.52)	138-0917-73
9H-Xanthen-9-one, 1,3-dihydroxy-4,7-dimethoxy-	MeOH	232(4.47),268(4.51), 313s(4.00),319(4.02), 388(3.81)	39-1329-73C
9H-Xanthen-9-one, 1,8-dihydroxy-3,5-dimethoxy-	EtOH	235(4.30),251(4.42), 275(4.21),296(3.80), 332(3.98)	36-0926-73

Compound	Solvent	λ_{max}(log ε)	Ref.
$C_{15}H_{12}O_7$			
Benzoic acid, 3,6-dihydroxy-2-(2-hydroxy-4-methoxybenzoyl)-	MeOH	210(4.56),228s(4.21), 278(4.15),325(4.07)	24-1182-73
1,4-Naphthalenedione, 5-(1,2-dioxopropyl)-6,8-dihydroxy-2-methoxy-7-methyl-	EtOH-HCl	209(4.41),287(4.35), 310(4.29),406(3.73)	33-2323-73
Naphtho[2,1-b]furan-1,6,9(2H)-trione, 2,5-dihydroxy-7-methoxy-2,4-dimethyl-	EtOH-HCl	270(4.33),300s(--), 400(3.61)	33-2323-73
$C_{15}H_{12}O_8$			
Benzoic acid, 2-(2-carboxy-5-methoxyphenoxy)-3,6-dihydroxy-	MeOH	212(4.62),251(4.16), 291(3.65),336(3.67)	24-1182-73
$C_{15}H_{12}S$			
Benzene, 1-(phenylethynyl)thio-4-methyl-	EtOH	251(4.48),308(4.11)	39-0063-73B
$C_{15}H_{13}BrN_2O_2$			
Benzenamine, 4-bromo-N-[3-(2-nitrophenyl)-2-propenyl]-, (E)-	MeOH	209(4.40),254(4.44), 310(3.87)	42-0694-73
$C_{15}H_{13}BrO_3$			
2H-Naphtho[1,2-b]pyran-5,6-dione, 3-bromo-3,4-dihydro-2,2-dimethyl-	EtOH	225(4.09),282(3.99), 330(3.22),445(2.84)	12-1121-73
$C_{15}H_{13}ClN_2O_2$			
Benzenamine, 4-chloro-N-[3-(2-nitrophenyl)-2-propenyl]-, (E)-	MeOH	209(3.76),253(3.86), 310(3.07)	42-0694-73
$C_{15}H_{13}ClN_2O_2S$			
Benzenesulfonamide, 4-chloro-N-(1-methyl-1H-indol-3-yl)-	EtOH	222(4.57),285(3.78)	39-1602-73C
$C_{15}H_{13}ClN_2O_5$			
Benzo[b]quinolizinium, 11-(acetylamino)-, perchlorate	EtOH	224(4.80),370(4.76), 387(4.76),408(4.76)	44-4167-73
$C_{15}H_{13}ClN_4$			
2H-1,4-Benzodiazepin-2-one, 7-chloro-1,3-dihydro-5-phenyl-, hydrazone	isoPrOH	250s(4.35)	94-2375-73
1,4,5-Benzotriazocin-2-amine, 8-chloro-3,4-dihydro-6-phenyl-	isoPrOH	263(4.35)	94-2375-73
$C_{15}H_{13}ClN_4O$			
3H-1,4-Benzodiazepine, 7-chloro-2-hydrazino-5-phenyl-, 4-oxide	isoPrOH	244(4.40),267(4.37)	94-2375-73
1,4,5-Benzotriazocin-2(1H)-one, 8-chloro-3,4-dihydro-6-phenyl-, oxime	isoPrOH	266(4.38)	94-2375-73
$C_{15}H_{13}ClO_3S$			
Benzenesulfonic acid, 4-[2-chloro-2-(4-methylphenyl)ethenyl]-	EtOH	255(4.00)	104-1511-73
$C_{15}H_{13}Cl_2NO$			
Aziridine, 2,2-dichloro-1-(3-methoxyphenyl)-3-phenyl-	heptane	240(4.10),277(3.49), 284(3.49)	104-2360-73
Aziridine, 2,2-dichloro-3-(3-methoxyphenyl)-1-phenyl-	heptane	224(4.20),237(4.04), 272(3.42),277(3.53), 285(3.45)	104-2360-73
$C_{15}H_{13}Cl_2NO_4$			
Phenanthridinium, 6-(chloromethyl)-5-methyl-, perchlorate	EtOH	248(4.56),352(3.60)	103-0076-73

Compound	Solvent	$\lambda_{max}(\log \epsilon)$	Ref.
$C_{15}H_{13}Cl_2N_3$			
3H-1,5-Benzodiazepin-2-amine, 4-(2-chlorophenyl)-, hydrochloride	EtOH	268(4.42),305s(3.44), 397(3.06)	4-0399-73
$C_{15}H_{13}NO$			
2,4,6-Cycloheptatrien-1-one, 2-amino-4-(2-phenylethenyl)-	pH 1.03	370(4.3),410s(4.2)	18-0544-73
	pH 6.34	432(4.0)	18-0544-73
	MeOH	233(3.84),323(4.56), 425(4.00)	18-0199-73
2,4,6-Cycloheptatrien-1-one, 2-amino-6-(2-phenylethenyl)-	MeOH	235(4.02),320(4.66), 425(4.00)	18-0199-73
1H-Indole, 2-(2-methoxyphenyl)-	MeOH	214(4.51),244(4.23), 318(4.35)	73-0224-73
1H-Indole, 3-(4-methoxyphenyl)-	EtOH	228(4.39),266(4.24), 290s(3.95)	94-2786-73
3H-Indol-3-ol, 3-methyl-2-phenyl-	EtOH	232s(4.20),238(4.25), 245(4.22),313(4.16)	117-0017-73
Isoxazole, 4,5-dihydro-3,5-diphenyl-	EtOH	262(4.15)	22-1390-73
7,1-Metheno-1H-benzo[3,4]cyclohepta[1,2-b]pyridin-3(2H)-one, 4,4a,7,11b-tetrahydro-	EtOH	265(2.18)	44-1893-73
isomer	EtOH	268(2.48)	44-1893-73
Oxazole, 2,5-dihydro-2,4-diphenyl-	EtOH	246(4.23),288s(2.69)	88-2283-73
Oxazole, 2,5-dihydro-4,5-diphenyl-	EtOH	245(4.10)	33-2588-73
2-Propen-1-one, 3-amino-1,3-diphenyl-	EtOH	248(4.12),351(4.31)	33-2588-73
2-Propen-1-one, 1,3-diphenyl-, oxime	EtOH	255(4.31)	33-2588-73
$C_{15}H_{13}NO_2$			
Benzamide, 2-(4-methylbenzoyl)-	EtOH	224(4.27)	39-1160-73B
Benzenepropanamide, β-oxo-N-phenyl-	pH 13	327(4.35)	39-0808-73B
1H-Isoindol-1-one, 2,3-dihydro-3-hydroxy-2-methyl-3-phenyl-	H_2SO_4	240(4.29),344(4.14)	24-1423-73
1H-Isoindol-1-one, 2,3-dihydro-3-hydroxy-3-methyl-2-phenyl-	H_2SO_4	239(4.45),354(3.72)	24-1423-73
4,7-Methanoisobenzofuran-1(3H)-one, 3a,4,7,7a-tetrahydro-3-(phenylimino)-	MeCN	255(3.61)	35-6792-73
4,7-Methano-1H-isoindole-1,3(2H)-dione, 3a,4,7,7a-tetrahydro-2-phenyl-	MeCN	255s(2.57)	35-6792-73
2-Propen-1-one, 3-(4-aminophenyl)-1-(2-hydroxyphenyl)-	dioxan	255(4.07),402(4.51)	83-0299-73
$C_{15}H_{13}NO_3$			
Benzene, 1-methoxy-4-[2-(4-nitrophenyl)-ethenyl]-	THF	258(4.14),270s(--), 374(4.29)	18-2828-73
Benzenepropanamide, N-(4-hydroxyphenyl)-β-oxo-	pH 13	327(4.26)	39-0808-73B
$C_{15}H_{13}NO_3S$			
Benzenecarbothioic acid, O-[2-(4-nitrophenyl)ethyl] ester	C_6H_{12}	272(4.29),418(2.26)	39-1575-73C
Benzenecarbothioic acid, 4-nitro-, O-(2-phenylethyl) ester	C_6H_{12}	256(4.08),298(4.13), 436(2.30)	39-1574-73C
4H-1-Benzopyran-4-one, 7-methoxy-2-methyl-3-(2-methyl-4-thiazolyl)-	n.s.g.	295(4.09)	104-2580-73
2H-1,2-Benzothiazin-4-ol, 2-methyl-3-phenyl-, 1,1-dioxide	EtOH	324(4.18)	4-0095-73
	EtOH-NaOH	236s(4.04),274(3.76), 377(4.06)	4-0095-73
Ethanone, 1-[4-[(4-methylphenyl)thio]-3-nitrophenyl]-	DMF	296(4.18),370(3.71)	39-1430-73B

Compound	Solvent	$\lambda_{max}(\log \epsilon)$	Ref.
$C_{15}H_{13}NO_3S_2$			
Methanesulfonamide, N-(10,11-dihydro-11-oxodibenzo[b,f]thiepin-2-yl)-	MeOH	227(4.34),245(4.38),265s(4.13),347(3.62)	73-2484-73
$C_{15}H_{13}NO_4$			
Pyrrolo[1,2-b]isoquinoline-2-carboxylic acid, 1,2,3,5-tetrahydro-1,5-dioxo-, ethyl ester	EtOH	249(4.06),254(4.10),261s(4.00),329(4.28),345(4.31),355(4.23)	78-0213-73
$C_{15}H_{13}NO_4S$			
Benzoic acid, 4-[(4-methylphenyl)thio]-3-nitro-, methyl ester	DMF	288(4.19),372(3.68)	39-1430-73B
4-Benzoxazolol, 3-methyl-, 4-methylbenzenesulfonate	MeOH	228(4.34),268(3.58),276(3.51)	39-2220-73C
$C_{15}H_{13}NO_5$			
1H-Pyrrole-3,4-dicarboxylic acid, 1-benzoyl-, dimethyl ester	MeOH	229(4.25),253(4.00)	23-1089-73
$C_{15}H_{13}NO_5S$			
2-Thiophenecarboxylic acid, 5-[2-(4-methoxyphenyl)ethenyl]-4-nitro-, methyl ester	EtOH	248(4.24),405(4.01)	118-0313B-73
$C_{15}H_{13}NO_6$			
Ethanone, 1-(2,4-dihydroxyphenyl)-2-(2-methoxy-5-nitrophenyl)-	EtOH	212(4.47),231(4.23),282(4.32),313(4.30)	95-1514-73
6,7-Isoquinolinedicarboxylic acid, 5,8-dihydro-5,8-dioxo-, diethyl ester	EtOH	206(4.15),254(4.18),310s(--)	39-0026-73C
6,7-Quinolinedicarboxylic acid, 5,8-dihydro-5,8-dioxo-, diethyl ester	EtOH	205(4.03),222s(--),242(4.26),345s(--)	39-0026-73C
$C_{15}H_{13}N_2O$			
Benzo[b]quinolizinium, 11-(acetylamino)-, perchlorate	EtOH	224(4.80),370(4.76),387(4.76),408(4.76)	44-4167-73
$C_{15}H_{13}N_3$			
Benzeneacetonitrile, α-[(2-phenylhydrazino)methylene]-	MeOH	288(4.20),306(4.16)	28-1457-73A
Benzenepropanenitrile, β-(phenylhydrazono)-	MeOH	295(4.00),330(4.26)	28-1457-73A
1H-Imidazo[1,2-a]benzimidazole, 2,3-dihydro-2-phenyl-	MeOH	245(4.0),285(4.1)	103-0726-73
$C_{15}H_{13}N_3O$			
4H-Indolo[6.5.4-cd]indol-8-amine, 4-acetyl-6,6a-dihydro-, acetate	EtOH	208(4.31),242(4.52),319(4.02),340(3.89)	39-0760-73C
2(1H)-Quinazolinone, 4-[4-(methylamino)-phenyl]-	EtOH	210(1.19),230(1.11),265(0.53),399(0.59)	30-0828-73
2H-1,2,3-Triazole, 4-methyl-2,5-diphenyl-, 1-oxide	EtOH	203(4.55),246(3.90),286(3.95)	103-0120-73
$C_{15}H_{13}N_3O_2S$			
3-Pyridinecarboxylic acid, 2-amino-4-phenyl-6-thiocyanato-, ethyl ester	MeOH	251(4.28),285s(3.45),341(3.91)	48-0679-73
$C_{15}H_{13}N_3O_2S_2$			
Pyridazino[4',5':5,6]thiopyrano[4,3-b]-indole-1,4-dione, 2,3,11,11a-tetrahydro-11a-methyl-6-(methylthio)-	EtOH	258(4.26),330(3.95)	94-2770-73

Compound	Solvent	$\lambda_{max}(\log \epsilon)$	Ref.
1,3,4-Thiadiazolium, 3-methyl-2-phenyl-5-[(phenylsulfonyl)amino]-, hydroxide, inner salt	MeOH	249(4.09),324(3.97)	103-1216-73
$C_{15}H_{13}N_3O_4$			
Benzenamine, 3-nitro-N-[3-(2-nitrophenyl)-2-propenyl]-	MeOH	209(4.39),243(4.67)	42-0694-73
Benzenamine, 4-nitro-N-[3-(2-nitrophenyl)-2-propenyl]-	MeOH	210(4.30),236(4.36), 383(4.33)	42-0694-73
Pyrrolo[3,4-b]quinolizine-10-carboxylic acid, 1,2,3,4-tetrahydro-1-imino-2-methyl-3,4-dioxo-, ethyl ester	EtOH	265(4.19),450(4.34)	94-1667-73
$C_{15}H_{13}N_3O_4S$			
Indole, 2,3-dihydro-3-methyl-2-(4-nitrophenylsulfonylimino)-	EtOH	261(4.20),291s(3.95)	39-1602-73C
$C_{15}H_{13}N_3S$			
Acetophenone, (2-benzothiazolylhydrazone), (E)-	EtOH	228(4.29),305(4.17)	40-1314-73
Naphtho[2',1':5,6]thiopyrano[4,3-c]pyrazol-1-amine, 11,11a-dihydro-11a-dimethyl-	EtOH	219(4.34),235(4.36), 300(4.33),312(4.38), 350(4.18)	32-1073-73
1H-Pyrazolo[4,3-g]benzothiazole, 4,5-dihydro-7-methyl-1-phenyl-	EtOH	312(4.06)	32-0755-73
1,2,4-Triazolidine-3-thione, 4-methyl-1,5-diphenyl-, meso-ionic didehydro deriv.	MeCN	308(3.36)	103-1048-73
1H-1,2,4-Triazolium, 4,5-dihydro-3-methyl-2,4-diphenyl-5-thioxo-, hydroxide, inner salt	MeCN	254(4.33),326(3.39)	103-1048-73
1H-1,2,4-Triazolium, 3-mercapto-4-phenyl-1-(phenylmethyl)-, hydroxide, inner salt	MeCN	306(3.36)	103-1048-73
$C_{15}H_{13}N_5O$			
Phenol, 4-methyl-2-[[4-(1H-1,2,4-triazol-1-yl)phenyl]azo]-	MeOH	333(4.3),395(3.9)	12-1585-73
Phenol, 4-methyl-2-[[4-(1H-1,2,4-triazol-4-yl)phenyl]azo]-	MeOH	330(4.4),395(4.3)	12-1585-73
1H-Pyrazole-4,5-dione, 3-methyl-1-phenyl)-, 4-(3-pyridinyl)hydrazone)	EtOH	249(4.30),381(4.39)	12-2723-73
1H-1,2,3-Triazole-4-carboxylic acid, 1,5-diphenyl-, hydrazide	EtOH	244(3.49)	42-0589-73
$C_{15}H_{13}N_5O_6$			
Diazene, (2,4-dinitrophenyl)(1-methyl-1-nitro-2-phenylethyl)-	$CHCl_3$	410(2.53)	78-3929-73
$C_{15}H_{13}N_5S$			
Isatin, β-4-phenylthiocarbonohydrazone	EtOH	238(4.24),273(4.11), 358(4.19)	104-2007-73
$C_{15}H_{13}O_4P$			
Phosphonic acid, (2-phenyl-4H-1-benzopyran-4-yl)-	EtOH	245(3.65)	65-0087-73
$C_{15}H_{14}BrNO_4$			
Furo[3,2-c]quinoline-4-carboxylic acid, 2-(bromomethyl)-2,3-dihydro-6-methoxy-, methyl ester	MeOH	247(4.64),351(3.77)	24-0355-73

Compound	Solvent	λmax(log ε)	Ref.
$C_{15}H_{14}ClNO_2S$			
Benzenesulfonamide, 4-[2-chloro-2-(4-methylphenyl)ethenyl]-	EtOH	255(4.33)	104-1511-73
$C_{15}H_{14}ClNO_3$			
Acetamide, 2-(4-chlorophenoxy)-N-hydroxy-N-(3-methylphenyl)-	EtOH	228(4.16),255(4.09)	112-0547-73
Acetamide, 2-(4-chlorophenoxy)-N-hydroxy-N-(4-methylphenyl)-	EtOH	228(4.14),254(4.10)	112-0547-73
$C_{15}H_{14}ClNO_4$			
2-Quinolinecarboxylic acid, 4-chloro-8-methoxy-3-(2-oxopropyl)-, methyl ester	MeOH	256(4.53)	24-0355-73
2-Quinolinecarboxylic acid, 3-(2-chloro-2-propenyl)-1,4-dihydro-8-methoxy-4-oxo-, methyl ester	MeOH	225(4.40),233(4.35), 312(3.65),342(3.88)	24-0355-73
$C_{15}H_{14}ClN_3O$			
Cyclohexanone, 2-(4-chloro-6-phenyl-1,3,5-triazin-2-yl)-	EtOH	268(3.83),317(3.80)	22-2039-73
$C_{15}H_{14}ClN_3O_2$			
Quinolinium, 1-[(1,2,3,4-tetrahydro-1-methyl-2,4-dioxo-5-pyrimidinyl)-methyl]-, chloride	EtOH	270(3.93),318(3.87)	69-2879-73
$C_{15}H_{14}INO$			
Isoquinolinium, 1-(2-furanylmethyl)-2-methyl-, iodide	MeOH	234(4.70),279(3.53), 335(3.77),343(3.77)	83-0592-73
$C_{15}H_{14}INS$			
Isoquinolinium, 2-methyl-1-(2-thienyl-methyl)-, iodide	MeOH	230(4.80),270(3.56), 278(3.56),335(3.79), 344(3.79)	83-0592-73
$C_{15}H_{14}NO$			
Pyridinium, 1-[3-(4-methylphenyl)-3-oxo-1-propenyl]-, diphenyl phosphate	H_2O	271(4.28),275s(4.27), 298s(4.12)	24-0435-73
$C_{15}H_{14}NO_2$			
Pyridinium, 1-[3-(4-methoxyphenyl)-3-oxo-1-propenyl]-, diphenyl phosphate	H_2O	267(4.32),330(4.08)	24-0435-73
$C_{15}H_{14}NO_4$			
Spiro[1,3-dioxolan-2,9'-[9H-1,3]dioxolo-[4,5-g]pyrrolo[1,2-b]isoquinolinium], 7',8'-dihydro- (triiodide)	EtOH	260(5.00)	78-0213-73
$C_{15}H_{14}N_2$			
Azepino[3,4,5,6-def]carbazole, 4,8,9,10-tetrahydro-9-methyl-	MeOH	245(4.53),253(4.50), 286(3.94),296(4.12), 327(3.65),341(3.69)	39-2818-73C
Benzenamine, 2-(3-methyl-1H-indol-2-yl)-	EtOH	229(4.83),245s(4.39), 302(4.24)	78-1429-73
3H-2,3-Benzodiazepine, 4,5-dihydro-3-phenyl-	EtOH	235(4.25),298s(3.91), 335(4.43)	118-0159B-73
5H-[1,4]Diazepino[1,2,3,4-lmn][1,10]-phenanthrolinediium, 6,7-dihydro-, bis(tetrafluoroborate)	MeCN	213(4.47),228(4.36), 283(4.63),314(3.93), 325s(3.79)	5-0339-73

Compound	Solvent	$\lambda_{max}(\log \epsilon)$	Ref.
3H-Indol-2-amine, N-methyl-3-phenyl-, hydrochloride	MeOH	210(4.49),262(3.94)	103-0471-73
2H-Indol-2-imine, 1,3-dihydro-1-methyl-3-phenyl-, hydrochloride	MeOH	212(4.25),265(4.06)	103-0471-73
2H-Indol-2-imine, 1,3-dihydro-3-methyl-1-phenyl-, hydrochloride	MeOH	217(4.34),263(3.81)	103-0471-73
1H-Indole-3-carbonitrile, 4,5,6,7-tetrahydro-2-phenyl-	MeOH	308(4.21)	88-2279-73
$C_{15}H_{14}N_2O$			
[1,4]Diazepino[3,2,1-kl]phenoxazine, 1,2,3,4-tetrahydro-	EtOH	246(4.50),318(3.81)	95-0020-73
1H-Indazole, 3-(4-methoxyphenyl)-1-methyl-	MeOH	205(4.49),247(4.19), 275s(3.82),313(4.12)	24-3432-73
3H-Indol-3-ol, 2-(2-aminophenyl)-3-methyl-	EtOH	232(4.07),300(3.56), 323s(3.40),391(3.47)	78-1429-73
1,2-Propanedione, 1-phenyl-, 1-(phenylhydrazone)	MeOH	240(4.13),285(3.89), 364(4.30)	80-0723-73
$C_{15}H_{14}N_2O_2$			
1H-Indazol-4-ol, 3-(4-methoxyphenyl)-1-methyl-	MeOH	212(4.46),245(4.10), 273(3.98),312(4.08)	24-3432-73
2,5-Piperazinedione, 3-(2-butenylidene)-6-(phenylmethylene)-	EtOH	345(4.54)	18-3876-73
2,5-Piperazinedione, 3-ethylidene-6-(3-phenyl-2-propenylidene)-	EtOH	365(4.44)	18-3876-73
Propanediamide, N,2-diphenyl-	EtOH	260(2.26),290(1.47)	103-0717-73
$C_{15}H_{14}N_2O_2S$			
7(4H)-Benzothiazolone, 5,6-dihydro-6-[[(2-hydroxyphenyl)amino]methylene]-2-methyl-	EtOH	212(4.26),241(4.07) 286(4.05),425(4.19)	32-1063-73
$C_{15}H_{14}N_2O_2S_2$			
Spiro[3H-indole-3,2'(3'H)-thiophene]-4'-carboxylic acid, 3'-imino-2-methyl-5'-(methylthio)-, methyl ester, hydrochloride	EtOH	232(4.38),280(4.10)	94-2344-73
$C_{15}H_{14}N_2O_3$			
2,5-Cyclohexadiene-1,4-dione, 3-acetyl-2-(methylamino)-5-(phenylamino)-	EtOH	243(3.95),295(3.90), 348(4.01),487(2.96)	39-0493-73C
Ethanediamide, N-(4-methoxyphenyl)-N'-phenyl-	dioxan	288(4.26)	30-0001-73
2H-Pyrrol-2-one, 3-acetyl-1,5-dihydro-4-hydroxy-5-(1H-indol-3-ylmethyl)-	MeOH	222(4.60),272(4.24), 279(4.33),290(4.19)	77-0812-73
$C_{15}H_{14}N_2O_4$			
Pyrazolo[5,1-a]isoquinoline-1,2-dicarboxylic acid, 5,6-dihydro-, dimethyl ester	EtOH	226(4.20),267(4.14)	95-0648-73
$C_{15}H_{14}N_2O_4S$			
Benzamide, 2-formyl-N-[2-[(methylamino)-sulfonyl]phenyl]-	EtOH	220(4.37),240(4.19), 300(3.66)	7-0635-73
Benzenepropanamide, N-[4-(aminosulfonyl)-phenyl]-β-oxo-	pH 13	335(4.36)	39-0808-73B
Benzoic acid, 2-(3,4-dihydro-2-methyl-2H-1,2,4-benzothiadiazin-3-yl)-, S,S-dioxide	EtOH	272(3.42),310(3.52)	7-0635-73

Compound	Solvent	$\lambda_{max}(\log \epsilon)$	Ref.
Benzoic acid, 2-(3,4-dihydro-4-methyl-2H-1,2,4-benzothiadiazin-3-yl)-, S,S-dioxide	EtOH	272(3.57),322(3.50)	7-0635-73
$C_{15}H_{14}N_2O_5S$			
Benzoic acid, 2-[[[2-[(methylamino)sulfonyl]phenyl]amino]carbonyl]-	EtOH	288(3.78)	7-0635-73
$C_{15}H_{14}N_2O_6$			
1H-Pyrazole-3,4,5-tricarboxylic acid, trimethyl ester	MeOH	250(3.83)	78-0101-73
	EtOH	250(3.73)	94-2026-73
$C_{15}H_{14}N_3O_2$			
Quinolinium, 1-[(1,2,3,4-tetrahydro-1-methyl-2,4-dioxo-5-pyrimidinyl)methyl]-, chloride	EtOH	270(3.93),318(3.87)	69-2879-73
$C_{15}H_{14}N_4O_2S$			
Pyrrolo[1,2-a][1,2,4]triazino[5,6-d][3,1]benzoxazepin-12(9aH)-one, 10,11-dihydro-9a-methyl-7-(methylthio)-	EtOH	238(4.44),388(4.14)	78-0639-73
$C_{15}H_{14}N_4O_3$			
2,4(1H,3H)-Pteridinedione, 7-methoxy-3,6-dimethyl-	MeOH	225s(4.16),262(4.04), 322(4.08)	24-3203-73
2,4,6(1H,3H,5H)-Pyrimidinetrione, 1-methyl-5-(3-methyl-1-phenyl-1H-pyrazol-5-yl)-, compd. with phenylhydrazine	EtOH	253(4.45)	94-2639-73
$C_{15}H_{14}N_4O_4$			
Adrenochrome, 2,4-dinitrophenylhydrazone	M NaOH	280(3.91),298s(--), 421s(--),585(4.64)	39-0509-73C
2,4(1H,3H)-Pteridinedione, 7-methoxy-3,6-dimethyl-1-phenyl-, 5-oxide	MeOH	248(4.35),285s(3.81), 340(3.92)	24-3203-73
$C_{15}H_{14}N_4O_4S$			
1(2H)-Pyrimidineacetic acid, 4-cyano-2-[[(4-methylphenyl)sulfonyl]imino]-, methyl ester	EtOH	224(4.27),253(4.30), 365(3.51)	44-1591-73
$C_{15}H_{14}N_4O_5$			
Phenol, 4-[(2,4-dinitrophenyl)azo]-3-ethyl-5-methyl- (in 50% DMSO)	acid	403(4.36)	1-3641-73
	KOH	564(4.65)	1-3641-73
Phenol, 4-[(2,4-dinitrophenyl)azo]-2-propyl- (in 50% DMSO)	acid	403(4.31)	1-3641-73
	KOH	595(4.72)	1-3641-73
Phenol, 4-[(2,4-dinitrophenyl)azo]-3-propyl- (first two spectra in 50% DMSO)	acid	404(4.33)	1-3641-73
	KOH	575(4.67)	1-3641-73
	C_2Cl_4	396(4.44)	1-3632-73
Phenol, 4-[(2,4-dinitrophenyl)azo]-2,3,5-trimethyl- (in 50% DMSO)	acid	412(4.27)	1-3641-73
	KOH	596(4.67)	1-3641-73
Phenol, 4-[(2,4-dinitrophenyl)azo]-2,3,6-trimethyl- (first two spectra in 50% DMSO)	acid	453(4.45)	1-3641-73
	KOH	610(4.78)	1-3641-73
	C_2Cl_4	399(4.60),435(4.66)	1-3632-73
Urea, N,N'-dimethyl-N,N'-bis(4-nitrophenyl)-	$CHCl_3$	325(4.3)	44-2590-73
$C_{15}H_{14}N_6O$			
5H-Tetrazol-5-imine, 1,4-dihydro-N-nitro-1,4-bis(phenylmethyl)-	MeOH	284(4.00)	39-1357-73C

Compound	Solvent	λ max (log ε)	Ref.
$C_{15}H_{14}N_6O_3$			
L-Phenylalanine, N-[(1H-purin-6-yl-amino)carbonyl]-	pH 1-2	276.5(4.29)	87-0139-73
	pH 5-7	270(4.28)	87-0139-73
	pH 12	278(4.23)	87-0139-73
$C_{15}H_{14}N_6O_4$			
L-Tyrosine, N-[(1H-purin-6-ylamino)-carbonyl]-	pH 1-2	277.5(4.31)	87-0139-73
	pH 5-7	270(4.28)	87-0139-73
	pH 12	278(4.24)	87-0139-73
$C_{15}H_{14}N_8$			
Formazan, 5-(4-methylphenyl)-3-phenyl-1-(1H-tetrazol-5-yl)- (also metal complexes)	pH 13	486(4.52)	103-1423-73
	EtOH	445(4.00)	103-1423-73
$C_{15}H_{14}O$			
2H-Indeno[5,4,3-cde]azulen-5-one, 1,5,6,8,9,9a-hexahydro-	C_6H_{12}	242s(4.37),247(4.51), 257s(4.36),268(4.29), 278(4.15),305(3.11), 318(3.32),336(1.79), 343s(2.39)	44-1445-73
$C_{15}H_{14}OS$			
Benzenecarbothioic acid, O-(2-phenyleth-yl) ester	C_6H_{12}	248(3.82),288(3.98), 420(2.08)	39-1571-73C
Benzenecarbothioic acid, 2-(phenylmeth-yl)-, O-methyl ester	C_6H_{12}	269(3.94),406(2.48)	39-1571-73C
3-Penten-2-one, 3-phenyl-4-(2-thienyl)-	EtOH	280(3.85),345(4.05)	48-0993-73
$C_{15}H_{14}O_2$			
1,3,5-Cycloheptatrienecarboxylic acid, phenylmethyl ester	EtOH	278(3.56)	78-3609-73
1,4-Naphthalenedione, 2-(3-methyl-2-but-enyl)-	EtOH	247(4.2),252(4.2), 264(4.1),334(3.4)	1-3211-73
2-Phenanthrenecarboxylic acid, 3,4,9,10-tetrahydro-	EtOH	353(4.29)	44-2093-73
1-Propanone, 3-hydroxy-1,3-diphenyl-	EtOH	241(4.12)	35-3310-73
$C_{15}H_{14}O_2S$			
Dibenzo[b,e]thiepin-11-ol, 6,11-dihydro-3-methoxy-	MeOH	220(4.39),253s(3.84), 290(3.30),297(3.27)	73-1596-73
Ethanone, 1-[2-[(4-methoxyphenyl)thio]-phenyl]-	MeOH	231(4.48),266(3.93), 335(3.60)	73-1579-73
$C_{15}H_{14}O_3$			
5H-Benzocyclohepten-5-one, 6-acetoxy-7,8-dimethyl-	EtOH	223(4.71),282(3.71)	39-1223-73C
α-Lapachone	EtOH	248(4.41),281(4.18), 333(3.43)	136-0247-73A
β-Lapachone	EtOH	257(4.45),333(3.24), 430(3.28)	136-0247-73A
Methanone, bis(4-methoxyphenyl)-	FSO_3H	315(4.04),400(4.66)	59-0807-73
at -75°	FSO_3H	309(4.11),387(4.60)	59-0807-73
at -75°	FSO_3H-SbF_5	285(4.04),336(4.32)	59-0807-73
Methanone, (3,4-dimethoxyphenyl)phenyl-	MeOH	246(4.15),282(4.02), 316(3.79)	39-1329-73C
1,4-Naphthalenedione, 2-hydroxy-3-(3-methyl-2-butenyl)- (lapachol)	EtOH	253(4.3),279(4.1), 333(3.4)	1-3211-73

Compound	Solvent	$\lambda_{max}(\log \epsilon)$	Ref.
$C_{15}H_{14}O_4$			
1(2H)-Anthracenone, 3,4-dihydro-8,9,10-trihydroxy-6-methyl-	dioxan	270(4.42),304(3.68), 314(3.57),332(3.35), 424(3.87)	78-3721-73
Benzoic acid, 2-[(4-hydroxy-3-methoxyphenyl)methyl]-	EtOH	208(4.35),284(3.59)	56-1949-73
2H-1-Benzopyran-2-one, 7-methoxy-8-(3-methyl-1-oxo-3-butenyl)-	EtOH	257(3.75),323(4.2)	102-3010-73
2-Butenal, 3-(7-methoxy-2-oxo-2H-1-benzopyran-8-yl)-2-methyl-, (E)-	EtOH and EtOH-base	236(4.17),320(4.16)	88-5005-73
Ethanone, 1-(4-acetoxy-1-hydroxy-3-methyl-2-naphthalenyl)-	n.s.g.	220(4.62),261(4.38), 270(4.33),274(3.58)	39-0235-73C
β-Lapachone, hydroxyiso-	EtOH	254s(4.26),261(4.35), 268(4.28),285s(3.82), 330(3.75),442(3.88)	12-1121-73
Methanone, (2-hydroxy-4-methoxyphenyl)-(4-methoxyphenyl)-	MeOH	294(4.22),332(4.13)	18-1498-73
2-Naphthalenecarboxylic acid, 3,7-dihydro-8-(1-methylethyl)-3,7-dioxo-, methyl ester	n.s.g.	229(4.41),258(4.32), 325s(3.52),370s(3.32)	88-4339-73
Naphtho[2,3-b]furan-4,9-dione, 2,3-dihydro-2-(1-hydroxy-1-methylethyl)-(stenocarpoquinone B)	EtOH	246(4.25),252(4.27), 283(3.97),335(3.31), 400(3.00)	12-1121-73
	EtOH-acid	252(3.86),282(3.74), 335(3.11),392(2.92)	12-1121-73
	EtOH-KOH	274(4.01),477(3.80)	12-1121-73
2H-Naphtho[1,2-b]pyran-5,6-dione, 3,4-dihydro-3-hydroxy-2,2-dimethyl-(stenocarpoquinone A)	EtOH	255(4.31),264s(4.22), 282(3.84),326s(3.30), 428(3.08)	12-1121-73
after 24 hours	EtOH-KOH	275(4.12),476(2.90)	12-1121-73
$C_{15}H_{14}O_5$			
Benzoic acid, 2,6-dihydroxy-, 4-hydroxy-2,6-dimethylphenyl ester	MeOH	208(4.20),220(4.37), 255(4.13),283(3.52), 326(3.52)	24-1198-73
Benzoic acid, 2,6-dihydroxy-, 4-hydroxy-3,5-dimethylphenyl ester	MeOH	208s(4.28),220(4.41), 255(4.09),283s(3.64), 326(3.57)	24-1198-73
2H-1-Benzopyran-2-one, 5-hydroxy-7-methoxy-6-(3-methyl-1-oxo-2-butenyl)-	EtOH	235s(3.78),300(3.54)	78-2943-73
	EtOH-NaOH	240(3.73),313(3.56), 392(3.39)	78-2943-73
2H-1-Benzopyran-2-one, 5-hydroxy-7-methoxy-8-(3-methyl-1-oxo-2-butenyl)-	EtOH	218s(4.13),251(4.08), 318(4.00)	78-2943-73
	EtOH-NaOH	255(4.05),325(3.91), 360(3.83)	78-2943-73
Methanone, bis(2-hydroxy-4-methoxyphenyl)-	MeOH	240s(3.94),253s(3.83), 288(4.06),344(4.06)	18-1498-73
Methanone, (2,4-dihydroxy-3,5-dimethoxyphenyl)phenyl-	MeOH	244s(4.02),303(4.07), 358(3.83)	39-1329-73C
Methanone, (3,6-dihydroxy-2,4-dimethylphenyl)(2,4-dihydroxyphenyl)-	MeOH	208(4.46),230s(4.10), 285(4.26),319(4.04)	24-1182-73
Methanone, (3,6-dihydroxy-2,4-dimethylphenyl)(2,6-dihydroxyphenyl)-	MeOH	209(4.30),221(4.17) 282(4.04),356(3.48)	24-1198-73
Methanone, (2,5-dihydroxy-4-methoxyphenyl)(2-methoxyphenyl)-	MeOH	243(4.12),286(4.04), 362(3.91)	39-1329-73C
Methanone, (2,5-dihydroxy-4-methoxyphenyl)(4-methoxyphenyl)-	MeOH	256(4.03),296(4.12), 370(3.92)	18-1498-73
1,8-Naphthalenediol, 3-methoxy-, diacetate	EtOH	212s(4.22),231(4.67), 267(3.52),279(3.62), 290(3.55),319(3.12), 333(3.45)	23-1617-73

Compound	Solvent	λ max (log ε)	Ref.
9H-Xanthen-9-one, 4,4a-dihydro-1,4,6-trihydroxy-3,4a-dimethyl-	MeOH	208(4.41),254(3.97), 313(3.78),395(4.24)	24-1198-73
9H-Xanthen-9-one, 4,4a-dihydro-1,4,8-trihydroxy-3,4a-dimethyl-	MeOH	210(4.29),225(4.24), 247s(3.87),277(3.84), 386(4.17),414(3.99)	24-1198-73
diastereoisomer	MeOH	210(4.29),225(4.21), 244s(3.86),277(3.74), 377(4.16),412(3.91)	24-1198-73
$C_{15}H_{14}S$			
7H-Benzo[3,4]cyclobuta[1,2-b][1]benzothiopyran, 4b,6,8,9-tetrahydro-	EtOH	224s(4.12),274(4.05), 363(3.79)	39-2253-73C
$C_{15}H_{14}S_2$			
Dicyclohepta[d,f][1,3]dithiepin, 5a,8a-dihydro-	dioxan	244(3.82),294(3.87)	88-2627-73
$C_{15}H_{15}$			
Cycloheptatrienylium, (2,4,6-cycloheptatrien-1-ylmethyl)-	pH 2	226(4.28),288(3.89), 596(4.70)	138-1169-73
Ethylium, 1-(4-methylphenyl)-1-phenyl-	H_2SO_4	318(3.95),441(4.62)	59-0807-73
at -75°	FSO_3H	317(3.95),436(4.61)	59-0803-73
at -75°	FSO_3H-SbF_5	317(4.04),436(4.60)	59-0807-73
$C_{15}H_{15}BrN_2O$			
Phenol, 4-bromo-2-[[[4-(dimethylamino)-phenyl]imino]methyl]-	benzene	280(3.89),332(3.94), 400(4.49)	80-1781-73
	EtOH	209(--),232(--), 252(--),329(--), 395(--)	80-1781-73
	ether	234(4.31),251(4.30), 333(3.86),396(4.38)	80-1781-73
	CH_2Cl_2	237(4.46),252(4.43), 335(3.97),401(4.53)	80-1781-73
$C_{15}H_{15}BrN_2O_3$			
Acetamide, N-acetyl-N-(1-acetyl-5-bromo-3-methyl-1H-indol-2-yl)-	MeOH	246(4.41),297(3.79), 306(3.77)	103-0471-73
$C_{15}H_{15}ClO_3$			
1-Cyclopentene-1-carboxylic acid, 3-[(4-chlorophenyl)methylene]-2-hydroxy-, ethyl ester	EtOH	235(3.90),330(4.64)	103-0628-73
$C_{15}H_{15}ClO_6$			
Benzofuro[3,2-c]pyrylium, 3-methyl-1-propyl-, perchlorate	n.s.g.	255(4.00),266(3.93), 315(3.65)	103-0416-73
$C_{15}H_{15}N$			
[1,1'-Biphenyl]-2-amine, N-(1-methylethylidene)-	ether	245(4.15),283(3.66)	44-1157-73
1H-Carbazole, 2,3,4,4a-tetrahydro-4a-(2-propynyl)-, hydrobromide	EtOH	206(4.14),212(4.13), 219(4.12),225(4.00), 239(3.65),261(3.71)	39-1913-73C
9H-Carbazole, 4,5,9-trimethyl-	MeOH	248(4.25),256(4.08), 265(3.84),295(3.77), 336(3.15),352(3.34)	39-2818-73C
$C_{15}H_{15}NO$			
Benzofuro[3,2-c]pyridine, 3-methyl-1-propyl-	n.s.g.	254(4.17),280(4.00), 289(3.96),299(3.94)	103-0416-73

Compound	Solvent	λ_{max}(log ϵ)	Ref.
2-Cyclobutene-1-carbonitrile, 1-(1,1-dimethylethyl)-4-oxo-2-phenyl-	EtOH	290(4.09)	88-0009-73
Isoquinoline, 1-(2-furanylmethyl)-1,2-dihydro-2-methyl-	MeOH	240s(3.98),333(4.08)	83-0592-73
Methanamine, N-[(4-methylphenyl)phenylmethylene]-, N-oxide, (E)-	EtOH	303(4.16)	44-4440-73
(Z)-	heptane	305(4.19)	44-4440-73
Methanone, [4-(dimethylamino)phenyl]-phenyl-	FSO_3H at -75°	286(4.18),332(4.43)	59-0807-73
$C_{15}H_{15}NO_2$			
1-Cyclohexene-1-carbonitrile, 2-ethoxy-6-oxo-4-phenyl-	EtOH	269(4.17)	70-0811-73
1H-Isoindole-1,3(2H)-dione, 3a,4,7,7a-tetrahydro-4-methyl-2-phenyl-, (1R,2R,3R)-	EtOH	219(4.14)	104-2317-73
(1R,2R,3S)-	EtOH	216(3.83)	104-2317-73
(1R,2S,3R)-	EtOH	216(4.00)	104-2317-73
(1R,2S,3S)-	EtOH	216(3.99)	104-2317-73
Pyridine, 1,4-diacetyl-1,4-dihydro-4-phenyl-	MeOH	255(4.26)	78-0391-73
$C_{15}H_{15}NO_2S$			
Benzene, 1,4-dimethyl-2-[(4-methylphenyl)thio]-5-nitro-	DMF	342(3.97)	32-0723-73
Sulfilimine, N-(ethoxycarbonyl)-S,S-diphenyl-	EtOH	226s(4.13)	44-4324-73
$C_{15}H_{15}NO_3$			
Benzamide, N-hydroxy-3-methoxy-N-(2-methylphenyl)-	EtOH	255(3.91)	112-0547-73
Benzamide, N-hydroxy-3-methoxy-N-(3-methylphenyl)-	EtOH	255(4.00)	112-0547-73
1H-Carbazol-1-one, 9-acetyl-2,3,4,9-tetrahydro-7-methoxy-	EtOH	233(4.20),260(4.02), 270s(3.99),333(4.47)	39-0878-73B
1H-Indene-2-pentanenitrile, 2,3-dihydro-5-methoxy-γ,1-dioxo-	MeOH	222(4.16),267(4.19), 287(4.07),294(4.07)	24-1303-73
2,4-Pentadienoic acid, 2-cyano-5-hydroxy-5-(4-methylphenyl)-, ethyl ester	CH_2Cl_2	260(4.23),372(3.18)	97-0132-73
$C_{15}H_{15}NO_3S$			
2-Thiophenecarboxylic acid, 3-methyl-5-[(phenylcarbonyl)amino]-, ethyl ester	MeOH	229(4.14),251s(4.93), 320(4.41)	48-0539-73
$C_{15}H_{15}NO_4$			
Benzamide, N-hydroxy-2,4-dimethoxy-N-phenyl-	EtOH	275(4.00)	112-0547-73
Furo[3,2-c]quinoline-4-carboxylic acid, 2,3-dihydro-6-methoxy-2-methyl-, methyl ester	MeOH	247(4.66),299(3.59), 314(3.57),351(3.77)	24-0355-73
Norskimmianine, O-ethyl-	MeOH	240s(4.77),248(4.96), 268(3.45),306s(3.77), 319(3.91),331(3.91), 344s(3.77)	78-1217-73
	MeOH-acid	252(4.92),279s(3.71), 308s(3.68),321(3.90), 348(3.93)	78-1217-73
Phenol, 2-[(2-hydroxy-5-methylphenyl)-methyl]-4-methyl-6-nitro-	neutral	285(3.87),375(3.44)	49-1315-73

Compound	Solvent	λ_{max}(log ε)	Ref.
Phenol, 2-[(2-hydroxy-5-methylphenyl)-methyl]-4-methyl-6-nitro- (cont.)	anion	285(3.79),428(3.63)	49-1315-73
	dianion	300(3.89),454(3.71)	49-1315-73
1H-Pyrano[3,4-b]quinolin-1-one, 3,4-dihydro-5,9-dimethoxy-3-methyl-	MeOH	258(4.59),308(3.52), 360(3.53)	24-0355-73
1H-Pyrrole-3-carboxylic acid, 4-acetyl-1-[(phenylmethoxy)methyl]-	EtOH	262(4.01)	23-1089-73
2-Quinolinecarboxylic acid, 1,4-dihydro-8-methoxy-4-oxo-3-(2-propenyl)-, methyl ester	ether	224(4.40),239(4.31), 295(3.61),308(3.69), 358(3.92)	24-0355-73
$C_{15}H_{15}NO_5$			
1-Cyclopentene-1-carboxylic acid, 2-hydroxy-3-[(4-nitrophenyl)methylene]-, ethyl ester	EtOH	290(4.27),367(4.60)	103-0628-73
2(1H)-Isoquinolinepropanoic acid, 3-carboxy-1-oxo-, ethyl ester	EtOH	225s(4.17),301(3.89), 325s(3.78)	78-0213-73
$C_{15}H_{15}NO_6$			
6,7-Isoquinolinedicarboxylic acid, 5,8-dihydroxy-, diethyl ester	EtOH	219(4.44),248(4.25), 254(3.90)	39-0026-73C
6,7-Quinolinedicarboxylic acid, 5,8-dihydroxy-, diethyl ester	EtOH	208(4.40),232(3.98), 268(4.46),341(3.56)	39-0026-73C
$C_{15}H_{15}NS$			
Isoquinoline, 1,2-dihydro-2-methyl-1-(2-thienylmethyl)-	MeOH	233(4.35),265s(3.72), 334(4.04)	83-0592-73
$C_{15}H_{15}N_2O_2$			
Pyridinium, 3-[[(acetyloxy)imino]methyl]-1-(phenylmethyl)-	pH 6.61	248(4.06)	36-1381-73
$C_{15}H_{15}N_2O_2$			
Anantine	n.s.g.	218(4.2),277(4.3)	88-1757-73
Isoanantine	n.s.g.	285(3.93)	88-1757-73
1,2,4-Triazin-4-ol, 2,3,4,5-tetrahydro-3,6-diphenyl-	EtOH	286(4.07)	103-0123-73
$C_{15}H_{15}N_3OS$			
7(4H)-Benzothiazolone, 5,6-dihydro-2-methyl-6-[[(2-aminophenyl)amino]-methylene]-	EtOH	222(4.35),285(4.16), 415(4.23)	32-1063-73
$C_{15}H_{15}N_3OS_3$			
4-Thiazolidinone, 3-ethyl-5-[4,5-dimethyl-3-(2-pyridinyl)thiazolin-2-ylidene]-2-thioxo-	EtOH	437(5.00)	103-0687-73
$C_{15}H_{15}N_3OS_4$			
4-Thiazolidinone, 3-ethyl-5-[4,5-dimethyl-3-(2-thiazolyl)thiazolin-2-ylidene]-2-thioxo-	EtOH	537(5.19)	103-0687-73
$C_{15}H_{15}N_3O_2$			
2,4(1H,3H)-Pyrimidinedione, 5-ethyl-1-(1H-indol-3-ylmethyl)- (spectra in 35% ethanol)	pH 6.5	217(4.62),274(4.17), 287s(4.05)	19-0257-73
	pH 13	273(4.12),287s(3.96)	19-0257-73
2,4(1H,3H)-Pyrimidinedione, 1-methyl-5-(1(2H)-quinolinylmethyl)-	EtOH	231(4.56),272(4.04), 351(4.44)	69-2879-73

Compound	Solvent	λ_{max}(log ϵ)	Ref.
$C_{15}H_{15}N_3O_2S_3$			
[5,5'-Bithiazolidine]-4,4'-dione, 3-methyl-2-(methylimino)-3'-(phenylmethyl)-2'-thioxo-	EtOH	264(4.35),295(4.26)	94-1132-73
$C_{15}H_{15}N_3O_3$			
Phenol, 2-[[[4-(dimethylamino)phenyl]-imino]methyl]-4-nitro-	benzene	280(4.04),318(4.13), 404(4.39)	80-1781-73
	EtOH	206(--),249(--), 260(--),317(--), 404(--)	80-1781-73
	ether	248(4.24),262(4.17), 317(4.10),399(4.34)	80-1781-73
	CH_2Cl_2	249(4.33),262(4.31), 318(4.20),406(4.48)	80-1781-73
Pyrazinecarboxylic acid, 3-amino-6-(2-phenylethenyl)-, ethyl ester, 4-oxide	EtOH	315(4.49),402(3.75)	35-6407-73
$C_{15}H_{15}N_3O_8$			
1H-Indole-3-carboxylic acid, 5-acetoxy-1,2-dimethyl-4,6-dinitro-, ethyl ester	MeOH or $CHCl_3$	267(4.28),324(3.96), 345(3.95)	103-1490-73
$C_{15}H_{15}N_5O$			
4(1H)-Pteridinone, 2-amino-6-(3-phenylpropyl)-	pH 13	254(4.33),364(3.78)	44-2073-73
4(1H)-Pteridinone, 2-amino-7-(3-phenylpropyl)-	pH 13	252(4.26),358(3.88)	44-2073-73
$C_{15}H_{15}N_5O_3$			
Carbamic acid, (3-ethyl-7,8-dihydro-8-oxo-3H-purin-6-yl)-, phenylmethyl ester	pH 1	228(4.44),305(4.26)	94-1954-73
	pH 7	238(4.24),307(4.22)	94-1954-73
	pH 13	248(4.20),323(4.36)	94-1954-73
	EtOH	243(4.24),314(4.20)	94-1954-73
$C_{15}H_{15}O$			
Ethylium, 1-(4-methoxyphenyl)-1-phenyl-	H_2SO_4	320(3.95),446(4.67)	59-0807-73
at -75°	FSO_3H	317(3.90),443(3.63)	59-0807-73
at -75°	FSO_3H-SbF_5	309(3.95),406(4.46)	59-0807-73
$C_{15}H_{15}O_2$			
Benzofuro[3,2-c]pyrylium, 3-methyl-1-propyl-, perchlorate	n.s.g.	255(4.00),266(3.93), 315(3.65)	103-0416-73
$C_{15}H_{15}S$			
Sulfonium, cyclopropyldiphenyl-, tetrafluoroborate	EtOH	231(3.58),261(2.71), 267(2.82),274(--)	35-5298-73
$C_{15}H_{16}$			
Azulene, 1-(3-methyl-1-butenyl)-	C_6H_{12}	236(4.33),288(4.63), 371(3.94),391(3.95), 595s(2.41),620s(2.46), 641(2.50),668s(2.41), 706(2.37),750s(1.97), 796(1.86)	5-0166-73
1,1'-Biphenyl, 2-(1-methylethyl)-	EtOH	233(4.06)	22-1517-73
1,1'-Biphenyl, 2-propyl-	EtOH	234(3.95)	35-5288-73
7H-Cycloocta[de]naphthalene, 8,9,10,11-tetrahydro-	n.s.g.	223(5.03),228(5.20), 245s(3.32),267s(3.73), 276(3.93),286(4.03),	35-2940-73

Compound	Solvent	λ max (log ε)	Ref.
7H-Cycloocta[de]naphthalene, 8,9,10,11-tetrahydro- (cont.)	n.s.g.	293s(3.86),303(3.87), 306(3.29),316(3.02), 321(3.08)	35-2940-73
Spiro[cyclopropane-1,1'-[1H]indene], 2',3'-dihydro-2-methylene-3-(1-methylethylidene)-	EtOH	245(4.27)	39-0278-73B
$C_{15}H_{16}BrNO$			
Pyridinium, 3-ethyl-1-(2-oxo-2-phenyl-ethyl)-, bromide	EtOH	249(4.20)	94-2695-73
$C_{15}H_{16}BrNO_4$			
1H-Indole-3-carboxylic acid, 5-acetoxy-6-bromo-1,2-dimethyl-, ethyl ester	isooctane	227(4.57),292(4.05), 300(4.03)	103-0306-73
$C_{15}H_{16}BrN_5O_3$			
L-Histidine, N-acetyl-2-[(4-bromophenyl)-azo]-, methyl ester	EtOH	387(4.41)	44-1971-73
L-Histidine, N-acetyl-5-[(4-bromophenyl)-azo]-, methyl ester	EtOH	354(4.39)	44-1971-73
$C_{15}H_{16}BrS$			
Sulfonium, (3-bromopropyl)diphenyl-, tetrafluoroborate	EtOH	235(3.51),261(2.77), 268(2.84),275(2.73)	35-5298-73
$C_{15}H_{16}ClNO_3S$			
Sulfamoyl chloride, [dihydro-5-methyl-3-(1-methylethylidene)-4-(phenyl-methylene)-2(3H)-furanylidene]-	EtOH	320.5(3.66)	44-1015-73
$C_{15}H_{16}ClN_3$			
Benzenamine, 4-[4-chloro-2-methylphen-yl)azo]-N,N-dimethyl-	C_6H_{12}	413(4.51)	18-3139-73
ammonium ion	50%EtOH-HCl	334(4.36)	18-3139-73
azonium ion	50%EtOH-HCl	511(3.54)	18-3139-73
Benzenamine, 4-[(4-chlorophenyl)azo]-N,N,2-trimethyl-	C_6H_{12}	415(4.52)	18-3139-73
ammonium ion	50%EtOH-HCl	332(3.87)	18-3139-73
azonium ion	50%EtOH-HCl	517(4.68)	18-3139-73
$C_{15}H_{16}ClN_5O$			
Morpholine, 4-[4-[2-(4-chlorophenyl)-2H-tetrazol-5-yl]-1,3-butadienyl]-, (E,E)-	EtOH	262(4.27),327(4.57)	88-4295-73
$C_{15}H_{16}ClS$			
Sulfonium, (3-chloropropyl)diphenyl-, tetrafluoroborate	EtOH	233(3.49),248(2.74), 265(2.80),273(2.70)	35-5298-73
$C_{15}H_{16}FNO_2$			
1H-Pyrrole-2-carboxylic acid, 4-fluoro-5-(2,4,6-trimethylphenyl)-, methyl ester	MeOH	215(4.26),267(3.92)	24-3544-73
$C_{15}H_{16}IS$			
Sulfonium, (3-iodopropyl)diphenyl-, tetrafluoroborate	EtOH	234(3.47),258(2.78), 265(2.82),273(2.73)	35-5298-73
$C_{15}H_{16}NO_2S$			
Thiopyrylium, 2-amino-3-(ethoxycarbon-yl)-6-(4-methylphenyl)- perchlorate	HOAc	283(3.59),317(3.27), 417(4.14)	97-0342-73

Compound	Solvent	$\lambda_{max}(\log \epsilon)$	Ref.
$C_{15}H_{16}NO_3$			
Pyrylium, 2-amino-3-(ethoxycarbonyl)-6-(4-methylphenyl)-, perchlorate	HOAc	267(3.94),395(4.30)	97-0132-73
$C_{15}H_{16}NO_4$			
Spiro[1,3-dioxolane-2,9'[9H-1,3]dioxolo-[4,5-g]pyrrolo[1,2-b]isoquinolinium], 7',8',9'a,10'-tetrahydro-, triiodide	EtOH	255(4.30),295(4.34), 370(4.31)	78-0213-73
$C_{15}H_{16}N_2$			
Cinnoline, 1,2,3,4-tetrahydro-1-methyl-4-phenyl-	MeCN	254(3.91),299(3.55)	22-3487-73
[1,4]Diazepino[3,2,1-jk]carbazole, 1,2,3,5,6,7-hexahydro-	EtOH	243(3.62),311(3.71), 340(3.42)	78-4045-73
9H-Pyrido[3,4-b]indole, 1-isobutyl-	MeOH	235(4.58),289(4.27), 336(3.70),350(3.71)	95-0033-73
$C_{15}H_{16}N_2O$			
1H-Indazole, 6,7-dihydro-3-(4-methoxyphenyl)-1-methyl-	MeOH	262(4.24)	24-3432-73
Phenol, 2-[[[4-(dimethylamino)phenyl]-imino]methyl]-	benzene	279(3.82),334(3.98), 390(4.39)	80-1781-73
	EtOH	225(--),246(--), 330(--),386(--)	80-1781-73
	ether	226(4.17),247(4.24), 333(3.96),387(4.37)	80-1781-73
	CH_2Cl_2	249(4.27),335(3.98), 392(4.38)	80-1781-73
	MeCN	226(--),246(--), 320(--),384(--)	80-1781-73
$C_{15}H_{16}N_2O_2$			
Canthin-6-one, 1,2,3,3a,4,5-hexahydro-8-hydroxy-3-methyl-	EtOH	215(4.06),243(4.12), 327(3.78)	35-7842-73
4H-Indazol-4-one, 1,5,6,7-tetrahydro-3-(4-methoxyphenyl)-1-methyl-	MeOH	237(4.28),280(3.95)	24-0450-73
6H-Indolo[3,4-gh][1,4]benzoxazine-9-methanol, 4,8,9,10a-tetrahydro-9-methyl-, hydrochloride	EtOH	224(4.52),287(3.85), 294(3.85)	39-0760-73C
1H-Pyrazole-3-carboxylic acid, 5-(1-methyl-2-phenylethenyl)-, ethyl ester	C_6H_{12} or EtOH	224(4.25),277(4.36)	4-0015-73
Pyridine, 1,4-dihydro-1-methyl-4-[1-(4-nitrophenyl)propylidene]-	hexane	490(--)	48-0901-73
	dioxan	273(3.93),534(--)	48-0901-73
(also other solvents)	DMF	590(--)	48-0901-73
Pyridine, 1-ethyl-1,4-dihydro-4-[1-(4-nitrophenyl)ethylidene]-	dioxan	270(3.89)	48-0901-73
$C_{15}H_{16}N_2O_2S$			
1,3(2H,4H)-Isoquinolinedione, 4-(mercapto-1-piperidinylmethylene)-	EtOH	289(3.25),360(2.54)	95-0322-73
$C_{15}H_{16}N_2O_3$			
Acetamide, N-(3,4-dihydrospirobenz[cd]-indole-5(1H),2'-[1,3]dioxolan]-4-yl)-	EtOH	203(4.33),224(4.54), 286(3.84),292(3.84)	39-0760-73C
1H-Pyrazole-3-carboxylic acid, 5-acetyl-1-(4-methylphenyl)-, ethyl ester	C_6H_{12} or EtOH	221(4.32),275(4.83)	4-0015-73
2,4(1H,3H)-Pyrimidinedione, 5-ethyl-1-(3-oxo-3-phenylpropyl)- (spectra in 10% ethanol)	pH 6.5	251(4.20),270s(4.07)	19-0257-73
	pH 13	249(4.19)	19-0257-73

Compound	Solvent	$\lambda_{max}(\log \epsilon)$	Ref.
$C_{15}H_{16}N_2O_3S$			
Acetamide, N-[3,4-dihydro-2-(1-methylethenyl)-4-oxo-2H-1,3-thiazin-5-yl]-2-phenoxy-	EtOH	320(3.89)	88-2159-73
1,3(2H,4H)-Isoquinolinedione, 4-(mercapto-4-morpholinylmethylene)-2-methyl-	EtOH	290(3.13)	95-0322-73
$C_{15}H_{16}N_2O_4$			
2,3-Quinoxalinedimethanol, α-methyl-, diacetate	EtOH	238(4.59),320(3.84)	33-1882-73
$C_{15}H_{16}N_2O_4S$			
Benzenamine, N,N-dimethyl-4-[[(4-nitrophenyl)sulfonyl]methyl]-	$CHCl_3$	364(2.72)	23-1187-73
at 47.8°	$CHCl_3$	360(2.73)	23-1187-73
at 17.8°	$CHCl_3$	368(2.72)	23-1187-73
Propanedioic acid, [(2-benzothiazolylamino)methylene]-, diethyl ester	EtOH	213(3.56),260(2.82), 330(3.59)	94-2019-73
$C_{15}H_{16}N_2O_5$			
1H-Indole-2-carboxylic acid, 4-[(dimethylamino)oxoacetyl]-5-hydroxy-, ethyl ester	n.s.g.	220(4.18),260(3.95), 363(4.07)	22-2046-73
	base	225(4.26),322(4.08), 432(3.99)	22-2046-73
Propanedioic acid, [(2-benzoxazolylamino)methylene]-, diethyl ester	EtOH	315(3.84)	94-2019-73
$C_{15}H_{16}N_2O_6$			
Acetamide, N-[3,4-diacetoxy-5-(2-furanyl)-1-methyl-1H-pyrrol-2-yl]-	n.s.g.	225(3.95),280(4.21)	12-2221-73
2-Butenedioic acid, 2-[(4-nitrophenyl)amino]-3-(2-propenyl)-, dimethyl ester, cis	ether	285(3.69),366(4.48)	24-0355-73
trans	ether	293(3.61),359(4.42)	24-0355-73
2-Butenedioic acid, 2-[(4-nitrophenyl)-2-propenylamino]-, dimethyl ester, cis	ether	258(4.04),272(4.05), 353(4.21)	24-0355-73
trans	ether	366(4.23)	24-0355-73
1H-Indole-3-carboxylic acid, 5-acetoxy-1,2-dimethyl-6-nitro-, ethyl ester	MeOH	211(4.42),380(3.42)	103-1490-73
$C_{15}H_{16}N_2S$			
Benzo[b]thiophen-2-amine, 4,5,6,7-tetrahydro-3-(iminophenylmethyl)-, hydrochloride	MeOH	270(4.13),440(3.59)	88-2279-73
1-Cyclohexene-1-acetonitrile, α-(aminophenylmethylene)-2-mercapto-	MeOH	294(3.79)	88-2279-73
Thiourea, N,N-bis(phenylmethyl)-	EtOH	250(3.92)	48-0144-73
$C_{15}H_{16}N_4OS$			
Spiro[cyclopentane-1,6'(7'H)-[1,2,4]-triazino[5,6-d][3,1]benzoxazepine], 3'-(methylthio)-	EtOH	206(4.33),238(4.46), 349(4.05),445(3.82)	78-0639-73
$C_{15}H_{16}N_4O_2$			
Benzenecarbohydrazonamide, N,N-dimethyl-N'-(2-nitrophenyl)-	MeOH	246(4.28),326(4.19), 470(3.89)	24-2530-73
Propanedinitrile, [3-cyano-1,5-dihydro-5-hydroxy-5-(1-methylethyl)-4-(2-methyl-1-oxopropyl)-2H-pyrrol-2-ylidene]-	EtOH	244(4.13),364(3.72)	12-1551-73

Compound	Solvent	$\lambda_{max}(\log \epsilon)$	Ref.
$C_{15}H_{16}N_4O_2S$			
2-Propanone, 1-[6,7-dihydro-6-methyl-3-(methylthio)-1,2,4-triazino[5,6-d][3,1]benzoxazepin-6-yl)]-	EtOH	228(4.29),308(4.24), 448(2.79)	78-0639-73
[1,2,4]Triazino[5,6-d][3,1]benzoxazepine, 7-acetyl-6,7-dihydro-6,6-dimethyl-3-(methylthio)-	EtOH	238(4.44),378(4.16)	78-0639-73
$C_{15}H_{16}N_4O_3S$			
[1,2,4]Triazino[5,6-d][3,1]benzoxazepine-6-propanoic acid, 6,7-dihydro-6-methyl-3-(methylthio)-	EtOH	202(4.38),238(4.41), 351(3.80),444(3.48)	78-0639-73
$C_{15}H_{16}N_4O_6$			
1H-Purine-2,6-dione, 7-(4-acetoxy-3,6-dihydro-6-methyl-3-oxo-2H-pyran-2-yl]-3,7-dihydro-1,3-dimethyl-, (2S-cis)-	n.s.g.	274(3.88)	136-0468-73B
$C_{15}H_{16}N_6O$			
Urea, N-(3-phenylpropyl)-N'-(1H-purin-6-yl)-	pH 1-2	278.5(4.30)	87-0139-73
	pH 5-7	269(4.25)	87-0139-73
	pH 12	278(4.20)	87-0139-73
$C_{15}H_{16}O$			
Bicyclo[3.1.0]hexan-2-one, 5-cyclopropyl-6-phenyl-, trans	EtOH	254(2.55),259(2.54), 264(2.43),284s(2.08)	35-6723-73
Bicyclo[3.1.0]hexan-2-one, 6-cyclopropyl-6-phenyl-, endo-exo-	EtOH	252(2.49),258(2.50), 280s(2.06),365(2.43)	35-6723-73
2-Cyclohexen-1-one, 4-cyclopropyl-3-phenyl-	EtOH	203(4.53),221(4.32), 282(4.29)	35-6723-73
2-Cyclohexen-1-one, 4-cyclopropyl-4-phenyl-	EtOH	208(4.18),220s(4.09), 262s(3.13),320s(1.72)	35-6723-73
1H-Cyclopenta[2,3]cyclopropa[1,2-a]naphthalen-1-one, 2,3,4,5,9b,9c-hexahydro-9b-methyl-	EtOH	240(4.01)	78-0309-73
Phenol, 4-(1-methyl-1-phenylethyl)-	$C_2H_4Cl_2$	278(3.29),284(3.23)	116-0305-73
Spiro[cyclopentane-1,2'(1'H)-naphthalen]-3-one, 3',4'-dihydro-1'-methylene-	EtOH	250(4.1)	78-0309-73
$C_{15}H_{16}OS$			
1-Propanone, 2-methyl-1-(2-methyl-5-phenyl-3-thienyl)-	EtOH	251(4.42),286(4.09)	78-0413-73
1-Propanone, 2-methyl-1-(5-methyl-2-phenyl-3-thienyl)-	EtOH	236(4.09),255s(3.93), 299(3.74)	78-0413-73
$C_{15}H_{16}O_2$			
Acetic acid, (1,2,7,8,9,9a-hexahydro-6H-benz[cd]azulen-6-ylidene)-	EtOH	269(4.04)	44-1447-73
Bicyclo[2.2.1]hept-2-ene-2-carboxylic acid, 3-phenyl-, methyl ester	MeCN	276(4.02)	5-0844-73
	C_6H_{12}	278(--)	5-0844-73
$C_{15}H_{16}O_3$			
2H-1-Benzopyran-2-one, 5-methyl-4-[(3-methyl-2-butenyl)oxy]-	MeOH	276(4.11),283(4.10)	24-0382-73
3H-2-Benzopyran-3-one, 1-(3-furanyl)-1,7,8,8a-tetrahydro-5,8a-dimethyl-(pyroangolensolide)	EtOH	277(4.29)	88-4869-73
diastereoisomer	EtOH	278(4.24)	88-4869-73

Compound	Solvent	λmax(log ε)	Ref.
Cyclopent[a]indene-2-carboxylic acid, 1,2,3,8-tetrahydro-6-methoxy-2-methyl-	EtOH	265(4.24)	39-2454-73C
4H-Furo[3,2-c][1]benzopyran-4-one, 2,3-dihydro-2,2,3,9-tetramethyl-	MeOH	289(4.00),298(4.10), 313(4.01),327(3.83)	24-0382-73
2,4-Hexadienoic acid, 2-benzoyl-, ethyl ester	EtOH	253(4.35),282(4.25)	70-2301-73
Isogerberacumarin	MeOH	289(4.02),298(4.12), 313(4.02),329(3.83)	24-0382-73
1,2-Naphthalenedione, 6-hydroxy-3,8-dimethyl-5-(1-methylethyl)-	EtOH	218(4.39),274(4.08), 410(3.89),550(3.35)	2-0974-73
Naphtho[2,3-b]furan-4,6-dione, 4a,5,7,8-tetrahydro-3,4a,5-trimethyl-	EtOH	218(4.14),234(3.86), 241(3.88),272(2.84), 337(3.71)	73-0739-73
2,4-Pentadienoic acid, 2-acetyl-5-phenyl-, ethyl ester	EtOH	273(3.93),331(4.48)	70-2301-73
1(2H)-Phenanthrenone, 3,4,9,10-tetrahydro-9,10-dihydroxy-9-methyl-	MeOH	228(4.12),232s(4.12), 300(4.23),320s(4.05)	88-1553-73
Photosantonene A	n.s.g.	252(4.26)	39-2563-73C
Photosantonene B	n.s.g.	255(4.52)	39-2563-73C
$C_{15}H_{16}O_3S$			
2-Thiophenecarboxaldehyde, 5-[5-(tetrahydro-2H-pyran-2-yloxy)-3-penten-1-ynyl]-, (E)-	ether	231(4.12),327(4.47)	24-3621-73
3-Thiophenecarboxylic acid, tetrahydro-5-[(4-methylphenyl)methylene]-4-oxo-, ethyl ester	EtOH	244(3.86),347(4.31), 361(4.29)	133-0157-73
$C_{15}H_{16}O_4$			
4,7-Benzofurandione, 6-methoxy-3-methyl-5-(3-methyl-2-butenyl)- (breviquinone)	n.s.g.	265(4.11),318(3.74), 498(3.06)	88-0003-73
2H-1-Benzopyran-7-ol, 6,8-diacetyl-2,2-dimethyl-	MeOH	260(4.70),349(3.79)	2-0100-73
2H-1-Benzopyran-2-one, 7-hydroxy-5-methoxy-8-(3-methyl-2-butenyl)-	MeOH	261(4.09),320(4.14)	2-1126-73
Butanedioic acid, 2-(3,4-dihydro-2-naphthalenyl)-2-methyl-	EtOH	265(4.2)	2-0131-73
Butanoic acid, 2-(2-oxocyclopentyl)-4-oxo-4-phenyl-	MeOH	249(4.63)	115-0381-73
Cyclopentanecarboxylic acid, 3-[(3-methoxyphenyl)methylene]-1-methyl-4-oxo-	EtOH	242(3.87),295(4.37)	39-2454-73C
1,4-Ethanonaphthalen-9-one, 1,4-dihydro-4,5,8-trimethoxy-	EtOH	297(3.56),305(3.51)	39-1840-73C
2H-Furo[2,3-h]-1-benzopyran-2-one, 8,9-dihydro-5-methoxy-8,8,9-trimethyl-	MeOH	256(3.97),264(4.02), 340(4.14)	2-1126-73
3H-Naphtho[1,8-bc]furan-3-propanoic acid, 4,5-dihydro-6-methoxy-	EtOH	253(3.97),292(3.56), 302(3.51)	18-1772-73
Spiro[cyclopropane-1,3'(2'H)-[1,2,4]-methenopentalene]-1',5'(3'aH)-dicarboxylic acid, 4',6'a-dihydro-, dimethyl ester	EtOH	232(3.90)	24-1822-73
$C_{15}H_{16}O_4S$			
3-Thiophenecarboxylic acid, tetrahydro-5-[(4-methoxyphenyl)methylene]-4-oxo-, ethyl ester	EtOH	215(3.98),251(4.44), 275(3.82),361(4.44)	133-0157-73

Compound	Solvent	λ_{max}(log ϵ)	Ref.
$C_{15}H_{16}O_5$			
Acetic acid, (4,7-dimethoxy-5-methyl-2H-1-benzopyran-2-ylidene)-, methyl ester	MeOH	278(3.87),299(3.89)	94-0149-73
4H-1-Benzopyran-4-one, 2,3-dihydro-7-hydroxy-2-methyl-2-(tetrahydro-3-methyl-5-oxo-2-furanyl)-	MeOH	212(4.30),217s(4.25), 228(3.99),275(4.05), 312(3.76)	24-1198-73
1-Cyclopentene-1-acetic acid, 2-(2,4-dimethoxyphenyl)-5-oxo-	EtOH	230(4.12),285(4.01), 308(4.06)	39-2420-73C
4H-Furo[3,2-c][1]benzopyran-4-one, 2,3-dihydro-8-hydroxy-3-(hydroxymethyl)-2,3,9-trimethyl- (glaupadiol)	EtOH	284s(3.72),295(4.15), 311(4.11)	95-0202-73
Lapachol, dihydrodihydroxy-, (±)-	EtOH	240(4.10),247s(4.15), 253(4.20),277(4.23), 287s(4.18),334(3.42), 388(3.12)	12-1121-73
	EtOH-KOH	275(4.36),479(3.37)	12-1121-73
Murrangatin	EtOH	248(3.52),254(3.50), 258(3.51),317(4.13)	78-2811-73
2,4-Pentadienoic acid, 3-acetoxy-5-(4-methoxyphenyl)-, methyl ester, (E,E)-	EtOH	241(4.08),338(4.56)	5-0650-73
(Z,E)-	EtOH	242(4.12),340(4.47)	5-0650-73
1H-Xanthene-1,9(2H)-dione, 3,4,4a,9a-tetrahydro-4,6-dihydroxy-3,4a-dimethyl-	MeOH	211(4.26),233(3.99), 278(4.07),311(3.90)	24-1198-73
9H-Xanthen-9-one, 2,3,4,4a-tetrahydro-1,4,6-trihydroxy-3,4a-dimethyl-	MeOH	204(4.21),220s(4.04), 242s(3.85),248(3.90), 301(3.99),350(4.20)	24-1198-73
isomer	MeOH	204(4.21),220s(4.04), 242s(3.85),248(3.86), 301(3.99),350(4.15)	24-1198-73
9H-Xanthen-9-one, 2,3,4,4a-tetrahydro-1,4,8-trihydroxy-3,4a-dimethyl-	MeOH	212(4.09),222(4.13), 270(3.54),279(3.58), 334(4.16)	24-1198-73
$C_{15}H_{16}O_5S$			
3-Thiophenecarboxylic acid, tetrahydro-5-[(4-hydroxy-3-methoxyphenyl)methylene]-4-oxo-, ethyl ester	EtOH	253(3.80),361(4.38), 377(4.29)	133-0157-73
$C_{15}H_{16}O_6$			
5,1-(Epoxymethano)naphthalene-8a(1H)-carboxylic acid, 4,4a,5,8-tetrahydro-5-methoxy-2-methyl-8,10-dioxo-, methyl ester	EtOH	252(4.18)	94-0528-73
$C_{15}H_{16}O_8$			
Benzoic acid, 2-acetoxy-4-(diacetoxymethyl)-, methyl ester	EtOH	232(4.11),283(3.04)	78-0857-73
$C_{15}H_{17}BO_7$			
Boron, bis(acetato-O)(ethyl β-oxobenzenepropanoato)-, (T-4)-	CH_2Cl_2	312(4.31)	39-1796-73B
Boron, bis(acetato-O)[1-(4-methoxyphenyl)-1,3-butanedionato]-, (T-4)-	CH_2Cl_2	363(4.68)	39-1796-73B
$C_{15}H_{17}ClN_2O_4S_2$			
Benzothiazolium, 2-[5-(dimethylamino)-2-thienyl]-3-ethyl-, perchlorate	$MeNO_2$	471(4.93)	103-0850-73

Compound	Solvent	$\lambda_{max}(\log \epsilon)$	Ref.
$C_{15}H_{17}IN_2$			
Pyridinium, 1-[[[4-(1-methylethyl)phenyl]methylene]amino]-, iodide	EtOH	215(4.46),302(4.30)	103-1108-73
$C_{15}H_{17}N$			
15-Azatricyclo[8.2.2.1^{4,7}]pentadeca-4,6,10,12,13-pentaene, 15-methyl-	EtOH	205(3.99),227(3.89), 269s(2.75),279s(2.61)	88-4017-73
1H-Carbazole, 2,3,4,4a-tetrahydro-4a-(2-propenyl)-	EtOH	210s(4.23),213(4.26), 219(4.25),223s(4.11), 262(3.78)	39-1913-73C
1H-Carbazole, 2,3,4,9-tetrahydro-9-(2-propenyl)-	EtOH	230(4.47),279s(3.74), 286(3.79),293(3.76)	39-1913-73C
7,8-Decadiene-1,3,5-triyn-1-amine, N,N-diethyl-9-methyl-	n.s.g.	209(4.60),214(4.71), 227(3.83),239(3.90), 254(3.89),268(4.00), 282(3.74),300(3.60), 309(3.62),351(3.42)	70-1029-73
5-Heptenenitrile, 6-methyl-2-(phenylmethylene)-	n.s.g.	218(3.94),269(4.16)	107-0393-73
Pyridine, 2,3,4,5-tetrahydro-6-(4-phenyl-1,3-butadienyl)-, (E,E)-	MeOH-acid	247(3.91),354(4.43)	33-1763-73
	MeOH-base	226(4.05),232(4.05), 302s(4.40),310(4.40)	33-1763-73
$C_{15}H_{17}NO$			
Benzeneethanamine, N-(3-methoxyphenyl)-	heptane	219(4.30),247(4.06), 280(3.45)	104-2360-73
Benzeneethanamine, 3-methoxy-N-phenyl-	heptane	224(3.87),247(4.06), 263(3.43),270(3.48), 284(3.23)	104-2360-73
Benzeneethanamine, 4-methoxy-N-phenyl-	heptane	227(3.65),246(3.80), 298(3.18),304(3.20), 315(3.00)	104-2360-73
Piperidine, 1-(5-phenyl-2-furanyl)-	EtOH	219(4.03),325(4.27)	39-2523-73C
2(1H)-Pyridinone, 3-ethyl-1-(2-phenylethyl)-	EtOH	233(3.74),303(3.83)	94-2695-73
2(1H)-Pyridinone, 5-ethyl-1-(2-phenylethyl)-	EtOH	232(3.96),313(3.79)	94-2695-73
2-Pyrrolidinone, 4-ethylidene-3-(1-methylethylidene)-5-phenyl-	EtOH	258s(3.88)	44-1015-73
isomer	EtOH	287.5(4.03)	44-1015-73
2-Pyrrolidinone, 5-methyl-3-(1-methylethylidene)-4-(phenylmethylene)-	EtOH	318.5(4.24)	44-1015-73
isomer	EtOH	297(3.92)	44-1015-73
2H-Pyrrol-2-one, 4-ethyl-1,3-dihydro-3-(1-methylethylidene)-5-phenyl-	EtOH	370(3.76)	44-1015-73
$C_{15}H_{17}NO_2$			
Azacyclotrideca-2,4,6,8,10,12-hexaene-1-carboxylic acid, ethyl ester	C_6H_{12}	213(4.26),275(4.52), 345(3.85)	89-0328-73
3-Azatetracyclo[7.4.0.0^{2,4}.0^{10,13}]trideca-5,7,11-triene-3-carboxylic acid, ethyl ester	MeOH	225s(3.60)	89-0328-73
11-Azatetracyclo[6.5.0.0^{2,7}.0^{3,6}]trideca-4,9,12-triene-11-carboxylic acid, ethyl ester	MeOH	231(4.28)	89-0328-73
11-Azatetracyclo[6.5.0.0^{9,13}.0^{10,12}]trideca-2,4,6-triene-11-carboxylic acid, ethyl ester	MeOH	253(3.18)	89-0328-73
1H-Benzo[de]quinoline, 2,3-dihydro-5,6-dimethoxy-1-methyl-, hydrochloride	EtOH	230(4.68),266(3.96), 350(3.87)	33-0759-73

Compound	Solvent	$\lambda_{max}(\log \epsilon)$	Ref.
2-Butenoic acid, 3-(2-methyl-1H-indol-3-yl)-, ethyl ester, cis	EtOH	226(4.37),283(3.72), 290(3.70),335(3.48)	104-1275-73
trans	EtOH	227(4.50),283(3.94), 289(3.93),330(4.05)	104-1275-73
1H-Carbazole-3-carboxylic acid, 2,3,4,9-tetrahydro-, ethyl ester	EtOH	226(4.53),274(3.83), 282(3.86),289(3.77)	44-2882-73
Morpholine, 4-[5-(4-methylphenyl)-2-furanyl]-	EtOH	221(4.03),316(4.32)	39-2523-73
2,4,6,8-Nonatetraenoic acid, 8-methyl-9-(1H-pyrrol-2-yl)-, methyl ester	EtOH	409(4.64)	39-1416-73C
$C_{15}H_{17}NO_2S$			
1-Benzothiepin-5(2H)-one, 3,4-dihydro-4-(4-morpholinylmethylene)-	EtOH	247(4.06)	44-2629-73
$C_{15}H_{17}NO_3$			
Benzamide, N-(4,4-dimethyl-2,6-dioxo-1-cyclohexyl)-	MeOH	274(4.04)	5-0407-73
	MeOH-HCl	265(4.07)	5-0407-73
	MeOH-NaOH	283(4.29)	5-0407-73
Morpholine, 4-[5-(4-methoxyphenyl)-2-furanyl]-	EtOH	224(4.00),310(4.34)	39-2523-73
2,4-Pentadienoic acid, 2-acetyl-5-(methylphenylamino)-, methyl ester	EtOH	250(3.90),410(4.68)	70-1963-73
Ribalinine, (±)-	0.3M HCl	236(4.41),300(3.82)	78-0205-73
	neutral and pH 12	237(4.34),314(3.83), 326(3.78)	78-0205-73
$C_{15}H_{17}NO_3S$			
Bicyclo[3.2.1]oct-3-en-2-one, p-tolylsulfonyloxime, anti	MeOH	230(4.40),274(2.85)	39-1661-73C
$C_{15}H_{17}NO_4$			
2,4-Hexadienoic acid, 6-[(4-ethoxyphenyl)amino]-6-oxo-, methyl ester	EtOH	264(4.67),339(4.33)	104-2527-73
1H-Pyrrole-2-acetic acid, 1-(4-ethoxyphenyl)-4,5-dihydro-5-oxo-, methyl ester	EtOH	262(4.60)	104-2527-73
Ribaline, (±)-	0.3M HCl	241(4.41),289s(3.92), 298(3.95),330(3.70)	78-0205-73
	pH 12	238s(4.30),257(4.47), 295s(3.70),307(3.77)	78-0205-73
	50% EtOH	235(4.37),245(4.34), 304(3.90),325(3.80), 339(3.71)	78-0205-73
Ribalinidine, (-)-	0.3M HCl	220(4.34),243(4.48), 301(3.90),342(3.64)	78-0205-73
	pH 12	240s(4.41),256(3.52), 296(3.63),300s(3.64), 307(3.70)	78-0205-73
	MeOH	220s(4.31),235(4.48), 245s(4.43),301(3.88), 331(3.87),346(3.81)	78-0205-73
Spiro[1,3-dioxolane-2,9'(5'H)-[1,3]dioxolo[4,5-g]pyrrolo[1,2-b]isoquinoline], 7',8',9'a,10'-tetrahydro-	EtOH	293(3.72)	78-0213-73
$C_{15}H_{17}NO_5Se$			
Benzo[b]selenophene-3-carboxylic acid, 2-[(3-carboxy-1-oxo-2-propenyl)amino]-4,5,6,7-tetrahydro-, ethyl ester	EtOH	285(3.98),340(4.02)	103-0300-73

Compound	Solvent	$\lambda_{max}(\log \epsilon)$	Ref.
$C_{15}H_{17}NO_6$			
Ethenetricarboxylic acid, [(phenylmethyl)amino]-, trimethyl ester	EtOH	293(4.32)	95-1008-73
$C_{15}H_{17}NS_2$			
Dithiobenzoic acid, 2,4,6-trimethylpyridine salt	EtOH	320(3.94),346(4.18), 506(2.13)	143-0359-73
$C_{15}H_{17}N_2$			
Pyridinium, 1-[[[4-(1-methylethyl)phenyl]methylene]amino]-, iodide	EtOH	215(4.46),302(4.30)	103-1108-73
$C_{15}H_{17}N_2S_2$			
Benzothiazolium, 2-[5-(dimethylamino)-2-thienyl]-3-ethyl-, perchlorate	$MeNO_2$	471(4.93)	103-0850-73
$C_{15}H_{17}N_3$			
Benzenamine, N,N-dimethyl-4-[(2-methylphenyl)azo]-	C_6H_{12}	394(4.48)	18-3139-73
ammonium ion	50%EtOH-HCl	327(4.29)	18-3139-73
azonium ion	50%EtOH-HCl	515(3.76)	18-3139-73
Benzenamine, N,N-dimethyl-4-[(4-methylphenyl)azo]-	C_6H_{12}	400(4.50)	18-0194-73
	50%EtOH-acid	331(4.12),528(4.48)	18-0194-73 +18-3139-73
Benzenamine, N,N,3-trimethyl-4-(phenylazo)-	C_6H_{12}	405(4.48)	18-3139-73
ammonium ion	50%EtOH-HCl	327(3.80)	18-3139-73
azonium ion	50%EtOH-HCl	516(4.67)	18-3139-73
$C_{15}H_{17}N_3O$			
Anantine, dihydro-	n.s.g.	260(2.37),265(2.35), 270(2.30)	88-1757-73
Benzenamine, 4-[(4-methoxyphenyl)azo]-N,N-dimethyl-	EtOH	410(4.46)	103-0850-73
	EtOH-HCl	560(4.43)	103-0850-73
Cycloheptanecarbonitrile, 1-(benzoylazo)-	C_6H_{12}	244(3.93),290s(3.15), 321s(2.44),408(1.70)	23-1378-73
Cyclohexanecarbonitrile, 1-[(4-methylbenzoyl)azo]-	C_6H_{12}	255(4.02),290s(3.48), 321s(2.71),409(1.67)	23-1378-73
2,4-Pentadienamide, 2-cyano-5-(ethylamino)-5-(4-methylphenyl)-	CH_2Cl_2	253(3.89),383(4.54)	97-0342-73
3-Pyridinol, 4-acetyl-2,5-dimethyl-, phenylhydrazone	n.s.g.	360(4.39)	70-1057-73
$C_{15}H_{17}N_3O_2$			
Cyclohexanecarbonitrile, 1-[(4-methoxybenzoyl)azo]-	MeCN	286(4.03),406s(1.75)	23-1378-73
3-Pyridinecarboxamide, 1-ethyl-1,2-dihydro-2-imino-6-(4-methoxyphenyl)-	CH_2Cl_2	257s(3.92),266(3.95), 382(3.80)	97-0342-73
$C_{15}H_{17}N_3O_2S_2$			
Carbamic acid, [[(3-methyl-4-phenyl-2(3H)-thiazolylidene)amino](methylthio)methylene]-, ethyl ester	dioxan	279(3.86),336(4.39)	94-0074-73
Carbamic acid, [[(3-methyl-5-phenyl-2(3H)-thiazolylidene)amino](methylthio)methylene]-, ethyl ester	dioxan	279(4.11)	94-0074-73
$C_{15}H_{17}N_3O_4$			
2-Naphthalenamine, N,N-diethyl-4-methyl-6,8-dinitro-	MeOH	235(4.43),260(4.68), 350(3.76),415(4.38), 470(4.40)	44-3136-73

Compound	Solvent	$\lambda_{max}(\log \epsilon)$	Ref.
2-Naphthalenamine, N,N-diethyl-4-methyl-6,8-dinitro- (cont.)	66% H_2SO_4	210(4.60),255(4.32), 295(4.15),360(3.43), 430(1.90)	44-3136-73
1H-Pyrrole-3-carboxylic acid, 2,5-dihydro-5-(methoxyimino)-1-methyl-2-oxo-4-[(phenylmethyl)amino]-, methyl ester	EtOH	243(3.92),347(4.12)	94-1667-73
Sydnone imine, N-benzoyl-3-(5-carboxypentyl)-	EtOH	200(4.10),260(4.00), 340(4.32)	103-1327-73
hydrochloride	EtOH	203(3.96),260(3.98), 340(4.25)	103-1327-73
$C_{15}H_{17}N_3O_4S$			
5-Pyrimidinecarboxylic acid, 1,2-dihydro-1-methyl-2-[[(4-methylphenyl)sulfonyl]imino]-, ethyl ester	EtOH	223(4.24),275(4.53), 323(3.49)	44-1591-73
5-Pyrimidinecarboxylic acid, 2-[methyl[(4-methylphenyl)sulfonyl]amino]-, ethyl ester	EtOH	232(4.17),260(4.34)	44-1591-73
$C_{15}H_{17}N_3O_6$			
4H,5H-Pyrano[3,4-e]-1,3-oxazine-4,5-dione, 2,7-dimorpholino-	$CHCl_3$	290(4.19),325(3.89)	39-2432-73C
$C_{15}H_{17}N_5$			
Pyrazinepropanamine, 3-amino-6-(1H-indol-3-yl)-	MeOH-HCl	221(4.37),275(4.17), 305(4.28),404(3.63)	78-3761-73
	MeOH-NaOH	227(4.35),273(4.28), 288s(4.19),362(3.90)	78-3761-73
$C_{15}H_{17}N_5O$			
Morpholine, 4-[4-(2-phenyl-2H-tetrazol-5-yl)-1,3-butadienyl]-, (E,E)-	EtOH	247(4.11),333(4.66)	88-4295-73
$C_{15}H_{17}N_5O_7$			
D-Galactitol, 1-deoxy-1-(3,4-dihydro-2,4-dioxopyrido[3,2-g]pteridin-10(2H)-yl)-	H_2O	237s(--),255s(--), 260(4.32),304(3.60), 388s(--),425(3.94)	4-0209-73
D-Glucitol, 1-deoxy-1-(3,4-dihydro-2,4-dioxopyrido[3,2-g]pteridin-10(2H)-yl-	H_2O	238s(--),255(4.32), 259(4.33),303(3.63), 389(3.89),423(3.97)	4-0209-73
$C_{15}H_{18}$			
Benzene, 1-methyl-4-[methylmethylene(1-methylethylidene)cyclopropyl]-	EtOH	245.0(4.24)	39-0278-73B
Benzene, 1,3,5-tris(1-methylethenyl)-	MeOH	239(4.58)	32-0849-73
1H-Cyclopent[jk]fluorene, 2,2a,3,4,5-5a,9b,9c-octahydro-	hexane	263(2.98),267(3.17), 275(3.27)	88-0865-73
2H-Indeno[5,4,3-cde]azulene, 1,5,6,6a,7-8,9,9a-octahydro-, cis	C_6H_{12}	262s(2.66),265(2.75), 269(2.96),274(2.85), 278(3.09)	44-1445-73
Naphthalene, 1-pentyl-	MeCN	274(3.73),284(3.78), 291(3.60)	88-2487-73
$C_{15}H_{18}BrClO_2$			
2H-Cyclopenta[b]furan-6-ol, 2-(1-bromopropyl)-3a-chloro-3,3a,6,6a-tetrahydro-6a-(2-penten-4-ynyl)- (chondriol)	MeOH	221(3.99)	88-0313-73

Compound	Solvent	$\lambda_{max}(\log \epsilon)$	Ref.
$C_{15}H_{18}BrClO_6$			
1,3-Dioxol-1-ium, 2-[2-(4-bromophenyl)-ethenyl]-4,5-dihydro-4,4,5,5-tetra-methyl-, perchlorate	$CHCl_3$	293(4.08)	104-0394-73
$C_{15}H_{18}BrNO_3$			
1H-Indole-3-carboxylic acid, 4-bromo-5-methoxy-1,2,6-trimethyl-, ethyl ester	isooctane	222(4.62),240(4.42), 286(4.08),297(4.04)	103-0306-73
	EtOH	220(4.56),240(4.33), 288(4.07),297(4.06)	103-0306-73
Piperidine, 1-[[4-(bromoacetyl)phenoxy]-acetyl]-	EtOH	212(4.44),267(4.22)	111-0574-73
$C_{15}H_{18}ClNO_4$			
Pyridinium, 2,4,6-trimethyl-1-(4-methyl-phenyl)-, perchlorate	EtOH	220(3.90),270(3.88)	103-0333-73
$C_{15}H_{18}ClNO_5$			
Pyridinium, 1-(4-methoxyphenyl)-2,4,6-trimethyl-, perchlorate	EtOH	224(4.63),270(4.72)	103-0333-73
α-D-Xylofuranuronimidoyl chloride, N-hydroxy-1,2-O-(1-methylethylidene)-3-O-(phenylmethyl)-	EtOH	212(3.15)	136-0297-73D
$C_{15}H_{18}ClN_3O_2$			
Cyclohexanone, 2,2'-(6-chloro-1,3,5-triazine-2,4-diyl)bis-	C_6H_{12}	331(4.80)	22-2039-73
$C_{15}H_{18}ClN_3O_4S$			
Acetic acid, [[6-chloro-3-[(oxo-1-pyrro-lidinylacetyl)amino]-2-pyridinyl]-thio]-, ethyl ester	EtOH	231(4.2),306(3.7)	103-0621-73
$C_{15}H_{18}IN_3$			
Benzenaminium, N,N,N-trimethyl-4-(phen-ylazo)-, iodide	EtOH	245(4.11),317(4.14), 438(2.87)	7-0727-73
$C_{15}H_{18}NO$			
Pyrylium, 4-[4-(dimethylamino)phenyl]-2,6-dimethyl-, perchlorate	MeCN	484(4.62)	78-0795-73
$C_{15}H_{18}N_2$			
1H-Indole, 2-[(1-methyl-4-piperidinyli-dene)methyl]-	MeOH	240(4.30),307(4.35), 313s(4.32)	23-0792-73
Spiro[cyclopentane-1,1'-[1H]pyrido[3,4-b]indene, 2',3',4',9'-tetrahydro-, hydrochloride	EtOH	222(4.68),272(3.94), 279(3.92),289(3.76)	44-4342-73
	EtOH	226(4.31),272(3.81), 278(3.86),290(3.74)	114-0105-73D
$C_{15}H_{18}N_2O$			
1H-Indazole, 4,5,6,7-tetrahydro-3-(4-methoxyphenyl)-1-methyl-	MeOH	259(4.31)	24-3432-73
2-Pyridinamine, N-methyl-N-(1-methyl-2-phenylethyl)-, 1-oxide, (S)-	MeOH	246(4.24),274(3.79), 333(3.52)	32-1083-73
$C_{15}H_{18}N_2O_2$			
Benzaldehyde, 4-methoxy-, methyl(2-meth-yl-3-oxo-1-cyclopenten-1-yl)hydrazone	MeOH	261(4.20),293(3.84), 306(3.99),346(4.64)	24-0450-73
Benzaldehyde, 4-methoxy-, methyl(3-oxo-1-cyclohexen-1-yl)hydrazone	MeOH	265(3.96),354(4.68)	24-0450-73

Compound	Solvent	λ_{max}(log ε)	Ref.
1,3-Butanedione, 2-(1,3-dimethyl-2-imid-azolidinylidene)-1-phenyl-	EtOH	234(4.14),290(4.16)	1-0258-73
Ephedrine, N-(2-pyridinyl)-, py-oxide, (R)-(+)-	MeOH	246(4.24),273(3.81), 333(3.53)	32-1083-73
1H-Indazol-4-ol, 4,5,6,7-tetrahydro-3-(4-methoxyphenyl)-1-methyl-	MeOH	257(4.30)	24-3432-73
$C_{15}H_{18}N_2O_3$			
9H-6,12b-Methano-2H-furo[2,3-d]pyrido-[1,2-b][1,2]diazocin-2-one, 7-acetyl-6,7,10,11,12,12a-hexahydro-, [6S-(6α,12aα,12bα)]-	EtOH	222(4.15)	78-1063-73
$C_{15}H_{18}N_2O_4$			
2H-1-Benzopyran-2-one, 4-(dipropyl-amino)-3-nitro-	EtOH	276(4.08),319(3.98), 390s(3.40)	103-0816-73
$C_{15}H_{18}N_2O_5$			
Pentanedioic acid, 3-oxo-2-(phenylazo)-, diethyl ester	EtOH	242(4.20),360(4.39)	70-2006-73
Pyridinium, 4-acetyl-1-[[3-ethoxy-2-(ethoxycarbonyl)-3-oxo-1-propenyl]-amino]-, hydroxide, inner salt	EtOH	236(4.15),287(4.15), 462(4.26)	39-2580-73C
1H-Pyrrolo[2,3-c]pyridine-3-acetic acid, 2-(ethoxycarbonyl)-5-methoxy-, ethyl ester	EtOH	283(4.11),292(4.20), 348(3.61)	44-1824-73
$C_{15}H_{18}N_2O_9$			
2,4(1H,3H)-Pyrimidinedione, 3-(2,3,5-tri-O-acetyl-β-D-arabinofuranosyl)-	pH 2	263(3.86)	88-2939-73
	pH 7	263(3.86)	88-2939-73
	pH 12	294(4.00)	88-2939-73
$C_{15}H_{18}N_3O_2$			
Pyridinium, 2-amino-3-(aminocarbonyl)-1-ethyl-6-(4-methoxyphenyl)-, per-chlorate	HOAc	254(3.99),278s(3.56), 344(4.10)	97-0342-73
$C_{15}H_{18}N_4$			
1-Propen-2-amine, N,N-dimethyl-1-(6-methyl-3-phenyl-1,2,4-triazin-5-yl)-	MeOH	245(4.33),385(4.47)	5-1963-73
$C_{15}H_{18}N_4OS$			
[1,2,4]Triazino[5,6-d][3,1]benzoxaze-pine, 3-(butylthio)-6,7-dihydro-6-methyl-	EtOH	205(4.25),239(4.34), 348(3.88),436(3.60)	78-0639-73
$C_{15}H_{18}N_4O_2$			
Benzo[g]pteridine-2,4(1H,3H)-dione, 5-ethyl-5,10-dihydro-7,8,10-trimethyl-	6M HCl	286(4.00),305(4.03)	5-1388-73
	pH 7	355(3.74)	5-1388-73
$C_{15}H_{18}N_4O_4$			
Camphenylone, 2,4-dinitrophenylhydra-zone	$CHCl_3$	369(4.36)	22-2472-73
2,5-Heptadien-4-one, 2,6-dimethyl-, 2,4-dinitrophenylhydrazone	50% DMSO-acid	400(4.42)	1-3641-73
	+KOH	475(4.36)	1-3641-73
$C_{15}H_{18}N_4O_5S$			
L-Aspartic acid, N-[1-oxo-5-(7H-pyrrolo-[2,3-d]pyrimidin-4-ylthio)pentyl]-	pH 1	219(4.33),257(3.99), 310(4.08)	73-1438-73

Compound	Solvent	λ_{max}(log ϵ)	Ref.
L-Aspartic acid, N-[1-oxo-5-(7H-pyrrolo-[2,3-d]pyrimidin-4-ylthio)pentyl]-	pH 13	219(4.29),247(3.96), 292(4.13)	73-1438-73
$C_{15}H_{18}N_4O_6S$			
Inosine, 7,8-dihydro-2',3'-O-(1-methylethylidene)-8-thioxo-, 5'-acetate	pH 1	216(4.10),294(4.35)	94-1143-73
	pH 7	216(4.02),294(4.24)	94-1143-73
	pH 13	291.5(4.32)	94-1143-73
$C_{15}H_{18}N_5$			
1H-[1,2,4]Triazolo[1,5-a]pyrimidin-8-ium, 2-amino-6-ethyl-5,7-dimethyl-1-phenyl-, perchlorate	n.s.g.	255(4.20),312(3.65)	124-1036-73
$C_{15}H_{18}N_5O$			
1H-[1,2,4]Triazolo[1,5-a]pyrimidin-8-ium, 2-amino-5-(ethoxymethyl)-7-methyl-1-phenyl-, perchlorate	n.s.g.	245(4.18),312(3.51)	124-1036-73
$C_{15}H_{18}N_6O$			
Acetylzoanthoxanthin	MeOH	290(4.29),428(4.10)	77-0099-73
$C_{15}H_{18}N_6O_9$			
L-Aspartic acid, N-[[(9-β-D-ribofuranosyl-9H-purin-6-yl]amino]carbonyl]-	pH 1-2	270s(--),276(4.39)	87-0139-73
	pH 5-7	269(4.39),277s(--)	87-0139-73
	pH 12	270(4.31),298(3.94)	87-0139-73
$C_{15}H_{18}O$			
Methanone, phenyl(1,2,3-trimethyl-2-cyclopenten-1-yl)-, (R)-	EtOH	244(3.99),265(3.18), 326(2.22)	33-1741-73
Naphtho[2,3-b]furan, 4,4a,7,8-tetrahydro-3,4a,5-trimethyl-	MeOH	293(4.00)	18-2840-73
Spiro[cyclopentane-1,2'(1'H)-naphthalen]-3-one, 3',4'-dihydro-1'-methyl-	EtOH	258(2.93),266(2.95), 273(2.94),277(2.81)	78-0309-73
$C_{15}H_{18}O_2$			
4(1H)-Phenanthrenone, 2,3,4a,9,10,10a-hexahydro-7-methoxy-, cis-(+)-	MeOH	277(3.30),287(3.27)	19-0009-73
(-)-	MeOH	278(3.30),287(3.27)	19-0009-73
(±)-	MeOH	277(3.28),285(3.25)	19-0009-73
$C_{15}H_{18}O_3$			
Acetic acid, (3,4-dihydro-6-methoxy-1(2H)-naphthalenylidene)-, ethyl ester, (E)-	EtOH	302s(4.21),315(4.27)	39-0615-73C
(Z)-	EtOH	304(4.01)	39-0615-73C
7H-Benz[e]inden-7-one, 3-(formyloxy)-1,2,3,3a,4,5,8,9-octahydro-3a-methyl-, (3S-cis)-	MeOH	303(4.34)	78-3631-73
Cyclopentaneacetic acid, 1,3-dimethyl-2-oxo-5-phenyl-	EtOH	242(2.02),248(2.15), 253(2.26),259(2.34), 264(2.22),268(2.08)	104-0835-73
Cyclopentaneacetic acid, 1-methyl-2-oxo-5-phenyl-, methyl ester, trans	EtOH	243(2.08),248(2.18), 254(2.30),259(2.38), 265(2.28)	104-0835-73
Ethanone, 1-(3,4-dihydro-4-hydroxy-3-methoxy-1,4-dimethyl-2-naphthalenyl)-	MeOH	221(4.08),225(4.09), 293(4.04)	88-1553-73
Ethanone, 1-(7,8-dihydro-2-hydroxy-4-methoxy-7,7-dimethyl-1-naphthalenyl)-	MeOH	258(3.67),297(2.95)	83-0857-73
Furanoeremophilane, 3,9-dioxo-	EtOH	282(4.19)	18-2840-73

Compound	Solvent	λ_{max}(log ε)	Ref.
1-Naphthaleneacetic acid, 3,4-dihydro-6-methoxy-, ethyl ester	EtOH	274(3.95)	39-0615-73C
Naphtho[2,3-b]furan-4,6-dione, 4a,5,7,8-8a,9-hexahydro-3,4a,5-trimethyl-(japonicindione)	EtOH	210(4.05),269(3.52)	73-0739-73
4H-Pyran-4-one, 2,3-dihydro-2-hydroxy-2,3,3,5-tetramethyl-6-phenyl-	EtOH	227(3.83),296(4.14)	44-0896-73
4H-Pyran-4-one, 5,6-dihydro-6-hydroxy-2,3,5,5-tetramethyl-6-phenyl-	EtOH	273(4.01)	44-0896-73
4βH-Pyrosantonin	EtOH	224(4.06),336(2.16)	39-0914-73C
$C_{15}H_{18}O_3S$			
2-Thiophenemethanol, 5-[5-(tetrahydro-2H-pyran-2-yloxy)-3-penten-1-ynyl]-, (E)-	ether	299(4.38),312(4.30)	24-3621-73
$C_{15}H_{18}O_4$			
Benzenepropanoic acid, 3-ethoxy-1-methyl-3-oxo-1-propenyl ester	EtOH	212(4.19)	22-3416-73
Complicatic acid	EtOH	234(3.65)	102-2717-73
1,4-Ethanonaphthalen-9-ol, 1,4-dihydro-4,5,8-trimethoxy-, endo	EtOH	290(3.52),300(3.36)	39-1840-73C
exo	EtOH	290(3.54),300(3.44)	39-1840-73C
Naphtho[1,2-b]furan-2,6(3H,4H)-dione, 3a,5,5a,9b-tetrahydro-3-hydroxy-3,5a,9-trimethyl-	EtOH	271(3.8),315(3.0)	73-1804-73
Naphtho[2,3-b]furan-4,6-dione, 4a,5,7,8-8a,9-hexahydro-8a-hydroxy-3,4a,5-trimethyl-, [4aR-(4aα,5α,8aα)]-	EtOH	210(4.03),271(3.54)	73-0739-73
$C_{15}H_{18}O_5$			
Ethanone, 1-[3-ethoxy-2,3-dihydro-6-hydroxy-2-(2-methyloxiranyl)-5-benzofuranyl]-	EtOH	218(4.31),223(4.39), 236(4.11),242(4.09), 277(4.13),319(3.86)	102-0429-73
$C_{15}H_{18}O_6$			
2-Propenoic acid, 3-(4-acetoxy-3,5-dimethoxyphenyl)-, ethyl ester	EtOH	224(4.31),292(4.26)	102-0893-73
$C_{15}H_{19}$			
Cyclopropenylium, phenyldipropyl-, perchlorate	2.9M HCl	262(4.42)	18-3881-73
$C_{15}H_{19}BrN_2O_3$			
Piperidine, 1-[[4-[2-bromo-1-(hydroxyimino)ethyl]phenoxy]acetyl]-	EtOH	214(4.48),259(4.23)	111-0574-73
$C_{15}H_{19}ClN_2O_4$			
4H,5H-Pyrano[3,4-e]-1,3-oxazine-4,5-dione, 7-chloro-2-(octylamino)-	MeCN	295(4.11),338(4.23)	39-2432-73C
$C_{15}H_{19}ClO_6$			
1,3-Dioxol-1-ium, 4,5-dihydro-4,4,5,5-tetramethyl-2-(2-phenylethenyl)-	$CHCl_3$	280(4.66)	104-0394-73
$C_{15}H_{19}ClO_7$			
1,3-Dioxol-1-ium, 4,5-dihydro-2-[2-(4-hydroxyphenyl)ethenyl]-4,4,5,5-tetramethyl-, perchlorate	$CHCl_3$	276(3.98),298(4.01)	104-0394-73

Compound	Solvent	$\lambda_{max}(\log \epsilon)$	Ref.
$C_{15}H_{19}F_3N_2O$			
1H-Indole-3-ethanamine, 5-methoxy-N,N,2-trimethyl-4-(trifluoromethyl)-	MeOH	229(4.35),306(3.97)	44-1504-73
compd. with borane	MeOH	230(4.42),308(4.04)	44-1504-73
$C_{15}H_{19}F_3N_2O_2$			
1H-Indole-3-methanol, α-[(dimethylamino)methyl]-5-methoxy-2-methyl-4-(trifluoromethyl)-	MeOH	228(4.43),305(4.03)	44-1504-73
$C_{15}H_{19}N$			
Benz[f]isoquinoline, 1,2,3,4,5,6-hexahydro-3,6-dimethyl-	EtOH	263(3.97)	87-0592-73
1H-Indole, 2-(2,2-dimethyl-3-butenyl)-3-methyl-	EtOH	229(4.51),285(3.92), 293(3.88)	39-1913-73C
1H-Indole, 3-(2,2-dimethyl-3-butenyl)-2-methyl-	EtOH	227(4.50),284(3.84), 291(3.79)	39-1913-73C
1H-Indole, 2,3-dimethyl-1-(3-methyl-2-butenyl)-	EtOH	231(4.50),281s(3.77), 287(3.82),293(3.80)	39-1913-73C
3H-Indole, 2,3-dimethyl-3-(3-methyl-2-butenyl)-	EtOH	212(4.30),217(4.27), 223s(4.11),256(3.74)	39-1913-73C
$C_{15}H_{19}NO$			
1H-Carbazole, 8-acetyl-2,3,4,4a,9,9a-hexahydro-4a-methyl- (or irradiation product)	EtOH	234(4.26),260(3.83), 307s(2.83),375(3.74)	33-2628-73
	EtOH-HCl	236(4.19),256s(3.71), 282s(3.06),317s(2.89), 375(3.57)	33-2628-73
1H-Carbazole, 9-acetyl-2,3,4,4a,9,9a-hexahydro-4a-methyl-	EtOH	254(4.08),275s(3.49), 288(3.38)	33-2628-73
Cyclohexanone, 2-[[4-(dimethylamino)-phenyl]methylene]-, (E)-	EtOH	381(4.38)	23-1458-73
Cyclohexanone, 5-methyl-2-[(methylphenylamino)methylene]-	EtOH	247(4.34)	77-0526-73
Pyridine, 1,2,3,4-tetrahydro-1-(1-oxo-2,4-decadien-6-ynyl)-, (E,E)-	ether	293(4.52)	24-1328-73
Pyridine, 1,2,3,4-tetrahydro-1-(1-oxo-2,4,6,8-decatetraenyl)-, (all-E)-	ether	332(4.87)	24-2087-73
2-Pyridineethanol, 3,4,5,6-tetrahydro-α-(2-phenylethenyl)-, (E)-, hydrochloride	MeOH	253(4.24),282(3.52), 291(3.42)	33-1763-73
$C_{15}H_{19}NO_2$			
Acetic acid, cyanotricyclo[3.3.1.1^{3,7}]-dec-2-ylidene-, ethyl ester	hexane	242(4.16)	78-1691-73
1H-Benzo[de]quinoline, 2,3,9,9a-tetrahydro-5,6-dimethoxy-1-methyl-, hydrochloride	EtOH	230(4.60),266(3.95), 305(3.28)	33-0759-73
1H-Carbazole, 2,3,4,4a-tetrahydro-6,7-dimethoxy-4a-methyl-	EtOH	219(4.33),290(3.83)	44-0215-73
	EtOH-HCl	223(4.39),245s(4.19), 330(3.71)	44-0215-73
9H-Carbazole-9-carboxaldehyde, 1,2,3,4-4a,9a-hexahydro-8-methoxy-4a-methyl-	EtOH	257(4.16)	33-2628-73
2-Cyclohexen-1-one, 3-[(4-methoxyphenyl)amino]-5,5-dimethyl-	EtOH	314(4.29)	18-2504-73
Ethanone, 1-(4-methoxyphenyl)-2-(1-methyl-2-piperidinylidene)-	EtOH	219(4.02),270(3.90), 341(4.48)	103-0880-73
2H-Pyrazole-3-carboxylic acid, 3,4-dihydro-2,2,3-trimethyl-5-phenyl-, methyl ester	C_6H_{12}	243(4.17)	35-1945-73

Compound	Solvent	$\lambda_{max}(\log \epsilon)$	Ref.
$C_{15}H_{19}NO_3$			
Acetamide, 2-(4-acetylphenoxy)-N-cyclopentyl-	EtOH	215(4.14),268(4.27)	111-0574-73
7H-Benzo[de]quinolin-7-one, 1,2,3,8,9-9a-hexahydro-5,6-dimethoxy-1-methyl-	EtOH	221(4.33),262(3.84), 329(3.52)	33-0759-73
5,9b-Ethano-9bH-benz[e]indole-5,7,8(1H)-triol, 2,3,3a,4-tetrahydro-3-methyl-, hydrochloride, (3aα,5α,9bβ)-(±)-	H_2O	282(3.58)	33-0347-73
Piperidine, 1-[(4-acetylphenoxy)acetyl]-	EtOH	212(4.29),268(4.28)	111-0574-73
$C_{15}H_{19}NO_4$			
2-Cyclohexene-1-carboxylic acid, 4-(1-cyano-2-ethoxy-2-oxoethylidene)-2-methyl-, ethyl ester	EtOH	300(4.46),430(1.79)	78-4103-73
	EtOH-NaOH	256(4.06),430(4.41)	78-4103-73
Morpholine, 4-[[4-(1-oxopropyl)phenoxy]-acetyl]-	EtOH	214(4.15),265(4.23)	111-0574-73
2,4(1H,3H)-Quinolinedione, 3-ethyl-6,8-dimethoxy-1,3-dimethyl- (same spectra in acid and base)	MeOH	244(4.39),288(3.25), 374(3.40)	78-1217-73
2(1H)-Quinolinone, 3-ethyl-4,6,8-trimethoxy-1-methyl-	MeOH	218(4.33),236(4.34), 257(4.24),282(3.74), 292(3.69),331s(3.32), 349(3.49),363(3.40)	78-1217-73
$C_{15}H_{19}NO_5$			
DL-Valine, N-[3-(4-hydroxy-3-methoxyphenyl)-1-oxo-2-propenyl]-	MeOH	295(4.18),320(4.26)	20-0243-73
	MeOH-KOH	310(3.79),365(4.28)	20-0243-73
$C_{15}H_{19}NS_2$			
1-Naphthalenecarbodithioic acid, diethylamine salt	EtOH	325(3.94),346(4.08), 479(2.20)	143-0359-73
$C_{15}H_{19}N_2O_2$			
1H-Imidazol-1-yloxy, 2,5-dihydro-2,2,5-5-tetramethyl-4-(2-phenylethenyl)-, 3-oxide	EtOH	233(4.05),238(4.07), 333(4.29)	104-1990-73
$C_{15}H_{19}N_3$			
3H-Azepin-2-amine, N,N-diethyl-4-(4-pyridinyl)-	EtOH	253(4.31),378(3.90)	39-1079-73C
3H-Azepin-2-amine, N,N-diethyl-5-(4-pyridinyl)-	EtOH	268(4.23)	39-1079-73C
3H-Azepin-2-amine, N,N-diethyl-6-(4-pyridinyl)-	EtOH	228(4.11),340(4.33)	39-1079-73C
$C_{15}H_{19}N_3O_5$			
Pyrano[3,4-e]-1,3-oxazine-4,5-dione, 2-(butylamino)-7-morpholino-	$CHCl_3$	287(4.32),323(3.90)	39-2432-73C
$C_{15}H_{19}N_3S_2$			
Propanedithioamide, 2-[3-(dimethylamino)-3-(4-methylphenyl)-2-propenylidene]-	CH_2Cl_2	275(3.98),331(3.87), 447(4.45)	97-0342-73
$C_{15}H_{19}N_5O$			
Benzenemethanol, α-[[4,6-bis(dimethylamino)-1,3,5-triazin-2-yl]methylene]-	C_6H_{12}	232(4.50),318(4.40)	22-2039-73

Compound	Solvent	$\lambda_{max}(\log \epsilon)$	Ref.
$C_{15}H_{19}N_5O_4S$			
Glycine, N-[N-[1-oxo-5-(1H-pyrrolo[2,3-d]pyrimidin-4-ylthio)pentyl]glycyl]-	pH 1	218(4.34),257(4.01), 310(4.05)	73-1438-73
	pH 13	220(4.32),248(3.95), 292(4.13)	73-1438-73
$C_{15}H_{19}O_3$			
1,3-Dioxol-1-ium, 4,5-dihydro-2-[2-(4-hydroxyphenyl)ethenyl]-4,4,5,5-tetramethyl-, perchlorate	$CHCl_3$	276(3.98),298(4.01)	104-0394-73
$C_{15}H_{20}$			
Naphthalene, 1,2-dihydro-4-pentyl-	EtOH	262(4.15)	88-2487-73
$C_{15}H_{20}Br_2O_2$			
Isoprelaurefucin	n.s.g.	209(3.94),219s(4.07), 224(4.12),232s(3.99)	88-4135-73
$C_{15}H_{20}N_2$			
9H-Carbazole-9-propanamine, 1,2,3,4-tetrahydro-, maleate	EtOH	228(4.56),279(3.81)	78-4045-73
hydrochloride	EtOH	231(4.52),279(3.80), 285(3.85),293(3.81)	78-4045-73
1H-Indole, 2-[(1-methyl-4-piperidinyl)-methyl]-	MeOH	275(3.88),281(3.88), 291(3.76)	23-0792-73
$C_{15}H_{20}N_2O$			
1-Hexanone, 1-(1H-indol-3-yl)-6-(methylamino)-	0.01M KOH	217(4.45),242(4.10), 263(4.07),274(4.02), 297(4.10),330(3.78)	103-0311-73
	EtOH	209(4.53),242(4.16), 256(4.00),297(4.13)	103-0311-73
$C_{15}H_{20}N_2OS$			
Pyrrolo[1,2-b][1,2,4]oxadiazole-2(1H)-thione, tetrahydro-5,5,7,7-tetramethyl-1-phenyl-	EtOH	219(4.04),268(3.97)	12-2473-73
$C_{15}H_{20}N_2O_2$			
1,3-Butanedione, 2-[bis(dimethylamino)-methylene]-1-phenyl-	EtOH	241(4.12),272s(4.09), 297(4.19)	1-0258-73
1H-Imidazole, 2,5-dihydro-1-hydroxy-2,2,5,5-tetramethyl-4-(2-phenylethenyl)-, 3-oxide	EtOH	231(3.96),237(3.95), 330(4.22)	104-1990-73
1,8-Naphthyridin-4(1H)-one, 5-butyl-1-ethyl-6-hydroxy-7-methyl-	EtOH	240(4.01),277s(--), 344(3.76)	77-0579-73
3,4-Pentamethylene-5-isoxazolinone, benzylammonium salt	EtOH	260(3.94)	1-2802-73
$C_{15}H_{20}N_2O_2S$			
4-Imidazolidinium, 5-ethoxy-5-(1-methylpropyl)-3-phenyl-2-thioxo-	EtOH	272.5(4.21)	63-1307-73
4-Imidazolidinium, 5-ethoxy-5-(2-methylpropyl)-3-phenyl-2-thioxo-	EtOH	272.5(4.21)	63-1307-73
$C_{15}H_{20}N_2O_2SSe$			
Benzo[b]selenophene-3-carboxylic acid, 4,5,6,7-tetrahydro-2-[[(2-propenylamino)thioxomethyl]amino]-	EtOH	235(3.56),242(3.50), 285(3.47),295(3.53), 318(3.42),340(3.70)	103-0300-73

Compound	Solvent	$\lambda_{max}(\log \epsilon)$	Ref.
$C_{15}H_{20}N_2O_3$			
Acetamide, N-cyclopentyl-2-[4-(1-hydroxyimino)ethyl]phenoxy]-	EtOH	207(4.31),256(4.22)	111-0574-73
Piperidine, 1-[[4-[1-(hydroxyimino)-ethyl]phenoxy]acetyl]-	EtOH	210(4.37),258(4.28)	111-0574-73
$C_{15}H_{20}N_2O_4$			
Isoxazolin-4-acetic acid, 3-methyl-5-oxo-, ethyl ester, benzylammonium salt	EtOH	255(3.94)	1-2802-73
$C_{15}H_{20}N_2O_5$			
Spiro[cyclohexane-1,4'-[2,3]diazabicyclo[3.1.0]hex[2]ene]-1',5'-dicarboxylic acid, 6',6'-dimethyl-2-oxo-, dimethyl ester	n.s.g.	335(2.18)	89-0240-73
$C_{15}H_{20}N_4O_3$			
1H-Pyrimido[5,4-b][1,4]oxazine-6-carboxylic acid, 7-methyl-4-piperidino-, ethyl ester	EtOH	244(4.3),282(4.1), 382(3.3)	103-1532-73
$C_{15}H_{20}N_4O_3S$			
Glycine, N-[1-oxo-5-(1H-pyrrolo[2,3-d]-pyrimidin-4-ylthio)pentyl]-, ethyl ester	pH 1	220(4.35),258(3.94), 311(4.02)	73-1438-73
	pH 13	222(4.33),249(3.94), 294(4.10)	73-1438-73
$C_{15}H_{20}N_4O_4$			
1H-Pyrimido[5,4-b][1,4]oxazine-6-carboxylic acid, 2,7-dimethyl-4-morpholino-, ethyl ester	EtOH	241(4.1),272(3.8), 384(3.2)	103-1532-73
$C_{15}H_{20}N_4O_4S$			
9H-Purine, 6-[(3-methyl-2-butenyl)thio]-9-β-D-ribofuranosyl-	MeOH	287s(4.31),292(4.32)	69-2179-73
	MeOH-HCl	296(4.26)	69-2179-73
	MeOH-NaOH	295(4.27)	69-2179-73
$C_{15}H_{20}N_4O_5S$			
Methanesulfonamide, N-(4,5,7,7a,10a,11-hexahydro-9,9-dimethyl-7,11-epoxy-8,10-dioxa-4,5,11a-triazacyclopenta-[6,7]cyclooct[1,2,3-cd]inden-3-ylidene)-, [7R-(7α,7aα,10aα,11α)]-	MeOH	222(4.26),240(4.19), 308(3.85)	18-0618-73
$C_{15}H_{20}N_4O_6S$			
7H-Pyrrolo[2,3-d]pyrimidin-4-amine, 7-[2,3-O-(1-methylethylidene)-5-O-(methylsulfonyl)-β-D-ribofuranosyl]-	MeOH	214(4.36),275(4.00), 293(4.05)	18-0618-73
$C_{15}H_{20}N_6O_7$			
Propanoic acid, 2-methyl-3-[[[(9-β-D-ribofuranosyl-9H-purin-6-yl)amino]-carbonyl]amino]-	pH 1-2	270s(--),277(4.33)	87-0139-73
	pH 5-7	269(4.32),277s(--)	87-0139-73
	pH 12	277(4.20),299(3.88)	87-0139-73
$C_{15}H_{20}N_6O_8$			
Threonine, N-[[(9-β-D-ribofuranosyl-9H-purin-6-yl)amino]carbonyl]-	pH 1-2	270s(--),277(4.31),	87-0139-73
	pH 5-7	270(4.37),277s(--)	87-0139-73
	pH 12	271(4.23),299(4.06)	87-0139-73

Compound	Solvent	λ_{max}(log ϵ)	Ref.
$C_{15}H_{20}O$			
5(6H)-Benzocyclodecenone, 7,8,9,10,11-12-hexahydro-1-methyl-	EtOH	244(3.71)	22-3493-73
Benzofuran, 3,5-dimethyl-4-pentyl-	EtOH	254.3(4.09)	18-2918-73
Benzofuran, 3,5-dimethyl-6-pentyl-	EtOH	251.5(4.05)	18-2918-73
4a(2H)-Biphenylenol, 1,3,4,8b-tetrahydro-4,4,8b-trimethyl-	EtOH	261(3.09),267(3.26), 272(3.22)	78-1843-73
Ethanone, 1-(2,3-dihydro-1,3,3,5-tetramethyl-1H-inden-1-yl)-	C_6H_{12}	266s(2.94),271(3.10), 278(3.16)	23-1598-73
Ethanone, 1-(2,3-dihydro-1,3,3,6-tetramethyl-1H-inden-1-yl)-	C_6H_{12}	264s(2.97),272(3.11), 278(3.15)	23-1598-73
3H-Fluoren-3-one, 1,2,6,7,8,8a,9,9a-octahydro-4,5-dimethyl-	EtOH	289(4.06)	22-1109-73
Isocapsidienone	EtOH	238(3.89),267s(3.63)	23-0748-73
1(2H)-Naphthalenone, 3,4-dihydro-2,2,4,4,6-pentamethyl-	C_6H_{12}	250(3.95),283(2.94), 293s(2.78)	23-1598-73
1(2H)-Naphthalenone, 3,4-dihydro-2,2,4,4,7-pentamethyl-	C_6H_{12}	248(3.78),393(3.08)	23-1598-73
Tricyclo[3.2.1.0^{2,7}]oct-3-en-6-one, 1,2,3,4,5,7-hexamethyl-8-methylene-	hexane	253(3.85)	33-2796-73
$C_{15}H_{20}O_2$			
Azuleno[5,6-c]furan-3(1H)-one, 4,4a,5,6-7,7a-hexahydro-6,6,8-trimethyl-	EtOH	270(3.78)	1-1573-73
Azuleno[5,6-c]furan-3(1H)-one, 4a,5,6,7-7a,8-hexahydro-6,6,8-trimethyl-	EtOH	282(3.63)	1-1573-73
3,5-Cycloheptadiene-1,2-dione, 7-(1,1-dimethyl-2-propenyl)-3,5,7-trimethyl-	n.s.g.	225s(3.76),313(3.51), 446(2.00)	39-1958-73C
3,6-Cycloheptadiene-1,2-dione, 5-(3-methyl-2-butenyl)-3,5,7-trimethyl-	n.s.g.	267(3.63),318(3.00), 405(1.90)	39-1958-73C
2,4,6-Cycloheptatrien-1-one, 2-[(3-methyl-2-butenyl)oxy]-3,5,7-trimethyl-	n.s.g.	244(4.34),325(3.88)	39-1958-73C
2-Cyclopenten-1-one, 3-[2-(1-acetylcyclopropyl)-1-propenyl]-5,5-dimethyl- (hypacrone)	EtOH	285(4.26)	138-0063-73
4a,8a-Ethenonaphthalene-1,5(2H,6H)-dione, 3,4,7,8-tetrahydro-4,9,10-trimethyl-, (4α,4aβ,8aα)-	EtOH	235(3.54),302(2.70)	44-4281-73
Isoligularone	EtOH	269(3.68)	88-3999-73
Naphtho[2,3-b]furan-6-ol, 4,4a,5,6,7,8-hexahydro-3,4a,5-trimethyl-	MeOH	292(4.00)	18-2840-73
4-Phenanthrenol, 1,2,3,4,4a,9,10,10a-octahydro-7-methoxy-, (+)-	MeOH	279(3.37),287(3.34)	19-0009-73
(-)-	MeOH	279(3.23),287(3.21)	19-0009-73
2,4,6,8,10-Tetradecapentaenoic acid, methyl ester	MeOH	365(4.76)	88-0881-73
Velleral	EtOH	220(4.36),245s(4.06)	78-1621-73
$C_{15}H_{20}O_3$			
Arteannuin B	n.s.g.	215(3.76)	88-3039-73
2H-Cyclopenta[b]furan-2-one, 3,3a,6,6a-tetrahydro-4-(3-oxo-1-octenyl)-, [3aα,4(E),6aα]-(±)-	n.s.g.	274(4.25)	88-1319-73
Furanoeremophilane, 3β-hydroxy-9-oxo-	EtOH	281(4.23)	18-2840-73
1,4-Methano-3-benzoxepin-5,10(4H)-dione, 1,2,7,8,9,9a-hexahydro-2,2,9,9a-tetramethyl-	EtOH	225(3.83),304(2.38), 318(2.37),349(2.24)	5-0432-73

Compound	Solvent	λ_{max}(log ϵ)	Ref.
$C_{15}H_{20}O_4$			
Cyclopentaneacetic acid, α,3-dimethyl-3-(2-methyl-3-oxo-1-cyclopenten-1-yl)-2-oxo-	EtOH	243(4.00)	39-0914-73C
Cyclopentaneacetic acid, α,3-dimethyl-3-(5-methyl-4-oxo-1-cyclopenten-1-yl)-2-oxo-	EtOH	241(4.03),294(2.39)	39-0914-73C
Ethanone, 1-(3,4-dihydro-5,7-dimethoxy-2,2-dimethyl-2H-1-benzopyran-8-yl)-	MeOH	212(4.25),225(4.13), 277(3.80)	119-0064-73
Isohirsutic acid	EtOH	232(3.65)	102-2717-73
3H-Oxireno[8,8a]naphtho[2,3-b]furan-3,5-diol, 1a,2,4,4a,5,9-hexahydro-4,4a,6-trimethyl-	EtOH	219(3.80)	73-0739-73
2,4-Pentadienoic acid, 5-(1-hydroxy-2,6,6-trimethyl-4-oxo-2-cyclohexen-1-yl)-3-methyl-, (+)-	MeOH	245(4.39)	35-0239-73
	MeOH-acid	261(4.38)	35-0239-73
trans isomer	MeOH	241(4.45)	35-0239-73
Spiro[1,3-dioxolan-2,2'(1'H)-naphthalene]-8'-carboxylic acid, 3',4',4'a-8'a-tetrahydro-4'a-methyl-, methyl ester, cis	MeOH	219(3.52),292(3.82)	35-2303-73
$C_{15}H_{20}O_5$			
Cordilin	EtOH	210(4.18)	102-1415-73
Isocordilin	EtOH	224(4.18)	102-1415-73
Spiro[1,3-dioxolane-2,2'(1'H)-naphthalene]-8'(3'H)-carboxylic acid, 4',6',7',8'-tetrahydro-5'-methyl-6'-oxo-, methyl ester, (R)-	EtOH	245(4.10)	39-2083-73C
Spiro[1,3-dioxolane-2,5'(1'aH)-naphth-[1,2-b]oxirene]-3'-carboxylic acid, 3'a,4',6',7',7'a,7'b-hexahydro-7'a-methyl-, methyl ester, (1'aα,3'aα,7'aα,7'bα)-	MeOH	230(3.69)	35-2303-73
(1'aα,3'aα,7'aβ,7'bα)-	MeOH	238(3.84)	35-2303-73
$C_{15}H_{20}O_6$			
2H-Pyran-2-one, 4-methoxy-6-(1,2-diacetoxypentyl)-	MeOH	220(3.30),280(3.80)	44-3542-73
$C_{15}H_{20}O_7$			
1,3-Cyclopentadiene-1,2-dicarboxylic acid, 5-(2,2-diethoxy-1-hydroxyethylidene)-, dimethyl ester	MeOH	239(4.05),320(4.42), 370(3.56)	24-3817-73
sodium deriv.	MeOH	288(4.70),331(4.28)	24-3817-73
$C_{15}H_{20}O_8$			
Fragilin	n.s.g.	267(3.0)	105-0127-73
	NaOH	269(2.96)	105-0127-73
$C_{15}H_{20}O_8S$			
1,5-Hexadiene-2,3,4,5-tetracarboxylic acid, 1-(methylthio)-, tetramethyl ester, (E)-	EtOH	207(3.87),286(4.20)	39-2016-73C
(Z)-	EtOH	207(3.91),295(4.13)	39-2016-73C
$C_{15}H_{20}S_4$			
3(2H)-Thiophenethione, 5-(1,1-dimethylethyl)-2-[5-(1,1-dimethylethyl)-3H-1,2-dithiol-3-ylidene]-	dioxan	262(4.57),368(3.98), 500(3.79)	22-1659-73

Compound	Solvent	$\lambda_{max}(\log \epsilon)$	Ref.
$C_{15}H_{21}BrO$			
4,7-Methanoazulen-3(3aH)-one, 2-bromo-4,5,6,7,8,8a-hexahydro-3a,4,8,8-tetramethyl-, (3aα,4α,7α,8aβ)-(-)-	EtOH	259.5(3.72)	78-2097-73
$C_{15}H_{21}ClN_3S$			
1H-Benzimidazolium, 2-[(chlorocyclohexylamino)thio]-1,3-dimethyl-, chloride	98% H_2SO_4	302(4.16)	104-2622-73
$C_{15}H_{21}F_3N_2O$			
1H-Indole-3-ethanamine, 2,3-dihydro-5-methoxy-N,N,2-trimethyl-4-(trifluoromethyl)-, cis	MeOH	248(3.89),325(3.59)	44-1504-73
trans	MeOH	248(3.88),325(3.54)	44-1504-73
$C_{15}H_{21}N$			
1H-Indole, 2,3-dimethyl-1-(3-methylbutyl)-	EtOH	231(4.47),282s(3.73), 288(3.78),294s(3.77)	39-1913-73C
$C_{15}H_{21}NO$			
Furo[3,2-c]pyridine, octahydro-2,5-dimethyl-7a-phenyl-	EtOH	257(3.67)	87-0592-73
Piperidine, 1-(1-oxo-2,4,6,8-decatetraenyl)-, (all-E)-	ether	311(4.69),323(4.81), 337(4.73)	24-2087-73
Pyridine, 1,2,3,4-tetrahydro-1-(1-oxo-2,4,6-decatrienyl)-, (E,E,Z)-	ether	302(4.59)	24-1328-73
2-Piperidinone, 3-ethyl-1-(2-phenylethyl)-	EtOH	248(2.14),253(2.23), 259(2.31),261s(2.25), 265(2.20),268(2.11)	94-2695-73
2-Piperidinone, 5-ethyl-1-(2-phenylethyl)-	EtOH	248(2.13),253(2.24), 259(2.32),261s(2.26), 265(2.21),268(2.13)	94-2695-73
$C_{15}H_{21}NO_2$			
1H,8H-Benzo[ij]quinolizin-8-one, 2,3,5,6,7,9,10,10a-octahydro-10-(2-oxopropyl)-, trans	MeOH	319(4.40)	35-8427-73
2-Pentenoic acid, 2-methyl-3-[(phenylmethyl)amino]-, ethyl ester	EtOH	303(4.24)	1-2802-73
2-Piperidinone, 3-ethyl-1-(2-hydroxy-2-phenylethyl)-	EtOH	247(2.16),252(2.23), 258(2.31),264(2.18), 268s(1.92)	94-2695-73
2-Piperidinone, 5-ethyl-1-(2-hydroxy-2-phenylethyl)-	EtOH	247(2.31),252(2.34), 258(2.35),264(2.19), 268s(1.94)	94-2695-73
$C_{15}H_{21}NO_4$			
1H,10bH-Benzo[ij]quinolizine-10b-carboxylic acid, 2,3,5,6,7,7a,8,10a-octahydro-10-methoxy-8-oxo-, methyl ester	MeOH	245(4.17)	35-8427-73
trans-trans	MeOH	250(4.12)	35-8427-73
Cyclohexanecarboxylic acid, 2-(1-cyano-2-ethoxy-2-oxoethylidene)-1-methyl-, ethyl ester	EtOH	236(3.24)	78-4103-73
$C_{15}H_{21}NO_8$			
L-Tyrosine, O-β-D-glucopyranosyl-	pH 6.5	270(3.0),276(2.9)	102-2243-73
	pH 13	270(3.0),276(2.9)	102-2243-73

Compound	Solvent	λ_{max}(log ϵ)	Ref.
$C_{15}H_{21}N_3O_4S$			
5-Pyrimidinecarboxylic acid, 1,4,5,6-tetrahydro-1-methyl-2-[[(4-methylphenyl)sulfonyl]amino]-, ethyl ester	EtOH	232(4.23)	44-1591-73
5-Pyrimidinecarboxylic acid, 1,4,5,6-tetrahydro-2-[methyl[(4-methylphenyl)-sulfonyl]amino]-, ethyl ester	EtOH	228(4.22)	44-1591-73
$C_{15}H_{21}N_5O_2S$			
1H-Purine-2,6-dione, 8-butyl-3,7-dihydro-7-(3-isocyanatopropyl)-1,3-dimethyl-	n.s.g.	210(4.39),277(4.03)	73-1571-73
$C_{15}H_{21}N_5O_3$			
Adenosine, 2'-deoxy-N-(3-methyl-2-butenyl)-	MeOH	268(4.28)	69-2179-73
$C_{15}H_{21}N_5O_4$			
Adenosine, N-cyclopentyl-	pH 1.0	266(4.36)	87-0358-73
	H_2O	270(4.30)	87-0358-73
	pH 13	269.5(4.31)	87-0358-73
Adenosine, N-(3-methyl-2-butenyl)-	MeOH	268(4.26)	69-2179-73
9H-Purin-6-amine, 9-β-D-arabinofuranosyl-N-(3-methyl-2-butenyl)-	MeOH	266.5(4.26)	69-2179-73
9H-Purine, 6-piperidino-9-β-D-ribofuranosyl-	pH 1	274(4.34)	87-0358-73
	H_2O	282(4.36)	87-0358-73
	pH 13	282(4.37)	87-0358-73
1H-Pyrazolo[4,3-d]pyrimidin-7-amine, N-(3-methyl-2-butenyl)-3-β-D-ribofuranosyl-	MeOH	239(3.80),288s(4.15), 296(4.20),307s(4.07)	69-2179-73
	MeOH-HCl	239(3.82),301(4.24), 311(4.22)	69-2179-73
	MeOH-NaOH	244(4.12),300(4.09)	69-2179-73
$C_{15}H_{21}N_5O_4S$			
9H-Purin-2-amine, 6-[(3-methyl-2-butenyl)thio]-9-β-D-ribofuranosyl-	MeOH	248(4.16),303(4.12)	69-2179-73
	MeOH-HCl	250(3.96),327(4.07)	69-2179-73
	MeOH-NaOH	248(4.09),314(4.12)	69-2179-73
$C_{15}H_{21}N_5O_5$			
Adenosine, N-ethoxy-2',3'-O-(1-methylethylidene)-	pH 1	268(4.25)	94-1676-73
	pH 7	270(4.18)	94-1676-73
	pH 13	284(4.05)	94-1676-73
	EtOH	269(4.14)	94-1676-73
Adenosine, 1-ethoxy-2',3'-O-(1-methylethylidene)-, HI salt	pH 1	259(4.13)	94-1676-73
	pH 7	259(4.13)	94-1676-73
	pH 13	258(4.09)	94-1676-73
	EtOH	260(4.11)	94-1676-73
$C_{15}H_{21}N_6O_{11}P$			
L-Threonine, [[(9-β-D-ribofuranosyl-9H-purin-6-yl)amino]carbonyl]-, 5'-(dihydrogen phosphate)	pH 1	277(4.28)	87-0956-73
	H_2O	269(4.38),276(4.31)	87-0956-73
	pH 13	269(4.35),276(4.30), 297(3.90)	87-0956-73
$C_{15}H_{21}N_7O_7$			
Adenosine, N-[[[1-(aminocarbonyl)-2-hydroxypropyl]amino]carbonyl]-, DL-	pH 1-2	270s(--),277(4.36)	87-0139-73
	pH 5-7	270(4.38),277s(--)	87-0139-73
	pH 12	270(4.06),300(4.36)	87-0139-73
L-isomer	pH 1-2	270s(--),277(4.30)	87-0139-73
	pH 5-7	269(4.40),277s(--)	87-0139-73
	pH 12	271(4.10),300(4.37)	87-0139-73

Compound	Solvent	λmax(log ε)	Ref.
$C_{15}H_{22}$			
Benzene, 1-cyclohexyl-2-(1-methylethyl)-	EtOH	257(2.54),263(2.57), 271(2.46)	22-1517-73
Benzene, [1-(1,1-dimethylethyl)-2,2-dimethylcyclopropyl]-	EtOH	250(2.19),255(2.29), 261(2.35),267(2.20)	35-1586-73
Benzene, [1-(1,1-dimethylethyl)-1,2-dimethyl-2-propenyl]-	EtOH	243(2.03),248(2.15), 253(2.28),259(2.36), 265(2.23)	35-1586-73
Benzene, 1-nonenyl-	MeOH	250.5(4.27)	24-1612-73
Benzene, 1-(propylidenehexyl)-, cis	EtOH	235(3.85)	88-0669-73
trans	EtOH	245(4.00)	88-0669-73
Cyclohexane, 1-(1-methylethyl)-2-phenyl-, cis	EtOH	250s(2.16),254(2.26), 259(2.31),262s(2.27), 265(2.20),269(2.10)	22-1517-73
trans	EtOH	249(2.52),254(2.58), 256s(2.57),259(2.62), 262(2.61),265(2.49), 269(2.49)	22-1517-73
1H-3a,7-Methanoazulene, 4,5,6,7,8,8a-hexahydro-4,9,9-trimethyl-1-methylene-, trans	EtOH	241(3.20)	78-2097-73
4H-3a,7-Methanoazulene, 5,6,7,8-tetrahydro-1,4,9,9-tetramethyl-, cis	EtOH	262(3.66)	78-2097-73
$C_{15}H_{22}BrClO_2$			
Spiro[5.5]undec-3-en-2-one, 8-bromo-9-chloro-1-hydroxy-1,5,5,9-tetramethyl-	EtOH	234(3.77)	88-2381-73
$C_{15}H_{22}ClN_3O_4$			
Benzimidazolium, 2-cyclohexylamino-1,3-dimethyl-, perchlorate	EtOH	281(4.21),287(4.22)	104-2622-73
$C_{15}H_{22}N_2$			
Pyrrolidine, 1,1'-(5-methyl-1,3-phenylene)bis-	EtOH	241(4.61),310(3.78)	78-1083-73
$C_{15}H_{22}N_2O$			
1H-Indole-3-ethanamine, 5-methoxy-N,N,2,4-tetramethyl-	MeOH	224(4.53),278(3.98), 297(3.86)	44-1504-73
$C_{15}H_{22}N_2O_2$			
Isoxazole, 5,5'-methylenebis[3-(1,1-dimethylethyl)-	n.s.g.	216.5(4.04)	32-0037-73
2H-Pyrrol-3-ol, 2-[(3,4-dimethyl-1H-pyrrol-2-yl)methylene]-5-ethoxy-3,4-dihydro-4,4-dimethyl-, (E)-	CH_2Cl_2	320(4.32),330s(4.23)	5-1067-73
$C_{15}H_{22}N_2O_5S$			
1H-Imidazole-4-hexanoic acid, 5-[(acetylthio)methyl]-2,3-dihydro-1-methyl-ε,2-dioxo-, ethyl ester	EtOH	308(4.02)	70-1641-73
$C_{15}H_{22}N_4O_2$			
2,4(1H,3H)-Pteridinedione, 6,7-bis(1,1-dimethylethyl)-1-methyl-	MeOH	230s(4.08),252(4.06), 326(3.95)	24-3149-73
$C_{15}H_{22}N_6O_3$			
Oxazolidine, 3-acetyl-5-[[6-(dimethylamino)-9H-purin-9-yl]methyl]-2-ethoxy-	pH 1	269(4.25)	87-0037-73
	pH 7	277(4.24)	87-0037-73
	pH 13	277(4.25)	87-0037-73

Compound	Solvent	$\lambda_{max}(\log \epsilon)$	Ref.
4H-Pyrazolo[3,4-d]pyrimidin-4-one, 1,5-dihydro-5,?-bis(4-morpholinylmethyl)-	EtOH	253(3.74)	103-1280-73
$C_{15}H_{22}N_6O_5$			
Adenosine, N-[[(1,1-dimethylethyl)-amino]carbonyl]-	pH 1-2	270s(--),277(4.38)	87-0139-73
	pH 5-7	270(4.39),277s(--)	87-0139-73
	pH 12	278(4.26),302(3.73)	87-0139-73
$C_{15}H_{22}N_6O_6$			
Adenosine, N-[[(4-hydroxybutyl)amino]-carbonyl]-	pH 1-2	270s(--),278(4.37)	87-0139-73
	pH 5-7	269(4.36),277s(--)	87-0139-73
	pH 12	278(4.20),298(4.00)	87-0139-73
$C_{15}H_{22}O$			
2,4-Cyclohexadien-1-one, 6-(2-butenyl)-2-(1,1-dimethylethyl)-6-methyl-, (E)-	EtOH	309(3.71)	33-0014-73
Cyclohexanone, 5-ethenyl-5-methyl-4-(1-methylethenyl)-2-(1-methylethylidene)-	EtOH	256.5(3.82)	39-2212-73C
Germacra-3,7(11),9-trien-6-one, (3Z,9E)-	EtOH	245(3.32),301(2.36)	39-2212-73C
3,5-Hexadien-2-one, 6-(3,3-dimethyl-bicyclo[2.2.1]hept-2-yl)-	EtOH	283(4.49)	22-3071-73
5,8-Methano-1H-benzocyclohepten-3(2H)-one, 5,6,7,8,9,9a-hexahydro-5,9,9-trimethyl-, [5S-(5α,8α,9aβ)]-	EtOH	242(4.19)	78-2097-73
Myliol	n.s.g.	220(3.70),278(2.44)	73-1084-73
Mylione, dihydro-	n.s.g.	263(2.63)	73-1084-73
isomer	n.s.g.	265(2.73)	73-1084-73
2(3H)-Naphthalenone, 4,4a,5,6,7,8-hexahydro-4a,5-dimethyl-3-(1-methylethylidene)- (dehydrofukinone)	EtOH	249(4.06),274(3.86)	102-2931-73
$C_{15}H_{22}O_2$			
Eremophilenolide, (±)-	MeOH	220(4.16)	23-2166-73
1H-Inden-1-one, 2,3,3a,4,5,6-hexahydro-7-methyl-2-(3-oxopentyl)-	EtOH	254(4.00)	22-1109-73
Ligularenolide, tetrahydro-, (±)-	MeOH	220(4.18)	23-2166-73
1(2H)-Naphthalenone, 3,4,4a,5,6,7-hexahydro-3-hydroxy-4,4a-dimethyl-6-(1-methylethenyl)- (capsenone)	EtOH	238(3.80)	23-0748-73
2(1H)-Naphthalenone, 3,4,6,7,8,8a-hexahydro-4-hydroxy-1,8a-dimethyl-7-(1-methylethenyl)-	EtOH	286(2.48)	23-0748-73
	EtOH-NaOH	290(4.06)	23-0748-73
Spiro[4.5]dec-6-ene-1-carboxylic acid, 4-methyl-8-methylene-, ethyl ester	MeOH	223(c.4.3)	33-1812-73
$C_{15}H_{22}O_3$			
3-Furanmethanol, tetrahydro-2-(2-hydroxy-6-methylphenyl)-4,4,5-trimethyl-	ether	271(3.30),279(3.31)	24-0382-73
Furanoeremophilane, 3β,9β-dihydroxy-	EtOH	222.5(3.86)	18-2840-73
1,4-Methano-3-benzoxepin-5(4H)-one, 1,2,7,8,9,9a-hexahydro-10-hydroxy-2,2,9,9a-tetramethyl- (nardofuran)	EtOH	246(3.79),338(2.00)	5-0432-73
4;7αH-5;6:11βH-Santan-6:13-olide, 2-oxo-	EtOH	277(1.83)	94-0296-73
5;7αH-4;6:11βH-Santan-6:13-olide, 2-oxo-	EtOH	292(1.33)	94-0296-73
$C_{15}H_{22}O_4$			
Arsantin	n.s.g.	214(2.36),290(1.26)	105-0162-73
Euryopsol	EtOH	220(3.85)	73-0739-73
1H-Indene-4-carboxylic acid, 1-(1,1-dimethylethoxy)-2,3,5,6,7,7a-hexahydro-7aβ-methyl-5-oxo-, cis	EtOH	249(3.99)	44-3239-73

Compound	Solvent	$\lambda_{max}(\log \epsilon)$	Ref.
1-Naphthalenecarboxylic acid, 1,2,3,4-4a,5,8,8a-octahydro-7-methoxy-1,4a-dimethyl-5-oxo-, methyl ester, [1R-(1α,4aβ,8aα)]-	EtOH	248(4.23)	78-1237-73
1-Naphthalenecarboxylic acid, 1,2,3,4-4a,7,8,8a-octahydro-5-methoxy-1,4a-dimethyl-7-oxo-, methyl ester, [1R-(1α,4aβ,8aα)]-	EtOH	250(4.33)	78-1237-73
1,4-Naphthalenedione, 8α-acetoxy-2α,5α,9β-trimethyl-, trans	EtOH	210(2.65)	23-3989-73
Naphtho[1,2-b]furan-2,7-dione, deca-hydro-8-hydroxy-3,5a,9-trimethyl-	$CHCl_3$	282(2.08)	94-0296-73
Naphtho[2,3-b]furan-4,6,8a(4aH)-triol, 4,5,6,7,8,9-hexahydro-3,4a,5-tri-methyl-	EtOH	218(3.8)	73-0739-73
5αH-Santan-6:13-olide, 3-hydroxy-2-oxo-	EtOH	281(2.22)	94-0296-73
α-Santonin, tetrahydro-2α-hydroxy-	$CHCl_3$	278(1.81)	94-0296-73
γ-Santonin, tetrahydro-2β-hydroxy-	$CHCl_3$	274(1.56)	94-0296-73
Spiro[1,3-dioxolane-2,1'(2'H)-naphtha-lene]-5',8'-dione, 4',7',8'a-tri-methyl-, (4'α,4'aα,7'β,8'aβ)-	EtOH	214(2.60)	23-3989-73
$C_{15}H_{22}O_5$			
1-Cyclopentene-1-heptanoic acid, 2-(methoxycarbonyl)-5-oxo-, methyl ester	MeOH	246(3.98)	44-4412-73
1,1-Cyclopropanedicarboxylic acid, 2-(3-oxo-1-octenyl)-, methyl ester, (E)-	MeOH	238(4.24)	88-0451-73
Lactarorufin B	EtOH	218(4.00)	19-0785-73
1-Naphthalenecarboxylic acid, 1,2,3,4-4a,7,8,8a-octahydro-1-hydroxy-5-meth-oxy-4a,8a-dimethyl-7-oxo-, methyl ester	EtOH	248(4.02)	78-1237-73
2,4-Pentadienoic acid, 5-(3,8-dihydroxy-1,5-dimethyl-6-oxabicyclo[3.2.1]oct-8-yl)-3-methyl- (dihydrophaseic acid)	MeOH	259(4.19)	138-0245-73
$C_{15}H_{22}O_6$			
1-Cyclopentene-1-heptanoic acid, 3-hy-droxy-2-(methoxycarbonyl)-5-oxo-, methyl ester	MeOH	237(4.07)	44-4412-73
$C_{15}H_{22}O_9$			
Mentzeloside	n.s.g.	205(3.53)	23-0760-73
$C_{15}H_{23}BrO_4$			
1(2H)-Naphthalenone, 7-acetoxy-2-bromo-octahydro-8a-hydroxy-4a,8,8-trimethyl-	EtOH	342(2.05)	78-2297-73
$C_{15}H_{23}NO$			
1-Piperidineethanol, 3-ethyl-α-phenyl-	EtOH	247s(2.34),252(2.37), 258(2.40),264(2.28), 267s(2.10)	94-2695-73
$C_{15}H_{23}N_3O_4$			
2,6-Pyridinedicarboxamide, N,N',1-tri-ethyl-1,4-dihydro-3-(2-hydroxyethyl)-4-oxo-	EtOH	276(4.15)	95-1183-73

Compound	Solvent	λ_{max}(log ε)	Ref.
$C_{15}H_{23}N_5O$			
4(1H)-Pteridinone, 2-amino-6-nonyl-	pH 13	253(4.34),362(3.79)	44-2073-73
$C_{15}H_{24}$			
Azulene, 2,3,3a,4,5,6-hexahydro-3a,7-dimethyl-1-(1-methylethyl)-	n.s.g.	244(4.17)	138-0133-73
1H-Benzocycloheptene, 7-ethyl-2,3,4,5,6,7-hexahydro-1,1-dimethyl-	C_6H_{12}	242(3.85)	22-3187-73
1H-Benzocycloheptene, 7-ethyl-2,3,4,6,7,8-hexahydro-1,1-dimethyl-	C_6H_{12}	232(3.74)	22-3187-73
1H-Benzocycloheptene, 7-ethyl-2,3,4,7,8,9-hexahydro-1,1-dimethyl-	C_6H_{12}	242(3.76)	22-3187-73
1H-Benzocycloheptene, 7-ethyl-2,3,4,8,9,9a-hexahydro-1,1-dimethyl-	C_6H_{12}	246(3.84)	22-3187-73
1H-Benzocycloheptene, 7-ethyl-2,3,5,6,7,8-hexahydro-1,1-dimethyl-	C_6H_{12}	242(4.19)	22-3187-73
1H-Benzocycloheptene, 7-ethyl-2,5,6,7,8,9-hexahydro-1,1-dimethyl-	C_6H_{12}	263(3.30)	22-3187-73
Naphthalene, 1,2,3,4,5,6-hexahydro-1,1-dimethyl-7-(1-methylethyl)-	MeOH	263(4.06)	35-8692-73
Naphthalene, 1,2,3,4,7,8-hexahydro-1,1-dimethyl-6-(1-methylethyl)-	MeOH	250(3.79),275s(3.48)	35-8692-73
Naphthalene, 1,2,3,5,6,7-hexahydro-1,1-dimethyl-7-(1-methylethyl)-	MeOH	241(4.34)	35-8692-73
Naphthalene, 1,2,3,4,4a,5,6,7-octahydro-1,1-dimethyl-7-(1-methylethylidene)-	EtOH	248(4.23)	35-8692-73
Naphthalene, 1,2,3,5,6,7,8,8a-octahydro-1,1-dimethyl-6-(1-methylethylidene)-	EtOH	240(4.26)	35-8692-73
$C_{15}H_{24}Cl_5N_3$			
Cyclobutenylcarboxamidinium, N,N'-diisopropyl-2-(isopropylamino)-3,3-dichloro-4-(dichloromethylene)-, chloride	n.s.g.	268(4.28)	44-1470-73
$C_{15}H_{24}N_2O$			
2-Pyridinamine, N-(2-cyclohexyl-1-methylethyl)-N-methyl-, 1-oxide, (S)-	MeOH	246(4.30),275(3.83), 335(3.53)	32-1083-73
$C_{15}H_{24}N_2O_2$			
2-Cyclopenten-1-one, 2-hydroxy-3,5-bis-(1-pyrrolidinylmethyl)-	EtOH	263(3.78)	44-0551-73
Isoxazole, 3-(1,1-dimethylethyl)-5-[[3-(1,1-dimethylethyl)-5-isoxazolyl]-methyl]-4,5-dihydro-	n.s.g.	214.5(4.08)	32-0037-73
$C_{15}H_{24}N_2O_3$			
1H-Pyrrole-2-carboxylic acid, 4-[2-(diethylamino)ethyl]-5-formyl-3-methyl-, ethyl ester	EtOH	233(4.16),307(4.33)	103-0186-73
$C_{15}H_{24}N_2O_4$			
2-Cyclopenten-1-one, 2-hydroxy-3,5-bis-(4-morpholinylmethyl)-	EtOH	266.5(3.71)	44-0551-73
$C_{15}H_{24}N_6O_4$			
Adenosine, N-[3-(dimethylamino)propyl]-	pH 1	264(4.27)	87-0358-73
	H_2O	267(4.28)	87-0358-73
	pH 13	269(4.30)	87-0358-73

Compound	Solvent	$\lambda_{max}(\log \epsilon)$	Ref.
$C_{15}H_{24}O$			
Acoragermacrone	MeOH	242(3.82)	88-2759-73
2(1H)-Azulenone, 4,5,6,7,8,8a-hexahydro-5,8a-dimethyl-3-(1-methylethyl)-	n.s.g.	234(4.32)	138-0727-73
4(1H)-Azulenone, 2,5,6,7,8,8a-hexahydro-3,8-dimethyl-5-(1-methylethyl)-	MeOH	256(3.92)	88-1687-73
5β,7βH,10α-Eudesm-4(14)-en-1-one	MeOH	248s(2.34),254s(2.38), 275(2.45)	88-3337-73
Fukinone	EtOH	251(3.66)	102-2931-73
Myliol, dihydro-	n.s.g.	210(2.81),248(1.80)	73-1084-73
isomer	n.s.g.	210(3.12),246(2.27)	73-1084-73
2-Naphthalenemethanol, 1,2,3,4,4a,8a-hexahydro-α,α,4a,8-tetramethyl- [(+)-occidentalol]	MeOH	264(3.67)	44-0728-73
(-)-trans	MeOH	264(3.67)	44-0728-73
1(4H)-Naphthalenone, 4a,5,6,7,8,8a-hexahydro-4,8a-dimethyl-6-(1-methylethyl)-	MeOH	225(3.90)	88-3337-73
2-Pentenal, 3-methyl-5-(2,6,6-trimethyl-1-cyclohexen-1-yl)- (β-cyclofarnesal)	EtOH	238(4.09)	65-2047-73
$C_{15}H_{24}OSi$			
Silane, triethyl[(3-phenyl-1-propenyl)-oxy]-	isooctane	256(2.81),263(2.79), 269(2.66)	22-2638-73
Silane, triethyl[(3-phenyl-2-propenyl)-oxy]-	isooctane	251(3.46),253(3.46), 283(2.71),293(3.57)	22-2638-73
$C_{15}H_{24}O_2$			
β-Cyclofarnesylic acid	EtOH	213(4.18)	65-2047-73
1-Cyclohexene-1-carboxaldehyde, 4-(1,5-dimethyl-3-oxohexyl)-	EtOH	232(4.23)	138-0491-73
Mogoltone	n.s.g.	310(3.15)	105-0583-73
Stemphol	EtOH	273(3.24),280(3.21)	102-1797-73
$C_{15}H_{24}O_3$			
1,3,5-Benzenetrimethanol, α,α,α',α',α",α"-hexamethyl-	MeOH	261(2.41)	32-0849-73
Furan, 5-(4-carbomethoxy-4-methylpent-yl)-2-isopropyl-	MeOH	223(3.85)	35-8692-73
$C_{15}H_{24}O_4$			
1(2H)-Naphthalenone, 7-acetoxyoctahydro-8a-hydroxy-4a,8,8-trimethyl-, (4aα,7α,8aβ)-	$CHCl_3$	305(1.40)	78-2297-73
1(2H)-Naphthalenone, 8-acetoxyoctahydro-4-hydroxy-2,5,8a-trimethyl-, (2α,4β,4aα,5α,8α,8aβ)-	EtOH	210(2.48)	23-3989-73
Spiro[1,3-dioxolane-2,1'(2'H)-naphthal-en]-8'(5'H)-one, hexahydro-5'-hydroxy-4',7',8'a-trimethyl-, (4'α,4'aα,5'β-7'α,8'aβ)-	EtOH	210(2.62)	23-3989-73
$C_{15}H_{24}O_4Si$			
Phenol, 3-[(5-ethyl-2-methyl-4-propyl-1,3-dioxa-2-silacyclohexen-2-yl)oxy]-	EtOH	204(3.94),273(3.21)	87-0729-73
$C_{15}H_{25}BO_6$			
Boron, bis(acetato-O)(2,2,6,6-tetrameth-yl-3,5-heptanedionato-O,O')-, (T-4)-	CH_2Cl_2	296(4.20)	39-1796-73B

Compound	Solvent	$\lambda_{max}(\log \epsilon)$	Ref.
$C_{15}H_{25}NO$			
Piperidine, 1-(1-oxo-2,4-decadienyl)-, (E,E)-	ether	250(4.48)	24-2087-73
$C_{15}H_{25}NS_2$			
Dithiobenzoic acid, dibutylamine salt	EtOH	285(4.05),361(3.99), 500(2.20)	143-0359-73
$C_{15}H_{25}N_3O_2S_2$			
Carbamic acid, [[(3-butyl-2(3H)-thiazolylidene)amino](butylthio)methylene]-, ethyl ester	dioxan	245(3.57),281(3.91), 332(4.37)	94-0074-73
$C_{15}H_{25}N_3O_5$			
Cytidine, 2',3',5'-tri-O-ethyl-	pH 2	280(4.13)	69-0194-73
	pH 12	271(3.96)	69-0194-73
$C_{15}H_{26}$			
Cyclohexene, 1,3,3-trimethyl-2-(3-methyl-1-pentenyl)-	C_6H_{12}	227(3.78)	22-3187-73
$C_{15}H_{26}N_4O$			
Acetamide, 2-cyano-N-[2-(diethylamino)-ethyl]-2-(1-methyl-2-piperidinylidene)-	EtOH	302(4.24)	103-0880-73
$C_{15}H_{26}O$			
Furan, 3-hexyl-4-pentyl-	n.s.g.	216(3.52)	35-0250-73
1(2H)-Naphthalenone, octahydro-4,8a-dimethyl-6-(1-methylethyl)-, (4R)-	MeOH	267(2.31)	88-3337-73
(4S)-	MeOH	278(2.26)	88-3337-73
$C_{15}H_{26}O_3$			
Cyclohexanepropanoic acid, 4-(1,1-dimethylethyl)-1-methyl-2-oxo-, methyl ester, axial isomer	EtOH	290(1.60)	44-1000-73
isomer	EtOH	290(1.54)	44-1000-73
$C_{15}H_{27}NO$			
Cyclohexanamine, N-(2,3,4-trimethyl-3-hexenylidene)-, N-oxide, (E)-	pentane	252(3.89)	33-2961-73
(Z)-	pentane	250(3.94)	33-2961-73
$C_{15}H_{27}N_3$			
Cyclopropene, 3-azido-1,2,3-tris(1,1-dimethylethyl)-	C_6H_{12}	295(1.45)	44-3149-73
$C_{15}H_{27}S_3$			
Cyclopropenylium, tris[(1,1-dimethylethyl)thio]-, perchlorate	MeCN	273(4.34)	88-3409-73
$C_{15}H_{28}Cl_4N_4$			
Diisopropyl[1,3,5-trichloro-5-(diisopropylamino)-2,4-diazapenta-2,4-dienylidene]ammonium chloride	$CHCl_3$	248(4.47),316(4.53)	114-0081-73A
Dipropyl[1,3,5-trichloro-5-(propylamino)-2,4-diazapenta-2,4-dienylidene]-ammonium chloride	$CHCl_3$	247(4.39),316(4.45)	114-0081-73A

Compound	Solvent	$\lambda_{max}(\log \epsilon)$	Ref.
$C_{15}H_{28}N_2O$			
2-Cyclopropen-1-one, 2,3-bis[bis(1-methylethyl)amino]-	MeCN	230(4.16),260s(3.36)	35-3043-73
2H-Pyran-4,6-diamine, N,N,N',N'-tetraethyl-2,2-dimethyl-	EtOH	245(3.83),302(4.20)	70-1033-73
$C_{15}H_{28}N_2S$			
2-Cyclopropene-1-thione, 2,3-bis[bis(1-methylethyl)amino]-	MeCN	234(4.14),271(4.25)	35-3043-73
$C_{15}H_{28}O$			
6-Dodecanone, 7-propylidene-	pentane	231(3.90)	33-2975-73
$C_{15}H_{28}O_2Si_2$			
Silane, [(5-ethynyl-4-methyl-4-cyclohexene-1,3-diyl)bis(oxy)]bis[trimethyl-	EtOH	230(4.05)	88-3649-73
$C_{15}H_{28}Si$			
Silane, [1-(1-butynyl)-2-ethyl-1-hexenyl]trimethyl-	n.s.g.	235(3.96)	39-0599-73B
$C_{15}H_{29}NSi_2$			
Benzenemethanamine, N,N-dimethyl-2,6-bis(trimethylsilyl)-	isooctane	256(2.90),265(2.85), 273(2.78)	101-0001-73H
$C_{15}H_{30}N_2$			
1H-Imidazole, 2-dodecyl-4,5-dihydro-	EtOH	220(3.61)	93-2424-73
$C_{15}H_{30}NiO_6P_2$			
Nickel, (η^5-2,4-cyclopentadien-1-yl)-(diethyl phosphito-P)(ethyl phosphite-P)-	MeOH	249(4.27),295(3.87), 374(3.04),507(1.75)	33-1620-73
$C_{15}H_{30}Si_3$			
Silane, (1-methyl-1,2,3,4-pentatetraen-1-yl-5-ylidene)tris[trimethyl-	n.s.g.	249(4.18)	39-0599-73B
Silane, [1-(1-propynyl)-1,2-propadien-1-yl-3-ylidene]tris[trimethyl-	n.s.g.	232(4.07),240(4.12), 252(4.14)	39-0599-73B

Compound	Solvent	λ_{max}(log ε)	Ref.
$C_{16}H_7D_5N_2O$			
Benzamide-2,3,4,5,6-d$_5$, N-1-isoquinolinyl-	EtOH	282(4.04),321(3.70), 357(3.94),375(3.90)	1-3647-73
Isoquinolinium, 2-(benzoyl-d$_5$-amino)-, hydroxide, inner salt	EtOH	274s(3.97),332(4.03)	1-3647-73
$C_{16}H_8Cl_4O_2S_2$			
Spiro[1,3-benzodioxole-2,2'-[1,3]dithiole], 4,5,6,7-tetrachloro-4'-(4-methylphenyl)-	benzene	292(3.63)	97-0465-73
Spiro[1,3-benzodioxole-2,2'-[1,3]dithiole], 4,5,6,7-tetrachloro-4'-methyl-5'-phenyl-	benzene	288(3.86)	97-0465-73
$C_{16}H_8O_2$			
Benzo[b]biphenylene-6,9-dione	EtOH-5% $CHCl_3$	223(4.46),242s(4.50), 248(4.53),305s(4.45), 314(4.47),362(2.80), 377(2.96)	39-2267-73C
$C_{16}H_8O_2S_2$			
Benzo[b]thiophen-3(2H)-one, 2-(3-oxobenzo[b]thien-2(3H)-ylidene)-, cis	benzene	484(4.14)	46-0831-73
trans	benzene	543(4.23)	46-0831-73
$C_{16}H_8O_2Se_2$			
Benzo[b]selenophen-3(2H)-one, 2-(3-oxobenzo[b]selenophen-2(3H)-ylidene)-, cis	benzene	485(4.02)	46-0831-73
trans	benzene	562(4.15)	46-0831-73
$C_{16}H_8O_3$			
Benz[d]indeno[1,2-b]pyran-5,11-dione	MeOH	222(4.56),245(4.42), 345(4.0)	2-0413-73
$C_{16}H_9BrClNO_2$			
1H-Pyrrole-2,5-dione, 3-(4-bromophenyl)-1-(4-chlorophenyl)-	n.s.g.	231(4.49),289(4.08)	48-0717-73
$C_{16}H_9ClN_2O_4$			
1H-Pyrrole-2,5-dione, 1-(4-chlorophenyl)-3-(4-nitrophenyl)-	n.s.g.	218(4.26),279(4.22)	48-0717-73
$C_{16}H_9Cl_2NO_2$			
1H-Pyrrole-2,5-dione, 1,3-bis(4-chlorophenyl)-	n.s.g.	231(4.51),286(4.11)	48-0717-73
$C_{16}H_9Cl_3O_2S$			
Ethanone, 2-chloro-1-(2,8-dichloro-11-hydroxydibenzo[b,f]thiepin-10-yl)-	MeOH	220(4.40),247(4.21), 273(4.01),323(4.05)	73-0115-73
$C_{16}H_9N_3$			
Propanedinitrile, 9(10H)-acridinylidene-	EtOH	240(4.3),294(4.0), 480(4.1)	18-0283-73
$C_{16}H_9N_3O_2$			
Pyrrolo[2,1-a]isoquinoline-3-carboxylic acid, 1,2-dicyano-, methyl ester	MeCN	323(3.95),339(3.97), 356(4.01)	94-1118-73

Compound	Solvent	$\lambda_{max}(\log \epsilon)$	Ref.
$C_{16}H_9N_3O_3S$			
Thiopyrano[3,4-b]indole-3-acetic acid, α,4-dicyano-1,9-dihydro-1-oxo-, methyl ester	EtOH	250(4.71),320(4.44), 382(4.32),447(4.21)	95-1523-73
$C_{16}H_9N_5O_4$			
3H-Imidazo[4,5-f]quinoline, 3-(2,4-dinitrophenyl)-	EtOH	250(4.79),300(4.02), 328(3.93)	78-0221-73
$C_{16}H_{10}$			
Dicyclopenta[ef,kl]heptalene	C_6H_{12}	252(4.73),267(5.03), 285(4.49),299(4.32), 308(4.27),334(4.07), 343(4.13),356(3.62), 409(2.92),442(3.17), 452(3.28),459(3.17), 470(3.49),483(4.11), 550(1.64),600(1.64), 645(1.60),663(1.60), 720(1.31),738(1.26), 770(0.96)	44-1445-73
$C_{16}H_{10}BrClN_2OS$			
4-Imidazolidinone, 3-(4-bromophenyl)-5-[(2-chlorophenyl)methylene]-2-thioxo-	EtOH	250s(4.10),363(4.51)	56-0181-73
	EtOH-NaOH	260(4.18),403(4.42)	56-0181-73
4-Imidazolidinone, 3-(4-bromophenyl)-5-[(3-chlorophenyl)methylene]-2-thioxo-	EtOH	252(4.15),373(4.54)	56-0181-73
	EtOH-NaOH	262(4.22),405(4.47)	56-0181-73
4-Imidazolidinone, 3-(4-bromophenyl)-5-[(4-chlorophenyl)methylene]-2-thioxo-	EtOH	228(4.23),248(4.18),	56-0181-73
	Et	378(4.61)	
	EtOH-NaOH	260(4.23),407(4.51)	56-0181-73
$C_{16}H_{10}F_2$			
Tricyclo[9.3.1.1^{4,8}]hexadeca-1(15),2,4,6,8(16),9,11,13-octaene, 15,16-difluoro-, (Z,Z)-	C_6H_{12}	278(3.52),337(2.92)	44-3928-73
$C_{16}H_{10}F_3NO_4$			
Furo[3,4-b]pyridine-3-carboxylic acid, 5,7-dihydro-2-methyl-5-oxo-4-[2-(trifluoromethyl)phenyl]-	EtOH	275(3.77)	87-0034-73
$C_{16}H_{10}F_6$			
Benzene, 1,1'-(1,2-ethenediyl)bis[4-(trifluoromethyl)-, cis	EtOH	225(4.32),280(4.11)	36-0910-73
trans	EtOH	226(4.15),298(4.49), 308(4.51),320(4.30)	36-0910-73
$C_{16}H_{10}N_2O$			
7H-Benzo[e]perimidin-7-one, 4-methyl-	EtOH	286(3.59),310(3.74), 350(3.96),368(4.15), 375(4.00),389(4.13)	104-1523-73
8H-Pyrazolo[5,1-a]isoindol-8-one, 2-phenyl-	EtOH	248(4.56),335(3.17)	28-1033-73A
$C_{16}H_{10}N_2OS$			
2H-Pyrimido[2,1-b]benzothiazol-2-one, 4-phenyl-	EtOH	233(4.98),250(4.09), 306(4.18)	94-2019-73

Compound	Solvent	λ_{max}(log ϵ)	Ref.
$C_{16}H_{10}N_2O_2$			
2-Indolinone, 3-(3-oxo-1-isoindolinylidene)-, (phthalaurin)	DMSO	377(4.20),455s(3.85)	24-3240-73
3-Indolinone, 2-(3-oxo-1-isoindolinylidene)-	DMSO	516(4.16)	24-3240-73
$C_{16}H_{10}N_2O_4$			
Benzo[lmn][3,8]phenanthroline-1,3,6,8-(2H,7H)-tetrone, 2,7-dimethyl-	HOAc	304s(3.75),322s(3.80), 341(4.06),359(4.30), 378(4.38)	5-0339-73
$C_{16}H_{10}N_4O_2$			
Methanone, 1,2,5,6-tetrazine-3,6-diylbis[phenyl-	n.s.g.	269(4.24),534(2.66)	5-0879-73
$C_{16}H_{10}N_6$			
2H-Triazolo[4,5-f]quinoline, 2-(5-indazolyl)-	EtOH	225(4.45),275(4.55), 340(4.37)	78-0221-73
$C_{16}H_{10}O_2$			
1,2-Naphthalenedione, 3-phenyl-	EtOH	265(4.46),340(3.37), 446(3.49)	48-0887-73
1,4-Naphthalenedione, 2-phenyl-	EtOH	250(4.36),301(3.85), 338s(--)	48-0887-73
$C_{16}H_{10}O_2S_2$			
18,20-Dioxa-2,19-dithiatetracyclo-[13.2.1.1^{3,6}.1^{9,12}]eicosa-3,5,7,9,11,13,15,17-octaene	n.s.g.	266(4.40),287(4.41), 418(3.43)	39-1786-73C
$C_{16}H_{10}O_3S$			
18,19,20-Trioxa-2-thiatetracyclo-[13.2.1.1^{3,6}.1^{9,12}]eicosa-3,5,7,9,11,13,15,17-octaene	n.s.g.	253(4.29),296s(4.48), 305(4.55),417(3.78)	39-1786-73C
$C_{16}H_{10}O_4$			
Benzoic acid, 2-(1-oxo-1H-2-benzopyran-3-yl)-	MeOH	230(4.24),292(4.0),	2-0413-73
Spiro[3H-2-benzopyran-3,1'(3'H)-isobenzofuran]-1,3'(4H)-dione	MeOH	220(4.26),275(3.52)	2-0413-73
$C_{16}H_{10}O_5$			
6H-Benzofuro[3,2-c][1]benzopyran-6-one, 8,9-dihydroxy-2-methyl-	n.s.g.	245(4.0),278(3.8), 344(4.0)	2-0115-73
6H-Benzofuro[3,2-c][1]benzopyran-6-one, 8,9-dihydroxy-3-methyl-	n.s.g.	245(4.2),285(4.2), 348(3.8)	2-0115-73
6H-Benzofuro[3,2-c][1]benzopyran-6-one, 8,9-dihydroxy-4-methyl-	n.s.g.	244(4.2),285(3.8), 347(4.3)	2-0115-73
$C_{16}H_{10}O_6$			
Furo[3,4-f]-1,3-benzodioxol-5(7H)-one, 7-(1,3-benzodioxol-5-yl)-	EtOH	223(4.46),245(3.90), 261(3.80),293(3.93), 308(3.76)	39-1266-73C
$C_{16}H_{10}S_2$			
8H-Acenaphtho[1,2-b]thiopyran-8-thione, 9-methyl-	C_6H_{12}	231(4.81),353(4.42), 370(4.51),416(4.29), 436(4.30)	22-3334-73
	MeOH	228(4.64),346(4.15), 362(4.04),409(3.76), 426(3.81)	22-3334-73

Compound	Solvent	λ_{max}(log ε)	Ref.
8H-Acenaphtho[1,2-b]thiopyran-8-thione, 9-methyl- (cont.)	MeCN	229(4.78),372(4.37), 408(4.22),428(4.29)	22-3334-73
8H-Acenaphtho[1,2-b]thiopyran-8-thione, 10-methyl-	C_6H_{12}	231(4.33),352(3.91), 367(4.00),408(3.93), 428(3.90)	22-3334-73
	MeOH	229(4.65),346(4.04), 418(3.97)	22-3334-73
	MeCN	232(4.53),370(4.18), 401(4.12),420(4.14)	22-3334-73
$C_{16}H_{11}Br$			
1,4-Ethenoanthracene, 2-bromo-1,4-dihydro-	hexane	236(4.69),255s(3.98), 265(3.99),274(3.92), 284(3.63),298(2.85), 311(2.63),321(2.28), 325(2.49)	23-3486-73
$C_{16}H_{11}BrO_3$			
3(2H)-Benzofuranone, 7-bromo-4-methoxy-2-(phenylmethylene)-	$CHCl_3$	267s(3.88),275s(3.94), 306(4.18),394(4.35)	78-1037-73
4H-1-Benzopyran-4-one, 8-bromo-5-methoxy-2-phenyl-	$CHCl_3$	267(4.35),295s(4.08), 327(4.04)	78-1037-73
$C_{16}H_{11}ClN_2OS$			
Methanone, (4-amino-2-phenyl-5-thiazolyl)(4-chlorophenyl)-	DMF	394(3.99)	48-0497-73
$C_{16}H_{11}ClN_2O_2$			
2H-Benzimidazol-2-one, 1-[3-(4-chlorophenyl)-1-oxo-2-propenyl]-1,3-dihydro-	HOAc	308(4.39)	48-1152-73
2-Naphthalenol, 1-[(4-chloro-2-hydroxyphenyl)azo]-	toluene	484(4.12)	33-2450-73
2-Naphthalenol, 1-[(5-chloro-2-hydroxyphenyl)azo]-	toluene	486(4.24)	33-2450-73
$C_{16}H_{11}ClN_2O_3$			
Ethanone, 1-(5-chloro-3-nitro-3-phenyl-3H-indol-2-yl)-	isoPrOH	241(4.13),317(3.88)	44-3077-73
$C_{16}H_{11}ClN_2O_4$			
2H-1,4-Oxazin-3(4H)-one, 2-chloro-6-(4-nitrophenyl)-4-phenyl-	EtOH	243(4.13),358(4.22)	4-0347-73
$C_{16}H_{11}ClN_4$			
Pyridazino[3,4-a]quinolizinium, 3-(2-pyridinyl)-, chloride	EtOH	263(4.35),282(4.45), 293(4.42),327(3.96), 340(4.01),361(4.01)	12-0389-73
4H-[1,2,4]Triazolo[4,3-a][1,4]benzodiazepine, 8-chloro-6-phenyl-	2M HCl	269(4.02)	94-2375-73
	MeOH	223(4.67),247s(4.23)	94-2375-73
$C_{16}H_{11}ClN_4O$			
4H-[1,2,4]Triazolo[4,3-a][1,4]benzodiazepine, 8-chloro-6-phenyl-, 5-oxide	2M HCl	233(4.39),307(4.02)	94-2375-73
	MeOH	230(4.47),256(4.25), 310(4.06)	94-2375-73
$C_{16}H_{11}ClN_4O_2$			
Benzoic acid, 2-[[2-(4-chlorophenyl)ethenyl]-1H-tetrazol-1-yl]-	n.s.g.	292(4.30)	48-1152-73

Compound	Solvent	λ_{max}(log ε)	Ref.
$C_{16}H_{11}ClO_2S$			
2H-1-Benzothiopyran, 2-[(4-chlorophenyl)methylene]-, 1,1-dioxide	MeOH	242(4.25),270(3.95), 293(4.05),349(4.33)	39-0163-73C
$C_{16}H_{11}Cl_2NO$			
Ethanone, 1-(3,5-dichloro-3-phenyl-3H-indol-2-yl)-	CH_2Cl_2	251(4.19),322(3.85)	44-3077-73
1H-Indole, 1-acetyl-2,5-dichloro-3-phenyl-	isoPrOH	243(4.36),280(4.06), 299(3.94),309(3.91)	44-3077-73
$C_{16}H_{11}FO$			
Furan, 3-fluoro-2,4-diphenyl-	EtOH	243(4.30),272(4.38)	22-0202-73
$C_{16}H_{11}NOS$			
1,2-Naphthalenedione, 1-(S-phenylthiooxime)	EtOH	227(4.43),271(4.00), 445(4.18)	39-1031-73C
1,2-Naphthalenedione, 2-(S-phenylthiooxime)	CH_2Cl_2	270(4.32),468(4.18)	39-1031-73C
1,4-Naphthalenedione, 1-(S-phenylthiooxime)	EtOH	275(4.23),337(3.61), 453(4.20)	39-1031-73C
Thiocyanic acid, 3-[1,1'-biphenyl]-4-yl-3-oxo-1-propenyl ester	dioxan	232(3.82),324(4.36)	24-0435-73
$C_{16}H_{11}NO_2$			
Acenaphtho[1,2-c]pyrrole-2-carboxylic acid, N-methyl-	n.s.g.	224(4.56),283(3.73), 310(3.72),322(3.75), 337(3.74)	48-1105-73
2H-1-Benzopyran-2-one, 4-[(phenylimino)-methyl]-	EtOH	240(4.18),302(4.06)	44-3874-73
$C_{16}H_{11}NO_3$			
Formamide, N-(9,10-dihydro-2-methyl-9,10-dioxo-1-anthracenyl)-	EtOH	260(4.68),335(3.63)	104-1523-73
Isoxazolium, 2,5-dihydro-3-hydroxy-5-oxo-4-phenyl-2-(phenylmethylene)-, hydroxide, inner salt, (Z)-	dioxan	480(3.60)	44-1782-73
1,3-Propanedione, 1-(2-benzofuranyl)-3-(4-pyridinyl)-	MeOH	290(3.94),385(4.17)	56-1053-73
4H-Quinolizine-1-carboxylic acid, 4-oxo-2-phenyl-	EtOH	225(4.49),400(4.23)	4-0139-73
$C_{16}H_{11}NO_4$			
Isoxazolium, 2,5-dihydro-3-hydroxy-2-[(2-hydroxyphenyl)methylene]-5-oxo-4-phenyl-, hydroxide, inner salt	dioxan	475(3.00)	44-1782-73
$C_{16}H_{11}NO_4S$			
1H-2-Benzothiopyran, 1-[(4-nitrophenyl)-methylene]-, 2,2-dioxide	MeOH	247(4.12),285(3.89), 333(3.99)	39-0163-73C
2H-1-Benzothiopyran, 2-[(4-nitrophenyl)-methylene]-, 1,1-dioxide	MeOH	244(4.17),298(4.19), 360(4.25)	39-0163-73C
$C_{16}H_{11}NO_5$			
4-Benzofurancarboxylic acid, 2-(4-nitrophenyl)-, methyl ester	90% EtOH	233(4.19),250s(4.03), 276s(3.77),287(3.81), 358(4.43)	12-1059-73
$C_{16}H_{11}NO_6$			
4H-1-Benzopyran-4-one, 7-hydroxy-3-(2-methoxy-5-nitrophenyl)-	EtOH	242(4.52),250(4.51), 305(4.42)	95-1514-73

Compound	Solvent	$\lambda_{max}(\log \epsilon)$	Ref.
$C_{16}H_{11}N_3$			
2H-Naphtho[1,2-d]triazole, 2-phenyl-	MeOH	225(4.86),278(4.51), 334(4.34)	73-0224-73
	$CHCl_3$	336(4.27)	73-0224-73
Quinoxaline, 2-(1H-indol-3-yl)-	EtOH	204(4.45),223(--), 346(--)	34-0102-73
$C_{16}H_{11}N_3O$			
1H-Imidazo[4,5-f]quinoline, 2-[2-(2-furanyl)ethenyl]-	MeOH	251(4.28),311(4.38), 357(4.72)	103-0406-73
1-Naphthalenol, 4-(2H-benzotriazol-2-yl)-	0.05M HCl	323(4.19)	73-0224-73
	0.05M NaOH	374(4.15)	73-0224-73
	MeOH	233(4.50),332(4.17)	73-0224-73
	dioxan	323(4.26)	73-0224-73
	$CHCl_3$	323(4.18)	73-0224-73
2-Naphthalenol, 1-(2H-benzotriazol-2-yl)-	heptane	319(4.11)	73-0224-73
	0.05M HCl	287(3.91),331(3.81)	73-0224-73
	0.05M NaOH	278(4.44),355(4.25)	73-0224-73
	MeOH	224(4.86),276(4.17), 284(4.16),318s(3.74), 331(3.78)	73-0224-73
	EtOH	318s(3.74)	73-0224-73
	dioxan	317(3.87),330(3.85)	73-0224-73
	50% dioxan	319s(3.72)	73-0224-73
	$CHCl_3$	320(4.15),356(4.11)	73-0224-73
Phenol, 2-(2H-naphtho[1,2-d]triazol-2-yl)-	0.05M HCl	277(4.20),350(4.22)	73-0224-73
	0.05M NaOH	350(3.87)	73-0224-73
	MeOH	226(4.59),276(4.36), 347(4.30)	73-0224-73
	dioxan	349(4.36)	73-0224-73
	$CHCl_3$	350(4.38)	73-0224-73
Phenol, 3-(2H-naphtho[1,2-d]triazol-2-yl)-	MeOH	224(4.59),276(4.44), 336(4.31)	73-0224-73
Phenol, 4-(2H-naphtho[1,2-d]triazol-2-yl)-	0.05M HCl	346(4.32)	73-0224-73
	0.05M NaOH	372(4.39)	73-0224-73
	MeOH	228(4.53),284(4.36), 342(4.37)	73-0224-73
	dioxan	346(4.38)	73-0224-73
	$CHCl_3$	344(4.33)	73-0224-73
4H-Pyridazino[4,5-b]indol-4-one, 3,5-dihydro-1-phenyl-	n.s.g.	230(4.58),253(4.45), 314(3.93)	103-1497-73
Pyrimido[1,2-a]benzimidazol-2(1H)-one, 4-phenyl-	MeOH	212(4.76),239(4.76), 297(4.30)	39-1588-73C
	EtOH	242(4.46),305(4.03)	94-2019-73
Pyrimido[1,2-a]benzimidazol-4(1H)-one, 2-phenyl-	EtOH	254(4.47),288(4.22), 345(3.97)	94-2019-73
$C_{16}H_{11}N_3OS$			
4H-Quinolizine-1-carbonitrile, 2-(methylthio)-4-oxo-3-(2-pyridinyl)-	EtOH	276(4.33),303(4.14), 396(4.28)	94-0921-73
5H-1,3,4-Thiadiazolo[2,3-b]quinazolin-5-one, 2-(4-methylphenyl)-	n.s.g.	238(4.94),253(5.07), 278(4.81),288(4.80), 290s(4.91),330(5.37), 345(5.25)	48-0185-73
$C_{16}H_{11}N_3O_2$			
Benzo[a]phenazine, 5,6-dihydro-2-nitro-	EtOH	209(--),253(4.44), 260(--),304(--), 363(--)	34-0102-73

Compound	Solvent	λ max (log ε)	Ref.
1,3(2H,4H)-Isoquinolinedione, 4-(1,3-dihydro-2H-benzimidazol-2-ylidene)-	EtOH	234(3.42),245(3.30), 293(3.17)	95-0322-73
$C_{16}H_{11}N_3O_2S$			
5H-1,3,4-Thiadiazolo[2,3-b]quinazolin-5-one, 2-(2-methoxyphenyl)-	n.s.g.	237(4.36),275(4.46), 303(4.24),323(4.01), 337(4.36),353(4.15), 365(4.03)	48-0185-73
$C_{16}H_{11}N_3O_3$			
Isoquinolinium, 2-[(2-nitrobenzoyl)-amino]-, hydroxide, inner salt	isoPrOH	276(3.92),323(3.99)	1-3647-73
Isoquinolinium, 2-[(3-nitrobenzoyl)-amino]-, hydroxide, inner salt	isoPrOH	268s(4.21),331(4.02)	1-3647-73
Isoquinolinium, 2-[(4-nitrobenzoyl)-amino]-, hydroxide, inner salt	isoPrOH	278(4.16),331(4.08)	1-3647-73
5H-1,3,4-Oxadiazolo[2,3-b]quinazolin-5-one, 2-(4-methoxyphenyl)-	n.s.g.	225(4.92),253(5.18), 291(4.81),322s(5.68)	48-0185-73
$C_{16}H_{11}N_3O_3S$			
Methanone, [4-amino-2-(4-nitrophenyl)-5-thiazolyl]phenyl-	DMF	426(4.06)	48-0497-73
Methanone, (4-amino-2-phenyl-5-thiazolyl)(4-nitrophenyl)-	DMF	407(4.12)	48-0497-73
4,5,6(1H)-Pyrimidinetrione, dihydro-1,3-diphenyl-2-thioxo-, 5-oxime	anion	343(4.28),570(2.76)	140-0395-73
$C_{16}H_{11}N_3O_4$			
2H-Benzimidazol-2-one, 1,3-dihydro-1-[3-(4-nitrophenyl)-1-oxo-2-propenyl]-	HOAc	316(4.41)	48-1152-73
2-Naphthalenol, 1-[(2-hydroxy-4-nitrophenyl)azo]-	toluene	512(4.35)	33-2450-73
2-Naphthalenol, 1-[(2-hydroxy-5-nitrophenyl)azo]-	toluene	485(4.26)	33-2450-73
2,4,5,6(1H,3H)-Pyrimidinetetrone, 1,3-diphenyl-, 5-oxime (anion)	pH 7	315(4.23),560(1.76)	140-0395-73
$C_{16}H_{11}N_3S$			
Sulfilimine, N-(2,2-dicyanoethenyl)-S,S-diphenyl-	EtOH	230s(4.10),295(4.35)	44-4324-73
$C_{16}H_{11}N_4$			
Pyridazino[3,4-a]quinolizinium, 3-(2-pyridinyl)-, chloride	EtOH	263(4.35),282(4.45), 293(4.42),327(3.96), 340(4.01),361(4.01)	12-0389-73
$C_{16}H_{11}N_5O_4$			
Benzoic acid, 2-[5-[2-(4-nitrophenyl)-ethenyl]-1H-tetrazol-1-yl]-	n.s.g.	318(4.37)	48-1152-73
$C_{16}H_{11}N_7$			
2H-1,2,3-Triazolo[4,5-f]quinoline, 2-(1-methyl-1H-benzotriazol-5-yl)-	EtOH	225(4.46),270(4.55), 294(4.51),335(4.37)	78-0221-73
$C_{16}H_{12}$			
Azulene, 1-phenyl-	heptane	233(4.54),296(4.56), 355(3.88),373(3.87), 615(1.51),670(1.45)	104-2389-73
Cyclobut[a]acenaphthylene, 6b,7,8,8a-tetrahydro-7,8-bis(methylene)-	n.s.g.	227(4.88),253(3.83), 271s(3.39),280(3.78),	35-1874-73

Compound	Solvent	λ max(log ε)	Ref.
Cyclobut[a]acenaphthylene, 6b,7,8,8a-tetrahydro-7,8-bis(methylene)- (cont.)	n.s.g.	290(3.83),302(3.66), 306(3.48),317(2.83), 322(2.80)	35-1874-73
Cyclobuta[5,6]cyclohepta[1,2,3-de]naphthalene, 8,9-dihydro-	n.s.g.	232(4.46),242(4.45), 249(4.42),279(3.58), 284(3.70),297(3.71), 312(3.57),334(3.81), 343(3.95),356(3.88), 367(3.75),379(3.78), 387(3.34),430(2.60), 457(3.69),489(2.68), 524(2.54),570(2.20)	35-1874-73
Cyclobuta[1,2-a:3,4-a']dipentalene, 3b,3c,7b,7c-tetrahydro-	hexane	254(4.21),259(4.22), 275(4.07),400(3.17)	89-0337-73
Cyclobuta[1,2-a:4,3-a']dipentalene, 3b,3c,7a,7b-tetrahydro-	hexane	254(4.16),387(3.02)	89-0337-73
9,10-Ethenoanthracene, 9,10-dihydro-	C_6H_{12}	253(3.00),266(3.00), 273(3.33),280(3.49)	78-1379-73
Naphthalene, 2,3-di-1,2-propadienyl-	MeOH	257(4.78)	88-3181-73
Naphthalene, 1-phenyl-	heptane	231(4.75),292(4.00)	104-2389-73
Naphthalene, 2-phenyl-	EtOH	252(4.68),287(4.05)	48-0887-73
$C_{16}H_{12}BrNO_3$			
1H-Indole-3-acetic acid, 5-bromo-2,3-dihydro-2-oxo-3-phenyl-	EtOH	258(4.02),295(3.08)	104-0861-73
$C_{16}H_{12}Br_2N_2O_2$			
Diazene, bis[2-(3-bromophenyl)ethenyl]-, 1,2-dioxide	benzene	326(4.4)	48-0796-73
$C_{16}H_{12}ClNO$			
Ethanone, 1-(5-chloro-3-phenyl-1H-indol-2-yl)-	isoPrOH	232s(4.32),244(4.34), 313(4.28),345s(3.82)	44-3077-73
$C_{16}H_{12}ClNO_2$			
Oxireno[c]quinolin-2(1aH)-one, 6-chloro-3,7b-dihydro-3-methyl-7b-phenyl-	isoPrOH	267(4.09),300s(3.46)	44-0449-73
2(1H)-Quinolinone, 6-chloro-3-hydroxy-1-methyl-4-phenyl-	EtOH	233(4.67),292(3.93), 315(3.87),327(3.99), 339(3.91)	94-0807-73
	isoPrOH	232(4.69),290(3.92), 315s(3.85),322(3.99), 339(3.88)	44-0449-73
$C_{16}H_{12}ClNO_3$			
1H-Indole-3-acetic acid, 5-chloro-2,3-dihydro-2-oxo-3-phenyl-	EtOH	258(4.28),294(3.23)	104-0861-73
$C_{16}H_{12}ClN_3$			
Imidazo[1,2-a]quinazoline, 7-chloro-1,2-dihydro-5-phenyl-	n.s.g.	249(4.46),266(4.37)	40-1944-73
$C_{16}H_{12}Cl_2$			
Benzene, 1,3-dichloro-2-(4-phenyl-1,3-butadienyl)-, (E,E)-	EtOH	317(4.56)	35-2058-73
$C_{16}H_{12}Cl_2N_2O_2$			
Diazene, bis[2-(3-chlorophenyl)ethenyl]-, 1,2-dioxide	benzene	328(4.3)	48-0796-73

Compound	Solvent	$\lambda_{max}(\log \epsilon)$	Ref.
$C_{16}H_{12}Cl_2N_2S$			
1H-Imidazole, 4,5-bis(4-chlorophenyl)-2-(methylthio)-	EtOH	230(4.32),273(4.21)	24-1628-73
$C_{16}H_{12}F_2O_2$			
3-Butenoic acid, 4,4-bis(4-fluorophenyl)-	EtOH	228(4.42),251(4.75), 281(4.15)	73-3879-73
$C_{16}H_{12}F_3HgO_2$			
Ethylium, 1,1-diphenyl-2-[(trifluoroacetato-O)mercurio]-	n.s.g.	374(3.87)	30-0932-73
$C_{16}H_{12}F_6$			
Benzene, 1,1'-(1,2-ethanediyl)bis[4-(trifluoromethyl)-	EtOH	253(2.74),258(2.85), 264(2.77),269(2.59)	36-0910-73
$C_{16}H_{12}N_2$			
2,3'-Bi-1H-indole	EtOH	207(4.11),229(4.16), 290(3.81)	34-0109-73
6H-Pyrido[4,3-b]carbazole, 5-methyl-	EtOH	225(4.43),274(4.72), 284(4.82),293(4.89)	78-3357-73
$C_{16}H_{12}N_2O$			
Imidazole, 2-benzoyl-1-phenyl-	EtOH	259(4.06),295(4.04)	12-0415-73
1-Naphthalenol, 4-(phenylazo)-	C_6H_{12}	204(4.42),238(4.08), 271(3.94),410(4.01), 445s(3.86)	131-0255-73
	EtOH	203(4.47),239(4.33), 274(4.18),410(4.24), 468s(4.11)	131-0255-73
2-Naphthalenol, 1-(phenylazo)-	C_6H_{12}	207(4.46),231(4.17), 266s(4.00),281s(3.82), 305(3.85),430s(4.08), 467(4.10)	131-0255-73
	EtOH	204(4.42),230(4.39), 257(4.00),317(3.69), 423s(3.86),485(4.02)	131-0255-73
1H-Perimidine, 2-(2-furanyl)-1-methyl-	MeOH	268(4.14),340(4.09), 346(4.13)	103-0922-73
Phenol, 2-(1-naphthalenylazo)-	EtOH	216(4.53),260(4.25), 298(3.93),396(3.93)	131-0255-73
Phenol, 4-(1-naphthalenylazo)-	C_6H_{12}	208(4.63),219(4.48), 249s(4.12),264(3.99), 274(3.93),378(4.24), 455s(3.15)	131-0255-73
	EtOH	206(4.69),226(4.38), 246s(4.19),277s(3.93), 378(4.32),445s(3.40)	131-0255-73
8H-Pyrazolo[5,1-a]isoindol-8-one, 3,3a-dihydro-2-phenyl-	EtOH	312(4.13)	28-1033-73A
Quinolinium, 1-(benzoylamino)-, hydroxide, inner salt	EtOH	234(4.51),320(3.90)	78-2359-73
$C_{16}H_{12}N_2OS$			
4-Imidazolidinone, 3-phenyl-5-(phenylmethylene)-2-thioxo-	EtOH	237(4.07),246(4.09), 373(4.53)	63-1307-73
Thiazole, 4-amino-5-benzoyl-2-phenyl-	DMF	393(4.14)	48-0497-73
$C_{16}H_{12}N_2O_2$			
9,10-Anthracenedione, 1,4-bis(methylamino)-	n.s.g.	630(4.28)	40-1738-73

Compound	Solvent	$\lambda_{max}(\log \epsilon)$	Ref.
Benzenepropanamide, N-(3-cyanophenyl)-β-oxo-	pH 13	330(4.41)	39-0808-73B
2H-Benzimidazol-2-one, 1,3-dihydro-1-(1-oxo-3-phenyl-2-propenyl)-	HOAc	302(4.39)	48-1152-73
2H-1-Benzopyran-4-carboxaldehyde, 2-oxo-, 4-(phenylhydrazone)	EtOH	260(4.11),410(4.35)	44-3874-73
2(3H)-Furanone, 5-phenyl-3-phenylhydrazono-	CH_2Cl_2	228(3.94),252(4.14), 294(3.66),431(4.51)	39-2532-73C
1H-Indole, 2-[2-(4-nitrophenyl)ethenyl]-, (E)-	MeOH	306(4.07),410(4.51)	23-0792-73
1-Naphthalenol, 4-[(2-hydroxyphenyl)-azo]-	C_6H_{12}	206(4.40),223(4.37), 257(3.98),268(3.93), 301(4.15),349(4.05), 465(4.17)	131-0255-73
	EtOH	202(4.59),240(4.27), 301(4.16),391(3.94), 519(4.25)	131-0255-73
1-Naphthalenol, 4-[(3-hydroxyphenyl)-azo]-	C_6H_{12}	213(4.45),232(4.40), 267(4.19),279(4.17), 391(4.20),406(4.18), 450s(3.92)	131-0255-73
	EtOH	204(4.53),236(4.28), 275(4.00),413(4.11), 467(3.96)	131-0255-73
1-Naphthalenol, 4-[(4-hydroxyphenyl)-azo]-	C_6H_{12}	209(4.47),240(4.29), 274(4.07),388(4.17), 405(4.16),479(3.44)	131-0255-73
	EtOH	203(4.48),242(4.17), 278s(3.97),397(4.12), 411(4.13)	131-0255-73
2-Naphthalenol, 1-[(2-hydroxyphenyl)-azo]-	C_6H_{12}	210(4.60),233(4.48), 264(3.94),275(3.80), 287(3.83),310(3.80), 366(3.81),405s(4.03), 465(4.21),481(4.21)	131-0255-73
	EtOH	209(4.69),231(4.62), 262(4.19),315(3.96), 428(4.00),508(4.42)	131-0255-73
2-Naphthalenol, 1-[(3-hydroxyphenyl)-azo]-	C_6H_{12}	211(4.40),230(4.46), 264(3.94),308(3.75), 413s(3.97),476(4.04)	131-0255-73
	EtOH	211(4.40),228(4.43), 265(3.98),316(3.72), 417s(3.88),488(4.03)	131-0255-73
2-Naphthalenol, 1-[(4-hydroxyphenyl)-azo]-	C_6H_{12}	209(4.40),230(4.41), 256(4.05),264(3.99), 286(3.74),373(3.79), 419(4.06),460(4.02)	131-0255-73
	EtOH	211(4.38),229(4.38), 265s(3.98),366s(3.79), 417(4.06),461(4.04)	131-0255-73
5-Oxazolidinecarbonitrile, 2-oxo-4,5-diphenyl-	EtOH	247(2.6),253(2.69), 259(2.75),264(3.79), 269(2.61)	48-0044-73
3-Pyrazolecarboxylic acid, 1,5-diphenyl-	CH_2Cl_2	253(4.05)	39-2532-73
s-Tetrazine, 3,6-dibenzoyl-1,2-dihydro-	n.s.g.	272(4.19),300(3.81)	5-0879-73
$C_{16}H_{12}N_2O_2S$			
4-Imidazolidinone, 5-[(4-hydroxyphenyl)-methylene]-3-phenyl-2-thioxo-	EtOH	254(4.01),291(3.82), 392(4.48)	63-1307-73

Compound	Solvent	λ_{max}(log ε)	Ref.
$C_{16}H_{12}N_2O_3$			
Ethanone, 1-(3-nitro-3-phenyl-3H-indol-2-yl)-	isoPrOH	235(4.10),315(3.81)	44-3077-73
$C_{16}H_{12}N_2O_4$			
3(2H)-Benzofuranone, 6-methyl-2-[[(4-nitrophenyl)amino]methylene]-	MeOH	284(3.83),348(4.02), 416(4.59)	103-0141-73
9,10-Ethanoanthracene, 9,10-dihydro-1,5-dinitro-, (-)-	EtOH	217(4.16),262(4.05), 309s(3.62)	18-0915-73
2H-1,4-Oxazin-3(4H)-one, 6-(4-nitrophenyl)-4-phenyl-	EtOH	248(4.18),368(4.19)	4-0347-73
$C_{16}H_{12}N_2O_5$			
2H-1,4-Oxazin-3(4H)-one, 2-hydroxy-6-(4-nitrophenyl)-4-phenyl-	EtOH	248(4.12),365(4.21)	4-0347-73
$C_{16}H_{12}N_2O_5S$			
Benzo[b]thiophen-3(2H)-one, 2-[2-nitro-1-(phenylamino)ethylidene]-, 1,1-dioxide	EtOH	237(3.96),425(4.15)	95-0612-73
$C_{16}H_{12}N_2O_6S$			
2H-1-Benzothiopyran, 4-(2,4-dinitrophenyl)-2-methyl-, 1,1-dioxide	40% MeOH	249(3.94),305s(3.48), 325s(3.15)	39-0163-73C
	MeOH-NaOH	278(3.83),387(3.56)	39-0163-73C
$C_{16}H_{12}N_4$			
2H-1,2,3-Triazolo[4,5-f]quinoline, 2-(4-methylphenyl)-	EtOH	295(4.41),330(4.25)	78-0221-73
$C_{16}H_{12}N_4O_2$			
Benzoic acid, 2-[5-(2-phenylethenyl)-1H-tetrazol-1-yl]-	n.s.g.	220(4.34),292(4.40)	48-1152-73
$C_{16}H_{12}N_6$			
3,5-Pyridinedicarbonitrile, 2-amino-4-(cyanomethyl)-6-(phenylmethyl)-amino]-	EtOH	234(4.49),285(4.34), 342(4.16)	12-2567-73
$C_{16}H_{12}O$			
1-Naphthalenol, 3-phenyl-	EtOH	256(4.66),303(3.87)	48-0887-73
$C_{16}H_{12}O_2$			
[16]Annulene 1,4:7,10-dioxide	C_6H_{12}	280(4.89),287(4.91), 535(2.45)	88-0361-73
9-Anthracenol, acetate	EtOH	216(4.05),219(4.04), 246s(5.00),252(5.28), 315s(3.12),329(3.47), 345(3.76),363(3.94), 383(3.91)	44-1167-73
Benzaldehyde, 3-(3-oxo-3-phenyl-1-propenyl)-	benzene	292(3.83)	23-3756-73
Benzaldehyde, 4-(3-oxo-3-phenyl-1-propenyl)-	benzene	280(3.52)	23-3756-73
2,4,6-Cycloheptatrien-1-one, 2,2'-(1,2-ethenediyl)bis-	EtOH	223(4.42),250s(4.24), 318(3.97),344s(3.92), 413(4.14)	88-0877-73
3,4:5,6-Dibenzocyclohepta-1,3,5-triene-1-carboxylic acid	EtOH	215(4.20),243(4.59), 277(4.04)	35-6277-73

Compound	Solvent	λ_{max}(log ε)	Ref.
2,3-Dioxanaphthacene, 1,4-dihydro-	MeOH	250s(4.91),256(5.21), 327(3.36),344(3.63), 362(3.71),382(3.63)	88-3181-73
7H-8,10b-Methano-1H-benzo[2,3]cyclopropa[1,2-c][1]benzopyran-7-one, 8,10a-dihydro-11-methylene-	n.s.g.	218(4.16),273(3.75), 279s(3.73)	33-2981-73
2-Propyn-1-one, 3-(4-methoxyphenyl)-1-phenyl-	EtOH	245(4.22),263(4.25), 327(4.38)	44-2544-73
Spiro[4H-1-benzopyran-4,1'-[3,5]cyclohexadien]-2'-one, 3-ethenylidene-2,3-dihydro-	n.s.g.	217(4.11),276(3.83), 282(3.84),300s(3.67)	33-2981-73
$C_{16}H_{12}O_2S$			
2H-1-Benzothiopyran, 2-(phenylmethylene)-, 1,1-dioxide	MeOH	240(4.16),291(4.04), 346(4.30)	39-0163-73C
$C_{16}H_{12}O_3$			
Aurone, 4-methoxy-	$CHCl_3$	308(4.22),389(4.34)	78-1037-73
3-Benzofurancarboxylic acid, 2-phenyl-, methyl ester	90% EtOH	224(4.22),303(4.21)	12-1079-73
2-Benzofuranone, 3-(methoxyphenylmethylene)-, cis or trans	90% EtOH	237(4.21),321(3.93), 346s(3.91)	12-1079-73
trans or cis	90% EtOH	222(4.03),252s(4.08), 255(4.10),306s(3.97), 327(4.03)	12-1079-73
3(2H)-Benzofuranone, 6-methoxy-2-(phenylmethylene)-, cis	MeOH	337(4.45)	78-0359-73
trans	MeOH	340(4.51)	78-0359-73
2H-1-Benzopyran-2-one, 5-methoxy-2-phenyl-	$CHCl_3$	263(4.41),290s(4.12), 320(4.07)	78-1037-73
2H-1-Benzopyran-2-one, 6-methoxy-3-phenyl-	MeOH	298(4.16),350(3.97)	24-0388-73
2H-1-Benzopyran-2-one, 6-methoxy-4-phenyl-	EtOH	223(4.43),254(3.90), 282(4.05),346(3.63)	12-0899-73
1,3-Butanedione, 1-naphtho[2,1-b]furan-2-yl-	MeOH	223(4.63),254(4.13), 309(4.21),342(4.23)	56-1053-73
$C_{16}H_{12}O_4$			
1,5-Acenaphthylenedicarboxylic acid, dimethyl ester	MeOH	226(4.46),248(4.43), 319(4.06),334(4.24)	88-1803-73
9,10-Anthracenedione, 1-hydroxy-8-methoxy-2-methyl-	EtOH	256(4.34),275s(4.04), 282s(3.98),402s(3.91), 419(3.97),442s(3.85)	64-0436-73C
Benz[e]inden-2-one, 1,3-dihydro-1,3-bis(hydroxymethylene)-7-methoxy-	MeOH	258(4.60),271(4.51), 297(4.32),330(4.27)	39-1780-73C
Benzoic acid, 2-(3,4-dihydro-1-oxo-1H-2-benzopyran-3-yl)-	MeOH	220(3.26),275(3.52)	2-0413-73
2H-1-Benzopyran-2-one, 6-hydroxy-7-methoxy-4-phenyl- (dalbergin)	MeOH	237(4.23),260(4.05), 301(3.85),355(4.0)	39-1737-73C
Chrysophanol, 1(and 8)-O-methyl-	MeOH	224(4.66),259(4.39), 283s(4.16),415(4.00)	94-1254-73
	MeOH-KOH	250(--),280(--), 319(--),490(--)	94-1254-73
1H-Indene-1,2(3H)-dione, 3-hydroxy-3-(2-methoxyphenyl)-	EtOH	273(3.98)	78-3337-73
$C_{16}H_{12}O_5$			
9,10-Anthracenedione, 1,7-dihydroxy-5-methoxy-7-methyl-	EtOH	254s(4.21),272s(4.32), 280(4.34),412(3.85)	64-0436-73C

Compound	Solvent	λmax(log ε)	Ref.
1,3-Benzodioxole-5-carboxaldehyde, 6-(1,3-benzodioxol-5-ylmethyl)-	EtOH	283(3.95),321(3.76)	39-1266-73C
2H-1-Benzopyran-2-one, 6-hydroxy-4-(3-hydroxyphenyl)-7-methoxy- (stevenin)	MeOH	222s(4.74),284(4.14), 340(4.05)	39-1737-73C
	MeOH-NaOMe	252(4.49),312(3.97), 397(4.08)	39-1737-73C
	MeOH-NaOAc	301(4.09),356(3.98)	39-1737-73C
Isoflavone, 4',7-dihydroxy-6-methoxy-	MeOH	256(4.35),319(3.98)	102-0169-73
(glycitein)	MeOH-NaOMe	259(--),344(--)	102-0169-73
9H-Xanthene-2,9(4aH)-dione, 6-acetoxy-4a-methyl-	MeOH	211(4.46),247s(4.13), 359(3.54)	24-1182-73
$C_{16}H_{12}O_6$			
1,3-Benzodioxole-5-carboxylic acid, 6-(1,3-benzodioxol-5-ylmethyl)-	EtOH	243(3.95),258(3.82), 260(3.95)	39-1266-73C
4H-1-Benzopyran-4-one, 5,7-dihydroxy-2-(4-hydroxyphenyl)-6-methoxy-	MeOH	212(4.42),267(4.48), 330s(--)	39-1737-73C
(tectorigenin)	MeOH-NaOAc	273(4.5),340(4.09)	39-1737-73C
	MeOH-$AlCl_3$	273(4.46),375s(--), 380(4.51)	39-1737-73C
4H-1-Benzopyran-4-one, 5,6,7-trihydroxy-2-(4-methoxyphenyl)-	EtOH	287(4.54),335(4.57)	95-0707-73
Hispidulin	MeOH	275(4.09),337(4.31)	102-2317-73
$C_{16}H_{12}O_7$			
Azareatin	EtOH	254(4.34),372(4.45)	95-1542-73
	EtOH-$AlCl_3$	266(--),433(--)	95-1542-73
	EtOH-NaOAc	274(--),380(--)	95-1542-73
Spiro[benzofuran-2(3H),1'-[2,4]cyclohexadiene]-2'-carboxylic acid, 3'-hydroxy-6-methoxy-3,6'-dioxo-, methyl ester	MeOH	207(4.40),232(4.32), 272(4.16),321(4.00)	24-1182-73
9H-Xanthene-1-carboxylic acid, 2,4a-dihydro-4a,6-dimethoxy-2,9-dioxo-	MeOH	204(4.39),273(3.92), 335(3.79)	24-1182-73
$C_{16}H_{12}S$			
Thiophene, 2,4-diphenyl-	C_6H_{12}	224s(4.30),256(4.73), 301s(4.06)	18-2253-73
$C_{16}H_{12}S_4$			
1,3-Benzodithiole, 2-(5-methyl-1,3-benzodithiol-2-ylidene)-	MeCN	256(4.25),287(4.26), 311(4.29),343s(--), 432(2.47)	5-0310-73
cation perchlorate	MeCN	283(3.71),314(3.84), 401s(--),423(4.17), 445(4.21),487s(--), 632s(--),660(4.08)	5-0310-73
$C_{16}H_{12}Se_2$			
1,3-Diselenole, 4-phenyl-2-(phenylmethylene)-	EtOH	340(4.26)	44-0338-73
$C_{16}H_{13}$			
Benzo[1,2:4,5]dicyclohepten-1-ium, 1,7-dihydro-, (deloc-1,2,3,4,5,5a,12a)-, tetrafluoroborate	MeCN	228(4.15),256(4.14), 261(4.11),293(4.05), 317(3.94),550(3.26)	44-3051-73
$C_{16}H_{13}Br$			
Benzene, 1,1'-(2-bromo-1,3-butadienylidene)bis-	$CHCl_3$	289(4.16)	108-0557-73

Compound	Solvent	$\lambda_{max}(\log \epsilon)$	Ref.
$C_{16}H_{13}BrN_2O_2$			
4H-Pyrido[1,2-a]pyrimidin-4-one, 9-[(2-bromophenyl)methoxy]-2-methyl-	EtOH	258(3.95),265(4.00), 300(3.86),310(3.90), 340(4.04),355(4.07)	4-0143-73
$C_{16}H_{13}BrO_2$			
2,4,6-Cycloheptatrien-1-one, 4-[2-(4-bromophenyl)ethenyl]-2-methoxy-, (E)-	MeOH	249(4.15),285(4.27), 315(4.27),393(4.36)	18-0199-73
2,4,6-Cycloheptatrien-1-one, 6-[2-(4-bromophenyl)ethenyl]-2-methoxy-, (E)-	MeOH	233(4.18),314(4.54)	18-0199-73
$C_{16}H_{13}ClN_2$			
12H-Indolo[2,3-a]quinolizin-5-ium, 1-methyl-, chloride	EtOH-HCl	224(4.54),249(4.61), 294(4.09),343(4.35), 394(3.28)	2-0621-73
	EtOH-KOH	229(4.39),253(4.33), 290(4.38),370(4.34), 447(3.73)	2-0621-73
$C_{16}H_{13}ClN_2O_4S$			
1H-Indole-2-carboxylic acid, 3-[[(4-chlorophenyl)sulfonyl]amino]-1-methyl-	EtOH	232(4.60),300(4.12), 315s(3.84)	39-1602-73C
$C_{16}H_{13}ClN_3$			
1H-Imidazo[1,2-a]quinazolin-10-ium, 7-chloro-2,3-dihydro-5-phenyl-, chloride hydrochloride	n.s.g.	247(4.55),264s(4.15), 295(3.97)	40-1944-73
$C_{16}H_{13}ClO_2$			
2,4,6-Cycloheptatrien-1-one, 4-[2-(3-chlorophenyl)ethenyl]-2-methoxy-, (E)-	MeOH	247(4.16),294(4.31), 392(4.30)	18-0199-73
2,4,6-Cycloheptatrien-1-one, 4-[2-(4-chlorophenyl)ethenyl]-2-methoxy-	MeOH	248(4.15),283(4.28), 314(4.27),398(4.36)	18-0199-73
2,4,6-Cycloheptatrien-1-one, 6-[2-(3-chlorophenyl)ethenyl]-2-methoxy-, (E)-	MeOH	234(4.17),307(4.55)	18-0199-73
2,4,6-Cycloheptatrien-1-one, 6-[2-(4-chlorophenyl)ethenyl]-2-methoxy-	MeOH	234(4.17),313(4.52)	18-0199-73
$C_{16}H_{13}ClO_3S$			
Benzenecarbothioic acid, 4-methoxy-, S-[2-(4-chlorophenyl)-2-oxoethyl] ester	EtOH	261(4.37),284(4.37)	48-0497-73
$C_{16}H_{13}Cl_2$			
Methylium, bis(4-chlorophenyl)cycloprop-yl-	FSO_3H at -75°	338(<4.18),468(4.86)	59-0803-73
$C_{16}H_{13}Cl_2NO_3$			
Benzenepropanamide, α,2-dichloro-N-(2-methoxyphenyl)-β-oxo-	pH 13	322(4.34)	39-0808-73B
$C_{16}H_{13}Cl_2N_3$			
2-Quinazolinamine, 6-chloro-N-(2-chloro-ethyl)-4-phenyl-	n.s.g.	245(4.51),275s(4.16)	40-1944-73
$C_{16}H_{13}CrNO_5$			
Chromium, pentacarbonyl(phenyl-1-pyrrol-idinylmethylene)-, (OC-6-21)-	n.s.g.	245(4.38),365(3.80)	101-0111-73I
$C_{16}H_{13}FO_2$			
Methanone, [3-(fluoromethyl)-3-phenyl-oxiranyl]phenyl-, cis	EtOH	248(4.18)	22-0202-73

Compound	Solvent	$\lambda_{max}(\log \epsilon)$	Ref.
Methanone, [3-(fluoromethyl)-3-phenyl-oxiranyl]phenyl-, trans	EtOH	248(4.18)	22-0202-73
$C_{16}H_{13}N$			
1H-Indole, 2-(2-phenylethenyl)-, trans	MeOH	264(4.50),285(4.42), 335(4.57),345(4.59), 363(4.43)	23-0792-73
Indolo[1,7-ab][1]benzazepine, 6,7-dihydro-	n.s.g.	210(4.50),259(4.10), 298(4.17),307(4.17)	39-1041-73C
Quinoline, 2-(4-methylphenyl)-	EtOH	263(4.47),325(3.95)	33-2588-73
$C_{16}H_{13}NO$			
Acetamide, N-9-anthracenyl-	EtOH	214(4.15),247s(4.98), 253(5.20),315s(3.07), 330(3.44),346(3.73), 364(3.89),384(3.84)	44-1167-73
8H-Indeno[1,2-d]isoxazole, 3a,8a-dihydro-3-phenyl-	EtOH	267(4.04)	32-0047-73
1H-Indole-2-carboxaldehyde, 5-methyl-3-phenyl-	EtOH	230(4.30),249(4.33), 322(4.38)	78-0603-73
1H-Indole-3-carboxaldehyde, 5-methyl-2-phenyl-	EtOH	224(4.40),261(4.52), 318(4.26)	78-0603-73
Indolizine, 1-acetyl-2-phenyl-	EtOH	236(4.56),321s(3.99), 354(4.28),370s(4.17)	39-2091-73C
3-Pyrrolin-2-one, 1,5-diphenyl-	CH_2Cl_2	274(3.67)	39-2523-73C
4-Quinolinemethanol, 2-phenyl-	EtOH	256(4.56)	33-2588-73
$C_{16}H_{13}NOS$			
Benzenemethanol, α-(3-methyl-2H-1,4-benzothiazin-2-ylidene)-	MeOH	471(3.59)	124-0922-73
	$CHCl_3$	448(3.38)	124-0922-73
$C_{16}H_{13}NO_2$			
Benzenamine, N-[(3-methoxy-2-benzofuranyl)methylene]-	MeOH	323(4.39),325(4.36)	103-0141-73
Benzo[a]cyclopenta[f]quinolizine-1,12-dione, 2,3,5,6-tetrahydro-	EtOH	255(4.58),273s(4.33), 308(4.08)	30-0445-73 +70-1794-73
3-Benzofuranol, 6-methyl-2-(phenyliminomethyl-	MeOH	272(4.05),338(4.05), 415(4.50)	103-0141-73
3(2H)-Benzofuranone, 2-[(methylphenylamino)methylene]-	MeOH	265(4.16),325(4.05), 405(4.44)	103-0141-73
2H-Benzofuro[2,3-b]pyrrol-2-one, 1,3,3a,8a-tetrahydro-1-phenyl-	EtOH	276(3.68),284(3.64)	44-3874-73
2H-Indol-2-one, 1,3-dihydro-3-[(2-hydroxyphenyl)methylene]-1-methyl-	EtOH	247(4.36)	103-0034-73
$C_{16}H_{13}NO_3$			
3-Benzofuranol, 2-[(4-methoxyphenylimino)methyl]-	MeOH	275(4.05),343(3.81), 426(4.43)	103-0141-73
2H-1-Benzopyran-2-one, 3-(4-aminophenyl)-6-methoxy-	MeOH	227(4.44),297(4.22), 369(4.26)	24-0388-73
1H-Indole-3-acetic acid, 2,3-dihydro-2-oxo-3-phenyl-	EtOH	250(3.90),282(3.20)	104-0861-73
$C_{16}H_{13}NO_3S$			
Thiazolo[3,2-a]pyridinium, 8-acetoxy-3-hydroxy-5-methyl-2-phenyl-, hydroxide, inner salt (spectra in 50% dioxan)	HCl	465(--)	1-1763-73
	NaOH	223(3.9),258(3.9), 290s(3.5),317(3.6), 430(4.0)	1-1763-73

Compound	Solvent	λmax(log ε)	Ref.
$C_{16}H_{13}NO_4$			
Benzoic acid, 4-[(1,3-dioxo-3-phenyl-propyl)amino]-	pH 13	338(4.39)	39-0808-73B
2H-1,4-Benzoxazine-6,7-dione, 5-acetyl-3,4-dihydro-2-phenyl-	EtOH	294(4.34),454(3.30)	78-2881-73
	CH_2Cl_2	291(4.34),448(3.40)	78-2881-73
2,4,6-Cycloheptatrien-1-one, 2-methoxy-4-[2-(3-nitrophenyl)ethenyl]-	MeOH	277(4.34),294(4.32), 359(4.17),391(4.20)	18-0199-73
2,4,6-Cycloheptatrien-1-one, 2-methoxy-4-[2-(4-nitrophenyl)ethenyl]-	MeOH	231(4.22),303(4.57)	18-0199-73
2,4,6-Cycloheptatrien-1-one, 2-methoxy-6-[2-(3-nitrophenyl)ethenyl]-, (E)-	MeOH	231(4.22),303(4.57)	18-0199-73
2,4,6-Cycloheptatrien-1-one, 2-methoxy-6-[2-(4-nitrophenyl)ethenyl]-, (E)-	MeOH	225(4.17),341(4.54)	18-0199-73
2-Naphthaleneacetic acid, α-cyano-1,4-dihydro-3-methyl-1,4-dioxo-, ethyl ester	EtOH	338(3.51)	83-0257-73
	EtOH-KOH	588(3.82)	83-0257-73
2-Propen-1-one, 3-(2-methoxyphenyl)-1-(4-nitrophenyl)-	isooctane	260s(--),305(4.42)	65-0638-73
	benzene	312(4.26)	65-0638-73
	EtOH	265s(--),312(4.33)	65-0638-73
$C_{16}H_{13}NO_4S$			
4H-1-Benzopyran-4-one, 7-acetoxy-2-methyl-3-(2-methyl-4-thiazolyl)-	n.s.g.	298(3.82)	104-2580-73
Thiopyrano[2,3-b]indole-2,3-dicarboxylic acid, 4-methyl-, dimethyl ester, hydrochloride	EtOH	249(4.20),284(4.43), 382(4.04)	94-2770-73
$C_{16}H_{13}NO_5$			
2H-1,4-Benzoxazine-5-carboxylic acid, 3,4,6,7-tetrahydro-6,7-dioxo-2-phenyl-, methyl ester	EtOH	270(4.13),277s(4.13), 308(4.23),457(3.34)	78-2881-73
	CH_2Cl_2	273(4.15),306(4.19), 446(3.42)	78-2881-73
$C_{16}H_{13}NO_5S$			
Benzenecarbothioic acid, 4-methoxy-, S-[2-(4-nitrophenyl)-2-oxoethyl] ester	MeCN	282(4.56),360(2.65)	48-0497-73
4H-1-Benzopyran-2-carboxylic acid, 7-hydroxy-3-(2-methyl-4-thiazolyl)-4-oxo-, ethyl ester	n.s.g.	312(4.03)	104-2580-73
$C_{16}H_{13}NO_6$			
Furo[3,4-c]isoquinoline-4(1H)-propanoic acid, 3,5-dihydro-1,3,5-trioxo-, ethyl ester	EtOH	214(4.56),299(4.05)	78-0213-73
$C_{16}H_{13}NO_7$			
Naphtho[2,1-b]furan-1,6,9(2H)-trione, 2-acetoxy-7-amino-5-hydroxy-2,4-dimethyl-	EtOH	232(4.34),263(4.22), 306(3.99),357(3.75)	33-2323-73
$C_{16}H_{13}NS_2$			
4H-Dithien[2,3-c:3',2'-e]azepine, 5,6-dihydro-5-phenyl-	C_6H_{12}	233(4.43),246s(4.35), 283(3.89),305s(3.56)	44-2814-73
Dithiobenzoic acid, isoquinoline salt	EtOH	305(3.94),355(3.73), 515(2.04)	143-0359-73
Dithiobenzoic acid, quinoline salt	EtOH	305(3.96),360(3.68), 520(2.04)	143-0359-73
1-Naphthalenedithioic acid, pyridine salt	EtOH	305(4.20),345(4.08), 506(2.22)	143-0359-73

Compound	Solvent	λ_{max}(log ϵ)	Ref.
$C_{16}H_{13}N_2$			
12H-Indolo[2,3-a]quinolizin-5-ium, 1-methyl-, chloride	EtOH-HCl	224(4.54),249(4.61), 294(4.09),343(4.35), 394(3.28)	2-0621-73
	EtOH-KOH	229(4.39),253(4.33), 290(4.38),370(4.34), 447(3.73)	2-0621-73
$C_{16}H_{13}N_3O$			
Benzaldehyde, 2-hydroxy-, 2-quinolinyl-hydrazone	EtOH	358(4.38)	77-0684-73
Benzaldehyde, 2-hydroxy-, 2(1H)-quino-linylidenehydrazone, (Z,Z)-	EtOH	395(4.22)	77-0684-73
Benzeneacetonitrile, α-[(2-acetylphen-yl)hydrazono]-, isomer A	MeOH	230(4.38),390(4.44)	80-0723-73
isomer B	MeOH	320(3.99),395(4.12)	80-0723-73
Benzeneacetonitrile, α-[(3-acetylphen-yl)hydrazono]-	MeOH	240(4.42),370(4.39)	80-0723-73
Benzeneacetonitrile, α-[(4-acetylphen-yl)hydrazono]-	MeOH	240(4.22),280(3.83), 374(4.56)	80-0723-73
2H-Naphtho[1,2-d]triazole, 4,5-dihydro-2-phenyl-, 1-oxide	EtOH	205(4.59),252(4.21), 301(4.38)	103-0120-73
5-Oxazolecarbonitrile, 2-amino-4,5-di-hydro-4,5-diphenyl-	EtOH	247(2.56),252(2.68), 259(2.75),265(2.67), 269(2.51)	48-0044-73
1,2,4-Triazine, 3-methoxy-5,6-diphenyl-	n.s.g.	217s(2.95),236(3.04), 280s(2.54),328(2.30)	22-2493-73
1,2,4-Triazine, 5-methyl-3,6-diphenyl-, 4-oxide	EtOH	271(4.52)	103-0123-73
$C_{16}H_{13}N_3OS$			
Spiro[benzothiazole-2(3H),3'-[3H]pyraz-ol]-4'(2'H)-one, 3-methyl-2'-phenyl-	EtOH	226s(4.20),257(4.10), 309(3.98),400(4.35)	94-0241-73
1,3,4-Thiadiazolium, 5-(benzoylamino)-3-methyl-2-phenyl-, hydroxide, inner salt	MeOH	238(4.30),264(4.07), 330(4.24)	103-1216-73
$C_{16}H_{13}N_3O_2$			
Benzamide, N-(3-amino-1-oxo-2(1H)-iso-quinolinyl)-	EtOH	233(4.57),302(4.26), 376(3.59)	95-1581-73
1(2H)-Isoquinolinone, 2,3-diamino-4-benzoyl-	EtOH	243(4.39),282(4.05), 379(4.04)	95-1581-73
$C_{16}H_{13}N_3O_3S$			
1H-Benzimidazole-1-carboxamide, 2,3-di-hydro-N-(phenoxyacetyl)-2-thioxo-	MeOH	248(4.23),306(4.27)	103-0639-73
$C_{16}H_{13}N_3O_4$			
3H-Indazole-3-carboxylic acid, 3-(4-ni-trophenyl)-, ethyl ester	EtOH	272(4.27),340(2.78)	78-1833-73
$C_{16}H_{13}N_3S$			
Pyrimido[5,4-g]benzothiazole, 5,6-di-hydro-8-methyl-2-phenyl-	EtOH	270(4.44),325(4.20), 337(4.13)	32-1063-73
1,2,4-Triazine, 3-(methylthio)-5,6-di-phenyl-	n.s.g.	220(4.11),276(4.11), 356(3.38)	22-2493-73
$C_{16}H_{13}O_2$			
17,18-Dioxatricyclo[12.2.1.1^{4,7}]octa-decaheptaenylium (bisulfate)	H_2SO_4	218(4.34),285(4.13), 334(4.48),349(4.52),	88-5065-73

Compound	Solvent	$\lambda_{max}(\log \epsilon)$	Ref.
17,18-Dioxatricyclo[12.2.1.1^{4,7}]octadecaheptaenylium (bisulfate) (cont.)	H_2SO_4	478(3.77),490(3.81), 514(3.90),548(3.93)	88-5065-73
$C_{16}H_{14}$			
Acenaphthylene, 1,2-diethenyl-1,2-dihydro-, cis	n.s.g.	218(4.77),229(4.88), 266(3.65),277(3.85), 288(3.93),299(3.76), 305(3.56),315(2.16), 319(2.16)	35-2940-73
Bicyclo[3.2.2]nona-2,6,8-triene, 4-(phenylmethylene)-	MeOH	265(4.10)	35-6770-73
Bicyclo[4.2.1]nona-2,4,7-triene, 9-(phenylmethylene)-	MeOH	245(4.36),270(4.06)	35-6770-73
1,3-Butadiene, 1,4-diphenyl-, carbonium ion	81.5% H_2SO_4	384(2.49),572(3.08)	48-0810-73
	95.8% H_2SO_4	427(3.43)	48-0810-73
	99.9% H_2SO_4	423(3.30),497(3.30)	48-0810-73
	+18% SO_3	425(3.15),488(3.08), 522(3.18)	48-0810-73
	+33% SO_3	390s(3.58),430s(3.32), 480s(3.34),522(3.26), 582(3.08)	48-0810-73
Cyclohepta[de]naphthalene, 8,9-dimethyl-	n.s.g.	242(4.21),250(4.91), 272(3.44),283(3.46), 299s(3.39),332(3.55), 343(3.71),358(3.67), 368(3.59),376(3.55), 387(3.25),422(2.66), 447(2.63),478(2.52), 513(1.25),655(0.82)	35-1874-73
1,3,5-Cycloheptatriene, 7,7'-(1,2-ethanediylidene)bis-	C_6H_{12}	242(4.20),412(4.61), 438(4.54)	89-0076-73
Cyclopropane, (diphenylmethylene)-	EtOH	226(4.30),234(4.23), 258(4.29)	78-1169-73
Dibenzopentalene, 3,6,7,8-tetrahydro-	EtOH	262(3.24),268(3.39), 275(3.41)	78-1321-73
9,10-Ethanoanthracene, 9,10-dihydro-	C_6H_{12}	258(2.91),266(3.17), 273(3.28)	78-1379-73
Naphtho[1',8']tricyclo[4.3.0.0^{5,9}]non-2-ene	n.s.g.	231(4.53),237(4.55), 272(3.69),281(3.68), 292(3.97),302(2.82), 307(3.54),317(3.07), 321(3.01)	35-2940-73
Naphtho[1',8']tricyclo[5.1.1.0^{2,6}]non-3-ene	n.s.g.	223(4.78),228(4.94), 243(3.20),268(3.64), 278(3.82),288(3.88), 299(3.70),304(3.54), 314(2.94),318(2.94	35-2940-73
Tricyclo[3.3.1.0^{2,8}]nona-3,6-diene, 9-(phenylmethylene)-	MeOH	265(4.156)	35-6770-73
$C_{16}H_{14}BrClN_2$			
Pyridinium, 1-[(2-chloro-3-quinolinyl)-methyl]-3-methyl-, bromide	H_2O	267(3.84),293(3.47), 307(3.50),321(3.52)	44-2351-73
$C_{16}H_{14}BrIN_2$			
Pyridinium, 1-[(2-iodo-3-quinolinyl)-methyl]-4-methyl-, bromide	H_2O	234(4.72),311(3.70), 325(3.73)	44-2351-73
$C_{16}H_{14}BrNO$			
2-Propen-1-one, 2-bromo-3-(methylamino)-1,3-diphenyl-	hexane	235(3.88),335(4.14)	40-2152-73

Compound	Solvent	$\lambda_{max}(\log \epsilon)$	Ref.
$C_{16}H_{14}Br_2N_2$			
Pyridinium, 1-[(2-bromo-3-quinolinyl)-methyl]-3-methyl-, bromide	H_2O	267(3.89),295(3.54), 308(3.58),322(3.59)	44-2351-73
Pyridinium, 1-[(2-bromo-3-quinolinyl)-methyl]-4-methyl-, bromide	H_2O	240(4.83),295(3.61), 308(3.65),322(3.67)	44-2351-73
$C_{16}H_{14}Br_2N_4O_6$			
2,4,6(1H,3H,5H)-Pyrimidinetrione, 5-[5-(dibromomethyl)-1,2,3,4-tetra-hydro-1,3-dimethyl-2,4-dioxo-7H-pyrano[2,3-d]pyrimidin-7-ylidene]-1,3-dimethyl-	pyridine	444(4.00)	39-0823-73C
$C_{16}H_{14}Cl$			
Methylium, (4-chlorophenyl)cyclopropyl-phenyl-	FSO_3H at -75°	328(<4.1),452(4.72)	59-0803-73
$C_{16}H_{14}ClNO$			
2-Buten-1-one, 2-chloro-1-phenyl-3-(phenylamino)-	hexane	246(4.00),361(4.27)	40-2152-73
1H-Indole, 5-chloro-2-ethoxy-3-phenyl-	isoPrOH	228(4.49),281(4.25)	44-3077-73
1H-Indole, 2-chloro-3-(4-methoxyphenyl)-1-methyl-	EtOH	230(4.50),263(4.17), 283s(4.08),294s(4.07)	94-2739-73
2-Propen-1-one, 2-chloro-3-(methylamino)-1,3-diphenyl-	hexane	241(3.93),356(4.17)	40-2152-73
$C_{16}H_{14}ClNO_3$			
Benzenepropanamide, 2-chloro-N-(2-meth-oxyphenyl)-β-oxo-	pH 13	314(4.29)	39-0808-73B
$C_{16}H_{14}ClNO_5$			
1-Pyrrolinium, 5-oxo-1,2-diphenyl-, perchlorate	CH_2Cl_2	236(3.97),298(3.34)	39-2523-73C
$C_{16}H_{14}ClNS$			
Benzenamine, 4-chloro-N-[3-(methylthio)-3-phenyl-2-propenylidene]-	EtOH	345(4.32)	104-1739-73
$C_{16}H_{14}ClN_3$			
Acetonitrile, [[[5-chloro-2-(methyl-amino)phenyl]phenylmethylene]-amino]-, anti	EtOH	232(4.45),388(3.83)	95-1253-73
syn	EtOH	253(4.42)	95-1253-73
$C_{16}H_{14}ClN_3O$			
Ethanol, 2-[(6-chloro-4-phenyl-2-quin-azolinyl)amino]-	n.s.g.	245(4.61),275s(4.32)	40-1944-73
$C_{16}H_{14}ClN_4O_7PS$			
Inosine, 8-[(4-chlorophenyl)thio]-, cyclic 3',5'-(dihydrogen phosphate), ammonium salt	pH 1	256(4.19),275s(4.18)	69-5310-73
	pH 11	244(4.11),282(4.20)	69-5310-73
$C_{16}H_{14}ClN_5NaO_7PS$			
Guanosine, 8-[(4-chlorophenyl)thio]-, cyclic 3',5'-(hydrogen phosphate), sodium salt	pH 1	275(4.33)	69-5310-73
	pH 11	296(4.33)	69-5310-73
$C_{16}H_{14}F_2O$			
1-Butanone, 1,4-bis(4-fluorophenyl)-	EtOH	246(4.18),273(3.35)	73-3879-73

Compound	Solvent	λmax(log ε)	Ref.
$C_{16}H_{14}F_2S_2$			
3,11-Dithiatricyclo[11.3.1.1^{5,9}]octadeca-1(17),5,7,9(18),13,15-hexaene, 17,18-difluoro-, syn	C_6H_{12}	218(4.21),242s(3.57), 261s(3.39),269(3.38)	44-3928-73
$C_{16}H_{14}HgO_2$			
Mercury, bis(2-oxo-2-phenylethyl)-	MeCN	244(4.42),320(3.14)	44-0514-73
$C_{16}H_{14}IN_7$			
2,4,6-Pyrimidinetriamine, N^4-(4-iodophenyl)-5-(phenylazo)-	EtOH	250(4.26),290(4.48), 420(4.36)	42-0260-73
$C_{16}H_{14}N$			
Heptafulvenylium, 8-cyano-8-cycloheptatrienyl-, tetrafluoroborate	pH 2	216(4.56),270(3.95), 300(3.53),592(4.41)	138-1169-73
$C_{16}H_{14}N_2$			
Benzenemethanamine, α-1H-isoindol-1-ylidene-2-methyl-	EtOH	252(4.28),307(3.95), 337(3.75)	107-0181-73
Benzo[lmn][3,8]phenanthrolinium, 2,7-dimethyl-, bis(tetrafluoroborate)	MeCN	247(4.83),293(3.56), 306(3.92),320(4.36), 335(4.56),372(3.42), 393(3.91),417(4.19),	5-0339-73
2,5'-Bi-1H-indole, 2',3'-dihydro-	EtOH	209(4.02),306(3.88), 347(3.87)	34-0109-73
2,3-Diazabicyclo[3.1.0]hex-2-ene, 4,4-diphenyl-	EtOH	334(2.31)	35-0980-73
9,10-Ethenoanthracene-1,5-diamine, (-)-	MeOH	200(4.50),204(4.52), 207s(4.49),224(4.62), 296(3.50)	18-0915-73
	MeOH-HCl	211s(4.59),215(4.63), 270(3.23),278(3.40), 295s(2.00)	18-0915-73
1H-Indole, 1-methyl-2-[2-(2-pyridinyl)ethenyl]-, trans (as methiodide)	MeOH	280(3.90),423(4.35)	23-0792-73
$C_{16}H_{14}N_2O$			
1H-Indole-2-carboxamide, 3-(phenylmethyl)-	n.s.g.	295(4.26)	103-1497-73
1H-Pyrazole, 3-(4-methoxyphenyl)-5-phenyl-	EtOH	260.0(4.62)	42-0589-73
1H-Pyrazole-3-carboxaldehyde, 4,5-dihydro-1,5-diphenyl-	C_6H_{12}	362(4.20)	104-0413-73
	EtOH	376(4.28)	104-0413-73
3H-Pyrazol-3-one, 2,4-dihydro-2-methyl-4,5-diphenyl-	EtOH	240s(4.17),265s(4.05), 300s(3.80)	23-0338-73
$C_{16}H_{14}N_2OS_2$			
[1]Benzothieno[2,3-d]pyrimidin-4(1H)-one, 2,3,5,6,7,8-hexahydro-3-phenyl-2-thioxo-	EtOH	287(4.09),340(4.20)	103-0525-73
$C_{16}H_{14}N_2O_2$			
Benzamide, 2-[p-(dimethylamino)benzoyl]-	EtOH	210(4.42),262(4.18), 352(3.96)	39-1160-73B
Benzenamine, 2-methyl-N-[3-(2-nitrophenyl)-2-propenylidene]-	MeOH	210(3.36),278(3.40), 338(3.08)	42-0277-73
Benzenamine, 4-methyl-N-[3-(2-nitrophenyl)-2-propenylidene]-	MeOH	208(4.19),233(4.19), 281(4.47),345(4.36)	42-0277-73
3H-Indazole-3-carboxylic acid, 3-phenyl-, ethyl ester	EtOH	221(4.28),268(3.78), 348(2.32)	78-1833-73

Compound	Solvent	$\lambda_{max}(\log \epsilon)$	Ref.
3H-Pyrazol-3-one, 2,4-dihydro-4-hydroxy-2-methyl-4,5-diphenyl-	EtOH	217(4.17),310(4.11)	23-0338-73
4H-Pyrazol-4-one, 2,3-dihydro-3-hydroxy-2-methyl-3,5-diphenyl-	EtOH	215s(4.13),271(4.20), 420(3.67)	23-0338-73
4(3H)-Quinazolinone, 3-ethyl-2-(2-hydroxyphenyl)-	EtOH	233(4.42),279(3.98), 304(3.55)	78-3173-73
$C_{16}H_{14}N_2O_3$			
Benzenamine, 4-methoxy-N-[3-(2-nitrophenyl)-2-propen-1-ylidene]-	MeOH	210(4.29),250(4.29), 284(4.38),361(4.31)	42-0277-73
Benzenamine, 4-methyl-N-[3-(2-nitrophenyl)-2-propenylidene]-, N-oxide	MeOH	228(4.22),278(4.11), 335(4.34)	2-0884-73
2H,4H-Oxazolo[5,4,3-ij]pyrido[3,2-g]-quinoline-4,8(11H)-dione, 6,10,11-trimethyl-	EtOH	258(4.45),289(4.38), 302(4.81),363(3.90)	35-5003-73
Sibiromycin, acid hydrolysis product	MeOH	290(4.69),375(4.00), 410(4.01),435(3.90)	105-0223-73
$C_{16}H_{14}N_2O_3S$			
Benzenesulfonamide, N-(1,3-dihydro-1-methyl-3-oxo-2H-indol-2-ylidene)-4-methyl-	$CHCl_3$	259(4.53),264(4.54), 300s(3.50),454(3.23)	39-1943-73C
$C_{16}H_{14}N_2O_4S$			
Benzenesulfonamide, 2-(1,3-dihydro-1,3-dioxo-2H-isoindol-2-yl)-N,N-dimethyl-	EtOH	220(4.43),268(3.34), 275(3.34),293(3.23)	7-0635-73
2-Propenoic acid, 3-(1-acetyl-3-hydroxy-1H-indol-2-yl)-2-cyano-3-(methylthio)-, methyl ester	EtOH	321(4.20)	94-1658-73
$C_{16}H_{14}N_2O_5$			
Benzenepropanamide, 4-methoxy-N-(3-nitrophenyl)-β-oxo-	pH 13	333(4.48)	39-0808-73B
$C_{16}H_{14}N_2O_5S$			
2H-1,2-Benzothiazine-3-carboxamide, N,4-dihydroxy-2-methyl-N-phenyl-, 1,1-dioxide	EtOH	334(4.06)	87-0044-73
$C_{16}H_{14}N_2O_6$			
1H-Azepine-4,5-dicarboxylic acid, 1-(4-nitrophenyl)-, dimethyl ester	MeCN	237(4.32),376(4.28)	24-3824-73
1,3-Cycloheptadiene-1,2-dicarboxylic acid, 5-[[(4-nitrophenyl)amino]-methylene]-, dimethyl ester	MeCN	227(4.12),249(4.18), 263s(4.10),305(3.40), 410(4.79)	24-3824-73
2,4(1H,3H)-Pyrimidinedione, 1-[5-[(benzoyloxy)methyl]tetrahydro-3-oxo-2-furanyl]-, [R-(R*,S*)]-	EtOH	228(4.22),258(4.06)	44-1283-73
$C_{16}H_{14}N_2S$			
1H-Imidazole, 2-(methylthio)-4,5-diphenyl-	EtOH	222(4.28),270(4.21)	24-1628-73
$C_{16}H_{14}N_2S_2$			
[1]Benzothieno[2,3-c]isothiazol-3-amine, 4,5,6,7-tetrahydro-N-(phenylmethylene)-	MeOH	285(4.29),408(4.08), 442s(3.74)	48-0539-73
$C_{16}H_{14}N_4OS_3$			
4-Thiazolidinone, 5-[1-(2-benzothiazolyl)-1,3-dihydro-3-methyl-2H-imidazol-2-ylidene]-3-ethyl-2-thioxo-	EtOH	427(4.11)	103-1078-73

Compound	Solvent	λ_{max}(log ε)	Ref.
$C_{16}H_{14}N_4O_2$			
Benzamide, N-[4-(4-methoxyphenyl)-1H-1,2,3-triazol-1-yl]-	EtOH	256(4.44)	78-2119-73
1H-Pyrano[2,3-c:6,5-c']dipyrazol-4(7H)-pne, 1,3,5-trimethyl-7-phenyl-	EtOH	235(4.28)	103-0911-73
$C_{16}H_{14}N_4O_2S_2$			
4-Thiazolidinone, 5-[1-(2-benzoxazolyl)-3-methyl-1H-imidazol-2(3H)-ylidene]-3-ethyl-2-thioxo-	EtOH	427(4.36)	103-1078-73
$C_{16}H_{14}N_4O_3$			
1H-Indole, 2-[(2-methoxy-4-nitrophenyl)-azo]-3-methyl-	EtOH	460(4.44)	35-3400-73
1H-Pyrazole, 1-acetyl-4,5-dihydro-3-(4-nitrophenyl)-4-(2-pyridinyl)-	$CHCl_3$	238(3.96),346(4.15)	103-0055-73
1H-Pyrazole, 1-acetyl-4,5-dihydro-4-(4-nitrophenyl)-3-(2-pyridinyl)-	$CHCl_3$	297(4.65)	103-0055-73
2,4,6(1H,3H,5H)-Pyrimidinetrione, 5-(2,2-diphenylhydrazino)-	EtOH	280(3.72),415(4.16)	103-0247-73
$C_{16}H_{14}N_4O_4$			
2-Propenoic acid, 2-methyl-, 2-(3,4-dihydro-2,4-dioxobenzo[g]pteridin-10(2H)-yl)ethyl ester	EtOH	215(4.45),266(4.48), 333(3.83),435(3.98)	126-0007-73L
$C_{16}H_{14}N_6$			
Formazan, 3-methyl-1-phenyl-5-(2-quinoxalinyl)-	benzene	435s(4.40)	103-1542-73
	EtOH	410(4.63)	103-1542-73
	EtOH-KOH	535(4.78)	103-1542-73
	dioxan	425(4.42)	103-1542-73
	H_2SO_4	491(4.20)	103-1542-73
$C_{16}H_{14}N_6O_4$			
3H-Indole-3-propanoic acid, α-amino-3-(2,3,6,7-tetrahydro-2,6-dioxo-1H-purin-8-yl)-	pH 0	235s(4.00),274(4.09)	69-5084-73
	pH 5.0	235s(4.00),275(4.10)	69-5084-73
	pH 8	240(4.09),279(4.09)	69-5084-73
	pH 11	243(4.18),283(4.08)	69-5084-73
isomer B	pH 0	235s(4.00),274(4.10)	69-5084-73
	pH 5	235s(3.99),275(4.11)	69-5084-73
	pH 8	241(4.09),279(4.09)	69-5084-73
	pH 11	244(4.18),283(4.05)	69-5084-73
$C_{16}H_{14}N_6O_8$			
Benzoic acid, 3-methoxy-, 2,2-bis(hexahydro-2,4,6-trioxo-5-pyrimidinyl)-hydrazide	EtOH	240(4.39)	103-0247-73
$C_{16}H_{14}N_7O_{10}P$			
Adenosine, 2'-O-(2,4-dinitrophenyl)-, cyclic 3',5'-(hydrogen phosphate)	pH 1	256(4.38),294s(--)	69-1010-73
	pH 11	258(4.38),291s(--)	69-1010-73
$C_{16}H_{14}O$			
Benzofuran, 2-methyl-3-(phenylmethyl)-(and isomers)	EtOH	247(4.11),276(3.54), 283(3.48)	103-0026-73
9H-Fluoren-9-one, 1,2,8-trimethyl-	EtOH	251(4.96),266(5.13), 295(3.57),309(3.63), 323(3.63),341(3.64), 412(3.04)	39-1511-73C
Tricyclo[9.3.1.1^{4,8}]hexadeca-1(15),4,6-8(16),11,13-hexaen-2-one	isooctane	207(4.61),275s(2.8), 309(2.6),318(2.6)	35-0621-73

Compound	Solvent	λ max(log ε)	Ref.
$C_{16}H_{14}OS$			
Dibenzo[b,f]thiepin, 2-ethoxy-	MeOH	242(4.30),262(3.82), 294(3.76)	73-1579-73
$C_{16}H_{14}O_2$			
Acetic acid, (2,3-dihydro-4(1H)-phenanthrenylidene)-, cis	EtOH	307(3.81)	39-0615-73C
trans	EtOH	312(3.98),331s(3.88)	39-0615-73C
Anthracene, 9,10-dimethoxy-	EtOH	345(3.13),361(3.45), 381(3.63),403(3.56)	3-1794-73
2(3H)-Benzofuranone, 3-ethyl-3-phenyl-	EtOH	271(3.19),278(3.15)	44-1993-73
1,4-Butanedione, 1,4-diphenyl-	EtOH	243(4.44),278(3.37)	22-0202-73
3-Butenoic acid, 3,4-diphenyl-, (E)-	EtOH	211(3.83),219(3.81), 274(3.96)	35-6277-73
2,4,6-Cycloheptatrien-1-one, 2-methoxy-6-(2-phenylethenyl)-	MeOH	233(4.04),308(4.51)	18-0199-73
17,18-Dioxatricyclo[12.2.1.1^{4,7}]octadeca-2,4,6,8,12,14,16-heptaene	C_6H_{12}	222s(4.45),227(4.52), 277(4.60),286(4.80), 365(3.95),375(3.99), 387(4.16),400(4.00), 412(4.09)	88-0361-73
2-Propen-1-one, 1-(2-hydroxyphenyl)-3-(2-methylpropyl)-	EtOH	210(4.31),224s(4.01), 236(3.81),277s(3.78), 328(4.18),368s(4.01)	42-0129-73
2-Propen-1-one, 1-(2-hydroxyphenyl)-3-(3-methylphenyl)-	EtOH	208(4.41),234(4.00), 275s(3.96),331(4.28), 364s(4.11)	42-0129-73
2-Propen-1-one, 1-(2-hydroxyphenyl)-3-(4-methylphenyl)-	isooctane	225(4.21),320(4.44), 355s(--)	65-0638-73
	benzene	332(4.39),360s(--)	65-0638-73
	EtOH	206(4.35),222s(4.21), 240(3.89),292s(3.77), 340(4.15),369s(4.15)	42-0129-73
	EtOH	235(4.05),330(4.42), 360s(--)	65-0638-73
2-Propen-1-one, 1-(2-methoxyphenyl)-3-phenyl-	isooctane	298(4.45)	65-0638-73
$C_{16}H_{14}O_2S$			
Dibenzo[b,f]thiepin-10(11H)-one, 8-ethoxy-	MeOH	238(4.35),257(4.03), 352(3.56)	73-1579-73
$C_{16}H_{14}O_2S_2$			
Ethanebis(thioic) acid, S,S-bis(2-methylphenyl) ester	$CHCl_3$	288(4.01),499(2.26)	143-0437-73
Ethanebis(thioic) acid, S,S-bis(4-methylphenyl) ester	$CHCl_3$	259(4.28),518(2.58)	143-0437-73
$C_{16}H_{14}O_3$			
2(3H)-Benzofuranone, 5-hydroxy-3-methyl-3-(phenylmethyl)-	EtOH	295(3.38)	94-1868-73
2,4,6-Cycloheptatrien-1-one, 2-methoxy-4-(2-phenylethenyl)-	MeOH	242(4.04),310(4.22), 355(4.15)	18-0199-73
2,5-Cyclohexadiene-1,4-dione, 2-methoxy-5-(1-phenyl-2-propenyl)-	MeOH	206(4.26),260(4.16)	39-1737-73C
17,18-Dioxatricyclo[12.2.1.1^{4,7}]octadeca-1(16),2,4,6,12,14-hexaene-9,11-diol, dehydration product 9	MeOH	261(4.45),375(4.00)	88-5065-73
dehydration product 10	MeOH	261(4.32),363(3.92), 375(3.91)	88-5065-73

Compound	Solvent	λ_{max}(log ε)	Ref.
dehydration product 11 (cont.)	MeOH	263(4.27),360(3.96)	88-5065-73
dehydration product 12	MeOH	261(4.14),360(3.85), 385s(3.68)	88-5065-73
7H-Furo[3,2-g][1]benzopyran-7-one, 6-(1,1-dimethyl-2-propenyl)- (chalepensin)	n.s.g.	247(4.3),292(3.9), 328(3.8)	49-0911-73
1(3H)-Isobenzofuranone, 3-methoxy-3-(4-methylphenyl)-	H_2O	221(4.29)	44-3383-73
4,9-Methanonaphtho[2,3-c]furan-1,3-dione, 3a,4,9,9a-tetrahydro-10-(1-methylethylidene)-	90% EtOH	219(3.85),262(3.06), 268(3.25),275(3.28)	12-1725-73
2-Propenal, 3-(6-oxo-8-phenyl-5-oxaspiro[3.4]oct-7-en-7-yl)-	EtOH	274(4.24)	78-3553-73
2-Propenoic acid, 3-phenyl-, 3-methoxyphenyl ester	EtOH	282(4.38)	12-0899-73
2-Propen-1-one, 1-(2,4-dihydroxyphenyl)-3-(2-methylphenyl)-	EtOH	206(4.55),236s(4.17), 261s(4.10),363(4.24)	42-0129-73
2-Propen-1-one, 1-(2,4-dihydroxyphenyl)-3-(3-methylphenyl)-	EtOH	207(4.45),226s(4.01), 264s(3.67),283s(3.90), 357(4.27)	42-0129-73
2-Propen-1-one, 1-(2,4-dihydroxyphenyl)-3-(4-methylphenyl)-	EtOH	209(4.32),225s(4.11), 258(3.67),360(4.38)	42-0129-73
2-Propen-1-one, 1-(2-hydroxyphenyl)-3-(2-methoxyphenyl)-	EtOH	209(4.45),252(4.06), 274s(4.03),308(4.20), 362(4.30)	42-0129-73
2-Propen-1-one, 1-(2-hydroxyphenyl)-3-(3-methoxyphenyl)-	EtOH	210(4.55),256(4.17), 345(4.32),368s(4.25)	42-0129-73
2-Propen-1-one, 1-(2-hydroxyphenyl)-3-(4-methoxyphenyl)-	isooctane	240(4.18),280(3.81), 345(4.49),365s(--)	65-0638-73
	benzene	365(4.44)	65-0638-73
	EtOH	206(4.46),212s(4.34), 244(4.31),276(4.16), 358(4.51)	42-0129-73
	EtOH	240(4.19),275(3.81), 365(4.45)	65-0638-73
$C_{16}H_{14}O_4$			
1,5-Acenaphthylenedicarboxylic acid, 1,2-dihydro-, dimethyl ester	MeOH	309(4.69)	88-1803-73
1,5-Acenaphthylenedicarboxylic acid, 4,5-dihydro-, dimethyl ester	MeOH	227(4.69),309(4.08)	88-1803-73
3(2H)-Benzofuranone, 2-hydroxy-4-methoxy-2-(phenylmethyl)-	EtOH	278(4.01),343(3.56)	114-0093-73B
4H-1-Benzopyran-4-one, 2,3-dihydro-3-hydroxy-6-methoxy-2-phenyl-	EtOH	225(3.84),350(3.56)	114-0093-73B
4H-1-Benzopyran-4-one, 2,3-dihydro-7-hydroxy-5-methoxy-2-phenyl- (alpinetin)	n.s.g.	286(4.26)	102-0238-73
1-Dibenzofurancarboxylic acid, 3,9b-dihydro-4,9b-dimethyl-3-oxo-, methyl ester	90% EtOH	217s(4.12),231(4.27), 260s(3.63),281s(3.32), 344(3.51)	12-1093-73
1(3H)-Isobenzofuranone, 3,6-dimethoxy-3-phenyl-	H_2O	218(4.50),304(3.43)	44-3383-73
1(3H)-Isobenzofuranone, 3-methoxy-3-(4-methoxyphenyl)-	H_2O	231(4.26)	44-3383-73
1,4-Naphthalenedione, 2-(1-acetyl-2-oxopropyl)-3-methyl-	EtOH	333(3.43)	83-0257-73
	EtOH-KOH	528(2.88)	83-0257-73
Naphtho[1,2-b]furan-5,6,9(4H)-trione, 4-ethenyl-2,3,3a,9b-tetrahydro-4-methyl-3-methylene- (cordiachrome H)	EtOH	248(3.89),382(3.01)	39-1556-73C

Compound	Solvent	λ_{max}(log ε)	Ref.
2,3-Phenanthrenediol, 5,7-dimethoxy-	n.s.g.	262(4.87),284(4.13), 290s(4.01),307(3.91)	39-1179-73C
2-Propenoic acid, 3-(6-oxo-8-phenyl-5-oxaspiro[3.4]oct-7-en-7-yl)-, (Z)-	EtOH	229(4.04),265s(4.00)	78-3553-73
2-Propen-1-one, 1-(2,4-dihydroxy-6-methoxyphenyl)-3-phenyl- (cardamonin)	n.s.g.	214(4.43),345(4.44)	102-0238-73
2-Propen-1-one, 1-(2-hydroxyphenyl)-3-(2-hydroxy-3-methoxyphenyl)-	EtOH	212(4.48),244(4.05), 270(4.16),380(4.44)	42-0129-73
9H-Xanthen-9-one, 3,7-dimethoxy-5-methyl-	MeOH	205(4.25),245(4.55), 269s(4.16),312(4.18), 352(3.74)	24-1182-73
$C_{16}H_{14}O_4S_2$			
2,5-Hexanedione, 3,4-bis(hydroxy-2-thienylmethylene)-	EtOH	204(4.05),275(4.07), 345(4.47)	128-0465-73
$C_{16}H_{14}O_5$			
5H-Benzocyclohepten-5-one, 6,9-diacetoxy-7-methyl-	EtOH	224(4.80),288(3.79)	39-1223-73C
1aH-Benz[b]oxireno[h]benzofuran-4-carboxylic acid, 2,4a-dihydro-1a,4a-dimethyl-2-oxo-, methyl ester	90% EtOH	220(3.97),234s(3.86), 270s(3.42)	12-1093-73
1,3-Benzodioxole-5-methanol, 6-(1,3-benzodioxol-5-ylmethyl)-	EtOH	239(3.94),290(3.91)	39-1266-73C
Benzoic acid, 2-(3,4-dimethoxybenzoyl)-	EtOH	211(4.38),279(4.06), 308(4.00)	56-1949-73
Benzoic acid, 2-(4-hydroxy-3-methoxybenzoyl)-	EtOH	211(4.34),286(4.00), 316(4.02)	56-1949-73
4H-1-Benzopyran-4-one, 2,3-dihydro-2,5-dihydroxy-7-methoxy-2-phenyl-	EtOH	287(3.99),330s(--)	22-1781-73
	EtOH-NaOH	295(3.78),385(3.96)	22-1781-73
	EtOH-$AlCl_3$	308(4.11),375(3.48)	22-1781-73
1,2-Dibenzofurandicarboxylic acid, 1,9b-dihydro-4,9b-dimethyl-	90% EtOH	235(3.90),286(3.64), 351(3.93)	12-1093-73
Isoflavanone, 5,7-dihydroxy-4'-methoxy-, (±)-	EtOH	222(4.38),294(4.15), 330(3.51)	102-1184-73
	EtOH-NaOH	231(4.36),250s(4.11), 331(4.39)	102-1184-73
Prangenin	EtOH	248(4.39),262(4.11)	64-0260-73C
2-Propen-1-one, 1-(2,4-dihydroxyphenyl)-3-(4-hydroxy-3-methoxyphenyl)-	EtOH	207(4.42),262(3.82), 383(4.44)	42-0129-73
Toralactone monomethyl ether	EtOH	269(4.60),279(4.78), 393(3.40)	95-0261-73
9H-Xanthen-9-one, 1,3,7-trimethoxy-	MeOH	239(4.47),255(4.60), 303(4.12),356(3.82)	39-1329-73C
9H-Xanthen-9-one, 1,5,6-trimethoxy-	MeOH	238(4.69),305(4.25), 337s(3.99)	39-1329-73C
9H-Xanthen-9-one, 1,6,7-trimethoxy-	MeOH	251(4.56),267s(4.10), 283(4.10),305s(3.66), 353(4.08),358(4.10)	39-1329-73C
9H-Xanthen-9-one, 2,3,4-trimethoxy-	MeOH	245(4.53),275(4.02), 302(4.06),350(3.81)	39-1329-73C
9H-Xanthen-9-one, 2,3,6-trimethoxy-	MeOH	246(4.55),267(4.06), 313(4.31),342s(4.01)	18-1498-73
$C_{16}H_{14}O_6$			
2,3-Furandicarboxylic acid, 4-benzoyl-5-methyl-, dimethyl ester	$CHCl_3$	265s(3.92),293(4.15)	103-1307-73
1,3,8-Naphthalenetriol, triacetate	EtOH	210(4.39),226(4.81), 283(3.70)	23-1617-73

Compound	Solvent	$\lambda_{max}(\log \epsilon)$	Ref.
9H-Xanthen-9-one, 1-hydroxy-3,4,7-tri-methoxy-	MeOH	233(4.44),264(4.57), 312(4.03),381(3.83)	39-1329-73C
9H-Xanthen-9-one, 1-hydroxy-3,5,6-tri-methoxy-	MeOH	245(4.68),282(4.03), 310(4.37),338(3.97)	39-1329-73C
9H-Xanthen-9-one, 1-hydroxy-3,5,8-tri-methoxy-	EtOH	220(4.08),233s(4.15), 250(4.40),274(3.92), 332(3.88)	36-0926-73
$C_{16}H_{14}O_7$			
Benzoic acid, 3,6-dihydroxy-2-(2-hydr-oxy-4-methoxybenzoyl)-, methyl ester	MeOH	214(4.53),232s(4.21), 281(4.13),333(4.01)	24-1182-73
Benzoic acid, 6-hydroxy-2-(2-hydroxy-4-methoxybenzoyl)-3-methoxy-	MeOH	209(4.59),230s(4.24), 279(4.13),327(4.10)	24-1182-73
1,4-Naphthalenedione, 5-(1,2-dioxoprop-yl)-2-hydroxy-6,8-dimethoxy-7-methyl-	EtOH-HCl	215(4.27),262(4.24), 298(4.19),369(3.79)	33-2287-73
Spiro[benzofuran-2,2'-cyclohex-6'-ene]-1'-carboxylic acid, 6'-hydroxy-3,3'-dioxo-6-methoxy-, methyl ester	MeOH	208(4.33),233(4.04), 270(4.15),317(3.97)	24-1182-73
$C_{16}H_{14}O_8$			
Benzoic acid, 2-(2-carboxy-5-methoxy-phenoxy)-3,6-dihydroxy-, 1-methyl ester	MeOH	210(4.61),238s(4.17), 288(3.51),342(3.61)	24-1182-73
Benzoic acid, 2-(2-carboxy-5-methoxy-phenoxy)-6-hydroxy-3-methoxy-	MeOH	213(4.59),251(4.18), 292(3.70),333(3.65)	24-1182-73
$C_{16}H_{14}S_4$			
Disulfide, bis[(2-methylphenyl)thioxo-methyl]	$CHCl_3$	310(4.17),514(2.38)	143-0437-73
Disulfide, bis[(4-methylphenyl)thioxo-methyl]	$CHCl_3$	323(4.02),523(2.47)	143-0437-73
$C_{16}H_{15}$			
Methylium, cyclopropyldiphenyl-	FSO_3H at -75°	318(<4.0),434(4.53)	59-0803-73
$C_{16}H_{15}BrN_2O$			
Isoquinolinium, 2-(benzoylamino)-3,4-di-hydro-, bromide	EtOH	267(3.64),272(3.65), 306(3.68)	95-0648-73
Pyridinium, 1-[(1,2-dihydro-2-oxo-3-quinolinyl)methyl]-3-methyl-, bromide	H_2O	223(4.51),247(4.04), 270(4.10),332(3.88)	44-2351-73
Pyridinium, 1-[(1,2-dihydro-2-oxo-3-quinolinyl)methyl]-4-methyl-, bromide	H_2O	225(4.53),247(4.06), 263(3.92),275(3.92), 331(3.83)	44-2351-73
$C_{16}H_{15}BrN_2O_2S$			
Benzenesulfonamide, N-(3-bromo-1,3-di-hydro-1-methyl-2H-indol-2-ylidene)-4-methyl-	n.s.g.	204(4.16),225(4.46), 263(4.03),281(4.02)	39-1943-73C
$C_{16}H_{15}BrN_4O_6$			
2,4,6(1H,3H,5H)-Pyrimidinetrione, 5-[5-(bromomethyl)-1,2,3,4-tetrahydro-1,3-dimethyl-2,4-dioxo-7H-pyrano[2,3-d]-pyrimidin-7-ylidene]-1,3-dimethyl-	MeOH	440(4.09)	39-0823-73C
$C_{16}H_{15}Cl$			
Bicyclo[3.3.1]nonadiene, 2-chloro-9-(phenylmethylene)-	MeOH	285(4.20)	35-6770-73

Compound	Solvent	$\lambda_{max}(\log \epsilon)$	Ref.
$C_{16}H_{15}ClN_2$			
6H-Indolo[2,3-a]quinolizin-5-ium, 7,12-dihydro-1-methyl-, chloride	EtOH-HCl	219(4.44),314(4.21), 386(4.30)	2-0621-73
	EtOH-KOH	223(4.52),266(4.11), 365(4.21),420(4.36)	2-0621-73
$C_{16}H_{15}ClN_2O_2S$			
Benzenesulfonamide, N-(3-chloro-1,3-dihydro-1-methyl-2H-indol-2-ylidene)-4-methyl-	n.s.g.	226(4.76),288(4.06)	39-1943-73C
Benzenesulfonamide, 4-chloro-N-[2-(1H-indol-3-yl)ethyl]-	EtOH	223(4.67),281(3.77), 291(3.70)	39-1602-73C
$C_{16}H_{15}ClN_2O_6$			
2,4(1H,3H)-Pyrimidinedione, 1-(5-O-benzoyl-3-chloro-3-deoxy-β-D-arabinofuranosyl)-	MeOH	227(4.18),259(4.03)	117-0075-73
$C_{16}H_{15}ClN_5O_6PS$			
Adenosine, 8-[(4-chlorophenyl)thio]-, cyclic 3',5'-(hydrogen phosphate)	pH 1	281(4.20)	69-5310-73
	pH 11	283(4.14)	69-5310-73
$C_{16}H_{15}Cl_2NO_3S$			
2-Phenoxathiinamine, N,N-bis(2-chloroethyl)-, 10,10-dioxide	EtOH	270(4.45),352(3.74)	80-1617-73
$C_{16}H_{15}IO_4$			
3H-3,10a-Methano-1H-indeno[2,1-c]oxepin-10-carboxylic acid, 4,5,5a,10-tetrahydro-4-iodo-9-methyl-1-oxo-	MeCN	262(2.94)	44-0741-73
$C_{16}H_{15}N$			
Indolo[1,7-ab][1]benzazepine, 1,2,6,7-tetrahydro-	n.s.g.	211(4.43),294(4.27)	39-1041-73C
Quinoline, 2-(1,3,5-heptatrienyl)-, (E,E,E)-	C_6H_{12}	293(4.47),329(4.49), 344(4.50),353(4.51), 360(4.52)	54-0683-73
$C_{16}H_{15}NO$			
Acetamide, N-(1,2-diphenylethenyl)-, cis	MeOH	294(4.37)	104-2119-73
trans	MeOH	291(4.11)	104-2119-73
Acetamide, N-(2,2-diphenylethenyl)-	MeOH	284(4.29)	104-2119-73
2,4,6-Cycloheptatrien-1-one, 2-amino-4-[2-(4-methylphenyl)ethenyl]-	MeOH	239(3.98),327(4.50), 430(3.94)	18-0199-73
2,4,6-Cycloheptatrien-1-one, 2-amino-6-[2-(4-methylphenyl)ethenyl]-	MeOH	245(4.10),328(4.62), 430(3.98)	18-0199-73
1H-Indole, 3-(4-methoxyphenyl)-1-methyl-	EtOH	237(4.41),266(4.22), 300s(4.00)	94-2786-73
3H-Indol-3-ol, 3,5-dimethyl-2-phenyl-	EtOH	235s(4.12),242(4.19), 249(4.16),324(4.09)	117-0017-73
Isoxazole, 4,5-dihydro-3-(4-methoxyphenyl)-5-phenyl-	EtOH	256(4.31)	33-2588-73
Oxazole, 2,5-dihydro-2-methyl-4,5-diphenyl-, cis	EtOH	245(4.09)	33-2611-73
trans	EtOH	246(4.08)	33-2611-73
Oxazole, 2,5-dihydro-4-(4-methylphenyl)-5-phenyl-	EtOH	254(4.16)	33-2588-73
Oxazole, 2,5-dihydro-5-(4-methylphenyl)-4-phenyl-	EtOH	220(4.21),244(4.15)	33-2611-73

Compound	Solvent	$\lambda_{max}(\log \epsilon)$	Ref.
Phenanthridine, 6-(methoxymethyl)-5-methyl-, perchlorate	EtOH	245(4.48),340(3.76)	103-0076-73
2-Propenamide, N-(4-methylphenyl)-3-phenyl-, cis	EtOH	266(4.03)	33-2588-73
trans	EtOH	292(4.43)	33-2588-73
2-Propen-1-one, 3-amino-3-(4-methylphenyl)-	EtOH	252(4.14),357(4.39)	33-2588-73
2-Propen-1-one, 1-(4-methylphenyl)-3-phenyl-, oxime, anti	EtOH	257(4.25)	33-2588-73
2:3 syn:anti mixture	EtOH	291(4.37)	33-2588-73
2-Propen-1-one, 3-(4-methylphenyl)-1-phenyl-, oxime, anti-cis	EtOH	253(4.29)	33-2588-73
$C_{16}H_{15}NOS$			
Acetamide, N-(6,11-dihydrodibenzo[b,e]thiepin-2-yl)-	MeOH	280(4.24)	73-1602-73
Ethanone, 1-(6,11-dihydrodibenzo[b,e]thiepin-2-yl)-, oxime	MeOH	231(3.87),317(4.22)	73-1602-73
$C_{16}H_{15}NO_2$			
2,4,6-Cycloheptatrien-1-one, 2-amino-4-[2-(4-methoxyphenyl)ethenyl]-	MeOH	245(4.11),337(4.57), 370(4.32),429(4.11)	18-0199-73
2,4,6-Cycloheptatrien-1-one, 2-amino-6-[2-(4-methoxyphenyl)ethenyl]-	MeOH	249(4.19),331(4.79), 428(4.19)	18-0199-73
2H-Indol-2-one, 1,3-dihydro-3-(4-methoxyphenyl)-1-methyl-	EtOH	226(4.49),255(4.13), 266s(4.05),277s(3.78), 284(3.70)	94-2739-73
1-Propanone, 1-phenyl-3-[(phenylmethylene)amino]-, N-oxide	EtOH	294(4.24)	104-0793-73
2H-Pyrrole-3-carboxylic acid, 3,4-dihydro-5-(2-naphthalenyl)-, methyl ester	C_6H_{12}	233(4.66),241(4.78), 248(4.77),264(3.89), 273(4.02),282(4.10), 290(3.95),293(4.00), 322(2.94),328(2.75), 337(2.94)	35-1945-73
2-Pyrrolidinone, 5-hydroxy-1,5-diphenyl-	H_2SO_4	261(4.03),298(4.17)	24-1423-73
$C_{16}H_{15}NO_2S$			
Dibenzo[b,f]thiepin, 2-(ethoxycarbonylamino)-	MeOH	225(4.48),264(4.57), 296(3.70)	73-2484-73
2,4,6-Heptatrienoic acid, 7-(2-benzothiazolyl)-, ethyl ester, (E,E,E)-	CH_2Cl_2	365(4.71)	54-0683-73
Isoquinoline, 6,7-dimethoxy-1-(2-thienylmethyl)-	MeOH	239(4.82),314(3.57), 327(3.64)	83-0592-73
Thiazolo[3,2-a]pyridinium, 8-ethoxy-3-hydroxy-5-methyl-2-phenyl-, hydroxide, inner salt	50% dioxan-HCl	448(--)	1-1763-73
	50% dioxan-NaOH	225s(3.9),242(4.0), 290(3.8),450(4.1)	1-1763-73
$C_{16}H_{15}NO_2S_2$			
Dibenzo[b,f]thiepin-2-sulfonamide, N,N-dimethyl-	MeOH	232(4.42),272(4.39), 296(3.79)	73-2137-73
$C_{16}H_{15}NO_3$			
Acetamide, 2-(4-acetylphenoxy)-N-phenyl-	EtOH	210(4.25),263(4.37)	111-0574-73
Acetic acid, cyano[3-(1-methylethylidene)-1(3H)-isobenzofuranylidene]-, ethyl ester	EtOH	266(4.30),277(4.27), 302(3.76),315(3.84), 332(3.82),372(4.12), 390s(3.95)	39-1731-73C

Compound	Solvent	λ max (log ε)	Ref.
9H-Carbazole, 9-acetyl-2,3-dimethoxy-	EtOH	224(4.65),240s(4.40), 295(4.19),303s(4.16), 324(4.07)	44-0215-73
2-Cyclopenten-1-one, 2-[(3,4-dihydro-1(2H)-isoquinolinylidene)acetyl]-3-hydroxy-	EtOH	263(4.20),400(4.43)	30-0445-73 +70-1794-73
Isoquinoline, 1-(2-furanylmethyl)-	MeOH	239(4.86),314(3.58), 326(3.64)	83-0592-73
Lycorinone, 1-deoxy-, racemic	MeOH	227(4.20),290(3.68)	88-4587-73
4,7-Methanoisobenzofuran-1(3H)-one, 3a,4,7,7a-tetrahydro-3-[(4-methoxyphenyl)imino]-	MeCN	266(3.86)	35-6792-73
4,7-Methano-1H-isoindole-1,3(2H)-dione, 3a,4,7,7a-tetrahydro-2-(4-methoxyphenyl)-	MeCN	273(3.15)	35-6792-73
$C_{16}H_{15}NO_3S_2$			
Dibenzo[b,f]thiepin-2-sulfonamide, 10,11-dihydro-N,N-dimethyl-11-oxo-	MeOH	229(4.30),241(4.27), 281(4.01),332(3.64)	73-2137-73
$C_{16}H_{15}NO_4$			
Benzoic acid, 2-hydroxy-, 2-[(ethylamino)carbonyl]phenyl ester	EtOH	238(4.22),304(3.86)	78-3173-73
$C_{16}H_{15}NO_6$			
5H-Cyclopropa[g]quinoline-5a,6a(6H,7H)-dicarboxylic acid, 5,7-dioxo-, diethyl ester	EtOH	218(4.36),243(3.88)	39-0026-73C
5H-Cycloprop[g]isoquinoline-5a,6a-dicarboxylic acid, 6,7-dihydro-5,7-dioxo-, diethyl ester	EtOH	212(4.33),238s(--), 297(3.52)	39-0026-73C
Ethenetricarboxylic acid, 1H-indol-3-yl-, trimethyl ester	EtOH	271(3.97),360(4.14)	95-1008-73
$C_{16}H_{15}NO_7$			
Spiro[1,3-dioxolane-2,6'(10'H)-[1H]pyrano[3,4-f]indolizine]-3'-carboxylic acid, 7',8'-dihydro-1',10'-dioxo-, ethyl ester	EtOH	240s(4.03),248(4.08), 262(4.06),298s(3.85), 313(3.99),325s(3.96), 364(3.88)	78-1949-73
$C_{16}H_{15}NS$			
4H-Thiepino[3,4,5,6-def]carbazole, 4-ethyl-8,10-dihydro-	EtOH	248(4.52),257(4.51), 266(4.48),288(3.92), 299(4.11),338(3.78), 353(3.88)	39-2818-73C
$C_{16}H_{15}N_2$			
6H-Indolo[2,3-a]quinolizin-5-ium, 7,12-dihydro-1-methyl-, chloride	EtOH-HCl	219(4.44),314(4.21), 386(4.30)	2-0621-73
	EtOH-KOH	223(4.52),266(4.11), 365(4.21),420(4.36)	2-0621-73
$C_{16}H_{15}N_2O$			
Isoquinolinium, 2-(benzoylamino)-3,4-dihydro-, bromide (see $C_{16}H_{15}BrN_2O$)	EtOH	267(3.64),272(3.65), 306(3.68)	95-0648-73
$C_{16}H_{15}N_3$			
Benzeneacetonitrile, α-[1-(2-phenylhydrazino)ethylidene]-	MeOH	278(4.26),300s(3.96)	28-1457-73A

Compound	Solvent	$\lambda_{max}(\log \epsilon)$	Ref.
1H-Imidazo[1,2-a]benzimidazole, 2,3-dihydro-1-methyl-2-phenyl-	MeOH	230(3.9),245(3.9), 280(4.0)	103-0726-73
3H-Imidazo[1,2-a]benzimidazole, 2,9-dihydro-9-methyl-2-phenyl-	MeOH	285(3.9),300(3.9)	103-0726-73
$C_{16}H_{15}N_3O$			
Azepino[1',2':1,2]pyrimido[4,5-b]quinolin-13(7H)-one, 8,9,10,11-tetrahydro-	MeOH	246(4.6),280(4.3), 360(3.7)	24-3533-73
2-Pyrazoline, 1-acetyl-4-phenyl-3-(2-pyridinyl)-	$CHCl_3$	301(4.07)	103-0055-73
Pyrimido[1,2-b]indazol-2(1H)-one, 7,8,9,10-tetrahydro-4-phenyl-	MeOH	242(4.50),294(4.00)	4-0261-73
Pyrimido[1,2-b]indazol-4(1H)-one, 7,8,9,10-tetrahydro-2-phenyl-	MeOH	250(4.60),328(3.60)	4-0261-73
2(1H)-Quinazolinone, 4-[4-(dimethylamino)phenyl]-	EtOH	210(1.05),230(1.10), 270(--),400(--)	30-0828-73
1,2,4-Triazine, 2,5-dihydro-3-methoxy-5,5-diphenyl-	n.s.g.	225(4.34),284(4.55), 348(3.86)	22-2493-73
$C_{16}H_{15}N_3OS_3$			
4-Thiazolidinone, N-ethyl-5-[1-methyl-2-[N-(2-pyridinyl)thiazol-2-ylidene]ethylidene]-2-thioxo-	EtOH	537(5.26)	103-0687-73
$C_{16}H_{15}N_3O_2S_2$			
1,3,4-Thiadiazolium, 3-methyl-2-(4-methylphenyl)-5-[(phenylsulfonyl)amino]-, hydroxide, inner salt	MeOH	313(3.92)	103-1216-73
$C_{16}H_{15}N_3O_3$			
Pyrido[2,3-d]pyrimidine-2,4,5(1H,3H,8H)-trione, 1,3,7-trimethyl-8-phenyl-	EtOH	218(4.18),247(4.56), 265(4.13)	94-2014-73
$C_{16}H_{15}N_3O_3S_2$			
1,3,4-Thiadiazolium, 2-(4-methoxyphenyl)-3-methyl-5-[(phenylsulfonyl)amino]-, hydroxide, inner salt	MeOH	274(3.87),330(4.18)	103-1216-73
$C_{16}H_{15}N_3O_5$			
Pyrrolo[3,4-b]quinolizine-10-carboxylic acid, 1,2,3,4-tetrahydro-1-(methoxyimino)-2-methyl-3,4-dioxo-, ethyl ester	EtOH	273(4.09),435(4.28), 460(4.43)	94-1667-73
$C_{16}H_{15}N_3S$			
1H-2-Benzothiopyran-4-carbonitrile, 3-amino-5,6,7,8-tetrahydro-1-(phenylimino)-	MeOH	225(4.73),306(4.24), 377(3.75)	48-0679-73
1,2,4-Triazine, 2,5-dihydro-3-(methylthio)-5,5-diphenyl-	n.s.g.	222(4.20),288(4.45), 351(3.48)	22-2493-73
$C_{16}H_{15}N_4O_4$			
Benzeneacetaldehyde, 2-[3-(2-methoxy-4-nitrophenyl)-1-triazenyl]- -methyl-, ion(1-)	50% dioxan	530(4.35)	35-3400-73
$C_{16}H_{15}N_5O$			
1H-1,2,3-Triazole-4-carboxylic acid, 5-(4-methylphenyl)-1-phenyl-, hydrazide	EtOH	239(4.39)	42-0589-73

Compound	Solvent	λ_{max}(log ε)	Ref.
$C_{16}H_{16}$			
9H-Fluorene, 1,2,8-trimethyl-	EtOH	226s(4.29),262s(4.27), 266s(4.32),271(4.36), 284(4.19),293(3.88), 297s(3.72),305(3.87)	39-1511-73C
9H-Fluorene, 1,4,6-trimethyl-	EtOH	258s(5.51),263(5.20), 268(5.22),272(5.20), 278s(5.06),288(4.91), 292s(4.86),299(4.87)	39-1511-73C
Heptafulvalene, dimethyl-	EtOH	233(4.36),368(4.34)	35-0826-73
Naphthalene, 1-methyl-4-(2,4-pentadien-yl)-	EtOH	226(4.83),279s(3.84), 288(3.92),298s(3.77), 316s(2.90),320s(2.66)	33-2479-73
Naphthalene, 2-methyl-1-(2,4-pentadien-yl)-	EtOH	227(4.95),276(3.81), 284(3.84),290s(3.75), 307(3.07),314s(2.85), 322(2.94)	33-2479-73
Naphthalene, 1,2,3,4-tetrahydro-6-phen-yl-	EtOH	213(4.65),254(4.43)	132-0051-73
Phenanthrene, 9,10-dihydro-2,7-dimethyl-	C_6H_{12}	273(4.34),302(3.77)	24-2190-73
$C_{16}H_{16}BrNO_6$			
5H-Cyclohepta[b]pyridine-6,8-dicarbox-ylic acid, 6-bromo-6,7-dihydro-9-hy-droxy-5-oxo-, ethyl ester	EtOH	208(4.04),223(4.09), 239(4.10),281(4.27), 320s(--)	39-0026-73C
$C_{16}H_{16}BrN_3O$			
Acetamide, N-[2-bromo-3,4-dimethyl-6-(phenylazo)phenyl]-	EtOH	330(4.25),450(3.02)	65-1574-73
$C_{16}H_{16}ClN_3$			
Pyrrolidine, 1-[5-[(4-chlorophenyl)azo]-phenyl]-	C_6H_{12}	417(4.54)	18-0194-73
	50%EtOH-HCl	329(3.48),520(4.76)	18-0194-73
$C_{16}H_{16}ClN_3O$			
3-Pyridinecarboxamide, 5-[(4-chloro-1H-indol-3-yl)methyl]-1,4-dihydro-1-methyl-	MeOH	221(4.57),281(3.86), 359(3.81)	33-0374-73
$C_{16}H_{16}ClN_5O_2$			
Imidodicarbonic dihydrazide, N'-[2-(4-chlorophenyl)ethylidene]-2-phenyl-	EtOH	228(4.37),327(4.39), 261s(4.11)	48-0492-73
$C_{16}H_{16}ClN_5O_4$			
Adenosine, N-(2-chlorophenyl)-	pH 1.0	274(4.34)	87-0358-73
	H_2O	279(4.32)	87-0358-73
	pH 13	281.5(4.30)	87-0358-73
Adenosine, N-(3-chlorophenyl)-	pH 1.0	277(4.27)	87-0358-73
	H_2O	293.5(4.37)	87-0358-73
	pH 13	294.5(4.38)	87-0358-73
Adenosine, N-(4-chlorophenyl)-	pH 1.0	277(4.31)	87-0358-73
	H_2O	294.5(4.40)	87-0358-73
	pH 13	294.5(4.41)	87-0358-73
$C_{16}H_{16}F_2O$			
Benzenebutanol, 4-fluoro-α-(4-fluoro-phenyl)-	EtOH	227(4.06),251(4.16)	73-3879-73
$C_{16}H_{16}NO$			
Isoxazolium, 4,5-dihydro-2-methyl-3,5-diphenyl-, perchlorate	EtOH	212s(--),300(3.99)	22-1390-73

Compound	Solvent	λ max(log ε)	Ref.
Pyridinium, 1-[3-(4-ethylphenyl)-3-oxo-1-propenyl]-, diphenyl phosphate	H_2O	271(4.28),298(4.14)	24-0435-73
$C_{16}H_{16}NO_3$			
Pyrylium, 2-amino-3-(ethoxycarbonyl)-6-(2-phenylethenyl)-, perchlorate	HOAc	280(3.93),325s(3.28), 425(4.31)	97-0132-73
$C_{16}H_{16}N_2$			
Benzenamine, 2-(3,3-dimethyl-3H-indol-2-yl)-	EtOH	238(4.36),246s(4.30), 264s(4.01),294(4.09), 306(4.07),321(3.85), 383(4.06)	78-1429-73
9,10-Ethanoanthracene-1,5-diamine, (-)-	MeOH	199(4.69),212s(4.56), 232s(4.32),288(3.56)	18-0915-73
	EtOH-HCl	209s(4.54),250s(2.98), 263(3.00),270(3.05), 290(2.32)	18-0915-73
5H-Indeno[2,1-c]cinnoline, 6,6a,7,11b-tetrahydro-5-methyl-	MeCN	253(3.90),294(3.47)	22-3487-73
Indol-2-amine, 3-methyl-1-(phenylmethyl)-, hydrochloride	MeOH	262(3.95)	103-0471-73
1H-Indole-3-ethanamine, 1-phenyl-	EtOH	217(4.32),258(4.20), 297(3.95)	103-0196-73
Pyridazine, 1,4,5,6-tetrahydro-3,6-diphenyl-	n.s.g.	386(2.89)	89-0224-73
$C_{16}H_{16}N_2O$			
Benzamide, N-(3,4-dihydro-2(1H)-isoquinolinyl)-	EtOH	265(3.73),272(3.66)	95-0648-73
1H-Cyclopenta[b]quinoline-9-carboxamide, 2,3-dihydro-N-2-propenyl-	EtOH	238(4.72),295(4.03), 308(4.07),322(4.11)	103-1005-73
1,2-Diazetidin-3-one, 4,4-dimethyl-1,2-diphenyl-	EtOH	245(4.01),263(4.04)	39-1297-73C
Propiophenone, benzoylhydrazone	EtOH	286(4.39)	78-2119-73
$C_{16}H_{16}N_2O_2$			
Benzamide, 2-[4-(dimethylamino)benzoyl]-	EtOH	210(4.42),262(4.18), 352(3.96)	39-1160-73B
	$CHCl_3$	348(3.96)	39-1160-73B
	dioxan	215(4.27),242(4.13), 346(4.28)	39-1160-73B
	MeCN	216(4.24),242(4.15), 350(4.26)	39-1160-73B
1H-Indazole, 4-methoxy-3-(4-methoxyphenyl)-1-methyl-	MeOH	212(4.42),244(4.13), 270(3.93),308(4.03)	24-3432-73
Lysergic acid	H_2O	309(3.92)	39-1312-73B
	EtOH	310(3.97)	39-1312-73B
2,5-Piperazinedione, 3-(3-phenyl-2-propenylidene)-6-propylidene-	EtOH	365(4.60)	18-3876-73
1-Propanone, 1-phenyl-3-[(phenylmethylene)amino]-, oxime N-oxide	EtOH	294(4.29)	104-0793-73
$C_{16}H_{16}N_2O_2S$			
Benzenesulfonamide, N-1H-indol-2-yl-N,4-dimethyl-	EtOH	218(4.56),273(3.90), 283(3.93),292(3.92)	39-1602-73C
$C_{16}H_{16}N_2O_3$			
Acetamide, [4-(1-hydroxyiminoethyl)phenoxy]-N-phenyl-	EtOH	208(4.44),252(4.44)	111-0574-73
Benzamide, 2-[(2-aminobenzoyl)oxy]-N-ethyl-	EtOH	254(3.03),288(3.46), 302(3.45),317(3.44)	78-3173-73

Compound	Solvent	λ_{max}(log ε)	Ref.
Benzenepropanoic acid, α-(2-cyanoethyl)-2-(3-cyano-1-oxopropyl)-	EtOH	244(3.81),287(3.00)	22-0691-73
1H-1,2-Diazepin-6-ol, 1-acetyl-5-methyl-4-phenyl-, acetate	MeOH	260s(--),352(2.70)	44-2939-73
$C_{16}H_{16}N_2O_4$			
Anthranilic acid, N,N'-ethylenedi-	MeOH	260(4.28),349(4.03)	80-0589-73
(also lanthanide complexes)	DMF	349(4.0)	80-0589-73
1-Azulenecarboxylic acid, 2-(acetylamino)-3-(formylamino)-, ethyl ester	MeOH	225s(4.32),248(4.35), 314(4.73),360(3.84), 375s(3.70),535(2.67)	18-3161-73
2,5-Cyclohexadiene-1,4-dione, 3-acetyl-2-[(2-hydroxyethyl)amino]-5-(phenylamino)-	EtOH	245(4.14),299(4.18), 350(4.31),490(3.25)	78-2881-73
	CH_2Cl_2	248(4.12),300(4.11), 353(4.32),488(3.21)	78-2881-73
Ethanediamide, N,N'-bis(4-methoxyphenyl)-	dioxan	295(4.35)	30-0001-73
2-Quinolinecarboxylic acid, 6-(acetylamino)-1,4-dihydro-4-oxo-3-(2-propenyl)-, methyl ester	MeOH	264(4.57),367(3.89)	24-0355-73
$C_{16}H_{16}N_2O_4S$			
Benzamide, N-[2-[(dimethylamino)sulfonyl]phenyl]-2-formyl-	EtOH	222(4.39),308(3.71)	7-0635-73
5-Thia-1-azabicyclo[4.2.0]oct-2-ene-2-carboxylic acid, 3-methyl-8-oxo-7-[(phenylacetyl)amino]-	EtOH	296(3.63)	39-1321-73C
$C_{16}H_{16}N_2O_5$			
Benzamide, N-[[4-acetoxy-4,5-dihydro-4-(1-methylethyl)-5-oxo-2-oxazolyl]methylene]-	ether	239(3.88)	88-2163-73
1,4-Cyclohexadiene-1-carboxylic acid, 2-[(2-hydroxyethyl)amino]-3,6-dioxo-5-(phenylamino)-, methyl ester	EtOH	250(4.17),283s(3.91), 350(4.32),499(3.02)	78-2881-73
	CH_2Cl_2	253(4.20),277s(4.06), 352(4.32),503(3.19)	78-2881-73
8H-Imidazo[5,1-c][1,4]oxazine-1-carboxylic acid, 5,6-dihydro-5-(4-methoxyphenyl)-6-methyl-8-oxo-, methyl ester	EtOH	213s(4.15),231(4.21), 263(4.14)	95-0893-73
$C_{16}H_{16}N_2O_5S$			
Benzoic acid, 2-[[[[2-(dimethylamino)sulfonyl]phenyl]amino]carbonyl]-	EtOH	293(3.81)	7-0635-73
$C_{16}H_{16}N_3O_3P$			
Phosphonic acid, [2-(phenylamino)-4-quinazolinyl]-, dimethyl ester	EtOH	266(3.97),288(3.99), 386(3.12)	48-0649-73
$C_{16}H_{16}N_3S$			
Thiazolo[3,2-a]pyrimidin-4-ium, 5-[2-[4-(dimethylamino)phenyl]ethenyl]-, perchlorate	n.s.g.	532(4.84)	124-1151-73
Thiazolo[3,2-a]pyrimidin-4-ium, 7-[2-[4-(dimethylamino)phenyl]ethenyl]-, perchlorate	n.s.g.	530(4.55)	124-1151-73
$C_{16}H_{16}N_4O_3$			
Acetamide, N-[2-[(3,5-dimethyl-1H-pyrazol-4-yl)methyl]-2,3-dihydro-1,3-dioxo-1H-isoindol-4-yl]-	EtOH	241(4.47),252(4.46), 261s(4.37),328(3.57)	87-0512-73

Compound	Solvent	λ_{max}(log ε)	Ref.
2,4,6(1H,3H,5H)-Pyrimidinetrione, 1,3-dimethyl-5-(3-methyl-1-phenyl-1H-pyrazol-5-yl)-, compd. with phenylhydrazine	EtOH	255(4.23)	94-2639-73
$C_{16}H_{16}N_4O_3S$			
Acetic acid, spiro[cyclopentane-1,6(7'H)-[1,2,4]triazino[5,6-d][3,1]benzoxazepin]-3'-ylthio-	EtOH	238(4.40),348(4.00), 444(3.78)	78-0639-73
$C_{16}H_{16}N_4O_4$			
3-Indazolecarboxaldehyde, 2,3-dihydro-3-methyl-2-[(2-methoxy-4-nitrophenyl)amino]-	EtOH	395(4.39)	35-3400-73
$C_{16}H_{16}N_4O_5$			
Phenol, 2-butyl-4-[(2,4-dinitrophenyl)-azo]- (spectra in 50% DMSO)	acid	405(4.32)	1-3641-73
	KOH	604(4.79)	1-3641-73
Phenol, 3-butyl-4-[(2,4-dinitrophenyl)-azo]- (spectra in 50% DMSO)	acid	405(4.29)	1-3641-73
	KOH	592(4.66)	1-3641-73
Phenol, 4-[(2,4-dinitrophenyl)azo]-2-methyl-5-propyl- (first two spectra in 50% DMSO)	acid	414(4.30)	1-3641-73
	KOH	593(4.71)	1-3641-73
	C_2Cl_4	392(--),427(--)	1-3632-73
Phenol, 4-[(2,4-dinitrophenyl)azo]-3-methyl-5-propyl- (spectra in 50% DMSO)	acid	402(4.25)	1-3641-73
	KOH	564(4.57)	1-3641-73
Phenol, 4-[(2,4-dinitrophenyl)azo]-5-methyl-2-propyl- (first two spectra in 50% DMSO)	acid	417(4.34)	1-3641-73
	KOH	596(4.80)	1-3641-73
	C_2Cl_4	393(4.54),430(4.60)	1-3632-73
Phenol, 2,3,5,6-tetramethyl-4-[(2,4-dinitrophenyl)azo]- (first two spectra in 50% DMSO)	acid	445(4.31)	1-3641-73
	KOH	608(4.66)	1-3641-73
	C_2Cl_4	391(4.49),421(4.47)	1-3632-73
$C_{16}H_{16}N_4O_6$			
2,4,6(1H,3H,5HO-Pyrimidinetrione, 1,3-dimethyl-5-(1,2,3,4-tetrahydro-1,3,5-trimethyl-2,4-dioxo-7H-pyrano[2,3-d]-pyrimidin-7-ylidene)-	$CHCl_3$	424(4.50),442(4.51)	39-0823-73C
$C_{16}H_{16}N_4O_9S$			
2H-Pyrano[2,3-d]pyrimidine-5-methane-sulfonic acid, 1,3,4,7-tetrahydro-1,3-dimethyl-2,4-dioxo-7-(tetrahydro-1,3-dimethyl-2,4,6-trioxo-5(2H)-pyrimidinylidene)-	H_2O	440(4.28),457(4.32)	39-0823-73C
$C_{16}H_{16}N_6O_2$			
Furo[3,2-c]pyridazin-4(1H)-one, 4a,6,7-7a-tetrahydro-7-hydroxy-1-(2-pyridinyl)-, 2-pyridinylhydrazone, [4aS-(4aα,7β,7aα)-	EtOH	247(4.04),307(3.90), 368(3.96)	136-0165-73E
$C_{16}H_{16}N_6O_3$			
L-Phenylalanine, N-[(1H-purin-6-yl-amino)carbonyl]-, methyl ester	pH 1-2	277(4.30)	87-0139-73
	pH 5-7	267(4.26)	87-0139-73
	pH 12	278(4.18)	87-0139-73
DL-Phenylalanine, N-(N-1H-purin-6-yl-glycyl)-	pH 1	278(4.19)	94-2349-73
	pH 7	267(4.16)	94-2349-73
	pH 13	274(4.13),281s(4.01)	94-2349-73

Compound	Solvent	$\lambda_{max}(\log \epsilon)$	Ref.
$C_{16}H_{16}O$			
1-Butanone, 1,3-diphenyl-	EtOH	243(4.10),278(3.08)	44-3893-73
Methanone, phenyl(2,4,6-trimethylphenyl)-	C_6H_{12}	245(4.29),270s(3.49), 335(2.13)	104-1986-73
2-Naphthalenol, 1,2-dihydro-1-methyl-1-(2,4-pentadienyl)-	EtOH	218(4.56),225s(4.52), 266(3.87)	33-2479-73
1(2H)-Naphthalenone, 2-methyl-2-(2,4-pentadienyl)-	EtOH	225(4.64),237(4.69), 264(3.72),271s(3.67), 282s(3.46),334(3.33)	33-2479-73
2(1H)-Naphthalenone, 1-methyl-1-(2,4-pentadienyl)-	EtOH	226(4.47),237s(4.37), 308(3.97)	33-2479-73
$C_{16}H_{16}OS$			
Benzenecarbothioic acid, O-(1-methyl-2-phenylethyl) ester	C_6H_{12}	252(3.98),289(4.06), 417(2.11)	39-1580-73C
Benzenecarbothioic acid, 2-(phenylmethyl)-, O-ethyl ester	C_6H_{12}	266(3.98),406(2.49)	39-1571-73C
3-Hexen-2-one, 3-phenyl-4-(2-thienyl)-	EtOH	253(4.09),335(3.93)	48-0993-73
non-crystalline stereoisomer	EtOH	245(4.04),329(3.95)	48-0993-73
$C_{16}H_{16}O_2$			
1,4-Naphthalenedione, 2-methyl-3-(3-methyl-2-butenyl)-	EtOH	245(4.2),249(4.2), 264(4.1),272(4.1), 334(3.4)	1-3211-73
Phenanthrene, 9,10-dihydro-2,7-dimethoxy-, cation radical	CH_2Cl_2-TFA	429(4.57),750(4.21)	39-1594-73B
$C_{16}H_{16}O_2S$			
Benzenecarbothioic acid, O-[2-(4-methoxyphenyl)ethyl] ester	C_6H_{12}	244(3.92),278(4.12), 283(4.13),290(4.07), 420(2.15)	39-1574-73C
Benzenecarbothioic acid, 4-methoxy-, O-(2-phenylethyl) ester	EtOH	228(4.07),233(4.06), 260(3.78),311(4.30), 415(2.36)	39-1574-73C
$C_{16}H_{16}O_3$			
Cordiachrome G	EtOH	248(4.10),326(2.76)	39-1556-73C
1-Dibenzofurancarboxylic acid, 1,9b-dihydro-4,9b-dimethyl-, methyl ester, cis	90% EtOH	216(3.85),233s(3.77), 265s(3.51),279(3.72), 298s(3.46)	12-1093-73
trans	90% EtOH	213(3.88),243(3.56), 283(3.70),312(3.38)	12-1093-73
1-Dibenzofurancarboxylic acid, 3,9b-dihydro-4,9b-dimethyl-, methyl ester	90% EtOH	232s(3.84),280(3.40), 284s(3.36)	12-1093-73
2,5-Hexadienoic acid, 5-(3-methyl-2-benzofuranyl)-, methyl ester	90% EtOH	213(4.20),281s(4.10), 287(4.15),294(4.16), 303s(4.08),348(3.32)	12-1093-73
Phenanthro[9,10-c]furan-1,3-dione, 4,5,6,7,8,9,10,11-octahydro-	MeCN	230(4.50),283(3.52), 325(3.54)	22-2121-73
$C_{16}H_{16}O_4$			
Butanedioic acid, 2-naphthalenyl-, dimethyl ester	EtOH	225(4.97),269(3.76), 274(3.78)	2-0131-73
1,3-Cyclohexadiene-1-carboxylic acid, 6-(2-hydroxyphenyl)-4,6-dimethyl-5-oxo-, methyl ester	90% EtOH	216(4.08),282(3.73), 302s(3.91),311(3.96), 323s(3.85)	12-1093-73
17,18-Dioxatricyclo[12.2.1.1^{4,7}]octadeca-1(16),2,4,6,12,14-hexaene-9,11-diol	MeOH	261(4.17),345(3.72), 364(3.76),383(3.67)	88-5065-73
	H_2SO_4	334(4.48),349(4.52)	88-5065-73

Compound	Solvent	λ max(log ε)	Ref.
Methanone, (2,4-dimethoxyphenyl)(3-methoxyphenyl)-	EtOH	219(4.26),240s(3.89), 250s(3.81),285(3.70), 308(3.78)	35-7752-73
3H-3,10a-Methano-1H-indeno[2,1-c]oxepin-10-carboxylic acid, 4,5,5a,10-tetrahydro-9-methyl-1-oxo-, (3α,5aβ,10β-10aα)-	MeCN	263(2.40),272(2.27)	44-0741-73
1,4-Naphthalenedione, 5,8-dihydroxy-2-(4-methyl-3-pentenyl)-	EtOH	226(4.10),280(3.98), 488(3.83),510(3.86), 540(3.70)	2-0528-73
Naphtho[1,2-b]furan-5(4H)-one, 4-ethenyl-2,3,3a,9b-tetrahydro-6,9-dihydroxy-4-methyl-3-methylene-, (3aα,4β,9bα)-(±)- (leucocordiachrome H)	EtOH	241s(3.97),271(3.69), 385(3.64)	39-1556-73C
$C_{16}H_{16}O_4S$			
Dibenzothiophene, 2,3,7,8-tetramethoxy-	MeOH	210(4.58),240(4.64), 310(4.24)	2-0863-73
$C_{16}H_{16}O_5$			
2H-1-Benzopyran-2-one, 5,7-dimethoxy-6-(3-methyl-1-oxo-2-butenyl)-	EtOH	218s(4.09),247(4.16), 268s(4.09),332(4.10)	78-2943-73
1-Dibenzofurancarboxylic acid, 4a,9b-dihydro-4a-hydroperoxy-4,9b-dimethyl-	90% EtOH	216(3.94),280(3.99)	12-1093-73
Methanone, (2-hydroxy-4,5-dimethoxyphenyl)(2-methoxyphenyl)-	MeOH	239(4.15),284(4.07), 351(3.95)	39-1329-73C
Methanone, (2-hydroxy-4-methoxyphenyl)-(2,4-dimethoxyphenyl)-	MeOH	233(4.18),285(4.20), 333(4.10)	18-1498-73
Methanone, (2-hydroxy-6-methoxyphenyl)-(3,6-dihydroxy-2,4-dimethylphenyl)-	MeOH	210(4.24),221s(4.17), 246(3.96),266(3.96), 283(3.94),344(3.52)	24-1198-73
Methanone, (4-methoxyphenyl)(3,4-dimethoxyphenyl)-	MeOH	237(4.24),290(4.18), 336(4.20)	18-1498-73
Nodakenetin acetate	EtOH	224(3.98),247(3.59), 259(3.54),299s(--), 332(4.14)	102-2312-73
$C_{16}H_{16}O_5S$			
Dibenzothiophene, 2,3,7,8-tetramethoxy-, 5-oxide	MeOH	260(4.7),320(3.84)	2-0863-73
2,5-Thiophenedicarboxylic acid, 3-hydroxy-4-phenyl-, diethyl ester	EtOH	275(4.13)	2-0313-73
$C_{16}H_{16}O_6$			
Byakangelicin, (+)-	EtOH	222(4.38),241(4.12), 248(4.13),269(4.26), 311(4.10)	100-0333-73
7H-Furo[3,2-g][1]benzopyran-7-one, 9-(2,3-dihydroxy-3-methylbutoxy)-	EtOH	250(4.35),263s(4.14), 302(4.07)	64-0260-73C
Methanone, (2-hydroxy-4-methoxyphenyl)-(2-hydroxy-4,5-dimethoxyphenyl)-	MeOH	233s(4.19),249s(4.12), 288(4.12),365(4.06)	18-1498-73
$C_{16}H_{16}O_6S$			
Dibenzothiophene, 2,3,7,8-tetramethoxy-, 5,5-dioxide	MeOH	250(4.6),320(4.06)	2-0863-73
$C_{16}H_{16}O_8$			
2H-1-Benzopyran-2-one, 7-acetoxy-6-(acetoxymethyl)-5,8-dimethoxy-	MeOH	209(4.36),225s(4.18), 251(3.84),293(4.06)	78-2645-73

Compound	Solvent	$\lambda_{max}(\log \epsilon)$	Ref.
$C_{16}H_{17}$			
Cycloheptatrienylium, [1-(2,4,6-cyclo-heptatrien-1-yl)ethyl]-, ion	pH 2	220(4.61),290(4.05), 612(4.21)	138-1169-73
Ethylium, 1,1-bis(4-methylphenyl)-	FSO_3H at -75°	320(4.04),450(4.78)	59-0803-73
$C_{16}H_{17}BF_4S$			
Sulfonium, (2-methylcyclopropyl)diphen-yl-, tetrafluoroborate	EtOH	234(3.33),258(2.76), 264(2.83),273(2.73)	35-5298-73
$C_{16}H_{17}Br$			
Cycloocta[b]naphthalene, 5-bromo-6,7,8,9,10,11-hexahydro-	EtOH	215s(4.88),233(5.00), 259s(3.40),269s(3.60), 278(3.76),289(3.80), 297s(3.63),300s(3.62), 318(2.56),322(2.59)	44-1207-73
$C_{16}H_{17}BrO_2$			
Benzene, 2-bromo-1-methoxy-3,5-dimethyl-5-(phenylmethoxy)-	MeOH	211(4.44),230s(4.02), 282s(3.49),289(3.52)	24-1198-73
Phenol, 2-bromo-6-[(2-hydroxy-3,5-di-methylphenyl)methyl]-4-methyl-	dioxan	288(3.75)	126-0039-73L
$C_{16}H_{17}BrO_3$			
Benzenemethanol, 3-[(3-bromo-2-hydroxy-5-methylphenyl)methyl]-2-hydroxy-5-methyl-	dioxan	289(3.80)	126-0039-73L
$C_{16}H_{17}Cl$			
Cycloocta[b]naphthalene, 5-chloro-6,7,8,9,10,11-hexahydro-	EtOH	215s(4.46),227s(4.87), 232(5.06),259s(3.38), 269s(3.59),278(3.74), 288(3.78),297(3.60), 300s(3.58),319(2.52), 323(2.52)	44-1207-73
$C_{16}H_{17}ClN_2O$			
4H-Indazol-4-one, 3-(4-chlorophenyl)-1,5,6,7-tetrahydro-1,6,6-trimethyl-	MeOH	232(4.41),266(4.14)	24-0450-73
$C_{16}H_{17}Cl_2NO$			
Benzenamine, N,N-bis(2-chloroethyl)-2-phenoxy-	EtOH	259(3.97),290(3.47)	80-1617-73
Benzenamine, N,N-bis(2-chloroethyl)-3-phenoxy-	EtOH	262(4.34),314(3.51)	80-1617-73
Benzenamine, N,N-bis(2-chloroethyl)-4-phenoxy-	EtOH	260(4.28),316(3.65)	80-1617-73
$C_{16}H_{17}Cl_2NS$			
Benzenamine, N,N-bis(2-chloroethyl)-3-(phenylthio)-	EtOH	270(4.16),337(3.55)	80-1617-73
Benzenamine, N,N-bis(2-chloroethyl)-4-(phenylthio)-	EtOH	278(4.42)	80-1617-73
$C_{16}H_{17}N$			
Benzo[h]quinoline, 1,2-dihydro-2,2,4-trimethyl-	EtOH	227(5.01),283(4.74)	33-0478-73
9H-Carbazole, 9-ethyl-4,5-dimethyl-	EtOH	248(4.64),257(4.50), 265(4.27),295(4.17), 337(3.59),352(3.75)	39-2818-73C

Compound	Solvent	$\lambda_{max}(\log \epsilon)$	Ref.
$C_{16}H_{17}NO$			
Benzophenone imine, N-isopropyl-, N-oxide	n.s.g.	308(4.13)	32-0681-73
4H-Indol-4-one, 1,5,6,7-tetrahydro-6,6-dimethyl-3-phenyl-	EtOH	237(3.89),263(3.95), 288s(3.74)	33-1351-73
$C_{16}H_{17}NO_2$			
12H-[1]Benzopyrano[2,3-g]indolizin-12-one, 1,2,3,5,6,12b-hexahydro-11-methyl-	EtOH	230(4.69),308(4.08)	78-1285-73
6(2H)-Isoquinolinone, 2-benzoyl-1,3,4-4a,5,8a-hexahydro-, (4aS,8aR)-	EtOH	218(4.26)	33-2834-73
(4aS,8aS)-	EtOH	222(4.29)	33-2834-73
Carbazole, 1-ethyl-6,7-dimethoxy-	EtOH	210(4.45),235(4.65), 250s(4.29),262(4.19), 303(4.24),335(3.72), 340(3.72)	44-0215-73
$C_{16}H_{17}NO_3$			
Demethylilludinic acid, methyl ester	MeOH	242(4.63),260s(4.33), 285(4.03),307(4.01), 333(3.98),348s(3.93), 385(3.66)	44-4305-73
2(1H)-Pyridinone, 1-butyl-3-[3-(2-furanyl)-1-oxo-2-propenyl]-	EtOH	217(4.04),261(3.59), 378(4.30)	103-0615-73
Tembamide	EtOH	230(4.34),275(3.41), 282(3.22)	102-2071-73
$C_{16}H_{17}NO_4$			
Benzamide, N-hydroxy-2,4-dimethoxy-N-(3-methylphenyl)-	EtOH	253(4.00),290(3.90)	112-0547-73
Benzamide, N-hydroxy-2,4-dimethoxy-N-(4-methylphenyl)-	EtOH	275(4.00)	112-0547-73
Propionuric acid, 2-(6-methoxy-2-naphthalenyl)-	MeOH	232(4.84),253(3.58), 262(3.67),272(3.67), 303(2.88),316(3.14), 324(3.09),331(3.24)	36-0937-73
2-Quinolinecarboxylic acid, 1,4-dihydro-8-methoxy-1-methyl-4-oxo-3-(2-propenyl)-, methyl ester	MeOH	233(4.49),300(3.83), 342(4.09)	24-0355-73
2-Quinolinecarboxylic acid, 4,8-dimethoxy-3-(2-propenyl)-, methyl ester	MeOH	246(4.57),302(3.52), 330(3.48)	24-0355-73
$C_{16}H_{17}NO_4S$			
Spiro[2H-indene-2,2'-thiazolidine]-4'-carboxylic acid, 1,3-dihydro-3',5',5'-trimethyl-1,3-dioxo-, methyl ester	MeOH	229(4.68),248s(4.11)	78-4271-73
$C_{16}H_{17}NO_5$			
1H-Pyrrole-3,4-dicarboxylic acid, 1-[(phenylmethoxy)methyl]-, 3-ethyl ester	EtOH	247(3.88),260(3.86)	23-1089-73
$C_{16}H_{17}NO_6$			
7H-Cyclohepta[b]pyridine-6,8-dicarboxylic acid, 5,9-dihydroxy-, diethyl ester	EtOH	204(4.11),225s(--), 239(4.18),281(4.35), 322s(--)	39-0026-73C
7H-Cyclohepta[c]pyridine-6,8-dicarboxylic acid, 5,9-dihydroxy-, diethyl ester	EtOH	206(4.08),218s(--), 252(4.27),272(4.18), 320(3.94)	39-0026-73C

Compound	Solvent	$\lambda_{max}(\log \epsilon)$	Ref.
$C_{16}H_{17}NO_8S$			
Benzene, 1-[(3,4-dimethoxyphenyl)sulfonyl]-4,5-dimethoxy-2-nitro-	MeOH	250(4.32),290(4.17)	2-0863-73
$C_{16}H_{17}N_2O_2$			
Pyridinium, 1-benzyl-3-(1-acetoxyimino)-ethyl-	pH 6.61	241(4.01)	36-1831-73
$C_{16}H_{17}N_3$			
2(1H)-Pentalenone, 1-(dimethylamino)-, phenylhydrazone	MeOH	365(3.94),382(4.20)	5-0750-73
	DMSO	387(3.89)	5-0750-73
	DMSO-NaOH	530(4.21)	5-0750-73
Pyrrolidine, 1-[4-(phenylazo)phenyl]-	C_6H_{12}	407(4.52)	18-0194-73
	50% EtOH-NaOH	324(3.48),516(4.76)	18-0194-73
$C_{16}H_{17}N_3O$			
Anantine, N-methyl-	n.s.g.	283(4.31)	88-1757-73
1,2,4-Triazin-4-ol, 2,3,4,5-tetrahydro-5-methyl-3,6-diphenyl-	EtOH	283(4.06)	103-0123-73
$C_{16}H_{17}N_3O_2$			
Benzene, 1-methyl-4-(1-methylethyl)-[(4-nitrophenyl)azo]-	EtOH-HCl	267(4.19),357(3.97)	83-0641-73
	EtOH-NaOH	342(4.05)	83-0641-73
	$CHCl_3$	350(4.22)	83-0641-73
Ethanediamide, N-[4-(dimethylamino)-phenyl]-N'-phenyl-	dioxan	257(4.15),323(4.16)	30-0001-73
2,4(1H,3H)-Pyrimidinedione, 1-(1H-indol-3-ylmethyl)-5-propyl- (spectra in 35% ethanol)	pH 6.5	217(4.62),277(4.18), 287s(4.08)	19-0257-73
	pH 13	273(4.11),287s(3.97)	19-0257-73
Pyrrolo[1,2-a]pyrazine-1,4-dione, hexahydro-3-(1H-indol-3-ylmethyl)-, D-isomer	EtOH	220(4.54),273(3.75), 280(3.78),290(3.70)	78-0107-73
L-isomer	EtOH	220(4.51),273(3.72), 280(3.74),290(3.66)	78-0107-73
$C_{16}H_{17}N_3O_3$			
Acetamide, N,N',N"-1,2,3-azulenetriyl-tris-	MeOH	246(4.34),307(4.72), 320s(4.36),365(3.69), 375(3.55),600(2.54)	18-3266-73
Phenol, 5-methyl-4-[(2-nitrophenyl)azo]-2-propyl-	C_2Cl_4	399(4.37),449(4.26)	1-3632-73
Phenol, 5-methyl-4-[(4-nitrophenyl)azo]-2-propyl-	C_2Cl_4	387(4.30)	1-3632-73
$C_{16}H_{17}N_3O_4$			
2,4,6(1H,3H,5H)-Pyrimidinetrione, 1,3-dimethyl-5-[3-oxo-1-(phenylamino)-butylidene]-	MeOH	223(4.28),310(4.45)	39-0823-73C
Urea, N-(4-methoxyphenyl)-N,N'-dimethyl-N'-(4-nitrophenyl)-	$CHCl_3$	290s(3.8),347(4.0)	44-2590-73
$C_{16}H_{17}N_3O_5$			
Cytidine, N-benzoyl-2'-deoxy-	EtOH	259(4.32),304(--)	138-0859-73
$C_{16}H_{17}N_3O_6$			
Cytidine, N-benzoyl-	EtOH	259(4.35),303(--)	138-0859-73

Compound	Solvent	λmax(log ε)	Ref.
$C_{16}H_{17}N_4O_4$			
1H-Purinium, 7-(2-ethoxy-2-oxoethyl)-2,3,6,9-tetrahydro-2,6-dioxo-9-(phenylmethyl)-	pH 0	240s(3.76),263(4.00)	24-1389-73
	pH 5	253(3.92),291(3.92)	24-1389-73
$C_{16}H_{17}N_5O_2$			
Imidodicarbonic hydrazide, 2-phenyl-N'-(2-phenylethylidene)-	EtOH	238(4.33),261s(4.09)	48-0492-73
$C_{16}H_{17}N_5O_4$			
Adenosine, N-phenyl-	pH 1.0	275(4.25)	87-0358-73
	H_2O	290(4.32)	87-0358-73
	pH 13	290(4.32)	87-0358-73
$C_{16}H_{17}N_5O_5$			
2,4,6(1H,3H,5H)-Pyrimidinetrione, 1,3-dimethyl-5-(2,3,4,8-tetrahydro-1,3,5-trimethyl-2,4-dioxopyrido[2,3-d]pyrimidin-7(1H)-ylidene)-	$CHCl_3$	382s(4.56),394(4.70)	39-0823-73C
$C_{16}H_{17}O$			
Ethylium, 1-(4-methoxyphenyl)-1-(4-methylphenyl)-	H_2SO_4	325(4.08),466(4.81)	59-0807-73
at -75°	FSO_3H	324(4.04),461(4.79)	59-0807-73
at -75°	FSO_3H-SbF_5	310(4.00),414(4.48)	59-0807-73
$C_{16}H_{17}O_2$			
Ethylium, 1,1-bis(4-methoxyphenyl)-	H_2SO_4	333(4.08),484(4.78)	59-0807-73
at -75°	FSO_3H	323(4.04),467(4.69)	59-0807-73
at -75°	FSO_3H-SbF_5	308(4.84),415(4.51)	59-0807-73
$C_{16}H_{17}S$			
Sulfonium, (2-methylcyclopropyl)diphenyl-, tetrafluoroborate	EtOH	234(3.33),258(2.76), 264(2.83),273(2.73)	35-5298-73
$C_{16}H_{18}$			
Acenaphthylene, 1-(1,1-dimethylethyl)-1,2-dihydro-	EtOH	227(4.88),287(3.83)	44-3122-73
Azulene, 1-(1-hexenyl)-	n.s.g.	235(4.07),286(4.38), 369(3.65),388(3.61), 640(2.18),699s(2.02)	5-0166-73
Bi-2,4,6-cycloheptatrien-1-yl, x,x'-dimethyl-	EtOH	254(3.87)	18-1785-73
3,5,7,9-Dodecatetrayne, 2,2,11,11-tetramethyl-	C_6H_{12}	242(5.54)	33-1752-73
Spiro[cyclopropane-1,1'(2'H)-naphthalene], 3',4'-dihydro-2-methylene-3-(1-methylethylidene)-	EtOH	243(4.23)	39-0278-73B
$C_{16}H_{18}BBrF_4S$			
Sulfonium, (3-bromobutyl)diphenyl-, tetrafluoroborate	EtOH	235(3.42),260(2.68), 267(2.76),274(2.68)	35-5298-73
$C_{16}H_{18}BClF_4S$			
Sulfonium, (3-chlorobutyl)diphenyl-, tetrafluoroborate	EtOH	234(3.45),257(2.74), 264(2.82),272(2.71)	35-5298-73
$C_{16}H_{18}BrCl$			
Naphthalene, 2-(6-bromohexyl)-3-chloro-	EtOH	238(5.00),252s(3.43), 260(3.58),269(3.69),	44-1207-73

Compound	Solvent	$\lambda_{max}(\log \epsilon)$	Ref.
Naphthalene, 2-(6-bromohexyl)-3-chloro- (cont.)	EtOH	279(3.70),289(3.49), 306(2.66),320(2.60)	44-1207-73
$C_{16}H_{18}BrNO_3$			
Pyridinium, 1-[2-(3,4-dimethoxyphenyl)-2-oxoethyl]-, bromide	EtOH	234(4.27),276(4.19), 312(4.02)	94-2695-73
$C_{16}H_{18}BrNO_4$			
1H-Indole-3-carboxylic acid, 5-acetoxy-4-bromo-1,2,6-trimethyl-, ethyl ester	EtOH	224(4.61),290(4.10), 298(4.08)	103-0306-73
$C_{16}H_{18}ClNO_2S$			
Benzenesulfonamide, N-(4-chloro-3-propylphenyl)-4-methyl-	EtOH	224(4.26),232(4.22)	12-1337-73
$C_{16}H_{18}ClNO_3S$			
Benzenesulfonamide, N-[4-chloro-3-(3-hydroxypropyl)phenyl]-4-methyl-	EtOH	225(4.24),232(4.20)	12-1337-73
$C_{16}H_{18}ClNO_5$			
2-Butenedioic acid, 2-[(2-chloro-2-propenyl)(2-methoxyphenyl)amino]-, dimethyl ester, (E)-	ether	283(4.34)	24-0355-73
Pyridinium, 1-(4-acetylphenyl)-2,4,6-trimethyl-, perchlorate	EtOH	234(4.12),272(3.97), 320(2.76)	103-0333-73
$C_{16}H_{18}ClNO_7$			
Isoquinolinium, 3-(ethoxycarbonyl)-2-methyl-4-(2-oxopropyl)-, perchlorate	EtOH	242(4.66),345(3.93)	78-0213-73
$C_{16}H_{18}ClN_3$			
Benzenamine, 4-[(4-chloro-2-methylphenyl)azo]-N,N,2'-trimethyl-	C_6H_{12}	411(4.49)	18-3139-73
ammonium ion	50%EtOH-HCl	335(4.30)	18-3139-73
azonium ion	50%EtOH-HCl	513(4.09)	18-3139-73
Benzenamine, 4-[(4-chlorophenyl)azo]-N,N-diethyl-	C_6H_{12}	416(4.53)	18-0194-73
	50%EtOH-HCl	325(4.32),518(3.85)	18-0194-73
$C_{16}H_{18}ClN_3O$			
3-Pyridinecarboxamide, 5-[(4-chloro-1H-indol-3-yl)methyl]-1,4,5,6-tetrahydro-1-methyl-	MeOH-HCl	222(4.50),310(4.38)	33-0374-73
$C_{16}H_{18}Cl_2N_6O_3$			
1,2-Cyclopentanediol, 3-[2-amino-6-chloro-5-[(4-chlorophenyl)azo]-4-pyrimidinyl]amino]-5-(hydroxymethyl)-, (1α,2α,3β,5β)-(±)-	pH 1	240(4.26),280(3.94), 372(4.42)	36-1432-73
	pH 7 and 13	227(4.21),280(4.03), 385(4.46)	36-1432-73
$C_{16}H_{18}Cl_4$			
1,3-Cyclopentadiene, 5-[2,3-bis(1,1-dimethylethyl)-2-cyclopropen-1-ylidene]-1,2,3,4-tetrachloro-	EtOH	220(3.58),317(4.26)	138-0561-73
$C_{16}H_{18}NO$			
Pyridinium, 1-(4-acetylphenyl)-2,4,6-trimethyl-, perchlorate	EtOH	234(4.12),272(3.97), 320(2.76)	103-0333-73
$C_{16}H_{18}NO_3$			
Isoquinolinium, 3-(ethoxycarbonyl)-2-methyl-4-(2-oxopropyl)-, perchlorate	EtOH	242(4.66),345(3.93)	78-0213-73

Compound	Solvent	λ_{max}(log ε)	Ref.
Pyridinium, 1-[2-(3,4-dimethoxyphenyl)-2-oxoethyl]-, bromide	EtOH	234(4.27),276(4.19), 312(4.02)	94-2695-73
$C_{16}H_{18}N_2$			
Agroclavine	EtOH	281(3.85),292(3.85)	39-1312-73B
	5% EtOH	279(3.85),289(3.85)	39-1312-73B
1-Aziridinamine, 2,3-dimethyl-N,N-diphenyl-, cis and trans	MeCN	253(3.77)	22-3487-73
Benzo[lmn][3,8]phenanthroline, 1,2,3,6-7,8-hexahydro-2,7-dimethyl-	MeCN	215s(4.39),230(4.79), 273s(3.59),284s(3.84), 295(3.94),298s(3.90), 302(3.81),313(3.69), 320(3.19),328(3.24)	5-0339-73
Diazene, phenyl(1-methyl-1-phenylpropyl)-	octane	261(4.06),416(2.08)	35-4361-73
Hydrazine, 2-(1-methyl-2-propenyl)-1,1-diphenyl-	MeCN	244(3.83),294(3.76)	22-3487-73
1H-Indene-1-propanenitrile, 2-(1-pyrrolidinyl)-	ether	231(4.00),306(4.30)	22-0691-73
1H-Indene-2-propanenitrile, 3-(1-pyrrolidinyl)-	ether	244(4.05),251(4.00), 289(3.37),299(3.30)	22-0691-73
9H-Pyrido[3,4-b]indole, 1-(2-methylbutyl)-	MeOH	235(4.58),289(4.27), 336(3.70),350(3.71)	95-0033-73
9H-Pyrrolo[3,4-b]indole, 1-(3-methylbutyl)-	MeOH	235(4.58),289(4.26), 336(3.70),350(3.71)	95-0033-73
$C_{16}H_{18}N_2O$			
1-Cyclohexene-1-carbonitrile, 4,4-dimethyl-6-oxo-2-[(phenylmethyl)amino]-	EtOH	232(3.70),288(4.28)	70-0811-73
1H-Cyclopenta[b]quinoline-9-carboxamide, 2,3-dihydro-N-(1-methylethyl)-	EtOH	238(4.69),295(4.00), 308(4.06),322(4.1)	103-1005-73
15-Oxatricyclo[8.2.2.1^{1,10}]pentadeca-11,13-diene-11,12-dicarbonitrile	EtOH	300(3.09)	88-4321-73
$C_{16}H_{18}N_2O_2$			
4H-Indazol-4-one, 1,5,6,7-tetrahydro-3-(2-hydroxyphenyl)-1,6,6-trimethyl-	MeOH	229(4.20),259(3.92), 280s(3.75),307(3.83)	24-0450-73
7,11-Methanoazocino[1,2-a]indol-6(7H)-one, 10-amino-8,9,10,11-tetrahydro-2-methoxy-	MeOH	253(4.52),298(3.86), 310s(3.81)	24-1474-73
Pyridine, 1-ethyl-1,4-dihydro-4-[1-(4-nitrophenyl)propylidene]-	dioxan	273(4.05)	48-0901-73
$C_{16}H_{18}N_2O_2S_4$			
Acetamide, N-[2-[[(ethylthio)(4-oxo-3-phenyl-2-thioxo-5-thiazolidinylidene)methyl]thio]ethyl]-	EtOH	299(3.87),402(4.44)	94-1431-73
[2,5'-Bithiazolidin]-4'-one, 3-acetyl-2-(ethylthio)-3'-phenyl-2'-thioxo-	EtOH	269(3.98),303(4.23)	94-1431-73
$C_{16}H_{18}N_2O_3$			
Acetamide, N-(3,4-dihydro-1-methylspiro-[benz[cd]indole-5(1H),2'-[1,3]dioxolan]-4-yl)-	EtOH	204(4.39),227(4.52), 294(3.85)	39-0760-73C
2H-1,4-Benzodiazepin-2-one, 5-(acetoxymethyl)-1,3-dihydro-1-methyl-3-(2-methylpropenyl)-	isoPrOH	227(4.53),250s(3.81), 300(3.20)	44-3502-73
4H-Indazol-4-one, 3-(3,4-dimethoxyphenyl)-1,5,6,7-tetrahydro-1-methyl-	MeOH	237(4.30),295(3.87)	24-0450-73
2,4(1H,3H)-Pyrimidinedione, 1-(3-oxo-2-phenylpropyl)-5-propyl- (in 10% ethanol)	pH 6.5	251(4.19),270s(4.07)	19-0257-73
	pH 13	249(4.18)	19-0257-73

Compound	Solvent	$\lambda_{max}(\log \epsilon)$	Ref.
Sibiromycin, acid hydrolysis product, octahydro deriv.	MeOH	229(4.53),260s(4.00), 350(3.60)	105-0223-73
$C_{16}H_{18}N_2O_3SSe$			
Acetic acid, [[3,4,5,6,7,8-hexahydro-4-oxo-3-(2-propenyl)[1]benzoseleno-[2,3-d]pyrimidin-2-yl]thio]-, methyl ester	EtOH	265(4.07),330(4.10)	103-0300-73
$C_{16}H_{18}N_2O_4$			
2,4(1H,3H)-Pyrimidinedione, 1-(phenyl-methyl)-5-(tetrahydro-2H-pyran-2-yl-oxy)-	pH 6.5	280(3.93)	39-1089-73C
	pH 12.0	277(3.83)	39-1089-73C
1H-Pyrrolo[1,2-b]pyrazole-2,3-dicarbox-ylic acid, 3a,4,5,6-tetrahydro-1-phen-yl-, dimethyl ester	EtOH	356(4.13)	44-4259-73
2,3-Quinoxalinedimethanol, α,α'-dimeth-yl-, diacetate	EtOH	237(4.58),320(3.87)	33-1882-73
$C_{16}H_{18}N_2O_4S$			
Benzenamine, N,N-dimethyl-4-[1-[(4-ni-trophenyl)sulfonyl]ethyl]-	$CHCl_3$	367(2.77)	23-1187-73
$C_{16}H_{18}N_2O_5$			
α-D-xylo-Hexofuranos-5-ulosurononitrile, 1,2-O-(1-methylethylidene)-3-O-(phen-ylmethyl)-, oxime	EtOH	228(3.70)	136-0311-73D
DL-Valine, N-[[5-oxo-2-(phenoxymethyl)-4(5H)-oxazolylidene]methyl]-	EtOH	322(4.46)	4-0935-73
$C_{16}H_{18}N_2O_5S$			
DL-Valine, 3-mercapto-N-[[5-oxo-2-(phen-oxymethyl)-4(5H)-oxazolylidene]methyl]-	EtOH	324(4.43)	4-0935-73
$C_{16}H_{18}N_2O_6$			
2(1H)-Pyrimidinone, 5-(phenylmethoxy)-1-β-D-ribofuranosyl-	pH 2 and 6	335(3.71)	73-1381-73
$C_{16}H_{18}N_2O_8S$			
2,4(1H,3H)-Pyrimidinedione, 1-[2-O-[(4-methylphenyl)sulfonyl]-β-D-lyxofurano-syl]-	EtOH	225(4.15),260(3.96)	44-1283-73
$C_{16}H_{18}N_4$			
1,2,3,4-Tetrazine, 1,4,5,6-tetrahydro-1,4-bis(4-methylphenyl)-	CH_2Cl_2	255s(--),326(4.32)	24-3097-73
$C_{16}H_{18}N_4O$			
Ethene-1,1-dicarbonitrile, 2-[4-(dimeth-ylamino)phenyl]-2-morpholino-	MeCN	340s(4.26),348(4.27)	39-0616-73B
$C_{16}H_{18}N_4OS$			
Spiro[cyclohexane-1,6'(7'H)-[1,2,4]tria-zino[5,6-d][3,1]benzoxazepine], 3'-(methylthio)-	EtOH	205(4.35),235(4.38), 348(3.87),438(3.52)	78-0639-73
$C_{16}H_{18}N_4O_3$			
Ethanol, 2-[ethyl[4-[(4-nitrophenyl)-azo]phenyl]amino]-	n.s.g.	496(4.52)	40-1738-73

Compound	Solvent	λmax(log ε)	Ref.
$C_{16}H_{18}N_4O_3S$			
[1,2,4]Triazino[5,6-d][3,1]benzoxazepine-6-acetic acid, 6,7-dihydro-6-methyl-3-(methylthio)-, ethyl ester	EtOH	206(4.32),240(4.43), 350(3.96),445(3.73)	78-0639-73
$C_{16}H_{18}N_4O_4$			
Benzo[g]pteridine-2,4(3H,10H)-dione, 10-(2-hydroxyethyl)-6-methoxy-3,7,8-trimethyl-	6M HCl	271(3.78),303(3.79), 371(3.42)	5-1388-73
	pH 7	280(3.94),356(3.70)	5-1388-73
	MeOH	277(3.97),352(3.77)	5-1388-73
4,4'-Bipyridinium, 1,1'-bis[(ethoxycarbonyl)amino]-, dihydroxide, bis(inner salt)	EtOH	244(3.88),287(3.78), 389(4.25)	4-0447-73
$C_{16}H_{18}N_4O_5S$			
9H-Purine, 9-(4,6-di-O-acetyl-2,3-dideoxy-α-D-erythro-hex-2-enopyranosyl)-	EtOH	283(4.26),290s(4.24)	87-1056-73
β-isomer	EtOH	283(4.27),290s(4.25)	87-1056-73
$C_{16}H_{18}N_4O_7$			
Compound from uridinedialadehyde and benzoylhydrazine	pH 1 and 7	261(3.98)	136-0255-73A
	pH 13	264(3.86)	136-0255-73A
$C_{16}H_{18}N_4O_8$			
Cyclopropane-1,1-dicarboxylic acid, 2-formyl-, 2,4-dinitrophenylhydrazone	EtOH	355(4.31)	23-3263-73
$C_{16}H_{18}N_6O$			
Urea, N-(4-phenylbutyl)-N'-(1H-purin-6-yl)-	pH 1-2	278(4.28)	87-0139-73
	pH 5-7	268.5(4.23)	87-0139-73
	pH 12	287.5(4.17)	87-0139-73
$C_{16}H_{18}N_6O_4$			
Adenosine, 2-amino-N-phenyl-	pH 1.0	257(4.11),306(4.25)	87-0358-73
	pH 13	252(4.14),305(4.38)	87-0358-73
$C_{16}H_{18}N_6O_5$			
Pyridinium, 1,1'-[oxybis(methylene)]-bis[2,4-bis(hydroxyimino)methyl]-, dibromide	0.05M HCl	305(4.44)	73-2788-73
	0.05M NaOH	375(4.61)	73-2788-73
$C_{16}H_{18}N_6O_6$			
Adenosine, N-[[(2-furanylmethyl)amino]-carbonyl]-	pH 1-2	270s(--),277(4.33)	87-0139-73
	pH 5-7	270(4.34),277s(--)	87-0139-73
	pH 12	278(4.14),297(4.23)	87-0139-73
$C_{16}H_{18}N_{10}O_6$			
Carbamic acid, (5,6,7,12,13,14-hexahydro-6,13-dioxodipyrimido[4,5-d:4',5'-i][1,3,6,8]tetrazecine-4,11-diyl)bis-, diethyl ester	H_2O	309(3.76)	4-1043-73
$C_{16}H_{18}O$			
1-Acenaphylenol, 1-(1,1-dimethylethyl)-1,2-dihydro-	EtOH	227(4.86),287(3.83)	44-3122-73
Benzo[a]cyclopropa[cd]pentalen-1(2H)-one, 2a,2b,6b,6c-tetrahydro-2,2,2b,6c-tetramethyl-	EtOH	208(5.00),251s(4.23), 261s(4.11),270s(4.00), 278(3.84),289(3.42), 300(3.38)	35-4592-73

Compound	Solvent	λ_{max}(log ε)	Ref.
Benzo[a]cyclopropa[cd]pentalen-2(1H)-one, 2a,2b,6b,6c-tetrahydro-1,1,2b,6c-tetramethyl-	EtOH	210(4.08),239s(4.04), 287(3.98)	35-4592-73
2,4-Cyclohexadien-1-one, 2,4,6-trimethyl-6-(phenylmethyl)-	EtOH	320(3.60)	33-0014-73
2,5-Cyclohexadien-1-one, 2,4,6-trimethyl-4-(phenylmethyl)-	EtOH	240(4.08)	33-0014-73
1,4-Ethanonaphthalen-9-one, 1,4-dihydro-2,3,10,10-tetramethyl-	EtOH	216(3.91),268(3.08), 273(3.04),300(2.59)	35-4592-73 +44-3805-73
Methanone, (6,6-dimethylbicyclo[3.1.1]hept-2-en-2-yl)phenyl-	C_6H_{12}	246(4.18)	22-1351-73
1-Naphthalenol, 1,2-dihydro-2-methyl-2-(2,4-pentadienyl)-	EtOH	223(4.58),263(3.96)	33-2479-73
$C_{16}H_{18}O_2$			
Cordiachrome A	EtOH	250(4.19),356(3.22)	39-1352-73C
Cordiachrome B	EtOH	250(4.13),350(2.87)	39-1352-73C
Cordiachrome C	EtOH	247(4.13),343(2.87)	39-1352-73C
Naphtho[2,3-b]furan, 5,6-dihydro-9-methoxy-3,4,5-trimethyl- (cacalohastine)	EtOH	223(3.59),241(3.47), 249(3.45),284(3.64), 293(3.57)	102-2931-73
9,10-Phenanthrenedione, 1,2,3,4,4a,10aα-hexahydro-1 ,4a -dimethyl-	EtOH	209(4.02),283(3.94)	23-3620-73
Phenol, 2-[(2-hydroxy-3,5-dimethylphenyl)methyl]-4-methyl-	dioxan	287(3.72)	126-0039-73L
$C_{16}H_{18}O_3$			
Benzene, 1,1'-[oxybis(methyleneoxy)]-bis[2-methyl-	C_6H_{12}	262(3.27),269(3.45), 275(3.38)	80-0883-73
Benzene, 1,1'-[oxybis(methyleneoxy)]-bis[3-methyl-	C_6H_{12}	264(3.26),270(3.44), 275(3.42)	80-0883-73
Benzene, 1,1'-[oxybis(methyleneoxy)]-bis[4-methyl-	C_6H_{12}	267(3.34),273(3.45), 275(3.50),282(3.45)	80-0883-73
Benzoic acid, (3,5,5-trimethyl-4-oxo-2-cyclohexen-1-yl) ester	MeOH	231(4.30)	35-0239-73
Cyclopent[a]indene-2-carboxylic acid, 1,2,3,8-tetrahydro-6-methoxy-2-methyl-, methyl ester	EtOH	264(4.2)	39-2454-73C
1,2-Naphthalenedione, 6-methoxy-3,8-dimethyl-5-(1-methylethyl)-	EtOH	218(4.32),244(4.09), 272(4.23),400(3.87)	2-0974-73
2,6-Octadienal, 8-(3,6-dioxo-1,4-cyclohexadien-1-yl)-2,6-dimethyl-	EtOH	227(4.33),294(3.64)	88-2955-73
1(2H)-Phenanthrenone, 3,4,9,10-tetrahydro-9-hydroxy-10-methoxy-9-methyl-	MeOH	228(4.14),232(4.13), 302(4.19)	88-1553-73
Phenanthro[9,10-c]furan-1,3-dione, 3b,4,5,6,7,8,9,10,11,11a-decahydro-	MeOH	248(3.57),310(2.69)	22-2121-73
$C_{16}H_{18}O_4$			
Bicyclo[4.2.1]nona-2,4,7-triene-2,5-dicarboxylic acid, 9-(1-methylethylidene)-, dimethyl ester	EtOH	308(4.06)	24-1837-73
Butanedioic acid, (3,4-dihydro-2-naphthalenyl)-, dimethyl ester	EtOH	265(4.2)	2-0131-73
Coumurrayin	MeOH	260(3.92),329(4.08)	2-1126-73
Cyclohexaneacetic acid, α-(2-oxo-2-phenylethyl)-2-oxo-	MeOH	249(4.14),282(3.35), 300(3.11)	115-0381-73
Cyclopentaneacetic acid, α-[2-(4-methylphenyl)-2-oxoethyl]-	MeOH	254(4.64),320(3.92)	115-0381-73
3-Cyclopentene-1-acetic acid, 2-oxo-5-[(phenylmethoxy)methyl]-, methyl ester, trans	n.s.g.	209(4.11)	39-0810-73C

Compound	Solvent	$\lambda_{max}(\log \epsilon)$	Ref.
4H,9H-Furo[2',3',4':4,5]naphtho[2,1-c]-pyran-4,9-dione, 1,2,3,3a,5a,7,10b-10c-octahydro-3a,10b-dimethyl-	EtOH	261(3.94)	32-1271-73
as-Indacene-4,5-dicarboxylic acid, 1,2-3,6,7,8-hexahydro-, dimethyl ester	MeOH	295(3.53)	22-2121-73
Naphtho[1,2-b]furan-5(4H)-one, 4-ethyl-3a,9b-dihydro-6,9-dihydroxy-3,4-dimethyl-, (3aα,4β,9bα)-	EtOH	242(4.02),260s(3.59), 383(3.68)	39-1556-73C
2,7-Octanedione, 4,5-di-2-furanyl-	MeOH	220(4.04)	18-2892-73
Tetracyclo[4.3.0.0^{2,4}.0^{3,7}]non-8-ene-2,8-dicarboxylic acid, 5-isopropylidene-, dimethyl ester	EtOH	237(4.04)	24-1822-73
Tricyclo[4.3.0.0^{2,9}]nona-3,7-diene-2,8-dicarboxylic acid, 5-isopropylidene-, dimethyl ester	EtOH	259(4.00)	24-1837-73
$C_{16}H_{18}O_5$			
4H,9H-Furo[2',3',4':4,5]naphtho[2,1-c]-pyran-4,9-dione, 1,2,3,3a,5a,7,10b-10c-octahydro-7-hydroxy-3a,10b-dimethyl-	MeOH	257(4.20)	32-1271-73
1-Naphthalenecarboxaldehyde, 4,5,6,7-tetramethoxy-2-methyl-	EtOH	229(4.21),245(4.13), 269(4.22),348(3.80)	39-2388-73C
$C_{16}H_{18}O_6$			
1-Naphthalenecarboxylic acid, 4,5,6,7-tetramethoxy-2-methyl-	EtOH	248(4.59),275(4.11)	39-2388-73C
Stachyoiphenone	MeOH	214(4.22),287(4.09), 325s(3.40)	119-0053-73
$C_{16}H_{18}O_7$			
4a(4H)-Naphthalenecarboxylic acid, 5-(acetoxymethyl)-1,5,8,8a-tetrahydro-2-methoxy-1,4-dioxo-, methyl ester	EtOH	273(4.04)	94-0528-73
1,8a(1H)-Naphthalenedicarboxylic acid, 4,4a,5,8-tetrahydro-6-methoxy-2-methyl-5,8-dioxo-, dimethyl ester	EtOH	271.5(4.00)	94-0528-73
isomer	EtOH	273(3.98)	94-0528-73
Tephrophenone	MeOH	223(4.27),239(4.28), 284(4.36),320s(3.78)	119-0053-73
$C_{16}H_{18}O_{10}$			
Fraxin	n.s.g.	350(3.95)	105-0586-73
$C_{16}H_{19}BrN_2$			
1H-Cyclopenta[b]quinolin-9-amine, 7-bromo-N-butyl-2,3-dihydro-	EtOH	224(4.26),252(4.28), 340(4.02),352(4.0)	103-0490-73
1H-Cyclopenta[b]quinolin-9-amine, 7-bromo-2,3-dihydro-N-(2-methylpropyl)-	EtOH	226(4.22),256(4.11), 336(3.68)	103-0490-73
$C_{16}H_{19}ClN_2$			
1H-Cyclopenta[b]quinolin-9-amine, N-butyl-5-chloro-2,3-dihydro-	EtOH	229(4.7),247(4.53), 338(4.32)	103-0490-73
1H-Cyclopenta[b]quinolin-9-amine, N-butyl-7-chloro-2,3-dihydro-	EtOH	223(4.74),252(4.57), 339(4.2),353(4.21)	103-0490-73
1H-Cyclopenta[b]quinolin-9-amine, 7-chloro-2,3-dihydro-N-(2-methylpropyl)-	EtOH	222(4.26),254(4.19), 334(3.79)	103-0490-73
$C_{16}H_{19}ClN_2O$			
Benzaldehyde, 4-chloro-, (5,5-dimethyl-3-oxo-1-cyclohexen-1-yl)methylhydrazone	MeOH	236(3.80),257(3.88), 350(4.62),360(4.62)	24-0450-73

Compound	Solvent	λ_{max}(log ε)	Ref.
$C_{16}H_{19}ClN_2O_2$			
6H-Indolo[3,4-gh][1,4]benzoxazinium, 4,8,9,10a-tetrahydro-9-(hydroxymethyl)-7,9-dimethyl-, chloride	EtOH	225(4.48),286(3.74), 295(3.76)	39-0760-73C
$C_{16}H_{19}ClN_4O_6$			
Benzo[g]pteridinium, 5-ethyl-2,3,4,9-tetrahydro-3,7,8,9-tetramethyl-2,4-dioxo-, perchlorate	pH 2	282(4.63),430(4.00), 548(3.88)	5-1388-73
	MeCN	412(4.03),555(3.95)	5-1388-73
$C_{16}H_{19}ClO_8$			
1,3-Dioxol-1-ium, 2-[2-(1,3-benzodioxol-5-yl)ethenyl]-4,5-dihydro-4,4,5,5-tetramethyl-, perchlorate	$CHCl_3$	292(4.07),330(4.22)	104-0394-73
$C_{16}H_{19}Cl_2NO_3$			
1H-Indole-2-propanoic acid, α,5-dichloro-β-ethoxy-3-methyl-, ethyl ester	isoPrOH	230(4.58),287(3.91), 294(3.91),304s(3.77)	44-3077-73
$C_{16}H_{19}Cl_3O$			
1(2H)-Pentalenone, 4,5,6-trichloro-2,3-bis(1,1-dimethylethyl)-	EtOH	235(4.18),265(4.09), 332(4.01),398(3.46)	138-0561-73
$C_{16}H_{19}N$			
1H-Carbazole, 2,3,4,9-tetrahydro-9-methyl-1-(2-propenyl)-	EtOH	232(4.55),281s(3.83), 287(3.87),293s(3.85)	39-1913-73C
Pyridine, 2-methyl-5-(3-phenylbutyl)-	MeOH	268(3.66)	103-1507-73
$C_{16}H_{19}NO$			
1-Propanol, 2-amino-2-methyl-1,1-diphenyl-	MeOH	250f(2.8)	83-0881-73
$C_{16}H_{19}NO_2$			
Morphinan-6-one, 3-hydroxy-, (-)-	EtOH	220s(3.90),282(3.38), 290s(3.31)	87-0352-73
4-Pentynoic acid, 2-[1-(phenylmethyl)-amino]ethylidene]-, ethyl ester	EtOH	298(4.24)	1-2802-73
$C_{16}H_{19}NO_3$			
12H-[1]Benzopyrano[2,3-g]indolizin-12-one, 1,2,3,5,6,6a,12a,12b-octahydro-6a-hydroxy-11-methyl-	EtOH	256(3.82),316(3.34)	78-1285-73
2-Butenoic acid, 3-(5-methoxy-2-methyl-1H-indol-3-yl)-, ethyl ester	EtOH	228(4.45),278(3.98), 297(4.03),333(4.07)	104-1275-73
Carbazole, 9-acetyl-1,2,3,4-tetrahydro-6,7-dimethoxy-	EtOH	260(4.37),285(3.97)	44-0215-73
2,4-Pentadienoic acid, 2-acetyl-5-(dimethylamino)-5-phenyl-, methyl ester	EtOH	245(3.93),417(4.61)	70-1963-73
2(1H)-Pyridinone, 1-[2-(3,4-dimethoxyphenyl)ethyl]-3-methyl-	EtOH	231(4.12),286(3.84), 302(3.83)	94-2695-73
2(1H)-Pyridinone, 1-[2-(3,4-dimethoxyphenyl)ethyl]-5-methyl-	EtOH	231(4.17),284(3.66), 314(3.74)	94-2695-73
$C_{16}H_{19}NO_3S$			
1H-Benz[e]indene-3-carbonitrile, 3a,4-6,7,8,9,9a,9b-octahydro-3a-methyl-6-(methylsulfonyl)-7-oxo-, [3aS-(3aα,6α,9aα,9bβ)]-	MeOH	215(4.03),300(2.22)	94-0335-73

Compound	Solvent	λ max(log ε)	Ref.
$C_{16}H_{19}NO_4$			
7H-Benzo[de]quinolin-7-one, 6-acetoxy-1,2,3,8,9,9a-hexahydro-5-methoxy-1-methyl-	EtOH	255(3.88),325(3.54)	33-0759-73
1,3-Octadien-4-ol, 2-methyl-, 4-nitrobenzoate	EtOH	231(4.34),255s(4.18), 296s(3.48)	33-0875-73
2,4-Octadien-4-ol, 2-methyl-, 4-nitrobenzoate	EtOH	237(4.33),257s(4.17), 295s(3.47)	33-0875-73
2H-Pyrrole-3,4-dicarboxylic acid, 3,4-dihydro-2,2-dimethyl-5-phenyl-, dimethyl ester, trans	C_6H_{12}	242(4.15)	35-1945-73
Ribalinidine, O^7-methyl-	0.3M HCl	223(4.50),244(4.67), 301(4.02),332(3.78), 345(3.76)	78-0205-73
	pH 12	220s(4.41),235(4.57), 245(4.56),302(3.98), 327(3.97),345(3.93)	78-0205-73
$C_{16}H_{19}NO_5$			
2-Butenedioic acid, 2-[(2-methoxyphenyl)-2-propenylamino]-, dimethyl ester, (E)-	ether	283(4.32)	24-0355-73
$C_{16}H_{19}NO_6S$			
Benzenamine, 2-[(3,4-dimethoxyphenyl)-sulfonyl]-4,5-dimethoxy-	MeOH	330(3.83)	2-0863-73
$C_{16}H_{19}NO_7$			
DL-Alanine, N-[3-[3-methoxy-4-[(methoxycarbonyl)oxy]phenyl]-1-oxo-2-propenyl]-, methyl ester	MeOH	277(4.26),306s(3.99)	20-0243-73
Glycine, N-[3-[3-methoxy-4-[(methoxycarbonyl)oxy]phenyl]-1-oxo-2-propenyl]-, ethyl ester	EtOH	280(4.29),310s(4.00)	20-0243-73
$C_{16}H_{19}NS_2$			
1-Naphthalenecarbodithioic acid, piperidine salt	EtOH	328(3.93),348(4.14), 481(2.21)	143-0359-73
$C_{16}H_{19}N_2$			
3H-Pyrido[3,4-b]indolium, 4,9-dihydro-2,9-dimethyl-3-(2-propenyl)-, perchlorate	n.s.g.	251(4.0),363(4.4)	83-0500-73
$C_{16}H_{19}N_2O_2$			
6H-Indolo[3,4-gh][1,4]benzoxazinium, 4,8,9,10a-tetrahydro-9-(hydroxymethyl)-7,9-dimethyl-, chloride	EtOH	225(4.48),286(3.74), 295(3.76)	39-0760-73C
$C_{16}H_{19}N_3$			
Benzenamine, N,N-diethyl-4-(phenylazo)-	C_6H_{12}	407(4.51)	18-0194-73
	50%EtOH-HCl	318(4.28),516(3.98)	18-0194-73
Benzenamine, 4-[(2,4-dimethylphenyl)-azo]-N,N-dimethyl-	C_6H_{12}	393(4.49)	18-3139-73
ammonium ion	50%EtOH-HCl	340(4.32)	18-3139-73
azonium ion	50%EtOH-HCl	522(3.61)	18-3139-73
Benzenamine, N,N,2-trimethyl-4-[(2-methylphenyl)azo]-	C_6H_{12}	400(4.46)	18-3139-73
ammonium ion	50%EtOH-HCl	330(4.17)	18-3139-73
azonium ion	50%EtOH-HCl	514(4.23)	18-3139-73

Compound	Solvent	$\lambda_{max}(\log \epsilon)$	Ref.
Benzenamine, N,N,2-trimethyl-4-[(4-methylphenyl)azo]-	C_6H_{12}	405(4.49)	18-3139-73
ammonium ion	50%EtOH-HCl	336(3.81)	18-3139-73
azonium ion	50%EtOH-HCl	528(4.65)	18-3139-73
$C_{16}H_{19}N_3O$			
4H-Indazol-4-one, 3-[4-(dimethylamino)-phenyl]-1,5,6,7-tetrahydro-1-methyl-	MeOH	205(4.40),250(4.23), 278(3.98),320(4.09)	24-0450-73
$C_{16}H_{19}N_3O_2$			
Cynometrine	n.s.g.	258(2.41),264(2.33)	88-1757-73
3,8(9)-p-Menthadiene, 3-(p-nitrophenyl-azo)-	HCl	275(4.3),400(4.05)	83-0641-73
	EtOH	420(4.29)	83-0641-73
$C_{16}H_{19}N_3O_3$			
Acetonitrile, [(2,2-diethoxyethyl)-amino](1,2-dihydro-2-oxo-3H-indol-3-ylidene)-	EtOH	280(4.12),287(4.09), 368(4.13)	95-1520-73
$C_{16}H_{19}N_3O_4$			
Sydnone imine, N-benzoyl-3-(6-carboxy-hexyl)-	EtOH	203(4.32),260(4.00), 340(4.61)	103-1327-73
hydrochloride	EtOH	200(4.32),260(4.00), 340(4.61)	103-1327-73
$C_{16}H_{19}N_3O_5$			
Cytidine, 2'-O-(phenylmethyl)-	pH 1.0	208(4.20),280(4.03)	24-0665-73
	pH 6.0	235s(3.85),271(3.91)	24-0665-73
Cytidine, 3'-O-(phenylmethyl)-	pH 1.0	208(4.23),278(4.13)	24-0665-73
	pH 6.0	230s(3.90),270(3.97)	24-0665-73
Cytidine, 5'-O-(phenylmethyl)-	pH 1.0	208(4.24),279(4.10)	24-0665-73
	pH 6.0	232s(3.86),271(3.93)	24-0665-73
$C_{16}H_{19}N_3O_7S$			
Cytidine, 5'-(4-methylbenzenesulfonate)	MeOH	224(4.22),271(3.58)	88-2811-73
$C_{16}H_{19}N_3O_{11}$			
1H-Imidazole-5-carboxylic acid, 4-nitro-1-(2,3,4-tri-O-acetyl-α-D-arabino-pyranosyl)-, methyl ester	EtOH	280.2(3.64)	5-1286-73
L-isomer	EtOH	280.2(3.63)	5-1286-73
1H-Imidazole-5-carboxylic acid, 4-nitro-1-(2,3,4-tri-O-acetyl-β-D-xylo-pyranosyl)-, methyl ester	EtOH	279.1(3.50)	5-1286-73
$C_{16}H_{19}N_4O_2$			
Benzo[g]pteridinium, 5-ethyl-2,3,4,9-tetrahydro-3,7,8,9-tetramethyl-2,4-dioxo-, perchlorate	pH 2	282(4.63),430(4.00), 548(3.88)	5-1388-73
	MeCN	412(4.03),555(3.95)	5-1388-73
$C_{16}H_{19}N_5O_2$			
Morpholine, 4-[4-[2-(4-methoxyphenyl)-2H-tetrazol-5-yl]-1,3-butadienyl]-, (E,E)-	EtOH	247(4.11),355(4.75)	88-4295-73
$C_{16}H_{19}N_5O_3$			
Benzo[g]pteridine-4a(2H)-acetamide, 3,4,5,10-tetrahydro-3,7,8,10-tetra-methyl-2,4-dioxo-	6M HCl	268(3.93),303(3.79), 395(3.45)	5-1388-73
	pH 7	271(3.97),330s(3.72), 360(3.73)	5-1388-73
	MeOH	272(3.99),355(3.77)	5-1388-73

Compound	Solvent	λ_{max}(log ε)	Ref.
$C_{16}H_{19}N_5O_6$			
Pyridinium, 1-[2-[(1,2-dihydro-2-oxo-1-β-D-ribofuranosyl-4-pyrimidinyl-hydrazono]-2-hydroxyethyl]-, hydroxide, inner salt	pH 2.8	267(4.11),278(4.09)	35-1323-73
	pH 6.2	260(4.07),267(4.08), 280s(4.03),306s(3.87)	35-1323-73
	pH 10.8	260(4.09),267(4.09), 306(4.18)	35-1323-73
Pyridinium, 3-[[(1,2-dihydro-2-oxo-1-β-D-ribofuranosyl-4-pyrimidinyl)hydrazono]hydroxymethyl]-1-methyl-, hydroxide, inner salt	M HCl	275s(4.09),292(4.25)	35-1323-73
	pH 2.8	270(4.05),340(3.73)	35-1323-73
	pH 6.2	260(3.97),340(4.21)	35-1323-73
	pH 10.8	257(3.98),345(4.26)	35-1323-73
Pyridinium, 4-[[(1,2-dihydro-2-oxo-1-β-D-ribofuranosyl-4-pyrimidinyl)hydrazono]hydroxymethyl]-1-methyl-, hydroxide, inner salt	pH 2.8	220(4.15),275(4.11), 376(3.84)	35-1323-73
	pH 6.2	227(4.11),264(4.07), 400(4.16)	35-1323-73
	pH 10.8	227(4.12),264(4.09), 403(4.20)	35-1323-73
$C_{16}H_{19}O_4$			
1,3-Dioxol-1-ium, 2-[2-(1,3-benzodioxol-5-yl)ethenyl]-4,5-dihydro-4,4,5,5-tetramethyl-, perchlorate	$CHCl_3$	292(4.07),330(4.22)	104-0394-73
$C_{16}H_{20}$			
Benzene, [3-methyl-3-(1-propenyl)-1-cyclohexen-1-yl]-, (Z)-	MeCN	248(4.25),254(4.23)	35-8670-73
Bicyclo[3.1.0]hexane, 5-methyl-1-phenyl-6-(1-cis-propenyl)-, endo	MeCN	258(2.94)	35-8670-73
trans	MeCN	258(3.05)	35-8670-73
Naphthalene, 1-methyl-2-pentyl-	EtOH	223s(4.80),228(4.95), 274(3.71),284(3.73), 291s(3.61),307(2.91), 313(2.65),322(2.77)	33-2479-73
Naphthalene, 1-methyl-4-pentyl-	EtOH	211s(4.47),228(4.75), 279s(3.77),289(3.84), 298s(3.69),316s(2.83), 320s(2.59)	33-2479-73
Naphthalene, 1-methyl-5-pentyl-	EtOH	210s(4.36),223s(4.78), 228(4.95),268s(3.63), 277(3.84),287(3.94), 298(3.77),310s(2.88), 316(2.73),320(2.61)	33-2479-73
$C_{16}H_{20}BrNO_2$			
Pyridinium, 1-[2-(3,4-dimethoxyphenyl)-ethyl]-3-methyl-, bromide	EtOH	268(3.80)	94-2695-73
$C_{16}H_{20}BrN_5O_6$			
D-Arabinitol, 1-C-(7-amino-1H-pyrazolo-[4,3-d]pyrimidin-3-yl)-1,4-anhydro-2-bromo-2-deoxy-, 5-(2-acetoxy-2-methylpropanoate), (S)-	MeOH-acid	237(3.93),298(4.06)	44-3179-73
	MeOH-base	236(4.25),306(3.85)	44-3179-73
D-Xylitol, 1-C-(7-amino-1H-pyrazolo-[4,3-d]pyrimidin-3-yl)-1,4-anhydro-3-bromo-3-deoxy-, 5-(2-acetoxy-2-methylpropanoate), (S)-	MeOH-acid	236(3.94),298(4.00)	44-3179-73
	MeOH-base	235(4.23),304(4.00)	44-3179-73
$C_{16}H_{20}F_2O_3$			
Cyclopropa[3,4]cyclopenta[1,2-b]furan-2(3H)-one, 4,4-difluorohexahydro-3b-(3-oxo-1-octenyl)-, α-	n.s.g.	238(4.17)	88-1319-73
β-form	n.s.g.	238(4.17)	88-1319-73

Compound	Solvent	λ_{max}(log ε)	Ref.
$C_{16}H_{20}FeN_6S_2$			
Ferrocene, 1,1'-bis[1-[(aminothioxomethyl]hydrazono]ethyl]-	EtOH	280(4.36),305(4.52), 318(4.50),458(3.20)	18-2896-73
$C_{16}H_{20}FeO_3$			
Iron, tricarbonyl[(1,2,3,4-η)-1,2,3,4-5,5-hexamethyl-6-methylene-1,3-cyclohexadiene]-	EtOH	204(4.41),246s(--), 294s(--)	101-0239-73H
$C_{16}H_{20}IN$			
1H-Carbazolium, 2,3,4,4a-tetrahydro-9-methyl-4a-(2-propenyl)-, iodide	EtOH	207s(4.30),211(4.29), 219(4.25),238s(3.88), 277(3.85)	39-1913-73C
$C_{16}H_{20}INO_4$			
Spiro[1,3-dioxolane-2,9'(5'H)-[1,3]dioxolo[4,5-g]pyrrolo[1,2-b]isoquinoline], 7',8',9'a,10'-tetrahydro-, methiodide	EtOH	293(3.71)	78-0213-73
$C_{16}H_{20}N_2$			
3H-Azepin-2-amine, N,N-diethyl-5-phenyl-	EtOH	252(4.31)	39-1079-73C
3H-Azepin-2-amine, N,N-diethyl-6-phenyl-	EtOH	318(4.23)	39-1079-73C
1H-Cyclopenta[b]quinolin-9-amine, N-butyl-2,3-dihydro-	EtOH	222(4.29),248(4.26), 330(3.94)	103-0490-73
Indole, 1-methyl-2-[(1-methyl-4-piperidinylidene)methyl]-	MeOH	243(4.31),301(4.22)	23-0792-73
1H-Indole-3-ethanamine, N-cyclohexylidene-	EtOH	274(3.75),280(3.78), 290(4.03)	114-0105-73D
1H-Pyrido[3,4-b]indole, 2,3,4,9-tetrahydro-2,9-dimethyl-3-(2-propenyl)-	n.s.g.	233(4.7),290(3.8)	83-0500-73
Spiro[cyclohexane-1,1'-[1H]pyrido[3,4-b]indole], 2',3',4',9'-tetrahydro-,	EtOH	222(4.62),272(3.92), 279(3.91),289(3.79)	44-4342-73
hydrochloride	EtOH	224(4.27),272(3.82), 278(3.82),288(3.69)	114-0105-73D
$C_{16}H_{20}N_2O$			
3H,4H-3a,6a-Diazafluoranthen-3-one, 10b-ethyl-1,2,5,6,10b,10c-hexahydro-	EtOH	251(3.93),299(3.44)	78-4049-73
Pyridine, 2-[ethyl(1-benzylethyl)amino]-, 1-oxide	MeOH	247(4.22),279(3.80), 335(3.51)	32-1083-73
$C_{16}H_{20}N_2O_2$			
[4,4'-Bipyridin]-1-iumyl, 4,4'-diacetyl-1,1',4,4'-tetrahydro-1,1'-dimethyl-	H_2SO_4	244(3.76),250(3.77), 262s(3.53),285s(3.40), 295s(3.42),305(3.46), 316(3.48),355s(3.92), 372(4.16),390(4.23)	44-2355-73
Cyclohexane-1-carbonitrile, 4,4-dimethyl-2,6-dioxo-, benzylamine salt	EtOH	232(3.91),272(4.35)	70-0811-73
$C_{16}H_{20}N_2O_3$			
Benzaldehyde, 3,4-dimethoxy-, methyl-(2-methyl-3-oxo-1-cyclohexen-1-yl)-hydrazone	MeOH	218s(4.10),233s(3.95), 267(3.95),359(4.72)	24-0450-73
Benzamide, N-[2-oxo-1-(1-piperidinocarbonyl)propyl]-	EtOH	226(4.03)	70-2505-73
$C_{16}H_{20}N_2O_4$			
Cyclohexanecarboxylic acid, 1-[(3-methoxyphenyl)azo]-2-oxo-, ethyl ester	EtOH	235(4.04),280(3.92), 330(3.50)	39-0872-73B

Compound	Solvent	$\lambda_{max}(\log \epsilon)$	Ref.
1H-Indole-3-carboxylic acid, 4-(acetylamino)-5-methoxy-1,2-dimethyl-, ethyl ester	MeOH	219(4.57),248(4.10), 293(3.98)	103-1490-73
2,4-Pentadienoic acid, 5-(diethylamino)-2-nitro-5-phenyl-, methyl ester	EtOH	250(3.82),310(3.94), 440(4.70)	70-1959-73
$C_{16}H_{20}N_2O_4S$			
1H-Pyrrole-3-carboxylic acid, 5,5'-thiobis[2-methyl-, diethyl ester	EtOH	247(4.19)	5-0207-73
$C_{16}H_{20}N_2O_4S_2$			
1H-Pyrrole-3-carboxylic acid, 5,5'-dithiobis[2-methyl-, diethyl ester	EtOH	263(4.20),316(3.91)	5-0207-73
$C_{16}H_{20}N_2O_6$			
Pyridinium, 4-(ethoxycarbonyl)-1-[[3-ethoxy-2-(ethoxycarbonyl)-3-oxo-1-propenyl]amino]-, hydroxide, inner salt	EtOH	231s(4.50),287(4.25), 457(4.34)	39-2580-73C
$C_{16}H_{20}N_2O_9S_3$			
1,3,4-Thiadiazole-2(3H)-thione, 5-[(2,3,4,6-tetra-O-acetyl-β-D-glucopyranosyl)thio]-	n.s.g.	324(4.01)	48-0915-73
$C_{16}H_{20}N_4$			
2-Tetrazene, 1,4-diethyl-1,4-diphenyl-	C_6H_{12}	353(4.50)	73-0046-73
	THF	355(4.52)	73-0046-73
$C_{16}H_{20}N_4O_2$			
Benzo[g]pteridine-2,4(1H,3H)-dione, 5-ethyl-5,10-dihydro-3,7,8,10-tetramethyl-	6M HCl	305(4.03)	5-1388-73
	pH 5	245(4.31),345(3.66)	5-1388-73
	pH 7	345(3.74)	5-1388-73
Benzo[g]pteridinium, 1,2,3,4,5,10-hexahydro-3,5,5,7,8,10-hexamethyl-2,4-dioxo-, hydroxide, inner salt	6M HCl	213(4.56),292(4.08), 318(4.13)	5-1388-73
	pH 7	265(4.43),293(4.26), 310(4.02)	5-1388-73
	MeOH	265(4.51),293(4.23), 310s(3.91)	5-1388-73
Propanoic acid, 3,3-bis(2-phenylhydrazino)-, methyl ester	EtOH	255(4.22)	22-2482-73
$C_{16}H_{20}N_4O_3$			
Benzo[g]pteridine-2,4(3H,4aH)-dione, 5-ethyl-5,10-dihydro-4a-hydroxy-3,7,8,10-tetramethyl-	pH 7	275s(3.75),315s(3.93), 352(3.96)	5-1388-73
	MeOH	275(3.86),308(3.93), 355(3.99)	5-1388-73
$C_{16}H_{20}N_4O_4$			
Norbornane-3-carboxaldehyde, 2,2-dimethyl-, 2,4-dinitrophenylhydrazone	$CHCl_3$	362(4.38)	22-2472-73
$C_{16}H_{20}N_4O_5$			
Tubercidin, 5'-O-acetyl-2',3'-O-(1-methylethylidene)-	MeOH	270(4.04)	18-0618-73
$C_{16}H_{20}N_4O_5S$			
L-Glutamic acid, N-[1-oxo-5(1H-pyrrolo-[2,3-d]pyrimidin-4-ylthio)pentyl]-	pH 1	218(4.33),257(4.00), 310(4.06)	73-1438-73
	pH 13	219(4.39),248(3.90), 294(4.10)	73-1438-73

Compound	Solvent	λ_{max}(log ε)	Ref.
$C_{16}H_{20}N_6O_2S$			
Thiazolo[2,3-f]purine, 6-methyl-2,4-dimorpholino-	pH 1	232(4.23),256(4.28), 280(4.12),321(4.28)	94-0256-73
$C_{16}H_{20}N_8O_5$			
Adenosine, N-[[[2-(1H-imidazol-4-yl)ethyl]amino]carbonyl]-	pH 1-2	270s(--),277(4.35)	87-0139-73
	pH 5-7	269(4.36),277s(--)	87-0139-73
	pH 12	278(4.20),299(4.05)	87-0139-73
$C_{16}H_{20}O$			
Cyclohexanol, 2,6-dimethyl-1-(phenylethynyl)-	EtOH	242(4.30),252(4.23)	23-3620-73
Ethanone, 1-(2,6-dimethyl-1-cyclohexen-1-yl)-2-phenyl-	EtOH	211(3.91),244(3.58)	23-3620-73
9(5H)-Phenanthrenone, 4b,6,7,8,8a,10-hexahydro-4b,8-dimethyl-, (4bα,8α,8aα)-	EtOH	209(3.97),282(3.14)	23-3620-73
$C_{16}H_{20}O_2$			
7H-Benz[e]inden-7-one, 3-acetyl-1,2,3-3a,4,5,8,9-octahydro-3a-methyl-, (3S-cis)	MeOH	305(4.36)	78-3631-73
Methanone, (4-methoxyphenyl)(1,2,3-trimethyl-2-cyclopenten-1-yl)-, (R)-	isooctane	265(4.21),329(2.15)	33-1741-73
	EtOH	275(4.11),323(2.46)	33-1741-73
$C_{16}H_{20}O_3$			
7H-Benz[e]inden-7-one, 3-acetoxy-1,2,3-3a,4,5,8,9-octahydro-3a-methyl-, (3S-cis)	MeOH	303(4.34)	78-3631-73
Cyclopentaneacetic acid, 1-methyl-2-oxo-5-phenyl-, ethyl ester, trans	EtOH	243(2.08),248(2.18), 254(2.30),260(2.38), 265(2.28)	104-0835-73
$C_{16}H_{20}O_3S$			
Bicyclo[3.1.1]hept-2-ene-6-methanol, 6-methyl-2-[(phenylsulfonyl)methyl]-	EtOH	258(3.00),265(3.00), 272(2.88)	39-2319-73C
7-Oxatricyclo[4.3.0.0^{3,9}]nonane, 9-methyl-6-[(phenylsulfonyl)methyl]-	EtOH	253(2.61),258(2.82), 265(2.97),272(3.25)	39-2319-73C
$C_{16}H_{20}O_4$			
1,2-Naphthalenedicarboxylic acid, 5,6,7,8-tetrahydro-5,5-dimethyl-, dimethyl ester	pentane	241(3.97),281(3.18), 289(3.16)	44-0399-73
Naphtho[1,2-b]furan-5(4H)-one, 4-ethyl-2,3,3a,9b-tetrahydro-6,9-dihydroxy-3,4-dimethyl-	EtOH	240(3.95),261s(3.69), 382(3.53)	39-1556-73C
Pentacyclo[6.2.2.0^{2,7}.0^{3,10}.0^{4,9}]dodecane-5,11-dione, 6,12-dihydroxy-1,4,6,12-tetramethyl-	EtOH	308(1.98)	5-1675-73
Pentacyclo[6.2.2.0^{2,7}.0^{3,10}.0^{4,9}]dodecane-5,11-dione, 6,12-dihydroxy-2,6,9,12-tetramethyl-	EtOH	307(1.95)	5-1675-73
$C_{16}H_{20}O_5$			
2H-1-Benzopyran-2,6(5H)-dione, 5-acetoxy-3,4-dihydro-4,4,5,7,8-pentamethyl-	MeOH	327(3.48)	35-8319-73
Propanoic acid, 3-(3,4-dimethoxyphenyl)-3-(2,2-dimethyl-1,3-dioxolan-4-yl)-2,3-epoxy-	EtOH	235(3.92),276(3.46)	39-2359-73C
2H-Pyran-2-one, 6-[2-(3,4-dimethoxyphenyl)ethyl]-5,6-dihydro-4-methoxy-, (S)-	EtOH	231(4.25),277(3.53), 284s(3.45)	102-1182-73

Compound	Solvent	$\lambda_{max}(\log \epsilon)$	Ref.
$C_{16}H_{20}O_6$			
4a(4H)-Naphthalenecarboxylic acid, 1,5,8,8a-tetrahydro-2-methoxy-6-methyl-1,4-dioxo-, methyl ester, (4aα,5β,8aβ)-	EtOH	272(4.00)	94-0528-73
Stachyoinolphenone	MeOH	224(4.12),291(4.17), 330s(3.49)	119-0053-73
Tricyclo[4.2.2.0^{3,8}]octane-2,7-dicarboxylic acid, 4,5-diacetyl-2,7-dimethyl-	EtOH	272(1.85)	5-1675-73
$C_{16}H_{20}O_7$			
4a(4H)-Naphthalenecarboxylic acid, 5-(acetoxymethyl)-1,5,8,8a-tetrahydro-1-hydroxy-2-methoxy-4-oxo-, methyl ester	EtOH	256(4.18)	94-0528-73
1,8a(1H)-Naphthalenedicarboxylic acid, 4,4a,5,8-tetrahydro-5-hydroxy-6-methoxy-2-methyl-8-oxo-, dimethyl ester	EtOH	253.5(4.18)	94-0528-73
isomer	EtOH	254(4.11)	94-0528-73
Stachyoinic acid, methyl ester	MeOH	226(4.27),269(4.23), 306(3.06)	119-0053-73
$C_{16}H_{20}O_8$			
1,3-Benzenedicarboxaldehyde, 2-(2-acetoxy-3-hydroxy-3-methylbutyl)-4,6-dihydroxy-5-methoxy-	MeOH	270(4.51)	78-2645-73
	MeOH-HCl	224(4.01),270(4.28)	78-2645-73
	MeOH-NaOH	266s(4.17),293(4.40), 340(3.97)	78-2645-73
$C_{16}H_{21}BO_5$			
4,9-Ethenonaphtho[2,3-d]-1,3,2-dioxaborol-6(4H)-one, 3a,4a,5,8a,9,9a-hexahydro-2,5-dihydroxy-3a,5,7,9-tetramethyl-	EtOH	310(2.13)	5-1675-73
1,2,5-Methenocyclobuta[1,8]naphtho-[2,3-d][1,3,2]dioxaborol-3(2H)-one, octahydro-4,7-dihydroxy-2,4,5a,8b-tetramethyl-	EtOH	308(1.70)	5-1675-73
$C_{16}H_{21}BrN_2O$			
Benzamide, 5-bromo-N-butyl-2-(cyclopentylideneamino)-	EtOH	226(4.63),351(3.66)	103-0490-73
Benzamide, 5-bromo-2-(cyclopentylideneamino)-N-(2-methylpropyl)-	EtOH	225(4.78),353(3.85)	103-0490-73
2-Propanamine, N-[4-[(4-bromophenyl)-methylene]-3-(1-methylethyl)-2-oxazolidinylidene]-	EtOH	228(4.20),295(4.21)	44-1051-73
$C_{16}H_{21}ClN_2O$			
Benzamide, N-butyl-5-chloro-2-(cyclopentylideneamino)-	EtOH	226(4.59),351(3.62)	103-0490-73
Benzamide, 5-chloro-2-(cyclopentylideneamino)-N-(2-methylpropyl)-	EtOH	226(4.64),351(3.73)	103-0490-73
2-Propanamine, N-[4-[(4-chlorophenyl)-methylene]-3-(1-methylethyl)-2-oxazolidinylidene]-, (?,E)-	EtOH	256(4.00),299(4.53)	44-1051-73
$C_{16}H_{21}ClN_2O_4$			
Pyridinium, 1-[4-(dimethylamino)phenyl]-2,4,6-trimethyl-, perchlorate	EtOH	224(3.92),266(4.46), 310(3.42)	103-0333-73

Compound	Solvent	λ_{max}(log ε)	Ref.
$C_{16}H_{21}ClO_7$			
1,3-Dioxol-1-ium, 4,5-dihydro-2-[2-(2-hydroxyphenyl)-1-methylethenyl]-4,4,5,5-tetramethyl-, perchlorate	$CHCl_3$	291(3.32),323(3.40), 408(3.03)	104-0394-73
1,3-Dioxol-1-ium, 4,5-dihydro-2-[2-(4-methoxyphenyl)ethenyl]-4,4,5,5-tetramethyl-	$CHCl_3$	315(5.21),405(4.51)	104-0394-73
$C_{16}H_{21}N$			
1H-Indole, 2-(2,2-dimethyl-3-butenyl)-1,3-dimethyl-	EtOH	232(4.49),282s(3.80), 288(3.85),295(3.83)	39-1913-73C
$C_{16}H_{21}NO_2$			
1H-Carbazole, 9-acetyl-2,3,4,4a,9,9a-hexahydro-8-methoxy-4a-methyl-	EtOH	255(4.07)	33-2628-73
1-Cyclohexene-1-carboxylic acid, 2-[(phenylmethyl)amino]-, ethyl ester	EtOH	303(4.17)	1-2802-73
Ethanone, 1-(2,3,4,4a,9,9a-hexahydro-8-methoxy-4a-methyl-1H-carbazol-6-yl)-	EtOH	249(3.94),343(4.23)	33-2628-73
2H-Indol-2-one, 1-cyclohexyl-1,3-dihydro-5-hydroxy-3,3-dimethyl-	MeOH	262(4.01),3?2s(3.35)	39-2618-73C
$C_{16}H_{21}NO_2S$			
5-Oxa-8-thia-6-azaspiro[3.4]octan-2-one, 1,1,3,3,6-pentamethyl-7-phenyl-	C_6H_{12}	219(3.84),297(2.97)	12-2491-73
$C_{16}H_{21}NO_3$			
Acetamide, 2-(4-acetylphenoxy)-N-cyclohexyl-	EtOH	214(4.14),266(4.27)	111-0574-73
Benzenepropanamide, N-cyclohexyl-4-methoxy-β-oxo-	pH 13	312(4.32)	39-0808-73B
N-Demethylmesembrine	MeOH	200(4.70),229(4.02), 277(3.56)	33-0347-73
3H,5H-Oxazolo[4,3-a]isoindol-5-one, 1,9b-dihydro-9b-hydroxy-1,1-dimethyl-3-(2-methylpropyl)-	EtOH	245(3.70),276(3.16), 283(3.04)	94-1164-73
Piperidine, 1-[(4-acetylphenoxy)acetyl]-4-methyl-	EtOH	214(4.42),268(4.43)	111-0574-73
Piperidine, 1-[[4-(1-oxopropyl)phenoxy]-acetyl]-	EtOH	214(4.24),266(4.24)	111-0574-73
$C_{16}H_{21}NO_4$			
1H-Isoindole-1,3(2H)-dione, 2-(4,4-diethoxybutyl)-	EtOH	232(4.13),239(3.97), 291(3.27)	78-3761-73
Morpholine, 4-[[4-(2-methyl-1-oxopropyl)phenoxy]acetyl]-	EtOH	214(4.28),267(4.25)	111-0574-73
Morpholine, 4-[[4-(1-oxobutyl)phenoxy]-acetyl]-	EtOH	214(4.26),266(4.26)	111-0574-73
$C_{16}H_{21}NO_5$			
L-Leucine, N-[3-(4-hydroxy-3-methoxyphenyl)-1-oxo-2-propenyl]-	MeOH	290(3.83),319(3.89)	20-0243-73
	MeOH-KOH	310(3.45),362(4.00)	20-0243-73
$C_{16}H_{21}NO_7S$			
α-D-Xylopentodialdo-1,4-furanose, 1,2-O-(1-methylethylidene)-3-O-p-tolylsulfonyl-, 5-(N-methyloxime)	EtOH	228(4.05),240s(--)	136-0159-73F
$C_{16}H_{21}N_2$			
Pyridinium, 1-[4-(dimethylamino)phenyl]-2,4,6-trimethyl-, perchlorate	EtOH	224(3.92),266(4.46), 310(3.42)	103-0333-73

Compound	Solvent	λ_{max}(log ϵ)	Ref.
$C_{16}H_{21}N_2O_2$			
1H-Imidazol-1-yloxy, 2,5-dihydro-2,2,5,5-tetramethyl-4-[2-(4-methylphenyl)ethenyl]-, 3-oxide	EtOH	235(4.09),241(4.08), 252(3.92),340(4.38)	104-1990-73
$C_{16}H_{21}N_3O_3$			
4H-Isoxazolo[3,4-d]azepin-3-ol, 6-acetyl-5,6,7,8-tetrahydro-, benzylammonium salt	THF	261(3.82)	1-3251-73
$C_{16}H_{21}N_3O_{10}$			
Acetamide, 2-diazo-N-(2,3,4,6-tetra-O-acetyl-β-D-glucopyranosyl)-	MeOH	253(4.15)	136-0101-73F
$C_{16}H_{21}N_5O_5$			
D-Mannitol, 1-(6-amino-9H-purin-9-yl)-3,6-anhydro-1-deoxy-4,5-O-(1-methylethylidene)-, 2-acetate	EtOH	260(4.24)	136-0243-73B
$C_{16}H_{21}N_5O_6$			
Formycin, 5'-O-(2-acetoxyisobutyryl)-3'-deoxy-	MeOH-acid	236(3.96),297(4.03)	44-3179-73
	MeOH-base	212(4.41),236(4.22), 305(3.83)	44-3179-73
$C_{16}H_{21}O_3$			
1,3-Dioxol-1-ium, 4,5-dihydro-2-[2-(2-hydroxyphenyl)-1-methylethenyl]-4,4,5,5-tetramethyl-, perchlorate	$CHCl_3$	291(3.32),323(3.40), 408(3.03)	104-0394-73
$C_{16}H_{21}ClNO_8$			
Carbamic acid, [3-chloro-4-(β-D-glucopyranosyloxy))phenyl]-, 1-methylethyl ester	pH 13	240(4.36),289(3.30)	98-0792-73
	75% MeOH	240(4.36),289(3.30)	98-0792-73
Carbamic acid, [5-chloro-2-(β-D-glucopyranosyloxy)phenyl]-, 1-methylethyl ester	pH 13	239(4.25),285(3.43)	98-0792-73
	75% MeOH	239(4.24),285(3.42)	98-0792-73
$C_{16}H_{22}ClN_2O_3P$			
Phosphonic acid, (2-chloro-4-quinazolinyl)-, dibutyl ester	EtOH	237(4.57),273(3.21), 284(3.23),298(3.32), 325(3.56)	48-0649-73
$C_{16}H_{22}FN_5O_{11}$			
β-D-Allofuranuronic acid, 5-[[2-amino-5-O-(aminocarbonyl)-2,3-dideoxy-L-erythro-pentonoyl]amino]-1,5-dideoxy-1-(3,4-dihydro-5-fluoro-2,4-dioxo-1(2H)-pyrimidinyl)-	0.05M HCl	267(3.90)	35-5788-73
	0.05M NaOH	268(3.81)	35-5788-73
$C_{16}H_{22}FN_5O_{12}$			
β-D-Allofuranuronic acid, 5-[[2-amino-5-O-(aminocarbonyl)-2-deoxy-L-xylonoyl]amino]-1,5-dideoxy-1-(5-fluoro-3,4-dihydro-2,4-dioxo-1(2H)-pyrimidinyl)-	0.05M HCl	267(3.91)	35-5788-73
	0.05M NaOH	268(3.81)	35-5788-73
$C_{16}H_{22}IN$			
3H-Indolium, 1,2,3-trimethyl-3-(3-methyl-2-butenyl)-, iodide	EtOH	219(4.26),238s(3.86), 278(3.84)	39-1913-73C

Compound	Solvent	λ_{max}(log ε)	Ref.
$C_{16}H_{22}N_2$			
4,4'-Bipyridinium, 1,1',2,2',6,6'-hexamethyl-, bis(tetrafluoroborate)	MeCN	337(3.97),366(4.22), 393(4.37),560(4.09), 595(4.20),635(4.09), 695(3.71)	5-1036-73
9H-Carbazole-9-propanamide, 1,2,3,4-tetrahydro-1-methyl-	EtOH	231(4.48),280(3.80), 286(3.85),294(3.80)	78-4045-73
maleate	EtOH	230(4.56),280(3.87), 285(3.90),294(3.85)	78-4045-73
Cyclobutanecarbonitrile, 3-(cyanomethylene)-2,2-diethyl-4-(1-ethylpropylidene)-	EtOH	282(4.26)	39-0885-73B
Cyclohept[b]indole-5(6H)-propanamine, 7,8,9,10-tetrahydro-, hydrochloride	EtOH	230(4.51),280(3.79), 287(3.85),294(3.84)	78-4045-73
1H-Pyrrole, 4-ethyl-2-[(4-ethyl-3,5-dimethyl-2H-pyrrol-2-ylidene)methyl]-3-methyl-, hydrobromide	$CHCl_3$	482(5.25)	65-0885-73
picrate	$CHCl_3$	481(4.91)	65-0885-73
$C_{16}H_{22}N_2O$			
Benzamide, N-butyl-2-(cyclopentylideneamino)-	EtOH	225(4.56),340(3.62)	103-0490-73
Benzamide, 2-(cyclopentylideneamino)-N-(2-methylpropyl)-	EtOH	225(4.50),340(3.20)	103-0490-73
2-Propanamine, N-[3-(1-methylethyl)-4-(phenylmethylene)-2-oxazolidinylidene]-, (E)-	EtOH	224(4.02),289(4.48)	44-1051-73
(Z)-	EtOH	225(4.13),284(4.18)	44-1051-73
2-Propanamine, N-[4-methyl-3-(1-methylethyl)-5-phenyl-2-oxazolidinylidene]-	EtOH	221(4.12),312(4.11)	44-1051-73
$C_{16}H_{22}N_2O_2$			
1H-Imidazole, 2,5-dihydro-1-hydroxy-2,2,5,5-tetramethyl-4-[2-(4-methylphenyl)ethenyl]-, 3-oxide	EtOH	233(4.04),238(4.03), 248(3.87),334(4.40)	104-1990-73
$C_{16}H_{22}N_2O_2S$			
1-Piperidinecarbothioamide, 3-methoxy-2-(2-oxopropyl)-N-phenyl-, cis	pH 13	214(4.30),242(4.29)	44-1933-73
	MeOH	225(4.25),255(4.19)	44-1933-73
trans	pH 13	214(4.30),242(4.28)	44-1933-73
	MeOH	224(4.25),255(4.16)	44-1933-73
$C_{16}H_{22}N_2O_3$			
Acetamide, N-cyclohexyl-2-[4-[1-(hydroxyimino)ethyl]phenoxy]-	EtOH	208(4.34),256(4.24)	111-0574-73
1H-Azepine, hexahydro-1-[[4-[1-(hydroxyimino)ethyl]phenoxy]acetyl]-	EtOH	212(4.46),257(4.41)	111-0574-73
Piperidine, 1-[[4-[1-(hydroxyimino)ethyl]phenoxy]acetyl]-4-methyl-	EtOH	208(4.40),256(4.26)	111-0574-73
Piperidine, 1-[[4-[1-(hydroxyimino)propyl]phenoxy]acetyl]-	EtOH	211(4.34),257(4.26)	111-0574-73
$C_{16}H_{22}N_2O_4$			
Morpholine, 4-[[4-[1-(hydroxyimino)butyl]phenoxy]acetyl]-	EtOH	212(4.33),257(4.25)	111-0574-73
Morpholine, 4-[[4-[1-(hydroxyimino)-2-methylpropyl]phenoxy]acetyl]-	EtOH	210(4.26)	111-0574-73
$C_{16}H_{22}N_2O_{11}$			
α-D-Glucopyranose, 2-(acetylnitrosoamino)-2-deoxy-, 1,3,4,6-tetraacetate	$CHCl_3$	389(--),405(--), 424(--)	136-0339-73C

Compound	Solvent	$\lambda_{max}(\log \epsilon)$	Ref.
β-D-Glucopyranose, 2-(acetylnitroso-amino)-2-deoxy-, 1,3,4,6-tetraacetate	$CHCl_3$	391(1.73),407(1.93), 426(1.94)	136-0339-73C
$C_{16}H_{22}N_4O_3$			
1H-Pyrimido[5,4-b][1,4]oxazine-6-carbox-ylic acid, 2,7-dimethyl-4-piperidino-, ethyl ester	EtOH	244(4.3),280(4.1), 384(3.3)	103-1532-73
$C_{16}H_{22}N_4O_3S$			
DL-Valine, N-[1-oxo-5-(1H-pyrrolo[2,3-d]pyrimidin-4-ylthio)pentyl]-	pH 1	220(4.35),258(3.99), 311(4.03)	73-1438-73
	pH 13	222(4.35),249(3.96), 293(4.11)	73-1438-73
$C_{16}H_{22}N_4O_4$			
1H-Imidazo[4,5-c]pyridin-4-amine, N-(3-methyl-2-butenyl)-1-β-D-ribofuranosyl-	M HCl	212(4.40),267(4.20)	102-2087-73
	EtOH	216(4.26),274(4.22)	102-2087-73
3H-Imidazo[4,5-b]pyridin-7-amine, N-(3-methyl-2-butenyl)-3-β-D-ribofuranosyl-	M HCl	223(4.20),265(3.88), 293(4.30)	102-2087-73
	EtOH	224(4.23),267(4.18), 287(4.20)	102-2087-73
$C_{16}H_{22}N_6O_7$			
L-Valine, N-[[(9-β-D-ribofuranosyl-9H-purin-6-yl)amino]carbonyl]-	pH 1-2	270s(--),277(4.32)	87-0139-73
	pH 5-7	270(4.34),277s(--)	87-0139-73
	pH 12	270(4.28),299(3.70)	87-0139-73
$C_{16}H_{22}N_6O_7S$			
L-Methionine, N-[[(9-β-D-ribofuranosyl-9H-purin-6-yl)amino]carbonyl]-	pH 1-2	270s(--),277(4.31)	87-0139-73
	pH 5-7	271(4.37),277s(--)	87-0139-73
	pH 12	272(4.26),297(3.96)	87-0139-73
$C_{16}H_{22}O$			
5(6H)-Benzocyclododecenone, 7,8,9,10-11,12,13,14-octahydro-	EtOH	241(3.81)	78-1857-73
5(6H)-Benzocyclooctenone, 8-(1,1-dimeth-ylethyl)-7,8,9,10-tetrahydro-	EtOH	248(3.81)	78-1843-73
5(6H)-Benzocyclooctenone, 7,8,9,10-tetrahydro-7,7,9,9-tetramethyl-	EtOH	249(3.95)	78-1851-73
4a(2H)-Biphenylenol, 2-(1,1-dimethyleth-yl)-1,3,4,8b-tetrahydro-, cis	EtOH	260(3.07),266(3.24), 273(3.20)	78-1843-73
trans	EtOH	261(3.04),267(3.20), 273(3.16)	78-1843-73
4a(2H)-Biphenylenol, 1,3,4,8b-tetra-hydro-1,1,3,3-tetramethyl-, cis	EtOH	260(3.12),266(3.25), 273(3.23)	78-1843-73
$C_{16}H_{22}O_2$			
7H-Benz[e]inden-7-one, 3-acetyl-1,2,3,3a,4,5,8,9,9a,9b-decahydro-3a-methyl-	EtOH	239(4.21)	94-0335-73
1,4-Methano-1H-indene-3,8(2H)-dione, 3a,4,5,7a-tetrahydro-1,2,3a,4,6,7-hexamethyl-	MeOH	292(1.85)	88-2871-73
1,4-Methano-5H-inden-5-one, 1,3a,4,7a-tetrahydro-7a-hydroxy-1,2,3a,4,6,7-hexamethyl-	MeOH	251(3.87),325(1.76)	88-2871-73
Tricyclo[4.4.0.0^{2,9}]dec-3-ene-7,10-di-one, 1,3,4,6,8,9-hexamethyl-	MeOH	246(2.82),300(1.85)	88-2871-73

Compound	Solvent	$\lambda_{max}(\log \epsilon)$	Ref.
$C_{16}H_{22}O_2Rh$			
Rodium, 9,9-dimethylbicyclo[6.1.0]nona-2,4,6-triene(pentane-2,4-dionato)-	hexane	229s(4.10),304(3.64), 353(3.16)	78-3903-73
$C_{16}H_{22}O_2S_2$			
2-Cyclohexen-1-one, 3,3'-dithiobis[5,5-dimethyl-	EtOH	208(3.96),277(4.26)	88-4319-73
Spiro[1,3-benzodithiole-2,1'-cyclohexane]-3',4'(5H)-dione, 6,7-dihydro-5',5',6,6-tetramethyl-	$CHCl_3$	250(3.71),350(3.71)	88-4319-73
$C_{16}H_{22}O_3$			
2H-1-Benzopyran-5,7-diol, 3,4-dihydro-2,2-dimethyl-3-(3-methyl-2-butenyl)-	EtOH	271(2.88)	39-0419-73C
	EtOH-base	334(--)	39-0419-73C
$C_{16}H_{22}O_4$			
2(3H)-Benzofuranone, 5-ethylidene-3a,4,5,7a-tetrahydro-3-(methoxymethyl)-6-(3-oxobutyl)-	EtOH	239(4.06)	44-0585-73
2H-1-Benzopyran-2,6(8aH)-dione, 8a-ethoxy-2,4-dihydro-4,4,5,7,8-pentamethyl-	MeOH	235(4.13),279(3.31)	35-8319-73
1-Butanone, 1-(3,4-dihydro-5,7-dihydroxy-2,2-dimethyl-2H-1-benzopyran-6-yl)-2-methyl-	EtOH	293(4.29)	39-0419-73C
	EtOH-base	303(--)	39-0419-73C
1-Butanone, 1-(3,4-dihydro-5,7-dihydroxy-2,2-dimethyl-2H-1-benzopyran-8-yl)-2-methyl-	EtOH	293(4.23)	39-0419-73C
	EtOH-base	303(--)	39-0419-73C
Cyclopentaneacetic acid, α,3-dimethyl-3-(2-methyl-3-oxo-1-cyclopenten-1-yl)-2-oxo-, methyl ester	EtOH	241(4.08)	39-0914-73C
Ketone A from heveadride	MeOH	216(3.76),256(3.71)	39-0194-73C
$C_{16}H_{22}O_5S$			
Cyclopenta[c]pyran-4-carboxylic acid, 5-[(butylthio)methylene]-1,4a,5,6-7,7a-hexahydro-1-methoxy-6-oxo-, methyl ester	EtOH	232(4.02),314(4.21)	35-0540-73
Cyclopenta[c]pyran-4-carboxylic acid, 7-[(butylthio)methylene]-1,4a,5,6-7,7a-hexahydro-1-methoxy-6-oxo-, methyl ester	EtOH	237(4.04),318(4.26)	35-0540-73
$C_{16}H_{22}O_6$			
4a(4H)-Naphthalenecarboxylic acid, 1,5,8,8a-tetrahydro-1-hydroxy-2-methoxy-5-(methoxymethyl)-6-methyl-4-oxo-, methyl ester	EtOH	255(4.18)	94-0528-73
isomer	EtOH	252(4.04)	94-0528-73
$C_{16}H_{22}O_{11}$			
Cyclopenta[c]pyran-4,7-dicarboxylic acid, 1-(β-D-glucopyranosyloxy)-1,4a,5,6,7,7a-hexahydro- (forsythid)	MeOH	234(4.06)	94-0497-73
$C_{16}H_{23}ClN_2O_2$			
Isoquinolinium, 2-(2-aminobutyl)-3,4-dihydro-6,7-dimethoxy-1-methyl-, chloride hydrochloride	pH 3	255(4.75),316(4.00), 329s(3.83)	39-2830-73C

Compound	Solvent	$\lambda_{max}(\log \epsilon)$	Ref.
$C_{16}H_{23}N$			
Thujopsene-3-carbonitrile	EtOH	246(4.03)	54-0985-73
$C_{16}H_{23}NO$			
1-Naphthalenol, 1,2,3,4-tetrahydro-1-(piperidinomethyl)-	EtOH	259s(2.53),266(2.62), 273(2.58)	25-1111-73
6-Oxa-1-azabicyclo[3.1.0]hexane, 5-(1,1-dimethylethyl)-2,2-dimethyl-3-phenyl-, cis	EtOH	244(2.16),249(2.24), 254(2.32),260(2.40), 266(2.28),270(2.15)	12-2159-73
$C_{16}H_{23}NO_3$			
2-Piperidinone, 1-[2-(3,4-dimethoxyphenyl)ethyl]-3-methyl-	EtOH	230(3.99),281(3.48)	94-2695-73
2-Piperidinone, 1-[2-(3,4-dimethoxyphenyl)ethyl]-5-methyl-	EtOH	229(3.97),281(3.48)	94-2695-73
$C_{16}H_{23}NO_4$			
1,4,6-Cycloheptatriene-1,4-dicarboxylic acid, 2-(diethylamino)-3-methyl-, dimethyl ester	dioxan	228(4.14),238s(4.08), 271(4.15),342(3.84), 400(3.99)	88-1213-73
2,4,7-Cycloheptatriene-1,4-dicarboxylic acid, 2-(diethylamino)-3-methyl-, dimethyl ester	dioxan	214(4.21),246s(3.88), 311(3.58)	88-1213-73
2-Piperidinone, 1-[2-(3,4-dimethoxyphenyl)-2-hydroxyethyl]-3-methyl-	EtOH	231(3.98),279(3.45)	94-2695-73
2-Piperidinone, 1-[2-(3,4-dimethoxyphenyl)-2-hydroxyethyl]-5-methyl-	EtOH	230(3.98),279(3.46)	94-2695-73
$C_{16}H_{23}NO_7$			
Alanine, N-(2,6-dimethoxybenzoyl)-3,3-diethoxy-	EtOH	280(3.33)	4-0935-73
$C_{16}H_{23}N_3O_2$			
4-Pyrimidinamine, 5-(dimethoxymethyl)-5,6-dihydro-2-phenyl-N-propyl-	EtOH	248(4.03),281(3.85)	18-0253-73
	EtOH-HCl	258(--),290(--), 305s(--)	18-0253-73
$C_{16}H_{23}N_5O_4$			
Adenosine, N-cyclohexyl-	pH 1.0	265.5(4.28)	87-0358-73
	H_2O	270(4.26)	87-0358-73
	pH 13	270(4.26)	87-0358-73
Adenosine, 2'-O-methyl-N-(3-methyl-2-butenyl)-	MeOH	268(4.26)	69-2179-73
Adenosine, 3'-O-methyl-N-(3-methyl-2-butenyl)-	MeOH	268(4.29)	69-2179-73
$C_{16}H_{23}N_7O_6$			
Adenosine, N-[[[1-(aminocarbonyl)-2-methylpropyl]amino]carbonyl]-, (S)-	pH 1-2	270s(--),277(4.37)	87-0139-73
	pH 5-7	269(4.36),277s(--)	87-0139-73
	pH 12	270(4.12),248(4.25)	87-0139-73
$C_{16}H_{24}$			
Benzene, [1-(1,1-dimethylethyl)-3,3-dimethyl-1-butenyl]-	EtOH	242(2.31),254(2.36), 259(2.40),266(2.28)	35-1586-73
Bicyclo[10.2.2]hexadeca-12,14,15-triene	EtOH	224(3.88),268(2.53)	49-0644-73
Cyclopropa[d]naphthalene, decahydro-4a,8,8-trimethyl-2,3-bis(methylene)-	EtOH	253(3.74)	54-0985-73
Tricyclo[8.6.0.0^{2,9}]hexadeca-2,16-diene (95%)	EtOH	250(3.82),259(3.91), 269(3.78)	22-3067-73

Compound	Solvent	$\lambda_{max}(\log \epsilon)$	Ref.
$C_{16}H_{24}NOS$			
Deoxynupharidin-6α-ol, 7β-(methylthio)-, perchlorate	EtOH-acid	294(3.39)	35-6342-73
7-Epideoxynupharidin-6β-ol, 7α-(methylthio)-, perchlorate	EtOH	295(3.21)	35-6342-73
$C_{16}H_{24}N_2$			
Piperidine, 1-(2,4-cyclopentadien-1-ylidene-1-piperidinylmethyl)-	hexane	259(3.96),347(4.47)	101-0243-73C
$C_{16}H_{24}N_2O_2$			
2-Propenamide, N-ethyl-3-(4-methoxyphenyl)-3-(propylamino)-	EtOH	207(3.97),227(4.02), 278(3.22),288(3.18)	33-1266-73
$C_{16}H_{24}N_2O_4$			
1H-Cyclopenta[d]pyridazine-2,3-dicarboxylic acid, 4,7a-dihydro-1,5,6,7,7a-pentamethyl-, dimethyl ester, cis	ether	264(3.60)	24-0008-73
trans	ether	258(3.64)	24-0008-73
$C_{16}H_{24}N_6O_4$			
Adenosine, 3'-[2-(acetylamino)ethyl]-3'-deoxy-N,N-dimethyl-	H_2O	274(4.38)	44-0198-73
Adenosine, 3'-deoxy-3'-[2-(dimethylamino)-2-oxoethyl]-N,N-dimethyl-	H_2O	275(4.16)	44-0193-73
$C_{16}H_{14}N_6O_5$			
Adenosine, N-[[(3-methylbutyl)amino]-carbonyl]-	pH 1-2	270s(--),278(4.40)	87-0139-73
	pH 5-7	270(4.39),277s(--)	87-0139-73
	pH 12	278(4.24),298(4.06)	87-0139-73
$C_{16}H_{24}O$			
Cyclopropa[d]naphthalene-3-carboxaldehyde, 1,1a,4,4a,5,6,7,8-octahydro-2,4a,8,8-tetramethyl-	EtOH	277(4.07)	54-0985-73
$C_{16}H_{24}O_2$			
Thujopsene-3-carboxylic acid	EtOH	253(3.95)	54-0985-73
$C_{16}H_{24}O_3$			
1H-Indene-2-carboxylic acid, 2-(1-formylethenyl)octahydro-3a,4-dimethyl-, methyl ester	EtOH	219(3.84),333(2.82)	94-2806-73
$C_{16}H_{24}O_4$			
Cyclopent[a]indene, 1,2,3,3a,5,6,7,8a-octahydro-2,2,6,6-tetramethoxy-	EtOH	244.5(4.23)	35-4582-73
1H-Indene-4-carboxylic acid, 1β-(1,1-dimethylethoxy)-2,3,5,6,7,7a-hexahydro-7aβ-methyl-5-oxo-, methyl ester	EtOH	240(4.02)	44-3239-73
2H-Inden-2-one, 4-acetoxy-3,3a,4,5,6,7-hexahydro-1-methoxy-4-methyl-7-(1-methylethyl)-	EtOH	252(3.99)	44-3663-73
$C_{16}H_{24}O_4S_2$			
Propanedioic acid, 2-butenyl[(2-butenylthio)thioxomethyl]-, diethyl ester	EtOH	320(3.96)	78-2077-73

Compound	Solvent	$\lambda_{max}(\log \epsilon)$	Ref.
$C_{16}H_{24}O_5$			
2,4-Pentadienoic acid, 5-(3,8-dihydroxy-1,5-dimethyl-6-oxabicyclo[3.2.1]oct-8-yl)-3-methyl-, methyl ester	EtOH	267(4.30)	88-0139-73
$C_{16}H_{24}O_6$			
Benzenebutanoic acid, β-hydroxy-3,4,5-trimethoxy-β-methyl-, ethyl ester	EtOH	213(3.84),217s(3.49), 273(2.60)	39-2388-73C
Eupacunin, deacetyldeangeloyl-11,13-dihydro-13-methoxy-	MeOH	210(3.64)(end abs.)	44-2189-73
$C_{16}H_{24}Si_2$			
Silane, 1,4-naphthalenediylbis[trimethyl-, tetracyanoethylene complex	CH_2Cl_2	446(1.95),588(1.91)	39-0447-73B
Silane, 1,5-naphthalenediylbis[trimethyl-, tetracyanoethylene complex	CH_2Cl_2	440(2.27),586(3.30)	39-0447-73B
Silane, 2,6-naphthalenediylbis[trimethyl-, tetracyanoethylene complex	CH_2Cl_2	463(2.62),590(2.69)	39-0447-73B
Silane, 2,7-naphthalenediylbis[trimethyl-, tetracyanoethylene complex	CH_2Cl_2	460(2.52),588(2.51)	39-0447-73B
$C_{16}H_{24}Si_4$			
1,4,7,10-Tetrasilacyclododeca-2,5,8,11-tetrayne, 1,1,4,4,7,7,10,10-octamethyl-	n.s.g.	202(3.43),209(3.48), 218(3.30)	65-1397-73
$C_{16}H_{25}BrN_2O_2$			
Isoquinolinium, 2-(2-aminobutyl)-3,4-dihydro-6,7-dimethoxy-1-methyl-, bromide hydrobromide	pH 3	246(4.19),309(4.02), 362(4.02)	39-2830-73C
$C_{16}H_{25}N$			
Bicyclo[10.2.2]hexadeca-12,14,15-trien-13-amine	EtOH	242(3.79),292(3.32)	49-0644-73
$C_{16}H_{25}NOS$			
Spiro[pyrrolo[1,2-b][1,4,2]oxathiazole-2,2'-tricyclo[3.3.1.1^{3,7}]decane], tetrahydro-5,5-dimethyl-	C_6H_{12}	213(3.50),243(3.49)	12-2491-73
$C_{16}H_{25}NO_3$			
1-Piperidineethanol, α-(3,4-dimethoxyphenyl)-3-methyl-	EtOH	230(3.96),279(3.48)	94-2695-73
$C_{16}H_{25}NO_4$			
1-Cyclopentene-1-carboxylic acid, 2-[7-(ethylamino)-7-oxoheptyl]-3-oxo-, methyl ester	MeOH	246(4.12)	44-4412-73
$C_{16}H_{25}NO_4Si$			
Silicon, [4-(1,1-dimethylethyl)phenolato][[2,2',2"-nitrilotris[ethanolato(3-)]]N,O,O',O"]-	H_2O	220(3.78),275(3.13)	30-0941-73
$C_{16}H_{25}NO_9$			
Acetonitrile, [6-(β-D-glucopyranosyloxy)-2-hydroxy-2,4-dimethoxycyclohexylidene]-, (1E,2α,3β,4β,6β)-	n.s.g.	217(4.04)	39-2209-73C

Compound	Solvent	$\lambda_{max}(\log \epsilon)$	Ref.
$C_{16}H_{25}NS$			
1H-Indene, octahydro-1-(1-isothiocyanato-2-methylpropyl)-3a-methyl-7-methylene-	CCl_4	243(3.40)	78-4259-73
$C_{16}H_{25}N_3O_6$			
1-Cyclopenteneheptanoic acid, 2-(methoxycarbonyl)-3-hydroxy-5-oxo-, methyl ester, semicarbazone	MeOH	296(4.38)	44-4412-73
$C_{16}H_{25}N_6O_8P$			
5'-Adenylic acid, N-[[(3-methylbutyl)-amino]carbonyl]-	pH 1	277(4.36)	87-0956-73
	H_2O	269(4.34),275(4.27)	87-0956-73
	pH 13	269(4.26),277(4.23), 297(3.88)	87-0956-73
$C_{16}H_{25}O_3P$			
Phosphonic acid, (2-phenylethenyl)-, dibutyl ester	nonane	217s(4.11),259(4.26), 285(--),294(3.18)	65-2164-73
	EtOH	217s(4.17),261(4.31), 295(3.26)	65-2164-73
	dioxan	217s(4.16),260(4.32), 294(3.18)	65-2164-73
	MeCN	216s(4.17),260(4.35), 292(3.18)	65-2164-73
$C_{16}H_{25}PS$			
Phosphine sulfide, bis(2-methylpropyl)-(2-phenylethenyl)-	nonane	218s(4.23),260(4.33), 286s(3.74),295(3.48)	65-2164-73
Phosphine sulfide, dibutyl(2-phenylethenyl)- (also spectra in other solvents)	nonane	218s(4.22),260(4.33), 284s(3.73),295(3.51)	65-2164-73
	EtOH	208(4.38),217s(4.26), 261(4.37),284s(3.93), 295(3.61)	65-2164-73
$C_{16}H_{26}Cl_2N_4O_8$			
Benzenaminium, N-[2-(dimethylamino)-1-[(dimethylimino)methyl]ethenyl]-N-[(dimethylamino)methylene]-, diperchlorate	H_2O	252(3.97),309(4.44)	73-2633-73
$C_{16}H_{26}N_4O_4$			
1H-Imidazol-1-yloxy, 4,4'-(1,2-ethenediyl)bis[2,5-dihydro-2,2,5,5-tetramethyl-, 3,3'-dioxide	EtOH	244(3.79),360(4.11), 378(4.19)	104-1990-73
$C_{16}H_{26}N_6O_4$			
Adenosine, N-[2-(diethylamino)ethyl]-	pH 1	269(4.23)	87-0358-73
	H_2O	267(4.28)	87-0358-73
	pH 13	269.5(4.29)	87-0358-73
$C_{16}H_{26}O$			
2(3H)-Benzocyclododecenone, 4,4a,5,6,7-8,9,10,11,12,13,14-dodecahydro-	EtOH	240(4.22)	39-0393-73C
3,5-Hexadien-2-one, 6-[5-methyl-2-(1-methylethyl)cyclohexyl]-	EtOH	279(4.51)	22-3071-73
Isomenthone, 2,4-diallyl-, (1R,2S,4S)-(+)-	dioxan	295(1.62)	22-1049-73

Compound	Solvent	$\lambda_{max}(\log \epsilon)$	Ref.
$C_{16}H_{26}O_2$			
5,6-Decamethylene-4-pyrone, 2,3-dihydro-2-methyl-	EtOH	270(4.33)	22-1409-73
Resorcinol, pentaethyl-	EtOH	249(4.00),293(3.60)	12-0899-73
	KOH	231(4.34),342(3.83)	12-0899-73
$C_{16}H_{26}O_3$			
4-Hexen-1-one, 5-methyl-1-(10-methyl-1,4-dioxaspiro[4.5]dec-7-yl)-	MeOH	285(1.76)	39-2113-73C
$C_{16}H_{26}O_4Si$			
Phenol, 3-[(2,5-diethyl-4-propyl-1,3-dioxo-2-silacyclohex-2-yl)oxy]-	EtOH	205(4.04),275(3.20)	87-0729-73
$C_{16}H_{27}NO$			
Cyclohexanamine, N-(3-cyclohexylidene-2-methylpropylidene)-, N-oxide	EtOH	237(3.97)	33-2961-73
$C_{16}H_{27}NS_2$			
Dithiobenzoic acid, 4-methyl-, dibutyl-amine salt	EtOH	302(4.10),353(3.90), 500(2.29)	143-0359-73
$C_{16}H_{27}N_5$			
1H-Pyrazolo[4,3-d]pyrimidin-7-amine, N-decyl-3-methyl- (all spectra in ethanol)	pH 1	261(3.74),310(4.03)	102-0025-73
	pH 7	237(3.74),295(4.03), 307(3.94),318s(--)	102-0025-73
	pH 12	243(4.12),263s(--), 307(3.85)	102-0025-73
$C_{16}H_{28}N_4O_4$			
1H-Imidazole, 4,4'-(1,2-ethenediyl)bis-[2,5-dihydro-1-hydroxy-2,2,5,5-tetra-methyl-, 3,3'-dioxide	EtOH	244(3.54),360(4.09), 378(4.33)	104-1990-73
$C_{16}H_{28}SSi$			
Silane, trimethyl[4-(2-thienyl)-3-non-enyl]-, cis	EtOH	251(3.85),278(3.87)	88-2487-73
trans	EtOH	255(3.82),293(3.78)	88-2487-73
$C_{16}H_{29}N_7O_6$			
Formamide, N-[2-amino-3,4-dihydro-4-oxo-6-(D-ribofuranosylamino)-5-pyrimidin-yl]-N-[2-(3-aminopropyl)methylamino]-ethyl]-	pH 1	270(4.30)	103-0377-73
	pH 6	272(4.26)	103-0377-73
	pH 13	265(4.12)	103-0377-73
$C_{16}H_{30}$			
Cyclobutene, 1,2,3-tris(1,1-dimethyl-ethyl)-	ether	215(3.42),225(2.47), 235(1.79)	35-8481-73
$C_{16}H_{30}O$			
Cyclohexanone, 2,2,6-triethyl-3-methyl-6-(1-methylethyl)-, (3R-cis)-	hexane	312(1.38)	22-1049-73
	MeOH	307(1.49)	22-1049-73
$C_{16}H_{31}ClN_2O_4S$			
Cyclopropenium, 1,2-bis[bis(1-methyl-ethyl)amino]-3-(methylthio)-, per-chlorate	MeOH	214(4.02),266(3.91)	35-3043-73
$C_{16}H_{32}N_2$			
1H-Imidazole, 4,5-dihydro-2-tridecyl-	EtOH	220(3.67)	93-2424-73

Compound	Solvent	$\lambda_{max}(\log \epsilon)$	Ref.
$C_{16}H_{32}Si_3$			
Silane, 1,6-heptadiyne-1,3,7-triyltris-[trimethyl-	n.s.g.	302(2.83)	39-0599-73B
$C_{16}H_{33}N_3O$			
5-Hexen-2-ol, 2-methyl-6,6-bis(propyl-amino)-4-(propylimino)-	EtOH	229(3.82),295(4.36)	70-1033-73
$C_{16}H_{36}AuCl_4N$			
Tetrabutylaminium tetrachloroaurate	MeCN	225(4.64),322(3.73)	33-2405-73

Compound	Solvent	$\lambda_{max}(\log \epsilon)$	Ref.
$C_{17}F_{25}N$			
Pyridine, 2,3,5-trifluoro-4,6-bis(undecafluorocyclohexyl)-	C_6H_{12}	279(3.73)	39-1710-73C
$C_{17}H_8Br_2O$			
7H-Benzo[c]fluoren-7-one, 2,9-dibromo-	EtOH	218(4.52),240(4.63), 273(4.50),285(4.55), 294(4.62),445(3.00)	115-0145-73A
$C_{17}H_8Cl_{10}$			
1,4:5,8-Dimethanonaphthalene, 1,2,3,4-tetrachloro-10-(2,2,3,4,5,5-hexachloro-3-cyclopenten-1-ylidene)-1,4,4a,5,8,8a-hexahydro-, (1aα,4α,4aα,5β,8β,8aα)-	C_6H_{12}	234(4.21)	77-0910-73
$C_{17}H_9ClN_2O_2$			
Acetonitrile, [(4-chlorophenyl)amino]-(1,3-dihydro-1,3-dioxo-2H-inden-2-ylidene)-	MeCN	236(4.30),264(4.12), 385(4.38)	39-1045-73B
$C_{17}H_9F_6N$			
Isoquinoline, 3-fluoro-1-(pentafluoroethyl)-4-phenyl-	hexane	224(4.73),283(3.71), 296(3.75),336(4.01)	30-0767-73
$C_{17}H_9NO$			
Fluorantheno[8,9-d]oxazole	EtOH	235(4.7),290s(4.5), 298(4.7),325(3.7), 347(3.7),360(3.8)	103-0561-73
$C_{17}H_9N_3$			
Propanedinitrile, (9-acridinylmethylene)-	EtOH	248(4.9),366(3.8)	18-0283-73
$C_{17}H_{10}BrN_3O_3$			
1H-Benzimidazole, 2-[5-(4-bromophenyl)-2-furanyl]-5-nitro-	EtOH	223(4.24),242(4.15), 262(4.17),325(4.38), 379(4.61)	73-1700-73
$C_{17}H_{10}Br_2$			
7H-Benzo[c]fluorene, 2,9-dibromo-	HOAc	250(4.53),319(4.25), 325(4.24),334(4.14), 340(4.25)	115-0145-73A
$C_{17}H_{10}Br_2O$			
17H-Cyclopenta[a]phenanthren-17-one, 15,15-dibromo-	EtOH	279(4.70),298(4.24), 315(4.18),360(3.30), 377(3.27)	39-2236-73C
17H-Cyclopenta[a]phenanthren-17-one, 15,16-dibromo-	EtOH	283(4.60),312(4.33), 361(3.19),380(3.18)	39-2236-73C
$C_{17}H_{10}ClNO_3$			
9H-Pyrano[2,3-g]-1,2-benzisoxazol-9-one, 7-(4-chlorophenyl)-3-methyl-	n.s.g.	220(4.4),272(4.6), 303(4.2)	2-0541-73
$C_{17}H_{10}ClN_3O_2$			
Pyrimido[4,5-b]quinoline-2,4(1H,3H)-dione, 3-(4-chlorophenyl)-	DMSO	258(4.6),356(3.5)	24-3533-73

Compound	Solvent	$\lambda_{max}(\log \epsilon)$	Ref.
$C_{17}H_{10}ClN_3O_3$			
1H-Benzimidazole, 2-[5-(4-chlorophenyl)-2-furanyl]-5-nitro-	EtOH	222(4.27),239(4.17), 259(4.18),321(4.39), 372(4.51)	73-1700-73
$C_{17}H_{10}Cl_2N_4$			
1H-Indole, 3-(4,6-dichloro-1,3,5-triazin-2-yl)-1-phenyl-	EtOH	244(3.81),259(3.63), 374(3.97)	39-2075-73B
$C_{17}H_{10}Cl_2N_4O_2$			
[1,3,5]Triazino[1,2-a][1,4]benzodiazepine-1,3(2H,5H)-dione, 9-chloro-7-(2-chlorophenyl)-	EtOH	215s(4.53),246s(4.12), 292s(3.20)	87-1256-73
$C_{17}H_{10}Cl_4N_2$			
Pyrimidine, 4,5,6-trichloro-2-(chlorophenylmethylene)-2,5-dihydro-5-phenyl-	C_6H_{12}	245(4.02)	18-0299-73
$C_{17}H_{10}F_6O_2$			
Benzeneacetic acid, 4-(trifluoromethyl)-α-[[4-(trifluoromethyl)phenyl]methylene]-, (Z)-	EtOH	275(4.15)	36-0910-73
$C_{17}H_{10}N_2O_2$			
Acetonitrile, (1,3-dihydro-1,3-dioxo-2H-inden-2-ylidene)(phenylamino)-	MeCN	233(4.30),260(4.13), 380(4.35)	39-1045-73B
$C_{17}H_{10}N_2O_2S_2$			
Thiazolo[2,3-a]isoquinolinium, 2-mercapto-3-(4-nitrophenyl)-, hydroxide, inner salt	MeOH	214(4.46),230(4.46), 256(4.55),273s(--), 310(4.41),435(4.20)	2-1257-73
$C_{17}H_{10}N_2O_5$			
9H-Pyrano[2,3-g]-1,2-benzisoxazol-9-one, 3-methyl-7-(4-nitrophenyl)-	n.s.g.	221(4.4),278(4.5), 310(4.4)	2-0541-73
$C_{17}H_{10}N_2O_6$			
1H-Benz[f]indole-1-carbonitrile, 3-formyl-4,9-dihydro-8-hydroxy-2-(1-hydroxy-2-oxopropyl)-4,9-dioxo-	EtOH	252.5(4.03)	94-0931-73
$C_{17}H_{10}N_4O_5$			
1H-Benzimidazole, 5-nitro-2-[5-(4-nitrophenyl)-2-furanyl]-	EtOH	217(4.21),239(4.19), 287(4.16),392(4.56)	73-1700-73
$C_{17}H_{10}N_4S$			
Sulfilimine, S,S-diphenyl-N-(tricyanoethenyl)-	EtOH	240s(4.01),342(4.27)	44-4324-73
2H-Triazolo[4,5-f]quinoline, 2-benzo[b]thien-5-yl-	EtOH	235(4.36),275(4.62), 295(4.54),340(4.48)	78-0221-73
$C_{17}H_{10}O_4$			
Benz[d]indeno[1,2-b]pyran-5,11-dione, 3-methoxy-	MeOH	280(4.37),355(3.94)	2-0413-73
$C_{17}H_{10}O_6$			
1H-2-Benzopyran-4-carboxylic acid, 3-(2-carboxyphenyl)-1-oxo- (3λ,2ε)	MeOH	230(4.47),275(4.06), 325(?)	2-0413-73
6,12-Epoxy-9H-benzocycloundecene-8,10-dicarboxylic acid, 9-oxo-	MeOH	293(4.64)	78-0533-73

Compound	Solvent	λmax(log ε)	Ref.
$C_{17}H_{11}BrN_2O$			
1H-Benzimidazole, 2-[5-(4-bromophenyl)-2-furanyl]-	EtOH	225s(4.31),241s(3.94), 276(4.04),342(4.54), 352(4.62),372(4.42)	73-1700-73
$C_{17}H_{11}BrN_4O_4S_2$			
Ethene, 1-(5-bromo-2-thienyl)-2-(5-formyl-2-thienyl)-, 2,4-dinitrophenylhydrazone	DMF	367(4.35),460(4.52)	24-0655-73
$C_{17}H_{11}BrO$			
17H-Cyclopenta[a]phenanthren-17-one, 15-bromo-15,16-dihydro-	EtOH	268(4.78),287(4.41), 299(4.36),310(4.13), 354(3.32),372(3.31)	39-2236-73C
17H-Cyclopenta[a]phenanthren-17-one, 16-bromo-15,16-dihydro-	EtOH	231(4.28),273(4.73), 301s(4.27),335s(3.00), 354(3.13),371(3.13)	39-2236-73C
$C_{17}H_{11}BrO_2$			
Methanone, (4-bromo-1-hydroxy-2-naphthalenyl)phenyl-	C_6H_{12}	224(4.40),266(4.47), 304s(3.78),318(3.50), 385(3.86)	19-0849-73
	MeOH	220(4.44),266(4.47), 302s(3.87),316s(3.54), 385(3.85)	19-0849-73
	50% MeOH	222(4.38),266(4.41), 304(3.93),314s(3.63), 385(3.81)	19-0849-73
$C_{17}H_{11}ClN_2O$			
1H-Benzimidazole, 2-[5-(4-chlorophenyl)-2-furanyl]-	EtOH	225(4.31),239s(4.01), 275(4.08),340(4.61), 350(4.68),360(4.49)	73-1700-73
$C_{17}H_{11}F_6N$			
Benzenepropanenitrile, 4-(trifluoromethyl)-α-[4-(trifluoromethyl)phenyl]-	EtOH	258(2.92),263(2.98), 269(2.90)	36-0910-73
$C_{17}H_{11}N$			
Benz[a]acridine	EtOH	222(4.57),233(4.50), 275(4.71),283s(4.66), 320s(3.59),334(3.71), 345(3.81),360(3.91), 379(3.92)	12-2315-73
	EtOH-acid	221(4.53),233(4.50), 250(4.43),257(4.44), 280(4.54),291(4.63), 380s(4.03),395(4.08)	12-2315-73
Cycloocta[b]naphthalene-8-carbonitrile	hexane	227(4.70),247s(4.27), 285(4.20),292s(4.16), 305s(3.84),343s(3.02)	23-3486-73
Cyclopropa[3,4]pentaleno[1,2-b]naphthalene-1-carbonitrile, 2a,2b,8b,8c-tetrahydro-	C_6H_{12}	233(4.89),262s(4.00), 286(3.82),297s(3.73), 307s(3.45),315(3.24), 322(2.99),329(3.25)	23-3486-73
Cyclopropa[3,4]pentaleno[1,2-b]naphthalene-8c(2aH)-carbonitrile, 2b,8b-dihydro-	C_6H_{12}	239(4.85),267s(3.66), 275(3.76),289(3.78), 299(3.58),314(2.79), 317s(2.54),322(2.46), 327(2.79)	23-3486-73

Compound	Solvent	λ max (log ε)	Ref.
1,4-Ethenoanthracene-2-carbonitrile, 1,4-dihydro-	hexane	232(4.74),237(4.79), 254(3.87),264(3.91), 273(3.90),283(3.71), 297s(2.51),311(2.40), 319(2.15),323(1.90)	23-3486-73
$C_{17}H_{11}NO$			
Benz[a]acridin-5-ol	EtOH	256(4.55),275(4.47), 280(4.27),287(4.51), 290s(4.36),296(4.45), 298(4.46),304(4.46), 322s(4.19),358(3.61), 410(3.70),465(4.06), 490(3.97)	12-2315-73
	EtOH-acid	242(4.64),251s(4.40), 284(4.49),293(4.49), 355s(3.66),376(3.92), 413(4.17),430(4.14)	12-2315-73
	EtOH-base	239(4.49),246(4.49), 255(4.49),272(4.40), 294(4.46),304(4.59), 317(4.53),343(4.02), 360(3.84),408(3.84)	12-2315-73
$C_{17}H_{11}NOS$			
Thiazolo[3,2-a]quinolinium, 1-hydroxy-2-phenyl-, hydroxide, inner salt	50% dioxan-HCl	238(4.4),269(3.8), 307(4.0),488(4.1)	1-1763-73
	50% dioxan-NaOH	238(4.4),269(3.8), 307(3.9),488(4.3)	1-1763-73
$C_{17}H_{11}NO_3$			
4H,5H-Benzo[a]pyrano[2,3-f]quinolizine-4,5-dione, 2-methyl-	EtOH	242(4.42),259(4.35), 308(4.21),320(4.19), 417(4.41),442(4.44)	70-1745-73
9H-Pyrano[2,3-g]-1,2-benzisoxazol-9-one, 3-methyl-7-phenyl-	n.s.g.	220(4.5),265(4.5), 305(4.3)	2-0541-73
$C_{17}H_{11}NO_4$			
Methanone, (1-hydroxy-4-nitro-2-naphthalenyl)phenyl-	C_6H_{12}	248s(4.47),252(4.48), 256s(4.46),262s(4.44), 286(4.25),296(4.26), 364(4.02)	19-0849-73
	MeOH	252(4.48),260s(4.44), 288(4.20),296(4.20), 364(4.04)	19-0849-73
	50% MeOH	236s(4.25),252(4.47), 258s(4.44),296(4.18), 366(4.06)	19-0849-73
$C_{17}H_{11}N_3O$			
1-Phthalazinecarbonitrile, 4-(2-oxo-2-phenylethyl)-	EtOH	231(4.55),297(4.12), 307(4.18),408(4.49), 423(4.48)	95-0409-73
2-Propyn-1-one, 3-phenyl-1-(5-phenyl-1H-1,2,3-triazol-4-yl)-	EtOH	227(4.41),300(4.37)	78-3271-73
anion	EtOH	226(4.42),277(4.32), 320(4.21)	78-3271-73
$C_{17}H_{11}N_3OS$			
Pyrimido[4,5-b]quinolin-4(1H)-one, 2,3-dihydro-3-phenyl-2-thioxo-	MeCN	287(4.5),368(3.8)	24-3533-73

Compound	Solvent	$\lambda_{max}(\log \epsilon)$	Ref.
$C_{17}H_{11}N_3O_2$			
Pyrimido[4,5-b]quinoline-2,4(1H,3H)-dione, 3-phenyl-	MeCN	264(4.8),274(4.8), 351(4.2)	24-3533-73
$C_{17}H_{11}N_3O_3$			
1H-Benzimidazole, 2-[5-(4-nitrophenyl)-2-furanyl]-	EtOH	217s(4.30),245(3.92), 307(4.19),379(4.45)	73-1700-73
1H-Benzimidazole, 5-nitro-2-(5-phenyl-2-furanyl)-	EtOH	219(4.02),239(4.04), 256(4.05),317(4.29), 372(4.39)	73-1700-73
$C_{17}H_{11}N_3O_3S$			
4H-Quinolizine-1-carbonitrile, 2-(methylthio)-3-(2-nitrophenyl)-4-oxo-	EtOH	278(4.36),314(4.14), 397(4.26)	94-0921-73
Thiopyrano[3,4-b]indole-3-acetic acid, α,4-dicyano-1,9-dihydro-9-methyl-1-oxo-, methyl ester	EtOH	253(4.52),320(4.25), 386(4.15),463(4.05)	95-1523-73
Thiopyrano[3,4-b]indole-3-acetic acid, α,4-dicyano-1,9-dihydro-1-oxo-, ethyl ester	EtOH	250(4.53),320(4.29), 382(4.15),447(4.04)	95-1523-73
$C_{17}H_{12}$			
17H-Cyclopenta[a]phenanthrene	EtOH	238(4.11),269(4.46), 273(4.42),292(3.93), 302(3.91),315(2.82), 343(2.45),360(2.44)	39-1255-73C
11H-Indeno[2,1-a]azulene	C_6H_{12}	236(4.02),300(4.65), 312(4.77),326(4.34), 340(3.51),358(3.70), 373(4.04),395(4.27)	78-1321-73
1,1'-Spiro[bi-1H-indene]	hexane	205(4.51),228(4.52), 234(4.53),269(3.86), 278(2.86),288(3.60), 300(3.40)	35-1229-73
(S)-(-)-	MeOH	226(4.42),267(3.79), 275(3.78),285(3.58), 297(3.28)	35-1217-73
$C_{17}H_{12}BrN_3O$			
3H-Imidazo[4,5-f]quinoline, 2-[2-(5-bromo-2-furanyl)ethenyl]-3-methyl-	MeOH	247(4.35),294(4.39), 350(4.32)	103-0406-73
$C_{17}H_{12}BrN_3OS$			
3H-Pyrazol-3-one, 5-(2-benzothiazolyl)-4-bromo-1,2-dihydro-1-methyl-2-phenyl-	EtOH	322(4.24)	95-0207-73
$C_{17}H_{12}Br_2N_2O_2$			
Methanimidamide, N'-(2,4-dibromo-9,10-dihydro-9,10-dioxo-1-anthracenyl)-N,N-dimethyl-	EtOH	245(4.67),275(4.49), 290(4.53),320(4.05), 395(3.72)	104-1523-73
hydrochloride	EtOH	212(4.49),258(4.61), 347(3.60)	104-1523-73
$C_{17}H_{12}ClNO_2$			
1(3H)-Isobenzofuranone, 3-(5-chloro-2-methyl-1H-indol-3-yl)-	n.s.g.	201(4.49),225(4.58), 280(3.76),297(3.57)	39-1943-73C
1H-Pyrrole-2,5-dione, 1-(4-chlorophenyl)-3-(4-methylphenyl)-	n.s.g.	231(4.49),294(4.08)	48-0717-73

Compound	Solvent	λ_{max}(log ε)	Ref.
$C_{17}H_{12}ClNO_3$			
1H-Pyrrole-2,5-dione, 1-(4-chlorophenyl)-3-(4-methoxyphenyl)-	n.s.g.	236(4.51),314(4.08), 375(3.78)	48-0717-73
$C_{17}H_{12}ClNO_4$			
1,3-Propanedione, 1-(4-chlorophenyl)-3-(6-hydroxy-3-methyl-1,2-benzisoxazol-7-yl)-	n.s.g.	220(4.1),242(4.3), 279(4.5),384(4.6)	2-0541-73
$C_{17}H_{12}Cl_2FNO_2$			
3H-Indole-2-carboxylic acid, 3,5-dichloro-3-(2-fluorophenyl)-, ethyl ester	CH_2Cl_2	245(4.26),322(3.82)	44-3077-73
$C_{17}H_{12}Cl_2N_2$			
Pyrimidine, 4,6-dichloro-5-phenyl-2-(phenylmethyl)-	C_6H_{12}	234(4.07),265s(3.82)	18-0299-73
$C_{17}H_{12}Cl_2N_2O_2$			
Methanimidamide, N-(2,4-dichloro-9,10-dihydro-9,10-dioxo-1-anthracenyl)-N,N-dimethyl-	EtOH	240(4.27),265(4.30), 330(3.85),395(3.70)	104-1523-73
$C_{17}H_{12}Cl_2N_2O_4$			
3H-Indole-2-carboxylic acid, 4,7-dichloro-3-nitro-3-phenyl-, ethyl ester	isoPrOH	240(4.13),294(3.69), 327(3.68)	44-3077-73
3H-Indole-2-carboxylic acid, 5,7-dichloro-3-nitro-3-phenyl-, ethyl ester	isoPrOH	244(4.13),323(3.83)	44-3077-73
3H-Indole-2-carboxylic acid, 6,7-dichloro-3-nitro-3-phenyl-, ethyl ester	isoPrOH	242(4.25),309(3.78)	44-3077-73
$C_{17}H_{12}Cl_2N_4$			
9H-Carbazole, 3-(4,6-dichloro-1,3,5-triazin-2-yl)-9-ethyl-	EtOH	244(3.59),276(3.40), 379(4.21)	39-2075-73B
$C_{17}H_{12}F_2O_4$			
Butanedioic acid, [bis(4-fluorophenyl)-methylene]-	MeOH	223(4.17),276(4.0)	73-3879-73
$C_{17}H_{12}N_2$			
α-Carboline, 4-phenyl-	n.s.g.	218(4.63),247(4.26), 300(4.09)	103-1154-73
Cyclopentadiene, 1-diazo-3,4-diphenyl-	EtOH	231(4.28),326(3.99)	78-4307-73
Spiro[2,4,6-cycloheptatriene-1,3'-tricyclo[3.2.2.0^{2,4}]nona[6,8]diene-2',6'-dicarbonitrile	MeOH	255(3.76)	88-4885-73
$C_{17}H_{12}N_2O$			
1H-Benzimidazole, 2-(5-phenyl-2-furanyl)-	EtOH	221(4.41),238s(3.98), 271(4.00),335(4.58), 345(4.65),364(4.45)	73-1700-73
$C_{17}H_{12}N_2O_2$			
[1]Benzopyrano[2,3-c]pyrazol-4(1H)-one, 3-methyl-1-phenyl-	EtOH	238(4.37),315(3.44)	103-0911-73
$C_{17}H_{12}N_2O_3$			
Indolizino[1,2-b]quinoline-7-carboxylic acid, 9,11-dihydro-, methyl ester	EtOH	223(4.74),254(4.34), 367(4.18)	4-0077-73

Compound	Solvent	$\lambda_{max}(\log \epsilon)$	Ref.
$C_{17}H_{12}N_2O_4$			
2H-Benzimidazol-2-one, 1-[3-(1,3-benzo-dioxol-5-yl)-1-oxo-2-propenyl]-1,3-dihydro-	HOAc	348(4.33)	48-1152-73
$C_{17}H_{12}N_2O_5$			
1H-Pyrrole-2,5-dione, 3-(4-methoxyphen-yl)-1-(4-nitrophenyl)-	n.s.g.	317(4.26)	48-0717-73
$C_{17}H_{12}N_2O_5S$			
2H,5H-[1,3]Oxazino[5,6-c][1,2]benzothia-zine-2,4(3H)-dione, 5-methyl-3-phen-yl-, 6,6-dioxide	EtOH	293(3.98),314(4.00)	87-0044-73
Propanedioic acid, (4-cyano-1,9-dihydro-thiopyrano[3,4-b]indol-3-yl)-, dimeth-yl ester	EtOH	255(4.50),320(4.26), 385(4.13),464(4.01)	95-1523-73
$C_{17}H_{12}N_2O_6$			
Propanedioic acid, (3-cyano-2,5-dihydro-2-oxopyrano[3,2-b]indol-4-yl)-, dimethyl ester	EtOH	256(4.18),394(4.34)	95-1523-73
1,3-Propanedione, 1-(6-hydroxy-3-methyl-1,2-benzisoxazol-7-yl)-3-(4-nitro-phenyl)-	n.s.g.	220(4.5),244(4.1), 271(4.0),383(4.3)	2-0541-73
$C_{17}H_{12}N_4O$			
1,2,3-Triazole, 4-phenyl-5-(3-phenyl-5-isoxazolyl)-	EtOH	235(4.38)	78-3271-73
	anion	237(4.58),291(4.13)	78-3271-73
$C_{17}H_{12}N_4O_3$			
3H-Imidazo[4,5-f]quinoline, 3-methyl-2-[2-(5-nitro-2-furanyl)ethenyl]-	MeOH	246(4.26),294(4.10), 404(4.16)	103-0406-73
$C_{17}H_{12}N_4O_4$			
Benzoic acid, 2-[5-[2-(1,3-benzodioxol-5-yl)ethenyl]-1H-tetrazol-1-yl]-	n.s.g.	330(4.10)	48-1152-73
$C_{17}H_{12}N_6$			
Pyrimido[5,4-e]-1,2,4-triazin-5-amine, 3,7-diphenyl-	EtOH	254(3.70),307(4.22), 396(3.34)	44-2238-73
$C_{17}H_{12}N_6O$			
Methanone, bis(5-phenyl-1H-1,2,3-tria-zol-4-yl)-	EtOH	226(4.36),288(3.98)	78-3271-73
	anion	231(4.40),303(3.98)	78-3271-73
$C_{17}H_{12}O$			
3H-Cyclopent[a]anthracen-3-one, 1,2-di-hydro-	EtOH	271(4.30),323(3.44), 342(3.26),360(3.21), 378(3.06),396(3.14)	39-1251-73C
16H-Cyclopenta[a]phenanthren-16-one, 15,17-dihydro-	EtOH	258(4.77),269(4.21), 278(4.11),300(4.21), 319(3.14),335(3.10), 350(3.03)	39-1255-73C
$C_{17}H_{12}OS_2$			
Ethanone, 1-phenyl-2-(4-phenyl-3H-1,2-dithiol-3-ylidene)-	C_6H_{12}	229(4.42),245s(4.28), 265s(4.01),285s(3.77), 305s(3.55),405s(3.89), 424(4.27),447(4.38)	33-0597-73

Compound	Solvent	$\lambda_{max}(\log \epsilon)$	Ref.
Ethanone, 1-phenyl-2-(4-phenyl-3H-1,2-dithiol-3-ylidene- (cont.)	EtOH	225(4.40),245(4.22), 270(3.96),290(3.80), 405(3.92),428(4.32), 448(4.45)	33-0597-73
Ethanone, 1-phenyl-2-(5-phenyl-3H-1,2-dithiol-3-ylidene)-	C_6H_{12}	230(4.54),236s(4.53), 264(4.40),285s(4.27), 295s(4.20),304s(4.15), 322s(3.85),430s(4.32), 450(4.44),465s(4.35)	33-0597-73
	EtOH	230(4.43),265(4.20), 305s(4.10),320s(3.93), 426s(4.20),451(4.42), 470s(4.33)	33-0597-73
$C_{17}H_{12}O_2$			
9,10-Anthracenedione, 2-(1-methylethen-yl)-	$CHCl_3$	259(4.50),332(3.65)	39-0850-73C
Methanone, (1-hydroxy-2-naphthalenyl)-phenyl-	C_6H_{12}	220(4.45),262(4.49), 299(4.02),310s(3.61), 381(3.83)	19-0849-73
	MeOH	204(4.32),220(4.45), 262(4.48),298(4.01), 310s(3.81),379(3.84), 384s(3.84)	19-0849-73
	20% MeOH	219(4.44),265(4.50), 300(4.05),310(3.87), 385(3.86)	19-0849-73
Methanone, (2-hydroxy-1-naphthalenyl)-phenyl-	C_6H_{12}	228(4.75),247(4.04), 259(4.09),321(3.72), 370(3.77)	19-0849-73
	MeOH	208(4.48),226(4.83), 250(4.24),276s(3.83), 288(3.73),320s(3.42), 334(3.49),360s(3.12)	19-0849-73
	20% MeOH	226(4.85),256(4.23), 288(3.80),320s(3.43), 330(3.48),360s(3.17)	19-0849-73
Methanone, (4-hydroxy-1-naphthalenyl)-phenyl-	C_6H_{12}	212(4.60),235(4.56), 250s(4.31),320(3.97), 330s(3.89)	19-0849-73
	MeOH	210(4.63),236(4.52), 254s(4.26),339(3.98)	19-0849-73
	20% MeOH	210(4.66),234(4.51), 242(4.02),252(4.30), 348(4.02)	19-0849-73
1,1'-Spirobi[1H-indene]-3,3'(2H,2'H)-dione	EtOH	208(4.73),246(4.38), 294(3.76)	35-1229-73
(S)-(+)-	MeOH	212(4.35),243(4.31), 289(3.62),293(3.64)	35-1217-73
$C_{17}H_{12}O_3$			
1,3-Propanedione, 1-(2-benzofuranyl)-3-phenyl-	MeOH	270(3.88),350(4.21)	56-1053-73
$C_{17}H_{12}O_3S$			
4H-Thiopyran-4-one, 2,6-diphenyl-, 1,1-dioxide	EtOH	226s(4.21),314(4.07), 327s(4.05)	18-1007-73
$C_{17}H_{12}O_4$			
4H-1-Benzopyran-5-acetic acid, 4-oxo-2-phenyl-	EtOH	257(4.34),294(4.34), 312s(4.21)	78-3091-73

Compound	Solvent	$\lambda_{max}(\log \epsilon)$	Ref.
2H-Furo[3,2-f][1]benzopyran-2,9(1H)-dione, 3a,9b-dihydro-7-phenyl-	EtOH	312(3.81)	78-3091-73
$C_{17}H_{12}O_5$			
Benzoic acid, 2-(7-methoxy-1-oxo-1H-2-benzopyran-3-yl)-	MeOH	236(4.55),300(4.34), 350(3.97)	2-0413-73
4-Cyclopentene-1,3-dione, 4-hydroxy-2,5-bis(4-hydroxyphenyl)- (gyrocyanin)	EtOH	225(4.18),264(4.28), 366(4.08)	24-3223-73
Metabolite E from Aspergillus terreus	MeOH	238(4.32),369(4.46)	102-2527-73
Spiro[3H-2-benzopyran-3,1'(3'H)-isobenzofuran]-1,3'(4H)-dione, 7-methoxy-	MeOH	232(4.46),280(3.49), 307(3.59)	2-0413-73
$C_{17}H_{12}O_6$			
4H-1-Benzopyran-4-one, 3-(1,3-benzodioxol-5-yl)-7-hydroxy-6-methoxy-	MeOH	259(4.48),295(4.36)	2-0098-73
8H-1,3-Dioxolo[4,5-g][1]benzopyran-8-one, 7-(4-hydroxyphenyl)-9-methoxy- (irisolone)	EtOH	265(4.55),322(3.88)	94-0600-73
2(5H)-Furanone, 5-[(3,4-dihydroxyphenyl)methylene]-4-hydroxy-3-(4-hydroxyphenyl)-	EtOH	243(4.12),308s(3.96), 343(4.10),378(4.14)	39-1921-73C
	10% EtOH	253(4.11),307s(4.07), 335(4.18),356s(4.08)	39-1921-73C
	+ NH_3	259(4.10),386(4.14)	39-1921-73C
Gyroporin	EtOH	226(4.13),273(4.22), 371(4.04)	24-3223-73
Isoflavone, 2'-hydroxy-5-methoxy-6,7-(methylenedioxy)-	EtOH	252(4.30),285s(4.08), 317(3.86)	78-2703-73
Metabolite G from Aspergillus terreus	MeOH	237(4.22),369(4.38)	102-2527-73
Spiro[2H-1-benzopyran-3(4H),5'(6'H)-cyclobuta[f][1,3]benzodioxol]-4-one, 5,7-dihydroxy-	EtOH	232(4.29),297(4.45), 340(3.72)	88-4569-73
$C_{17}H_{12}O_7$			
Iriflogenin	EtOH	251s(4.35),274(4.47), 335(3.65)	94-2323-73
	EtOH-$AlCl_3$	248(4.28),284(4.44)	94-2323-73
$C_{17}H_{13}BrN_2OS$			
4-Imidazolidinone, 3-(4-bromophenyl)-5-[(2-methylphenyl)methylene]-2-thioxo-	EtOH	225s(4.15),248s(4.05), 363(4.46)	56-0181-73
	EtOH-NaOH	223(4.25),258s(3.15), 278(4.03),398(4.44)	56-0181-73
4-Imidazolidinone, 3-(4-bromophenyl)-5-[(4-methylphenyl)methylene]-2-thioxo-	EtOH	227s(4.23),248(4.16), 377(4.55)	56-0181-73
	EtOH-NaOH	225(4.43),250(4.27), 276(4.13),393(4.52)	56-0181-73
$C_{17}H_{13}BrN_2O_2$			
Methanimidamide, N'-(2-bromo-9,10-dihydro-9,10-dioxo-1-anthracenyl)-N,N-dimethyl-	EtOH	245(4.19),275(4.10), 315(3.65),395(3.43), 460(3.15)	104-1523-73
hydrochloride	EtOH	206(4.34),261(4.45), 335(3.54)	104-1523-73
$C_{17}H_{13}BrN_2O_2S$			
4-Imidazolidinone, 3-(4-bromophenyl)-5-[(2-methoxyphenyl)methylene]-2-thioxo-	EtOH	250s(4.11),381(4.49)	56-0181-73
	EtOH-NaOH	232(4.25),258s(4.14), 405(4.48)	56-0181-73
4-Imidazolidinone, 3-(4-bromophenyl)-5-[(3-methoxyphenyl)methylene]-2-thioxo-	EtOH	214(4.43),348(4.14), 378(4.54)	56-0181-73

Compound	Solvent	λ max(log ε)	Ref.
4-Imidazolidinone, 3-(4-bromophenyl)-5-[(3-methoxyphenyl)methylene]-2-thioxo- (cont.)	EtOH-NaOH	233(4.28),256s(4.20), 405(4.46)	56-0181-73
4-Imidazolidinone, 3-(4-bromophenyl)-5-[(4-methoxyphenyl)methylene]-2-thioxo-	EtOH	225s(4.28),250(4.18), 392(4.62)	56-0181-73
	EtOH-NaOH	230(4.38),290(4.07), 405(4.49)	56-0181-73
$C_{17}H_{13}BrO_2$			
Cyclopropenylium, (methoxycarbonyl)diphenyl-, bromide	MeOH	215(4.60),252(4.18), 299(4.17),314(4.06)	104-1449-73
$C_{17}H_{13}BrO_4$			
3(2H)-Benzofuranone, 7-bromo-4,6-dimethoxy-2-(phenylmethylene)-	$CHCl_3$	246s(4.18),314(4.26), 383(4.29)	78-1037-73
4H-1-Benzopyran-4-one, 8-bromo-5,7-dimethoxy-2-phenyl-	$CHCl_3$	267(4.46),285s(4.20), 323(4.09)	78-1037-73
$C_{17}H_{13}ClFNO_3$			
1H-Indole-3-carboxylic acid, 5-chloro-3-(2-fluorophenyl)-2,3-dihydro-2-oxo-, ethyl ester	isoPrOH	257(4.04),299(3.23)	44-3077-73
$C_{17}H_{13}ClN_2O_2$			
Methanaimidamide, N'-(2-chloro-9,10-dihydro-9,10-dioxo-1-anthracenyl)-N,N-dimethyl-	EtOH	245(4.29),260(4.24), 305(4.28),415(3.84)	104-1523-73
$C_{17}H_{13}ClN_2O_2S$			
Methanone, [4-amino-2-(4-methoxyphenyl)-5-thiazolyl](4-chlorophenyl)-	DMF	399(4.29)	48-0497-73
$C_{17}H_{13}ClN_2O_4$			
3H-Indole-2-carboxylic acid, 5-chloro-3-nitro-3-phenyl-, ethyl ester	isoPrOH	238(4.19),321(3.83)	44-3077-73
$C_{17}H_{13}ClN_4O_3$			
1H-Pyrazole-4,5-dione, 3-acetoxy-1-phenyl-, 4-[(4-chlorophenyl)hydrazone]	EtOH	206(4.15),250(4.25), 396(4.34)	4-1051-73
$C_{17}H_{13}ClO_2S$			
2H-1-Benzothiopyran, 2-[(4-chlorophenyl)methylene]-3-methyl-, 1,1-dioxide	MeOH	237(4.29),292(4.18), 340(4.06)	39-0163-73C
2H-1-Benzothiopyran, 2-[(4-chlorophenyl)methylene]-6-methyl-, 1,1-dioxide	MeOH	245(4.20),273(4.06), 292(4.07),348(4.29)	39-0163-73C
4H-1-Benzothiopyran, 4-[(4-chlorophenyl)methylene]-2-methyl-, 1,1-dioxide	MeOH	245(3.93),327(4.27)	39-0163-73C
$C_{17}H_{13}ClO_4Se$			
Seleninium, 2,6-diphenyl-, perchlorate	MeCN-$HClO_4$	420(4.33)	103-0790-73
$C_{17}H_{13}Cl_2FN_2O$			
3H-Indole-2-carboxamide, 3,5-dichloro-N-ethyl-3-(2-fluorophenyl)-	isoPrOH	243(4.30),269s(3.70), 320(3.84)	44-3077-73
$C_{17}H_{13}Cl_2NO_2$			
1H-Indole-2-carboxylic acid, 4,7-dichloro-3-phenyl-, ethyl ester	isoPrOH	241(4.58),297(4.21), 320(3.92)	44-3077-73
1H-Indole-2-carboxylic acid, 5,7-dichloro-3-phenyl-, ethyl ester	isoPrOH	239(4.59),299(4.16), 320s(3.86)	44-3077-73

Compound	Solvent	λ_{max}(log ε)	Ref.
1H-Indole-2-carboxylic acid, 6,7-dichloro-3-phenyl-, ethyl ester	isoPrOH	241(4.59),303(4.26), 325s(3.93)	44-3077-73
3H-Indole-2-carboxylic acid, 3,5-dichloro-3-phenyl-, ethyl ester	CH_2Cl_2	246(4.23),325(3.81)	44-3077-73
$C_{17}H_{13}Cl_2NO_3$			
1H-Indole-3-carboxylic acid, 4,7-dichloro-2,3-dihydro-2-oxo-3-phenyl-, ethyl ester	isoPrOH	248(3.92),255(3.92), 268s(3.70),295(3.30), 301(3.29)	44-3077-73
1H-Indole-3-carboxylic acid, 5,7-dichloro-2,3-dihydro-2-oxo-3-phenyl-, ethyl ester	isoPrOH	258(4.07),303(3.34)	44-3077-73
1H-Indole-3-carboxylic acid, 6,7-dichloro-2,3-dihydro-2-oxo-3-phenyl-, ethyl ester	isoPrOH	257(3.80),269s(3.65), 294(3.32),300s(3.30)	44-3077-73
$C_{17}H_{13}Cl_3O_5$			
Caloploicin	EtOH	226s(4.51),258s(3.89), 323(3.79)	94-1547-73
$C_{17}H_{13}NO$			
Isoxazole, 3-phenyl-5-(2-phenylethenyl)- (plus shoulders)	C_6H_{12}	227(4.33),235(4.27), 247(4.04),303(4.54)	32-0309-73
	MeOH	227(4.32),233(4.24), 247(4.08),305(4.55)	32-0309-73
Isoxazole, 5-phenyl-3-(2-phenylethenyl)- (plus shoulders)	C_6H_{12}	208(4.46),218(4.33), 226(4.11),281(4.62)	32-0309-73
	MeOH	207(4.48),225(4.14), 281(4.63)	32-0309-73
2(1H)-Pyridinone, 3,5-diphenyl-	EtOH	252(4.29),338(3.93)	94-1090-73
$C_{17}H_{13}NO_2$			
Ethanone, 1-(3-benzoyl-1-indolizinyl)-	EtOH	229(4.12),236s(4.11), 254(4.14),284s(3.96), 292(4.00),336s(4.14), 353(4.16),365s(4.12)	39-2091-73C
2-Naphthalenecarboxamide, N-hydroxy-N-phenyl-	EtOH	226(4.61),275(4.14)	112-0547-73
4(1H)-Pyridinone, 1-hydroxy-3,5-diphenyl-	EtOH	242(4.43),298(4.02), 334(3.82)	4-0665-73
$C_{17}H_{13}NO_2S_3$			
Thiophene, 2-[2-(5-methyl-2-thienyl)-ethenyl]-5-[2-(5-nitro-2-thienyl)-ethenyl]-	DMF	296(3.90),378(4.14), 488(4.51)	24-0655-73
$C_{17}H_{13}NO_3$			
4H,5H-Benzo[a]pyrano[2,3-f]quinolizine-4,5-dione, 6,6a-dihydro-2-methyl-	EtOH	240(4.16),310(4.06)	30-0486-73 +70-1745-73
4H,5H-Benzo[a]pyrano[2,3-g]quinolizine-4,5-dione, 7,8-dihydro-2-methyl-	EtOH	250(4.26),300(4.07), 350(4.14),417(3.90)	70-1745-73
4-Isoxazolecarboxylic acid, 3,5-diphenyl-, methyl ester	heptane	234(3.87),265(3.90)	104-0732-73
1H-Pyrrole-2,5-dione, 3-(4-methoxyphenyl)-1-phenyl-	n.s.g.	316(3.93),375(3.85)	48-0717-73
$C_{17}H_{13}NO_3S$			
Ethanone, 1-(2,4-dihydroxyphenyl)-2-(2-phenyl-4-thiazolyl)-	n.s.g.	285(4.37)	104-2580-73

Compound	Solvent	λ_{max}(log ϵ)	Ref.
$C_{17}H_{13}NO_4$			
Isoxazolium, 2,5-dihydro-3-hydroxy-2-[(4-methoxyphenyl)methylene]-5-oxo-4-phenyl-, hydroxide, inner salt	dioxan	466(3.60)	44-1782-73
1,3-Propanedione, 1-(6-hydroxy-3-methyl-1,2-benzisoxazol-7-yl)-3-phenyl-	n.s.g.	238(4.5),285(4.5), 370(4.6)	2-0541-73
$C_{17}H_{13}NO_4S$			
4H-1-Benzothiopyran, 2-methyl-4-[(4-nitrophenyl)methylene]-, 2,2-dioxide	MeOH	248(4.07),340(4.31)	39-0163-73C
$C_{17}H_{13}NO_5$			
6H-Benzofuro[3,2-c][1]benzopyran-6-one, 2-amino-8,9-dimethoxy-	n.s.g.	243(4.3),280(3.7), 348(4.1)	2-0115-73
6H-Benzofuro[3,2-c][1]benzopyran-6-one, 3-amino-8,9-dimethoxy-	n.s.g.	248(4.0),285(3.8), 315(3.9),355(4.2)	2-0115-73
Isoxazolium, 2,5-dihydro-3-hydroxy-2-[(4-hydroxy-3-methoxyphenyl)methylene]-5-oxo-4-phenyl-, hydroxide, inner salt	dioxan	460(3.30)	44-1782-73
$C_{17}H_{13}N_3O$			
Acetonitrile, (1,2-dihydro-2-oxo-3H-indol-3-ylidene)[(phenylmethyl)amino]-	EtOH	280(4.15),370(4.18)	95-1520-73
2H-Naphtho[1,2-d]triazole, 2-(2-methoxyphenyl)-	MeOH	217(4.60),240(4.10), 329(4.04)	73-0224-73
Pyrimido[1,2-a]benzimidazol-2(1H)-one, 1-methyl-4-phenyl-	EtOH	252(4.00),296(3.00)	94-2019-73
	EtOH-HCl	253(4.00),288(3.00)	94-2019-73
	EtOH-NaOH	251(4.00),298(4.00)	94-2019-73
Pyrimido[1,2-a]benzimidazol-2(10H)-one, 10-methyl-4-phenyl-	EtOH	241(4.00),307(3.00)	94-2019-73
	EtOH-HCl	242(4.00),294(3.00)	94-2019-73
	EtOH-NaOH	240(4.00),295(4.00)	94-2019-73
Pyrimido[1,2-a]benzimidazol-4(10H)-one, 10-methyl-2-phenyl-	EtOH	255(4.00),287(4.00), 347(3.00)	94-2019-73
	EtOH-HCl	253(4.00),287(4.00), 348(3.00)	94-2019-73
	EtOH-NaOH	254(4.00),298(4.00)	94-2019-73
$C_{17}H_{13}N_3OS$			
Pyrazolo[4,3-b][1,4]benzothiazine, 9-acetyl-1,9-dihydro-1-phenyl-	EtOH	224s(4.17),274(4.24), 332s(3.79),415(3.43)	94-0241-73
3H-Pyridazino[4,5-b][1,4]benzothiazin-4(10H)-one, 10-methyl-3-phenyl-	EtOH	234s(4.07),275(4.51), 316(3.92),433(3.08)	94-0241-73
$C_{17}H_{13}N_3O_2$			
4H-Pyridazino[4,5-b]indol-4-one, 3,5-dihydro-1-(4-methoxyphenyl)-	n.s.g.	230(4.48),260(4.49), 315(3.89)	103-1497-73
$C_{17}H_{13}N_3O_2S$			
Spiro[benzothiazole-2(3H),3'-[3H]pyrazol]-4'(2'H)-one, 3-acetyl-2'-phenyl-	EtOH	224s(4.34),246s(3.96), 316(4.04)	94-0241-73
$C_{17}H_{13}N_3O_4S$			
Methanone, [4-amino-2-(4-methoxyphenyl)-5-thiazolyl](4-nitrophenyl)-	DMF	411(4.20)	48-0497-73
$C_{17}H_{13}N_3S$			
Benzothiazole, 2-(3-methyl-1-phenyl-1H-pyrazol-5-yl)-	MeOH	212(3.84),234(3.71), 275(4.11)	103-0944-73

Compound	Solvent	$\lambda_{max}(\log \epsilon)$	Ref.
$C_{17}H_{13}N_5$			
1H-1,2,3-Triazole, 4-phenyl-5-(5-phenyl-1H-pyrazol-3-yl)-	EtOH	253.5(4.52)	78-3271-73
	anion	251(4.47)	78-3271-73
$C_{17}H_{13}N_5O_3S$			
[1,2,4]Triazino[5,6-d][3,1]benzoxazepine, 6,7-dihydro-3-(methylthio)-6-(4-nitrophenyl)-	EtOH	241(4.66),255s(4.52), 351(4.18),437(3.88)	78-0639-73
$C_{17}H_{13}O_2$			
Cyclopropenylium, (methoxycarbonyl)diphenyl-, bromide	MeOH	215(4.60),252(4.18), 299(4.17),314(4.06)	104-1449-73
$C_{17}H_{13}Se$			
Seleninium, 2,6-diphenyl-, perchlorate	MeCN-$HClO_4$	420(4.33)	103-0790-73
$C_{17}H_{14}$			
Phenanthrene, 9-cyclopropyl-	hexane	221(4.48),252(4.78)	44-1703-73
1,1'-Spirobi[1H-indene], 2,3-dihydro-, (R)-(+)-	MeOH	218(4.48),222s(4.42), 258(3.91),265(3.90), 272(3.76)	35-1217-73
$C_{17}H_{14}BrClO_2S_2$			
Benzo[b]thiophene, 6-bromo-3-[(4-chlorophenyl)thio]-2-propyl-, 1,1-dioxide	EtOH	230(3.94),280(3.78), 325(3.72)	2-0628-73
$C_{17}H_{14}Br_2N_2O$			
Pyridinium, 4-acetyl-1-[(2-bromo-3-quinolinyl)methyl]-, bromide	H_2O	240(4.21),275(3.88), 308(3.63),322(3.62)	44-2351-73
$C_{17}H_{14}Br_2N_4S$			
7H-1,2,4-Triazolo[4,3-b][1,3,4]thiadiazinium, 6-(4-bromophenyl)-1-(phenylmethyl)-, bromide	MeOH	228(3.95),286(4.21), 315s(--)	48-1131-73
$C_{17}H_{14}Br_2O_2$			
Cyclopropanecarboxylic acid, 2,3-dibromo-2,3-diphenyl-, methyl ester, cis-cis	MeOH	299(3.00),316(2.82)	104-1449-73
cis-trans	MeOH	285(3.71),301(3.71), 316(3.58)	104-1449-73
$C_{17}H_{14}ClFN_2O$			
1H-Indole-2-carboxamide, 5-chloro-N-ethyl-3-(2-fluorophenyl)-	isoPrOH	233(4.54),300(4.20)	44-3077-73
$C_{17}H_{14}ClFN_2O_2$			
1H-Indole-3-carboxamide, 5-chloro-N-ethyl-3-(2-fluorophenyl)-2,3-dihydro-2-oxo-	isoPrOH	260(4.01),269s(3.90), 295(3.25)	44-3077-73
$C_{17}H_{14}ClFO_2S_2$			
Benzo[b]thiophene, 3-[(4-chlorophenyl)thio]-6-fluoro-2-propyl-, 1,1-dioxide	EtOH	225(3.94),248(3.47), 277(3.65),321(3.63)	2-0628-73
$C_{17}H_{14}ClNO_2S$			
4H-1,4-Benzothiazine-2-carboxylic acid, 6-chloro-3-phenyl-, ethyl ester	EtOH	205(4.45),220s(4.28), 265(4.44),340(3.41), 428(3.15)	7-0045-73

Compound	Solvent	λ_{max}(log ε)	Ref.
4H-1,4-Benzothiazine-2-carboxylic acid, 7-chloro-3-phenyl-, ethyl ester	EtOH	206(4.39),218(4.22), 265(4.40),340(3.47), 431(3.15)	7-0045-73
$C_{17}H_{14}ClNO_3$			
Acetamide, N-[4-[3-(5-chloro-2-hydroxy-phenyl)-3-oxo-1-propenyl]phenyl]-	dioxan	228(4.20),251(4.18), 375(4.43)	83-0299-73
1H-Indole-3-carboxylic acid, 5-chloro-2,3-dihydro-2-oxo-3-phenyl-, ethyl ester	isoPrOH	259(4.07),300(3.26)	44-3077-73
4-Isoxazolecarboxylic acid, 5-chloro-4,5-dihydro-3,5-diphenyl-	heptane	255(4.26)	104-0732-73
Propanamide, N-(2-benzoyl-4-chlorophen-yl)-N-methyl-2-oxo-	EtOH	252.1(4.24)	94-0742-73
$C_{17}H_{14}ClN_3$			
1H-Pyrimido[1,2-a]quinazoline, 8-chloro-2,3-dihydro-6-phenyl-	n.s.g.	245(4.47),260(4.20)	40-1944-73
$C_{17}H_{14}ClN_3O_2$			
1H-1,2,3-Triazole-4-carboxylic acid, 5-(4-chlorophenyl)-1-phenyl-, ethyl ester	EtOH	250(4.21)	42-0589-73
1H-1,2,3-Triazole-5-carboxylic acid, 4-(4-chlorophenyl)-1-phenyl-, ethyl ester	EtOH	274(4.15)	42-0589-73
$C_{17}H_{14}ClN_3O_3S$			
1H-Benzimidazole-1-carboxamide, N-[(4-chloro-2-methylphenoxy)acetyl]-2,3-dihydro-2-thioxo-	MeOH	250(4.48),306(4.54)	103-0639-73
$C_{17}H_{14}Cl_2N_4$			
Benzenamine, 4-(4,6-dichloro-1,3,5-tria-zin-2-yl)-N-ethyl-N-phenyl-	EtOH	263(3.32),291(3.34), 398(4.10)	39-2075-73B
$C_{17}H_{14}F_3NO_3$			
Acetamide, 2-(4-acetylphenoxy)-N-[2-(trifluoromethyl)phenyl]-	EtOH	210(4.18),262(4.23)	111-0574-73
$C_{17}H_{14}F_6O_2$			
Benzene, 1,1'-[methylenebis(oxymethyl-ene)bis[4-(trifluoromethyl)-	EtOH	257(2.90),262(2.95), 268(2.86)	36-0910-73
$C_{17}H_{14}INOS$			
Ethanone, 2-(3-ethyl-2(3H)-benzothiazo-lylidene)-1-(4-iodophenyl)-	EtOH	220(4.48),266(4.28), 388(4.61)	73-3616-73
$C_{17}H_{14}NO_2$			
1,2-Oxazin-1-ium, 6-methoxy-3,5-diphen-yl-, tetrachloroferrate	CH_2Cl_2	327(4.02),375(4.33)	104-2006-73
$C_{17}H_{14}N_2$			
Indolo[1,2-c]quinazoline, 6,12-dimethyl-	EtOH	238(4.14),261s(4.25), 271(4.51),280(4.63), 295(3.79),324(3.67), 343(3.90),359(3.91)	78-1429-73
2H-Pyrrole-3-carbonitrile, 3,4-dihydro-2,5-diphenyl-	EtOH	247(4.18)	35-1945-73
Quinoxaline, 2-(2,3-dihydro-1H-inden-5-yl)-	EtOH	209(4.47),252(--), 329(--)	34-0102-73

Compound	Solvent	λ_{max}(log ε)	Ref.
$C_{17}H_{14}N_2O$			
2,3-Diazabicyclo[4.1.0]hept-3-en-5-one, 6,7-diphenyl-	MeOH	327(3.71)	44-2954-73
Imidazole, 2-benzoyl-1-benzyl-	EtOH	259(3.72),297(3.91)	12-0415-73
Isoquinolinium, 2-(benzoylimino)-1-methyl-, hydroxide, inner salt	EtOH	231(4.59),320(3.89)	78-2359-73
Quinolinium, 1-(benzoylimino)-2-methyl-, hydroxide, inner salt	EtOH	238(4.65),321(4.22)	78-2359-73
$C_{17}H_{14}N_2O_2$			
Methanimidamide, N'-(9,10-dihydro-9,10-dioxo-1-anthracenyl)-N,N-dimethyl-, hydrochloride	EtOH	204(4.41),216(4.40), 264(4.56),390(3.76)	104-1523-73
2-Naphthalenol, 1-[(2-hydroxy-4-methylphenyl)azo]-	toluene	480(4.30)	33-2450-73
2-Naphthalenol, 1-[(2-hydroxy-5-methylphenyl)azo]-	toluene	480(4.24)	33-2450-73
$C_{17}H_{14}N_2O_2S$			
1H-Indole, 3-[1-(methylthio)-2-nitroethenyl]-2-phenyl-	EtOH	308(4.39)	95-0612-73
Methanone, [4-amino-2-(4-methoxyphenyl)-5-thiazolyl]phenyl-	DMF	393(4.30)	48-0497-73
Pyridinium, 1-[([1,1'-biphenyl]-2-ylsulfonyl)amino]-, hydroxide, inner salt	EtOH	238(4.14),307(3.48)	44-3311-73
$C_{17}H_{14}N_2O_3$			
Benzenepropanamide, N-(3-cyanophenyl)-4-methoxy-β-oxo-	pH 13	334(4.53)	39-0808-73B
2H-Benzimidazol-2-one, 1,3-dihydro-1-[3-(4-methoxyphenyl)-1-oxo-2-propenyl]-	HOAc	285(3.92),312(4.16), 338(4.33)	48-1152-73
2-Naphthalenol, 1-[(2-hydroxy-4-methoxyphenyl)azo]-	toluene	466(4.32)	33-2450-73
2-Naphthalenol, 1-[(2-hydroxy-5-methoxyphenyl)azo]-	toluene	493(4.18)	33-2450-73
$C_{17}H_{14}N_2O_3S$			
Ethanone, 2-(3-ethyl-2(3H)-benzothiazolylidene)-1-(3-nitrophenyl)-	EtOH	221(4.51),389(4.53)	73-3616-73
Ethanone, 2-(3-ethyl-2(3H)-benzothiazolylidene)-1-(4-nitrophenyl)-	EtOH	225(4.41),263(4.23), 320(3.99),418(4.40)	73-3616-73
$C_{17}H_{14}N_2O_3Se$			
Ethanone, 2-(3-ethyl-2(3H)-benzoselenazolylidene)-1-(3-nitrophenyl)-	EtOH	229(4.70),390(4.51)	73-3616-73
Ethanone, 2-(3-ethyl-2(3H)-benzoselenazolylidene)-1-(4-nitrophenyl)-	EtOH	228(4.38),260(4.28), 318(3.91),421(4.37)	73-3616-73
$C_{17}H_{14}N_2O_4$			
Benzoic acid, 2-hydroxy-5-[[4-(2-methyl-3-oxo-1-propenyl)phenyl]azo]-	EtOH	382(4.53)	7-0379-73
1H-Indole-2-carboxylic acid, 3-(4-nitrophenyl)-, ethyl ester	EtOH	230(4.49),295(4.29), 358(3.97)	94-2786-73
3H-Indole-2-carboxylic acid, 3-nitro-3-phenyl-, ethyl ester	isoPrOH	233(4.21),311(3.78)	44-3077-73
$C_{17}H_{14}N_2O_5$			
2H-1,4-Oxazin-3(4H)-one, 2-methoxy-6-(4-nitrophenyl)-4-phenyl-	EtOH	245(4.16),363(4.25)	4-0347-73
2H-1,4-Oxazin-3(4H)-one, 4-(2-methoxyphenyl)-6-(4-nitrophenyl)-	EtOH	248(4.00),368(4.22)	4-0347-73

Compound	Solvent	λmax(log ε)	Ref.
$C_{17}H_{14}N_2O_6S$			
Ethanone, 1-[3-[[(4-methylphenyl)sulfonyl]oxy]-1H-indol-2-yl]-2-nitro-	EtOH	318(4.22),390(4.07)	95-0971-73
$C_{17}H_{14}N_2S$			
Pyridazine, 6-(methylthio)-3,4-diphenyl-	n.s.g.	270(4.4)	106-0641-73
3(2H)-Pyridazinethione, 2-methyl-5,6-diphenyl-	n.s.g.	320(4.4),390(3.5)	106-0641-73
$C_{17}H_{14}N_4OS$			
[1,2,4]Triazino[5,6-d][3,1]benzoxazepine, 6,7-dihydro-3-(methylthio)-6-phenyl-	EtOH	239(4.44),352(3.94), 443(3.70)	78-0639-73
$C_{17}H_{14}N_4O_3$			
Benzoic acid, 2-[5-[2-(4-methoxyphenyl)-ethenyl]-1H-tetrazol-1-yl]-	n.s.g.	225(4.19),318(4.39)	48-1152-73
$C_{17}H_{14}N_4O_4$			
Sydnone imine, 3-[(4-carboxyphenyl)methyl]-N-[(phenylamino)carbonyl]-	EtOH	203(4.28),225(3.95), 262(4.15),346(3.95)	103-1327-73
$C_{17}H_{14}N_4S_3$			
Benzenamine, N,N'-(3,4-dihydro-2H,5H-1,6,6a-trithia(6a-S^{IV})-2a,4a-diazacyclopenta[cd]pentalene-2,5-diylidene)bis-	CH_2Cl_2	259(4.65),309(4.21)	88-2989-73
$C_{17}H_{14}O$			
Benzaldehyde, 3-(4-phenyl-1,3-butadienyl)-	benzene	325(4.62),335(4.65), 354(4.47)	23-3756-73
Benzaldehyde, 4-(4-phenyl-1,3-butadienyl)-	benzene	347(4.60),362(4.69), 379(4.55)	23-3756-73
9,10-Ethanoanthracene-1-carboxaldehyde, 9,10-dihydro-	EtOH	251(3.97),300(3.37)	49-0274-73
2,4-Pentadienal, 4,5-diphenyl-	MeOH	228(4.02),236(4.04), 326(4.60)	44-2169-73
1,1'-Spirobi[1H-inden]-3(2H)-one, 2',3'-dihydro-, (R)-(-)-	MeOH	212(4.29),244(4.00), 265(3.29),272(3.35), 293(3.39)	35-1217-73
$C_{17}H_{14}OS$			
1-Benzothiepin-5(2H)-one, 3,4-dihydro-4-(phenylmethylene)-	EtOH	235(4.07),304(4.20)	44-2629-73
$C_{17}H_{14}OS_2$			
2,5-Cyclohexadien-1-one, 2,6-dimethyl-4-(5-phenyl-3H-1,2-dithiol-3-ylidene)-	C_6H_{12}	257(3.98),284(3.98), 302(4.10),322s(3.98), 337(3.85),380(4.01), 517(4.38)	22-1032-73
	MeOH	258(3.90),278(3.74), 312(3.86),340(4.02), 365s(3.97),550(3.86), 574(4.40)	22-1032-73
	MeCN	257(3.96),282(3.85), 312(4.05),324(4.04), 370(4.01),538(4.43), 560s(4.42)	22-1032-73
2H-Pyran, 3,6-bis(phenylthio)- (or isomeric furan)	EtOH	211s(4.36),246(4.64)	44-0187-73

Compound	Solvent	λ_{max}(log ε)	Ref.
$C_{17}H_{14}O_2$			
15H-Cyclopenta[a]phenanthrene-16,17-diol, 16,17-dihydro-, cis	EtOH	251(4.71),257(4.83), 279(4.16),287(4.06), 299(4.16),320(2.71), 328(4.83),335(2.87), 343(2.49),350(2.86)	39-1255-73C
15H-Cyclopenta[a]phenanthrene-16,17-diol, 16,17-dihydro-, trans	EtOH	251(4.71),257(4.82), 279(4.16),287(4.05), 299(4.17),320(2.65), 328(2.49),335(2.84), 343(2.44),350(2.84)	39-1255-73C
2-Cyclopenten-1-one, 4-hydroxy-3,4-diphenyl-	EtOH	288(4.26)	44-1749-73
9,10-Ethanoanthracene-1-carboxylic acid, 9,10-dihydro-	EtOH	284(3.43)	49-0274-73
9,10-Ethanoanthracene-2-carboxylic acid, 9,10-dihydro-	EtOH	246(3.98),264s(3.59), 271s(3.37),276s(3.21), 285s(2.96)	49-0274-73
1,5-Methano-2-benzoxepin-3(1H)-one, 4,5-dihydro-5-phenyl-, (1R-cis)-	isooctane	213(4.06),251(3.01), 257(3.07),263(3.08), 270(2.98)	35-1217-73
$C_{17}H_{14}O_2S$			
1-Benzothiepin-5(2H)-one, 3,4-dihydro-4-(phenylmethylene)-, 1-oxide	EtOH	233(4.22),316(4.16)	44-2629-73
$C_{17}H_{14}O_3$			
2-Cyclopropene-1-carboxylic acid, 1-hydroxy-2,3-diphenyl-, methyl ester	MeOH	222(4.54),229(4.47), 286(4.47),301(4.59), 316(4.49)	104-1449-73
5,11-Epoxy-6,10-etheno-7H-cyclohepta[b]-naphthalen-7-one, 5,5a,6,10,10a,11-hexahydro-6-hydroxy-	EtOH	265(3.23),270(2.99), 340(1.92)	44-4100-73
2(5H)-Furanone, 5-methoxy-3,4-diphenyl-	EtOH	295(4.03)	44-4348-73
3(2H)-Furanone, 5-methoxy-2,4-diphenyl-	EtOH	253(4.35),287(3.95)	44-4348-73
1H-Indene-1-acetic acid, 2,3-dihydro-3-oxo-1-phenyl-	MeOH	209(4.31),244(4.01), 292(3.32)	35-1217-73
	EtOH	207(4.62),245(4.09), 293(3.34)	35-1229-73
$C_{17}H_{14}O_3S$			
1-Benzothiepin-5(2H)-one, 3,4-dihydro-4-(phenylmethylene)-, 1,1-dioxide	EtOH	232(4.04),305(4.16)	44-2629-73
$C_{17}H_{14}O_4$			
2-Benzofuranacetic acid, α-(2-hydroxyphenyl)-, methyl ester	90% EtOH	215(4.22),250(4.21), 278(3.87),284(3.88)	12-1079-73
3-Benzofurancarboxylic acid, 2-[(2-hydroxyphenyl)methyl]-, methyl ester	90% EtOH	245(3.92),263(3.99), 277(4.03),284(3.91)	12-1079-73
1H-2-Benzopyran-1-one, 8-methoxy-3-(4-methoxyphenyl)-	EtOH	262(4.29),306(4.28), 318(4.29),362(4.29)	102-2279-73
Cryptocaryone	EtOH	237(4.00),243(3.96), 287(4.00),385(4.36), 396(4.36)	78-3091-73
Ethanone, 2-(2-hydroxyphenyl)-1-(2-methoxy-3-benzofuranyl)-	90% EtOH	225(4.25),247(4.10), 276(4.11),280s(4.11)	12-1079-73
Phenanthro[2,3-d][1,3]dioxole, 1,3-dimethoxy-	n.s.g.	259(4.93),283(4.15), 291(4.06),306(3.78)	39-1179-73C

Compound	Solvent	λ_{max}(log ε)	Ref.
$C_{17}H_{14}O_5$			
9,10-Anthracenedione, 3-(hydroxymethyl)-1,8-dimethoxy- (1,8-di-O-methyl-aloe-emodin)	MeOH	223(4.60),257(4.34), 392(3.87)	94-1254-73
	MeOH	223(4.56),258(4.31), 275s(4.06),390(3.85)	94-1254-73
	MeOH-KOH	225(--),257(--), 392(--)	94-1254-73
	MeOH-KOH	223(--),258(--), 390(--)	94-1254-73
9,10-Anthracenedione, 1,3,8-trihydroxy-6-propyl-	MeOH	254(4.16),264s(--), 291(4.14),302s(--), 400(3.85)	78-3699-73
9,10-Anthracenedione, 1,3,8-trimethoxy-	EtOH	225(4.44),276(4.34), 397(3.81)	39-2853-73C
Benzoic acid, 2-(3,4-dihydro-7-methoxy-1H-2-benzopyran-3-yl)-	MeOH	222(4.34),282(3.64)	2-0413-73
4H-1-Benzopyran-4-one, 3-(2,4-dimethoxy-phenyl)-7-hydroxy-	MeOH	253(4.5),280s(--), 345(4.13)	39-1737-73C
Emodin, 1,6-di-O-methyl-	MeOH	222(4.25),250(3.93), 265(3.96),283(4.00), 425(3.68)	94-1254-73
	MeOH-KOH	257(--),296(--), 490(--)	94-1254-73
Emodin, 6,8-di-O-methyl-	MeOH	225(4.25),246(3.77), 269(3.97),280(3.97), 425(3.63)	94-1254-73
	MeOH-KOH	265(--),296(--), 490(--)	94-1254-73
Flemmichapparin B, dihydro- (pterocar-pin)	EtOH	281(3.62),287(3.67), 313(3.93)	102-0425-73
$C_{17}H_{14}O_6$			
4H-1-Benzopyran-4-one, 3,5-dihydroxy-7-methoxy-2-(4-methoxyphenyl)-	EtOH	270(4.40),328(4.21), 370(4.45)	102-0913-73
Methanone, (2,4-dihydroxyphenyl)(5,6-di-methoxy-3-benzofuranyl)-	EtOH	245(4.18),296(4.20), 327s(4.07)	39-1277-73C
Pilloin	EtOH	254(4.2),270(4.3), 342(4.3)	102-1455-73
Toralactone monoacetate	EtOH	275(4.60),286(4.80), 382(3.40)	95-0261-73
Velutin	EtOH	252(4.19),270(4.15), 348(4.29)	102-1455-73
	EtOH-NaOEt	400(4.34)	102-1455-73
$C_{17}H_{14}O_7$			
4H-1-Benzopyran-4-one, 5,6-dihydroxy-2-(4-hydroxy-3-methoxyphenyl)-7-methoxy-	MeOH	225(4.32),249s(3.92), 293(4.11),342(4.32)	24-0020-73
4H-1-Benzopyran-4-one, 5,7-dihydroxy-2-(4-hydroxy-3-methoxyphenyl)-6-methoxy-	MeOH	240(4.04),273(4.13), 342(4.38)	24-0020-73
$C_{17}H_{15}BrN_4S$			
1,2,4-Triazolo[3,4-b]-1,3,4-thiadiazin-4-ium, 1,7-dihydro-6-phenyl-1-(phen-ylmethyl)-, bromide	MeOH	228(3.82),275(4.06), 308s(--)	48-1131-73
$C_{17}H_{15}BrN_6O_4$			
Propanenitrile, 3-[[4-(2-bromo-4,6-di-nitrophenyl)azo]phenyl]ethylamino]-	MeOH	498(4.53)	89-0926-73

Compound	Solvent	λ_{max}(log ϵ)	Ref.
$C_{17}H_{15}Br_2N_3O$			
Phenol, 2,4-dibromo-6-[[(4,5-dihydro-5-methyl-1-phenyl-1H-pyrazol-3-yl)imino]methyl]-	EtOH	240(4.00),272(3.92), 445(3.81)	104-1776-73
$C_{17}H_{15}Br_5O_4$			
Benzene, 1,2,4-tribromo-3-[(2,3-dibromo-4,5-dimethoxyphenyl)methyl]-5,6-dimethoxy-	n.s.g.	216(4.91),227s(4.59), 284s(3.34),291(3.36)	39-0891-73C
$C_{17}H_{15}ClN_2O_2$			
2(1H)-Quinolinone, 6-chloro-3-[(2-hydroxyethyl)amino]-4-phenyl-	EtOH	238(4.54),260(4.16), 300(3.93),311(3.98), 337(4.25),351(4.26)	94-0807-73
$C_{17}H_{15}ClN_2O_4S$			
1H-Indole-2-carboxylic acid, 3-[[(4-chlorophenyl)sulfonyl]amino]-, ethyl ester	EtOH	203(4.28),229(4.60), 300(4.20)	39-1602-73C
$C_{17}H_{15}ClN_3$			
Pyrimido[1,2-a]quinazolin-11-ium, 8-chloro-1,2,3,4-tetrahydro-6-phenyl-, chloride, hydrochloride	n.s.g.	245(4.51),261s(4.18), 290(3.92)	40-1944-73
$C_{17}H_{15}ClN_4O$			
1,4-Benzenediamine, N'-[(3-chloro-2-quinoxalinyl)methylene]-N,N-dimethyl-, N'-oxide	EtOH	242(4.49),315(4.16)	103-0785-73
$C_{17}H_{15}ClN_4O_2$			
1,4,5-Benzotriazocin-2(1H)-one, 4-acetyl-8-chloro-3,4-dihydro-6-phenyl-, 2-oxime	MeOH	259(4.32)	94-2375-73
$C_{17}H_{15}ClO_2$			
Benzoic acid, 4-(2-chloro-2-phenylethenyl)-, ethyl ester	EtOH	235(4.23)	104-1511-73
$C_{17}H_{15}ClS_4$			
3(2H)-Thiophenethione, 5-(4-chlorophenyl)-2-[5-(1,1-dimethylethyl)-3H-1,2-dithiol-3-ylidene]-	dioxan	238s(4.44),256s(4.48), 282(4.59),390(4.28), 516(3.96)	22-1659-73
$C_{17}H_{15}Cl_2N_3$			
2-Quinazolinamine, 6-chloro-N-(3-chloropropyl)-4-phenyl-	n.s.g.	245(4.57),272s(4.19)	40-1944-73
$C_{17}H_{15}Cl_2N_5O_2$			
Propanenitrile, 3-[[4-(2,6-dichloro-4-nitrophenyl)azo]phenyl]ethylamino]-	MeOH	417(4.49)	89-0926-73
$C_{17}H_{15}N$			
1H-Indole, 2-(2,3-dihydro-1H-inden-5-yl)-	EtOH	206(4.00),235(4.18), 288(3.45)	34-0109-73
[2.2]Metacyclophane-4-carbonitrile	EtOH	250(4.0),296(3.0)	49-0644-73
$C_{17}H_{15}NO$			
Indeno[1,2-b]azirin-6(1H)-one, 1-ethyl-1a,6a-dihydro-1a-phenyl-	isooctane	229(4.27),240(4.16), 275(3.5)	44-0654-73

Compound	Solvent	λ_{max}(log ϵ)	Ref.
1,4-Pentadien-3-one, 1,5-diphenyl-, oxime	C_6H_{12}	200(4.49),220(4.30), 223s(--),250s(--), 285(4.62)	32-0309-73
	MeOH	199(4.34),218(4.25), 225s(--),257s(--), 287(4.59)	32-0309-73
2,4-Pentadien-1-one, 1,5-diphenyl-, oxime	C_6H_{12}	215s(--),230(4.01), 238(4.03),243s(--), 257(3.93),267s(--), 307s(--),317(4.60), 330s(--)	32-0309-73
	MeOH	230s(--),238(4.03), 243s(--),257(3.93), 320(4.64),330s(--)	32-0309-73
4-Quinolinemethanol, 2-(4-methylphenyl)-	EtOH	263(4.46)	33-2588-73
$C_{17}H_{15}NOS$			
Ethanone, 2-(3-ethyl-2(3H)-benzothiazolylidene)-1-phenyl-	EtOH	220(4.43),246(4.31), 384(4.61)	73-3616-73
$C_{17}H_{15}NOSe$			
Ethanone, 2-(3-ethyl-2(3H)-benzoselenazolylidene)-1-phenyl-	EtOH	224(4.31),248(4.30), 386(4.52)	73-3616-73
$C_{17}H_{15}NO_2$			
1H-Dibenzo[a,f]quinolizine-1,13(2H)-dione, 3,4,6,7-tetrahydro-	EtOH	263(4.62),303(3.93)	30-0445-73 +70-1794-73
5,11-Epoxy-6,10-etheno-7H-cyclohepta-[b]naphthalen-7-one, 6-amino-5,5a,6,10,10a,11-hexahydro-, (5α,5aβ,6β,10α,10aβ,11α)-	EtOH	225(3.79),263(3.21), 271(3.02),340(2.03)	44-4100-73
1-Indolizinecarboxylic acid, 2-phenyl-, ethyl ester	EtOH	238(4.88),257s(4.81), 298s(3.41),309(3.24), 334s(3.95),347(3.97)	94-1139-73
$C_{17}H_{15}NO_2S$			
Pyridine, 1,2-dihydro-1-methyl-2-(5-phenyl-2H-thiopyran-2-ylidene)-, S,S-dioxide	MeOH and MeOH-base	245(4.10),262(3.99), 306(3.83),334s(--), 380(3.54),490(4.25)	39-1184-73B
Pyridine, 1,4-dihydro-1-methyl-4-(3-phenyl-4H-thiopyran-4-ylidene)-, S,S-dioxide	MeOH	238(4.22),280(3.46), 333(3.65),457(4.62)	39-1184-73B
$C_{17}H_{15}NO_2S_2$			
Dibenzo[b,f]thiepin, 2-(methylsulfonamido)-, (1/3 benzene solvate)	MeOH	224(4.54),263(4.50), 296(3.77)	73-2484-73
$C_{17}H_{15}NO_3$			
Acetamide, N-[4-[3-(2-hydroxyphenyl)-3-oxo-1-propenyl]phenyl]-	dioxan	249(4.28),367(4.60)	83-0299-73
Benzene, 1-methoxy-4-[4-(4-nitrophenyl)-1,3-butadienyl]-	THF	248(4.06),295(4.21), 400(4.56)	18-2828-73
Benzenepropanamide, N-(3-acetylphenyl)-β-oxo-	pH 13	328(4.38)	39-0808-73B
Benzenepropanamide, N-(4-acetylphenyl)-β-oxo-	pH 13	354(4.58)	39-0808-73B
2(3H)-Benzofuranone, 5-hydroxy-3-[1-[(phenylmethyl)amino]ethylidene]-	dioxan	270(4.18),350(4.27)	78-0921-73
3(2H)-Benzofuranone, 2-[[(4-methoxyphenyl)amino]methylene]-6-methyl-	MeOH	275(4.10),337(4.03), 428(4.51)	103-0141-73

Compound	Solvent	$\lambda_{max}(\log \epsilon)$	Ref.
1H,13H-Benzo[a]pyrano[3,4-f]quinolizine-1,13-dione, 3,4,6,7-tetrahydro-3-methyl-	$CHCl_3$	233(4.32),247(4.50), 283(3.97),290(3.98), 330(3.97),353(3.72)	70-1258-73
1H,13H-Benzo[a]pyrano[3,4-f]quinolizine-1,13-dione, 6,7,11b,12-tetrahydro-3-methyl-	EtOH	247(4.50),290(3.98), 330(3.96)	70-1258-73
4H,5H-Benzo[a]pyrano[2,3-f]quinolizine-4,5-dione, 6,6a,11,12-tetrahydro-2-methyl-	EtOH	260(4.02),303(3.71)	70-1745-73
4H,5H-Benzo[a]pyrano[2,3-g]quinolizine-4,5-dione, 7,8,12b,13-tetrahydro-2-methyl-	EtOH	244(4.10),303(3.00)	30-0486-73 +70-1745-73
1H-Indole-3-acetic acid, 2,3-dihydro-5-methyl-2-oxo-3-phenyl-	EtOH	256(3.86),290(3.13)	104-0861-73
1H-Indole-3-acetic acid, 2,3-dihydro-7-methyl-2-oxo-3-phenyl-	EtOH	256(3.87),285(3.28)	104-0861-73
1H-Indole-3-carboxylic acid, 2,3-dihydro-2-oxo-3-phenyl-, ethyl ester	isoPrOH	254(3.89),265s(3.75), 289(3.26)	44-3077-73
$C_{17}H_{15}NO_3S$			
Carbamic acid, (10,11-dihydro-11-oxo-dibenzo[b,f]thiepin-2-yl)-, ethyl ester	MeOH	247(4.46),270s(4.21), 354(3.63)	73-2484-73
$C_{17}H_{15}NO_4$			
Benzoic acid, 3-[(1,3-dioxo-3-phenyl-propyl)amino]-, methyl ester	pH 13	328(4.38)	39-0808-73B
2H-Benzo[a]quinolizine-2,4(3H)-dione, 3-(1,3-dioxobutyl)-1,11b-dihydro-	EtOH	268(4.10),330(4.17)	70-1745-73
1H-Indole-3-acetic acid, 2,3-dihydro-5-methoxy-2-oxo-3-phenyl-	EtOH	260(3.89),304(3.31)	104-0861-73
$C_{17}H_{15}NO_4S$			
2H-1,2-Benzothiazin-4-ol, 2-methyl-3-phenyl-, acetate, 1,1-dioxide	EtOH	290(4.15)	4-0095-73
$C_{17}H_{15}NO_5$			
6,9-Ethanobenzo[g]quinoline-2-carboxylic acid, 1,4,6,9-tetrahydro-5,10-dihydroxy-4-oxo-, methyl ester	$CHCl_3$	265(3.91),305(3.66), 330s(3.47),398(3.13)	39-2374-73C
$C_{17}H_{15}NS_2$			
4H-Dithien[2,3-c:3',2'-e]azepine, 5,6-dihydro-5-(phenylmethyl)-	C_6H_{12}	230(4.38),282s(3.74), 291(3.80),302s(3.64)	44-2814-73
1-Naphthalenecarbodithioic acid, 3-methylpyridine salt	EtOH	325(3.90),346(4.04), 502(2.07)	143-0359-73
$C_{17}H_{15}N_3$			
2-Azulenamine, 1-[(4-methylphenyl)azo]-	MeOH	238(4.27),285(4.29), 316(4.28),375s(4.64), 388(4.66),535s(3.69)	18-3266-73
$C_{17}H_{15}N_3O$			
Benzaldehyde, 2-hydroxy-, (1,2-dihydro-1-methyl-2-quinolinylidene)hydrazone	EtOH	398(4.37)	77-0684-73
1H-Indole, 1-[2-oxo-1-(phenylhydrazono)-propyl]-	EtOH	275(3.93),284s(3.84), 345(4.30)	78-3159-73
Spiro[3H-indole-3,3'-[3H]pyrazol-2(1H)-one, 2',4'-dihydro-1-methyl-5'-phenyl-	EtOH	265(3.33)	103-0034-73

Compound	Solvent	$\lambda_{max}(\log \epsilon)$	Ref.
$C_{17}H_{15}N_3OS$			
1,3,4-Thiadiazolium, 5-(benzoylamino)-3-methyl-2-(4-methylphenyl)-, hydroxide, inner salt	MeOH	236(4.20),268(4.05), 331(4.22)	103-1216-73
$C_{17}H_{15}N_3O_2$			
3H-Pyrrolo[1,2-a]indole-2-carbonitrile, 9-hydroxy-3-oxo-1-(1-piperidinyl)-	EtOH	235(4.47),290(4.09), 370(3.82)	95-0964-73
1H-1,2,3-Triazole-4-carboxylic acid, 1,5-diphenyl-, ethyl ester	EtOH	246(4.10)	42-0589-73
1H-1,2,3-Triazole-5-carboxylic acid, 1,4-diphenyl-, ethyl ester	EtOH	272(4.05)	42-0589-73
$C_{17}H_{15}N_3O_2S$			
1,3,4-Thiadiazolium, 5-(benzoylamino)-2-(4-methoxyphenyl)-3-methyl-, hydroxide, inner salt	MeOH	274(4.08),335(4.30)	103-1216-73
$C_{17}H_{15}N_3O_3$			
2H-Indol-2-one, 1,3-dihydro-3-[2-nitro-1-[(phenylmethyl)amino]ethylidene]-	EtOH	283(4.29),342(4.13)	95-0612-73
3H-Pyrrolo[1,2-a]indole-2-carbonitrile, 9-methoxy-1-(4-morpholinyl)-3-oxo-	EtOH	237(4.42),322(4.26), 364(4.27)	95-0964-73
$C_{17}H_{15}N_3O_5$			
Pyrido[2,3-d]pyrimidine-5-carboxylic acid, 1,2,3,4,7,8-hexahydro-1,3-dimethyl-2,4,7-trioxo-8-phenyl-, methyl ester	EtOH	286(3.94),336(3.71)	94-2014-73
Pyrido[2,3-d]pyrimidine-7-carboxylic acid, 1,2,3,4,5,8-hexahydro-1,3-dimethyl-2,4,5-trioxo-8-phenyl-, methyl ester	EtOH	235(4.10),281(4.30)	94-2014-73
$C_{17}H_{15}N_4S$			
1,2,4-Triazolo[3,4-b]-1,3,4-thiadiazin-4-ium, 1,7-dihydro-6-phenyl-1-(phenylmethyl)-, bromide	MeOH	228(3.82),275(4.06), 308s(--)	48-1131-73
$C_{17}H_{15}N_5O_2$			
Ethanone, 2,2'-(5-imino-1H-tetrazole-1,4(5H)-diyl)bis[1-methyl-	EtOH	249f(4.13)	22-1854-73
$C_{17}H_{15}N_7O_6$			
Propanenitrile, 3-[ethyl-[4-[(2,4,6-trinitrophenyl)azo]phenyl]amino]-	MeOH	520(4.68)	89-0926-73
$C_{17}H_{15}O_4P$			
Phosphonic acid, (2,6-diphenyl-4H-pyran-4-yl)- (hydrate)	EtOH	245(5.312)	65-0087-73
$C_{17}H_{15}O_6P$			
Phosphonic acid, [2,6-bis(3-hydroxyphenyl)-4H-pyran-4-yl]-	EtOH	250(4.172)	65-0087-73
$C_{17}H_{16}$			
Anthracene, 1,4,6-trimethyl-	EtOH	239s(4.39),250s(4.92), 257(5.18),330(3.44), 343s(3.63),348(3.69), 364(3.78),385(3.73)	39-1511-73C

Compound	Solvent	λ_{max}(log ε)	Ref.
Benzene, 1,1'-(1,2-propadienylidene)bis-[4-methyl-	hexane	266(5.04)	107-0013-73
7H-Cyclopenta[3,4]cyclobut[1,2-a]acenaphthylene, 6b,6c,8,9,9a,9b-hexahydro-	n.s.g.	225s(4.76),230(4.94), 247(3.12),273(3.65), 289(3.89),298(3.93), 302(3.74),307(3.70), 316(3.13),320(3.19)	35-2940-73
Cyclopropene, 3,3-dimethyl-1,2-diphenyl-	hexane	224(4.18),230(4.20), 237(4.08),309(4.34), 319(4.45),337(4.32)	118-0611-73
Naphtho[1',8']tricyclo[4.4.0.0^{5,10}]dec-2-ene	n.s.g.	228(4.40),236(4.30), 272s(3.42),279(3.62), 290(3.72),302(3.54), 307(3.39),316(2.81), 321(2.87)	35-2940-73
1,1'-Spirobi[1H-indene], 1,1',3,3'-tetrahydro-	C_6H_{12}	194(4.87),215s(4.31), 220s(4.20),224(3.98), 253(2.86),261(3.13), 267(3.34),273(3.41)	35-1229-73
(S)-(-)-	MeOH	213(4.15),220(3.89), 223s(3.86),253s(3.87), 260(3.11),265(3.30), 272(3.36)	35-1217-73
$C_{17}H_{16}BrClN_2$			
Pyridinium, 1-[(2-chloro-3-quinolinyl)-methyl]-3,4-dimethyl-, bromide	H_2O	237(4.75),262(3.89), 294(3.54),307(3.57), 321(3.58)	44-2351-73
$C_{17}H_{16}BrNO_3S_2$			
Butanethioamide, N-(4-bromophenyl)-2-[(4-methylphenyl)sulfonyl]-3-oxo-	EtOH	320(4.2)	104-0352-73
$C_{17}H_{16}ClNO_2S$			
Benzenecarbothioic acid, 4-(dimethylamino)-S-[2-(4-chlorophenyl)-2-oxoethyl] ester	EtOH	244(4.51),345(4.57)	48-0497-73
$C_{17}H_{16}ClNO_4$			
Isoquinolinium, 2-methyl-3-(phenylmethyl)-, perchlorate	MeOH	232(4.64),270(3.45), 280(3.49),339(3.78)	83-0648-73
$C_{17}H_{16}ClN_3$			
Imidazo[1,2-a]quinazoline, 7-chloro-1,2,4,5-tetrahydro-4-methyl-5-phenyl-	n.s.g.	220(4.27),271(4.03)	40-1944-73
1H-Pyrazol-3-amine, N-[(2-chlorophenyl)-methylene]-4,5-dihydro-5-methyl-1-phenyl-	EtOH	270(4.13),424(4.30), 436(4.34)	104-1776-73
$C_{17}H_{16}ClN_3O$			
1-Propanol, 3-[(6-chloro-4-phenyl-2-quinazolinyl)amino]-	n.s.g.	246(4.55),276s(4.26)	40-1944-73
$C_{17}H_{16}ClN_5O_2$			
Propanenitrile, 3-[[4-[(2-chloro-4-nitrophenyl)azo]phenyl]ethylamino]-	MeOH	475(4.60)	89-0926-73
$C_{17}H_{16}Cl_2N_4$			
Propanenitrile, 3-[[4-[(2,6-dichlorophenyl)azo]phenyl]ethylamino]-	MeOH	396(4.34)	89-0926-73

Compound	Solvent	λ_{max}(log ε)	Ref.
$C_{17}H_{16}Cl_4N_4$			
Benzenaminium, N-[chloro[[chloro[[chloro(methylphenylamino)methylene]amino]-methylene]amino]methylene]-N-methyl-, chloride	$CHCl_3$	247(4.71)	114-0081-73A
$C_{17}H_{16}NO_2S$			
Pyridinium, 1-methyl-2-(3-phenyl-2H-thiopyran-6-yl)-, perchlorate, S,S-dioxide	MeOH-$HClO_4$	245(3.77),269(3.87), 343(4.19)	39-1184-73B
Pyridinium, 1-methyl-4-(3-phenyl-2H-thiopyran-4-yl)-, tetrafluoroborate, S,S-dioxide	MeOH-$HClO_4$	271(4.13),340(3.38)	39-1184-73B
$C_{17}H_{16}N_2$			
Benzenamine, N-[5-(phenylamino)-2,4-pentadienylidene]-, tetrafluoroborate	MeOH	486(4.85)	44-3990-73
2,3-Diazabicyclo[3.1.0]hex-2-ene, 1-methyl-4,4-diphenyl-	EtOH	333(2.23)	35-0980-73
1H-Pyrazole, 1,4-dimethyl-3,5-diphenyl-	EtOH	248(4.35)	78-4159-73
1H-Pyrazole, 3,4-dimethyl-1,5-diphenyl-	EtOH	256(4.19)	78-4159-73
1H-Pyrazole, 4,5-dimethyl-1,3-diphenyl-	EtOH	266(4.27)	78-4159-73
$C_{17}H_{16}N_2O$			
2-Cyclopropen-1-one, 2,3-bis(methylphenylamino)-	MeOH	281(4.45),290(4.42)	88-2619-73
1H-Indole-3-ethanol, 2-[2-(3-pyridinyl)-ethenyl]-, (E)-	MeOH	261(3.67),360(4.16)	23-0792-73
2-Pyridinamine, N-[1-(1-naphthalenyl)-ethyl]-, 1-oxide, (S)-	MeOH	222(4.92),252(4.03), 272(3.94),282(3.92), 294(3.80),325(3.77)	32-1083-73
4(3H)-Quinazolinone, 3-(1-methylethyl)-2-phenyl-	MeOH	205(4.72),228(4.47), 278(4.03),305s(3.72), 315s(3.60)	78-2153-73
$C_{17}H_{16}N_2O_2$			
Azuleno[2,1-b]pyrazine-10-carboxylic acid, 2,3-dimethyl-	MeOH	227(4.34),255(4.39), 325(4.68),338(4.74), 373(3.85),395(3.89), 416(3.89),520(2.38), 554(2.41),600s(2.29), 660s(1.75)	18-3161-73
20,21-Dinoreburnamenine-14,17(15H)-dione, (3α)-(±)-	EtOH	242(4.35),265(4.04), 295(3.67),303(3.67)	22-2705-73
1H-Indole-2-carboxamide, 3-[(4-methoxyphenyl)methyl]-	n.s.g.	225(4.49),295(4.23)	103-1497-73
$C_{17}H_{16}N_2O_2S$			
1H-Indole, 2-(ethylthio)-1-methyl-3-(4-nitrophenyl)-	EtOH	228(4.22),292(3.84), 380(3.70)	94-2739-73
$C_{17}H_{16}N_2O_3$			
Benzenamine, 4-ethoxy-N-[3-(2-nitrophenyl)-2-propen-1-ylidene]-	MeOH	210(4.36),249(4.37), 285(4.46),361(4.40)	42-0277-73
$C_{17}H_{16}N_2O_3S$			
7(4H)-Benzothiazolone, 6-[[[2-(acetyloxy)phenyl]amino]methylene]-5,6-dihydro-2-methyl-	EtOH	239(4.14),274(4.12), 410(4.25)	32-1063-73

Compound	Solvent	$\lambda_{max}(\log \epsilon)$	Ref.
$C_{17}H_{16}N_2O_3S_2$			
1H-Indole-2-carboximidothioic acid, 3-hydroxy-N-[(4-methylphenyl)sulfonyl]-, methyl ester	EtOH	223(4.35),252(4.12), 275(4.05),350(4.23)	95-0971-73
$C_{17}H_{16}N_2O_4S$			
2H-1,2-Benzothiazine-3-carboxamide, 4-hydroxy-N,2-dimethyl-N-phenyl-, 1,1-dioxide	EtOH	232s(4.11),323(4.09)	87-0044-73
1H-Indole-2-carboxylic acid, 1-methyl-3-[[(4-methylphenyl)sulfonyl]amino]-	EtOH	229(4.43),300(4.03), 320s(3.69)	39-1602-73C
2-Propenoic acid, 3-(1-acetyl-3-methoxy-1H-indol-2-yl)-2-cyano-3-(methylthio)-, methyl ester	EtOH	245(4.12),280(3.99), 324(4.14)	94-1658-73
$C_{17}H_{16}N_2O_5S$			
1,4-Thiazepine-3-carboxylic acid, 6-(1,3-dihydro-1,3-dioxo-2H-isoindol-2-yl)-2,3,4,5-tetrahydro-2,2-dimethyl-7-oxo-, methyl ester, (S)-	MeOH	217(4.63),238(4.11), 256(3.92),304(4.07)	1-0677-73
1,4-Thiazepine-3-carboxylic acid, 6-(1,3-dihydro-1,3-dioxo-2H-isoindol-2-yl)-2,3,4,7-tetrahydro-2,2-dimethyl-7-oxo-, methyl ester, (S)-	MeOH	218(4.66),238(4.11), 250(3.89),304(4.08)	1-0677-73
$C_{17}H_{16}N_2O_8S$			
2,5-Methano-5H,9H-pyrimido[2,1-b][1,5,3]-dioxazepin-9-one, 3-[(benzoyloxy)methyl]-2,3-dihydro-11-[(methylsulfonyl)-oxy]-, [2S-(2α,3β,5α,11R*)]-	MeOH	227(4.35),250s(3.91)	117-0075-73
$C_{17}H_{16}N_4$			
4H-1,2-Diazepine, 5-hydrazino-3,7-diphenyl-	MeOH	210(4.28),256(4.02), 300(3.41)	103-0321-73
4H-Indene-5,5,6,6-tetracarbonitrile, 3a,7a-dihydro-1,2,3,3a-tetramethyl-	dioxan	272(3.67)	24-0008-73
$C_{17}H_{16}N_4O$			
Acetamide, N-[2-(5-methyl-3-phenyl-1H-1,2,4-triazol-1-yl)phenyl]-	MeOH	244(4.47)	24-2530-73
$C_{17}H_{16}N_4O_2$			
1H-Pyrazol-3-amine, 4,5-dihydro-5-methyl-N-[(2-nitrophenyl)methylene]-1-phenyl-	EtOH	286(4.12),485(4.26)	104-1776-73
$C_{17}H_{16}N_4O_3$			
Furo[2,3-g]pteridine-8-carboxylic acid, 1,5,5a,8a-tetrahydro-7-methyl-, phenylmethyl ester	$CHCl_3$	245(4.31),301(3.93)	39-1615-73C
1H-Indole-2-carboxaldehyde, 3-methyl-, (2-methoxy-4-nitrophenyl)hydrazone	n.s.g.	340(4.11),445(4.49)	35-3400-73
4-Pteridineacetic acid, α-benzoyl-1,4-dihydro-, ethyl ester	$CHCl_3$	252(4.13),332(3.92)	39-1615-73C
$C_{17}H_{16}N_4O_6$			
Inosine, 5'-benzoate	EtOH	230(4.27),248s(4.08), 260s(3.83)	44-2896-73

Compound	Solvent	$\lambda_{max}(\log \epsilon)$	Ref.
$C_{17}H_{16}N_4O_6S$			
Inosine, 2',3'-didehydro-3'-deoxy-, 2'-(4-methylbenzenesulfonate)	EtOH	230(4.16),248s(4.02), 263s(3.75),271s(3.64)	44-2896-73
$C_{17}H_{16}N_6$			
Formazan, 3-methyl-1-(4-methylphenyl)-5-(2-quinoxalinyl)-	benzene	435s(4.30)	103-1542-73
	EtOH	398(4.60)	103-1542-73
	EtOH-KOH	538(4.77)	103-1542-73
	dioxan	408(4.42)	103-1542-73
	H_2SO_4	530(3.51)	103-1542-73
$C_{17}H_{16}N_6O_4$			
Propanenitrile, 3-[[4-[(2,4-dinitrophenyl)azo]phenyl]ethylamino]-	MeOH	491(4.58)	89-0926-73
Propanenitrile, 3-[[4-[(2,6-dinitrophenyl)azo]phenyl]ethylamino]-	MeOH	450(4.43)	89-0926-73
$C_{17}H_{16}O$			
5H-Benzocyclohepten-5-one, 6,7,8,9-tetrahydro-6-phenyl-	EtOH	247(3.88),287(3.07)	78-1851-73
3H-Cyclopent[a]anthracen-3-one, 1,2,7,8,9,10-hexahydro-	EtOH	246(4.67),261(4.74), 284(3.92),295(4.01), 305(3.90),337(3.48), 351(3.45)	39-1251-73C
17H-Cyclopenta[a]phenanthren-17-one, 1,2,3,4,15,16-hexahydro-	EtOH	257(3.96),282(3.25), 293(3.27),334(2.86), 348(2.91)	39-1251-73C
13H-Dibenzo[a,d]cyclononen-13-one, 5,6,7,8-tetrahydro-	EtOH	264(4.17)	78-1851-73
9,10-Ethanoanthracene-1-methanol, 9,10-dihydro-	EtOH	266(3.09),271(3.11), 274(3.15)	49-0274-73
Oxirane, 2-phenyl-2-(2-phenylcyclopropyl)-	MeOH	244(4.08)	39-2030-73C
1-Penten-3-one, 1,5-diphenyl-, (E)-	EtOH	210(4.20),220(3.98), 290(4.28)	12-0183-73
3-Penten-2-one, 3,4-diphenyl-, cis	EtOH	257(4.00),310(3.96)	78-1745-73
trans	EtOH	265(4.05),317(3.95)	78-1745-73
$C_{17}H_{16}OS$			
1-Propanone, 1-(6,11-dihydrodibenzo-[b,e]thiepin-2-yl)-	MeOH	241(3.86),315(4.21)	73-1602-73
$C_{17}H_{16}O_2$			
Acetic acid, (2,3-dihydro-3-methyl-4(1H)-phenanthrenylidene)-, (E)-	EtOH	307(3.97),330s(3.79)	39-0615-73C
Benzoic acid, 4-(2-phenylethenyl)-, ethyl ester	EtOH	302(4.24)	104-1511-73
Bicyclo[3.3.1]nona-3,6-diene-2,8-dione, 4,6-dimethyl-9-phenyl-	EtOH	217s(4.27),270s(3.40)	94-1213-73
Bicyclo[3.3.1]nona-3,7-diene-2,6-dione, 4,8-dimethyl-9-phenyl-	EtOH	238(4.12),270s(3.17), 350(2.81)	94-1213-73
2,4,6-Cycloheptatrien-1-one, 2-methoxy-4-[2-(4-methylphenyl)ethenyl]-, (E)-	MeOH	248(4.12),280(4.12), 318(4.10),386(4.24)	18-0199-73
2,4,6-Cycloheptatrien-1-one, 2-methoxy-6-[2-(4-methylphenyl)ethenyl]-	MeOH	251(4.27),317(4.24), 363(4.17)	18-0199-73
1H-Indene-1-acetic acid, 2,3-dihydro-1-phenyl-, (S)-	MeOH	214(3.98),259(3.01), 264(3.08),271(3.05)	35-1217-73
[2.2]Metacyclophane-4-carboxylic acid	C_6H_{12}	257(4.0),295(3.0)	49-0644-73
2-Propen-1-one, 3-(2-furanyl)-1-(5,6,7-8-tetrahydro-2-naphthalenyl)-	EtOH	239(3.60),342(4.23)	39-1251-73C

Compound	Solvent	$\lambda_{max}(\log \epsilon)$	Ref.
$C_{17}H_{16}O_2S$			
1-Benzothiepin-5(2H)-one, 3,4-dihydro-4-(hydroxyphenylmethyl)-	EtOH	240(4.28),263(3.75)	44-2629-73
3-Penten-2-one, 5-(5-acetyl-2-thienyl)-3-phenyl-	EtOH	257(4.00),348(4.00)	48-0993-73
$C_{17}H_{16}O_2S_2$			
1,3-Cyclohexanedione, 5,5-dimethyl-2-(4-phenyl-1,3-dithiol-2-ylidene)-	EtOH	395(4.51)	94-2224-73
	MeCN	395(4.50)	94-2224-73
3,3'(4H,4'H)-Spirobi[2H-1,5-benzoxathiepin]	THF	262(4.21),286(3.59)	78-2337-73
$C_{17}H_{16}O_3$			
Benzeneacetic acid, α-(methoxyphenylmethylene)-, methyl ester, (Z)-	EtOH	225(4.08),280(4.04)	39-0221-73C
Benzenebutanoic acid, β-oxo-α-phenyl-, methyl ester	MeOH	210(4.13),254(3.57), 264s(3.53)	18-2908-73
Benzoic acid, 3,6-dimethyl-2-(4-methylbenzoyl)-	C_6H_{12}	225s(4.20),288(3.36)	39-1511-73C
2,4,6-Cycloheptatrien-1-one, 2-methoxy-4-[2-(4-methoxyphenyl)ethenyl]-, (E)-	MeOH	250(4.20),281(4.10), 332(4.09),400(4.39)	18-0199-73
2,4,6-Cycloheptatrien-1-one, 2-methoxy-6-[2-(4-methoxyphenyl)ethenyl]-, (E)-	MeOH	237(4.24),314(4.55), 350(4.48)	18-0199-73
1H,3H-Fluoreno[8a,9-c]furan-1,5(4H)-dione, 6,7,7a,11b-tetrahydro-11-methyl-3-methylene-, (3aS*,7aα,11bβ)-	MeCN	266(2.51),274(2.41)	44-0741-73
Spiro[cyclobutane-1,3'(6'aH)-oxireno[h]-[1,2]benzodioxin], 7'a,7'b-dihydro-4'-phenyl-, (6'aα,7'aα,7'bβ)-	EtOH	262(4.18)	78-3553-73
$C_{17}H_{16}O_3S$			
1,3-Cyclohexanedione, 5,5-dimethyl-2-(5-phenyl-1,3-oxathiol-2-ylidene)-	EtOH	361(4.40)	94-2224-73
	MeCN	359(4.38)	94-2224-73
$C_{17}H_{16}O_4$			
4H-1-Benzopyran-4-one, 2,3-dihydro-5,7-dihydroxy-6,8-dimethyl-2-phenyl-	MeOH	210(4.38),296(4.15), 347(3.41)	100-0422-73
	MeOH-KOH	220(--),250s(3.33), 338(4.10)	100-0422-73
1,4-Naphthalenedione, 2-acetoxy-3-(3-methyl-2-butenyl)-	EtOH	245(4.2),251(4.2), 264(4.1),269(4.1), 336(3.4)	1-3211-73
3-Phenanthrenol, 2,5,7-trimethoxy-	EtOH	252s(4.77),261(4.94), 283(4.22),295s(4.02), 307(3.96),328(3.64), 344(3.85),362(4.03)	102-2789-73
2-Propen-1-one, 3-(2,3-dimethoxyphenyl)-1-(2-hydroxyphenyl)-	EtOH	216(4.52),255(3.97), 287s(3.97),332(4.22), 368s(4.07)	42-0129-73
2-Propen-1-one, 1-(2-hydroxy-4,6-dimethoxyphenyl)-3-phenyl-	n.s.g.	214(4.43),345(4.44)	102-0238-73
Spiro[1,2-benzodioxin-3(7H),1'-cyclobutan]-7-one, 8,8a-dihydro-8-hydroxy-4-phenyl-, trans	EtOH	302(4.24)	78-3553-73
Spiro[cyclobutane-1,6'(2'H)-pyrano[3,4-b]pyran-2'-one, 8',8'a-dihydro-8'-hydroxy-5'-phenyl-, cis	EtOH	285(4.18)	78-3553-73
$C_{17}H_{16}O_5$			
Benzeneacetic acid, α-[(3-hydroxyphenyl)methylene]-3,5-dimethoxy-	n.s.g.	230(4.29),295(4.11)	39-1263-73C

Compound	Solvent	λ_{max}(log ε)	Ref.
3aH-Benz[e]indene-3a-carboxylic acid, 2,3,4,5-tetrahydro-3-(hydroxymethylene)-7-methoxy-2-oxo-, methyl ester	MeOH	238(3.84),300s(4.27), 399(4.47)	39-1780-73C
2H,5H-Benz[4,5]indeno[1,7a-c]furan-2,5-dione, 2a,3,6,7-tetrahydro-3α,9-dimethoxy-	MeOH	243(3.90),332(4.39)	39-1780-73C
5H-Benzocyclohepten-5-one, 6,9-diacetoxy-7,8-dimethyl-	EtOH	225(4.84),285(3.76)	39-1223-73C
Benzoic acid, 2-(3,4-dimethoxybenzoyl)-, methyl ester	EtOH	212(4.41),281(4.06), 315(4.01)	56-1949-73
2-Naphthaleneacetic acid, α-acetyl-1,4-dihydro-3-methyl-1,4-dioxo-, ethyl ester	EtOH	332(3.37)	83-0257-73
	EtOH-KOH	530(2.88)	83-0257-73
1-Oxaspiro[4.5]dec-3-ene-6-acetic acid, 2,8-dioxo-10-phenyl-	EtOH	259(2.72),264(2.64), 270(2.51)	78-3091-73
3,6-Phenanthrenediol, 2,4,7-trimethoxy-	n.s.g.	258(4.95),283(4.58), 290s(4.43),313(4.16)	39-1179-73C
2-Propen-1-one, 1-(2,6-dihydroxy-3,4-dimethoxyphenyl)-3-phenyl-	MeOH	336(4.39)	2-0009-73
	MeOH-NaOAc	235(--),292s(--)	2-0009-73
	MeOH-AlCl$_3$	317s(--),366(--)	2-0009-73
2-Propen-1-one, 1-(2-hydroxy-4,6-dimethoxyphenyl)-3-(4-hydroxyphenyl)-	EtOH	245(3.86),265(4.39), 370(4.58)	2-0509-73
Stenocarpoquinone A acetate	EtOH	255(4.40),262(4.33), 280(3.91),335(3.22), 420(3.21)	12-1121-73
Toralactone dimethyl ether	EtOH	268(4.61),278(4.79), 392(3.39)	95-0261-73
$C_{17}H_{16}O_6$			
7,4'-Aromadendrine, O-methyl-	EtOH	228(4.24),292(4.08)	102-0913-73
Benzoic acid, 4-methoxy-3-[4-(methoxycarbonyl)phenoxy]-, methyl ester	EtOH	256(4.44)	33-1266-73
1,2-Dibenzofurandicarboxylic acid, 1,9b-dihydro-7-methoxy-4,9b-dimethyl-, trans	90% EtOH	214(4.26),286(3.70), 351(3.78)	12-1093-73
1H-Phenalen-1-one, 3,9-dihydroxy-6,7,8-trimethoxy-4-methyl-	EtOH	217(4.47),239s(4.28), 270s(4.11),374(4.28), 398(4.31),414s(4.26)	39-2388-73C
9H-Xanthen-9-one, 1,3,4,7-tetramethoxy-	MeOH	236(4.45),259(4.26), 300s(4.00),310(4.06), 369(3.94)	39-1329-73C
9H-Xanthen-9-one, 1,3,5,6-tetramethoxy-	MeOH	244(4.68),287(4.11), 306(4.34),330s(4.05)	39-1329-73C
9H-Xanthen-9-one, 1,3,6,7-tetramethoxy-	MeOH	247s(4.49),254(4.60), 266s(4.12),300(4.22), 347(4.14)	39-1329-73C
9H-Xanthen-9-one, 2,3,4,5-tetramethoxy-	MeOH	247(4.44),254(4.55), 285s(3.98),308s(3.72), 353s(3.81),363(3.82)	39-1329-73C
$C_{17}H_{16}O_7$			
Acetic acid, (4,7-diacetoxy-5-methyl-2H-1-benzopyran-2-ylidene)-	MeOH	290(3.92)	94-0149-73
Benzoic acid, 6-hydroxy-2-(2-hydroxy-4-methoxybenzoyl)-3-methoxy-, methyl ester	MeOH	215(4.54),232s(4.25), 281(4.14),332(4.04)	24-1182-73
4H-1-Benzopyran-4-one, 2-(2,5-dihydroxy-4-methoxyphenyl)-2,3-dihydro-5-hydroxy-7-methoxy-	n.s.g.	288(4.30),340s(4.00)	88-0007-73
Parvisoflavanone	MeOH	287(4.35),320s(3.58)	102-1188-73

Compound	Solvent	$\lambda_{max}(\log \epsilon)$	Ref.
Parvisoflavanone (cont.)	MeOH-NaOH	243(4.45),322(4.66)	102-1188-73
	MeOH-NaOAc	292(4.35),323(4.08)	102-1188-73
9H-Xanthen-9-one, 1-hydroxy-3,5,6,7-tetramethoxy-	MeOH	240(4.35),258(4.49), 275(3.94),312(4.18), 364(3.81)	39-1329-73C
9H-Xanthen-9-one, 1-hydroxy-3,5,7,8-tetramethoxy-	EtOH	241(4.27),264(4.41), 315(3.92),384(3.60)	102-2542-73
$C_{17}H_{16}O_8$			
Benzoic acid, 3,6-dihydroxy-2-[5-methoxy-2-(methoxycarbonyl)phenoxy]-, methyl ester	MeOH	216(4.58),252(4.22), 292(3.73),342(3.60)	24-1182-73
$C_{17}H_{17}$			
1,3,5,7,9,11,13,15-Cycloheptadecaoctaene, ion(1-), lithium salt	ether at -70°	295(4.72),426(4.56), 447(5.32),580(3.38), 616(3.40),673(3.89)	89-0325-73
Methylium, cyclopropyl(4-methylphenyl)-phenyl-	FSO_3H at -75°	321(<4.1),446(4.63)	59-0803-73
Phenanthrenylium, 9,10-dihydro-9,9,10-trimethyl-	70% $HClO_4$	267(4.29),339(3.89), 538(3.64)	88-0539-73 +104-1057-73
	75% H_2SO_4	266(4.28),338(3.92)	104-1057-73
$C_{17}H_{17}ClN_2O_3$			
Glycine, N-[(2-amino-5-chlorophenyl)-phenylmethylene]-, ethyl ester, anti	EtOH	232(4.43),364(3.72)	95-1253-73
syn	EtOH	247(4.39)	95-1253-73
$C_{17}H_{17}ClN_2O_8S$			
2,4(1H,3H)-Pyrimidinedione, 1-[5-O-benzoyl-3-chloro-3-deoxy-2-O-(methylsulfonyl)-β-D-arabinofuranosyl]-	MeOH	227(4.05),259(3.89)	117-0075-73
$C_{17}H_{17}ClN_4$			
Propanenitrile, 3-[[4-[(2-chlorophenyl)-azo]phenyl]ethylamino]-	MeOH	412(4.57)	89-0926-73
Propanenitrile, 3-[[4-[(4-chlorophenyl)-azo]phenyl]ethylamino]-	MeOH	409(4.62)	89-0926-73
$C_{17}H_{17}ClN_6O_5$			
Adenosine, N-[[(2-chlorophenyl)amino]-carbonyl]-	pH 1-2	280(4.45)	87-0139-73
	pH 5-7	280(4.44)	87-0139-73
	pH 12	309(4.54),315(4.65)	87-0139-73
$C_{17}H_{17}ClO_3$			
1-Propanone, 3-(5-chloro-2,4-dimethoxyphenyl)-1-phenyl-	EtOH	238(3.62),283(3.08)	2-1099-73
Spiro[1,2-benzodioxin-3(7H),1'-cyclobutan]-8-ol, 7-chloro-8,8a-dihydro-4-phenyl-, (7α,8β,8aα)-	EtOH	255(4.35)	78-3553-73
$C_{17}H_{17}ClO_4$			
Hydroperoxide, 7-chloro-8,8a-dihydro-4-phenylspiro[1,2-benzodioxin-3(7H),1'-cyclobut]-8-yl, (7α,8β,8aα)-	EtOH	256(4.33)	78-3553-73
$C_{17}H_{17}Cl_3N_2O_2$			
1-Piperidinecarboxylic acid, 4-(1H-indol-2-ylmethylene)-, 2,2,2-trichloroethyl ester	MeOH	245(4.20),307(4.35), 313(4.32)	23-0792-73

Compound	Solvent	λ_{max}(log ε)	Ref.
$C_{17}H_{17}IO_4$			
3H-3,10a-Methano-1H-indeno[2,1-c]oxepin-10-carboxylic acid, 4,5,5a,10-tetrahydro-4-iodo-8-methyl-1-oxo-, methyl ester, (3α,4α,5aβ,10β,10aα)-	EtOH	263(2.96),270s(2.85)	44-0741-73
$C_{17}H_{17}N$			
2,4-Pentadien-1-amine, 4,5-diphenyl-, hydrochloride, (E,Z)-	MeOH	224(4.09),232(4.05), 287(4.45),308(4.23)	44-2169-73
$C_{17}H_{17}NO$			
Benzeneacetamide, α-(3-phenylpropylidene)-, (Z)-	EtOH	249(4.17),283s(3.10), 291(2.83)	44-2913-73
Oxazole, 2,5-dihydro-2,2-dimethyl-4,5-diphenyl-	EtOH	243(4.08)	33-2611-73
Phenol, 4-[2-(3,4-dihydro-1-isoquinolinyl)ethyl]-	pH 1	218(4.22),277(4.13)	4-0519-73
	pH 13	242(4.25),290(3.63)	4-0519-73
	EtOH	250(4.00),279(3.61)	4-0519-73
$C_{17}H_{17}NO_2$			
Apomorphine, (±)-, hydriodide	MeOH	217(4.61),273(4.23), 309(3.52)	87-1223-73
Aporphine, 1,2-dihydroxy-, hydriodide	MeOH	213(4.65),271(4.20), 310(3.64)	87-1228-73
Benzamide, 2-(2,4,6-trimethylbenzoyl)-	EtOH	214(4.45),244(4.02)	39-1160-73B
6H,8H-Benzo[a]pyrano[3,2-g]quinolizin-8-one, 5,9,10,11-tetrahydro-11-methyl-	EtOH	233(4.27),329(4.15)	30-0234-73 +70-1263-73
Caaverine, d-	n.s.g.	273(4.19),313(3.70)	105-0727-73
1,3-Cyclohexanedione, 5,5-dimethyl-2-(2(1H)-quinolinylidene)-	$CHCl_3$	282(3.93),385(4.28), 428(4.15)	4-0115-73
1H-Dibenzo[a,f]quinolizine-1,13(2H)-dione, 3,4,6,7,11b,12-hexahydro-	EtOH	255(4.50),277(4.16)	70-1794-73
4,9-Methano-1H-benz[f]isoindole-1,3(2H)-dione, 3a,4,9,9a-tetrahydro-2-methyl-10-(1-methylethylidene)-, (4λ,3ε)	90% EtOH	219(3.91),260(3.01), 266(3.11),273(?)	12-1725-73
exo isomer	90% EtOH	221(3.83),262(3.11), 267(3.21),274(3.24)	12-1725-73
9,13-Metheno-13H-1,3-dioxolo[4,5-l][2]-benzazacycloundecine, 5,6,7,8-tetrahydro-6-methyl-	EtOH	256(3.92),303(3.85)	23-2338-73
2-Propen-1-one, 3-[4-(dimethylamino)-phenyl]-1-(2-hydroxyphenyl)-	isooctane	250(4.05),267(4.12), 324(3.59),405(4.57), 415s(--)	65-0638-73
	benzene	330(3.59),420s(--), 430(4.54)	65-0638-73
	EtOH	250s(--),275(4.13), 325(4.50),410s(--), 435(4.54)	65-0638-73
$C_{17}H_{17}NO_2S$			
Benzenecarbothioic acid, 4-(dimethylamino)-, S-(2-oxo-2-phenylethyl) ester	EtOH	244(4.25),345(4.48)	48-0497-73
$C_{17}H_{17}NO_3$			
1H,13H-Benzo[a]pyrano[4,3-f]quinolizine-1,13-dione, 3,4,6,7,11b,12-hexahydro-3-methyl-	EtOH	249(4.11),305(4.17)	70-1258-73

Compound	Solvent	$\lambda_{max}(\log \epsilon)$	Ref.
$C_{17}H_{17}NO_4$			
Aporphine, 1,2,9,10-tetrahydroxy-, (+)-, hydriodide	MeOH	219(4.68),279(4.08), 304(4.14)	87-1228-73
3-Azatricyclo[3.2.1.0^{2,4}]oct-6-ene-6,7-dicarboxylic acid, 3-phenyl-, dimethyl ester, exo	EtOH	235(4.37)	12-0619-73
3,4-Azocinedicarboxylic acid, 1,8-dihydro-1-phenyl-, dimethyl ester	MeOH	253(4.15),297(4.28)	77-0665-73
Benzenepropanamide, 4-methoxy-N-(4-methoxyphenyl)-β-oxo-	pH 13	330(4.36)	39-0808-73B
1,3-Butanedione, 1-(1,6,7,11b-tetrahydro-2-hydroxy-4-oxo-4H-benzo[a]-quinolizin-3-yl)-	$CHCl_3$	283(4.14),333(3.30)	30-0486-73 +70-1745-73
Demethylcephalotaxinone	EtOH	230s(3.95),295(3.92), 318(3.94)	95-0916-73
	EtOH	317(4.01)	102-2987-73
7H-Furo[3,2-g][1]benzopyran-7-one, 9-methoxy-4-[(3-methyl-2-butenyl)amino]-	EtOH	230(4.39),294(4.32), 327(4.00)	4-0443-73
1H,13H-Pyrano[3',4':2,3][1,4]oxazepino-[5,4-a]isoquinoline-1,13-dione, 3,4,6,7,11b,12-hexahydro-3-methyl-	$CHCl_3$	295(4.26)	70-1258-73
$C_{17}H_{17}NO_4S_2$			
Thiopyrano[4,3-b]indole-3,4-dicarboxylic acid, 4a,5-dihydro-4a-methyl-1-(methylthio)-, dimethyl ester	EtOH	256(4.17),364(3.79)	94-2770-73
$C_{17}H_{17}NO_5$			
3,4-Pyridinedicarboxylic acid, 1,6-dihydro-2-methyl-6-oxo-5-(phenylmethyl)-, dimethyl ester	EtOH	267(3.89),307(3.68)	39-0404-73C
3,4-Pyridinedicarboxylic acid, 1,6-dihydro-5-methyl-6-oxo-2-(phenylmethyl)-, dimethyl ester	EtOH	266(3.79),308(3.58)	39-0404-73C
1H-Pyrrole-3,4-dicarboxylic acid, 1-benzoyl-, diethyl ester	EtOH	227(4.07),242(3.99)	23-1089-73
$C_{17}H_{17}NO_6$			
Ethanone, 1-(2,4-dimethoxyphenyl)-2-(2-methoxy-5-nitrophenyl)-	EtOH	229(4.17),269(4.03), 307(4.11)	95-1514-73
1,4-Naphthalenedione, 5-(1,2-dioxopropyl)-6,8-dimethoxy-7-methyl-2-(methylamino)-	EtOH	230(4.45),277(4.30), 306s(4.08),360s(3.53), 465(3.56)	33-2287-73
$C_{17}H_{17}NO_6S$			
7-Azabicyclo[2.2.1]hepta-2,5-diene-2,3-dicarboxylic acid, 7-[(4-methylphenyl)sulfonyl]-, dimethyl ester	EtOH	290(3.04)	24-3824-73
3-Azatetracyclo[3.2.0.0^{2,7}.0^{4,6}]heptane-1,5-dicarboxylic acid, 3-[(4-methylphenyl)sulfonyl]-, dimethyl ester	EtOH	230(4.05),251s(2.89), 255s(2.74),263(2.61), 267s(2.52),274(2.38)	24-3824-73
1H-Azepine-4,5-dicarboxylic acid, 1-[(4-methylphenyl)sulfonyl]-, dimethyl ester	MeCN	238s(4.04),259s(3.72), 273s(3.46),350(2.91)	24-3824-73
1,2-Benzenedicarboxylic acid, 4-[[(4-methylphenyl)sulfonyl]amino]-, dimethyl ester	EtOH	222s(3.32),256s(3.08), 264(3.11),276s(3.02), 283s(2.88),292s(2.71)	24-3824-73
Propanedioic acid, [(1-acetyl-3-hydroxy-1H-indol-2-yl)(methylthio)methylene]-, dimethyl ester	EtOH	290(4.35),306(4.36)	94-1658-73

Compound	Solvent	λ_{max}(log ε)	Ref.
$C_{17}H_{17}NO_7$			
Benzaldehyde, 4,5-dimethoxy-2-(2-methoxy-5-methyl-4-nitrophenoxy)-	MeOH	236(4.33),277(4.12), 329(4.05)	35-2995-73
Ethenetricarboxylic acid, (2,3-dihydro-1-methyl-2-oxo-1H-indol-3-yl)-, trimethyl ester	EtOH	265(4.49),300(3.83)	95-1008-73
$C_{17}H_{17}N_2O_3P$			
Phosphonic acid, (2',4'-dihydrospiro-[9H-fluorene-9,3'-[3H]pyrazol-5'-yl)-, dimethyl ester	EtOH	270(4.15),308(3.48)	65-1226-73
$C_{17}H_{17}N_3$			
1H-1,2,5-Triazepine, 6,7-dihydro-1-methyl-3,4-diphenyl-	EtOH	230(4.19),253(4.11), 290s(3.84),360(3.55)	77-0642-73
	EtOH-HCl	263(--),405(--)	77-0642-73
$C_{17}H_{17}N_3O$			
Pyrimido[1,2-b]indazol-2(1H)-one, 7,8,9,10-tetrahydro-7-methyl-4-phenyl-	MeOH	246(4.48),289(3.95)	4-0261-73
Pyrimido[1,2-b]indazol-4(1H)-one, 7,8,9,10-tetrahydro-7-methyl-2-phenyl-	MeOH	250(4.70),328(3.70)	4-0261-73
1,2,5-Triazabicyclo[3.2.1]oct-3-ene, 2-hydroxy-3,4-diphenyl-	EtOH	242(4.02)	77-0642-73
	EtOH-HCl	256(--)	77-0642-73
1,2,4-Triazine, 2,5-dihydro-3-methoxy-5-methyl-5,6-diphenyl-	n.s.g.	229(4.12),278(3.63)	22-2493-73
$C_{17}H_{17}N_3OS$			
3H-Pyrrolo[1,2-a]indole-2-carbonitrile, 9-(diethylamino)-1-(methylthio)-3-oxo-	EtOH	232(4.37),325(4.20)	95-0964-73
$C_{17}H_{17}N_3O_2$			
Anantine, N-acetyl-	n.s.g.	222(4.14),292(4.29)	88-1757-73
$C_{17}H_{17}N_3O_2S$			
Acetamide, N-[2-[[(4,7-dihydro-2-methyl-7-oxo-6(5H)-benzothiazolylidene)-methyl]amino]phenyl]-	EtOH	220(4.22),275(4.14), 410(4.36)	32-1063-73
$C_{17}H_{17}N_3O_3$			
Benzenamine, 4-[4,5-dihydro-3-(4-nitrophenyl)-5-isoxazolyl]-N,N-dimethyl-	EtOH	265(4.32),310(4.25)	39-1574-73C
Pyrido[2,3-d]pyrimidine-2,4,5(1H,3H,8H)-trione, 1,3,7-trimethyl-8-(phenylmethyl)-	EtOH	232(4.30),248(3.93), 264(3.70),297(3.57)	94-2014-73
$C_{17}H_{17}N_3O_4$			
Glycine, N-[(2-amino-5-nitrophenyl)phenylmethylene]-, ethyl ester, anti	EtOH	230(4.33),365(4.22)	95-1253-73
4,7-Methano-1H-benzotriazole-5,6-dicarboxylic acid, 3a,4,7,7a-tetrahydro-1-phenyl-, dimethyl ester, (3aα,4β,7β,7aα)-	EtOH	228(4.28),277(3.85), 285s(3.84),303(3.80)	12-0619-73
$C_{17}H_{17}N_3O_5$			
Uridine, 5'-deoxy-5'-(1H-indol-1-yl)-	EtOH	263(4.13),291(3.85)	104-2223-73
$C_{17}H_{17}N_3S$			
1,2,4-Triazine, 2,5-dihydro-5-methyl-3-(methylthio)-5,6-diphenyl-	n.s.g.	233(4.09),296s(3.69)	22-2493-73

Compound	Solvent	$\lambda_{max}(\log \epsilon)$	Ref.
$C_{17}H_{17}N_4O_7PS$			
Inosine, 8-[(phenylmethyl)thio]-, cyclic 3',5'-(hydrogen phosphate)	pH 1	276(4.12)	69-5310-73
	pH 11	283(4.13)	69-5310-73
$C_{17}H_{17}N_5O_2$			
Propanenitrile, 3-[ethyl[4-[(2-nitrophenyl)azo]phenyl]amino]-	MeOH	425(4.56)	89-0926-73
Propanenitrile, 3-[ethyl[4-[(4-nitrophenyl)azo]phenyl]amino]-	MeOH	453(4.64)	89-0926-73
7H-Purine-7-propanenitrile, 1,2,3,6-tetrahydro-1,3-dimethyl-2,6-dioxo-8-(phenylmethyl)-	n.s.g.	210(4.48),278(4.04)	73-1571-73
$C_{17}H_{17}N_5O_5$			
Adenosine, N^6-benzoyl-	pH 1	292(4.38)	18-3858-73
	pH 7	281(4.37)	18-3858-73
	pH 12	303(4.40)	18-3858-73
$C_{17}H_{17}N_5O_5S$			
Adenosine, 2',3'-didehydro-3'-deoxy-, 2'-(4-methylbenzenesulfonate)	EtOH	228(4.16),258(4.16)	44-2896-73
9H-Purine, 9-(2-deoxy-β-D-erythro-pentofuranosyl)-6-[[(4-nitrophenyl)methyl]thio]-	MeOH	284(4.50),290s(4.48)	23-3161-73
$C_{17}H_{17}N_6O_7P$			
Adenosine, N-[(phenylamino)carbonyl]-, cyclic 3',5'-(hydrogen phosphate)	pH 1	285(4.45)	87-1075-73
	pH 7	277(4.46)	87-1075-73
	pH 11	277(4.46)	87-1075-73
$C_{17}H_{17}N_7$			
2,4,6-Pyrimidinetriamine, N^4-(4-methylphenyl)-5-(phenylazo)-	EtOH	250(4.18),280(4.34), 400(4.37)	42-0260-73
$C_{17}H_{17}N_7O$			
2,4,6-Pyrimidinetriamine, N^4-(4-methoxyphenyl)-5-(phenylazo)-	EtOH	245(4.41),280(4.41), 320(3.57),420(4.28)	42-0260-73
$C_{17}H_{18}$			
1,3,5,7,9,11,13,15-Cycloheptadecaoctaene	ether	225(4.20),260(4.43), 276(4.48),365(3.58)	89-0325-73
isomer (oil)	ether	225(4.15),260(4.42), 276(4.45),362(3.54)	89-0325-73
Cyclopropane, 1-(diphenylmethylene)-2-methyl-	EtOH	226(4.20),235(4.13), 259(4.20)	78-1169-73
[2.2]Metacyclophane, 4-methyl-	C_6H_{12}	230(4.0),276(2.8)	49-0644-73
$C_{17}H_{18}Br_2O_4$			
Benzene, 1,1'-methylenebis[2-bromo-4,5-dimethoxy-	n.s.g.	236s(4.34),286(3.85)	39-0891-73C
$C_{17}H_{18}ClNO_5$			
Phenanthridinium, 6-(ethoxymethyl)-5-methyl-, perchlorate	EtOH	240(4.70),350(3.90)	103-0076-73
$C_{17}H_{18}ClN_3O$			
Ethanol, 2-[(6-chloro-3,4-dihydro-3-methyl-4-phenyl-2-quinazolinyl)amino]-	n.s.g.	220(4.31),296(3.98)	40-1944-73

Compound	Solvent	λ_{max}(log ε)	Ref.
$C_{17}H_{18}INO_2S$			
Isoquinolinium, 6,7-dimethoxy-2-methyl-1-(2-thienylmethyl)-, iodide	MeOH	258(4.88),318(4.12)	83-0592-73
$C_{17}H_{18}INO_3$			
Isoquinolinium, 1-(2-furanylmethyl)-6,7-dimethoxy-2-methyl-, iodide	MeOH	257(4.86),318(4.11)	83-0592-73
$C_{17}H_{18}N_2$			
1H-Indole-3-ethanamine, 1-(phenylmethyl)-	EtOH	220(4.63),278s(3.76), 287(3.79),295(3.72)	103-0196-73
2H-Indol-2-imine, 3-ethyl-1,3-dihydro-1-(phenylmethyl)-, hydrochloride	MeOH	209(4.34),262(3.88)	103-0471-73
$C_{17}H_{18}N_2O$			
1-Cyclohexene-1-carbonitrile, 6-oxo-4-phenyl-2-(1-pyrrolidinyl)-	EtOH	236(3.92),300(4.39)	70-0811-73
Deethylibogamine, 8-oxo-	MeOH	245(4.15),266(3.99), 303(4.01)	24-1459-73
Pyrazolidine, 2-acetyl-1,3-diphenyl-	EtOH	240(4.12),277(3.57), 350(2.93)	103-0503-73
$C_{17}H_{18}N_2O_2$			
Benzamide, 2-[4-(dimethylamino)benzoyl]-N-methyl-	EtOH	211(4.42),262(4.17)	39-1160-73B
	dioxan	216(4.30),264(4.19), 348(3.18)	39-1160-73B
	$CHCl_3$	346(3.26)	39-1160-73B
	MeCN	216(4.22),266(4.15), 352(3.13)	39-1160-73B
Ergoline-8-carboxylic acid, 7,8-didehydro-6-methyl-, methyl ester	CH_2Cl_2	223(4.50),292(4.39)	88-5095-73
Isoxazole, 5-[[3-(1,1-dimethylethyl)-5-isoxazolyl]methyl]-3-phenyl-	n.s.g.	206(4.37),240(4.20)	32-0037-73
2H-1,2,5-Oxadiazin-3-ol, 3,4-dihydro-4,4-dimethyl-3,6-diphenyl-	EtOH	260(3.49)	103-1008-73
2,5-Piperazinedione, 3-butylidene-6-(3-phenyl-2-propenylidene)-	EtOH	365(4.64)	18-3876-73
2,5-Piperazinedione, 3-(2-methylpropylidene)-6-(3-phenyl-2-propenylidene)-	EtOH	366(4.63)	18-3876-73
2(1H)-Pyridinone, 1-butyl-3-[1-oxo-3-(3-pyridinyl)-2-propenyl]-	EtOH	223(4.21),244(4.05), 308(4.08),371(4.0)	103-0615-73
1H-Pyrrolo[3,4-b]quinoline-3,9(2H,4H)-dione, 2-cyclohexyl-	n.s.g.	245(4.57),333(4.13), 348(4.41)	4-0225-73
$C_{17}H_{18}N_2O_3$			
Benzenamine, 4-ethoxy-N-[3-(2-nitrophenyl)-2-propenyl]-	MeOH	208(4.55),243(4.59), 310(4.04)	42-0694-73
$C_{17}H_{18}N_2O_4$			
1-Azulenecarboxylic acid, 2,3-diacetamido-, ethyl ester	MeOH	235s(4.31),248(4.33), 314(4.72),360(3.82), 370s(3.77),395s(3.21), 535(2.68)	18-3266-73
2,5-Cyclohexadiene-1,4-dione, 3-acetyl-2-[(2-hydroxy-1-methylethyl)amino]-5-(phenylamino)-	EtOH	245(4.12),296(4.12), 351(4.29),485(3.26)	78-2881-73
	CH_2Cl_2	247(4.13),297(4.07), 355(4.29),490(3.22)	78-2881-73
2,5-Cyclohexadiene-1,4-dione, 3-acetyl-2-[(2-hydroxypropyl)amino]-5-(phenylamino)-	EtOH	244(4.16),291(4.14), 352(4.28),475(3.20)	78-2881-73
	CH_2Cl_2	248(4.13),297(4.09), 353(4.29),488(3.20)	78-2881-73

Compound	Solvent	λ_{max}(log ε)	Ref.
$C_{17}H_{18}N_2O_5$			
Acetamide, N-(3,4-diacetoxy-1-methyl-5-phenyl-1H-pyrrol-2-yl)-	n.s.g.	219(4.07),277(4.09)	12-2221-73
1,4-Cyclohexadiene-1-carboxylic acid, 2-[(2-hydroxypropyl)amino]-3,6-dioxo-5-(phenylamino)-, methyl ester	EtOH	250(4.18),275s(3.97), 350(4.30),496(3.14)	78-2881-73
	CH_2Cl_2	253(4.17),277s(3.96), 351(4.29),490(3.03)	78-2881-73
1H-Pyrrole-2,4-dipropanoic acid, 3-(benzoylamino)-	EtOH	226(4.46)	70-1859-73
$C_{17}H_{18}N_2O_5S$			
Acetamide, N-[2-(1-methylethylidene)-3,8-dioxo-5-thia-1-azabicyclo[4.2.0]-oct-7-yl]-2-phenoxy-, S-oxide, (R)-	n.s.g.	221(4.14),261(3.83), 268(3.89),275(3.91), 282s(3.85)	39-2105-73C
(S)-	n.s.g.	217(4.12),262s(3.82), 268(3.90),274(3.91), 278s(3.85)	39-2105-73C
Spiro[cyclohexane-1,3'-[3H]furo[3,4-c]-pyrazole]-4,6-dione, 3'a,6'a-dihydro-2-[(4-methylphenyl)sulfonyl]-	EtOH	290(4.00)	39-1922-73B
$C_{17}H_{18}N_2O_6S$			
Acetamide, N-[2-(1-methylethylidene)-3,8-dioxo-5-thia-1-azabicyclo[4.2.0]-oct-7-yl]-2-methoxy-, S,S-dioxide, (6R-trans)-	n.s.g.	216(3.96),262s(3.62), 268(3.72),274(3.72)	39-2105-73C
$C_{17}H_{18}N_2O_7S$			
2,4(1H,3H)-Pyrimidinedione, 1-[2,3-anhydro-5-O-(methylsulfonyl)-β-D-lyxo-furanosyl]-3-(phenylmethyl)-	EtOH	258(3.98)	44-0598-73
$C_{17}H_{18}N_2O_8$			
Benzene, 1,1'-methylenebis[4,5-dimethoxy-2-nitro-	n.s.g.	244(4.41),286(4.07), 337(4.07)	39-0891-73C
$C_{17}H_{18}N_3S$			
Thiazolo[3,2-a]pyrimidin-4-ium, 5-[2-[4-(dimethylamino)phenyl]ethenyl]-7-methyl-, perchlorate	n.s.g.	515(4.91)	124-1151-73
$C_{17}H_{18}N_4$			
Propanenitrile, 3-[ethyl[4-(phenylazo)-phenyl]amino]-	MeOH	399(4.60)	89-0926-73
$C_{17}H_{18}N_4O_2$			
Pyrrolidine, 1-[[(2-nitrophenyl)hydrazono]phenylmethyl]-	MeOH	266(4.32),302(4.09), 522(3.83)	24-2530-73
$C_{17}H_{18}N_4O_2S_2$			
Thieno[2,3-d]thiazole-5-carboxylic acid, 2-[[4-(dimethylamino)phenyl]azo]-6-methyl-, ethyl ester	CH_2Cl_2	253(4.06),299(3.87), 326(3.89),353s(3.72), 369s(3.71),537(4.71)	48-0539-73
$C_{17}H_{18}N_4O_3$			
1H-Pyrimido[5,4-b][1,4]oxazine-6-carboxylic acid, 7-methyl-4-[(phenylmethyl)-amino]-, ethyl ester	EtOH	231(4.4),273(4.2), 402(3.2)	103-1532-73

Compound	Solvent	λ_{max}(log ε)	Ref.
$C_{17}H_{18}N_4O_4$			
2(3H)-Naphthalenone, 4,6,7,8-tetrahydro-6-methyl-, 2,4-dinitrophenylhydrazone	n.s.g.	397(4.51)	39-1757-73C
$C_{17}H_{18}N_4O_5$			
2,5-Cyclohexadiene-1,4-dione, 2-methyl-5-propyl-, 1-[(2,4-dinitrophenyl)-methylhydrazone]	C_2Cl_4	346(3.90),448(4.08)	1-3632-73
Phenol, 2-butyl-4-[(2,4-dinitrophenyl)-azo]-5-methyl- (in 50% DMSO)	acid	421(4.22)	1-3641-73
	KOH	601(4.70)	1-3641-73
Phenol, 2-butyl-4-[(2,4-dinitrophenyl)-azo]-6-methyl- (in 50% DMSO)	acid	455(4.41)	1-3641-73
	KOH	612(4.76)	1-3641-73
Phenol, 3-butyl-4-[(2,4-dinitrophenyl)-azo]-5-methyl- (in 50% DMSO)	acid	406(4.20)	1-3641-73
	KOH	576(4.60)	1-3641-73
	C_2Cl_4	402(4.38)	1-3632-73
Spiro[5.5]undec-7-ene-1,9-dione, 9-(2,4-dinitrophenylhydrazone)	EtOH	372(4.43)	39-0393-73C
$C_{17}H_{18}N_4O_5S$			
1,2,4-Triazino[5,6-d][3,1]benzoxazepine-6,6(7H)-dimethanol, 3-(methylthio)-, diacetate	EtOH	205(4.31),238(4.40), 354(4.00),455(3.80)	78-0639-73
$C_{17}H_{18}N_4O_6$			
Inosine, 1-(phenylmethoxy)-	pH 1	244s(3.99),251(4.04), 267s(3.78)	44-3046-73
	pH 13	244s(3.99),251(4.03), 267s(3.78)	44-3046-73
$C_{17}H_{18}N_4O_7S$			
Inosine, 5'-(4-methylbenzenesulfonate)	MeOH	224(4.17),249(3.99)	88-2811-73
$C_{17}H_{18}N_5O_7PS$			
Guanosine, 8-[(phenylmethyl)thio]-, cyclic 3',5'-(hydrogen phosphate)	pH 1	273(4.14),290s(4.06)	69-5310-73
	pH 7	277(4.20)	69-5310-73
	pH 11	275s(3.99),293(4.13)	69-5310-73
$C_{17}H_{18}N_6O_5$			
Adenosine, N-[(phenylamino)carbonyl]-	pH 1-2	283(4.41)	87-0139-73
	pH 5-7	279(4.43)	87-0139-73
	pH 12	308(4.51),313(4.65)	87-0139-73
$C_{17}H_{18}O$			
2(1H)-Naphthalenone, 1-methyl-1,4-di-2-propenyl-	EtOH	244(4.07),305(3.95)	33-0014-73
$C_{17}H_{18}OS$			
Benzenecarbothioic acid, O-[1-(phenyl-methyl)propyl] ester	C_6H_{12}	253(3.99),291(4.05), 421(2.08)	39-1580-73C
1-Pentanethione, 3-hydroxy-1,2-diphenyl-	C_6H_{12}	229(3.91),234(3.88), 250(3.66),316(4.10), 553(1.97)	39-1580-73C
$C_{17}H_{18}O_2$			
Acetic acid, (1,2,3,4-tetrahydro-5H-fluoren-4-ylidene)-, ethyl ester	C_6H_{12}	229(3.94),236(3.96), 243(4.05),252(3.96), 330(4.49)	44-1445-73
1H-Cyclopent[a]anthracene-3,5(2H,4H)-dione, 3a,7,8,9,10,11b-hexahydro-	EtOH	221(4.36),264(4.12), 302(3.35)	39-1251-73C

Compound	Solvent	λ max (log ε)	Ref.
1H-Cyclopenta[a]phenanthrene-11,17-dione, 2,3,4,12,13,14,15,16-octahydro-	EtOH	200(4.25),257(3.91), 308(3.33)	39-1251-73C
Phenol, 2-benzoyl-4-(1,1-dimethylethyl)-	C_6H_{12}	257(4.09),267(4.07), 349(3.64)	22-1442-73
	EtOH	263(4.07),348(3.59)	22-1442-73
Phenol, 2-benzoyl-3,4,5,6-tetramethyl-	MeOH	248(4.5),275(3.94), 340s(3.7)	5-1893-73
Phenol, 4-(1,1-dimethylethyl)-, benzoate	C_6H_{12}	230(4.24)	22-1442-73
	EtOH	232(4.24)	22-1442-73
$C_{17}H_{18}O_3$			
1H-Cyclopenta[2,3]cyclopropa[1,2-a]naphthalene-3-carboxylic acid, 1,2,3,3a,4,5,9b,9c-octahydro-3-methyl-1-oxo-, methyl ester	EtOH	234(4.06)	78-0309-73
Spiro[1,2-benzodioxin-3(7H),1'-cyclobutan]-8-ol, 8,8a-dihydro-4-phenyl-, trans	EtOH	248(4.29)	78-3553-73
$C_{17}H_{18}O_4$			
Butanedioic acid, 2-methyl-2-(2-naphthalenyl)-, dimethyl ester	EtOH	226(4.99),266(3.8), 275(3.81)	2-0131-73
2-Cyclohexen-1-one, 5,6-dihydroxy-4-[(1-hydroxycyclobutyl)phenylmethylene]-, (4Z,5α,6α)-	EtOH	297(4.19)	78-3553-73
3H-3,10a-Methano-1H-indeno[2,1-c]oxepin-10-carboxylic acid, 4,5,5a,10-tetrahydro-9-methyl-1-oxo-, methyl ester, (3α,5aβ,10β,10aα)-	EtOH	260s(2.34),264(2.40), 272(2.25)	44-0741-73
Spiro[1,2-benzodioxin-3(7H),1'-cyclobutane]-7,8-diol, 8,8a-dihydro-4-phenyl-, (7α,8β,8aα)-	EtOH	250(4.31)	78-3553-73
isomer	EtOH	249(4.32)	78-3553-73
Spiro[cyclobutane-1,6'(2'H)-pyrano[3,4-b]pyran]-2',8'-diol, 8',8'a-dihydro-5'-phenyl-, (2'α,8'β,8'aβ)-	EtOH	249(4.32)	78-3553-73
Virolane	EtOH	234(4.13),285(3.95)	102-0417-73
	EtOH-NaOH	241(4.20),291(4.03)	102-0417-73
Virolanol	EtOH	231(4.03),284(3.82),	102-0417-73
	EtOH-NaOH	236(4.04),292(3.94)	102-0417-73
$C_{17}H_{18}O_5$			
Benzoic acid, 2,6-dimethoxy-, (4-hydroxy-2,6-dimethylphenyl) ester	MeOH	209(4.42),245(3.61), 278(3.66)	24-1198-73
2H-1-Benzopyran-7-ol, 3,4-dihydro-3-(3-hydroxy-2,4-dimethoxyphenyl)-	MeOH	282(3.62),292(3.79)	102-1157-73
2H-1-Benzopyran-2-one, 8-(3-acetoxy-1,2-dimethyl-1-propenyl)-7-methoxy-	EtOH	257(3.67),318(4.18)	88-5005-73
8aH-Fluorene-8a,9-dicarboxylic acid, 4b,5,6,7,8,9-hexahydro-1-methyl-7-oxo-, 9-methyl ester, (4bα,8aα,9aα)-	EtOH	265(2.38),270(2.30), 274s(2.19)	44-0741-73
Methanone, (2,3,4,5-tetramethoxyphenyl)phenyl-	MeOH	253(4.20),279(3.80), 314s(3.40)	39-1329-73C
3,6-Phenanthrenediol, 9,10-dihydro-2,4,7-trimethoxy-	n.s.g.	260(4.05),283(4.15), 318(4.12)	39-1179-73C
1-Propanone, 2-hydroxy-1-(2-hydroxy-6-methoxyphenyl)-3-methoxy-3-phenyl-	EtOH	277(4.10),343(3.55)	114-0093-73B
Spiro[1,2-benzodioxin-3(7H),1'-cyclobutan]-7-ol, 8,8a-dihydro-8-hydroperoxy-4-phenyl-, (7α,8β,8aα)-	EtOH	249(4.26)	78-3553-73

Compound	Solvent	λ_{max}(log ε)	Ref.
$C_{17}H_{18}O_6$			
Epierythrostominol	n.s.g.	231(4.51),277(3.91), 317(3.90),482s(3.87), 514(3.93),551(3.73)	39-2975-73C
7H-Furo[3,2-g][1]benzopyran-7-one, 9-(2-hydroxy-3-methoxy-3-methylbutoxy)-, (+)-	EtOH	220(4.58),249(4.45), 300(4.18)	2-0410-73
Methanone, (2,6-dimethoxyphenyl)(2-hydroxy-4,5-dimethoxyphenyl)-	MeOH	246(4.11),283(4.16), 350(3.99)	39-1329-73C
Methanone, (2-hydroxy-3,4,5-trimethoxyphenyl)(2-methoxyphenyl)-	MeOH	246(3.95),290(4.13), 362(3.79)	39-1329-73C
1,2-Naphthalenedione, 3-(2-acetoxy-1-hydroxy-1-methylethyl)-6-methoxy-5-methyl-	EtOH	218(4.23),244(4.08), 280(4.20),405(3.83)	78-1773-73
1H,3H-Naphtho[1,8-cd]pyran-1-one, 6,7,8,9-tetramethoxy-4-methyl-	EtOH	224(4.36),254(4.61), 338(3.98)	44-1944-73
Spiro[cyclopropane-1,3'(2'H)-[1,2,4]-methenopentalene]-1',5',6'(3'aH)-tricarboxylic acid, 4',6'a-dihydro-, trimethyl ester	EtOH	237(3.83)	24-1822-73
Spiro[cyclopropane-1,3'(2'H)-[1,2,4]-methenopentalene]-1',5',6'a-tricarboxylic acid, 3'a,4'-dihydro-, trimethyl ester	EtOH	227(3.84)	24-1822-73
Spiro[cyclopropane-1,5'-[5H]cycloprop-[cd]indene]-2',2'a,2'b-tricarboxylic acid, 5'a,5'b-dihydro-, trimethyl ester	EtOH	214s(3.88)	24-1837-73
$C_{17}H_{18}O_7$			
Melampodin B	MeOH	end absorption	77-0614-73
$C_{17}H_{19}BrN_2OS$			
Thiazolo[3,2-a]pyridinium, 5-[2-[4-(dimethylamino)phenyl]ethenyl]-2,3-dihydro-3-hydroxy-, bromide	MeOH	509(4.27)	103-1138-73
$C_{17}H_{19}BrN_2O_5S$			
2(3H)-Isothiazoleacetic acid, 5-bromo-α-(1-methylethyl)-3-oxo-4-[[(phenylmethoxy)carbonyl]amino]-, methyl ester, (S)-	MeOH	283(4.00)	88-5213-73
$C_{17}H_{19}Cl$			
6H-5,13-Methenobenzocyclododecene, 15-chloro-7,8,9,10,11,12-hexahydro-	EtOH	235s(4.70),241(4.83), 271s(3.58),282s(3.70), 289(3.73),300s(3.58), 320s(2.55),333s(2.35)	44-1207-73
$C_{17}H_{19}ClN_2O_5S$			
2(3H)-Isothiazoleacetic acid, 5-chloro-α-(1-methylethyl)-3-oxo-4-[[(phenylmethoxy)carbonyl]amino]-, methyl ester, (S)-	MeOH	284(4.05)	88-5213-73
Thiazolo[3,2-a]pyridinium, 7-[2-[4-(dimethylamino)phenyl]ethenyl]-2,3-dihydro-3-hydroxy-, perchlorate	MeOH	510(4.54)	103-1138-73

Compound	Solvent	$\lambda_{max}(\log \epsilon)$	Ref.
$C_{17}H_{19}ClN_4O_7$			
9H-Purine, 6-chloro-9-(2,3,4-tri-O-acetyl-6-deoxy-β-L-galactopyranosyl)-	n.s.g.	265(3.92)	136-0192-73E
$C_{17}H_{19}ClN_4O_7S$			
9H-Purine, 6-chloro-2-(methylthio)-9-(2,3,5-tri-O-acetyl-β-D-ribofuranosyl)-	EtOH	235(4.24),265(4.10), 308(3.96)	94-0692-73
$C_{17}H_{19}Cl_2NO_3S$			
2H-1,4-Thiazine-3-carboxylic acid, 4-(dichlorophenylacetyl)-3,4-dihydro-, 1,1-dimethylethyl ester	EtOH	279(3.63)	39-1321-73C
$C_{17}H_{19}F_3N_2O_3$			
1H-Indole-3-acetamide, α-hydroxy-5-methoxy-2-methyl-N-(2-methyl-2-propenyl)-4-(trifluoromethyl)-	MeOH	225(4.45),305(4.05)	44-1504-73
$C_{17}H_{19}INP$			
Phosphonium, (1H-indol-2-ylmethyl)dimethylphenyl-, iodide	MeOH	271(4.00),276(4.00), 285(3.99),293(3.90)	23-0792-73
$C_{17}H_{19}IN_2S_2$			
Benzothiazolium, 2-[2-[5-(dimethylamino)-2-thienyl]ethenyl]-3-ethyl-, iodide	$MeNO_2$	567(5.13)	103-0850-73
$C_{17}H_{19}N$			
Quinoline, 1,2,3,4-tetrahydro-4-methyl-2-(4-methylphenyl)-	EtOH	254(4.14)	33-2588-73
$C_{17}H_{19}NO$			
Benzeneethanol, α-(2-aminoethyl)-β-(phenylmethylene)-, (E)-	MeOH	221(4.19),255(4.13)	44-2169-73
Benzenemethanamine, 4-methoxy-α-methyl-N-(1-phenylethylidene)-	C_6H_{12}	230(4.218)	35-2971-73
Benzenemethanamine, N-[1-(4-methoxyphenyl)ethylidene]-α-methyl-	C_6H_{12}	262(4.28)	35-2971-73
Phenol, 4-[2-(1,2,3,4-tetrahydro-1-isoquinolinyl)ethyl]-	pH 1	275(3.20)	4-0519-73
	pH 13	238(4.11),295(3.40)	4-0519-73
$C_{17}H_{19}NOS$			
Benzenecarbothioic acid, O-[2-[4-(dimethylamino)phenyl]ethyl] ester	C_6H_{12}	258(4.10),290(3.81), 420(2.62)	39-1574-73C
Benzenecarbothioic acid, 4-(dimethylamino)-, O-(2-phenylethyl) ester	C_6H_{12}	246(4.11),355(4.57), 410(3.14)	39-1574-73C
$C_{17}H_{19}NO_2$			
7-Azabicyclo[4.2.1]nona-2,4-diene-7-carboxylic acid, 8-phenyl-, ethyl ester	EtOH	264(3.59)	44-3094-73
6H,8H-Benzo[a]pyrano[3,2-g]quinolizin-8-one, 5,9,10,11,13,13a-hexahydro-11-methyl-	EtOH	262(3.72)	30-0234-73 +70-1263-73
Methanone, 1-[5-(1,1-dimethylethyl)-2-hydroxyphenyl]phenyl-, oxime	MeOH	260(4.104)	30-0394-73
	CCl_4	318(3.584)	30-0394-73
L-Proline, 1-(2-naphthalenyl)-, ethyl ester	MeOH	248(5.23),278(4.43), 288(4.60),298(4.58), 355(4.00)	94-0054-73

Compound	Solvent	$\lambda_{max}(\log \epsilon)$	Ref.
$C_{17}H_{19}NO_2S$			
Isoquinoline, 1,2-dihydro-6,7-dimethoxy-2-methyl-1-(2-thienylmethyl)-	MeOH	230s(4.40),333(4.06)	83-0592-73
$C_{17}H_{19}NO_2S_2$			
Spiro[1,3-dithiolane-2,5'-[5H]indole, 7'-(1,3-benzodioxol-5-yl)-1',2',3'-6',7',7'a-hexahydro-	MeOH	225(3.88),286(3.62)	88-4587-73
$C_{17}H_{19}NO_3$			
1,3-Benzodioxole-5-methanol, 6-[3-[2-(methylamino)ethyl]phenyl]-	EtOH	259(3.85),294(3.74)	23-2338-73
1H,6H-Benzo[a]pyrano[4,3-f]quinolizin-1-one, 3,4,7,11b,12,13-hexahydro-13-hydroxy-3-methyl-	EtOH	263(3.97)	70-1258-73
Isoquinoline, 1-(2-furanylmethyl)-1,2-dihydro-6,7-dimethoxy-2-methyl-	MeOH	255s(4.03),331(4.04)	83-0592-73
Tembamide, O-methyl-	n.s.g.	228(4.32),269(3.36), 279(3.23)	12-0687-73
$C_{17}H_{19}NO_4$			
3,4-Azocinedicarboxylic acid, 1,4,5,8-tetrahydro-1-phenyl-, dimethyl ester	MeOH	242s(3.61),308(4.38)	77-0665-73
3,4-Azocinedicarboxylic acid, 1,6,7,8-tetrahydro-1-phenyl-, dimethyl ester	MeOH	286(4.08),326(4.16)	77-0665-73
1-Buten-2-ol, 1-(1-cyclohexen-1-yl)-, 4-nitrobenzoate	EtOH	236(4.39),244s(4.33), 296s(3.42)	33-0875-73
α-D-xylo-5-Heptenofuranurononitrile, 5,6-dideoxy-1,2-O-(1-methylethylidene)-3-O-(phenylmethyl)-, (Z)-	EtOH	211(4.02),257(2.47)	33-1310-73
$C_{17}H_{19}NO_5$			
α-D-xylo-Heptofuranos-5-ulose, 6,7-dideoxy-6,6,7,7-tetradehydro-2-O-(1-methylethylidene)-3-O-(phenylmethyl)-, oxime	EtOH	214(3.63),229(3.53)	136-0311-73D
Isoxazole, 5-phenyl-3-(tetrahydro-6-methoxy-2,2-dimethylfuro[2,3-d]-1,3-dioxol-5-yl)-, [3aR-(3aα,5α,6α,6aα)]-	CHCl	265(4.45)	136-0311-73D
Isoxazole, 3-[tetrahydro-2,2-dimethyl-6-(phenylmethoxy)furo[2,3-d]-1,3-dioxol-5-yl]-	EtOH	218(4.40)	136-0311-73D
$C_{17}H_{19}NO_5S$			
Spiro[2H-indene-2,2'-thiazolidine]-1,3-diol, 3'-acetyl-1,3-dihydro-, diacetate	EtOH	212(4.05),271(3.76)	78-4271-73
less polar isomer	EtOH	212(4.09),270(3.78)	78-4271-73
$C_{17}H_{19}NP$			
Phosphonium, (1H-indol-2-ylmethyl)dimethylphenyl-, iodide	MeOH	271(4.00),276(4.00), 285(3.99),293(3.90)	23-0792-73
$C_{17}H_{19}N_2OS$			
Thiazolo[3,2-a]pyridinium, 5-[2-[4-(dimethylamino)phenyl]ethenyl]-2,3-dihydro-3-hydroxy-, bromide	MeOH	509(4.27)	103-1138-73
perchlorate	MeOH	510(4.54)	103-1138-73

Compound	Solvent	λ max(log ε)	Ref.
$C_{17}H_{19}N_2S_2$			
Benzothiazolium, 2-[2-[5-(dimethyl-amino)-2-thienyl]ethenyl]-3-ethyl-, iodide	MeNO	567(5.13)	103-0850-73
$C_{17}H_{19}N_3$			
1H-Indole-3-ethanamine, 1-[2-(2-pyridin-yl)ethyl]-	EtOH	222(4.91),267(4.04), 285(3.98),298s(3.91)	103-0196-73
Pyrrolidine, 1-[4-[(4-methylphenyl)azo]-phenyl]-	C_6H_{12}	407(4.52)	18-0194-73
	50%EtOH-HCl	335(3.46),528(4.74)	18-0194-73
$C_{17}H_{19}N_3O_2$			
2,4(1H,3H)-Pyrimidinedione, 5-butyl-1-(1H-indol-3-ylmethyl)- (in 35% ethanol)	pH 6.5	217(4.63),276(4.19), 287s(4.08)	19-0257-73
	pH 13	273(4.13),287s(3.98)	19-0257-73
$C_{17}H_{19}N_3O_2S_4$			
4-Thiazolidinone, 3-ethyl-5-[2-[[4,5-dimethyl-3-(2-thiazolyl)thiazolin-2-ylidene]-1-ethoxy]ethyl]-	EtOH	532(5.16)	103-0687-73
$C_{17}H_{19}N_3O_3$			
2,5-Cyclohexadiene-1,4-dione, 2-methyl-5-propyl-, 1-[methyl(4-nitrophenyl)-hydrazone]	MeCN	461(4.44)	1-3632-73
$C_{17}H_{19}N_3O_6$			
2,3-Diazabicyclo[2.2.1]hept-5-ene-2,3-dicarboxylic acid, 7-[[[(phenylamino)-carbonyl]oxy]methyl]-, dimethyl ester, anti	EtOH	236(4.25),273(2.89), 281(2.78)	35-7813-73
$C_{17}H_{19}N_5O_3$			
Adenosine, 2'-deoxy-N-(phenylmethyl)-	MeOH	269(4.35)	23-3161-73
	MeOH	267s(4.33),270(4.34)	69-2179-73
Adenosine, 3'-deoxy-N-(phenylmethyl)-	MeOH	267s(4.32),271(4.32)	69-2179-73
Imidodicarbonic dihydrazide, N'-[2-(4-methoxyphenyl)ethylidene]-2-phenyl-	EtOH	230(4.40),236(4.38), 261s(4.13)	48-0492-73
$C_{17}H_{19}N_5O_4$			
Adenosine, N-(phenylmethyl)-	pH 1	265(4.28)	18-3858-73
	pH 7	268(4.30)	18-3858-73
	pH 12	270(4.30)	18-3858-73
	MeOH	267s(4.31),270(4.32)	69-2179-73
Benzo[g]pteridine-2,4(3H,10H)-dione, 10-(2-acetoxyethyl)-8-(dimethyl-amino)-7-methyl-	MeOH	219(4.18),259(4.65), 300s(4.83),496(3.59)	77-0703-73
9H-Purin-6-amine, 9-β-D-arabinofurano-syl-N-(phenylmethyl)-	MeOH	267(4.30)	69-2179-73
D-Ribitol, 1,4-anhydro-1-C-[7-(phenyl-methyl)amino]-1H-pyrazolo[4,3-d]-pyrimidin-3-yl]-, (S)-	MeOH	239(3.83),289s(4.11), 297(4.17),307(4.08)	69-2179-73
	MeOH-HCl	291(4.21),301(4.19)	69-2179-73
	MeOH-NaOH	243(4.10),305(4.03)	69-2179-73
$C_{17}H_{19}N_5O_5$			
Adenosine, N-(2-methoxyphenyl)-	pH 1.0	272(4.27)	87-0358-73
	H_2O	282.5(4.24)	87-0358-73
	pH 13	282.5(4.25)	87-0358-73
Adenosine, N-(3-methoxyphenyl)-	pH 1.0	276(4.27)	87-0358-73
	H_2O	298(4.32)	87-0358-73

Compound	Solvent	$\lambda_{max}(\log \epsilon)$	Ref.
Adenosine, N-(3-methoxyphenyl)- (cont.)	pH 13	298(4.33)	87-0358-73
Adenosine, N-(4-methoxyphenyl)-	pH 1.0	275(4.32)	87-0358-73
	H_2O	288.5(4.34)	87-0358-73
	pH 13	288.5(4.35)	87-0358-73
Adenosine, N-(phenylmethoxy)-	pH 1	269(4.22)	94-1676-73
	pH 7	269(4.21)	94-1676-73
	pH 13	285(4.10)	94-1676-73
	EtOH	268(4.20)	94-1676-73
L-Histidine, N-acetyl-2-[[4-(methoxy-carbonyl)phenyl]azo]-, methyl ester	EtOH	388(4.44)	44-1971-73
L-Histidine, N-acetyl-5-[[4-(methoxy-carbonyl)phenyl]azo]-, methyl ester	EtOH	358(4.45)	44-1971-73
$C_{17}H_{19}N_5O_7S$			
Guanosine, 5'-(4-methylbenzenesulfonate)	MeOH	224(4.15),253(4.01)	88-2811-73
$C_{17}H_{19}N_6O_7P$			
Guanosine, 8-[(phenylmethyl)amino]-, cyclic 3',5'-(hydrogen phosphate)	pH 1	255(4.30),288(4.00)	69-5310-73
	pH 11	263(4.24)	69-5310-73
$C_{17}H_{20}$			
Bicyclo[5.3.1]undeca-7,9-diene, 10-meth-yl-	C_6H_{12}	230(3.79),315(3.94)	35-5088-73
5H-Indeno[2,1-a]azulene, 4b,6,7,8,9,10-10b,11-octahydro-, cis	EtOH	259(3.06),266(3.20), 272(3.23)	78-1321-73
$C_{17}H_{20}BrNO_3$			
Pyridinium, 1-[2-(3,4-dimethoxyphenyl)-2-oxoethyl]-3-ethyl-, bromide	EtOH	233(4.28),276(4.19), 311(4.01)	94-2695-73
$C_{17}H_{20}BrN_2$			
Methanaminium, N-[4-bromo[4-(dimethyl-amino)phenyl]methylene]-2,5-cyclo-hexadien-1-ylidene]-N-methyl-	$MeNO_2$	630(3.79)	104-1766-73
$C_{17}H_{20}ClNO_3S$			
2H-1,4-Thiazine-5-carboxylic acid, 4-(chlorophenylacetyl)-3,4-dihydro-, 1,1-dimethylethyl ester	EtOH	281(3.87)	39-1321-73C
$C_{17}H_{20}ClNO_6S$			
Isoquinolinium, 3,4-dihydro-6,7-dimeth-oxy-2-methyl-3-(2-thienylmethyl)-, perchlorate	MeOH	248(4.45),313(4.10), 372(4.06)	83-0592-73
$C_{17}H_{20}ClNO_7$			
Isoquinolinium, 3-(2-furanylmethyl)-3,4-dihydro-6,7-dimethoxy-2-methyl-, per-chlorate	MeOH	213(4.35),251(4.41), 313(4.14),373(4.08)	83-0592-73
$C_{17}H_{20}ClNO_8$			
Isoquinolinium, 3-(ethoxycarbonyl)-4-(2-ethoxy-2-oxoethyl)-2-methyl-, perchlorate	EtOH	240(4.89),280(3.62), 343(4.00)	78-0213-73
$C_{17}H_{20}ClN_2$			
Methanaminium, N-[4-[chloro[4-(dimethyl-amino)phenyl]methylene]-2,5-cyclohexa-dien-1-ylidene]-N-methyl-, chloride	$MeNO_2$	626(4.80)	104-1766-73

Compound	Solvent	λ_{max}(log ϵ)	Ref.
$C_{17}H_{20}FN_2$			
Methanaminium, N-[4-[[4-(dimethylamino)-phenyl]fluoromethylene]-2,5-cyclohexa-dien-1-ylidene]-N-methyl-, fluoride	MeNO	588(4.53)	104-1766-73
	MeCN	586(--)	104-1766-73
	CH_2Cl_2	588(--)	104-1766-73
$C_{17}H_{20}F_3NO_3$			
1H,8H-Benzo[ij]quinolizin-8-one, 2,3,7,7a,9,10,10a,10b-octahydro-10-(2-oxopropyl)-6-(trifluoroacetyl)-	MeOH	321(4.50)	35-8427-73
isomer	MeOH	322(4.44)	35-8427-73
$C_{17}H_{20}NOS_2$			
Methanaminium, N-[[5-ethyl-2-[(2-oxo-2-phenylethyl)thio]-3-thienyl]meth-ylene]-N-methyl-, bromide	EtOH	252(4.18),275(4.00), 362(3.33)	70-2017-73
$C_{17}H_{20}NO_2S$			
Isoquinolinium, 3,4-dihydro-6,7-dimeth-oxy-2-methyl-3-(2-thienylmethyl)-, perchlorate	MeOH	248(4.45),313(4.10), 372(4.06)	83-0592-73
$C_{17}H_{20}NO_3$			
Isoquinolinium, 3-(2-furanylmethyl)-3,4-dihydro-6,7-dimethoxy-2-methyl-, per-chlorate	MeOH	213(4.35),251(4.41), 313(4.14),373(4.08)	83-0592-73
Pyridinium, 1-[2-(3,4-dimethoxyphenyl)-2-oxoethyl]-3-ethyl-, bromide	EtOH	233(4.28),276(4.19), 311(4.01)	94-2695-73
$C_{17}H_{20}NO_4$			
Isoquinolinium, 3-(ethoxycarbonyl)-4-(2-ethoxy-2-oxoethyl)-2-methyl-, per-chlorate	EtOH	240(4.89),280(3.62), 343(4.00)	78-0213-73
$C_{17}H_{20}NO_6P$			
Morphine 3-phosphate	pH 1	280(2.80)	95-1302-73
	pH 13	283(3.00)	95-1302-73
Morphine 6-phosphate	pH 1	286(2.82)	95-1302-73
	pH 13	300(3.08)	95-1302-73
$C_{17}H_{20}N_2$			
Deethylibogamine	MeOH	283(3.98),291(3.94)	24-1459-73
6,9-Methanocyclohept[b]indole-5(6H)-propanamine, 9,10-dihydro-, maleate	EtOH	231(4.45),288(3.79), 294(3.79)	78-4049-73
2-Naphthalenepropanenitrile, 1,2-di-hydro-3-(1-pyrrolidinyl)-	EtOH	228s(4.01),315(4.15)	22-0691-73
2-Naphthalenepropanenitrile, 3,4-di-hydro-1-(1-pyrrolidinyl)-	ether	256(4.03),288s(3.57), 300(3.52)	22-0691-73
$C_{17}H_{20}N_2O$			
1H-Cyclopenta[b]quinoline-9-carboxamide, N-butyl-2,3-dihydro-	EtOH	238(4.73),295(4.05), 308(4.09),322(4.13)	103-1005-73
1H-Indazole, 6,7-dihydro-3-(4-methoxy-phenyl)-1,6,6-trimethyl-	MeOH	254s(4.26),266(4.29)	24-3432-73
Methanone, bis[4-(dimethylamino)phenyl]-	FSO_3H at -75°	285(4.04),324(4.42)	59-0807-73
$C_{17}H_{20}N_2O_2$			
Isoxazole, 5-[[3-(1,1-dimethylethyl)-1,2-oxazol-5-yl]methyl]-3-phenyl-	n.s.g.	208(4.33),241(4.23)	32-0037-73

Compound	Solvent	$\lambda_{max}(\log \epsilon)$	Ref.
2,4-Pentadienoic acid, 2-cyano-5-(dimethylamino)-5-(4-methylphenyl)-, ethyl ester	CH_2Cl_2	284(3.84),403(4.30)	97-0132-73
2,4-Pentadienoic acid, 2-cyano-5-(ethylamino)-5-(4-methylphenyl)-, ethyl ester	CH_2Cl_2	390(4.30)	97-0132-73
$C_{17}H_{20}N_2O_2S$			
2,1-Benzisothiazole-5-ethanamine, 1,3-dihydro-1-methyl-N-(phenylmethyl)-, 2,2-dioxide, hydrochloride	EtOH	239(4.10),261(2.76), 263(2.76),268(2.81), 290(3.22)	4-0249-73
$C_{17}H_{20}N_2O_3$			
Cyclohexanecarboxylic acid, 4-(hydroxyimino)-3-(1H-indol-2-yl)-, ethyl ester, cis	MeOH	272(3.90),273(--), 281(3.89),289(3.79)	24-1459-73
[1,4]Diazepino[7,1-a]isoquinolin-2(3H)-one, 4-ethyl-4,5-dihydro-10,11-dimethoxy-	EtOH-HOAc	261(4.72),325(4.01), 395(3.07),413(3.03)	39-2830-73C
	EtOH-NaOH	236(4.55),262s(4.15), 271(4.17),284(4.20), 292(4.26),340s(3.76), 378s(4.07),395(4.20), 413(4.09)	39-2830-73C
$C_{17}H_{20}N_2O_4S$			
Acetamide, N-[3-hydroxy-2-(1-methylethylidene)-8-oxo-5-thia-1-azabicyclo-[4.2.0]oct-7-yl]-2-phenoxy-, [6R-(6aα,7β)]-	n.s.g.	223(4.37),261(3.73), 268(3.75),275(3.64)	39-2106-73C
1,4-Thiazepine-3-carboxylic acid, 2,3,4,5-tetrahydro-2,2-dimethyl-5-oxo-6-[(phenylacetyl)amino]-, methyl ester, (S)-	EtOH	235(3.98),305(3.72)	1-0677-73
1,4-Thiazepine-3-carboxylic acid, 2,3,4,7-tetrahydro-2,2-dimethyl-7-oxo-6-[(phenylacetyl)amino]-, methyl ester	MeOH	204(4.16),258(3.81), 315(3.98)	1-0677-73
$C_{17}H_{20}N_2O_5$			
2-Butenedioic acid, 2-[[4-(acetylamino)-phenyl]amino]-3-(2-propenyl)-, dimethyl ester, (E)-	MeOH	251(4.11),291(4.24)	24-0355-73
$C_{17}H_{20}N_2O_5S$			
Acetamide, N-[3-hydroxy-2-(1-methylethylidene)-8-oxo-5-thia-1-azabicyclo-[4.2.0]oct-7-yl]-2-phenoxy-, S-oxide, [6R-(6α,7β)]-	n.s.g.	219(4.11),238s(3.81), 262s(3.38),269(3.30), 276(3.18)	39-2105-73C
2(3H)-Isothiazoleacetic acid, α-(1-methylethyl)-3-oxo-4-[[(phenylmethoxy)-carbonyl]amino]-, methyl ester	MeOH	290(3.97)	88-5213-73
$C_{17}H_{20}N_2O_6S$			
2(3H)-Isothiazoleacetic acid, α-(1-methylethyl)-3-oxo-4-[[(phenylmethoxy)-carbonyl]amino]-, methyl ester, 1-oxide	MeOH	230(3.82),280(3.49)	88-2159-73
$C_{17}H_{20}N_2O_7$			
Isoxazole, 4,5-dihydro-3-(4-nitrophenyl)-5-(tetrahydro-6-methoxy-2,2-dimethylfuro[2,3-d]-1,3-dioxol-5-yl)-	$CHCl_3$	312(4.14)	33-1303-73

Compound	Solvent	λ_{max}(log ε)	Ref.
$C_{17}H_{20}N_2O_7S$			
Acetic acid, [[1-(2-hydroxy-2-methyl-1-oxopropyl)-4-oxo-3-[(phenoxyacetyl)-amino]-2-azetidinyl]thio]-, (2R-cis)-	n.s.g.	219(4.13),264(3.23), 270(3.28),276(3.20)	39-2105-73C
2(3H)-Isothiazoleacetic acid, α-(1-methylethyl)-3-oxo-4-[[(phenylmethoxy)-carbonyl]amino]-, methyl ester, 1,1-dioxide	MeOH	237(4.23),276(3.65)?	88-2159-73
$C_{17}H_{20}N_2O_9$			
6H-Furo[2',3':4,5]oxazolo[3,2-a]pyrimidin-6-one, 3-acetoxy-2,3,3a,9a-tetrahydro-2-(2,5,5-trimethyl-4-oxo-1,3-dioxolan-2-yl)-	MeOH	225(3.97),249(3.90)	35-4016-73
$C_{17}H_{20}N_3O_8P$			
3-Isoquinolinecarboxylic acid, 6-amino-1,2,3,4-tetrahydro-7-hydroxy-1-[3-hydroxy-2-methyl-5-[(phosphonooxy)methyl]-4-pyridinyl]-	pH 7.0	240s(4.06),305s(3.85), 325(3.98)	35-1621-73
$C_{17}H_{20}N_4$			
Propanedinitrile, [[[4-(dimethylamino)-phenyl]piperidino]methylene]-	MeCN	322(4.32),335(4.32)	39-0616-73B
$C_{17}H_{20}N_4O$			
1H-1,2,4-Triazolo[4,3-b]pyridazin-4-ium, 7-butyl-8-hydroxy-6-methyl-1-(phenylmethyl)-, hydroxide, inner salt	n.s.g.	226(3.78),280(3.92), 315(4.08)	48-0097-73
$C_{17}H_{20}N_4O_2$			
Benzo[g]pteridine-2,4(3H,4aH)-dione, 5,10-dihydro-3,7,8,10-tetramethyl-4a-(2-propenyl)-	6M HCl	268(4.07),303(3.81), 395(3.45)	5-1388-73
	pH 7	271(4.15),300s(3.83), 362(3.80)	5-1388-73
	MeOH	273(4.15),360(3.81)	5-1388-73
$C_{17}H_{20}N_4O_3S$			
1,2,4-Triazino[5,6-d][3,1]benzoxazepine-6-propanoic acid, 6,7-dihydro-6-methyl-3-(methylthio)-, ethyl ester	EtOH	205(4.31),238(4.43), 348(3.98),446(3.73)	78-0639-73
$C_{17}H_{20}N_4O_4$			
2-Cyclohexene-1-carboxaldehyde, 2-methyl-5-(1-methylethenyl)-, 2,4-dinitrophenylhydrazone	$CHCl_3$	388(4.58)(anom.)	22-2472-73
2,4,6-Heptatrienoic acid, 7-(2,3,6,7-tetrahydro-1,3,7-trimethyl-2,6-dioxo-1H-purin-8-yl)-, ethyl ester, (E,E,E)-	CH_2Cl_2	375(4.62),390(4.63)	54-0683-73
$C_{17}H_{20}N_4O_6$			
Bicyclo[2.2.2]octane-2-carboxylic acid, 5-[(2,4-dinitrophenyl)hydrazono]-1-methyl-, methyl ester	n.s.g.	367(4.39)	39-1757-73C
3-Cyclohexene-1-propanoic acid, 2-[(2,4-dinitrophenyl)hydrazono]-4-methyl-, methyl ester	n.s.g.	382(4.42)	39-1757-73C
Riboflavine	pH 0	245(3.97),312(3.99), 370(4.00)	33-1908-73
	pH 6	256(4.21),275s(--), 318(3.76),410(4.06)	33-1908-73

Compound	Solvent	λ_{max}(log ε)	Ref.
Riboflavine (cont.)	pH 13	245(4.25),318(4.40), 379(3.68)	33-1908-73
$C_{17}H_{20}N_6O$			
2-Propenenitrile, 3-[[4,6-bis(dimethyl-amino)-1,3,5-triazin-2-yl]oxy]-2-methyl-3-phenyl-	EtOH	226(4.69)	22-2039-73
$C_{17}H_{20}N_6O_4$			
1,3-Butanedione, 2-[4,6-bis(dimethyl-amino)-1,3,5-triazin-2-yl]-1-(4-ni-trophenyl)-	C_6H_{12}	230(3.29),274(3.08)	22-2039-73
$C_{17}H_{20}O$			
Bicyclo[3.1.0]hexan-3-one, 2-methyl-6-(1-methylethyl)-4-(phenylmethyl-ene)-, (1α,2β,5α,6α)-	MeOH	228(3.80),311(4.11)	39-2671-73C
5H-Cyclopent[a]anthracen-5-one, 1,2,3,3a,4,7,8,9,10,11b-decahydro-	EtOH	219(4.24),262(3.98), 306(3.72)	39-1251-73C
Methanone, (7,7-dimethyltricyclo-[4.1.1.0^{2,4}]oct-2-yl)phenyl-	C_6H_{12}	315(1.95)	22-1351-73
$C_{17}H_{20}O_2$			
Benzenemethanol, 2-hydroxy-3,4,5,6-tetramethyl-α-phenyl-	EtOH	287(3.43)	5-1893-73
Phenol, 2,2'-methylenebis[4,6-dimethyl-	dioxan	287(3.70)	126-0039-73L
$C_{17}H_{20}O_3$			
1,4-Anthracenedione, 5,6,8a,9,10,10a-hexahydro-2(or 3)-methoxy-8,10a-di-methyl-, cis	EtOH	276(4.07),355(2.59)	39-1352-73C
1,4-Anthracenedione, 5,6,7,8,8a,9,10,10a-octahydro-2(or 3)-methoxy-8a-methyl-5-methylene-, cis	EtOH	275(4.07),360(2.61)	39-1352-73C
Benzenemethanol, 2-hydroxy-3-[(2-hy-droxy-3,5-dimethylphenyl)methyl]-5-methyl-	dioxan	287(3.74)	126-0039-73L
4-Cyclohexene-1,2-diol, 3-[(1-hydroxy-cyclobutyl)phenylmethylene]-, (1α,2α,3Z)-	EtOH	250(4.02)	78-3553-73
1,4-Naphthalenedione, 6-ethenyl-5,6,7,8-tetrahydro-2(or 3)-methoxy-6-methyl-7-(1-methylethenyl)-, cis	EtOH	275(4.13),365(2.70)	39-1352-73C
9,10-Phenanthrenedione, 1,2,3,4,4a,10aα-hexahydro-7-methoxy-1α,4aα-dimethyl-	EtOH	226(4.24),286(3.77)	23-3620-73
$C_{17}H_{20}O_4$			
Benzene, 1,1'-methylenebis[3,4-dimeth-oxy-	n.s.g.	230s(4.19),281(3.80), 287s(3.73)	39-0891-73C
Benzenebutanoic acid, α-(1-methyl-2-oxo-cyclohexyl)-γ-oxo-	MeOH	241(4.29),275(3.48), 320(3.37)	115-0381-73
Benzenebutanoic acid, 4-methyl-γ-oxo-α-(2-oxocyclohexyl)-	MeOH	258(4.17),305(3.47), 338(3.46)	115-0381-73
Butanedioic acid, 2-(3,4-dihydro-2-naph-thalenyl)-2-methyl-, dimethyl ester	EtOH	265(4.12)	2-0131-73
4-Cyclohexene-1,2,3-triol, 6-[(1-hy-droxycyclobutyl)phenylmethylene]-	EtOH	252(4.26)	78-3553-73
isomer	EtOH	253(4.25)	78-3553-73
2-Naphthaleneheptanoic acid, γ,ζ-dioxo-5,6,7,8-tetrahydro-	EtOH	216(4.14),258(4.06)	39-1251-73C

Compound	Solvent	$\lambda_{max}(\log \epsilon)$	Ref.
$C_{17}H_{20}O_4S$			
2-Thiophenemethanol, 5-[5-[(tetrahydro-2H-pyran-2-yl)oxy]-3-penten-1-ynyl]-, acetate, (E)-	ether	298(4.38),313(4.31)	24-3621-73
$C_{17}H_{20}O_5$			
8aH-Fluorene-8a,9-dicarboxylic acid, 4b,5,6,7,8,9-hexahydro-7-hydroxy-1-methyl-, 9-methyl ester, (4bα,7α,8aα,9α)-	EtOH	263(2.43),273s(2.32)	44-0741-73
4H,9H-Furo[2',3',4':4,5]naphtho[2,1-c]-pyran-4,9-dione, 1,2,3,3a,5a,7,10b-10c-octahydro-7-methoxy-3a,10b-di-methyl- (antibiotic LL-Z1271α)	MeOH	257(4.12)	32-1271-73
isomer	MeOH	259(4.00)	32-1271-73
$C_{17}H_{20}O_6$			
1H-Indene-4,5,6-tricarboxylic acid, 2,3-dihydro-2,2-dimethyl-, trimethyl ester	EtOH	294(3.26)	44-2870-73
$C_{17}H_{20}O_7$			
4a(4H)-Naphthalenecarboxylic acid, 5-(acetoxymethyl)-1,5,8,8a-tetrahydro-2-methoxy-6-methyl-1,4-dioxo-, methyl ester	EtOH	274(4.00)	94-0528-73
Unknown phenol, m. 150-156°	EtOH	232(4.11),349(3.54)	94-0528-73
$C_{17}H_{20}O_{10}$			
2H-1-Benzopyran-2-one, 6-(β-D-gluco-pyranosyloxy)-5,7-dimethoxy-	n.s.g.	330(3.98)	105-0586-73
$C_{17}H_{21}BO_6$			
Boron, bis(acetato-O)(4,4-dimethyl-1-phenyl-1,3-pentanedionato-O,O')-, (T-4)-	CH_2Cl_2	337(4.39)	39-1796-73B
$C_{17}H_{21}ClN_2O_9$			
Uridine, 2'-chloro-2'-deoxy-, 3'-acetate 5'-(2-acetoxy-2-methylpropanoate)	MeOH	258(4.00)	35-4016-73
Uridine, 2'-chloro-2'-deoxy-5'-O-(2,4,4-trimethyl-5-oxo-1,3-dioxolan-2-yl)-, 3'-acetate	MeOH	259(4.00)	35-4016-73
$C_{17}H_{21}ClO_6$			
1,3-Dioxol-1-ium, 4,5-dihydro-4,4,5,5-tetramethyl-2-(4-phenyl-1,3-butadien-yl)-, perchlorate	$CHCl_3$	285(4.18)	104-0394-73
$C_{17}H_{21}ClO_8$			
1,3-Dioxol-1-ium, 2-[2-(1,3-benzodioxol-5-yl)-1-methylethenyl]-4,5-dihydro-4,4,5,5-tetramethyl-, perchlorate	$CHCl_3$	288(4.32),323(4.43), 408(4.35)	104-0394-73
$C_{17}H_{21}F_3N_2O$			
1H-Indole, 5-methoxy-2-methyl-3-[2-(1-pyrrolidinyl)ethyl]-4-(trifluoro-methyl)-	MeOH	228(4.40),305(4.00)	44-1504-73

Compound	Solvent	λ_{max}(log ε)	Ref.
$C_{17}H_{21}N$			
1H-Carbazole, 2,3,4,4a-tetrahydro-4a-(3-methyl-2-butenyl)-	EtOH	213(4.27),217(4.25), 223s(4.12),256(3.77)	39-1913-73C
1H-Carbazole, 2,3,4,9-tetrahydro-9-(3-methyl-2-butenyl)-	EtOH	232(4.48),281s(3.76), 287(3.81),294(3.80)	39-1913-73C
$C_{17}H_{21}NO_2$			
2-Cyclohexen-1-one, 2-acetyl-5,5-dimethyl-3-[(phenylmethyl)amino]-	EtOH	261(4.06),294(4.09)	94-1372-73
2-Cyclohexen-1-one, 3-[acetyl(phenylmethyl)amino]-5,5-dimethyl-	EtOH	288(4.07)	94-1372-73
4,6,8,10-Undecatetraen-3-one, 5-hydroxy-2,10-dimethyl-11-(1H-pyrrol-2-yl)-	EtOH	425(4.69)	39-1416-73C
$C_{17}H_{21}NO_3$			
2H-Benzo[a]quinolizine-2,4(3H)-dione, 1,6,7,11b-tetrahydro-3-(3-hydroxybutyl)-	EtOH	266(2.95)	70-1263-73
2(1H)-Pyridinone, 1-(3,4-dimethoxyphenethyl)-3-ethyl-	EtOH	232(4.08),286(3.81), 303(3.81)	94-2695-73
2(1H)-Pyridinone, 1-(3,4-dimethoxyphenethyl)-5-ethyl-	EtOH	232(4.19),284(3.68), 313(3.76)	94-2695-73
$C_{17}H_{21}NO_3S$			
2H-1,4-Thiazine-5-carboxylic acid, 3,4-dihydro-4-(phenylacetyl)-, 1,1-dimethylethyl ester	EtOH	286(4.05)	39-1321-73C
$C_{17}H_{21}NO_4$			
3,4-Azocinedicarboxylic acid, 1,4,5,6-7,8-hexahydro-1-phenyl-, dimethyl ester	MeOH	256(3.38),307(4.49)	77-0665-73
Preskimmianine (same spectrum in acid or base)	MeOH	218(4.67),232s(4.43), 249(4.22),257(4.23), 287(3.91),297(3.95), 309(4.00),321(4.09), 334(3.99)	78-1217-73
$C_{17}H_{21}N_2$			
Methanaminium, N-[4-[[4-(dimethylamino)-phenyl]methylene]-2,5-cyclohexadien-1-ylidene]-N-methyl-	98% HOAc	607.5(5.17)	39-2151-73B
$C_{17}H_{21}N_3$			
Benzenamine, N,N-diethyl-4-[(4-methylphenyl)azo]-	C_6H_{12}	407(4.52)	18-0194-73
	50% EtOH-acid	332(4.34),528(3.83)	18-0194-73
Benzenamine, 4-[(2,4-dimethylphenyl)-azo]-N,N,2-trimethyl-	C_6H_{12}	399(4.48)	18-3139-73
	50% EtOH-acid	342(4.25),525(4.10)	18-3139-73
$C_{17}H_{21}N_3O$			
4,7-Methano-1H-benzotriazole, 8-(1,1-dimethylethoxy)-3a,4,7,7a-tetrahydro-1-phenyl-, syn-endo	EtOH	218(4.10),287(3.99), 305(4.01)	12-0619-73
$C_{17}H_{21}N_3O_3$			
2H-Indol-2-one, 3-(dimorpholinomethylene)-1,3-dihydro-	EtOH	274(4.34),360(4.21)	95-1520-73

Compound	Solvent	λ_{max}(log ε)	Ref.
$C_{17}H_{21}N_3O_5$			
1H-Indole-3-carboxylic acid, 4,6-bis-(acetylamino)-5-hydroxy-1,2-dimethyl-, ethyl ester	MeOH	266(4.48),318(4.18)	103-1490-73
$C_{17}H_{21}N_4O_8PS$			
Riboflavine, 2-thio-, 5'-(dihydrogen phosphate)	n.s.g.	272(4.10),317(4.30), 400(3.86),490(4.16)	65-0918-73
$C_{17}H_{21}N_5O_2$			
1,3-Butanedione, 2-[4,6-bis(dimethylamino)-1,3,5-triazin-2-yl]-1-phenyl-	C_6H_{12}	227(4.76),273(3.59), 281(3.58),300(3.57)	22-2039-73
1H-Purine-2,6-dione, 7-(3-aminopropyl)-3,7-dihydro-1,3-dimethyl-8-(phenylmethyl)-, hydrochloride	n.s.g.	211(4.49),278(4.05)	73-1571-73
$C_{17}H_{21}N_5O_3S_2$			
Spiro[furo[2,3-d]thiazole-2(3H),4'-imidazolidine]-2'-thione, tetrahydro-5'-imino-1',3',3a-trimethyl-3-(4-nitrophenyl)-	EtOH	271(4.01)	94-1300-73
$C_{17}H_{21}N_5O_6$			
1H-Imidazole-4-carboximidamide, 5-(formylamino)-N-(phenylmethoxy)-1-β-D-ribofuranosyl-	pH 1	249(3.91)	94-1676-73
	pH 7	249(3.81)	94-1676-73
	pH 13	249(4.10)	94-1676-73
	EtOH	222s(4.17),256s(3.81)	94-1676-73
$C_{17}H_{21}O_2$			
1,3-Dioxol-1-ium, 4,5-dihydro-4,4,5,5-tetramethyl-2-(4-phenyl-1,3-butadienyl)-, perchlorate	$CHCl_3$	285(4.18)	104-0394-73
$C_{17}H_{22}$			
5H-Indeno[2,1-a]azulene, 4b,5a,6,7,8,9-10,10a,10b,11-decahydro-	EtOH	260(2.98),267(3.16), 274(3.22)	78-1321-73
$C_{17}H_{22}BrNO_2$			
Pyridinium, 1-[2-(3,4-dimethoxyphenyl)-ethyl]-3-ethyl-, bromide	EtOH	268(3.81)	94-2695-73
$C_{17}H_{22}IN_5O_6$			
Pyridinium, 3-[[(2,3-dihydro-3-methyl-2-oxo-1-β-D-ribofuranosyl-4(1H)-pyrimidinylidene)hydrazino]carbonyl]-1-methyl-, iodide	M HCl	275s(4.08),292(4.23)	35-1323-73
	pH 2.8	272(4.07),286s(4.06)	35-1323-73
	pH 6.2	272(4.06),286s(4.06)	35-1323-73
	pH 10.8	258s(4.03),331(4.02)	35-1323-73
$C_{17}H_{22}N_2$			
1H-Cyclopenta[b]quinolin-9-amine, N-butyl-2,3-dihydro-5-methyl-	EtOH	238(4.7),247(4.69), 333(4.45),346(4.49)	103-0490-73
1H-Cyclopenta[b]quinolin-9-amine, N-butyl-2,3-dihydro-7-methyl-	EtOH	224(4.13),248(4.24), 332(4.06),348(4.07)	103-0490-73
6,9-Methanocyclohept[b]indole-5(6H)-propanamine, 7,8,9,10-tetrahydro-, maleate	EtOH	231(4.52),286(3.83), 294(3.82)	78-4049-73
Spiro[bicyclo[2.2.1]heptane-2,10'(2'H)-pyrimido[1,2-a]indole], 1',3',4',10'a-tetrahydro-, maleate	EtOH	244(4.00),294(3.45)	78-4049-73

Compound	Solvent	λ_{max}(log ε)	Ref.
$C_{17}H_{22}N_2O$			
1H-Cyclopenta[b]quinolin-9-amine, N-butyl-2,3-dihydro-7-methoxy-	EtOH	228(4.48),253(4.66), 312(4.05),341(4.27), 356(4.28)	103-0490-73
$C_{17}H_{22}N_2O_2$			
Cyclopenta[5,6]pyrimido[2,1-a]isoquinoline, 1,2,3,3a,5,6,12,12a-octahydro-8,9-dimethoxy-, cis	EtOH	232(4.36),276(3.99), 314(3.91)	4-0021-73
hydrochloride	EtOH	231(4.44),277(4.10), 312(4.01)	4-0021-73
trans	EtOH	230(4.39),275(4.05), 313(3.96)	4-0021-73
trans, hydrochloride	EtOH	233(4.19),277(3.85), 316(3.76)	4-0021-73
1H-Indazol-4-ol, 4,5,6,7-tetrahydro-3-(4-methoxyphenyl)-1,6,6-trimethyl-	MeOH	258(4.26)	24-3432-73
2H-Pyrrol-3-ol, 2-[(3,4-dimethyl-1H-pyrrol-2-yl)methylene]-5-ethoxy-3-ethynyl-3,4-dihydro-4,4-dimethyl-, (E)-	CH_2Cl_2	323(4.37)	5-1067-73
$C_{17}H_{22}N_2O_3$			
[1,4]Diazepino[7,1-a]isoquinolin-2(3H)-one, 4-ethyl-4,5,7,8-tetrahydro-10,11-dimethoxy-	EtOH-NaOH	231(4.37),275(3.73), 333(4.26)	39-2830-73C
Propanamide, N-[2,6-dioxo-1-(2-phenylethyl)-3-piperidinyl]-2-methyl-	EtOH	210(4.24)	78-4071-73 +142-0043-73
1H-Pyrido[3,4-b]indole-1-propanoic acid, 2,3,4,9-tetrahydro-8-methoxy-2-methyl-, methyl ester	EtOH	223(4.32),269(4.03), 279s(3.97),283(3.90), 289(3.73)	35-7842-73
$C_{17}H_{22}N_2O_4$			
Butanoic acid, 4-[[2-(7-methoxy-1H-indol-3-yl)ethyl]methylamino]-4-oxo-, methyl ester	EtOH	224(4.17),271(3.76), 279s(3.73),290(3.59)	35-7842-73
$C_{17}H_{22}N_2O_5S$			
L-Cysteine, N-acetyl-S-(5,6-dimethoxy-1-methyl-1H-indol-3-yl)-, methyl ester	EtOH	232(4.43),295s(--), 307(3.97)	130-0191-73
$C_{17}H_{22}N_2O_9S_3$			
β-D-Glucopyranoside, 5-(methylthio)-1,3,4-thiadiazol-2-yl-1-thio-, 2,3,4,6-tetraacetate	n.s.g.	288(4.03)	48-0915-73
1,3,4-Thiadiazole-2(3H)-thione, 3-methyl-5-(2,3,4,6-tetra-O-acetyl-β-D-glucopyranosyl)thio]-	n.s.g.	323(4.11)	48-0915-73
1,3,4-Thiadiazole-2(3H)-thione, 5-(methylthio)-3-(2,3,4,6-tetra-O-acetyl-β-D-glucopyranosyl)-	n.s.g.	321(4.20)	48-0915-73
$C_{17}H_{22}N_2O_{10}$			
α-D-Glucopyranoside, methyl 6-deoxy-6-(3,4-dihydro-2,4-dioxo-1(2H)-pyrimidinyl)-, 2,3,4-triacetate	MeOH	260(4.01)	18-3165-73
Uridine, 5-O-(2,4,4-trimethyl-5-oxo-1,3-dioxolan-2-yl)-, 2'-acetate	MeOH	261(3.90)	35-4016-73

Compound	Solvent	λ_{max}(log ε)	Ref.
$C_{17}H_{22}N_3O_8P$			
L-Tyrosine, 3-amino-N-[[3-hydroxy-2-methyl-5-(phosphonooxy)methyl]-4-pyrimidinyl]methyl]-	pH 7.0	240s(3.93),294(3.72), 325(3.90)	35-1621-73
$C_{17}H_{22}N_4O_2$			
Benzo[g]pteridine-2,4(1H,3H)-dione, 5,10-dihydro-3,7,8,10-tetramethyl-5-(1-methylethyl)-	pH 5	340(3.83)	5-1388-73
	pH 9	325(3.79)	5-1388-73
	MeOH	335(3.63)	5-1388-73
	6M HCl	285(3.97),300(3.94)	5-1388-73
Benzo[g]pteridine-2,4(3H,4aH)-dione, 5,10-dihydro-3,7,8,10-tetramethyl-4a-(1-methylethyl)-	pH 7	363(3.72)	5-1388-73
	MeOH	365(3.77)	5-1388-73
	6M HCl	400(3.42)	5-1388-73
$C_{17}H_{22}N_4O_3$			
Benzo[g]pteridine-2,4(3H,4aH)-dione, 5,10-dihydro-4a-hydroxy-3,7,8,10-tetramethyl-5-(1-methylethyl)-	pH 3	320s(3.93),345(3.95)	5-1388-73
	MeCN	282(3.80),310s(3.91), 335(3.97)	5-1388-73
$C_{17}H_{22}N_4O_4$			
Isopulegonecarboxaldehyde, 2,4-dinitrophenylhydrazone	$CHCl_3$	396(4.62),446s(4.58) (anom.)	22-2472-73
Pulegonecarboxaldehyde, 2,4-dinitrophenylhydrazone	$CHCl_3$	371(4.30)(anom.)	22-2472-73
$C_{17}H_{22}N_4O_8S$			
Acetamide, N-[4-(aminothioxomethyl)-1-(2,3,5-tri-O-acetyl-β-D-ribofuranosyl)-1H-imidazol-5-yl]-	EtOH	268(3.92),313(3.87)	94-0692-73
$C_{17}H_{22}N_5O_6$			
Pyridinium, 3-[[(2,3-dihydro-3-methyl-2-oxo-1-β-D-ribofuranosyl-4(1H)-pyrimidinylidene)hydrazino]carbonyl]-1-methyl-, iodide	M HCl	275s(4.08),292(4.23)	35-1323-73
	pH 2.8	272(4.07),286s(4.06)	35-1323-73
	pH 6.2	272(4.06),286s(4.06)	35-1323-73
	pH 10.8	258s(4.03),331(4.02)	35-1323-73
$C_{17}H_{22}N_6O_5S$			
Glycine, N-[N-[N-[1-oxo-5-(1H-pyrrolo-[2,3-d]pyrimidin-4-yl)thio]pentyl]-glycyl]glycyl]-	pH 1	219(4.36),258(4.03), 311(4.11)	73-1438-73
	pH 13	220(4.33),248(4.00), 293(4.16)	73-1438-73
$C_{17}H_{22}O$			
Phenanthrene, 1,2,3,4,4a,10a-hexahydro-10-methoxy-1,4a-dimethyl-	n.s.g.	222(4.19),277(4.07)	23-3620-73
$C_{17}H_{22}OS$			
Benzenecarbothioic acid, O-neothujyl ester	CH_2Cl_2	249(3.85),287(4.08), 420(2.11)	39-1574-73C
Benzenecarbothioic acid, O-thujyl ester	CH_2Cl_2	249(3.86),287(4.07), 420(2.08)	39-1574-73C
$C_{17}H_{22}O_2$			
Cyclohexanol, 1-[(2-methoxyphenyl)ethynyl]-2,6-dimethyl-	EtOH	243(4.25),255(4.30), 292(3.79),301(3.79)	23-3620-73
Cyclohexanol, 1-[(3-methoxyphenyl)ethynyl]-2,6-dimethyl-	EtOH	244(4.19),252(4.19), 290(3.46),298(3.47)	23-3620-73
Cyclohexanol, 1-[(4-methoxyphenyl)ethynyl]-2,6-dimethyl-	EtOH	252(4.40),261(4.37), 286(3.62),297(3.52)	23-3620-73
Cyclopentaneacetic acid, 2-(5,6,7,8-tetrahydro-2-naphthalenyl)-	EtOH	208(3.98),217(3.83), 270(2.90),279(2.97)	39-1251-73C

Compound	Solvent	λ_{max}(log ε)	Ref.
Ethanone, 1-(2,6-dimethyl-1-cyclohexen-1-yl)-2-(3-methoxyphenyl)-	EtOH	208(4.20),275(3.48), 282(3.43),310(2.84)	23-3620-73
A-Nor-3-oxaestra-1,5(10),9(11)-trien-17β-ol, 2-methyl-	EtOH	212(4.05),242(4.02)	94-0335-73
8αH-isomer	EtOH	207(4.45),240(4.07)	94-0335-73
$C_{17}H_{22}O_3$			
1H-Benz[cd]azulene-6-acetic acid, 2,6,7,8,9,9a-hexahydro-6-hydroxy-, ethyl ester	C_6H_{12}	263s(2.77),268(2.95), 276(3.00)	44-1445-73
1H-Benz[e]inden-3-ol, 2,3,3a,4,5,9b-hexahydro-7-methoxy-3a-methyl-, acetate, [3S-(3α,3aα,9bβ)]-	MeOH	279(3.48)	78-3631-73
Chimgin	n.s.g.	260(4.27)	105-0646-73
1,3-Dioxolane, 4-(5-heptene-1,3-diynyl)-5-(5-hydroxy-1-pentenyl)-2,2-dimethyl-, trans-trans	ether	209(4.59),216(4.67), 243(3.71),255(4.00), 270(4.15),286(3.93)	39-0140-73C
9-Hexadecene-12,14-diynoic acid, 16-oxo-, methyl ester, (Z)-	EtOH	232(3.26),244(3.39), 257(3.66),272(3.84), 288(3.76)	39-0743-73C
4-Phenanthrenol, 1,2,3,4,4a,9,10,10b-octahydro-7-methoxy-, acetate, [4S-(4α,4aβ,10aβ)]-	MeOH	278(3.32),286(3.30)	19-0009-73
$C_{17}H_{22}O_3S$			
Bicyclo[3.1.1]hept-2-ene-6-methanol, 6-methyl-3-[1-(phenylsulfonyl)ethylidene]-, [1R-[1α,2(Z),5α,6β]]-	EtOH	267(3.08),272(2.88)	39-2319-73C
$C_{17}H_{22}O_4$			
Butanedioic acid, dispiro[2.1.2.3]dec-4-ylidenemethylene-, dimethyl ester	EtOH	210(4.00),250(3.48)	77-0859-73
2-Butenedioic acid, 2-[(dispiro-[2.1.2.3]dec-4-ylidene)methyl]-, dimethyl ester	EtOH	210(4.00),300(3.60)	77-0859-73
$C_{17}H_{22}O_4S$			
2(1H)-Naphthalenone, octahydro-6-[[(4-methylphenyl)sulfonyl]oxy]-	MeOH	273.2(2.66)	44-2077-73
α-D-xylo-Hex-5-enofuranose, 5-deoxy-6-S-methyl-1,2-O-(1-methylethylidene)-3-O-(phenylmethyl)-6-thio-	EtOH	245(3.70)	33-1310-73
$C_{17}H_{22}O_5$			
1H-Naphtho[1,8a-c]furan-7-propanoic acid, 3,3a,4,5,6,6a,7,8-octahydro-7-methyl-3,8-dioxo-, methyl ester, (3aα,6aα,7α,10aS*)-	n.s.g.	225(3.85)	78-2575-73
Ovatifolin	EtOH	209(4.23)	102-2469-73
$C_{17}H_{22}O_6$			
1H-Indene-4,5,6-tricarboxylic acid, 2,2,3a,6-tetrahydro-2,2-dimethyl-, trimethyl ester, trans	EtOH	264s(3.23)	44-2870-73
1H-Indene-4,5,6-tricarboxylic acid, 2,3,5,6-tetrahydro-2,2-dimethyl-, trimethyl ester, trans	EtOH	301(4.04)	44-2870-73
1H-3a,7-Methanoazulene-3,6-dicarboxylic acid, 2,3,4,7,8,8a-hexahydro-8-(hydroxymethyl)-8-methyl-4-oxo-, dimethyl ester, [3R-(3α,3aβ,7β,8α,8aα)]-	MeOH	230(3.67)	2-0991-73

Compound	Solvent	λ max(log ε)	Ref.
$C_{17}H_{22}O_6S$			
α-D-xylo-Hex-5-enofuranose, 5,6-dideoxy-1,2-O-(1-methylethylidene)-6-(methylsulfonyl)-3-O-(phenylmethyl)-, cis	EtOH	221(3.47)	33-1310-73
$C_{17}H_{22}O_7$			
4a(4H)-Naphthalenecarboxylic acid, 5-[(acetyloxy)methyl]-1,5,8,8a-tetrahydro-1-hydroxy-2-methoxy-6-methyl-4-oxo-, methyl ester, (1α,4aβ,5α,8aβ)-	EtOH	252(4.04)	94-0528-73
$C_{17}H_{23}ClO_7$			
1,3-Dioxol-1-ium, 4,5-dihydro-2-[2-(4-methoxyphenyl)-1-methylethenyl]-4,4,5,5-tetramethyl-, perchlorate	$CHCl_3$	298(4.18),388(4.23)	104-0394-73
$C_{17}H_{23}ClO_8$			
1,3-Dioxol-1-ium, 2-[2-(3,4-dimethoxyphenyl)ethenyl]-4,5-dihydro-4,4,5,5-tetramethyl-, perchlorate	$CHCl_3$	300(4.04),330(4.15), 427(3.26)	104-0394-73
$C_{17}H_{23}F_3N_2O$			
1H-Indole, 2,3-dihydro-5-methoxy-2-methyl-3-[2-(1-pyrrolidinyl)ethyl]-4-(trifluoromethyl)-, borane adduct	MeOH	232(4.43),308(4.00)	44-1504-73
$C_{17}H_{23}N$			
Bicyclo[10.2.2]hexadeca-12,14,15-triene-13-carbonitrile	EtOH	233(3.76),285(3.04)	49-0644-73
Isoquinoline, 1,2,3,4,5,6,7,8-octahydro-1-(2-phenylethyl)-, hydrochloride	EtOH	253(2.22),259(2.30), 264(2.19),268(2.12)	4-0217-73
$C_{17}H_{23}NO$			
4-Azaestra-1,3,5(10)-trien-17β-ol	EtOH	268(3.68)	28-0959-73A
Cyclohexanamine, N-[(1,2,3,4-tetrahydro-1-naphthalenyl)methylene]-, N-oxide	pentane	250(3.90)	33-2961-73
1-Oxa-3-azaspiro[5.5]undec-2-ene, 2-(2-phenylethyl)-, hydrobromide	EtOH	end absorption	4-0217-73
$C_{17}H_{23}NO_2$			
1-Cycloheptene-1-carboxylic acid, 2-[(phenylmethyl)amino]-, ethyl ester	EtOH	309(4.18)	1-2802-73
6H-Dibenzo[b,d]pyran-1-ol, 6a,7,10,10a-tetrahydro-6,6,9-trimethyl-3-(methylamino)-, (6aR-trans)-	EtOH	218(4.65),248(3.94), 292(3.23)	33-0510-73
1-Oxa-3-azaspiro[5.5]undec-2-ene, 2-[(2-methoxyphenyl)methyl]-, hydrochloride	EtOH	272(3.37),278(3.37)	4-0217-73
$C_{17}H_{23}NO_3$			
5,9b-Ethano-9bH-benz[e]indol-5(1H)-ol, 2,3,3a,4-tetrahydro-7,8-dimethoxy-3-methyl-, (3aα,5α,9bβ)-(±)-	MeOH	228(3.86),282(3.62)	33-0347-73
9-Hexadecene-12,14-diynoic acid, 16-amino-16-oxo-, methyl ester	EtOH	221s(3.84),232(3.71), 245(3.69),259(3.77), 274(3.59)	39-0743-73C
Piperidine, 1-[[4-(2-methyl-1-oxopropyl)phenoxy]acetyl]-	EtOH	214(4.27),267(4.25)	111-0574-73
Piperidine, 1-[[4-(1-oxobutyl)phenoxy]-acetyl]-	EtOH	213(4.26),267(4.26)	111-0574-73

Compound	Solvent	λ_{max}(log ϵ)	Ref.
$C_{17}H_{23}NO_4$			
Butanedioic acid, [1-(phenylmethyl)-amino]ethylidene]-, diethyl ester	EtOH	297(4.29)	1-2802-73
Morpholine, 4-[[4-(3-methyl-1-oxobutyl)-phenoxy]acetyl]-	EtOH	213(4.26),267(4.25)	111-0574-73
Morpholine, 4-[[4-(1-oxopentyl)phenoxy]-acetyl]-	EtOH	211(4.28),257(4.18)	111-0574-73
$C_{17}H_{23}NO_8S$			
1,2-Benzisothiazol-3(2H)-one, 2-(2,3,4,6-tetra-O-methyl-β-D-glucopyranosyl)-, 1,1-dioxide	MeOH	276(3.78),285(3.64)	5-1943-73
α-D-Glucopyranoside, 1,2-benzisothiazol-3-yl 2,3,4,6-tetra-O-methyl-, S,S-dioxide	MeOH	268(3.72)	5-1943-73
$C_{17}H_{23}NS_2$			
1-Naphthalenecarbodithioic acid, triethylamine salt	EtOH	326(4.08),348(4.14), 472(2.22)	143-0359-73
$C_{17}H_{23}N_3$			
9H-Pyrido[3,4-b]indole-4-propanamine, 3,4-dihydro-N,N,1-trimethyl-	pH 2	246(4.00),354(4.28)	103-0311-73
	EtOH	235(4.16),317(4.12)	103-0311-73
$C_{17}H_{23}N_3O_4$			
4H-Isoxazolo[3,4-d]azepine-6-carboxylic acid, 5,6,7,8-tetrahydro-3-hydroxy-, ethyl ester, benzylammonium salt	THF	260(3.82)	1-3251-73
$C_{17}H_{23}N_5O_4S$			
Glycine, N-[N-[1-oxo-5-(1H-pyrrolo[2,3-d]pyrimidin-4-ylthio)pentyl]glycyl]-, ethyl ester	pH 1	218(4.30),257(3.97), 310(4.06)	73-1438-73
	pH 13	222(4.29),247(3.92), 292(4.12)	73-1438-73
$C_{17}H_{23}O_3$			
1,3-Dioxol-1-ium, 4,5-dihydro-2-[2-(4-methoxyphenyl)-1-methylethenyl]-4,4,5,5-tetramethyl-, perchlorate	$CHCl_3$	298(4.18),388(4.23)	104-0394-73
$C_{17}H_{23}O_4$			
1,3-Dioxol-1-ium, 2-[2-(3,4-dimethoxyphenyl)ethenyl]-4,5-dihydro-4,4,5,5-tetramethyl-, perchlorate	$CHCl_3$	300(4.04),330(4.15), 427(3.26)	104-0394-73
$C_{17}H_{24}B_7Co_3$			
Cobalt, tris(η^5-2,4-cyclopentadien-1-yl)[μ_3-[η^4:η^4:η^5-nonahydrodicarbanonaborato(4-)], tri-(Co-Co)-	MeCN	248(4.40),294(4.55), 414(3.38),484(3.12), 648(3.36)	77-0706-73
$C_{17}H_{24}ClNO_6$			
1,3-Dioxol-1-ium, 2-[2-[4-(dimethylamino)phenyl]ethenyl]-4,5-dihydro-4,4,5,5-tetramethyl-, perchlorate	$CHCl_3$	282(3.97),370(3.28), 500(4.82)	104-0394-73
$C_{17}H_{24}N_2$			
9H-Carbazole-9-butanamine, 1,2,3,4-tetrahydro-α-methyl-, hydrochloride	EtOH	231(4.54),279(3.79), 286(3.84),293(3.82)	78-4045-73
5H-Cyclooct[b]indole-5-propanamine, 6,7,8,9,10,11-hexahydro-, hydrochloride	EtOH	231(4.48),280(3.79), 287(3.85),294(3.83)	78-4045-73

Compound	Solvent	$\lambda_{max}(\log \epsilon)$	Ref.
$C_{17}H_{24}N_2O$			
Benzamide, N-butyl-2-(cyclopentylidene-amino)-5-methyl-	EtOH	225(5.16),346(3.23)	103-0490-73
$C_{17}H_{24}N_2O_2$			
Oxazolidin-2-imine, N,3-diisopropyl-4-[(4-methoxyphenyl)methylene]-, (E)-	EtOH	225(4.12),280(4.23)	44-1051-73
$C_{17}H_{24}N_2O_3$			
Piperidine, 1-[[4-[1-(hydroxyimino)-butyl]phenoxy]acetyl]-	EtOH	212(4.29),258(4.20)	111-0574-73
Piperidine, 1-[[4-[1-(hydroxyimino)-2-methylpropyl]phenoxy]acetyl]-	EtOH	212(4.26)	111-0574-73
$C_{17}H_{24}N_2O_4$			
Morpholine, 4-[[4-[1-(hydroxyimino)-pentyl]phenoxy]acetyl]-	EtOH	213(4.33),266(4.33)	111-0574-73
$C_{17}H_{24}N_4O_3S$			
L-Leucine, N-[1-oxo-5-(1H-pyrrolo[2,3-d]pyrimidin-4-ylthio)pentyl]-	pH 1	220(4.27),258(3.89), 311(3.98)	73-1438-73
	pH 13	222(4.29),249(3.85), 294(4.05)	73-1438-73
$C_{17}H_{14}N_6O_3$			
4-Pyrimidinol, 2-(dimethylamino)-5,6-di-methyl-, carbonate (2:1)	EtOH	243(4.61),308(3.90)	54-0705-73
$C_{17}H_{14}N_6O_7$			
Isoleucine, N-[[(9-β-D-ribofuranosyl-9H-purin-6-yl)amino]carbonyl]-	pH 1-2	270s(--),277(4.30)	87-0139-73
	pH 5-7	270(4.32),277s(--)	87-0139-73
	pH 12	270(4.26),299(3.77)	87-0139-73
L-Leucine, N-[[(9-β-D-ribofuranosyl-9H-purin-6-yl)amino]carbonyl]-	pH 1-2	270s(--),277(4.34)	87-0139-73
	pH 5-7	270(4.38)	87-0139-73
	pH 12	271(4.30),298(3.81)	87-0139-73
$C_{17}H_{24}O$			
1-Undecen-3-one, 1-phenyl-, (E)-	EtOH	221(3.72),288(3.95)	12-0183-73
$C_{17}H_{24}O_2$			
Bicyclo[10.2.2]hexadeca-12,14,15-triene-13-carboxylic acid	EtOH	230(3.84),290(3.11)	49-0644-73
A-Nor-3-oxaestra-1,5(10)-dien-17β-ol, 2-methyl-	EtOH	225.5(3.86)	94-0335-73
Orcinol, 4-(3-p-menth-4-enyl)-, trans	EtOH	283(3.37)	32-0127-73
Spiro[3-cyclohexene-1,1'(2'H)-naphtha-lene]-2,2'-dione, 3',4',4'a,5',6',7'-8',8'a-octahydro-3,4-dimethyl-	C_6H_{12}	243(3.98)	28-0883-73A
$C_{17}H_{24}O_3$			
7H-Benz[e]inden-7-one, 1,2,3,3a,4,5,8-9,9a,9b-decahydro-3-hydroxy-3a-methyl-6-(2-oxopropyl)-, [3S-(3α,3aα,9aα,9bβ)]-	EtOH	249(4.13)	94-0335-73
2H-Cyclobuta[4,5]cyclopenta[1,2-b]furan-2-one, octahydro-4-(3-oxo-1-octenyl)-, [3aα,4α(E),4aα,6aα,6bα]-(±)-	n.s.g.	228(4.19)	39-0810-73C
$C_{17}H_{24}O_3S$			
2-Naphthalenol, decahydro-, 4-methyl-benzenesulfonate	MeOH	273.2(2.65)	44-2077-73

Compound	Solvent	λ_{max}(log ε)	Ref.
$C_{17}H_{24}O_3S_2$			
Spiro[1,3-dithiolane-2,8'(4'H)-naphtho-[1,2-b]furan]-2',7'(3'H,5'H)-dione, hexahydro-3',5'a,9'-trimethyl-, α-	EtOH	225(2.99),251(2.76), 305(2.42)	94-0296-73
β-	EtOH	226(3.04),249(2.86), 307(2.48)	94-0296-73
$C_{17}H_{24}O_4$			
1H-Indene-1-heptanoic acid, 5,6,7,7a-tetrahydro-2-hydroxy-5-oxo-, methyl ester	MeOH	230(3.46),314(4.33), 361(3.91)	78-1447-73
	MeOH-base	223(3.78),361(4.83)	78-1447-73
1H-Indene-3-heptanoic acid, 2,4,5,6-7,7a-hexahydro-2,6-dioxo-, methyl ester	MeOH	237(4.10),312(--), 362(--)	78-1447-73
$C_{17}H_{24}O_4S$			
7H-Benz[e]inden-7-one, 1,2,3,3a,4,5,8-9,9a,9b-decahydro-3a-methyl-3-[(methylsulfonyl)acetyl]-	EtOH	239(4.24),300(3.83)	94-0335-73
$C_{17}H_{24}O_5$			
2H-Cyclopenta[b]furan-2-one, 6-acetoxy-hexahydro-4-(3-oxo-1-octenyl)-	n.s.g.	224(4.10)	77-0119-73
2-Naphthaleneacetic acid, 1,2,3,5,6,7-8,8a-octahydro-2-(methoxycarbonyl)-8,8a-dimethyl-3-oxo-, methyl ester, (2α,8β,8aβ)-(±)-	MeOH	242(4.14)	23-2166-73
5αH-Santan-6:13-olide, 3β-acetoxy-2-oxo-	EtOH	286(1.43)	94-0296-73
$C_{17}H_{24}O_7$			
1-Cyclopentene-1-heptanoic acid, 3-acetoxy-2-(methoxycarbonyl)-5-oxo-, methyl ester	MeOH	238(4.11)	44-4412-73
	MeOH-KOH	252(3.89),422(3.92)	44-4412-73
$C_{17}H_{24}O_{10}$			
Geniposide	EtOH	236.5(4.08)	94-2684-73
$C_{17}H_{24}O_{11}$			
Cyclopenta[c]pyran-4,7-dicarboxylic acid, 1-(β-D-glucopyranosyloxy)-1,4a,5,6,7,7a-hexahydro-, 7-methyl ester (forsythid methyl ester)	MeOH	233.5(4.05)	94-0497-73
$C_{17}H_{25}ClN_4O_4S$			
Acetic acid, [[6-chloro-3-[[[[2-(diethylamino)ethyl]amino]oxoacetyl]amino]-2-pyridinyl]thio]-, ethyl ester	EtOH	236(4.2),284(4.0), 306(3.9)	103-0621-73
$C_{17}H_{25}ClO$			
2,5-Cyclohexadien-1-one, 4-chloro-2,6-bis(1,1-dimethylethyl)-4-(2-propenyl)-	n.s.g.	240(4.08)	70-1998-73
Spiro[2.5]octa-4,7-dien-6-one, 1-(chloromethyl)-5,7-bis(1,1-dimethylethyl)-	n.s.g.	270(4.24)	70-1998-73
$C_{17}H_{25}NO_2$			
5-Benzoxazolol, 4,7-bis(1,1-dimethylethyl)-2-ethyl-	EtOH	242(4.00),295(3.61)	39-0268-73C

Compound	Solvent	λ max(log ε)	Ref.
$C_{17}H_{25}NO_3$			
2-Piperidinone, 1-[2-(3,4-dimethoxyphenyl)ethyl]-3-ethyl-	EtOH	229(3.96),280(3.43)	94-2695-73
2-Piperidinone, 1-[2-(3,4-dimethoxyphenyl)ethyl]-5-ethyl-	EtOH	230(3.95),280(3.45)	94-2695-73
$C_{17}H_{25}NO_4$			
1H,5H-Benzo[ij]quinolizine-8-acetic acid, α-acetyldecahydro-10-oxo-, methyl ester	MeOH	255(3.28)	35-8427-73
8,12-Methano-1H,5H-cycloocta[ij]quinolizine-9-carboxylic acid, 2,3,6,7,7a-8,11,12,12a,12b-decahydro-10,12-dihydroxy-, methyl ester	MeOH	256(4.04)	35-8427-73
	MeOH-KOH	282(4.29)	35-8427-73
2-Piperidinone, 1-[2-(3,4-dimethoxyphenyl)-2-hydroxyethyl]-3-ethyl-	EtOH	231(3.97),279(3.57)	94-2695-73
2-Piperidinone, 1-[2-(3,4-dimethoxyphenyl)-2-hydroxyethyl]-5-ethyl-	EtOH	230(3.94),279(3.65)	94-2695-73
$C_{17}H_{25}N_3O$			
Propanedinitrile, [2-methyl-1-[3-(4-morpholinyl)-3-cyclohexen-1-yl]propyl]-	MeOH	224(4.00),294(2.20)	49-0447-73
$C_{17}H_{25}N_5O_4$			
Adenosine, N-cycloheptyl-	pH 1	265.5(4.34)	87-0358-73
	H_2O	271(4.29)	87-0358-73
	pH 13	271(4.32)	87-0358-73
$C_{17}H_{25}N_5O_5$			
Adenosine, 5'-O-(1-ethoxyethyl)-2',3'-O-(1-methylethylidene)-	MeOH	260(4.11)	18-3228-73
$C_{17}H_{25}N_7O_6$			
Adenosine, N-[[[1-(aminocarbonyl)-2-methylbutyl]amino]carbcnyl]-	pH 1-2	270s(--),277(4.36)	87-0139-73
	pH 5-7	269(4.37),277s(--)	87-0139-73
	pH 12	270(4.12),298(4.27)	87-0139-73
Adenosine, N-[[[1-(aminocarbonyl)-3-methylbutyl]amino]carbonyl]-	pH 1-2	270s(--),277(4.35)	87-0139-73
	pH 5-7	269(4.36),277s(--)	87-0139-73
	pH 12	270(4.05),299(4.32)	87-0139-73
$C_{17}H_{26}$			
Benzene, (2,2,6,6-tetramethyl-3-hepten-4-yl)-, cis	EtOH	237(4.08)	35-1586-73
trans	EtOH	230(3.85)	35-1586-73
Bicyclo[10.2.2]hexadeca-12,14,15-triene, 13-methyl-	EtOH	215(3.78),270(2.51)	49-0644-73
Bicyclo[3.2.1]octa-2,6-diene, 1,2,3,5-6,7,8,8-octamethyl-4-methylene-	EtOH	247(4.14)	35-4096-73
$C_{17}H_{26}N_2O_5S$			
4-Thia-1-azabicyclo[4.2.0]oct-2-ene-2-carboxylic acid, 7-[[(1,1-dimethylethoxy)carbonyl]amino]-, 1,1-dimethylethyl ester, trans	EtOH	262(3.60),305(3.57)	39-1321-73C
$C_{17}H_{26}N_6O$			
4H-Pyrazolo[3,4-d]pyrimidin-4-one, 1,5-dihydro-5,?-bis(1-piperidinylmethyl)-	EtOH	253(3.74)	103-1280-73

Compound	Solvent	$\lambda_{max}(\log \epsilon)$	Ref.
$C_{17}H_{26}N_6O_5$			
9H-Purin-6-amine, 9-[3-deoxy-3-[2-(dimethylamino)-2-oxoethyl]-β-D-allo-furanosyl]-N,N-dimethyl-	MeOH	275(4.30)	44-0193-73
$C_{17}H_{26}O$			
Thujopsene, 3-acetyl-	EtOH	275(3.91)	54-0985-73
$C_{17}H_{26}O_2$			
Bicyclo[9.3.1]pentadec-11-ene-1-carbox-aldehyde, 12-methyl-15-oxo-	EtOH	252(4.03)	39-0393-73C
2,5-Cyclohexadiene-1,4-dione, 2-undecyl-	EtOH	249(3.8)	1-3211-73
Spiro[5.11]heptadec-1-ene-3,7-dione	EtOH	221(3.79),246(3.71)	39-0393-73C
$C_{17}H_{26}O_3$			
1H-2-Benzopyran-6,8-diol, 3-heptyl-3,4-dihydro-7-methyl-	MeOH	225s(3.9),281(3.06)	33-2694-73
	MeOH-NaOH	285(3.27),339(2.12) (changing)	33-2694-73
2,5-Cyclohexadiene-1,4-dione, 2-methoxy-3,5-dipentyl-	EtOH	278(4.2),380(2.8)	1-3211-73
Cyclohexanepropanoic acid, 2-(3,4-dimethyl-2-oxo-3-cyclohexen-1-yl)-	C_6H_{12}	242(4.04)	28-0883-73
1H-Indene-3-propanoic acid, 2,4,5,6-7,7a-hexahydro-α,α,7,7-tetramethyl-2-oxo-, methyl ester, (S)-	EtOH	239(4.08)	78-1465-73
$C_{17}H_{26}O_5$			
1-Cyclopentene-1-heptanoic acid, 2-(ethoxycarbonyl)-5-oxo-, ethyl ester	MeOH	246(3.99)	44-4412-73
2H-Furo[3,2-b]pyran-2-one, 3-ethylhexahydro-7-hydroxy-3a-methoxy-6,6-dimethyl-5-(1,3-pentadienyl)-	MeOH	243(4.32)	88-2823-73
$C_{17}H_{26}O_{10}$			
Cyclopenta[c]pyran-4-carboxylic acid, 1-(β-D-glucopyranosyloxy)-1,4a,5,6-7,7a-hexahydro-5-hydroxy-7-methyl-, methyl ester (dihydrocornin)	EtOH	238(4.05)	1-2581-73
Cyclopenta[c]pyran-4-carboxylic acid, 1-(β-D-glucopyranosyloxy)-1,4a,5,6-7,7a-hexahydro-7-(hydroxymethyl)-, methyl ester (dihydrogeniposide)	MeOH	238(4.07)	94-0497-73
isomer	MeOH	238.5(4.12)	94-0497-73
Loganin	EtOH	236(4.11)	95-0030-73
$C_{17}H_{26}O_{11}$			
Morroniside	MeOH	240(4.07)	94-0846-73
$C_{17}H_{26}O_{12}$			
Lamalbid	MeOH	235(3.96)	88-4037-73
$C_{17}H_{27}$			
1-Pentalenylium, 1,3a,4,6a-tetrahydro-1,2,3,3a,4,4,5,6,6a-nonamethyl-, deloc-1,2,3, cis	H_2SO_4	326(3.66)	88-3891-73
$C_{17}H_{27}NO$			
2(3H)-Naphthalenone, 1-[1-(diethylamino)-1-propenyl]-4,4a,5,6,7,8-hexahydro-	C_6H_{12}	237(4.24)	28-0803-73A

Compound	Solvent	λ_{max}(log ε)	Ref.
$C_{17}H_{27}NO_3$			
7-Oxabicyclo[4.1.0]hept-3-ene-2,5-dione, 1,4-bis(1,1-dimethylethyl)-3-(propylamino)-	EtOH	214(3.91),280(3.67), 377(3.65)	39-0268-73C
1-Piperidineethanol, α-(3,4-dimethoxyphenyl)-3-ethyl-	EtOH	230(3.79),279(3.43)	94-2695-73
$C_{17}H_{27}NO_6$			
2,3-Pyridinedicarboxylic acid, 1,4,5,6-tetrahydro-1-[4-(2-methyl-1,3-dioxolan-2-yl)butyl]-, dimethyl ester	MeOH	298(4.30)	107-0073-73
$C_{17}H_{28}Cl_2N_4O_8$			
Benzenemethanaminium, N-[2-(dimethylamino)-1-[(dimethyliminio)methyl]ethenyl]-N-[(dimethylamino)methylene]-, diperchlorate	H_2O	206(4.32),308(4.51)	73-2633-73
$C_{17}H_{28}N_2O$			
1-Cyclohexene-1-carbonitrile, 2-(dibutylamino)-4,4-dimethyl-6-oxo-	EtOH	232(3.89),270(4.40)	70-0811-73
$C_{17}H_{28}N_2O_2$			
2-Cyclopenten-1-one, 2-hydroxy-3,5-bis-(1-piperidinylmethyl)-	EtOH	262(3.75)	44-0551-73
$C_{17}H_{28}N_8O$			
4H-Pyrazolo[3,4-d]pyrimidin-4-one, 1,5-dihydro-5,?-bis[(4-methyl-1-piperazinyl)methyl]-	EtOH	253(3.91)	103-1280-73
$C_{17}H_{28}O_2$			
2-Pentenoic acid, 3-methyl-5-(2,6,6-trimethyl-1-cyclohexen-1-yl)-, ethyl ester (β-cyclofarnesylic acid ethyl ester)	EtOH	215(4.26)	65-2047-73
$C_{17}H_{28}O_6$			
2-Butenedioic acid, (E)-, mono(11-carboxy-1-methylundecyl) ester	MeOH	213(3.91)	78-3687-73
$C_{17}H_{29}N$			
Pyridine, 2-methyl-5-undecyl-	MeOH	268(3.61)	103-1507-73
$C_{17}H_{30}O_2$			
2,4-Dodecadienoic acid, 3,7,11-trimethyl-, ethyl ester, trans-trans	hexane	262(4.45)	98-0354-73
2-cis-4-trans	hexane	264(4.25)	98-0354-73
$C_{17}H_{34}Si_3$			
Silane, [1,6-dimethyl-3-(trimethylsilyl)-1,2-hexadien-4-yne-1,6-diyl]bis-[trimethyl-	n.s.g.	234(3.17),250(3.07)	39-0599-73B
Silane, [1-(1-pentynyl)-1,2-propadien-1-yl-3-ylidene]tris[trimethyl-	n.s.g.	234(4.11),243(4.16), 255(4.17)	39-0599-73B
$C_{17}H_{36}Ge_4$			
Germane, 3,4-pentadien-1-yne-1,3-diyl-5-ylidenetetrakis[trimethyl-	EtOH	245(4.11)	35-3324-73

Compound	Solvent	$\lambda_{max}(\log \epsilon)$	Ref.
Germane, 1,3-pentadiyn-1-yl-5-ylidenetetrakis[trimethyl-	EtOH	224(4.85),256(2.84), 270(2.90),286(2.72)	35-3324-73
$C_{17}H_{36}Si_4$			
Silane, (1,2-pentadien-4-yne-1,1,3,5-tetrayl)tetrakis[trimethyl-	EtOH	258(4.26)	35-3324-73

Compound	Solvent	$\lambda_{max}(\log \epsilon)$	Ref.
$C_{18}H_3F_{24}NO$			
Pyridine, 2,5-difluoro-3-methoxy-4,6-bis(undecafluorocyclohexyl)-	C_6H_{12}	288(3.68)	39-1710-73C
$C_{18}H_8Br_2N_2O$			
Benz[g]indeno[1,2,3-de]phthalazin-7(6H)-one, 3,11-dibromo-	HOAc	252(4.36),267(4.22), 291(4.15),322(3.89), 363s(3.74),378(3.76)	115-0145-73A
$C_{18}H_8Br_2O_3$			
7H-Benzo[c]fluorene-6-carboxylic acid, 2,9-dibromo-7-oxo-	EtOH	220(4.53),246(4.64), 268(4.90),287(4.42), 297(4.44),335s(3.92), 438(3.03)	115-0145-73A
$C_{18}H_8N_2$			
8,9-Fluoranthenedicarbonitrile	MeCN	215(4.44),234(4.61), 242(4.61),260(4.31), 288(4.28),299(4.56), 312(3.77),321s(3.67), 327(3.97),366(4.09), 382(4.16)	33-3004-73
$C_{18}H_9BrN_2O$			
7H-Benzimidazo[2,1-a]benz[de]isoquinolin-7-one, 2-bromo-	HOAc	283(4.17),294(4.18), 358(4.03),390(4.11)	4-0705-73
7H-Benzimidazo[2,1-a]benz[de]isoquinolin-7-one, 5-bromo-	EtOH	269(4.32),284(4.26), 296(4.26),344(3.83), 390(4.03)	4-0705-73
	HOAc	284(4.26),295(4.26), 343s(3.88),386(4.07)	4-0705-73
$C_{18}H_9ClO_3$			
Benz[a]anthracene-7,12-dione, 8(or 11)-chloro-11(or 8)-hydroxy-	benzene	423(3.85)	40-1328-73
$C_{18}H_9ClO_4$			
Benz[a]anthracene-7,12-dione, x-chloro-8,11-dihydroxy-	benzene	495(4.11),511(4.08)	40-1328-73
$C_{18}H_9NO_5$			
8H-Bis[1,3]benzodioxolo[6,5,4-de:5',6'-g]quinolin-8-one (cassameridine)	EtOH	249(4.50),272(4.35), 320(4.16),349(4.06), 386(3.98),440(3.91)	78-2245-73
	EtOH-HCl	259(4.60),290(4.51), 380(4.16),508(3.74)	78-2245-73
$C_{18}H_9N_3O_3$			
7H-Benzimidazo[2,1-a]benz[de]isoquinolin-7-one, 1-nitro-	HOAc	281(4.11),291(4.08), 387(4.06)	4-0705-73
7H-Benzimidazo[2,1-a]benz[de]isoquinolin-7-one, 2-nitro-	HOAc	273(4.33),281(4.23), 292(4.38),385(4.03)	4-0705-73
7H-Benzimidazo[2,1-a]benz[de]isoquinolin-7-one, 3-nitro-	HOAc	283(4.18),343s(4.00), 403(4.27)	4-0705-73
7H-Benzimidazo[2,1-a]benz[de]isoquinolin-7-onem 4-nitro-	HOAc	288(4.21),347(3.79), 404(3.81)	4-0705-73
7H-Benzimidazo[2,1-a]benz[de]isoquinolin-7-one, 5-nitro-	HOAc	282(4.41),292(4.44), 397(3.93)	4-0705-73
7H-Benzimidazo[2,1-a]benz[de]isoquinolin-7-one, 6-nitro-	HOAc	284(4.32),294(4.34), 344(3.81),399(3.97)	4-0705-73

Compound	Solvent	$\lambda_{max}(\log \epsilon)$	Ref.
$C_{18}H_{10}BrNO_2S$			
3-Thiophenecarbonitrile, 5-(4-bromobenzoyl)-4-hydroxy-2-phenyl-	CH_2Cl_2	353(4.33)	48-0497-73
$C_{18}H_{10}Br_2$			
Chrysene, 2,8-dibromo-	C_6H_{12}	249(4.20),267(3.92), 277(5.26),299(4.30), 310(4.20),323(3.97), 348(2.59),355(2.53), 366(2.23)	5-1112-73
$C_{18}H_{10}Br_2N_2O_2$			
Benz[a]anthracene-7,12-dione, 8,11-diamino-9,10-dibromo-	benzene	592(4.11),634(4.00)	40-1328-73
Benzo[g]phthalazine-1,4-dione, 7-bromo-5-(4-bromophenyl)-2,3-dihydro- (2λ,3ε)	EtOH	253(4.69),342(4.94), ?(3.95)	115-0145-73A
$C_{18}H_{10}Br_2S$			
Naphtho[1,2-b]thiophene, 6-bromo-3-(4-bromophenyl)-	MeOH	250(4.72),274(4.63), 333(3.32)	5-1112-73
$C_{18}H_{10}Cl_4$			
Benzene, [phenyl(2,3,4,5-tetrachloro-2,4-cyclopentadien-1-ylidene)methyl]-	hexane	220(4.15),244(4.01), 362(4.34),483(2.69)	88-5101-73
$C_{18}H_{10}Cl_4O_3$			
2-Propen-1-one, 3,3'-oxybis[1-(3,4-dichlorophenyl)-	dioxan	270(4.35),307(4.59)	24-0435-73
$C_{18}H_{10}N_2O$			
7H-Benzimidazo[2,1-a]benz[de]isoquinolin-7-one	EtOH	272s(4.45),283(4.22), 293(4.26),382(4.11)	4-0705-73
	HOAc	271(4.02),282(4.13), 292(4.17),384(4.07)	4-0705-73
Benz[g]indeno[1,2,3-de]phthalazin-7(6H)-one	n.s.g.	247(4.64),272(4.70), 291(4.63),315(4.21), 326s(4.18)	115-0145-73A
Benz[h]indeno[1,2,3-de]phthalazin-3(2H)-one	HOAc	287(4.45),310s(4.18), 375(3.95)	115-0145-73A
$C_{18}H_{10}N_2O_3S$			
1H-Indene-1,3(2H)-dione, 2-(5-oxo-1-phenyl-2-thioxo-4-imidazolidinylidene)-	EtOH	226(4.41),240(4.30), 275(4.07),405(4.44)	63-1307-73
$C_{18}H_{10}O_2S_2$			
3,3'-Bibenzo[b]thiophene-2,2'-dicarboxaldehyde	EtOH	232(4.47),250s(4.29), 303(4.39),345s(3.86)	44-2814-73
$C_{18}H_{10}O_2S_3$			
6H-[1,2]Dithiolo[1',5':1,5][1,2]dithiolo[4,3-c][1]benzopyran-10-S^{IV}-6-one, 8-phenyl-	EtOH	258(4.64),280(4.47), 325(4.38),479(4.08)	39-1022-73C
$C_{18}H_{10}O_3S_2$			
6H-[1,2]Dithiolo[1',5':2,3][1,2]oxathiolo[4,5-c][1]benzopyran-10-S^{IV}-6-one, 8-phenyl-	EtOH	231(4.46),250(4.34), 280(4.18),293(4.18), 293(4.18),327(4.15), 436(4.53)	39-1022-73C

Compound	Solvent	λ_{max}(log ϵ)	Ref.
$C_{18}H_{10}O_4$			
Benz[a]anthracene-7,12-dione, 8,11-dihydroxy-	benzene	496(4.08),514(4.08)	40-1328-73
5,12-Naphthacenedione, 1,4-dihydroxy-	CH_2Cl_2	464(4.1)	22-2856-73
$C_{18}H_{10}O_5W$			
Tungsten, pentacarbonyl(diphenylmethylene)-, (OC-6-21)-	hexane	232(4.67),485(4.02)	35-5833-73
$C_{18}H_{10}O_8$			
2(3H)-Benzofuranone, 5,6-dihydroxy-3-[3-hydroxy-4-(4-hydroxyphenyl)-5-oxo-2(5H)-furanylidene]-	EtOH	257(4.14),275(4.10), 287s(4.03),364s(3.70), 497(4.24)	39-1529-73C
$C_{18}H_{10}S_2$			
Naphtho[2',3':4,5]thieno[3,2-b][1]benzothiophene	C_6H_{12}	208(3.64),236(3.67), 253(3.63),273(3.67), 282(3.67),293(3.68), 309(3.61),320(3.63), 335(3.61),353(3.62), 375(3.62)	39-0734-73C
$C_{18}H_{10}S_4$			
Benzo[1,2-b:4,3-b']dithiophene, 2-(2-thieno[2,3-b]thien-2-ylethenyl)-	benzene	300(4.13),364(4.31), 383(4.36),404(4.20)	35-3692-73
$C_{18}H_{11}BrClOP$			
10H-Phenoxaphosphine, 7-bromo-2-chloro-10-phenyl-	EtOH	239(4.26),247s(4.23), 268(3.26),275(3.33), 289s(3.43),301(3.61), 309(3.64)	39-1972-73C
$C_{18}H_{11}BrClO_2P$			
10H-Phenoxaphosphine, 7-bromo-2-chloro-10-phenyl-, 10-oxide	EtOH	235(4.56),247s(4.49), 268(3.45),276(3.47), 290s(3.52),301(3.67), 310(3.68)	39-1972-73C
$C_{18}H_{11}BrN_2OS$			
Phenol, 4-bromo-2-[(naphtho[2,3-d]thiazol-2-ylimino)methyl-	benzene	290(4.28),408(4.27), 416(4.27)	80-1781-73
	EtOH	227(--),245(--), 260(--),268(--), 287(--),315(--), 404(--)	80-1781-73
	ether	247(4.67),287(4.45), 404(4.38)	80-1781-73
	CH_2Cl_2	247(4.66),287(4.44), 409(4.37)	80-1781-73
3-Thiophenecarbonitrile, 4-amino-5-(4-bromobenzoyl)-2-phenyl-	CH_2Cl_2	378(4.03)	48-0497-73
$C_{18}H_{11}NO$			
Fluorantheno[8,9-d]oxazole, 9-methyl-	EtOH	235(4.7),290s(4.5), 298(4.7),325(3.7), 347(3.7),360(3.8)	103-0561-73
$C_{18}H_{11}NOS_2$			
Benzenepropanenitrile, β-oxo-α-(5-phenyl-3H-1,2-dithiol-3-ylidene)-	C_6H_{12}	232(4.52),292(4.19), 444(4.37)	33-0597-73

Compound	Solvent	λ max (log ε)	Ref.
Benzenepropanenitrile, β-oxo-α-(5-phenyl-3H-1,2-dithiol-3-ylidene)- (cont.)	EtOH	229(4.50),300(4.17), 440(4.44)	33-0597-73
$C_{18}H_{11}NO_2S$			
3-Thiophenecarbonitrile, 5-benzoyl-4-hydroxy-2-phenyl-	CH_2Cl_2	351(4.28)	48-0497-73
$C_{18}H_{11}NO_3$			
Benz[a]anthracene-7,12-dione, 8(or 11)-amino-11(or 8)-hydroxy-	benzene	556(3.85),597(3.70)	40-1328-73
$C_{18}H_{11}NO_5$			
9H-Pyrano[2,3-g]-1,2-benzisoxazol-9-one, 3-methyl-7-piperonyl-	n.s.g.	224(4.4),265(4.5), 309(4.4)	2-0541-73
$C_{18}H_{11}N_3$			
Propanedinitrile, (9(10H)-acridinylideneethylidene)-	EtOH	253(4.65),318(4.0), 570(4.5)	18-0283-73
$C_{18}H_{11}N_3O$			
7H-Benzimidazo[2,1-a]benz[de]isoquinolin-7-one, 1-amino-	EtOH	273(4.47),303(4.26), 335(3.90),440(4.11), 456(4.11)	4-0705-73
$C_{18}H_{11}N_3O_3S$			
Phenol, 2-[(naphtho[2,3-d]thiazol-2-ylimino)methyl]-4-nitro-	benzene	287(4.37),398(4.21), 413(4.20)	80-1781-73
	EtOH	231(--),258(--), 265(--),301(--), 312(--),374(--), 450(--)	80-1781-73
	ether	267(4.53),284(4.58), 307(4.37),393(4.34), 406(4.32)	80-1781-73
	CH_2Cl_2	243(4.57),266(4.50), 284(4.51),310(4.31), 397(4.31),411(3.91)	80-1781-73
Phenol, 2-[(naphtho[2,3-d]thiazol-2-ylimino)methyl]-6-nitro-	benzene	398(4.29),413(4.26)	80-1781-73
	EtOH	232(--),262(--), 267(--),302(--), 313(--),413(--)	80-1781-73
	ether	243(4.51),269(4.43), 284(4.48),307(4.30), 394(4.31),406(4.30)	80-1781-73
	CH_2Cl_2	243(--),283(--), 308(--),394(--), 410(--)	80-1781-73
$C_{18}H_{11}N_5$			
2H-1,2,3-Triazolo[4,5-f]quinoline, 2-(6-quinolinyl)-	EtOH	225(4.72),270(4.83), 295(4.68),340(4.61)	78-0221-73
$C_{18}H_{11}N_5O_{11}$			
Pyridinium, 1-(2,4-dinitrophenyl)-, 3,5-dinitrosalicylate	EtOH	228(4.56),344(4.20)	39-2949-73C
$C_{18}H_{12}$			
Benzo[3,4]cyclobut[1,2-a]acenaphthylene, 6b,10b-dihydro-	$C_5H_{11}Me$	213(4.51),226(4.63), 291(3.90)	35-7391-73
[2,2,2](1,3,5)-Cyclophane-1,9,17-triene	EtOH	252(3.29),325(1.95)	35-3201-73

Compound	Solvent	$\lambda_{max}(\log \epsilon)$	Ref.
$C_{18}H_{12}BrN_3O_3$			
1H-Benzimidazole, 2-[5-(4-bromophenyl)-2-furanyl]-1-methyl-5-nitro-	EtOH	223(4.18),239(4.10),261(4.20),329(4.43),348(4.44),362(4.55)	73-1700-73
$C_{18}H_{12}Br_2O$			
17H-Cyclopenta[a]phenanthren-17-one, 15,15-dibromo-15,16-dihydro-11-methyl-	EtOH	268(4.68),303(4.32),315s(4.12),369(3.29),384(3.31)	39-2236-73C
$C_{18}H_{12}ClNO_3$			
9H-Pyrano[2,3-g]-1,2-benzisoxazol-9-one, 7-(4-chlorophenyl)-3,8-dimethyl-	n.s.g.	221(4.4),252(4.5),313(3.8)	2-0541-73
$C_{18}H_{12}ClNO_5S$			
Furan, 2-[2-(3-chlorophenyl)-1-(phenylsulfonyl)ethenyl]-5-nitro-	EtOH	211(4.69),231s(4.54),286(4.53),323s(4.14)	73-1705-73
Furan, 2-[2-(4-chlorophenyl)-1-(phenylsulfonyl)ethenyl]-5-nitro-	EtOH	209(4.51),219(4.49),296(4.55)	73-1705-73
$C_{18}H_{12}ClN_3O$			
Ethanone, [(4-chlorophenyl)imino]di-2-pyridinyl-	EtOH	237(4.26),274(4.09),338(3.32)	12-2027-73
$C_{18}H_{12}ClN_3O_3$			
1H-Benzimidazole, 2-[5-(4-chlorophenyl)-2-furanyl]-1-methyl-5-nitro-	EtOH	224(4.19),239s(4.12),261(4.20),327(4.44),347(4.44),364(4.46)	73-1700-73
$C_{18}H_{12}F_6O_2$			
Benzeneacetic acid, 4-(trifluoromethyl)-α-[[4-(trifluoromethyl)phenyl]methylene]-, methyl ester, (Z)-	EtOH	277(4.30)	36-0910-73
$C_{18}H_{12}INO_5S$			
Furan, 2-[2-(4-iodophenyl)-1-(phenylsulfonyl)ethenyl]-5-nitro-	EtOH	210(4.55),217s(4.51),304(4.71)	73-1705-73
$C_{18}H_{12}N_2$			
8,9-Fluoranthenedicarbonitrile, 6b,7,10,10a-tetrahydrc-	MeCN	224(4.09),245(3.84),252s(3.78),288(3.82)	33-3004-73
$C_{18}H_{12}N_2OS$			
Phenol, 2-[(naphtho[2,3-d]thiazol-2-ylimino)methyl]-	benzene	292(4.26),398(4.22),410(4.20)	80-1781-73
	EtOH	247(--),260(--),265(--),290(--),312(--),396(--)	80-1781-73
	ether	227(4.67),244(4.62),267(4.43),284(4.39),394(4.30)	80-1781-73
	CH_2Cl_2	247(4.71),266(4.49),290(4.53),397(4.44)	80-1781-73
	MeCN	225(--),244(--),264(--),287(--),391(--)	80-1781-73
3-Thiophenecarbonitrile, 4-amino-5-benzoyl-2-phenyl-	CH_2Cl_2	380(4.03)	48-0497-73

Compound	Solvent	$\lambda_{max}(\log \epsilon)$	Ref.
$C_{18}H_{12}N_2O_2$			
Acetamide, 2-cyano-2-(2,3-dihydro-3-oxo-2-phenyl-1H-inden-1-ylidene)-	EtOH	252s(4.04),261(3.97), 298(4.01),330(3.42)	39-1731-73C
Acetonitrile, (1,3-dihydro-1,3-dioxo-2H-inden-2-ylidene)[(2-methylphenyl)-amino]-	MeCN	237(4.27),264(4.13), 375(4.32)	39-1045-73B
Acetonitrile, (1,3-dihydro-1,3-dioxo-2H-inden-2-ylidene)[(3-methylphenyl)-amino]-	MeCN	233(4.33),260(4.16), 382(4.38)	39-1045-73B
Acetonitrile, (1,3-dihydro-1,3-dioxo-2H-inden-2-ylidene)[(4-methylphenyl)-amino]-	MeCN	235(4.38),264(4.18), 390(4.38)	39-1045-73B
Benz[a]anthracene-7,12-dione, 8,11-di-amino-	benzene	585(4.20),628(4.11)	40-1328-73
Benzeneacetonitrile, α-(1,3-dihydro-1,3-dioxo-2H-inden-2-ylidene)-4-(methyl-amino)-	MeOH	250(4.48),557(4.50)	88-2993-73
$C_{18}H_{12}N_2O_2S$			
4H-Quinolizine-1-carbonitrile, 3-benz-oyl-2-(methylthio)-4-oxo-	EtOH	270(4.33),310s(3.96), 398(4.28)	94-0921-73
$C_{18}H_{12}N_2O_2S_2$			
5-Cyclohexene-1,2,3,4-tetrone, 1,3-bis-(S-phenylthiooxime)	CH_2Cl_2	270(4.08),421(4.51)	39-1031-73C
$C_{18}H_{12}N_2O_3$			
Acetonitrile, (1,3-dihydro-1,3-dioxo-2H-inden-2-ylidene)[(4-methoxyphen-yl)amino]-	MeCN	236(4.36),262(4.11), 391(4.28)	39-1045-73B
$C_{18}H_{12}N_2O_3S_2$			
Benzenesulfonic acid, 2-(3H-phenothia-zin-3-ylideneamino)-	pH 3	304(4.53),640(4.70)	80-1005-73
	pH 11	290(4.47),546(4.36)	80-1005-73
Benzenesulfonic acid, 3-(3H-phenothia-zin-3-ylideneamino)-	pH 6	304(4.46),648(4.56)	80-1005-73
	pH 11	290(4.44),560(4.36)	80-1005-73
Benzenesulfonic acid, 4-(3H-phenothia-zin-3-ylideneamino)-	pH 2.2	308(4.63),660(4.70)	80-1005-73
	pH 11	294(4.58),560(4.44)	80-1005-73
$C_{18}H_{12}N_2O_7S$			
Furan, 2-nitro-5-[2-(4-nitrophenyl)-1-(phenylsulfonyl)ethenyl]-	EtOH	217(4.58),298(4.62)	73-1705-73
Furan, 2-nitro-5-[2-(4-nitrophenyl)-2-(phenylsulfonyl)ethenyl]-	EtOH	208(4.53),219s(4.46), 248s(4.42),270(4.46), 347(4.43)	73-1705-73
$C_{18}H_{12}N_4$			
Tricyclo[6.2.1.0^{2,7}]undeca-2,4,6-triene-5,5,6,6-tetracarbonitrile, 11-isoprop-ylidene-	90% EtOH	229(4.19),261(3.4), 269(3.53),274(3.54)	12-1725-73
$C_{18}H_{12}N_4O_2$			
2,4(1H,3H)-Pteridinedione, 6,7-diphenyl-	pH 5.0	220(4.43),272(4.16), 361(4.17)	24-3149-73
	pH 11.0	220s(4.41),288(4.30), 376(4.06)	24-3149-73
$C_{18}H_{12}N_4O_3$			
2,4(1H,3H)-Pteridinedione, 6,7-diphen-yl-, 8-oxide	pH 2.0	260(4.41),368(3.92)	24-3149-73
	pH 9.0	291(4.40),400(3.92)	24-3149-73

Compound	Solvent	$\lambda_{max}(\log \epsilon)$	Ref.
2,4(1H,3H)-Pteridinedione, 6,7-diphenyl-, 8-oxide (cont.)	pH 14.0	269(4.44),405(4.00)	24-3149-73
$C_{18}H_{12}N_4O_4$			
4,5-Isoxazoledione, 3-phenyl-, 4-[(5-hydroxy-3-phenyl-4-isoxazolyl)hydrazone]	EtOH	238(4.41),300(3.87), 520(3.79)	32-1045-73
$C_{18}H_{12}N_4O_5$			
1H-Benzimidazole, 1-methyl-5-nitro-2-[5-(4-nitrophenyl)-2-furanyl]-	EtOH	219(4.10),241(4.14), 288(4.16),373(4.45)	73-1700-73
[1,1'-Biphenyl]-2-ol, 5-[(2,4-dinitrophenyl)azo]- (first two spectra in 50% DMSO)	acid	402(4.23)	1-3641-73
	KOH	586(4.63)	1-3641-73
	C_2Cl_4	394(4.27)	1-3632-73
[1,1'-Biphenyl]-3-ol, 6-[(2,4-dinitrophenyl)azo]- (first two spectra in 50% DMSO)	acid	398(4.20)	1-3641-73
	KOH	564(4.52)	1-3641-73
	C_2Cl_4	396(4.31)	1-3632-73
$C_{18}H_{12}O_3$			
Benzoic acid, 2-(1-naphthalenylcarbonyl)-	M H_2SO_4	323(4.87)	44-3375-73
3,4-Furandicarboxaldehyde, 2,5-diphenyl-	$CHCl_3$	323(4.1)	22-1154-73
$C_{18}H_{12}O_4$			
9,10-Ethenoanthracene-1,5-dicarboxylic acid, 9,10-dihydro-, (-)-	MeOH	205(4.55),222(4.52), 305(3.81)	18-0915-73
$C_{18}H_{12}O_7$			
1H-2-Benzopyran-4-carboxylic acid, 3-(2-carboxyphenyl)-7-methoxy-1-oxo-	MeOH	230(4.44),280(3.9)	2-0413-73
$C_{18}H_{12}S$			
4,9[1',2']-Benzenonaphtho[2,3-c]thiophene, 4,9-dihydro-	C_6H_{12}	265(3.71),268(3.76), 278(3.57)	78-1379-73
Benzo[b]thiophene, 2-(2-naphthalenyl)-	MeOH	234(4.5),272(4.3), 282(4.4),320(4.5), 332(4.4)	5-1112-73
$C_{18}H_{12}S_4$			
Thieno[2,3-b]thiophene, 2,5-bis[2-(2-thienyl)ethenyl]-	benzene	336s(4.48),352s(4.53), 368(4.58)	35-3692-73
$C_{18}H_{13}BrO$			
17H-Cyclopenta[a]phenanthren-17-one, 15-bromo-15,16-dihydro-11-methyl-	EtOH	268(4.68),290(4.37), 303(4.29),363(3.31), 381(3.35)	39-2236-73C
$C_{18}H_{13}BrO_2$			
Methanone, (4-bromo-1-methoxy-2-naphthalenyl)phenyl-	C_6H_{12}	240(4.50),274s(4.03), 290s(3.86),306s(3.71), 336(3.33)	19-0849-73
$C_{18}H_{13}Cl$			
Azulene, 1-chloro-3-(2-phenylethenyl)-, cis	hexane	657(2.19)	5-0166-73
trans	hexane	262(3.55),307s(3.61), 319(3.70),402(3.43), 675(2.24),750s(2.10)	5-0166-73
$C_{18}H_{13}ClFNO_3$			
3-Quinolinecarboxylic acid, 6-chloro-4-(2-fluorophenyl)-1,2-dihydro-2-oxo-, ethyl ester	isoPrOH	238(4.65),272(3.85), 280s(3.82),333s(3.67), 338(3.80),360s(3.73)	44-0449-73

Compound	Solvent	λ_{max}(log ε)	Ref.
$C_{18}H_{13}ClN_4O_2$			
[1,3,5]Triazino[1,2-a][1,4]benzodiazepine-1,3(2H,4H)-dione, 9-chloro-4-methyl-7-phenyl-	EtOH	225(4.45),272(4.23), 379(3.83)	87-1256-73
[1,3,5]Triazino[1,2-a][1,4]benzodiazepine-1,3(2H,5H)-dione, 9-chloro-2-methyl-7-phenyl-	EtOH	219(4.46),249(4.15), 265s(4.02),290s(3.53), 380(2.39)	87-1256-73
$C_{18}H_{13}ClO_6$			
Benzofuro[3,2-c]pyrylium, 3-methyl-1-phenyl-, perchlorate	n.s.g.	253(3.48),284(4.00), 370(3.69)	103-0416-73
$C_{18}H_{13}Cl_2N_3O_3$			
Ethanone, 1-[3-(2,4-dichlorophenyl)-5-methyl-1-(4-nitrophenyl)-1H-pyrazol-4-yl)-	EtOH	230s(5.46),250s(5.33), 295(5.20)	78-0121-73
$C_{18}H_{13}F_6IN_2S$			
Benzothiazolium, 2-[2-[4-[bis(trifluoromethyl)amino]phenyl]ethenyl]-3-methyl-, iodide	EtOH	366(4.46)	104-2181-73
$C_{18}H_{13}IN_2O_2S_2$			
Thiazolo[2,3-a]isoquinolinium, 2-(methylthio)-3-(4-nitrophenyl)-, iodide	MeOH	228(4.59),286(4.18), 340(4.11),358(4.12)	2-1257-73
$C_{18}H_{13}N$			
1H-Indole, 2-(2-naphthalenyl)-	EtOH	208(4.49),235(4.63), 342(4.45)	34-0109-73
$C_{18}H_{13}NO$			
Benz[a]acridine, 5-methoxy-	EtOH	224(4.77),238s(4.70), 243(4.75),274s(4.75), 282(4.84),294(4.79), 318(3.87),334(3.91), 352(3.86),374(4.08), 394(4.11)	12-2315-73
	EtOH-acid	228(4.70),242(4.76), 252(4.63),285(4.72), 297(4.63),380s(4.23), 400(4.35),414(4.14)	12-2315-73
Benz[c]acridin-7(12H)-one, 12-methyl-	EtOH	234(4.39),254(4.38), 274s(4.54),282(4.71), 310(4.07),320s(3.79), 336(3.75),385(3.93), 400(3.95)	12-2315-73
$C_{18}H_{13}NO_2S_2$			
Methanone, [4,5-dihydro-3-phenyl-5-(2-thienyl)-4-isoxazolyl]-2-thienyl-, trans	EtOH	264.5(4.39)	39-1148-73C
$C_{18}H_{13}NO_3$			
Furo[2,3-b]quinolin-4(9H)-one, 8-(phenylmethoxy)-	EtOH	244(4.64),260s(3.89), 286s(3.55),297(3.64), 316s(3.82),330(4.02)	2-1088-73
Isoxazolium, 2,5-dihydro-3-hydroxy-5-oxo-4-phenyl-2-(3-phenyl-2-propenylidene)-, hydroxide, inner salt	dioxan	525(3.70)	44-1782-73

Compound	Solvent	$\lambda_{max}(\log \epsilon)$	Ref.
9H-Pyrano[2,3-g]-1,2-benzisoxazol-9-one, 3,8-dimethyl-7-phenyl-	n.s.g.	220(4.5),253(4.6), 315(3.9)	2-0541-73
9H-Pyrano[2,3-g]-1,2-benzisoxazol-9-one, 3-methyl-7-(4-methylphenyl)-	n.s.g.	220(4.14),269(4.4), 309(4.4)	2-0541-73
$C_{18}H_{13}NO_3S$			
Methanone, [4,5-dihydro-3-phenyl-5-(2-thienyl)-4-isoxazolyl]-2-furanyl-	EtOH	275.5(4.39)	39-1148-73C
Methanone, [5-(2-furanyl)-4,5-dihydro-3-phenyl-4-isoxazolyl]-2-thienyl-, trans	EtOH	265(4.37)	39-1148-73C
$C_{18}H_{13}NO_4$			
Furo[2,3-b]quinoline-3,4(2H,9H)-dione, 8-(phenylmethoxy)-	EtOH	248(4.64),266s(4.21), 279s(4.10)	2-1088-73
6-Isoquinolinecarboxylic acid, 5-(benzoyloxy)-, methyl ester	EtOH	228(4.74),268s(3.81), 338(3.56)	78-0857-73
6-Isoquinolinecarboxylic acid, 7-(benzoyloxy)-, methyl ester, hydrochloride	EtOH	230(4.79),338(3.46)	78-0857-73
Methanone, 2-furanyl[4-(2-furanyl)-4,5-dihydro-3-phenyl-5-isoxazolyl]-, trans	EtOH	276(4.36)	39-1148-73C
Methanone, (1-methoxy-4-nitro-2-naphthalenyl)phenyl-	C_6H_{12}	250(4.49),280s(3.94), 340(3.80)	19-0849-73
$C_{18}H_{13}NO_5S$			
Furan, 2-nitro-5-[2-phenyl-1-(phenylsulfonyl)ethenyl]-	EtOH	209(4.59),217s(4.57), 289(4.65)	73-1705-73
$C_{18}H_{13}NO_6$			
1,3-Propanedione, 3-(1,3-benzodioxol-5-yl)-1-(6-hydroxy-3-methyl-1,2-benzisoxazol-7-yl)-	n.s.g.	242(4.1),274(4.5), 386(4.3)	2-0541-73
$C_{18}H_{13}NO_7$			
4,5-Benzofurandicarboxylic acid, 2-(4-nitrophenyl)-, dimethyl ester	90% EtOH	237(4.37),350(4.47)	12-1059-73
$C_{18}H_{13}N_3$			
Benzo[c]cinnolin-4-amine, N-phenyl-	C_6H_{12}	241(4.58),297(4.63), 338(3.46),354(3.63), 364(3.57),372(3.73), 510(3.65)	44-0507-73
$C_{18}H_{13}N_3O$			
Ethanone, 2-(phenylimino)-1,2-di-2-pyridinyl-	EtOH	235(4.47),273(4.01), 335(3.42)	12-2027-73
2(1H)-Quinazolinone, 4-(1-amino-2-naphthalenyl)-	EtOH	230(1.25),280(0.40), 450(0.31)	30-0828-73
$C_{18}H_{13}N_3OS$			
4-Imidazolidinone, 5-(1H-indol-3-ylmethylene)-3-phenyl-2-thioxo-	EtOH	224(4.42),281(4.07), 290(4.06),429(4.56)	63-1307-73
$C_{18}H_{13}N_3O_2$			
Acetonitrile, (2,3-dihydro-2-methyl-1,3-dioxo-4(1H)-isoquinolinylidene)-(phenylamino)-	EtOH	223(3.38),262(3.16), 417(3.35)	95-0322-73
Ethanone, 1-[5-[2-(1H-imidazo[4,3-f]-quinolin-2-yl)ethenyl]-2-furanyl]-	MeOH	251(4.02),280(3.81), 385(4.23)	103-0406-73

Compound	Solvent	λ_{max}(log ε)	Ref.
1H-Indole, 3,3'-(nitroethenylidene)bis-	EtOH	280(4.23),430(4.23)	95-0612-73
Pyrimido[4,5-b]quinoline-2,4(1H,3H)-dione, 3-(phenylmethyl)-	MeCN	248(4.6),302(3.9), 352(3.4)	24-3533-73
$C_{18}H_{13}N_3O_2S$			
1H-Pyridazino[4,5-b][1,4]benzothiazin-1-one, 10-acetyl-2,10-dihydro-2-phenyl-	EtOH	220(3.43),250s(2.98), 322(2.89)	94-0241-73
3H-Pyridazino[4,5-b][1,4]benzothiazin-4(10H)-one, 10-acetyl-3-phenyl-	EtOH	225(3.50),263s(3.15), 313(2.97)	94-0241-73
$C_{18}H_{13}N_3O_3$			
1H-Benzimidazole, 1-methyl-5-nitro-2-(5-phenyl-2-furanyl)-	EtOH	220(4.19),240s(4.07), 260(4.16),328(4.40), 366(4.38)	73-1700-73
1H-Benzimidazole, 2-[5-(4-methylphenyl)-2-furanyl]-5-nitro-	EtOH	219(4.25),241(4.13), 258(4.42),321(4.35), 376(4.46)	73-1700-73
$C_{18}H_{13}N_3O_3S$			
Thiopyrano[3,4-b]indole-3-acetic acid, α,4-dicyano-1,9-dihydro-9-methyl-1-oxo-, ethyl ester	EtOH	250(4.53),320(4.28), 385(4.18),463(4.01)	95-1523-73
$C_{18}H_{13}N_3O_4$			
1H-Benzimidazole, 2-[5-(4-methoxyphenyl)-2-furanyl]-5-nitro-	EtOH	218s(4.33),262(4.03), 327(4.42),384(4.55)	73-1700-73
Pyrrolo[2,1-a]isoquinoline-1,1(10bH)-dicarboxylic acid, 2,3-dicyano-, dimethyl ester	MeCN	416(4.01)	94-1118-73
Pyrrolo[2,1-a]isoquinoline-3,3(2H)-dicarboxylic acid, 1,2-dicyano-, dimethyl ester	MeOH	390(3.86),411(3.94), 436(3.73)	94-1118-73
$C_{18}H_{13}N_3O_6$			
Azulene, 4-ethenyl-, 1,3,5-trinitrobenzene complex	CH_2Cl_2	261(4.53),292(4.55), 347(3.61),592(2.64), 644(2.55),713(2.06)	44-1106-73
Azulene, 6-ethenyl-, 1,3,5-trinitrobenzene complex	C_6H_{12}	291(4.80),347(3.67), 355(3.75),363(3.64), 372(3.88),592(2.46), 613(2.51),639(2.45), 672(2.40),708(2.10), 752(1.96)	44-1106-73
$C_{18}H_{13}N_5$			
Pyridine, 2,2',2"-(1H-imidazole-2,4,5-triyl)tris-	EtOH	320(4.71)	94-1927-73
Pyridine, 4,4',4"-(1H-imidazole-2,4,5-triyl)tris-	EtOH	315(4.71)	94-1927-73
$C_{18}H_{13}N_5O$			
4(1H)-Pteridinone, 2-amino-6,7-diphenyl-	pH 0	277(4.15),360(4.17)	24-3175-73
	pH 5	293(4.31),374(4.07)	24-3175-73
	pH 10	273(4.33),385(4.10)	24-3175-73
$C_{18}H_{13}N_5O_2$			
4(1H)-Pteridinone, 2-amino-6,7-diphenyl-, 8-oxide	pH -3.0	259(4.41),272s(4.18), 365(3.91)	24-3175-73
	pH 3.0	291(4.40),390(3.92)	24-3175-73
	pH 9.0	269(4.46),397(4.01)	24-3175-73

Compound	Solvent	$\lambda_{max}(\log \epsilon)$	Ref.
$C_{18}H_{13}N_5O_3$			
4(1H)-Pteridinone, 2-amino-6,7-diphenyl-, 5,8-dioxide	pH -3.0	255(4.43),367(3.92)	24-3175-73
	pH 2.0	258(4.41),373(3.90)	24-3175-73
	pH 13.0	287(4.48),392(4.00)	24-3175-73
$C_{18}H_{13}O_2$			
Benzofuro[3,2-c]pyrylium, 3-methyl-1-phenyl-, perchlorate	n.s.g.	253(3.48),284(4.00), 370(3.69)	103-0416-73
$C_{18}H_{14}$			
Azulene, 1-(2-phenylethenyl)-, cis	C_6H_{12}	259(4.31),313(4.56), 626(2.49)	5-0166-73
Azulene, 1-(2-phenylethenyl)-, trans	C_6H_{12}	254(4.46),317(4.54), 335(4.41),379(4.29), 397(4.34),648(2.52), 717(2.32)	5-0166-73
15H-Cyclopenta[a]phenanthrene, 11-methyl-	EtOH	222(4.47),267(4.65), 274(4.65),294(4.08), 306(4.08),317(2.83), 348(2.85),364(2.74)	39-1255-73C
Naphthacene, 5,12-dihydro-	C_6H_{12}	224(4.95),230(5.09), 251s(3.50),262s(3.70), 271(2.82),280(3.77), 290(3.58),306(2.82), 316(2.50),320(2.77)	78-1379-73
Tetracyclo[6.6.2.1^{3,13}.1^{6,10}]octadeca-1,3(17),4,6,8,10(18),11,13-octaene	C_6H_{12}	245s(3.35),281s(2.78), 322(1.92)	35-3201-73
$C_{18}H_{14}BrNO_3$			
4H-Quinolizine-1-carboxylic acid, 3-bromo-4-oxo-2-phenyl-, ethyl ester	EtOH	265(4.25),400(4.24)	4-0139-73
$C_{18}H_{14}BrNO_5$			
1H-Indole-1,3-diacetic acid, 5-bromo-2,3-dihydro-2-oxo-3-phenyl-	EtOH	261(4.09),290(3.27)	104-0831-73
$C_{18}H_{14}BrN_3$			
1H-Pyrrolo[1,2-b][1,2,4]triazole, 6-(4-bromophenyl)-2-methyl-1-phenyl-	MeOH	224(3.78),279(4.12)	118-0414-73
$C_{18}H_{14}Br_2$			
Benzene, [(4,5-dibromo-2-cyclopenten-1-ylidene)phenylmethyl]-, trans	C_6H_{12}	245(4.19),305(4.31)	78-2699-73
$C_{18}H_{14}Br_2N_2$			
2-Propenal, 3-(4-bromophenyl)-, [3-(4-bromophenyl)-2-propenylidene]hydrazone	$CHCl_3$	355(4.81),369(4.80)	22-3303-73
$C_{18}H_{14}Br_4$			
Benzene, [phenyl(2,3,4,5-tetrabromocyclopentylidene)methyl]-, trans-cis-trans	C_6H_{12}	226(4.22),292(4.08)	78-2699-73
trans-trans-trans	C_6H_{12}	232(4.20),305(3.95)	78-2699-73
unsymmetrical form	C_6H_{12}	227(4.20),294(4.11)	78-2699-73
$C_{18}H_{14}ClNO$			
Ethanone, 1-(5-chloro-2-ethenyl-3-phenyl-2H-isoindol-1-yl)-	EtOH	263(4.38),308s(3.70), 384(4.23)	94-1404-73

Compound	Solvent	λ_{max}(log ε)	Ref.
$C_{18}H_{14}ClNO_5$			
1H-Indole-1,3-diacetic acid, 5-chloro-2,3-dihydro-2-oxo-3-phenyl-	EtOH	260(4.08),290(3.26)	104-0831-73
$C_{18}H_{14}ClN_3$			
1H-Pyrrolo[1,2-b][1,2,4]triazole, 6-(4-chlorophenyl)-2-methyl-1-phenyl-	MeOH	223(3.78),277(4.12)	118-0414-73
$C_{18}H_{14}ClN_3O_3$			
Ethanone, 1-[3-(2-chlorophenyl)-5-methyl-1-(4-nitrophenyl)-1H-pyrazol-4-yl]-	EtOH	252s(5.20),295(5.26)	78-0121-73
Ethanone, 1-[3-(4-chlorophenyl)-5-methyl-1-(4-nitrophenyl)-1H-pyrazol-4-yl]-	EtOH	230(5.42),255s(5.26), 300(5.20)	78-0121-73
$C_{18}H_{14}Cl_2N_2O$			
2H-Isoindole-1-carboxamide, 5-chloro-3-(2-chlorophenyl)-2-ethenyl-N-methyl-	EtOH	230(4.36),259(4.40), 304s(3.72),318(3.66), 361(4.04)	94-1404-73
$C_{18}H_{14}CrN_2O_4$			
Chromium, tetracarbonyl[α-methyl-N-(2-pyridinylmethylene)benzenemethanamine-N,N']-	acetone	382(3.39),510(3.69)	101-0183-73K
$C_{18}H_{14}I_2N_2O_6$			
3H-Phenoxazine-1,9-dicarboxylic acid, 2-amino-4,6-diiodo-3-oxo-, diethyl ester	EtOH	250(4.62),435s(4.50), 445(4.52)	104-2560-73
$C_{18}H_{14}MoN_2O_4$			
Molybdenum, tetracarbonyl[α-methyl-N-(2-pyridinylmethylene)benzenemethanamine-N,N']-	acetone	382(3.38),490(3.60)	101-0183-73K
$C_{18}H_{14}NO$			
[1,1'-Biphenyl]-4-yl phenyl nitroxide	hexane	243(4.00),294(4.02), 329(4.29),400s(--)	44-0165-73
	EtOH	243(3.96),294(3.96), 332(4.27)	44-0165-73
$C_{18}H_{14}N_2$			
1H-Pyrido[2,3-b]indole, 4-methyl-2-phenyl-	MeOH	218(4.54),250(4.60), 312(4.58)	103-0968-73
9H-Pyrido[2,3-b]indole, 2-methyl-4-phenyl-	MeOH	220(4.75),251(4.38), 305(4.19)	103-0968-73
Pyrimido[1,2-a]indole, 2(4)-methyl-4(2)-phenyl-	MeOH	266(4.65),320(3.70), 432(3.20)	103-0968-73
$C_{18}H_{14}N_2O$			
1H-Benzimidazole, 2-[5-(4-methylphenyl)-2-furanyl]-	EtOH	222s(4.47),238s(4.09), 277(4.13),343s(4.65), 352(4.70),371(4.51)	73-1700-73
Propanal, 3-(1H-inden-1-ylidene)-2-(phenylhydrazono)-	hexane	312(4.03),392(3.97)	5-0750-73
	50% EtOH	330(4.11),391(4.28)	5-0750-73
after 24 hours	hexane	318(4.04),343(4.02), 377(4.02),463(4.12)	5-0750-73
$C_{18}H_{14}N_2O_2$			
Acetic acid, 9(10H)-acridinylidenecyano-, ethyl ester	EtOH	247(4.7),293(4.1), 480(3.9)	18-0283-73

Compound	Solvent	λ_{max}(log ε)	Ref.
1H-Benzimidazole, 2-[5-(4-methoxyphenyl)-2-furanyl]-	EtOH	222(4.55),238(4.22), 274(4.23),338(4.79), 348(4.85),367(4.66)	73-1700-73
2H-Benzimidazol-2-one, 1,3-dihydro-1-(1-oxo-5-phenyl-2,4-pentadienyl)-	HOAc	336(4.53)	48-1152-73
2H-Indol-2-one, 3-(1,3-dihydro-5-methyl-3-oxo-2H-indol-2-ylidene)-1,3-dihydro-5-methyl-	EtOH	296(4.37),460(3.8)	95-0008-73
$C_{18}H_{14}N_2O_3S_2$			
4H-Quinolizine-1-carbonitrile, 3-[(2-methylphenyl)sulfonyl]-2-(methylthio)-4-oxo-	EtOH	271(4.26),320(4.12), 408(4.36)	94-0921-73
$C_{18}H_{14}N_2O_4$			
1H-Pyrrole-3-carboxylic acid, 2,5-dihydro-2,5-dioxo-1-phenyl-4-(phenylamino)-, methyl ester	EtOH	235(4.48),392(3.82)	95-1008-73
$C_{18}H_{14}N_2O_4W$			
Tungsten, tetracarbonyl[α-methyl-N-(2-pyridinylmethylene)benzenemethanamine-N,N']-	acetone	383(3.40),497(3.75)	101-0183-73K
$C_{18}H_{14}N_2O_5$			
Pyrano[3,2-b]indole-4-acetic acid, α-acetyl-3-cyano-2,5-dihydro-2-oxo-, ethyl ester	EtOH	253(4.19),376(4.39), 393(4.37)	95-1523-73
$C_{18}H_{14}N_4$			
Pyrimido[4,5-d]pyrimidine, 3,4-dihydro-2,7-diphenyl-	MeCN	254(4.86),312(4.14), 350(3.99)	18-0253-73
$C_{18}H_{14}N_4O$			
1H-1,2,4-Triazolo[4,3-b]pyridazin-4-ium, 8-hydroxy-6-phenyl-1-(1-phenylmethyl)-, hydroxide, inner salt	n.s.g.	253(4.10),315(4.14)	48-0097-73
$C_{18}H_{14}N_4O_2$			
Benzenamine, 4-[(4-nitrophenyl)azo]-N-phenyl-	n.s.g.	480(4.46)	40-1738-73
Benzoic acid, 2-[5-(4-phenyl-1,3-butadienyl)-1H-tetrazol-1-yl]-	n.s.g.	320(4.57)	48-1152-73
$C_{18}H_{14}N_4O_3$			
Benzo[a]pyrrolo[3,4-g]quinolizine-12-carbonitrile, 5,6,8,9,10,11-hexahydro-11-(methoxyimino)-10-methyl-8,9-dioxo-	EtOH	398(4.30),408(4.32)	94-1667-73
$C_{18}H_{14}N_4O_4$			
Methanone, 1,2,4,5-tetrazine-3,6-diylbis[(4-methoxyphenyl)-	n.s.g.	265(4.22),313(4.30), 532(2.64)	5-0879-73
$C_{18}H_{14}N_4O_5$			
Ethanone, 1-[5-methyl-1,3-bis(4-nitrophenyl)-1H-pyrazol-4-yl]-	EtOH	214s(5.45),295(5.41)	78-0121-73
$C_{18}H_{14}N_6$			
2,4-Pteridinediamine, 6,7-diphenyl-	pH 2.0	223s(4.44),267(4.32), 370(4.26)	24-3175-73

Compound	Solvent	λ_{max}(log ε)	Ref.
2,4-Pteridinediamine, 6,7-diphenyl- (cont.)	pH 8.0	223(4.43),270(4.38), 389(4.14)	24-3175-73
2H-1,2,3-Triazolo[4,5-f]quinoline, 2-(1,2-dimethyl-1H-benzimidazol-5-yl)-	EtOH	224(4.38),254(4.45), 290(4.45),337(4.37)	78-0221-73
$C_{18}H_{14}N_6O_2$			
2,4-Pteridinediamine, 6,7-diphenyl-, 5,8-dioxide	pH -1.0	260(4.46),382(3.98)	24-3175-73
	pH 5.0	278(4.52),398(4.06)	24-3175-73
$C_{18}H_{14}O$			
16H-Cyclopenta[a]phenanthren-16-one, 15,17-dihydro-11-methyl-	EtOH	257(4.77),282(4.06), 295(4.08),307(4.16), 324(2.99),339(3.06), 355(3.04)	39-1255-73C
16H-Cyclopenta[a]phenanthren-16-one, 15,17-dihydro-17-methyl-	EtOH	259(4.80),278(4.23), 288(4.10),300(4.14), 319(3.06),334(3.03), 350(2.96)	39-1255-73C
Dibenzobicyclo[2.2.2]octadien-2-one, 1-methyl-3-methylene-	MeOH	284(3.37),342(2.64)	35-6294-73
Dibenzobicyclo[2.2.2]octadien-2-one, 4-methyl-3-methylene-	MeOH	286(3.53),340(2.85)	35-6294-73
$C_{18}H_{14}OS$			
Methanone, (2-methyl-5-phenyl-3-thien-yl)phenyl-	EtOH	260(4.49),290(4.20)	78-0413-73
Methanone, (5-methyl-2-phenyl-3-thien-yl)phenyl-	EtOH	259(4.32),322(3.58)	78-0413-73
$C_{18}H_{14}O_2$			
Methanone, (1-methoxy-2-naphthalenyl)-phenyl-	C_6H_{12}	244(4.43),288s(3.83), 332(3.24)	19-0849-73
Methanone, (2-methoxy-1-naphthalenyl)-phenyl-	C_6H_{12}	229(4.84),246s(4.31), 269(3.79),280(3.83), 290s(3.74),310s(3.32), 322(3.41),336(3.47), 384s(1.71)	19-0849-73
Methanone, (4-methoxy-1-naphthalenyl)-phenyl-	C_6H_{12}	212(4.61),237(4.56), 250s(4.33),310s(3.95), 321(4.01),336s(3.88), 360s(3.71)	19-0849-73
$C_{18}H_{14}O_4$			
1,5-Anthracenedicarboxylic acid, dimeth-yl ester	dioxan	222(4.30),224s(4.29), 261(4.08),348s(3.61), 365(3.89),385(3.99), 406(3.92)	18-0605-73
4H-1-Benzopyran-5-acetic acid, 4-oxo-2-phenyl-, methyl ester	EtOH	258(4.30),294(4.31), 311s(4.21)	78-3091-73
9,10-Ethanoanthracene-1,5-dicarboxylic acid, 9,10-dihydro-	MeOH	198(4.58),202(4.48), 207(4.47),211(4.46), 229(4.32),254(3.39), 257(3.23),260s(3.20), 263s(3.18),291(3.71)	18-0915-73
Osajaxanthone, 7-deoxy-	MeOH	258(4.42),292(4.48), 312(4.21),348(4.06)	2-1237-73
$C_{18}H_{14}O_4S$			
Benzo[b]thiophene-6-carboxylic acid, 4-acetoxy-7-phenyl-, methyl ester	EtOH	238s(4.70),285(4.05), 330(3.85)	48-0300-73

Compound	Solvent	$\lambda_{max}(\log \epsilon)$	Ref.
$C_{18}H_{14}O_5$			
4-Cyclopentene-1,3-dione, 4-hydroxy-5-(4-hydroxyphenyl)-2-(4-methoxyphenyl)-	EtOH	225(4.16),264(4.23), 364(4.03)	24-3223-73
1H-Indene-1,2(3H)-dione, 3-acetoxy-3-(2-methoxyphenyl)-	EtOH	273(3.98)	78-3337-73
$C_{18}H_{14}O_6$			
Pyrano[3,2-a]xanthen-12(1H)-one, 5,9,11-trihydroxy-1,1-dimethyl-	n.s.g.	242(4.45),262(4.45), 332(4.26),392(4.06)	2-0518-73
9H-Xanthen-9-one, 2,6-diacetoxy-4-methyl-	MeOH	206(4.27),242(4.64), 265(4.19),292(3.88), 339(3.83)	24-1182-73
$C_{18}H_{14}O_7$			
Spiro[2H-1-benzopyran-3(4H),5'(6'H)-cyclobuta[f][1,3]benzodioxol]-4-one, 2,5-dihydroxy-7-methoxy-	EtOH	229(4.56),294(4.68), 336(3.89)	88-4569-73
$C_{18}H_{14}O_8$			
[1,1'-Biphenyl]-2,2',6,6'-tetracarboxylic acid, 2,2'-dimethyl ester	EtOH	289(3.27)	33-2255-73
$C_{18}H_{15}$			
Cyclopropenylium, cyclopropyldiphenyl-, tetrafluoroborate	MeCN	264(4.19),288(4.26), 303(4.32),318(4.22)	35-3239-73
$C_{18}H_{15}AsAuCl$			
Gold, chloro(triphenylarsine)-	MeCN	253(3.20),259(3.20), 264(3.22),271(3.10)	33-2405-73
$C_{18}H_{15}AsCl_2$			
Arsenic, dichlorotriphenyl-	MeCN	259(3.28),265(3.29), 271(3.16)	33-2405-73
$C_{18}H_{15}AuClP$			
Gold, chloro(triphenylphosphine)-	MeCN	260(3.41),267(3.41), 271(3.30)	33-2405-73
$C_{18}H_{15}AuClSb$			
Gold, chloro(triphenylstibine)-	MeCN	257(3.38),263(3.32), 270(3.16)	33-2405-73
$C_{18}H_{15}BrF_3N_5O_2$			
Propanenitrile, 3-[[4-[[2-bromo-4-nitro-6-(trifluoromethyl)azo]phenyl]ethylamino]-	MeOH	423(4.42)	89-0926-73
$C_{18}H_{15}BrN_2OS$			
4-Imidazolidinone, 3-(4-bromophenyl)-5-(2,4-dimethylphenyl)methylene]-2-thioxo-	EtOH	226s(4.25),253(4.13), 369(4.51)	56-0181-73
	EtOH-NaOH	258(4.23),285(4.10), 400(4.51)	56-0181-73
4-Imidazolidinone, 3-(4-bromophenyl)-5-(3,4-dimethylphenyl)methylene]-2-thioxo-	EtOH	230(4.21),253(4.11), 372(4.50)	56-0181-73
	EtOH-NaOH	255(4.18),285(4.02), 398(4.40)	56-0181-73

Compound	Solvent	λ max (log ε)	Ref.
$C_{18}H_{15}BrN_2O_3S$			
4-Imidazolidinone, 3-(4-bromophenyl)-5-[(2,3-dimethoxyphenyl)methylene]-2-thioxo-	EtOH	217(4.53),255s(4.08),376(4.53)	56-0181-73
	EtOH-NaOH	230(4.51),258s(4.28),280(4.13),403(4.54)	56-0181-73
4-Imidazolidinone, 3-(4-bromophenyl)-5-[(2,4-dimethoxyphenyl)methylene]-2-thioxo-	EtOH	260(4.15),405(4.56)	56-0181-73
	EtOH-NaOH	232(4.40),260(4.26),290s(4.12),413(4.62)	56-0181-73
4-Imidazolidinone, 3-(4-bromophenyl)-5-[(2,5-dimethoxyphenyl)methylene]-2-thioxo-	EtOH	217(4.43),256s(4.08),360s(4.23),400(4.33)	56-0181-73
	EtOH-NaOH	229(4.37),263(4.16),418(4.47)	56-0181-73
4-Imidazolidinone, 3-(4-bromophenyl)-5-[(3,4-dimethoxyphenyl)methylene]-2-thioxo-	EtOH	220s(4.39),257(4.19),393(4.58)	56-0181-73
	EtOH-NaOH	230(4.39),258s(4.22),295(3.97),412(4.55)	56-0181-73
$C_{18}H_{15}BrN_6O_2$			
Benzonitrile, 3-bromo-2-[[4-[(2-cyanoethyl)ethylamino]phenyl]azo]-5-nitro-	MeOH	506(4.57)	89-0926-73
$C_{18}H_{15}ClN_2O$			
2H-Isoindole-1-carboxamide, 5-chloro-2-ethenyl-N-methyl-3-phenyl-	EtOH	230(4.27),259(4.41),300s(3.80),368(4.02)	94-1404-73
$C_{18}H_{15}ClO_4S$			
Sulfonium, triphenyl-, perchlorate	MeOH	267(3.61),275(3.46)	35-1908-73
	$CHCl_3$	268(3.68),276(3.53)	35-1908-73
$C_{18}H_{15}ClO_4Se$			
Seleninium, 4-methyl-2,6-diphenyl-, perchlorate	MeCN-$HClO_4$	410(4.33)	103-0790-73
$C_{18}H_{15}Cl_2NO_2$			
Ethanone, 1-[5-chloro-3-(2-chlorophenyl)-2-(2-hydroxyethyl)-2H-isoindol-1-yl]-	EtOH	237(4.17),270(4.37),300s(4.70),363(4.20),377(4.25)	94-1404-73
$C_{18}H_{15}Cl_2N_3O_2$			
1H-Pyrazole-5-carboxylic acid, 4-amino-1,3-bis(4-chlorophenyl)-, ethyl ester	EtOH	244(4.60),280s(--)	22-2843-73
$C_{18}H_{15}Cl_2P$			
Phosphorus, dichlorotriphenyl-	MeCN	254(3.03),259(3.18),272(3.19)	33-2405-73
$C_{18}H_{15}Cl_2Sb$			
Antimony, dichlorotriphenyl-	MeCN	258(--),263(3.21),270(3.08)	33-2405-73
$C_{18}H_{15}IO$			
Oxonium, triphenyl-, iodide	MeOH	254(2.96),257(2.96),263(2.77)	35-1908-73
$C_{18}H_{15}N$			
3H-Indole, 3-methyl-2-phenyl-3-(2-propynyl)-	EtOH	222s(4.06),228(4.11),233(4.10),244(3.99),306(4.12)	39-1913-73C
Pyridine, 2-(diphenylmethyl)-	pH 2	262(3.85)	39-2111-73B
	pH 8	260(3.66),270s(3.53)	39-2111-73B

Compound	Solvent	$\lambda_{max}(\log \epsilon)$	Ref.
[2.2](2,5)Pyrrolo[1,4]naphthalenophane	EtOH	227(4.28),243s(4.13), 301(3.43)	88-4017-73
$C_{18}H_{15}NO$			
4H-Carbazol-4-one, 1,2,3,4-tetrahydro-9-phenyl-	MeOH	207(4.49),242(4.37), 266(4.05),298(4.21)	24-0745-73
4(1H)-Pyridinone, 1-methyl-3,5-diphenyl-	EtOH	237(4.42),299(4.10)	4-0665-73
1H-Pyrrole, 1-acetyl-3,4-diphenyl-	EtOH	244(4.43),269s(4.15), 286s(4.02),294s(3.87), 303s(3.54)	24-3824-73
$C_{18}H_{15}NOSe$			
3-Buten-2-one, 1-(3-methyl-2(3H)-benzoselenazolylidene)-4-phenyl-	EtOH	228(4.45),280(4.14), 412(4.44)	73-3616-73
$C_{18}H_{15}NO_2$			
2H-1-Benzopyran-2-one, 4-[[(3,4-dimethylphenyl)imino]methyl]-	EtOH	245(4.09),315(4.08)	44-3874-73
Ethanone, 1-(3-benzoyl-6-methyl-1-indolizinyl)-	EtOH	232(4.18),253(4.22), 261s(4.20),285s(4.07), 294(4.12),347(4.21), 367s(4.19)	39-2091-73C
Ethanone, 1-(3-benzoyl-7-methyl-1-indolizinyl)-	EtOH	232s(4.20),238(4.22), 251s(4.21),286s(3.93), 296(4.01),337s(4.21), 359(4.26)	39-2091-73C
Ethanone, 1-(3-benzoyl-8-methyl-1-indolizinyl)-	EtOH	236(4.16),264(4.15), 292(3.89),337(4.06), 370(4.11)	39-2091-73C
Indole, 1,2-dimethyl-3-phthalidyl-	n.s.g.	202(4.61),223(4.74), 280(4.02),290(3.88)	39-1943-73C
2-Naphthalenecarboxamide, N-hydroxy-N-(3-methylphenyl)-	EtOH	226(4.62),275(4.15)	112-0547-73
2-Naphthalenecarboxamide, N-hydroxy-N-(4-methylphenyl)-	EtOH	226(4.62),274(4.15)	112-0547-73
$C_{18}H_{15}NO_3$			
1H-Pyrrole-2,5-dione, 3-(4-methoxyphenyl)-1-(4-methylphenyl)-	n.s.g.	322(3.93),375(3.85)	48-0717-73
4H-Quinolizine-1-carboxylic acid, 4-oxo-2-phenyl-, ethyl ester	EtOH	260(4.50),386(4.24)	4-0139-73
$C_{18}H_{15}NO_4$			
9-Anthracenecarbonitrile, 10-hydroxy-2,4,5-trimethoxy-	EtOH	228(4.26),272(4.80), 308(4.21),349(3.59), 368(3.82),392s(3.60), 413(3.81),435(3.87), 461(3.80)	39-2853-73C
1,3-Propanedione, 1-(6-hydroxy-3-methyl-1,2-benzisoxazol-7-yl)-3-(4-methylphenyl)-	n.s.g.	220(4.3),247(4.5), 271(4.1),384(4.5)	2-0541-73
1H-Pyrrole-2,5-dione, 1,3-bis(4-methoxyphenyl)-	n.s.g.	334(3.95),375(3.85)	48-0717-73
$C_{18}H_{15}NO_5$			
Carbamic acid, [4-(6-methoxy-2-oxo-2H-1-benzopyran-3-yl)phenyl]-, methyl ester	MeOH	230(4.57),247(4.25), 282(3.88),355(4.23)	24-0388-73
1H-Indole-1,3-diacetic acid, 2,3-dihydro-2-oxo-3-phenyl-	EtOH	255(3.92),283(3.32)	104-0831-73

Compound	Solvent	$\lambda_{max}(\log \epsilon)$	Ref.
Isoxazolium, 2-[(2,3-dimethoxyphenyl)-methylene]-2,5-dihydro-3-hydroxy-5-oxo-4-phenyl]-, hydroxide, inner salt	dioxan	468(3.60)	44-1782-73
Isoxazolium, 2-[(2,4-dimethoxyphenyl)-methylene]-2,5-dihydro-3-hydroxy-5-oxo-4-phenyl]-, hydroxide, inner salt	dioxan	466(3.63)	44-1782-73
Isoxazolium, 2-[(3,4-dimethoxyphenyl)-methylene]-2,5-dihydro-3-hydroxy-5-oxo-4-phenyl]-, hydroxide, inner salt	dioxan	468(3.30)	44-1782-73
$C_{18}H_{15}NO_5S$			
Benzenesulfonic acid, 4-nitro-, 2-(4-azulenyl)ethyl ester	CH_2Cl_2	280(4.66),286(4.63), 329(3.48),343(3.62), 571(2.56),616(2.46), 676(2.08)	44-1106-73
Benzenesulfonic acid, 4-nitro-, 2-(6-azulenyl)ethyl ester	CH_2Cl_2	279(4.85),285(3.67), 330(3.67),337(3.65), 344(3.80),573(2.48), 590(2.45),622(2.41), 684(1.98)	44-1106-73
$C_{18}H_{15}NO_6$			
Benzofuro[3,2-h]quinoline-2-carboxylic acid, 1,4,7,8-tetrahydro-5-hydroxy-9-methoxy-4-oxo-, methyl ester	$CHCl_3$	338(4.46),385s(3.85)	39-2374-73C
$C_{18}H_{15}NO_7S$			
2-Quinolinecarboxylic acid, 1,4-dihydro-5,8-dihydroxy-6-[(4-methylphenyl)sulfonyl]-4-oxo-, methyl ester	EtOH	245(4.41),262s(4.30), 290s(3.73),343(3.95), 392s(3.58)	39-2374-73C
$C_{18}H_{15}NO_8$			
Acetamide, N-[2-(acetyloxy)-1,2,6,9-tetrahydro-5-hydroxy-2-methyl-1,6,9-trioxonaphtho[2,1-b]furan-7-yl]-	EtOH-HCl	212(4.34),234(4.41), 274(4.39),328(4.01), 386(3.68)	33-2323-73
$C_{18}H_{15}NS_2$			
6H-[1,2]Dithiolo[5,1-e]isothiazole-7-S^{IV}, 6-methyl-2,4-diphenyl-	MeOH	236(4.52),280s(4.18), 447(4.24)	39-2351-73C
$C_{18}H_{15}NS_3$			
Benzenesulfenamide, N,N-bis(phenylthio)-	EtOH	235(4.33),368(2.93)	39-1031-73C
$C_{18}H_{15}N_3$			
Benzenamine, N-phenyl-2-(phenylazo)-	C_6H_{12}	288(4.48),322(4.35), 457(4.03)	44-0507-73
1H-Indole, 1-methyl-3-(5-phenyl-1H-pyrazol-3-yl)-	EtOH	205(4.61),222(4.58), 279(4.17)	103-0038-73
Naphtho[2,1-e][1,2,4]triazine, 1,2-dihydro-3-methyl-2-phenyl-	MeOH	242(4.77),266(3.98), 314(3.74),326(3.71)	103-0145-73
1H-Pyrrolo[1,2-b][1,2,4]triazole, 2-methyl-1,6-diphenyl-	MeOH	220(3.81),251(4.21), 270(4.25)	118-0414-73
$C_{18}H_{15}N_3O_2S$			
3(2H)-Benzothiazolecarboxaldehyde, 2-(2,5-dihydro-2-methyl-5-oxo-1-phenyl-1H-pyrazol-3-yl)-	EtOH	290(3.99)	95-0207-73
$C_{18}H_{15}N_3O_3$			
Ethanone, 1-[5-methyl-1-(4-nitrophenyl)-3-phenyl-1H-pyrazol-4-yl]-	EtOH	226(5.41),255s(5.22), 300(5.21)	78-0121-73

Compound	Solvent	λmax(log ε)	Ref.
$C_{18}H_{15}N_3O_4$			
3-Isoxazoleacetic acid, 4,5-dihydro-5-oxo-α-(phenylhydrazono)-, phenylmethyl ester	EtOH	278(4.28)	70-2006-73
2H-1,4-Oxazin-3(4H)-one, 2-(1-aziridinyl)-6-(4-nitrophenyl)-4-phenyl-	EtOH	249(4.15),366(4.10)	4-0347-73
$C_{18}H_{15}N_3O_4S$			
1H-Benzimidazole-1-carboxamide, 3-acetyl-2,3-dihydro-N-(phenoxyacetyl)-2-thioxo-	MeOH	249(4.32),301(4.28)	103-0639-73
5H-1,3,4-Thiadiazolo[2,3-b]quinazolin-5-one, 2-(3,4,5-trimethoxyphenyl)-	n.s.g.	220(5.44),291(5.57), 300(5.56)	48-0185-73
$C_{18}H_{15}O$			
Oxonium, triphenyl-, tetrafluoroborate	MeOH	252(2.81),257(2.83), 263(2.63)	35-1908-73
	$CHCl_3$	255(2.97),257(2.99), 263(2.73)	35-1908-73
$C_{18}H_{15}S$			
Sulfonium, triphenyl-, perchlorate	MeOH	267(3.61),275(3.46)	35-1908-73
	$CHCl_3$	268(3.68),276(3.53)	35-1908-73
$C_{18}H_{15}Se$			
Seleninium, 4-methyl-2,6-diphenyl-, perchlorate	MeCN-$HClO_4$	410(4.33)	103-0790-73
$C_{18}H_{16}$			
Benzene, 1,1'-(1,3,5-hexatriene-1,6-diyl)bis-	81.5% H_2SO_4	370(3.30),440(3.23)	48-0810-73
	95.8% H_2SO_4	393(4.19),475(4.53)	48-0810-73
	99.9% H_2SO_4	428(4.00),470(4.09), 600s(3.72)	48-0810-73
	18% SO_3	390(3.83),471(4.44), 545(4.06),581(4.14)	48-0810-73
	33% SO_3	385(4.17),530(3.76), 580(3.70)	48-0810-73
Cyclobuta[1,2-a:4,3-a']dipentalene, 3b,3c,7a,7b-tetrahydro-2,5-dimethyl-	hexane	257(4.20),272(4.11), 382(2.90)	89-0337-73
isomer	hexane	258(4.25),263(4.28), 276(4.15),392(3.06)	89-0337-73
9,10-Ethenoanthracene, 9,10-dihydro-1,5-dimethyl-, (-)-	isooctane	195(4.48),215s(4.59), 220(4.73),237s(3.63), 273(2.92),281(3.10)	18-0915-73
Naphthalene, 2,3-dimethyl-1-phenyl-	hexane	228(4.78),275(3.85), 284(3.90),319(2.90), 324(2.74)	54-0845-73
Tetracyclo[6.6.2.1^{3,13}.1^{6,10}]octadeca-1,3(17),4,6,8,10(18),13-heptaene	C_6H_{12}	281s(2.77),318(1.95)	35-3201-73
$C_{18}H_{16}BrClN_2O_2$			
2H-Isoindole-1-carboxamide, 5-bromo-3-(2-chlorophenyl)-2-(2-hydroxyethyl)-N-methyl-	EtOH	265(4.40),344(3.08), 361s(--)	94-0742-73
$C_{18}H_{16}BrNO_3$			
1H-Indole-3-acetic acid, 5-bromo-2,3-dihydro-2-oxo-3-phenyl-, ethyl ester	EtOH	258(4.12),295(3.20)	104-0861-73
1H-Indole-3-carboxylic acid, 6-bromo-5-hydroxy-2-methyl-1-phenyl-, ethyl ester	EtOH	216(4.62),244(4.52), 292(4.20)	103-0306-73

Compound	Solvent	λ_{max}(log ε)	Ref.
$C_{18}H_{16}Br_2$			
Chrysene, 2,8-dibromo-4b,5,6,10b,11,12-hexahydro-, cis	C_6H_{12}	260s(3.21),273(3.39), 281(3.42)	5-1112-73
$C_{18}H_{16}ClNO_2S_2$			
Morpholine, 4-[2-[2-(4-chlorophenyl)-thio]phenyl]-2-oxo-1-thioxoethyl]-	MeOH	227(4.40),269(4.28), 344(3.79)	73-0115-73
$C_{18}H_{16}ClNO_3$			
1H-Indole-3-acetic acid, 5-chloro-2,3-dihydro-2-oxo-3-phenyl-, ethyl ester	EtOH	258(4.03),294(3.20)	104-0861-73
1H-Indole-3-carboxylic acid, 1-(2-chlorophenyl)-6-hydroxy-2-methyl-	dioxan	275(4.04),300(3.99)	83-0446-73
$C_{18}H_{16}ClN_3OS$			
Methanone, [4-amino-2-[4-(dimethylamino)-phenyl]-5-thiazolyl](4-chlorophenyl)-	DMF	429(4.72)	48-0497-73
$C_{18}H_{16}ClN_3O_9$			
Uridine, 2'-chloro-2'-deoxy-, 3'-acetate 5'-(4-nitrobenzoate)	MeOH	257(4.35)	35-4016-73
$C_{18}H_{16}Cl_2N_2O_2$			
2H-Isoindole-1-carboxamide, 5-chloro-3-(2-chlorophenyl)-2-(2-hydroxyethyl)-N-methyl-	EtOH	265(4.38),344(4.09), 360s(--)	94-0742-73 +94-1404-73
$C_{18}H_{16}Cl_2N_2O_4S$			
Acetic acid, dichloro-, 2,3-dihydro-1-methyl-2-[[(4-methylphenyl)sulfonyl]-imino]-1H-indol-3-yl ester	n.s.g.	230(4.47),276(4.06), 285(4.05),311(3.83)	39-1943-73C
$C_{18}H_{16}Cl_2O_5$			
Ethanone, 1,1'-[oxybis[methylene(5-chloro-2-hydroxy-3,1-phenylene]]bis-	$CHCl_3$	258(4.15),350(3.92)	104-1927-73
Vicanicin	EtOH	226s(4.50),270(3.89), 325(3.38)	94-1547-73
$C_{18}H_{16}F_3NO_5$			
3,5-Pyridinedicarboxylic acid, 2,6-dimethyl-4-[2-(trifluoromethyl)phenyl]-, mono(2-hydroxyethyl) ester	EtOH	272(3.70)	87-0034-73
$C_{18}H_{16}F_3N_5O_2$			
Propanenitrile, 3-[ethyl[4-[[4-nitro-2-(trifluoromethyl)phenyl]azo]-phenyl]amino]-	MeOH	480(4.64)	89-0926-73
$C_{18}H_{16}NO_2$			
1,2-Oxazin-1-ium, 6-ethoxy-3,5-diphenyl-, tetrachloroferrate	CH_2Cl_2	326(4.03),375(4.31)	104-2006-73
$C_{18}H_{16}N_2$			
2-Propenal, 3-phenyl-, (3-phenyl-2-propenylidene)hydrazone	$CHCl_3$	349(4.79),362(4.78)	22-3303-73
Pyrimidine, 2,4-dimethyl-5,6-diphenyl-	C_6H_{12}	225(4.27),273(4.01)	44-1333-73
2H-Pyrrole-3-carbonitrile, 3,4-dihydro-3-methyl-2,5-diphenyl-, cis	EtOH	248(4.26)	35-1945-73

Compound	Solvent	$\lambda_{max}(\log \epsilon)$	Ref.
$C_{18}H_{16}N_2O$			
Acetamide, N-[1H-isoindol-1-ylidene-(2-methylphenyl)methylene]-	EtOH	241(4.38),290(3.96), 340(3.82)	107-0181-73
4H-1,2-Diazepine, 6-methoxy-4,5-diphenyl-	MeOH	263(3.98),303(3.92), 334(3.95)	44-2954-73
3H-Indol-3-one, 1,2-dihydro-2-methyl-2-(2-methyl-1H-indol-3-yl)-	EtOH	259(4.16),288s(3.97), 405(3.54)	78-0603-73
$C_{18}H_{16}N_2OS$			
Benzamide, N-(3,4-dimethyl-2-phenyl-5-thiazolidinylidene)-, meso-ionic didehydro deriv.	EtOH	298(3.86),382(4.25)	18-0964-73
$C_{18}H_{16}N_2OS_2$			
Benzamide, N-[3-methyl-2-(methylthio)-4-phenyl-5-thiazolidinylidene]-, meso-ionic didehydro deriv.	EtOH	230(4.30),330(4.06), 382(4.21)	18-0964-73
$C_{18}H_{16}N_2O_2$			
Carbamic acid, (8-phenyl-2-quinolinyl)-, ethyl ester	EtOH	230s(4.41),248(4.66), 295(3.77),324(3.68)	12-2213-73
2,4-Hexadienediamide, N,N'-diphenyl-, (E,E)-	EtOH	229(4.08),274(4.37), 320(4.49)	104-2527-73
Pyrrolidine, 1-(10-nitro-9-anthracen-9-yl)-	MeCN	252(5.02),275s(4.38), 307s(3.90),355s(3.75), 373(3.81),385s(3.77), 420s(3.60),550(3.62)	22-1305-73
$C_{18}H_{16}N_2O_2S$			
1,3(2H,4H)-Isoquinolinedione, 4-[(methylthio)[(phenylmethyl)amino]methylene]-	EtOH	227(3.40),290(3.12), 330(3.00)	95-0322-73
Sulfilimine, N-(2-cyano-3-ethoxy-3-oxo-1-propenyl)-S,S-diphenyl-	EtOH	230s(4.16),300(4.46)	44-4324-73
Sulfoxonium, dimethyl-, 2-oxo-2-phenyl-1-(2-quinoxalinyl)ethylide	EtOH	239(4.32),282(4.02), 384(3.83)	95-1064-73
$C_{18}H_{16}N_2O_3$			
2H-1-Benzopyran-2-one, 8-ethyl-4-hydroxy-6-methyl-3-(phenylazo)-	MeOH	213(4.49),253(4.00), 365(4.11)	2-0433-73
Isoxazolium, 2-[[4-(dimethylamino)phenyl]methylene]-2,5-dihydro-3-hydroxy-5-oxo-4-phenyl-, hydroxide, inner salt	dioxan	408(4.40)	44-1782-73
$C_{18}H_{16}N_2O_4$			
3H-Indol-5-ol, 2,3,3-trimethyl-, 4-nitrobenzoate	EtOH	261(4.36)	88-0903-73
2H-1,4-Oxazin-3(4H)-one, 2,2-dimethyl-6-(4-nitrophenyl)-4-phenyl-	EtOH	253(4.17),373(4.20)	4-0347-73
$C_{18}H_{16}N_2O_4S$			
1H-Indole, 1-[(4-methylphenyl)sulfonyl]-3-(2-nitro-1-propenyl)-	EtOH	235(4.19),249(4.15), 352(4.04)	12-2555-73
$C_{18}H_{16}N_2O_4S_2$			
Thiopyrano[4,3-b]indole-3,4-dicarboxylic acid, 1-[(cyanomethyl)thio]-4a,5-dihydro-4a-methyl-, dimethyl ester	EtOH	257(4.23),380(3.85)	94-2770-73

Compound	Solvent	λ_{max}(log ε)	Ref.
$C_{18}H_{16}N_2O_5S$			
2H-1,2-Benzothiazine-3-carboxamide, 4-acetoxy-2-methyl-N-phenyl-, 1,1-dioxide	EtOH	230(4.15),280s(3.95), 314(4.05)	87-0044-73
2-Propenoic acid, 3-[1-acetyl-3-(acetyloxy)-1H-indol-2-yl]-2-cyano-3-(methylthio)-, methyl ester	EtOH	242(4.28),265(4.16), 326(4.26)	94-1658-73
$C_{18}H_{16}N_2O_8$			
Pyrido[2,3-g]quinoline-2,7-dicarboxylic acid, 1,4,6,9-tetrahydro-5,10-dimethoxy-4,9-dioxo-, dimethyl ester	$CHCl_3$	265(4.66),298(4.08), 356(3.89),443(4.01), 465(4.08)	39-2374-73C
$C_{18}H_{16}N_4O$			
Benzamide, N-[(4-amino-2-phenyl-5-pyrimidinyl)methyl]-	MeCN	210(4.07),298(4.08)	18-0253-73
	MeCN-HCl	254(--)	18-0253-73
Benzenecarboximidamide, N-[(3,4-dihydro-4-oxo-2-phenyl-5-pyrimidinyl)methyl]-	MeOH	235(4.45),295(4.00)	18-0580-73
	MeOH-HCl	235(--),285(--)	18-0580-73
	MeOH-NaOH	234(--),285(--), 294(--)	18-0580-73
$C_{18}H_{16}N_4O_3S$			
Methanone, [4-amino-2-[4-(dimethylamino)-phenyl]-5-thiazolyl](4-nitrophenyl)-	DMF	444(4.40)	48-0497-73
$C_{18}H_{16}N_4O_4$			
2,4,6(1H,3H,5H)-Pyrimidinetrione, 5-acetoxy-, 2-(diphenylhydrazone)	EtOH	405(4.05)	103-0247-73
$C_{18}H_{16}N_5$			
1H-[1,2,4]Triazolo[1,5-a]pyrimidin-8-ium, 2-amino-7-methyl-1,5-diphenyl-, perchlorate	n.s.g.	236(4.20),290(4.02), 328(3.80)	124-1036-73
$C_{18}H_{16}N_6$			
1H-1,2,3-Triazolo[4,5-c]pyridine-4,6-diamine, 1-(diphenylmethyl)-	10% MeOH-pH 7	228s(4.40),285(3.80), 322(3.85)	44-1095-73
3H-1,2,3-Triazolo[4,5-b]pyridine-5,7-diamine, 3-(diphenylmethyl)-	10% MeOH-pH 7	292(4.20)	44-1095-73
$C_{18}H_{16}N_6O_2$			
Benzonitrile, 2-[[4-(2-cyanoethyl)ethylamino]phenyl]azo]-5-nitro-	MeOH	504(4.65)	89-0926-73
$C_{18}H_{16}N_8$			
1H,6H-Bis[1,2,4]triazolo[4,3-b:4',3'-e]-[1,2,4,5]tetrazine, 1,6-bis(phenylmethyl)-	MeOH	300(4.12)	48-1131-73
$C_{18}H_{16}O$			
15H-Cyclopenta[a]phenanthren-17-ol, 16,17-dihydro-11-methyl-	EtOH	227(4.22),255(4.78), 281(4.02),293(4.02), 305(4.10),323(2.79), 339(2.96),354(2.98)	39-1255-73C
Ethanone, 1-(9,10-dihydro-9,10-ethanoanthracen-1-yl)-	EtOH	245(3.99),292(3.40)	49-0274-73
Ethanone, 1-(9,10-dihydro-9,10-ethanoanthracen-2-yl)-	EtOH	260(4.08),270s(3.99), 295s(3.26)	49-0274-73
2-Propanone, 1-(3-phenyl-1H-inden-1-yl)-	EtOH	207(4.4),232(4.35), 267(3.78)	104-2377-73

Compound	Solvent	$\lambda_{max}(\log \epsilon)$	Ref.
$C_{18}H_{16}O_2$			
1-Butanone, 1-(3-phenyl-2-benzofuranyl)-	EtOH	208(4.16),230(4.18), 300(4.28)	44-1993-73
1,7-Chrysenedione, 2,3,4,8,9,10-hexahydro-	EtOH	237(3.90),252s(4.19), 259(4.43),281(3.57), 292(3.75),302(3.78), 360(3.01),379(3.07)	39-0044-73C
Cyclobuta[b]naphthalene-3,8-dione, 2a,3a,4,7,7a,8a-hexahydro-1-phenyl-	EtOH	230(3.92),257(3.91), 266(3.85),283(3.42), 294s(2.45),309s(2.32)	104-2389-73
15H-Cyclopenta[a]phenanthrene-16,17-diol, 16,17-dihydro-11-methyl-, cis	EtOH	227(4.19),255(4.83), 281(4.07),293(4.03), 304(4.11),324(2.80), 339(2.96),354(2.94)	39-1255-73C
trans	EtOH	227(4.22),256(4.85), 281(4.07),293(4.04), 305(4.13),323(2.82), 339(2.97),354(2.98)	39-1255-73C
2-Cyclopenten-1-one, 4-hydroxy-2-methyl-3,4-diphenyl-	EtOH	276(4.30)	44-1749-73
2-Cyclopenten-1-one, 4-hydroxy-5-methyl-3,4-diphenyl-, (4SR,5RS)-	EtOH	285(4.29)	44-1749-73
(4SR,5SR)-	EtOH	286(4.32)	44-1749-73
Dicyclopenta[a,f]naphthalene-1,6-dione, 2,3,7,8-tetrahydro-3,8-dimethyl-	EtOH	234(4.64),240(4.72), 312(4.18),344(3.72)	132-0279-73
9,10-Ethanoanthracene-1-carboxylic acid, 9,10-dihydro-, methyl ester	EtOH	285(3.48)	49-0274-73
9,10-Ethanoanthracene-2-carboxylic acid, 9,10-dihydro-, methyl ester	EtOH	248(4.01)	49-0274-73
9,10-Ethenoanthracene, 9,10-dihydro-1,5-dimethoxy-, (+)-	EtOH	219(4.62),277(3.36), 285(3.39)	18-0915-73
9,10-Ethenoanthracene-1,5-dimethanol, 9,10-dihydro-, (-)-	MeOH	193s(4.63),196s(4.62), 200s(4.58),203s(4.57), 207s(4.55),215s(4.59), 220(4.64),257s(3.07), 267s(3.02),276(3.30), 284(3.54)	18-0915-73
6H-Phenaleno[1,2-b]furan-6-one, 8,9-dihydro-1,8,8-trimethyl-	EtOH	264s(4.45),271(4.53), 338(3.92),430(4.29)	39-2159-73C
7H-Phenaleno[1,2-b]furan-7-one, 8,9-dihydro-8,8,9-trimethyl-	EtOH	213(4.32),235(4.41), 256s(3.92),339(4.03), 356s(3.91),428(3.34)	39-2159-73C
7H-Phenaleno[1,2-b]furan-7-one, 8,9-dihydro-8,9,9-trimethyl-	EtOH	214(4.32),235(4.42), 258s(3.80),340(4.07), 356s(3.96)	39-2159-73C
1H-Phenalen-1-one, 3-[(3-methyl-2-butenyl)oxy]-	EtOH	226(4.32),245(4.32), 327(4.09),352(4.00), 394s(3.75)	39-2159-73C
$C_{18}H_{16}O_3$			
2-Cyclopropene-1-carboxylic acid, 1-methoxy-2,3-diphenyl-, methyl ester	MeOH	222(3.84),229(3.90), 287(3.96),300(4.11), 316(4.02)	104-1449-73
5,11-Epoxy-6,10-etheno-7H-cyclohepta[b]naphthalen-7-one, 5,5a,6,10,10a,11-hexahydro-8-methoxy-	EtOH	265(3.49),267(3.51), 274(3.53),280(3.50), 330(2.24)	44-4100-73
3,4-Furandimethanol, 2,5-diphenyl-	$CHCl_3$	300(4.4)	22-1154-73

Compound	Solvent	λ_{max}(log ε)	Ref.
$C_{18}H_{16}O_4$			
2-Butenoic acid, 3-methyl-, 7-(2,4-hexa-diynylidene)-1,6-dioxaspiro[4.4]nona-2,8-dien-4-yl ester, (E)-	ether	212(4.52),314(4.32)	24-0845-73
(Z)-	ether	211(4.50),308s(4.34), 319(4.37),338s(4.14)	24-0845-73
7-Phenanthrenol, 2,4-dimethoxy-, acetate	n.s.g.	258(4.86),279s(4.31)	39-1263-73C
2-Propenoic acid, 2-methyl-, 1,5-naph-thalenediyl ester	dioxan	296.5(3.83)	126-0025-73B
2-Propenoic acid, 2-methyl-, 1,7-naph-thalenediyl ester	dioxan	294(3.76),319(--)	126-0025-73B
2-Propenoic acid, 2-methyl-, 2,7-naph-thalenediyl ester	dioxan	292(3.73),315(--)	126-0025-73B
2H,6H-Pyrano[3,2-b]xanthen-6-one, 3,4-dihydro-5-hydroxy-2,2-dimethyl-	MeOH	254(4.52),292(4.16), 314(4.28),360(4.01)	2-1237-73
2H,12H-Pyrano[2,3-a]xanthen-12-one, 3,4-dihydro-5-hydroxy-2,2-dimethyl-	MeOH	251(4.28),285(4.39), 312(4.11),354(3.98)	2-1237-73
9H-Xanthen-9-one, 1,3-dihydroxy-2-(3-methyl-2-butenyl)-	MeOH	263(4.42),301(4.46), 341(4.21)	2-1237-73
$C_{18}H_{16}O_4S$			
4H-Thiopyran-4-one, 2,3-dihydro-2-meth-oxy-2,6-diphenyl-, 1,1-dioxide	EtOH	217(4.34),292(4.00)	18-1007-73
$C_{18}H_{16}O_5$			
9,10-Anthracenedione, 1,3,8-trimethoxy-6-methyl-	EtOH	225(4.45),278(4.38), 403(3.61)	39-2853-73C
Butanedioic acid, [3-(2-furanyl)-1-phen-yl-2-propenylidene]-, 1-methyl ester	EtOH	248(3.95),365(3.96)	42-0430-73
Flavone, 5,6,7-trimethoxy-	EtOH	216(4.58),264(4.40), 306(4.35)	102-3014-73
Phenanthro[3,4-d]-1,3-dioxole, 4,9,10-trimethoxy-	EtOH	212s(4.17),236(4.69), 285(3.90),309(3.68), 322(3.86),348(4.47)	12-2035-73
2-Propen-1-one, 1-(1,3-benzodioxol-5-yl)-3-(3,4-dimethoxyphenyl)-	EtOH	254(4.20),360(4.45)	4-0085-73
2-Propen-1-one, 3-(1,3-benzodioxol-5-yl)-1-(3,4-dimethoxyphenyl)-	EtOH	242(4.23),360(4.53)	4-0867-73
2H,6H-Pyrano[3,2-b]xanthen-6-one, 3,4-dihydro-5,8-dihydroxy-2,2-dimethyl-	MeOH	264(4.32),313(4.40), 372(3.64)	2-1233-73
2H,12H-Pyrano[2,3-a]xanthen-12-one, 3,4-dihydro-5,10-dihydroxy-2,2-dimethyl-	MeOH	264(4.21),308(4.42), 378(4.01)	2-1233-73
9H-Xanthen-9-one, 1,3,7-trihydroxy-2-(3-methyl-2-butenyl)-	MeOH	268(4.42),308(4.48), 372(4.04)	2-1233-73
$C_{18}H_{16}O_6$			
[1]Benzopyrano[3,4-b][1]benzopyran-12(6H)-one, 6a,12a-dihydro-9-hydroxy-2,3-dimethoxy-, cis-(±)-	EtOH	202(4.61),233(4.14), 282(4.15),317(3.90)	39-1277-73C
Flavanone, 2',5-dimethoxy-6,7-(methyl-enedioxy)-	EtOH	242(3.84),279(3.68), 335(3.33)	78-2703-73
Flavone, 5-hydroxy-4',6,7-trimethoxy-	EtOH	279(4.38),330(4.50)	95-0707-73
5H-Furo[3,2-b]xanthen-5-one, 2,3-di-hydro-4,8,9-trihydroxy-2,3,3-tri-methyl-	n.s.g.	248(4.54),286(4.26), 336(4.17)	2-0518-73
Isoflavone, 2'-hydroxy-4',5',7-trimeth-oxy-	EtOH	221(4.45),247s(4.28), 266(4.22),299(4.26)	39-1277-73C
Methanone, (5,6-dimethoxy-3-benzofuran-yl)(2-hydroxy-4-methoxyphenyl)-	EtOH	245(4.19),293(4.21), 325(4.06)	39-1277-73C

Compound	Solvent	$\lambda_{max}(\log \epsilon)$	Ref.
2-Propen-1-one, 1-(6-hydroxy-4-methoxy-1,3-benzodioxol-5-yl)-3-(2-methoxyphenyl)-	EtOH	240(4.09),312(4.21), 358(4.30)	78-2703-73
$C_{18}H_{16}O_7$			
4H-1-Benzopyran-4-one, 5,7-dihydroxy-3,6-dimethoxy-2-(4-methoxyphenyl)-	EtOH	273(4.31),341(4.29)	78-2575-73
	EtOH-NaOH	276(4.46),296s(4.34), 378(4.12)	78-2575-73
4H-1-Benzopyran-4-one, 5-hydroxy-2-(4-hydroxy-3-methoxyphenyl)-6,7-dimethoxy-	MeOH	275(4.2),345(4.3)	2-0201-73
4H-1-Benzopyran-4-one, 5-hydroxy-2-(2-hydroxyphenyl)-3,7,8-trimethoxy-	EtOH	252s(4.32),265(4.41), 304s(3.82),346(3.88)	77-0555-73
Furo[3,4-f]-1,3-benzodioxol-5(7H)-one, 7-(3,4,5-trimethoxyphenyl)-	EtOH	302(3.83)	39-1266-73C
Quercitin, 3,3',7-trimethyl-	EtOH	255(4.32),267s(4.24), 357(4.31)	12-1111-73
	EtOH-KOH	265(4.30),404(4.42)	12-1111-73
$C_{18}H_{16}S_3$			
Thiophene, 2,5-bis[2-(5-methyl-2-thienyl)ethenyl]-	DMF	419(4.70),440(4.60)	24-0655-73
$C_{18}H_{17}$			
Cyclopropenylium, diphenylpropyl-, tetrafluoroborate	2.9M HCl	246(4.20),293(4.53), 307(4.54)	18-3881-73
$C_{18}H_{17}ClN_2O_2$			
2H-Isoindole-1-carboxamide, 5-chloro-2-(2-hydroxyethyl)-N-methyl-3-phenyl-	EtOH	228(4.38),263(4.42), 298(3.78),358(4.08)	94-1404-73
2(1H)-Quinolinone, 6-chloro-3-[(2-hydroxyethyl)amino]-1-methyl-4-phenyl-	EtOH	238(4.52),261(4.17), 303(3.89),314(3.97), 338(4.23),352(4.24)	94-0807-73
$C_{18}H_{17}ClN_2O_2S$			
Benzenesulfonamide, 4-chloro-N-spiro-[cyclopentane-1,3'-[3H]indol]-2'(1'H)-ylidene-	EtOH	227(4.44),280(4.15)	39-1809-73C
Benzenesulfonamide, 4-chloro-N-(1,2,3,4-tetrahydro-4aH-carbazol-4a-yl)-	EtOH	216(4.21),220(4.22), 233s(3.94),260s(3.48)	39-1809-73C
$C_{18}H_{17}ClN_2O_4S$			
1H-Indole-2-carboxylic acid, 3-[[(4-chlorophenyl)sulfonyl]amino]-1-methyl-, ethyl ester	EtOH	230(4.62),301s(4.21), 320(3.84)	39-1602-73C
$C_{18}H_{17}ClN_4$			
2-Propanone, (7-chloro-5-phenyl-3H-1,4-benzodiazepin-2-yl)hydrazone	MeOH	260(4.47)	94-2375-73
$C_{18}H_{17}ClN_4O$			
2-Propanone, (7-chloro-5-phenyl-3H-1,4-benzodiazepin-2-yl)hydrazone, N-oxide	MeOH	246(4.42),280(4.47)	94-2375-73
$C_{18}H_{17}ClO_2$			
Benzoic acid, 4-[2-chloro-2-(4-methylphenyl)ethenyl]-, ethyl ester	EtOH	310(4.48)	104-1511-73

Compound	Solvent	λ_{max}(log ε)	Ref.
$C_{18}H_{17}Cl_2NO_6S$			
4H-1,4-Benzothiazinium, 6-chloro-2-(ethoxycarbonyl)-1-methyl-3-phenyl-, perchlorate	EtOH	213(4.42),224(4.44), 254(4.15),280(4.03), 378(4.06)	7-0045-73
4H-1,4-Benzothiazinium, 7-chloro-2-(ethoxycarbonyl)-1-methyl-3-phenyl-, perchlorate	EtOH	207(4.44),223(4.37), 261(4.22),280(4.09), 380(4.07)	7-0045-73
$C_{18}H_{17}Cl_3N_2O_4S$			
6αH-4-Thia-1-azabicyclo[4.2.0]oct-2-ene-2-carboxylic acid, 7α-methyl-8-oxo-7β-[(phenylacetyl)amino]-, 2,2,2-trichloroethyl ester	EtOH	264(3.75),306(3.71)	39-1321-73C
$C_{18}H_{17}F_3N_4$			
Propanenitrile, 3-[ethyl[4-[[2-(trifluoromethyl)phenyl]azo]phenyl]amino]-	MeOH	416(4.53)	89-0926-73
Propanenitrile, 3-[ethyl[4-[[4-(trifluoromethyl)phenyl]azo]phenyl]amino]-	MeOH	416(4.61)	89-0926-73
$C_{18}H_{17}N$			
1H-Indole, 3-methyl-2-phenyl-1-(2-propenyl)-	EtOH	228(4.45),238s(4.32), 299(4.11)	39-1913-73C
3H-Indole, 3-methyl-2-phenyl-3-(2-propenyl)-	EtOH	201(4.48),228(4.09), 233(4.09),236s(4.09), 244s(4.00),306(4.15)	39-1913-73C
$C_{18}H_{17}NO$			
2H-Pyrrol-2-one, 1,3-dihydro-3,4-dimethyl-3,5-diphenyl-	MeOH	218(4.22),280(3.8)	32-0003-73
2H-Pyrrol-2-one, 1,5-dihydro-4,5-dimethyl-3,5-diphenyl-	C_6H_{12}	211(4.12),240(4.18)	32-0003-73
$C_{18}H_{17}NO_2$			
3(2H)-Benzofuranone, 2-[[(2,4,6-trimethylphenyl)amino]methylene]-	MeOH	265(3.97),322(4.06), 397(4.41)	103-0141-73
2H-Benzofuro[2,3-b]pyrrol-2-one, 1-(3,4-dimethylphenyl)-1,3,3a,8a-tetrahydro-	EtOH	276(3.68),284(3.60)	44-3874-73
2,4,6-Heptatrienoic acid, 7-(2-quinolinyl)-, ethyl ester, (E,E,E)-	EtOH	239(4.00),300(4.44), 353(4.75),369(4.73)	54-0683-73
1-Indolizinecarboxylic acid, 5-methyl-2-phenyl-, ethyl ester	EtOH	238(4.40),257s(4.24), 300s(3.81),312(3.92), 328s(3.98),340(4.04), 355s(3.91)	94-1139-73
1-Indolizinecarboxylic acid, 8-methyl-2-phenyl-, ethyl ester	EtOH	237(4.46),258s(4.29), 296s(3.83),311(3.98), 325s(4.02),340(4.10), 356s(3.95)	94-1139-73
Pyrano[3,2-a]carbazole-5-methanol, 3,11-dihydro-3,3-dimethyl-	EtOH	226(4.60),282(4.57), 302(4.58)	44-2728-73
2H-Pyrrole-3-carboxylic acid, 3,4-dihydro-2,5-diphenyl-, methyl ester, cis	EtOH	247(4.26)	35-1945-73
$C_{18}H_{17}NO_2S$			
Benzenamine, 4-(2H-1-benzothiopyran-2-ylidenemethyl)-N,N-dimethyl-, S,S-dioxide	50% MeOH	240(4.22),270(4.03), 328(3.62),451(4.54)	39-0163-73C
	MeOH-HCl	244(4.16),275(4.16), 353(4.23)	39-0163-73C

Compound	Solvent	$\lambda_{max}(\log \epsilon)$	Ref.
Ethanone, 2-(3-ethyl-2(3H)-benzothiazolylidene)-1-(4-methoxyphenyl)-	EtOH	220(4.42),272(4.01), 386(4.63)	73-3616-73
Pyridine, 1,2-dihydro-1-methyl-2-(6-methyl-3-phenyl-2H-thiopyran-2-ylidene)-, S,S-dioxide	MeOH	245(4.12),278s(--), 341(3.78),483(4.02)	39-1184-73B
Pyridine, 1,4-dihydro-1-methyl-4-(2-methyl-5-phenyl-4H-thiopyran-4-ylidene)-, S,S-dioxide	MeOH	240(4.24),285(3.58), 337(3.72),470(4.61)	39-1184-73B
$C_{18}H_{17}NO_2Se$			
Ethanone, 2-(3-ethyl-2(3H)-benzoselenazolylidene)-1-(4-methoxyphenyl)-	EtOH	223(4.46),272(4.21), 389(4.62)	73-3616-73
$C_{18}H_{17}NO_3$			
1H-Indole-3-acetic acid, 2,3-dihydro-2-oxo-3-phenyl-, ethyl ester	EtOH	250(3.82),282(3.12)	104-0861-73
6H-Pyrano[3,2-b]acridin-6-one, 2,3,4,11-tetrahydro-5-hydroxy-2,2-dimethyl-	EtOH	226(4.3),245(4.5), 272(4.7),328(3.9), 403(3.7)	12-2311-73
Pyrano[3,2-a]carbazol-1(11H)-one, 2,3-dihydro-5-(hydroxymethyl)-3,3-dimethyl-	EtOH	228(4.65),283(4.08), 290(4.23)	44-2728-73
$C_{18}H_{17}NO_3S_2$			
Pyrrolidine, 1-[(10,11-dihydro-11-oxodibenzo[b,f]thiepin-2-yl)sulfonyl]-	MeOH	231(4.30),245(4.30), 284(4.05),335(3.72)	73-2137-73
$C_{18}H_{17}NO_5S$			
Acetic acid, [[2-methyl-3-(2-methyl-4-triazolyl)-4-oxo-4H-1-benzopyran-7-yl]oxy]-, ethyl ester	n.s.g.	295(4.06)	104-2580-73
$C_{18}H_{17}NO_6$			
Furo[3,4-c]phenanthridine-1,3,5(3aH)-trione, 3b,4,11,11a-tetrahydro-7,8-dimethoxy-4-methyl-	EtOH	230(3.86),253(4.06), 313(3.67)	78-3881-73
Pyrrolo[1,2-b]isoquinoline-2,10-dicarboxylic acid, 1,2,3,5-tetrahydro-1,5-dioxo-, diethyl ester	EtOH	214(4.41),256s(3.93), 322s(4.17),347(4.22), 356(4.15)	78-0213-73
$C_{18}H_{17}NS_2$			
Cycloheptano[1,2-b:4,3-b']dithiophene, 7-(phenylmethylamino)-	C_6H_{12}	238(4.32),268(4.11), 277(4.08),292(4.13), 304(4.26),332(3.88)	44-2814-73
$C_{18}H_{17}N_3$			
1H-Pyrrolo[2,3-b]quinolin-4-amine, 2,3-dihydro-1-methyl-N-phenyl-	EtOH	206(4.51),247(4.52), 330(4.10)	44-2614-73
$C_{18}H_{17}N_3O$			
2-Naphthalenol, 1-[[2-(dimethylamino)-phenyl]azo]-	$CHCl_3$	510(4.28)	48-0725-73
1,2-Propanedione, 1-(2-methyl-1H-indol-3-yl)-, 1-(phenylhydrazone)	EtOH	282(4.01),350(4.23)	78-3159-73
$C_{18}H_{17}N_3OS$			
Methanone, [4-amino-2-[4-(dimethylamino)phenyl]-5-thiazolyl]phenyl-	DMF	427(4.64)	48-0497-73

Compound	Solvent	$\lambda_{max}(\log \epsilon)$	Ref.
$C_{18}H_{17}N_3O_2$			
Spiro[3H-indole-3,3'-[3H]pyrazol]-2(1H)-one, 2',4'-dihydro-5'-(4-methoxyphenyl)-1-methyl-	EtOH	290(3.28)	103-0034-73
1H-1,2,3-Triazole-4-carboxylic acid, 5-(4-methylphenyl)-1-phenyl-, ethyl ester	EtOH	250(4.16)	42-0589-73
1H-1,2,3-Triazole-5-carboxylic acid, 4-(4-methylphenyl)-1-phenyl-, ethyl ester	EtOH	276(4.22)	42-0589-73
$C_{18}H_{17}N_3O_2S_2$			
7(4H)-Benzothiazolone, 6,6'-(iminodimethylidyne)bis[5,6-dihydro-2-methyl-	EtOH	290(3.94),335(3.65), 433(4.36)	32-1063-73
$C_{18}H_{17}N_3O_3$			
2H-Indol-2-one, 1,3-dihydro-1-methyl-3-(2-nitro-1-[(phenylmethyl)amino]-ethylidene]-	EtOH	280(4.23),340(4.10)	95-0612-73
1H-1,2,3-Triazole-4-carboxylic acid, 5-(4-methoxyphenyl)-1-phenyl-, ethyl ester	EtOH	260(4.17)	42-0589-73
$C_{18}H_{17}N_3O_4$			
2-Propenoic acid, 2-cyano-3-[2-[(2-cyano-3-ethoxy-3-oxo-1-propenyl)-amino]phenyl]-, ethyl ester	EtOH	212(4.37),234(4.42), 307(4.47),329(4.44)	94-1943-73
$C_{18}H_{17}N_3O_6$			
2,3-Diazabicyclo[2.2.1]hept-5-ene-2,3-dicarboxylic acid, 1-(1,3-dihydro-1,3-dioxo-2H-isoindol-2-yl)methyl]-, dimethyl ester	EtOH	218(4.66),241(3.98), 294(3.30)	35-7813-73
2,3-Diazabicyclo[2.2.1]hept-5-ene-2,3-dicarboxylic acid, 5-(1,3-dihydro-1,3-dioxo-2H-isoindol-2-yl)methyl]-, dimethyl ester	EtOH	221(4.67),238(4.02), 293(3.25)	35-7813-73
$C_{18}H_{17}N_3O_6S$			
1H-Indole-2-carboxylic acid, 1-methyl-3-[[(4-nitrophenyl)sulfonyl]amino]-, ethyl ester	$CHCl_3$	242(4.35),304(4.15), 310s(3.95),465(2.95)	39-1602-73C
$C_{18}H_{17}N_3O_6Se$			
Benzo[b]selenophene-3-carboxylic acid, 2-[(2,4-dinitrophenyl)methylene]-amino]-4,5,6,7-tetrahydro-, ethyl ester	EtOH	240(4.59),305(3.76)	103-0300-73
$C_{18}H_{17}N_5$			
Benzenecarboximidamide, N-[(4-amino-2-phenyl-5-pyrimidinyl)methyl]-	MeCN	237(4.36),260s(--), 284(3.91),297(3.88)	18-0253-73
	MeCN-HCl	254(--)	18-0253-73
Benzonitrile, 2-[[4-[(2-cyanoethyl)ethylamino]phenyl]azo]-	MeOH	434(4.62)	89-0926-73
Benzonitrile, 4-[[4-[(2-cyanoethyl)ethylamino]phenyl]azo]-	MeOH	433(4.65)	89-0926-73
$C_{18}H_{18}$			
[2.2.2](1,2,4)Cyclophane	EtOH	223(4.08),291(2.64), 305s(2.34)	35-5825-73

Compound	Solvent	λ max (log ε)	Ref.
[2.2.2](1,3,5)Cyclophane	hexane	258(3.08),312(1.98)	35-3201-73
9,10-Ethanoanthracene, 9,10-dihydro-1,5-dimethyl-, (-)-	isooctane	192s(4.97),194s(4.89), 196s(4.85),201(4.81), 204(4.80),208(4.76), 215s(4.60),243(2.99), 249(2.99),255(3.08), 261(3.03),265s(2.82), 268s(2.76),274(2.66)	18-0915-73
1,5,7,9,11,15-Hexadecahexaene-3,13-diyne, 2,15-dimethyl-, (all-E)-	benzene	384(4.96),404(4.87)	5-1339-73
(E,E,Z,Z)-	benzene	375(4.83),395s(4.69)	5-1339-73
3,5,7,9,11-Tetradecapentayne, 2,2,13,13-tetramethyl-	C_6H_{12}	242(--),254(--), 268(5.67)	33-1752-73
50% each solvent (also other mixtures)	$C_6H_{12}-CS_2$	277(5.37)	33-1752-73
$C_{18}H_{18}BrN_5O_4S$			
Propanenitrile, 3-[[4-[[2-bromo-6-(methylsulfonyl)-4-nitrophenyl]azo]phenyl]-ethylamino]-	MeOH	433(4.48)	89-0926-73
$C_{18}H_{18}ClN_3$			
1H-Pyrimido[1,2-a]quinazoline, 8-chloro-2,3,5,6-tetrahydro-5-methyl-6-phenyl-	n.s.g.	222(4.40),266(4.05)	40-1944-73
$C_{18}H_{18}F_2S_2$			
Tricyclo[9.3.1.$1^{4,8}$]hexadeca-1(15),4,6-8(16),11,13-hexaene, 15,16-difluoro-1,9-bis(methylthio)-	C_6H_{12}	274(2.96),281(2.92)	44-3928-73
$C_{18}H_{18}NO_2S$			
Pyridinium, 1-methyl-2-(6-methyl-3-phenyl-2H-thiopyran-2-yl)-, perchlorate, S,S-dioxide	$MeOH-HClO_4$	275(4.12),310(3.86)	39-1184-73B
$C_{18}H_{18}N_2$			
Azocyclopropane, 1,1'-diphenyl-	benzene	365(1.51)	24-2890-73
1,3-Diazabicyclo[3.1.0]hex-3-ene, 2,6-dimethyl-4,5-diphenyl-, exo	C_6H_{12}	230(4.10)	44-1333-73
1H-Indole, 2,3-dihydro-3-(1H-indol-3-ylmethyl)-3-methyl-	MeOH	225(4.47),284(3.98), 292(3.96)	44-1504-73
$C_{18}H_{18}N_2O$			
1H-1,2-Diazepine, 1-benzoyl-4,5,6,7-tetrahydro-3-phenyl-	EtOH	240(4.04),307(3.70)	88-0603-73
5-Isoxazoleethanamine, 3-methyl-N,α-diphenyl-	EtOH	247(4.15),297(3.38)	18-3533-73
2-Pyridinamine, N-methyl-N-[1-(1-naphthalenyl)ethyl]-, 1-oxide, (S)-(-)-	MeOH	223(4.83),245(4.29), 273(4.01),285(4.04), 295(3.99),330(3.59)	32-1083-73
4(3H)-Quinazolinone, 3-(1-methylethyl)-2-(4-methylphenyl)-	MeOH	206(4.62),230(4.45), 279(4.04),305s(3.76), 315s(3.59)	78-2153-73
$C_{18}H_{18}N_2O_2$			
Diazene, bis[2-(3-methylphenyl)ethenyl]-, 1,2-dioxide	benzene	335(4.4)	48-0796-73
Indolo[3,2,1-de]pyrido[3,2,1-ij][1,5]-12a-homonaphthyridine, 1,2,3,5,6,12-13,14-octahydro-1,12-dioxo-	EtOH	242(5.34),266(5.02), 292(4.80),301(4.79)	22-2705-73
Methanol, (9,10-didehydroergolin-8-ylidene)-, acetate	MeOH	248(4.19),339(4.11)	44-2249-73

Compound	Solvent	λ_{max}(log ε)	Ref.
$C_{18}H_{18}N_2O_2S$			
1H-Imidazole, 4,5-bis(4-methoxyphenyl)-2-(methylthio)-	EtOH	238(4.31),275(4.32)	24-1628-73
$C_{18}H_{18}N_2O_3S$			
4-Imidazolidinone, 5-ethoxy-5-[(4-hydroxyphenyl)methyl]-3-phenyl-2-thioxo-	EtOH	272(4.19)	63-1307-73
$C_{18}H_{18}N_2O_4$			
Diazene, bis[2-(3-methoxyphenyl)ethenyl]-, 1,2-dioxide	benzene	326(4.2)	48-0796-73
$C_{18}H_{18}N_2O_4S$			
1H-Indole, 1-[(4-methylphenyl)sulfonyl]-	EtOH	215(4.43),246s(4.15), 283(3.62),292(3.59)	12-2555-73
Sulfur diimide, bis[4-(ethoxycarbonyl)-phenyl]-	C_6H_{12}	376(4.10),425(4.19)	143-0285-73
$C_{18}H_{18}N_2O_5$			
Acetamide, N-[2-[1-methyl-1-[(4-nitrobenzoyl)oxy]ethyl]phenyl]-	EtOH	257(4.20)	88-0903-73
$C_{18}H_{18}N_2O_7$			
2-Propenoic acid, 2-hydroxy-3-[2-(4-methoxyphenyl)methoxy]-5-nitro-4-pyridinyl]-, ethyl ester	EtOH	224(4.39),282(3.99)	44-1824-73
$C_{18}H_{18}N_4$			
4H-Indene-5,5,6,6-tetracarbonitrile, 3a,7-dihydro-1,2,3,3a,4-pentamethyl-, cis	dioxan	272(3.68)	24-0008-73
trans	dioxan	274(3.65)	24-0008-73
$C_{18}H_{18}N_4O_4$			
L-threo-2,3-Hexodiulosonic acid, γ-lactone, 2,3-bis(phenylhydrazone), red form	EtOH	236s(3.69),264(4.09), 276s(4.00),357(3.74), 465(4.00)	95-0304-73
yellow form	EtOH	262(4.17),281(4.16), 350(3.77),433(4.22)	95-0304-73
3H-Pyrazol-3-one, 2,4-dihydro-2-phenyl-4-(phenylazo)-5-(1,2,3-trihydroxypropyl)-, [R-(R*,R*)]-	$CHCl_3$	252(4.25),258s(4.16), 398(4.21)	95-0304-73
Tubercidin, 2',3'-O-benzylidene-	MeOH	270(4.08)	18-3228-73
$C_{18}H_{18}N_4O_6$			
1-Naphthalenecarboxylic acid, 3-[(2,4-dinitrophenylhydrazono]-3,4,4a,5,8,8a-hexahydro-, methyl ester	MeOH	387(4.29)	18-0880-73
$C_{18}H_{18}O$			
Cyclopenta[c][1]benzopyran, 1,2,3,3a,4-9b-hexahydro-4-phenyl-	EtOH	220(3.97),260(3.34), 280(3.55),285(3.52)	44-1993-73
17H-Cyclopenta[a]phenanthren-17-one, 1,2,3,4,15,16-hexahydro-11-methyl-	EtOH	223(4.23),261(4.77), 287(3.97),298(4.02), 308(3.87),344(3.69), 354(3.74)	39-1251-73C
[2.2]Metacyclophane, 4-acetyl-	EtOH	259(3.6),297(3.0), 330(2.0)	49-0644-73
Methanone, phenyl(6,7,8,9-tetrahydro-5H-benzocyclohepten-2-yl)-	MeOH	260(4.20)	73-2768-73

Compound	Solvent	λmax(log ε)	Ref.
Phenol, 2-(1-phenyl-1,5-hexadienyl)-	EtOH	210(4.19),250(3.93), 283s(3.38)	44-1993-73
Phenol, 2-(6-phenyl-1,5-hexadienyl)-	EtOH	255(4.49),285(3.73), 293(3.83),301(3.80)	44-1993-73
2-Propen-1-one, 3-phenyl-1-(2,4,6-trimethylphenyl)-	EtOH	295(4.40)	35-3310-73
$C_{18}H_{18}OS_4$			
Ethanethione, 2-[3-(1,1-dimethylethyl)-5H-thieno[3,2-c]-1,2-dithiol-5-ylidene]-	dioxan	260(4.57),332(4.57), 376(4.42),578(4.53)	22-1659-73
3(2H)-Thiophenethione, 2-[5-(1,1-dimethylethyl)-3H-1,2-dithiol-3-ylidene]-5-(4-methoxyphenyl)-	dioxan	264(4.43),322s(3.85), 400(4.22),510(3.96)	22-1659-73
3(2H)-Thiophenethione, 5-(1,1-dimethylethyl)-2-[5-(4-methoxyphenyl)-3H-1,2-dithiol-3-ylidene]-	dioxan	270(4.70),356(4.38), 520(4.20)	22-1659-73
$C_{18}H_{18}O_2$			
Acetic acid, (2,3-dihydro-4(1H)-phenanthrenylidene)-, ethyl ester, cis	EtOH	307(3.79)	39-0615-73C
trans	EtOH	315(4.00),332s(3.92)	39-0615-73C
1-Cyclohexene-1-carboxaldehyde, 2,2'-(1,3-butadiyne-1,4-diyl)bis-	EtOH	206(4.34),231s(4.00), 239(4.13),258s(4.09), 270(4.16),290(4.20), 317(4.20),334(4.23), 358(4.09)	18-2565-73
1H-Cyclopropa[c]cyclobuta[1,2-a:3,4-a']-dicyclooctene-1-carboxylic acid, 1a,5a,5b,11a,11b,11c-hexahydro-	ether	228s(3.90),258(3.34)	89-0325-73
isomer	ether	228s(3.86),258(3.28)	89-0325-73
1H-Cyclopropa[c]cyclobuta[1,2-a:3,4-a']-dicyclooctene-1-carboxylic acid, 1a,3a,3b,9a,9b,11a-hexahydro-	ether	250(3.30)	89-0325-73
Estra-1,3,5(10),6,8-pentaen-17-one, 3-hydroxy- (Kober test)	H_2SO_4	510(4.36)	94-1720-73
Honokiol	EtOH	294(3.91)	95-0422-73
Magnolol	EtOH	294(3.90)	95-0422-73
[2.2]Metacyclophane-4-carboxylic acid, methyl ester	C_6H_{12}	252(4.0),292(3.0)	49-0644-73
1,8-(1,4-Naphthaleno)octane-3,6-dione	EtOH	231(4.65),298(3.70)	88-4017-73
Oxirane, 2-[2-(4-methoxyphenyl)cyclopropyl]-2-phenyl-	MeOH	229(4.19),243s(4.14)	39-2030-73C
1H-Phenalen-1-one, 8-(2-hydroxy-1,1-dimethylethyl)-6-methyl-	EtOH	257(4.49),267(4.48), 321(3.70),375s(4.10), 400(4.11)	39-2159-73C
4-Phenanthreneacetic acid, 1,2-dihydro-, ethyl ester	EtOH	312(3.88),335(3.68)	39-0615-73C
$C_{18}H_{18}O_2S$			
1,4-Butanediol, 1-(dibenzo[b,f]thiepin-10-yl)-	MeOH	256(4.28),281(3.66)	73-0115-73
Dibenzo[b,f]thiepin-10(11H)-one, 8-butoxy-	MeOH	239(4.37),256s(4.04), 352(3.53)	73-1579-73
2H-Thiopyran, 3,6-dihydro-4-methyl-2,6-diphenyl-, 1,1-dioxide, cis	EtOH	209(4.34),253(2.74), 259(2.82),265(2.73), 270(2.53)	39-0410-73C

Compound	Solvent	$\lambda_{max}(\log \epsilon)$	Ref.
$C_{18}H_{18}O_2S_3$			
3(2H)-Thiophenone, 2-[5-(1,1-dimethylethyl)-3H-thiol-3-ylidene]-5-(4-methoxyphenyl)-	dioxan	238s(4.15),268(4.18), 370(4.23),463s(4.38), 486(4.50)	22-1659-73
3(2H)-Thiophenone, 5-(1,1-dimethylethyl)-2-[5-(4-methoxyphenyl)-3H-1,2-dithiol-3-ylidene]-	dioxan	238(4.50),246s(4.42), 336(4.52),486(4.48)	22-1659-73
$C_{18}H_{18}O_3$			
1H-Indene-1-acetic acid, 2,3-dihydro-3-hydroxy-1-phenyl-, methyl ester, (1R-trans)-	MeOH	211(4.08),257(2.78), 263(2.85),270(2.78)	35-1217-73
1H-Phenalen-1-one, 2-(2-hydroxy-1,1-dimethylethyl)-4-methoxy-	EtOH	208(4.42),266(4.44), 322(3.65),418(4.03), 436(4.06)	39-2159-73C
$C_{18}H_{18}O_4$			
4H-Benzopyran-4-one, 2,3-dihydro-7-hydroxy-5-methoxy-6,8-dimethyl-2-phenyl-	MeOH	214(4.35),287(4.13), 345s(3.51)	100-0422-73
	MeOH-KOH	235s(--),250(4.85), 340(4.42)	100-0422-73
Butanedioic acid, bicyclo[5.4.1]dodeca-1(11),2,5,7,9-pentaen-4-ylidene-, dimethyl ester	n.s.g.	237(4.36),305(4.28), 370s(3.62)	35-2359-73
Butanoic acid, 3-methyl-, 7-(2,4-hexadiynylidene)-1,6-dioxaspiro[4.4]nona-2,8-dien-4-yl ester, (Z)-	ether	206(4.28),232(4.11), 241(4.09),306s(4.34), 318(4.37),337s(4.15)	24-0845-73
4a,1-(Epoxymethano)-7,9a-methanobenz[a]-azoluene, 4a,7-dihydroxy-1-methyl-8-methylene-2-oxo-	MeOH	233(3.79),338(2.15), 351(2.12),371(1.93)	78-3425-73
2-Naphthalenepropanoic acid, 6-(2-carboxy-1-methylethenyl)-β-methyl-	EtOH	216(4.41),260(4.37), 298(4.08)	132-0279-73
Spiro[bicyclo[5.4.1]dodeca-2,5,7,9,11-pentaene-4,1'-cyclopropane]-2',3'-dicarboxylic acid, dimethyl ester	n.s.g.	240(4.34),258(4.40), 317(3.43)	35-2359-73
$C_{18}H_{18}O_5$			
Benzoic acid, 2-methoxy-6-[2-(4-methoxyphenyl)-2-oxoethyl]-, methyl ester	EtOH	287.5(4.21)	102-2279-73
1,3-Cyclohexadiene-1-carboxylic acid, 6-(2-acetoxyphenyl)-4,6-dimethyl-5-oxo-, methyl ester	90% EtOH	213(4.13),303s(3.92), 312(3.96),323s(3.85)	12-1093-73
1,2-Dibenzofurandicarboxylic acid, 1,9b-dihydro-4,9b-dimethyl-, dimethyl ester	90% EtOH	209(3.71),235(3.76), 286(3.48),357(3.92)	12-1093-73
1,2-Dibenzofurandicarboxylic acid, 3,9b-dihydro-4,9b-dimethyl-, dimethyl ester	90% EtOH	230s(4.06),280(3.50), 285s(3.48)	12-1093-73
Methanone, [2-methoxy-6-(methoxymethoxy)phenyl](3-phenyloxiranyl)-	EtOH	273(3.99)	114-0093-73B
1-Oxaspiro[4.5]dec-3-ene-6-acetic acid, 2,8-dioxo-10-phenyl-, methyl ester	EtOH	258(2.65),264(2.54), 270(2.30)	78-3091-73
1-Phenanthrenol, 2,5,6,7-tetramethoxy-(5λ,4ε)	$CHCl_3$	295(4.03),309(4.02), 330(3.15),347(3.23), 364(?)	102-0228-73
Spiro[1,2-benzodioxin-3(7H),1'-cyclobutane]-7,8-diol, 8,8a-dihydro-4-phenyl-, 7-formate, (7α,8β,8aα)-	EtOH	251(4.37)	78-3553-73

Compound	Solvent	$\lambda_{max}(\log \epsilon)$	Ref.
$C_{18}H_{18}O_6$			
1,3-Benzodioxole-5-carboxaldehyde, 6-[(3,4,5-trimethoxyphenyl)methyl]-	EtOH	280(3.91),322(3.88)	39-1266-73C
1,3-Cyclohexadiene-1,2-dicarboxylic acid, 6-(2-hydroxyphenyl)-4,6-dimethyl-5-oxo-, dimethyl ester	90% EtOH	215(4.11),284(3.62), 306(3.71),345s(2.94)	12-1093-73
	NH_3	215(4.11),284(3.62), 306(3.71),345s(2.94), 416(3.36)	12-1093-73
1,2-Dibenzofurandicarboxylic acid, 1,9b-dihydro-1-hydroxy-4,9b-dimethyl-, dimethyl ester	90% EtOH	233(4.08),283s(3.80), 288(3.81),350(4.07)	12-1093-73
Furo[3,4-f]-1,3-benzodioxole, 5,7-dihydro-5-(3,4,5-trimethoxyphenyl)-	EtOH	294(3.80)	39-1266-73C
Pedicin	MeOH	308(4.35)	2-0009-73
1H-Phenalen-1-one, 3-hydroxy-6,7,8,9-tetramethoxy-4-methyl-	EtOH	216(4.42),271(4.45), 353(3.98),388(4.04), 407(4.06),430s(3.92)	39-2388-73C
Propanedioic acid, (1,4-dihydro-3-methyl-1,4-dioxo-2-naphthalenyl)-, diethyl ester	EtOH	337(3.50)	83-0257-73
	EtOH-KOH	559(3.26)	83-0257-73
Spiro[1,2-benzodioxin-3(7H),1'-cyclobutan]-7-ol, 8,8a-dihydro-8-hydroperoxy-4-phenyl-, formate, (7α,8β,8aα)-	EtOH	251(4.36)	78-3553-73
$C_{18}H_{18}O_7$			
1,2-Dibenzofurandicarboxylic acid, 1,9b-dihydro-7,9-dimethoxy-4,9b-dimethyl-	90% EtOH	219(4.43),257(4.28), 352(3.83)	12-1093-73
Furo[3,4-f]-1,3-benzodioxol-5-ol, 5,7-dihydro-7-(3,4,5-trimethoxyphenyl)-	EtOH	283s(--),290(3.73), 295s(--)	39-1266-73C
7H-Furo[3,2-g][1]benzopyran-7-one, 9-(2-acetoxy-3-hydroxy-3-methylbutoxy)-	MeOH	220(4.62),250(4.60), 300(4.30)	2-0530-73
9H-Xanthen-9-one, 1,3,5,6,7-pentamethoxy-	MeOH	244(4.54),253(4.64), 303(4.26),347s(3.94), 351(3.94)	39-1329-73C
$C_{18}H_{18}O_8$			
Benzoic acid, 2-[2-(ethoxycarbonyl)-5-methoxyphenoxy]-3,6-dihydroxy-, methyl ester	MeOH	216(4.63),253(4.27), 292(3.80),342(3.67)	24-1182-73
Benzoic acid, 6-hydroxy-3-methoxy-2-[5-methoxy-2-(methoxycarbonyl)phenoxy]-, methyl ester	MeOH	216(4.59),254(4.18), 294(3.80),335(3.42)	24-1182-73
$C_{18}H_{18}O_9$			
4,5-Benzofurandicarboxylic acid, 6,7-dihydro-7-[3-methoxy-1-(methoxycarbonyl)-3-oxo-1-propenyl]-, dimethyl ester, (E)-	90% EtOH	229(4.35),256s(3.93), 300(3.60),345(3.13), 362s(3.00)	12-1059-73
$C_{18}H_{18}S_3$			
5,13,18-Trithiatetracyclo[7.7.3.1^{3,15}-1^{7,11}]heneicosa-1,3(20),7,9,11(21),15-hexaene	EtOH	241(3.79)	35-3201-73
$C_{18}H_{18}Si_2$			
Silane, 1,4-phenylenebis[phenyl-	heptane	279.2(2.21)	70-1825-73
$C_{18}H_{19}$			
Methylium, cyclopropylbis(4-methylphenyl)-	FSO_3H at -75°	326(<4.2),462(4.79)	59-0803-73

Compound	Solvent	λ_{max}(log ε)	Ref.
$C_{18}H_{19}ClN_2OS$			
Piperazine, 1-(8-chloro-10,11-dihydrodibenzo[b,f]thiepin-10-yl)-, S-oxide	MeOH	233.5(4.20)	73-0599-73
$C_{18}H_{19}ClN_2O_2$			
Glycine, N-[[5-chloro-2-(methylamino)-phenyl]phenylmethylene]-, ethyl ester, anti	EtOH	232(4.46),383(3.79)	95-1253-73
syn	EtOH	252(4.39)	95-1253-73
$C_{18}H_{19}ClN_4O_5$			
2,5-Cyclohexadiene-1,4-dione, 2-chloro-3,5-dipropyl-, 1-(2,4-dinitrophenyl-hydrazone)	50% DMSO-acid	452(4.52)	1-3641-73
	+ KOH	606(4.79)	1-3641-73
	C_2Cl_4	395(4.42),440(4.60)	1-3632-73
$C_{18}H_{19}Cl_3$			
1a,9-Metheno-2H-benzocyclopropa[c]-cyclododecene, 1,1,14-trichloro-1,3,4,5,6,7,8,13b-octahydro-	EtOH	228s(4.25),235(4.39), 242(4.35),299(3.69)	44-1207-73
$C_{18}H_{19}N$			
2,4-Pentadien-1-amine, N-methyl-4,5-diphenyl-, hydrochloride	MeOH	207(4.29),224(4.09), 232(4.08),288(4.44)	44-2169-73
1H-Pyrrole, 2,5-dihydro-2,3-dimethyl-2,4-diphenyl-, hydrochloride	H_2O	242(4.18)	32-0003-73
$C_{18}H_{19}NO$			
Carbazol-4-one, 1,2,3,4,5,6,7,8-octahydro-9-phenyl-	MeOH	201(4.31),255(4.28), 295s(3.70)	24-0745-73
2-Cyclohexen-1-one, 3-(1,2,3,4-tetrahydro-9H-carbazol-9-yl)-	MeOH	222(4.51),279(4.07), 342(3.98)	24-0745-73
Oxazole, 2,5-dihydro-2,2-dimethyl-5-(4-methylphenyl)-4-phenyl-	EtOH	222(4.13),243(4.14)	33-2611-73
$C_{18}H_{19}NO_2$			
Aporphine, 11-hydroxy-10-methoxy-, hydriodide, (±)-	MeOH	270(4.22),306(3.60)	87-1223-73
Benzamide, N-methyl-2-(2,4,6-trimethyl-benzoyl)-	EtOH	214(4.44),246(3.97)	39-1160-73B
Benzenepropanamide, 2,4,6-trimethyl-β-oxo-N-phenyl-	pH 13	303(4.36)	39-0808-73B
2-Propen-1-one, 3-[4-(dimethylamino)-phenyl]-1-(2-methoxyphenyl)-	isooctane	255(4.13),328(4.00), 372(4.52)	65-0638-73
	benzene	325(3.89),395(4.49)	65-0638-73
	EtOH	325(3.72),360(4.04), 407(4.48)	65-0638-73
2(1H)-Pyridinone, 1-butyl-3-(1-oxo-1-phenyl-2-propenyl)-	EtOH	220(4.17),233(4.10), 323(4.14),370(4.10)	103-0615-73
$C_{18}H_{19}NO_3$			
Acetamide, 2-(4-acetylphenoxy)-N-(2,3-dimethylphenyl)-	EtOH	212(4.37),265(4.27)	111-0574-73
6,8(2H,7H)-Isoquinolinedione, 3-(1,3,5-heptatrienyl)-7-hydroxy-2,7-dimethyl-, (E,E,E)-	CH_2Cl_2	250(2.71),370(3.12)	33-2694-73
2-Propenamide, 3-[4-(2-methoxy-5-methyl-phenoxy)phenyl]-N-methyl-, (E)-	EtOH	215(4.28),223(4.29), 295(4.39),308s(4.35)	33-1266-73
Pyrano[3,2-a]carbazole-5-methanol, 1,2,3,11-tetrahydro-1-hydroxy-3,3-dimethyl-	EtOH	238(4.56),288(4.3), 330(3.64)	44-2728-73

Compound	Solvent	$\lambda_{max}(\log \epsilon)$	Ref.
$C_{18}H_{19}NO_4$			
Acetic acid, (6,7-dihydro-9,10-dimethoxy-2H-benzo[a]quinolizin-2-ylidene)-, methyl ester	EtOH	240(4.15),259s(--), 290(4.02),320(4.03), 378(4.28)	78-4153-73
	EtOH-HCl	226s(--),266s(--), 287(4.09),370(4.11)	78-4153-73
Cephalotaxinone	EtOH	245(3.96),288(3.70)	95-0916-73
	EtOH	242(4.00),290(3.69)	102-2987-73
Demethylcephalotaxinone methyl ester	EtOH	237(4.00),298s(3.95), 313(3.99)	95-0916-73
Erythrinine	EtOH	209(4.35),230(4.26), 289(3.70)	95-1211-73 +95-1215-73
$C_{18}H_{19}NO_4S_2$			
Thiopyrano[4,3-b]indole-3,4-dicarboxylic acid, 4a,5-dihydro-4a,5-dimethyl-1-(methylthio)-, dimethyl ester	EtOH	258(4.30),380(3.88)	94-2770-73
$C_{18}H_{19}NO_6$			
1,4-Naphthalenedione, 2-(dimethylamino)-5-(1,2-dioxopropyl)-6,8-dimethoxy-7-methyl-	EtOH	207(4.35),236(4.31), 282(4.27),458(3.69)	33-2287-73
1H-Pyrrole-3-acetic acid, 2-(methoxycarbonyl)-5-methyl-4-[(phenylmethoxy)carbonyl]-, methyl ester	MeOH	275(4.20)	39-1546-73C
$C_{18}H_{19}NO_6S$			
2-Pyrimidinedione, 1-(5,6-dihydro-8,9-dimethoxynaphth[2,1-c][1,2]oxathiin-2-yl)-, S,S-dioxide	EtOH	255(4.37),315(4.25)	4-0137-73
$C_{18}H_{19}N_3O$			
2(1H)-Pentalenone, 1-morpholino-, phenylhydrazone	MeOH	270(4.02),424(4.39)	5-0750-73
	DMSO	431(4.37)	5-0750-73
	DMSO-NaOH	592(4.73)	5-0750-73
$C_{18}H_{19}N_3O_2$			
2-Propenal, 3-[4-[(4-amino-5-methoxy-2-methylphenyl)azo]phenyl]-2-methyl-	EtOH	445(4.49)	7-0379-73
$C_{18}H_{19}N_3O_2S_2$			
7(4H)-Benzothiazolone, 6-[[[(4,7-dihydro-2-methyl-7-oxo-6(5H)-benzothiazolylidene)methyl]amino]methyl]-5,6-dihydro-2-methyl-	EtOH	277(4.36),385(4.30)	32-1063-73
$C_{18}H_{19}N_3O_3$			
2-Propenal, 3-[4-[(4-amino-2,5-dimethoxyphenyl)azo]phenyl]-2-methyl-	EtOH	486(4.55)	7-0379-73
$C_{18}H_{19}N_3O_4$			
Pyrano[3,2-b]indole-3-carbonitrile, 4-[(2,2-diethoxyethyl)amino]-2,5-dihydro-2-oxo-	EtOH	294(4.11),338(4.28)	95-0964-73
$C_{18}H_{19}N_3S$			
1,2,4-Triazolidine-3-thione, 4-butyl-1,5-diphenyl-, meso-ionic didehydro deriv.	MeCN	256(4.46),324(3.42)	103-1048-73

Compound	Solvent	λ_{max}(log ε)	Ref.
$C_{18}H_{19}N_4O_{14}P$			
6H-Furo[2',3':4,5]oxazolo[3,2-c]pyrimidine-6,8(7H)-dione, 3-[[[(2,3,3a,7,8-9a-hexahydro-3-hydroxy-6,8-dioxo-6H-furo[2',3':4,5]oxazolo[3,2-c]pyrimidin-2-yl)methoxy]hydroxyphosphinyl]-oxy]-2,3,3a,9a-tetrahydro-2-(hydroxymethyl)-	pH 3	253(4.25)	35-4054-73
	H_2O	253(4.23)	35-4054-73
	pH 11	255(4.10)	35-4054-73
$C_{18}H_{19}N_5O_2$			
Imidodicarbonic dihydrazide, 2-phenyl-N'-(4-phenyl-3-butenylidene)-	EtOH	268(4.09),293s(4.10)	48-0492-73
Propanenitrile, 3-[ethyl[4-[(2-methyl-4-nitrophenyl)azo]phenyl]amino]-	MeOH	454(4.62)	89-0926-73
$C_{18}H_{19}N_5O_2S$			
1H-Purine-2,6-dione, 3,7-dihydro-7-(3-isothiocyanatopropyl)-1,3-dimethyl-8-(phenylmethyl)-	n.s.g.	211(4.50),278(4.04)	73-1571-73
$C_{18}H_{19}N_5O_4S$			
Propanenitrile, 3-[ethyl[4-[[2-(methylsulfonyl)-4-nitrophenyl]azo]phenyl]-amino]-	MeOH	500(4.54)	89-0926-73
$C_{18}H_{19}N_5O_5$			
Adenosine, 2'-(4-methoxybenzoate)	EtOH	260(4.45)	30-0521-73
$C_{18}H_{19}N_5O_7S_2$			
3,5'-Cycloadenosine, 3'-deoxy-2'-O-tosyl-2',3'-didehydro-, mesylate	EtOH	216(4.27),274(4.10)	44-2896-73
$C_{18}H_{19}N_7$			
Benzenamine, N,N-dimethyl-4-[3-methyl-5-(2-quinoxalinyl)-1-formazano]-	benzene	492(4.65)	103-1542-73
	EtOH	488(4.68)	103-1542-73
	EtOH-KOH	558(4.78)	103-1542-73
	dioxan	490(4.69)	103-1542-73
	H_2SO_4	404(4.35)	103-1542-73
$C_{18}H_{19}O_2P$			
Phosphinic acid, diphenyl-, 1-cyclohexen-1-yl ester	EtOH	254(2.96),260(3.08), 266(3.19),273(3.10)	139-0209-73A
$C_{18}H_{20}$			
Dicyclopenta[a,f]naphthalene, 1,2,3,6,7-8-hexahydro-1,6-dimethyl-	EtOH	229(4.07),236(4.22), 272(3.12),281(3.15), 292(3.06),312(2.71), 317(2.78),328(2.74), 334(2.90)	132-0279-73
[2.2]Metacyclophane, 4-ethyl-	C_6H_{12}	230(4.0),277(2.8)	49-0644-73
$C_{18}H_{20}ClNO_3$			
Cephalotaxine, 6-chloro-6-deoxy-	EtOH	240s(3.68),292(3.60)	95-0916-73
$C_{18}H_{20}ClN_3O$			
1-Propanol, 3-[(6-chloro-3,4-dihydro-3-methyl-4-phenyl-2-quinazolinyl)-amino]-	n.s.g.	220(4.26),295(3.88)	40-1944-73

Compound	Solvent	$\lambda_{max}(\log \epsilon)$	Ref.
$C_{18}H_{20}ClN_3O_4$			
Quinolinium, 2-[2-(1,3-dimethyl-1H-pyrazol-4-yl)ethenyl]-1-ethyl-, perchlorate	EtOH	456(3.65),570(4.10)	104-1792-73
Quinolinium, 2-[2-(1,5-dimethyl-1H-pyrazol-4-yl)ethenyl]-1-ethyl-, perchlorate	EtOH	430(3.03),570(5.10)	104-1792-73
$C_{18}H_{20}ClN_3O_7$			
1H-Imidazo[4,5-c]pyridine, 4-chloro-2-methyl-1-(2,3,5-tri-O-acetyl-β-D-ribofuranosyl)-	pH 1	271(3.76)	124-0703-73
	pH 13	252(3.75),269(3.73)	124-0703-73
	MeOH	253(3.79),267(3.68)	124-0703-73
$C_{18}H_{20}F_3N_2$			
Methanaminium, N-[4-[1-[4-(dimethylamino)phenyl]-2,2,2-trifluoroethylidene]-2,5-cyclohexadien-1-ylidene]-N-methyl-	MeNO	693(4.33)	104-1766-73
	98% HOAc	610(0.85),690(0.70)	39-2151-73B
	at 70°	610(1.36),690(1.51)	39-2151-73B
Methanaminium, N-[4-[[4-(dimethylamino)-2-(trifluoromethyl)phenyl]methylene]-2,5-cyclohexadien-1-ylidene]-N-methyl-	98% HOAc	624(4.64+)	39-1792-73B
$C_{18}H_{20}N_2O$			
1H,10H-3a,9b-Diazabenzo[a]naphth[2,1,8-cde]azulen-10-one, 2,3,4,5,11,12,12a-12b-octahydro-	EtOH	243(5.34),267(4.14), 293(3.83),302(3.83)	22-2705-73
1H-Indole-3-ethanamine, 5-methoxy-7-(phenylmethyl)-	EtOH	225(4.43),274s(3.79), 280(3.83),303(3.68)	103-0196-73
Pyrazolidine, 1-acetyl-5-methyl-2,3-diphenyl-	EtOH	238(3.91)	103-0503-73
$C_{18}H_{20}N_2O_2$			
Benzamide, 2-[4-(dimethylamino)benzoyl]-N,N-dimethyl-	EtOH	214(4.18),248(4.15), 352(4.39)	39-1160-73B
Benzamide, 2-[4-(dimethylamino)benzoyl]-N-ethyl-	EtOH	212(4.42),262(4.18), 352(3.28)	39-1160-73B
	$CHCl_3$	346(3.26)	39-1160-73B
	dioxan	215(4.31),264(4.21), 342(3.19)	39-1160-73B
	MeCN	216(4.27),264(4.17), 352(3.99)	39-1160-73B
Benzoic acid, 2-[[[(1-methylethyl)amino]phenylmethylene]amino]-, methyl ester	MeOH	227(4.42),278(3.96)	78-2153-73
2-Buten-1-one, 1-(3-pyridinyl)-3-[3-(1-butyl-2-oxo-3(1H)-pyridinyl)]-	EtOH	278(3.85),313(3.77)	103-0615-73
Estra-1,3,5(10)-trien-17-one, 16-diazo-3-hydroxy-	EtOH	251(3.51),282(3.05), 288(3.06),305s(--), 381(0.6)	44-3525-73
1-Isoquinolinamine, 3,4-dihydro-6,7-dimethoxy-3-methyl-N-phenyl-	EtOH	265(4.18),300(4.09)	106-0364-73
	EtOH-acid	282(4.16),320(4.09)	106-0364-73
$C_{18}H_{20}N_2O_2S_2$			
Benzo[b]thiophene-3-carboxylic acid, 4,5,6,7-tetrahydro-2-[[(phenylamino)-thioxomethyl]amino]-, ethyl ester	EtOH	272(4.01),345(4.12)	103-0525-73
$C_{18}H_{20}N_2O_3$			
Acetamide, N-(2,3-dimethylphenyl)-2-[2-[1-(hydroxyimino)ethyl]phenoxy]-	EtOH	209(4.46),254(4.24)	111-0574-73

Compound	Solvent	$\lambda_{max}(\log \epsilon)$	Ref.
Pyrrolidine, 1-(1,6,7,11b-tetrahydro-2-hydroxy-4-oxo-4H-benzo[a]quinolizin-3-yl)carbonyl]-	$CHCl_3$	273(4.00),333(2.78)	70-1745-73
$C_{18}H_{20}N_2O_6$			
Carbamic acid, [1-[4-acetoxy-4,5-dihydro-4-(1-methylethyl)-5-oxo-2-oxazolyl]ethenyl]-, phenylmethyl ester	ether	250(3.48)	88-2163-73
Spiro[cyclopropane-1,1'(3'aH)-cycloprop[3,4]indeno[2,1-c]pyrazole-3'a,3'b,3'c-tricarboxylic acid, 6',6'a,6'b,6'c-tetrahydro-, trimethyl ester, (3'aα,3'bα,3'cβ,6'aβ,6'bα,6'cα)-	EtOH	212s(4.12),322(2.30)	24-1837-73
$C_{18}H_{20}N_2O_9S_2$			
Uridine, 2',3'-didehydro-3'-deoxy-3-(phenylmethyl)-, 2',5'-dimethanesulfonate	EtOH	257(3.95)	44-0598-73
$C_{18}H_{20}N_2S$			
Benzenamine, 3-(2-benzothiazolyl)-N,N-diethyl-5-methyl-	MeOH	224(4.29),250(3.90), 347(3.85)	103-0944-73
$C_{18}H_{20}N_3$			
Methanaminium, N-[4-[cyano[4-(dimethylamino)phenyl]methylene]-2,5-cyclohexadien-1-ylidene]-N-methyl-	$MeNO_2$	716(4.74)	104-1766-73
Quinolinium, 2-[2-(1,3-dimethyl-1H-pyrazol-4-yl)ethenyl]-1-ethyl-, perchlorate	EtOH	456(3.65),570(4.10)	104-1792-73
Quinolinium, 2-[2-(1,5-dimethyl-1H-pyrazol-4-yl)ethenyl]-1-ethyl-, perchlorate	EtOH	430(3.03),570(5.10)	104-1792-73
$C_{18}H_{20}N_3O_9P$			
5'-Cytidylic acid, N-benzoyl-2'-deoxy-, 3'-acetate	pH 7	258(4.27),302(--)	138-0859-73
$C_{18}H_{20}N_4$			
Propanenitrile, 3-[ethyl[4-(2-methylphenyl)azo]phenyl]amino]-	MeOH	402(4.26)	89-0926-73
Propanenitrile, 3-[ethyl[4-(4-methylphenyl)azo]phenyl]amino]-	MeOH	399(4.72)	89-0926-73
$C_{18}H_{20}N_4O_2$			
Acetamide, N-[[[2-(acetylamino)phenyl]hydrazono]phenylmethylene]-N-methyl-	MeOH	325(4.08)	24-2530-73
$C_{18}H_{20}N_4O_5$			
Phenol, 4-[(2,4-dinitrophenyl)azo]-2,5-dipropyl-	50% DMSO-acid	417(4.34)	1-3641-73
	+ KOH	598(4.80)	1-3641-73
	C_2Cl_4	396(4.31),432(4.37)	1-3632-73
Phenol, 4-[(2,4-dinitrophenyl)azo]-2,6-dipropyl- (spectra in 50% DMSO)	acid	454(4.45)	1-3641-73
	KOH	612(4.88)	1-3641-73
Spiro[5.6]dodec-1-ene-3,7-dione, 3-(2,4-dinitrophenylhydrazone)	$CHCl_3$	378(4.47)	39-0393-73C

Compound	Solvent	$\lambda_{max}(\log \epsilon)$	Ref.
$C_{18}H_{20}N_4O_5S$			
Propanoic acid, 3-[[1,2,3,4,5,6-hexahydro-1-methyl-5-[(4-nitrophenyl)hydrazono]-6-oxo-3aH-indol-3a-yl]thio]-	0.1M $NaHCO_3$	229(4.16),416(4.67)	39-0509-73C
$C_{18}H_{20}N_4O_6$			
1-Naphthalenecarboxylic acid, 3-[(2,4-dinitrophenyl)hydrazono]-3,4,4a,5,6-7,8,8a-octahydro-, methyl ester	MeOH	385(4.27)	18-0880-73
$C_{18}H_{20}N_4O_6S$			
Propanoic acid, 3-[[1,2,3,4,5,6-hexahydro-3-hydroxy-1-methyl-5-[(4-nitrophenyl)hydrazono]-6-oxo-3aH-indol-3a-yl]thio]-	0.1M $NaHCO_3$	231(4.13),416(4.67)	39-0509-73C
$C_{18}H_{20}N_6O_2$			
Phenol, 4,4'-(1,2-diethyl-1,2-ethanediyl)bis[2-azido-	EtOH	244(4.16),297(3.98)	44-3525-73
$C_{18}H_{20}N_6O_3$			
L-Valine, N-[(1H-purin-6-ylamino)carbonyl]-, phenylmethyl ester	pH 1-2	275(4.27)	87-0139-73
	pH 5-7	267(4.26)	87-0139-73
	pH 12	276(4.18)	87-0139-73
$C_{18}H_{20}N_6O_4$			
Pyridinium, 1,1'-(2-butene-1,4-diyl)-bis[2,4-bis[(hydroxyimino)methyl]-, dibromide, (E)-	0.05M HCl	300(4.44)	73-2788-73
	0.05M NaOH	365(4.64)	73-2788-73
$C_{18}H_{20}N_6O_5$			
Adenosine, N-[[(phenylmethyl)amino]carbonyl]-	pH 1-2	270s(--),277(4.41)	87-0139-73
	pH 5-7	269(4.41),277s(--)	87-0139-73
	pH 12	299(4.15)	87-0139-73
$C_{18}H_{20}N_6O_8$			
1H-1,2,3-Triazole-4,5-dicarboxylic acid, 1,1'-[2,3-bis(methylene)-1,4-butanediyl]bis-, tetramethyl ester	EtOH	217(4.39)	88-2361-73
$C_{18}H_{20}O$			
1,3,5-Cycloheptatriene, 7-(2,4,6-cycloheptatrien-1-ylidene)-1-methoxy-3-(1-methylethyl)-	isooctane	235(4.30),287(3.80), 352(4.23)	138-0067-73
Phenol, 2-[2-(phenylmethyl)cyclopentyl]-	EtOH	218(4.02),270s(3.36), 277(3.43),281s(3.40)	44-1993-73
$C_{18}H_{20}OS$			
Benzenecarbothioic acid, O-[2-methyl-1-(phenylmethyl)propyl] ester	CH_2Cl_2	250(3.85),286(3.99), 420(2.08)	39-1580-73C
1-Pentanethione, 3-hydroxy-4-methyl-1,2-diphenyl-	C_6H_{12}	229(3.95),234(3.93), 247(3.70),316(4.10), 553(2.01)	39-1580-73C
$C_{18}H_{20}O_2$			
2,3,8:4,5,7-Dimethenodicyclopenta[a,f]pentalene-3b(1H)-carboxylic acid, dodecahydro-, methyl ester, cis	EtOH	212(2.34)	24-1804-73
Estra-1,3,5(10),9(11)-tetraen-17-one, 3-hydroxy-	n.s.g.	263(4.25)	22-1433-73

Compound	Solvent	λ_{max}(log ε)	Ref.
Estra-1,3,5(10),9(11)-tetraen-17-one, 3-hydroxy-, Kober test	H_2SO_4	470s(3.65),510(3.80)	94-1720-73
1-Propanone, 3-hydroxy-1-(2,4,6-triphenyl)-3-phenyl-	EtOH	252(3.55)	35-3310-73
$C_{18}H_{20}O_3$			
2H-1-Benzopyran-5-ol, 3,4-dihydro-2,2-dimethyl-7-(phenylmethoxy)-	EtOH	211(4.6),270(3.5)	12-2291-73
1-Cyclopentene-1-acetic acid, 5-oxo-2-(5,6,7,8-tetrahydro-2-naphthalenyl)-, methyl ester	EtOH	226(3.39),284(3.60)	39-1251-73C
Estra-1,3,5(10),8-tetraen-17-one, 3,11-dihydroxy-, Kober test	H_2SO_4	420s(3.95),470(4.22), 495s(4.11)	94-1720-73
2-Naphthalenepropanoic acid, 6-acetyl-β-methyl-, ethyl ester	EtOH	215(4.39),224(4.36), 240(4.46),251(4.49), 291(3.86),320(3.44)	132-0279-73
$C_{18}H_{20}O_4$			
1H-Fluorene-9-carboxylic acid, 9a-acetyl-2,3,4,4a,9,9a-hexahydro-8-methyl-2-oxo-, methyl ester	EtOH	265(4.48),269s(2.42), 273(2.35)	44-0741-73
Gibba-1,3,4a(10a)-triene-10-carboxylic acid, 7-hydroxy-1-methyl-9-oxo-, methyl ester, (4bβ,10β)-(±)-	EtOH	263(2.42),270(2.32)	44-0741-73
2,6-Naphthalenedipropanoic acid, β,β'-dimethyl-	EtOH	220(4.67),230(4.83), 261(3.47),272(3.51), 281(3.31)	132-0279-73
$C_{18}H_{20}O_5$			
1,3-Benzodioxole, 5-methyl-6-[(3,4,5-trimethoxyphenyl)methyl]-	EtOH	292(3.70)	39-1266-73C
4-Cyclohexene-1,2,3-triol, 6-[(1-hydroxycyclobutyl)phenylmethylene]-, 3-formate, (1α,2α,3β,6Z)-	EtOH	252(4.26)	78-3553-73
8aH-Fluorene-8a-acetic acid, 4b,5,6,7-8,9-hexahydro-9-(methoxycarbonyl)-1-methyl-7-oxo-, (4bα,8aα,9α)-(±)-	EtOH	264(2.43),270(2.34)	44-1398-73
Methanone, (2,6-dimethoxyphenyl)(3-hydroxy-6-methoxy-2,4-dimethylphenyl)-	MeOH	210(4.49),226(4.17), 260(3.87),325(3.53)	24-1198-73
1-Oxaspiro[4.5]decane-6-acetic acid, 2,8-dioxo-10-phenyl-, methyl ester	EtOH	252(2.51),258(2.41), 264(2.48)	78-3091-73
$C_{18}H_{20}O_6$			
1,3-Benzodioxole-5-methanol, 6-[(3,4,5-trimethoxyphenyl)methyl]-	EtOH	285(3.64)	39-1266-73C
Bicyclo[4.2.1]nona-2,4,7-triene-2,3,5-tricarboxylic acid, 9-isopropylidene-, trimethyl ester	EtOH	213s(4.15),232s(4.03), 269s(3.57)	24-1837-73
Cyclobuta[b]naphthalene-1,2-dicarboxylic acid, 2a,3a,4,7,7a,8a-hexahydro-3,8-dioxo-, diethyl ester	EtOH	252s(3.59),293s(3.01), 305s(2.87)	104-2389-73
1H-Cyclonona[1,2-c:5,6-c']difuran-1,3,6-8(4H)-tetrone, 10-ethyl-5,9,10,11-tetrahydro-4-propyl- (heveadride)	C_6H_{12}	244(3.98)	39-0194-73C
4H,9H-Furo[2',3',4':4,5]naphtho[2,1-c]-pyran-4,9-dione, 7-acetoxy-1,2,3,3a-5a,7,10b,10c-octahydro-3a,10b-dimethyl-	EtOH	258(4.11)	32-1271-73
isomer	MeOH	255(4.15)	32-1271-73
3aH-Indene-3a,4,6-tricarboxylic acid, 3a,7a-dihydro-3-(1-methylethylidene)-, trimethyl ester	EtOH	235s(3.77),240s(3.70), 290(3.83)	24-1837-73

Compound	Solvent	$\lambda_{max}(\log \epsilon)$	Ref.
Machaerol A	EtOH	295(3.74)	102-2544-73
Spiro[cyclopropane-1,1'(3'aH)-dicyclopropa[a,cd]indene]-3'a,3'b,3'c-tricarboxylic acid, 4',4'a,4'b,4'c-tetrahydro-, trimethyl ester, (3'aα,3'bα,3'cβ,4'aβ,4'bα,4'cα)-	EtOH	220(3.94)	24-1837-73
Tetracyclo[4.3.0.0^{2,4}.0^{3,7}]non-8-ene-1,2,8-tricarboxylic acid, 5-isopropylidene-, trimethyl ester	EtOH	236(4.03)	24-1822-73
Tetracyclo[4.3.0.0^{2,4}.0^{3,7}]non-8-ene-2,8,9-tricarboxylic acid, 5-isopropylidene-, trimethyl ester	EtOH	250(4.02)	24-1822-73
Tricyclo[4.3.0.0^{2,9}]nona-3,7-diene-1,2,8-tricarboxylic acid, 5-isopropylidene-, trimethyl ester	EtOH	255(4.03)	24-1837-73
Tricyclo[4.3.0.0^{2,9}]nona-3,7-diene-2,8,9-tricarboxylic acid, 5-isopropylidene-, trimethyl ester	EtOH	262(4.08)	24-1837-73
$C_{18}H_{20}O_6S$			
1H-Fluorene-9-carboxylic acid, 2,3,4,4a-9,9a-hexahydro-8-methyl-9a-[(methylsulfonyl)acetyl]-2-oxo-, (4aα,9α,9aα)-	MeCN	256s(2.39),263s(2.51), 267(2.58),276(2.52), 293(1.49)	44-0741-73
$C_{18}H_{20}O_7$			
Machaerol C	EtOH	284(3.55)	102-2544-73
Methanone, (2,3-dimethoxyphenyl)(2-hydroxy-3,4,5-trimethoxyphenyl)-	MeOH	245(3.83),273(4.13), 351(3.65)	39-1329-73C
Methanone, (2-hydroxy-3,4,5-trimethoxyphenyl)(2,6-dimethoxyphenyl)-	MeOH	245(3.76),286(4.13), 360(3.74)	39-1329-73C
$C_{18}H_{20}O_8$			
2H-1-Benzopyran-6-carboxaldehyde, 5-(2-acetoxy-3-hydroxy-3-methylbutyl)-7-hydroxy-8-methoxy-2-oxo-	MeOH	273(4.41),345s(3.90)	78-2645-73
	MeOH-HCl	205(4.64),263(4.00), 326(4.14)	78-2645-73
	MeOH-NaOH	236(4.32),268(4.16), 300(4.06),357(4.08)	78-2645-73
Tephrophenol diacetate	MeOH	221(4.24),240s(4.05), 284(3.48),310(3.08)	119-0053-73
$C_{18}H_{21}NO$			
2,5-Cyclohexadien-1-one, 2,3,5-trimethyl-4-[(2,3,4-trimethylphenyl)imino]-	EtOH	276(4.29),443(3.24)	78-0085-73
$C_{18}H_{21}NO_2$			
6-Azaestra-1,3,5(10),9(11)-tetraen-17-one, 3-methoxy-	EtOH	235(4.40),270(4.04), 332(3.78)	65-0663-73
$C_{18}H_{21}NO_3$			
1H-Carbazole, 2,3,4,9-tetrahydro-6,7-dimethoxy-9-(1-oxo-2-butenyl)-	EtOH	220(4.43),281(4.24), 320s(3.76)	44-0215-73
Erysodine	EtOH	228(4.25),284(3.60)	95-1211-73
Estra-1,3,5(10)-triene-16,17-dione, 3-hydroxy-, 16-oxime	EtOH	232(4.14),280(3.46)	44-3525-73
3H-Indolo[7a,1-a]isoquinolin-3-one, 1,2,5,6,8,9-hexahydro-11,12-dimethoxy-	EtOH	231(4.18),284(4.48)	39-0874-73C
Pyrano[3,2-a]carbazol-1(7H)-one, 2,3,8,9,10,11-hexahydro-5-(hydroxymethyl)-3,3-dimethyl-1-oxo-	EtOH	226(4.54),282(4.09), 290(4.21)	44-2728-73

Compound	Solvent	λ_{max}(log ε)	Ref.
$C_{18}H_{21}NO_4$			
Cephalotaxine	EtOH	240(3.57),290(3.65)	95-0916-73
7-Isoquinolinol, 1,2,3,4-tetrahydro-1-[(4-hydroxy-3-methoxyphenyl)methyl]-6-methoxy-, (R)-	EtOH	210(4.60),228(4.12), 286(3.83)	95-1211-73
Pseudocephalotaxine	EtOH	256(3.89),297(3.66)	95-0916-73
$C_{18}H_{21}NO_5$			
Alkaloid G	EtOH	243(3.52),291(3.61)	95-0916-73
Ribalinidine, O^3-acetyl-O^7-methoxy-	0.3M HCl	224s(4.43),244(4.71), 288s(3.92),299(4.04), 332(3.79)	78-0205-73
	MeOH	220(4.41),235(4.58), 245(4.57),288s(3.80), 300(3.97),315s(3.82), 328(3.99),342(3.95)	78-0205-73
Stephabyssine	MeOH	284(3.52)	44-0151-73
$C_{18}H_{21}NO_6$			
5H-Cyclohepta[b]pyridine-6,8-dicarboxylic acid, 6,7,8,9-tetrahydro-6,8-dimethyl-5,9-dioxo-, diethyl ester	EtOH	213(4.33),244(3.84), 275s(--),322s(--)	39-0026-73C
4(1H)-Quinolinone, 2-(acetoxymethyl)-3-(2-acetoxypropyl)-8-methoxy-	MeOH	233(4.66),300(3.91), 328(4.16)	24-0355-73
$C_{18}H_{21}N_3O_2$			
Estra-1,3,5(10)-trien-17-one, 2-azido-3-hydroxy-	EtOH	253(3.86),300(3.73)	44-3525-73
Estra-1,3,5(10)-trien-17-one, 4-azido-3-hydroxy-	EtOH	258(3.92),289(3.69)	44-3525-73
4-Pentenamide, N-[2-[3-(1-methyl-1H-imidazol-5-yl)-3-oxopropyl]phenyl]-	MeOH	255(4.04)	35-5098-73
	MeOH-acid	232(4.06)	35-5098-73
Phenol, 2-azido-4-[1-ethyl-2-(4-hydroxyphenyl)butyl]-	EtOH	250(3.84),288(3.69), 297(3.66)	44-3525-73
$C_{18}H_{21}N_3O_3$			
Benzo[f]quinazoline, 3-amino-1-[2-(2-ethoxyethoxy)ethoxy]-	EtOH-pH 1	239s(4.36),246(4.43), 262(4.79),278s(4.23), 288s(4.07),300(4.23), 347(3.48),360(3.48)	4-0059-73
Hydrazinecarboxamide, N-[4-(4-methylphenoxy)-1-oxobutyl]-1-phenyl-	MeOH	227(4.29),279(3.55)	104-1200-73
Phenol, 4-[(2-nitrophenyl)azo]-2,6-dipropyl-	C_2Cl_4	395(4.29),457(4.21)	1-3632-73
Phenol, 4-[(4-nitrophenyl)azo]-2,6-dipropyl-	C_2Cl_4	386(4.45)	1-3632-73
$C_{18}H_{21}N_3O_4$			
2,4,6(1H,3H,5H)-Pyrimidinetrione, 1,3-diethyl-5-[3-oxo-1-(phenylamino)butylidene]-	MeOH	224(4.27),312(4.45)	39-0823-73C
$C_{18}H_{21}N_3O_8S$			
Cytidine, N-acetyl-, 5'-(4-methylbenzenesulfonate)	MeOH	222(4.28),248(4.19), 297(3.91)	88-2811-73
$C_{18}H_{21}N_3S$			
Benzothiepino[2,3-b]pyridine, 5,6-dihydro-6-(4-methyl-1-piperazinyl)-	MeOH	248(3.89),280(3.90), 288s(3.83)	73-1693-73

Compound	Solvent	$\lambda_{max}(\log \epsilon)$	Ref.
$C_{18}H_{21}N_5O_4$			
Adenosine, 2'-O-methyl-N-(phenylmethyl)-	MeOH	267s(4.30),271(4.30)	69-2179-73
	MeOH-NaOH	269.5(4.30)	69-2179-73
Adenosine, 3'-O-methyl-N-(phenylmethyl)-	MeOH	271.5(4.31)	69-2179-73
$C_{18}H_{21}N_5O_8S_2$			
Benzamide, N-[[1,2,3,4,5,6-hexahydro-4,5-bis[(methylsulfonyl)oxy]-3,6-epoxyimidazo[1,5-a][1,3]diazocin-10-yl]iminomethyl]-, [3S-(3α,4β,5β,6α)]-	EtOH	244(4.14),264(4.16), 325(4.17)	44-2896-73
$C_{18}H_{21}N_5O_9$			
Acetamide, N-[6,7-dihydro-6-oxo-7-(2,3,4-tri-O-acetyl-β-D-ribopyranosyl)-1H-purin-2-yl]-	EtOH	265(4.12),285s(3.98)	136-0149-73B
Acetamide, N-[6,9-dihydro-6-oxo-9-(2,3,4-tri-O-acetyl-α-D-ribopyranosyl)-1H-purin-2-yl]-	EtOH	257(4.20),277s(4.04)	136-0149-73B
β-isomer	EtOH	257(4.23),282s(4.08)	136-0149-73B
Acetamide, N-[6,7-dihydro-6-oxo-7-(2,3,4-tri-O-acetyl-β-D-xylopyranosyl)-1H-purin-2-yl]-	EtOH	263(4.12),283s(4.00)	136-0149-73B
Acetamide, N-[6,9-dihydro-6-oxo-9-(2,3,4-tri-O-acetyl-β-D-xylopyranosyl)-1H-purin-2-yl]-	EtOH	256(4.21),280s(4.05)	136-0149-73B
$C_{18}H_{22}$			
Azulene, 1-(1-octenyl)-	C_6H_{12}	238(4.37),284(4.64), 371(3.94),391(3.93), 627s(2.47),638(2.48), 666s(2.43),700s(2.32)	5-0166-73
Bi-2,4,6-cycloheptatrien-1-yl, x,x'-diethyl-	EtOH	254(3.85)	18-1785-73
Estra-1,3,5(10),16-tetraene, Kober test	H_2SO_4	470s(3.82),490(3.86)	94-1720-73
$C_{18}H_{22}BrNO$			
2-Hexen-1-one, 1-(4-bromophenyl)-4-(1-piperidinylmethylene)-	EtOH	260(4.25),351(4.49)	48-1161-73
$C_{18}H_{22}BrN_5O_7$			
9H-Purin-6-amine, 9-[2-O-acetyl-3-bromo-3-deoxy-5-O-(2,4,4-trimethyl-5-oxo-1,3-dioxolan-2-yl)-β-D-xylofuranosyl]-	MeOH	258(4.18)	35-4025-73
$C_{18}H_{22}ClNO$			
2-Hexen-1-one, 1-(4-chlorophenyl)-4-(1-piperidinylmethylene)-	EtOH	252(4.23),350(4.47)	48-1161-73
$C_{18}H_{22}ClN_3O_4$			
3H-Indolium, 2-[2-(1,3-dimethyl-1H-pyrazol-4-yl)ethenyl]-1,3,3-trimethyl-, perchlorate	EtOH	416(4.29)	104-1792-73
3H-Indolium, 2-[2-(1,5-dimethyl-1H-pyrazol-4-yl)ethenyl]-1,3,3-trimethyl-, perchlorate	EtOH	416(4.59)	104-1792-73
$C_{18}H_{22}NO_4$			
Furo[2,3-b]quinolinium, 2,3-dihydro-4,6,8-trimethoxy-9-methyl-2-(1-methylethenyl)-	MeOH	214(4.50),255(4.76), 283s(--),292(3.92), 301(3.94),335(3.70), 347(3.67)	102-2552-73

Compound	Solvent	λ_{max}(log ε)	Ref.
$C_{18}H_{22}N_2$			
Benzenamine, 4,4'-ethenylidenebis[N,N-dimethyl-	FSO_3H at -75°	308(4.08),409(4.45)	59-0807-73
5H-Benzocycloheptene-8-propanenitrile, 6,7-dihydro-9-(1-pyrrolidinyl)-	ether	238(4.04),303(3.57)	22-0691-73
Diazene, bis(2,3,4-trimethylphenyl)-	EtOH	242(4.10),345(4.21), 445(3.06)	78-0085-73
Diazene, bis(2,4,6-trimethylphenyl)-	EtOH	237(3.97),324(4.17), 462(2.98)	23-3143-73
	EtOH-KOH	237(3.95),324(4.16), 462(2.98)	23-3143-73
	86% H_2SO_4	252(3.62),315(3.40), 475(4.55)	23-3143-73
2-Naphthalenepropanenitrile, 3,4-dihydro-1-(1-piperidinyl)-	ether	259(3.90),290s(3.56), 302s(3.52)	22-0691-73
$C_{18}H_{22}N_2O$			
Benzenemethanol, 3,5-dimethyl-4-[(2,4,6-trimethylphenyl)azo]-	MeOH	235(3.93),322(4.11), 461(3.02)	23-3143-73
	MeOH-KOH	236(3.90),321(4.06), 450s(2.93)	23-3143-73
	86% H_2SO_4	245(3.62),312(3.48), 463(4.45)	23-3143-73
Diazene, bis(2,4,6-trimethylphenyl)-, 1-oxide	MeOH	214s(4.26),240s(3.88), 307(3.58)	23-3143-73
	MeOH-KOH	240(3.88),307(3.58)	23-3143-73
	86% H_2SO_4	387(3.67)	23-3143-73
Phenol, 3-(1-methylethyl)-2-[[2-(1-methylethyl)phenyl]azo]-	EtOH	243(3.90),248(3.91), 337(4.27)	23-3827-73
Phenol, 2,3,5-trimethyl-4-[(2,4,6-trimethylphenyl)azo]-	MeOH	249(3.99),340(4.18), 463(3.13)	23-3143-73
	MeOH-KOH	264(3.94),379(4.27)	23-3143-73
	86% H_2SO_4	258(3.75),312(3.45), 488(4.52)	23-3143-73
$C_{18}H_{22}N_2O_3$			
4H-Indazol-4-one, 3-(3,4-dimethoxyphenyl)-1,5,6,7-tetrahydro-1,6,6-trimethyl-	MeOH	237(4.37),265s(3.92), 298(3.96)	24-0450-73
$C_{18}H_{22}N_2O_3S_2$			
Benzeneacetamide, 2-[[4-(dimethylamino)-sulfonyl]phenyl]thio]-N,N-dimethyl-	MeOH	270(4.23),277(4.23)	73-2137-73
$C_{18}H_{22}N_2O_4$			
3H-Azepinium, 2-(diethylamino)-4-phenyl-, oxalate	EtOH	240(4.26),310(3.94)	39-1079-73C
3H-Azepinium, 2-(diethylamino)-6-phenyl-, oxalate		293(4.11)	39-1079-73C
$C_{18}H_{22}N_2O_5$			
Diazene, bis[2-(dimethoxymethyl)phenyl]-, 1-oxide, (Z)-	EtOH	232(4.0),307(3.9)	23-3827-73
$C_{18}H_{22}N_2O_{10}S_2$			
Uridine, 3-(phenylmethyl)-, 2',3'-dimethanesulfonate	EtOH	257(4.01)	44-0598-73

Compound	Solvent	λmax(log ε)	Ref.
$C_{18}H_{22}N_3$			
3H-Indolium, 2-[2-(1,3-dimethyl-1H-pyrazol-4-yl)ethenyl]-1,3,3-trimethyl-, perchlorate	EtOH	416(4.29)	104-1792-73
3H-Indolium, 2-[2-(1,5-dimethyl-1H-pyrazol-4-yl)ethenyl]-1,3,3-trimethyl-, perchlorate	EtOH	416(4.59)	104-1792-73
$C_{18}H_{22}N_4O_2$			
Benzo[g]pteridine-2,4(3H,4aH)-dione, 5,10-dihydro-3,5,7,8,10-pentamethyl-4a-(2-propenyl)-	pH 7	218(4.43),272(3.82), 328(4.03)	5-1388-73
	MeOH	222(4.39),285(3.90), 303(3.96),328(3.94)	5-1388-73
	6M HCl	217(4.30),312(3.95)	5-1388-73
Ethanediamide, N,N'-bis[4-(dimethylamino)phenyl]-	dioxan	252(4.08),329(4.36)	30-0001-73
$C_{18}H_{22}N_4O_3$			
4,5,6(1H)-Quinazolinetrione, 2,8-di-1-piperidinyl-	EtOH	246(4.32),280(4.14), 390(4.26)	103-1535-73
$C_{18}H_{22}N_4O_4$			
Benzo[g]pteridine-5(1H)-acetic acid, 2,3,4,10-tetrahydro-3,7,8,10-tetramethyl-2,4-dioxo-, ethyl ester	pH 7	338(3.86)	5-1388-73
	MeOH	335(3.63)	5-1388-73
	6M HCl	287(4.04),305(4.01)	5-1388-73
2-Propenal, 3-(3,3-dimethylbicyclo[2.2.1]hept-2-yl)-, 2,4-dinitrophenylhydrazone	$CHCl_3$	380(4.51)	22-3071-73
$C_{18}H_{22}N_4O_6$			
Acetamide, N-[7-[5-O-acetyl-2,3-O-(1-methylethylidene)-β-D-ribofuranosyl]-7H-pyrrolo[2,3-d]pyrimidin-4-yl]-	MeOH	287(3.89)	18-3228-73
1-Naphthalenecarboxylic acid, 3-[(2,4-dinitrophenyl)hydrazono]decahydro-, methyl ester	MeOH	363(4.26)	18-0880-73
$C_{18}H_{22}N_4O_{13}S$			
Uridine, 5',5'"-sulfite	pH 1	259(4.25)	136-0455-73B
	pH 11	260(4.16)	136-0455-73B
$C_{18}H_{22}N_6O_5$			
Adenosine, 2-amino-N-[2-(4-hydroxyphenyl)ethyl]-	pH 1	256(4.17)	87-0358-73
	H_2O	283(4.19)	87-0358-73
	pH 13	285(4.26)	87-0358-73
$C_{18}H_{22}N_8O_{10}$			
Hexanedioic acid, bis[2-(5-acetoxy-1,4,5,6-tetrahydro-4,6-dioxo-2-pyrimidinyl)hydrazide	EtOH	223(4.26)	103-0247-73
$C_{18}H_{22}O$			
Estra-1,3,5(10)-trien-17-one, Kober test	H_2SO_4	400s(3.51),490(4.06)	94-1720-73
$C_{18}H_{22}OS$			
Benzenecarbothioic acid, O-[2-(6,6-dimethylbicyclo[3.1.1]hept-2-en-2-yl)ethyl ester	EtOH	241(3.96),286(4.04)	39-1574-73C

Compound	Solvent	$\lambda_{max}(\log \epsilon)$	Ref.
$C_{18}H_{22}O_2$			
1,1'-Biphenyl, 4,4'-dipropoxy-	n.s.g.	267(3.77)	18-0263-73
2,8-Decadiene-4,6-diynedial, 3,8-bis-(1,1-dimethylethyl)-	EtOH	225(4.12),232(4.16), 254(4.12),265(4.16), 280(4.15),304s(4.02), 322(4.09),344(3.92)	18-2565-73
Estra-4,9-diene-3,17-dione	n.s.g.	302(4.28)	22-1433-73
Estra-1,3,5(10),6-tetraene-3,17β-diol, Kober test	H_2SO_4	512(3.43)	94-1720-73
Estra-1,3,5(10)-trien-16-one, 3-hydroxy-, Kober test	H_2SO_4	420(3.76),520s(3.33)	94-1720-73
Estra-1,3,5(10)-trien-17-one, 3-hydroxy-, Kober test	H_2SO_4	514(4.65)	94-1720-73
1,4-Ethanonaphthalen-9-ol, 1,4-dihydro-2,3,10,10-tetramethyl-, acetate, anti	EtOH	208(4.72),223(4.45), 260s(3.04),266(3.15), 273(3.11),288s(2.43)	35-4592-73
syn	EtOH	207(4.56),226(4.58), 260(3.24),265(3.28), 272(3.28),279s(3.11), 288s(2.76)	35-4592-73
2,7-Ethanonaphth[2,3-b]oxiren-8-one, 1a,2,7,7a-tetrahydro-1a,2,7,7a,9,9-hexamethyl-, (1aα,2α,7α,7aα)-	C_6H_{12}	227(3.70),258(2.48), 264(2.71),271(2.67), 282(2.42),295(2.52), 305(2.53),316(2.30)	44-3805-73
Furan, 2,2'-(1,2-ethynediyl)bis[3-(1,1-dimethylethyl)-	EtOH	253(4.21),296s(4.29), 301(4.30),319s(4.10)	18-2565-73
$C_{18}H_{22}O_3$			
Benzene, 1,1'-[oxybis(methyleneoxy)]bis-[2,3-dimethyl-	C_6H_{12}	264(3.12),268(3.18), 271(3.19),277(3.26)	80-0883-73
Benzene, 1,1'-[oxybis(methyleneoxy)]bis-[2,4-dimethyl-	C_6H_{12}	268(3.32),273(3.51), 276(3.45),282(3.41)	80-0883-73
Benzene, 1,1'-[oxybis(methyleneoxy)]bis-[2,5-dimethyl-	C_6H_{12}	265(3.30),270(3.43), 273(3.46),279(3.45)	80-0883-73
Benzene, 1,1'-[oxybis(methyleneoxy)]bis-[2,6-dimethyl-	C_6H_{12}	261(3.10),264(3.11), 267(3.10),272(3.02)	80-0883-73
Benzene, 1,1'-[oxybis(methyleneoxy)]bis-[3,4-dimethyl-	C_6H_{12}	267(3.30),272(3.42), 275(3.44),282(3.40)	80-0883-73
Benzene, 1,1'-[oxybis(methyleneoxy)]bis-[3,5-dimethyl-	C_6H_{12}	263(3.11),270(3.26), 273(3.20),278(3.30)	80-0883-73
Estra-1,3,5(10)-trien-17-one, 2,3-di-hydroxy-, Kober test	H_2SO_4	414(4.14),490s(4.24), 510s(4.24),536(4.32)	94-1720-73
Estra-1,3,5(10)-trien-17-one, 3,15α-di-hydroxy-, Kober test	H_2SO_4	512(3.79)	94-1720-73
Estra-1,3,5(10)-trien-16-one, 3,17β-di-hydroxy-, Kober test	H_2SO_4	512(4.61)	94-1720-73
$C_{18}H_{22}O_4$			
Butanoic acid, 4-(4-methylphenyl)-2-(1-methyl-2-oxocyclohexyl)-4-oxo-	MeOH	253.5(4.47)	115-0381-73
Debenzylidenerubranine	EtOH	235(4.21),293(4.29), 335(3.51)	78-1243-73
Ethanone, 1-(3,3a,4,5-tetrahydro-8-hy-droxy-2,5,5-trimethyl-2,4-ethano-2H-pyrano[4,3,2-de]-1-benzopyran-7-yl-	EtOH	235(4.18),293(4.27), 335(3.48)	78-1243-73
Gibba-1,3,4a(10a)-triene-10-carboxylic acid, 7,8-dihydroxy-1-methyl-, methyl ester	EtOH	265(2.46),273(2.31)	44-1398-73
1-Naphthalenecarboxaldehyde, 2,3,8-tri-methoxy-6-methyl-4-(1-methylethyl)-	MeOH	235(3.10),273(3.81), 353(4.00)	2-0825-73

Compound	Solvent	λmax(log ε)	Ref.
9,10-Phenanthrenedicarboxylic acid, 1,2,3,4,5,6,7,8-octahydro-, dimethyl ester	MeOH	290(3.38)	22-2121-73
$C_{18}H_{22}O_6$			
1,4:5,8-Diepoxy-2,3-naphthalenedicarboxylic acid, 1,4,4a,5,8,8a-hexahydro-1,4,5,8-tetramethyl-, dimethyl ester	MeOH	234(3.66)	24-0674-73
$C_{18}H_{22}O_6P_2$			
Phosphonic acid, (1,2-diphenyl-1,2-ethenediyl)bis-, P,P'-diethyl ester	H_2O	260(4.06)	18-0643-73
$C_{18}H_{22}O_7S_2$			
Ethanol, 2,2'-oxybis-, bis(4-methylbenzenesulfonate)	n.s.g.	225(4.37)	78-1659-73
$C_{18}H_{23}BrO_6$			
1H-3a,7-Methanoazulene-3,6-dicarboxylic acid, 8-(acetoxymethyl)-4-bromo-2,3,4-7,8,8a-hexahydro-8-methyl-, 6-methyl ester, [3R-(3α,3aβ,4α,7β,8α,8aα)]-	MeOH	235(3.79)	2-0991-73
$C_{18}H_{23}ClO_6$			
1,3-Dioxol-1-ium, 4,5-dihydro-4,4,5,5-tetramethyl-2-(1-methyl-4-phenyl-1,3-butadienyl)-, perchlorate	$CHCl_3$	318(4.49),400(4.45)	104-0394-73
$C_{18}H_{23}FO_2$			
Estra-1,3,5(10)-triene-3,17-diol, 7-fluoro-, (7α,17β)-	EtOH	280(3.30),287(3.26)	39-1462-73C
	EtOH-KOH	300(3.43)	39-1462-73C
Estr-5(10)-ene-3,17-dione, 2β-fluoro-	dioxan	294(1.68)	78-4053-73
$C_{18}H_{23}N$			
1H-Carbazole, 1-(1,1-dimethyl-2-propenyl)-2,3,4,9-tetrahydro-9-methyl-	EtOH	233(4.57),281s(4.13), 287(4.18),294(4.16)	39-1913-73C
Indole, 6-(3-methyl-2-butenyl)-2-(1,1-dimethyl-2-propenyl)-	hexane	225(4.47),270(3.83), 283(3.70),288(3.68), 296(3.70)	32-0141-73
$C_{18}H_{23}NO$			
Benzo[g]cycloprop[f]isoquinoline-10-carboxaldehyde, 1,2,3,4,5,5a,6,10b-octahydro-2,2,5a-trimethyl-	EtOH	215(4.33),259(3.95), 297(3.54)	54-0985-73
2-Hexen-1-one, 1-phenyl-4-(1-piperidinylmethylene)-	EtOH	245(4.31),346(4.64)	48-1161-73
1-Propanone, 2,2-dimethyl-1-(2,3,4,4a-tetrahydro-4a-methyl-1H-carbazol-8-yl)-	EtOH	260s(3.95),278(4.08), 330s(2.74)	33-2628-73
$C_{18}H_{23}NOS$			
Spiro[1,4,2-oxathiazolidine-5,2'-tricyclo[3.3.1.1^{3,7}]decane], 2-methyl-3-phenyl-	C_6H_{12}	219(3.84),295(2.76)	12-2491-73
$C_{18}H_{23}NO_2$			
6-Azaestra-1,3,5(10),9(11)-tetraen-17-ol, 3-methoxy-, (17β)-	EtOH	235(4.46),270(4.04), 332(3.73)	65-0663-73
Estra-1,3,5(10)-trien-17-one, 3-hydroxy-, oxime, Kober test	H_2SO_4	515(2.32)	94-1720-73

Compound	Solvent	λ_{max}(log ε)	Ref.
$C_{18}H_{23}NO_3$			
10H-Dibenzo[de,g]quinolin-10-one, 4,5,6,6a,7,7a,8,9,11,11a-decahydro-1-hydroxy-2-methoxy-6-methyl-	$CHCl_3$	288(3.56)	4-0307-73
isomer	$CHCl_3$	288(3.56)	4-0307-73
Glycine, N-(5-methyl-3-oxo-1-cyclohexen-1-yl)-N-(phenylmethyl)-, ethyl ester	n.s.g.	214(3.84),290s(4.14), 306(4.21)	44-3487-73
$C_{18}H_{23}NO_3S$			
2-Naphthalenecarbonitrile, decahydro-6-[[(4-methylphenyl)sulfonyl]oxy]-	MeOH	273.2(2.66)	44-2077-73
$C_{18}H_{23}NO_3S_2$			
1H,3H-Oxazolo[4,3-c][1,4]thiazine-6-carboxylic acid, 8,8a-dihydro-3,3,8,8-tetramethyl-1-(phenylthio)-, methyl ester	EtOH	249(3.86),321(4.00)	39-1985-73C
$C_{18}H_{23}NO_4$			
Propanedioic acid, ethyl(1H-indol-3-ylmethyl)-, diethyl ester	EtOH	280(3.80),290(3.75)	103-1367-73
$C_{18}H_{23}NO_5$			
1H-Indole-2-carboxylic acid, 5-(2-ethoxy-1,1-dimethyl-2-oxoethoxy)-1-methyl-, ethyl ester	EtOH	225(4.32),250(4.12), 260s(4.00),317(4.30)	39-0872-73B
Stephaboline	MeOH	281(3.44)	44-0151-73
hydrochloride	MeOH	283(3.47)	44-0151-73
$C_{18}H_{23}N_2S$			
Methanaminium, N-[4-[[4-(dimethylamino)-phenyl](methylthio)methylene]-2,5-cyclohexadien-1-ylidene]-N-methyl-	MeNO	592(4.68)	104-1766-73
$C_{18}H_{23}N_3O$			
4H-Indazol-4-one, 3-[4-(dimethylamino)-phenyl]-1,5,6,7-tetrahydro-1,6,6-trimethyl-	MeOH	251(4.39),279(4.13), 320(4.21)	24-0450-73
$C_{18}H_{23}N_3O_2$			
Estra-1,3,5(10)-triene-3,17-diol, 2-azido-, (17β)-	EtOH	254(3.88),301(3.75)	44-3525-73
Estra-1,3,5(10)-triene-3,17-diol, 4-azido-, (17β)-	EtOH	257(3.80),292(3.50)	44-3525-73
$C_{18}H_{23}N_3O_8S$			
Ethyl 3'-deoxy-3'-(N-pyridinium)thymidine uronate methyl sulfonate	H_2O	235(3.61),260(4.21)	44-0990-73
$C_{18}H_{23}N_7O_{11}P_2$			
Pyridinium, 3-(aminocarbonyl)-1-[5-O-[6-(6-amino-9H-purin-9-yl)-1,3-dihydroxy-2,4-dioxa-1,3-diphosphahex-1-yl]-β-D-ribofuranosyl]-, hydroxide, inner salt, P,P'-dioxide, reduced	pH 9.5	261(4.14),344(3.79)	5-0531-73
oxidized form	pH 9.5	261(4.26)	5-0531-73
cyanide addition product	pH 10	326(4.16)	5-0531-73

Compound	Solvent	$\lambda_{max}(\log \epsilon)$	Ref.
$C_{18}H_{23}O_2$			
1,3-Dioxol-1-ium, 4,5-dihydro-4,4,5,5-tetramethyl-2-(1-methyl-4-phenyl-1,3-butadienyl)-, perchlorate	$CHCl_3$	318(4.49),400(4.45)	104-0394-73
$C_{18}H_{24}$			
Estra-1,3,5(10)-triene, Kober test	H_2SO_4	430(3.59)	94-1720-73
Naphthalene, 1,4-bis(1,1-dimethylethyl)-, tetracyanoethylene complex	CH_2Cl_2	445(1.72),626(1.67)	39-0447-73B
Naphthalene, 2,6-bis(1,1-dimethylethyl)-, tetracyanoethylene complex	CH_2Cl_2	487(2.80),620(2.76)	39-0447-73B
Naphthalene, 2,7-bis(1,1-dimethylethyl)-, tetracyanoethylene complex	CH_2Cl_2	501(2.75),610(2.80)	39-0447-73B
$C_{18}H_{24}Br_2O_{12}$			
2H-Cyclopenta[b]furan-4,5,6-tricarboxylic acid, 3a,6-dibromo-3,3a,6,6a-tetrahydro-2,2,3,3,6a-pentamethoxy-, trimethyl ester	MeOH	214(3.9),240(3.9)	24-1758-73
isomer	MeOH	208(3.9),240(3.9)	24-1758-73
$C_{18}H_{24}CuF_3O_3S$			
Bis(1,5-cyclooctadiene)copper(I) trifluoroacetate	n.s.g.	236(3.49),282(3.23)	35-1889-73
$C_{18}H_{24}IN$			
1H-Carbazolium, 2,3,4,4a-tetrahydro-9-methyl-4a-(3-methyl-2-butenyl)-, iodide	EtOH	218(4.25),237s(3.87), 276(3.82)	39-1913-73C
$C_{18}H_{24}N_2$			
[1,1'-Biphenyl]-2,3-diamine, N^3,N^3-diethyl-N^2,N^2-dimethyl-, hydrochloride	EtOH	230s(3.91)	39-1079-73C
$C_{18}H_{24}N_2O_2$			
1H-Carbazole-1-carboxylic acid, 9-(3-aminopropyl)-2,3,4,9-tetrahydro-, ethyl ester, hydrochloride	EtOH	229(4.48),279(3.81), 285(3.84),293(3.79)	78-4045-73
$C_{18}H_{24}N_2O_3$			
1H-Azepine-4-carboxylic acid, 1-acetyl-2,3,6,7-tetrahydro-5-[(phenylmethyl)amino]-, ethyl ester	EtOH	304(4.12)	1-3251-73
Butanamide, N-[2,6-dioxo-1-(2-phenylethyl)-3-piperidinyl]-2-methyl-	EtOH	210(4.27)	78-4071-73 +142-0043-73
$C_{18}H_{24}N_2O_4S$			
1H-Pyrrole-2-carboxylic acid, 4,4'-thiobis[3,5-dimethyl-, diethyl ester	EtOH	263s(--),282(4.11)	5-0207-73
$C_{18}H_{24}N_2O_5S$			
1H-Pyrrole-2-carboxylic acid, 4,4'-sulfinylbis[3,5-dimethyl-, diethyl ester	EtOH	277(3.98)	5-0207-73
$C_{18}H_{24}N_2O_6$			
Acetamide, N,N'-[[2,5-bis(acetyloxy)-1,4-phenylene]di-2,1-ethanediyl]bis-	EtOH	269(2.71),276(2.73)	39-0832-73C
Cyclopent[g]indazole-3a,4,8b(3H,4H)-tricarboxylic acid, 6,7,8,8a-tetrahydro-7,7-dimethyl-, trimethyl ester, (3aα,4α,8aβ,8bα)-	EtOH	220(3.73),324(2.13)	44-2870-73

Compound	Solvent	$\lambda_{max}(\log \epsilon)$	Ref.
$C_{18}H_{24}N_4O_2$			
Benzo[g]pteridine-2,4(3H,4aH)-dione, 4a,5-diethyl-5,10-dihydro-3,7,8,10-tetramethyl-	pH 7	327(3.99)	5-1388-73
	MeOH	283(3.91),305(3.97), 330s(3.91)	5-1388-73
	6M HCl	322(4.02)	5-1388-73
Benzo[g]pteridinium, 5,5-diethyl-2,3,4,4a,5,10-hexahydro-3,7,8,10-tetramethyl-2,4-dioxo-, hydroxide, inner salt	pH 7	265(4.29),290(4.18), 310(3.92)	5-1388-73
	MeOH	266(4.40),290(4.17), 310s(3.81)	5-1388-73
	6M HCl	289(4.03),318(4.06)	5-1388-73
$C_{18}H_{24}N_4O_4$			
6,10-Etheno[1,2]diazepino[5,4-c]-1,2-diazepine-1,7-dicarboxylic acid, 5a,6,10,10a-tetrahydro-5,11-dimethyl-, diethyl ester, (5aα,6β,10β,10aα)-	MeOH	235(4.06),308(3.20)	88-4167-73
$C_{18}H_{24}O$			
Drupanol	EtOH	263.5(4.35)	105-0007-73
Phenol, 4-(3-ethenyl-3,6-dimethyl-1-methylene-5-heptenyl)- (bakuchiol)	EtOH	260(4.26)	78-1119-73
	EtOH-KOH	285(4.32)	78-1119-73
$C_{18}H_{24}O_2$			
Cyclobuta[1,2-c:4,3-c']diindene-1,12-dione, tetradecahydro-	hexane	312(2.08)	88-3441-73
7H-Diindeno[7,1-bc:1',7'a-e]pyran-7-one, 1,2,2a,3,4,5,8,9,10,10a,11,12,12a,12b-tetradecahydro-	hexane	303(1.93)	88-3441-73
Estra-1,3,5(10)-triene-2,17β-diol, Kober test	H_2SO_4	514(4.50)	94-1720-73
Estra-1,3,5(10)-triene-3,16β-diol, Kober test	H_2SO_4	462(4.40),514(4.24)	94-1720-73
Estra-1,3,5(10)-triene-3,17α-diol, Kober test	H_2SO_4	436s(4.11),462(4.35), 517(4.32)	94-1720-73
Estra-1,3,5(10)-triene-3,17β-diol, Kober test	H_2SO_4	436s(4.02),465(4.26), 490s(4.27),515(4.32)	94-1720-73
Estra-5(10),6,8-triene-3α,17β-diol, Kober test	H_2SO_4	416(4.10)	94-1720-73
Estra-5(10),6,8-triene-3β,17β-diol, Kober test	H_2SO_4	416(4.10)	94-1720-73
Ethanone, 1-[4-hydroxy-3,5-bis(3-methyl-2-butenyl)phenyl]-	ether	219(4.33),269(4.13)	24-0382-73
$C_{18}H_{24}O_3$			
Estra-1,3,5(10)-triene-2,3,17β-triol, Kober test	H_2SO_4	412(3.85),490s(4.09), 508s(4.20),540(4.21)	94-1720-73
Estra-1,3,5(10)-triene-3,6α,17β-triol	EtOH	222(3.89),229s(3.77), 282(3.34),288s(3.30)	44-3797-73
Estra-1,3,5(10)-triene-3,6β,17β-triol	EtOH	221(3.87),228s(3.77), 282(3.32),288s(3.28)	44-3797-73
Estra-1,3,5(10)-triene-3,16α,17β-triol, Kober test	H_2SO_4	462(4.22),512(4.57)	94-1720-73
Estra-1,3,5(10)-triene-3,16β,17β-triol, Kober test	H_2SO_4	513(4.63)	94-1720-73
Ethanone, 1-[2,4-dihydroxy-3,5-bis(3-methyl-2-butenyl)phenyl]-	EtOH	285(4.34),328(3.92)	94-1777-73
Heptanoic acid, 7-(2,3-dihydro-5-methoxy-1H-inden-1-ylidene)-, methyl ester	MeOH	261(4.13)	78-1447-73
B-Norandrost-4-ene-3,17-dione, 6-hydroxy-, (6α)-	EtOH	238(4.36),300(1.66)	73-1398-73

Compound	Solvent	λ_{max}(log ε)	Ref.
9,17-Octadecadiene-12,14-diynoic acid, 16-hydroxy-, [R-(Z)]-	EtOH	231(3.06),243(2.99), 256(2.78),274(2.42), 291(2.31)	88-3131-73
$C_{18}H_{24}O_4$			
Acetic acid, (2,2a,3,4,5,5a,8a,8b-octahydro-2a,5a,7-trimethyl-2-oxo-6H-naphtho[1,8-bc]furan-6-ylidene)-, ethyl ester	EtOH	254(3.80)	32-1271-73
1,3,5-Cyclohexanetrione, 2-acetyl-4,4-bis(3-methyl-2-butenyl)-	EtOH	273(3.83),338(3.90)	39-0419-73C
4-Deoxyacetohumulone	EtOH	292(4.20)	39-0419-73C
	EtOH-base	333(4.18)	39-0419-73C
Estra-1,3,5(10)-triene-2,3,16α,17β-tetrol, Kober test	H_2SO_4	415(3.84),490s(4.11), 510s(4.18),537(4.21)	94-1720-73
Ethanone, 1-[3,4-dihydro-5,7-dihydroxy-2,2-dimethyl-3-(3-methyl-2-butenyl)-2H-1-benzopyran-6-yl]-	EtOH	292(4.28)	39-0419-73C
Ethanone, 1-[3,4-dihydro-5,7-dihydroxy-2,2-dimethyl-3-(3-methyl-2-butenyl)-2H-1-benzopyran-8-yl]-	EtOH	292(4.24)	39-0419-73C
Ethanone, 1-(3,4,9,10-tetrahydro-5-hydroxy-2,2,8,8-tetramethyl-2H,8H-benzo[1,2-b:3,4-b']dipyran-6-yl)-	MeOH	298(4.02)	2-0100-73
Ethanone, 1-[2,4,6-trihydroxy-3,3-bis-(3-methyl-2-butenyl)]phenyl-	MeOH	251(2.85),347(4.15)	2-0100-73
Pentacyclo[$6.2.2.0^{2,7}.0^{3,10}.0^{4,9}$]dodecane-5,11-dione, 6,12-dihydroxy-1,2,4,6,9,12-hexamethyl-	EtOH	307(2.00)	5-1675-73
$C_{18}H_{24}O_5$			
3,13-Metheno-1,2-cyclotrideca-1,12-diene-1,2-dicarboxylic acid, 12-hydroxy-, dimethyl ester	pentane	243(5.15),329(5.08), 387(4.70)	88-4325-73
$C_{18}H_{24}O_7$			
8aα-Naphthalenecarboxylic acid, 1,4,4aα-5,8,8a-hexahydro-4β-hydroxy-3-methoxy-8β-(methoxymethyl)-7-methyl-1-oxo-, acetate	EtOH	247(4.08)	94-0528-73
Oxiranecarboxylic acid, 3-(3,4-dimethoxyphenyl)-3-(2,2-dimethyl-1,3-dioxolan-4-yl)-, ethyl ester	EtOH	203(4.62),235(3.94), 280(3.45)	39-2359-73C
$C_{18}H_{24}O_8$			
Colletodiol diacetate	MeOH	219(3.68)	39-1487-73C
$C_{18}H_{24}O_{12}$			
2H-Cyclopenta[b]furan-4,5,6-tricarboxylic acid, 3,6a-dihydro-2,2,3,3,6a-pentamethoxy-, trimethyl ester	MeOH	211(3.8),265(3.6), 305(3.5)	24-1758-73
$C_{18}H_{25}Cl_2NO$			
1(2H)-Pentalenone, 4,5-dichloro-6-(dimethylamino)-2,3-bis(1,1-dimethylethyl)-	EtOH	216(4.42),235(4.31), 326(4.15),386(3.67), 457(3.74)	138-0561-73
$C_{18}H_{25}CoO$			
(η-C_5H_5)Co[[(Me_3C)C≡CH)$_2$]CO]-, orange-yellow isomer	EtOH	282(4.30),357(3.36), 424(2.44)	12-1911-73

Compound	Solvent	$\lambda_{max}(\log \epsilon)$	Ref.
(η-C_5H_5)Co[[(Me$_3$C)C≡CH)$_2$]CO]-, red isomer	EtOH	284(4.37),352(3.26), 435(3.00)	12-1911-73
yellow hydrate	EtOH	279(4.22),360(3.38), 413(2.82)	12-1911-73
$C_{18}H_{25}N$			
Isoquinoline, 1,2,3,4,5,6,7,8-octahydro-2-methyl-1-phenylethyl-	EtOH	258(2.57)	4-0217-73
$C_{18}H_{25}NO$			
1H-Carbazole, 2,3,4,4a,9,9a-hexahydro-4a-methyl-9-(2,2-dimethyl-1-oxopropyl)-	EtOH	253(4.14),275s(3.67), 285(3.49)	33-2628-73
Isoquinoline, 1,2,3,4,5,6,7,8-octahydro-1-[2-(3-methoxyphenyl)ethyl]-	EtOH	273(3.31),280(3.28)	4-0217-73
hydrochloride	EtOH	272(3.33),279(3.29)	4-0217-73
1-Propanone, 1-(2,3,4,4a,9,9a-hexahydro-4a-methyl-1H-carbazol-8-yl)-2,2-dimethyl-	EtOH	234(4.22),260(3.58), 376(3.71)	33-2628-73
	EtOH-HCl	236(4.01),374(3.71)	33-2628-73
$C_{18}H_{25}NO_2$			
6-Azaestra-1,3,5(10)-trien-17-ol, 3-methoxy-, (17β)-	EtOH	212(4.39),251(3.84), 299(3.57)	65-0663-73
Benzenepropanamide, N-[2-(1-cyclohexen-1-yl)ethyl]-3-methoxy-	EtOH	229(3.24),272(3.27)	4-0217-73
Crepidamine	EtOH	209(4.04),251s(2.66), 258(2.58),264(2.43), 268s(2.20)	1-1907-73
6H-Dibenzo[b,d]pyran-3-amine, 6a,7,10,10a-tetrahydro-1-methoxy-N,6,6,9-tetramethyl-, (6aR-trans)	EtOH	217(4.45),249(3.92), 289(3.30)	33-0510-73
Isocrepidamine	EtOH	209(3.98),242(1.99), 247(2.11),251(2.26), 257(2.38),260(2.23), 263(2.26),267(2.04)	1-1907-73
1-Oxa-3-azaspiro[5.5]undec-2-ene, 2-[2-(3-methoxyphenyl)ethyl]-, hydrochloride	EtOH	273(3.30),280(3.26)	4-0217-73
$C_{18}H_{25}NO_3$			
Piperidine, 1-[[4-(3-methyl-1-oxobutyl)-phenoxy]acetyl]-	EtOH	214(4.27),267(4.26)	111-0574-73
Piperidine, 1-[[4-(1-oxopentyl)phenoxy]-acetyl]-	EtOH	214(4.29),268(4.27)	111-0574-73
$C_{18}H_{25}N_3O$			
Benzaldehyde, 4-(dimethylamino)-, (5,5-dimethyl-3-oxo-1-cyclohexen-1-yl)methylhydrazone	MeOH	238(3.97),292(4.06), 308(4.06),328s(4.06), 381(4.70)	24-0450-73
$C_{18}H_{25}N_5O_{11}$			
2(1H)-Pteridinone, 1-β-D-glucopyranosyl-4-(β-D-glucopyranosylamino)-	pH -2	238(4.10),333(3.92)	24-2982-73
	pH 7.0	241(4.14),280(3.77), 333(3.99)	24-2982-73
$C_{18}H_{25}N_7NaO_8P$			
Adenosine, N-[(propylamino)carbonyl]-, 2'-(propylcarbamate), Na salt	pH 1	276(4.40),285s(4.29)	87-1075-73
	pH 7	267(4.37),275s(4.30)	87-1075-73
	pH 11	267(4.37),275s(4.30)	87-1075-73

Compound	Solvent	λmax(log ε)	Ref.
$C_{18}H_{26}$			
1,1'-Bicyclohexyl, 2-phenyl-, trans	EtOH	249(2.11),254(2.24), 256(2.23),260(2.31), 262(2.33),265(2.20), 269(2.24)	22-1517-73
$C_{18}H_{26}N_2$			
5H-Cyclooct[b]indole-5-propanamine, 6,7,8,9,10,11-hexahydro-β-methyl-, maleate	EtOH	230(4.51),280(3.81), 288(3.87),295(3.85)	78-4045-73
$C_{18}H_{26}N_2O_3$			
Piperidine, 1-[[4-[1-(hydroxyimino)pent-yl]phenoxy]acetyl]-	EtOH	212(4.29),268(4.18)	111-0574-73
$C_{18}H_{26}N_2O_{10}$			
1,2,5-Oxadiazole, 3,4-bis(1,2-O-isoprop-ylidene-3-O-methyl-α-D-xylotetro-1,4-furanos-4-yl)-, 2-oxide	EtOH	265(3.62)	136-0311-73D
$C_{18}H_{26}N_4O_3S$			
DL-Valine, N-[1-oxo-5-(1H-pyrrolo[2,3-d]pyrimidin-4-ylthio)pentyl]-, ethyl ester	pH 1	219(4.43),257(4.00), 312(4.08)	73-1438-73
	pH 13	221(4.38),246(4.03), 291(4.15)	73-1438-73
$C_{18}H_{26}N_6O_6$			
Adenosine, 3'-deoxy-3'-[2-[(2-ethoxy-2-oxoethyl)amino]-2-oxoethyl]-N,N-dimethyl-	H_2O	275(4.16)	44-0198-73
$C_{18}H_{26}O$			
5(6H)-Benzocyclotetradecenone, 7,8,9,10-11,12,13,14,15,16-decahydro-	EtOH	242(3.81)	78-1857-73
Phenol, 4-(3-ethenyl-3,7-dimethyl-6-oct-enyl)-	EtOH	222(3.80),277(3.16)	78-1119-73
$C_{18}H_{26}O_2$			
Benzoic acid, 2,5-(decamethylene)-, methyl ester	EtOH	230(3.93),290(3.20)	49-0644-73
Estr-4-en-3-one, 17β-hydroxy-, Kober test	H_2SO_4	398(3.84),465(3.81), 515(3.66)	94-1720-73
9,17-Octadecadiene-12,14-diyne-1,16-diol	EtOH	231(3.02),243(2.98), 256(2.89),269(2.82), 285(2.73)	88-3131-73
$C_{18}H_{26}O_4S$			
2-Naphthalenol, decahydro-6-methoxy-, 4-methylbenzenesulfonate	MeOH	273.2(2.66)	44-2077-73
$C_{18}H_{26}O_6S_2$			
7H-Benz[e]inden-7-one, 1,2,3,3a,4,6,8,9-9a,9b-decahydro-3a-methyl-6-(methyl-sulfonyl)-3-[(methylsulfonyl)acetyl]-, [3S-(3α,3aα,6α,9aα,9bβ)]-	dioxan	225(3.47),300(2.39)	94-0335-73
$C_{18}H_{26}O_8$			
3-Hexyne-1,1,6,6-tetracarboxylic acid, tetraethyl ester	isooctane	211(2.65),240s(2.53), 286(1.90),292(1.89)	33-0625-73

Compound	Solvent	λ_{max}(log ε)	Ref.
$C_{18}H_{26}O_{11}$			
Cyclopenta[c]pyran-4,7-dicarboxylic acid, 1-(β-D-glucopyranosyloxy)-1,4a,5,6,7,7a-hexahydro-, dimethyl ester (forsythid dimethyl ester)	MeOH	236.5(4.09)	94-0497-73
$C_{18}H_{27}NO_2$			
5-Benzoxazolol, 4,7-bis(1,1-dimethylethyl)-2-propyl-	EtOH	244(4.02),295(3.64)	39-0268-73C
2,5-Cyclohexadiene-1,4-dione, 5-(1,1-dimethylethyl)-2-(2-methyl-1-propenyl)-	EtOH	229(4.33),260s(4.10), 512(3.40)	39-0268-73C
$C_{18}H_{27}NO_9S$			
Benzoic acid, 2-[[(2,3,4,6-tetra-O-methyl-β-D-glucopyranosyl)amino]sulfonyl]-, methyl ester	MeOH	276(3.09)	5-1943-73
$C_{18}H_{27}N_3O_6S$			
Guanidine, N'-(2-ethoxycarbonylethyl)-N"-(2-methoxycarbonylethyl)-N'-methyl-N-p-toluenesulfonyl-	EtOH	230(4.19)	44-1591-73
$C_{18}H_{27}N_5O_4$			
Adenosine, N-cyclooctyl-	pH 1	265(4.34)	87-0358-73
	H_2O	270.5(4.28)	87-0358-73
	pH 13	270.5(4.32)	87-0358-73
$C_{18}H_{28}N_3O_{10}PS$			
Uridine, 5'-O-[2,2-dihydro-5,5-dimethyl-2-[(methylsulfonyl)imino]-1,3,2-dioxaphosphorinan-2-yl]-2',3'-O-(1-methylethylidene)-	MeOH	256(4.02)	89-0070-73
$C_{18}H_{28}O$			
2-Dodecanone, 1-phenyl-	C_6H_{12}	287(2.18),294(--), 302(--),313(--)	28-0407-73B
	MeOH	285(2.19)	28-0407-73B
β-Ionylideneethylideneacetone, 7,8-dihydro-	EtOH	293(4.46)	65-2047-73
5,7,9,13-Pentadecatetraen-2-one, 6,10,14-trimethyl-	EtOH	225(4.43),315(3.90)	65-0409-73
Phenol, 4-(3-ethyl-3,7-dimethyl-6-octenyl)-, (R)-	EtOH	224(3.82),276(3.19)	78-1119-73
Spiro[2.5]octa-4,7-dien-6-one, 5,7-bis-(1,1-dimethylethyl)-1,2-dimethyl-, trans	n.s.g.	281(4.32)	70-1998-73
$C_{18}H_{28}O_4$			
1H-Indene-1-heptanoic acid, 2,3,4,5,6,7-hexahydro-5-hydroxy-4-methyl-2-oxo-, methyl ester	MeOH	239(4.13)	78-1447-73
$C_{18}H_{29}Cl_4N_3$			
1-Cyclobutene-1-carboximidamide, 3,3-dichloro-4-(dichloromethylene)-N,N'-bis-(1,1-dimethylethyl)-2-[(1,1-dimethylethyl)amino]-	n.s.g.	272(4.20)	44-1470-73
bisulfate	n.s.g.	272(4.32)	44-1470-73
monohydrochloride	n.s.g.	273(4.13)	44-1470-73
mononitrate	n.s.g.	273(4.27)	44-1470-73

Compound	Solvent	λmax(log ε)	Ref.
$C_{18}H_{29}NOS$			
Spiro[pyrrolo[1,2-b][1,4,2]oxathiazole-2,2'-tricyclo[3.3.1.1 ']decane], tetrahydro-5,5,7,7-tetramethyl-	C_6H_{12}	223s(--),243(4.10)	12-2491-73
$C_{18}H_{29}NO_3$			
7-Oxabicyclo[4.1.0]hept-3-ene-2,5-dione, 3-(butylamino)-1,4-bis(1,1-dimethylethyl)-	n.s.g.	215(4.08),280(3.91), 379(3.88)	39-0268-73C
$C_{18}H_{29}N_3O_2$			
Hydrazinecarboxamide, 2-(7-oxospiro-[5.11]heptadec-1-en-3-ylidene)-	EtOH	272(4.34)	39-0393-73C
$C_{18}H_{29}N_3O_5$			
1-Cyclopentene-1-heptanoic acid, 5-[(aminocarbonyl)hydrazono]-2-(ethoxycarbonyl)-, ethyl ester	MeOH	298(4.37)	44-4412-73
$C_{18}H_{30}N$			
Methanaminium, N-methyl-N-[(1,1a,4,4a-5,6,7,8-octahydro-2,4a,8,8-tetramethylcyclopropa[d]naphthalen-3-yl)methylene]-, perchlorate	EtOH	325(4.06)	54-0985-73
Methanaminium, N-methyl-N-[2-(octahydro-4a,8,8-trimethylcyclopropa[d]naphthalen-2(3H)-ylidene)ethylidene]-, perchlorate	EtOH	320(4.41)	54-0985-73
$C_{18}H_{30}O$			
Phenol, 4-(3-ethyl-3,7-dimethyloctyl)-, (R)-	EtOH	224(3.69),278(3.09)	78-1119-73
$C_{18}H_{30}O_3$			
1,3,5-Benzenetrimethanol, α,α',α"-triethyl-α,α',α"-trimethyl-	MeOH	261(2.37)	32-0849-73
1,3,5-Benzenetrimethanol, α,α',α"-tripropyl-	MeOH	263(2.37)	32-0849-73
$C_{18}H_{30}O_4$			
2,4-Hexadiyne, 1,6-bis(1-butoxyethoxy)-	n.s.g.	220(3.7),232(3.8), 245(3.9),257(3.8)	104-1830-73
$C_{18}H_{30}O_6$			
1-Cyclopentene-1-heptanoic acid, 2,4,4-triethoxy-5-oxo-	MeOH	263(4.17)	88-2213-73
$C_{18}H_{31}NO$			
2,4-Cyclohexadien-1-one, 2,4,6-tris(1,1-dimethylethyl)-, oxime	n.s.g.	216(3.78),306(3.46)	88-3947-73
$C_{18}H_{32}N_4O_4S$			
Glycinamide, 1-[(1,1-dimethylethoxy)-carbonyl]-L-prolyl-L-leucyl-thio-	EtOH	267(4.09)	35-5677-73
$C_{18}H_{32}N_5O$			
1H-Purinium, 2-amino-7-dodecyl-6,9-dihydro-9-methyl-6-oxo-, bromide	pH 4	253(4.07),280(3.86)	24-1389-73
	pH 10	219(4.29),249(3.74), 281(3.88)	24-1389-73

Compound	Solvent	$\lambda_{max}(\log \epsilon)$	Ref.
$C_{18}H_{32}O_5$			
Oxacyclooctadec-3-en-2-one, 5,6,7-trihydroxy-18-methyl- (aspicilin)	MeOH	211(4.10)	78-3687-73
$C_{18}H_{34}OS$			
7-Tridecanone, 6-[(butylthio)methylene]-	n.s.g.	295(4.18)	35-0250-73
$C_{18}H_{34}O_5$			
Oxacyclooctadecan-2-one, 5,6,7-trihydroxy-18-methyl-	MeOH	205(3.08)	78-3687-73
$C_{18}H_{38}Si_4$			
Silane, [3-[bis(trimethylsilyl)methylene]-2,5-cyclopentadiene-1,2-diyl]-bis[trimethyl-	n.s.g.	233(3.56),283(4.11), 323(3.08)	88-0911-73
Silane, 2,3-hexadien-5-yne-1,2,4,6-tetrayltetrakis[trimethyl-	n.s.g.	233(4.07),242(4.12), 253(4.10)	39-0599-73B

Compound	Solvent	λ_{max}(log ϵ)	Ref.
$C_{19}H_{10}Br_2O_3$			
7H-Benzo[c]fluorene-6-carboxylic acid, 2,9-dibromo-7-oxo-, methyl ester	EtOH	222(4.39),246(4.56), 272(--),297(4.42), 445(2.94)	115-0145-73A
$C_{19}H_{10}N_6$			
1-Phthalazinecarbonitrile, 4,4'-methylenebis-	EtOH	212(4.72),372(4.30)	95-0409-73
$C_{19}H_{11}ClO_2$			
Methanone, (2-chlorophenyl)(2-dibenzofuranyl)-	EtOH	236(4.34),242(4.43), 261(4.52),276(4.40)	40-1505-73
Methanone, (2-chlorophenyl)(3-dibenzofuranyl)-	EtOH	276(3.85),278(3.95), 309(4.44)	40-1505-73
Methanone, (3-chlorophenyl)(2-dibenzofuranyl)-	EtOH	247(4.41),263(4.43), 279(4.34)	40-1505-73
Methanone, (3-chlorophenyl)(3-dibenzofuranyl)-	EtOH	247(4.28),301(4.24)	40-1505-73
Methanone, (4-chlorophenyl)(2-dibenzofuranyl)-	EtOH	247(4.44),262(4.56)	40-1505-73
$C_{19}H_{11}ClO_4$			
4H-1-Benzopyran-4-one, 3-[(4-chloro-1-oxo-1H-2-benzopyran-3-yl)methylene]-2,3-dihydro-	EtOH	252(4.13),364(4.31)	22-2093-73
$C_{19}H_{11}NOS$			
Benzothiazole, 2-(2-dibenzofuranyl)-	THF	290(4.3),312(4.3), 325(4.3),343(4.3)	104-2601-73
Benzothiazole, 2-(4-dibenzofuranyl)-	THF	295(4.4),320s(4.3), 330s(4.1)	104-2601-73
$C_{19}H_{11}N_3$			
A triazapentaphene, m. 215°d.	EtOH	247(4.7),325(4.0), 436(2.3)	18-0942-73
$C_{19}H_{12}Br_2O_4$			
2,3-Naphthalenedicarboxylic acid, 7-bromo-1-(4-bromophenyl)-, 3-methyl ester	EtOH	246(4.91),290(4.06)	115-0145-73A
$C_{19}H_{12}ClNO_3S$			
3-Thiophenecarbonitrile, 5-(4-chlorobenzoyl)-4-hydroxy-2-(4-methoxyphenyl)-	CH_2Cl_2	375(4.33)	48-0497-73
$C_{19}H_{12}F_3S$			
Dibenzothiophenium, 5-[3-(trifluoromethyl)phenyl]-, tetrafluoroborate	EtOH	235(4.50),270(4.50), 275(3.96),318(3.52)	35-5288-73
Dibenzothiophenium, 5-[4-(trifluoromethyl)phenyl]-, tetrafluoroborate	EtOH	235(4.53),243(4.52), 270(4.03),315(3.51)	35-5288-73
$C_{19}H_{12}NO_2$			
Nitroxide, 9-oxo-9H-fluoren-2-yl phenyl	$CHCl_3$	250(4.59),304(4.26), 312(4.27),338(4.20), 380s(3.72),405s(3.52), 470(3.08),500(3.04), 670s(2.08)	44-0165-73

Compound	Solvent	$\lambda_{max}(\log \epsilon)$	Ref.
$C_{19}H_{12}N_2O_2$			
7H-Benzimidazo[2,1-a]benz[de]isoquinolin-7-one, 10-methoxy-	EtOH	306(4.33),409(4.03)	4-0705-73
7H-Benzimidazo[2,1-a]benz[de]isoquinolin-7-one, 11-methoxy-	EtOH	289(4.32),299(4.43), 344(4.03),373(4.05)	4-0705-73
	HOAc	289(4.33),299(4.41), 344(4.06),371(4.07)	4-0705-73
$C_{19}H_{12}N_2O_5S$			
Benzonitrile, 4-[2-(5-nitro-2-furanyl)-2-(phenylsulfonyl)ethenyl]-	EtOH	209(4.51),217s(4.48), 289(4.47)	73-1705-73
$C_{19}H_{12}O_2$			
7,8-Benzocoumarin, 3-phenyl-	EtOH	242(4.4),279(4.4), 338(4.2),375(4.1)	2-0707-73
	EtOH	242(4.36),279(4.38), 338(4.22),375(4.08)	39-1802-73C
1,3-Cyclobutanedione, 2-(2,3-diphenyl-2-cyclopropen-1-ylidene)-	EtOH	225s(4.23),266(4.28), 325(4.65)	18-1008-73
	EtOH-NaOH	265(4.12),328(4.39), 342(4.37)	18-1008-73
3H-Naphtho[2,1-b]pyran-3-one, 1-phenyl-	MeOH	229(4.7),252s(4.0), 307s(3.9),320(3.9), 350(4.0)	2-1245-73
3H-Naphtho[2,1-b]pyran-3-one, 2-phenyl-	EtOH	231(4.9),270s(3.7), 280(3.8),292(3.6), 328(3.8)	2-1245-73
4H-Naphtho[1,2-b]pyran-2-one, 4-phenyl-	MeOH	230(4.6),257s(4.3), 267(4.5),277(4.5), 308(3.9),323(3.9), 370(3.7)	2-1245-73
$C_{19}H_{12}O_2S_3$			
4H-[1,2]Dithiolo[1',5':1,5][1,2]dithiolo[3,4-b][1]benzopyran-11-S^{IV}-4-one, 6-methyl-2-phenyl-	EtOH	245(4.78),270(4.63), 293(4.59),321(4.51), 356(4.40),460(4.03)	39-1022-73C
$C_{19}H_{12}O_3$			
Methanone, 2-dibenzofuranyl(2-hydroxyphenyl)-	EtOH	249(4.37),265(4.44), 330(3.82)	40-1505-73
$C_{19}H_{12}O_6$			
Lasiocephalin	EtOH	261(4.18),272(3.20), 296s(--),326(4.12)	25-0792-73
$C_{19}H_{12}S_2$			
Naphtho[2',3':4,5]thieno[3,2-b][1]benzothiophene, 7-methyl-	C_6H_{12}	208(3.64),237(3.66), 254(3.63),276(3.66), 284(3.66),296(3.67), 310(3.60),322(3.62), 338(3.60),354(3.61), 378(3.62)	39-0734-73C
Naphtho[2',3':4,5]thieno[3,2-b][1]benzothiophene, 8-methyl-	C_6H_{12}	208(3.65),236(3.68), 255(3.64),275(3.67), 284(3.67),296(3.68), 310(3.61),321(3.63), 334(3.61),348(3.62), 358(3.61),378(3.61)	39-0734-73C
Naphtho[2',3':4,5]thieno[3,2-b][1]benzothiophene, 9-methyl-	C_6H_{12}	208(3.66),236(3.68), 253(3.65),273(3.67),	39-0734-73C

Compound	Solvent	λmax(log ε)	Ref.
Naphtho[2',3':4,5]thieno[3,2-b][1]benzothiophene, 9-methyl- (cont.)	C_6H_{12}	282(3.68),293(3.69), 308(3.63),320(3.64), 340(3.63),354(3.63) 372(3.63)	39-0734-73C
$C_{19}H_{13}BrO_3$			
Naphthalene, 1-acetoxy-2-benzoyl-4-bromo-	C_6H_{12}	240(4.54),260s(4.36), 294(3.84),304(3.78), 336(3.38)	19-0849-73
	MeOH	246(4.45),260s(4.39), 292(3.91),306s(3.78), 332(3.38),342s(3.33), 400s(2.34)	19-0849-73
	50% MeOH	250s(4.40),258(4.41), 300s(3.88),334(3.41), 342(3.40)	19-0849-73
$C_{19}H_{13}BrS$			
Benzo[b]thiophene, 2-(4-bromo-1-naphthalenyl)-6-methyl-	MeOH	260s(4.16),314(4.22), 325(4.16)	5-1112-73
Benzo[b]thiophene, 2-(6-bromo-2-naphthalenyl)-6-methyl-	MeOH	238(4.64),270(4.35), 284(4.33),325(4.53), 336(4.42)	5-1112-73
$C_{19}H_{13}ClN_2O_2S$			
3-Thiophenecarbonitrile, 4-amino-5-(4-chlorobenzoyl)-2-(4-methoxyphenyl)-	CH_2Cl_2	380(4.17)	48-0497-73
$C_{19}H_{13}Cl_3O$			
Benzenemethanol, 4-chloro-α,α-bis(4-chlorophenyl)-	99% H_2SO_4	465(5.01)	39-0095-73B
$C_{19}H_{13}Cl_6N_7O$			
Acetamide, N-[2-[2,5-bis[(2,4,6-trichlorophenyl)azo]-1H-imidazol-4-yl)-ethyl]-	EtOH	385(4.23)	44-1971-73
$C_{19}H_{13}F_3$			
1,1':2',1"-Terphenyl, 3-(trifluoromethyl)-	EtOH	215(4.22),265(3.15), 272(2.98)	35-5288-73
1,1':2',1"-Terphenyl, 4-(trifluoromethyl)-	EtOH	220(4.09),225s(3.79), 250(3.65)	35-5288-73
$C_{19}H_{13}NO$			
Benzeneacetonitrile, α-[(4-hydroxy-1-naphthalenyl)methylene]-	MeOH	244(4.3),360(4.2)	88-4203-73
9H-Fluoren-9-one, 1-(phenylamino)-	EtOH	257(4.68),296(4.04), 500(3.88)	44-0165-73
9H-Fluoren-9-one, 2-(phenylamino)-	EtOH	245(4.34),250s(4.29), 293(4.59),343(4.28), 506(3.04)	44-0165-73
9H-Fluoren-9-one, 3-(phenylamino)-	EtOH	252(4.59),267s(4.22), 322(4.24),388(3.80), 444(3.92)	44-0165-73
$C_{19}H_{13}NO_2$			
1-Acenaphthylenecarboxylic acid, 2-(4-pyridinyl)-, methyl ester	MeOH	316(3.87),343(4.00)	44-4404-73
Benz[a]acridin-5-ol, acetate	EtOH	223(4.63),239(4.49), 279(4.74),288(4.68), 323(3.72),334(3.77),	12-2315-73

Compound	Solvent	$\lambda_{max}(\log \epsilon)$	Ref.
Benz[a]acridin-5-ol, acetate (cont.)	EtOH	347(3.83),364(3.93), 383(3.94)	12-2315-73
	EtOH-acid	239(4.52),253(4.57), 262(4.42),289(4.61), 293(4.62),375s(4.09), 394(4.16)	12-2315-73
2-Naphthaleneacetonitrile, 1,4-dihydro-3-methyl-1,4-dioxo-α-phenyl-	EtOH	330(3.68)	83-0257-73
	EtOH-KOH	588(3.83)	83-0257-73
$C_{19}H_{13}NO_2S$			
Dibenzo[b,f]thiepin-10(11H)-one, 8-(2-pyridinyloxy)-, hydrochloride	MeOH	223(4.44),263(4.28), 296(3.79)	73-1579-73
$C_{19}H_{13}NO_3$			
1H-Benz[de]isoquinoline-1,3(2H)-dione, 2-(phenylmethoxy)-	EtOH	235(4.64),334(4.15)	104-0165-73
$C_{19}H_{13}NO_3S$			
4H-Benzopyran-4-one, 7-hydroxy-2-methyl-3-(2-phenyl-4-thiazolyl)-	n.s.g.	300(4.11)	104-2580-73
3-Thiophenecarbonitrile, 5-benzoyl-4-hydroxy-2-(4-methoxyphenyl)-	CH_2Cl_2	371(4.37)	48-0497-73
$C_{19}H_{13}NO_4$			
1,3-Dioxolo[4,5-h]isoquinoline, 7-(6-ethenyl-1,3-benzodioxol-5-yl)-	MeOH	232(4.68),328(4.17), 343s(4.03),384(3.69)	94-1410-73
$C_{19}H_{13}NO_5$			
Nandazurine	EtOH or EtOH-base	221(4.41),230s(4.43), 260(4.38),324(4.58), 394(3.84),426(3.78), 450s(3.73),606(3.53)	31-0518-73
Naphthalene, 1-acetoxy-2-benzoyl-4-nitro-	C_6H_{12}	250(4.51),254(4.51), 280s(4.03),331(3.73)	19-0849-73
	4:1 MeOH-C_6H_{12}	250(4.46),280s(4.09), 338(3.73)	19-0849-73
$C_{19}H_{13}NO_7S$			
1,3-Benzodioxole, 5-[2-(5-nitro-2-furanyl)-2-(phenylsulfonyl)ethenyl]-	EtOH	211(4.59),233s(4.42), 302(4.43)	73-1705-73
$C_{19}H_{13}N_3O$			
Benzo[c]cinnolinium, 5-(benzoylamino)-, hydroxide, inner salt	EtOH	250(4.63),340(3.92), 360(3.93),428(4.09)	24-1589-73
2-Naphthalenol, 1-[(8-quinolinyl)azo]-	$CHCl_3$	504(4.46)	48-0725-73
(also cobalt complexes)	30% acetone	500(4.35)	140-1973-73
$C_{19}H_{13}N_3OS_4$			
4-Thiazolidinone, 5-[2,3'(2'H)-bibenzothiazol-2'-ylidene]-3-ethyl-2-thioxo-	EtOH	429(4.93)	103-1078-73
$C_{19}H_{13}N_3O_2$			
1H-Imidazo[4,5-f]quinoline, 2-(2-furanyl)-3-(2-furanylmethyl)-	MeOH	242(4.37),285(4.50), 331(4.18)	103-0406-73
Propanedinitrile, (2,3-dihydro-1,3-dioxo-1H-inden-2-yl)[4-(methylamino)-phenyl]-	MeCN	228(4.63),258(4.33)	39-1045-73B
enol form	MeOH	250(4.60),405(3.31)	88-2993-73
Pyrano[3,2-b]indole-3-carbonitrile, 2,5-dihydro-2-oxo-4-[(phenylmethyl)amino]-	EtOH	224(4.44),294(4.13), 338(4.21)	95-0964-73

Compound	Solvent	$\lambda_{max}(\log \epsilon)$	Ref.
$C_{19}H_{13}N_3O_3S$			
1H-Thieno[3,2-d]pyrazol-4(5H)-one, 3-methyl-5-[(4-nitrophenyl)benzylidene]-1-phenyl-	EtOH	305(3.82)	104-2429-73
$C_{19}H_{13}N_5OS$			
3H-Pyrazolo[4',3':4,5]thieno[3,2-d]-1,2,3-triazin-4(6H)-one, 8-methyl-3,6-diphenyl-	EtOH	275(4.26),315(3.80)	104-2429-73
$C_{19}H_{14}ClNO_2S$			
Dibenzo[b,f]thiepin-10(11H)-one, 8-(2-pyridinyloxy)-, hydrochloride	MeOH	223(4.44),263(4.28), 296(3.79)	73-1579-73
$C_{19}H_{14}ClNO_3$			
4H-[1]Benzopyrano[3,4-d]oxazol-4-one, 2-(4-chlorophenyl)-6-ethyl-8-methyl-	MeOH	218(4.52),255(4.12), 308(4.51),325(4.47)	2-0433-73
$C_{19}H_{14}ClN_3O_4S$			
Pyrimido[2,1-b]benzothiazol-5-ium, 4-[(3-methyl-2(3H)-benzothiazolylidene)methyl]-, perchlorate	n.s.g.	496(4.99)	124-1151-73
$C_{19}H_{14}ClN_3O_6$			
1H-Pyrazole-4,5-dicarboxylic acid, 3-(4-chlorophenyl)-1-(4-nitrophenyl)-, dimethyl ester	EtOH	226(4.39),246(3.39), 306(4.21)	94-2026-73
$C_{19}H_{14}Cl_2N_4O_2$			
[1,3,5]Triazino[3,2-a][1,4]benzodiazepine-1,3(2H,4H)-dione, 9-chloro-7-(2-chlorophenyl)-2,4-dimethyl-	EtOH	220(4.51),265(4.12), 374(3.71)	87-1256-73
$C_{19}H_{14}FN_3O$			
Carbamic fluoride, phenyl[4-(phenylazo)-phenyl]-	MeOH	331(4.29)	69-3023-73
$C_{19}H_{14}F_3N_2S_2$			
Benzothiazolium, 3-methyl-2-[1,2,3-trifluoro-3-(3-methyl-2(3H)-benzothiazolylidene)-1-propenyl]-, tetrafluoroborate	EtOH	578(5.14)	104-0852-73
$C_{19}H_{14}N_2$			
6,13-Etheno-4,8:11,15-dimetheno-3H-cyclotetradecapyrazole, 3a,15a-dihydro-, cis	EtOH	322(2.49)	35-3201-73
$C_{19}H_{14}N_2O_2$			
Benzeneacetonitrile, α-(1,3-dihydro-1,3-dioxo-2H-inden-2-ylidene)-4-(dimethylamino)-	MeOH	256(4.31),565(4.59)	88-2993-73
$C_{19}H_{14}N_2O_2S$			
Phenanthridinium, 5-[(phenylsulfonyl)-amino]-, hydroxide, inner salt	EtOH	255(4.98),324(3.28), 339(3.62),356(3.86), 378(3.67)	44-3311-73
3-Thiophenecarbonitrile, 4-amino-5-benzoyl-2-(4-methoxyphenyl)-	CH_2Cl_2	379(4.12)	48-0497-73

Compound	Solvent	λ_{max}(log ε)	Ref.
$C_{19}H_{14}N_2O_3S$			
Benzoic acid, 2-[1-cyano-2-(methylthio)-4-oxo-4H-quinolizin-3-yl]-, methyl ester	EtOH	278(4.26),314(4.00), 396(4.21)	94-0921-73
$C_{19}H_{14}N_2O_4$			
Acetonitrile, (1,3-dihydro-1,3-dioxo-2H-inden-2-ylidene)[(2,4-dimethoxyphenyl)amino]-	MeCN	245(4.26),265(4.06), 305s(3.82),426(4.20)	39-1045-73B
$C_{19}H_{14}N_3S_2$			
Pyrimido[2,1-b]benzothiazol-5-ium, 4-[(3-methyl-2(3H)-benzothiazolylidene)-methyl]-, perchlorate	n.s.g.	496(4.99)	124-1151-73
$C_{19}H_{14}N_4$			
Benzo[c]cinnolinium, 5-[(iminophenylmethyl)amino]-, hydroxide, inner salt	EtOH	252(4.56),355s(3.91), 400s(4.08),420(4.14), 437(4.13)	24-1589-73
$C_{19}H_{14}N_4O_2$			
2,4(1H,3H)-Pteridinedione, 1-methyl-6,7-diphenyl-	pH 6.0	222(4.44),276(4.21), 365(4.18)	24-1401-73 +24-3149-73
	pH 11.0	220s(4.32),266(4.25), 367(4.16)	24-1401-73 +24-3149-73
2,4(1H,3H)-Pteridinedione, 3-methyl-6,7-diphenyl-	pH 2.0	223(4.44),270(4.16), 361(4.19)	24-1401-73 +24-3149-73
	pH 11.0	240s(4.31),288(4.34), 384(4.09)	24-1401-73 +24-3149-73
$C_{19}H_{14}N_4O_3$			
2,4(1H,3H)-Pteridinedione, 1-methyl-6,7-diphenyl-, 5-oxide	pH 5.0	253(4.40),300s(4.01), 373(4.01)	24-3149-73
	pH 12.0	258(4.47),372(4.04)	24-3149-73
2,4(1H,3H)-Pteridinedione, 3-methyl-6,7-diphenyl-, 8-oxide	pH 2.0	255(4.43),367(3.94)	24-3149-73
	pH 9.0	258(4.32),290(4.37), 402(3.93)	24-3149-73
$C_{19}H_{14}N_4O_4$			
4,5-Isoxazoledione, 3-phenyl-, 4-[(5-methoxy-3-phenyl-4-isoxazolyl)hydrazone]	EtOH	230(4.32),270s(3.80), 325s(--),375(4.10), 410s(--)	32-1045-73
$C_{19}H_{14}N_4O_4S$			
1H-Pyrrole-4-carbonitrile, 2,3-dihydro-5-[3-[[(4-methylphenyl)sulfonyl]oxy]-1H-indol-2-yl]-3-oxo-	EtOH	225(4.62),302(4.32)	95-0964-73
$C_{19}H_{14}N_4O_4S$			
1H-Pyrrole-4-carbonitrile, 2,3-dihydro-5-[3-[[(4-methylphenyl)sulfonyl]oxy]-1H-indol-2-yl]-3-oxo-	EtOH	225(4.62),302(4.32)	95-0964-73
$C_{19}H_{14}N_4O_8$			
1H-Pyrazole-4,5-dicarboxylic acid, 1,3-bis(4-nitrophenyl)-, dimethyl ester	EtOH	301(4.22)	94-2026-73
$C_{19}H_{14}N_4S$			
Methanone, phenyl-2-pyridinyl-, 2-benzothiazolylhydrazone, (E)-	EtOH	224(4.42),250(4.19), 335(4.38)	40-1314-73

Compound	Solvent	λ_{max}(log ε)	Ref.
Methanone, phenyl-2-pyridinyl-, 2-benzothiazolylhydrazone, (Z)-	EtOH	222(4.43),258(4.21), 363(4.33)	40-1314-73
$C_{19}H_{14}O_2$			
Naphtho[1,2-b]furan-2(3H)-one, 3-methyl-3-phenyl-	EtOH	230(4.67),288(3.78), 309(3.36),345(3.36)	39-1802-73C
Naphtho[2,1-b]furan-2(1H)-one, 1-methyl-1-phenyl-	MeOH	231(4.67),269(2.58), 280(2.69),291(2.64), 314(2.21),328(2.34)	39-1802-73C
2H-Naphtho[1,2-b]pyran-2-one, 3,4-dihydro-3-phenyl-	MeOH	231(4.5),278s(3.5), 288(3.5),323(3.0)	39-1802-73C
2H-Naphtho[1,2-b]pyran-2-one, 3,4-dihydro-4-phenyl-	MeOH	229(4.8),286(3.8)	2-1245-73
3H-Naphtho[2,1-b]pyran-3-one, 1,2-dihydro-1-phenyl-	MeOH	230(4.7),280(3.8), 291(3.7),323(3.3)	2-1245-73
3H-Naphtho[2,1-b]pyran-3-one, 1,2-dihydro-2-phenyl-	EtOH	230(4.95),268(3.53), 280(3.73),292(3.64)	2-1245-73
$C_{19}H_{14}O_3$			
Cyclopent[a]anthracen-3-one, 5-acetoxy-1,2-dihydro-	EtOH	265(4.48),277(4.45), 329(3.53),347(3.58), 364(3.61),378(3.55), 398(3.47)	39-1251-73C
17H-Cyclopenta[a]phenanthren-17-one, 15-acetoxy-15,16-dihydro-	EtOH	269(4.76),297(4.26), 330s(3.10),349(3.09), 366(3.07)	39-2236-73C
1(3H)-Isobenzofuranone, 3-methoxy-3-(1-naphthalenyl)-	MeOH	282(4.81)	44-3375-73
Naphthalene, 1-acetoxy-2-benzoyl-	C_6H_{12}	246(4.49),288(3.84), 296s(3.72),332(3.22)	19-0849-73
	MeOH	252(4.48),286(3.93), 298s(3.82),332(3.28)	19-0849-73
	50% MeOH	256(4.45),288(3.94), 298s(3.88),334(3.38)	19-0849-73
Naphthalene, 1-acetoxy-4-benzoyl-	C_6H_{12}	246(4.30),288s(3.80), 306(3.87),325s(3.70), 360s(2.30)	19-0849-73
	MeOH	248(4.24),286(3.85), 306s(3.82)	19-0849-73
	50% MeOH	252(4.22),286s(3.84), 320s(3.74)	19-0849-73
Naphthalene, 2-acetoxy-1-benzoyl-	C_6H_{12}	222(4.88),248(4.26), 278(3.82),290s(3.68), 300s(3.48),320s(3.25)	19-0849-73
	4:1 MeOH C_6H_{12}	220(4.88),250(4.23), 280s(3.85),320s(3.26)	19-0849-73
$C_{19}H_{14}O_4S$			
3-Thiophenecarboxylic acid, 5-benzoyl-4-hydroxy-2-phenyl-	CH_2Cl_2	342(4.16)	48-0497-73
$C_{19}H_{14}O_6$			
6,12-Epoxy-9H-benzocycloundecene-8,10-dicarboxylic acid, 9-oxo-, dimethyl ester	$C_2H_4Cl_2$	302(4.71)	78-0533-73
$C_{19}H_{14}O_7$			
Isoflavone, 7-acetoxy-6-methoxy-3',4'-(methylenedioxy)-	MeOH	256(4.14),292(3.9)	2-0098-73

Compound	Solvent	λmax(log ε)	Ref.
$C_{19}H_{14}O_8$			
Benzeneacetic acid, 3,4-dihydroxy-α-[3-hydroxy-4-(4-hydroxyphenyl)-5-oxo-2(5H)-furanylidene]-, methyl ester	EtOH	248(4.25),268(4.26), 283s(4.17),345s(3.98), 396(4.15)	39-1529-73C
	10% EtOH	234s(4.28),257(4.33), 310s(4.25),329(4.30), 372s(4.03)	39-1529-73C
	+ NH_3	263(4.37),386(4.28)	39-1529-73C
Benzeneacetic acid, α-[4-(3,4-dihydroxyphenyl)-3-hydroxy-5-oxo-2(5H)-furanylidene]-4-hydroxy-, methyl ester	EtOH	250(4.27),270(4.27), 278s(4.26),341s(4.04), 397(4.14)	39-1529-73C
	10% EtOH	235(4.22),253(4.23), 322(4.23),372s(4.04)	39-1529-73C
	+ NH_3	246(4.25),396(4.32), 601(3.48)	39-1529-73C
$C_{19}H_{14}S$			
Benzo[b]thiophene, 6-methyl-2-(2-naphthalenyl)-	MeOH	238(4.50),267(4.31), 283(4.31),323(4.42), 335(4.29)	5-1112-73
$C_{19}H_{14}Se$			
9H-Selenoxanthene, 9-phenyl-	EtOH	211(4.15),256(3.80), 277(2.50)	138-0391-73
10H-Selenoxanthene, 10-phenyl-	EtOH	211(4.25),258s(3.83), 278s(3.59)	138-0391-73
$C_{19}H_{15}BF_4OS$			
Dibenzothiophenium, 5-(4-methoxyphenyl)-, tetrafluoroborate	EtOH	227(4.25),236(4.23), 260(4.16),285s(3.84), 315(3.26)	35-5288-73
$C_{19}H_{15}BF_4S$			
Dibenzothiophenium, 5-(4-methylphenyl)-, tetrafluoroborate	EtOH	243(4.55),273s(4.05), 320(3.40)	35-5288-73
$C_{19}H_{15}BrN_2O_3$			
1H-Pyrazole-3-carboxylic acid, 5-benzoyl-1-(4-bromophenyl)-, ethyl ester	C_6H_{12} or EtOH	214(4.22),259(4.75)	4-0015-73
$C_{19}H_{15}ClN_2O$			
11H-Pyrrolo[2,1-c][1,4]benzodiazepin-11-one, 7-chloro-5,10-dihydro-10-methyl-5-phenyl-	isoPrOH	242(4.20),278(4.01)	44-3502-73
$C_{19}H_{15}ClN_2O_3$			
1H-Pyrazole-3-carboxylic acid, 5-benzoyl-1-(4-chlorophenyl)-, ethyl ester	C_6H_{12} or EtOH	222(4.05),258(4.11)	4-0015-73
$C_{19}H_{15}ClN_2O_4$			
1H-Pyrazole-4,5-dicarboxylic acid, 3-(4-chlorophenyl)-1-phenyl-, dimethyl ester	EtOH	247(4.10)	94-2026-73
$C_{19}H_{15}ClN_2O_6$			
Benzoic acid, 4-[2-chloro-2,3-dihydro-6-(4-nitrophenyl)-3-oxo-4H-1,4-oxazin-4-yl]-, ethyl ester	EtOH	230(4.24),245(4.12), 358(4.28)	4-0347-73

Compound	Solvent	$\lambda_{max}(\log \epsilon)$	Ref.
$C_{19}H_{15}ClN_4O_2S$			
1,2,4-Triazino[5,6-d][3,1]benzoxazepine, 7-acetyl-6-(4-chlorophenyl)-6,7-dihydro-3-(methylthio)-	EtOH	224(4.44),234s(4.36), 383(4.06)	78-0639-73
$C_{19}H_{15}ClO$			
Benzenemethanol, 4-chloro-α,α-diphenyl-	99% H_2SO_4	444(4.70)	39-0095-73B
1(2H)-Naphthalenone, 2-(3-chloro-3-phenyl-2-propenylidene)-3,4-dihydro-	EtOH	226(4.06),352(4.49)	22-2093-73
$C_{19}H_{15}ClO_7$			
Benzofuro[3,2-c]pyrylium, 1-(4-methoxyphenyl)-3-methyl-, perchlorate	n.s.g.	250(4.18),295(4.23), 395(3.63)	103-0416-73
$C_{19}H_{15}F_2N_2S_2$			
Benzothiazolium, 2-[1,2-difluoro-3-(3-methyl-2(3H)-benzothiazolylidene)-1-propenyl]-3-methyl-, methyl sulfate	n.s.g.	545(4.27)	30-0207-73
$C_{19}H_{15}IN_2O_3$			
1H-Pyrazole-3-carboxylic acid, 5-benzoyl-1-(4-iodophenyl)-, ethyl ester (hydrate)	C_6H_{12} or EtOH	221(4.40),255(4.57)	4-0015-73
$C_{19}H_{15}N$			
9H-Fluoren-3-amine, N-phenyl-	EtOH	264(4.45),298(4.25)	44-0165-73
$C_{19}H_{15}NO$			
Cyclobuta[a]naphthalene-8b(1H)-carbonitrile, 2,2a-dihydro-1-phenoxy-	MeCN	265(3.95),273(3.89), 300(2.75)	138-0187-73
9H-Fluoren-9-ol, 2-(phenylamino)-	EtOH	328(4.48)	44-0165-73
Isoxazole, 3,5-bis(2-phenylethenyl)-	C_6H_{12}	204(4.35),214(4.30), 220(4.35),227(4.32), 234(4.03),285s(--), 298s(--),304(4.67), 310s(--),325s(--)	32-0309-73
	MeOH	208(4.34),214(4.29), 219(4.33),226(4.31), 233(4.05),285s(--), 305(4.70),325s(--)	32-0309-73
$C_{19}H_{15}NOS$			
Sulfilimine, N-benzoyl-S,S-diphenyl-	EtOH	231(4.31),254(4.06)	44-4324-73
$C_{19}H_{15}NO_2$			
Benz[a]acridin-12(7H)-one, 5-methoxy-7-methyl-	EtOH	258(4.43),285(4.61), 293(4.70),301(4.38), 326(3.78),342(3.97), 369(3.94),388(4.01)	12-2315-73
Benzofuro[3,2-c]pyridine, 1-(4-methoxyphenyl)-3-methyl-	n.s.g.	260(4.17),304(4.04)	103-0416-73
1-Naphthalenepropanenitrile, β,4-dihydroxy-α-phenyl-	MeOH	242(4.4),310(4.0), 328(3.9)	88-4203-73
$C_{19}H_{15}NO_2S$			
Dibenzo[b,f]thiepin-10-ol, 10,11-dihydro-8-(2-pyridinyloxy)-	MeOH	270(4.20)	73-1579-73
Dibenzo[b,f]thiepin-10(11H)-one, 8-[(1,2-dihydro-2-pyridinyl)oxy]-, hydrochloride	MeOH	220(4.37),241(4.34), 262(4.18),340(3.62)	73-1579-73

Compound	Solvent	λ_{max}(log ε)	Ref.
$C_{19}H_{15}NO_3$			
4H-[1]Benzopyrano[3,4-d]oxazol-4-one, 6-ethyl-8-methyl-2-phenyl-	MeOH	213(4.35),295(4.31), 305(4.33),325(4.27)	2-0433-73
Dictamnine, 8-(phenylmethoxy)-	EtOH	245(4.79),299s(3.75), 312(3.86),326(3.83), 338(3.78)	2-1088-73
$C_{19}H_{15}NO_4$			
Aporphine, 1,2:9,10-bis(methylenedioxy)-6a,7-dehydro-	n.s.g.	262(4.69),304(3.89), 338(4.05)	39-0349-73C
5H-Bis[1,3]benzodioxolo[6,5,4-de:5',6'-g]quinoline, 6,7-dihydro-7-methyl- (dehydroneolitsine)	EtOH	262(4.97),305(3.87), 338(4.18)	78-2245-73
1H-Dibenzo[de,g]quinolin-1-one, 2,9,10-trimethoxy-	EtOH	231(4.57),246s(4.43), 274s(4.18),284s(4.11), 295s(4.02),406(3.98), 462(3.90)	35-4062-73
	EtOH	232(4.13),245s(4.49), 273s(4.22),285s(4.13), 295s(4.04),402(3.98), 463(3.92)	44-2394-73
Furo[2,3-b]quinolin-4(9H)-one, 8-methoxy-7-(phenylmethoxy)-	EtOH	234(4.47),254(4.61), 291s(3.77),326(3.94)	2-1088-73
3H-Oxazolo[4,3-a]isoquinolin-3-one, 1-(3,4-dimethoxyphenyl)-	EtOH	227(4.11),325(4.35), 352(4.08)	44-2291-73
$C_{19}H_{15}NO_5$			
Furo[2,3-b]quinoline-3,4(2H,9H)-dione, 8-methoxy-7-(phenylmethoxy)-	EtOH	253s(4.70),260(4.75), 293(4.09)	2-1088-73
9H-Pyrano[2,3-g]-1,2-benzisoxazol-9-one, 7-(3,4-dimethoxyphenyl)-3-methyl-	n.s.g.	221(4.5),262(4.5), 315(4.2)	2-0541-73
$C_{19}H_{15}NO_6S$			
Furan, 2-[2-(4-methoxyphenyl)-1-(phenylsulfonyl)ethenyl]-5-nitro-	EtOH	209(4.59),213(4.53), 311(4.67)	73-1705-73
$C_{19}H_{15}NS$			
Benzenesulfonamide, N-(diphenylmethylene)-	$CHCl_3$	277(3.94),340(4.12)	39-1037-73C
$C_{19}H_{15}N_2O_3P$			
Phosphonium, triphenyl-, nitronitrosomethylide	EtOH	345(3.95)	104-0922-73
$C_{19}H_{15}N_3$			
Propanedinitrile, [3-(4-methylphenyl)-3-(phenylamino)-2-propenylidene]-	CH_2Cl_2	274s(3.81),408(4.32)	97-0132-73
	CH_2Cl_2	274(3.81),408(4.30)	97-0342-73
$C_{19}H_{15}N_3O$			
Indolo[2',3' 3,4]pyrido[1,2-b][2,7]naphthyridin-5(7H)-one, 8,13-dihydro-2-methyl- (angustidine)	EtOH	223(4.19),233(4.27), 251(4.12),288(3.72), 299(3.62),371(4.32), 390(4.33)	39-0013-73C
$C_{19}H_{15}N_3O_2$			
Ethanone, [(4-methoxyphenyl)imino]di-2-pyridinyl-	EtOH	235(4.37),275(4.20), 345(3.67)	12-2027-73

Compound	Solvent	$\lambda_{max}(\log \epsilon)$	Ref.
$C_{19}H_{15}N_3O_3$			
1H-Benzimidazole, 1-methyl-2-[5-(4-methylphenyl)-2-furanyl]-5-nitro-	EtOH	219(4.21),240(4.11), 259(4.21),329(4.42), 342(4.42),366(4.43)	73-1700-73
4H-Quinolizine-3-carboxylic acid, 1-cyano-2-[(phenylmethyl)amino]-4-oxo-, methyl ester	EtOH	260(4.59),304(4.19), 396(3.98)	94-0921-73
$C_{19}H_{15}N_3O_4$			
1H-Benzimidazole, 2-[5-(4-methoxyphenyl)-2-furanyl]-1-methyl-5-nitro-	EtOH	219s(4.12),263(4.19), 346(4.33),373(4.34)	73-1700-73
$C_{19}H_{15}N_3O_6$			
1H-Pyrazole-4,5-dicarboxylic acid, 1-(4-nitrophenyl)-3-phenyl-, dimethyl ester	EtOH	224(4.40),306(4.19)	94-2026-73
1H-Pyrazole-4,5-dicarboxylic acid, 3-(4-nitrophenyl)-1-phenyl-, dimethyl ester	EtOH	218(4.16),294(4.00)	94-2026-73
$C_{19}H_{15}N_5O$			
Pteridine, 4-amino-2-methoxy-6,7-diphenyl-	pH 7	222(4.36),255(4.26), 278s(4.20),370(4.12)	33-1225-73
	MeOH	220s(4.43),257(4.28), 278s(4.25),372(4.10)	33-1225-73
2(1H)-Pteridinone, 4-amino-1-methyl-6,7-diphenyl-	pH 0.0	222(4.46),282(4.23), 383(4.18)	33-1225-73
	pH 7.0	222(4.36),278(4.30), 374(4.20)	33-1225-73
	MeOH	221(4.43),272(4.33), 374(4.21)	33-1225-73
1H-Pyrazole-4,5-dione, 3-methyl-1-phenyl-, 4-(3-quinolinylhydrazone)	EtOH	248(4.34),400(4.36)	12-2723-73
$C_{19}H_{15}N_7O_2$			
1,3-Benzenedicarbonitrile, 2-[[4-[(2-cyanoethyl)ethylamino]phenyl]azo]-5-nitro-	MeOH	549(4.58)	89-0926-73
$C_{19}H_{15}OS$			
Dibenzothiophenium, 5-(4-methoxyphenyl)-, tetrafluoroborate	EtOH	227(4.25),236(4.23), 260(4.16),285s(3.84), 315(3.26)	35-5288-73
$C_{19}H_{15}S$			
Dibenzothiophenium, 5-(4-methylphenyl)-, tetrafluoroborate	EtOH	243(4.55),273s(4.05), 320(3.40)	35-5288-73
$C_{19}H_{16}$			
1,4-Methanotriphenylene, 1,2,3,4-tetrahydro-	MeCN	224(4.36),236s(4.19), 241s(4.40),248(4.61), 256(4.72),266s(4.23), 271(4.24),284(3.87), 297(3.99),309(4.05), 329(2.74),345(2.99), 362(3.07)	5-0844-73
1,4-Pentadiyne, 3,3-dimethyl-1,1-diphenyl-	MeOH	240(4.57),256(4.63)	35-3246-73
1,1':2',1"-Terphenyl, 4-methyl-	EtOH	236(4.39),244s(4.09)	35-5288-73

Compound	Solvent	$\lambda_{max}(\log \epsilon)$	Ref.
$C_{19}H_{16}AsNO_2$			
Arsonium, triphenyl-, nitromethylide	MeOH	223(4.39),265(3.76), 298(3.81)	78-1697-73
$C_{19}H_{16}BrClN_2$			
9-Acridinamine, N-(3-bromophenyl)-6-chloro-1,2,3,4-tetrahydro-	n.s.g.	232(5.0),252(4.7), 328(4.3),348(4.2)	103-0488-73
9-Acridinamine, N-(4-bromophenyl)-6-chloro-1,2,3,4-tetrahydro-	n.s.g.	232(4.9),258(4.6), 328(4.1),350(4.18)	103-0488-73
$C_{19}H_{16}BrNO_3$			
Benzenebutanoic acid, 4-bromo-α-cyano-γ-oxo-β-phenyl-, ethyl ester	C_6H_{12}	261(4.27)	104-1834-73
3-Furancarboxylic acid, 2-amino-5-(4-bromophenyl)-4-phenyl-, ethyl ester	C_6H_{12}	323(4.34)	104-1834-73
$C_{19}H_{16}ClNO_3$			
Benzenebutanoic acid, 4-chloro-α-cyano-γ-oxo-β-phenyl-, ethyl ester	C_6H_{12}	259(4.24)	104-1834-73
3-Furancarboxylic acid, 2-amino-5-(4-chlorophenyl)-4-phenyl-, ethyl ester	C_6H_{12}	321(4.33)	104-1834-73
1H-Indole-3-acetaldehyde, 1-(4-chlorobenzoyl)-5-methoxy-2-methyl-	MeOH	232(4.31),263(4.20), 320(3.80)	87-0176-73
$C_{19}H_{16}ClN_3O_4$			
1H-Pyrazole-4-carboxylic acid, 3-(2-chlorophenyl)-5-methyl-1-(4-nitrophenyl)-, ethyl ester	EtOH	296(5.25)	78-0121-73
1H-Pyrazole-4-carboxylic acid, 3-(4-chlorophenyl)-5-methyl-1-(4-nitrophenyl)-, ethyl ester	EtOH	218(5.54),303(5.26)	78-0121-73
$C_{19}H_{16}Cl_2N_2$			
9-Acridinamine, 6-chloro-N-(4-chlorophenyl)-1,2,3,4-tetrahydro-	n.s.g.	230(4.32),262(4.07), 330(3.57),352(3.61)	103-0488-73
Pyrimidine, 4,6-dichloro-2,5-dihydro-5-methyl-5-phenyl-2-(1-phenylethylidene)-	C_6H_{12}	296(4.35)	18-0299-73
Pyrimidine, 4,6-dichloro-2-(phenylethyl)-5-(phenylmethyl)-	C_6H_{12}	260(3.79)	18-0299-73
$C_{19}H_{16}Cl_2N_2O_2$			
Morpholine, 4-[(6,7-dichloro-3-phenyl-1H-indol-2-yl)carbonyl]-	isoPrOH	233(4.51),298(4.06)	44-3077-73
$C_{19}H_{16}Cl_2N_2O_3$			
Morpholine, 4-[(6,7-dichloro-2,3-dihydro-2-oxo-3-phenyl-1H-indol-3-yl)carbonyl]-	isoPrOH	216(4.51),260s(3.66), 292(3.25)	44-3077-73
$C_{19}H_{16}FN_2S_2$			
Benzothiazolium, 2-[1-fluoro-3-(3-methyl-2(3H)-benzothiazolylidene)-1-propenyl]-3-methyl-, perchlorate	n.s.g.	567(4.01)	30-0207-73
$C_{19}H_{16}F_2O_4$			
Butanedioic acid, [bis(4-fluorophenyl)-methylene]-, 1-ethyl ester	MeOH	225(4.16),268(4.00)	73-3879-73

Compound	Solvent	$\lambda_{max}(\log \epsilon)$	Ref.
$C_{19}H_{16}FeO_4$			
Iron, tricarbonyl[[1-(2,3,4,5-η)-2,4-cyclohexadien-1-yl]-4-phenyl-3-buten-2-one]-	EtOH	224(4.33),291(4.40)	39-1882-73C
$C_{19}H_{16}N_2$			
Acenaphtho[1,2-c]cinnoline, 5,6,6a,12b-tetrahydro-5-methyl-	MeCN	223(3.84),290(2.93)	22-3487-73
Benzene, 1,1'-(4-diazo-3,5-dimethyl-1,4-cyclopentadiene-1,2-diyl)bis-	CH_2Cl_2	248(4.62),318(4.61)	78-4307-73
Benzophenone, phenylhydrazone	MeOH	237(4.27),298(4.06),340(4.31)	80-0723-73
$C_{19}H_{16}N_2O$			
1H-Cyclopenta[b]quinoline-8-carboxamide, 2,3-dihydro-N-phenyl-	EtOH	239(4.75),292(4.19),308(4.11),322(4.10)	103-1005-73
4H-Indazol-4-one, 1,5,6,7-tetrahydro-1,3-diphenyl-	MeOH	241(4.45),260s(4.26)	24-0745-73
Pyrazolo[1,2-a]pyridazin-6-one, 7,8-diphenyl-	n.s.g.	210(4.34),300(4.00)	39-0221-73C
$C_{19}H_{16}N_2OS$			
Sulfilimine, S,S-diphenyl-N-[(phenylamino)carbonyl]-	EtOH	242(4.33)	44-4324-73
$C_{19}H_{16}N_2OS_3$			
4-Thiazolidinone, 3-phenyl-5-[3-(phenylmethyl)-2-thiazolidinylidene]-2-thioxo-	EtOH	283(4.08),397(4.52)	94-1431-73
$C_{19}H_{16}N_2O_2$			
4H-Cyclopenta[1,2-d:4,3-d']diisoxazole, 3a,4a,7a,7b-tetrahydro-3,5-diphenyl-, anti	EtOH	263(4.38)	32-0047-73
syn	EtOH	262(4.27)	32-0047-73
7H-Cyclopenta[1,2-d:3,4-d']diisoxazole, 3a,3b,6a,7a-tetrahydro-3,6-diphenyl-, anti	MeOH	264(4.42)	32-0047-73
syn	MeOH	262(4.38)	32-0047-73
7H-Cyclopenta[2,1-d:3,4-d']diisoxazole, 3a,3b,6a,7a-tetrahydro-3,4-diphenyl-	EtOH	257(4.27)	32-0047-73
2H-Indol-2-one, 3-[(1,2-dihydro-1-methyl-2-oxo-3H-indol-3-ylidene)methyl]-1,3-dihydro-1-methyl-	EtOH	263(4.09),278(4.13),271(4.49)	103-1152-73
Isoxazole, 4,5-dihydro-3-phenyl-5-[(3-phenyl-5-isoxazolyl)methyl]-	n.s.g.	205(4.61),247(4.61)	32-0037-73
$C_{19}H_{16}N_2O_3$			
Pyridinium 1-benzoyl-3-cyano-4-ethoxy-4-oxo-2-butenylide	EtOH	223s(4.34),247(4.23),361(4.77)	39-2091-73C
$C_{19}H_{16}N_2O_4$			
1H-4,5-Pyrazoledicarboxylic acid, 1,3-phenyl-, dimethyl ester	EtOH	238(3.93)	94-2026-73
	MeOH	232(4.26)	78-0101-73
$C_{19}H_{16}N_2O_6$			
Benzoic acid, 4-[2,3-dihydro-6-(4-nitrophenyl)-3-oxo-4H-1,4-oxazin-4-yl]-, ethyl ester	EtOH	221(4.18),269(4.24),368(4.11)	4-0347-73
Propanedioic acid, (3-cyano-2,5-dihydro-2-oxopyrano[3,2-b]indol-4-yl)-, ethyl ester	EtOH	258(4.01),392(4.28)	95-1523-73

Compound	Solvent	$\lambda_{max}(\log \epsilon)$	Ref.
$C_{19}H_{16}N_2O_7$			
Benzoic acid, 4-[2,3-dihydro-2-hydroxy-6-(4-nitrophenyl)-3-oxo-4H-1,4-oxazin-4-yl]-, ethyl ester	EtOH	230(4.19),255(4.15), 363(4.18)	4-0347-73
$C_{19}H_{16}N_4$			
Benzenamine, N-[[(2-aminophenyl)azo]-phenylmethylene]-	EtOH	250(4.43),450(3.51)	24-2530-73
9,10-Methanoanthracene-2,3,6,7-tetracarbonitrile, 1,4,4a,5,8,8a,9,9a,10,10a-decahydro-	MeOH	237(4.34)	33-3004-73
1,3,3(4H)-Naphthalenetricarbonitrile, 2-amino-4a,5,6,7-tetrahydro-4-phenyl-	MeOH	240(3.88),300(4.14)	49-0447-73
$C_{19}H_{16}N_4OS$			
1H-Thieno[2,3-c]pyrazole-5-carboxamide, 4-amino-3-methyl-N,1-diphenyl-	EtOH	260(4.33),330(4.30)	104-2429-73
$C_{19}H_{16}N_4O_2$			
Benzenecarboximidic acid, N-phenyl-, 2-(2-nitrophenyl)hydrazide	MeOH	242(4.44),325(4.21), 467(3.89)	24-2530-73
$C_{19}H_{16}N_4O_6$			
1H-Pyrazole-4-carboxylic acid, 5-methyl-3-(3-nitrophenyl)-1-(4-nitrophenyl)-, ethyl ester	EtOH	250(5.36),295(5.30)	78-0121-73
$C_{19}H_{16}O$			
Azulene, 1-[2-(4-methoxyphenyl)ethenyl]-, cis	C_6H_{12}	266(4.32),311(4.49), 627(2.48)	5-0166-73
trans	C_6H_{12}	263(4.24),317(4.46), 347(4.32),380(4.23), 613s(2.37),657(2.43), 724(2.24)	5-0166-73
1,1':2',1"-Terphenyl, 4-methoxy-	EtOH	242(4.07),267(4.11)	35-5288-73
$C_{19}H_{16}OS$			
2-Naphthalenecarbothioic acid, O-(2-phenylethyl) ester	EtOH	217(4.56),250(4.40), 261(4.36),312(4.17), 420(1.93)	39-1574-73C
$C_{19}H_{16}O_2$			
2H-Pyran-2-one, 4,5-dimethyl-3,6-diphenyl-	96% H_2SO_4	221(4.18),248(3.98), 345(4.16)	35-7914-73
4H-Pyran-4-one, 2,6-dimethyl-3,5-diphenyl-	96% H_2SO_4	225(4.27),290(3.76)	35-7914-73
$C_{19}H_{16}O_3$			
2-Furanpropanoic acid, 5-[1,1'-biphenyl]-4-yl-	EtOH	310(4.49)	2-0301-73
2H-Pyran-2-one, 6-ethoxy-3,4-diphenyl-	CH_2Cl_2	240(4.16),345(3.95)	78-1697-73
$C_{19}H_{16}O_4$			
5,11-Epoxy-6,10-etheno-7H-cyclohepta-[b]naphthalen-7-one, 6-acetoxy-5,5a,6,10,10a,11-hexahydro-	EtOH	260(3.21),269(3.01), 340(2.14)	44-4100-73
5,11-Epoxy-6,10-etheno-7H-cyclohepta-[b]naphthalen-7-one, 8-acetoxy-5,5a,6,10,10a,11-hexahydro-	EtOH	265(3.34),270(3.16), 340(1.77)	44-4100-73
1,4,6-Heptatrien-3-one, 5-hydroxy-1,7-bis(4-hydroxyphenyl)-	EtOH	248(4.07),418(4.57)	39-2379-73C

Compound	Solvent	λ_{max}(log ε)	Ref.
2-Propanone, 1-[2-(1,3-benzodioxol-5-yl)-3-methyl-5-benzofuranyl]-	EtOH	318(4.44)	12-1111-73
$C_{19}H_{16}O_5$			
1,2,4-Cyclopentanetrione, 3,5-bis(4-methoxyphenyl)-	MeOH	251(4.31),349(4.20)	102-2527-73
4-Cyclopentene-1,3-dione, 4-hydroxy-2,5-bis(4-methoxyphenyl)-	EtOH	225(4.21),264(4.26),361(4.04)	24-3223-73
2(5H)-Furanone, 4-hydroxy-3-(4-methoxyphenyl)-5-[(4-methoxyphenyl)methylene]-	MeOH	236(4.26),365(4.34)	102-2527-73
$C_{19}H_{16}O_6$			
Lorostemin	EtOH	275(4.62),338(4.28)	102-0947-73
	EtOH-$AlCl_3$	270(4.54),350(4.23)	102-0947-73
	EtOH-NaOH	268(4.59),372(4.40)	102-0947-73
	EtOH-NaOAc	263(4.59),370(4.47)	102-0947-73
	EtOH-NaOAc-H_3BO_3	270(4.57),347(4.29)	102-0947-73
$C_{19}H_{16}O_7$			
1(3H)-Isobenzofuranone, 3-acetoxy-3-(4-acetoxy-3-methoxyphenyl)-	EtOH	211(4.42),278(3.65),284(3.65)	56-1949-73
Phenanthro[3,4-d]-1,3-dioxole-6-carboxylic acid, 4,9,10-trimethoxy-	EtOH	223(4.19),262(4.71),282s(4.51),318(3.96)	12-2035-73
	EtOH-NaOH	262(4.85),283(4.51),314(4.02),343s(3.29)	12-2035-73
Toralactone diacetate	EtOH	274(4.61),284(4.78),311(3.60),323(3.60),380(3.39)	95-0261-73
$C_{19}H_{16}S$			
Pyrene, 2-methyl-7-[(methylthio)methyl]-	EtOH	238(5.19),249(5.17),267(4.97),280(5.00),308(4.75),322(4.78),339(4.83)	35-3201-73
$C_{19}H_{17}BO_6$			
Boron, bis(acetato-O)(1,3-diphenyl-1,3-propanedionato-O,O')-, (T-4)-	CH_2Cl_2	370(4.57)	39-1796-73B
$C_{19}H_{17}BrN_2O_2$			
Oxazolo[3,2-d][1,4]benzodiazepin-6(5H)-one, 10-bromo-2,3,7,11b-tetrahydro-7-methyl-5-methylene-11b-phenyl-	EtOH	244.3(4.61)	94-0742-73
$C_{19}H_{17}BrN_4$			
1H-Pyrrolo[1,2-b][1,2,4]triazol-1-amine, 2-methyl-N-(phenylmethyl)-	MeOH	227(3.82),272(4.21)	118-0414-73
$C_{19}H_{17}Br_2N_7O$			
Acetamide, N-[2-[2,5-bis[(4-bromophenyl)azo]-1H-imidazol-4-yl]ethyl]-	EtOH	427(4.47)	44-1971-73
$C_{19}H_{17}ClN_2$			
9-Acridinamine, 6-chloro-1,2,3,4-tetrahydro-N-phenyl-	n.s.g.	234(4.5),254(4.07),328(3.62),354(3.7)	103-0488-73
5H-Pyrrolo[2,1-c][1,4]benzodiazepine, 7-chloro-10,11-dihydro-10-methyl-5-phenyl-	isoPrOH	272(4.02),310(3.34)	44-3502-73

Compound	Solvent	$\lambda_{max}(\log \epsilon)$	Ref.
$C_{19}H_{17}ClN_2O_2$			
2H-1,4-Benzodiazepin-2-one, 7-chloro-1,3-dihydro-1-methyl-5-phenyl-3-(2-propenyl)-, 4-oxide	isoPrOH	241(4.48),270s(4.13), 317(4.06)	44-3502-73
1H-Pyrrolo[2,1-c][1,4]benzodiazepine-3,11(2H,11aH)-dione, 7-chloro-5,10-dihydro-10-methyl-5-phenyl-	isoPrOH	240(4.04),253(4.05), 290s(2.90)	44-3502-73
$C_{19}H_{17}ClN_2O_2S$			
Benzenesulfonamide, 4-chloro-N-(1,2,3,5-tetrahydro-5-methyl-4H-cyclopenta[c]-quinolin-4-ylidene)-	EtOH	216(4.55),263(4.43), 293(3.75),304(3.76), 342s(4.10),351(4.18), 362(4.05)	39-1809-73C
$C_{19}H_{17}ClN_2O_4$			
1H-Pyrazole-4,5-dicarboxylic acid, 3-(4-chlorophenyl)-4,5-dihydro-1-phenyl-, dimethyl ester, trans	EtOH	246(4.44),297(4.04), 363(4.40)	94-2026-73
$C_{19}H_{17}ClN_4$			
1H-Pyrrolo[1,2-b][1,2,4]triazol-1-amine, 6-(4-chlorophenyl)-2-methyl-N-(phenylmethyl)-	MeOH	223(3.93),268(4.16)	118-0414-73
$C_{19}H_{17}ClN_4O_3$			
1,4,5-Benzotriazocin-2(1H)-one, 4-acetyl-8-chloro-3,4-dihydro-6-phenyl-, 2-(O-acetyloxime)	MeOH	253(4.42)	94-2375-73
$C_{19}H_{17}NO$			
2H-Benzo[b]pyrano[3',4':4,5]pyrrolo-[3,2,1-jk][1]benzazepine, 1,4,8,9-tetrahydro-	n.s.g.	210(4.45),263(4.15), 308(4.17)	39-1041-73C
4H-Carbazol-4-one, 1,2,3,9-tetrahydro-9-(phenylmethyl)-	MeOH	243(4.25),265(4.10), 297(4.16)	24-0745-73
Cyclobuta[l]phenanthrene-2a(2H)-carbonitrile, 2-ethoxy-1,10b-dihydro-	MeCN	272(4.09)	138-0309-73
$C_{19}H_{17}NOS$			
Sulfonium, dimethyl-, 2-oxo-2-phenyl-1-(2-quinolinyl)ethylide	EtOH	271(4.07),364(3.97)	95-1064-73
$C_{19}H_{17}NO_2S$			
Sulfoxonium, dimethyl-, 1-(1-isoquinolinyl)-2-oxo-2-phenylethylide	EtOH	282(4.11)	95-1064-73
Sulfoxonium, dimethyl-, 2-oxo-2-phenyl-1-(2-quinolinyl)ethylide	EtOH	276(4.08),348(3.99)	95-1064-73
$C_{19}H_{17}NO_3$			
Acetamide, N-(5,5a,7,10,10a,11-hexahydro-7-oxo-5,11-epoxy-6,10-etheno-6H-cyclohepta[b]naphthalen-6-yl)-	EtOH	240(3.63),265(3.41), 270(3.22),330(1.87)	44-4100-73
isomer	EtOH	262(3.32),272(3.08), 340(2.00)	44-4100-73
Acetamide, N-(5,5a,7,10,10a,11-hexahydro-7-oxo-5,11-epoxy-6,10-etheno-6H-cyclohepta[b]naphthalen-8-yl)-	EtOH	264(3.49),271(3.51), 284(3.53),345(2.28)	44-4100-73
Benzene, 1-methoxy-4-[6-(4-nitrophenyl)-1,3,5-hexatrienyl]-	THF	254(4.14),325(4.32), 336(4.32),419(4.06)	18-2828-73

Compound	Solvent	$\lambda_{max}(\log \epsilon)$	Ref.
Benzenebutanoic acid, α-cyano-γ-oxo-β-phenyl-, ethyl ester	C_6H_{12}	249(4.10)	104-1834-73
3-Furancarboxylic acid, 2-amino-4,5-diphenyl-, ethyl ester	C_6H_{12}	310(4.28)	104-1834-73
Pyridinium 3-acetyl-1-benzoyl-4-oxo-2-pentenylide	EtOH	250(3.99),282s(3.87), 375(4.35)	39-2091-73C
$C_{19}H_{17}NO_4$			
9-Anthracenecarbonitrile, 10-hydroxy-2,4,5-trimethoxy-7-methyl-	EtOH	235(4.14),275(4.79), 301(4.31),350(3.52), 368(3.69),392s(3.60), 411(3.78),433(3.82), 456s(3.60)	39-2853-73C
7H-Pyrano[2,3-c]acridin-7-one, 3,12-dihydro-6,11-dihydroxy-3,3,12-trimethyl-	EtOH	238(4.24),267(4.62), 284(4.61),293s(4.57), 325(4.27),341s(4.07), 424(3.73)	39-1173-73C
	EtOH-NaOMe	237(--),281(--), 293s(--),343(--), 456(--)	39-1173-73C
$C_{19}H_{17}NO_5$			
1,3-Benzodioxole-5-acetonitrile, α-[2-(3,4-dimethoxyphenyl)-2-oxoethyl]-	EtOH	230(4.34),278(4.16), 306s(3.98)	4-0867-73
1H-Indole-1,3-diacetic acid, 2,3-dihydro-5-methyl-2-oxo-3-phenyl-	EtOH	259(3.95),290(3.31)	104-0831-73
1H-Pyrrole-2,5-dione, 3-(3,4-dimethoxyphenyl)-4-methoxy-1-phenyl-	EtOH	249(4.26),297s(3.54), 400(3.65)	39-1538-73C
$C_{19}H_{17}NO_6$			
1,3-Propanedione, 1-(3,4-dimethoxyphenyl)-3-(6-hydroxy-3-methyl-1,2-benzisoxazol-7-yl)-	n.s.g.	240(4.2),275(4.5), 383(4.3)	2-0541-73
$C_{19}H_{17}NO_9$			
1,3-Benzodioxole-5-acetic acid, α-[(4,5-dimethoxy-2-nitrophenyl)methylene]-7-methoxy-, (E)-	EtOH	210(4.62),247(4.25), 264(4.24)	12-2035-73
	EtOH-NaOH	207(5.14),242s(4.30), 297s(4.22)	12-2035-73
$C_{19}H_{17}N_3O$			
2,2'-Bipyridinium, 1-(benzoylamino)-4,4'-dimethyl-, hydroxide, inner salt	dioxan	247(4.29),278(4.11), 357(3.62)	4-0447-73
2,4-Pentadienamide, 2-cyano-5-(4-methylphenyl)-5-(phenylamino)-	CH_2Cl_2	264(4.06),339(4.43)	97-0132-73
$C_{19}H_{17}N_3OS$			
7(4H)-Benzothiazolone, 6-[[(2-amino-1-naphthalenyl)amino]methylene]-5,6-dihydro-2-methyl-	EtOH	215(4.45),247(4.35), 313(4.10),435(4.17)	32-1063-73
$C_{19}H_{17}N_3O_2$			
Acetamide, N-[5-(4-hydroxyphenyl)-3-(phenylmethyl)pyrazinyl]-	DMF	277(4.13),297(4.17), 334(4.13)	77-0492-73
4H-Pyridazino[4,5-b]indol-4-one, 3,5-dihydro-1-(4-methoxyphenyl)-3,5-dimethyl-	n.s.g.	235(4.50),263(4.49), 325(3.92)	103-1497-73

Compound	Solvent	$\lambda_{max}(\log \epsilon)$	Ref.
$C_{19}H_{17}N_3O_3$			
1H-Pyrazole-4-carboxylic acid, 3-benzoyl-1-[2-(methylamino)phenyl]-, methyl ester	MeOH	210(4.17),235(4.10), 313(3.36)	25-0952-73
3-Quinolinecarboxylic acid, 2-[[(phenylamino)carbonyl]amino]-, ethyl ester	MeOH	223(4.5),253(4.5), 350(3.4)	24-3533-73
$C_{19}H_{17}N_3O_4$			
1H-Pyrazole-4-carboxylic acid, 5-methyl-1-(4-nitrophenyl)-3-phenyl-, ethyl ester	EtOH	222(5.46),250s(5.28), 300(5.18)	78-0121-73
$C_{19}H_{17}N_3O_7$			
4-Azulenepropanol, trinitrobenzene complex	CH_2Cl_2	280(4.73),285(4.73), 329(3.63),343(3.75), 355s(--),566(2.64), 657s(--),670s(--)	44-1106-73
$C_{19}H_{18}$			
Bicyclo[2.2.1]hept-2-ene, 2,3-diphenyl-	MeCN	225(4.21),229s(4.20), 240s(3.98),288(4.03), 312s(3.77)	5-0844-73
at 20°	EtOH-ether	287(--)	5-0844-73
at -190°	EtOH-ether	301(--)	5-0844-73
Cyclopentadiene, 5,5-dimethyl-2,3-diphenyl-	MeOH	225(4.31),238(4.37)	35-3246-73
7,8:9,10-Dibenzotricyclo[4.2.2.1^{2,5}]-undeca-7,9-diene	MeCN	255s(2.80),263s(2.92), 269(3.10),276(3.22)	5-0844-73
8,9:10,11-Dibenzotricyclo[5.2.2.0^{2,6}]-undeca-8,10-diene	MeCN	253s(2.82),260s(2.95), 266(3.15),272(3.25)	5-0844-73
Naphthalene, 1,2-dihydro-6-methyl-3-(2-phenylethenyl)-	MeOH	213(4.22),230(4.04), 237s(4.00),245(3.99), 252s(3.90),261(3.82), 309s(4.26),325(4.49), 340(4.60),358(4.47)	18-2908-73
1-Penten-4-yne, 3,3-dimethyl-1,5-diphenyl-, cis	MeOH	240(4.40),252(4.32)	35-3246-73
$C_{19}H_{18}BrClN_2O$			
Benzamide, N-(3-bromophenyl)-4-chloro-2-(cyclohexylideneamino)-	n.s.g.	230(4.60),344(3.51)	103-0488-73
Benzamide, N-(4-bromophenyl)-4-chloro-2-(cyclohexylideneamino)-	n.s.g.	234(4.70),344(3.44)	103-0488-73
$C_{19}H_{18}BrNO_3$			
1H-Indole-3-carboxylic acid, 6-bromo-5-methoxy-2-methyl-1-phenyl-, ethyl ester	EtOH	238(4.48),288(4.06), 298(4.04)	103-0306-73
$C_{19}H_{18}ClNO_3$			
1H-Indole-3-carboxylic acid, 1-(2-chlorophenyl)-6-methoxy-2-methyl-, ethyl ester	dioxan	275(4.09),295(4.03)	83-0446-73
1H-Indole-3-ethanol, 1-(4-chlorobenzoyl)-5-methoxy-2-methyl-	MeOH	231(4.31),263(4.19), 320(3.80)	87-0176-73
$C_{19}H_{18}ClNO_4$			
Morpholine, 4-[[4-(4-chlorobenzoyl)phenoxy]acetyl]-	EtOH	207(4.41),286(4.27)	111-0574-73
Pyridinium, 1,2-dimethyl-4,6-diphenyl-, perchlorate	EtOH	296(4.05)	103-0333-73

Compound	Solvent	$\lambda_{max}(\log \epsilon)$	Ref.
$C_{19}H_{18}Cl_2N_2O$			
Benzamide, 4-chloro-N-(4-chlorophenyl)-3-(cyclohexylideneamino)-	n.s.g.	232(4.54),334(3.59)	103-0488-73
$C_{19}H_{18}Cl_2N_2O_2$			
2H-Isoindole-1-carboxamide, 5-chloro-3-(2-chlorophenyl)-2-(2-hydroxypropyl)-N-methyl-	EtOH	228(4.47),264(4.37), 347(4.10),359(4.09)	94-0742-73
$C_{19}H_{18}Cl_3N_3$			
2(1H)-Pentalenone, 1-(1-piperidinyl)-, (2,4,6-trichlorophenyl)hydrazone	MeOH	375(3.90),384(4.11)	5-0750-73
	MeOH-NaOH	577(4.57)	5-0750-73
	DMSO	386(4.31)	5-0750-73
$C_{19}H_{18}N$			
Pyridinium, 2-(diphenylmethyl)-1-methyl-, iodide	neutral	370(4.18)	39-2111-73B
	pH 12	265(3.85),275s(3.83)	39-2111-73B
$C_{19}H_{18}N_2$			
Benz[g]indolo[2,3-a]quinolizine, 5,7,8,13,13b,14-hexahydro-, (S)-	n.s.g.	226(4.27),274(3.55), 283(3.55),291(3.47)	102-0199-73
1,2-Diazabicyclo[3.2.0]hepta-2,6-diene, 4,4-dimethyl-3,7-diphenyl-	EtOH	254(4.13)	35-3970-73
3,4-Diazabicyclo[4.1.0]hepta-2,4-diene, 7,7-dimethyl-2,5-diphenyl-	EtOH and isopentane	259(4.08),321(4.20)	35-3970-73
4H-1,2-Diazepine, 4,4-dimethyl-3,7-diphenyl-	EtOH	284(4.13)	35-3970-73
Pyridazine, 4-(1-methylethyl)-3,6-diphenyl-	EtOH	258(4.38)	35-3970-73
$C_{19}H_{18}N_2O$			
Benzaldehyde, (3-oxo-1-cyclohexen-1-yl)-phenylhydrazone	MeOH	226(3.90),231(3.92), 248(3.99),341(4.66), 352(4.66)	24-0745-73
2-Pyridinamine, N-(1,2-diphenylethyl)-, N(py)-oxide	MeOH	233(4.43),252(3.93), 326(3.70)	32-1083-73
Pyrimido[1,2-a]indole, 1-benzoyl-1,2,3,4-tetrahydro-3-methyl-	MeOH	303(4.07)	103-0598-73
2H-Pyrrol-2-one, 4-ethyl-1,5-dihydro-5-phenyl-3-(phenylmethylene)amino]-	EtOH	211(3.36),280(3.26)	88-2615-73
$C_{19}H_{18}N_2O_2$			
5H-Indolo[2,3-a]pyrano[3,2-g]quinolizin-5-one, 2,3,4,7,8,13-hexahydro-2-methyl-	EtOH	221(4.54),231(4.42), 294(3.60),340(4.29), 357(4.43)	30-0234-73 +70-1263-73
$C_{19}H_{18}N_2O_2S$			
Benzenesulfonamide, N-(1,2,3,5-tetrahydro-4H-cyclopenta[c]quinolin-4-ylidene)-4-methyl-	EtOH	213(4.60),222s(4.46), 262(4.36),330s(4.12), 341(4.27),350(4.11)	39-1809-73C
$C_{19}H_{18}N_2O_3$			
1H-Indole-3-acetamide, 7-methoxy-N-methyl-α-oxo-N-(phenylmethyl)-	EtOH	219(4.28),247(4.19), 263s(4.05),326(4.03)	35-7842-73
$C_{19}H_{18}N_2O_4$			
3H-Indole-2-carboxylic acid, 5,7-dimethyl-3-nitro-3-phenyl-	isoPrOH	245(4.16),338(3.86)	44-3077-73
1H-Pyrazole-4,5-dicarboxylic acid, 4,5-dihydro-1,3-diphenyl-, dimethyl ester	MeOH	244(3.78),302(3.78), 356(4.26)	78-0101-73

Compound	Solvent	$\lambda_{max}(\log \epsilon)$	Ref.
2(1H)-Pyridinone, 3,3'-(phenylmethylene)bis[4-hydroxy-6-methyl-	EtOH	230(3.90),300(4.16)	107-0355-73
$C_{19}H_{18}N_2O_4S_2$			
Carbonimidothioic acid, [(4-methylphenyl)sulfonyl]-, O-(1-acetyl-1H-indol-3-yl) S-methyl ester	EtOH	240(4.60),262(4.30)	95-0971-73
$C_{19}H_{18}N_2O_5$			
1H-Pyrrole-2,5-dione, 1-(2-aminophenyl)-3-(3,4-dimethoxyphenyl)-4-methoxy-	EtOH	239(4.33),287s(3.70), 396(3.64)	39-1538-73C
$C_{19}H_{18}N_2O_6$			
Isoquinoline, 3,4-dihydro-6,7-dimethoxy-1-[(6-nitro-1,3-benzodioxol-5-yl)methyl]-	MeOH	228(4.53),275(4.03), 310(4.01)	2-0342-73
$C_{19}H_{18}N_4$			
1H-Pyrrolo[1,2-b][1,2,4]triazol-1-amine, 2-methyl-6-phenyl-N-(phenylmethyl)-	MeOH	225(3.95),287(3.70)	118-0414-73
$C_{19}H_{18}N_4O$			
Benzamide, N-[[4-amino-2-(4-methylphenyl)-5-pyrimidinyl]methyl]-	EtOH	208(4.18),250(4.10), 263s(--),282(3.81), 297s(--)	18-0253-73
	EtOH-HCl	205(--),258(--), 278s(--)	18-0253-73
Benzamide, N-[(4-amino-2-phenyl-5-pyrimidinyl)methyl]-4-methyl-	MeOH	206(4.19),240(4.21), 257s(--),281(3.70), 295s(--)	18-0253-73
	MeOH-HCl	205(--),252(--)	18-0253-73
$C_{19}H_{18}O$			
2-Cyclohepten-1-one, 2,3-diphenyl-	EtOH	222(4.25),272(4.10)	18-1257-73
3-Cyclohepten-1-one, 2,3-diphenyl-	EtOH	245(4.18)	18-1257-73
11H-9,10[1',3']-endo-Cyclopentanthracen-9(10H)-ol, 12,13,14,15-tetrahydro-	EtOH	262(2.85),268(3.02), 277(3.11)	88-2221-73
6H-Cyclopenta[a]phenanthrene, 7,17-dihydro-3-methoxy-17-methyl-	isooctane	225(4.15),237(4.17), 255(4.35),262(4.50), 283(4.15),292(4.14), 302(4.13),326(2.93), 341(3.14),358(3.17)	94-1741-73
17H-Cyclopenta[a]phenanthrene, 15,16-dihydro-3-methoxy-17-methyl-	EtOH	263(3.6),286(3.04), 294(2.99),304(2.88)	70-1574-73
1(4H)-Naphthalenone, 4,4-dimethyl-2-(phenylmethyl)-	isooctane	255(4.1),285s(3.4), 300(3.3)	44-4226-73
$C_{19}H_{18}O_2$			
9-Anthracenol, 1,4,7-trimethyl-, acetate	C_6H_{12}	240s(4.27),253s(4.85), 261(5.13),320s(3.17), 337(3.41),354(3.68), 373(3.82),393(3.77)	39-1511-73C
2-Cyclopenten-1-one, 4-hydroxy-2,5-dimethyl-3,4-diphenyl-, 4SR,5RS	EtOH	274(4.12)	44-1749-73
4SR,5SR	EtOH	275(4.18)	44-1749-73
2-Cyclopenten-1-one, 4-hydroxy-5,5-dimethyl-3,4-diphenyl-	EtOH	287(4.29)	44-1749-73
14-Dehydroequilenin methyl ether, racemic-	EtOH	243(4.49),253(4.61), 262(4.61),283(4.04), 294(4.16),306(4.13), 335(3.39),353(3.18)	19-0091-73

Compound	Solvent	$\lambda_{max}(\log \epsilon)$	Ref.
1(2H)-Naphthalenone, 3,4-dihydro-7-methyl-2-(phenylacetyl)-	MeOH	236(4.04),245s(3.96), 258(3.84),310(4.03), 347(4.26)	18-2908-73
$C_{19}H_{18}O_3$			
1,3-Cyclopentanedione, 2-[2-(6-methoxy-1-naphthalenyl)ethenyl]-2-methyl-	EtOH	233(4.61),301(3.96)	19-0091-73
3H-Cyclopent[a]anthracen-3-one, 5-acetoxy-1,2,7,8,9,10-hexahydro-	EtOH	263(4.57),287(3.91), 298(3.96),308(3.86), 338(3.67),352(3.69)	39-1251-73C
17H-Cyclopenta[a]phenanthren-17-one, 11-acetoxy-1,2,3,4,15,16-hexahydro-	EtOH	222(4.27),258(4.84), 286(4.00),296(4.04), 307(3.91),340(3.72), 352(4.84)	39-1251-73C
2-Cyclopropene-1-carboxylic acid, 1-ethoxy-2,3-diphenyl-, methyl ester	MeOH	224(4.54),231(4.48), 290(4.46),302(4.56), 317(4.46)	104-1449-73
2,4a-Ethano-4aH-fluorene-9-carboxylic acid, 1,2-dihydro-2,8-dimethyl-11-oxo-, methyl ester	n.s.g.	234(4.10),281(3.73), 292s(3.69),300s(3.65)	39-1476-73C
3,9a-Ethano-9aH-fluorene-9α-carboxylic acid, 1,2,3,9-tetrahydro-8-methyl-2-methylene-11-oxo-, methyl ester	n.s.g.	230s(4.04),252s(4.00), 260(4.15),271(4.24), 292(3.62),303(3.68), 310s(3.56),320(3.34)	39-1476-73C
9β-	n.s.g.	230s(4.10),252s(4.02), 261(3.22),272(4.27), 293(3.57),304(3.65), 312s(3.55),322s(3.30)	39-1476-73C
Spiro[3H-benz[e]indene-3,1'-[2]cyclobuten]-2(3H)-one, 3'-acetyl-4,5-dihydro-7-methoxy-	MeOH	230(4.26),300s(4.15), 324(4.39)	39-1780-73C
$C_{19}H_{18}O_3S$			
4-Azuleneethanol, 4-methylbenzenesulfonate	CH_2Cl_2	280(4.68),286(4.64), 342(3.70),355(3.18), 572(2.61),615(2.55), 674(2.16)	44-1106-73
6-Azuleneethanol, 4-methylbenzenesulfonate	CH_2Cl_2	279(4.76),285(4.77), 330(3.58),336(3.56), 344(3.73),571(2.49), 588(2.47),620(2.42), 681(2.00)	44-1106-73
$C_{19}H_{18}O_4$			
5-Benzofuranethanol, 2-(1,3-benzodioxol-5-yl)-α,3-dimethyl-, (R)-	EtOH	315(4.41)	12-1111-73
1,3-Cyclopentanedione, 2-[2-(6-methoxy-1-naphthalenyl)-2-oxoethyl]-2-methyl-	EtOH	246(4.38),312(3.84), 216[sic](3.67)	19-0091-73
3,9a-Ethano-9aH-fluorene-9-carboxylic acid, 1,2,3,9-tetrahydro-8,11-dimethyl-1,2-dioxo-, methyl ester	n.s.g.	227s(4.05),251s(3.97), 261(4.07),272(4.05), 281(2.71),303(2.70), 450(2.64)	39-1476-73C
2-Furanpropanoic acid, 5-(6-methoxy-2-naphthalenyl)-β-methyl-	EtOH	220(4.43),236(4.36), 264(4.38),273(4.38), 307(4.45),321(4.40)	39-2420-73C
Gibba-1,3,4a(10a),4b-tetraene-10-carboxylic acid, 1,7-dimethyl-6,8-dioxo-, methyl ester	n.s.g.	238(3.96),290s(4.21), 299(4.30),325(4.16)	39-1476-73C
1,4-Naphthalenedione, 2-(4,4-dimethyl-2,6-dioxocyclohexyl)-3-methyl-	EtOH	332(3.50)	83-0257-73
	EtOH-KOH	494(3.45)	83-0257-73

Compound	Solvent	λ_{max}(log ϵ)	Ref.
2H-Pentaleno[1,6a-a]naphthalene-2,5-(2aH)-dione, 4-acetyl-3,4,6,7-tetrahydro-9-methoxy-	MeOH	243(4.00),301(4.37),328(4.40)	39-1780-73C
1H-Phenalene-2-acetic acid, 4-methoxy-α,α-dimethyl-1-oxo-, methyl ester	EtOH	206(4.49),265(4.45),309s(3.55),321(3.66),417s(4.11),436(4.16)	39-2159-73C
7H-Phenaleno[1,2-b]furan-7-one, 8,9-dihydro-6-hydroxy-1-methoxy-8,8,9-trimethyl-	EtOH	215(4.50),252(4.15),275(4.12),285(4.15),358(4.04),385(4.15),405(4.18),434(4.20)	39-2159-73C
1H-Phenalen-1-one, 9-hydroxy-4-methoxy-3-[(3-methyl-2-butenyl)oxy]-	EtOH	215(4.44),236s(4.35),254s(4.12),273(3.93),283(3.87),383(4.19),400(4.17),428(4.03)	39-2159-73C
9H-Xanthen-9-one, 1-hydroxy-3-methoxy-2-(3-methyl-2-butenyl)-	MeOH	254(4.46),298(4.58),341(4.20),382(3.81)	2-1237-73
9H-Xanthen-9-one, 1-hydroxy-3-methoxy-4-(3-methyl-2-butenyl)-	MeOH	256(4.48),290(4.12),310(4.02)	2-1237-73
$C_{19}H_{18}O_5$			
6H-2-Benzopyran-6,8(7H)-dione, 7-acetoxy-3-(1,3,5-heptatrienyl)-7-methyl-, (E,E,E)- (chrysodin)	CH_2Cl_2	243(3.99),309(4.12),380(4.61)	33-2694-73
1(2H)-Naphthalenone, 2-(1,3-benzodioxol-5-yl)-3,4-dihydro-6,7-dimethoxy-	EtOH	233(4.31),277(4.13),313(3.91)	4-0867-73
Naphtho[2,3-d][1,3]dioxol-5(6H)-one, 6-(3,4-dimethoxyphenyl)-7,8-dihydro-	EtOH	232(4.41),275(4.05),318(3.97)	4-0085-73
1H-Phenalene-2-acetic acid, 4,9-dimethoxy-α,α-dimethyl-1-oxo-	EtOH	208(4.41),230(4.14),264(4.35),384(4.22),419(4.04)	39-2159-73C
2-Phenanthrenol, 3,5,7-trimethoxy-, acetate	EtOH	252s(4.64),260(4.80),280s(4.17),290s(4.04),300s(3.77)	102-2789-73
Spiro[furan-3(2H),6'-[6H]naphtho[1,8-bc]furan]-2,2'(4'H)-dione, 5-(3-furanyl)-3',4,5,5',5'a,7'-hexahydro-7'-methyl-	EtOH	210(3.90),281(4.23)	105-0027-73
$C_{19}H_{18}O_6$			
3(2H)-Benzofuranone, 2-ethenyl-2-(2-hydroxy-4,5-dimethoxyphenyl)-6-methoxy-	EtOH	233(4.28),270(4.09),293(3.99),313(3.91)	39-1277-73C
4H-1-Benzopyran-4-one, 5,6,7-trimethoxy-2-(4-methoxyphenyl)-	EtOH	267(4.30),320(4.57)	95-0707-73
	EtOH	267(4.21),320(4.49)	95-1087-73
	EtOH	216(4.62),266(4.24),319(4.52)	102-3014-73
$C_{19}H_{18}O_7$			
1,3-Benzodioxole-5-acetic acid, α-[2-(3,4-dimethoxyphenyl)-2-oxoethyl]-	EtOH	228(4.35),274(4.27),294s(4.14)	4-0867-73
1,3-Benzodioxole-5-butanoic acid, α-(3,4-dimethoxyphenyl)-γ-oxo-	EtOH	230(4.41),274(3.97),307(3.92)	4-0085-73
$C_{19}H_{18}O_8$			
4H-1-Benzopyran-4-one, 2-(3,4-dimethoxyphenyl)-5,7-dihydroxy-3,8-dimethoxy-	MeOH	256(4.3),277(4.4),330(4.2)	2-0201-73
$C_{19}H_{18}O_9$			
4H-1-Benzopyran-4-one, 2-(3,5-dihydroxy-4-methoxyphenyl)-5-hydroxy-6,7,8-trimethoxy- (also other solvents)	MeOH	280(4.37),325(4.36)	2-1092-73
	MeOH-$AlCl_3$	307(--),343(--)	2-1092-73

Compound	Solvent	λmax(log ε)	Ref.
Chromomycinonic acid, 2-formyl-	EtOH	232(4.37),282(4.57), 325(3.83),340(3.86), 415(3.88)	105-0498-73
$C_{19}H_{18}S_3$			
3H-1,2-Dithiole, 4-(4-methylphenyl)-3-[(2-phenyl-1-propenyl)thio]-	C_6H_{12}	225s(4.10),275(3.95)	88-1561-73
$C_{19}H_{19}ClN_2O$			
Benzamide, 4-chloro-2-(cyclohexylidene-amino)-N-phenyl-	n.s.g.	232(4.50),334(3.36)	103-0488-73
1H-Indole-2-carboxamide, 5-chloro-N,N-diethyl-3-phenyl-	isoPrOH	226(4.54),265s(4.04), 295(4.06)	44-3077-73
$C_{19}H_{19}ClN_2O_2$			
1H-1,4-Benzodiazepin-2(3H)-one, 7-chlo-ro-1-methyl-3-(1-methylethoxy)-5-phenyl-	MeCN	231(4.53),255s(4.24), 317(3.44)	44-4206-73
1H-Indole-3-carboxamide, 5-chloro-N,N-diethyl-2,3-dihydro-2-oxo-3-phenyl-	isoPrOH	262(3.96),300(3.23)	44-3077-73
Oxazolo[3,2-d][1,4]benzodiazepin-6(5H)-one, 10-chloro-2,3,7,11b-tetrahydro-5,7-dimethyl-11b-phenyl-	EtOH	244.2(4.12)	94-0742-73
$C_{19}H_{19}ClN_2O_2S$			
Benzenesulfonamide, 4-chloro-N-(2-meth-ylspiro[cyclopentane-1,3'-[3H]indol]-2'(1'H)-ylidene)-	EtOH	225(4.42),279(4.22), 290s(4.11)	39-1809-73C
Benzenesulfonamide, 4-chloro-N-methyl-N-(2,3,4,9-tetrahydro-1H-carbazol-1-yl)-	EtOH	204(4.41),227(4.62), 276(3.99),283(3.98), 295(3.85)	39-1809-73C
$C_{19}H_{19}F_6N_2$			
Methanaminium, N-[4-[[4-(dimethylamino)-2-(trifluoromethyl)phenyl]methylene]-3-(trifluoromethyl)-2,5-cyclohexadien-1-ylidene]-N-methyl-	98% HOAc	650(3.53+)	39-1792-73B
$C_{19}H_{19}N$			
1-Azulenemethanamine, N,N-dimethyl-α-phenyl-	hexane	238(4.45),281(4.91), 345(3.99),361(3.81), 576s(2.70),594(2.76), 619s(2.70),651(2.69), 719(--)	5-0166-73
Indolo[1,7-ab][1]benzazepine, 1-ethyl-6,7-dihydro-2-methyl-	n.s.g.	207(4.49),267(4.12), 312(4.09)	39-1041-73C
$C_{19}H_{19}NO_2$			
1H-Dibenzo[a,f]quinolizine-1,13(2H)-di-one, 3,4,6,7-tetrahydro-3,3-dimethyl-	EtOH	263(4.55),300(3.90)	30-0445-73 +70-1794-73
8H-Indeno[2,1-e]pyrido[2,1-a]isoindole-12,13-dione, 4b,6a,6b,7,9,10,12a,12b-octahydro-	MeOH	242(4.07),288(3.32)	33-1763-73
1H-Indole-2-carboxylic acid, 5,7-dimeth-yl-3-phenyl-, ethyl ester	isoPrOH	225(4.40),242(4.42), 302(4.27),335s(3.83)	44-3077-73
2H-Pyrrole-3-carboxylic acid, 3,4-di-hydro-3-methyl-2,5-diphenyl-, methyl ester	EtOH	244(4.14)	35-1945-73
isomer?	EtOH	246(4.10)	35-1945-73

Compound	Solvent	λ_{max}(log ε)	Ref.
$C_{19}H_{19}NO_3$			
1H-Indole-3-acetic acid, 2,3-dihydro-5-methyl-2-oxo-3-phenyl-, ethyl ester	EtOH	257(4.12),290(3.31)	104-0861-73
1H-Indole-3-acetic acid, 2,3-dihydro-7-methyl-2-oxo-3-phenyl-, ethyl ester	EtOH	256(3.91),285(3.32)	104-0861-73
1H-Indole-3-carboxylic acid, 2,3-dihydro-5,7-dimethyl-2-oxo-3-phenyl-, ethyl ester	isoPrOH	259(3.86),298(3.31)	44-3077-73
6H-Pyrano[3,2-b]acridin-6-one, 2,3,4,11-tetrahydro-5-hydroxy-2,2,11-trimethyl-(nordihydroisoacronycine)	EtOH	227(4.2),248(4.5), 265(4.6),275(4.7), 330(4.0),406(3.7)	12-2311-73
$C_{19}H_{19}NO_4$			
4H-Dibenzo[de,g]quinolin-1-ol, 5,6-dihydro-2,9,10-trimethoxy-	EtOH	257s(4.33),266(4.34), 310(3.70),335(3.57), 380(3.10)	44-2394-73
Erytharbine	EtOH	233(4.17),265(4.16), 350s(3.17)	95-1617-73
6,8(2H,7H)-Isoquinolinedione, 7-acetoxy-3-(1,3,5-heptatrienyl)-7-methyl-	CH_2Cl_2	256(3.11),374(3.53)	33-2694-73
Morpholine, 4-[(4-benzoylphenoxy)acetyl]-	EtOH	211(4.29),283(4.21)	111-0574-73
2(1H)-Quinolinone, 4-hydroxy-6-methoxy-3-[2-(phenylmethoxy)ethyl]-	EtOH	232(4.62),276(3.96), 286(3.96),324s(3.79), 336(3.90),353s(3.81)	18-0577-73
2(1H)-Quinolinone, 4-hydroxy-7-methoxy-3-[2-(phenylmethoxy)ethyl]-	EtOH	222(4.78),242s(4.17), 249(4.08),272s(3.91), 282(3.94),302(4.01), 314(4.22),328(4.22)	18-0577-73
2(1H)-Quinolinone, 4-hydroxy-8-methoxy-3-[2-(phenylmethoxy)ethyl]-	EtOH	244(4.46),251(4.44), 270s(3.89),279(3.96), 290(3.95),320(3.59), 334s(3.44)	18-0577-73
$C_{19}H_{19}NO_5$			
Benzeneacetonitrile, 2-(2,6-dimethoxybenzoyl)-3,5-dimethoxy-	EtOH	223(4.12),238s(4.07), 277(3.94),305s(3.85)	39-2853-73C
Demethylacetylcephalotaxinone	EtOH	232(4.13),290(3.90), 318(3.91)	95-0916-73
Nandazurine, hexahydro-	EtOH	221(4.86),239s(4.11), 288(4.08),310(4.16)	31-0518-73
$C_{19}H_{19}NO_8$			
6,7-Quinolinedicarboxylic acid, 5,8-diacetoxy-, diethyl ester	EtOH	211(4.50),243(4.64), 280s(--)	39-0026-73C
$C_{19}H_{19}N_3O$			
Ethanone, 1-(1,3a,8,8a-tetrahydro-3a,8-dimethyl-1-phenylpyrazolo[3,4-b]indol-3-yl)-	EtOH	244(4.30),298(3.74), 354(4.10)	78-3159-73
1,3-Propanedione, 1-(1,2-dimethyl-1H-indol-3-yl)-, 1-(phenylhydrazone)	EtOH	283(4.04),352(4.22)	78-3159-73
$C_{19}H_{19}N_3O_2$			
1H-Indole-3-acetic acid, 2-methyl-α-(phenylhydrazono)-, ethyl ester	EtOH	283(4.01),340(4.15)	78-3159-73
$C_{19}H_{19}N_3O_7$			
1H-Indazole-3-carbonitrile, 1-(2,3,5-tri-O-acetyl-β-D-ribofuranosyl)-	EtOH	261s(3.76),269(3.81), 294(3.84)	104-0882-73

Compound	Solvent	$\lambda_{max}(\log \epsilon)$	Ref.
$C_{19}H_{19}N_7O_6$			
L-Glutamic acid, N-[4-[[(2-amino-1,4-dihydro-4-oxo-6-pteridinyl)methyl]amino]benzoyl]-	pH 1	246(4.12),296(4.29)	87-0697-73
	pH 7	281(4.44),346(3.85)	87-0697-73
	pH 13	256(4.39),283(4.38), 364(3.93)	87-0697-73
$C_{19}H_{19}O_4P$			
Phosphonic acid, (3,5-dimethyl-2,6-diphenyl-4H-pyran-4-yl)-	EtOH	245(4.25)	65-0087-73
$C_{19}H_{20}$			
[2.2.3](1,2,4)Cyclophane	EtOH	227(4.26),291(2.30), 302s(2.20)	35-5825-73
$C_{19}H_{20}ClIN_2O_3S$			
Carbamic acid, [1-[[(4-chlorophenyl)amino]carbonyl]-2-(iodothio)-2-methylpropyl]-, phenylmethyl ester, (±)-	CH_2Cl_2	250(4.2),325s(2.8), 425(1.23)	143-0539-73
$C_{19}H_{20}FNO_7$			
1H-Indole, 5-fluoro-1-(2,3,4-tri-O-acetyl-α-D-ribopyranosyl)-	EtOH	220(4.50),266(4.04), 294(3.75)	104-0611-73
β-isomer	EtOH	220(4.34),266(3.80), 294(3.50)	104-0611-73
1H-Indole, 6-fluoro-1-(2,3,4-tri-O-acetyl-β-D-ribopyranosyl)-	EtOH	226(4.47),263(3.65), 288(3.37)	104-0611-73
$C_{19}H_{20}INO$			
Isoquinolinium, 3,4-dihydro-1-[2-(4-methoxyphenyl)ethenyl]-2-methyl-, iodide, (E)-	EtOH	253(4.06),276(4.05), 295(4.05),385(4.38)	4-0519-73
$C_{19}H_{20}N$			
Cyclopropenylium, (diethylamino)diphenyl-, tetrafluoroborate	EtOH	315(4.37)	35-3239-73
$C_{19}H_{20}N_2$			
1,2-Diazepine, 5,6-dihydro-4,4-dimethyl-3,7-diphenyl-	EtOH	244(4.14),286(4.07)	35-3970-73
Phenazine, 1,2,3,4,6,7,8,9-octahydro-1-(phenylmethylene)-	dioxan	225(3.76),277(4.07), 345(4.09)	56-0943-73
1H-Pyrazole, 3,5-dimethyl-1,4-bis(phenylmethyl)-	EtOH	202(4.39),228s(3.90), 252s(2.8),259(2.78), 262(2.74),269(2.60)	78-4159-73
$C_{19}H_{20}N_2O$			
Ajmalan-11-ol, 1,2,19,20-tetradehydro-1-demethyl-	MeOH	232(4.40),276(3.47), 304(3.30)	94-1783-73
2-Cyclohexen-1-one, 3-[1-phenyl-2-(phenylmethyl)hydrazino]-	MeOH	303(4.44)	24-0745-73
5-Isoxazoleethanamine, 3-methyl-N-(4-methylphenyl)-α-phenyl-	EtOH	249(4.15),306(3.36)	18-3533-73
$C_{19}H_{20}N_2O_2$			
8H-Indeno[2,1-e]pyrido[2,1-a]isoindole-12,13-dione, 4b,6a,6b,7,9,10,12a,12b-octahydro-, 13-oxime	MeOH	247(3.95),284(3.51)	33-1763-73
Indolizino[1,2-c]phenanthridine-12,14-(4bH,6bH)-dione, 6a,6,8,9,10,12a,12b-13-octahydro-	MeOH	231(3.99),276(2.99)	33-1763-73

Compound	Solvent	λ max (log ε)	Ref.
Indolizino[1,2-c]phenanthridine-12,14-(4bH,6bH)-dione, 6a,7,8,9,10,12a,12b-13-octahydro-, isomer	MeOH	232(3.97),278s(3.00), 286s(2.85)	33-1763-73
5H-Indolo[2,3-a]pyrano[3,2-g]quinolizin-5-one, 2,3,4,7,8,13,13b,14-octahydro-2-methyl-	EtOH	225(4.60),271(4.00), 290(3.78)	30-0234-73 +70-1263-73
Quebrachamine, 14,15-dehydro-5,16-dioxo-	MeOH	243(4.26),319(4.31)	35-7458-73
$C_{19}H_{20}N_2O_2S$			
Benzenesulfonamide, 4-methyl-N-(2,3,4,9-tetrahydro-1H-carbazol-1-yl)-	EtOH	202(4.77),227(4.70), 276(3.95),284(3.96), 294(3.81)	39-1809-73C
$C_{19}H_{20}N_2O_3$			
2H-1,2,5-Oxadiazin-3-ol, 3,4-dihydro-4,4,6-trimethyl-3-phenyl-, benzoate	EtOH	231(4.24)	103-1008-73
hydrochloride	EtOH	228(4.18)	103-1008-73
Pyrrolidine, 1-[[4-(hydroxyimino)phenyl-methyl]phenoxy]acetyl]-	EtOH	211(4.40),241(4.23)	111-0574-73
$C_{19}H_{20}N_2O_4$			
Morpholine, 4-[[4-[(hydroxyimino)phenyl-methyl]phenoxy]acetyl]-	EtOH	212(4.42),240(4.21)	111-0574-73
$C_{19}H_{20}N_2O_4S$			
2H-1,2-Benzothiazine-3-carboxamide, 2-methyl-4-(1-methylethoxy)-N-phenyl-, 1,1-dioxide	EtOH	316(4.17)	87-0044-73
1H-Indole-2-carboxylic acid, 1-methyl-3-[[(4-methylphenyl)sulfonyl]amino]-, ethyl ester	EtOH	228(4.45),300(4.08), 315s(3.78)	39-1602-73C
$C_{19}H_{20}N_2O_7$			
1,3-Benzodioxole-5-acetamide, N-[2-(3,4-dimethoxyphenyl)ethyl]-6-nitro-	MeOH	237(4.24),280(3.71), 345(3.69)	2-0342-73
$C_{19}H_{20}N_2O_9$			
2-Butenedioic acid, 2-[[1,4-dihydro-5,8-dimethoxy-2-(methoxycarbonyl)-4-oxo-4-quinolinyl]amino]-, dimethyl ester	$CHCl_3$	291(4.23),360(4.18)	39-2374-73C
$C_{19}H_{20}N_3O_4P$			
Phosphoramidic acid, [2-[(1,5-dihydro-3-methyl-5-oxo-1-phenyl-4H-pyrazol-4-ylidene)methyl]phenyl]-, dimethyl ester	EtOH	243(4.57),295(3.95)	39-1606-73C
$C_{19}H_{20}N_4$			
4H-Indene-5,5,6,6-tetracarbonitrile, 3a,7-dihydro-1,2,3,3a,4,4-hexamethyl-	dioxan	272(3.66)	24-0008-73
$C_{19}H_{20}N_4O_4$			
5(6H)-Benzocyclooctenone, 7,8,9,10-tetrahydro-8-methyl-, 2,4-dinitro-phenylhydrazone	EtOH	364(3.38)	78-1843-73
$C_{19}H_{20}O$			
Benzene, 1-methoxy-2-(6-phenyl-1,5-hexa-dienyl)-	EtOH	213(4.39),255(4.47), 285(3.77),293(3.81), 300(3.74)	44-1993-73

Compound	Solvent	$\lambda_{max}(\log \epsilon)$	Ref.
Cyclohexene, 1-(4-methoxyphenyl)-2-phenyl-	EtOH	255(3.96)	35-5288-73
6H-Cyclopenta[a]phenanthrene, 7,15,16-17-tetrahydro-3-methoxy-17-methyl-	isooctane	282(4.41)	94-1741-73
Gona-1,3,5,7,9,16-hexaene, 3-methoxy-17-methyl- (5λ,4ε)	EtOH	268(3.77),279(3.84), 311(4.19),324(4.32), 338(?)	70-1574-73
4-Hepten-2-one, 3,4-diphenyl-	EtOH	245(4.13)	18-1257-73
$C_{19}H_{20}O_2$			
Acetic acid, (2,3-dihydro-3-methyl-4(1H)-phenanthrenylidene)-, ethyl ester, cis	EtOH	307(3.80)	39-0615-73C
trans	EtOH	312(3.95)	39-0615-73C
Estra-1,3,5(10),8(14),9,15-hexaen-17β-ol, 3-methoxy-, (±)-	EtOH	273(4.52)	94-0697-73
Estra-1,3,5(10),8,14-pentaen-17-one, 3-methoxy-, Kober test	H_2SO_4	444s(3.75),474(3.84)	94-1720-73
2,4a-Ethano-4aH-fluorene-9-carboxylic acid, 1,2-dihydro-2,8-dimethyl-, methyl ester	n.s.g.	233(4.13),275(3.87), 290s(3.72),299s(3.62)	39-1476-73C
2,4a-Ethano-4aH-fluorene-9-carboxylic acid, 1,2-dihydro-8,11-dimethyl-, methyl ester	n.s.g.	234(4.11),274(3.86), 280s(3.85),300s(3.62)	39-1476-73C
Oxirane, 2-[2-(4-methoxyphenyl)cyclopropyl]-2-(4-methylphenyl)-	MeOH	227(4.23),247(4.24)	39-2030-73C
$C_{19}H_{20}O_3$			
2H,8H-Benzo[1,2-b:5,4-b']dipyran-2-one, 8,8-dimethyl-3-(1,1-dimethyl-2-propenyl)-	EtOH	226(4.36),266(4.28), 346(4.15)	102-2073-73
1,3-Cyclopentanedione, 2-[2-(6-methoxy-1-naphthalenyl)ethyl]-2-methoxy-	EtOH	230(4.70),267(3.72), 277(3.79),288(3.72), 317(3.38),332(3.43)	19-0091-73
1H-Fluorene-9-carboxylic acid, 9,9a-dihydro-8-methyl-9a-(2-oxopropyl)-, methyl ester, (9aS-cis)-	n.s.g.	233(3.91),240(3.92), 248(3.82),295s(4.02), 308(4.13),320(4.17), 333s(4.06)	39-1476-73C
Gibba-1,3,4a(10a),4b-tetraene-10-carboxylic acid, 1,7-dimethyl-6-oxo-, methyl ester	n.s.g.	229(4.05),235(4.06), 286s(4.28),295(4.37), 315(4.19)	39-1476-73C
Gibberic acid, didehydro-, methyl ester	n.s.g.	250s(4.03),260(4.16), 270(4.11),288(3.46), 299(3.40)	39-1476-73C
1H-Indene-1,5(6H)-dione, 2,3,7,7a-tetrahydro-4-[2-(3-methoxyphenyl)ethenyl]-7a-methyl-, (S)-	EtOH	219(4.37),279(4.21), 315s(4.11)	44-3229-73
Oxirane, 2-(4-methoxyphenyl)-2-[2-(4-methoxyphenyl)cyclopropyl]-	MeOH	229(4.00),256(4.27)	39-2030-73C
1H-Phenalen-1-one, 2-(2-hydroxy-1,1-dimethylethyl)-4-methoxy-9-methyl-	EtOH	265(4.40),322(3.30), 377s(3.77),403s(3.94), 422(3.96)	39-2159-73C
2-Propenoic acid, 3-ethoxy-2,3-diphenyl-, ethyl ester, cis	EtOH	225(4.00),280(4.00)	39-0221-73C
$C_{19}H_{20}O_4$			
4H-1-Benzopyran-4-one, 2,3-dihydro-5,7-dimethoxy-6,8-dimethyl-2-phenyl-	MeOH	212(3.33),272(3.80), 330(3.34)	100-0422-73
Butanedioic acid, 2-phenyl-3-(phenylmethyl)-, dimethyl ester, erythro	MeOH	223(3.81),260(2.60)	39-1221-73C

Compound	Solvent	λ_{max}(log ε)	Ref.
Butanedioic acid, 2-phenyl-3-(phenylmethyl)-, dimethyl ester, threo	MeOH	223(4.74),260(3.66)	39-1221-73C
Gibba-1,3,4a(10a),4b-tetraene-10-carboxylic acid, 6-hydroxy-1,7-dimethyl-8-oxo-, methyl ester	n.s.g.	262(4.11),271(4.11), 288(3.56),300(3.50)	39-1476-73C
17-Norpodocarpa-5(10),6,8,11,13-pentaen-15-oic acid, 7-hydroxy-, methyl ester	EtOH	231(5.18),287(3.76)	94-0487-73
$C_{19}H_{20}O_5$			
4H,8H-Benzo[1,2-b:3,4-b']dipyran-4,8-dione, 2,3-dihydro-2,2-dimethyl-5-[(3-methyl-2-butenyl)oxy]-	EtOH	235(3.76),274(4.37), 325(4.09)	78-2943-73
2H-1-Benzopyran-2-one, 5-hydroxy-7-[(3-methyl-2-butenyl)oxy]-6-(3-methyl-1-oxo-2-butenyl)-	EtOH	239(3.52),302(4.31)	78-2943-73
	EtOH-NaOH	240(4.20),315(4.13), 393(3.93)	78-2943-73
Eriobrucinol, hydroxy-	EtOH	232(4.00)	78-0903-73
	EtOH-NaOH	243(3.78),279(3.85), 343(3.76),407(3.74)	78-0903-73
$C_{19}H_{20}O_6$			
1,2-Dibenzofurandicarboxylic acid, 1,9b-dihydro-7-methoxy-4,9b-dimethyl-, dimethyl ester	90% EtOH	214(4.22),283(3.72), 293s(3.62),355(3.88)	12-1093-73
1,2-Dibenzofurandicarboxylic acid, 3,9b-dihydro-7-methoxy-4,9b-dimethyl-, dimethyl ester	90% EtOH	222(4.02),286(3.51), 291s(2.45)	12-1093-73
1,2-Phenanthrenedicarboxylic acid, 1,2,3,4,9,10-hexahydro-7-methoxy-4-oxo-, dimethyl ester	EtOH	236(4.43),280(3.90)	65-2058-73
Spiro[1,2-benzodioxin-3(7H),1'-cyclobutan]-7-ol, 8,8a-dihydro-8-hydroperoxy-4-phenyl-, 7-acetate, (7α,8β,8aα)-	EtOH	251(4.31)	78-3553-73
$C_{19}H_{20}O_8$			
Melampodin B acetate	MeOH	206(4.48)	77-0614-73
$C_{19}H_{21}BF_4N_2$			
Benzenaminium, N-methyl-N-[5-(methylphenylamino)-2,4-pentadienylidene]-, tetrafluoroborate	EtOH	449(4.88)	44-3990-73
$C_{19}H_{21}BrN_2OS_2$			
Thiazolo[3,2-a]pyridinium, 3-ethoxy-5-[(3-ethyl-2(3H)-benzothiazolylidene)-methyl]-2,3-dihydro-, bromide	MeOH	458(4.63)	103-1138-73
$C_{19}H_{21}ClN_2$			
1H-Pyrrolo[2,1-c][1,4]benzodiazepine, 7-chloro-2,3,5,10,11,11a-hexahydro-10-methyl-5-phenyl-	isoPrOH	263(4.04),300s(3.38)	44-3502-73
$C_{19}H_{21}ClN_2OS$			
Piperazine, 1-(8-chloro-10,11-dihydrodibenzo[b,f]thiepin-10-yl)-4-methyl-, S-oxide	MeOH	232s(4.14)	73-0599-73
4-oxide	MeOH	256(4.00),265(4.01)	73-0599-73
$C_{19}H_{21}ClN_2O_2$			
2H-1,4-Benzodiazepin-2-one, 7-chloro-1,3,4,5-tetrahydro-4-(2-hydroxyethyl)-1,3-dimethyl-5-phenyl-	EtOH	241.6(4.09)	94-0742-73

Compound	Solvent	$\lambda_{max}(\log \epsilon)$	Ref.
$C_{19}H_{21}ClN_2O_2S$			
Piperazine, 1-(8-chloro-10,11-dihydro-dibenzo[b,f]thiepin-10-yl)-4-methyl-, S,4-dioxide	MeOH	258(3.95),265(3.97)	73-0599-73
$C_{19}H_{21}ClN_2O_3S$			
Piperazine, 1-(8-chloro-10,11-dihydro-dibenzo[b,f]thiepin-10-yl)-4-methyl-, S,S,4-trioxide	MeOH	242(4.22)	73-0599-73
$C_{19}H_{21}ClN_2O_4S_2$			
Benzothiazolium, 2-[4-[5-(dimethylamino)-2-thienyl]-1,3-butadienyl]-3-ethyl-, perchlorate	MeNO	659(5.21)	103-0580-73
$C_{19}H_{21}ClN_2O_5S_2$			
Thiazolo[3,2-a]pyridinium, 3-ethoxy-7-[(3-ethyl-2(3H)-benzothiazolylidene)-methyl]-2,3-dihydro-, perchlorate	MeOH	455(4.84)	103-1138-73
$C_{19}H_{21}IN_2O$			
Pyridinium, 4-(1,1-dimethylethyl)-1-[2-(1H-indol-3-yl)-2-oxoethyl]-, iodide	EtOH	214(4.46),243(4.20), 265(4.13),305(4.11)	44-2831-73
$C_{19}H_{21}N$			
2,4-Pentadien-1-amine, N-ethyl-4,5-di-phenyl-, hydrochloride	MeOH	207(4.37),233(4.08), 288(4.49),308(4.26)	44-2169-73
Piperidine, 1-(2,3-dihydro-3-phenyl-1-pentalenyl)-	hexane	315(4.44),323(4.45)	89-0335-73
$C_{19}H_{21}NO$			
4H-Carbazol-4-one, 1,2,3,5,6,7,8,9-octa-hydro-9-(phenylmethyl)-	MeOH	203(4.33),255(4.15), 285(3.64)	24-0745-73
9H-Fluoren-9-ol, 9-(1-piperidinylmeth-yl)-	EtOH	225s(4.49),231s(4.38), 270(4.20),283s(4.07), 291s(3.89),301(3.53)	25-1111-73
Isoquinoline, 1,2,3,4-tetrahydro-1-[2-(4-methoxyphenyl)ethenyl]-2-methyl-, hydrochloride	EtOH	270(4.40)	4-0519-73
Isoquinoline, 1,2,3,4-tetrahydro-1-[2-(4-methoxyphenyl)ethylidene]-2-meth-yl-, hydrochloride	EtOH	225(3.95)	4-0519-73
$C_{19}H_{21}NOS$			
1-Propanamine, 3-(3-methoxydibenzo[b,e]-thiepin-11(6H)-ylidene)-N-methyl-, hydrochloride, (E)-	MeOH	239(4.37),279(3.86)	73-1596-73
$C_{19}H_{21}NO_2$			
Benzamide, N,N-dimethyl-2-(2,4,6-tri-methylbenzoyl)-	EtOH	248(4.02)	39-1160-73B
4H-Dibenzo[de,g]quinoline, 5,6,6a,7-tetrahydro-1,2-dihydroxy-6-propyl-, hydriodide	MeOH	215(4.63),273(4.23), 307(3.49)	87-1223-73
4H-Dibenzo[de,g]quinoline, 5,6,6a,7-tetrahydro-1,2-dimethoxy-6-methyl-, (R)-	MeOH	215(4.57),269(4.26), 316s(3.36)	87-1223-73
4H-Dibenzo[de,g]quinoline, 5,6,6a,7-tetrahydro-2,10-dimethoxy-6-methyl-	EtOH	266(4.09),272(4.11), 298s(3.69),310(3.75), 318(3.75)	35-5742-73

Compound	Solvent	λ_{max}(log ε)	Ref.
4H-Dibenzo[de,g]quinoline, 5,6,6a,7-tetrahydro-10,11-dimethoxy-6-methyl-, (±)-, hydriodide	MeOH	216(4.67),269(4.28), 306s(3.36)	87-1223-73
$C_{19}H_{21}NO_3$			
Acetamide, 2-(4-benzoylphenoxy)-N,N-diethyl-	EtOH	210(4.29),284(4.25)	111-0574-73
2-Cyclohexen-1-one, 2-[(3,4-dihydro-1(2H)-isoquinolinylidene)acetyl]-3-hydroxy-5,5-dimethyl-	EtOH	270(4.12),400(4.51)	30-0445-73 +70-1794-73
4H-Dibenzo[de,g]quinolin-1-ol, 5,6,6a,7-tetrahydro-2,10-dimethoxy-6-methyl-, (±)-	EtOH	266(4.03),274(4.05), 305(3.88)	88-2923-73
hydrochloride	EtOH	265(3.91),274(3.92), 306(3.77)	2-1086-73
Isoxazolium, 2-(3,7-dimethyl-2,6-octadienylidene)-2,5-dihydro-3-hydroxy-5-oxo-4-phenyl-, hydroxide, inner salt	dioxan	466(3.60)	44-1782-73
$C_{19}H_{21}NO_4$			
Acetamide, N-[2-[3-[6-(hydroxymethyl)-1,3-benzodioxol-5-yl]phenyl]ethyl]-N-methyl-	EtOH	259(3.85),294(3.75)	23-2338-73
Alkaloid AA1 from Argemone albiflora HORNEM.	MeOH	232s(3.96),284(3.65)	73-3312-73
Erysotramidine	EtOH	212(4.02),236(4.07), 257s(3.70),316s(3.15)	95-1617-73
Lirinine N-oxide	EtOH	218(4.40),284(4.03)	105-0475-73
Northaliporphine	EtOH	279(4.04),302(4.07)	44-2394-73
Pallidine	MeOH	206(4.36),235(3.92), 283(3.61)	102-1505-73
$C_{19}H_{21}NO_6$			
1H-Pyrrole-3-propanoic acid, 4-(2-methoxy-2-oxoethyl)-5-[(phenylmethoxy)-carbonyl]-, methyl ester	MeOH	275(4.22)	39-1546-73C
$C_{19}H_{21}NO_7$			
5-Isoxazolecarboxylic acid, 3-[tetrahydro-2,2-dimethyl-6-(phenylmethoxy)-furo[2,3-d]-1,3-dioxol-5-yl]-, methyl ester, [3aR-(3aα,5α,6α,6aα)]-	$CHCl_3$	275(3.71)	136-0311-73D
$C_{19}H_{21}N_2$			
Benzenaminium, N-methyl-N-[5-(methylphenylamino)-2,4-pentadienylidene]-, tetrafluoroborate	EtOH	449(4.88)	44-3990-73
1,4-Diazepinylium, 2,3,4,?-tetrahydro-2,2-dimethyl-5,7-diphenyl-, perchlorate	MeOH	267(4.17),352(4.36)	39-1729-73B
$C_{19}H_{21}N_2O$			
Pyridinium, 4-(1,1-dimethylethyl)-1-[2-(1H-indol-3-yl)-2-oxoethyl]-, iodide	EtOH	214(4.46),243(4.20), 265(4.13),305(4.11)	44-2831-73
$C_{19}H_{21}N_2O_2$			
1H-Imidazol-1-yloxy, 2,5-dihydro-2,2,5,5-tetramethyl-4-[2-(2-naphthalenyl)ethenyl]-, 3-oxide	EtOH	232(4.42),247(4.28), 258(4.22),282(4.20), 294(4.20),351(4.50)	104-1990-73

Compound	Solvent	λ max (log ε)	Ref.
$C_{19}H_{21}N_2O_3P$			
Phosphonic acid, (2',4'-dihydrospiro-[9H-fluorene-9,3'-[3H]pyrazol]-5'-yl)-, diethyl ester	EtOH	268(4.32),305(3.45)	65-1226-73
$C_{19}H_{21}N_2S_2$			
Benzothiazolium, 2-[4-[5-(dimethylamino)-2-thienyl]-1,3-butadienyl]-3-ethyl-, perchlorate	MeNO	659(5.21)	103-0850-73
$C_{19}H_{21}N_3$			
2(1H)-Pentalenone, 1-(1-piperidinyl)-, phenylhydrazone	MeOH	273(4.13),428(4.43)	5-0750-73
	MeOH-DMSO	592.5(4.71)	5-0750-73
	DMSO	431(4.42)	5-0750-73
$C_{19}H_{21}N_3O_6$			
Cytidine, N-benzoyl-2',3'-O-(1-methylethylidene)-	MeOH	258(4.32),303(3.93)	24-0665-73
$C_{19}H_{21}N_5O_2$			
Propanenitrile, 3-[[4-(2,6-dimethyl-4-nitrophenyl)azo]phenyl]ethylamino]-	MeOH	383(4.38)	89-0926-73
$C_{19}H_{21}N_5O_4$			
Imidazole, N^5,4'-anhydro-(5'-deoxy-2',3'-O-isopropylidene-α-L-lyxosyl)-4-benzoylcarboximidino-5-amino-	EtOH	244(4.18),266(4.14), 336(4.28)	35-1350-73
$C_{19}H_{22}$			
Fluorene, 9-(1-methylpentyl)- (also spectra of lithium derivs.)	hexane	222s(4.44),229(4.05), 250s(4.19),257s(4.37), 260s(4.39),263(4.42), 265(4.40),267(4.41), 274s(4.22),280s(4.07), 291(3.89),295s(3.79), 302(4.06)	35-7009-73
$C_{19}H_{22}ClNO_6$			
Isoquinolinium, 3,4-dihydro-6,7-dimethoxy-2-methyl-3-(phenylmethyl)-, perchlorate	MeOH	250(4.32),313(4.01), 370(3.98)	83-0784-73
$C_{19}H_{22}FNO_7$			
1H-Indole, 5-fluoro-2,3-dihydro-1-(2,3-4-tri-O-acetyl-β-D-ribopyranosyl)-	EtOH	207(4.20),240(3.96), 304(3.43)	104-0611-73
1H-Indole, 6-fluoro-2,3-dihydro-1-(2,3-4-tri-O-acetyl-β-D-ribopyranosyl)-	EtOH	205(4.19),243(4.06), 294(3.56)	104-0611-73
$C_{19}H_{22}F_3N_2$			
Methanaminium, N-[4-[1-[4-(dimethylamino)-2-methylphenyl]-2,2,2-trifluoroethylidene]-2,5-cyclohexadien-1-ylidene]-N-methyl-	98% HOAc	362(1.62),684(1.00)	39-2151-73B
$C_{19}H_{22}IN_5O_8$			
Acetamide, N-[9-(2,3,4-tri-O-acetyl-6-deoxy-6-iodo-β-D-glucopyranosyl)-9H-purin-6-yl]-	EtOH	272(4.36)	136-0378-73C

Compound	Solvent	λ_{max}(log ϵ)	Ref.
$C_{19}H_{22}N_2$			
Ajmalan, 1,2-didehydro-1-demethyl-	MeOH	227s(4.15),259(3.68)	94-1783-73
1H-Carbazole, 9-(2,6-dimethyl-4-pyridinyl)-2,3,4,4a,9,9a-hexahydro-	MeOH	207(4.31),238(3.98), 339(4.32)	103-0321-73
1,2-Diazepine, 1,5,6,7-tetrahydro-4,4-dimethyl-3,7-diphenyl-	EtOH	264(3.59)	35-3970-73
Indolo[1,7-ab][1]benzazepine-2-methanamine, 1,2,6,7-tetrahydro-N,N-dimethyl-, hydrochloride	n.s.g.	213(4.38),294(4.27)	39-1041-73C
Quebrachamine, 14,15,16,17-tetradehydro-	MeOH	226(4.57),282(3.95), 291(3.83)	35-7458-73
$C_{19}H_{22}N_2O$			
1H-Cyclopenta[b]quinoline-9-carboxamide, N-cyclohexyl-2,3-dihydro-	EtOH	238(4.69),295(4.04), 308(4.07),322(4.09)	103-1005-73
Deformoakuammidinol, O-acetyl-	EtOH	233(4.50),281(3.83), 290(3.75)	102-0451-73
1H-Indole-3-ethanamine, 7-methoxy-N-methyl-N-(phenylmethyl)-	EtOH	224(4.25),270(3.75), 282(3.71),291(3.60)	35-7842-73
Indolizino[1,2-c]phenanthridin-14(4bH)-one, 6a,6b,7,8,9,10,12,12a,12b,13-decahydro-	MeOH	230(3.92),280s(2.95)	33-1763-73
Normacusine B	EtOH	225(4.46),282(3.90), 290(3.82)	33-2719-73
$C_{19}H_{22}N_2OS$			
Piperazine, 1-(10,11-dihydrodibenzo-[b,f]thiepin-10-yl)-4-methyl-, 4-oxide	MeOH	229(4.08),258(3.90), 264(3.87)	73-0599-73
Piperazine, 1-(10,11-dihydro-8-hydroxy-dibenzo[b,f]thiepin-10-yl)-4-methyl-	MeOH	242(3.94),269(3.71), 293(3.53)	73-1579-73
$C_{19}H_{22}N_2O_2$			
Benzenepropanamide, N-[4-(dimethylamino)phenyl]-β-oxo-	pH 13	332(4.35)	39-0808-73B
1H-Imidazole, 2,5-dihydro-1-hydroxy-2,2,5,5-tetramethyl-4-[2-(2-naphthalenyl)ethenyl]-, 3-oxide	EtOH	231(4.60),246(4.49), 255(4.41),280(4.36), 290(4.36),349(4.63)	104-1990-73
Indolizino[1,2-c]phenanthridine-12,14-(4bH,6bH)-dione, 5,6,6a,7,8,9,10,12a-12b,13-decahydro-	MeOH	233(3.99),276(2.97), 288s(2.85)	33-1763-73
1-Isoquinolinamine, 3,4-dihydro-6,7-dimethoxy-3-methyl-N-(2-methylphenyl)-	EtOH	265(4.30),300(4.13)	106-0364-73
	EtOH-acid	282(4.28),320(4.15)	106-0364-73
1-Isoquinolinamine, 3,4-dihydro-6,7-dimethoxy-3-methyl-N-(3-methylphenyl)-	EtOH	265(4.18),300(4.10)	106-0364-73
	EtOH-acid	282(4.17),320(4.10)	106-0364-73
1-Isoquinolinamine, 3,4-dihydro-6,7-dimethoxy-3-methyl-N-(4-methylphenyl)-	EtOH	265(4.46),300(4.34)	106-0364-73
	EtOH-acid	282(4.49),320(4.45)	106-0364-73
2,5-Piperazinedione, 3-benzylidene-6-octylidene-	EtOH	344(4.57)	18-3876-73
6H-Pyrrolo[3,2-f]indolizine-2-carboxylic acid, 7-ethyl-3,4,8-trimethyl-6-methylene-, ethyl ester	EtOH	276(4.68),283(4.66), 338(3.47),353(3.39), 395(3.47)	65-1587-73
$C_{19}H_{22}N_2O_3$			
Indolo[2,3-a]quinolizine-2,4(1H,3H)-dione, 6,7,12,12b-tetrahydro-3-(3-hydroxybutyl)-	EtOH	224(4.34),281(3.86), 290(3.78)	70-1263-73
Indolo[2,3-a]quinolizine-1-propanoic acid, 1,2,3,4,6,7,12,12b-octahydro-2-oxo-, methyl ester	EtOH	274(4.89),282(4.90), 290(4.81)	22-2705-73

Compound	Solvent	$\lambda_{max}(\log \epsilon)$	Ref.
$C_{19}H_{22}N_2O_3S$			
3-Pyridinecarboxylic acid, 2-(methylthio)-6-morpholino-4-phenyl-, ethyl ester	MeOH	243(4.55),290(4.08), 331(3.98)	48-0679-73
$C_{19}H_{22}N_2O_4$			
Isoquinoline, 1,2,3,4-tetrahydro-1-(4,5-dimethoxy-2-nitrobenzyl)-2-methyl-	MeOH	242(4.05),271(3.55), 300(3.66),340(3.70)	87-1228-73
$C_{19}H_{22}N_2O_6$			
6,9-Methano-9aH-cyclooctapyrazole-4,5,9a-tricarboxylic acid, 3,3a,6,9-tetrahydro-10-(1-methylethylidene)-, trimethyl ester, (3aα,6β,9β,9aβ)-	EtOH	230s(3.91),245s(3.73), 324(2.00)	24-1837-73
Propanediamide, N,N'-bis(2,3-dimethoxyphenyl)-	MeOH	249(4.26),284s(3.32)	78-1721-73
$C_{19}H_{22}N_4O_2S$			
Propanenitrile, 3-[ethyl[4-[[2-(ethylsulfonyl)phenyl]azo]phenyl]amino]-	MeOH	429(4.65)	89-0926-73
Propanenitrile, 3-[ethyl[4-[[4-(ethylsulfonyl)phenyl]azo]phenyl]amino]-	MeOH	430(4.60)	89-0926-73
$C_{19}H_{22}N_4O_3S$			
Benzenecarbothioic acid, S-[2-[[(4-amino-2-methyl-5-pyrimidinyl)methyl]formylamino]tetrahydro-2-methyl-3-furanyl] ester	EtOH	239(4.25),271(4.13)	94-0785-73
$C_{19}H_{22}N_4O_4S$			
Acetamide, N-(4",5"-dihydro-4",4"-dimethyl-8'-oxodispiro[oxirane-2,3'-[5]thia[1]azabicyclo[4.2.0]octane-2',3"-[3H]pyrazole]-7'-yl)-2-phenoxy-	n.s.g.	212(4.03),263(2.95), 270(3.11),277(3.04)	39-2105-73C
$C_{19}H_{22}N_4O_5$			
1H-Purine-2,6-dione, 3,4-dihydro-1,3,7-trimethyl-8-[2-(3,4,5-trimethoxyphenyl)ethenyl]-	MeOH	268(4.04),327(4.11)	36-1885-73
$C_{19}H_{22}N_6O_5$			
Adenosine, N-[[(2-phenylethyl)amino]carbonyl]-	pH 1-2	270s(--),278(4.37)	87-0139-73
	pH 5-7	270(4.35),277s(--)	87-0139-73
	pH 12	277(4.20),299(3.99)	87-0139-73
$C_{19}H_{22}O$			
5H-Benzocycloheptene-2-methanol, 6,7,8,9-tetrahydro-α-methyl-α-phenyl-	MeOH	253(3.42),258(3.49), 264(3.49),274(3.31)	73-2768-73
Cyclohexanol, 1-(4-methylphenyl)-2-phenyl-	EtOH	223(3.83),255(3.54)	35-5288-73
5,9-Methanobenzocycloocten-11-one, 1,2-3,4,5,6,7,8,9,?-decahydro-10-phenyl-	EtOH	238(4.05),287(3.11)	35-3310-73
$C_{19}H_{22}OS$			
Benzenecarbothioic acid, O-[2,2-dimethyl-1-(phenylmethyl)propyl] ester	C_6H_{12}	254(4.00),293(4.02), 421(2.10)	39-1580-73C
1-Pentanethione, 3-hydroxy-4,4-dimethyl-1,2-diphenyl-	C_6H_{12}	230(3.90),235(3.88), 247(3.71),314(4.00), 554(2.00)	39-1580-73C

Compound	Solvent	λ_{max}(log ϵ)	Ref.
$C_{19}H_{22}O_2$			
Androsta-4,8,14-triene-3,17-dione, (13ξ)-	MeOH	241(4.56)	24-3636-73
Cyclohexanol, 1-(4-methoxyphenyl)-2-phenyl-	EtOH	225s(3.92),267(3.48), 282(3.36)	35-5288-73
Estra-1,3,5(10),8,14-pentaen-17-ol, 3-methoxy-, (17α)-(±)-	EtOH	311(4.30)	94-0107-73
(-)-	EtOH	310(4.44)	94-0107-73
(13α,17β)-(±)-	EtOH	311(4.30)	94-0703-73
Estra-1,3,5(10),9(11)-tetraen-11-one, 3-methoxy-, (+)-	EtOH	263(4.24)	44-3229-73
1-Isobenzofuranol, 1,3-dihydro-3,3-dimethyl-1-(2,4,6-trimethylphenyl)-	C_6H_{12}	255(3.89),290s(3.43), 335(2.99)	104-1986-73
2-Naphthalenemethanol, 1,2,3,4-tetrahydro-1-hydroxy-7-methyl-α-(phenylmethyl)-	MeOH	262s(2.78),264(2.81), 269(2.89),279(2.88)	18-2908-73
$C_{19}H_{22}O_3$			
2H-1-Benzopyran, 3,4-dihydro-5-methoxy-2,2-dimethyl-7-(phenylmethoxy)-	EtOH	217(4.4),269(2.9)	12-2291-73
1-Cyclohexene-1-carboxaldehyde, 2-[3-(4,5,6,7-tetrahydro-3-methoxy-1(3H)-isobenzofuranylidene)-1-propynyl]-, cis	EtOH	249s(4.04),256(4.05), 287(3.94),360(4.31)	18-2565-73
2,4a-Ethano-4aH-fluorene-9-carboxylic acid, 1,2,3,4,9,9a-hexahydro-2,8-dimethyl-3-oxo-, methyl ester	n.s.g.	270(2.67)	39-1476-73C
3,9a-Ethano-9aH-fluorene-9-carboxylic acid, 1,2,3,9-tetrahydro-2-hydroxy-8,11-dimethyl-, methyl ester, [2S-(2α,3α,9α,9aα,11S*)]-	n.s.g.	223s(4.05),254s(4.13), 263(4.26),273(4.20), 291(3.53),303(3.53)	39-1476-73C
1H-Indene-1,5(6H)-dione, 2,3,7,7a-tetrahydro-4-[2-(3-methoxyphenyl)ethyl]-7a-methyl-, (±)-	EtOH	220(4.02),250(3.92)	44-3229-73
(S)-	EtOH	220(4.06),250(3.97), 278(3.42)	44-3229-73
A-Nor-3-oxaestra-1,5,7,9-tetraen-17-ol, 2-methyl-, acetate, (17β)-	isooctane	210(4.44),251s(4.09), 255(4.13),261s(3.98), 279(3.31),284(3.20), 289(3.31)	94-0335-73
8,14-Secoestra-1,3,5(10),9,15-pentaen-14-one, 17α-hydroxy-3-methoxy-, (±)-	EtOH	265(4.25)	94-0697-73
Spiro[3H-cyclopent[a]anthracene-3,2'-[1,3]dioxolan]-5(2H)-one, 1,3a,4,7-8,9,10,11b-octahydro-	EtOH	217(4.59),262(4.30), 304(3.58)	39-1251-73C
Spiro[17H-cyclopenta[a]phenanthrene-17,2'-[1,3]dioxolan]-11(1H)-one, 2,3,4,12,13,14,15,16-octahydro-	EtOH	218(4.29),256(3.88), 309(3.33)	39-1251-73C
$C_{19}H_{22}O_4$			
1,3-Cyclopentanedione, 2-[2-(7-methoxy-2-methyl-2H-1-benzopyran-4-yl)ethyl]-2-methyl-	EtOH	215(4.40),266(4.00), 308(3.85)	2-0847-73
2,7-Dioxabicyclo[3.2.1]octane, 3-(3-furanyl)-5-(4,5,6,7-tetrahydro-4-isobenzofuranyl)-8-methyl-	EtOH	212(3.93)	105-0165-73
1H-Indene-1,5(6H)-dione, 2,3,7,7a-tetrahydro-4-[2-hydroxy-2-(3-methoxyphenyl)ethyl]-7a-methyl-	EtOH	217(4.03),251(3.97), 279(3.42)	44-3229-73

Compound	Solvent	λ_{max}(log ε)	Ref.
$C_{19}H_{22}O_5$			
1(3H)-Isobenzofuranone, 7-[3-(3-furanyl)-8-methyl-2,7-dioxabicyclo[3.2.1]oct-5-yl]-4,5,6,7-tetrahydro-	EtOH	203(4.11)	105-0027-73
$C_{19}H_{22}O_6$			
Tricyclo[5.2.1.0^{4,6}]deca-2,8-diene-2,3,6-tricarboxylic acid, 10-(1-methylethylidene)-, trimethyl ester	EtOH	232(4.03)	24-1837-73
$C_{19}H_{22}O_6S$			
1H-Fluorene-9-carboxylic acid, 2,3,4,4a-9,9a-hexahydro-8-methyl-9a-[(methylsulfonyl)acetyl]-2-oxo-, methyl ester, (4aα,9α,9aα)-	MeCN	266(2.50),271s(2.42), 275(2.36),290(1.88)	44-0741-73
$C_{19}H_{22}O_7$			
Machaerol B	EtOH	284(3.65)	102-2544-73
1,2-Phenanthrenedicarboxylic acid, 1,2-3,4,4a,9,10,10a-octahydro-4a-hydroxy-7-methoxy-4-oxo-, dimethyl ester	EtOH	275(3.2),285(3.2)	65-2058-73
$C_{19}H_{22}O_8$			
2H-1-Benzopyran-5-carboxaldehyde, 5-(2-acetoxy-3-hydroxy-3-methylbutyl)-7,8-dimethoxy-2-oxo-	MeOH	219(4.23),266(4.37), 305s(3.97)	78-2645-73
$C_{19}H_{22}O_{10}$			
Aloearbonaside	MeOH	302(3.81)	94-0149-73
$C_{19}H_{23}BrN_4O_7$			
7H-Pyrrolo[2,3-d]pyrimidin-4-amine, 7-[2-O-acetyl-3-bromo-3-deoxy-5-O-(2,4,4-trimethyl-5-oxo-1,3-dioxolan-2-yl)-β-D-xylofuranosyl]-	MeOH-base	271(4.07)	44-3179-73
$C_{19}H_{23}ClN_2O_2$			
Benzenamine, 4-chloro-2-[[(2,2-diethoxyethyl)amino]phenylmethyl]-	EtOH	230(4.44),360(3.71)	95-1263-73
$C_{19}H_{23}ClN_2O_5S$			
Thiazolo[3,2-a]pyridinium, 5-[2-[4-(dimethylamino)phenyl]ethenyl]-3-ethoxy-2,3-dihydro-, perchlorate	MeOH	480(4.48)	103-1138-73
Thiazolo[3,2-a]pyridinium, 7-[2-[4-(dimethylamino)phenyl]ethenyl]-3-ethoxy-2,3-dihydro-, perchlorate	MeOH	490(4.20)	103-1138-73
$C_{19}H_{23}ClN_4O$			
2-Quinoxalinemethanamine, N-(4-chlorophenyl)-1,2,3,4-tetrahydro-1-[[(2-methoxyethyl)imino]methyl]-	EtOH	250(4.41),318(3.94)	35-8414-73
$C_{19}H_{23}ClN_4O_7$			
7H-Pyrrolo[2,3-d]pyrimidin-4-amine, 7-[2-O-acetyl-3-chloro-3-deoxy-5-O-(2,4,4-trimethyl-5-oxo-1,3-dioxolan-2-yl)-β-D-xylofuranosyl]-, hydrochloride	MeOH-acid	227(4.35),271(4.04)	44-3179-73
	MeOH-base	271(4.07)	44-3179-73

Compound	Solvent	λ max (log ε)	Ref.
$C_{19}H_{23}Cl_2N$			
2,13-Metheno-13H-1-benzazacyclopentadecine, 3,18-dichloro-3,4,5,6,7,8-9,10,11,12-decahydro-	EtOH	215(4.42),238(4.62), 314(3.52),328(3.43)	44-0927-73
$C_{19}H_{23}FO_2$			
Androsta-4,6-diene-3,17-dione, 6-fluoro-	n.s.g.	284(4.39)	35-6655-73
$C_{19}H_{23}IN_4O_7$			
7H-Pyrrolo[2,3-d]pyrimidin-4-amine, 7-[2-O-acetyl-3-deoxy-3-iodo-5-O-(2,4,4-trimethyl-5-oxo-1,3-dioxolan-2-yl)-β-D-xylofuranosyl]-	pH 1	271(4.07)	23-1313-73
	pH 13	270(4.09)	23-1313-73
	MeOH	268(4.13)	23-1313-73
$C_{19}H_{23}NO$			
2-Cyclobutene-1-carbonitrile, 1,2-bis-(1,1-dimethylethyl)-4-oxo-3-phenyl-	EtOH	278(4.03)	88-0009-73
2,5-Cyclohexadien-1-one, 4-[[2,6-dimethyl-4-(1-methylethyl)phenyl]imino]-2,6-dimethyl-	EtOH	276(4.49),495(3.12)	78-0085-73
1H-Indole, 1-ethyl-2,3-dihydro-2-methoxy-3,3-dimethyl-2-phenyl-	C_6H_{12}	254(4.03),295(3.53)	104-0407-73
	EtOH	245(4.05),295(3.58)	104-0407-73
	MeCN	250(4.06),300(3.58)	104-0407-73
1H-Indole-3-carboxaldehyde, 2-(1,1-dimethyl-2-propenyl)-6-(3-methyl-2-butenyl)-	EtOH	217(4.51),250(4.26), 273(4.05),312(4.02)	32-0141-73
$C_{19}H_{23}NO_2$			
2,5-Cyclohexadien-1-one, 3-(methoxymethyl)-2,6-dimethyl-4-[(2,4,6-trimethylphenyl)imino]-	EtOH	209(4.35),277(4.35), 515(3.02)	44-0183-73
Isoquinoline, 1-[(3,4-dimethoxyphenyl)-methyl]-1,2,3,4-tetrahydro-2-methyl-, hydrochloride	EtOH	232(3.99),279(3.47)	87-1228-73
Morphinan-6-one, 3-hydroxy-17-(2-propenyl)-, (-)-	EtOH	225s(3.80),283(3.34)	87-0352-73
$C_{19}H_{23}NO_3$			
Benzeneethanamine, 3-[(6-ethoxymethyl)-1,3-benzodioxol-5-yl]-N-methyl-	EtOH	258(3.81),293(3.68)	23-2338-73
3-Epischelhammericine	EtOH	236(3.72),289(3.65)	95-0916-73
Spiro[7H-benzo[de]quinoline-7,1'-[2]-cyclohexan]-4'-one, 1,2,3,8,9,9a-hexahydro-6-hydroxy-5-methoxy-1-methyl- (jolantamine)	MeOH	240s(4.1),262(3.9), 288s(3.3)	30-0139-73
$C_{19}H_{23}NO_4$			
6H,8H-Benzo[a]pyrano[3,2-g]quinolizin-8-one, 5,9,10,11,13,13a-hexahydro-2,3-dimethoxy-11-methyl-	EtOH	273(3.78),284(3.76)	30-0234-73 +70-1263-73
1-Cyclopenteneheptanamide, 2-carboxy-5-oxo-N-phenyl-	MeOH	242(4.42)	44-4412-73
Erysotrine, 11-hydroxy-	EtOH	229(4.16),287(3.51)	95-1617-73
Erythratidinone	EtOH	231(4.29),284(3.60)	39-0874-73C
Phenol, 2-methoxy-4-(1,2,3,4-tetrahydro-6,7-dimethoxy-2-methyl-1-isoquinolinyl)-, (R)-	MeOH	207(4.82),235s(4.15), 282(3.79)	78-0031-73
	20% MeOH-HCl	208(4.79),234(4.17), 281(3.79)	78-0031-73
	20& MeOH-KOH	247(4.11),291(3.83)	78-0031-73

Compound	Solvent	λmax(log ε)	Ref.
$C_{19}H_{23}NO_5$			
Isoxazole, 3-[5-(2,2-dimethyl-1,3-dioxolan-4-yl)-2,2-dimethyl-1,3-dioxolan-4-yl]-5-phenyl-, [4R-(4α,5β(R*)]]-	CHCl	258(4.34)	136-0311-73D
Prostephabyssine (methiodide)	MeOH	282(3.58)	44-0151-73
$C_{19}H_{23}N_3O_2$			
Ergometrine	H_2O	311(3.91)	39-1312-73B
	EtOH	311(3.96)	39-1312-73B
Ergometrinine	H_2O	312(3.88)	39-1312-73B
	EtOH	311(3.96)	39-1312-73B
1H,5H-Pyrazolo[1,2-a][1,2,4]triazole-1,3(2H)-dione, dihydro-5,5-dimethyl-6,7-bis(1-methylethylidene)-2-phenyl-	EtOH	222(4.31),255(3.77)	35-1553-73
$C_{19}H_{23}N_3O_4$			
Benzenamine, 2-[[(2,2-diethoxyethyl)-imino]phenylmethyl]-4-nitro-	EtOH	229(4.33),370(4.20)	95-1263-73
$C_{19}H_{23}N_3O_5$			
Thymidine, α-(3,4-dihydro-1(2H)-quinolinyl)-	EtOH	260(4.12),304(3.41)	69-2879-73
$C_{19}H_{23}N_3O_6$			
1H-Indole-3-carboxylic acid, 4,6-bis-(acetylamino)-5-acetoxy-1,2-dimethyl-, ethyl ester	MeOH	223(4.57),250(4.04)	103-1490-73
$C_{19}H_{23}N_3O_7S_2$			
L-Cysteine, N-acetyl-S-[2-[[2-[(5-sulfo-1-naphthalenyl)amino]ethyl]amino]-2-oxoethyl]-	pH 7.0	336(3.78)	69-4154-73
$(C_{19}H_{23}N_3O_8)_n$			
Poly(L-glutamyl-L-tyrosyl-L-glutamyl)	0.2M NaOH	243(4.02),294(3.36)	39-1001-73C
$C_{19}H_{24}$			
Phenanthrene, 1,9,10,10a-tetrahydro-2,10a-dimethyl-7-(1-methylethyl)-	MeOH	306(3.84),318(3.86)	88-2385-73
$C_{19}H_{24}Cl_3NO_3$			
Benzo[a]cyclopropa[d]cyclohepten-3-ol, 1,1,8-trichloro-1,1a,2,2a,3,4,5,8a-octahydro-2a-methyl-8a-(4-morpholinyl)-, acetate, (1aα,2aα,3α,8aα)-	EtOH	253(4.28)	78-4263-73
(1aα,2aβ,3β,8bα)-	EtOH	250(3.70)	78-4263-73
$C_{19}H_{24}N_2$			
Ajmalan, 1-demethyl-, 2-epi-	MeOH	242(3.78),292(3.45)	94-1783-73
Indolo[2,3-a]quinolizine, 2-(1,1-dimethylethyl)-1,4,6,7,12,12b-hexahydro-	EtOH	233(4.23),284(3.84), 291(3.77)	44-2831-73
Quebrachamine, 14,15-dehydro-	MeOH	231(4.49),287(3.79), 295(3.76)	35-7458-73
$C_{19}H_{24}N_2O$			
Antirhine	EtOH	227(4.56),283(3.89), 291(3.83)	95-0483-73

Compound	Solvent	λ_{max}(log ε)	Ref.
$C_{19}H_{24}N_2O_2$			
Indolo[2,3-a]quinolizine-1-propanoic acid, 1,2,3,4,6,7,12,12b-octahydro-, methyl ester	EtOH	228(5.32),282(4.74), 292(4.67)	22-2705-73
Isoquinoline, 1-(2-amino-3,4-dimethoxybenzyl)-2-methyl-1,2,3,4-tetrahydro-	MeOH	212(4.59),265(4.04), 272(3.15),285(3.20)	87-1223-73
Norajmaline	EtOH	245(3.55),291(3.05)	102-1167-73
6H-Pyrrolo[3,2-f]indolizine-2-carboxylic acid, 7-ethyl-3,4,6,8-tetramethyl-, ethyl ester, hydrochloride	EtOH	262(4.68),312(4.37), 323(4.39)	65-1587-73
$C_{19}H_{24}N_2O_7$			
Isoxazole, 4,5-dihydro-5-(1,2:3,4-di-O-isopropylidene-D-arabino-1,2,3,4-tetrahydroxybutyl)-3-(4-nitrophenyl)-	EtOH	227(4.19),305(4.34)	33-1303-73
$C_{19}H_{24}N_2O_{11}$			
Uridine, 5'-O-(2,4,4-trimethyl-5-oxo-1,3-dioxolan-2-yl)-, 2',3'-diacetate	MeOH	259(4.07)	35-4016-73
$C_{19}H_{24}N_2O_{12}S_3$			
Uridine, 3-(phenylmethyl)-, 2',3',5'-trimethanesulfonate	EtOH	257(4.00)	44-0598-73
$C_{19}H_{24}N_4O_4$			
2-Propenal, 3-(1,3,3-trimethylbicyclo-[2.2.1]hept-2-yl)-, 2,4-dinitrophenylhydrazone	$CHCl_3$	380(4.53)	22-3071-73
$C_{19}H_{24}N_4O_5$			
1H-Purine-2,6-dione, 3,7-dihydro-1,3,7-trimethyl-8-[2-(3,4,5-trimethoxyphenyl)ethyl]-	MeOH	276(4.08)	36-1885-73
$C_{19}H_{24}O$			
Estra-1,3,5(10),16-tetraene, 3-methoxy-, Kober test	H_2SO_4	466(4.93),521(4.71)	94-1720-73
Gona-1,3,5(10),13(17)-tetraene, 1-methoxy-17-methyl-	MeOH	272(3.34),279(3.33)	35-7501-73
Gona-1,3,5(10),13-tetraene, 3-methoxy-17β-methyl-, Kober test	H_2SO_4	466(4.61),521(4.47)	94-1720-73
Gona-1,3,5(10),13(17)-tetraene, 3-methoxy-17-methyl-	MeOH	277(3.43),286(3.39)	35-7501-73
$C_{19}H_{24}O_2$			
Androsta-8,14-diene-3,17-dione, (5α,13ξ)-	MeOH	244(4.24)	24-3636-73
7H-Benz[e]inden-7-one, 3-acetyl-1,2,3-3a,4,5,8,9,9a,9b-decahydro-3a-methyl-7-(2-propynyl)-, [3S-(3α,3aα,9aα,9bβ)]-	EtOH	246(4.18)	94-0335-73
Estra-1,3,5(10),8-tetraen-17-ol, 3-methoxy-, (17α)-(±)-	EtOH	277(4.20)	94-0107-73
Estra-1,3,5(10)-trien-17-one, 3-hydroxy-1-methyl-, Kober test	H_2SO_4	430s(3.91),520(4.45)	94-1720-73
Estra-1,3,5(10)-trien-17-one, 3-methoxy-, Kober test	H_2SO_4	470s(4.44),515(4.57)	94-1720-73
2,4a-Ethano-4aH-fluorene-9-carboxylic acid, 1,2,3,4,9,9a-hexahydro-2,8-dimethyl-, methyl ester	n.s.g.	266(2.60),273(2.58)	39-1476-73C
12α-Etiojerva-4,6-diene-3,17-dione	MeOH	284(4.38)	87-0568-73

Compound	Solvent	λ_{max}(log ϵ)	Ref.
5,9-Methanobenzocycloocten-11-one, dodecahydro-4a-hydroxy-10-phenyl-	EtOH	294(4.01)	35-3310-73
9-Octadecene-12,14,16-triynoic acid, methyl ester			
$C_{19}H_{24}O_3$			
Androsta-4,9(11)-diene-3,17-dione, 14-hydroxy-, (13ξ,14ξ)-	MeOH	235(4.16)	24-3636-73
Androst-1-ene-3,11,17-trione, (5β)-	n.s.g.	224(3.97)	39-1361-73C
Androst-2-ene-1,11,17-trione, (5β)-	n.s.g.	225(3.85)	39-1361-73C
7H-Benz[e]inden-7-one, 3-acetoxy-1,2,3,3a,4,5,8,9,9a,9b-decahydro-3a-methyl-6-(2-propynyl)-	EtOH	245.5(4.18)	94-0335-73
1,3-Cyclopentanedione, 2-[2-(3,4,6,7,8-8a-hexahydro-8a-methyl-6-oxo-1-naphthalenyl)ethyl]-2-methyl-, (R)-	MeOH	236(4.20)	24-3636-73
1,3-Cyclopentanedione, 2-[2-(3,4,6,7,8-8a-hexahydro-8a-methyl-6-oxo-1(2H)-naphthylidene)ethyl]-2-methyl-, (R)-	MeOH	238(4.24)	24-3636-73
1,3-Cyclopentanedione, 2-methyl-2-[2-(1,2,3,4-tetrahydro-6-methoxy-1-naphthalenyl)ethyl]-	EtOH	280(3.38),288(3.35)	70-1574-73
Cyclopentanone, 2-[2-(3,4-dihydro-6-methoxy-1(2H)-naphthylidene)ethyl]-3-hydroxy-2-methyl-	EtOH	266.5(4.29)	94-0107-73
Estra-4,9-diene-3,17-dione, 11-methoxy-, (11β)-	EtOH	292(4.32)	111-0451-73
Estra-1,3,5(10)-trien-17-one, 1,11-dihydroxy-4-methyl-, Kober test	H_2SO_4	505(3.86)	94-1720-73
2(3H)-Naphthalenone, 4,4a,5,6,7,8-hexahydro-4a-methyl-5-[2-[(2-methyl-3-oxo-1-cyclopenten-1-yl)oxy]ethylidene]-, (R)-	MeOH	251(4.49)	24-3636-73
A-Nor-3-oxaestra-1,5(10),9(11)-trien-17β-ol, 2-methyl-, acetate	EtOH	213(4.18),242(4.04)	94-0335-73
9-Octadecene-12,14,16-triynoic acid, 18-hydroxy-, methyl ester, (Z)-	EtOH	213(5.15)	39-0743-73C
Spiro[cyclopenta[b]pyran-2(5H),1'(2'H)-naphthalen]-5-one, 3,3',4,4',4a,6,7-7a-octahydro-6'-methoxy-4a-methyl-	EtOH	276(3.19),283(3.18)	94-0107-73 +94-0703-73
isomer	EtOH	276(3.15),282(3.12)	94-0703-73
$C_{19}H_{24}O_4$			
Estra-1,3,5(10)-trien-17-one, 3,16-dihydroxy-11-methoxy-, (11β,16α)-	EtOH	220(3.88),281(3.29), 287(3.25)	111-0451-73
	EtOH-NaOH	243(3.95),299(3.43)	111-0451-73
Ferutinin	n.s.g.	261(4.16)	105-0025-73
$C_{19}H_{24}O_5$			
α-D-ribo-Hexofuranose, 3-deoxy-1,2:5,6-bis-O-(1-methylethylidene)-3-(phenylmethylene)-, cis	EtOH	214(3.42),255(3.82)	136-0129-73C
trans	EtOH	212(3.59),252(4.17)	136-0129-73C
α-D-xyo-Hexofuranose, 3-deoxy-1,2:5,6-bis-O-(1-methylethylidene)-3-(phenylmethylene)-, cis	EtOH	212(3.52),252(4.01)	136-0129-73C
trans	EtOH	213(3.76),254(4.26)	136-0129-73C
A-Nor-3-oxaestr-1(10)-ene-5-acetic acid, 2,17-dioxo-, methyl ester	EtOH	216(4.19)	64-0675-73C

Compound	Solvent	λ_{max}(log ϵ)	Ref.
$C_{19}H_{24}O_6$			
Anhydrolactarorufin B diacetate	EtOH	274(3.86)	19-0785-73
2H-Naphtho[1,8-bc]furan-2-one, 6-[2-(3-furanyl)-2-hydroxyethyl]-3,4,5,5a,6,7-8,8a-octahydro-8-hydroxy-6-(hydroxymethyl)-7-methyl-	EtOH	209(3.93),220(4.01)	105-0165-73
Ovatifolin acetate	EtOH	212(4.00)	102-2469-73
3H-Oxireno[8,8a]naphtho[2,3-b]furan-3,5-diol, 1a,2,4,4a,5,9-hexahydro-4,4a,6-trimethyl-, diacetate	EtOH	219(3.80)	73-0739-73
Pectorolide	EtOH	217(4.33)	28-1799-73A
$C_{19}H_{24}O_7$			
Christinine	EtOH	215(3.36)	44-1759-73
1,2-Phenanthrenedicarboxylic acid, 1,2,3,4,4a,9,10,10a-octahydro-4,4a-dihydroxy-7-methoxy-, dimethyl ester	EtOH	275(3.2),285(3.2)	65-2058-73
$C_{19}H_{25}BrO_3$			
1,3-Cyclopentanedione, 2-[2-(1-bromo-1,2,3,4,6,7,8,8a-octahydro-8a-methyl-6-oxo-1-naphthalenyl)ethyl]-2-methyl-	MeOH	238(4.18)	24-3636-73
$C_{19}H_{25}BrO_6$			
1H-3a,7-Methanoazulene-3,6-dicarboxylic acid, 8-[(acetyloxy)methyl]-4-bromo-2,3,4,7,8,8a-hexahydro-8-methyl-, dimethyl ester, [3R-(3α,3aβ,4α,7β,8α-8aα)]-	MeOH	235(3.77)	2-0991-73
$C_{19}H_{25}NO$			
2-Hexen-1-one, 1-(4-methylphenyl)-4-(1-piperidinyl)methylene)-	EtOH	252(4.13),347(4.52)	48-1161-73
$C_{19}H_{25}NO_2$			
Morphinan-3,6-diol, 17-(2-propenyl)-, (6β)-	EtOH	220s(3.90),282(3.38), 289s(3.34)	87-0352-73
hydrobromide	EtOH	220(3.85),282(3.37), 289s(3.31)	87-0352-73
$C_{19}H_{25}NO_3$			
1H-Carbazole, 2,3,4,4a,9,9a-hexahydro-6,7-dimethoxy-4a-methyl-9-(1-oxo-2-butenyl)-	EtOH	212(4.35),295(4.02), 316(4.10)	44-0215-73
Glycine, N-(5,5-dimethyl-3-oxo-1-cyclohexen-1-yl)-N-(phenylmethyl)-, ethyl ester	n.s.g.	208(3.68),298(4.20)	44-3487-73
Schelhammera alkaloid B	EtOH	230s(3.82),283(3.52), 289s(3.48)	95-0916-73
$C_{19}H_{25}NO_4$			
2,4-Decadienamide, N-(2,5-dioxo-7-oxabicyclo[4.1.0]hept-3-en-3-yl)-2,4,6-trimethyl-	MeOH	245(4.03),320(4.06)	88-4995-73
Erythratidine	EtOH	219(4.35),232s(3.76), 284(3.41)	39-0874-73C
$C_{19}H_{25}NO_5$			
2H-Benzo[a]quinolizine-2,4(3H)-dione, 1,6,7,11b-tetrahydro-3-(3-hydroxybutyl)-9,10-dimethoxy-	EtOH	286(3.64)	70-1263-73

Compound	Solvent	$\lambda_{max}(\log \epsilon)$	Ref.
Furo[2,3-d]-1,3-dioxol-6-ol, 6-[4,5-dihydro-3-(2,4,6-trimethylphenyl)-5-isoxazolyl]-tetrahydro-2,2-dimethyl-	EtOH	216(4.08)	33-1303-73
$C_{19}H_{25}N_3O_{10}$			
α-D-Glucopyranoside, methyl 6-[4-(acetylamino)-2-oxo-1(2H)-pyrimidinyl]-6-deoxy-, 2,3,4-triacetate	MeOH	243(4.19),301(3.86)	18-3165-73
$C_{19}H_{25}N_7O_{11}P_2$			
Pyridinium, 3-(aminocarbonyl)-1-[5-O-[7-(6-amino-9H-purin-9-yl)-1,3-dihydroxy-2,4-dioxa-1,3-diphosphahept-1-yl]-β-D-ribofuranosyl]-, hydroxide, inner salt, P,P'-dioxide, reduced	pH 9.5	262(4.15),340(3.79)	5-0531-73
oxidized form	pH 9.5	262(4.28)	5-0531-73
cyanide addition compd.	pH 10	327(4.16)	5-0531-73
$C_{19}H_{26}$			
Phenanthrene, 1,2,3,4,4a,10a-hexahydro-1,10a-dimethyl-7-(1-methylethyl)-	MeOH	266(3.89)	88-2385-73
Phenanthrene, 1,2,3,9,10,10a-hexahydro-1,10a-dimethyl-7-(1-methylethyl)-	MeOH	256(3.97)	88-2385-73
cis	EtOH	255(4.21),287(3.28), 296(3.18)	23-3236-73
$C_{19}H_{26}N_2$			
Indolo[2,3-a]quinolizine, 2-(1,1-dimethylethyl)-1,2,3,4,6,7,12,12b-octahydro-, cis	EtOH	227(4.22),284(3.62), 291(3.55)	44-2831-73
trans	EtOH	229(4.21),283(3.77), 291(3.72)	44-2831-73
Spiro[cyclopentane-1,1'-[1H]pyrido[3,4-b]indole], 3,4-diethyl-2',3',4',9'-tetrahydro-, (1α,3α,4β)-	EtOH	226(4.38),272(3.87), 279(3.86),290(3.75)	114-0105-73D
$C_{19}H_{26}N_2O_3$			
1H-Pyrrole-2-carboxylic acid, 4-acetyl-5-[(4-ethyl-3,5-dimethyl-1H-pyrrol-2-yl)methyl]-3-methyl-, ethyl ester	hexane	229(4.48),261(4.13), 276(4.09)	65-1593-73
enol form	hexane	229(4.42),261(4.09), 276(4.05)	65-1593-73
$C_{19}H_{26}N_2O_4$			
1H-Azepine-1,4-dicarboxylic acid, 5-[(phenylmethyl)amino]-2,3,6,7-tetrahydro-, diethyl ester	EtOH	304(4.16)	1-3251-73
$C_{19}H_{26}N_2O_6$			
3-Azacyclonona[8,9-b]indole-6,12b-dicarboxylic acid, 10,11-dimethoxy-3-methyl-	EtOH-HCl	239(3.72),282(3.65)	44-0215-73
$C_{19}H_{26}N_2O_7S$			
L-Threonine, N-[S-acetyl-N-[(phenylmethoxy)carbonyl]-L-cysteinyl]-, ethyl ester	n.s.g.	230(3.67)	44-0270-73

Compound	Solvent	λmax(log ε)	Ref.
$C_{19}H_{26}N_4O_4$			
2-Propenal, 3-[5-methyl-2-(1-methylethyl)cyclohexyl]-, 2,4-dinitrophenylhydrazone	$CHCl_3$	375(4.53)	22-3071-73
$C_{19}H_{26}N_4O_5S$			
L-Aspartic acid, N-[1-oxo-5-(1H-pyrrolo-[2,3-d]pyrimidin-4-ylthio)pentyl]-, diethyl ester	pH 1	220(4.32),258(3.99), 312(4.08)	73-1438-73
	pH 13	219(4.36),245(3.97), 292(4.13)	73-1438-73
$C_{19}H_{26}N_6O_5S$			
Glycine, N-[N-[N-[1-oxo-5-(1H-pyrrolo-[2,3-d]pyrimidin-4-ylthio)pentyl]-glycyl]glycyl]-, ethyl ester	pH 1	219(4.33),256(3.97), 308(4.07)	73-1438-73
	pH 13	222(4.33),250(3.96), 294(4.19)	73-1438-73
$C_{19}H_{26}N_8$			
1H-Naphtho[2,1-d]tetrazolo[1,5-a]azepine-4-propanenitrile, 3-azido-2,3,4-4a,5,6,12,13,13a,13b-decahydro-3,13a-dimethyl-, [3S-(3α,4β,4aβ,13aβ,13bα)]-	EtOH	242(4.23)	88-2587-73
7H-Tetrazolo[5,1-b]tetrazolo[1',5':1,2]-quino[6,5-g][3]benzazepine, 4,5,5a,5b-6,13,14,14a,14b,15,16,16a-dodecahydro-14a,16a-dimethyl-, [5aS-(5aα,5bβ,14aβ-14bα,16aβ)]-	EtOH	242(4.25)	88-2587-73
$C_{19}H_{26}O$			
Benzene, 1-(3-ethenyl-3,7-dimethyl-1,6-octadienyl)-4-methoxy-, (E)-	EtOH	260(4.37)	78-1119-73
Estra-1,3,5(10)-triene, 3-methoxy-, Kober test	H SO	523(3.11)	94-1720-73
Gona-1,3,5(10)-triene, 3-methoxy-17-methyl-, (8ξ,9ξ,13ξ,14ξ)-	isooctane	221(3.60),278(3.34), 287(3.39)	94-1741-73
9(1H)-Phenanthrenone, 2,3,4,4a,10,10a-hexahydro-1,10a-dimethyl-7-(1-methylethyl)-, [1S-(1α,4aβ,10aα)]-	MeOH	258(4.20)	44-2732-73
1,12-Tridecadien-3-one, 1-phenyl-, (E)-	EtOH	221(3.63),288(3.95)	12-0183-73
$C_{19}H_{26}O_2$			
Androsta-8,14-dien-3-one, 17-hydroxy-, (5α,13ξ)-	MeOH	247(4.22)	24-3636-73
Androst-1-ene-3,17-dione, (5β)-	n.s.g.	230(3.98)	39-1361-73C
Androst-2-ene-1,17-dione, (5β)-	n.s.g.	225(3.88)	39-1361-73C
1H-Dibenzo[a,d]cycloheptene-1,6(2H)-dione, 3,4,5,7,8,9,10,11-octahydro-3,3,8,8-tetramethyl-	EtOH	240(4.28)	88-2351-73
4,19-Dinor-3-oxapregna-1,5(10)-dien-20-one, 2-methyl-	isooctane	226(3.89)	94-0335-73
Estra-4,14-dien-3-one, 17-hydroxy-7-methyl-, (7α,17β)-	n.s.g.	240(4.26)	13-0107-73B
Estra-1,3,5(10)-trien-16β-ol, 3-methoxy-	n.s.g.	222(3.89),278(3.29), 287(3.26)	39-1493-73C
Estra-1,3,5(10)-trien-17α-ol, 3-methoxy-	EtOH	280(3.30),288(3.28)	94-0107-73
Kober test	H_2SO_4	438s(4.00),468(4.27), 524(4.41)	94-1720-73
Estra-1,3,5(10)-trien-17β-ol, 3-methoxy-, Kober test	H_2SO_4	436s(4.08),467(4.36), 517(4.34)	94-1720-73
12α-Etiojerva-4,6-dien-3-one, 17α-hydroxy-	MeOH	286(4.43)	87-0568-73

Compound	Solvent	λ max(log ε)	Ref.
12α-Etiojerva-4,6-dien-3-one, 17β-hydroxy-	MeOH	286(4.37)	87-0568-73
2(3H)-Naphthalenone, 5-[2-(3-furanyl)-ethyl]-4,4a,5,6,7,8-hexahydro-1,5,6-trimethyl-, (4aα,5α,6α)-	EtOH	257(4.11)	23-1332-73
(4aα,5α,6β)-	EtOH	257(4.11)	23-1332-73
	$CHCl_3$	252(4.16)	23-1332-73
9,16-Octadecadiene-12,14-diynoic acid, methyl ester, (E,Z)-	EtOH	214(4.76),228(3.60), 240(3.86),253(4.18), 267(4.35),282(4.23)	39-0743-73C
(Z,Z)-	EtOH	213(4.75),228(3.51), 239(3.76),252(4.01), 266(4.18),282(4.07)	39-0743-73C
$C_{19}H_{26}O_3$			
Androst-4-ene-3,17-dione, 4-hydroxy-	EtOH	278(4.04)	39-1830-73C
7H-Benz[e]inden-7-one, 3-acetyl-1,2,3-3a,4,5,8,9,9a,9b-decahydro-3a-methyl-6-(2-oxopropyl)-, [3S-(3α,3aα,9aα,9bβ)]-	EtOH	248(4.17)	94-0335-73
Estra-4,9-dien-3-one, 17-hydroxy-19-methoxy-, (11β,17β)-	EtOH	295(4.29)	111-0451-73
Estra-1,3,5(10)-triene-2,17β-diol, 3-methoxy-, Kober test	H_2SO_4	412(3.87),490s(4.18), 510s(4.22),536s(4.16)	94-1720-73
Estra-1,3,5(10)-triene-3,17β-diol, 2-methoxy-, Kober test	H_2SO_4	411(3.91),490s(4.18), 510s(4.23),538(4.25)	94-1720-73
Estra-1,3,5(10)-triene-16α,17β-diol, 3-methoxy-, Kober test	H_2SO_4	515(4.51)	94-1720-73
Estr-4-ene-3,17-dione, 6-(hydroxymethyl)-, (6β)-	EtOH	240.5(4.20)	33-2396-73
2-Naphthalenebutanoic acid, 1,2,3,4-tetrahydro-γ,2-dimethyl-6-(1-methylethyl)-1-oxo-	MeOH	261(4.14)	44-2732-73
A-Nor-3-oxaestra-1,5(10)-dien-17-ol, 2-methyl-, acetate, (17β)-	EtOH	225.5(3.88)	94-0335-73
9,16-Octadecadiene-12,14-diynoic acid, 18-hydroxy-, methyl ester, (E,Z)-	EtOH	228(3.48),239(3.65), 252(4.13),266(4.29), 283(4.20)	39-0743-73C
7-Oxaandrosta-1,4-dien-3-one, 17-hydroxy-17-methyl-, (17β)-	EtOH	240(4.16)	87-0257-73
$C_{19}H_{26}O_4$			
Androst-4-ene-3,17-dione, 9,14-dihydroxy-, (9ξ,13ξ,14ξ)-	MeOH	240(4.20)	24-3636-73
7H-Benz[e]inden-7-one, 3-acetoxy-1,2,3-3a,4,5,8,9,9a,9b-decahydro-3a-methyl-6-(2-oxopropyl)-	EtOH	247.5(4.14)	94-0335-73
Estra-1,3,5(10)-triene-3,16,17-triol, 11β-methoxy-	EtOH	220(3.80),281(3.25), 287s(3.21)	111-0451-73
	EtOH-NaOH	242(3.91),299(3.40)	111-0451-73
$C_{19}H_{26}O_5$			
Nemosenin C	EtOH	218(3.75)	73-0739-73
$C_{19}H_{26}O_5S$			
2-Naphthalenecarboxylic acid, decahydro-6-[[(4-methylphenyl)sulfonyl]oxy]-, methyl ester	MeOH	273.2(2.66)	44-2077-73

Compound	Solvent	$\lambda_{max}(\log \epsilon)$	Ref.
$C_{19}H_{26}O_6$			
1,2-Methanodicyclopropa[cd,gh]pentalene-2c,2d-dicarboperoxoic acid, hexahydro-, bis(1,1-dimethylethyl) ester	EtOH	243(3.71)	24-1804-73
Naphtho[2,3-b]furan-4,6,8a(4aH)-triol, 4,5,6,7,8,9-hexahydro-3,4a,5-trimethyl-, 4,6-diacetate	EtOH	217(3.86)	73-0739-73
$C_{19}H_{26}O_7$			
1H-3a,7-Methanoazulene-3,6-dicarboxylic acid, 8-(acetoxymethyl)-2,3,4,7,8,8a-hexahydro-4-hydroxy-8-methyl-, dimethyl ester	MeOH	230(3.78)	2-0991-73
$C_{19}H_{27}NO$			
1H-Carbazole, 2,3,4,4a,9,9a-hexahydro-4a-methyl-9-(1-oxohexyl)-	EtOH	255(4.18),276s(3.67), 287(3.55)	33-2628-73
1-Hexanone, 1-(2,3,4,4a,9,9a-hexahydro-4a-methyl-1H-carbazol-8-yl)-	EtOH	236(4.24),260(3.59), 374(3.76)	33-2628-73
	EtOH-HCl	236(4.17),358s(3.43), 374(3.64)	33-2628-73
Isoquinoline, 1,2,3,4,5,6,7,8-octahydro-1-[2-(3-methoxyphenyl)ethyl]-2-methyl-, hydrobromide	EtOH	273(3.30),280(3.26)	4-0217-73
1-Propanone, 3-(1-piperidinyl)-1-(6,7,8-9-tetrahydro-5H-benzocyclohepten-2-yl)-	MeOH	262(4.16)	73-2768-73
$C_{19}H_{27}NO_2$			
1H-Carbazole, 9-(2,2-dimethyl-1-oxopropyl)-8-methoxy-4a-methyl-2,3,4,4a,9,9a-hexahydro-	EtOH	257(3.95),280s(3.65)	33-2628-73
Isoquinoline, 1-[2-(3,4-dimethoxyphenyl)ethyl]-1,2,3,4,5,6,7,8-octahydro-hydrobromide	EtOH	229(3.96),279(3.49), 283s(3.42)	4-0217-73
	EtOH	229(3.95),279(3.49), 284s(3.41)	4-0217-73
$C_{19}H_{27}NO_3$			
Benzenepropanamide, N-[2-(1-cyclohexen-1-yl)ethyl]-3,4-dimethoxy-, hydrochloride	EtOH	229(3.91),280(3.48), 284s(3.42)	4-0217-73
$C_{19}H_{27}NS_2$			
1-Naphthalenecarbodithioic acid, dibutylamine salt	EtOH	325(4.11),347(3.89), 470(2.46)	143-0359-73
$C_{19}H_{28}$			
Phenanthrene, 1,2,3,4,4a,9,10,10a-octahydro-1,10a-dimethyl-7-(1-methylethyl)-	MeOH	272(3.28),280(3.28)	88-2385-73
Phenanthrene, 1,2,3,4,4a,9,10,10a-octahydro-2,10a-dimethyl-7-(1-methylethyl)-	MeOH	272(3.10),280(3.15)	88-2385-73
$C_{19}H_{28}N_4O_3S$			
L-Leucine, N-[1-oxo-5(1H-pyrrolo[2,3-d]-pyrimidin-4-ylthio)pentyl]-, ethyl ester	pH 1	217(4.37),257(4.04), 311(4.10)	73-1438-73
	pH 13	219(4.40),246(3.96), 292(4.10)	73-1438-73

Compound	Solvent	$\lambda_{max}(\log \epsilon)$	Ref.
$C_{19}H_{28}N_4O_7$			
D-Mannitol, 1-deoxy-3,4:5,6-bis-O-(1-methylethylidene)-1-(1,2,3,6-tetrahydro-1,3-dimethyl-2,6-dioxo-7H-purin-7-yl)-	EtOH	273(3.97)	136-0154-73F
$C_{19}H_{28}N_4O_{12}$			
1H-Purine-2,6-dione, 7-(4-O-α-D-glucopyranosyl- -D-glucopyranosyl)-3,7-dihydro-1,3-dimethyl-	pH 7	274(3.99)	136-0378-73C
$C_{19}H_{28}N_6O_4$			
1H-Pyrimido[5,4-b][1,4]oxazine-6-carboxazine-6-carboxylic acid, 4-[4-(diethylamino)carbonyl]-1-piper zinyl]-7-methyl-, ethyl ester	EtOH	243(4.4),273(4.1), 384(3.3)	103-1532-73
$C_{19}H_{28}O_2$			
Androstane-3,17-dione, Kober test, (5α)-	H_2SO_4	380(3.61),412(3.47)	94-1720-73
Androst-4-en-3-one, 17β-hydroxy- (testosterone)	hexane	232)4.24)	10-0528-73F
Kober test	H_2SO_4	416(3.87),483(3.87), 593(3.74)	94-1720-73
Estr-4-en-3-one, 17β-hydroxy-17α-methyl-, Kober test	H_2SO_4	384(3.71),490(3.33)	94-1720-73
Ethanone, 1-[2,4,5,6,7,7a-hexahydro-7-(3-hydroxy-3-methyl-4-pentenyl)-7a-methyl-6-methylene-1H-inden-3-yl]-	EtOH	259(4.15)	78-2047-73
2,4,6-Octatrienoic acid, 6-methyl-8-(2,6,6-trimethyl-1-cyclohexen-1-yl)-, methyl ester	ether	303(4.32)	24-3779-73
$C_{19}H_{28}O_3$			
Androst-15-en-17-one, 3,5-dihydroxy-, (3β,5β)-	EtOH	237(3.92)	94-2452-73
7-Oxaandrost-1-en-3-one, 17-hydroxy-17-methyl-, (5α,17β)-	EtOH	225(4.03)	87-0257-73
1-Undecen-3-one, 1-(3,5-dimethoxyphenyl)-, (E)-	EtOH	285(3.71)	12-0183-73
$C_{19}H_{29}NO$			
Cyclopropa[d]naphthalene-2-acetaldehyde, α-[(dimethylamino)methylene]-1,1a,4-4a,5,6,7,8-octahydro-4a,8,8-trimethyl-	EtOH	293(4.40)	54-0985-73
$C_{19}H_{29}NO_2$			
Resorcinol, 2'-(3,4-trans-p-1,8-menthadien-3-yl)-5'-(dimethylamino)-, (-)-	EtOH	254s(3.60),286(2.96)	33-0510-73
$C_{19}H_{29}NO_3$			
Benzoic acid, 2-[(2,2-dimethyl-1-oxobutyl)amino]-4-(3-methylbutyl)-	EtOH	230(4.47),233(4.47), 250(4.10),265(4.02), 310(3.76)	32-0141-73
Decanamide, N-(3,6-dioxo-1,4-cyclohexadien-1-yl)-2,4,6-trimethyl-	MeOH	224(3.86),256(3.71), 380(3.04)	88-4995-73
$C_{19}H_{29}NO_4$			
Decanamide, N-[4(or 5)-hydroxy-3,6-dioxo-1,4-cyclohexadien-1-yl]-2,4,6-trimethyl-	MeOH	220(4.18),293(4.35), 400(3.00)	88-4995-73

Compound	Solvent	λ_{max}(log ε)	Ref.
$C_{19}H_{30}$			
Benzene, 1-tridecenyl-, (E)-	MeOH	251(4.28)	24-1612-73
Naphthalene, 2-butyl-1,2,3,4-tetrahydro-1-pentyl-	EtOH	262(2.79),268(2.89), 275(2.92)	88-2487-73
$C_{19}H_{30}O$			
Benzene, 1-(3-ethyl-3,7-dimethyl-1-octenyl)-4-methoxy-, [R-(E)]-	EtOH	212(4.30),259(4.38)	78-1119-73
Cyclohexanone, 3-methyl-6-(1-methylethyl)-2,2,6-tri-2-propenyl-, (3R-cis)-	hexane	309(1.95)	22-1049-73
	MeOH	308(2.06)	22-1049-73
2-Tridecanone, 1-phenyl-	C_6H_{12}	287(2.21),294(--), 303(--),312(--)	28-0407-73B
	MeOH	286.5(2.19)	28-0407-73B
$C_{19}H_{30}O_2$			
5α-Androstan-17-one, 3α-hydroxy-, Kober test	H_2SO_4	390s(3.92),410(3.94)	94-1720-73
5α-Androstan-17-one, 3β-hydroxy-, Kober test	H_2SO_4	384s(4.06),410(4.14)	94-1720-73
5β-Androstan-17-one, 3α-hydroxy-, Kober test	H_2SO_4	390s(4.00),410(4.04)	94-1720-73
Androst-5-ene-3β,17β-diol, Kober test	H_2SO_4	384(4.02),410(3.97), 465(3.48)	94-1720-73
Butanoic acid, 3-methyl-, 5,7,9,11-tetradecatetraenyl ester, (E,E,Z,E)-	ether	288(4.71),301(4.85), 315(4.79)	24-2140-73
$C_{19}H_{30}O_5$			
2-Naphthalenecarboxylic acid, 3-(2-ethoxy-1-methyl-2-oxoethoxy)-1,4,4a,5,6-7,8,8a-octahydro-8,8a-dimethyl-, methyl ester	EtOH	245(3.68)	138-0929-73
more polar diastereoisomer	EtOH	247(4.08)	138-0929-73
$C_{19}H_{30}O_7$			
2H-Pyran-2-acetic acid, 4-acetoxytetrahydro-6-(4-methoxy-1,3-dimethyl-4-oxo-2-butenyl)-3,5-dimethyl-, methyl ester	EtOH	219(4.13)	33-2287-73
$C_{19}H_{32}N_2O$			
Androstan-17-one, 3-hydroxy-, hydrazone, (3α,5α)-	MeOH	198(3.59)	88-2289-73
$C_{19}H_{32}O$			
Benzene, 1-(3-ethyl-3,7-dimethyloctyl)-4-methoxy-	EtOH	279(3.21)	78-1119-73
$C_{19}H_{32}O_4$			
1,4-Hexanedione, 1-[2-ethyl-5-(1-ethyl-2-oxobutyl)tetrahydro-4-methyl-2-furanyl]-	isoPrOH	285(2.10)	44-3431-73
$C_{19}H_{34}O_4$			
3-Hexanone, 6-[2-ethyl-5-(1-ethyl-2-oxobutyl)tetrahydro-4-methyl-2-furanyl]-6-hydroxy-	isoPrOH	278(2.01)	44-3431-73
$C_{19}H_{34}O_4Si$			
1-Cyclopentene-1-heptanoic acid, 3-[[(1,1-dimethylethyl)dimethylsilyl]oxy]-5-oxo-, methyl ester, (R)-	MeOH	259(4.31)	35-1676-73

Compound	Solvent	$\lambda_{max}(\log \epsilon)$	Ref.
$C_{19}H_{36}Cl_3N_4$			
1-Butanaminium, N-butyl-N-[chloro-[chloro[[chloro(dibutylamino)methylene]amino]methylene]amino]methylene]-, chloride	$CHCl_3$	249(4.50),317(4.51)	114-0081-73A
$C_{19}H_{40}Si_4$			
Silane, 1,6-heptadiyne-1,3,5,7-tetrayltetrakis[trimethyl-	n.s.g.	256(2.56),307(2.75)	39-0599-73B

Compound	Solvent	$\lambda_{max}(\log \epsilon)$	Ref.
$C_{20}F_{24}S_8$			
1,2,4,5-Tetrathiane, 3,6-bis[2-[4,5-bis(trifluoromethyl)-1,3-dithiol-2-ylidene]-3,3,3-trifluoro-1-(trifluoromethyl)propylidene]-	isooctane	288(4.22)	35-4379-73
$C_{20}F_{31}N$			
Pyridine, 3,5-difluoro-4-[1,2,2,2-tetrafluoro-1-(trifluoromethyl)ethyl]-2,6-bis(undecafluorocyclohexyl)-	C_6H_{12}	271(3.61)	39-1710-73C
$C_{20}H_8ClIO_2S_2$			
Naphtho[1,8-bc]thiopyran-3(2H)-one, 2-(6-chloro-3-oxobenzo[b]thien-2(3H)-ylidene)-7-iodo-, cis	n.s.g.	486.5(4.23)	103-0960-73
trans	n.s.g.	598.5(4.52)	103-0960-73
$C_{20}H_8INO_4S_2$			
Naphtho[1,8-bc]thiopyran-3(2H)-one, 7-iodo-2-(5-nitro-3-oxobenzo[b]-thien-2(3H)-ylidene)-, cis	n.s.g.	494.5(4.34)	103-0960-73
trans	n.s.g.	603.5(4.60)	103-0960-73
$C_{20}H_9IO_2S_2$			
Naphtho[1,8-bc]thiopyran-3(2H)-one, 7-iodo-2-(3-oxobenzo[b]thien-2(3H)-ylidene)-, cis	n.s.g.	487.5(4.20)	103-0960-73
trans	n.s.g.	600(4.48)	103-0960-73
$C_{20}H_9NO_4$			
Benzo[3,4]cyclobut[1,2-b]anthracene-6,11-dione	$CHCl_3$	320(4.60),372(3.66), 390(3.68),452(3.01)	39-2267-73C
$C_{20}H_{10}O_2$			
Benzo[3,4]cyclobut[1,2-b]anthracene-6,11-dione	$CHCl_3$	253(4.30),259(4.29), 264(4.25),308s(4.83), 312(4.86),340(3.64), 363s(3.62),367(3.67), 383(3.72),433(3.05)	39-2267-73C
Benzo[a]pyrene-1,6-dione	$CHCl_3$	315(2.29),327(2.28)	34-0332-73
Benzo[a]pyrene-3,6-dione	$CHCl_3$	290(2.96),303(2.81), 317(2.84),347(2.79), 385(2.56),405(2.52)	34-0332-73
Benzo[a]pyrene-4,5-dione	$CHCl_3$	267(3.72),275(3.77), 312(2.83),337(3.08), 350(3.97)	34-0332-73
Benzo[a]pyrene-6,12-dione	$CHCl_3$	282(3.37),291(3.39), 303(3.32),352(3.01), 370(3.07)	34-0332-73
$C_{20}H_{11}ClF_2OS$			
9H-Xanthene, 9-[[(4-chlorophenyl)thio]-methylene]-2,7-difluoro-	dioxan	255(3.96),295(4.00), 368(4.34)	44-0841-73
$C_{20}H_{11}N_5$			
2H-Pyrrole-3,3,4,4-tetracarbonitrile, 2,5-diphenyl-	EtOH	263(4.02)	35-1945-73
$C_{20}H_{12}$			
Benzo[3,4]cyclobut[1,2-b]anthracene	$CHCl_3$	248(5.27),277s(5.61),	39-2267-73C

Compound	Solvent	$\lambda_{max}(\log \epsilon)$	Ref.
Benzo[3,4]cyclobut[1,2-b]anthracene (cont.)	$CHCl_3$	286(5.91),298(6.14), 319(5.95),340(5.27), 356(5.24)	39-2267-73C
Benzo[a]pyrene, compd. with osmium oxide, dipyridine complex	$CHCl_3$	267(4.51),274(4.55), 298(4.13),314(4.00), 327(4.90),350(3.62), 367(3.56),379(3.48), 387(3.52),403(3.34)	34-0332-73
$C_{20}H_{12}Br_2O_4$			
1(3H)-Isobenzofuranone, 3-(3,5-dibromo-2,4-dihydroxyphenyl)-3-phenyl-	pH 7.9	530(3.66)	64-0468-73B
	EtOH	530(3.66)	64-0468-73B
$C_{20}H_{12}F_2$			
9,10[1',2']-Benzenoanthracene, 1,5-difluoro-9,10-dihydro-, (9R)-	MeOH	213(4.78),235s(3.90), 255s(3.33),260s(3.32), 268(3.23),276(3.12)	18-0605-73
$C_{20}H_{12}F_3N_3O_2$			
1H-Benzimidazole-1-carboxamide, 5-fluoro-N,3-bis(4-fluorophenyl)-2,3-dihydro-2-oxo-	THF	242(4.52),283s(3.82), 288(3.75)	44-1316-73
$C_{20}H_{12}N_2O$			
Indeno[1,2,3-de]phthalazin-3(2H)-one, 2-phenyl-	n.s.g.	233(4.65),248(4.57), 256s(4.50),327(4.14)	115-0145-73A
$C_{20}H_{12}N_2OS_2$			
Benzothiazole, 2-[5-[2-[2-benzothiazolyl)ethenyl]-2-furanyl]-	EtOH	305(4.24),410(4.47)	104-2596-73
diprotonated	H_2O	330(4.46),450(4.52)	104-2596-73
$C_{20}H_{12}N_2O_4$			
9,10[1',2']-Benzenoanthracene, 9,10-dihydro-1,5-dinitro-, (9S)-	MeOH	207s(4.79),254(4.05), 315(3.64)	18-0605-73
$C_{20}H_{12}N_2S_3$			
Benzothiazole, 2-[5-[2-(2-benzothiazolyl)ethenyl]-2-thienyl]-	EtOH	300(4.19),405(4.38)	104-2596-73
diprotonated	H_2O	322(4.16),445(4.43)	104-2596-73
$C_{20}H_{12}N_4$			
1,3-Cyclobutanedicarbonitrile, 2,4-bis-(2-cyanophenyl)-	THF	226(4.67),277(3.78), 285(3.80)	142-0021-73
$C_{20}H_{12}N_4O$			
Cyclobuta[3,4]naphth[1,2-c][1,2,5]oxadiazole-5-carbonitrile, 4-(2-cyanophenyl)-3b,4,5,5a-tetrahydro-	THF	225(4.73),260(4.42), 286(4.02),299(3.97)	142-0021-73
$C_{20}H_{12}N_4O_2$			
Dibenzo[3,4:5,6]biphenyleno[1,2-c:7,8-c']bis[1,2,5]oxadiazole, 7b,7c,14b-14c-tetrahydro-	THF	234(4.35),260(4.37), 293(3.76),302(3.75)	142-0021-73
Dibenzo[3,4:7,8]biphenyleno[1,2-c:5,6-c']bis[1,2,5]oxadiazole, 7b,7c,14b-14c-tetrahydro-	THF	225(4.60),260(4.29), 293(3.76),302(4.08)	142-0021-73
$C_{20}H_{12}O_3$			
Benzeneacetic acid, α-(2-oxo-1(2H)-acenaphthylenylidene)-	EtOH	250(3.99),316(3.55), 340(3.54)	2-1333-73

Compound	Solvent	λmax(log ε)	Ref.
Spiro[isobenzofuran-1(3H),9'-[9H]-xan-then]-3-one	EtOH	203(4.59),217(4.59), 286(3.70),292(3.69)	56-2101-73
	80% H_2SO_4	202(4.67),260(4.71), 281(3.76),376(4.55), 435(3.59)	56-2101-73
$C_{20}H_{12}O_4$			
1,4-Naphthalenedione, 2-(2,3-dihydro-1,3-dioxo-1H-inden-2-yl)-3-methyl-	EtOH	328(3.68)	83-0257-73
	EtOH-KOH	512(3.61)	83-0257-73
Spiro[isobenzofuran-1(3H),9'-[9H]-xan-then]-3-one, 3'-hydroxy-	EtOH	203(4.58),222(4.59), 275(3.65),286(3.67), 294(3.64)	56-2101-73
	80% H_2SO_4	202(4.67),222(4.48), 259(4.60),282(3.80), 394(3.50)	56-2101-73
$C_{20}H_{12}O_6$			
Helioxanthin	EtOH	219(4.39),267(4.50), 289(3.32),356(3.61)	2-0203-73
$C_{20}H_{12}O_7$			
Chromocyclin, 2-deacetyl-12a-deoxy-	EtOH	236(4.33),267(4.44), 343(3.74),435(4.38), 459(4.40)	105-0498-73
$C_{20}H_{12}S_3$			
Naphtho[2,1-b]thiophene, 2-(2-thieno-[2,3-b]thien-2-ylethenyl)-	benzene	364(4.24),383(4.25), 405(4.20)	35-3692-73
$C_{20}H_{13}BrN_2O$			
Benzoxazole, 2-[5-[2-(4-bromophenyl)eth-enyl]-2-pyridinyl]-	n.s.g.	357(4.79)	40-0991-73
$C_{20}H_{13}ClN_2$			
11H-Isoindolo[2,1-a]benzimidazole, 11-(4-chlorophenyl)-	EtOH	222(4.52),242(4.17), 251(3.99),306(4.35), 319(4.26)	44-3872-73
$C_{20}H_{13}ClN_2O$			
Benzoxazole, 2-[5-[2-(4-chlorophenyl)-ethenyl]-2-pyridinyl]-	n.s.g.	356(4.78)	40-0991-73
Benzoxazole, 2-[6-[2-(4-chlorophenyl)-ethenyl]-3-pyridinyl]-	n.s.g.	356(4.76)	40-0991-73
11H-Isoindolo[2,1-a]benzimidazol-11-ol, 11-(4-chlorophenyl)-	EtOH	248(4.27),261(4.29), 305s(4.09)	44-3872-73
$C_{20}H_{13}ClN_2S$			
Benzothiazole, 2-[5-[2-(4-chlorophenyl)-ethenyl]-2-pyridinyl]-	n.s.g.	364(4.70)	40-0991-73
$C_{20}H_{13}ClO_2S$			
9H-Thioxanthene, 9-[(4-chlorophenyl)-methylene]-, 10,10-dioxide	MeOH	277s(3.80),285(3.86), 329(4.19)	39-0163-73C
$C_{20}H_{13}N_3$			
Benzenamine, N-(10-diazo-9(10H)-anthra-cenylidene)-	EtOH	233(4.41),258(4.23), 322(4.15),407(4.05)	22-1305-73
tetrafluoroborate	EtOH	232(4.45),254(4.34), 292s(4.14),320(4.15), 407(4.02),490s(3.37)	22-1305-73

Compound	Solvent	$\lambda_{max}(\log \epsilon)$	Ref.
$C_{20}H_{13}N_3O_2S$			
Benzothiazole, 2-[5-[2-(4-nitrophenyl)-ethenyl]-2-pyridinyl]-	n.s.g.	380(4.70)	40-0991-73
$C_{20}H_{13}N_3O_3$			
Benzoxazole, 2-[5-[2-(4-nitrophenyl)ethenyl]-2-pyridinyl]-	n.s.g.	372(4.69)	40-0991-73
$C_{20}H_{14}$			
9,10[1',2']-Benzenoanthracene, 9,10-dihydro-	C_6H_{12}	265s(3.26),271(3.53), 279(3.61)	78-1379-73
	EtOH	197(4.80),211(4.81), 270(3.56),278(3.69)	18-2907-73
Benzo[5,6]cyclopropa[3,4]pentaleno[1,2-b]naphthalene, 4b,10b,10c,10d-tetrahydro-	C_6H_{12}	240(4.82),264(3.84), 276(3.87),284(3.84), 296s(3.60),313(3.10), 320(2.87),328(3.23)	35-1274-73
2,2'-Binaphthalene	EtOH	212(4.56),245s(4.69), 254(4.86),304(4.10)	132-0051-73
Cyclopropa[3,4]pentaleno[1,2-b]anthracene, 2a,2b,10b,10c-tetrahydro-	C_6H_{12}	255s(4.90),263(5.21), 315s(3.16),330(3.45), 345(3.69),362(3.82), 382(3.71)	35-3977-73
1,4-Ethenonaphthacene, 1,4-dihydro-	C_6H_{12}	238s(4.25),259s(4.91), 267(5.16),304(3.19), 317(3.50),332(3.76), 349(3.89),369(3.78)	35-3977-73
5,12-Ethenonaphthacene, 5,12-dihydro-	C_6H_{12}	224s(2.74),233(4.86), 240(4.95),255(4.01), 266(4.14),274(4.18), 284(3.74),293(2.92), 299(2.82),300(3.15), 311(2.82),319(3.25)	35-1274-73
$C_{20}H_{14}BrN_3S$			
1,2,4-Triazolidine-3-thione, 1-(4-bromophenyl)-4,5-diphenyl-, meso-ionic didehydro deriv.	MeOH	240(--),320(3.46)	42-0154-73
1,2,4-Triazolidine-3-thione, 5-(4-bromophenyl)-1,4-diphenyl-, meso-ionic didehydro deriv.	MeOH	215(4.40),246(4.47), 325(3.51)	42-0154-73
$C_{20}H_{14}Br_2O_2$			
Naphtho[2,3-c]furan-1(3H)-one, 7-bromo-9-(4-bromophenyl)-3,3-dimethyl-	n.s.g.	246(4.92),289(4.07), 348(3.70)	115-0145-73A
$C_{20}H_{14}Br_2O_3$			
7H-Benzo[c]fluorene-6-carboxylic acid, 2,9-dibromo-7-hydroxy-7-methyl-, methyl ester	EtOH	235(4.74),259(4.76), 332(4.29),353s(4.16)	115-0145-73A
$C_{20}H_{14}Br_2O_4$			
2,3-Naphthalenedicarboxylic acid, 7-bromo-1-(4-bromophenyl)-, dimethyl ester	EtOH	223(4.74),249(4.96), 292(4.17),341(3.56)	115-0145-73A
$C_{20}H_{14}ClNO$			
Ethanone, [(4-chlorophenyl)imino]diphenyl-	EtOH	259(4.49),330s(3.58)	12-2027-73

Compound	Solvent	λ_{max}(log ε)	Ref.
$C_{20}H_{14}ClNO_2$			
Benzamide, 2-benzoyl-N-(4-chlorophenyl)-	EtOH	268(3.88)	39-2448-73C
$C_{20}H_{14}ClN_3$			
11H-Isoindolo[2,1-a]benzimidazol-11-amine, 11-(4-chlorophenyl)-	EtOH	222(4.52),295s(4.15), 309(4.26),321(4.13)	44-3872-73
$C_{20}H_{14}ClN_3S$			
1,2,4-Triazolidine-3-thione, 5-(3-chlorophenyl)-1,4-diphenyl-, meso-ionic didehydro deriv.	MeOH	220(4.41),242(4.39), 325(3.49)	42-0154-73
$C_{20}H_{14}Cl_2N_4$			
Quinoxalino[2,3-b]phenazinium, 2,9(or 10)-dichloro-5,12-dihydro-5,12-dimethyl-, diperchlorate	EtOH	545(4.11),585(4.47), 635(4.55)	22-1289-73
	EtOH-NaOH	492(3.64),528(4.23), 568(4.69)	22-1289-73
$C_{20}H_{14}Cl_4O$			
Cyclohexanone, 2,6-bis[(2,4-dichlorophenyl)methylene]-	EtOH	318(4.34)	23-1458-73
Cyclohexanone, 2,6-bis[(2,6-dichlorophenyl)methylene]-	EtOH	289(4.17)	23-1458-73
Cyclohexanone, 2,6-bis[(3,4-dichlorophenyl)methylene]-	EtOH	329(4.54)	23-1458-73
$C_{20}H_{14}F_6$			
Benzene, 1,1'-[3-[2,2,2-trifluoro-1-(trifluoromethyl)ethylidene]-1-cyclopropene-1,2-diyl]bis[4-methyl-	C_6H_{12}	237s(4.29),244s(4.38), 253(4.51),300(3.92), 342(4.30)	88-4079-73
	benzene	342(--)	88-4079-73
	EtOH	338(--)	88-4079-73
	MeCN	334(--)	88-4079-73
$C_{20}H_{14}IN_3S$			
1,2,4-Triazolidine-3-thione, 5-(4-iodophenyl)-1,4-diphenyl-, meso-ionic didehydro deriv.	MeOH	215(4.46),254(4.49), 326(3.73)	42-0154-73
$C_{20}H_{14}NO$			
1H-Isoindolium, 1-oxo-2,3-diphenyl-, hexachloroantimonate	MeCN	231(4.15),271(4.12)	24-1423-73
	H_2SO_4	244(3.94),370(4.25)	24-1423-73
$C_{20}H_{14}N_2$			
4a,8a-Diazoniapentaphene, dication, bis(tetrafluoroborate)	MeCN	215(4.68),252(4.58), 274(4.21),286(4.34), 297(4.42),326s(--), 339(4.72),353(4.72), 362(4.55),383(4.66), 395s(--),420(3.76), 446(3.75)	5-0339-73
4a,12a-Diazoniapentaphene, dication, bis(tetrafluoroborate)	MeCN	215(4.57),235(4.54), 257(4.61),286(4.34), 296(4.35),321s(--), 343(4.65),356(4.80), 374(4.52),402(3.82), 426(3.72)	5-0339-73
12a,14a-Diazoniapentaphene, dication, bis(tetrafluoroborate)	MeCN	211(4.34),230(4.56), 242(4.50),262(4.64), 296(4.28),323s(--), 338(4.49),349(4.29),	5-0339-73

Compound	Solvent	$\lambda_{max}(\log \epsilon)$	Ref.
12a,14a-Diazoniapentaphene, dication, bis(tetrafluoroborate) (cont.)	MeCN	368(4.53),388(4.57), 395s(--),415(3.71)	5-0339-73
$C_{20}H_{14}N_2O$			
Benzoxazole, 2-[5-(2-phenylethenyl)-2-pyridinyl]-	n.s.g.	354(4.70)	40-0991-73
Benzoxazole, 2-[6-(2-phenylethenyl)-3-pyridinyl]-	n.s.g.	354(4.75)	40-0991-73
1H-Indeno[1,2-b]pyridine, 3-carbonitrile, 4,5-dihydro-2-methyl-5-oxo-4-phenyl-	EtOH	229s(4.33),234(4.37), 253s(4.38),260(4.38), 302s(3.64),320(3.62), 343(3.67),467(3.40)	103-0636-73
	EtOH-NaOH	241s(4.34),245(4.35), 270s(4.09),278(4.10), 312(3.79),333(3.66), 368(3.64),533(3.79), 563(3.81)	103-0636-73
11H-Isoindolo[2,1-a]benzimidazol-11-ol, 11-phenyl-	EtOH	242(4.28),291(4.09), 305s(4.06)	44-3872-73
$C_{20}H_{14}N_2OS_2$			
Benzothiazole, 2-[5-[2-(2-benzothiazolyl)ethyl]-2-furanyl]-	EtOH	250(4.06),330(4.44)	104-2596-73
diprotonated	H_2O	295(3.83),367(4.60)	104-2596-73
$C_{20}H_{14}N_2O_4$			
2H-1,4-Oxazin-3(4H)-one, 4-(1-naphthalenyl)-6-(4-nitrophenyl)-	EtOH	364(4.23)	4-0347-73
$C_{20}H_{14}N_2O_4S_2$			
9-Deoxyepiquinine-9-thiosulfuric acid (hemithiosulfate)	MeOH-HCl	256(4.32),330s(3.61), 359(3.74)	87-1042-73
$C_{20}H_{14}N_2S$			
Acridinium, 9-phenyl-, thiocyanate	EtOH	210(4.2),219s(4.1), 255(4.7),281(3.5), 326s(3.5),336s(3.6), 359(4.0),364s(--), 369s(--),389(3.7), 439s(--)	97-0072-73
Benzenesulfenamide, N-(2-phenyl-3H-indol-3-ylidene)-	$CHCl_3$	267(4.50),413(4.23)	39-1037-73C
Benzothiazole, 2-[5-(2-phenylethenyl)-2-pyridinyl]-	n.s.g.	362(4.69)	40-0991-73
Sulfur diimide, di-1-naphthalenyl-	C_6H_{12}	287(4.10),460(4.10)	143-0285-73
$C_{20}H_{14}N_2S_3$			
Benzothiazole, 2-[5-[2-(2-benzothiazolyl)ethyl]-2-thienyl]-	EtOH	254(3.96),335(4.18)	104-2596-73
diprotonated	H_2O	295(3.70),370(4.33)	104-2596-73
$C_{20}H_{14}N_4$			
Dipyrido[3,2-a:3',2'-h]phenazine, 3,10-dimethyl-	EtOH	214(4.60),221(4.58), 254(4.37),305(5.02), 353(3.97),362(3.93), 372(4.17),382(3.97), 393(4.34)	54-1377-73

Compound	Solvent	$\lambda_{max}(\log \epsilon)$	Ref.
$C_{20}H_{14}N_4O$			
Pyridazino[4,3-f:5,6-f']diquinoline, 8,13-dimethyl-, 3-oxide	EtOH	206(4.67),244(4.31), 303(4.50),354(4.15), 371(4.08),405(3.58), 429(3.59)	54-1377-73
$C_{20}H_{14}N_4O_2S$			
1,2,4-Triazolidine-3-thione, 5-(4-nitrophenyl)-1,4-diphenyl-, meso-ionic didehydro deriv.	MeOH	216(4.36),252(4.45), 375(3.55)	42-0154-73
$C_{20}H_{14}N_4O_2S_2$			
1,2,4-Oxadiazole, 3,3'-[dithiobis(4,1-phenylene-2,1-ethenediyl)]bis-	EtOH	227(4.37),301(4.67)	39-2241-73C
$C_{20}H_{14}O$			
Benzo-2,3-naphthobicyclo[3.3.0]octadien-4-one	C_6H_{12}	229(4.83),275(3.79), 284(3.84),293s(3.27), 307(3.16),314s(2.88), 321(3.22)	35-1274-73
Benzo-2,3-naphthobicyclo[3.3.0]octadien-6-one	C_6H_{12}	250(4.84),282s(3.77), 293(3.96),305(4.03), 322(2.82),336(2.98), 353(3.00)	35-1274-73
$C_{20}H_{14}O_2$			
9,10[1',2']-Benzenoanthracene-1,5-diol, 9,10-dihydro-, (9R)-	MeOH	217(4.71),234(4.11), 240s(4.00),262s(3.50), 268(3.61),277(3.58), 286(3.55)	18-0605-73
	MeOH-NaOH	217(4.69),245s(4.35), 270(3.66),278(3.66), 330(3.75)	18-0605-73
Benzo[a]pyrene-4,5-diol, 4,5-dihydro-	EtOH	263(4.55),272(4.74), 297(4.04),310(4.02), 323(3.97)	34-0332-73
1(3H)-Isobenzofuranone, 3,3-diphenyl-	EtOH	202(4.65)	56-2101-73
	80% H_2SO_4	195(4.54)	56-2101-73
$C_{20}H_{14}O_3$			
Benzoic acid, 2-benzoyl-, phenyl ester	C_6H_{12}	262(4.12),339(3.68)	22-1442-73
	EtOH	262(4.09),338(3.60)	22-1442-73
4,7-Isobenzofurandione, 5,6-dihydro-1,3-diphenyl-	$CHCl_3$	340(4.3)	22-1154-73
1(3H)-Isobenzofuranone, 3-(4-hydroxyphenyl)-3-phenyl-	pH 12	500(3.01)	64-0468-73B
	EtOH	204(4.71),278(3.40), 286(3.38)	56-2101-73
	80% H_2SO_4	200(4.42),227(3.92), 465(3.91)	56-2101-73
Methanone, 2-dibenzofuranyl(2-methoxyphenyl)-	EtOH	242(4.46),255(4.38), 259(4.54)	40-1505-73
Methanone, 3-dibenzofuranyl(2-methoxyphenyl)-	EtOH	277(3.97),307(4.46)	40-1505-73
Phenol, 2,4-dibenzoyl-	C_6H_{12}	253(4.45),268s(--), 338(3.65)	22-1442-73
	EtOH	255(4.43),275s(--), 325(3.59)	22-1442-73
$C_{20}H_{14}O_4$			
1,4-Benzenediol, dibenzoate	C_6H_{12}	255(4.40)	22-1442-73
	EtOH	259(4.41)	22-1442-73

Compound	Solvent	λ_{max}(log ε)	Ref.
2,2'-Bifuran, 5,5'-bis[2-(2-furanylethenyl)-, (E,E)-	$CHCl_3$	268(4.37),278(4.38), 318(4.74),445(4.65)	39-1786-73C
Haemodorin	MeOH	240s(4.06),285(4.24), 294(4.25),374(3.83), 520(3.62)	12-1377-73
1(3H)-Isobenzofuranone, 3-(2,3-dihydroxyphenyl)-3-phenyl-	pH 12.2	450(3.30)	64-0468-73B
1(3H)-Isobenzofuranone, 3-(2,4-dihydroxyphenyl)-3-phenyl-	neutral	480(3.38)	64-0468-73B
	pH 9.8	490(3.85)	64-0468-73B
1(3H)-Isobenzofuranone, 3-(2,5-dihydroxyphenyl)-3-phenyl-	pH 12.5	460(4.23)	64-0468-73B
5,12-Naphthacenedione, 1,4-dihydroxy-6,11-dimethyl-	CH_2Cl_2	277(4.3),465(4.0)	22-2856-73
Phenolphthalein	EtOH	203(4.71),230(4.35), 276(3.56)	56-2101-73
	80% H_2SO_4	196(4.61),265(3.97), 392(4.13),498(4.80)	56-2101-73
2,6-Pyrenedicarboxylic acid, dimethyl ester	EtOH	263(4.76),280s(4.45), 311(3.92),325(4.30), 339(4.51),374(3.24), 395(3.34)	88-3401-73
$C_{20}H_{14}O_5$			
1(3H)-Isobenzofuranone, 3-phenyl-3-(2,3,4-trihydroxyphenyl)-	pH 8.8	510(3.41)	64-0468-73B
1(3H)-Isobenzofuranone, 3-phenyl-3-(2,4,6-trihydroxyphenyl)-	pH 9.5	490(3.40)	64-0468-73B
$C_{20}H_{14}O_6$			
2H-1-Benzopyran-2-one, 7,7'-[1,2-ethanediylbis(oxy)]bis-	CH_2Cl_2	323(4.49)	44-0957-73
$C_{20}H_{14}O_6S_2$			
18,20-Dioxa-2,19-dithiatetracyclo[13.2-1.1^{3,6}.1^{9,12}]eicosa-3,5,7,9,11,13,15-17-octaene-7,14-dicarboxylic acid, dimethyl ester	$CHCl_3$	289(4.48),296(4.50)	39-1786-73C
$C_{20}H_{14}O_7S$			
18,19,20-Trioxa-2-thiatetracyclo[13.2.1-1^{3,6},1^{9,12}]eicosa-3,5,7,9,11,13,15,17-octaene-7,14-dicarboxylic acid, dimethyl ester	$CHCl_3$	291(4.39)	39-1786-73C
$C_{20}H_{14}S_6$			
3,3'-Bi-3H-1,2-dithiolo[3,4-b][1]benzothiophene, 6,6'-dimethyl-	isoPrOH	225(4.18),262(3.96), 309(3.58),340(3.07)	88-1561-73
$C_{20}H_{15}ClO_5S$			
3-Thiophenecarboxylic acid, 5-(4-chlorobenzoyl)-4-hydroxy-2-(4-methoxyphenyl)-, methyl ester	CH_2Cl_2	364(4.28)	48-0497-73
$C_{20}H_{15}ClO_6$			
Benzofuro[3,2-c]pyrylium, 3-methyl-1-(2-phenylethenyl)-, perchlorate	n.s.g.	255(4.14),308(4.23), 420(4.45)	103-0416-73
$C_{20}H_{15}LiO$			
Ethanone, 1,2,2-triphenyl-, lithium deriv.	DMF	288(5.64)	35-8118-73

Compound	Solvent	$\lambda_{max}(\log \epsilon)$	Ref.
$C_{20}H_{15}N$			
2H-Azirine, 2,2,3-triphenyl-	EtOH	250(4.39),285s(3.15), 310(3.04)	33-1679-73
11bH-Indeno[1',2':3,4]cyclobuta[1,2-a]-naphthalene-11b-carbonitrile, 6a,6b,11,11a-tetrahydro-	MeCN	265(3.89),273(3.89),	138-0187-73
1H-Indole, 2-[1,1'-biphenyl]-4-yl-	EtOH	210(4.35),276(4.32)	34-0109-73
$C_{20}H_{15}NO$			
Benzofuro[3,2-c]pyridine, 3-methyl-1-(2-phenylethenyl)-	n.s.g.	257(4.33),300(4.07), 333(4.00)	103-0416-73
Ethanone, 1,2-diphenyl-2-(phenylimino)-	EtOH	256(4.47),320s(3.78)	12-2027-73
$C_{20}H_{15}NO_2$			
Benzamide, 2-benzoyl-N-phenyl-	EtOH	265(3.79)	39-2448-73C
1H-Isoindol-1-one, 2,3-dihydro-3-hydroxy-2,3-diphenyl-	H_2SO_4	243(4.36),376(4.22)	24-1423-73
$C_{20}H_{15}NO_2S$			
Methanone, (4,5-dihydro-3,4-diphenyl-5-isoxazolyl)-2-thienyl-	EtOH	269(4.30)	39-1148-73C
Methanone, [4,5-dihydro-3-phenyl-4-(2-thienyl)-5-isoxazolyl]phenyl-	EtOH	252(4.42)	39-1148-73C
$C_{20}H_{15}NO_3$			
Acetic acid, cyano-, (2,3-dihydro-3-oxo-2-phenyl-1H-inden-1-ylidene)-, ethyl ester	EtOH-HCl	251s(4.15),260s(4.10), 300(4.23),332s(3.81)	39-1731-73C
Methanone, (4,5-dihydro-3,4-diphenyl-5-isoxazolyl)-2-furanyl-, trans	EtOH	276(4.36)	39-1148-73C
Methanone, (4,5-dihydro-3,5-diphenyl-4-isoxazolyl)-2-furanyl-, trans	EtOH	280(4.41)	39-1148-73C
$C_{20}H_{15}NO_4$			
[1,3]Benzodioxolo[5,6-c]phenanthridine, 2,3-dimethoxy-	EtOH	229(4.36),274(4.73), 278s(4.71),311(4.15), 330s(3.89),348(3.60), 367(3.46)	4-0085-73
Benzo[c][1,3]dioxolo[4,5-j]phenanthridine, 2,3-dimethoxy-	$CHCl_3$	273(4.83),283(4.08), 305(4.38),333(3.98), 351(3.76),368(3.48)	4-0867-73
2H-Benzofuro[2,3-b]pyrrol-2-one, 1,3,3a-8a-tetrahydro-1-[(2-oxo-2H-1-benzopyran-4-yl)methyl]-	EtOH	275(4.05),312(3.72)	44-3874-73
$C_{20}H_{15}NO_5$			
Benzo[c]phenanthridine-1,4,6(5H)-trione, 8,9-dimethoxy-5-methyl-	EtOH	202(4.33),254(4.13)	78-3881-73
$C_{20}H_{15}NO_6$			
Thalicminine	EtOH	254(4.70),280(4.53), 357(4.43),452(3.4)	102-0948-73
$C_{20}H_{15}N_3$			
11H-Isoindolo[2,1-a]benzimidazol-11-amine, 11-phenyl-	EtOH	295s(4.16),309(4.27), 321(4.16)	44-3872-73
$C_{20}H_{15}N_3O$			
Angustine	EtOH	220(4.54),255(4.32), 291(4.10),304(4.03), 380(4.58),400(4.59)	39-0013-73C

Compound	Solvent	$\lambda_{max}(\log \epsilon)$	Ref.
$C_{20}H_{15}N_3O_2$			
Ethanone, 1-phenyl-2-[(2-phenylimidazo-[1,2-a]pyrimidin-5-yl)oxy]-	MeOH	238(4.59),273(4.08), 317(4.05)	7-0619-73
Ethanone, 1-phenyl-2-[(2-phenylimidazo-[1,2-a]pyrimidin-7-yl)oxy]-	MeOH	237(4.61),267s(4.28), 315(4.05)	7-0619-73
Ethanone, 1-phenyl-2-[(2-phenylimidazo-[1,2-c]pyrimidin-5-yl)oxy]-	MeOH	242(4.59),285(4.19), 310s(3.91)	7-0619-73
Propanedinitrile, (4-amino-3,5-dimethyl-phenyl)(2,3-dihydro-1,3-dioxo-1H-ind-en-2-yl)-	MeCN	231(4.63),252(4.34), 293(3.50)	39-1045-73B
Propanedinitrile, (2,3-dihydro-1,3-di-oxo-1H-inden-2-yl)[4-(dimethylamino)-phenyl]-	MeCN	229(4.58),267(4.27)	39-1045-73B
enol form	MeOH	264(4.60),410(3.34)	88-2993-73
$C_{20}H_{15}N_3O_3$			
9H-Azuleno[1,2-b]cyclohepta[e]pyrazine-13-carboxylic acid, 9-(hydroxyimino)-, ethyl ester	MeOH	229(3.41),245(4.35), 314(4.55),397(4.58), 590(2.80),630(2.79), 690s(2.56)	18-3161-73
$C_{20}H_{15}N_3O_4$			
Propanedinitrile, (4-amino-3,5-dimeth-oxyphenyl)(2,3-dihydro-1,3-dioxo-1H-inden-2-yl)-	MeCN	227(4.73),252(4.28), 302(3.86)	39-1045-73B
$C_{20}H_{15}N_3S$			
1,2,4-Triazolidine-3-thione, 1,4,5-tri-phenyl-, meso-ionic didehydro deriv.	MeCN	234(4.32),330(3.38)	103-1048-73
$C_{20}H_{15}N_5O_2$			
Benzamide, N-benzoyl-N-(9-methyl-9H-purin-6-yl)-	MeOH	249(4.42),270s(4.30)	18-3228-73
$C_{20}H_{15}O_2$			
Benzofuro[3,2-c]pyrylium, 3-methyl-1-(2-phenylethenyl)-, perchlorate	n.s.g.	255(4.14),308(4.23), 420(4.45)	103-0416-73
$C_{20}H_{16}$			
Chrysene, 1,7-dimethyl-	EtOH	226(4.24),230(4.28), 243s(3.97),254s(4.33), 262(4.58),271(3.81), 288(3.74),301(3.79), 313(3.93),328(3.93), 348(2.92),352(2.57), 366(2.76)	39-0044-73C
$C_{20}H_{16}Br_2ClNO$			
1H-Cyclopenta[b]quinolinium, 3-bromo-3-(3-chlorobenzoyl)-2,3-dihydro-4-methyl-, bromide	EtOH	247(4.48),334(4.05)	103-1253-73
$C_{20}H_{16}Br_2O_4$			
2,5-Hexanedione, 3,4-bis[(4-bromophen-yl)hydroxymethylene]-	EtOH	212(4.33),262(4.30), 315(4.11)	128-0465-73
$C_{20}H_{16}Cl_2O_4$			
9,10-Ethanoanthracene-1,5-dicarboxylic acid, 11,12-dichloro-9,10-dihydro-, dimethyl ester, cis	dioxan	211(4.60),227s(4.36), 291(3.65)	18-0915-73

Compound	Solvent	$\lambda_{max}(\log \epsilon)$	Ref.
9,10-Ethanoanthracene-1,5-dicarboxylic acid, 11,12-dichloro-9,10-dihydro-, dimethyl ester, trans	dioxan	211(4.57),228(4.38), 290(3.63)	18-0915-73
higher melting isomer	dioxan	212(4.64),230s(4.37), 287s(3.62),292(3.62)	18-0915-73
2,5-Hexanedione, 3,4-bis[(4-chlorophenyl)hydroxymethylene]-	$CHCl_3$	261(4.14),317(4.28)	128-0465-73
$C_{20}H_{16}Cl_4O_4$			
Dibenzo[a,f]cyclopropa[cd]pentalene, 1,2,3,4-tetrachloro-4b,8b,8c,8d-tetrahydro-4b,8b,8c,8d-tetramethoxy-	C_6H_{12}	216(4.86),223(4.73), 300(3.20)	88-0821-73
9,10-Ethenoanthracene, 1,2,3,4-tetrachloro-9,10-dihydro-9,10,11,12-tetramethoxy-	C_6H_{12}	227(4.40),276(3.39)	88-0821-73
$C_{20}H_{16}NO$			
Pyridinium, 1-(3-[1,1'-biphenyl]-4-yl-3-oxo-1-propenyl)-, (diphenyl phosphate)	H_2O	272(4.55),328(4.40)	24-0435-73
$C_{20}H_{16}N_2$			
1,4-Benzenediamine, N,N'-bis(phenylmethylene)-	n.s.g.	358(4.41)	65-1400-73
9,10[1',2']-Benzenoanthracene-1,5-diamine, 9,10-dihydro-, (+)-	MeOH	194(4.75),220(4.75), 240s(4.32),269(3.61), 275(3.52),295(3.56)	18-0605-73
	MeOH-HCl	213(4.81),262s(3.12), 269(3.35),277(3.46)	18-0605-73
1-Cyclohexene-1,2-dicarbonitrile, 4,5-diphenyl-	MeOH	214(4.23),232(4.11)	33-3004-73
$C_{20}H_{16}N_2O_2$			
Benz[a]anthracene-7,12-dione, 8,11-bis-(methylamino)-	benzene	638(4.18),682(4.11)	40-1328-73
2,2'-Bioxazole, 4,4'-dimethyl-5,5'-diphenyl-	toluene	339(4.52)	34-0436-73
2-Butenoic acid, 4-(9(10H)-acridinylidene)-2-cyano-, ethyl ester	EtOH	252(4.65),316(3.95), 550(4.4)	18-0283-73
2(10H)-Phenazinone, 8-hydroxy-3,7-dimethyl-10-phenyl-	n.s.g.	225(4.3),290(4.5), 390(4.0),530(4.0)	83-0481-73
2,5-Piperazinedione, 3-(phenylmethylene)-6-(3-phenyl-2-propenylidene)-	EtOH	383(4.71)	18-3876-73
2-Propenal, 3-[4-(2-hydroxy-1-naphthalenyl)azo]phenyl]-2-methyl-	EtOH	501(4.46)	7-0379-73
$C_{20}H_{16}N_2O_2S$			
3-Thiophenecarbonitrile, 5-benzoyl-2-[4-(dimethylamino)phenyl]-4-hydroxy-	CH_2Cl_2	359(4.19),434s(3.45)	48-0497-73
$C_{20}H_{16}N_2O_2S_2$			
Spiro[3H-indole-3,2'(3'H)-thiophene]-4'-carboxylic acid, 3'-imino-5'-(methylthio)-2-phenyl-, methyl ester	EtOH	231(4.48),265(4.37), 300(4.11)	94-2344-73
$C_{20}H_{16}N_2O_2S_4$			
[5,5'-Bithiazolidine]-4,4'-dione, 3,3'-bis(phenylmethyl)-2,2'-dithioxo-	EtOH	262(4.24),299(4.36)	94-0279-73

Compound	Solvent	$\lambda_{max}(\log \epsilon)$	Ref.
$C_{20}H_{16}N_2O_3S$			
Benzenesulfonamide, N-[2-(2-benzoxazol-yl)phenyl]-4-methyl-	$C_2H_4Cl_2$	290s(4.2),300(4.3), 320(4.1)	103-0435-73
1H-Pyrazino[3,2,1-kl]phenoxazine, 2,3-dihydro-3-(phenylsulfonyl)-	EtOH	222(4.49),245(4.56), 324(3.89)	95-0020-73
1H-Pyrazino[3,2,1-kl]phenoxazine, 2,3-dihydro-6-(phenylsulfonyl)-	EtOH	229(4.49),288(4.37)	95-0020-73
$C_{20}H_{16}N_2O_3S_3$			
[5,5'-Bithiazolidine]-2,4,4'-trione, 3,3'-bis(phenylmethyl)-2'-thioxo-	EtOH	260(4.00),295(4.13)	94-1132-73
$C_{20}H_{16}N_2O_4$			
3H-Pyrrolo[1,2-a]indole-2-carboxylic acid, 9-hydroxy-3-oxo-1-[(phenyl-methyl)amino]-, methyl ester	EtOH	235(4.80)	95-0964-73
$C_{20}H_{16}N_3S_2$			
Pyrimido[2,1-b]benzothiazol-5-ium, 4-methyl-2-[(3-methyl-2(3H)-benzothi-azolylidene)methyl]-, perchlorate	n.s.g.	473(5.25)	124-1151-73
$C_{20}H_{16}N_4$			
Quinoxalino[2,3-b]phenazine, 5,12-di-hydro-5,12-dimethyl-	EtOH	487(3.74),522(4.27), 562(4.69)	22-1289-73
diperchlorate	EtOH	540(3.82),580(4.17), 630(4.25)	22-1289-73
$C_{20}H_{16}N_4O_2$			
2,4(1H,3H)-Pteridinedione, 1,3-dimethyl-6,7-diphenyl-	pH 7.0	228(4.41),275(4.19), 365(4.18)	24-1401-73 +24-3149-73
$C_{20}H_{16}N_4O_3$			
2,4(1H,3H)-Pteridinedione, 1,3-dimethyl-6,7-diphenyl-, 5-oxide	MeOH	255(4.41),301s(4.00), 374(4.00)	24-3149-73
$C_{20}H_{16}N_4O_4$			
Benzophenone, 2-methyl-, 2,4-dinitro-phenylhydrazone, (E)-	$CHCl_3$	382(4.43)	40-0771-73
(Z)-	$CHCl_3$	387.5(4.46)	40-0771-73
Benzophenone, 4-methyl-, 2,4-dinitro-phenylhydrazone, (E)-	$CHCl_3$	394(4.47)	40-0771-73
(Z)-	$CHCl_3$	391(4.46)	40-0771-73
4,5-Isoxazoledione, 3-phenyl-, 4-[(5-methoxy-3-phenyl-4-isoxazolyl)meth-ylhydrazone]	EtOH	225(4.36),325s(--), 371s(--)	32-1045-73
5(2H)-Isoxazolone, 4-[(5-methoxy-3-phen-yl-4-isoxazolyl)azo]-2-methyl-3-phenyl-	EtOH	231(4.24),268(4.13), 361(4.15),420s(--)	32-1045-73
$C_{20}H_{16}N_4O_5$			
Benzophenone, 4-methoxy-, 2,4-dinitro-phenylhydrazone, (E)-	$CHCl_3$	399(4.47)	40-0771-73
(Z)-	$CHCl_3$	392(4.46)	40-0771-73
$C_{20}H_{16}O$			
Ethanone, 1,2,2-triphenyl-, lithium deriv.	DMF	288(5.64)	35-8118-73
$C_{20}H_{16}OS$			
3-Buten-2-one, 3,4-diphenyl-4-(2-thien-yl)-	EtOH	273(4.06),355(4.01)	48-0993-73

Compound	Solvent	$\lambda_{max}(\log \epsilon)$	Ref.
$C_{20}H_{16}O_2S_2$			
3-Buten-2-one, 4-(5-acetyl-2-thienyl)-3-phenyl-4-(2-thienyl)-	EtOH	257(4.14),359(4.00)	48-0993-73
$C_{20}H_{16}O_4$			
9,10-Ethenoanthracene-1,5-dicarboxylic acid, 9,10-dihydro-, dimethyl ester	MeOH	205(4.53),223(4.49), 243s(4.21),284s(3.45), 306(3.82)	18-0915-73
6H,10H-Furo[3,2-c:4,5-g']bis[1]benzopyran-3-ol, 10,10-dimethyl- (anhydrotuberosid)	EtOH	240(4.47),332(4.27), 345(4.28)	39-0907-73C
Pyrano[2",3":7,6]coumarin, 4-hydroxy-6",6"-dimethyl-3-phenyl-	MeOH	248s(4.37),367s(4.28), 335(4.24)	2-0106-73
Pyrano[2",3":7,8]coumarin, 4-hydroxy-6",6"-dimethyl-3-phenyl-	MeOH	238(4.34),284(4.15)	2-0106-73
$C_{20}H_{16}O_4S_2$			
Benzo[b]thiophen-3(2H)-one, 6-ethoxy-2-(6-ethoxy-3-oxobenzo[b]thien-2(3H)-ylidene)-, cis	benzene	460(4.08)	46-0831-73
trans	benzene	516(4.17)	46-0831-73
$C_{20}H_{16}O_5$			
2H,6H-Benzo[1,2-b:5,4-b']dipyran-6-one, 5,7-dihydroxy-2,2-dimethyl-8-phenyl-	MeOH	268(3.91),341(4.32)	78-3347-73
$C_{20}H_{16}O_6$			
Elliptone	MeOH	238(4.63),275(3.95)	78-2731-73
Parvisoflavones A and B	EtOH	268(4.67),306(3.80)	102-1188-73
$C_{20}H_{16}O_7$			
17,18-Dioxatricyclo[12.2.1.$1^{4,7}$]octadeca-1(16),2,4,6,8,11,14-heptaene-9,11-dicarboxylic acid, 10-oxo-, dimethyl ester, (E,Z,Z)-	MeOH	221(4.17),260(4.41), 270(4.39),390(4.47), 448(3.99)	88-5065-73
$C_{20}H_{16}O_9$			
9H-Xanthene-4-carboxylic acid, 8-acetoxy-1,5-dimethoxy-9-oxo-, anhydride with acetic acid	MeOH	207(4.38),246(4.58), 273s(4.11),310(3.93), 354(3.81)	24-1182-73
$C_{20}H_{16}S$			
Methanethione, phenyl[2-(phenylmethyl)-phenyl]-	EtOH	322(4.16),603(2.03)	143-0427-73
$C_{20}H_{16}Se$			
9H-Selenoxanthene, 9-methyl-9-phenyl-	EtOH	218s(4.15),257(3.58), 280(3.59)	138-0391-73
$C_{20}H_{17}BrNO$			
1H-Cyclopenta[b]quinolinium, 3-benzoyl-3-bromo-2,3-dihydro-4-methyl-, bromide	EtOH	249(4.49),355(4.06)	103-1253-73
tribromide	EtOH	250(4.44),334(4.00)	103-1253-73
$C_{20}H_{17}ClN_2O$			
11H-Pyrrolo[2,1-c][1,4]benzodiazepin-11-one, 7-chloro-5,10-dihydro-3,10-dimethyl-5-phenyl-	isoPrOH	244(4.25),265s(4.02), 288(4.11)	44-3502-73

Compound	Solvent	λ_{max}(log ε)	Ref.
$C_{20}H_{17}ClN_2O_2$			
11H-Pyrrolo[2,1-c][1,4]benzodiazepin-11-one, 7-chloro-5,10-dihydro-10-(methoxymethyl)-5-phenyl-	isoPrOH	240(4.25),279(4.07)	44-3502-73
$C_{20}H_{17}ClO_8$			
Benzofuro[3,2-c]pyrylium, 1-(3,4-dimethoxyphenyl)-3-methyl-, perchlorate	n.s.g.	250(3.63),267(3.66), 310(3.47),425(3.60)	103-0416-73
$C_{20}H_{17}F_3N_6O_5$			
Adenine, 9-(2-O-acetyl-3-deoxy-3-trifluoroacetamido-β-L-erythro-furanosyl)-6-benzamido-	EtOH	261s(--),281(4.20)	33-2689-73
$C_{20}H_{17}IN_2$			
Benz[cd]indolium, 1-methyl-2-[2-(phenylamino)ethenyl]-, iodide	EtOH	511(4.30)	103-0314-73
$C_{20}H_{17}N$			
Benzenemethanamine, α-phenyl-N-(phenylmethylene)-	EtOH	252(4.33)	2-0499-73
$C_{20}H_{17}NO_2$			
3-Buten-2-one, 4-(1-acetyl-2-phenyl-3-indolizinyl)-	EtOH	234(4.32),272(3.98), 315(3.98),371(4.06), 413s(3.93)	39-2091-73C
$C_{20}H_{17}NO_2S$			
Benzenesulfonamide, 4-(2,2-diphenylethenyl)-	EtOH	230(4.09)	104-1511-73
$C_{20}H_{17}NO_4$			
Benzo[c]phenanthridine, 5,6-dihydro-8,9-dimethoxy-2,3-(methylenedioxy)-	$CHCl_3$	242(4.28),270(4.52), 277(4.60),326(4.34)	4-0085-73
4H-[1]Benzopyrano[3,4-d]oxazol-4-one, 6-ethyl-2-(4-methoxyphenyl)-8-methyl-	MeOH	212(4.45),310(4.46), 330(4.48)	2-0433-73
Dictamnine, 8-methoxy-7-(phenylmethoxy)-	EtOH	243s(4.73),251(4.93), 320(4.31),332(4.29)	2-1088-73
$C_{20}H_{17}NO_5$			
Benzamide, N-[6-(1,3-benzodioxol-5-yl)-2-hydroxy-4-oxo-2-cyclohexen-1-yl]-	MeOH-HCl	246(4.37)	88-4587-73
	MeOH-NaOH	283(4.51)	88-4587-73
7H-Dibenzo[de,g]quinolin-7-one, 1,2,3,4-tetramethoxy- (imenine)	EtOH	240(4.30),275(4.38), 335(3.71),345(3.71), 434(4.03)	44-0060-73
	EtOH-HCl	244(4.07),290(4.11), 360(3.77),484(3.67)	44-0060-73
Fagaridine	EtOH	228(4.55),284(4.65), 322s(4.14)	102-2315-73
Oxyberberine	$CHCl_3$	287(4.5),315(4.1), 369(3.9)	102-1822-73
9H-Pyrano[2,3-g]-1,2-benzisoxazol-9-one, 7-(3,4-dimethoxyphenyl)-3,8-dimethyl-	n.s.g.	221(4.5),252(4.7), 313(3.7)	2-0541-73
$C_{20}H_{17}NO_6$			
9H-Pyrano[2,3-g]-1,2-benzisoxazol-9-one, 3-methyl-7-(3,4,5-trimethoxyphenyl)-	n.s.g.	222(4.4),262(4.6), 315(4.3)	2-0541-73
$C_{20}H_{17}N_3O$			
Angustine, dihydro-	MeOH	221(4.44),252(4.15), 290(3.90),300(3.81),	88-4837-73

Compound	Solvent	$\lambda_{max}(\log \epsilon)$	Ref.
Angustine, dihydro- (cont.)	MeOH	375(4.46),395(4.48)	88-4837-73
	MeOH-acid	220(4.53),248(4.16), 260(4.19),289s(3.96), 299s(3.91),326(4.01), 439(4.68)	88-4837-73
	EtOH	221(4.44),252(4.15), 290(3.90),300(3.81), 375(4.46),395(4.48)	39-0013-73C
Ethanone, 1-(5,6-dihydro-8-phenyl-4H,8H-pyrazolo[4',3':4,5]pyrrolo[3,2,1-ij]-quinolin-10-yl)-	EtOH	264(4.19),319(3.99)	78-3159-73
$C_{20}H_{17}N_3OS$			
3-Thiophenecarbonitrile, 4-amino-5-benz-oyl-2-[4-(dimethylamino)phenyl]-	CH_2Cl_2	384(4.06)	48-0497-73
$C_{20}H_{17}N_3O_2$			
Angustoline	EtOH	221(4.49),251(4.37), 289(4.13),308(3.94), 375(4.59),395(4.60)	39-0013-73C
$C_{20}H_{17}N_3O_4$			
2-Butenedioic acid, 2-(8-methylindazolo-[1,2-a][1,2,3]benzotriazol-6-N^V-7-yl)-, dimethyl ester	EtOH	241(4.48),260(4.14), 350(4.04),365(4.25), 382(4.44),500(3.63)	88-0597-73
Glycine, N-(N-benzoyl-α,β-didehydro-tryptophyl)-	67% MeOH	274(4.0),336(4.25)	105-0273-73
2H-Indol-2-one, 3-[1-(2,3-dihydro-1-methyl-2-oxo-1H-indol-3-yl)-2-nitro-ethylidene]-1,3-dihydro-1-methyl-	EtOH	259(4.43),300(4.03)	95-0612-73
10bH-2a,6b,10c-Triazabenzo[2,3]penta-leno[1,6-ab]indene-1,2-dicarboxylic acid, 10-methyl-, dimethyl ester	EtOH	237(4.34),269(4.29), 300(3.86),395(3.58)	88-0597-73
10bH-2a,6b,10c-Triazabenzo[2,3]penta-leno[1,6-ab]indene-1,2-dicarboxylic acid, 10b-methyl-, dimethyl ester	EtOH	240(3.80),299(3.50), 365(3.47)	88-0597-73
$C_{20}H_{17}N_3O_6$			
1H-Pyrazole-4,5-dicarboxylic acid, 3-(4-methylphenyl)-1-(4-nitrophenyl)-, dimethyl ester	EtOH	243(4.02),312(3.81)	94-2026-73
$C_{20}H_{17}N_3O_7$			
1H-Pyrazole-4,5-dicarboxylic acid, 3-(4-methoxyphenyl)-1-(4-nitrophenyl)-, dimethyl ester	EtOH	258(4.05),323(3.70)	94-2026-73
$C_{20}H_{17}N_3O_8$			
Acetic acid, 2-(6-azulenyl)ethyl ester, trinitrobenzene complex	CH_2Cl_2	279(4.79),285(4.79), 329(3.59),336(3.56), 344(3.74),569(2.50), 588(2.47),612(2.42), 676(1.99)	44-1106-73
$C_{20}H_{17}N_5$			
1H-Imidazo[1',2':2,3][1,2,4]triazino-[5,6-b]indole, 2-phenyl-3-propyl-	EtOH	275(4.27),375(4.02)	103-1082-73

Compound	Solvent	$\lambda_{max}(\log \epsilon)$	Ref.
$C_{20}H_{17}N_5O_2$			
3H-Pyrazol-3-one, 4-[(1,5-dihydro-3-methyl-5-oxo-1-phenyl-4H-pyrazol-4-ylidene)amino]-2,4-dihydro-5-methyl-2-phenyl-	DMF	350(4.3),540(4.2)	104-1291-73
	DMSO	350(4.3),550(4.2)	104-1291-73
$C_{20}H_{17}N_5O_3$			
Carbamic acid, [7,8-dihydro-8-oxo-3-(phenylmethyl)-3H-purin-6-yl]-, phenylmethyl ester	pH 1	230(4.49),308(4.29)	94-1954-73
	pH 7	242(4.32),310(4.23)	94-1954-73
	pH 13	252(4.30),327(4.39)	94-1954-73
	EtOH	245(4.32),315(4.23)	94-1954-73
$C_{20}H_{17}O$			
Benzofuro[3,2-c]pyrylium, 1-(3,4-dimethoxyphenyl)-3-methyl-, perchlorate	n.s.g.	250(3.63),267(3.66),	103-0416-73
$C_{20}H_{17}PS$			
Phosphine sulfide, diphenyl(2-phenylethenyl)-	nonane	193(4.82),263(4.41), 295(3.78)	65-2164-73
$C_{20}H_{18}$			
Benzene, 1,1'-(1,3,5,7-octatetraene-1,8-diyl)bis-	81.5% H_2SO_4	370(3.72),400(3.69), 460(3.57),555(3.69)	48-0810-73
	95.8% H_2SO_4	473(4.28),545(4.49)	48-0810-73
	99.9% H_2SO_4	355(3.48),536(4.49), 635(3.51)	48-0810-73
	18% SO_3	385(4.02),475(4.38), 515(4.23),595(4.34), 645(4.54)	48-0810-73
	33% SO_3	388(4.37),465(4.03), 595(3.86),650(3.96)	48-0810-73
Pentalene, 1,3a,4,6a-tetrahydro-2,5-diphenyl-	MeCN	253(4.48),258(4.51), 267s(4.42),283s(3.64), 292(3.23)	5-0844-73
Pentalene, 1,3a,6,6a-tetrahydro-2,5-diphenyl-	MeCN	248s(4.26),253s(4.32), 260s(4.38),269(4.45), 276s(4.41),285s(4.16), 292(3.77)	5-0844-73
Tetracyclo[3.3.0.0^{3,4}.0^{3,7}]octane, 1,5-diphenyl-	MeCN	269(2.78)(end abs.)	5-0844-73
$C_{20}H_{18}BrIN_2O$			
1H-Cyclopenta[b]quinolinium, 3-bromo-2,3-dihydro-4-methyl-3-[(phenylamino)carbonyl]-, iodide	EtOH	244(4.56),329(3.92)	103-1253-73
$C_{20}H_{18}BrNO_4$			
1H-Indole-3-carboxylic acid, 5-acetoxy-6-bromo-2-methyl-1-phenyl-, ethyl ester	EtOH	224(4.59),234(4.60), 290(4.20),297(4.15)	103-0306-73
1H-Indole-3-carboxylic acid, 5-(benzoyloxy)-5-bromo-1,2-dimethyl-, ethyl ester	EtOH	222(4.65),292(3.94)	103-0306-73
$C_{20}H_{18}Br_2N_2$			
3-Buten-2-one, 4-(4-bromophenyl)-, [3-(4-bromophenyl)-1-methyl-2-propenylidene]hydrazone	$CHCl_3$	335(4.71),345(4.70)	22-3303-73
2-Propenal, 3-(4-bromophenyl)-2-methyl-, [3-(4-bromophenyl)-2-methyl-2-propenylidene]hydrazone	$CHCl_3$	341(4.80)	22-3303-73

Compound	Solvent	$\lambda_{max}(\log \epsilon)$	Ref.
$C_{20}H_{18}Br_2N_2O$			
1H-Cyclopenta[b]quinolinium, 3-bromo-2,3-dihydro-4-methyl-3-[(phenylamino)carbonyl]-, bromide	EtOH	248(4.55),334(4.05)	103-1253-73
$C_{20}H_{18}ClN_3O_2$			
Morpholine, 4-[3-[(4-chlorophenyl)azo]-5-phenyl-2-furanyl]-	CH_2Cl_2	254(4.26),331(4.16), 470(4.49)	39-2523-73C
tetrafluoroborate	CH_2Cl_2	267(4.27),276(4.26), 294(4.25),483(4.59)	39-2523-73C
$C_{20}H_{18}Cl_2N_2O$			
Compound 10b, m. 156°	EtOH	275(4.62),350(2.71)	18-2504-73
$C_{20}H_{18}Cl_2N_2O_3$			
2H-Isoindole-1-carboxamide, 5-chloro-3-(2-chlorophenyl)-N-methyl-2-(2-acetoxyethyl)-	EtOH	226(4.47),264(4.41), 295(3.64),350(4.12), 360(4.10)	94-1404-73
$C_{20}H_{18}FeN_2$			
Ferrocene, 1,1'-(2,3-dihydro-2-methyl-1H-1,5-benzodiazepine-2,4-diyl)-	EtOH	237(4.42),296(3.62), 344(3.70),443(2.82)	18-3315-73
$C_{20}H_{18}N_2$			
Cinnoline, 1,2,3,4-tetrahydro-1,4-diphenyl-	MeCN	291(4.18)	22-3487-73
$C_{20}H_{18}N_2O$			
4H-Benzo[a]quinolizin-4-one, 1,11b-dihydro-2-[(phenylmethyl)amino]-	EtOH	238(4.14),275(4.53), 340(4.19)	70-1745-73
1H-Cyclopenta[b]quinoline-9-carboxamide, 2,3-dihydro-N-(4-methylphenyl)-	EtOH	238(4.76),282(4.15), 308(4.12),322(4.09)	103-1005-73
1H-Cyclopenta[b]quinoline-9-carboxamide, 2,3-dihydro-N-(phenylmethyl)-	EtOH	238(4.63),295(3.91), 308(3.97),322(4.01)	103-1005-73
4H-Indazol-4-one, 1,5,6,7-tetrahydro-3-phenyl-1-(phenylmethyl)-	MeOH	229(4.44),257(4.03)	24-0450-73
$C_{20}H_{18}N_2O_2$			
Benzamide, N-[(1-benzoyl-4-methyl-1H-pyrrol-2-yl)methyl]-	EtOH	230(4.41)	70-2036-73
Diazene, bis[2-(4-ethenylphenyl)ethenyl]-, 1,2-dioxide	benzene	362(4.9)	48-0796-73
1H-Pyrazole-3-carboxylic acid, 5-(1,2-diphenylethenyl)-	C_6H_{12} or EtOH	215(4.36),230(4.36), 289(4.41)	4-0015-73
3-Pyridinecarboxamide, 1,2-dihydro-2-oxo-N,1-bis(phenylmethyl)-	EtOH	238(3.81),333(3.98)	70-1959-73
$C_{20}H_{18}N_2O_2S$			
Benzenesulfonic acid, 4-methyl-, (2-phenyl-2,4,6-cycloheptatrien-1-ylidene)hydrazide	EtOH	223(4.35),314(3.95)	35-0826-73
3-Pyridinecarboxylic acid, 2-amino-1,6-dihydro-1,4-diphenyl-6-thioxo-, ethyl ester	MeOH	270(4.06),300(3.99), 397(4.38)	48-0679-73
$C_{20}H_{18}N_2O_3$			
Acetamide, N-acetyl-N-(1-acetyl-3-phenyl-1H-indol-2-yl)-	MeOH	231(4.49),243(4.47), 296(4.03)	103-0471-73
2,5-Piperazinedione, 1-acetyl-6-(phenylmethyl)-3-(phenylmethylene)-, (Z)-	EtOH	230(4.17),320(4.20)	39-0404-73C

Compound	Solvent	$\lambda_{max}(\log \epsilon)$	Ref.
3-Pyrazoleearboxylic acid, 5-benzoyl-1-(4-methylphenyl)-	C_6H_{12} or EtOH	214(4.21),255(4.05)	4-0015-73
$C_{20}H_{18}N_2O_4$			
Corydamine, hydrochloride	MeOH	245(4.51),312(4.18), 380(3.59)	94-1410-73
$C_{20}H_{18}N_2O_5S$			
Benzenamine, N,N-dimethyl-4-[2-(5-nitro-2-furanyl)-2-(phenylsulfonyl)ethenyl]-	EtOH	208(4.35),249s(4.10), 303(4.17),376(4.33)	73-1705-73
$C_{20}H_{18}N_2O_6S$			
1,2-Benzothiazine-3-carboxamide, N-acetyl-4-(acetyloxy)-2-methyl-N-phenyl-, 1,1-dioxide	EtOH	317(3.99)	87-0044-73
$C_{20}H_{18}N_2S_2$			
2,5-Cyclohexadiene-1,4-dione, 2,6-dimethyl-, bis(S-phenylthiooxime)	$CHCl_3$	280(4.12),468(4.68)	39-1031-73C
3,5-Cyclohexadiene-1,2-dione, 4,6-dimethyl-, bis(S-phenylthiooxime)	$CHCl_3$	430(3.99),500(4.12)	39-1031-73C
$C_{20}H_{18}N_2S_3$			
Compd., m. 248°	$CHCl_3$	248(4.22),319(4.06), 525(4.18)	25-1162-73
$C_{20}H_{18}N_3S$			
Pyrimido[2,1-b]benzothiazol-5-ium, 4-[2-[4-(dimethylamino)phenyl]ethenyl]-, perchlorate	n.s.g.	565(4.97)	124-1151-73
$C_{20}H_{18}N_4O$			
1H-1,2,4-Triazolo[4,3-b]pyridazin-4-ium, 8-hydroxy-6-methyl-1,7-bis(phenylmethyl)-, hydroxide, inner salt	n.s.g.	225(3.71),285(3.88), 317(4.04)	48-0097-73
$C_{20}H_{18}N_4OS$			
1H-Thieno[2,3-c]pyrazol-4(5H)-one, 5-[[4-(dimethylamino)phenyl]imino]-3-methyl-1-phenyl-	EtOH	245(4.42),475(4.31)	104-2429-73
$C_{20}H_{18}N_4O_2$			
2-Propenal, 3-[4-(4,5-dihydro-3-methyl-5-oxo-1H-pyrazol-4-yl)azo]phenyl]-2-methyl-	EtOH	415(4.58)	7-0379-73
$C_{20}H_{18}N_4O_4$			
Morpholine, 4-[3-[(4-nitrophenyl)azo]-5-phenyl-2-furanyl]-	CH_2Cl_2	284(4.16),328(4.21), 526(4.53)	39-2523-73C
tetrafluoroborate	CH_2Cl_2	286(4.26),478(4.57), 502(4.58),570s(3.80)	39-2523-73C
1,4-Phthalazinedione, 2-[2-[(3,4-dihydro-3-methyl-4-oxo-1-phthalazinyl)oxy]ethyl]-2,3-dihydro-3-methyl-	MeOH	262(3.76),299(3.97)	1-1891-73
1(2H)-Phthalazinone, 4,4'-[1,2-ethanediylbis(oxy)]bis[2-methyl-	$CHCl_3$	254(3.87),264(3.90), 302(4.11)	1-1891-73
$C_{20}H_{18}N_5O_{12}P$			
Adenosine, N^6,$O^{2'}$-bis(ethyl-2-diazomalonyl)-, 3',5'-cyclic phosphate	pH 4.1	255(4.33),281(4.51)	69-4074-73
	pH 9.1	255(4.42),268(4.40)	69-4074-73

Compound	Solvent	$\lambda_{max}(\log \epsilon)$	Ref.
$C_{20}H_{18}N_6$			
Quinoxalino[2,3-b]phenazine-2,9-diamine, 7,14-dihydro-7,14-dimethyl-, compd. with BF_3 (1:2)	H_2O	540(3.76)	22-1289-73
	2% HCl	445(3.83),470(3.83), 670(4.00)	22-1289-73
$C_{20}H_{18}N_8O_{12}$			
(4-Pyridyl)viologen nitrate, dinitric acid salt	H_2O	286(3.39)	44-3993-73
$C_{20}H_{18}O$			
Benzenemethanol, 4-methyl-α,α-diphenyl-	99% H_2SO_4	450(4.66)	39-0095-73B
Cyclohexanone, 2,6-bis(phenylmethylene)-	EtOH	330(4.60)	23-1458-73
7,12-Ethanobenz[a]anthracen-1(2H)-one, 3,4,7,12-tetrahydro-	EtOH	253(3.82),310(3.25)	49-0274-73
7,12-Ethanobenz[a]anthracen-4(1H)-one, 2,3,7,12-tetrahydro-	EtOH	266(4.08),272(4.10), 305s(3.16)	49-0274-73
5,12-Ethanonaphthacen-7(8H)-one, 5,9,10,12-tetrahydro-	EtOH	264(4.12),270s(4.08), 300(3.51)	49-0274-73
$C_{20}H_{18}O_2$			
1-Acenaphthyleneacetic acid, 2a,3,4,5-tetrahydro-2-phenyl-	EtOH	221(4.13),230(4.10), 237(4.10),302(4.32)	39-1983-73C
$C_{20}H_{18}O_3$			
9,10-Ethano-2-anthracenebutanoic acid, γ-oxo-9,10-dihydro-	EtOH	259(4.10),295s(3.21)	49-0274-73
Isolonchocarpin, (-)-	EtOH	268(4.59),310(3.84)	2-0209-73
Lonchocarpin	MeOH	230(4.33),295s(4.35), 302(4.36),350(4.43)	32-0779-73
2-Propen-1-one, 1-(7-hydroxy-2,2-dimethyl-2H-1-benzopyran-6-yl)-3-phenyl-	MeOH	223(4.39),234s(4.35), 280(4.33),308(4.39), 320s(4.38),385(4.10)	32-0779-73
$C_{20}H_{18}O_4$			
2H-1-Benzopyran-2-one, 4,7-dihydroxy-6-(3-methyl-2-butenyl)-3-phenyl-	MeOH	251s(3.78),317(4.20)	2-0106-73
2H-1-Benzopyran-2-one, 4,7-dihydroxy-8-(3-methyl-2-butenyl)-3-phenyl-	MeOH	247(3.88),312(4.10)	2-0106-73
Cyclobuta[1]phenanthrene-1,2-dicarboxylic acid, 1,2,2a,10b-tetrahydro-, dimethyl ester	EtOH	242(4.01),273(4.18), 279(4.19),310(3.39)	39-0138-73C
9,10-Ethanoanthracene-1,5-dicarboxylic acid, 9,10-dihydro-, dimethyl ester	MeOH	202(4.67),230(4.32), 291(3.72)	18-0915-73
3,5-Hexadienoic acid, 3-(methoxycarbonyl)-4,6-diphenyl-	EtOH	240(4.15),315(4.27)	42-0430-73
2,5-Hexanedione, 3,4-bis(hydroxyphenylmethylene)-	$CHCl_3$	262(4.06),324(4.09)	128-0465-73
2,5-Hexanedione, 3,4-dibenzoyl-	$CHCl_3$	254.5(4.432)	128-0465-73
2-Propenoic acid, 2-methyl-, [1,1'-biphenyl]-4,4'-diyl ester	dioxan	262.5(4.32)	126-0025-73B
$C_{20}H_{18}O_5$			
2H,6H-Benzo[1,2-b:5,4-b']dipyran-6-one, 3,4-dihydro-5,7-dihydroxy-2,2-dimethyl-8-phenyl-	MeOH	272(4.28),358(4.46)	78-3347-73
4H-1-Benzopyran-4-one, 3,5,7-trihydroxy-6-(3-methyl-2-butenyl)-2-phenyl-	MeOH	212(4.28),358(3.30)	78-3347-73
2(5H)-Furanone, 4-methoxy-3-(4-methoxyphenyl)-5-[(4-methoxyphenyl)methylene]-	MeOH	237(4.26),353(4.52)	102-2527-73

Compound	Solvent	λ_{max}(log ε)	Ref.
1,6-Heptadiene-3,5-dione, 1-(4-hydroxy-3-methoxyphenyl)-7-(4-hydroxyphenyl)-	EtOH	251(4.13),423(4.71)	39-2379-73C
[1,1':4',1"-Terphenyl]-2,4,4"-triol, 2',5'-dimethoxy-	EtOH	225s(4.06),275(4.06)	77-0555-73
Tuberosin	EtOH	223(4.81),280(3.80), 286(3.82),310(3.78), 317(3.74),323(3.72)	39-0907-73C
$C_{20}H_{18}O_6$			
1,2,4-Cyclopentanetrione, 3-(3,4-dimethoxyphenyl)-5-(4-methoxyphenyl)-	EtOH	223s(4.04),269(3.78), 366(3.81)	39-1921-73C
2,5-Phenanthrenediol, 6,7-dimethoxy-, diacetate	$CHCl_3$	260(4.83),280(4.22), 288(4.10),301(3.91), 322(2.76),337(2.80), 354(2.80)	102-0228-73
Pyrano[3,2-a]xanthen-12(3H)-one, 11-hydroxy-5,9-dimethoxy-3,3-dimethyl-	MeOH	210(4.41),243(4.57), 264(4.47),321(4.44), 378(3.89)	39-1329-73C
Tachrosinol, 5,7-O,O-bisdemethyl-	MeOH	212(4.56),248s(4.17), 273(4.56),315(4.04)	119-0064-73
$C_{20}H_{18}O_7$			
Naphtho[2,3-c]furan-1(3H)-one, 9-(3,4-dihydroxy-5-methoxyphenyl)-4,9-dihydro-7-hydroxy-6-methoxy-	EtOH	283.5(3.75)	23-0482-73
Phenanthro[2,3-d][1,3]dioxole-6-carboxylic acid, 2,3,11-trimethoxy-, methyl ester	EtOH	200s(4.30),224(4.20), 263(4.58),282(4.40), 345(3.82)	12-2035-73
Phenanthro[3,4-d]-1,3-dioxole-6-carboxylic acid, 4,9,10-trimethoxy-, methyl ester	EtOH	204s(4.31),224(4.17), 266(4.70),284s(4.48), 329(3.97)	12-2035-73
$C_{20}H_{18}O_8$			
Chromocyclin, 2-deacetyl-	EtOH	231(4.40),276(4.68), 326(3.89),340(3.90), 418(4.01)	105-0492-73
Irisflorentin	EtOH	266(4.46),321(3.82)	94-0600-73
$C_{20}H_{18}O_9$			
Cryptosporin triacetate	MeOH	248(4.37),279(4.05), 342(3.46)	33-0619-73
$C_{20}H_{18}O_{10}$			
Benzoic acid, 3,6-diacetoxy-2-(2-carboxy-5-methoxyphenoxy)-, 1-methyl ester	MeOH	208(4.52),253(4.09), 282(3.75)	24-1182-73
$C_{20}H_{19}ClN_2$			
9-Acridinamine, 6-chloro-1,2,3,4-tetrahydro-N-(2-methylphenyl)-	n.s.g.	234(4.87),352(4.38)	103-0488-73
9-Acridinamine, 6-chloro-1,2,3,4-tetrahydro-N-(3-methylphenyl)-	n.s.g.	234(4.95),256(4.59), 328(4.15),346(4.18)	103-0488-73
9-Acridinamine, 6-chloro-1,2,3,4-tetrahydro-N-(4-methylphenyl)-	n.s.g.	234(4.6),258(4.3), 328(3.73),352(3.86)	103-0488-73
$C_{20}H_{19}ClN_2O$			
9-Acridinamine, 6-chloro-1,2,3,4-tetrahydro-N-(4-methoxyphenyl)-	n.s.g.	232(4.9),258(4.5), 328(4.1),355(4.14)	103-0488-73

Compound	Solvent	$\lambda_{max}(\log \epsilon)$	Ref.
$C_{20}H_{19}ClN_2O_2$			
Oxazolo[3,2-d][1,4]benzodiazepin-6(5H)-one, 10-chloro-2,3,7,11b-tetrahydro-2,7-dimethyl-5-methylene-11b-phenyl-	EtOH	247(4.28)	94-0742-73
Oxazolo[3,2-d][1,4]benzodiazepin-6(5H)-one, 10-chloro-2,3,7,11b-tetrahydro-3,7-dimethyl-5-methylene-11b-phenyl-	EtOH	243(4.26)	94-0742-73
$C_{20}H_{19}ClN_2O_4$			
Alkaloid TN-23	MeOH	245(4.21),312(4.14), 380(3.24)	95-0087-73
$C_{20}H_{19}ClN_2O_7$			
2-Naphthacenecarboxamide, 4-amino-7-chloro-1,4,4a,5,5a,6,11,12a-octahydro-3,10,12,12a-tetrahydroxy-N-methyl-1,11-dioxo-	MeOH-borate	225(4.25),245s(4.21), 266(4.21),375(4.05)	88-4907-73
$C_{20}H_{19}ClO_4Se$			
Seleninium, 4-methyl-2,6-bis(4-methylphenyl)-, perchlorate	$MeCN-HClO_4$	434(4.47)	103-0790-73
$C_{20}H_{19}ClO_6Se$			
Seleninium, 2,6-bis(4-methoxyphenyl)-4-methyl-, perchlorate	$MeCN-HClO_4$	482(4.48)	103-0790-73
$C_{20}H_{19}N$			
[1]Benzazepino[3,2,1-jk]carbazole, 1,2,3,4,8,9-hexahydro-	n.s.g.	210(4.43),265(4.14), 311(4.16)	39-1041-73C
$C_{20}H_{19}NO$			
4H-Carbazol-4-one, 1,2,3,9-tetrahydro-2,2-dimethyl-9-phenyl-	MeOH	208(4.54),243(4.36), 265(4.00),301(4.20)	24-0745-73
2-Cyclohexen-1-one, 3-(9H-carbazol-9-yl)-5,5-dimethyl-	MeOH	232(4.68),283(4.08), 336(4.10)	24-0745-73
$C_{20}H_{19}NO_2$			
2-Butanone, 4-(1-acetyl-2-phenyl-3-indolizinyl)-	EtOH	236(4.39),327s(3.80), 361(4.07),381(3.97)	39-2091-73C
$C_{20}H_{19}NO_2S$			
Sulfoxonium, dimethyl-, 1-(4-methyl-2-quinolinyl)-2-oxo-2-phenylethylide	EtOH	278(4.19),345(4.01)	95-1064-73
$C_{20}H_{19}NO_3$			
Benzenebutanoic acid, α-cyano-4-methyl-γ-oxo-β-phenyl-, ethyl ester	C_6H_{12}	256(4.28)	104-1834-73
3-Furancarboxylic acid, 2-amino-5-(4-methylphenyl)-4-phenyl-, ethyl ester	C_6H_{12}	309(4.27)	104-1834-73
Pyridinium, 2-methyl-, 3-acetyl-1-benzoyl-4-oxo-2-pentenylide	EtOH	260(4.25),375(4.48)	39-2091-73C
Pyridinium, 4-methyl-, 3-acetyl-1-benzoyl-4-oxo-2-pentenylide	EtOH	246(4.23),282(4.09) 376(4.56)	39-2091-73C
$C_{20}H_{19}NO_4$			
Benzenebutanoic acid, α-cyano-4-methoxy-γ-oxo-β-phenyl-, ethyl ester	C_6H_{12}	279(4.28)	104-1834-73
3H,6H-[1,3]Benzodioxolo[4',5',6':4,5]-[2]benzopyrano[1,8,7-hij]isoquinoline, 4,5,5a,11-tetrahydro-1-methoxy-5-methyl-, (±)-	EtOH	221(4.49),233s(4.34), 278s(3.86),286(3.98), 312(4.07),323s(4.05)	142-0031-73

Compound	Solvent	$\lambda_{max}(\log \epsilon)$	Ref.
[1,3]Benzodioxolo[5,6-c]phenanthridine, 4b,5,6,11b-tetrahydro-2,3-dimethoxy-	EtOH	233(4.52),285(4.07)	4-0085-73
Benzo[c][1,3]dioxolo[4,5-j]phenanthridine, 4b,11b,12,13-tetrahydro-2,3-dimethoxy-	EtOH	232(4.61),280(4.02), 316(3.72)	4-0867-73
2H-1-Benzopyran-2-one, 8-ethyl-4-hydroxy-3-[[(4-methoxyphenyl)methylene]-amino]-6-methyl-	MeOH	218(4.44),255(4.19), 270(4.31)	2-0433-73
3-Furancarboxylic acid, 2-amino-5-(4-methoxyphenyl)-4-phenyl-, ethyl ester	C_6H_{12}	306(4.30)	104-1834-73
Indeno[1,2-j]isoquinoline, 2,3,10,11-tetramethoxy-	EtOH	246(4.17),265s(4.00), 308s(3.33),335s(3.28), 359(3.38)	44-2394-73
7H-Pyrano[2,3-c]acridin-7-one, 3,12-dihydro-6-hydroxy-11-methoxy-3,3,12-trimethyl-	EtOH	240(4.13),272s(4.38), 280s(4.40),296(4.46), 320s(3.96),346(3.88), 428(3.46)	39-1173-73C
2H-Pyrrole-3,4-dicarboxylic acid, 3,4-dihydro-2,5-diphenyl-, dimethyl ester, cis-cis	EtOH	254(4.28)	35-1945-73
trans-cis	EtOH	249(4.25)	35-1945-73
$C_{20}H_{19}NO_5$			
Alkaloid TN-21	MeOH	249(4.15),295(3.76), 370(4.13)	95-0087-73
Protopine	MeOH	291(3.94)	95-0087-73
$C_{20}H_{19}NO_5S$			
Benz[a]acridine, 5-methoxy-, methyl sulfate	EtOH	228(4.56),242(4.55), 255(4.46),289(4.56), 300s(4.55),406(4.27), 426(4.24)	12-2315-73
$C_{20}H_{19}NO_6$			
6,9-Methanobenzo[g]quinoline-5a,9a-dicarboxylic acid, 5,6,9,10-tetrahydro-5,10-dioxo-, diethyl ester	EtOH	216(4.22),243(3.74), 275s(--)	39-0026-73C
$C_{20}H_{19}NO_7$			
1,3-Propanedione, 1-(6-hydroxy-3-methyl-1,2-benzisoxazol-7-yl)-3-(3,4,5-trimethoxyphenyl)-	n.s.g.	237(4.6),275(4.6), 370(4.6)	2-0541-73
$C_{20}H_{19}NO_9$			
1,3-Benzodioxole-5-acetic acid, α-[4,5-dimethoxy-2-nitrophenyl)methylene]-	EtOH	211(4.98),249(4.19), 268(4.17)	12-2035-73
$C_{20}H_{19}N_3O$			
Ethanone, 1-(5,6,7a,10a-tetrahydro-8-phenyl-4H,8H-pyrazolo[4',5':4,5]pyrrolo[3,2,1-ij]quinolin-10-yl)-	EtOH	245(4.24),301s(3.75), 352(4.13)	78-3159-73
2-Naphthalenol, 1-[[2-(1-pyrrolidinyl)-phenyl]azo]-	$CHCl_3$	525(4.18)	48-0725-73
1,2-Propanedione, 1-(5,6-dihydro-4H-pyrrolo[3,2,1-ij]quinolin-1-yl)-, 1-(phenylhydrazone)	EtOH	293(4.00),365(4.20)	78-3159-73
$C_{20}H_{19}N_3O_2$			
Acetamide, N-[5-(4-methoxyphenyl)-3-(phenylmethyl)pyrazinyl]-	DMF	294(4.19),330(4.17)	77-0492-73

Compound	Solvent	λ_{max}(log ε)	Ref.
1-Azulenecarboxylic acid, 2-amino-3-[(4-methylphenyl)azo]-, ethyl ester	MeOH	254(4.23),295s(4.42), 328(4.51),345s(4.35), 385(4.54),510(4.04)	18-3266-73
Morpholine, 4-[(1,5-diphenyl-1H-pyrazol-3-yl)carbonyl]-	CH_2Cl_2	248(4.15)	39-2532-73C
Morpholine, 4-[5-phenyl-3-(phenylazo)-2-furanyl]-	CH_2Cl_2	247(4.35),333(4.25), 463(4.53)	39-2523-73C
tetrafluoroborate	CH_2Cl_2	263(4.22),270(4.22), 294(4.26),480(4.52), 500s(4.46)	39-2523-73C
$C_{20}H_{19}N_3O_2S$			
4-Imidazolidinone, 5-ethoxy-5-(1H-indol-3-ylmethyl)-3-phenyl-2-thioxo-	EtOH	215(4.60),271(4.29), 476(2.26)	63-1307-73
3-Pyridinecarboxylic acid, 2-amino-1,6-dihydro-4-phenyl-1-(phenylamino)-6-thioxo-, ethyl ester	MeOH	281(4.16),301(4.08), 395(4.39)	48-0679-73
$C_{20}H_{19}N_3O_3$			
5H,10H-5,10-Etheno-5a,9a-(methanoxymethano)-1H-[1,2,4]triazolo[1,2-b]phthalazine-1,3(2H)-dione, dihydro-2-phenyl-, (5α,5aβ,9aβ,10α)-	MeCN	217(4.21),267(3.31)	78-2373-73
1H-Indole-2-carboxylic acid, 1-methyl-3-[2-oxo-1-(phenylhydrazono)propyl]-, methyl ester, (E)-	EtOH	229(4.56),293(4.31), 348(4.32)	78-3159-73
Pyrazolo[3,4-b]indole-8a(1H)-carboxylic acid, 3-acetyl-3a,8-dihydro-8-methyl-1-phenyl-, methyl ester	EtOH	244(4.30),308(4.04), 325(4.02)	78-3159-73
$C_{20}H_{19}N_3O_4$			
Isoquinoline, 1-(5,6-dimethoxy-1H-indazol-3-yl)-6,7-dimethoxy-	EtOH	245(4.36),307(3.72), 341(3.82)	44-2394-73
2H-1,4-Oxazin-3(4H)-one, 6-(4-nitrophenyl)-4-phenyl-2-pyrrolidino-	EtOH	254(4.29),371(4.03)	4-0347-73
1H-Pyrazole-4-carboxylic acid, 5-methyl-3-(4-methylphenyl)-1-(4-nitrophenyl)-, ethyl ester	EtOH	222(5.54),250s(5.23), 307(5.15)	78-0121-73
2H-Pyrrole-3-carboxylic acid, 2-oxo-5-[(phenylmethoxy)amino]-4-(phenylmethyl)amino]-, methyl ester	EtOH	350(4.01)	94-1667-73
1H-1,2,3-Triazole-4-carboxylic acid, 1-(4-ethoxy-5-oxo-1,3,6-cycloheptatrien-1-yl)-5-phenyl-, ethyl ester	n.s.g.	228(4.52),246s(4.48), 328(4.12)	18-1212-73
$C_{20}H_{19}N_3O_5S$			
3-Quinolinecarboxylic acid, 2-[[[[(4-methylphenyl)sulfonyl]amino]carbonyl]amino]-, ethyl ester	MeOH	222(4.3),258(4.2)	24-3533-73
$C_{20}H_{19}N_3O_5S$			
Benzenesulfonamide, N-[-(methylthio)-α-(1-acetylindol-3-yloxy)]methylene-p-acetamido-	EtOH	240(4.56),264(4.49)	95-0971-73
$C_{20}H_{19}N_5O$			
4(1H)-Pteridinone, 2-amino-7,8-dihydro-6,7-bis(phenylmethyl)-, hydrochloride	pH 1	258(4.18),368(3.80)	87-0869-73

Compound	Solvent	$\lambda_{max}(\log \epsilon)$	Ref.
$C_{20}H_{19}N_5O_4$			
Adenosine, N-(1-naphthalenyl)-	pH 1	265(4.28),283s(4.25)	87-0358-73
	H_2O	273s(4.22),283(4.24)	87-0358-73
	pH 13	273s(4.22),283(4.24)	87-0358-73
Adenosine, N-(2-naphthalenyl)-	pH 1	277(4.47)	87-0358-73
	H_2O	272s(4.36),280(4.42), 310(4.32)	87-0358-73
	pH 13	272s(4.38),280(4.44), 310(4.35)	87-0358-73
3,5'-Cycloadenosine, N-benzoyl-2',3'-O-isopropylidene-	MeOH	266(4.10),308(4.10)	35-4404-73
$C_{20}H_{19}OP$			
Phosphine oxide, (2,4,6-cycloheptatrien-1-yl)methyldiphenyl-	EtOH	218s(4.50),272(4.09), 303(3.79)	35-4292-73
$C_{20}H_{19}O_2Se$			
Seleninium, 2,6-bis(4-methoxyphenyl)-4-methyl-, perchlorate	MeCN-$HClO_4$	482(4.48)	103-0790-73
$C_{20}H_{19}Se$			
Seleninium, 4-methyl-2,6-bis(4-methylphenyl)-, perchlorate	MeCN-$HClO_4$	434(4.47)	103-0790-73
$C_{20}H_{20}$			
Cyclobuta[1,2-a:4,3-a']dipentalene, 3b,3c-dihydro-1,3,3c,7-tetramethyl-	hexane	256(4.22),262(4.24), 279(4.05),408(3.21)	89-0337-73
Cyclobuta[1,2-a:4,3-a']dipentalene, 3b,3c-dihydro-3b,3c,7,8-tetramethyl-	hexane	267(4.38),379(3.14)	89-0337-73
stereoisomer 8b	hexane	261(--),389(--)	89-0337-73
stereoisomer 8c	hexane	259(4.31),267(4.38), 284(4.08),404(3.23)	89-0337-73
1,3,5-Hexatriene, 1,6-bis(2-methylphenyl)-	C_6H_{12}	241(3.92),346(4.70),	39-0044-73C
Naphthalene, 1,2,3,4-tetramethyl-5-phenyl-	EtOH	242(4.77),310(4.04)	5-1893-73
$C_{20}H_{20}BrN_5O_5$			
Benzamide, N-[[4-(bromomethyl)-5-formyl-3a,4,10,10a-tetrahydro-2,2-dimethyl-4,10-epoxy-5H-1,3-dioxolo[4,5-e]imidazo[1,5-a][1,3]diazepin-6-yl)iminomethyl]-, [3aS-(3aα,4β,10β,10aα)]-	EtOH	244(4.17),266(4.15), 334(4.26)	35-1350-73
$C_{20}H_{20}Br_2N_2O_2$			
Pyridinium, 1-[(2-bromo-3-quinolinyl)-methyl]-4-(2-ethyl-1,3-dioxolan-2-yl)-, bromide	H_2O	239(4.35),295(3.56), 308(3.59),322(3.60)	44-2351-73
$C_{20}H_{20}Br_2N_2O_2S$			
Benzenesulfonamide, N-[5',7'-dibromo-1'-methylspiro[cyclopentane-1,2'-[2H]-indol]-3'(1'H)-ylidene]-4-methyl-	EtOH	258(4.13),481(3.64)	39-1809-73C
$C_{20}H_{20}ClNO_3$			
Piperidine, 1-[[4-(4-chlorobenzoyl)phenoxy]acetyl]-	EtOH	208(4.40),288(4.26)	111-0574-73

Compound	Solvent	$\lambda_{max}(\log \epsilon)$	Ref.
$C_{20}H_{20}ClNO_6$			
Isoquinolinium, 3-(ethoxycarbonyl)-1,4-dihydro-2-methyl-4-(phenylmethylene)-, perchlorate	EtOH	237(4.79),282(3.85), 342(3.92)	78-0213-73
$C_{20}H_{20}ClN_5O$			
Morpholine, 4-[4-[2-(4-chlorophenyl)hydrazino]-6-phenyl-3-pyridazinyl]-	CH_2Cl_2	251(4.56)	39-2532-73C
$C_{20}H_{20}FeN_2$			
Ferrocene, 1,1'-(2,3,4,5-tetrahydro-2-methyl-1H-1,5-benzodiazepine-2,4-diyl)-	EtOH	222(4.45),308(3.46), 441(2.26)	18-3315-73
$C_{20}H_{20}N_2$			
3,3'-Bi-1H-isoindole, 1,1,1',1'-tetramethyl-	C_6H_{12}	223(4.28),259(4.01), 287s(3.72),293(3.57)	44-1333-73
2-Butenal, 3-phenyl-, (3-phenyl-2-butenylidene)hydrazone	$CHCl_3$	335(4.76)	22-3303-73
3-Buten-2-one, 4-phenyl-, (1-methyl-3-phenyl-2-propenylidene)hydrazone	$CHCl_3$	327(4.71),342(4.70)	22-3303-73
5,11-Diazachrysene, 6,12-dihydro-6,6,12,12-tetramethyl-	MeOH	225(4.48),230s(4.46), 268(4.36),291(4.20), 302(4.17),365(2.60)	44-1333-73
2-Propenal, 2-methyl-3-phenyl-, (2-methyl-3-phenyl-2-propenylidene)hydrazone	$CHCl_3$	355(4.72)	22-3303-73
$C_{20}H_{20}N_2O$			
Benzaldehyde, (3-oxo-1-cyclohexen-1-yl)-(phenylmethyl)hydrazone	MeOH	230(3.94),254(3.94), 342(4.72),353(4.73)	24-0450-73
4H-Benzo[a]quinolizin-4-one, 1,6,7,11b-tetrahydro-2-[(phenylmethyl)amino]-	EtOH	305(4.34)	70-1745-73
2-Cyclohexen-1-one, 3-(phenylamino)-, ketene adduct	EtOH	271.5(4.66)	18-2505-73
1,3-Diazatricyclo[3.3.1.1^{3,7}]decan-6-one, 5,7-diphenyl-	EtOH	250(3.22)	44-1648-73
	EtOH-HCl	249(3.05),256(3.02)	44-1648-73
1H-Pyrido[3,4-b]indole, 2-benzoyl-2,3,4,9-tetrahydro-1,1-dimethyl-	EtOH	225(4.60),273(3.72), 279(3.69),289(3.61)	44-4342-73
$C_{20}H_{20}N_2O_2$			
Benzamide, N,N'-[2,3-bis(methylene)-1,4-butanediyl]bis-	EtOH	225(4.45)	88-2361-73
1,3-Diazatricyclo[3.3.1.1^{3,7}]decan-6-one, 5,7-diphenyl-, 1-oxide	EtOH	250(3.01),256(2.98), 262(2.83)	44-1648-73
2,4-Hexadienediamide, N,N'-bis(3-methylphenyl)-, (E,E)-	EtOH	273(4.45),324(4.56)	104-2527-73
$C_{20}H_{20}N_2O_2S$			
Benzenesulfonamide, N-(2,3-dihydro-1H-cyclopenta[c]quinolin-4-yl)-N,4-dimethyl-	EtOH	225(4.70),240s(4.36), 310(3.64),324(3.72)	39-1809-73C
Pyridinium, 1-[([1,1'-biphenyl]-2-ylsulfonyl)amino]-2,4,6-trimethyl-, hydroxide, inner salt	EtOH	241(4.23),297s(3.00)	44-3311-73
$C_{20}H_{20}N_2O_3$			
Sarpagan-18-al, 6,17-epoxy-11-methoxy-	MeOH	224(4.84),256s(3.47), 294(3.44),310s(3.35)	94-1783-73

Compound	Solvent	λ_{max}(log ϵ)	Ref.
$C_{20}H_{20}N_2O_4$			
Phenol, 2-[2-(2,3-dihydro-9,9-dimethyl-oxazolo[3,2-a]indol-9a(9H)-yl)ethen-yl]-6-nitro-	hexane	240(4.35),370(3.59)	103-1233-73
	EtOH	240(--),350(--), 435(--),550(--)	103-1233-73
Spiro[2H-1-benzopyran-2,2'-[2H]indole]-1'-ethanol, 1',3'-dihydro-3',3'-di-methyl-6-nitro-	EtOH	268(4.20),342(3.93)	103-1233-73
$C_{20}H_{20}N_2O_5$			
1H-Indole-3-carboxylic acid, 1,2-dimeth-yl-4-nitro-5-(phenylmethoxy)-, ethyl ester	MeOH or $CHCl_3$	290(3.91)	103-1490-73
1H-Pyrazole-4,5-dicarboxylic acid, 4,5-dihydro-3-(4-methoxyphenyl)-1-phenyl-, dimethyl ester	EtOH	248(4.11),304(3.94), 355(4.20)	94-2026-73
1H-Pyrrolo[2,3-c]pyridine-2,3-dicarbox-ylic acid, 5-(phenylmethoxy)-, dieth-yl ester	EtOH	235(4.17),263(4.03), 318(3.74)	44-1824-73
$C_{20}H_{20}N_2O_6$			
Isoquinoline, 4,5,6,7-tetramethoxy-1-[(2-nitrophenyl)methyl]-	EtOH	248(4.46),296(3.80), 300(3.78),330(3.65), 340(3.68)	44-0060-73
$C_{20}H_{20}N_3S$			
Thiazolo[3,2-a]pyrimidin-4-ium, 5-[3-(1,3-dihydro-1,3,3-trimethyl-2H-indol-2-ylidene)-1-propenyl]-, perchlorate	n.s.g.	562(5.24)	124-1151-73
$C_{20}H_{20}N_4$			
Phenazinium, 3,7-diamino-2,8-dimethyl-5-phenyl-	n.s.g.	270(4.6),525(4.7)	83-0481-73
diazonium salt	n.s.g.	230(4.0),280(4.3), 340(4.1),400s(3.8), 570(3.7)	83-0481-73
$C_{20}H_{20}N_4O$			
Benzamide, N-[[4-amino-2-(4-methylphen-yl)-5-pyrimidinyl]methyl]-4-methyl-	MeOH	205(4.22),242(4.17), 260s(--),282(3.81), 296s(--)	18-0253-73
	MeOH-HCl	204(--),256(--), 286s(--)	18-0253-73
3H-Pyrrolo[1,2-a]indole-2-carbonitrile, 3-oxo-1,9-di-1-pyrrolidinyl-	EtOH	240(4.45),315(4.32), 420(4.11)	95-0964-73
$C_{20}H_{20}N_6$			
3(2H)-Pyridazinone, 4,5-dihydro-6-phen-yl-, (4,5-dihydro-6-phenyl-3-pyrida-zinyl)hydrazone	CH_2Cl_2	230(4.13),348(4.59)	39-2532-73C
$C_{20}H_{20}N_6O_3$			
Morpholine, 4-[4-[2-(4-nitrophenyl)hy-drazino]-6-phenyl-3-pyridazinyl]-	CH_2Cl_2	255(4.55),290s(4.25), 368(4.37)	39-2532-73C
$C_{20}H_{20}N_6O_{10}S_2$			
Acetamide, N,N'-1,2-ethanediylbis[2-(2,4-dinitrophenyl)thio]-N-methyl-	acetone	335(4.34)	44-0937-73
$C_{20}H_{20}O$			
Cyclohexanone, 2-(1,2-diphenylethenyl)-	EtOH	220(4.23),270(4.11)	18-1257-73

Compound	Solvent	λmax(log ε)	Ref.
1(2H)-Naphthalenone, 3,4-dihydro-7-(5,6,7,8-tetrahydro-2-naphthalenyl)-	EtOH	213(4.44),249(4.45)	132-0051-73
$C_{20}H_{20}O_2$			
1-Acenaphthyleneacetic acid, 1,2,2a,3-4,5-hexahydro-2-phenyl-	EtOH	220(4.16)	39-1983-73C
1,7-Chrysenedione, 2,3,4,8,9,10-hexahydro-2,8-dimethyl-	EtOH	238(4.46),252(4.79), 260(4.99),281(4.14), 292(4.29),302(4.31), 344s(3.39),359(3.59), 375(3.61)	39-0044-73C
1,3-Dioxolane, 5-(9H-fluoren-9-ylidene)-2,2,4,4-tetramethyl-	EtOH	283(4.27),294(4.31), 317(4.16),331(4.17)	23-1995-73
$C_{20}H_{20}O_3$			
Benzenebutanoic acid, γ-oxo-4-(5,6,7,8-tetrahydro-2-naphthalenyl)-	EtOH	211(4.55),293(4.34)	132-0051-73
2H,6H-Benzo[1,2-b:5,4-b']dipyran-6-one, 3,4,7,8-tetrahydro-2,2-dimethyl-8-phenyl-	MeOH	243(4.25),283(4.34), 323(4.03)	32-0779-73
4H,8H-Benzo[1,2-b:3,4-b']dipyran-4-one, 2,3,9,10-tetrahydro-8,8-dimethyl-2-phenyl-	MeOH	235(4.04),246(4.03), 285(4.16),312(3.88)	32-0779-73
4H-1-Benzopyran-4-one, 2,3-dihydro-7-hydroxy-8-(3-methyl-2-butenyl)-2-phenyl-	MeOH	238(4.09),285(4.13), 315s(3.82)	32-0771-73
4H-1-Benzopyran-4-one, 2,3-dihydro-7-[(3-methylbutenyl)oxy]-2-phenyl-	MeOH	230(4.16),235s(4.13), 274(4.23),311(3.96)	32-0771-73
Calycopterin, 4'-methyl ether	n.s.g.	276(4.38),333(4.44)	2-0403-73
Gona-1,3,5(10),8,14-pentaenyl-13β-acetic acid, 17β-hydroxy-3-methoxy-, lactone, (±)-	EtOH	310(4.43)	94-2427-73
Isolonchocarpin, dihydro-	EtOH	237(4.08),284(4.23), 315s(--)	2-0209-73
2-Propen-1-one, 1-(3,4-dihydro-5-hydroxy-2,2-dimethyl-2H-1-benzopyran-6-yl)-3-phenyl-	MeOH	222s(4.20),264s(3.71), 340(4.37)	32-0779-73
	MeOH-NaOMe	320(--),435s(--)	32-0779-73
2-Propen-1-one, 1-(3,4-dihydro-5-hydroxy-2,2-dimethyl-2H-1-benzopyran-8-yl)-3-phenyl-	MeOH	305(4.34),350s(4.12)	32-0779-73
	MeOH-NaOMe	270s(--),300(--), 397(--)	32-0779-73
2-Propen-1-one, 1-(3,4-dihydro-7-hydroxy-2,2-dimethyl-2H-1-benzopyran-6-yl)-3-phenyl-	MeOH	315(4.19)	2-1225-73
	MeOH	228s(4.25),275(4.03), 320(4.43),360s(4.35)	32-0779-73
2-Propen-1-one, 1-[2,4-dihydroxy-3-(3-methyl-2-butenyl)phenyl]-3-phenyl- (isocordoin)	MeOH	343(4.14)	2-1225-73
	MeOH	222s(4.32),310s(4.34), 340(4.38)	32-0771-73
2-Propen-1-one, 1-[2,4-dihydroxy-5-(3-methyl-2-butenyl)phenyl]-3-phenyl-	MeOH	272(3.84),320(4.24)	2-1225-73
$C_{20}H_{20}O_4$			
[3,6'-Bi-2H-1-benzopyran]-5',7-diol, 3,4-dihydro-2',2'-dimethyl-	EtOH	265(4.29),273(4.30), 288(4.19),327(4.48)	39-0907-73C
1(2H)-Chrysenone, 3,4,11,12-tetrahydro-11,12-dihydroxy-8-methoxy-11-methyl-	C_6H_{12}	216s(4.29),224(4.37), 261s(3.87),268s(3.97), 276(4.30),287(4.49), 345s(3.94),353(3.97), 372s(3.88)	88-1553-73
1(2H)-Chrysenone, 3,4,11,12-tetrahydro-11-hydroxy-8,12-dimethoxy-	C_6H_{12}	224(4.38),267s(4.10), 277(4.37),286(4.50), 356(4.03),370s(3.96)	88-1553-73
Licarin B	EtOH	220(4.55),272(4.30)	102-1163-73

Compound	Solvent	λ_{max}(log ε)	Ref.
1H-Phenalene-2-acetic acid, 4-methoxy-α,α,9-trimethyl-1-oxo-, methyl ester	EtOH	207(4.56),264(4.50), 319(3.67),374(3.95), 402(4.15),421(4.19)	39-2159-73C
7H-Phenaleno[1,2-b]furan-7-one, 8,9-dihydro-1,6-dimethoxy-8,8,9-trimethyl-	EtOH	215(4.87),253(4.74), 269(4.47),279(4.34), 374(4.73),422(4.13)	39-2159-73C
1-Phenalenone, 2-(1,1-dimethyl-2-oxopropyl)-4,9-dimethoxy-	EtOH	228(4.31),263(4.33), 389(4.33),424(4.16), 451(3.96)	39-2159-73C
3,6-Phenanthrenedione, 4,4a-dihydro-5,8-dihydroxy-1,2,4a-trimethyl-7-(2-propenyl)-, (S)- (coleon F)	ether	280(4.20),336-440(4.16)	33-1129-73
Spiro[3-cyclohexene-1,2'(1'H)-naphthalene]-2,5,5',8'-tetrone, 3',4'-dihydro-3,4,6',7'-tetramethyl-6-methylene-	EtOH	259(4.43),265(4.38)	44-0813-73
$C_{20}H_{20}O_5$			
Archangelenone	EtOH	227(4.38),294(4.28), 331(3.95)	2-0407-73
	EtOH-$AlCl_3$	225(4.10),301(4.23), 375(3.71)	2-0407-73
Guianin	EtOH	235(3.93),265(4.01)	102-1805-73
1H-Phenalene-2-acetic acid, 4,9-dimethoxy-α,α-dimethyl-1-oxo-, methyl ester	EtOH	204(4.49),230(4.08), 264(4.21),270s(4.58), 280s(3.91),315(3.28), 384(4.23),420(4.04), 441(3.81)	39-2159-73C
Ugonin D	EtOH	296(4.05),337s(3.32)	94-1851-73
9H-Xanthen-9-one, 1-hydroxy-3,7-dimethoxy-2-(3-methyl-2-butenyl)-	MeOH	262(4.34),317(4.08), 381(3.64)	2-1233-73
$C_{20}H_{20}O_6$			
9,10-Anthracenedione, 1,8-dihydroxy-3-(2-hydroxypentyl)-6-methoxy-	MeOH	226(4.38),255(4.18), 263(4.17),286(4.08), 433(3.92)	78-3699-73
Benzeneacetic acid, α-[2-hydroxy-1-methoxy-3-(4-methoxyphenyl)-2-propenylidene]-4-methoxy-	MeOH	225(4.38),275(3.78)	102-2527-73
Benz[4,5]indeno[1,7a-c]furan-2,5-dione, 2a,3,6,7-tetrahydro-3-hydroxy-9-methoxy-2a-(3-oxobutyl)-	MeOH	244(3.93),334(4.44)	39-1780-73C
α-Conidendrin	EtOH	231s(4.20),284(3.86)	94-1114-73
	EtOH-NaOH	249(4.30),300(4.02)	94-1114-73
	n.s.g.	229(4.37),284(3.97), 289s(3.95)	105-0252-73
7H-1,3-Dioxolo[4,5-h][2]benzopyran, 7-(6-ethyl-1,3-benzodioxol-5-yl)-9-methoxy-	EtOH	211(4.29),238(4.00), 290(3.95)	73-2799-73
Ketomatairesinol	n.s.g.	233(4.61),283(4.41), 310(4.29)	105-0252-73
Naphtho[1,2-b]furan-5(4H)-one, 6,9-diacetoxy-4-ethenyl-2,3,3a,9b-tetrahydro-4-methyl-3-methylene-, (3aα,4β-9bα)-	EtOH	248(3.93),303(3.44)	39-1556-73C
$C_{20}H_{20}O_8$			
Methanone, [6-(1,3-dioxolan-2-yl)-1,3-benzodioxol-5-yl](3,4,5-trimethoxyphenyl)-	EtOH	294(4.10)	39-1266-73C

Compound	Solvent	λ_{max}(log ε)	Ref.
$C_{20}H_{20}O_9$			
4H-1-Benzopyran-4-one, 2-(3,5-dihydroxy-4-methoxyphenyl)-5,6,7,8-tetramethoxy-	MeOH	269(4.34),317(4.39)	2-1092-73
	MeOH-$AlCl_3$	269(--),317(--)	2-1092-73
4H-1-Benzopyran-4-one, 5-hydroxy-2-(3-hydroxy-4,5-dimethoxyphenyl)-6,7,8-trimethoxy-	MeOH	304(4.18),323(4.20)	2-0096-73
$C_{20}H_{20}O_{11}$			
Irisxanthone	EtOH	245(4.75),277(4.31),323(4.39),360(4.37)	94-2562-73
	EtOH-NaOAc	244(4.73),263s(4.45),275s(4.39),368(4.45)	94-2562-73
	EtOH-$AlCl_3$	238(4.63),250(4.68),262(4.57),338(4.57),380(4.23)	94-2562-73
	EtOH-NaOAc-H_3BO_3	245(4.75),277(4.31),323(4.39),360(4.37)	94-2562-73
$C_{20}H_{21}BrN_4O$			
Pyrido[1',2':2,3]pyrazolo[5,4-c]quinazolin-6(5H)-one, 2-bromo-5-[2-(diethylamino)ethyl]-	isoPrOH	221(4.51),233s(4.44),245s(4.53),251(4.59),263s(4.40),270s(4.33),317s(4.10),331(4.22),350(4.06),366(3.89)	44-3995-73
$C_{20}H_{21}ClN_2O$			
Benzamide, 4-chloro-2-(cyclohexylideneamino)-N-(2-methylphenyl)-	n.s.g.	232(4.63),342(3.58)	103-0488-73
Benzamide, 4-chloro-2-(cyclohexylideneamino)-N-(3-methylphenyl)-	n.s.g.	232(4.40),344(3.53)	103-0488-73
Benzamide, 4-chloro-2-(cyclohexylideneamino)-N-(4-methylphenyl)-	n.s.g.	232(4.52),344(3.44)	103-0488-73
Pyrimido[1,2-a]indole, 1-(4-chlorobenzoyl)-1,2,3,4,10,10a-hexahydro-10,10-dimethyl-	EtOH	246(4.26),296(3.50)	78-4049-73
$C_{20}H_{21}ClN_2O_2$			
Benzamide, 4-chloro-2-(cyclohexylideneamino)-N-(4-methoxyphenyl)-	n.s.g.	232(4.89),340(3.73)	103-0488-73
$C_{20}H_{21}ClN_2O_3$			
1H-1,4-Benzodiazepine-3-propanoic acid, 7-chloro-2,3-dihydro-1-methyl-2-oxo-5-phenyl-, methyl ester	isoPrOH	240(4.17),290s(3.11)	44-3502-73
Piperazine, 1-[(4-acetylphenoxy)acetyl]-4-(4-chlorophenyl)-	EtOH	210(4.46),260(4.54)	111-0574-73
$C_{20}H_{21}ClSi_2$			
Silane, chloromethyl[4-(methylphenylsilyl)phenyl]phenyl-	heptane	278.1(2.63)	70-1825-73
$C_{20}H_{21}N$			
[1]Benzazepino[3,2,1-jk]carbazole, 1,2,3,4,4a,8,9,14a-octahydro-	n.s.g.	210(4.46),300(4.24)	39-1041-73C
1H-Indole, 3-methyl-1-(3-methyl-2-butenyl)-2-phenyl-	EtOH	224(4.54),238s(4.34),298(4.17)	39-1913-73C
3H-Indole, 3-methyl-3-(3-methyl-2-butenyl)-2-phenyl-	EtOH	228(4.13),234(4.13),242s(4.04),307(4.15)	39-1913-73C

Compound	Solvent	$\lambda_{max}(\log \epsilon)$	Ref.
$C_{20}H_{21}NO$			
1-Butanone, 1-(9-propyl-2-acridinyl)-	EtOH	212(4.12),244s(4.48), 252(4.58),276(4.80), 333s(3.53),348(3.78), 367(3.87),382s(3.65), 400s(3.54)	39-1259-73C
1H-Carbazole, 9-benzoyl-2,3,4,4a,9,9a-hexahydro-4a-methyl-	EtOH	266(4.07),288s(3.91)	33-2628-73
Methanone, (2,3,4,4a,9,9a-hexahydro-4a-methyl-1H-carbazol-8-yl)phenyl-	EtOH	244(4.20),270(3.88), 321s(2.77),396(3.64)	33-2628-73
	EtOH-HCl	245(4.14),265s(3.91), 320s(2.73),396(3.64)	33-2628-73
$C_{20}H_{21}NO_3$			
Acetamide, 2-(4-benzoylphenoxy)-N-cyclopentyl-	EtOH	210(4.15),282(4.18)	111-0574-73
Piperidine, 1-[(4-benzoylphenoxy)acetyl]-	EtOH	211(4.34),283(4.26)	111-0574-73
$C_{20}H_{21}NO_3S$			
1H-Carbazole-3-methanol, 2,3,4,9-tetrahydro-, 4-methylbenzenesulfonate	EtOH	226(4.60),283(3.78), 290(3.71)	44-2882-73
$C_{20}H_{21}NO_4$			
Eschscholtzidine, (±)- (as methiodide)	EtOH	290(3.88)	2-1084-73
6,8(2H,7H)-Isoquinolinedione, 7-acetoxy-3-(1,3,5-heptatrienyl)-2,7-dimethyl-, (E,E,E)-	CH_2Cl_2	249(4.14),370(4.66), 496(3.52)	33-2694-73
Nantenine	MeOH	222(4.54),282(4.07), 308(4.16)	2-0342-73
Norglaucine, 6a,7-dehydro-	EtOH	259(4.81),335(3.89), 380(3.35)	44-2394-73
2(1H)-Quinolinone, 4,6-dimethoxy-3-[2-(phenylmethoxy)ethyl]-	EtOH	234(4.62),262(3.89), 272(3.91),282s(3.82), 329s(3.71),344(3.89), 361s(3.78)	18-0577-73
2(1H)-Quinolinone, 4,7-dimethoxy-3-[2-(phenylmethoxy)ethyl]-	EtOH	238s(4.55),255(3.84), 283(3.82),309(4.01), 323(4.24)	18-0577-73
2(1H)-Quinolinone, 4,8-dimethoxy-3-[2-(phenylmethoxy)ethyl]-	EtOH	236(4.34),252(4.45), 279(3.95),329(3.55), 343s(3.37)	18-0577-73
$C_{20}H_{21}NO_5$			
Alkaloid AA2 from Argemone albiflora HORNEM.	MeOH	230s(4.00),288(3.88)	73-3312-73
Benzeneacetonitrile, 2-(2,6-dimethoxy-4-methylbenzoyl)-3,5-dimethoxy-	EtOH	226(4.14),277(3.93), 299(3.88)	39-2853-73C
Formamide, N-[2-(1,3-benzodioxol-5-yl)-1,2,3,4-tetrahydro-6,7-dimethoxy-1-naphthalenyl]-	EtOH	233(4.19),285(3.98)	4-0867-73
Formamide, N-[6-(3,4-dimethoxyphenyl)-5,6,7,8-tetrahydronaphtho[2,3-d]-1,3-dioxol-5-yl]-	EtOH	230(4.20),285(3.90), 293s(3.79)	4-0085-73
Papaverine N-oxide	MeOH	232s(4.37),256(4.74), 303s(4.06),312s(3.99)	12-0437-73
2(1H)-Quinolinone, 4-hydroxy-6,8-dimethoxy-3-[2-(phenylmethoxy)ethyl]-	EtOH	228s(4.43),251(4.50), 280(4.00),290(3.97), 338(3.77),353s(3.70)	18-0577-73

Compound	Solvent	$\lambda_{max}(\log \epsilon)$	Ref.
$C_{20}H_{21}NO_7$			
1,3-Benzodioxole-5-acetic acid, α-[(2-amino-4,5-dimethoxyphenyl)methylene]-7-methoxy-, methyl ester	EtOH	217(4.61),236s(4.37), 255s(4.09),302(3.85)	12-2035-73
7H-Furo[2,3-f]indole-3,7-dicarboxylic acid, 7-acetoxy-2,6-dimethyl-, diethyl ester	dioxan	255(4.12),305(3.87)	78-0921-73
$C_{20}H_{21}NO_8$			
7H-Cyclohepta[b]pyridine-6,8-dicarboxylic acid, 5,9-diacetoxy-, diethyl ester	EtOH	205(4.09),236(4.44), 252s(--)	39-0026-73C
7H-Cyclohepta[c]pyridine-6,8-dicarboxylic acid, 5,9-diacetoxy-, diethyl ester	EtOH	212s(--),241(4.45), 308s(--)	39-0026-73C
$C_{20}H_{21}NO_{10}$			
Ethanone, 1-[4-(β-D-glucopyranosyloxy)-2-hydroxyphenyl]-2-(4-nitrophenyl)-	EtOH	216(4.17),278(4.27), 310(3.92)	114-0435-73B
$C_{20}H_{21}N_3$			
6,13-Imino-5H-pyrido[3',4':5,6]cyclooct-[1,2-b]indole, 4-ethyl-6,7,12,13-tetrahydro-7-methyl- (sauveoline)	EtOH	227(4.47),272(3.88), 285(3.82)	102-1167-73
$C_{20}H_{21}N_3O$			
2-Naphthalenol, 1-[[2-(diethylamino)-phenyl]azo]-	$CHCl_3$	518(4.30)	48-0725-73
$C_{20}H_{21}N_3O_2$			
1H-Indole-3-acetic acid, 1,2-dimethyl-α-(phenylhydrazono)-, ethyl ester	EtOH	285(4.09),341(4.21)	78-3159-73
$C_{20}H_{21}N_3O_3S$			
2H-1,2-Benzothiazine-3-carboxamide, 2-methyl-N-phenyl-4-pyrrolidino-, S,S-dioxide	EtOH	236(4.24),266s(3.94), 366(4.12)	87-0044-73
$C_{20}H_{21}N_3O_3S_2$			
Acetamide, N-[(4,7-dihydro-2-methyl-7-oxo-6(5H)-benzothiazolylidene)methyl]-N-[(4,5,6,7-tetrahydro-2-methyl-7-oxo-6-benzothiazolyl)methyl]-	EtOH	280(4.08),310(4.03)	32-1063-73
	EtOH-NaOH	370(3.92)	32-1063-73
$C_{20}H_{21}N_3O_5$			
Uridine, 5'-(1H-indol-1-yl)-5'-deoxy-2',3'-O-(1-methylethylidene)-	EtOH	258(4.02),296(3.08)	104-2223-73
$C_{20}H_{21}N_3O_5S$			
5-Phthalimidovaleronitrile, 2-amino-, 4-methylbenzenesulfonate	EtOH	233(4.17),238(3.98), 241(4.00),257(2.83), 262(2.92),268(2.97), 294(3.31)	78-3761-73
$C_{20}H_{21}N_5O$			
Morpholine, 4-[6-phenyl-4-(2-phenylhydrazino)-3-pyridazinyl]-	CH_2Cl_2	251(4.48)	39-2532-73C

Compound	Solvent	$\lambda_{max}(\log \epsilon)$	Ref.
$C_{20}H_{21}N_5O_6$			
Quinolinium, 4-[[(1,2-dihydro-2-oxo-1-β-D-ribofuranosyl-4-pyrimidinyl)hydrazino]hydroxymethyl]-1-methyl-, hydroxide, inner salt	M HCl	292(4.23),322s(3.97)	35-1323-73
	pH 2.8	278(4.07),322(4.00)	35-1323-73
	pH 6.2	310(4.24),420(3.54)	35-1323-73
	pH 10.8	308(4.28),422(3.62)	35-1323-73
$C_{20}H_{21}N_7O_6$			
Neohomofolic acid	pH 1	232(4.19),245(4.14), 282(3.62),321(3.92)	87-0697-73
	pH 7	242(4.36),272(4.25), 346(3.85)	87-0697-73
	pH 13	254(4.53),275s(--), 365(3.94)	87-0697-73
$C_{20}H_{22}$			
6,6'-Ditetralin	EtOH	213(4.65),258(4.29)	132-0051-73
Naphthalene, 1,2-dihydro-5,6,7,8-tetramethyl-4-phenyl-	EtOH	235(4.33),266(4.00)	132-0051-73
$C_{20}H_{22}BrP$			
9-Phosphoniatricyclo[4.2.1.0^{2,5}]nonane, 9,9-diphenyl-, bromide	EtOH	230(4.31),256s(3.05), 261(3.19),267(3.29), 274(3.17)	35-4292-73
$C_{20}H_{22}ClN_3O_3$			
Piperazine, 1-(4-chlorophenyl)-4-[[4-[1-(hydroxyimino)ethyl]phenoxy]acetyl]-	EtOH	211(4.49),256(4.55)	111-0574-73
$C_{20}H_{22}ClN_3O_9$			
1H-Imidazo[4,5-c]pyridine, 4-chloro-1-(2,3,4,6-tetra-O-acetyl-β-D-glucopyranosyl)-	pH 1	254(3.79),265(3.79)	124-0703-73
	pH 13	252(3.84),265(3.81)	124-0703-73
	MeOH	250(3.80),265(3.70)	124-0703-73
$C_{20}H_{22}N_2$			
Azocyclobutane, 1,1'-diphenyl-	C_6H_{12}	362(1.51)	24-2890-73
1,2'-Bi-1H-indole, 2',3'-dihydro-2,3,3',3'-tetramethyl-	MeOH	230(4.46),295(3.79)	88-4229-73
1,3-Diazabicyclo[3.1.0]hex-3-ene, 2,2,6,6-tetramethyl-4,5-diphenyl-	C_6H_{12}	232(4.13)	44-1333-73
1,2-Ethenediamine, N,N'-bis(1-methylethylidene)-1,2-diphenyl-, cis	C_6H_{12}	228(4.19),312(4.03)	44-1333-73
trans	C_6H_{12}	230(4.08),320(4.05)	44-1333-73
1,4-Methanobenzo[c]cinnoline, 1,2,3,4-4a,5,6,10b-octahydro-6-methyl-4a-phenyl-	MeCN	253(3.78),292(3.38)	22-3487-73
$C_{20}H_{22}N_2O$			
Ajmalan, 1,2,19,20-tetradehydro-1-demethyl-11-methoxy-	MeOH	230(4.37),275(3.51), 300(3.34)	94-1783-73
1,3-Diazatricyclo[3.3.1.1^{3,7}]decan-6-ol, 5,7-diphenyl-	EtOH	250(2.87),256(2.80), 262(2.63)	44-1648-73
1H-Pyrrole, 2-[[4,5-dimethyl-3-(phenylmethoxy)-2H-pyrrol-2-ylidene]methyl]-3,4-dimethyl-, hydrobromide	CH_2Cl_2	466(4.81)	5-0146-73
$C_{20}H_{22}N_2OS$			
Piperazine, 1-(7-methoxydibenzo[b,f]thiepin-10-yl)-4-methyl-	MeOH	250(4.38),268(4.17), 302(3.94)	73-2301-73

Compound	Solvent	λ_{max}(log ε)	Ref.
$C_{20}H_{22}N_2O_2$			
Hydroperoxide, 6,7-dihydro-5,7,7-trimethyl-2,3-diphenyl-5H-1,4-diazepin-5-yl-	MeOH	228(4.10),259(3.91)	44-1333-73
Quinidinone	EtOH	213(4.59),240s(4.20), 260s(3.85),343(3.69)	33-1494-73
Sarpagan, 1,2-didehydro-7,17-epoxy-2,7-dihydro-11-methoxy-, (16S)-	MeOH	285(3.42)	94-1783-73
$C_{20}H_{22}N_2O_2S$			
Benzenesulfonamide, 4-methyl-N-(2-methylspiro[cyclopentane-1,3'[3H]indol]-2'(1'H)-indol]-2'(1'H)-ylidene)-	EtOH	222(4.36),282(4.15), 291s(4.04)	39-1809-73C
$C_{20}H_{22}N_2O_3$			
Acetamide, N-cyclopentyl-2-[4-[(hydroxyimino)methylphenyl]phenoxy]-	EtOH	210(4.35),240(4.17), 263(4.18)	111-0574-73
Estra-1,3,5(10)-trien-17-one, 3-[(diazoacetyl)oxy]-	EtOH	215(3.96),250(4.24)	44-3525-73
1H-Indole-3-carboxylic acid, 1-[4-(dimethylamino)phenyl]-6-hydroxy-2-methyl-	MeOH	208(4.64),266(4.38), 305(4.28)	83-0446-73
Picrinine	n.s.g.	236(3.90),288(3.50)	102-2058-73
Piperidine, 1-[[4-(hydroxyimino)phenylmethyl]phenoxy]acetyl]-	EtOH	212(4.43),238(4.27)	111-0574-73
$C_{20}H_{22}N_2O_4S$			
1H-Indole-2-carboxylic acid, 1-methyl-3-[methyl[(4-methylphenyl)sulfonyl]amino]-, ethyl ester	EtOH	226(4.54),298(4.22)	39-1602-73C
$C_{20}H_{22}N_2O_6$			
2-Butenedioic acid, 2-[5-amino-2-(phenylmethoxy)-4-pyridinyl]-3-hydroxy-, diethyl ester	EtOH	240(4.34),296(3.71)	44-1824-73
$C_{20}H_{22}N_3O_4P$			
Phosphonic acid, (9,9a-dihydro-9a-methoxy-3-methyl-1-phenyl-1H-pyrazolo[3,4-b]quinolin-4-yl)-, dimethyl ester	n.s.g.	248(4.28),276(4.30), 338(3.78),365(3.64)	39-1606-73C
$C_{20}H_{22}N_3O_{11}P$			
5'-Cytidylic acid, N-benzoyl-, 2',3'-diacetate	pH 7	258(4.27),302(--)	138-0859-73
$C_{20}H_{22}N_4O$			
Pyrido[1',2':2,3]pyrazolo[5,4-c]quinolin-6(5H)-one, 5-[2-(diethylamino)ethyl]-	isoPrOH	215(4.54),228s(4.43), 236(4.43),249(4.55), 257s(4.48),266s(4.27), 292s(3.79),305(3.98), 319s(4.11),330(4.17), 351s(3.95),368s(3.72)	44-3995-73
7H-Pyrido[2',3':3,2]pyrrolo[5,4-c]quinolin-6(5H)-one, 5-[2-(diethylamino)ethyl]-	isoPrOH	233(4.65),250(4.46), 257(4.45),274s(4.02), 308s(4.16),314(4.18), 342(4.02),357(3.93)	44-3995-73
$C_{20}H_{22}N_4O_2S_2$			
7(4H)-Benzothiazolone, 6,6'-[1,2-ethanediylbis(iminomethylidyne)]bis[5,6-dihydro-2-methyl-	EtOH	214(4.28),278(4.29), 370(4.45)	32-1063-73

Compound	Solvent	λ_{max}(log ϵ)	Ref.
$C_{20}H_{22}N_4O_{10}$			
7(8H)-Pteridinone, 8-(2,3,4,6-tetra-O-acetyl-β-D-glucopyranosyl)-	MeOH	212(4.29),250(3.73), 259(3.71),269(3.65), 301(3.94)	24-0317-73
$C_{20}H_{22}N_4O_{11}$			
2,4(1H,3H)-Pteridinedione, 1-(2,3,4,6-tetra-O-acetyl-β-D-glucopyranosyl)-	pH 5.0	228(4.19),313(3.93)	24-2982-73
	pH 10.0	238(4.20),280s(3.69), 316(3.95)	24-2982-73
$C_{20}H_{22}N_6O_7$			
L-Phenylalanine, N-[[(9-β-D-ribofuranosyl-9H-purin-6-yl)amino]carbonyl]-	pH 1-2	270s(--),277(4.27)	87-0139-73
	pH 5-7	270(4.34),277s(--)	87-0139-73
	pH 12	271(4.24),300(3.90)	87-0139-73
$C_{20}H_{22}N_6O_8$			
L-Tyrosine, N-[[(9-β-D-ribofuranosyl-9H-purin-6-yl)amino]carbonyl]-	pH 1-2	270s(--),277(4.35)	87-0139-73
	pH 5-7	270(4.36),277s(--)	87-0139-73
	pH 12	272(4.30),297(3.85)	87-0139-73
$C_{20}H_{22}O$			
Furan, 2,3-dihydro-2,2,3,3-tetramethyl-4,5-diphenyl-	EtOH	285(4.04)	35-5416-73
Naphthalene, 1,2-dihydro-3-(1-methoxy-2-phenylethyl)-6-methyl-	MeOH	266(4.08),274(4.04), 303(3.23)	18-2908-73
$C_{20}H_{22}O_2$			
Benzenebutanoic acid, 4-(5,6,7,8-tetrahydro-2-naphthalenyl)-	EtOH	211(4.59),258(4.34)	132-0051-73
3H-Cyclopenta[a]phenanthren-3-one, 6,7,10,15,16,17-hexahydro-11-hydroxy-17,17-dimethyl-	EtOH	232(4.39),282(3.77), 291(3.69)	39-1967-73C
1H-Cyclopropa[c]cyclobuta[1,2-a:3,4-a']-dicyclooctene-1-carboxylic acid, 1a,5a,5b,11a,11b,11c-hexahydro-, ethyl ester	ether	228s(3.83),258s(3.36)	89-0325-73
1H-Cyclopropa[e]cyclobuta[1,2-a:3,4-a']-dicyclooctene-1-carboxylic acid, 1a,3a,3b,9a,9b,11a-hexahydro-, ethyl ester	ether	258s(3.30)	89-0325-73
$C_{20}H_{22}O_3$			
Estra-1,3,5(10),8-tetraene-18-carboxylic acid, 17-hydroxy-3-methoxy-, γ-lactone, (17β)-(±)-	EtOH	279(4.16)	94-2427-73
19-Norpregna-1,3,5(10)-trien-20-yn-6-one, 3,17-dihydroxy-, (17α)-	MeOH	222(4.32),256(3.48)	24-0723-73
$C_{20}H_{22}O_4$			
2H,8H-Benzo[1,2-b:5,4-b']dipyran-2-one, 10-(1,1-dimethyl-2-propenyl)-5-methoxy-8,8-dimethyl-	EtOH	230(4.31),270(4.36), 330(4.02)	102-1831B-73
[3,6'-Bi-2H-1-benzopyran]-7,7'-diol, 3,3',4,4'-tetrahydro-2',2'-dimethyl-	EtOH	285(3.89),290(3.89)	39-0907-73C
Eriobrucinol methyl ether	n.s.g.	224(4.05),333(4.02)	78-0903-73
Gibba-1,3,4a(10a),8-tetraene-10-carboxylic acid, 7-acetoxy-1-methyl-, methyl ester, (4bβ,10β)-(±)-	EtOH	265(2.52)	44-0741-73
Licarin A	MeOH	220(4.52),273(4.43)	102-1163-73

Compound	Solvent	λ_{max}(log ε)	Ref.
1H-Phenalen-1-one, 2-(2-hydroxy-1,1-dimethylpropyl)-4,9-dimethoxy-	EtOH	211(4.45),229(4.23), 265(4.25),388(4.21), 425(4.05),450(3.84)	39-2159-73C
$C_{20}H_{22}O_4S$			
6H-Cyclopenta[a]phenanthrene-2-sulfonic acid, 7,15,16,17-tetrahydro-3-methoxy-17-methyl-, methyl ester	MeOH	282.5(4.40)	94-1741-73
$C_{20}H_{22}O_5$			
3aH-Benz[e]indene-3a-carboxylic acid, 2,3,4,5-tetrahydro-7-methoxy-2-oxo-3-(3-oxobutyl)-, methyl ester	MeOH	239(3.98),300s(4.27), 319(4.41)	39-1780-73C
2H-1-Benzopyran-2-one, 5-methoxy-7-[(3-methyl-2-butenyl)oxy]-6-(3-methyl-1-oxo-2-butenyl)-	EtOH	246(4.08),270s(3.95), 324(4.05)	78-2943-73
[3,6'-Bi-2H-1-benzopyran]-3,7,7'(4H)-triol, 3',4'-dihydro-2',2'-dimethyl-, (R)-	EtOH	285(3.83)	39-0907-73C
Eriobrucinol, hydroxy-, methyl ether	n.s.g.	225(3.97),332(3.94)	78-0903-73
2(3H)-Furanone, 3-[(2,7-dimethoxy-1-naphthalenyl)methylene]dihydro-5-hydroxy-4,4,5-trimethyl-	EtOH	238(4.76)	39-2159-73C
Gibba-1,3,4a(10a)-triene-10-carboxylic acid, 7-acetoxy-1-methyl-9-oxo-, methyl ester, (4bβ,10β)-(±)-	EtOH	262(2.30),270(2.19)	44-0741-73
$C_{20}H_{22}O_6$			
Matairesinol	EtOH	232(4.10),283(3.79)	23-1050-73
	EtOH-NaOH	251(4.33),299(4.03)	23-1050-73
	n.s.g.	231(4.08),283(3.73)	105-0252-73
Pinoresinol, (+)-	n.s.g.	233(4.33),281(3.91)	105-0252-73
2-Propen-1-one, 2-methoxy-3-(4-methoxyphenyl)-1-(2,4,6-trimethoxyphenyl)-, cis	CHCl	243(4.09),300(3.95), 340s(--)	88-1001-73
trans	CHCl	242(4.10),328(4.31)	88-1001-73
$C_{20}H_{22}O_7$			
1,3-Benzodioxole-5-carboxylic acid, 6-[(3,4,5-trimethoxyphenyl)methyl]-, ethyl ester	EtOH	263(3.87),300(3.70)	39-1266-73C
1,2-Dibenzofurandicarboxylic acid, 3,9b-dihydro-7,9-dimethoxy-4,9b-dimethyl-, dimethyl ester	90% EtOH	221(4.32),272s(3.28)	12-1093-73
1,2-Dibenzofurandicarboxylic acid, 1,9b-dihydro-7,9-dimethoxy-4,9b-dimethyl-, dimethyl ester	90% EtOH	218(4.40),226s(3.77), 280s(3.52),362(3.81)	12-1093-73
Ethanone, 1-[4-(β-D-glucopyranosyloxy)-phenyl]-2-phenyl-	EtOH	212(4.08),268(4.15)	114-0435-73B
Matairesinol, hydroxy-	n.s.g.	232(4.29),283(3.99)	105-0252-73
Nortrachelogenin	EtOH	231(4.09),283(3.75)	94-1108-73
	EtOH	231(3.93),283(3.61)	94-1114-73
	EtOH-NaOH	248(4.29),297(3.96)	94-1108-73
	EtOH-NaOH	250(4.09),298(3.80)	94-1114-73
$C_{20}H_{22}O_8$			
Ethanone, 1-[4-(β-D-glucopyranosyloxy)-2-hydroxyphenyl]-2-phenyl-	EtOH	216(4.14),274(4.08), 320(3.77)	114-0435-73B
Nubilactone A	EtOH	263(4.36)	102-0883-73

Compound	Solvent	$\lambda_{max}(\log \epsilon)$	Ref.
$C_{20}H_{22}P$			
9-Phosphoniatricyclo[4.2.1.0^{2,5}]nonane, 9,9-diphenyl-, bromide	EtOH	230(4.31),256s(3.05), 261(3.19),267(3.29), 274(3.17)	35-4292-73
$C_{20}H_{22}S_4Si_2$			
Silane, [2,2'-bithiophene]-5,5'-diylbis-[dimethyl-2-thienyl-	$CHCl_3$	244(4.18),325(4.07)	88-4043-73
$C_{20}H_{22}Si_2$			
Silane, 1,4-phenylenebis[methylphenyl-	heptane	278(2.37)	70-1825-73
$C_{20}H_{23}BrN_4O_5S$			
L-Cysteine, N-acetyl-S-[5-[(4-bromophenyl)hydrazono]-1,2,3,4,5,6-hexahydro-3-hydroxy-1-methyl-6-oxo-3aH-indol-3a-yl]-	$NaHCO_3$	240(4.18),263s(--), 387(4.53)	39-0509-73C
$C_{20}H_{23}BrO_3$			
Estra-1,3,5(10)-trien-17-one, 3-acetoxy-16α-bromo-, Kober test	H_2SO_4	428(3.76),506(4.07)	94-1720-73
$C_{20}H_{23}ClN_2O_8$			
Pyrylium, 2,6-bis(1,1-dimethylethyl)-4-(6-nitro-2,1-benzisoxazol-3-yl)-, perchlorate	MeCN	244(4.50)	44-2834-73
$C_{20}H_{23}ClO_{12}$			
α-D-Glucopyranose, 1,2-O-[1-(3-chlorobenzoyl)dioxyethylidene]-2-C-methoxy-, 4,6-diacetate	EtOH	232(4.02)	23-0394-73
$C_{20}H_{23}Cl_3N_2O_4S$			
2-Butenoic acid, 2-[[3-(ethylthio)-3-oxo-2-[(phenylacetyl)amino]-1-propenyl]amino]-3-methyl-, 2,2,2-trichloroethyl ester, (E)-	EtOH	284(3.89)	39-1182-73C
$C_{20}H_{23}N$			
2,4-Pentadien-1-amine, N-(1-methylethyl)-4,5-diphenyl-, hydrochloride, (E,Z)-	MeOH	232(4.11),288(4.50), 308(4.26)	44-2169-73
$C_{20}H_{23}NO$			
4H-Carbazol-4-one, 1,2,3,5,6,7,8,9-octahydro-2,2-dimethyl-9-phenyl-	MeOH	204(4.31),256(4.22), 298s(3.59)	24-0745-73
2-Cyclohexen-1-one, 5,5-dimethyl-3-(1,2,3,4-tetrahydro-9H-carbazol-9-yl)-	MeOH	222(4.51),280(4.06), 346(3.97)	24-0745-73
$C_{20}H_{23}NOS$			
1-Propanamine, 3-(3-methoxydibenzo[b,e]-thiepin-11(6H)-ylidene)-N,N-dimethyl-, (E)-	MeOH	239(4.39),279(3.89)	73-1596-73
$C_{20}H_{23}NO_2$			
2H-Benz[g]indol-2-one, 1-cyclohexyl-1,3-dihydro-5-hydroxy-3,3-dimethyl-	MeOH	238(4.41),300(3.80), 311(3.71),324(3.56)	39-2618-73C
$C_{20}H_{23}NO_3$			
Lirinine, O-methyl ether	EtOH	222(4.46),283(4.22)	105-0475-73

Compound	Solvent	$\lambda_{max}(\log \epsilon)$	Ref.
$C_{20}H_{23}NO_3S$			
1H-Indole-3-butanol, 1-methyl-, 4-methylbenzenesulfonate	EtOH	230(4.84),285(4.21)	39-0548-73B
1H-Indole-3-butanol, 2-methyl-, 4-methylbenzenesulfonate	EtOH	231(4.88),275(3.91), 285(3.80),292(3.61)	39-0548-73B
$C_{20}H_{23}NO_4$			
Acetic acid, (3-ethyl-6,7-dihydro-9,10-dimethoxy-2H-benzo[a]quinolizin-2-ylidene)-, methyl ester, (E)-	EtOH	241(4.20),260s(--), 290(4.08),317(4.07), 384(4.27)	78-4153-73
	EtOH-HCl	230s(--),267s(--), 287(4.18),369(4.12)	78-4153-73
5H-Benzo[d]-1,3-dioxolo[4,5-j][1]benzazonine, 6,7,12,13-tetrahydro-9,10-dimethoxy-5-methyl-	EtOH	290(3.9)	88-2923-73
Corydalidzine	EtOH	212(4.46),225s(4.27), 284(3.78)	88-0803-73
Corydine, (+)-	EtOH	218(4.19),262(3.72), 270(3.70),302(3.40)	102-1505-73
Isoquinoline, 6,7-dimethoxy-1-(3,4-methylenedioxybenzyl)-2-methyl-	MeOH	213(4.48),285(3.97)	2-0342-73
Thalicmidine	n.s.g.	220(4.58),280(4.14), 305(4.18)	105-0661-73
$C_{20}H_{23}NO_5$			
Cephalotaxine, acetate	EtOH	240(3.56),290(3.63)	95-0916-73
$C_{20}H_{23}NO_6$			
Acetylalkaloid G	EtOH	243(3.62),291(3.68)	95-0916-73
Isoxazole, 3-(1,2:3,4-di-O-isopropylidene-α-D-galactopento-1,5-pyranos-5-yl)-5-phenyl-	CHCl	258(4.27)	136-0311-73D
1H-Pyrrole-3-propanoic acid, 4-(2-methoxy-2-oxoethyl)-2-methyl-5-[(phenylmethoxy)carbonyl]-, methyl ester	MeOH	285(4.29)	39-1546-73C
$C_{20}H_{23}N_2O_4$			
Pyrylium, 2,6-bis(1,1-dimethylethyl)-4-(6-nitro-2,1-benzisoxazol-3-yl)-, perchlorate	MeCN	244(4.50)	44-2834-73
$C_{20}H_{23}N_3$			
1H-Benzimidazol-1-amine, 3a,4,5,6,7,7a-hexahydro-2-methyl-N,N-diphenyl-	MeCN	291(4.27)	22-3487-73
$C_{20}H_{23}N_3O_2$			
Indolo[2',3':3,4]pyrido[1,2-b][2,7]-naphthyridin-5(1H)-one, 1-ethyl-2,3,7,8,13,13b,14,14a-octahydro-2-hydroxy-	MeOH	226(4.31),285(4.17), 290(4.16)	88-4837-73
	MeOH-acid	225(4.31),284s(4.03), 292s(4.06),306(4.11)	88-4837-73
2-Propenal, 3-[4-[[4-[ethyl(2-hydroxyethyl)amino]phenyl]azo]phenyl]-2-methyl-	EtOH	464(4.60)	7-0379-73
$C_{20}H_{23}N_3O_3$			
5H,10H-5,10-Ethano-5a,9a-(methanoxymethano)-1H-[1,2,4]triazolo[1,2-b]phthalazine-1,3(2H)-dione, tetrahydro-2-phenyl-, (5α,5aα,9aα,10α)-	MeCN	217(4.24)	78-2373-73
2-Propenal, 3-[4-[(4-amino-2,5-diethoxyphenyl)azo]phenyl]-2-methyl-	EtOH	483(4.50)	7-0379-73

Compound	Solvent	λ_{max}(log ε)	Ref.
2-Propenal, 3-[4-[[4-[bis(2-hydroxyethyl)amino]phenyl]azo]phenyl]-2-methyl-	EtOH	456(4.54)	7-0379-73
$C_{20}H_{23}N_5O_5$			
Adenosine, 2',3'-O-(1-methylethylidene)-N-(phenylmethoxy)-	pH 1	269(4.24)	94-1676-73
	pH 7	269(4.23)	94-1676-73
	pH 13	285(4.09)	94-1676-73
	EtOH	269(4.20)	94-1676-73
Adenosine, 2',3'-O-(1-methylethylidene)-1-(phenylmethoxy)-, hydrobromide	pH 1	260(4.09)	94-1676-73
	pH 7	260(4.09)	94-1676-73
	pH 13	259(4.07)	94-1676-73
	EtOH	261(4.08)	94-1676-73
$C_{20}H_{23}N_5O_7S$			
L-Cysteine, N-acetyl-S-[(1,2,3,4,5,6-hexahydro-3-hydroxy-1-methyl-5-[(4-nitrophenyl)hydrazono]-6-oxo-3aH-indol-3a-yl]-	$NaHCO_3$	233(4.14),416(4.68)	39-0509-73C
$C_{20}H_{23}N_5O_{10}$			
2(1H)-Pteridinone, 4-amino-1-(2,3,4,6-tetra-O-acetyl-β-D-glucopyranosyl)-	MeOH	238(4.34),290(3.84), 332(4.04)	24-2982-73
$C_{20}H_{23}N_5O_{11}S_4$			
3,5'-Cycloadenosine, 3'-deoxy-2',3'-didehydro-N^6-dimesyl-2'-O-tosyl-, mesylate	EtOH	219(4.15),269(4.03)	44-2896-73
$C_{20}H_{23}N_7O_4$			
Glycine, N-[N-(N-1H-purin-6-yl-DL-phenylalanyl)glycyl]-, ethyl ester	pH 1	280(4.25)	94-2349-73
	pH 7	268(4.21)	94-2349-73
	pH 13	275(4.17),280s(--)	94-2349-73
$C_{20}H_{23}N_7O_6$			
Adenosine, N-[[[2-amino-2-oxo-1-(phenylmethyl)ethyl]amino]carbonyl]-, (S)-	pH 1-2	270s(--),277(4.32)	87-0139-73
	pH 5-7	269(4.33),277s(--)	87-0139-73
	pH 12	271(4.08),301(4.24)	87-0139-73
$C_{20}H_{24}BrP$			
9-Phosphoniabicyclo[4.2.1]nonane, 9,9-diphenyl-, bromide	EtOH	233(4.30),256s(3.08), 261(3.23),267(3.33), 274(3.21)	35-4292-73
$C_{20}H_{24}F_3N_2$			
Methanaminium, N-[4-[1-[4-(dimethylamino)-2-methylphenyl]-2,2,2-trifluoroethylidene]-3-methyl-2,5-cyclohexadien-1-ylidene]-N-methyl-	98% HOAc	354(1.00),646(0.78)	39-2151-73B
$C_{20}H_{24}INO_4$			
Magnoflorine iodide	MeOH	270(3.89),305(3.60)	95-0624-73
$C_{20}H_{24}N_2O$			
Ajmalan, 19,20-didehydro-1-demethyl-11-methoxy-	MeOH	237s(3.68),295(3.66)	94-1783-73
Anhydrovobasinediol	EtOH	227(4.31),283(3.87), 292(3.81)	102-0451-73
1H-Naphtho[1,2-e][1,2]oxazine-2-carbonitrile, 3-cyclohexyl-2,3,4a,10b-tetrahydro-1-methyl-	pentane	262(3.74),268s(3.72)	33-2961-73

Compound	Solvent	$\lambda_{max}(\log \epsilon)$	Ref.
4H-Oxepino[3,4,5,6-def]carbazole-4-ethanamine, N,N-diethyl-8,10-dihydro-	n.s.g.	247(4.55),256(4.50), 263(4.33),297(4.09), 333(3.57),347(3.66)	39-2818-73C
$C_{20}H_{24}N_2OS$			
Piperazine, 1-(10,11-dihydro-7-methoxydibenzo[b,f]thiepin-10-yl)-4-methyl-	MeOH	227(4.33),262s(3.85), 291s(3.51)	73-2301-73
9H-Thioxanthen-9-one, 1-[[2-(diethylamino)ethyl]methylamino]-	EtOH	262(4.54),315(3.61), 322s(3.60),375(3.42), 428(3.56)	44-1743-73
$C_{20}H_{24}N_2O_2$			
Benzenemethanol, 3,5-dimethyl-4-[(2,4,6-trimethylphenyl)azo]-, acetate	MeOH	239(3.94),317(4.09), 458(3.02)	23-3143-73
9-Epiquinidine	EtOH	231(4.64),272s(3.64), 281(3.69),292s(3.62), 324s(3.76),334(3.80)	33-1494-73
$C_{20}H_{24}N_2O_2S$			
9H-Thioxanthen-9-one, 1-[[2-(diethylamino)ethyl]amino]-4-(hydroxymethyl)- (hycanthone)	EtOH	223(4.27),234(4.35), 257(4.65),331(3.93), 441(3.91)	44-1743-73
$C_{20}H_{24}N_2O_3$			
Benzenepropanamide, N-[2-(diethylamino)-phenyl]-4-methoxy-β-oxo-	pH 13	333(4.45)	39-0808-73B
Estra-1,3,5(10)-triene-3,17-diol, 17-(diazoacetate), (17β)-	EtOH	246(3.20),283(4.37)	44-3525-73
2(1H)-Pyridinone, 3,3'-(1-methyl-3-oxo-1-propene-1,3-diyl)bis[1-propyl-	EtOH	241(4.0),326(3.88)	103-0615-73
Talbotinic acid, deformyl-, methyl ester	EtOH	228(4.44),277s(3.82), 282(3.85),290s(3.77)	33-2719-73
$C_{20}H_{24}N_2O_4$			
1-Azulenecarboxylic acid, 2,3-bis(acetylamino)-7-(1-methylethyl)-, ethyl ester	MeOH	255(4.33),318(4.72), 357(3.85),540(2.80)	18-3266-73
D-Ribitol, 1,4-anhydro-1-C-(1,3-diphenyl-2-imidazolidinyl)-, (S)-	MeOH	250(4.57),295(3.73)	44-1836-73
Spiro[2H-indole-2,4'-[4H]pyrimidin]-3(1H)-one, 2',6'-bis(1,1-dimethylethyl)-6-nitro-	MeCN	247(4.34),273(4.18), 305(4.05)	44-2834-73
$C_{20}H_{24}N_2O_5$			
4-Nonene-3,7-dione, 2,2,8,8-tetramethyl-5-(6-nitro-2,1-benzisoxazol-3-yl)-	MeCN	276(4.22),332(3.98), 360(3.94)	44-2834-73
Spiro[2H-indole-2,4'-[4H]pyrimidin]-3(1H)-one, 2',6'-bis(1,1-dimethylethyl)-1-hydroxy-6-nitro-	MeCN	249(4.48),425(3.30)	44-2834-73
$C_{20}H_{24}N_2S$			
4H-Thiepino[3,4,5,6-def]carbazole-4-ethanamine, N,N-diethyl-8,10-dihydro-	MeOH	231(4.27),247(4.36), 265(4.23),298(3.91), 337(3.56),351(3.69)	39-2818-73C
$C_{20}H_{24}N_4O_4S_2$			
4,6(1H,5H)-Pyrimidinedione, 5-(1,3-diethyl-1,2,3,4-tetrahydro-5-methyl-4-oxo-2-thioxo-7H-pyrano[2,3-d]pyrimidin-7-ylidene)-1,3-diethyldihydro-2-thioxo-	C_6H_{12}	452(4.65),482(4.64)	39-0823-73C
	MeOH	450(4.63),475(4.75)	39-0823-73C
	$CHCl_3$	454(4.66),482(4.73)	39-0823-73C

Compound	Solvent	$\lambda_{max}(\log \epsilon)$	Ref.
$C_{20}H_{24}N_4O_5$			
7H,15H-6,15:7,14-Diethano-6a,14a-(methanoxymethano)-6H,14H-pyridazino[1,2-a]pyridazino[1',2':1,2]pyridazino-[4,5-d]pyridazine-1,4,9,12-tetrone, tetrahydro-, (6α,6aα,7β,14β,14aα,15α)-	MeCN	224(4.01),254(3.27)	78-2373-73
Phenol, 2,5-dibutyl-4-[(2,4-dinitrophenyl)azo]- (in 50% DMSO)	acid	427(4.24)	1-3641-73
	KOH	614(4.83)	1-3641-73
Phenol, 2,6-dibutyl-4-[(2,4-dinitrophenyl)azo]- (first two spectra in 50% DMSO)	acid	456(4.44)	1-3641-73
	KOH	613(4.91)	1-3641-73
	C_2Cl_4	401(4.46),440(4.52)	1-3632-73
$C_{20}H_{24}N_4O_6$			
Pyrano[2,3-d]pyrimidine-2,4-dione, 7-(1,3-diethylhexahydro-2,4,6-trioxopyrimidin-5-ylidene)-1,3-diethyl-1,7-dihydro-5-methyl-	C_6H_{12}	421(4.52),442(4.45)	39-0823-73C
	MeOH	420(4.51),441(4.58)	39-0823-73C
	$CHCl_3$	423(4.51),444(4.53)	39-0823-73C
$C_{20}H_{24}N_4O_6S$			
Propanoic acid, 3-[[1,2,3,4,5,6-hexahydro-3-hydroxy-1-(1-methylethyl)-5-[(4-nitrophenyl)hydrazono]-6-oxo-3aH-indol-3a-yl]thio]-	NaHCO	231(4.10),417(4.67)	39-0509-73C
$C_{20}H_{24}N_6O_5$			
Adenosine, N-[[(3-phenylpropyl)amino]-carbonyl]-	pH 1-2	270s(--),277(4.35)	87-0139-73
	pH 5-7	270(4.32),277s(--)	87-0139-73
	pH 12	276(4.20),299(3.86)	87-0139-73
$C_{20}H_{24}O$			
1-Naphthalenol, 1,2,3,4-tetrahydro-5,6,7,8-tetramethyl-1-phenyl-	EtOH	225s(4.18),254(3.65), 269(3.82),274(3.79), 280(3.63),285(3.61)	5-1893-73
$C_{20}H_{24}O_2$			
3H-Cyclopenta[a]phenanthren-3-one, 1,2,6,7,10,15,16,17-octahydro-11-hydroxy-10,17,17-trimethyl-, (S)-	EtOH	236(4.34),290(3.64)	39-1967-73C
Estra-1,3,5(10),15-tetraen-17-one, 3-methoxy-7α-methyl-	n.s.g.	224(4.10),272(3.32),	13-0107-73B
Isobenzofuran, 1,3-dihydro-1-methoxy-3,3-dimethyl-1-(2,4,6-trimethylphenyl)-	C_6H_{12}	257(3.5),290s(3.02)	104-1986-73
$C_{20}H_{24}O_3$			
2H-1-Benzopyran-2,4(3H)-dione, 5-methyl-3,3-bis(3-methyl-2-butenyl)-	MeOH	256(3.93),312(3.45)	24-0382-73
Estra-1,3,5(10)-trien-17-one, 3-acetoxy-, Kober test	H_2SO_4	465s(4.30),514(4.60)	94-1720-73
$C_{20}H_{24}O_4$			
2H-1-Benzopyran-2-one, 7-(3,7-dimethyl-2,6-octadienyl)oxy]-6-methoxy-, (E)-	EtOH	229(4.17),260s(4.47), 293(4.56)	102-0236-73
1,3,5-Cyclohexanetrione, 6-acetyl-2,2,4,4-tetra-2-propenyl-	EtOH-acid	282(4.03)	39-2013-73C
	EtOH-base	278(4.25)	39-2013-73C
1-Cyclopentene-1-heptanoic acid, 3-hydroxy-5-oxo-2-(2-phenylethenyl)-, (+)-	MeOH	325(4.56)	35-2664-73
Estra-1,4-diene-3,17-dione, 10β-acetoxy-, Kober test	H_2SO_4	515(4.14)	94-1720-73

Compound	Solvent	λ_{max}(log ε)	Ref.
Estra-2,5(10)-diene-1,4-dione, 17-acetoxy-, (17β)-	hexane	248(4.12),254(4.05), 330(3.00),450(1.65)	22-2086-73
	EtOH	246(4.00),340(2.74), 445(1.48)	22-2086-73
Estra-1,3,5(10)-trien-6-one, 17-acetoxy-3-hydroxy-, (17β)-	MeOH	221(4.29),254(3.93), 325(3.47)	24-0723-73
9-Octadecene-2,4,6-triynedioic acid, dimethyl ester, (Z)-	EtOH	210s(4.88),219(5.01), 228(5.06),258(3.04), 272(3.28),289(3.63), 308(3.76),329(3.58)	39-0743-73C
$C_{20}H_{24}O_5$			
2-Butenoic acid, 2-methyl-, 4,4a,5,6,8a-9-hexahydro-8a-hydroxy-3,4a,5-trimethyl-6-oxonaphtho[2,3-b]furan-4-yl ester	EtOH	222(4.22)	73-0739-73
Ethanone, 1-[9-acetoxy-3,4,5,6-tetrahydro-7-hydroxy-2-methyl-5-(1-methylethylidene)-2,6-methano-2H-1-benzoxocin-8-yl]-	EtOH	293(4.16)	78-1243-73
2(3H)-Furanone, 3-[(2,7-dimethoxy-1-naphthalenyl)hydroxymethyl]dihydro-4,4,5-trimethyl-	EtOH	238(4.17),278s(3.50)	39-2159-73C
Gibba-1,3,4a(10a)-triene-10-carboxylic acid, 7-acetoxy-9-hydroxy-1-methyl-, methyl ester	EtOH	264(2.50),272(2.41)	44-0741-73
Gibba-1,3,4a(10a)-triene-10-carboxylic acid, 8-acetoxy-7-hydroxy-1-methyl-, methyl ester	EtOH	255(2.44),273(2.28)	44-1398-73
$C_{20}H_{24}O_6$			
Benzenebutanoic acid, α-(3,4-dimethoxyphenyl)-3,4-dimethoxy-	EtOH	230(4.42),279(3.92)	4-0867-73
1-Cyclopentene-1-heptanoic acid, 2-(benzoyloxy)-4-hydroxy-5-oxo-, methyl ester, (R)-	MeOH	241(4.30)	35-1676-73
Isolariciresinol	n.s.g.	285(3.75)	105-0252-73
Pentacyclo[6.2.2.0^{2,7}.0^{3,10}.0^{4,9}]dodecane-5,11-dione, 6,12-diacetoxy-1,4,6,12-tetramethyl-	EtOH	310(1.93)	5-1675-73
4,12-Tetradecadiene-8,10-diyne-1,6,7-triol, triacetate, (E,E)-	ether	215(4.48),240(3.64), 253(3.91),267(4.04), 283(3.91)	39-0140-73C
$C_{20}H_{24}O_6S$			
Gibba-1,3,4a(10a),8-tetraene-10-carboxylic acid, 7-hydroxy-9-methoxy-1-methyl-8-(methylsulfonyl)-, methyl ester, (4bβ,10β)-(±)-	EtOH	202(4.42)(end abs.)	44-0741-73
$C_{20}H_{24}O_7$			
Punctatin	MeOH	232(4.25)	102-1421-73
$C_{20}H_{24}O_9$			
2H-1-Benzopyran-2-one, 6-acetoxy-5-(2-acetoxy-3-hydroxy-3-methylbutyl)-7,8-dimethoxy-	MeOH	208(4.56),248s(3.66), 303(4.07)	78-2645-73
7H-Furo[3,2-g][1]benzopyran-7-one, 2-[1-(glucosyloxy)-1-methylethyl)-2,3-dihydro-, (S)- (marmesinin)	EtOH	244(4.09),247(3.67), 257(3.59),335(4.24)	100-0333-73

Compound	Solvent	$\lambda_{max}(\log \epsilon)$	Ref.
$C_{20}H_{24}O_{10}$			
Acetic acid, [4-(β-D-glucopyranosyloxy)-7-methoxy-5-methyl-2H-1-benzopyran-2-ylidene]-, methyl ester	MeOH	300(3.75)	94-0149-73
$C_{20}H_{24}P$			
9-Phosphoniabicyclo[4.2.1]nonane, 9,9-diphenyl-, bromide	EtOH	233(4.30),256s(3.08), 261(3.23),267(3.33), 274(3.21)	35-4292-73
$C_{20}H_{24}S$			
1H-Thioxanthene, 2,3,4,4a,5,6,7,8-octahydro-4a-(phenylmethyl)-	n.s.g.	237(3.90),272(3.20)	104-2190-73
1H-Thioxanthene, 2,3,4,5,6,7,8,9-octahydro-9-(phenylmethyl)-	n.s.g.	244(4.20)	104-2190-73
$C_{20}H_{25}ClN_2O_2$			
Benzenamine, 4-chloro-2-[[(2,2-diethoxyethyl)imino]phenylmethyl]-N-methyl-	EtOH	230(4.46),378(3.79)	95-1263-73
$C_{20}H_{25}FO_3$			
Estra-1,3,5(10)-triene-3,17-diol, 2-fluoro-, 17-acetate, 17β-	EtOH	281(3.42)	78-4053-73
$C_{20}H_{25}NO$			
2,5-Cyclohexadien-1-one, 2,6-bis(1,1-dimethylethyl)-4-(phenylimino)-	EtOH	275(4.49),492(3.07)	78-0085-73
1-Penten-3-one, 4-methyl-1-[2-(1-piperidinyl)-1H-inden-3-yl]-	EtOH	232(4.13),260(4.00), 309(4.27),443(4.28)	48-1161-73
$C_{20}H_{25}NOS$			
2,5-Cyclohexadiene-1,4-dione, 2,6-bis-(1,1-dimethylethyl)-, 4-(S-phenylthiooxime)	$CHCl_3$	278(4.28),340(3.53), 434(4.28)	39-1031-73C
$C_{20}H_{25}NO_2$			
Acetamide, N-(17-oxoestra-1,3,5(10)-trien-3-yl)-, Kober test	H_2SO_4	483(4.01)	94-1720-73
$C_{20}H_{25}NO_3$			
Phenanthro[2,3-d]isoxazole-4-carboxylic acid, 1,2,3,4,4a,5,6,11b-octahydro-4,8,11b-trimethyl-, methyl ester, [4S-(4α,4aβ,11bα)]-	EtOH	242(3.93),247(3.97), 254(3.85),295(3.58)	12-1763-73
Phenanthro[2,3-d]oxazole-4-carboxylic acid, 1,2,3,4,4a,5,6,11b-octahydro-4,9,11b-trimethyl-, methyl ester, [4S-(4α,4aβ,11bα)]-	EtOH	238(3.71),274(3.33), 280(3.50),283(3.47), 290(3.52)	12-1763-73
$C_{20}H_{25}NO_4$			
Acetic acid, (3-ethyl-3,4,6,7-tetrahydro-9,10-dimethoxy-2H-benzo[a]quinolizin-2-ylidene)-, methyl ester	EtOH	237(4.30),292(4.00), 418(4.45)	78-4153-73
	EtOH-HCl	234(3.86),264(4.10), 316(4.14),396(3.96)	78-4153-73
	HOAc	263(4.08),318(4.14), 396(3.95)	78-4153-73
Erybidine	EtOH	216(4.50),284(3.92)	95-1211-73 +95-1218-73
Erythristemine	EtOH	235(4.3),283(3.5)	39-0874-73C

Compound	Solvent	$\lambda_{max}(\log \epsilon)$	Ref.
$C_{20}H_{25}NO_5$			
6-Isoquinolinemethanol, 1,2,3,4-tetra-hydro-5-hydroxy-1-[(3,4,5-trimethoxy-phenyl)methyl]-	EtOH	278(3.30)	78-0857-73
6-Isoquinolinemethanol, 1,2,3,4-tetra-hydro-7-hydroxy-1-[(3,4,5-trimethoxy-phenyl)methyl]-	EtOH	285(3.48)	78-0857-73
7-Isoquinolinemethanol, 1,2,3,4-tetra-hydro-6-hydroxy-1-[(3,4,5-trimethoxy-phenyl)methyl]-	EtOH	282(3.48)	78-0857-73
$C_{20}H_{25}N_2O_2$			
Methanaminium, N-[4-[1-[4-(dimethyl-amino)phenyl]-2-ethoxy-2-oxoethyl-idene]-2,5-cyclohexadien-1-ylidene]-N-methyl-, chloride	$MeNO_2$	646(4.65)	104-1766-73
$C_{20}H_{25}N_3O$			
LSD (tartrate)	H_2O	312(4.14)	39-1312-73B
	EtOH	311(4.22)	39-1312-73B
$C_{20}H_{25}N_3O_3$			
Phenol, 2,6-dibutyl-4-[(2-nitrophenyl)-azo]-	C_2Cl_4	395(4.23),457(4.41)	1-3632-73
$C_{20}H_{25}N_3O_{10}S$			
4H-Pyrrolo[2,3-d]pyrimidin-4-one, 3,5,6,7-tetrahydro-2-[(2,3,4,6-tetra-O-acetyl-β-D-glucopyranosyl)thio]-	EtOH	228(4.74),272(4.11)	104-1995-73
$C_{20}H_{26}$			
Bi-2,4,6-cycloheptatrien-1-yl, x,x-bis-(1-methylethyl)-	EtOH	254(3.89)	18-1785-73
5,7,9,11-Hexadecatetraene-3,13-diyne, 2,2,15,15-tetramethyl-, (all-E)-	hexane	310(4.24),329(4.74), 346(5.00),365(5.07)	5-1339-73
$C_{20}H_{26}Cl_2N_4$			
2-Tetrazene, 1,4-bis(3-chlorophenyl)-1,4-bis(1,1-dimethylethyl)-	EtOH	250(3.93),311(3.75)	35-8707-73
$C_{20}H_{26}INO_4$			
Orientaline methiodide	EtOH	225s(4.23),283(3.73)	39-0874-73C
	EtOH-NaOH	252(4.17),310(3.84)	39-0874-73C
$C_{20}H_{26}N_2O_2$			
Aspidospermidin-20-ol, 1,2-didehydro-16-methoxy-	EtOH	230(3.93),255(3.53), 282(3.49)	25-1032-73
Isoquinoline, 1-(2-amino-3-hydroxy-4-methoxybenzyl)-2-propyl-1,2,3,4-tetrahydro-	EtOH	264(3.18),271(3.21)	87-1223-73
	EtOH-NaOH	271(--),290(--)	87-1223-73
1H-Pyrido[3,2-c]carbazole-6β-carboxylic acid, 4aα-ethyl-2,3,4,4a,5,6,7,11cα-octahydro-7-methyl-, methyl ester	MeOH	221(4.49),277(3.83), 282(3.84),291s(3.76)	35-7146-73
$C_{20}H_{26}N_2O_2S$			
Ajmalan, 1-demethyl-1-(methylsulfonyl)-, (2α)-	MeOH	231(3.88),277(3.26), 283(3.23)	94-1783-73
(2α,20α)-	MeOH	231(3.80),277(3.26), 283(3.21)	94-1783-73

Compound	Solvent	$\lambda_{max}(\log \epsilon)$	Ref.
$C_{20}H_{26}N_2O_4$			
1H-Pyrrole-3-ethanol, 2-[[4-[2-(acetyl-oxy)ethyl]-3,5-dimethyl-2H-pyrrol-2-ylidene]methyl]-4-methyl-, acetate, hydrobromide	$CHCl_3$	366(3.85),479(4.82)	39-2923-73C
$C_{20}H_{26}N_2O_5$			
1H-Indole-4-acetic acid, 3-(ethoxycarbo-nyl)-5-hydroxy-1,2-dimethyl-α-[1-(methylamino)ethylidene]-, ethyl ester, (Z)-	dioxan	220(4.40),255(4.24), 285(4.25),315s(3.90)	78-0921-73
$C_{20}H_{26}N_4O_6$			
1-Cyclopentene-1-heptanoic acid, 5-(2,4-dinitrophenylhydrazone), ethyl ester	EtOH	381(4.29)	32-0031-73
$C_{20}H_{26}N_5O_{10}$			
1H-Purinium, 2-amino-6,9-dihydro-9-meth-yl-6-oxo-7-(2,3,4,6-tetra-O-acetyl-β-D-glucopyranosyl)-, bromide	pH 4	253(4.06),286(3.82)	24-1389-73
	pH 9	223(4.26),290(3.80)	24-1389-73
$C_{20}H_{26}N_8O$			
Benzamide, 4-[[(2,4-diamino-6-pteridin-yl)methyl]methylamino]-N-(1-methyl-butyl)-	EtOH	261(4.41),291(4.38), 375(3.89)	4-0425-73
$C_{20}H_{26}O$			
Gona-1,3,5(10),13-tetraene, 3-methoxy-17,17-dimethyl-, Kober test	H_2SO_4	440s(4.10),466(4.27), 520(3.42)	94-1720-73
$C_{20}H_{26}O_2$			
Androsta-4,6-diene-3,17-dione, 6-meth-yl-, (9β,10α)-	EtOH	288(4.35)	33-2396-73
Androsta-1,4,6-trien-3-one, 17-hydroxy-17-methyl-, (17β)-	MeOH	223(4.38),258(4.30), 299(1.40)	13-0763-73B
3'H-Cycloprop[15,16]androsta-4,15-diene-3,17-dione, 15,16-dihydro-	MeOH	239(4.21)	24-0888-73
1,4-Ethanonaphthalen-9-ol, 1,4-dihydro-1,2,3,4,10,10-hexamethyl-, acetate, syn	EtOH	209(4.27),257(2.93), 264(3.03),272(2.93)	35-4592-73
Gona-1,3,5(10),8-tetraen-17α-ol, 13β-ethyl-3-methoxy-, (±)-	EtOH	275(4.21)	94-0107-73
2(1H)-Phenanthrenone, 4a,9,10,10a-tetra-hydro-6-hydroxy-1,1,4a-trimethyl-8-(1-methylethyl)-	EtOH	225(4.44),284(3.58)	138-0321-73
4(1H)-Phenanthrenone, 4a,9,10,10a-tetra-hydro-6-hydroxy-1,1,4a-trimethyl-8-(1-methylethyl)-	EtOH	223(4.21),285(3.38)	138-1117-73
4(1H)-Phenanthrenone, 4a,9,10,10a-tetra-hydro-8-hydroxy-1,1,4a-trimethyl-6-(1-methylethyl)-	EtOH	223(4.22),281(3.34)	138-1117-73
Phenol, 4-(3-ethenyl-3,6-dimethyl-1-methylene-5-heptenyl)-, acetate	EtOH	250(4.28)	78-1119-73
1-Propanone, 1-[1,4,4a,5,6,7,8,8a-octa-hydro-2-(phenylmethoxy)-1-naphthalen-yl]-	C_6H_{12}	230(3.06)	28-0883-73A
$C_{20}H_{26}O_3$			
1H-Cyclopenta[a]cyclopropa[f]cycloundec-ene-4,7-dione, 1a,5,6,10,11,11a-hexa-	EtOH	220(4.03),263(3.96), 332(3.53)	78-0403-73

Compound	Solvent	λ_{max}(log ϵ)	Ref.
hydro-10-hydroxy-1,1,3,6,9-pentamethyl- (bertyadionol) (cont.)			
1H-Cyclopenta[a]cyclopropa[f]cycloundecene-4,7,10(1aH)-trione, 4a,5,6,7a,11-11a-hexahydro-1,1,3,6,9-pentamethyl-	EtOH	215(3.40),245(3.51), 275(3.53)	78-0403-73
Estra-1,3,5(10)-trien-17-one, 2,3-dimethoxy-, Kober test	H_2SO_4	410(4.07),490(4.20), 508s(4.32),536(4.37)	94-1720-73
D-Homoestra-1,3,5(10)-trien-17a-one, 14β-hydroxy-3-methoxy-, (8α,9α)-	EtOH	277(3.4)	70-0088-73
(8α,9β)-	EtOH	277(3.3)	70-0088-73
Maytenoquinone	EtOH	317(4.21),324s(4.20), 414(3.33)	78-2553-73
4a(2H)-Naphthalenecarboxaldehyde, 1-[2-(3-furanyl)ethyl]-1,3,4,7,8,8a-hexahydro-1,2,5-trimethyl-7-oxo-	EtOH	243(3.85)	23-1332-73
isomer	EtOH	244(3.98)	23-1332-73
1H-Naphtho[1,8a-c]furan-3(5H)-one, 7-[2-(3-furanyl)ethyl]-6,6a,7,8,9,10-hexahydro-7,8-dimethyl-	EtOH	210(4.26)	23-1346-73
$C_{20}H_{26}O_4$			
[1,1'-Biphenyl]-2,2'-diol, 3,3'-dimethoxy-5,5'-dipropyl-	EtOH	249(4.00),289(3.76)	12-1337-73
	EtOH-KOH	258(4.13),310(3.97)	12-1337-73
1-Cyclopentene-1-heptanoic acid, 3-hydroxy-5-oxo-2-(2-phenylethyl)-, (+)-	MeOH	236(4.15)	35-2664-73
Estra-1,3,5(10)-triene-3,6,17-triol, 17-acetate, (6β,17β)-	EtOH	221(3.85),283(3.30), 288s(3.27)	78-4053-73
Estr-4-ene-3,6-dione, 17β-acetoxy-	MeOH	251(4.05)	24-0723-73
1-Naphthalenecarboxylic acid, 5-[2-(3-furanyl)ethyl]-4a,5,6,7,8,8a-hexahydro-8a-(hydroxymethyl)-5,6-dimethyl-	n.s.g.	286(3.96)	78-2575-73
2,9-Octadecadiene-4,6-diynedioic acid, dimethyl ester, (E,Z)-	EtOH	215(4.46),223(4.54), 271(4.02),287(4.29), 305(4.28)	39-0743-73C
(Z,Z)-	EtOH	217(4.40),225(4.46), 275(3.97),289(4.18), 307(4.15)	39-0743-73C
2,9(1H,3H)-Phenanthrenedione, 4,4a,10-10a-tetrahydro-5-hydroxy-6-methoxy-1,4a-dimethyl-7-(1-methylethyl)-, [1S-(1α,4aβ,10aα)]-	pH 13	256(4.46),296(3.85), 377(3.63)	78-1227-73
	EtOH	229(4.20),273(3.95), 316(3.54)	78-1227-73
Senemorin	EtOH	219(4.11)	73-0739-73
$C_{20}H_{26}O_5$			
Nemosenin A	EtOH	220(4.09)	73-0739-73
Spiro[1,3-dioxolane-2,2'(1'H)-phenanthrene]-10'a-carboxylic acid, 4'b,5'-6',7',9',10'-hexahydro-4'b,8-dimethyl-7'-oxo-, methyl ester, (4'aS-cis)-	EtOH	248(4.01)	39-2083-73C
$C_{20}H_{26}O_6$			
Coleon C	EtOH	266(4.05),283(3.87), 327(3.67),395(3.77)	33-2534-73
Coleon D	EtOH	283(3.74),346(3.76), 421(3.88)	33-2534-73
Deacetyleupacunin	MeOH	208(4.15)(end abs.)	44-2189-73
Podocarp-7-eno-16,6β-lactone, 3,17-epoxy-3α-hydroxy-13-(hydroxyacetyl)-13-methyl-	MeOH	205(3.70)	39-2551-73C

Compound	Solvent	λ_{max}(log ϵ)	Ref.
$C_{20}H_{26}O_7$			
3,6-Epoxy-1H,3H,11H-furo[3,4-e][3]benz-oxepin-11-one, 8-(hexahydrofuro[2,3-b]furan-2-yl)-3a,4,6,7,7a,8-hexa-hydro-3a-hydroxy-8,9-dimethyl-	MeOH	248(3.95)	39-0712-73C
Punctatin, dihydro-	MeOH	216(4.11),232s(3.95)	102-1421-73
$C_{20}H_{27}BrO_3$			
Androst-4-ene-3,11-dione, 9α-bromo-17β-hydroxy-17α-methyl-	EtOH	237(4.21)	39-1967-73C
$C_{20}H_{27}ClN_2O$			
Antirhine methochloride	MeOH	220(4.56),272(3.88), 279(3.86),289(3.75)	95-0483-73
$C_{20}H_{27}ClO$			
Dehydroabietyl chloride	isooctane	267(2.87),275(2.87)	23-3236-73
$C_{20}H_{27}ClO_2$			
Androsta-4,6-dien-3-one, 7-chloro-17β-hydroxy-17α-methyl-	EtOH	293(4.47)	87-0065-73
$C_{20}H_{27}FO_4$			
Estr-4-en-3-one, 17β-acetoxy-2α-fluoro-10β-hydroxy-	C_6H_{12}	227.5(4.13)	78-4053-73
	EtOH	234(4.11)	78-4053-73
Estr-4-en-3-one, 17β-acetoxy-2β-fluoro-10α-hydroxy-	C_6H_{12}	225(4.11)	78-4053-73
	EtOH	233(4.15)	78-4053-73
Estr-4-en-3-one, 17β-acetoxy-2β-fluoro-10β-hydroxy-	C_6H_{12}	236.5(4.10)	78-4053-73
	EtOH	239(4.08)	78-4053-73
$C_{20}H_{27}NO_4$			
1-Phenanthrenecarboxylic acid, 1,2,3,4-4a,9,10,10a-octahydro-6-hydroxy-7-[1-(hydroxyimino)ethyl]-1,4a-dimeth-yl-, methyl ester, [1S-(1α,4aα,10aβ)]-	EtOH	259(4.02),267(3.92), 315(3.65)	12-1763-73
Spiro[1,3-dioxolane-2,5'-[5H]inden]-1'(4'H)-one, hexahydro-4'-[[(3-meth-oxyphenyl)amino]methyl]-7'a-methyl-, (3'aα,4'α,7'aβ)-	EtOH	250(3.70),290(3.00)	65-0663-73
$C_{20}H_{27}NO_5$			
Carbamic acid, [2-[1-(3,4-dimethoxyphen-yl)-4-oxo-2-cyclohexen-1-yl]ethyl]-methyl-, ethyl ester, (±)-	MeOH	226(4.37),278(3.55)	33-0347-73
Isoquinoline, 1,2,3,4,5,6,7,8-octahydro-1-[2-(3-methoxyphenyl)ethyl]-, oxalate	EtOH	272(3.32),279(3.27)	4-0217-73
$C_{20}H_{27}NO_6$			
Stephasunoline	EtOH	286(3.30)	88-4263-73
$C_{20}H_{27}NO_8S$			
Butanoic acid, 4-[[[3,4-dihydro-6,7-di-methoxy-2-(methoxysulfonyl)-1(2H)-naphthalenylidene]acetyl]amino]-, methyl ester	pH 1	247(4.03),357(4.16)	4-0137-73
	pH 11	233(4.04),276(4.12), 313(4.04)	4-0137-73
$C_{20}H_{27}N_2$			
Piperidinium, 1-[4-(1,3-dihydro-1,3,3-trimethyl-2H-indol-2-ylidene)-2-but-enylidene]-, perchlorate	n.s.g.	476(5.11)	104-1286-73

Compound	Solvent	λ max (log ε)	Ref.
$C_{20}H_{27}N_7O_3$			
Benzenepropanamide, α-amino-N-[3-[6-(dimethylamino)-9H-purin-9-yl]-2-hydroxypropyl]-4-methoxy-	pH 1	269(4.27)	87-0037-73
	pH 7	276(4.29)	87-0037-73
	pH 13	276(4.29)	87-0037-73
diastereoisomer	pH 1	269(4.28)	87-0037-73
	pH 7	276(4.29)	87-0037-73
	pH 13	275(4.30)	87-0037-73
$C_{20}H_{27}N_7O_{11}P_2$			
Pyridinium, 3-(aminocarbonyl)-1-[5-O-[8-(6-amino-9H-purin-9-yl)-1,3-dihydroxy-2,4-dioxa-1,3-diphosphaoct-1-yl]-β-D-ribofuranosyl]-, hydroxide, inner salt, P,P'-dioxide, reduced	pH 9.5	262(4.15),339(3.79)	5-0531-73
oxidized	pH 9.5	261.5(4.27)	5-0531-73
cyanide addition compd.	pH 10	327(4.16)	5-0531-73
$C_{20}H_{28}N_2O$			
2'H-Androsta-2,4-dieno[3,2-c]pyrazol-17-ol, (17β)-	n.s.g.	260(3.86)	65-0403-73
$C_{20}H_{28}N_2O_2$			
2H-3,7-Methanoazacycloundecino[5,4-b]indole-7(4H)-methanol, 1,5,6,8,9,10-hexahydro-12-methoxy-α-methyl-	EtOH	230(4.37),270(3.64), 300(3.64)	25-1032-73
$C_{20}H_{28}N_4$			
2-Tetrazene, 1,4-bis(1,1-dimethylethyl)-1,4-diphenyl-	C_6H_{12}	312(3.80)	73-0046-73
	THF	312(3.86)	73-0046-73
$C_{20}H_{28}N_4OS$			
1,2,4-Triazino[5,6-d][3,1]benzoxazepine, 6,7-dihydro-6,6-dimethyl-3-(octylthio)-	EtOH	240(4.40),351(3.99), 444(3.80)	78-0639-73
$C_{20}H_{28}N_4O_5S$			
L-Glutamic acid, N-[1-oxo-5-(7H-pyrrolo-[2,3-d]pyrimidin-4-ylthio)pentyl]-, diethyl ester	pH 1	220(4.30),258(3.99), 311(3.98)	73-1438-73
	pH 13	222(4.26),249(3.88), 294(4.06)	73-1438-73
$C_{20}H_{28}N_4O_6$			
Cyclopentaneheptanoic acid, 2-[(2,4-dinitrophenyl)hydrazono]-, ethyl ester	EtOH	364(4.24)	32-0031-73
$C_{20}H_{28}O$			
Retinol, 11,12-didehydro-, 13-cis	EtOH	317(4.51)	104-1868-73
$C_{20}H_{28}O_2$			
Androsta-1,4-dien-3-one, 17-hydroxy-17-methyl-, (17β)-	MeOH	243(4.10)	13-0763-73B
Cyclobuta[1,2-c:4,3-c']diindene-1,12-dione, tetradecahydro-6a,6b-dimethyl-	hexane	302(2.10)	88-3441-73
Cyclobuta[b]naphthalene-3,8-dione, 1,2-butyl-2a,3a,4,7,7a,8a-hexahydro-	EtOH	294(2.69)	104-2389-73
3'H-Cycloprop[15,16]androsta-4,15-dien-3-one, 15,16-dihydro-17-hydroxy-, (15β,16β,17β)-	MeOH	240(4.22)	24-0888-73
Estra-1,3,5(10)-triene, 3,17β-dimethoxy-, Kober test	H_2SO_4	440s(3.96),468(4.14), 513(4.13)	94-1720-73

Compound	Solvent	λ_{max}(log ε)	Ref.
Gona-1,3,5(10)-trien-17-ol, 13-ethyl-3-methoxy-, (17α)-(±)-	EtOH	279(3.29),288(3.26)	94-0107-73
Gon-4-en-3-one, 17-hydroxy-13-(2-propenyl)-, (17α)-(±)-	EtOH	234(4.18)	94-2202-73
(17β)-(±)-	EtOH	240(--)	94-2195-73
2(1H)-Naphthalenone, 8-[2-(3-furanyl)-ethyl]-4a,5,6,7,8,8a-hexahydro-4,4a-7,8-tetramethyl-, (4aα,7α,8β,8aβ)-	EtOH	247(3.88)	23-1332-73
2(1H)-Phenanthrenone, 3,4,4a,9,10,10a-hexahydro-8-hydroxy-1,1,4a-trimethyl-6-(1-methylethyl)-	EtOH	225(4.29),279(3.15)	138-1117-73
Retinoic acid (vitamin A acid)	EtOH	350(4.61)	22-0746-73
13-cis	EtOH	351(4.59)	32-0117-73
all-trans	EtOH	350(4.65)	32-0117-73
Retinoic acid, 11,12-dihydro-11-hydroxy-, δ-lactone	EtOH	230(4.19),270(4.03)	32-0117-73
Sugiol (7-oxoferruginol)	EtOH	233(4.16),284(4.10), 290s(4.09)	78-2553-73
$C_{20}H_{28}O_3$			
Allocyathin B	MeOH	235(3.71)	23-3842-73
Androst-4-ene-3,17-dione, 6-(hydroxymethyl)-, (6α)-	EtOH	239(4.19)	33-2396-73
(6β)-	EtOH	242(4.20)	33-2396-73
(6β,9β,10α)-	EtOH	241(4.19)	33-2396-73
Cyathin B_3-C_3 (mixture)	dioxan	233(3.83)	23-3157-73
1H-Cyclopenta[a]cyclopropa[f]cycloundecene-4,7-dione, 1a,4a,5a,7a,10,11,11a-octahydro-10-hydroxy-1,1,3,6,9-pentamethyl-	EtOH	275(4.20)	78-0403-73
Dispermone (17-hydroxy-7-oxototarol)	EtOH	241(4.09),285(3.95), 325(3.74)	78-2553-73
Estra-1,3,5(10)-trien-17-ol, 3,16-dimethoxy-, (16α,17β)-(±)-	EtOH	278(3.15),287(3.14)	94-0697-73
Gona-1,3,5(10)-triene-13-ethanol, 17-hydroxy-3-methoxy-	EtOH	279(3.29),287(3.26)	94-2427-73
19-Norpregn-4-ene-3,20-dione, 10β-hydroxy-	n.s.g.	236(4.164)	105-0174-73
1,4-Phenanthrenedione, 4b,5,6,7,8,8a,9-10-octahydro-3-hydroxy-4b,7,8-trimethyl-2-propyl-, [4bS-(4bα,7α,8α,8aβ)]-	ether	271(4.11),280s(4.09), 403(2.7)	33-1129-73
2(1H)-Phenanthrenone, 3,4,4a,9,10,10a-hexahydro-5-hydroxy-6-methoxy-1,4a-dimethyl-7-(1-methylethyl)-	EtOH	273(3.11),279(3.11)	78-1227-73
$C_{20}H_{28}O_4$			
Estr-4-ene-3,17-dione, 2,6-bis(hydroxymethyl)-, (2α,6β)-	EtOH	244(4.10)	33-2396-73
Estr-4-en-3-one, 17-acetoxy-2-hydroxy-, (2β,17β)-	EtOH	242(4.17)	39-1830-73C
Estr-4-en-3-one, 17-acetoxy-10-hydroxy-, (10α,17β)-	C_6H_{12}	224(4.23)	78-4053-73
	EtOH	232.5(4.29)	78-4053-73
(10β,17β)-	C_6H_{12}	227(4.17)	78-4053-73
	EtOH	234(4.15)	78-4053-73
Furanoeremophilane, 3β-angeloyloxy-9β-hydroxy-	EtOH	219(4.16)	18-2840-73
Furanoeremophilane, 10β-hydroxy-6β-senecioyloxy-	EtOH	218(4.32)	18-2840-73
Marrubiagenin	MeCN	209(4.30)	24-2929-73
19-Norpregn-4-ene-3,20-dione, 10β-hydroperoxy-	n.s.g.	237(4.19)	105-0174-73

Compound	Solvent	$\lambda_{max}(\log \epsilon)$	Ref.
9(1H)-Phenanthrenone, 2,3,4,4a,10,10a-hexahydro-2,5-dihydroxy-6-methoxy-1,4a-dimethyl-7-(1-methylethyl)-, [1S-(1α,2β,4aβ,10aβ)]-	EtOH	229(4.02),273(3.79), 317(3.30)	78-1227-73
1-Propanone, 2-methyl-1-(2,4,6-trihydroxy-3,5-bis(3-methyl-2-butenyl)phenyl]-	EtOH	293(4.21)	39-0419-73C
$C_{20}H_{28}O_5$			
Andrographolide, 14-deoxy-11-oxo-	n.s.g.	227(3.95)	39-1247-73C
Cyclopentaneheptenoic acid, 2-(3-cyclopentyl-3-oxo-1-propynyl)-3-hydroxy-5-oxo-	EtOH	222(3.98)	87-0429-73
2H-Naphtho[1,8-bc]furan-6-carboxylic acid, 3,4,5,5a,6,7,8,8a-octahydro-7-methyl-2-oxo-6-[2-(tetrahydro-3-furanyl)ethyl]-, methyl ester	EtOH	223(4.11)	105-0027-73
Nemosenin B	EtOH	218(3.76)	73-0739-73
$C_{20}H_{28}O_6$			
Benzoic acid, 4-[(3,7-dimethyl-2,6-octadienyl)oxy]-2-hydroxy-3-(hydroxymethyl)-6-methoxy-, methyl ester	EtOH	225(4.15),270(3.95), 303(3.26)	12-2459-73
	EtOH-KOH	230(4.02),272(3.26), 300(3.26)	12-2459-73
Benzoic acid, 6-[(3,7-dimethyl-2,6-octadienyl)oxy]-2-hydroxy-3-(hydroxymethyl)-4-methoxy-, methyl ester	EtOH	226(4.20),270(3.90), 304(3.40)	12-2459-73
	EtOH-KOH	224(4.08),272(3.26), 306(3.30)	12-2459-73
$C_{20}H_{28}S_3$			
Dispiro[adamantane-2,3'-[1,2,4]trithiolane]-5',2"-adamantane	C_6H_{12}	222(3.11),253(2.98)	39-2862-73C
$C_{20}H_{29}BrO_3$			
Androst-4-en-3-one, 9-bromo-11,17-dihydroxy-17-methyl-, (11β,17β)-	EtOH	244(4.18)	39-1967-73C
$C_{20}H_{29}ClN_4O_6$			
Benzo[g]pteridinium, 2-ethoxy-5,5-diethyl-3,4,5,10-tetrahydro-3,7,8,10-tetramethyl-4-oxo-, perchlorate	pH 7	215(4.16),245(4.15), 265(4.02),295(4.07), 315(3.98)	5-1388-73
$C_{20}H_{29}ClO$			
Androsta-4,6-dien-17-ol, 7-chloro-17-methyl-, (17β)-	EtOH	240(4.28),246(4.35), 253(4.21)	87-0065-73
$C_{20}H_{29}ClO_2$			
Androsta-5,7-diene-3,17-diol, 7-chloro-17-methyl-, (3β,17β)-	EtOH	263(3.83),273(3.95), 283(3.95),295(3.68)	87-0065-73
$C_{20}H_{29}FO_2$			
D-Homoandrost-16-en-17a-one, 17-fluoro-3-hydroxy-, (3β,5α)-	n.s.g.	234(3.86)	35-6655-73
$C_{20}H_{29}NO_2$			
Cyclopropa[d]naphthalene-2-acetaldehyde, α-[(dimethylamino)methylene]-3-formyl-1,1a,4,4a,5,6,7,8-octahydro-4,8,8-trimethyl-, [1aα,2(Z),4aβ,8aS*]-	EtOH	286(4.50)	54-0985-73

Compound	Solvent	$\lambda_{max}(\log \epsilon)$	Ref.
Isoquinoline, 1-[2-(3,4-dimethoxyphenyl)ethyl]-1,2,3,4,5,6,7,8-octahydro-2-methyl-	EtOH	229(3.96),280(3.51), 283s(3.46)	4-0217-73
hydrobromide	EtOH	229(3.94),279(3.51), 284s(3.44)	4-0217-73
$C_{20}H_{29}NO_3$			
7-Oxa-5α-androstano[2,3-d]isoxazole, 17β-hydroxy-17α-methyl-	MeOH	228(3.70)	87-0257-73
7-Oxa-5α-androstano[3,2-c]isoxazole, 17β-hydroxy-17α-methyl-	MeOH	225(3.59)	87-0257-73
$C_{20}H_{30}$			
Pentalene, 1,3,5-tris(1,1-dimethylethyl)-	hexane	211(4.27),280(3.34), 333(3.50),598(1.81)	89-0575-73
$C_{20}H_{30}N_2O$			
Androstano[3,2-c]pyrazole, 17β-hydroxy-	n.s.g.	230(4.07)	65-0403-73
$C_{20}H_{30}N_2O_2$			
Androst-4-en-3-one, 17-hydroxy-2-(hydroxymethylene)-, hydrazone	n.s.g.	252(3.96)	65-0403-73
7-Oxa-5α-androstano[3,2-c]pyrazole, 17β-hydroxy-17α-methyl-	EtOH	222(3.67)	87-0257-73
$C_{20}H_{30}N_2O_3$			
Quino[6,5-f]quinoline-2,8-dione, 1,3,4-4a,4b,5,6,6a,7,9,10,10a,10b,11-tetradecahydro-1-(2-hydroxyethyl)-4a,6a-dimethyl-, [4aR-(4aα,4bβ,6aα,10aβ,10bα)]-	MeOH	235(4.01)	39-1204-73C
$C_{20}H_{30}O$			
Androsta-1,3-dien-17-ol, 5-methyl-, (5α,17β)-	MeOH	266(3.49)	35-3932-73C
1(2H)-Naphthalenone, 3,4-dihydro-4,4,6-8-tetramethyl-7-(3-methylpentyl)-	EtOH	220(4.42),264(4.18), 303(3.40)	39-1754-73C
$C_{20}H_{30}O_2$			
β-Dicarvelone	EtOH	210(3.85),286(1.98)	12-0883-73
γ-Dicarvelone	EtOH	235(4.26)	12-0883-73
Estr-4-en-3-one, 16-ethyl-17-hydroxy-, (16β,17β)-(±)-	EtOH	240(4.19)	95-0566-73
Gon-4-en-3-one, 17-hydroxy-13-propyl-, (17β)-(±)-	EtOH	240(4.17)	94-2195-73
Kaur-16-en-15-one, 11-hydroxy-, (11β)-	n.s.g.	238(3.85)	39-0736-73C
2,7-Nonadien-4-yne-1,6-diol, 3,7-dimethyl-9-(2,6,6-trimethyl-1-cyclohexen-1-yl)-, (E,E)-	EtOH	230(4.22)	104-1868-73
Retinoic acid, 7,8-dihydro-	EtOH	300(4.21)	65-2047-73
$C_{20}H_{30}O_3$			
Allocyathin B_3, 11,12-dihydro-	MeOH	253(3.26)	23-3842-73
Cyathin A_3	MeOH	230s(3.36),315(1.71)	23-3842-73
	dioxan	324(1.63)	23-3842-73
4H-5,9a-Epoxydicyclopenta[a,d]cyclooct-en-4-one, 1,2,5,6,6a,7,8,8,9,10a-decahydro-9-(hydroxymethyl)-6,10a-dimethyl-3-(1-methylethyl)-	n.s.g.	255(3.88)	39-1590-73C
Estr-4-en-3-one, 17-hydroxy-6-(hydroxymethyl)-17-methyl-, (6α,17β)-	EtOH	241(4.19)	33-2396-73
(6β,17β)-	EtOH	242(4.18)	33-2396-73

Compound	Solvent	λ_{max}(log ε)	Ref.
$C_{20}H_{30}O_4$			
Haplopappic acid	EtOH	220(4.29)	102-1755-73
Marrubiagenin, 13,14-dihydro-	MeCN	216(4.01)	24-2929-73
Mebadonin	EtOH	232(3.92)	138-0255-73
7-Oxa-5α-androstan-3-one, 17β-hydroxy-2-(hydroxymethylene)-17α-methyl-	EtOH	281(3.95)	87-0257-73
Prost-8(12)-en-13-yn-1-oic acid, 9-hydroxy-11-oxo-, (±)-	MeOH	263(4.20)	88-2213-73
$C_{20}H_{30}O_6$			
2-Propenal, 3-[2-hydroxy-5-[1-hydroxy-2-[4-hydroxy-6,6-dimethyl-3-oxabicyclo[3.1.0]hex-2-yl)propyl]-3-methyl-6-oxabicyclo[3.1.0]hex-1-yl]-2-methyl-	n.s.g.	192(3.60),244(3.99), 310(2.02)	88-3611-73
$C_{20}H_{30}O_7S_2$			
Ethanone, 1-[1,2,3,3a,4,6,8,9,9a,9b-decahydro-3a-methyl-6-(methylsulfonyl)spiro[7H-benz[e]inden-7,2'-[1,3]-dioxolan]-3-yl]-2-(methylsulfonyl)-, [3S-(3α,3aα,6α,9aα,9bβ)]-	$CHCl_3$	298(1.73)	94-0335-73
$C_{20}H_{30}S_2$			
[2,2'-Bicyclo[2.2.1]heptane]-3,3'-dithione, 4,4',7,7,7',7'-hexamethyl-, (1S-exo)-(1'S-exo)-	EtOH	244(4.26),283(3.70), 494(1.34)	39-2866-73C
Disulfide, bis(1,7,7-trimethylbicyclo-[2.2.1]hept-2-en-1-yl)-, (1S)-(1'S)-	C_6H_{12}	277(4.04)	39-2866-73C
$C_{20}H_{31}N_5O_4$			
Adenosine, N-(4-cyclohexylbutyl)-	pH 1.0	264.5(4.32)	87-0358-73
	H_2O	270(4.23)	87-0358-73
	pH 13	269.5(4.25)	87-0358-73
$C_{20}H_{32}$			
Naphthalene, 1,2,3,4-tetrahydro-1,1,5,7-tetramethyl-6-(3-methylpentyl)-	EtOH	270(2.58),275(2.50), 280(2.52)	39-1754-73C
$C_{20}H_{32}N_2O_2$			
Androstan-3-one, 17-hydroxy-2-(hydroxymethylene)-, hydrazone, (17β)-	n.s.g.	231(4.11)	65-0403-73
5-Benzoxazolol, 4,7-bis(1,1-dimethylethyl)-2-ethyl-6-(propylamino)-	$CHCl_3$	240(4.03),300(3.79), 304s(3.78)	39-0268-73C
$C_{20}H_{32}O$			
2-Tetradecanone, 1-phenyl-	C_6H_{12}	287(2.23),294(--), 303(--),312(--)	28-0407-73B
	MeOH	286.5(2.23)	28-0407-73B
$C_{20}H_{32}O_2$			
5α-Androstan-3-one, 17β-hydroxy-17α-methyl-, Kober test	H_2SO_4	383(3.78)	94-1720-73
Androst-5-ene-3β,17β-diol, 17α-methyl-, Kober test	H_2SO_4	388(3.54),415(3.44), 497(3.51)	94-1720-73
2,6,11-Cyclotetradecatrien-1-one, 13-hydroxy-3,7,13-trimethyl-10-(1-methylethyl)-	EtOH	243(3.97)	102-0731-73
3,7,12-Pentadecatriene-2,14-dione, 4,8-dimethyl-11-(1-methylethyl)-, 3,4-cis?	EtOH	229(4.25)	102-0731-73
3,4-trans?	EtOH	229(4.34)	102-0731-73

Compound	Solvent	$\lambda_{max}(\log \epsilon)$	Ref.
$C_{20}H_{32}O_3$			
Cyathin A_3, 12,13-dihydro-	MeOH	295(1.18)	23-3842-73
$C_{20}H_{32}O_4$			
Haplopappic acid, dihydro-	EtOH	216(4.07)	102-1755-73
$C_{20}H_{32}O_5$			
8(12),13-Prostadienoic acid, 11,15-dihydroxy-9-oxo-, (11R,15S)-(+)-	MeOH	276.5(4.41)	35-2664-73
$C_{20}H_{32}Si_3$			
Silane, [1-(phenylethynyl)-1,2-propadien-1-yl)-3-ylidene]tris[trimethyl-	n.s.g.	252(4.05)	39-0599-73B
$C_{20}H_{34}O_2$			
1,3-Cyclohexadiene-1-carboxylic acid, 6-decyl-2-methyl-, ethyl ester	ether	278(3.84)	24-3779-73
$C_{20}H_{35}Cl_2N_3O_2$			
1-Cyclobutene-1-carboximidamide, N,N'-bis(1,1-dimethylethyl)-2-[(1,1-dimethylethyl)amino]-3,3-dimethoxy-4-(dichloromethylene)-	n.s.g.	278(4.17)	44-1470-73
hydrochloride	n.s.g.	277(4.24)	44-1470-73
$C_{20}H_{36}N_4$			
2-Butenedinitrile, 2,3-bis[(1,1,3,3-tetramethylbutyl)amino]-, (E)-	isooctane or MeOH	340(4.05)	44-2604-73
$C_{20}H_{38}N_2$			
Diazene, bis[2-(1,1-dimethylethyl)-3,3-dimethyl-1-butenyl]-, trans	n.s.g.	313(4.45),322(4.45), 337(4.26),440(2.37)	89-0655-73
$C_{20}H_{40}N_2$			
1H-Imidazole, 2-heptadecyl-4,5-dihydro-	EtOH	220(3.64)	93-2424-73

Compound	Solvent	$\lambda_{max}(\log \epsilon)$	Ref.
$C_{21}H_{10}ClIO_2S_2$			
Naphtho[1,8-bc]thiopyran-3(2H)-one, 2-(6-chloro-4-methyl-3-oxobenzo[b]thien-2(3H)-ylidene)-7-iodo-, cis	n.s.g.	485(4.26)	103-0960-73
trans	n.s.g.	597.5(4.57)	103-0960-73
$C_{21}H_{10}Cl_4O_2S_2$			
Spiro[1,3-benzodioxole-2,2'-[1,3]dithiole], 4,5,6,7-tetrachloro-4',5'-diphenyl-	benzene	300(3.89)	97-0465-73
$C_{21}H_{11}NO_4$			
1H,3H-Naphtho[1,8-cd]pyran-1,3-dione, 6-(5-phenyl-2-oxazolyl)-	toluene	295(4.03),398(4.34)	103-1204-73
$C_{21}H_{12}Cl_2N_4$			
9H-Carbazole, 9-[4-(4,6-dichloro-1,3,5-triazin-2-yl)phenyl]-	EtOH	240(3.63),281(4.32), 364(4.24)	39-2075-73B
$C_{21}H_{12}N_4O_{10}S$			
2H-1-Benzothiopyran, 2,4-bis(2,4-dinitrophenyl)-, 1,1-dioxide	MeOH	244(4.22),304s(3.68), 360s(3.18),518s(3.48), 608(3.69)	39-0163-73C
	MeOH-HCl	246(4.58),296(4.13)	39-0163-73C
	MeOH-NaOH?	246(4.47),359(3.86), 520(4.18),607(4.36)	39-0163-73C
$C_{21}H_{12}O$			
4H-Benzo[b]cyclopenta[4,5]phenanthro-[9,10-d]furan	EtOH	243s(4.58),248(4.67), 254(4.68),261s(4.65), 269s(4.55),281s(4.17), 297(4.12),306s(4.16), 313(4.33),321(4.24), 329(4.45),334s(3.88), 343s(3.44),353(3.47)	88-2675-73
$C_{21}H_{12}S_2$			
8H-Acenaphtho[1,2-b]thiopyran-8-thione, 9-phenyl-	C_6H_{12}	232(4.68),357(4.23), 375(4.21),420(3.99), 438(3.97)	22-3334-73
	MeOH	228(4.55),354(4.17), 431(3.80)	22-3334-73
	MeCN	227(4.64),352(4.23), 431(3.78)	22-3334-73
$C_{21}H_{13}Br_2ClN_2$			
1H-Imidazole, 4,5-bis(4-bromophenyl)-2-(3-chlorophenyl)-	EtOH	305(4.39)	103-0085-73
$C_{21}H_{13}Br_2N_3O_2$			
1H-Imidazole, 4,5-bis(4-bromophenyl)-2-(4-nitrophenyl)-	EtOH	300(4.12),375(4.15)	103-0085-73
$C_{21}H_{13}Br_3N_2$			
1H-Imidazole, 2,4,5-tris(4-bromophenyl)-	EtOH	235(4.24),310(4.35)	103-0085-73
$C_{21}H_{13}ClO$			
1H-Inden-1-one, 2-(4-chlorophenyl)-3-phenyl-	EtOH	263(4.54),434(3.32)	48-0353-73

Compound	Solvent	$\lambda_{max}(\log \epsilon)$	Ref.
$C_{21}H_{13}N_3$			
Benzo[f]quinoline, 3-(2-quinoxalinyl)-, Cu(I) complex	EtOH	400(4.66),552(3.89)	103-1391-73
$C_{21}H_{13}N_3O$			
Benzonitrile, 3-[2-[6-(2-benzoxazolyl)-3-pyridinyl]ethenyl]-	n.s.g.	350(4.75)	40-0991-73
Benzonitrile, 4-[2-[5-(2-benzoxazolyl)-2-pyridinyl]ethenyl]-	n.s.g.	360(4.78)	40-0991-73
Benzonitrile, 4-[2-[6-(2-benzoxazolyl)-3-pyridinyl]ethenyl]-	n.s.g.	359(4.80)	40-0991-73
$C_{21}H_{13}N_3S$			
Benzonitrile, 4-[2-[6-(2-benzothiazol-yl)-3-pyridinyl]ethenyl]-	n.s.g.	367(4.78)	40-0991-73
$C_{21}H_{14}$			
13H-Dibenzo[a,h]fluorene	EtOH	251(4.50),260(4.73), 279(4.13),288(3.83), 298(3.83),310(4.09), 324(4.13),338(3.68), 348(3.88),352(3.43)	132-0015-73
$C_{21}H_{14}BrN_3O$			
Naphtho[2,1-e]-1,2,4-triazine, 3-(5-bromo-2-furanyl)-1,2-dihydro-2-phenyl-	MeOH	231(4.61),282(4.64), 302(4.34),314(4.38), 337(4.47),353(4.50)	103-0145-73
$C_{21}H_{14}Br_2N_2$			
1H-Imidazole, 4,5-bis(4-bromophenyl)-2-phenyl-	EtOH	302(4.26)	103-0085-73
$C_{21}H_{14}ClNS_2$			
Benzenecarbothioamide, 4-chloro-N-(3-phenylbenzo[b]thien-2-yl)-	EtOH	228(4.50),264s(4.34), 376(3.73)	78-2783-73
$C_{21}H_{14}ClN_3O$			
Methanone, (4-chlorophenyl)(1,4-diphenyl-1H-1,2,3-triazol-5-yl)-	EtOH	266(4.28)	42-0589-73
Methanone, (4-chlorophenyl)(1,5-diphenyl-1H-1,2,3-triazol-4-yl)-	EtOH	268.0(4.37)	42-0589-73
$C_{21}H_{14}ClN_3O_2S$			
1H-Benzimidazole-1-carboxamide, 3-benzoyl-N-(3-chlorophenyl)-2,3-dihydro-2-thioxo-	MeOH	248(4.56),306(4.69)	103-0639-73
1H-Benzimidazole-1-carboxamide, 3-benzoyl-N-(4-chlorophenyl)-2,3-dihydro-2-thioxo-	MeOH	262(4.58),308(4.49)	103-0639-73
$C_{21}H_{14}N_2$			
Quinoxaline, 2-(9H-fluoren-2-yl)-	EtOH	208(4.56),238(--), 270(--),343(--)	34-0102-73
$C_{21}H_{14}N_2O$			
11H-Indeno[1,2-b]quinoxalin-11-ol, 11-phenyl-	EtOH	259s(4.39),268(4.47), 352(4.20),369(4.24)	78-3337-73
$C_{21}H_{14}N_2O_2$			
Formamidine, N-phenyl-N'-(1-anthraquinonyl)-	EtOH	240(4.18),465(3.48)	104-1523-73

Compound	Solvent	λmax(log ε)	Ref.
$C_{21}H_{14}N_2O_3$			
Benzoic acid, 4-[2-[6-(2-benzoxazolyl)-3-pyridinyl]ethenyl]-	dioxan	356(4.77)	40-0991-73
$C_{21}H_{14}N_4$			
1,2,4-Triazolo[4,3-c]quinazoline, 3,5-diphenyl-	H_2SO_4	286(4.98),341(4.41)	116-0483-73
$C_{21}H_{14}N_4O_3$			
1H-Naphtho[2,1-e]-1,2,4-triazine, 1,2-dihydro-3-(5-nitro-2-furanyl)-2-phenyl-	MeOH	228(4.62),268(4.50), 392(4.34),398(4.36)	103-0145-73
$C_{21}H_{14}N_4S$			
Benzonitrile, 4-(2,4-diphenyl-5-thioxo-1,2,4-triazolidin-3-yl)-, meso-ionic didehydro deriv.	MeOH	217(4.35),246(4.52), 350(3.60)	42-0154-73
$C_{21}H_{14}O$			
4H-Benzo[b]cyclopenta[4,5]phenanthro-[9,10-d]furan, 8a,12a-dihydro-	EtOH	241s(4.49),251s(4.61), 256(4.71),258(4.71), 280s(4.15),300(4.11), 311(4.14),327(3.92), 351(2.94)	88-2675-73
1H-Inden-1-one, 2,3-diphenyl-	EtOH	259(4.55),434(3.25)	48-0353-73
$C_{21}H_{14}O_3$			
1,2-Anthracenedione, 4-(phenylmethoxy)-	EtOH	224(4.48),291(4.43), 420(3.58)	28-1215-73A
Benzeneacetic acid, α-(2-oxo-1(2H)-acenaphthalenylidene)-, methyl ester	EtOH	244(4.01),316(3.66), 339(3.61)	2-1333-73
Spiro[isobenzofuran-1(3H),9'-[9H]xanthen]-3-one, 3'-methyl-	EtOH	202(4.57),220(4.60), 286(3.65)	56-2101-73
	80% H_2SO_4	203(4.54),260(4.58), 278(3.58),388(3.39)	56-2101-73
Triptycene, 7-carboxy-2-hydroxy-, (+)-	EtOH	214s(4.66),269(3.53), 286(3.64),300s(3.53)	18-0611-73
$C_{21}H_{14}O_4$			
Spiro[isobenzofuran-1(3H),9'-[9H]xanthen]-3-one, 3'-methoxy-	EtOH	203(4.55),222(4.58), 278(3.54),286(3.63)	56-2101-73
	80% H_2SO_4	202(4.60),222(4.43), 259(4.52),286(3.74), 397(4.44)	56-2101-73
$C_{21}H_{14}O_5$			
6H-Benzofuro[2,3-d]naphtho[1,2-b]pyran-6-one, 8,9-dimethoxy-	n.s.g.	244(4.1),265(3.9), 359(4.0),375(4.0)	2-0115-73
8H-Benzofuro[2,3-d]naphtho[2,1-b]pyran-8-one, 10,11-dimethoxy-	n.s.g.	231(4.5),280(3.9), 366(4.4),380(4.4)	2-0115-73
$C_{21}H_{14}O_7$			
Furo[3',4':6,7]naphtho[2,3-d]-1,3-dioxole-6,8-dione, 5-(3,4-dimethoxyphenyl)-	EtOH	215(4.59),260(4.82), 290(4.61)	2-0203-73
$C_{21}H_{15}$			
Cyclopropenylium, 1,2,3-triphenyl-, tetrafluoroborate	2.9M HCl	259(4.26),309(4.81), 324(4.74)	18-3881-73
	EtOH	317(4.13)	35-3239-73

Compound	Solvent	$\lambda_{max}(\log \epsilon)$	Ref.
$C_{21}H_{15}AsN_2$			
Arsonium, triphenyl-, dicyanomethylide	MeOH	223(4.38),265(3.57)	78-1697-73
$C_{21}H_{15}ClN_2$			
1H-Pyrazole, 3-(4-chlorophenyl)-1,5-diphenyl-	EtOH	255.5(4.56)	42-0589-73
$C_{21}H_{15}ClN_2OS$			
Benzenepropanethioamide, 4-chloro-β-oxo-N-phenyl-α-(phenylimino)-	MeOH	248(4.32),284(4.09), 360(3.82)	19-0893-73
Co complex	MeOH	403(4.16)	19-0893-73
Cu complex	MeOH	420(4.18)	19-0893-73
Ni complex	MeOH	410(4.17)	19-0893-73
Benzenepropanethioamide, α-[(4-chlorophenyl)imino]-β-oxo-N-phenyl-	MeOH	248(4.51),280(4.16), 361(3.74)	19-0893-73
Co complex	MeOH	407(4.04)	19-0893-73
Cu complex	MeOH	422(4.08)	19-0893-73
Ni complex	MeOH	413(4.10)	19-0893-73
Benzenepropanethioamide, N-(4-chlorophenyl)-β-oxo-α-(phenylimino)-	MeOH	242(4.61),281(4.23), 360(3.89)	19-0893-73
Co complex	MeOH	402(4.09)	19-0893-73
Cu complex	MeOH	418(4.05)	19-0893-73
Ni complex	MeOH	408(4.03)	19-0893-73
$C_{22}H_{15}ClO$			
Triptycene, 2-chloro-7-methoxy-, (+)-	dioxan	217(4.78),264(3.42), 268s(3.41),273s(3.42), 276(3.42),280(3.40)	18-0611-73
(-)-	dioxan	217(4.78),264(3.44), 268s(3.41),273s(3.43), 276(3.44),280(3.40)	18-0611-73
$C_{22}H_{15}F_3S$			
1,1':2',1"-Terphenyl, 2-(ethenylthio)-3"-(trifluoromethyl)-	EtOH	228(4.41),275(3.90), 283(3.81),320(2.49)	35-5288-73
1,1':2',1"-Terphenyl, 2-(ethenylthio)-4"-(trifluoromethyl)-	EtOH	230s(4.37),248s(4.23)	35-5288-73
$C_{22}H_{15}N$			
1H-Indole, 2-(9H-fluoren-2-yl)-	EtOH	209(3.55),269(3.44), 350(3.35)	34-0109-73
$C_{22}H_{15}NOS$			
Benzamide, N-(3-phenylbenzo[b]thien-2-yl)-	EtOH	231(4.50),248s(4.24), 308(4.05)	78-2783-73
2-Thiazolin-4-one, 2,5,5-triphenyl-	EtOH	282(4.36),325s(3.50)	78-2783-73
$C_{22}H_{15}NO_2$			
Benzeneacetonitrile, α-(benzoyloxy)-α-phenyl-	EtOH	227(4.25),260s(3.20)	78-2795-73
Benzo[f]quinoline, 3-(1,3-benzodioxol-5-yl)-1-methyl-	EtOH	235(4.59),258(4.56), 280(4.59),318(4.40), 348(4.07),364(4.05)	103-0633-73
4(5H)-Oxazolone, 2,5,5-triphenyl-	EtOH	202(4.72),267(4.35)	78-2795-73
5(2H)-Oxazolone, 2,2,4-triphenyl-	EtOH	261s(4.09),267(4.15), 271s(4.14)	33-1679-73
$C_{22}H_{15}NO_4S$			
4H-1-Benzopyran-4-one, 7-acetoxy-2-methyl-3-(2-phenyl-4-thiazolyl)-	n.s.g.	298(4.26)	104-2580-73

Compound	Solvent	$\lambda_{max}(\log \epsilon)$	Ref.
$C_{21}H_{15}NO_5S$			
4H-1-Benzopyran-2-carboxylic acid, 7-hydroxy-4-oxo-3-(2-phenyl-4-thiazolyl)-, ethyl ester	n.s.g.	308(4.30)	104-2580-73
$C_{21}H_{15}NS$			
Thiepino[3,4,5,6-lmn]phenanthridine, 9,11-dihydro-5-phenyl-	MeOH	222(4.53),253(4.51), 365(3.41)	39-2818-73C
$C_{21}H_{15}NS_2$			
Benzenecarbothioamide, N-(3-phenylbenzo-[b]thien-2-yl)-	EtOH	224(4.51),231(4.53), 254s(4.33),372(3.81)	78-2783-73
$C_{21}H_{15}N_3O$			
Methanone, (1,4-diphenyl-1H-1,2,3-triazol-5-yl)phenyl-	EtOH	259.0(4.34)	42-0589-73
Naphtho[2,1-e]-1,2,4-triazine, 3-(2-furanyl)-1,2-dihydro-2-phenyl-	MeOH	231(4.42),279(4.53), 300(4.14),311(4.14), 334(4.22),348(4.30)	103-0145-73
$C_{21}H_{15}N_3OS_2$			
4-Thiazolidinone, 3-methyl-5-(7-methylbenzo[a]phenazin-5(7H)-ylidene)-2-thioxo-	$CHCl_3$	620(3.96),668(4.05), 730s(3.85)	103-1407-73
$C_{21}H_{15}S_3$			
Cyclopropenylium, tris(phenylthio)-, perchlorate	MeCN	281(4.32)	88-3409-73
$C_{21}H_{16}$			
9,12-Methanobenzo[3,4]cyclobuta[1,2-l]-phenanthrene, 8c,9,12,12a-tetrahydro-, (8aα,9α,12α,12aα)-	EtOH	250s(4.65),256(4.72), 273(4.23),282(3.83), 295(3.85),306(3.94)	39-0138-73C
$C_{21}H_{16}BrNO$			
2-Propen-1-one, 2-bromo-1,3-diphenyl-3-(phenylamino)-	hexane	251(4.11),382(4.20)	40-2152-73
$C_{21}H_{16}BrNO_3S_2$			
Benzenepropanethioamide, N-(4-bromophenyl)-β-oxo-α-(phenylsulfonyl)-	EtOH	320(4.3)	104-0352-73
$C_{21}H_{16}BrO_5P$			
Phosphoric acid, 3-(4-bromophenyl)-3-oxo-1-propenyl diphenyl ester	dioxan	266(4.37)	24-0435-73
$C_{21}H_{16}ClNO$			
Oxazole, 5-(4-chlorophenyl)-2,5-dihydro-2,4-diphenyl-, cis	EtOH	226(4.34),246(4.25)	33-2611-73
trans	EtOH	226(4.34),244(4.24)	33-2611-73
2-Propen-1-one, 2-chloro-1,3-diphenyl-3-(phenylamino)-	hexane	254(4.14),382(4.23)	40-2152-73
$C_{21}H_{16}ClNO_2$			
Benzamide, N-(4-chlorophenyl)-2-(4-methylbenzoyl)-	EtOH	268(3.88)	39-2448-73C
$C_{21}H_{16}ClNO_3S_2$			
Benzenepropanethioamide, α-[(4-chlorophenyl)sulfonyl]-β-oxo-N-phenyl-	EtOH	320(4.0)	104-0352-73

Compound	Solvent	$\lambda_{max}(\log \epsilon)$	Ref.
$C_{21}H_{16}ClO_5P$			
Phosphoric acid, 3-(4-chlorophenyl)-3-oxo-1-propenyl diphenyl ester	dioxan	265(4.26)	24-0435-73
$C_{21}H_{16}FO_5P$			
Phosphoric acid, 3-(4-fluorophenyl)-3-oxo-1-propenyl diphenyl ester	dioxan	259(4.19)	24-0435-73
$C_{21}H_{16}IO_5P$			
Phosphoric acid, 3-(4-iodophenyl)-3-oxo-1-propenyl diphenyl ester	dioxan	280(4.28)	24-0435-73
$C_{21}H_{16}N_2$			
1H-Pyrazole, 1,3,5-triphenyl-	EtOH	253.0(4.49)	42-0589-73
$C_{21}H_{16}N_2O$			
Benzoxazole, 2-[5-[2-(4-methylphenyl)-ethenyl]-2-pyridinyl]-	n.s.g.	359(4.75)	40-0991-73
Benzoxazole, 2-[6-[2-(4-methylphenyl)-ethenyl]-3-pyridinyl]-	n.s.g.	360(4.74)	40-0991-73
Phenol, 2-(1,3-diphenyl-1H-pyrazol-5-yl)-	EtOH	212(4.64),270(4.60)	103-0038-73
$C_{21}H_{16}N_2OS$			
Benzenepropanethioamide, β-oxo-N-phenyl-α-(phenylimino)-	MeOH	230(4.33),252(4.28), 360(3.82)	19-0893-73
Co complex	MeOH	402(4.07)	19-0893-73
Cu complex	MeOH	414(4.12)	19-0893-73
Ni complex	MeOH	403(4.11)	19-0893-73
Benzothiazole, 2-[5-[2-(4-methoxyphenyl)ethenyl]-2-pyridinyl]-	n.s.g.	377(4.72)	40-0991-73
4-Imidazolidinone, 1,5,5-triphenyl-2-thioxo-	EtOH	234(4.39),279(4.38), 328s(2.60)	78-3571-73
4-Imidazolidinone, 3,5,5-triphenyl-2-thioxo-	EtOH	274(4.33),322(2.27)	78-3571-73
$C_{21}H_{16}N_2O_2$			
Benzoxazole, 2-[5-[2-(4-methoxyphenyl)-ethenyl]-2-pyridinyl]-	n.s.g.	367(4.71)	40-0991-73
Benzoxazole, 2-[6-[2-(4-methoxyphenyl)-ethenyl]-3-pyridinyl]-	n.s.g.	370(4.69)	40-0991-73
3,5-Pyrazolidinedione, 1,2,4-triphenyl-	EtOH	265(4.4)	103-0717-73
	EtOH-HCl	240(4.3)	103-0717-73
$C_{21}H_{16}N_2O_5$			
1,4-Naphthalenedione, 6,8-dihydroxy-2-methoxy-7-methyl-5-(3-methyl-2-quinoxalinyl)-	DMF	310s(--),330(4.33), 410s(--),430(4.39)	33-2323-73
$C_{21}H_{16}N_2O_5S$			
Benzenesulfonamide, 4-amino-N-[4-(3-hydroxy-4-oxo-4H-1-benzopyran-2-yl)-phenyl]-	dioxan	256(4.38),309(4.34)	83-0299-73
$C_{21}H_{16}N_2O_6S$			
Benzenepropanamide, N-[4-[(4-nitrophenyl)sulfonyl]phenyl-β-oxo-	pH 13	355(4.53)	39-0808-73B

Compound	Solvent	λ_{max}(log ε)	Ref.
$C_{21}H_{16}N_3S_2$			
Thiazolo[3,2-a]pyrimidin-4-ium, 5-[(3-methyl-2(3H)-benzothiazolylidene)-methyl]-3-phenyl-, perchlorate	n.s.g.	448(4.77),469(4.89)	124-1151-73
Thiazolo[3,2-a]pyrimidin-4-ium, 7-[(3-methyl-2(3H)-benzothiazolylidene)-methyl]-3-phenyl-, perchlorate	n.s.g.	485(4.73)	124-1151-73
$C_{21}H_{16}N_4O$			
Benzamide, N-[2-(5-phenyl-1H-1,2,4-triazol-3-yl)phenyl]-	H_2SO_4	280(4.70),338(4.10)	116-0483-73
$C_{21}H_{16}N_4O_2$			
1H-Pyrano[2,3-c:6,5-c']dipyrazol-4(7H)-one, 3,5-dimethyl-1,7-diphenyl-	EtOH	232(4.42)	103-0911-73
$C_{21}H_{16}N_6$			
Formazan, 1,3-diphenyl-5-(2-quinoxalin-yl)-	benzene	476(4.19)	103-1542-73
	EtOH	452(4.14)	103-1542-73
	EtOH-KOH	538(4.76)	103-1542-73
	dioxan	460(3.87)	103-1542-73
	H_2SO_4	643(4.27)	103-1542-73
$C_{21}H_{16}O$			
Anthracene, 9-methoxy-1-phenyl-	EtOH	212(4.36),258(5.02), 340s(3.49),356(3.78), 375(3.94),394(3.89)	44-1167-73
$C_{21}H_{16}OS$			
Dibenzo[b,f]thiepin, 2-(phenylmethoxy)-	MeOH	242(4.31),262(4.42), 293(3.75)	73-1579-73
$C_{21}H_{16}O_2$			
Benzoic acid, 4-(2,2-diphenylethenyl)-	EtOH	240(4.23)	104-1511-73
1(3H)-Isobenzofuranone, 3-(4-methylphenyl)-3-phenyl-	EtOH	202(4.68),286(3.15)	56-2101-73
	80% H_2SO_4	198(4.74),286(3.28), 455(3.38)	56-2101-73
$C_{21}H_{16}O_2S$			
Dibenzo[b,f]thiepin-10(11H)-one, 8-(phenylmethoxy)-	MeOH	239(4.40),257s(4.08), 351(3.55)	73-1579-73
$C_{21}H_{16}O_3$			
1(3H)-Isobenzofuranone, 3-(4-hydroxy-phenyl)-3-(4-methylphenyl)-	EtOH	202(4.84),225(4.42), 282(3.54)	56-0415-73
	2M NaOH	227(3.18),244(3.20)	56-0415-73
	80% H_2SO_4	194(4.64),394(4.07), 483(4.74)	56-0415-73
1(3H)-Isobenzofuranone, 3-(4-methoxy-phenyl)-3-phenyl-	EtOH	203(4.69),227(4.27), 278(3.42),286(3.40)	56-2101-73
	80% H_2SO_4	200(4.70),286(3.53), 385(3.74),472(4.38)	56-2101-73
$C_{21}H_{16}O_4$			
1(3H)-Isobenzofuranone, 3-(2,4-dihydr-oxy-6-methylphenyl)-3-phenyl-	pH 12.5	490(3.45)	64-0468-73B
1(3H)-Isobenzofuranone, 3-(4-hydroxy-3-methoxyphenyl)-3-phenyl-	EtOH	204(4.82),286(3.76)	56-0415-73
	2M NaOH	227(3.11),299(2.62)	56-0415-73
	80% H_2SO_4	200(4.65),385(3.96), 490(4.22)	56-0415-73

Compound	Solvent	λ max(log ε)	Ref.
1(3H)-Isobenzofuranone, 3-(4-hydroxy-phenyl)-3-(4-methoxyphenyl)-	EtOH	203(4.82),231(4.44), 278(3.63)	56-0415-73
	2M NaOH	230(3.22)	56-0415-73
	80% H_2SO_4	196(4.61),267(3.94), 397(4.12),507(4.77)	56-0415-73
$C_{21}H_{16}O_5$			
4H-Furo[3',2':4,5]furo[2,3-h]-1-benzo-pyran-4,10(9H)-dione, 7a,10a-dihydro-9,9-dimethyl-2-phenyl-, cis (semi-glabrinone)	MeOH	217(4.35),259(4.22), 311(4.15)	78-3099-73
$C_{21}H_{16}O_6$			
2H-1-Benzopyran-2-one, 7,7'-[1,3-prop-anediylbis(oxy)]bis-	CH_2Cl_2	324(4.49)	44-0957-73
2,3-Furandicarboxylic acid, 4-benzoyl-5-phenyl-, dimethyl ester	$CHCl_3$	270(4.29),317(4.28)	103-1307-73
Isotachrosin, 5,7-O,O-bisdemethyl-	MeOH	218(4.54),276(4.61), 321(4.26)	119-0064-73
Tachrosin, 5,7-O,O-bisdemethyl-	MeOH	216(4.56),276(4.54)	119-0064-73
$C_{21}H_{17}ClN_2$			
1H-Benz[3,4]cyclobuta[1,2-c]pyrazole, 3-(4-chlorophenyl)-3a,3b,7a,7b-tetra-hydro-1-phenyl-	EtOH	250(4.28),260(4.27), 307(3.98),387(4.21)	78-2405-73
$C_{21}H_{17}ClN_2O_4S$			
Benzenesulfonamide, 4-amino-N-[4-[3-(5-chloro-2-hydroxyphenyl)-3-oxo-1-prop-enyl]phenyl]-	dioxan	265(4.41),377(4.41)	83-0299-73
$C_{21}H_{17}ClN_4O_3$			
Oxazolo[4,5-b][1,4,5]benzotriazocine, 4,11-diacetyl-8-chloro-4,11-dihydro-2-methyl-6-phenyl-	MeOH	254(4.33)	94-2375-73
$C_{21}H_{17}ClO$			
1(2H)-Naphthalenone, 2-[(1-chloro-3,4-dihydro-2-naphthalenyl)methylene]-3,4-dihydro-	EtOH	274(4.47),360(4.53)	22-2093-73
$C_{21}H_{17}Cl_2N_3O_4S_2$			
Benzenesulfonamide, N,N-(3-methyl-3H-indole-2,3-diyl)bis[4-chloro-	$CHCl_3$	240(4.17),273s(3.98), 278(3.99),298(3.82)	39-1602-73C
$C_{21}H_{17}NO$			
Oxazole, 2,5-dihydro-2,4,5-triphenyl-, cis	EtOH	245(4.24)	33-2611-73
trans	EtOH	246(4.25)	33-2611-73
	EtOH	247(4.24),288(2.73)	44-1333-73
$C_{21}H_{17}NOS$			
Benzamide, N-(5,7-dihydrodibenzo[c,e]-thiepin-1-yl)-	n.s.g.	246(4.40)	39-2818-73C
$C_{21}H_{17}NO_2$			
Benzamide, 2-benzoyl-N-(4-methylphenyl)-	EtOH	265(3.76)	39-2448-73C
Benzamide, N-(5,7-dihydrodibenzo[c,e]-oxepin-1-yl)-	n.s.g.	234(4.36)	39-2818-73C
Benzamide, 2-(4-methylbenzoyl)-N-phenyl-	EtOH	265(3.81)	39-2448-73C

Compound	Solvent	$\lambda_{max}(\log \epsilon)$	Ref.
Ethanone, 1-[4-[(4-benzoylphenyl)amino]-phenyl]-	EtOH	246(4.33),309(3.94), 377(4.67)	39-1259-73C
Ethanone, 2-[(4-methoxyphenyl)imino]-1,2-diphenyl-	EtOH	257(4.42),338(3.74)	12-2027-73
$C_{21}H_{17}NO_3$			
Acetamide, 2-(4-benzoylphenoxy)-N-phenyl-	EtOH	209(4.34),245(4.35), 280(4.29)	111-0574-73
$C_{21}H_{17}NO_3S_2$			
Benzenepropanethioamide, β-oxo-N-phenyl-α-(phenylsulfonyl)-	EtOH	335(4.3)	104-0352-73
$C_{21}H_{17}NO_5$			
Oxynitidine	EtOH	276(4.59),288(4.65), 335(4.13)	4-0031-73
$C_{21}H_{17}NO_5S$			
Benzenepropanamide, β-oxo-N-[4-(phenylsulfonyl)oxy]phenyl]-	pH 13	332(4.36)	39-0808-73B
$C_{21}H_{17}NO_6$			
7H-Bis[1,3]benzodioxolo[6,5,4-de:5',6'-g]quinoline-7-carboxylic acid, 5,6-dihydro-, ethyl ester	dioxan	264(4.99),270(4.97), 295(4.25),327(4.32), 340(4.33),363(3.89), 382(3.83)	78-2245-73
	n.s.g.	238(4.85),291s(4.28), 328(4.27),338(4.28), 360(3.97),380(3.97)	39-0349-73C
$C_{21}H_{17}N_3OS$			
1,2,4-Triazolidine-3-thione, 5-(4-methoxyphenyl)-1,4-diphenyl-, meso-ionic didehydro deriv.	MeOH	223(4.38),252(4.38), 316(3.71)	42-0154-73
$C_{21}H_{17}N_3O_4$			
Euxylophoricine E	$CHCl_3$	255(4.65),289(4.55), 292s(4.48),307(4.54), 355(4.57),376(4.62), 398(4.64)	102-2521-73
$C_{21}H_{17}N_3S$			
2H-Imidazole-2-thione, 4-amino-1,5-dihydro-1,5,5-triphenyl-	EtOH	280(4.40),350s(2.50)	78-3571-73
2-Imidazolidinethione, 5-imino-1,4,4-triphenyl-	EtOH	268(4.48),304s(2.54)	78-3571-73
1,2,4-Triazolidine-3-thione, 5-(4-methylphenyl)-1,4-diphenyl-, meso-ionic didehydro deriv.	MeOH	223(4.33),246(4.42), 320(3.56)	42-0154-73
$C_{21}H_{17}N_5O_2$			
Benzamide, N-benzoyl-4-methyl-N-(9-methyl-9H-purin-6-yl)-	MeOH	255(4.30),270s(4.27)	18-3228-73
Benzamide, 4-methyl-N-(4-methylbenzoyl)-N-1H-purin-6-yl-	MeOH	240(4.52),290s(3.81)	18-3228-73
$C_{21}H_{17}N_5O_8S_2$			
Benzenesulfonamide, N,N'-(3-methyl-3H-indole-2,3-diyl)bis[4-nitro-	EtOH	205(4.53),263(4.46), 290s(4.19)	39-1602-73C

Compound	Solvent	$\lambda_{max}(\log \epsilon)$	Ref.
$C_{21}H_{17}O_5P$			
Phosphoric acid, 3-oxo-3-phenyl-1-propenyl diphenyl ester	dioxan	257(4.21)	24-0435-73
$C_{21}H_{18}$			
3,8[1',2']-Benzeno-3H-cyclobuta[3,4]-cyclopenta[1,2-b]naphthalene, 2a,2b,8,8a,9,9a-hexahydro-	EtOH	266(3.12),273(3.20)	35-5632-73
5,11[1',2']-Benzeno-5H-cyclohepta[b]-naphthalene, 5a,6,10a,11-tetrahydro-	EtOH	248(3.54),266(3.38), 272(3.26)	35-5632-73
Bicyclo[6.1.0]nona-2,4,6-triene, 2,7-diphenyl-	isooctane	254(4.39),299(3.99)	35-6717-73
11H-9,10[1',3']-endo-Cycloheptanthracene, 9,10,12,13-tetrahydro-	EtOH	254(3.69),262(2.73), 274(3.61)	35-5632-73
11H-9,10[1',4']-endo-Cycloheptanthracene, 9,10,14,15-tetrahydro-	EtOH	272(3.26),278(3.23), 280(3.34)	35-5632-73
1H-Indene, 3a,7a-dihydro-3,7-diphenyl-	isooctane	234(4.18),305(3.84)	35-6717-73
$C_{21}H_{18}AsNO_3$			
Arsonium, triphenyl-, 1-nitro-2-oxopropylide	MeOH	222(4.40),315(4.06)	78-1697-73
$C_{21}H_{18}BrNO_6$			
1,3-Dioxolo[4,5-g]isoquinoline-6(5H)-carboxylic acid, 5-[(6-bromo-1,3-benzodioxol-5-yl)methylene]-7,8-dihydro-, ethyl ester, (E)-	EtOH	223(4.66),300(4.32), 333(4.14)	78-2245-73
$C_{21}H_{18}ClNO_4$			
Nitidine chloride	MeOH	234(4.39),270(4.67), 290(4.62),299(4.61), 327(4.60),380(4.07)	4-0085-73
$C_{21}H_{18}ClN_2OP$			
Phosphonium, (1,2,4-oxadiazol-3-ylmethyl)triphenyl-, chloride	EtOH	227(4.42),262(3.42), 268(3.53),275(3.46)	39-2241-73C
$C_{21}H_{18}Cl_3NO_4$			
Berberinechloroform	MeOH	281(3.8),361(4.1)	102-1822-73
$C_{21}H_{18}N_2$			
Azepino[3,4,5,6-def]carbazole, 4,8,9,10-tetrahydro-9-(phenylmethyl)-	MeOH	245(4.43),253(4.42), 296(4.02),328(3.61), 342(3.67)	39-2818-73C
Cinnoline, 1,4-dihydro-1-methyl-3,4-diphenyl-	MeCN	230(4.24),343(4.11)	22-3487-73
3,4-Diazatricyclo[5.4.0.0 ']undeca-4,8,10-triene, 3,5-diphenyl-	EtOH	257(4.21),312(4.01), 379(4.20)	78-2405-73
5H-Indeno[2,1-c]cinnoline, 6,6a,7,11b-tetrahydro-5-phenyl-	MeCN	292(4.18)	22-3487-73
$C_{21}H_{18}N_2O_2$			
Benzeneacetonitrile, 4-(diethylamino)-α-(1,3-dihydro-1,3-dioxo-2H-inden-2-ylidene)-	MeOH	252(4.53),578(4.69)	88-2993-73
5H-Dibenz[c,e]azepine, 6,7-dihydro-1-nitro-6-(phenylmethyl)-	MeOH	233(4.33)	39-2818-73C
$C_{21}H_{18}N_2O_3$			
Acetamide, 2-[4-(hydroxyimino)phenylmethyl]phenoxy]-N-phenyl-	EtOH	209(4.47),243(4.51)	111-0574-73

Compound	Solvent	$\lambda_{max}(\log \epsilon)$	Ref.
$C_{21}H_{18}N_2O_3S$			
[1,4]Diazepino[3,2,1-kl]phenoxazine, 1,2,3,4-tetrahydro-4-(phenylsulfonyl)-	EtOH	239(4.48),317(3.80)	95-0020-73
[1,4]Diazepino[3,2,1-kl]phenoxazine, 1,2,3,4-tetrahydro-7-(phenylsulfonyl)-	EtOH	230(4.52),292(4.45)	95-0020-73
1H-Pyrazino[3,2,1-kl]phenoxazine, 2,3-dihydro-3-[(4-methylphenyl)sulfonyl]-	EtOH	228(4.55),242(4.22), 320(3.64)	95-0020-73
1H-Pyrazino[3,2,1-kl]phenoxazine, 2,3-dihydro-6-[(4-methylphenyl)sulfonyl]-	EtOH	234(4.46),288(4.37)	95-0020-73
$C_{21}H_{18}N_2O_4S$			
Benzenesulfonamide, 4-amino-N-[4-[3-(2-hydroxyphenyl)-3-oxo-1-propenyl]phenyl]-	dioxan	267(4.39),367(4.42)	83-0299-73
$C_{21}H_{18}N_2O_5$			
Alkaloid TN-12 from corydalis incisa Pers.	MeOH	244(4.60),309(4.14), 376(3.53)	95-0087-73
Corydamine, N-formyl-	MeOH	244(4.60),309(4.14), 376(3.53)	94-1410-73
$C_{21}H_{18}N_2O_5S_2$			
2-Propenoic acid, 2-cyano-3-[3-[[(4-methylphenyl)sulfonyl]oxy]-1H-indol-2-yl]-3-(methylthio)-, methyl ester	EtOH	263(4.09),342(4.18)	94-1658-73
$C_{21}H_{18}N_2O_7$			
Kinamycin C, isopropylidene-	EtOH	264.5(2.39)	94-0931-73
$C_{21}H_{18}N_4O_2S$			
1H-Thieno[2,3-c]pyrazole-5-carboxamide, 4-(acetylamino)-3-methyl-N,1-diphenyl-	EtOH	265(4.41),320(4.20)	104-2429-73
$C_{21}H_{18}N_4O_4$			
Benzophenone, 2,4-dimethyl-, 2,4-dinitrophenylhydrazone, (E)-	$CHCl_3$	387.5(4.44)	40-0771-73
(Z)-	$CHCl_3$	390(4.47)	40-0771-73
Benzophenone, 2,5-dimethyl-, 2,4-dinitrophenylhydrazone, (E)-	$CHCl_3$	386(4.44)	40-0771-73
Benzophenone, 3,4-dimethyl-, 2,4-dinitrophenylhydrazone, (E)-	$CHCl_3$	394(4.48)	40-0771-73
$C_{21}H_{18}O$			
9H-Xanthene, 2,6-dimethyl-9-phenyl-	EtOH	204(4.73),256(3.92), 290(3.47)	56-1191-73
	97% H_2SO_4	194(4.61),213(4.56), 269(4.63),392(4.54), 460(3.75)	56-1191-73
9H-Xanthene, 2,7-dimethyl-9-phenyl-	EtOH	203(4.78),255(4.04), 292(3.53)	56-1191-73
	97% H_2SO_4	201(4.60),212(4.60), 270(4.51),383(4.34), 472(3.67)	56-1191-73
9H-Xanthene, 3,6-dimethyl-9-phenyl-	EtOH	205(4.73),255(3.83), 286(3.43)	56-1191-73
	97% H_2SO_4	192(4.67),222(4.55), 270(4.85),402(4.66)	56-1191-73
$C_{21}H_{18}OS$			
Benzenecarbothioic acid, O-(1,2-diphenylethyl) ester	C_6H_{12}	250(3.99),294(4.04), 408(2.08)	39-1580-73C

Compound	Solvent	$\lambda_{max}(\log \epsilon)$	Ref.
Benzenecarbothioic acid, O-(2,2-diphenylethyl) ester	CH_2Cl_2	254(3.95),291(4.10), 406(2.06)	39-1580-73C
$C_{21}H_{18}O_2$			
1H-Dibenzo[a,h]fluorene-1,8(2H)-dione, 3,4,9,10,11,13-hexahydro-	EtOH	220(4.33),252(4.63), 274(4.26),280(4.23), 310(3.39)	132-0015-73
$C_{21}H_{18}O_3$			
Ethanone, 2-hydroxy-1-(4-methoxyphenyl)-2,2-diphenyl-	EtOH	284(4.23)	42-0586-73
$C_{21}H_{18}O_4$			
Anhydrotuberosin, 3-O-methyl-	EtOH	228(4.43),249(4.39), 325(4.17)	39-0907-73C
1H-Cyclopenta[a]phenanthrene-16,17-diol, 16,17-dihydro-, diacetate, cis	EtOH	250(4.74),257(4.88), 279(4.17),287(4.06), 299(4.18),319(2.64), 327(2.51),334(2.83), 342(2.45),350(2.80)	39-1255-73C
15H-Cyclopenta[a]phenanthrene-15,16-diol, 16,17-dihydro-, diacetate, cis	EtOH	223(4.29),255(4.76), 279(4.13),288(4.06), 300(4.11),319(2.58), 326(2.49),334(2.59), 340(2.35),350(2.23)	39-1255-73C
15H-Cyclopenta[a]phenanthrene-16,17-diol, 16,17-dihydro-, diacetate, cis	EtOH	250(4.74),257(4.87), 279(4.20),286(4.09), 298(4.18),320(2.63), 328(2.48),335(2.82), 343(2.43),350(2.82)	39-1255-73C
$C_{21}H_{18}O_5$			
Felamedin	EtOH	226(4.35),248(3.67), 259(3.58),310(3.78), 336(4.23)	105-0397-73
$C_{21}H_{18}O_6$			
Butanedioic acid, [3-(1,3-benzodioxol-5-yl)-1-phenyl-2-propenylidene]-, 1-methyl ester	EtOH	244(3.99),290(3.83), 348(3.95)	42-0430-73
$C_{21}H_{18}O_7$			
1,12(4H,5H)-Naphthacenedione, 2-acetyl-4a,12a-dihydro-3,10,11,12a-tetrahydroxy-6-methyl-, (4aS-cis)-	EtOH	224(4.34),271(4.58), 424(3.82)	105-0492-73
$C_{21}H_{18}O_8$			
Pulvinic acid, 3,4,4'-trimethoxy-	EtOH	260(4.19),392(3.84)	39-1921-73C
Pulvinic acid, 3',4,4'-trimethoxy-	EtOH	242s(4.35),259(4.41), 392(4.15)	39-1921-73C
$C_{21}H_{18}S$			
1,1'-Biphenyl, 2-ethenyl-2'-[(4-methylphenyl)thio]-	EtOH	215(4.12),235s(3.94), 248(3.83),284(3.36)	35-5288-73
1,1':2',1"-Terphenyl, 2-(ethenylthio)-4"-methyl-	EtOH	212s(3.94),231(3.89), 235s(3.86),252(3.60), 261(3.52),285(3.18), 322(2.40)	35-5288-73

Compound	Solvent	λ max (log ε)	Ref.
$C_{21}H_{19}BrN_2O_2$			
1H-Pyrazole-3-carboxylic acid, 1-(4-bromophenyl)-5-(1-methyl-2-phenylethenyl)-, ethyl ester	C_6H_{12} or EtOH	222(4.64),258(4.84)	4-0015-73
$C_{21}H_{19}Br_2NO$			
1H-Cyclopenta[b]quinolinium, 3-bromo-2,3-dihydro-4-methyl-3-(4-methylbenzoyl)-, bromide	EtOH	250(4.52),337(4.52)	103-1253-73
$C_{21}H_{19}Br_2NO_2$			
1H-Cyclopenta[b]quinolinium, 3-bromo-2,3-dihydro-3-(4-methoxybenzoyl)-4-methyl-, bromide	EtOH	245(4.45),333(4.13)	103-1253-73
$C_{21}H_{19}Br_2N_7O_3$			
L-Histidine, N-acetyl-2,5-bis[(4-bromophenyl)azo]-, methyl ester	EtOH	428(4.44)	44-1971-73
$C_{21}H_{19}ClN_2O$			
2H-1,4-Benzodiazepin-2-one, 7-chloro-1,3-dihydro-1-methyl-3-(3-methyl-2-butenylidene)-5-phenyl-	isoPrOH	206(4.54),230s(4.43), 236(4.43),255s(4.35), 290(4.25),380(3.73)	44-3502-73
$C_{21}H_{19}ClN_2O_2$			
1H-Pyrazole-3-carboxylic acid, 1-(4-chlorophenyl)-5-(1-methyl-2-phenylethenyl)-, ethyl ester	C_6H_{12} or EtOH	214(4.16),258(4.25)	4-0015-73
11H-Pyrrolo[2,1-c][1,4]benzodiazepin-11-one, 7-chloro-10-(ethoxymethyl)-5,10-dihydro-5-phenyl-	isoPrOH	239(4.21),278(4.05)	44-3502-73
$C_{21}H_{19}NO$			
Benzenemethanamine, N-[(4-methylphenyl)phenylmethylene]-, N-oxide	EtOH	300(4.11)	44-4440-73
2-Cyclobutene-1-carbonitrile, 1-(1,1-dimethylethyl)-4-oxo-2,3-diphenyl-	EtOH	230(4.26),315(4.08)	88-0009-73
Methanone, (4-methylphenyl)phenyl-, O-(phenylmethyl)oxime, (Z)-	EtOH	236(4.21),263(4.11)	44-4440-73
$C_{21}H_{19}NO_2$			
3-Buten-2-one, 4-(1-acetyl-6-methyl-2-phenylindolizin-3-yl)-	EtOH	231(4.33),273(4.01), 319(4.08),370(4.18), 422s(3.95)	39-2091-73C
3-Buten-2-one, 4-(1-acetyl-7-methyl-2-phenylindolizin-3-yl)-	EtOH	227(4.42),272(4.16), 319(4.13),369(4.24), 409(4.18)	39-2091-73C
Pyridine, 3,5-dibenzoyl-1,4-dihydro-2,6-dimethyl-	EtOH	252(4.16),315(3.58), 413(3.83)	103-0636-73
$C_{21}H_{19}NO_3$			
Benzene, 1-methoxy-4-[8-(4-nitrophenyl)-1,3,5,7-octatetraenyl]-	THF	265(4.06),360(4.41), 430(4.75),445s(--)	18-2828-73
$C_{21}H_{19}NO_3S$			
Methanone, 5-(2-furanyl)-4,5-dihydro-3-(2,4,6-trimethylphenyl)-4-isoxazolyl]-2-thienyl-, trans	EtOH	267(3.98),297(3.95)	39-1148-73C

Compound	Solvent	$\lambda_{max}(\log \epsilon)$	Ref.
$C_{21}H_{19}NO_4$			
Chelerythrine, dihydro-	n.s.g.	228(4.62),282(4.69), 322(4.30)	105-0664-73
Methanone, 2-furanyl[5-(2-furanyl)-4,5-dihydro-3-(2,4,6-trimethylphenyl)-4-isoxazolyl]-, trans	EtOH	283.5(4.14)	39-1148-73C
$C_{21}H_{19}NO_5$			
4H-[1]Benzopyrano[3,4-d]oxazol-4-one, 2-(3,4-dimethoxyphenyl)-6-ethyl-8-methyl-	MeOH	213(4.53),315(4.40), 331(4.43)	2-0433-73
Thalixine	EtOH	237(4.22),265(4.48), 313(3.96),390(3.60)	105-0421-73
$C_{21}H_{19}NO_6$			
Adlumidiceine enol lactone	EtOH	224(4.45),238s(4.39), 306(4.14),388(4.26)	102-2513-73
1,3-Dioxolo[4,5-g]isoquinoline-6(5H)-carboxylic acid, 5-(1,3-benzodioxol-5-ylmethylene)-7,8-dihydro-, ethyl ester, (E)-	EtOH	230(4.39),283(3.88), 312(3.83)	39-0349-73C
(Z)-	EtOH	217(4.55),244s(4.50), 298s(4.22),337(4.48)	39-0349-73C
8H-1,3-Dioxolo[4,5-h]isoindolo[1,2-b]-[3]benzazepin-8-one, 5,6-dihydro-9,10,14-trimethoxy-	MeOH	269(4.11),314(3.99), 380(4.49)	25-0478-73
9H-Pyrano[2,3-g]-1,2-benzisoxazol-9-one, 3,8-dimethyl-7-(3,4,5-trimethoxyphenyl)-	n.s.g.	223(4.4),249(4.6), 319(3.7)	2-0541-73
$C_{21}H_{19}N_3O_2$			
4H,8H-Pyrazolo[4',3':4,5]pyrrolo[3,2,1-ij]quinoline-10-carboxylic acid, 5,6-dihydro-8-phenyl-, ethyl ester	EtOH	261(4.27),303(4.04)	78-3159-73
1H,5H-Pyrazolo[1,2-a][1,2,4]triazole-1,3(2H)-dione, 6,7-dihydro-6-methylene-5-(1-methylethylidene)-2,7-diphenyl-	EtOH	222(4.31),265(3.21)	35-1553-73
	EtOH	223(4.31),274(4.30)	35-1553-73
$C_{21}H_{19}N_3O_2S$			
1H-Imidazo[2,1-a]isoquinolin-4-ium, 1-butyl-2-mercapto-3-(4-nitrophenyl)-, hydroxide, inner salt	MeOH	246(4.57),263(4.51), 273(4.50),300(4.30), 375(4.09),425s(4.01)	2-1257-73
	acetone	398(4.01),480(4.13)	2-1257-73
	$CHCl_3$	397(4.30),460(4.26)	2-1257-73
	MeCN	390(4.08),467(4.10)	2-1257-73
$C_{21}H_{19}N_3O_4$			
Euxylophoricine D	MeCN	252(4.44),341(4.45), 356(4.48),374(4.32)	102-2521-73
1H-Pyrazole-3-carboxylic acid, 5-(1-methyl-2-phenylethenyl)-1-(4-nitrophenyl)-	C_6H_{12} or EtOH	223(4.4),270(4.52)	4-0015-73
$C_{21}H_{19}N_3O_4S$			
Carbamothioic acid, [[2-oxo-4,6-bis-(phenylamino)-2H-pyran-3-yl]carbonyl]-, S-ethyl ester	MeCN	252(4.33),327(4.39)	39-2432-73C

Compound	Solvent	$\lambda_{max}(\log \epsilon)$	Ref.
$C_{21}H_{19}N_3O_6$			
Benzoic acid, 4-[2-(1-aziridinyl)-2,3-dihydro-6-(4-nitrophenyl)-3-oxo-4H-1,4-oxazin-4-yl]-, ethyl ester	EtOH	232(4.16),260(4.13), 364(4.14)	4-0347-73
$C_{21}H_{19}N_3O_7$			
Glycine, N-[4-[2,3-dihydro-6-(4-nitrophenyl)-3-oxo-4H-1,4-oxazin-4-yl]-benzoyl]-, ethyl ester	EtOH	222(4.21),253(4.17), 367(4.23)	4-0347-73
1H-Pyrazole-4,5-dicarboxylic acid, 3-(4-ethoxyphenyl)-1-(4-nitrophenyl)-, dimethyl ester	EtOH	258(4.06),323(3.71)	94-2026-73
$C_{21}H_{19}N_3O_8$			
4-Azulenepropanol, acetate, trinitrobenzene complex	CH_2Cl_2	280(4.89),286(4.89), 330(3.82),342(3.92), 352(3.46),563(2.56), 605s(--),656s(--)	44-1106-73
1H-Pyrazole-4,5-dicarboxylic acid, 3-(3,4-dimethoxyphenyl)-1-(4-nitrophenyl)-, dimethyl ester	EtOH	264(3.96),317(3.60)	94-2026-73
$C_{21}H_{19}N_5O_4$			
Benzophenone, 4-(dimethylamino)-, 2,4-dinitrophenylhydrazone, (E)-	$CHCl_3$	439(4.48)	40-0771-73
(Z)-	$CHCl_3$	399(4.47)	40-0771-73
$C_{21}H_{20}$			
Bicyclo[5.2.0]nona-2,5-diene, 2,2-diphenyl-, cis	isooctane	243(4.18)	35-6717-73
$C_{21}H_{20}ClNO_8$			
Isoquinolinium, 4-(1,3-benzodioxol-5-ylmethylene)-3-(ethoxycarbonyl)-1,4-dihydro-2-methyl-, perchlorate	EtOH	238(4.71),344(3.90)	78-0213-73
$C_{21}H_{20}ClN_3O$			
Morpholine, 4-[4-[(4-chlorophenyl)methyl]-6-phenyl-3-pyridazinyl]-	CH_2Cl_2	264(4.23)	39-2532-73C
	CH_2Cl_2 -HCl	264(4.20)	39-2532-73C
$C_{21}H_{20}Cl_2N_4OS_2$			
Spiro[furo[2,3-d]thiazole-2(3H),4'-imidazolidine]-2'-thione, 1,3'-bis(4-chlorophenyl)tetrahydro-5'-imino-3,3a-dimethyl-	EtOH	273(4.12)	94-1300-73
$C_{21}H_{20}F_3NO_5$			
Benzo[6,7]cyclohept[1,2,3-ij]isoquinoline-2,10-diol, 4,5,6,6a,7,8-hexahydro-6,11-dimethoxy-6-(trifluoroacetyl)-	MeOH	210(4.61),267(4.06), 287(4.00)	88-4553-73
12H-Dibenzo[d,f]quinolin-12-one, 1,2,3,3a,4,5-hexahydro-7-hydroxy-8,11-dimethoxy-3-(trifluoroacetyl)-	MeOH	242(4.33),284(3.87)	88-4553-73
$C_{21}H_{20}FeN_2$			
Ferrocene, 1,1'-(2,3-dihydro-2,7(or 8)-dimethyl-1H-1,5-benzodiazepine-2,4-diyl)-	EtOH	237(4.42),266(3.94), 306(3.61),346(3.69), 438(2.83)	18-3315-73

Compound	Solvent	λ max(log ε)	Ref.
$C_{21}H_{20}FeO_4$			
Iron, tricarbonyl[4-(2,3,4,5-η)-2,4-cyclohexadien-1-yl-4-methyl-1-phenyl-1-penten-3-one]-	EtOH	223(4.43),294(4.34)	39-1882-73C
$C_{21}H_{20}NO_5$			
1,3-Dioxolo[4,5-h]isoindolo[1,2-b][3]benzazepinium, 5,6-dihydro-9,10,14-trimethoxy-, chloride	MeOH	262(4.06),334(4.01), 362(4.04),507(4.23)	25-0478-73
$C_{21}H_{20}N_2$			
Cinnoline, 1,2,3,4-tetrahydro-1-methyl-3,4-diphenyl-	MeCN	253(3.50),305(3.38)	22-3487-73
Cinnoline, 1,2,3,4-tetrahydro-1-methyl-4,4-diphenyl-	MeCN	255(3.85),302(3.55)	22-3487-73
1H-Pyrazole, 3,5-diphenyl-1,4-di-2-propenyl-	EtOH	250(4.32)	78-4159-73
$C_{21}H_{20}N_2O$			
Piperidine, 1-benzoyl-4-(1H-indol-2-ylmethylene)-	MeOH	241(4.42),308(4.34), 314(4.31)	23-0792-73
$C_{21}H_{20}N_2O_2$			
Acetamide, N-methyl-N-[1,3,4,5-tetrahydro-5-oxo-1-(phenylmethyl)benz[cd]indol-4-yl]-	EtOH	206(4.55),254(3.23), 330(3.66),365(3.71)	39-0760-73C
2,4-Pentadienoic acid, 2-cyano-5-(4-methylphenyl)-5-(phenylamino)-, ethyl ester	CH_2Cl_2	252(3.89),267s(3.84), 277s(3.82),407(4.40)	97-0132-73
1-Piperidinecarboxylic acid, 4-(1H-indol-2-ylmethylene)-, phenyl ester	MeOH	240(4.40),307(4.37), 314(4.32)	23-0792-73
$C_{21}H_{20}N_2O_2S$			
3-Pyridinecarboxylic acid, 2-amino-1,6-dihydro-4-phenyl-1-(phenylmethyl)-6-thioxo-, ethyl ester	MeOH	270(3.86),301(3.77), 397(4.23)	48-0679-73
$C_{21}H_{20}N_2O_4$			
Talbotine, 3,4,5,6-tetradehydro-	EtOH	235(4.59),240(4.58), 251s(4.33),278s(3.90), 281(3.93),287(4.24), 339(3.79),352(3.88)	33-2719-73
$C_{21}H_{20}N_2O_4S$			
1H-Pyrrole-3-carboxylic acid, 2,5-dihydro-4-(methylthio)-2-oxo-5-[(phenylmethoxy)imino]-1-(phenylmethyl)-, methyl ester	EtOH	340(4.18)	94-1667-73
$C_{21}H_{20}N_2O_5$			
1-Isoquinolinecarbonitrile, 2-benzoyl-1,2-dihydro-4,5,6,7-tetramethoxy-	EtOH	240(4.38),299(4.13), 317(4.07)	44-0060-73
$C_{21}H_{20}N_4O$			
Benzenecarboximidic acid, N-phenyl-, 2-[2-(acetylamino)phenyl]hydrazide	MeOH	336(4.29)	24-2530-73
Phenol, 3-methyl-2,4-bis[(2-methylphenyl)azo]-	EtOH	235(4.04),350(4.51), 420s(3.77)	23-3827-73

Compound	Solvent	λ_{max}(log ϵ)	Ref.
$C_{21}H_{20}N_4O_2$			
3-Pyridinecarboxamide, N-[(cyanophenyl-amino)carbonyl]-1,4,5,6-tetrahydro-1-methyl-N-phenyl-	MeOH	277.5(4.16)	33-0374-73
$C_{21}H_{20}N_4O_2S_2$			
Benzenesulfenamide, N-[1-methyl-1-[(4-nitrophenyl)azo]ethyl]-N-(phenylthio)-	$CHCl_3$	278(4.28)	39-1037-73C
$C_{21}H_{20}N_4O_4$			
2H-Pyran-3-carboxamide, N-(aminocarbonyl)-2-oxo-4,6-bis[(phenylmethyl)amino]-	MeCN	248(4.09),311(4.23)	39-2432-73C
$C_{21}H_{20}N_6O_2$			
Carbamic acid, [4-amino-1-(diphenylmethyl)-1H-1,2,3-triazolo[4,5-c]pyridin-6-yl]-, ethyl ester	10% MeOH-pH 7	233(4.45),290(4.06), 303s(4.03)	44-1095-73
Carbamic acid, [7-amino-3-(diphenylmethyl)-3H-1,2,3-triazolo[4,5-b]pyridin-5-yl]-, ethyl ester	10% MeOH-pH 7	232(4.36),283(4.22), 297s(4.15)	44-1085-73
$C_{21}H_{20}O$			
Methanone, phenyl[3-(phenylmethylene)-1-cyclohepten-1-yl]-	MeOH	226(4.31),255(4.18), 326(4.34)	44-1178-73
$C_{21}H_{20}O_4$			
4H-1-Benzopyran-4-one, 8-(3-hydroxy-3-methyl-1-butenyl)-7-methoxy-2-phenyl-, (E)-, (lanceolatin A)	MeOH	223(4.42),262(4.41), 317(4.16)	2-0085-73
$C_{21}H_{20}O_5$			
2H,6H-Benzo[1,2-b:5,4-b']dipyran-6-one, 3,4-dihydro-5-hydroxy-7-methoxy-2,2-dimethyl-8-phenyl-	MeOH	268(4.46),320(4.13)	12-0641-73
4H-1-Benzopyran-4-one, 5,7-dihydroxy-3-methoxy-6-(3-methyl-2-butenyl)-2-phenyl-	MeOH	245(4.16),270(4.34), 325(4.14)	12-0641-73
4H-1-Benzopyran-4-one, 5,7-dihydroxy-3-methoxy-8-(3-methyl-2-butenyl)-2-phenyl-	MeOH	215(4.55),272(4.53), 356(3.51)	12-0641-73
4H-1-Benzopyran-4-one, 5-hydroxy-3-methoxy-7-[(3-methyl-2-butenyl)oxy]-2-phenyl-	MeOH	268(4.40)	12-0641-73
Butanedioic acid, [3-(4-methoxyphenyl)-1-phenyl-2-propenylidene]-, 1-methyl ester	EtOH	228(4.04),246(4.00), 334(4.11)	42-0430-73
9H-Fluorene-2,7-dibutanoic acid, γ-oxo-	EtOH	219(3.97),290(4.12), 314(4.25)	132-0015-73
2H-Pentaleno[1,6a-a]naphthalene-2,5(2aH)-dione, 4-(1-acetoxyethylidene)-3,4,6,7-tetrahydro-9-methoxy-	MeOH	245(4.30),267s(4.09), 330(4.42)	39-1780-73C
Tephroglabrinol	MeOH	213(4.43),247s(4.25), 257(4.28),311(4.28)	78-3099-73
$C_{21}H_{20}O_6$			
4H-1-Benzopyran-4-one, 5,7-diacetoxy-2,3-dihydro-6,8-dimethyl-2-phenyl-	MeOH	264(3.62),327(4.11)	100-0422-73
Curcumin	EtOH	268(4.09),430(4.74)	39-2379-73C

Compound	Solvent	λ max(log ε)	Ref.
4-Cyclopentene-1,3-dione, 2-(3,4-dimethoxyphenyl)-4-methoxy-5-(4-methoxyphenyl)-	EtOH	241s(4.31),251(4.35), 354(4.24)	39-1529-73C
4-Cyclopentene-1,3-dione, 4-(3,4-dimethoxyphenyl)-5-methoxy-2-(4-methoxyphenyl)-	EtOH	220s(4.34),257(4.19), 270s(4.11),325s(3.75), 366(4.01)	39-1529-73C
2,3-Naphthalenedimethanol, 6,7-methylenedioxy)-1-(3,4-dimethoxyphenyl)-	EtOH	243(4.42),290(4.05)	2-0203-73
Pulvinone, 3,4,4'-trimethoxy-O-methyl-	EtOH	239(4.33),357(4.56)	39-1921-73C
Pulvinone, 3',4,4'-trimethoxy-O-methyl-	EtOH	240(4.34),259s(4.17), 367(4.60)	39-1921-73C
Tachrosinol, 5-O-demethyl-	MeOH	211(4.57),273(4.53), 335s(3.87)	119-0064-73
Ugonin C	EtOH	273(4.17),309(3.96), 364(4.01)	94-1851-73
$C_{21}H_{20}O_7$			
Ethanone, (2-hydroxy-4,5-dimethoxyphenyl)[4-hydroxy-2-(1-methylethyl)-5-benzofuranyl]-	EtOH	240(5.4),249s(4.48), 284(4.26),356(3.99)	39-1277-73C
Excelsin, demethoxy-, (+)-	EtOH	237(3.99),285(3.72)	102-1799-73
Melannene acetate	MeOH	243s(4.46),285(4.03), 315(4.03)	39-0965-73C
1,5-Phenanthrenediol, 2,6,7-trimethoxy-, diacetate	$CHCl_3$	263(5.00),284(4.37), 291(4.24),306(4.22), 322(3.04),340(3.14), 356(3.09)	102-0228-73
3,6-Phenanthrenediol, 2,4,7-trimethoxy-, diacetate	n.s.g.	258(4.91),280(4.27), 292(4.18),301(3.92)	39-1179-73C
$C_{21}H_{20}O_8$			
4H-1-Benzopyran-4-one, 3,5-diacetoxy-2,3-dihydro-7-methoxy-2-(4-methoxyphenyl)-	EtOH	237(4.47),248(4.30), 294(4.30)	102-0913-73
4H-1-Benzopyran-4-one, 6-(β-D-glucopyranosyloxy)-3-phenyl-	dioxan	251(4.45),294(4.45), 304(3.93)	114-0365-73D
Isoflavone, 7-β-D-glucosyloxy-	EtOH	250(4.32),298(3.89)	114-0435-73B
$C_{21}H_{20}O_9$			
Chrysophanol, 1(and 8)-O-β-D-glucopyranosyl-	MeOH	222(4.45),283(4.19), 412(3.96)	94-1254-73
$C_{21}H_{20}O_{10}$			
9,10-Anthracenedione, 1-(β-D-glucopyranosyloxy)-6,8-dihydroxy-3-methyl-	MeOH	253(4.34),287(4.36), 425(3.92)	94-1254-73
9,10-Anthracenedione, 3-[(β-D-glucopyranosyloxy)methyl]-1,8-dihydroxy-	MeOH	226(4.72),256(4.40), 433(4.05)	94-1254-73
Apigenin 7-glucoside	EtOH	268(3.99),338(4.09)	95-1231-73
	EtOH-NaOAc	269(--),349(--)	95-1231-73
	EtOH-$AlCl_3$	274(--),304(--), 322(--),361(--)	95-1231-73
4H-1-Benzopyran-4-one, 3-[4-(β-D-glucopyranosyloxy)phenyl]-5,7-dihydroxy-	95% dioxan	262(4.56),320s(3.89)	114-0365-73D
Kaempferol rhamnoside	MeOH	254s(--),267(4.27), 324s(--),368(4.32)	105-0526-73
$C_{21}H_{20}O_{11}$			
4H-1-Benzopyran-4-one, 2-(3,4-dihydroxyphenyl)-7-(β-D-glucopyranosyloxy)-5-hydroxy- (luteolin 7-glucoside)	EtOH	257(4.39),269s(4.34), 351(4.40)	95-1231-73

Compound	Solvent	λ max (log ε)	Ref.
4H-1-Benzopyran-4-one, 2-(3,4-dihydroxyphenyl)-7-(β-D-glucopyranosyloxy)-5-hydroxy- (cont.)	EtOH-NaOAc	257(--),268(-), 361(--),410s(--)	95-1231-73
	EtOH-AlCl$_3$	271(--),404(--)	95-1231-73
4H-1-Benzopyran-4-one, 2-[4-(β-D-glucopyranosyloxy)-3-hydroxyphenyl]-5,7-dihydroxy- (luteolin 4'-glucoside)	EtOH	243(4.17),271(4.28), 337(4.28)	95-1231-73
	EtOH-NaOAc	278(--),360(--)	95-1231-73
	EtOH-AlCl$_3$	269(--),369(--)	95-1231-73
$C_{21}H_{20}O_{12}$			
Hypolaetin 7-glucoside	MeOH	258s(4.27),277(4.29), 301(4.19),344(4.29)	105-0521-73
Isoquercitrin	n.s.g.	260(4.40),362(4.32)	103-0407-73
Myricitrin	MeOH	257(4.31),305(3.97), 355(4.23)	105-0644-73
$C_{21}H_{21}BrO_3$			
1(2H)-Chrysenone, 8-bromo-12-ethyl-3,4,11,12-tetrahydro-11-hydroxy-11-methyl-	C_6H_{12}	226(4.57),264s(4.25), 273(4.57),283(4.69), 327s(4.16),339(4.23), 360(3.95)	88-1553-73
isomer	C_6H_{12}	227(4.53),263s(4.28), 272(4.58),283(4.68), 342(4.16)	88-1553-73
$C_{21}H_{21}ClN_2O_7$			
2-Naphthacenecarboxamide, 4-amino-7-chloro-1,4,4a,5,5a,6,11,12a-octahydro-3,12,12a-trihydroxy-10-methoxy-N-methyl-1,11-dioxo-	MeOH-borate	223(4.35),267(4.23), 338(4.16)	88-4907-73
$C_{21}H_{21}IN_4O_4$			
Benzamide, N-[7-[5-deoxy-5-iodo-2,3-O-(1-methylethylidene)-β-D-ribofuranosyl]-7H-pyrrolo[2,3-d]pyrimidin-4-yl]-	MeOH	223(4.43),235s(4.34), 299(3.99)	18-0618-73
$C_{21}H_{21}N$			
4,7-Methano-1H-isoindole, 3a,4,5,6,7,7a-hexahydro-1,3-diphenyl-	EtOH	246(4.03)	44-1333-73
$C_{21}H_{21}NO$			
4H-Carbazol-4-one, 1,2,3,9-tetrahydro-2,2-dimethyl-9-(phenylmethyl)-	MeOH	212(4.52),244(4.24), 267(4.05),301(4.13)	24-0745-73
1H-Isoindol-1-one, 2,3,3a,6,7,7a-hexahydro-2-methyl-5,6-diphenyl-, cis	MeOH	243(4.10)	44-2169-73
trans	MeOH	245(4.08)	44-2169-73
2-Propenamide, N-(4,5-diphenyl-2,4-pentadienyl)-N-methyl-	MeOH	230(4.17),288(4.51), 307(4.27)	44-2169-73
4(1H)-Pyridinone, 1-butyl-3,5-diphenyl-	EtOH	239(4.28),299(4.04)	4-0665-73
$C_{21}H_{21}NOSn$			
Stannanecarboxamide, N,N-dimethyl-1,1,1-triphenyl-	C_6H_{12}	205(--),233(3.93), 257(--)	101-0207-73M
$C_{21}H_{21}NO_3$			
Pyridinium, 2,4-dimethyl-, 3-acetyl-1-benzoyl-4-oxo-2-pentenylide	EtOH	225s(3.98),261(3.81), 376(4.15)	39-2091-73C
$C_{21}H_{21}NO_4$			
Cyclohepta[def]carbazole-9,9(4H)-dicarboxylic acid, 8,10-dihydro-, diethyl ester	MeOH	243(4.51),292(4.00), 326(3.50),420(3.60)	39-2818-73C

Compound	Solvent	λ_{max}(log ϵ)	Ref.
7H-Pyrano[2,3-c]acridin-7-one, 3,12-dihydro-6,11-dimethoxy-3,3,12-trimethyl-	EtOH	234s(3.98),263(4.32), 281(4.31),292s(4.23), 315(3.97),335s(3.61), 396(3.50)	39-1173-73C
$C_{21}H_{21}NO_5$			
2H-1-Benzopyran-2-one, 3-[[(3,4-dimethoxyphenyl)methylene]amino]-8-ethyl-4-hydroxy-6-methyl-	MeOH	218(4.55),273(4.27), 310(4.24)	2-0433-73
Corycavine	MeOH	291(3.86)	95-0087-73
Corynoline	MeOH	238(4.06),289(3.97)	95-0087-73
Spiro[1,3-dioxolo[4,5-g]isoquinolin-5(6H),2'-[2H]inden]-1'(3'H)-one, 7,8-dihydro-4',5'-dimethoxy-6-methyl-	EtOH	237(4.38),292(4.33)	88-2795-73
$C_{21}H_{21}NO_6$			
6H-Dibenzo[a,c]cycloheptene-6,6-dicarboxylic acid, 5,7-dihydro-1-nitro-, diethyl ester	MeOH	241(4.15)	39-2818-73C
1,3-Dioxolo[4,5-g]isoquinoline-6(5H)-carboxylic acid, 5-(1,3-benzodioxol-5-ylmethyl)-7,8-dihydro-, ethyl ester	n.s.g.	237(4.05),290(4.06)	39-0349-73C
6-Isoquinolinecarboxylic acid, 5-hydroxy-1-[(3,4,5-trimethoxyphenyl)-methyl]-, methyl ester	EtOH	256(4.36),290s(3.80), 300s(3.73),354(3.68), 368(3.68)	78-0857-73
6-Isoquinolinecarboxylic acid, 7-hydroxy-1-[(3,4,5-trimethoxyphenyl)-methyl]-, methyl ester	EtOH	240(4.72),270s(3.90), 383(3.58)	78-0857-73
$C_{21}H_{21}NO_7$			
Adlumidiceine	EtOH	232s(4.14),294(3.87), 306s(3.75)	102-2513-73
	EtOH-HCl	222s(4.21),295(3.73), 316(3.74)	102-2513-73
	EtOH-NaOH	230(4.08),289(3.82), 307s(3.72)	102-2513-73
1(3H)-Isobenzofuranone, 6,7-dimethoxy-3-[[6-[2-(hydroxymethylamino)ethyl]-1,3-benzodioxol-5-yl]methylene]-, (Z)-	EtOH	228(4.59),243s(4.24), 310(4.06),388(4.24)	33-2107-73
Spiro[6H-1,3-dioxolo[4,5-i][3,4]benzoxazocine-6,1'(3'H)-isobenzofuran]-3'-one, 5,8,9,10-tetrahydro-4'.5'-dimethoxy-8-methyl-	EtOH	218(4.62),245s(--), 300(3.78)	33-2107-73
$C_{21}H_{21}N_3$			
Benzenamine, 4-methyl-N-(3-methylphenyl)-2-[(3-methylphenyl)azo]-	C_6H_{12}	293(4.32),323(4.15), 482(3.92)	44-0507-73
Benzenamine, 5-methyl-N-(4-methylphenyl)-2-[(4-methylphenyl)azo]-	THF	292(4.31),353(4.27), 465(4.05)	44-0507-73
$C_{21}H_{21}N_3O$			
Morpholine, 4-[6-phenyl-4-(phenylmethyl)-3-pyridazinyl]-	CH_2Cl_2	262(4.21)	39-2532-73C
	CH_2Cl_2-HCl	262(4.21)	39-2532-73C
2-Naphthalenol, 1-[[2-(1-piperidinyl)-phenyl]azo]-	$CHCl_3$	516(4.32)	48-0725-73
$C_{21}H_{21}N_3O_2$			
Acetic acid, cyano(3-ethyl-3,4,7,12-tetrahydroindolo[2,3-a]quinolizin-2(6H)-ylidene)-, methyl ester	EtOH	223(4.45),250s(--), 344(4.05),449(4.70), 476(4.81)	78-4153-73

Compound	Solvent	λ max (log ε)	Ref.
Morpholine, 4-[3-[(4-methylphenyl)azo]-5-phenyl-2-furanyl]-	CH_2Cl_2	246(4.26),333(4.16), 461(4.44)	39-2523-73C
tetrafluoroborate	CH_2Cl_2	267(4.21),276(4.22), 294(4.24),488(4.56)	39-2523-73C
4H,8H-Pyrazolo[4',3':4,5]pyrrolo[3,2,1-ij]quinoline-10-carboxylic acid, 5,6,7a,10a-tetrahydro-8-phenyl-, ethyl ester, cis	EtOH	245(4.23),303s(3.89), 336(4.08)	78-3159-73
10H,15H-Pyrrolo[1",2":4',5']pyrazino-[1',2':1,2]azocino[5,4-b]indole-10,15-dione, 5,6,12,13,15a,16-hexahydro-6,6-dimethyl-	EtOH	224(4.44),272(3.93), 284(3.84),292(3.71)	78-0107-73
4H-Pyrrolo[3,2,1-ij]quinoline-1-acetic acid, 5,6-dihydro-α-(phenylhydrazono)-, ethyl ester	EtOH	286(4.04),351(4.27)	78-3159-73
$C_{21}H_{21}N_3O_2S_2$			
Carbamic acid, [[[3-(phenylmethyl)-2(3H)-thiazolylidene]amino](phenylmethyl)thio]methylene]-, ethyl ester	dioxan	281(3.94),411(4.38)	94-0074-73
$C_{21}H_{21}N_3O_3$			
Austamide	EtOH	234(4.42),256(3.07), 268s(3.04),282(3.94), 392(3.43)	78-0107-73
Benzenamine, 5-methoxy-N-(4-methoxyphenyl)-2-[(4-methoxyphenyl)azo]-	THF	288(4.23),347(4.26), 451(4.18)	44-0507-73
1H-Indole-2-carboxylic acid, 1-methyl-3-[2-oxo-1-(phenylhydrazono)propyl]-, ethyl ester, (E)-	EtOH	229(4.56),293(4.26), 347(4.26)	78-3159-73
Morpholine, 4-[3-[(4-methoxyphenyl)azo]-5-phenyl-2-furanyl]-	CH_2Cl_2	241(4.33),333(4.21), 463(4.98)	39-2523-73C
tetrafluoroborate	CH_2Cl_2	242(4.17),258(4.17), 295(4.25),507(4.53)	39-2523-73C
Pyrazolo[3,4-b]indole-8a(1H)-carboxylic acid, 3-acetyl-3a,8-dihydro-8-methyl-1-phenyl-, ethyl ester	EtOH	244(4.26),309(3.99), 325s(3.98)	78-3159-73
$C_{21}H_{21}N_3O_4$			
2H-1,4-Oxazin-3(4H)-one, 6-(4-nitrophenyl)-4-phenyl-2-(1-piperidinyl)-	EtOH	254(4.29),373(4.01)	4-0347-73
$C_{21}H_{22}$			
Dibenzo[a,h]fluorene, 2,3,4,8,9,10,11-13-octahydro-	EtOH	214(4.74),269(4.30), 300(3.80),303(3.94), 310(4.01),318(4.07)	132-0015-73
$C_{21}H_{22}BrN_5O_5$			
L-erythro-2-Pentofuranoside, methyl 5-C-[6-(benzoylamino)-9H-purin-9-yl]-1-bromo-1-deoxy-3,4-O-(1-methylethylidene)-, (R)-	EtOH	230(4.07),277(4.24)	35-1350-73
$C_{21}H_{22}FeN_2$			
Ferrocene, 1,1'-(2,3,4,5-tetrahydro-2,7(or 8)-dimethyl-1H-1,5-benzodiazepine-2,4-diyl)-	EtOH	222(4.49),312(3.47), 444(2.29)	18-3315-73
$C_{21}H_{22}NO$			
Pyrylium, 4-(dimethylamino)-2,6-diphenyl-, perchlorate	MeCN	250(4.10),335(4.24), 422(4.61),443(4.59)	78-1031-73

Compound	Solvent	$\lambda_{max}(\log \epsilon)$	Ref.
$C_{21}H_{22}NO_5$			
6H-Benzo[g]-1,3-benzodioxolo[5,6-a]quinolizinium, 5,8,13,13a-tetrahydro-9,10-dimethoxy-7-methyl-13-oxo-	MeOH	230(4.29),287(4.30)	88-2795-73
	MeOH-base	270(4.10),362(4.35)	88-2795-73
Pyridinium 1-benzoyl-3,3-bis(ethoxycarbonyl)allylide	EtOH	245(4.05),388(4.35), 448(4.35)	39-2091-73C
$C_{21}H_{22}N_2$			
1H-Indole, 2-[[1-(phenylmethyl)-4-piperidinylidene]methyl]-	MeOH	243(4.20),307(4.35), 313s(4.32)	23-0792-73
$C_{21}H_{22}N_2O$			
3,6-Diazatricyclo[4.3.1.1^{3,8}]undecan-9-one, 1,8-diphenyl-	EtOH	250s(3.27),256s(3.22), 263s(3.13)	44-1648-73
	EtOH-HCl	250(3.07),262(3.10)	44-1648-73
$C_{21}H_{22}N_2O_2$			
Apo Δ^{14}-vincamine	EtOH	229(4.56),275(4.14), 317(3.90)	102-1475-73
1-Piperidinecarboxylic acid, 4-(1H-indol-2-ylmethyl)-, phenyl ester	MeOH	275(3.91),282(3.90), 291(3.81)	23-0792-73
$C_{21}H_{22}N_2O_4$			
2-Butenedioic acid, 2-[(1-methyl-2-phenylethylidene)phenylhydrazino]-, dimethyl ester	MeOH	286(3.00)	78-0101-73
2,4(1H,3H)-Pyrimidinedione, 1,3-bis-[(2-hydroxy-3-methylphenyl)methyl]-5-methyl-	pH 2-7	276(4.10)	56-1645-73
	pH 13	288(4.16)	56-1645-73
Talbotine, 3,4-didehydro-	EtOH	209(4.34),240(4.24), 316(4.18)	33-2719-73
	EtOH-HCl	209(4.34),245(3.99), 349(4.31)	33-2719-73
	EtOH-KOH	233(4.25),240s(4.21), 317(4.18)	33-2719-73
$C_{21}H_{22}N_2O_6$			
DL-Phenylalanine, N-[N-[3-(4-hydroxy-3-methoxyphenyl)-1-oxo-2-propenyl]-glycyl]-	MeOH-HCl	296(4.05),320(4.16)	20-0259-73
	MeOH-KOH	298(3.60),308(3.69), 365(4.28)	20-0259-73
L-isomer	MeOH-HCl	296(4.06),319(4.16)	20-0259-73
	MeOH-KOH	296s(3.63),308(3.74), 365(4.28)	20-0259-73
$C_{21}H_{22}N_3S$			
Thiazolo[3,2-a]pyrimidin-4-ium, 7-[3-(1,3-dihydro-1,3,3-trimethyl-2H-indol-2-ylidene)-1-propenyl]-5-methyl-, perchlorate	n.s.g.	566(5.37)	124-1151-73
$C_{21}H_{22}N_4O$			
2-Propen-1-one, 3-(diethylamino)-3-phenyl-1-(5-phenyl-1H-1,2,3-triazol-4-yl)-	EtOH	344(4.47)	78-3271-73
anion	EtOH	234(4.28),344(4.52)	78-3271-73
$C_{21}H_{22}N_4O_2$			
Benzo[g]pteridine-2,4(3H,4aH)-dione, 5,10-dihydro-4a,7,8,10-tetramethyl-3-(phenylmethyl)-	pH 7	360(3.94)	5-1388-73
	6M HCl	385(3.57)	5-1388-73

Compound	Solvent	$\lambda_{max}(\log \epsilon)$	Ref.
$C_{21}H_{22}N_4O_4$			
Benzamide, N-[7-[5-deoxy-2,3-O-(1-methylethylidene)-β-D-ribofuranosyl]-7H-pyrrolo[2,3-d]pyrimidin-4-yl]-	MeOH	224(4.42),300(3.97)	18-0618-73
$C_{21}H_{22}N_4O_5S$			
Tubercidin, 2',3'-O-isopropylidene-N - p-toluenesulfonyl-	MeOH	220(4.52),313(4.14)	18-0618-73
$C_{21}H_{22}O_2$			
17H-Cyclopenta[a]phenanthren-17-one, 11,12,13,16-tetrahydro-3-methoxy-13-(2-propenyl)-, (±)-	EtOH	314(4.49)	94-2195-73
$C_{21}H_{22}O_3$			
11H-Cyclopenta[a]phenanthren-17-ol, 12,13,14,15-tetrahydro-3-methoxy-13-methyl-, acetate	EtOH	268(4.71),280(4.76), 292(4.63),326(4.42), 342(4.44)	70-1574-73
11H-Cyclopenta[a]phenanthren-17-ol, 12,13,16,17-tetrahydro-3-methoxy-13-methyl-, acetate, (13S-cis)-	EtOH	310(4.4)	70-1574-73
4-Cyclopentene-1,3-dione, 2-[2-(3,4-dihydro-6-methoxy-1(2H)-naphthalenylidene)ethyl]-2-(2-propenyl)-	EtOH	267(4.25)	94-2195-73
2-Propen-1-one, 1-[2-hydroxy-4-methoxy-3-(3-methyl-2-butenyl)phenyl]-3-phenyl-, (E)- (derricin)	MeOH	343(4.44)	2-1225-73
2-Propen-1-one, 1-[2-hydroxy-4-methoxy-5-(3-methyl-2-butenyl)phenyl]-3-phenyl-, (E)-	MeOH	310(4.03),365(4.09)	2-1225-73
$C_{21}H_{22}O_4$			
Benzaldehyde, 3-[5-(3,6-dioxo-1,4-cyclohexadien-1-yl)-3-methyl-3-pentenyl]-6-hydroxy-2,4-dimethyl-, (E)-	MeOH	248(4.16),274(4.06), 346(3.58),440(1.18)	78-2565-73
Benzaldehyde, 6-hydroxy-3-[2-(6-hydroxy-2-methyl-2H-1-benzopyran-2-yl)ethyl]-2,4-dimethyl- (panicein B_2)	MeOH	273(3.91),340(3.45)	78-2565-73
Benzofuran, 2-(3,4-dimethoxyphenyl)-7-methoxy-3-methyl-5-(1-propenyl)-, (E)-	EtOH	233(4.38),265(4.43), 308(4.42)	12-1111-73
1(2H)-Chrysenone, 3,4,11,12-tetrahydro-11-hydroxy-8,12-dimethoxy-11-methyl-	C_6H_{12}	224(4.37),260s(3.90), 267s(4.01),276(4.33), 287(4.49),352(4.06)	88-1553-73
9H-Fluorene-2,7-dibutanoic acid	EtOH	220(4.30),260(4.42), 268(4.46),278(4.35), 294(3.98),300(3.94), 306(4.08)	132-0015-73
1H-Phenalen-1-one, 2-(2-acetoxy-1,1-dimethylethyl)-4-methoxy-9-methyl-	EtOH	264(4.48),335(3.83), 418(4.15)	39-2159-73C
$C_{21}H_{22}O_5S$			
1H-Phenalene-2-acetic acid, 4-methoxy-9-[(methylsulfinyl)methyl]-α,α-dimethyl-1-oxo-, methyl ester	EtOH	208(4.47),268(4.45), 324(3.61),380(3.77), 417(3.98),437(4.01)	39-2159-73C
$C_{21}H_{22}O_6$			
2H,5H-Benz[4,5]indeno[1,7a-c]furan-2,5-dione, 2a,3,6,7-tetrahydro-3α,9-dimethoxy-2aα-(3-oxobutyl)-	MeOH	244(3.98),336(4.44)	39-1780-73C

Compound	Solvent	$\lambda_{max}(\log \epsilon)$	Ref.
$C_{21}H_{22}O_7$			
3,6-Phenanthrenediol, 9,10-dihydro-2,4,7-trimethoxy-, diacetate	n.s.g.	284(4.37),295s(4.25), 306s(4.06)	39-1179-73C
Ribose, 2,3-bis(4-methylbenzoate)	MeOH	236(4.33)	18-3228-73
$C_{21}H_{22}O_8$			
4H-1-Benzopyran-4-one, 3,5,6,7,8-pentamethoxy-2-(4-methoxyphenyl)-	MeOH	270(4.44),305(4.23)	2-0201-73
Chromomycinonic acid, 2-formyl-6-methyl-, methyl ester	EtOH	224(4.0),278(4.64), 326(3.66),335(3.89)	105-0498-73
$C_{21}H_{22}O_9$			
Barbaloin	MeOH	261(3.85),269(3.92), 297(3.98),362(4.08)	94-0149-73
	MeOH-KOH	269(--),302(--), 379(--)	94-0149-73
4H-1-Benzopyran-4-one, 2-(3-hydroxy-4,5-dimethoxyphenyl)-5,6,7,8-tetramethoxy-	MeOH	272(4.38),322(4.53)	2-0096-73
$C_{21}H_{22}O_{11}$			
Saponaretin	MeOH	273(4.32),335(4.34)	105-0640-73
$C_{21}H_{23}ClN_2O_3$			
1H-Indole-3-carboxylic acid, 1-(4-chlorophenyl)-1-[(dimethylamino)methyl]-6-hydroxy-2-methyl-, ethyl ester	dioxan	275(4.15),302(4.03)	83-0446-73
Yohimbanium, 17-hydroxy-16-(methoxycarbonyl)-, chloride, (6α,17β)-	MeOH	253(4.45),307(4.29), 368(3.63)	95-0483-73
$C_{21}H_{23}ClN_2O_4S_2$			
Benzothiazolium, 2-[6-[5-(dimethylamino)-2-thienyl]-1,3,5-hexatrienyl]-3-ethyl-, perchlorate	$MeNO_2$	762(5.04)	103-0850-73
$C_{21}H_{23}F_3N_4O_2$			
Benzoic acid, 4-[[[1,2,3,4-tetrahydro-1-[[(2,2,2-trifluoroethyl)imino]methyl]-2-quinoxalinyl]methyl]amino]-, ethyl ester	EtOH	274(4.24),306(4.49)	35-8414-73
$C_{21}H_{23}IN_4O_5S$			
Benzenesulfonamide, N-[7-[5-deoxy-5-iodo-2,3-O-(1-methylethylidene)-β-D-ribofuranosyl]-7H-pyrrolo[2,3-d]pyrimidin-4-yl]-4-methyl-	MeOH	290(4.29)	18-0618-73
$C_{21}H_{23}N$			
Cyclohexanamine, N-(2,3-dihydro-1H-inden-1-ylidene)-	isooctane	248(4.24),280(4.54), 287(4.67),297(4.64)	44-0654-73
1H-Isoindole, 2,3,3a,4,5,7a-hexahydro-2-methyl-5,6-diphenyl-, cis, hydrochloride	MeOH	241(4.09)	44-2169-73
trans, cyclohexylsulfamate	MeOH	243(4.00)	44-2169-73
2,4-Pentadien-1-amine, N-methyl-4,5-diphenyl-N-2-propenyl-, hydrochloride	MeOH	222(4.15),232(4.11), 289(4.51),306(4.32)	44-2169-73
$C_{21}H_{23}NO_3$			
Acetamide, 2-(4-benzoylphenoxy)-N-cyclohexyl-	EtOH	210(4.21),283(4.24)	111-0574-73

Compound	Solvent	λ max (log ε)	Ref.
Cyclopentanecarboxylic acid, 2-oxo-3-[phenyl(phenylamino)methyl]-, ethyl ester	EtOH	264(4.22),309(3.94)	103-0628-73
1H-Indole-3-acetic acid, 2,3-dihydro-α-(1-methylethyl)-2-oxo-3-phenyl-, ethyl ester	EtOH	255(3.84),285(3.00)	104-0861-73
$C_{21}H_{23}NO_4$			
Benzo[e][1,3]dioxolo[4,5-k][3]benzazecine, 5,6,7,8-tetrahydro-3,4-dimethoxy-6-methyl-, cis	C_6H_{12}	295(3.80)	33-0553-73
	EtOH	294(3.85)	33-0553-73
trans	C_6H_{12}	281(3.98)	33-0553-73
	EtOH	233(4.10)	33-0553-73
1H-Isoindole, 1-[(6-ethenyl-1,3-benzodioxol-5-yl)methyl]-2,3-dihydro-4,5-dimethoxy-2-methyl-	EtOH	264(4.02),306(3.70)	33-0553-73
Spiro[2H-indene-2,1'(2'H)-isoquinoline]-5,6'-diol, 1,3,3',4'-tetrahydro-6,7'-dimethoxy-2'-methyl-1-methylene-	EtOH	266s(3.94),272s(3.94), 294(3.75),316(3.95), 328s(3.92)	78-1265-73
$C_{21}H_{23}NO_5$			
Corycavine, dihydro-	MeOH	243(3.88),292(3.85)	95-0087-73
6H-1,3-Dioxolo[4,5-h]isoindolo[1,2-b]-[3]benzazepine, 5,8,12b,13-tetrahydro-9,10,14-trimethoxy-	MeOH	236s(4.06),280(3.61)	25-0478-73
2(1H)-Quinolinone, 4,6,8-trimethoxy-3-[2-(phenylmethoxy)ethyl]-	EtOH	232(4.34),255(4.37), 279(3.91),290s(3.80), 347(3.75),363s(3.66)	18-0577-73
$C_{21}H_{23}NO_6$			
Cephalotaxine, 5,6-didehydro-O^7-demethyl-7,8-dihydro-	EtOH	235(4.02),291(3.60)	95-0916-73
Colchinal	EtOH	256(4.42),346(3.72)	63-0421-73
Colchicine, 2-demethyl-	EtOH	240s(4.50),352(4.22)	63-0421-73
Colchicine, 10-demethyl-	EtOH	244(4.47),348(4.20)	63-0421-73
Rhoeageninemethine, dihydro-	EtOH	212(4.30),237(4.03), 290(3.94)	73-2799-73
$C_{21}H_{23}NO_{12}S$			
1,2-Benzisothiazol-3(2H)-one, 2-(2,3,4-6-tetra-O-acetyl-β-D-glucopyranosyl)-	MeOH	276(3.05),285(2.94)	5-1943-73
α-D-Glucopyranoside, 1,2-benzisothiazol-3-yl, 2,3,4,6-tetraacetate, S,S-dioxide	MeOH	268(3.36)	5-1943-73
$C_{21}H_{23}N_2S_2$			
Benzothiazolium, 2-[6-[5-(dimethylamino)-2-thienyl]-1,3,5-hexatrienyl]-3-ethyl-, perchlorate	$MeNO_2$	762(5.04)	103-0850-73
$C_{21}H_{23}N_3$			
Suaveoline, N_b-methyl-	EtOH	227(4.57),272(4.01), 284(3.97)	102-1167-73
$C_{21}H_{23}N_3O$			
5H-Pyrido[4,3-b]indole-5-propanamine, 2-benzoyl-1,2,3,4-tetrahydro-, maleate(1:1)	EtOH	225(4.36),275(3.88), 282(3.89),292(3.81)	78-4045-73

Compound	Solvent	λ_{max}(log ε)	Ref.
$C_{21}H_{23}N_3O_2$			
2H,7H-1,12b:4,7-Dimethanopyrido[2',3'-6,7]oxocino[3,4-b]indol-14-imine, 3-ethylidene-3,4,4a,5,13,13a-hexahydro-10-methoxy-, [1R-(1α,3E,4α-4aβ,7α,12bβ,13aβ)]-	EtOH	234(4.44),279(3.53), 310s(3.18)	95-1165-73
Pyrrolo[1,2-a]pyrazine-1,4-dione, 3-[[2-(1,1-dimethyl-2-propenyl)-1H-indol-3-yl)methyl]-2,3,6,7-tetrahydro-, (S)-	EtOH	223(4.54),268(4.03), 283(4.00),292(3.89)	78-0107-73
$C_{21}H_{23}N_3O_3$			
Spiro[2H-indole-2,7'(8'H)-[5H,12H]pyrrolo[1',2':4,5]pyrazino[1,2-a]azepine]-3,5',12'-trione, 1,1',2',3,3',5'a,6'-12'a-octahydro-8',8'-dimethyl-, [2S-(2α,5'aβ,12'aα)]-	EtOH	234(4.40),256(4.05), 392(3.46)	78-0107-73
Spiro[2H-indole-2,7'(8'H)-[5H,12H]pyrrolo[1',2':4,5]pyrazino[1,2-a]azepine]-3,5',12'(1H)-trione, 1',2',3',5'a,6'-12'a-hexahydro-8',8'-dimethyl-	EtOH	238(4.49),256(4.13), 390(3.52)	78-0107-73
$C_{21}H_{23}N_5O$			
Morpholine, 4-[4-[2-(4-methylphenyl)hydrazino]-6-phenyl-3-pyridazinyl]-	CH_2Cl_2	254(4.48)	39-2532-73C
$C_{21}H_{23}N_5O_2$			
Carbamic acid, [4,5-diamino-6-[(diphenylmethyl)amino]-2-pyridinyl]-, ethyl ester	10% MeOH-pH 7	222(4.54),296(3.91)	44-1095-73
Morpholine, 4-[4-[2-(4-methoxyphenyl)-hydrazino]-6-phenyl-3-pyridazinyl]-	CH_2Cl_2	250(4.49),290s(4.09)	39-2532-73C
$C_{21}H_{23}N_5O_6$			
1,3-Azulenedicarboxylic acid, 2-amino-6-[5-amino-4-(ethoxycarbonyl)-1H-1,2,3-triazol-1-yl]-, diethyl ester	n.s.g.	246(4.3),332(4.7), 418(3.9)	18-1212-73
$C_{21}H_{23}N_7O_6$			
Neobishomofolic acid	pH 1	232(4.16),246(4.12), 281(3.61),321(3.91)	87-0697-73
	pH 7	240(4.35),273(4.15), 346(3.83)	87-0697-73
	pH 13	254(4.51),278s(--), 364(3.91)	87-0697-73
$C_{21}H_{23}O_8P$			
Phosphonic acid, [2,6-bis(2,4-dimethoxyphenyl)-4H-pyran-4-yl]-	EtOH	260(4.367)	65-0087-73
Phosphonic acid, [2,6-bis(3,4-dimethoxyphenyl)-4H-pyran-4-yl]-	EtOH	275(4.214)	65-0087-73
$C_{21}H_{24}BrNO_4$			
6H-Dibenzo[a,g]quinolizinium, 5,8-dihydro-3,11-dihydroxy-2,11-dimethoxy-7,13-dimethyl-, bromide	EtOH	230(4.45),231(4.55)	78-1265-73
$C_{21}H_{24}Br_2O_2$			
6H-Cyclopenta[a]phenanthren-17-ol, 13-(2,3-dibromopropyl)-7,11,12,13,16,17-hexahydro-3-methoxy-	EtOH	276(4.23)	94-2202-73

Compound	Solvent	λ_{max}(log ϵ)	Ref.
$C_{21}H_{24}ClNO_2$			
Benzoic acid, 4-(2-chloro-2-phenylethenyl)-, 2-(diethylamino)ethyl ester	EtOH	298(4.05)	104-1511-73
$C_{21}H_{24}ClN_3O_9$			
1H-Imidazo[4,5-c]pyridine, 4-chloro-2-methyl-1-(2,3,4,6-tetra-O-acetyl-β-D-galactopyranosyl)-	pH 1	272(3.71)	124-0703-73
	pH 13	251(3.68),269(3.66)	124-0703-73
	MeOH	250(3.76),265(3.58)	124-0703-73
1H-Imidazo[4,5-c]pyridine, 4-chloro-2-methyl-1-(2,3,4,6-tetra-O-acetyl-β-D-glucopyranosyl)-	pH 1	272(3.66)	124-0703-73
	pH 13	252(3.59),268(3.58)	124-0703-73
	MeOH	250(3.74),265(3.64)	124-0703-73
$C_{21}H_{24}FeO_7$			
Iron, tricarbonyl[(4a,9,10,10a-η)-dimethyl 1,2,3,4,4b,5,6,7,8,8a-decahydro-9,10-phenanthrenedicarboxylate]-	EtOH	238(4.16)	22-2121-73
$C_{21}H_{24}N_2O_2S$			
Benzenesulfonamide, 4-methyl-N-(2,3,4,9-tetrahydro-1,9-dimethyl-1H-carbazol-1-yl)-	EtOH	203(4.49),229(4.76), 288(3.94)	39-1809-73C
9H-Thioxanthene-4-carboxaldehyde, 1-[[2-(diethylamino)ethyl]methylamino]-9-oxo-	EtOH	256(4.39),272s(4.21), 301(4.15),333(4.20), 415(3.83)	44-1743-73
$C_{21}H_{24}N_2O_3$			
Acetamide, N-cyclohexyl-2-[4-(hydroxyimino)phenylmethyl]phenoxy]-	EtOH	210(4.40),264(4.25)	111-0574-73
4H-Benzo[a]quinolizin-4-one, 1,6,7,11b-tetrahydro-2-hydroxy-3-[1-oxo-3-(1-pyrrolidinyl)-2-butenyl]-	$CHCl_3$	271(4.09),386(4.75)	70-1745-73
Coronaridine, 19-oxo-	EtOH	222(4.46),276s(3.81), 284(3.85),292(3.78)	36-1199-73
Estra-1,3,5(10)-trien-17-one, 3-(3-diazo-2-oxopropoxy)-	EtOH	272(3.89)	44-3532-73
2-Propanone, 1-diazo-3-[4-[1-ethyl-2-(4-hydroxyphenyl)butyl]phenoxy]-	EtOH	274(4.00)	44-3525-73
$C_{21}H_{24}N_2O_4$			
Acetic acid, cyano(3-ethyl-3,4,6,7-tetrahydro-9,10-dimethoxy-2H-benzo-[a]quinolizin-2-ylidene)-, methyl ester	EtOH	245(4.25),302(3.82), 344(3.93),448(4.67),	78-4153-73
	EtOH-HCl	246(4.20),304(3.82), 344(3.90),446(4.58), 468(4.62)	78-4153-73
	HOAc	302(3.78),348(3.88), 448(4.57),466(4.62)	78-4153-73
$C_{21}H_{24}N_2O_5S$			
Thiopyrano[4,3-b]indole-3,4-dicarboxylic acid, 4a,5-dihydro-4a,5-dimethyl-1-(4-morpholinyl)-, dimethyl ester	EtOH	225(4.17),255(4.16), 366(3.83)	94-2770-73
$C_{21}H_{24}N_3O_4P$			
Phosphonic acid, [9,9a-dihydro-9a-methoxy-3-methyl-1-(3-methylphenyl)-1H-pyrazolo[3,4-b]quinolin-4-yl]-, dimethyl ester	n.s.g.	248(4.41),276(4.38), 338(3.78),370(3.72)	39-1606-73C
Phosphonic acid, [9,9a-dihydro-9a-methoxy-3-methyl-1-(4-methylphenyl)-1H-pyrazolo[3,4-b]quinolin-4-yl]-, dimethyl ester	n.s.g.	248(4.34),277(4.35), 338(3.84),375(3.74)	39-1606-73C

Compound	Solvent	$\lambda_{max}(\log \epsilon)$	Ref.
$C_{21}H_{24}N_4O_2$			
4-Cyclopentapyrazoleacetaldehyde, 1,3a-4,5,6,6a-hexahydro-5,6-dihydroxy-α-methyl-1-phenyl-, phenylhydrazone	n.s.g.	243(4.11),276(4.44)	23-0760-73
$C_{21}H_{24}N_4O_4$			
Spiro[2H-indole-2,7'(8'H)-[5H,12H]pyrrolo[1',2':4,5]pyrazino[1,2-a]azepine]-3,5',12'-trione, 1,1',2',3,3',5'a,6'-9',10',12'a-decahydro-8',8'-dimethyl-1-nitroso-, [2S-(2α,5'aβ,12'aβ)]-	EtOH	206(4.20),237(4.08), 252(4.10),283(3.79), 328(3.67)	78-0107-73
$C_{21}H_{24}N_4O_5S$			
Benzenesul onamide, N-(4,5,7,7a,10,11-hexahydro-9,9-dimethyl-7,11-epoxy-3H,6H-8,10-dioxa-4,5a,11a-triaza-cyclopenta[6,7]cyclooct[1,2,3-cd]-inden-3-ylidene)-4-methyl-, [7R-(7α,7aα,10aα,11α)]-	MeOH	220(4.24),245s(3.92), 312(3.76)	18-0618-73
$C_{21}H_{24}N_4O_6S$			
Tubercidin, 2',3'-O-isopropylidene-N[6]-p-toluenesulfonyl-	MeOH	220(4.27),291(4.21)	18-0618-73
$C_{21}H_{24}O_2$			
6H-Cyclopenta[a]phenanthren-17-ol, 7,11-12,13,16,17-hexahydro-3-methoxy-13-(2-propenyl)-, cis-(±)-	EtOH	312(4.41)	94-2195-73
Estra-1,3,5(10),8,14-pentaen-17-one, 16-ethyl-3-methoxy-, (±)-	EtOH	313(4.46)	95-0566-73
14β-Estra-1,3,5(10),8,15-pentaen-17-one, 16-ethyl-3-methoxy-, (±)-	EtOH	271(4.16)	95-0566-73
Naphth[2',1':4,5]indeno[1,7a-b]furan, 1,2,3a,4,6,7,12,13-octahydro-9-methoxy-2-methyl-	EtOH	310(4.48)	94-2195-73
$C_{21}H_{24}O_3$			
1,3-Cyclopentanedione, 2-[2-(3,4-dihydro-6-methoxy-1(2H)-naphthalenylidene)ethyl]-2-(2-propenyl)-	EtOH	267(4.34)	94-2195-73
18,19-Dinorpregna-1,3,5(10)-trien-20-yn-6-one, 13-ethyl-3,17-dihydroxy-, (17α)-	MeOH	221(4.26),254(3.89), 324(3.42)	24-0723-73
$C_{21}H_{24}O_4$			
Benzaldehyde, 3-[5-(2,5-dihydroxyphenyl)-3-methyl-3-pentenyl]-6-hydroxy-2,4-dimethyl-	MeOH	276(4.10),294s(3.71), 346(3.53)	78-2565-73
2-Cyclopenten-1-one, 4-acetoxy-5-[2-(3,4-dihydro-6-methoxy-1(2H)-naphthalenylidene)ethyl]-5-methyl-	EtOH	265(4.24)	94-0697-73
Ethanone, 1-[3,4-dihydro-5-methoxy-2,2-dimethyl-7-(phenylmethoxy)-2H-1-benzopyran-8-yl]-	EtOH	210(4.6),228(4.3), 279(3.8)	12-2291-73
Gibba-1,3,4a(10a),4b-tetraene-10-carboxylic acid, 6α-ethoxy-1,7-dimethyl-8-oxo-, methyl ester	n.s.g.	254s(4.05),262(4.19), 271(4.19),288(3.61), 299(3.53)	39-1476-73C
6β-	n.s.g.	253s(4.05),260(4.20), 270(4.15),288(3.52), 299(3.48)	39-1476-73C

Compound	Solvent	λmax(log ε)	Ref.
6-Oxagona-1,3,5(10),8,14-pentaen-17-one, 3-methoxy-7,13β-dimethyl-	EtOH	247(4.18),307(4.11), 334(4.26)	2-0847-73
1H-Phenanthro[3,2-b]pyran-4-carboxylic acid, 2,3,4,4a,5,6,8,12b-octahydro-4α,12bβ-dimethyl-8-oxo-, methyl ester	EtOH	225(4.26),231(4.19), 244(4.03),251(3.99), 267(3.66),312(3.72)	12-1763-73
$C_{21}H_{24}O_5$			
Benzaldehyde, 3-[5-(2,5-dihydroxyphenyl)-3-methyl-3-pentenyl]-5,6-dihydroxy-2,4-dimethyl-, (E)- (panicein C)	MeOH	291(4.18),380(3.32)	78-2565-73
3aH-Benz[e]indene-3a-carboxylic acid, 2,3,4,5-tetrahydro-7-methoxy-2-oxo-3-(3-oxopentyl)-, methyl ester	MeOH	239(3.98),300s(4.28), 318(4.41)	39-1780-73C
1H-Indene-1,5(6H)-dione, 4-[2-acetoxy-2-(3-methoxyphenyl)ethyl]-2,3,7,7a-tetrahydro-7a-methyl-, (R*,S*)-(±)-	EtOH	220(4.04),249(3.96), 275(3.48),281(3.42)	44-3229-73
$C_{21}H_{24}O_6$			
Arctigenin	EtOH	231(4.17),282(3.75)	95-1231-73
4'-β-gentiobioside	EtOH	230(4.20),280(3.79)	94-1114-73
Benzenepropanoic acid, 4-methoxy-3-[4-(3-methoxy-3-oxopropyl)phenoxy]-, methyl ester	EtOH	209(4.32),220(4.29), 273(3.61),281(3.58)	33-1266-73
Butanedioic acid, [(2,7-dimethoxy-1-naphthalenyl)methylene]dimethyl-, 4-ethyl ester	EtOH	215(4.36),239(4.81), 308(2.72),318(2.73), 331(2.72)	39-2159-73C
3-Furancarboxylic acid, 2-(2,7-dimethoxy-1-naphthalenyl)tetrahydro-4,4-dimethyl-5-oxo-, ethyl ester	EtOH	238(4.49),279(3.80), 315(3.30),322(3.15), 331(3.26)	39-2159-73C
$C_{21}H_{24}O_7$			
Chromomycinonic acid, 2-deoxy-6,9-dimethyl-, methyl ester	EtOH	224(4.34),278(4.68), 325(3.84),340s(3.81), 388(3.78)	105-0498-73
Chromomycinonic acid, 2-deoxy-6,8,9-trimethyl-	EtOH	226(4.18),267(4.68), 329(3.94),360s(3.64)	105-0498-73
$C_{21}H_{24}O_8$			
Chromomycinonic acid, 6,9-dimethyl-, methyl ester	EtOH	224(4.35),279(4.67), 327(3.81),340(3.74), 390(3.73)	105-0498-73
$C_{21}H_{24}O_9$			
1-Propanone, 1-[2-(-D-glucopyranosyloxy)-6-hydroxyphenyl]-3-(4-hydroxyphenyl)-	EtOH	218(4.17),272(4.15), 320(3.83)	114-0435-73B
$C_{21}H_{24}S_3$			
Pyrene, 4,5,9,10-tetrahydro-2-methyl-4,9-bis(methylthio)-7-[(methylthio)-methyl]-	C_6H_{12}	263(4.01),282(4.20), 292(4.30),306(4.16)	35-3201-73
$C_{21}H_{25}ClN_2O_2S$			
1-Piperazinepropanol, 4-(8-chloro-10,11-dihydrodibenzo[b,f]thiepin-10-yl)-, 1-oxide	MeOH	234(4.20)	73-0599-73
$C_{21}H_{25}ClN_2O_3$			
1H-Isoindol-3-amine, 1-(4-chlorophenyl)-N-(2,2-diethoxyethyl)-1-methoxy-	EtOH	227(4.38)	44-3872-73

Compound	Solvent	λmax(log ε)	Ref.
$C_{21}H_{25}Cl_3N_4O_4S$			
3H-Pyrazole-3-carboxylic acid, 3-[2-(ethylthio)-4-oxo-3-[(phenylacetyl)-amino]-1-azetidinyl]-4,5-dihydro-4,4-dimethyl-, 2,2,2-trichloroethyl ester	EtOH	330(2.36)	39-1182-73C
more polar epimer	EtOH	330(2.04)	39-1182-73C
$C_{21}H_{25}N$			
2,4-Pentadien-1-amine, N-(1,1-dimethyl-ethyl)-4,5-diphenyl-	MeOH	206(4.40),224(4.13), 232(4.08),288(4.49), 308(4.26)	44-2169-73
$C_{21}H_{25}NO$			
4H-Carbazol-4-one, 1,2,3,5,6,7,8,9-octa-hydro-2,2-dimethyl-9-(phenylmethyl)-	MeOH	206(4.29),257(4.16), 292(3.69)	24-0745-73
$C_{21}H_{25}NO_2$			
Noraporphine, 10,11-dimethoxy-N-propyl-, hydrobromide	MeOH	216(4.69),269(4.26), 306s(3.34)	87-1223-73
hydriodide	MeOH	216(4.69),269(4.26), 307(3.34)	87-1223-73
$C_{21}H_{25}NO_3$			
2H-1-Benzopyran-6-methanimide, 3,4-di-hydro-5-methoxy-α,2,2-trimethyl-7-(phenylmethoxy)-, hydrochloride	EtOH	211(3.4),315(2.7)	12-2291-73
$C_{21}H_{25}NO_4$			
1-Phenanthrenecarboxylic acid, 1,2,3,4-4a,9,10,10a-octahydro-6-hydroxy-1,4a-dimethyl-7-(3-isoxazolyl)-, methyl ester, [1S-(1α,4aα,10aβ)]-	EtOH	225(4.00),255(3.73), 310(3.45)	12-1763-73
$C_{21}H_{25}NO_5$			
Acetic acid, [[(3-methoxy-17-oxoestra-1,3,5(10)-trien-6-ylidene)amino]oxy]-	EtOH	258(3.94),308(3.52)	13-0327-73B
Floramultine, (R)-	EtOH	218(4.60),260(4.10), 291(3.71)	73-1712-73
Floramultine, (S)- (bechuanine)	EtOH	218(4.60),260(4.11), 291(3.71)	73-1712-73
Homoaporphine, 4,5,6,6a-tetrahydro-1,12-dihydroxy-2,10,11-trimethoxy-6-methyl-	MeOH	221(4.45),258(4.12), 289(3.84),298(3.76)	78-2027-73
$C_{21}H_{25}NO_6$			
6-Isoquinolinecarboxylic acid, 1,2,3,4-tetrahydro-5-hydroxy-1-[(3,4,5-tri-methoxyphenyl)methyl]-, methyl ester, hydrochloride	EtOH	248(4.10),312(3.59)	78-0857-73
6-Isoquinolinecarboxylic acid, 1,2,3,4-tetrahydro-7-hydroxy-1-[(3,4,5-tri-methoxyphenyl)methyl]-, methyl ester, hydrochloride	EtOH	243(4.11),320(3.61)	78-0857-73
7-Isoquinolinecarboxylic acid, 1,2,3,4-tetrahydro-6-hydroxy-1-[(3,4,5-tri-methoxyphenyl)methyl]-, methyl ester, hydrochloride	EtOH	216(4.70),238s(4.22), 313(3.60)	78-0857-73
Rhoeageninemethinediol, dihydro-	EtOH	213(4.30),236(3.90), 291(3.85)	73-2799-73

Compound	Solvent	$\lambda_{max}(\log \epsilon)$	Ref.
$C_{21}H_{25}NO_7$			
Benzoic acid, 2-hydroxy-4-[2-[[(3,4,5-trimethoxyphenyl)acetyl]amino]ethyl]-, methyl ester	EtOH	244(4.21),310(3.62)	78-0857-73
Oxostephamiersine	EtOH	286(3.30)	88-4263-73
$C_{21}H_{25}N_3O_2$			
4H-Isoxazolo[3,4-d]azepin-3-ol, 6-benzyl-5,6,7,8-tetrahydro-, benzylammonium salt	THF	261(4.77)	1-3251-73
10H,15H-Pyrrolo[1",2":4',5']pyrazino-[1',2":1,2]azocino[5,4-b]indole-10,15-dione, 5,6,7,8,10a,11,12,13,15a,16-decahydro-6,6-dimethyl-	EtOH	225(4.51),275s(3.85), 283(3.91),291(3.85)	78-0107-73
$C_{21}H_{25}N_3O_2S_2$			
Dibenzo[b,f]thiepin-2-sulfonamide, N,N-dimethyl-11-(4-methylpiperazino)-	MeOH	226(4.48),280(4.40), 305(4.21)	73-2137-73
$C_{21}H_{25}N_3O_3$			
Austamide, tetrahydro-, (12S)-	EtOH	225(4.23),265s(3.76), 394(3.50)	78-0107-73
$C_{21}H_{25}N_5O_{11}$			
Acetamide, N-[6,7-dihydro-6-oxo-7-(2,3,4,6-tetra-O-acetyl-β-D-glucopyranosyl)-1H-purin-2-yl]-	EtOH	263(4.13),283s(4.01)	136-0149-73B
Acetamide, N-[6,9-dihydro-6-oxo-9-(2,3,4,6-tetra-O-acetyl-β-D-glucopyranosyl)-1H-purin-2-yl]-	EtOH	256(4.20),282s(4.05)	136-0149-73B
$C_{21}H_{26}Br_2O_3$			
Spiro[cyclopenta[b]pyran-2(5H),1'(2'H)-naphthalen]-5-one, 4a-(2,3-dibromopropyl)-3,3',4,4',4a,6,7,7a-octahydro-6'-methoxy-	EtOH	277(3.20),283(3.18)	94-2202-73
$C_{21}H_{26}NO_4$			
Isoquinolinium, 3,4-dihydro-3-[(3,4-dimethoxyphenyl)methyl]-6,7-dimethoxy-2-methyl-, perchlorate	MeOH	249(4.31),312(4.03), 368(3.96)	83-0784-73
$C_{21}H_{26}N_2O_2$			
Akuammilan-17-oic acid, 1,2-dihydro-1-methyl-, methyl ester	EtOH	253(4.03),293(3.53)	88-1425-73
	EtOH-acid	249(4.00),291(3.45)	88-1425-73
Epivincadine, 6,7-dehydro-, (+)-	EtOH	226(4.57),285(3.94), 292(3.91)	25-0229-73
Vincadine, 6,7-dehydro-	EtOH	226(4.58),284(3.90), 292(3.86)	25-0229-73
$C_{21}H_{26}N_2O_3$			
8H-3,8a-Diazacycloocta[jk]fluoren-8-one, 7-ethylidene-1,2,3,3a,4,5,6,7-octahydro-10,11-dimethoxy-3-methyl-	EtOH	230(4.31),281(4.28), 320s(3.76)	44-0215-73
Podocarpa-8,11,13-trien-19-oic acid, 12-hydroxy-13-(3-pyrazolyl)-, methyl ester	EtOH	220(4.06),252(3.97), 262(4.00),304(3.61), 311(3.61)	12-1763-73
2-Propanone, 1-diazo-3-[[(17β)-17-hydroxyestra-1,3,5(10)-trien-3-yl]oxy]-	EtOH	273(3.90)	44-3525-73
Rauwolscine (α-yohimbine)	EtOH	225(4.54),280(3.92), 291(3.76)	2-0007-73

Compound	Solvent	λ_{max}(log ϵ)	Ref.
Rauwolscine isomer	EtOH	225(4.54),281(3.91), 290(3.77)	2-0007-73
2,3-Secoakuammigine	MeOH	224(4.62),245s(4.10), 284(3.75),292(3.57)	78-2015-73
3,4-Secogardnerine, N_b-methyl-3-oxo-	EtOH	232(4.10),234(4.08), 263(3.85),345(4.35)	95-1165-73
Δ^{14}-Vincamine	EtOH	222(4.49),270(3.93), 279(3.88),289(3.72)	102-1475-73
16-epi-	EtOH	222(4.28),271(3.84), 278(3.77),290(3.59)	102-1475-73
$C_{21}H_{26}N_2O_5$			
Spiro[2H-indole-2,4'-[4'H]pyran]-3(1H)-one, 2',6'-bis(1,1-dimethylethyl)-1-methoxy-6-nitro-	MeCN	249(4.30),400(3.04)	44-2834-73
$C_{21}H_{26}N_4O_2$			
Ergovalide	MeOH	315(4.02)	105-0139-73
$C_{21}H_{26}N_4O_4$			
3,5-Hexadien-2-one, 6-(3,3-dimethylbicyclo[2.2.1]hept-2-yl)-, 2,4-dinitrophenylhydrazone	$CHCl_3$	400(4.66)	22-3071-73
$C_{21}H_{26}N_4O_5S$			
Tubercidin, 1,2-dihydro-2',3'-O-isopropylidene-N^6-p-toluenesulfonyl-	MeOH	222(4.30),252(4.15), 308(3.84)	18-0618-73
$C_{21}H_{26}N_4O_{10}$			
α-D-ribo-Pentodialdo-1,4-furanose, 1,2-O-cyclohexylidene-3-C-(2-ethoxy-2-oxoethyl)-, 2,4-dinitrophenylhydrazone	n.s.g.	300(4.15)	30-0676-73
$C_{21}H_{26}N_6O_5$			
Adenosine, N-[[(4-phenylbutyl)amino]-carbonyl]-	pH 1-2	270s(--),278(4.35)	87-0139-73
	pH 5-7	269(4.34),277s(--)	87-0139-73
	pH 12	278(4.17),299(4.03)	87-0139-73
$C_{21}H_{26}O_2$			
Estra-1,3,5(10),8,14-pentaen-17β-ol, 16-ethyl-3-methoxy-, (±)-	EtOH	313(4.47)	95-0566-73
2'H-Gona-1,3,5(10),8-tetraeno[17,13-b]-furan, 4',5'-dihydro-3-methoxy-5'-methyl-, (17α)-(±)-	EtOH	228(4.48),278(4.09)	94-2195-73
Gona-1,3,5(10),8-tetraen-17α-ol, 3-methoxy-13β-(2-propenyl)-	EtOH	278(4.14)	94-2202-73
Gona-1,3,5(10)-trien-17-one, 3-methoxy-13β-(2-propenyl)-, (±)-	EtOH	278(3.30),286(3.27)	94-2427-73
Methanone, [3,5-bis(1,1-dimethylethyl)-2-hydroxyphenyl]phenyl-	isooctane	252(4.08),273(4.08), 358(3.68)	88-0197-73
$C_{21}H_{26}O_3$			
Carbonic acid, bis(p-tert-butylphenyl) ester	$C_2H_4Cl_2$	262(2.88),270(3.80)	116-0305-73
1,3-Cyclopentanedione, 2-[2-(3,4-dihydro-6-methoxy-1(2H)-naphthalenylidene)ethyl]-4-ethyl-2-methyl-	EtOH	268(4.16)	95-0566-73
Cyclopentanone, 2-[2-(3,4-dihydro-6-methoxy-1(2H)-naphthalenylidene)-ethyl]-3-hydroxy-2-(2-propenyl)-	EtOH	266(4.28)	94-2202-73
isomer	EtOH	271(4.03)	94-2202-73

Compound	Solvent	λ_{max}(log ε)	Ref.
Gibba-1,3,4a(10a),4b-tetraene-10-carboxylic acid, 6-ethoxy-1,7-dimethyl-, methyl ester, (7β,9aβ,10β)-	n.s.g.	250s(4.07),259(4.20), 268(4.11),287(3.43), 296(3.37)	39-1476-73C
Gibba-1,3,4a(10a),4b-tetraene-10-carboxylic acid, 6-ethoxy-1,8-dimethyl-, methyl ester, (10β)-	n.s.g.	250s(4.12),259(4.24), 268(4.17),287(3.46), 298(3.40)	39-1476-73C
19-Norpregna-1,3,5(10)-trien-20-yne-3,17-diol, 11-methoxy-, (11β,17α)-	EtOH	221(3.84),280(3.28), 286s(3.24)	111-0451-73
Spiro[cyclopenta[b]pyran-2(5H),1'(2'H)-naphthalen-5-one, 3,3',4,4',4a,6,7,7a-octahydro-6'-methoxy-4a-(2-propenyl)-	EtOH	277(3.23),283(3.21)	94-2202-73
isomer	EtOH	277(3.23),283(3.21)	94-2202-73
$C_{21}H_{26}O_4$			
Cyclopentanone, 3-acetoxy-2-[2-(3,4-dihydro-6-methoxy-1(2H)-naphthalenylidene)ethyl]-2-methyl-	EtOH	265(4.42)	94-0107-73
Gona-1,3,5(10),8-tetraene-13-propanol, β,14-epoxy-17-hydroxy-3-methoxy-, (14β,17α)-(±)-	EtOH	274(4.12)	94-2202-73
6-Oxaestra-1,3,5(10),8-tetraen-17β-ol, 3-methoxy-7-methyl-, acetate	EtOH	275(4.18),318(3.74)	2-0847-73
$C_{21}H_{26}O_5$			
Estra-2,5(10)-diene-1,4-dione, 17-acetoxy-3-methoxy-, (17β)-	hexane	272(4.45),350(2.66), 420s(2.08)	22-2086-73
	EtOH	273(4.26),356(2.68)	22-2086-73
5H-Inden-5-one, 4-[2-acetoxy-2-(3-methoxyphenyl)ethyl]-1,2,3,6,7,7a-hexahydro-1-hydroxy-7a-methyl-, [1α,4(S*),7aα]-(±)-	EtOH	219(3.96),248(3.97)	44-3229-73
Porosin	EtOH	237(4.16),258(4.34), 285s(3.66)	102-0413-73
$C_{21}H_{26}O_7$			
Erioflorin acetate	EtOH	208(4.19)	102-2469-73
$C_{21}H_{26}S$			
1H-Thioxanthene, 2,3,4,4a,5,6,7,8-octahydro-9-methyl-4a-(phenylmethyl)-	n.s.g.	240(4.04),280(3.53)	104-2190-73
1H-Thioxanthene, 2,3,4,5,6,7,8,9-octahydro-9-methyl-9-(phenylmethyl)-	n.s.g.	245(4.30)	104-2190-73
$C_{21}H_{27}ClO$			
18-Norpregna-3,5,13-trien-20-one, 3-chloro-17-methyl-, (17α)-	EtOH	246(4.38)	22-2032-73
$C_{21}H_{27}ClO_3$			
Pregn-4-ene-3,11,20-trione, 21-chloro-	MeOH	238(4.20)	44-2328-73
$C_{21}H_{27}FO_4$			
Pregna-4,17(20)-dien-21-al, 9-fluoro-11β,20-dihydroxy-3-oxo-	MeOH	239(4.24),285(4.03)	24-2263-73
$C_{21}H_{27}NO_5$			
Acetic acid, [[[(17β)-17-hydroxy-3-methoxyestra-1,3,5(10)-trien-6-ylidene]amino]oxy]-	EtOH	258(4.01),308(3.58)	13-0327-73B
Escholinine	MeOH	234(4.06),286(3.83)	73-3514-73
Stephodeline	EtOH	230(3.90),275(4.06)	105-0613-73

Compound	Solvent	λ_{max}(log ε)	Ref.
$C_{21}H_{27}NO_6$			
Epistephamiersine	EtOH	286(3.36)	88-4263-73
Stephamiersine	EtOH	286(3.34)	88-4263-73
$C_{21}H_{27}NO_7$			
Tricyclo[3.3.1.1^{3,7}]decane-1-carboxylic acid, 1,2-dihydro-2-oxo-1-β-D-ribo-furanosyl-4-pyridinyl ester	pH 1	296(3.75)	87-0294-73
	pH 13	257(3.86),272s(3.74)	87-0294-73
	EtOH	300(3.72)	87-0294-73
$C_{21}H_{27}N_3O_2$			
Pyrrolo[1,2-a]pyrazine-1,4-dione, 3-[[2-(1,1-dimethylpropyl)-1H-indol-3-yl]methyl]hexahydro-	EtOH	224(4.42),275(3.75), 284(3.80),292(3.75)	78-0107-73
$C_{21}H_{27}N_3O_6$			
2-Propenamide, N-[2-(1-β-D-glucopyrano-syl-1H-imidazol-4-yl)ethyl]-N-methyl-3-phenyl-, cis	pH 1	261(3.96)	35-8737-73
	pH 11	249(4.20)	35-8737-73
	EtOH	256(4.11)	35-8737-73
trans (casimiroedine)	pH 1	218(4.26),224s(4.19), 283(4.31)	35-8737-73
	pH 11	225s(4.08),282(4.30)	35-8737-73
	EtOH	219(4.25),224s(4.18), 281(4.31)	35-8737-73
$C_{21}H_{27}N_3O_{11}S$			
5-Pyrimidinecarboxylic acid, 4-amino-1,2-dihydro-1-(2,3,4,6-tetraacetyl-β-D-glucopyranosyl)-2-thioxo-, ethyl ester	MeOH	222(4.2),238(4.2), 255(4.2),305(4.0)	24-3039-73
$C_{21}H_{28}N_2O_2$			
Dendrochrysine, cis	EtOH	210(4.24),253(4.06)	1-1982-73
Dendrochrysine, trans	EtOH	218(4.14),224(4.05), 281(4.31)	1-1982-73
Epivincadine	EtOH	226(4.58),285(3.96), 292(3.93)	25-0229-73
Vincadine	MeOH	226(4.58),285(3.94), 292(3.91)	114-0207-73C
$C_{21}H_{28}N_2O_3$			
Geissovelline, deacetyl-	EtOH	230(4.10),305(3.80)	44-0215-73
	EtOH-HCl	234(3.94),283(3.67)	44-0215-73
5-Isoquinolinecarboxylic acid, deca-hydro-6-hydroxy-2-[2-(1H-indol-3-yl)ethyl]-, methyl ester	MeOH	221(4.52),282(3.73), 290(3.65)	78-2015-73
$C_{21}H_{28}N_2O_5$			
Spiro[2H-indole-2,4'-[4'H]pyran]-3-ol, 2',6'-bis(1,1-dimethylethyl)-1,3-di-hydro-1-methoxy-6-nitro-	MeCN	250(4.36),360(3.26)	44-2834-73
$C_{21}H_{28}N_6O_5$			
Adenosine, N-[(tricyclo[3.3.1.1^{3,7}]dec-1-ylamino)carbonyl]-	pH 1-2	270s(--),278(4.28)	87-0139-73
	pH 5-7	270(4.21),277s(--)	87-0139-73
	pH 12	278(4.06),300(3.59)	87-0139-73
$C_{21}H_{28}N_6O_{11}P_2$			
Adenosine, 5'-(trihydrogen phosphate), mono[4-(3-acetylpyridinio)butyl] ester, hydroxide, inner salt	pH 9.5	259(4.25)	5-0961-73

Compound	Solvent	λ_{max}(log ϵ)	Ref.
$C_{21}H_{28}O$			
Pregna-3,5,16-trien-20-one	EtOH	229(4.29),236(4.31), 244(4.16)	94-1240-73
$C_{21}H_{28}O_2$			
Abieta-6,8,11,13-tetraen-18-oic acid, methyl ester	isooctane	221(3.4),266(3.0)	8-0185-73
13α-Androst-4-en-3-one, 17α-ethynyl-17β-hydroxy-	EtOH	244(4.21)	94-0565-73
13α-Androst-4-en-3-one, 17β-ethynyl-17α-hydroxy-	EtOH	243(4.21)	94-0565-73
Estra-1,3,5(10),8-tetraen-17β-ol, 16-ethyl-3-methoxy-, (±)-	EtOH	279(4.16)	95-0566-73
12α-Etiojerva-4,6-dien-3-one, 17α-acetoxy-	MeOH	285(4.41)	87-0568-73
Gona-1,3,5(10),8-tetraen-17α-ol, 3-methoxy-13β-propyl-, (±)-	EtOH	278(4.28)	94-2202-73
Gona-1,3,5(10)-trien-17α-ol, 3-methoxy-13β-(2-propenyl)-, (±)-	EtOH	278(3.48),285(3.26)	94-2202-73
2'H-Gona-1,3,5(10)-trieno[17,13-b]furan, 4',5'-dihydro-3-methoxy-5'-methyl-, (8α,17α)-(±)-	EtOH	278(3.42),286(3.38)	94-2195-73
(17β)-(±)-	EtOH	278(3.28),286(3.25)	94-2195-73
Isozonarone	MeOH	248(4.33),330(3.16)	44-2383-73
18-Nor-17α-pregna-4,13-diene-3,21-dione, 17β-methyl-	EtOH	239(4.20)	22-2032-73
19-Norpregna-4,9-diene-3,20-dione, 17α-methyl-	EtOH	214(3.80),302(4.32)	22-2694-73
19-Norpregn-4-en-20-yn-3-one, 17-hydroxy-9-methyl-	n.s.g.	240(4.19)	39-2095-73C
Zonarone	MeOH	248(4.10),331(2.90)	44-2383-73
$C_{21}H_{28}O_2S$			
Benzene, [[3-methyl-5-(2,6,6-trimethyl-1-cyclohexen-1-yl)-2,4-pentadienyl]-sulfonyl]-, (E,E)-	EtOH	240(4.13),272(4.17)	22-0746-73
$C_{21}H_{28}O_3$			
18-Nor-17α-pregn-4-ene-3,20-dione, 13ξ,14ξ-epoxy-17β-methyl-	EtOH	242(4.19)	22-2032-73
1-Phenanthrenecarboxylic acid, 1,2,3,4-4a,9,10,10a-octahydro-1,4a-dimethyl-7-(1-methylethyl)-9-oxo-, methyl ester, [1R-(1α,4aβ,10aα)]-	EtOH	254(3.95),300(3.23)	78-1227-73
$C_{21}H_{28}O_3S$			
12α-Etiojerv-4-ene-3,17-dione, 7α-(acetylthio)-	MeOH	238(4.21)	87-0568-73
$C_{21}H_{28}O_4$			
5α-Androst-8-ene-11,17-dione, 3β-acetoxy-	EtOH	253(3.95)	39-1967-73C
1-Phenanthrenecarboxylic acid, 1,2,3,4-4a,5,8,9,10,10a-decahydro-1,4a-dimethyl-7-(1-methylethyl)-5,8-dioxo-, methyl ester	hexane	257(4.30),260(4.27), 332(2.57),456(1.60)	22-2086-73
	EtOH	260(4.43),338(2.65), 420s(1.90)	22-2086-73
13α-Pregn-4-ene-3,6,20-trione, 17β-hydroxy-	EtOH	252(4.04)	94-0565-73
Spiro[cyclopenta[b]pyran-2(3H),1'(2'H)-naphthalen]-5-ol, 3',4,4',4a,5,6,7,7a-	EtOH	277(3.26),283(3.24)	94-0107-73

Compound	Solvent	λ_{max}(log ε)	Ref.
octahydro-6'-methoxy-4a-methyl-, acetate, [2R-(2α,4aβ,5α,7aβ)]- (cont.)			
$C_{21}H_{28}O_5$			
Marrubiagenin, 2-oxo-, methyl ester	EtOH	207(4.28),245s(3.67)	24-2929-73
Pregna-1,4-diene-3,20-dione, 11β,17α,21-trihydroxy-, Kober test	H_2SO_4	418(3.75)	94-1720-73
5β-Pregn-1-ene-3,11,20-trione, 17,21-dihydroxy-	n.s.g.	223(3.98)	39-1361-73C
5β-Pregn-2-ene-1,11,20-trione, 17,21-dihydroxy-	n.s.g.	224(3.85)	39-1361-73C
Spiro[cyclopenta[b]pyran-2(5H),1'(2'H)-naphthalen]-5-one, 4a-(2,3-dihydroxypropyl)-3,3',4,4',4a,6,7,7a-octahydro-6'-methoxy-	EtOH	277(3.24),283(3.22)	94-2202-73
$C_{21}H_{28}O_5S$			
1H-6,4,10a-Ethanylylideneindeno[5,6-e]-[1,2]oxaselenepinium, 6-formyldecahydro-3-hydroxy-5a-(methoxycarbonyl)-9-methyl-5-(1-methylethylidene)-, hydroxide, inner salt, (4α,5aβ,6β,6aβ-9β,9aα,10aα)-	EtOH	210(3.87),255s(3.11)	35-7917-73
$C_{21}H_{28}O_6$			
Nemosenin D	EtOH	217(3.83)	73-0739-73
A-Nor-3-oxaestr-1(10)-ene-5-acetic acid, 17-acetoxy-2-oxo-, methyl ester	EtOH	215(4.21)	64-0675-73C
$C_{21}H_{28}O_8$			
Chromomycinonic acid, 2-acetyl-2-deoxy-6,8,9-trimethyl-, methyl ester	EtOH	231(4.40),268(4.34), 302(3.93),316(3.95), 366(4.35)	105-0498-73
$C_{21}H_{29}Br_2N_3O_2$			
2H-Pyrrole-4-propanoic acid, 2-[[5-bromo-3-[2-(diethylamino)ethyl]-4-methyl-1H-pyrrol-2-yl]methylene]-5-(bromomethyl)-3-methyl-, dihydrobromide	EtOH-HBr	489(4.58)	103-0186-73
$C_{21}H_{29}ClO_2$			
Pregna-1,4-dien-3-one, 20-chloro-16β-hydroxy-, (20R)-	MeOH	244(4.0)	5-2048-73
(20S)-	MeOH	244(4.1)	5-2048-73
$C_{21}H_{29}F_3N_2O$			
3-Azabicyclo[3.2.2]nonane, 3-[2-[2,3-dihydro-5-methoxy-2-methyl-4-(trifluoromethyl)-1H-indol-3-yl]ethyl]-, cis	MeOH	246(3.91),322(3.58)	44-1504-73
trans	MeOH	240(3.88),320(3.60)	44-1504-73
$C_{21}H_{29}IO_2$			
Pregn-4-ene-3,20-dione, 21-iodo-	MeOH	241(4.24)	44-2335-73
$C_{21}H_{29}NO$			
Malouetafrine	n.s.g.	241(4.00)	102-1813-73
$C_{21}H_{29}NO_3$			
Crepidine	hexane	240(3.48),252s(3.30), 257s(3.18),264s(2.95), 295(2.15)	1-1907-73

Compound	Solvent	λ max (log ε)	Ref.
Crepidine (cont.)	EtOH	208(4.34),240s(3.28), 257s(3.04),264s(2.88), 294(2.28)	1-1907-73
$C_{21}H_{29}NO_5$			
Acetic acid, [[[(3β)-3-hydroxy-17-oxo-androst-5-en-7-ylidene]amino]oxy]-	EtOH	239(4.11)	13-0723-73A
$C_{21}H_{29}N_2$			
Methanaminium, N-[4-[1-[4-(dimethylamino)phenyl]-2,2-dimethylpropylidene]-2,5-cyclohexadien-1-ylidene]-N-methyl-	98% HOAc	384(3.89),618(3.81)	39-2151-73B
$C_{21}H_{29}N_3$			
1H,6H-Pyrrolo[1",2":4',5']pyrazino-[1',2':1,2]azocino[4,5-b]indole, 2,3,3a,4,7,8,13,14,14a,15-decahydro-8,8-dimethyl-, (3aR-cis)-	EtOH	227(4.44),276(3.69), 285(3.73),292(3.71)	78-0107-73
$C_{21}H_{29}N_3O_2S_2$			
Benzenesulfonamide, N-[3-cyclohexyl-4-(cyclohexylimino)-1,3-thiazetidin-2-ylidene]-4-methyl-	C_6H_{12}	229s(4.43),235s(4.50), 248(4.55),262s(4.46)	18-2559-73
$C_{21}H_{29}N_7O_{11}P_2$			
Pyridinium, 3-(aminocarbonyl)-1-[5-O-[9-(6-amino-9H-purin-9-yl)-1,3-dihydroxy-2,4-dioxa-1,3-diphosphanon-1-yl]-β-D-ribofuranosyl]-, hydroxide, inner salt, P,P'-dioxide, reduced form	pH 9.5	262(4.14),339(3.80)	5-0531-73
oxidized form	pH 9.5	262(4.28)	5-0531-73
cyanide addition compd.	pH 10	327(4.16)	5-0531-73
$C_{21}H_{30}N_2O$			
Androst-4-eno[3,2-c]pyrazol-17β-ol, 17α-methyl-	n.s.g.	259(4.05)	65-0403-73
$C_{21}H_{30}N_2O_3$			
Geissovelline, deacetyldihydro-	EtOH	235s(4.05),303(3.70)	44-0215-73
	EtOH-HCl	230(3.94),280(3.68)	44-0215-73
$C_{21}H_{30}N_6O_{11}P_2$			
Adenosine, 5'-(trihydrogen phosphate), mono[4-(3-acetyl-1(4H)-pyridinyl)-butyl] ester	pH 9.5	258(4.16),382(4.03)	5-0961-73
$C_{21}H_{30}O$			
1,8-Pentadecadien-3-one, 1-phenyl-, (E,Z)-	EtOH	221(3.84),288(4.09)	12-0183-73
$C_{21}H_{30}O_2$			
Abieta-8,11,13-trien-18-oic acid, methyl ester	isooctane	200(4.7),268(1.8), 276(1.9)	8-0186-73
Androsta-4,6-dien-3-one, 17-hydroxy-6,17-dimethyl-, (9β,10α,17β)	EtOH	292(4.38)	33-2396-73
Androst-4-en-3-one, 17-hydroxy-17-methyl-6-methylene-, (9β,10α,17β)-	EtOH	255(4.00)	33-2396-73
1,4-Benzenediol, 2-[(decahydro-5,5,8a-trimethyl-2-methylene-1-naphthalenyl)-methyl]-, [1S-(1α,4aβ,8aα)]-	MeOH	211(3.92),295(3.50)	44-2383-73

Compound	Solvent	λmax(log ε)	Ref.
1,4-Benzenediol, 2-[(1,4,4a,5,6,7,8,8a-octahydro-2,5,5,8a-tetramethyl-1-naphthalenyl)methyl]-, [1S-(1α,4aβ,8aα)]-(isozonarol)	MeOH	209(3.91),296(3.43)	44-2383-73
Cannabidiol	hexane	212(4.25),282(3.32)	106-0129-73
	pH 3.3	233(3.70),283(3.34)	106-0129-73
	pH 4.4	230(3.74),283(3.28)	106-0129-73
	pH 8.0	220(3.97),283(3.23)	106-0129-73
and other pH values not listed	pH 10.6	218(4.08),283(3.23)	106-0129-73
	MeOH	212(4.27),283(3.31)	106-0129-73
18,21-Cyclopregn-18(21)-en-20-one, 3-hydroxy-, (3β,5α)-	n.s.g.	230(3.91)	33-2698-73
Estra-1,3,5(10)-trien-17-ol, 16-ethyl-3-methoxy-, (17β)-(±)-	EtOH	279(3.22),288(3.19)	95-0566-73
18-Norpregna-4,13-dien-3-one, 20-hydroxy-17-methyl-, (17α,20R)-	EtOH	242(4.19)	22-2032-73
19-Norpregna-4,9-dien-3-one, 20-hydroxy-17-methyl-, (20R)-	EtOH	216(3.79),307(4.32)	22-2694-73
19-Norpregn-4-ene-3,20-dione, 9α-methyl-	n.s.g.	241(4.22)	39-2095-73C
Pregna-5,16-dien-20-one, 3β-hydroxy-	EtOH	239(4.26)	94-1240-73
	n.s.g.	239.5(3.95)	102-1509-73
Pregna-14,17(20)-dien-16-one, 3-hydroxy-, (3β,5α)-	n.s.g.	255(4.24)	33-1078-73
Pregn-4-ene-3,20-dione, Kober test	H_2SO_4	388(3.00),480(2.85)	94-1720-73
Retinoic acid, methyl ester (isomer)	EtOH	335(4.33)	22-0746-73
13-cis	EtOH	359(4.58)	32-0117-73
$C_{21}H_{30}O_3$			
Allocyathin B_3 methyl ketal	isooctane	256(3.62)	23-3842-73
Cyathin B_3 methyl ketal	isooctane	233(3.72)	23-3157-73
Cyathin C_3 methyl ketal	isooctane	236(3.87),257s(3.63)	23-3157-73
Estr-4-en-3-one, 17β-acetoxy-1α-methyl-	EtOH	242(4.18)	54-1267-73
Estr-4-en-3-one, 17β-acetoxy-1β-methyl-	EtOH	244(4.19)	54-1267-73
13α-D-Homoandrost-4-ene-3,17-dione, 17aα-hydroxy-17aβ-methyl-	EtOH	242(4.18)	94-0565-73
13α-D-Homoandrost-4-ene-3,17a-dione, 17β-hydroxy-17α-methyl-	EtOH	242(4.19)	94-0565-73
18-Nor-17α-pregn-4-en-3-one, 13ξ,14ξ-epoxy-20β-hydroxy-17β-methyl-	EtOH	242(4.18)	22-2032-73
5α-Pregn-1-ene-3,20-dione, 11α-hydroxy-	n.s.g.	231(4.03)	39-2137-73C
Pregn-4-ene-3,16-dione, 20α-hydroxy-	EtOH	241.5(4.21)	78-0823-73
13α-Pregn-4-ene-3,20-dione, 17β-hydroxy-	EtOH	244(4.18)	94-0565-73
$C_{21}H_{30}O_3S$			
12α-Etiojerv-4-en-3-one, 7α-(acetylthio)-17α-hydroxy-	MeOH	238(4.24)	87-0568-73
12α-Etiojerv-4-en-3-one, 7α-(acetylthio)-17β-hydroxy-	MeOH	238(4.27)	87-0568-73
$C_{21}H_{30}O_4$			
1-Butanone, 2-methyl-1-[2,4,6-trihydroxy-3,5-bis(3-methyl-2-butenyl)phenyl]-	EtOH	273(3.79),325(3.97)	39-0419-73C
4-Deoxyhumulone	EtOH	292(4.21)	39-0419-73C
Marrubiagenin, methyl ester	MeCN	211(4.33)	24-2929-73
Δ^1-Marrubiagenin, 13,14-dihydro-, methyl ester	MeCN	293.5(3.70)	24-2929-73
Retinoic acid, 12-carboxy-7,8-dihydro-	EtOH	285(4.48)	65-2047-73
$C_{21}H_{30}O_5$			
Cannabinol, hexahydro-6-oxo-	EtOH	276(3.11),283(3.15)	78-1615-73

Compound	Solvent	λmax(log ε)	Ref.
Marrubiagenin, 3,4-epoxy-, methyl ester	EtOH	208(4.17)	24-2929-73
Marrubiagenin, 2-hydroxy-, methyl ester	MeCN	208(4.32)	24-2929-73
5β-Pregn-1-ene-3,11-dione, 17,20β,21-trihydroxy-	n.s.g.	225(3.97)	39-1361-73C
5β-Pregn-2-ene-1,11-dione, 17,20β,21-trihydroxy-	n.s.g.	225(3.87)	39-1361-73C
Pregn-4-ene-3,20-dione, 11β,17α,21-trihydroxy-, Kober test	H_2SO_4	422(3.93)	94-1720-73
$C_{21}H_{30}O_7$			
Eupacunin, deacetyl-11,13-dihydro-13-methoxy-	MeOH	217(4.04)	44-2189-73
Nigakilactone N	MeOH	270(3.45)	78-1515-73
$C_{21}H_{31}ClO_2$			
Pregn-4-en-3-one, 20-chloro-16-hydroxy-, (16β,20R)-	MeOH	241(4.3)	5-2048-73
(16β,20S)-	MeOH	241(4.2)	5-2048-73
$C_{21}H_{31}N_3O$			
Spiro[2H-indole-2,7'(8'H)-[1H,3H]pyrrolo[1',2':4,5]pyrazino[1,2-a]azepin-3-ol, 1,2',3,3',5'a,6',9',10',12',12'a-decahydro-8',8'-dimethyl-, [3aR-(3aα,4β,13β,13aα)]-	EtOH	212(4.22),251(3.94), 308(3.34)	78-0107-73
$C_{21}H_{31}N_3O_2$			
2H-Pyrrole-4-propanoic acid, 2-[[4-[2-(diethylamino)ethyl]-3,5-dimethyl-1H-pyrrol-2-yl]methylene]-3-methyl-, dihydrobromide	EtOH-HBr	471(4.97)	103-0186-73
$C_{21}H_{32}N_2$			
5H-Cyclododec[b]indole-5-propanamine, 6,7,8,9,10,11,12,13,14,15-decahydro-, hydrochloride	EtOH	231(4.51),280(3.81), 286(3.86),294(3.83)	78-4045-73
$C_{21}H_{32}N_2O$			
2'H-Androst-2-eno[3,2-c]pyrazol-17-ol, 17α-methyl-	n.s.g.	230(3.78)	65-0403-73
$C_{21}H_{32}N_2O_2$			
Androst-4-en-3-one, 17-hydroxy-2-(hydroxymethylene)-17-methyl-, hydrazone, (17β)-	n.s.g.	257(4.02)	65-0403-73
$C_{21}H_{32}N_2O_{10}$			
Uridine, 2',5'-bis-O-(tetrahydro-4-methoxy-2H-pyran-4-yl)-	EtOH	262(3.99)	39-2513-73C
$C_{21}H_{32}O$			
5H-Benzocycloheptadecen-5-one, 6,7,8,9-10,11,12,13,14,15,16,17,18,19-tetradecahydro-	EtOH	242(3.90)	78-1857-73
$C_{21}H_{32}O_2$			
Abieta-7,13-dien-18-oic acid, methyl ester	isooctane	234(3.3),242(3.4), 250(3.2)	8-0187-73
Abieta-8,13-dien-18-oic acid, methyl ester	isooctane	265(2.9)	8-0188-73

Compound	Solvent	$\lambda_{max}(\log \epsilon)$	Ref.
Abieta-8,13(15)-dien-18-oic acid, methyl ester	isooctane	195(3.3)	8-0189-73
Abieta-8(14),12-dien-18-oic acid, methyl ester	isooctane	273(2.7)	8-0190-73
Abieta-8(14),13(15)-dien-18-oic acid, methyl ester	isooctane	252(2.4)	8-0191-73
13β-Abieta-7,9(11)-dien-18-oic acid, methyl ester	isooctane	241(2.2)	8-0192-73
1H-Cyclohepta[a]naphthalene-4-carboxylic acid, 2,3,4,4a,5,6,8,11,11a,11b-decahydro-4,8,9,11b-tetramethyl-, methyl ester (methyl strobate)	isooctane	193.6(4.19)	78-1441-73
14S,17-Cyclolabda-8(17),12-dien-18-oic acid, methyl ester	isooctane	194(3.2)	8-0214-73
7,15-Isopimaradien-18-oic acid, methyl ester	isooctane	205s(2.9)	8-0206-73
8,15-Isopimaradien-18-oic acid, methyl ester	isooctane	none	8-0207-73
8(14),15-Isopimaradien-18-oic acid, methyl ester	isooctane	204(3.1)	8-0208-73
8(17),E-12,14-Labdatrien-19-oic acid, methyl ester	isooctane	193(3.1),232(3.4)	8-0212-73
1-Naphthalenecarboxylic acid, decahydro-1,4a-dimethyl-6-methylene-5-(3-methylene-4-pentenyl)-, methyl ester, [1S-(1α,4aβ,5β,8aα)]-	n.s.g.	226(4.00)	78-3379-73
8(14),15-Pimaradien-18-oic acid, methyl ester	isooctane	200s(3.0)	8-0203-73
8,15-Pimaradien-18-oic acid, methyl ester	isooctane	none	8-0202-73
Pregn-4-en-3-one, 21-hydroxy-	MeOH	242(4.22)	44-2328-73
Pregn-5-en-20-one, 3β-hydroxy-, Kober test	H_2SO_4	400(3.57)	94-1720-73
Retinoic acid, 7,8-dihydro-, methyl ester	EtOH	315(4.57)	65-2047-73
$C_{21}H_{32}O_3$			
Androst-4-en-3-one, 17-hydroxy-6-(hydroxymethyl)-17-methyl-, (6β,9β,10α,17β)	EtOH	241(4.20)	33-2396-73
Cannabinol, hexahydro-6α-hydroxy-	EtOH	228s(4.04),275(3.09), 283(3.11)	78-1615-73
Cannabinol, hexahydro-6β-hydroxy-	EtOH	230s(3.81),276(3.09), 282(3.09)	78-1615-73
6,9-Epoxycyclohept[e]indene-8-carboxaldehyde, 2,3,3a,4,5,5a,6,7,8,9,10,10a-dodecahydro-6-methoxy-3a,5a-dimethyl-1-(methylethyl)-, [3aR-(3aα,5aβ,6β,8β-9β,10aα)]-	isooctane	282(2.09)	23-3842-73
D-Homo-5α,13α-androstane-16,17a-dione, 3β-hydroxy-17-methyl-	EtOH-HCl	266(4.13)	44-1270-73
Pregn-4-en-3-one, 16β,20α-dihydroxy-	EtOH	241.5(4.23)	78-0823-73
Retinoic acid, 11,12-dihydro-11-hydroxy-, methyl ester, 13-cis	EtOH	228(4.22),267(4.15)	32-0117-73
1-Tridecen-3-one, 1-(3,5-dimethoxyphenyl)-, (E)-	EtOH	278(3.77),285(3.79)	12-0183-73
$C_{21}H_{32}O_4$			
Estr-4-en-3-one, 17-hydroxy-2,6-bis(hydroxymethyl)-17-methyl-, (2α,6β,17β)-	EtOH	246(4.18)	33-2396-73

Compound	Solvent	$\lambda_{max}(\log \epsilon)$	Ref.
Prosta-5,10,13-trien-1-oic acid, 15α-hydroxy-11-methyl-9-oxo-	MeOH	226(3.99),316(2.78)	33-0557-73
Prosta-5,11,13-trien-1-oic acid, 15-hydroxy-8-methyl-9-oxo-	MeOH	234(4.16)	35-8483-73
$C_{21}H_{33}IO$			
5α-Pregnan-20-one, 18-iodo-	EtOH	260(2.65)	22-1456-73
$C_{21}H_{34}O$			
2-Pentadecanone, 1-phenyl-	C_6H_{12}	287(2.21),294(--), 301(--)	28-0407-73B
$C_{21}H_{34}O_2$			
7-Abieten-18-oic acid, methyl ester	isooctane	203(2.8)	8-0193-73
8-Abieten-18-oic acid, methyl ester	isooctane	197(2.9)	8-0195-73
8(14)-Abieten-18-oic acid, methyl ester	isooctane	207(2.9)	8-0197-73
13-Abieten-18-oic acid, methyl ester	isooctane	190(3.0)	8-0199-73
13(15)-Abieten-18-oic acid, methyl ester	isooctane	197(3.1)	8-0200-73
13β-Abiet-7-en-18-oic acid, methyl ester	isooctane	205(2.8)	8-0194-73
13β-Abiet-8-en-18-oic acid, methyl ester	isooctane	195(3.0)	8-0196-73
13β-Abiet-8(14)-en-18-oic acid, methyl ester	isooctane	201(3.0)	8-0198-73
1H-Cyclohepta[a]naphthalene-4-carboxylic acid, 2,3,4,4a,5,6,6a,7,10,11-11a,11b-dodecahydro-4,8,9,11b-tetramethyl-, methyl ester	EtOH	195(3.94)	78-1441-73
1H-Cyclohepta[a]naphthalene-4-carboxylic acid, 2,3,4,4a,5,6,8,9,10,11-11a,11b-dodecahydro-4,8,9,11b-tetramethyl-, methyl ester	EtOH	203.2(3.98)	78-1441-73
7-Isopimaren-18-oic acid, methyl ester	isooctane	203(2.8)	8-0209-73
8-Isopimaren-18-oic acid, methyl ester	isooctane	195(2.9)	8-0210-73
8(14)-Isopimaren-18-oic acid, methyl ester	isooctane	201(3.0)	8-0211-73
8(17),E-13-Labdadien-15-oic acid, methyl ester	isooctane	200(3.2),217(3.2)	8-0213-73
8-Pimaren-18-oic acid, methyl ester	isooctane	194(2.9)	8-0204-73
8(14)-Pimaren-18-oic acid, methyl ester	isooctane	202(3.0)	8-0205-73
$C_{21}H_{34}O_3$			
Benzenemethanol, α-(2-ethyl-2,6-dimethylheptyl)-4-methoxy-, acetate	EtOH	225(4.00),270(3.71)	78-1119-73
Labda-8,14-dien-19-oic acid, 13β-hydroxy-, methyl ester	EtOH	205(3.85),210(3.70), 215(3.47)(end abs.)	12-0209-73
$C_{21}H_{34}O_4$			
2-Cyclohexen-1-one, 6-ethyl-3-[2-ethyl-5-(1-ethyl-2-oxobutyl)tetrahydro-4-methyl-2-furanyl]-6-hydroxy-, [2α(S*),4α,5β(S*)]-	MeOH	238(4.04)	44-3431-73
14S,17-Cyclolabd-8(17)-en-18-oic acid, 12α,13α-dihydroxy-, methyl ester, osmate	EtOH	245(3.89),252(3.93), 257(3.95),263(3.86)	78-1441-73
$C_{21}H_{35}IO$			
Pregnan-20-ol, 18-iodo-, (5α,20R)-	EtOH	260(2.81)	22-1456-73

Compound	Solvent	$\lambda_{max}(\log \epsilon)$	Ref.
$C_{21}H_{35}NO_2$			
Tetradecanamide, N-hydroxy-N-(3-methylphenyl)-	EtOH	254(4.00)	112-0547-73
$C_{21}H_{35}NO_3$			
2-Nonenoic acid, 7-[(cyclohexylimino)-methyl]-3-methyl-6-(1-methylethylidene)-, methyl ester, N-oxide	hexane	243(4.10)	33-2961-73
$C_{21}H_{36}O_2$			
8α,13β-Abietan-18-oic acid, methyl ester	isooctane	none	8-0201-73
$C_{21}H_{36}O_4$			
14S,17-Cyclolabdan-18-oic acid, 12α,13α-dihydroxy-, methyl ester	EtOH	200(2.62)	78-1441-73
$C_{21}H_{36}O_5$			
3-Hexanone, 6-acetoxy-6-[2-ethyl-5-(1-ethyl-2-oxobutyl)tetrahydro-4-methyl-2-furanyl]-	isoPrOH	281(1.90)	44-3431-73
$C_{21}H_{37}N_5$			
2-Pentenedinitrile, 3-amino-2-[(1,1,3,3-tetramethylbutyl)amino]-4-[(1,1,3,3-tetramethylbutyl)imino]-	isooctane	234(3.92),400(3.75)	44-2604-73
$C_{21}H_{38}N_5O_8P$			
Phosphorane, tris(diethylamino)(4-pyridinylimino)-, dioxalate	EtOH	295(4.39)	39-1079-73C
$C_{21}H_{38}O_7$			
8-Epierythronolide B	EtOH	283(1.67)	78-0935-73
$C_{21}H_{44}Si_4$			
Silane, 3,4-pentadien-1-yne-1,3-diyl-5-ylidenetetrakis[ethyldimethyl-	EtOH	250(4.07)	35-3324-73

Compound	Solvent	λ_{max}(log ε)	Ref.
$C_{22}H_{10}Cl_2O_4$			
Benzo[1,2-b:4,3-b']difuran, 2,2'-(1,2-ethenediyl)bis[7-chloro-, (E)-	n.s.g.	347s(4.46),363(4.74), 383(3.98),407(4.99)	1-3133-73
$C_{22}H_{10}N_4$			
10,10,11,11-Triphenylenetetracarbonitrile	$C_2H_4Cl_2$	245(4.70),253(4.73), 273(4.35),367(3.82)	88-0043-73
$C_{22}H_{11}BrN_2O$			
14H-Benz[4,5]isoquino[2,1-a]perimidin-14-one, 10-bromo-	C_6H_5Cl	495(3.69)	103-1257-73
$C_{22}H_{12}ClN_2O_4P$			
Phosphine, (4-chlorophenyl)bis[(4-nitrophenyl)ethenyl]-	EtOH	301(4.60)	65-2627-73
$C_{22}H_{12}ClN_2O_5P$			
Phosphine oxide, (4-chlorophenyl)bis-[(4-nitrophenyl)ethynyl]-	EtOH	288(4.61),350s(3.11)	65-2627-73
$C_{22}H_{12}N_2$			
9,10[1',2']-Benzenoanthracene-1,5-dicarbonitrile, 9,10-dihydro-, (9R)-	EtOH	212s(4.58),222s(4.59), 235s(4.31),280s(3.68), 289(3.80),298(3.91)	18-0605-73
$C_{22}H_{12}N_2O_2$			
14H-Benz[4,5]isoquino[2,1-a]perimidin-14-one, 10-hydroxy-	C_6H_5Cl	482(3.71)	103-1257-73
$C_{22}H_{12}O_2$			
Dibenz[a,h]anthracene-7,14-dione	MeCN	218(4.62),237s(4.43), 295(4.66),332(3.64), 387(3.66)	24-1341-73
Dibenz[a,j]anthracene-7,14-dione	MeCN	218(4.75),234(4.45), 280(4.34),297(4.63), 325(3.77),355(3.56)	24-1341-73
$C_{22}H_{13}F_5$			
Phenanthrene, 9,10-dihydro-9-methyl-10-methylene-9-(pentafluorophenyl)-	heptane	221(4.47),250(4.39), 287(4.12)	104-1057-73
	96% H_2SO_4	270(4.46),343(4.01), 557(3.87)	104-1057-73
$C_{22}H_{13}IO_3S_2$			
Naphtho[1,8-bc]thiopyran-3(2H)-one, 2-(6-ethoxy-3-oxobenzo[b]thien-2(3H)-ylidene)-7-iodo-, cis	n.s.g.	471.5(4.20)	103-0960-73
trans	n.s.g.	589(4.52)	103-0960-73
$C_{22}H_{13}N_2O_4P$			
Phosphine, bis(4-nitrophenyl)ethynyl]-phenyl-	EtOH	307(4.45)	65-2627-73
$C_{22}H_{13}N_2O_5P$			
Phosphine oxide, bis(4-nitrophenyl)ethynyl]phenyl-	EtOH	289(4.40),360s(3.00)	65-2627-73
$C_{22}H_{13}N_3O$			
14H-Benz[4,5]isoquino[2,1-a]perimidin-14-one, 10-amino-	C_6H_5Cl	486(3.86)	103-1257-73

Compound	Solvent	$\lambda_{max}(\log \epsilon)$	Ref.
$C_{22}H_{13}N_3O_2$			
Benzo[f]quinoline-1-carboxylic acid, 3-(2-quinoxalinyl)-, Cu(I) complex	EtOH	400(4.61),552(3.95)	103-1391-73
$C_{22}H_{13}N_3O_2S$			
Quinoline, 6-(2-benzothiazolyl)-2-(2-nitrophenyl)-	aq dioxan	230(4.59),270(4.47), 337(4.50)	7-0373-73
Quinoline, 6-(2-benzothiazolyl)-2-(3-nitrophenyl)-	dioxan	230(4.54),274(4.54), 345(4.55)	7-0373-73
Quinoline, 6-(2-benzothiazolyl)-2-(4-nitrophenyl)-	dioxan	230(4.59),287(4.56), 361(4.65)	7-0373-73
$C_{22}H_{14}$			
9,10[1',2']-Benzeneanthracene, 2-ethynyl-9,10-dihydro-	EtOH	198(4.77),211(4.80), 270(3.45),277(3.56)	18-2907-73
Benzo[c]chrysene	EtOH	222(4.51),232(4.47), 245(4.25),262(4.22), 282(4.73),292(4.91), 320(4.49),346s(2.65), 367(2.68),386(2.49)	24-1341-73
Dibenz[a,j]anthracene	isooctane	225(4.61),258(4.56), 285(4.86),296(5.10), 321(4.23)	24-1341-73
Naphtho[2,1-j]cyclobut[a]acenaphthylene, 6b,12b-dihydro-	3-Mepentane	219(4.96),224(4.96), 295(4.12)	35-7391-73
Naphtho[2,3-j]cyclobut[a]acenaphthylene, 6b,10b-dihydro-	3-Mepentane	222(4.84),288(4.85), 292(4.04)	35-7391-73
$C_{22}H_{14}ClN_3$			
4-Isoquinolinecarbonitrile, 1-[(4-chlorophenyl)amino]-3-phenyl-	EtOH	223(4.51),256(4.50), 362(4.45)	39-0817-73C
4-Isoquinolinecarbonitrile, 7-chloro-3-phenyl-1-(phenylamino)-	EtOH	238(4.74),255(4.65), 372(4.46)	39-0817-73C
$C_{22}H_{14}Cl_2O_4$			
Furan, 2,2'-(1,2-ethenediyl)bis[5-[2-(5-chloro-2-furanyl)ethenyl]-, (E,E,E)-	n.s.g.	282s(4.07),286(4.09), 330(3.95),345(4.14), 416s(4.22),440(4.39), 470(4.33)	1-3133-73
$C_{22}H_{14}N_2$			
Benzo[f]quinoline, 2-(2-quinolinyl)-	n.s.g.	280(4.62),327(4.35), 365(3.96)	103-0220-73
Cu(I) complex	isoAmOH	535(3.86)	103-0220-73
$C_{22}H_{14}O$			
Dibenz[a,j]anthracen-7(14H)-one	$CHCl_3$	280(3.97),310(3.59), 360(3.08)	24-1341-73
Dibenz[a,j]anthracen-14(7H)-one	$CHCl_3$	265s(3.94),337(3.72), 355s(3.61)	24-1341-73
$C_{22}H_{14}O_2$			
Benzeneacetaldehyde, α-(10-oxo-9(10H)-anthracenylidene)-	hexane	270(4.30),350(3.78)	54-0845-73
9,10[1',2']-Benzenoanthracene-1,5-dicarboxaldehyde, 9,10-dihydro-, (+)-	MeOH	209(4.74),215s(4.67), 238s(4.27),251(4.31), 260s(4.20),278(3.36), 305s(3.68),318(3.74)	18-0605-73
Ethanone, 1-naphtho[1,2,3-kl]xanthen-13-yl-	hexane	226(4.74),260(4.57), 288(4.15),300(4.04),	54-0845-73

Compound	Solvent	λ_{max}(log ϵ)	Ref.
Ethanone, 1-naphtho[1,2,3-kl]xanthen-13-yl- (cont.)	hexane	353(4.08),368(4.11), 387(4.11)	54-0845-73
Furan, 3-phenyl-2-[(4-phenyl-2-furanyl)-ethynyl]-	EtOH	232(4.52),259s(4.17), 343(4.24)	18-2565-73
2-Naphthalenecarboxaldehyde, 1-(1-naphthalenylcarbonyl)-	dioxan	212(4.77),247(4.71), 254(4.74),298(4.09), 308s(4.03),328s(3.98)	24-1341-73
Naphtho[1,2-c]furan-1(3H)-one, 3-(1-naphthalenyl)-	dioxan	223(5.03),238(4.85), 274s(4.09),283(4.16), 293(4.07),315(3.35), 330(3.45)	24-1341-73
$C_{22}H_{14}O_3$			
2-Naphthalenecarboxylic acid, 1-(1-naphthalenylcarbonyl)-	MeOH	213(4.79),235(4.81), 288s(3.95),297(4.00), 321(3.97)	24-1341-73
$C_{22}H_{14}O_4$			
9,10[1',2']-Benzenoanthracene-1,5-dicarboxylic acid, 9,10-dihydro-	EtOH	211(4.65),288(3.75), 299(3.79)	18-0605-73
$C_{22}H_{14}O_6$			
[1,1'-Binaphthalene]-5,5',8,8'-tetrone, 4,4'-dihydroxy-7,7'-dimethyl- (maritinone)	EtOH	264(4.42),436(3.87)	102-0175-73
Euclein (7-methyljuglone dimer)	EtOH	218(4.59),235(4.45), 432(4.02)	102-0433-73
	EtOH-base	226(4.74),288(4.30), 357s(3.51),548(4.25)	102-0433-73
$C_{22}H_{14}O_7$			
[1,2'-Binaphthalene]-1',4',5,8-tetrone, 4,5',8'-trihydroxy-2,3'-dimethyl-	$CHCl_3$	253(4.24),300(3.93), 434(3.84),460(3.92), 484(3.91),514(3.90), 554(3.66)	102-0175-73
$C_{22}H_{14}S$			
4,11[1',2']-Benzenoanthra[2,3-b]thiophene, 4,11-dihydro-	C_6H_{12}	225s(4.79),232(4.89), 254(4.29),258(4.28), 269(4.29),278(4.26), 286(3.75),298(2.99), 304(2.92),311(3.26), 317(2.95),325(3.39)	78-1379-73
4,11[1',2']-Benzenoanthra[2,3-c]thiophene, 4,11-dihydro-	C_6H_{12}	229(4.81),235(4.82), 256(4.51),266s(4.19), 276(4.05),288(3.66), 295s(2.97),302(2.81), 309(3.15),315(2.83), 323(3.28)	78-1379-73
$C_{22}H_{14}S_4$			
Disulfide, bis(1-naphthalenylthioxomethyl)-	$CHCl_3$	342(4.24),517(2.41)	143-0437-73
$C_{22}H_{15}ClN_4O_3$			
1H-Pyrazole-4,5-dione, 3-(benzoyloxy)-1-phenyl-, 4-[(4-chlorophenyl)hydrazone]	EtOH	206(4.24),243(4.37), 397(4.29)	4-1051-73

Compound	Solvent	$\lambda_{max}(\log \epsilon)$	Ref.
$C_{22}H_{15}ClO_2$			
Triptycene, 2-chloro-7-(methoxycarbonyl)-	EtOH	216(4.75),263(3.19), 280s(3.43),295(3.60)	18-0611-73
Triptycene, 5-chloro-7-(methoxycarbonyl)-	EtOH	216(4.74),263(3.19), 280s(3.41),295(3.57)	18-0611-73
$C_{22}H_{15}N_3$			
4-Isoquinolinecarbonitrile, 3-phenyl-1-(phenylamino)-	EtOH	224(4.49),255(4.38), 364(4.38)	39-0817-73C
$C_{22}H_{15}N_3O_2$			
Pyrimidine, 2-(4-nitrophenyl)-4,5-diphenyl-	EtOH	244(4.18),283s(4.26), 303(4.29),345s(3.76)	33-1351-73
$C_{22}H_{15}N_3O_2S$			
Benzenamine, 4-(2-benzothiazolyl)-N-[3-(2-nitrophenyl)-2-propenylidene]-	dioxan	314(4.48),363(4.44)	7-0373-73
Benzenamine, 4-(2-benzothiazolyl)-N-[3-(3-nitrophenyl)-2-propenylidene]-	dioxan	314(4.52),358(4.50)	7-0373-73
Benzenamine, 4-(2-benzothiazolyl)-N-[3-(4-nitrophenyl)-2-propenylidene]-	dioxan	323(4.56),379(4.54)	7-0373-73
$C_{22}H_{16}$			
Azulene, 1,1'-(1,2-ethenediyl)bis-	$C_2H_4Cl_2$	250(4.49),282(4.40), 318(4.34),662(2.87)	5-0166-73
Cyclohexene, 3-(1,3,5-heptatriynyl)-4-(1-nonene-3,5,7-triynyl)-, (E)-	ether	211(5.16),273(3.85), 290(4.12),309(4.24), 330(4.04)	24-2745-73
Phenanthrene, 2-(2-phenylethenyl)-, (E)-	dioxan	220(4.40),235s(4.15), 244(4.14),274s(4.53), 283(4.68),301(4.69), 316s(4.59),327(4.70), 342s(4.55),372(3.24)	24-1341-73
Phenanthrene, 2-(2-phenylethenyl)-, (Z)-	dioxan	219s(4.55),249(4.53), 273s(4.61),282(4.65), 295(4.54),312(4.28)	24-1341-73
$C_{22}H_{16}Br_2N_2$			
1H-Imidazole, 4,5-bis(4-bromophenyl)-2-(3-methylphenyl)-	EtOH	305(4.31)	103-0085-73
1H-Imidazole, 4,5-bis(4-bromophenyl)-2-(4-methylphenyl)-	EtOH	300(4.39)	103-0085-73
$C_{22}H_{16}ClNO_5S$			
Benzenesulfonamide, N-[4-(6-chloro-3-hydroxy-4-oxo-4H-1-benzopyran-2-yl)phenyl]-4-methyl-	dioxan	227(4.44),260(4.25), 329(4.20),358(4.36)	83-0299-73
$C_{22}H_{16}Cl_2N_2O_4S_2$			
2,2'-Bis(3-ethoxycarbonyl-6-chloro-2H-1,4-benzothiazine)	EtOH	212(4.56),252(4.60), 284(3.97),336(3.73), 390(3.45)	7-0045-73
2,2'-Bis(3-ethoxycarbonyl-7-chloro-2H-1,4-benzothiazine)	EtOH	212(4.51),249(4.43), 256(4.43),286(3.97), 346(3.87)	7-0045-73
$C_{22}H_{16}N_2$			
4,4'-Bipyridine, 2,6-diphenyl-	MeCN	245(4.66),318(3.90)	5-1036-73

Compound	Solvent	λ_{max}(log ε)	Ref.
$C_{22}H_{16}N_2O_2$			
11H-Indeno[1,2-b]quinoxalin-11-ol, 11-(2-methoxyphenyl)-	EtOH	262s(4.32),269(4.37), 347(4.19),365(4.21)	78-3337-73
11H-Indeno[1,2-b]quinoxalin-11-ol, 11-(4-methoxyphenyl)-	EtOH	262s(4.45),269(4.46), 353(4.16),370(4.17)	78-3337-73
Methanimidamide, N-(9,10-dihydro-9,10-dioxo-1-anthracenyl)-N'-(4-methylphenyl)-	EtOH	230(4.25),470(3.58)	104-1523-73
$C_{22}H_{16}N_2O_2S$			
Benzoic acid, 4-[2-[6-(2-benzothiazolyl)-3-pyridinyl]ethenyl]-, methyl ester	n.s.g.	366(4.75)	40-0991-73
$C_{22}H_{16}N_2O_3$			
Benzoic acid, 4-[2-[5-(2-benzoxazolyl)-2-pyridinyl]ethenyl]-, methyl ester	n.s.g.	361(4.68)	40-0991-73
Benzoic acid, 4-[2-[6-(2-benzoxazolyl)-3-pyridinyl]ethenyl]-, methyl ester	n.s.g.	358(4.77)	40-0991-73
$C_{22}H_{16}N_2S_2$			
1,2-Naphthalenedione, bis(S-phenylthiooxime)	CH_2Cl_2	267(4.09),440(4.04), 489(4.09)	39-1031-73C
$C_{22}H_{16}N_4O$			
4H-Quinolizine-1-carbonitrile, 4-oxo-2-[(phenylmethyl)amino]-3-(2-pyridinyl)-	EtOH	268(4.60),320(4.15), 390(4.03)	94-0921-73
$C_{22}H_{16}N_4O_2$			
Benzamide, N-benzoyl-N-(4-phenyl-1H-1,2,3-triazol-1-yl)-	EtOH	230(4.23),284(4.21), 336(4.33)	78-2119-73
$C_{22}H_{16}N_4O_3$			
1H-Pyrazole-4,5-dione, 3-(benzoyloxy)-1-phenyl-, 4-(phenylhydrazone)	EtOH	207(4.41),235(4.26), 248s(4.43),255s(4.23), 296(4.17)	4-1051-73
$C_{22}H_{16}O$			
Methanone, (2-methyl-1-naphthalenyl)-1-naphthalenyl-	MeCN	224(5.00),240s(4.31), 313(4.03)	24-1341-73
$C_{22}H_{16}O_2$			
9-Anthracenol, 1-phenyl-, acetate	EtOH	214(4.34),256(5.10), 319s(3.10),335(3.49), 351(3.79),369(3.96), 389(3.90)	44-1167-73
2-Naphthalenecarboxylic acid, 1-(1-naphthalenylmethyl)-	MeOH	223(5.00),274s(4.05), 284(4.14),294(4.05), 318(3.29)	24-1341-73
2-Propanone, 1-phenyl-1-(9H-xanthen-9-ylidene)-	hexane	220(4.54),280(3.85), 324(3.99)	54-0845-73
$C_{22}H_{16}O_3$			
Benzeneacetic acid, α-(oxodiphenylethylidene)-	EtOH	283(4.04)	2-1333-73
Spiro[isobenzofuran-1(3H),9'-[9H]xanthen]-3-one, 2',6'-dimethyl-	EtOH	203(4.74),220(4.69), 290(3.68),299(3.67)	56-1191-73
	80% H_2SO_4	203(4.67),230(4.44), 265(4.65),286(3.84), 399(4.62),451(3.69)	56-1191-73

Compound	Solvent	$\lambda_{max}(\log \epsilon)$	Ref.
Spiro[isobenzofuran-1(3H),9'-[9H]xanthe]-3-one, 2',7'-dimethyl-	EtOH	202(4.75),216(4.65), 302(3.73)	56-1191-73
	80% H_2SO_4	201(4,77),230(4.54), 268(4.80),390(4.51), 461(3.73)	56-1191-73
Spiro[isobenzofuran-1(3H),9'-[9H]xanthen]-3-one, 3',6'-dimethyl-	EtOH	202(4.76),221(4.75), 284(3.70),293(3.68)	56-1191-73
	80% H_2SO_4	204(4.71),225(4.47), 243(4.44),261(4.75), 287(3.99),398(4.68)	56-1191-73
Triptycene, 7-carboxy-2-methoxy-	dioxan	224(4.49),269(3.54), 285(3.60),298(3.58)	18-0611-73
$C_{22}H_{16}O_3S$			
1,4-Oxathiin, 2,3,5-triphenyl-, 4,4-dioxide	EtOH	228(4.35),240(4.32), 266(4.12)	18-0667-73
$C_{22}H_{16}O_4$			
9,10[1',2']-Benzenoanthracene-1-carboxylic acid, 9,10-dihydro-5,8-dihydroxy-, methyl ester	dioxan	215(4.66),262(3.37), 270(3.47),298(3.94)	18-0651-73
9,10[1',2']-Benzenoanthracene-2-carboxylic acid, 5,8,8a,9,10,10a-hexahydro-5,8-dioxo-, methyl ester, endo	dioxan	239(4.21),244(4.19), 249(4.20),255(4.18), 261(3.96),271s(3.43), 284s(3.14),360s(1.84), 377(1.90),395s(1.80), 410s(1.26)	18-1520-73
exo	dioxan	240s(4.19),247s(4.13), 251s(4.09),257s(3.96), 262s(3.81),269s(3.49), 275s(3.34),284s(3.14), 360s(1.86),378(1.88), 400s(1.75),420s(1.35)	18-1520-73
2,3-Triphenylenedicarboxylic acid, dimethyl ester	MeCN	224(4.33),234(4.35), 248s(4.58),257s(4.78), 265(4.92),284s(4.40), 296s(4.17),309s(3.90), 318s(3.70),338(3.18), 355(3.06)	5-0844-73
$C_{22}H_{16}O_4S$			
4,9-o-Benzenonaphtho[2,3-c]thiophene-1,3-dicarboxylic acid, 4,9-dihydro-, dimethyl ester	$CHCl_3$	277(4.25),286(4.16), 300s(3.79),313(4.00), 327(3.94)	78-1379-73
$C_{22}H_{16}O_6$			
Stachyoidin, 5-O-demethyldehydro-	MeOH	217(4.53),234(4.53), 279(4.59)	119-0053-73
$C_{22}H_{16}O_7$			
Chromocyclin, 2-deacetyl-12a-deoxy-, dimethyl ether	EtOH	224(4.32),258(4.37), 281(4.20),332(3.92), 420(4.39)	105-0498-73
9,10[3',4]-Furanoanthracene-1,5-dicarboxylic acid, 9,10,11,15-tetrahydro-12,14-dioxo-, dimethyl ester	dioxan	223(4.38),289(3.62)	18-0605-73
$C_{22}H_{16}O_9$			
Naphtho[2,3-d]-1,3-dioxole-6,7-dicarboxylic acid, 5-(1,3-benzodioxol-5-yl)-8-	EtOH	239(4.32),270(4.59), 276(4.60),300(4.11),	39-1266-73C

Compound	Solvent	λ_{max}(log ε)	Ref.
hydroxy-, dimethyl ester (cont.)	EtOH	314(3.94),347(3.49), 356(3.49)	39-1266-73C
$C_{22}H_{16}S_2$			
Thieno[2,3-b]thiophene, 2,5-bis(2-phenylethenyl)-	benzene	319(4.53),332(4.52), 358(4.52)	35-3692-73
Thiophene, 2,2'-(2,7-naphthalenediyldi-2,1-ethenediyl)bis-	benzene	330s(4.43),343(4.54), 357s(4.49),395s(2.76)	35-3692-73
$C_{22}H_{17}BrO_7$			
Naphtho[2,3-c]furan-1,3-dione, 4-(2-bromo-4,5-dimethoxyphenyl)-6,7-dimethoxy-	EtOH	215(4.68),260(4.86), 290(4.64)	2-0203-73
$C_{22}H_{17}Cl$			
Phenanthrene, 9-(4-chlorophenyl)-9,10-dihydro-9-methyl-10-methylene-	C_6H_{12}	221(4.52),246(4.38), 283(4.05)	104-1057-73
	96% H_2SO_4	270(4.46),332(4.00), 400(3.46),559(3.74)	104-1057-73
	70% $HClO_4$	270(4.46),335(3.97), 382(3.54),556(3.75)	104-1057-73
$C_{22}H_{17}ClN_2O_2S$			
Benzenesulfonamide, 4-chloro-N-[1,3-dihydro-1-methyl-3-(phenylmethylene)-2H-indol-2-ylidene]-, (E)-	n.s.g.	210(4.67),275(4.48), 320(3.76),360s(3.48)	39-1943-73C
1H-Pyrazole, 3-[(4-chlorophenyl)sulfonyl]-4,5-dihydro-4-methylene-5,5-diphenyl-	EtOH	332(3.95)	22-2746-73
$C_{22}H_{17}ClO_2$			
2-Propen-1-one, 1-[5-chloro-2-(phenylmethoxy)phenyl]-3-phenyl-	EtOH	227(4.38),312(4.23)	114-0093-73B
$C_{22}H_{17}ClO_3$			
Methanone, [5-chloro-2-(phenylmethoxyphenyl](3-phenyloxiranyl)-	EtOH	250(4.50),329(3.62)	114-0093-73B
$C_{22}H_{17}CoO$			
Cobalt, (η^5-2,4-cyclopentadien-1-yl)-[(2,3,4,5-η)-2,4-diphenyl-2,4-cyclopentadien-1-one]-	EtOH	252(4.35),327(4.17), 437(2.85)	12-1911-73
isomer (dihydrate)	EtOH	270(4.43),304(4.11), 379(3.51)	12-1911-73
$C_{22}H_{17}F$			
Phenanthrene, 9-(3-fluorophenyl)-9,10-dihydro-9-methyl-10-methylene-	heptane	218(4.42),240s(--), 245(4.32),267s(--), 273s(--),284(3.97)	104-1057-73
	96% H_2SO_4	270(4.62),332(4.05), 372s(--),558(3.88)	104-1057-73
	70% $HClO_4$	268(4.32),331(4.24), 372s(--),553(4.08)	104-1057-73
Phenanthrene, 9-(4-fluorophenyl)-9,10-dihydro-9-methyl-10-methylene-	heptane	218(4.42),245(4.32), 284(3.97)	104-1057-73
	96% H_2SO_4	269(4.49),332(3.95), 393(3.42),556(3.74)	104-1057-73
	70% $HClO_4$	269(4.50),336(4.00), 376s(--),556(3.81)	104-1057-73

Compound	Solvent	λ_{max}(log ε)	Ref.
$C_{22}H_{17}F_3S$			
1,1':2',1"-Terphenyl, 2-(1-propenyl-thio)-3"-(trifluoromethyl)-	EtOH	235(4.66)	35-5288-73
$C_{22}H_{17}N$			
Methanamine, 1-(9H-fluoren-9-ylidene)-N-[(4-methylphenyl)methylene]-	EtOH	236(4.64),261(4.56), 271(4.56),375(4.56)	23-1995-73
$C_{22}H_{17}NO$			
4H-1,4-Oxazine, 2,4,6-triphenyl-	EtOH	238(4.30),348(4.31), 440(3.49)	44-3433-73
$C_{22}H_{17}NO_2$			
Aziridine, 1,2-dibenzoyl-2-phenyl-	EtOH	247(4.33)	35-1954-73
9,10[1',2']-Benzenoanthracene-1-carboxylic acid, 5-amino-9,10-dihydro-, methyl ester, (+)-	MeOH	208(4.65),217(4.56), 240s(4.28),269(3.53), 294(3.76)	18-0605-73
	MeOH-HCl	209(4.72),240s(4.10), 270s(3.33),276(3.47), 293(3.59)	18-0605-73
$C_{22}H_{17}NO_2$			
Methanone, (4,5-dihydro-3,4-diphenyl-5-isoxazolyl)phenyl-	EtOH	255(4.29),333(3.27)	39-1148-73C
Methanone, (4,5-dihydro-3,5-diphenyl-4-isoxazolyl)phenyl-	EtOH	253(4.41)	39-1148-73C
$C_{22}H_{17}NO_4$			
Pyrido[1,2-a]indol-3-ol, 10-(4-acetoxyphenyl)-, acetate	n.s.g.	270(5.1),300(4.3), 330(4.1),410(3.8)	83-0360-73
$C_{22}H_{17}NO_5S$			
Benzenesulfonamide, N-[4-(3-hydroxy-4-oxo-4H-1-benzopyran-2-yl)phenyl]-4-methyl-	dioxan	229(4.42),317(4.17), 353(4.40)	83-0299-73
$C_{22}H_{17}N_3$			
4H-Imidazo[1,5-a]benzimidazole, 1-phenyl-4-(phenylmethyl)-	EtOH	230s(4.22),251s(4.02), 281(4.05),351(4.18)	103-0366-73
$C_{22}H_{17}N_3OS$			
Acetamide, N-[4-[2-[6-(2-benzothiazolyl)-3-pyridinyl]ethenyl]phenyl]-	n.s.g.	381(4.71)	40-0991-73
$C_{22}H_{17}N_3OS_4$			
4-Thiazolidinone, 5-[2-[2,3'(2'H)-bibenzothiazol]-2'-ylidene)-1-methylethylidene)-3-ethyl-2-thioxo-	EtOH	529(5.06)	103-1078-73
$C_{22}H_{17}N_3O_2$			
Acetamide, N-[4-[2-[6-(2-benzoxazolyl)-3-pyridinyl]ethenyl]phenyl]-	n.s.g.	374(4.72)	40-0991-73
Acetic acid, cyano(7-methylbenzo[a]phenazin-5(7H)-ylidene)-, ethyl ester	n.s.g.	556s(4.19),594(4.32), 640s(4.18)	103-1407-73
1,3-Diazabicyclo[3.1.0]hex-3-ene, 2-(4-nitrophenyl)-4,5-diphenyl-	EtOH	253(4.28),260(4.27)	33-1351-73
Methanone, (1,4-diphenyl-1H-1,2,3-triazol-5-yl)(4-methoxyphenyl)-	EtOH	234(4.41),303(4.29)	42-0589-73
Methanone, (1,5-diphenyl-1H-1,2,3-triazol-4-yl)(4-methoxyphenyl)-	EtOH	223(4.30),266(4.33)	42-0589-73

Compound	Solvent	$\lambda_{max}(\log \epsilon)$	Ref.
Pyrimidine, 1,4-dihydro-2-(4-nitrophenyl)-5,6-diphenyl-	EtOH	263(4.30),399(3.47)	33-1351-73
$C_{22}H_{17}N_3O_3$			
Pyrrolidine, 1-[(13-oxo-11H,13H-furo[3',4':6,7]indolizino[1,2-b]quinolin-3-yl)carbonyl]-	MeOH	252(4.57),289(4.38), 378(4.34),397(4.34)	88-1307-73
$C_{22}H_{17}N_3O_6S$			
1,4,2-Oxathiazole, 3-(4-nitrophenyl)-5-[2-(4-nitrophenyl)ethoxy]-5-phenyl-	EtOH	270.5(4.42)	39-1574-73C
$C_{22}H_{17}N_5O$			
5H-Pyrimido[5,4-b]indole, 5-(methoxymethyl)-2,4-di-2-pyridinyl-	EtOH	237s(4.25),249(4.38), 255(4.39),287s(3.85), 388(3.89)	44-3324-73
$C_{22}H_{18}$			
9,10[1',2']-Benzenoanthracene, 9,10-dihydro-1,5-dimethyl-	MeOH	198(4.80),214s(4.85), 218(4.86),240s(3.78), 257s(3.15),263(3.14), 271(3.28),275s(3.16), 279(3.37)	18-0605-73
Naphthalene, 2-(6-phenyl-1,3,5-hexatrienyl)-, (E,E,E)-	C_6H_{12}	216(4.49),220(4.57), 245(4.01),252(4.08), 260(3.99),277(3.85), 290(4.10),299(4.20), 306(4.14),330(4.39), 347(4.71),363(4.81), 385(4.74)	39-0044-73C
Naphthalene, 2-(6-phenyl-1,3,5-hexatrienyl)-, (E,E,Z)-	C_6H_{12}	216(4.60),220(4.69), 255(4.31),277(4.10), 290(4.24),300(4.31), 306(4.27),330(4.62), 346(4.84),363(4.96), 384(4.84)	39-0044-73C
Phenanthrene, 9,10-dihydro-9-methyl-10-methylene-9-phenyl-	C_6H_{12}	222(4.74),246(4.64), 284(4.28)	104-1057-73
	96% H_2SO_4	270(4.42),334(3.96), 390(3.52),555(3.77)	104-1057-73
	70% $HClO_4$	269(4.50),335(3.99), 373s(--),558(3.79)	104-1057-73
$C_{22}H_{18}BrNO_8$			
2,4-Cyclopentadiene-1,2,3,4-tetracarboxylic acid, 5-(4-bromo-2-quinolinyl)-, tetramethyl ester	MeOH	247(4.53),278s(4.19), 285s(4.12),356(3.98), 382(3.73)	39-1338-73C
$C_{22}H_{18}Br_2O_2$			
Naphtho[2,3-c]furan-1(3H)-one, 7-bromo-9-(4-bromophenyl)-3,3-diethyl-	n.s.g.	248(4.93),289(4.05), 352(3.68)	115-0145-73A
$C_{22}H_{18}Cl$			
9-Phenanthrenylium, 10-(4-chlorophenyl)-9,10-dihydro-9,10-dimethyl-	96% H_2SO_4	270(4.46),332(4.00), 400(3.46),559(3.74)	88-0539-73
	70% $HClO_4$	270(4.46),335(3.97), 382(3.54),556(3.75)	88-0539-73
$C_{22}H_{18}ClNO_2$			
Benzamide, N-(4-chlorophenyl)-2-(2,5-dimethylbenzoyl)-	EtOH	270(4.02)	39-2448-73C

Compound	Solvent	$\lambda_{max}(\log \epsilon)$	Ref.
$C_{22}H_{18}ClNO_4S$			
Benzenesulfonamide, N-[4-[3-(5-chloro-2-hydroxyphenyl)-3-oxo-1-propenyl]-phenyl]-4-methyl-	dioxan	227(4.39),364(4.38)	83-0299-73
$C_{22}H_{18}ClN_3O_4S_2$			
Benzothiazolium, 3-methyl-2-[[5-[(3-methyl-2(3H)-benzothiazolylidene)-methyl]-2H-pyrrol-2-ylidene]methyl]-, perchlorate	EtOH	330(4.53),545(4.09), 618(4.39),664(4.58)	104-2202-73
$C_{22}H_{18}F_2$			
9-Phenanthrenylium, 10-(4-fluorophenyl)-9,10-dihydro-9,10-dimethyl-	96% H_2SO_4	269(4.49),332(3.95), 393(3.42),556(3.74)	88-0539-73
	70% $HClO_4$	269(4.50),336(4.00), 376s(--),556(3.81)	88-0539-73
$C_{22}H_{18}N_2$			
1,3-Diazabicyclo[3.1.0]hex-3-ene, 2,4,5-triphenyl-, endo	EtOH	247(4.06)	44-1333-73
exo	EtOH	248(4.18)	44-1333-73
$C_{22}H_{18}N_2O$			
1H-Pyrazole, 3-(4-methoxyphenyl)-1,5-di-phenyl-	EtOH	260.0(4.61)	42-0589-73
$C_{22}H_{18}N_2OS$			
Benzenepropanethioamide, 4-methyl-β-oxo-N-phenyl-α-(phenylimino)-	MeOH	260(4.52),356(3.92)	19-0893-73
Co complex	MeOH	405(4.11)	19-0893-73
Cu complex	MeOH	412(4.23)	19-0893-73
Ni complex	MeOH	404(4.14)	19-0893-73
Benzenepropanethioamide, α-[(4-methyl-phenyl)imino]-β-oxo-N-phenyl-	MeOH	242(4.62),258(4.20), 364(3.93)	19-0893-73
Co complex	MeOH	398(4.18)	19-0893-73
Cu complex	MeOH	418(4.15)	19-0893-73
Ni complex	MeOH	406(4.12)	19-0893-73
Benzenepropanethioamide, N-(4-methyl-phenyl)-β-oxo-α-(phenylimino)-	MeOH	246(4.40),263(4.12), 361(3.74)	19-0893-73
Co complex	MeOH	405(4.09)	19-0893-73
Cu complex	MeOH	421(4.17)	19-0893-73
Ni complex	MeOH	403(4.06)	19-0893-73
4H-Imidazol-4-one, 1,5-dihydro-2-(meth-ylthio)-1,5,5-triphenyl-	EtOH	250(4.25)	78-3571-73
3H-Pyrazole, 4,5-dihydro-3,3-diphenyl-5-[(phenylsulfinyl)methylene]-	EtOH	255(4.09)	22-2746-73
$C_{22}H_{18}N_2OS_2$			
Benzothiazolium, 3-methyl-2-[5-[2-(3-methylbenzothiazolium-2-yl)ethenyl]-2-furanyl]-, dibromide	H_2O	327(4.05),455(4.44)	104-2596-73
$C_{22}H_{18}N_2O_2S$			
Benzenepropanethioamide, N-(4-methoxy-phenyl)-β-oxo-α-(phenylimino)-	MeOH	253(4.67),289(4.26),	19-0893-73
Co complex	MeOH	418(4.15)	19-0893-73
Cu complex	MeOH	430(4.12)	19-0893-73
Ni complex	MeOH	422(4.18)	19-0893-73
1H-Pyrazole, 4,5-dihydro-4-methylene-	EtOH	225(3.88),350(--)	22-2739-73
5,5-diphenyl-3-(phenylsulfonyl)-	EtOH	330(3.88)	22-2746-73

Compound	Solvent	λ_{max}(log ε)	Ref.
$C_{22}H_{18}N_2S_3$			
Benzothiazolium, 3-methyl-2-[5-[2-(3-methylbenzothiazolium-2-yl)ethenyl]-2-thienyl]-, diperchlorate	H_2O	310(4.06),460(4.43)	104-2596-73
$C_{22}H_{18}N_3S_2$			
Benzothiazolium, 3-methyl-2-[[5-[(3-methyl-2(3H)-benzothiazolylidene)-methyl]-2H-pyrrol-2-ylidene]methyl]-, perchlorate	EtOH	330(4.53),545(4.09), 618(4.39),664(4.58)	104-2202-73
$C_{22}H_{18}N_4O_4$			
Biuret, 3-anilino-1,5-dibenzoyl-	MeOH	238(4.66),278(3.95)	104-1200-73
$C_{22}H_{18}O$			
3-Buten-2-one, 3,4,4-triphenyl-	hexane	239(4.26),293(3.93)	54-0845-73
	EtOH	240(3.64),330(3.88)	78-1745-73
$C_{22}H_{18}O_2$			
Benzeneacetaldehyde, α-(diphenylmethylene)-4-methoxy-	hexane	345(3.94)	54-0845-73
1(3H)-Isobenzofuranone, 3,3-bis(4-methylphenyl)-	EtOH	202(4.69),222(4.35), 286(3.11)	56-2101-73
	80% H_2SO_4	198(4.73),323(3.04), 400(3.85),467(4.38)	56-2101-73
Triptycene, 2,7-bis(hydroxymethyl)-, (+)-	MeOH	215(4.78),240s(3.68), 264s(3.20),273(3.42), 277s(3.45),281(3.57)	18-0605-73
Triptycene, 2,5-dimethoxy-	dioxan	217(4.76),262(3.43), 271(3.48),278(3.65), 294(3.61)	18-0651-73
Triptycene, 2,7-dimethoxy-, (+)-	dioxan	219(4.67),240s(3.97), 263s(3.53),268(3.61), 277(3.55),285(3.49)	18-0605-73
$C_{22}H_{18}O_3$			
Benzoic acid, 2-(2,6-dimethyl-9H-xanthen-9-yl)-	EtOH	203(4.75),287(3.67)	56-1191-73
Benzoic acid, 2-(2,7-dimethyl-9H-xanthen-9-yl)-	EtOH	203(4.73),289(3.66)	56-1191-73
Benzoic acid, 2-(3,6-dimethyl-9H-xanthen-9-yl)-	EtOH	204(4.72),276(3.66), 285(3.64)	56-1191-73
2-Propenoic acid, 3-phenyl-, 3-(phenylmethoxy)phenyl ester	EtOH	283(4.41)	12-0899-73
$C_{22}H_{18}O_4$			
1(3H)-Isobenzofuranone, 3,3-bis(4-methoxyphenyl)-	EtOH	203(4.71),232(4.35), 276(3.56)	56-2101-73
	80% H_2SO_4	198(4.63),267(4.00), 397(4.17),513(4.85)	56-2101-73
1(3H)-Isobenzofuranone, 3-(4-hydroxy-3-methoxyphenyl)-3-(4-methylphenyl)-	EtOH	204(4.84),286(3.75)	56-0415-73
	80% H_2SO_4	198(4.63),394(4.10), 510(4.45)	56-0415-73
	2M NaOH	227(3.25),299(2.77)	56-0415-73
$C_{22}H_{18}O_5$			
6H,10H-Furo[3,2-c:4,5-g']bis[1]benzopyran-3-ol, 10,10-dimethyl-, acetate	EtOH	225(4.39),243(4.52), 330(4.24),345(4.28)	39-0907-73C
1(3H)-Isobenzofuranone, 3-(4-hydroxy-3-methoxyphenyl)-3-(4-methoxyphenyl)-	EtOH	204(4.86),230(4.43), 286(3.81)	56-0415-73

Compound	Solvent	$\lambda_{max}(\log \epsilon)$	Ref.
1(3H)-Isobenzofuranone, 3-(4-hydroxy-3-methoxyphenyl)-3-(4-methoxyphenyl)-	80% H_2SO_4	198(4.64),276(3.91), 397(4.09),535(4.64)	56-0415-73
	2M NaOH	230(3.29),299(2.64)	56-0415-73
Tephroglabrin	MeOH	217(4.49),257(4.52), 284s(4.29),312(4.34)	78-3099-73
$C_{22}H_{18}O_6$			
2H-1-Benzopyran-2-one, 7,7'-[1,4-butanediylbis(oxy)]bis-	CH_2Cl_2	324(4.50)	44-0957-73
Stachyoidin, 5-O-demethyl-	MeOH	214(4.38),247(4.11), 274(4.44)	119-0053-73
Tachrosin, 5-O-demethyl-	MeOH	216(4.67),275(4.67), 340(3.98)	119-0064-73
$C_{22}H_{18}O_7$			
Naphtho[2,3-c]furan-1,3-dione, 6,7-dimethoxy-4-(3,4-dimethoxyphenyl)-	EtOH	210(4.5),255(4.8), 290(4.6)	2-0203-73
Tephrodinol, 5-O-demethyl-	MeOH	218(4.38),274(4.42), 310(4.16)	119-0053-73
$C_{22}H_{18}O_8$			
2(3H)-Benzofuranone, 5,6-dimethoxy-3-[3-methoxy-4-(4-methoxyphenyl)-5-oxo-2(5H)-furanylidene]-	$CHCl_3$	272(3.88),372(3.62), 454(3.83)	39-1529-73C
Benzoic acid, 2,6-dihydroxy-, 2,6-dimethyl-1,4-phenylene ester	MeOH	208s(4.46),220(4.61), 254(4.32),284(3.60), 325(3.85)	24-1198-73
Podophyllotoxin, tetradehydro- (6λ,5ε)	EtOH	226(4.48),263(4.57), 269s(3.90),312s(3.98), 323(3.70),355(?)	39-1266-73C
$C_{22}H_{19}$			
Phenanthrenylium, 9,10-dihydro-9,10-dimethyl-10-phenyl-	96% H_2SO_4	270(4.42),334(3.96), 390(3.52),555(3.77)	88-0539-73
	70% $HClO_4$	269(4.50),335(3.99), 373s(--),558(3.79)	88-0539-73
$C_{22}H_{19}ClN_2O_4$			
[3,6'-Bi-1H-indole]-2,2'-dicarboxylic acid, 6-chloro-, diethyl ester	EtOH	236(4.62),306(4.50)	78-1991-73 +94-1481-73
$C_{22}H_{19}NO_2$			
Benzamide, 2-(2,5-dimethylbenzoyl)-N-phenyl-	EtOH	270(3.82)	39-2448-73C
Benzamide, 2-(4-methylbenzoyl)-N-(4-methylphenyl)-	EtOH	265(3.78)	39-2448-73C
Ethanone, 2,2'-(phenylimino)bis[1-phenyl-	dioxan	252(4.43),282(3.56)	44-3433-73
1(2H)-Naphthalenone, 2,2'-(iminodimethylidyne)bis[3,4-dihydro-	MeOH	220(4.15),270(4.23), 435(4.67)	39-1802-73C
$C_{22}H_{19}NO_2S$			
Benzenamine, N,N-dimethyl-4-(9H-thioxanthen-9-ylidenemethyl)-, S,S-dioxide	50% MeOH	261(4.16),293s(3.83), 410(4.18)	39-0163-73C
	MeOH-HCl	282(3.96),321(4.17)	39-0163-73C
$C_{22}H_{19}NO_3S_2$			
Benzenepropanethioamide, α-[(4-methylphenyl)sulfonyl]-β-oxo-N-phenyl-	EtOH	340(4.1)	104-0352-73

Compound	Solvent	λmax(log ε)	Ref.
$C_{22}H_{19}NO_4S$			
Benzenepropanamide, N-[4-[(4-methylphenyl)sulfonyl]phenyl]-β-oxo-	pH 13	347(4.60)	39-0808-73B
$C_{22}H_{19}NO_4S_2$			
Thiopyran[4,3-b]indole-3,4-dicarboxylic acid, 4a,5-dihydro-1-(methylthio)-4a-phenyl-, dimethyl ester	EtOH	260(4.23),370(3.88)	94-2770-73
$C_{22}H_{19}NO_7$			
1,2,3-Benzenetricarboxylic acid, 5-hydroxy-4-(8-methyl-2-quinolinyl)-, trimethyl ester	MeOH	208(4.62),246(4.58), 271s(4.31),325(4.03)	39-1338-73C
	MeOH-HClO4	208(4.63),249(4.69), 325(4.01)	39-1338-73C
	MeOH-NaOH	254(4.65),300(4.17), 355(3.85)	39-1338-73C
$C_{22}H_{19}NO_8$			
Benzofuro[3,2-h]quinoline-2-carboxylic acid, 4,5-diacetoxy-7,8-dihydro-9-methoxy-, methyl ester	CHCl3	318(4.42),332s(4.41), 347(4.44)	39-2374-73C
2,4-Cyclopentadiene-1,2,3,4-tetracarboxylic acid, 5-(2-quinolinyl)-, tetramethyl ester	MeOH	245(4.54),343(3.96)	39-1338-73C
$C_{22}H_{19}N_3$			
4H-1,2-Diazepine, 3,7-diphenyl-5-(1-methyl-2-pyrrolyl)-	EtOH	205(4.64),270(4.35)	103-0038-73
$C_{22}H_{19}N_3O$			
Benzamide, N-[[1-(phenylmethyl)-1H-benzimidazol-2-yl]methyl]-	EtOH	224s(4.26),246s(4.12), 270(3.86),277(3.91), 284(3.82)	103-0366-73
Benzenamine, 4-[2-[6-(2-benzoxazolyl)-3-pyridinyl]ethenyl]-N,N-dimethyl-	n.s.g.	415(4.61)	40-0991-73
$C_{22}H_{19}N_3OS$			
1,2,4-Triazolidine-3-thione, 5-(3-ethoxyphenyl)-1,4-diphenyl-, meso-ionic didehydro deriv.	MeOH	228(4.42),244s(--), 300(3.57)	42-0154-73
$C_{22}H_{19}N_3O_2$			
Propanedinitrile, [4-(diethylamino)phenyl](2,3-dihydro-1,3-dioxo-1H-inden-2-yl)-	MeOH	252(4.73),405(3.47)	88-2993-73
1,2,4-Triazoline-3,5-dione, 1-[1,4-dihydro-9-(1-methylethenyl)-1,4-methanonaphthalen-9-yl]-4-phenyl-	90% EtOH	229(3.93)	12-1725-73
$C_{22}H_{19}N_3O_3$			
Angustoline acetate	EtOH	221(4.45),252(4.20), 290(3.11),301(3.88), 378(4.58),397(4.59)	39-0013-73C
$C_{22}H_{19}N_3O_4$			
Euxylophorine D	MeCN	277(4.33),360(4.65)	102-2521-73
$C_{22}H_{19}N_3S$			
Benzenamine, 4-[2-[6-(2-benzothiazolyl)-3-pyridinyl]ethenyl]-N,N-dimethyl-	n.s.g.	425(4.55)	40-0991-73

Compound	Solvent	λmax(log ε)	Ref.
4H-Imidazol-4-imine, 1,5-dihydro-2-(methylthio)-1,5,5-triphenyl-	EtOH	240(4.33),280(4.21)	78-3571-73
$C_{22}H_{19}N_5O_2$			
Benzamide, 2-methyl-N-(2-methylbenzoyl)-N-(9-methyl-9H-purin-6-yl)-	MeOH	252(4.30),270(4.26)	18-3228-73
Benzamide, 4-methyl-N-(4-methylbenzoyl)-N-(9-methyl-9H-purin-6-yl)-	MeOH	262(4.48)	18-3228-73
$C_{22}H_{19}O_5P$			
Phosphoric acid, 3-(4-methylphenyl)-3-oxo-1-propenyl diphenyl ester	dioxan	267(4.17)	24-0435-73
$C_{22}H_{19}O_6P$			
Phosphoric acid, 3-(4-methoxyphenyl)-3-oxo-1-propenyl diphenyl ester	dioxan	226(4.15),292(4.38)	24-0435-73
$C_{22}H_{20}$			
Chrysene, 1,2,7,8-tetramethyl-	EtOH	228(4.50),238(4.53), 246(4.33),257s(4.57), 265(4.90),275(5.14), 291s(4.09),303(4.08), 315(4.12),329(4.11), 350(3.24),354s(2.64), 370(3.05)	39-0044-73C
1,3,5,7,9-Decapentaene, 1,10-diphenyl-	81.5% H_2SO_4	370(3.58),440(3.79), 600(3.94),690(3.80)	48-0810-73
	95.8% H_2SO_4	400(4.00),470(4.07), 550(4.42),600(4.78), 693(3.45)	48-0810-73
	99.9% H_2SO_4	415(3.45),540(4.25), 600s(4.32),638(4.53), 700(4.79)	48-0810-73
	33% SO_3	600(3.79)	48-0810-73
5,12-Ethanonaphthacene, 13-ethyl-5,12-dihydro-	C_6H_{12}	217s(4.60),233(4.93), 236s(4.89),259(3.85), 267(3.95),271(3.93), 278(3.90),287(3.68), 289(3.65),306(2.87), 317s(2.57),320(2.90)	78-1379-73
$C_{22}H_{20}ClNO$			
2-Propen-1-one, 1-(4-chlorophenyl)-3-[2-(1-pyrrolidinyl)-1H-inden-3-yl]-	EtOH	276(4.27),490(4.52)	48-1161-73
$C_{22}H_{20}ClN_2OP$			
Phosphonium, [(5-methyl-1,2,4-oxadiazol-3-yl)methyl]triphenyl-, chloride	EtOH	226.5(4.42)	39-2769-73C
$C_{22}H_{20}Fe_2$			
Ethene, 1,2-diferrocenyl-, trans	EtOH	244(4.30),313(4.23), 459(3.10)	101-0323-73J
$C_{22}H_{20}INO_5$			
6H-Benzo[g]-1,3-dioxolo[7,8][1]benzopyrano[3,4,5-ija]quinolizinium, 5,8-dihydro-9,10-dimethoxy-13-methyl-, iodide	EtOH	290(4.46),348(4.00)	73-1614-73

Compound	Solvent	λ_{max}(log ε)	Ref.
$C_{22}H_{20}N_2$			
8,9-Diazatricyclo[4.4.0.0^{2,5}]deca-3,7,9-triene, 1,6-dimethyl-7,10-diphenyl-, (1α,2β,5β,6α)-	ether	306(4.19)	88-0861-73
$C_{22}H_{20}N_2O$			
Pyrazolidine, 1-benzoyl-2,3-diphenyl-	EtOH	227(3.50)	103-0503-73
$C_{22}H_{20}N_2OS_2$			
Benzothiazolium, 3-methyl-2-[5-[2-(3-methylbenzothiazolium-2-yl)ethyl]-2-furanyl]-, diiodide	H_2O	287(3.97),355(4.24)	104-2596-73
$C_{22}H_{20}N_2O_2$			
Benzamide, 2-[4-(dimethylamino)benzoyl]-N-phenyl-	EtOH	212(4.51),242(4.29), 350(4.23)	39-1160-73B
	dioxan	215(4.34),240(4.30), 348(4.33)	39-1160-73B
	$CHCl_3$	346(4.28)	39-1160-73B
1,4-Benzenediamine, N,N'-bis[(4-methoxyphenyl)methylene]-	n.s.g.	360(4.56)	65-1400-73
2,2'-Bioxazole, 5,5'-bis(2,4-dimethylphenyl)-	toluene	334(4.50)	34-0436-73
2,2'-Bioxazole, 5,5'-bis(4-ethylphenyl)-	toluene	336(4.57)	34-0436-73
2,4,6-Heptatrienoic acid, 2-cyano-5-(phenylamino)-7-phenyl-, ethyl ester	CH_2Cl_2	314(4.23),439(4.28)	97-0132-73
Stenocarpoquinone,A, quinoxaline deriv.	EtOH	226(4.55),238(4.58), 277(4.53),302(3.75), 368s(--),408(4.00), 424(4.00)	12-1121-73
$C_{22}H_{20}N_2O_3S$			
[1,4]Diazepino[3,2,1-kl]phenoxazine, 1,2,3,4-tetrahydro-4-[(4-methylphenyl)sulfonyl]-	EtOH	235(4.52),320(3.79)	95-0020-73
[1,4]Diazepino[3,2,1-kl]phenoxazine, 1,2,3,4-tetrahydro-7-[(4-methylphenyl)sulfonyl]-	EtOH	234(4.51),292(4.40)	95-0020-73
$C_{22}H_{20}N_2O_4$			
Benz[a]anthracene-7,12-dione, 8,11-bis-[(2-hydroxyethyl)amino]-	benzene	633(4.26),682(4.23)	40-1328-73
2,2'-Bioxazole, 5,5'-bis(4-ethoxyphenyl)-	toluene	337(4.50)	34-0436-73
2,5-Cyclohexadiene-1,4-dione, 3-acetyl-2-[(2-hydroxy-2-phenylethyl)amino]-5-(phenylamino)-	EtOH	244(4.11),300(4.09), 352(4.31),490(3.24)	78-2881-73
	CH_2Cl_2	248(4.14),298(4.09), 355(4.31),487(3.20)	78-2881-73
$C_{22}H_{20}N_2O_5$			
Corydamine acetate	MeOH	244(4.61),309(4.20), 378(3.67)	94-1410-73
1,4-Cyclohexadiene-1-carboxylic acid, 2-[(2-hydroxy-2-phenylethyl)amino]-3,6-dioxo-5-(phenylamino)-, methyl ester	EtOH	250(4.17),275s(3.95), 352(4.33),500(3.10)	78-2881-73
	CH_2Cl_2	252(4.21),276s(4.00), 354(4.34),506(3.16)	78-2881-73
Pyrazolo[5,1-a]isoquinoline-1,2-dicarboxylic acid, 3-benzoyl-3,5,6,10b-tetrahydro-, dimethyl ester	EtOH	272(3.65),310(3.67)	95-0648-73

Compound	Solvent	$\lambda_{max}(\log \epsilon)$	Ref.
$C_{22}H_{20}N_2S_3$			
Benzothiazolium, 3-methyl-2-[5-[2-(3-methylbenzothiazolium-2-yl)ethyl]-2-thienyl]-, dibromide	H_2O	285(4.01),357(4.29)	104-2596-73
$C_{22}H_{20}N_3S$			
Thiazolo[3,2-a]pyrimidin-4-ium, 5-[2-[4-(dimethylamino)phenyl]ethenyl]-3-phenyl-, perchlorate	n.s.g.	540(4.65)	124-1151-73
Thiazolo[3,2-a]pyrimidin-4-ium, 7-[2-[4-(dimethylamino)phenyl]ethenyl]-3-phenyl-, perchlorate	n.s.g.	538(4.53)	124-1151-73
Thiazolo[3,2-a]pyrimidin-4-ium, 7-[2-[4-(dimethylamino)phenyl]ethenyl]-5-phenyl-, perchlorate	n.s.g.	538(4.57)	124-1151-73
$C_{22}H_{20}N_4$			
Quinoxalino[2,3-b]phenazine, 5,12-dihydro-2,5,9(or 10),12-tetramethyl-diperchlorate	EtOH-2% NaOH	492(3.72),528(4.26), 570(4.67)	22-1289-73
	EtOH	550(4.07),590(4.46), 645(4.55)	22-1289-73
$C_{22}H_{20}N_4O_2$			
Indolo[2,3-a]quinolizine-3-prop noic acid, 2-(dicyanomethylene)-2,3,4,6-7,12-hexahydro-, methyl ester, (±)-	MeOH	221(4.27),246(3.88), 348(3.98),448(4.57), 475(4.64)	44-2501-73
$C_{22}H_{20}N_8O_8$			
Spiro[4.5]dec-6-ene-1,8-dione, bis(2,4-dinitrophenylhydrazone)	$CHCl_3$	370(4.62)	39-0393-73C
$C_{22}H_{20}OS$			
Benzenecarbothioic acid, O-(2,3-diphenylpropyl) ester	CH_2Cl_2	253(3.87),290(4.04), 410(2.11)	39-1580-73C
1,1'-Biphenyl, 2-[(4-methoxyphenyl)thio]-2'-(1-propenyl)-	EtOH	228(4.12),255(3.95)	35-5288-73
$C_{22}H_{20}OSi$			
3-Buten-2-one, 3-(triphenylsilyl)-	C_6H_{12}	329f(1.88)	23-2024-73
$C_{22}H_{20}O_3$			
1-Propanone, 2-hydroxy-1-(4-methoxyphenyl)-2,3-diphenyl-	EtOH	282(4.18)	42-0586-73
$C_{22}H_{20}O_4$			
1,3-Azulenedicarboxylic acid, 2-phenyl-, diethyl ester	C_6H_{12}	235(4.55),269(4.43), 305(4.65),310(4.58), 345(3.97),365(3.93), 520(2.77),540(2.76)	88-3883-73
1,3-Azulenedicarboxylic acid, 4-phenyl-, diethyl ester	C_6H_{12}	273(4.45),265(4.42), 295(4.43),308(4.46), 340(3.99),377(3.92), 550(2.97)	88-3883-73
1,3-Azulenedicarboxylic acid, 6-phenyl-, diethyl ester	C_6H_{12}	272(4.35),277(4.36), 327(4.72),507(2.88), 542(2.75)	88-3883-73
15H-Cyclopenta[a]phenanthrene-16,17-diol, 16,17-dihydro-11-methyl-, diacetate, cis	EtOH	226(4.15),255(4.88), 281(4.11),292(4.06), 304(4.14),324(2.81), 339(2.97),354(2.98)	39-1255-73C

Compound	Solvent	λmax(log ε)	Ref.
15H-Cyclopenta[a]phenanthrene-16,17-diol, 16,17-dihydro-11-methyl-, diacetate, trans	EtOH	224(4.14),254(4.88), 281(4.09),292(4.05), 304(4.15),323(2.80), 338(2.97),354(2.97)	39-1255-73C
Ethanone, 2-hydroxy-1,2-bis(4-methoxyphenyl)-2-phenyl-	EtOH	280(4.23)	42-0586-73
Ethanone, 2-hydroxy-1-(2-methoxyphenyl)-2-(4-methoxyphenyl)-2-phenyl-	EtOH	276(4.27)	42-0586-73
2,3-Triphenylenedicarboxylic acid, 1,2,3,4-tetrahydro-, dimethyl ester, cis	MeCN	224(4.42),240s(4.51), 247(4.73),254(4.83), 260s(4.46),270s(4.20), 278(4.16),286(4.03), 298(4.05),318(3.63), 325(2.61),333(2.81), 340(2.64),349(2.84), 363s(2.11)	5-0844-73
$C_{22}H_{20}O_6$			
5H-Cycloprop[cd]indene-2,2b,5b-tricarboxylic acid, 2a,5a-dihydro-5-(phenylmethylene)-, trimethyl ester	EtOH	225(4.15),280(4.20)	24-1837-73
isomer	EtOH	225s(4.28),286(4.26)	24-1837-73
Guaialignan-9,9'-olide, 4,4'-dimethyl-, (8R,8'R)-	EtOH	232(4.20),280(3.79)	105-0512-73
1,2,4-Methenopentalene-1,5,6a-tricarboxylic acid, 2,3,3a,4-tetrahydro-3-(phenylmethylene)-, trimethyl ester, (E)-	EtOH	241(4.16),266(4.14)	24-1822-73
(Z)-	EtOH	242(4.18),266(4.14)	24-1822-73
Naphtho[2,3-c]furan-1(3H)-one, 4-(3,4-dimethoxyphenyl)-6,7-dimethoxy-	EtOH	224(4.53),258(4.80), 320(4.13)	95-0541-73
$C_{22}H_{20}O_8$			
12a-Deoxychromocycin	EtOH	240(4.45),289(4.19), 337(3.98),374(4.26), 443(4.49),476(4.32)	105-0492-73
Pulvinic acid, 3,4,4'-trimethoxy-, methyl ester	EtOH	271(4.04),310s(3.95), 326s(3.87),396(3.87)	39-1529-73C
Pulvinic acid, 3',4,4'-trimethoxy-, methyl ester	EtOH	240(4.24),266(4.22), 276s(4.18),394(4.09)	39-1529-73C
Steganone	EtOH	238(4.44),276(3.96), 317(2.77)	35-1335-73
$C_{22}H_{20}O_9$			
Chromocyclin	EtOH	232(4.46),284(4.67), 328(3.91),420(4.03)	105-0492-73
$C_{22}H_{20}S_2$			
Ethene, 1,2-bis(p-tolylthio)-2-phenyl-	EtOH	257(4.18),295(4.21), 315(4.21)	39-0063-73B
$C_{22}H_{21}ClN_2O_7$			
2-Naphthacenecarboxamide, 7-chloro-4-(dimethylamino)-1,4,4a,5,12,12a-hexahydro-3,10,11,12a-tetrahydroxy-6-methyl-1,12-dioxo-, [4S-(4α,4aα,12aα)]- (anhydroaureomycin)	pH 2	228(4.46),274(4.70), 337(3.63),435(3.92)	89-0497-73
$C_{22}H_{21}ClO_2$			
1H-1,5-Etheno-8,14a:9,14-dimethanocyclooctacyclodecene-2,16(5H)-dione, 3-chloro-6,8,9,14-tetrahydro-6,6-dimethyl-	C_6H_{12}	203(4.04),260(3.58), 270(3.46)	33-0545-73

Compound	Solvent	$\lambda_{max}(\log \epsilon)$	Ref.
$C_{22}H_{21}IN_2$			
Benz[cd]indolium, 2-[3-(1-ethyl-2(1H)-pyridinylidene)-1-propenyl]-1-methyl-, iodide	EtOH	570(4.57)	103-0314-73
$C_{22}H_{21}NO$			
4H-Isoindol-4-one, 2,5,6,7-tetrahydro-6,6-dimethyl-1,3-diphenyl-	EtOH	288(4.17),253(4.26), 297(3.97),312s(3.92)	33-1351-73
2-Propen-1-one, 1-phenyl-3-[3-(1-pyrrolidinyl)-1H-inden-2-yl]-	EtOH	255(4.21),270(4.26), 290(4.21),488(4.66), 510(4.65)	48-1161-73
$C_{22}H_{21}NO_5$			
Allonitidine, 5,6-dihydro-6-methoxy-	$CHCl_3$	281(4.63),311(4.38)	4-0867-73
6H,8H-Benzo[g]-1,3-dioxolo[7,8][1]benzopyrano[3,4,5-ija]quinolizine, 5,13-dihydro-9,10-dimethoxy-13-methyl-	EtOH	238(4.31),271(4.09), 379(4.15)	73-1614-73
Nitidine, 5,6-dihydro-6-methoxy-	$CHCl_3$	238(4.53),283(4.60), 310(4.40),325s(4.25)	4-0085-73
$C_{22}H_{21}NO_6$			
Nordicentrine, N-carbethoxydehydro-	dioxan	241(4.56),263(4.80), 272(5.04),326(4.33), 339(4.35),360(3.88), 384(3.78)	78-2245-73
Thelflavidine	n.s.g.	254(4.38),263(4.49), 296(3.94),400(3.60)	105-0660-73
$C_{22}H_{21}NO_8S$			
Allonitidine methyl sulfate	MeOH	231(4.43),272(4.80), 302(4.59),328(4.51), 390(3.98)	4-0867-73
Nitidine methyl sulfate	EtOH	230(4.38),272(4.68), 280s(4.62),300(4.54), 328(4.50),388(4.00)	4-0085-73
$C_{22}H_{21}NO_{10}$			
4H-1-Benzopyran-4-one, 7-(β-D-glucopyranosyloxy)-2-methyl-3-(4-nitrophenyl)-	EtOH	222(4.12),282(3.92)	114-0435-73B
$C_{22}H_{21}NP$			
Phosphonium, (1H-indol-2-ylmethyl)methyldiphenyl-, iodide	MeOH	271(4.07),277(4.07), 285(4.04),293(3.97)	23-0792-73
$C_{22}H_{21}N_3O_2$			
1H,5H-Pyrazolo[1,2-a][1,2,4]triazole-1,3(2H)-dione, 6,7-dihydro-5-methyl-7-(1-methylethylidene)-2-phenyl-6-(phenylmethylene)-, (E)-	EtOH	222(4.35),273(4.12)	35-1553-73
(Z)-	EtOH	222(4.35),268(3.97)	35-1553-73
1H,5H-Pyrazolo[1,2-a][1,2,4]triazole-1,3(2H)-dione, 6-ethylidenedihydro-5-(1-methylethylidene)-2,7-diphenyl-	EtOH	222(4.31),261(3.27)	35-1553-73
$C_{22}H_{21}N_3O_3$			
Ethanone, 1-[4-[[2-(4-morpholinyl)-5-phenyl-3-furanyl]azo]phenyl]-	CH_2Cl_2	275(4.29),321(4.21), 495(4.58)	39-2523-73C
tetrafluoroborate	CH_2Cl_2	282(4.36),483(4.60), 505s(4.56)	39-2523-73C

Compound	Solvent	λ_{max}(log ε)	Ref.
Morpholine, 4-[4-(1,3-benzodioxol-5-yl-methyl)-6-phenyl-3-pyridazinyl]-	CH_2Cl_2	261s(4.23),280(4.26)	39-2532-73C
	CH_2Cl_2-HCl	262s(4.09),280(4.10)	39-2532-73C
4H,7aH-Pyrazolo[4',3':4,5]pyrrolo[3,2,1-ij]quinoline-7a-carboxylic acid, 10-acetyl-5,6,8,10a-tetrahydro-8-phenyl-, methyl ester	EtOH	249(4.25),313(4.07), 334(4.04)	78-3159-73
4H-Pyrrolo[3,2,1-ij]quinoline-2-carboxylic acid, 5,6-dihydro-1-[2-oxo-1-(phenylhydrazono)propyl]-, methyl ester	EtOH	234(4.59),294(4.29), 347(4.33)	78-3159-73
$C_{22}H_{21}N_3O_4$			
2-Butenedioic acid, 2-(8-methylindazolo-[1,2-a][1,2,3]benzotriazol-6-N^V-7-yl)-, diethyl ester	EtOH	241(4.48),262(4.14), 350(4.04),365(4.25), 384(4.45),508(3.65)	88-0597-73
Euxylophorine C	EtOH	389(--)	102-2521-73
	MeCN	303(4.14),408(4.40)	102-2521-73
	$CHCl_3$	425(4.51)	102-2521-73
10bH-2a,6b,10c-Triazabenzo[2,3]pentaleno[1,6-ab]indene-1,2-dicarboxylic acid, 10-methyl-, diethyl ester	EtOH	238(4.36),271(4.28), 300(3.95),399(3.59)	88-0597-73
$C_{22}H_{21}N_3O_4S$			
Benzamide, N-[2-oxo-2-[[[[1-(5-oxo-2-phenyl-4(5H)-oxazolylidene)ethyl]-thio]ethyl]amino]ethyl]-	EtOH	349(4.40)	39-0465-73C
	EtOH-base	288(4.16)	39-0465-73C
Ethanethioic acid, (benzoylamino)-, S-[2-[[1-(5-oxo-2-phenyl-4(5H)-oxazol-ylidene)ethyl]amino]ethyl] ester	EtOH	349(4.45)	39-0465-73C
	EtOH-base	352(4.47)	39-0465-73C
1(2H)-Pyrimidineacetic acid, 2-[[(4-methylphenyl)sulfonyl]imino]-4-(2-phenylethenyl)-, methyl ester	EtOH	225(4.23),246(4.22), 343(4.38)	44-1591-73
$C_{22}H_{21}N_3O_5$			
Piperidine, 1-[4-[2,3-dihydro-6-(4-nitrophenyl)-3-oxo-4H-1,4-oxazin-4-yl]-benzoyl]-	EtOH	254(4.25),366(4.11)	4-0347-73
$C_{22}H_{21}N_3O_6$			
1H-Pyrazole-4,5-dicarboxylic acid, 3-[4-(1-methylethyl)phenyl]-1-(4-nitrophenyl)-, dimethyl ester	EtOH	244(4.15),312(3.91)	94-2026-73
$C_{22}H_{22}$			
Tetracyclo[6.2.0.0^{4,10}.0^{5,9}]decane, 9,10-diphenyl-	hexane	223(4.03),248(3.18), 253(2.96),262(2.90), 272(2.69)	44-1762-73
$C_{22}H_{22}BrNO$			
2,4-Pentadien-1-one, 1-(4-bromophenyl)-4-phenyl-5-(1-piperidinyl)-	EtOH	275(3.98),439(4.52)	48-1161-73
$C_{22}H_{22}BrNO_5$			
1H-Indole-1,3-diacetic acid, 5-bromo-2,3-dihydro-2-oxo-3-phenyl-, diethyl ester	EtOH	261(4.10),290(3.27)	104-0831-73
$C_{22}H_{22}BrNO_8$			
Spiro[6H-1,3-dioxolo[4,5-i][3,4]benzoxazocine-6,1'(3'H)-isobenzofuran]-3'-	EtOH	214(4.81),308(3.44)	33-2107-73

Compound	Solvent	$\lambda_{max}(\log \epsilon)$	Ref.
one, 11-bromo-5,8,9,10-tetrahydro-4,4',5'-trimethoxy-8-methyl- (cont.)			
$C_{22}H_{22}ClNO$			
2,4-Pentadien-1-one, 1-(4-chlorophenyl)-4-phenyl-5-(1-piperidinyl)-	EtOH	275(4.13),438(4.69)	48-1161-73
$C_{22}H_{22}ClNO_5$			
1H-Indole-1,3-diacetic acid, 5-chloro-2,3-dihydro-2-oxo-3-phenyl-, diethyl ester	EtOH	259(4.07),292(3.24)	104-0831-73
$C_{22}H_{22}ClNO_6$			
1,3-Dioxolo[4,5-g]isoquinoline-6(5H)-carboxylic acid, 5-[(2-chloro-4,5-dimethoxyphenyl)methylene]-7,8-dihydro-, ethyl ester, (E)-	EtOH	222(4.78),298(4.51), 335(4.70)	78-2245-73
$C_{22}H_{22}Cl_3NO_4$			
6H-Dibenzo[a,g]quinolizine, 5,8-dihydro-2,3,9,10-tetramethoxy-8-(trichloromethyl)- (palmatinechloroform)	MeOH	280(4.0),362(4.1)	102-1822-73
$C_{22}H_{22}NO$			
Pyrylium, 4-[2-(dimethylamino)-1-methylethenyl]-2,6-diphenyl-, perchlorate	MeCN	253(4.25),284(3.88), 332(4.24),444(4.56)	78-1031-73
$C_{22}H_{22}N_2O$			
Cinnoline, 4-ethoxy-1,2,3,4-tetrahydro-1,2-diphenyl-	MeCN	245(4.23),280(4.11)	22-3487-73
1H-Cyclopenta[b]quinoline-9-carboxamide, 2,3-dihydro-N-(1-methyl-2-phenylethyl)-	EtOH	238(4.72),295(4.00), 308(4.06),322(4.11)	103-1005-73
$C_{22}H_{22}N_2O_2$			
1H-Pyrazole-3-carboxylic acid, 1-(4-methylphenyl)-5-(1-methyl-2-phenylethenyl)-, ethyl ester	C_6H_{12} or EtOH	217(4.4),258(4.51)	4-0015-73
$C_{22}H_{22}N_2O_3$			
Acetamide, N-[3,4-dihydro-1-(phenylmethyl)spiro[benz[cd]indole-5(1H),2'-[1,3]dioxolan]-4-yl]-	EtOH	206(4.35),227(4.37), 293(3.73)	39-0760-73C
$C_{22}H_{22}N_8O_8$			
Spiro[4.5]decane-1,8-dione, bis(2,4-dinitrophenylhydrazone)	$CHCl_3$	365(4.69)	39-0393-73C
$C_{22}H_{22}OS$			
Dibenzo[b,h]benzo[3,4]cyclobuta[1,2-e]thionin, 1,2,3,4,6,7,8,9-octahydro-, 5-oxide, cis	EtOH	267(4.58),359(3.90)	39-2253-73C
trans	EtOH	225(4.22),315(3.98)	39-2253-73C
isomer (oil)	ether	292(--),298s(--), 318s(--)	39-2253-73C
$C_{22}H_{22}O_3$			
2-Propen-1-one, 3,3'-oxybis[1-(3,4-dimethylphenyl)-	dioxan	301(4.61)	24-0435-73

Compound	Solvent	$\lambda_{max}(\log \epsilon)$	Ref.
$C_{22}H_{22}O_4$			
4H-1-Benzopyran-4-one, 5,7-dimethoxy-8-(3-methyl-2-butenyl)-2-phenyl-	MeOH	217(4.61),268(4.61), 330(4.06)	119-0064-73
Bicyclo[4.2.1]nona-2,4,7-triene-2,4-dicarboxylic acid, 9-(1-methylethylidene)-5-phenyl-, dimethyl ester	EtOH	320(4.05)	24-1837-73
4-Cyclohexene-1,2-dicarboxylic acid, 4,5-diphenyl-, dimethyl ester, cis	MeCN	220s(4.02),231s(3.94), 243s(3.90),275s(3.58)	5-0844-73
5H-Cycloprop[cd]indene-2a,2b-dicarboxylic acid, 5a,5b-dihydro-5-(1-methylethylidene)-2-phenyl-, dimethyl ester	EtOH	242(4.17),255s(4.10)	24-1837-73
2,5-Hexanedione, 3,4-bis(4-methylbenzoyl)-	EtOH	207(4.38),268(4.47)	128-0465-73
Tetracyclo[4.3.0.0^{2,4}.0^{3,7}]non-8-ene-1,8-dicarboxylic acid, 5-(1-methylethylidene)-2-phenyl-, dimethyl ester	EtOH	234(4.05)	24-1837-73
Tetracyclo[4.3.0.0^{2,4}.0^{3,7}]non-8-ene-2,9-dicarboxylic acid, 5-(1-methylethylidene)-8-phenyl-, dimethyl ester	EtOH	275(4.00)	24-1822-73
$C_{22}H_{22}O_5$			
7H,9H-Benzo[1,2]fluoreno[4a,4b-c]furan-7,12-dione, 5,6,10,11-tetrahydro-3α,9-dimethoxy-13-methyl-	MeOH	253(3.71),370(4.37)	39-1780-73C
4H-1-Benzopyran-4-one, 3-(3,4-dihydro-7-methoxy-2,2-dimethyl-2H-1-benzopyran-6-yl)-7-methoxy-	EtOH	240(4.34),248(4.35), 294(4.21)	39-0907-73C
4H-1-Benzopyran-4-one, 8-[(3,3-dimethyloxiranyl)methyl]-5,7-dimethoxy-2-phenyl-	MeOH	212(4.51),267(4.49), 325(4.02)	119-0064-73
4H-1-Benzopyran-4-one, 5-hydroxy-3,7-dimethoxy-6-(3-methyl-2-butenyl)-2-phenyl-	MeOH	246(4.33),271(4.56), 315(4.28)	12-0641-73
4H-1-Benzopyran-4-one, 8-(3-hydroxy-3-methyl-1-butenyl)-5,7-dimethoxy-2-phenyl-, (Z)- (tephrostachin)	MeOH	215(4.52),270(4.56), 332(4.00)	119-0071-73
Coleon F acetate	ether	246(3.94),253s(3.91), 282s(4.09),289(4.11), 431(4.09),480s(4.04)	33-1129-73
$C_{22}H_{22}O_6$			
Butanedioic acid, [3-(3,4-dimethoxyphenyl)-1-phenyl-2-propenylidene]-, 1-methyl ester	EtOH	230(4.39),336(4.29)	42-0430-73
Licoricone	EtOH	238(4.32),248(4.29), 284(4.01),302(3.89)	94-1338-73
	EtOH-NaOAc	250(--),253s(--), 303s(--),330(--)	94-1338-73
2-Naphthalenol, 4-(2,6-dimethoxyphenyl)-5,7-dimethoxy-, acetate	EtOH	245(4.72),289(3.79), 300s(3.76),320s(3.48), 334(3.48)	39-2853-73C
$C_{22}H_{22}O_7$			
2-Propen-1-one, 3,3'-oxybis[1-(3,4-dimethoxyphenyl)-	dioxan	234(4.66),280(4.26), 322(4.32)	24-0435-73
$C_{22}H_{22}O_8$			
4H-1-Benzopyran-4-one, 7-(β-D-glucopyranosyloxy)-2-methyl-3-phenyl-	EtOH	233(4.35),287(3.91)	114-0435-73B
Epiexcelsin, (+)-	EtOH	242(4.04),275(3.45)	102-1799-73

Compound	Solvent	$\lambda_{max}(\log \epsilon)$	Ref.
Episteganol	EtOH	254(3.91),288(3.73)	35-1335-73
Excelsin, (+)-	EtOH	242(4.02),275(3.46)	102-1799-73
Steganol	EtOH	255(4.05),287(3.75)	35-1335-73
$C_{22}H_{22}O_9$			
4H-1-Benzopyran-4-one, 7-(β-D-gluco-pyranosyloxy)-3-(4-methoxyphenyl)-	EtOH	260(4.42),305(3.87)	114-0435-73B
	dioxan	263(4.45),302s(3.82)	114-0365-73D
$C_{22}H_{22}S$			
Dibenzo[b,h]benzo[3,4]cyclobuta[1,2-e]-thionin, 1,2,3,4,6,7,8,9-octahydro-, (E,Z)-	EtOH	224s(4.25),285s(3.82), 314(4.06)	39-2253-73C
(Z,Z)-	EtOH	223s(4.16),268(4.49), 375(3.79)	39-2253-73C
$C_{22}H_{23}BrN_2O_8$			
Tetracycline, 11a-bromo-, 6,12-hemi-ketal	MeOH-HCl	268(4.29),350(3.57)	128-0357-73
$C_{22}H_{23}BrN_2O_{11}S$			
Anhydrotetracycline, 9-bromo-, sulfate	pH 1	228(4.50),275(4.67), 433(3.88)	128-0357-73
$C_{22}H_{23}ClN_2O_7$			
2-Naphthacenecarboxamide, 7-chloro-4-(dimethylamino)-1,4,4a,5,5a,6,11,12a-octahydro-3,10,12,12a-tetrahydroxy-6-methyl-1,11-dioxo-, (4α,4aα,5aβ-6α,12aα)-(±)-	MeOH-HCl	231(4.16),268(4.23), 347(4.07),368(4.07)	89-0497-73
	MeOH-NaOH	228(4.14),244(4.19), 264(4.13),386(4.17)	89-0497-73
	MeOH-borate	220(4.14),244(4.20), 268(4.10),384(4.21)	89-0497-73
$C_{22}H_{23}NO$			
2,4-Pentadien-1-one, 1,4-diphenyl-5-(1-piperidinyl)-	EtOH	267(4.06),431(4.67)	48-1161-73
2-Propenamide, N-(4,5-diphenyl-2,4-pentadienyl)-N-ethyl-, (E,Z)-	MeOH	224(4.19),234(4.18), 289(4.51),308(4.27)	44-2169-73
$C_{22}H_{23}NO_4$			
Propanedioic acid, (1H-indol-3-ylmethyl)phenyl-, diethyl ester	EtOH	280(3.74),290(3.68)	103-1367-73
Tylophorinidine	EtOH	260(4.64),287(4.41), 313(3.90),340(3.17)	78-0891-73
	EtOH-NaOH	256(4.73),298(4.53), 335(4.00)	78-0891-73
$C_{22}H_{23}NO_5$			
1H-Indole-1,3-diacetic acid, 2,3-di-hydro-2-oxo-3-phenyl-, diethyl ester	EtOH	255(3.84),280(3.24)	104-0831-73
$C_{22}H_{23}NO_6$			
Alkaloid TN-4 from corydalis incisa Pers.	MeOH	240(4.07),289(3.96)	95-0087-73
Corydalic acid, methyl ester	MeOH	240(4.07),289(3.96)	94-1020-73
7H-1,3-Dioxolo[4,5-h][2]benzopyran-6-amine, 7-(6-ethenyl)-1,3-benzodioxol-5-yl)-6,9-dihydro-9-methoxy-N,N-di-methyl-	EtOH	270(3.91),294s(3.81)	73-2799-73
$C_{22}H_{23}NO_8$			
Spiro[6H-1,3-dioxolo[4,5-i][3,4]benzox-azocine-6,1'(3'H)-isobenzofuran]-3'-	EtOH	218(4.73),312(3.67)	33-2107-73

Compound	Solvent	$\lambda_{max}(\log \epsilon)$	Ref.
one, 5,8,9,10-tetrahydro-4,4',5'-trimethoxy-8-methyl- (cont.)			
$C_{22}H_{23}N_3O$			
Morpholine, 4-[4-[(4-methylphenyl)methyl]-6-phenyl-3-pyridazinyl]-	CH_2Cl_2	262(4.21)	39-2532-73C
	CH_2Cl_2-HCl	262(4.20)	39-2532-73C
Suaveoline, N_b-acetyl-	EtOH	224(4.26),274(3.6), 286(3.5)	102-1167-73
$C_{22}H_{23}N_3O_2$			
Apogardnerine, N_b-cyano-	EtOH	225(4.43),266s(3.54), 277(3.62),298(3.77)	95-1165-73
Morpholine, 4-[4-[(4-methoxyphenyl)methyl]-6-phenyl-3-pyridazinyl]-	CH_2Cl_2	263s(4.20),275(4.22)	39-2532-73C
	CH_2Cl_2-HCl	263s(4.25),275(4.27)	39-2532-73C
$C_{22}H_{23}N_3O_4$			
Euxylophorine C, dihydro-	MeCN	268(4.18)	102-2521-73
$C_{22}H_{23}N_5OS$			
1H-Thieno[2,3-c]pyrazol-4-ol, 5-[[4-(diethylamino)phenyl]azo]-3-methyl-1-phenyl-	EtOH	245(4.0),480(3.94)	104-2429-73
$C_{22}H_{23}N_7O_7$			
L-Tryptophan, N-[[(9-β-D-ribofuranosyl)-9H-purin-6-yl)amino]carbonyl]-	pH 1-2	270s(--),277(4.38)	87-0139-73
	pH 5-7	270(4.37),277s(--)	87-0139-73
	pH 12	270(4.34),300(3.53)	87-0139-73
$C_{22}H_{24}ClNO_8$			
Isoquinolinium, 4-[(3,4-dimethoxyphenyl)methylene]-3-(ethoxycarbonyl)-1,4-dihydro-2-methyl-, perchlorate	EtOH	237(4.62),344(3.86)	78-0213-73
$C_{22}H_{24}N_2O_3$			
Icajine	EtOH	253(4.23),291(3.52)	78-4137-73
Vinorine, 10-methoxy-	n.s.g.	223(4.07),280(3.66)	105-0657-73
$C_{22}H_{24}N_2O_4$			
2,4-Hexadienediamide, N,N'-bis(4-ethoxyphenyl)-, (E,E)-	EtOH	266(4.40),345(4.51)	104-2527-73
16,19-Secostrychnidine-10,16-dione, 14-hydroxy-19-methyl-	EtOH	254(4.25),279s(3.79), 291(3.61)	78-4137-73
$C_{22}H_{24}N_2O_5$			
Aspidophytine, 10-oxo-	EtOH	222(4.46),259(3.68), 306(3.19)	23-3102-73
Cimicine, 10-oxo-	EtOH	220(4.31),256(3.77), 294(3.26)	23-3102-73
	EtOH-NaOH	234(4.29),259s(3.71), 315(3.67)	23-3102-73
16,19-Secostrychnidine-10,16-dione, 21,22-epoxy-4-hydroxy-19-methyl-	EtOH	229(4.44),267(4.04), 300(3.75)	78-4137-73
16,19-Secostrychnidine-10,16-dione, 21,22-epoxy-14-hydroxy-19-methyl-, (21α,22α)-	EtOH	254(4.28),282s(3.81), 290(3.67)	78-4137-73
$C_{22}H_{24}N_2O_6$			
L-Phenylalanine, N-[N-[3-(4-hydroxy-3-methoxyphenyl)-1-oxo-2-propenyl]glycyl]-	MeOH-HCl	279s(3.79),295(4.10), 319(4.21)	20-0259-73
	MeOH-KOH	296s(3.62),308(3.74), 365(4.26)	20-0259-73

Compound	Solvent	λ_{max}(log ε)	Ref.
16,19-Secostrychnidine-10,16-dione, 21,22-epoxy-21,22-dihydro-4,14-dihydroxy-19-methyl-, (21α,22α)-	EtOH	228(4.28),266(3.90), 298(3.60)	78-4137-73
$C_{22}H_{24}N_2O_7S$			
L-Cysteine, N-[N-[(phenylmethoxy)carbonyl]-L-seryl-, methyl ester, benzoate	EtOH	264(3.89)	44-0270-73
$C_{22}H_{24}N_2O_9S_3$			
1,3,4-Thiadiazole-2(3H)-thione, 3-phenyl-5-[(2,3,4,6-tetra-O-acetyl-β-D-glycopyranosyl)thio]-	n.s.g.	331(4.07)	48-0915-73
$C_{22}H_{24}N_4O_2$			
[1,2,4,5]Tetrazino[6,1-a:3,4-a']diisoquinoline, 8,16-diacetyl-5,6,8,13-14,16-hexahydro-	EtOH	266(2.97),274(3.00)	95-0648-73
$C_{22}H_{24}N_5O_6$			
Pyridinium, 3-[[2-(1,2-dihydro-2-oxo-1-β-D-ribofuranosyl-4-pyrimidinyl)-hydrazino]carbonyl]-1-(phenylmethyl)-, bromide	pH 2.8	274(4.12),340(3.78)	35-1323-73
	pH 6.2	265(4.06),344(4.03)	35-1323-73
	pH 10.8	258(4.03),347(4.25)	35-1323-73
Pyridinium, 4-[[2-(1,2-dihydro-2-oxo-1-β-D-ribofuranosyl-4-pyrimidinyl)-hydrazino]carbonyl]-1-(phenylmethyl)-, bromide	pH 2.8	275(4.19),375(3.73)	35-1323-73
	pH 6.2	266(4.11),408(4.04)	35-1323-73
	pH 10.8	265(4.13),412(4.07)	35-1323-73
$C_{22}H_{24}N_8O_2$			
1H-1,2,3-Triazol-5-amine, N-[[5-amino-1-(phenylmethyl)-1H-1,2,3-triazol-4-yl]methylene]-4-(dimethoxymethyl)-1-(phenylmethyl)-	n.s.g.	337(4.30)	39-2037-73C
$C_{22}H_{24}O_3$			
3H-Cyclopenta[a]phenanthren-3-one 11-acetoxy-6,7,10,15,16,17-hexahydro-10,17,17-trimethyl-, (S)-	EtOH	207(4.54),231(4.36)	39-1967-73C
$C_{22}H_{24}O_4$			
13H-Cyclopenta[c]phenanthrene-13-acetic acid, 6,7,11,14,16,17-hexahydro-3-methoxy-17-oxo-, ethyl ester, (±)-	EtOH	313(4.43)	94-2427-73
Estra-1,3,5(10),7,9-pentaene-18-carboxaldehyde, 17,17-[1,2-ethanediylbis-(oxy)]-3-methoxy-, (±)-	EtOH	231(4.76),267(--), 277(3.73),288(--), 322(--),337(--)	94-2427-73
α-D-xylo-Hex-5-enofuranose, 5,6-dideoxy-1,2-O-(1-methylethylidene)-6-phenyl-3-(O-phenylmethyl)-, cis	EtOH	208(4.30),242(4.10), 289(2.20)	33-1310-73
19-Norpregna-1,3,5(10)-trien-20-yn-6-one, 17β-acetoxy-3-hydroxy-	MeOH	223(4.29),256(3.92), 327(3.46)	24-0723-73
1H-Phenalen-1-one, 2-(1,1-dimethyl-2-oxopropyl)-4-methoxy-9-(1-methylethoxy)-	EtOH	212(4.30),230(4.23), 265(4.27),389(4.27), 420(4.09),445(3.85)	39-2159-73C
$C_{22}H_{24}O_5$			
1,3-Propanedione, 1-[2-hydroxy-4,6-dimethoxy-3-(3-methyl-2-butenyl)phenyl]-3-phenyl-	MeOH	207(4.43),239(4.32), 291(4.22),368(4.05)	119-0064-73
Tephrostachin, dihydro-	MeOH	213(4.69),270(4.67), 332(4.11)	119-0071-73

Compound	Solvent	$\lambda_{max}(\log \epsilon)$	Ref.
$C_{22}H_{24}O_6$			
2H,5H-Benz[4,5]indeno[1,7a-c]furan-2,5-dione, 2a,3,6,7-tetrahydro-3α,9-dimethoxy-2aα-(3-oxopentyl)-	MeOH	244(3.94),336(4.46)	39-1780-73C
3β-	MeOH	244(3.94),332(4.44)	39-1780-73C
4H-1-Benzopyran-4-one, 8-(2,3-dihydroxy-3-methylbutyl)-5,7-dimethoxy-2-phenyl-	MeOH	212(4.58),269(4.58), 330(3.99)	119-0064-73
2(3H)-Furanone, 4-[(3,4-dimethoxyphenyl)methyl]-3-[(3,4-dimethoxyphenyl)-methylene]dihydro-	EtOH	233(4.21),287(3.94), 332(4.08)	95-0374-73
2(5H)-Furanone, 3,4-bis[(3,4-dimethoxyphenyl)methyl]-	EtOH	282(3.82)	95-0374-73
2,3-Naphthalenedimethanol, 1-(3,4-dimethoxyphenyl)-6,7-dimethoxy-	EtOH	243(4.42),285(4.06)	2-0203-73
7H-Phenaleno[1,2-b]furan-7-one, 8,9-dihydro-1-hydroxy-2,3,4-trimethoxy-6,8,9,9-tetramethyl-	$CHCl_3$	217(4.43),242s(4.25), 270(4.32),367(4.13), 384(4.09),410(4.05), 434s(3.86)	39-2388-73C
7H-Phenaleno[1,2-b]furan-7-one, 8,9-dihydro-6-hydroxy-3,4,5-trimethoxy-1,8,9,9-tetramethyl-	$CHCl_3$	217(4.60),270s(4.15), 377(4.29),403(4.30), 423s(4.22)	39-2388-73C
1H-Phenalen-1-one, 9-hydroxy-6,7,8-trimethoxy-4-methyl-3-[(2-methyl-2-butenyl)oxy]-	$CHCl_3$	214(4.62),240(4.30), 270s(4.04),376s(4.25), 395(4.28),411s(4.24)	39-2388-73C
$C_{22}H_{24}O_7$			
Epiaschantin	EtOH	229(4.13),285(3.66)	88-0335-73
$C_{22}H_{24}O_9$			
Chromomycinonic acid, 2-formyl-6,9-dimethyl-, methyl ester	EtOH	224(4.36),278(4.69), 327(3.83),340(3.79), 391(?)	105-0498-73
$C_{22}H_{25}ClO_5$			
Pentanoic acid, 5-chloro-2-[(2,7-dimethoxy-1-naphthalenyl)methyle e]-3,3-dimethyl-4-oxo-, ethyl ester	EtOH	239(4.70),328(3.80)	39-2159-73C
$C_{22}H_{25}ClO_{13}$			
α-D-Glucopyranose, 1,2-O-[1-(3-chlorobenzoyl)dioxyethylidene]-2-C-methoxy-, triacetate	EtOH	233(4.01)	23-0394-73
$C_{22}H_{25}FO_5$			
Estra-1,3,5(10)-trien-6-one, 3,17-diacetoxy-7-fluoro-, (7α,17β)-	EtOH	211(4.30),255(4.02), 305(3.34)	39-1462-73C
Estra-1,3,5(10)-trien-7-one, 3,17-diacetoxy-6-fluoro-, (6β,17β)-	EtOH	267(2.88),272(2.89)	39-1462-73C
$C_{22}H_{25}NO_4$			
7H-Furo[3,2-g][1]benzopyran-7-one, 4-[bis(3-methyl-2-butenyl)amino]-9-methoxy-	EtOH	226(4.39),273(4.18), 315(3.96)	4-0443-73
Spiro[2H-indene-2,1'(2'H)-isoquinolin]-5-ol, 1,3,3',4'-tetrahydro-6,6',7'-trimethoxy-2'-methyl-1-methylene-	EtOH	263s(4.04),272s(4.04), 292s(3.83),315(4.02), 328s(3.99)	78-1265-73
Spiro[2H-indene-2,1'(2'H)-isoquinolin]-5-ol, 1,3,3',4'-tetrahydro-6,6',7'-trimethoxy-2'-methyl-3-methylene-	EtOH	262(4.11),270(4.09), 287s(3.75),293(3.78), 316(4.00),327s(3.96)	78-1265-73

Compound	Solvent	λmax(log ε)	Ref.
$C_{22}H_{25}NO_6$			
1,3-Benzodioxole-5-ethanamine, 6-(6,7-dihydro-4-methoxy-4H-1,3-dioxolo[4,5-c][1]benzopyran-6-yl)-N,N-dimethyl-, (4S-trans)-	EtOH	238(3.98),291(3.93)	73-2799-73
Colchicine	benzene	344(4.22)	23-2821-73
	H_2O	199(--),234(4.43), 246(4.50),354(4.21)	23-2821-73
	MeOH	206(--),234(4.44), 243(4.46),352(4.22)	23-2821-73
	EtOH	202(4.40),234(4.43), 243(4.47),351(4.22)	23-2821-73
	EtOH	242(4.48),350(4.24)	63-0421-73
	PrOH	202(--),244(4.42), 351(4.19)	23-2821-73
	isoPrOH	234(4.44),243(4.60), 350(4.23)	23-2821-73
	BuOH	244(4.45),351(4.21)	23-2821-73
	tert-BuOH	204(--),242(4.40), 350(4.20)	23-2821-73
	dioxan	266(4.11),342(4.19)	23-2821-73
	CCl_4	260(4.21),347(4.20)	23-2821-73
	$CHCl_3$	242(4.42),350(4.21)	23-2821-73
	CH_2Cl_2	248(4.42),343(4.22)	23-2821-73
	$HCONH_2$	255(4.29),350(4.22)	23-2821-73
	DMF	262(4.09),344(4.14)	23-2821-73
	MeCN	230(4.45),343(4.19)	23-2821-73
7H-1,3-Dioxolo[4,5-h][2]benzopyran-6-amine, 7-(6-ethyl-1,3-benzodioxol-5-yl)-6,9-dihydro-9-methoxy-N,N-dimethyl-	EtOH	241(3.74),292(3.89)	73-2799-73
$C_{22}H_{25}N_3O_3S$			
1H-Indole-3-carboximidamide, N-cyclohexyl-3-hydroxy-N-[(4-methylphenyl)sulfonyl]-	EtOH	245(4.39),321(4.37)	95-0971-73
$C_{22}H_{25}N_3O_{11}$			
Acetamide, 2-diazo-N-[4-[(2,3,4,6-tetra-O-acetyl-α-D-mannopyranosyl)oxy]-phenyl]-	MeOH	275(4.37)	136-0101-73F
	MeOH-acid	248(4.19)	136-0101-73F
$C_{22}H_{25}N_5O_7$			
1H-Pyrrole, 4-ethyl-2-[(4-ethyl-3,5-dimethyl-2H-pyrrol-2-ylidene)methyl]-3-methyl-, picrate	$CHCl_3$	481(4.91)	65-0885-73
$C_{22}H_{26}$			
Cyclohepta[de]naphthalene, 2,5-bis(1,1-dimethylethyl)-	n.s.g.	232(4.39),246(4.35), 253(4.43),294(3.41), 308(3.46),332(3.59), 348(3.68),367(3.43), 420(2.43),444(2.51), 473(2.48),507(2.30)	35-1874-73
$C_{22}H_{26}BrNO_4$			
Dibenzo[a,g]quinolizinium, 5,6,7,8-tetrahydro-3-hydroxy-2,10,11-trimethoxy-7,13-dimethyl-, bromide	EtOH	233(4.39),329(4.39)	78-1265-73

Compound	Solvent	λ_{max}(log ϵ)	Ref.
Dibenzo[a,g]quinolizinium, 5,6,7,8-tetrahydro-10-hydroxy-2,3,11-trimethoxy-7,13-dimethyl-, bromide	EtOH	235(4.33),330(4.42)	78-1265-73
6H-Dibenzo[a,g]quinolizinium, 7,8-dihydro-11-hydroxy-2,3,10-trimethoxy-7,13-dimethyl-, bromide	EtOH	233(4.23),290(4.00), 327(4.24)	78-1265-73
$C_{22}H_{26}N_2$			
Azocyclopentane, 1,1'-diphenyl-	C_6H_{12}	370(1.28)	24-2890-73
$C_{22}H_{26}N_2O$			
2H-Benzo[b]pyrano[3',4':4,5]pyrrolo-[3,2,1-jk][1]benzazepine-1-methanamine, 1,4,4a,8,9,14a-hexahydro-N,N-dimethyl-	n.s.g.	213(4.40),295(4.16)	39-1041-73C
$C_{22}H_{26}N_2O_2$			
Icajidine	EtOH	214(4.31),258(4.00), 319(3.48)	78-4137-73
$C_{22}H_{26}N_2O_3$			
Hirsuteine	MeOH	225(4.57),284s(3.82), 291(3.78)	95-0448-73
Icajine, dihydro-	EtOH	253(4.36),291(3.76)	78-4137-73
$C_{22}H_{26}N_2O_4$			
Aspidophytine	EtOH	222(4.46),256(3.77), 304(3.38)	35-7842-73
Cimicine	EtOH	221(4.50),257(3.94), 295(3.66)	23-3102-73
	EtOH-NaOH	235(4.36),260s(3.76), 311(3.71)	23-3102-73
Gardnerine, 3-hydroxy-, acetate	EtOH	229(4.49),268(3.69), 297(3.77),305(3.68), 345(3.33)	95-1165-73
	EtOH-HCl	218(4.30),261(3.71), 295(3.50),346(4.16)	95-1165-73
1-Isoquinolinecarbonitrile, 3-[(3,4-dimethoxyphenyl)methyl]-1,2,3,4-tetrahydro-6,7-dimethoxy-2-methyl-	MeOH	249(4.28),312(3.99), 368(3.92)	83-0784-73
Δ^{14}-Vincamine, 12-methoxy-	EtOH	228(4.5),271(3.87), 286(3.77),293(3.68)	78-1131-73
$C_{22}H_{26}N_2O_4S$			
1,5-Benzothiazepin-4(5H)-one, 3-acetoxy-5-[2-(dimethylamino)ethyl]-2,3-dihydro-2-(4-methoxyphenyl)-, hydrochloride, cis	EtOH	238(4.38)	95-0729-73
Thiopyrano[4,3-b]indole-3,4-dicarboxylic acid, 4a,5-dihydro-4a,5-dimethyl-1-(1-piperidinyl)-, dimethyl ester	EtOH	225(4.27),252(4.24), 366(3.92)	94-2770-73
$C_{22}H_{26}N_2O_5S$			
Allosecurinine phenyldimethylhydrazinium mesitylenesulfonate	EtOH	224(3.69),256(3.76)	78-1063-73
Securinine phenyldimethylhydrazinium mesitylenesulfonate	EtOH	224(3.88),258(3.93)	78-1063-73
$C_{22}H_{26}N_4$			
Camphor osazone	EtOH	254(4.22),304(4.12), 375(4.23)	18-3319-73

Compound	Solvent	$\lambda_{max}(\log \epsilon)$	Ref.
$C_{22}H_{26}O_2$			
1,5-Heptanedione, 4,6,6-trimethyl-1,3-diphenyl-	EtOH	242(4.08)	22-0263-73
$C_{22}H_{26}O_3$			
2,5-Cyclohexadiene-1,4-dione, 2-[5-(4-methoxy-2,3,6-trimethylphenyl)-3-methyl-2-pentenyl]-, (E)-	MeOH	245(4.15),282(3.43), 315(2.34),440(1.18)	78-2565-73
3H-Cyclopenta[a]phenanthren-3-one, 11-acetoxy-1,2,6,7,10,15,16,17-octahydro-10,17,17-trimethyl-	EtOH	233(4.35),272(3.36), 281(3.26)	39-1967-73C
$C_{22}H_{26}O_4$			
[3,6'-Bi-2H-1-benzopyran]-7,7'-diol, 3,3',4,4'-tetrahydro-7,7'-dimethoxy-2',2'-dimethyl-	EtOH	284(3.89),290(3.89)	39-0907-73C
Estra-1,3,5(10),8-tetraene-18-carboxylic acid, 3-methoxy-17-oxo-, ethyl ester, (±)-	EtOH	280(4.20)	94-2427-73
Gona-1,3,5(10)-trien-17-one, 3-methoxy-13β-(2-oxoethyl)-, 17-ethylene ketal	EtOH	278(3.30),286(3.26)	94-2427-73
2-Naphthalenepropanoic acid, 6-(3-ethoxy-1-methyl-3-oxo-1-propenyl)-β-methyl-, ethyl ester	EtOH	220(4.62),250(4.41), 262(4.13),298(4.03)	132-0279-73
Spiro[1,3-dioxolane-2,17'(16'H)-[8,13]-ethano[7H]cyclopenta[a]phenanthren]-8'a-one, 6',9',11',12',14',15'-hexahydro-3'-methoxy-, (8'α,9'β,13'α,14'β)-(±)-	EtOH	276(3.26),281(3.22)	94-2427-73
$C_{22}H_{26}O_5$			
2H,6H,12H-Benzo[1,2-b:3,4-b':5,6-b"]tripyran-2,12-dione, 3,4,10,11-tetrahydro-6,6,10,11-tetramethyl-4-propyl-	EtOH	226(4.08),248(3.98), 274(4.16),303(3.98)	102-0185-73
Cyclopentaneacetic acid, 1-[2-(3,4-dihydro-6-methoxy-1(2H)-naphthalenylidene)ethyl]-2,5-dioxo-, ethyl ester	EtOH	267(4.20)	94-2427-73
Estra-1,3,5(10)-trien-6-one, 3,17-diacetoxy-, (17β)-	MeOH	209(4.40),247(4.01), 299(3.33)	24-0723-73
Estra-1,3,5(10)-trien-17-one, 1,3-diacetoxy-, Kober test	H_2SO_4	528(3.47)	94-1720-73
Pentanoic acid, 2-[(2,7-dimethoxy-1-naphthalenyl)methylene]-3,3-dimethyl-4-oxo-, ethyl ester	EtOH	238(4.77)	39-2159-73C
Pregna-4,17(20)-diene-3,11-dione, 20,21-[carbonylbis(oxy)]-, cis	MeOH	238(4.20)	44-2335-73
trans	MeOH	238(4.19)	44-2335-73
Pregna-4,20-diene-3,11-dione, 20,21-[carbonylbis(oxy)]-	MeOH	238(4.21)	44-2335-73
$C_{22}H_{26}O_6$			
2(3H)-Furanone, 3,4-bis[(3,4-dimethoxyphenyl)methyl]dihydro-, trans	EtOH	232(4.21),281(3.80)	95-0374-73
1H,3H-Furo[3,4-c]furan, 1,4-bis(3,4-dimethoxyphenyl)tetrahydro-, (1α,3aα-4α,6aα)-	MeOH	233(4.14),283(3.59)	95-0044-73
3H-Nidulinic acid, O-methyltridechloro-, methyl ester	n.s.g.	245s(4.22),280(3.62)	1-2710-73

Compound	Solvent	$\lambda_{max}(\log \epsilon)$	Ref.
$C_{22}H_{26}O_7$			
Chromomycinonic acid, 2-deoxy-6,8,9-tri-methyl-, methyl ester	EtOH	227(4.21),268(4.66), 329(3.94),360s(3.64)	105-0498-73
$C_{22}H_{26}O_8$			
Eupacunin, 1,10-epoxy-9-dehydro-	MeOH	210(4.16)	44-2189-73
Eupacunolin, dehydro- (9-acetoxy-10-formyl-2,3,3a,4,7,8,9,11a-octahydro-7-hydroxy-6-methyl-3-methylene-2-oxo-cyclodeca[b]furan-4-yl ester of 2-methyl-2-butenoic acid)	MeOH	212(4.34)	44-2189-73
2(3H)-Furanone, 3,4-bis[(3,4-dimethoxy-phenyl)methyl]dihydro-3,4-dihydroxy-, cis	EtOH	231(4.37),280(3.91)	95-0374-73
3S-trans	EtOH	231(4.37),280(3.90)	95-0374-73
$C_{22}H_{26}O_9$			
Oxiranecarboxylic acid, 2,3-dimethyl-, 3-acetoxy-1a,2,3,5a,7,8,8a,9,10,10a-decahydro-4,10a-dimethyl-8-methylene-7-oxooxireno[5,6]cyclodeca[1,2-b]-furan-9-yl ester	MeOH	210(4.19)	44-2189-73
$C_{22}H_{26}O_{11}$			
Heraclenol, tert-O-β-glucosyl-	EtOH	225(4.58),250(4.61), 300(4.33)	2-0410-73
$C_{22}H_{26}Si_2$			
Silane, 1,4-phenylenebis[ethylphenyl-	heptane	277(2.32)	70-1825-73
$C_{22}H_{27}ClO_5$			
Pregn-4-ene-3,11-dione, 20α-chloro-20,21-[carbonylbis(oxy)]-	MeOH	238(4.22)	44-2328-73
20β-	MeOH	237(4.21)	44-2328-73
$C_{22}H_{27}FO_3$			
Pregna-4,6-diene-3,20-dione, 16α,17β-epoxy-6-fluoro-16β-methyl-	n.s.g.	282(4.37)	39-0227-73C
$C_{22}H_{27}FO_4$			
Estra-1,3,5(10)-triene-3,17-diol, 7-fluoro-, diacetate, (7α,17β)-	EtOH	267(2.98),274(2.95)	39-1462-73C
Pregna-14,17(20)-trien-21-al, 9-fluoro-11β,20-dihydroxy-16α-methyl-3-oxo-	MeOH	240(4.19),281(4.14)	24-2263-73
$C_{22}H_{27}FO_5$			
Estra-1,3,5(10)-triene-3,6,17-triol, 7-fluoro-, 3,17-diacetate, (6α,7α,17β)-	EtOH	267(2.73),274(2.71)	39-1462-73C
Estra-1,3,5(10)-triene-3,7,17-triol, 6-fluoro-, 3,17-diacetate, (6β,7α,17β)-	EtOH	270(2.87),277(2.85)	39-1462-73C
$C_{22}H_{27}F_3O_3$			
Androsta-3,5-dien-7-one, 17-methyl-17-[(trifluoroacetyl)oxy]-, (17β)-	EtOH	279(4.38)	87-0065-73
$C_{22}H_{27}NO$			
2,5-Cyclohexadien-1-one, 4-[(4-cyclohex-yl-2,6-dimethylphenyl)imino]-2,6-di-methyl-	EtOH	275(4.51),490(3.08)	78-0085-73

Compound	Solvent	λ max (log ε)	Ref.
$C_{22}H_{27}NO_3$			
Estra-1(10),2,4-trieno[2,3-d]isoxazole, 17β-hydroxy-3'-methyl-, acetate	EtOH	243(4.00),249(4.04), 255(3.96),296(3.64)	12-1763-73
Estra-1(10),2,4-trieno[2,3-d]oxazole, 17β-hydroxy-2'-methyl-, acetate	EtOH	240(4.05),274(3.70), 279(3.83),284(3.81), 289(3.82)	12-1763-73
$C_{22}H_{27}NO_4$			
Benz[d]indeno[1,2-b]azepin-3-ol, 5,6,7-7a,12,12a-hexahydro-2,9,10-trimethoxy-7,7a-dimethyl-, isomer A	EtOH	232(4.12),285(3.88)	78-1265-73
isomer B	EtOH	230s(4.20),286(3.99)	78-1265-73
Homoargemonine, (±)-	MeOH	277(3.53)	44-2099-73
Spiro[2H-indene-2,1'(2'H)-isoquinolin]-5-ol, 1,3,3',4'-tetrahydro-6,6',7'-trimethoxy-1,2'-dimethyl-	EtOH	231s(4.07),291(3.89)	78-1265-73
Spiro[2H-indene-2,1'(2'H)-isoquinolin]-5-ol, 1,3,3',4'-tetrahydro-6,6',7'-trimethoxy-2',3-dimethyl-	EtOH	230s(4.06),290(3.82)	78-1265-73
$C_{22}H_{27}N_5O_{10}$			
β-D-Glucopyranoside, 2-(dimethylamino)-7-pteridinyl-, tetraacetate	MeOH	244(4.36),283(3.97), 384(4.00)	24-0317-73
2(1H)-Pteridinone, 4-amino-6,7-dimethyl-1-(2,3,4,6-tetra-O-acetyl-β-D-glucopyranosyl)-	MeOH	246(4.12),287(3.63), 338(3.97)	24-2982-73
7(8H)-Pteridinone, 2-(dimethylamino)-8-(2,3,4,6-tetra-O-acetyl-β-D-glucopyranosyl)-	MeOH	219(4.15),244(4.11), 310s(3.71),365(4.20)	24-0317-73
$C_{22}H_{28}ClF_3O_2$			
Androsta-4,6-dien-17β-ol, 7-chloro-17α-methyl-, trifluoroacetate	EtOH	239(4.31),246(4.38), 255(4.26)	87-0065-73
$C_{22}H_{28}N_2O$			
Methanone, phenyl(6,7,8,9-tetrahydro-5H-benzocyclohepten-2-yl)-, O-[2-(dimethylamino)ethyl]oxime, hydrochloride	MeOH	238(4.10),260(4.09)	73-2768-73
$C_{22}H_{28}N_2O_2$			
Apogardnerine, N_a,N_b-dimethyl-	EtOH	228(4.52),283s(3.80), 299(3.92)	95-1165-73
$C_{22}H_{28}N_2O_2S_2$			
1-Piperazinepropanol, 4-(10,11-dihydro-8-methoxydibenzo[b,f]thiepin-10-yl)-, dihydrochloride	MeOH	277(4.04)	73-0599-73
$C_{22}H_{28}N_2O_3$			
Haplocine	EtOH	220(4.53),260(3.92), 292(3.60)	23-3102-73
	EtOH-NaOH	235(4.46),262s(3.78), 311(3.77)	23-3102-73
Hirsutine	MeOH	226(4.57),284s(3.84), 291(3.78)	95-0448-73
2(1H)-Pyridinone, 3,3'-(1-methyl-3-oxo-1-propene-1,3-diyl)bis[1-butyl-	EtOH	278(3.76),334(3.96)	103-0615-73
3,4-Secogardnerine, N_a,N_b-dimethyl-3-oxo-	EtOH	219(4.35),243s(4.02), 263(3.86),342(4.36)	95-1165-73

Compound	Solvent	λ_{max}(log ε)	Ref.
$C_{22}H_{28}N_2O_6S$			
Carbamic acid, [1-[4-acetoxy-4,5-dihydro-4-(1-methylethyl)-5-oxo-2-oxazolyl]-2-[(1,1-dimethylethyl)-thio]ethenyl]-, phenylmethyl ester	ether	301(3.92)	88-2163-73
$C_{22}H_{28}N_4$			
Bicyclo[2.2.1]heptan-2-one, 1,7,7-trimethyl-3-(2-phenylhydrazino)-, phenylhydrazone	EtOH	242(4.38),280(4.51), 346(3.39)	18-3319-73
$C_{22}H_{28}N_4O_3$			
Benzoic acid, 4-[[[1,2,3,4-tetrahydro-1-[[(2-methoxyethyl)imino]methyl]-2-quinoxalinyl]methyl]amino]-, ethyl ester	EtOH	275(4.26),308(4.48)	35-8414-73
$C_{22}H_{28}N_4O_6$			
Benzo[g]pteridine-4a,5-diacetic acid, 2,3,4,10-tetrahydro-3,7,8,10-tetramethyl-2,4-dioxo-, diethyl ester	6M HCl	271(3.78),302(3.79), 373(3.42)	5-1388-73
	pH 7	277(3.92),304(3.80), 355(3.74)	5-1388-73
	MeOH	276(3.98),350(3.77)	5-1388-73
$C_{22}H_{28}O_2$			
18,19-Dinorpregn-4-en-21-yn-3-one, 17-hydroxy-13-(2-propenyl)-, (17α)-(±)-	EtOH	240(4.20)	94-2195-73
$C_{22}H_{28}O_2S_2$			
Bicyclo[2.2.1]heptan-2-one, 3,3'-(1,3-dithietane-2,4-diylidene)bis[1,7,7-trimethyl-	n.s.g.	343(4.54),364(4.22)	28-1115-73A
$C_{22}H_{28}O_2S_3$			
Bicyclo[2.2.1]heptan-2-one, 3,3'-(1,2,4-trithiolane-3,5-diylidene)-bis[1,7,7-trimethyl-	n.s.g.	329(4.38)	28-1115-73A
$C_{22}H_{28}O_2S_4$			
Bicyclo[2.2.1]heptan-2-one, 3,3'-(1,2,4,5-tetrathiane-3,6-diylidene)bis[1,7,7-trimethyl-	n.s.g.	300(4.15),350(3.90)	28-1115-73A
$C_{22}H_{28}O_4$			
Androsta-1,4-diene-3,11,17-trione, 9α-methyl-, 17-(1,2-ethanediyl acetal)	n.s.g.	240(4.18)	39-2095-73C
Gona-1,3,5(10),8-tetraen-17-one, 13β-(2-hydroxyethyl)-, cyclic 1,2-ethanediyl acetal	EtOH	272(4.18)	94-2427-73
Pregna-4,17(20)-dien-3-one, 20,21-[carbonylbis(oxy)]-, cis	MeOH	240(4.24)	44-2335-73
trans	MeOH	241(4.23)	44-2335-73
Pregna-4,20-dien-3-one, 20,21-[carbonylbis(oxy)]-	MeOH	240(4.24)	44-2335-73
$C_{22}H_{28}O_5$			
2H,8H,10H-Benzo[1,2-b:3,4-b']5,6-b"]tripyran-2,8-dione, 3,4,6,7,11,12-hexahydro-6,7,10,10-tetramethyl-4-propyl-	EtOH	282(4.18),336(3.65)	102-0185-73
7-Oxapregna-1,4-diene-3,20-dione, 17-acetoxy-	EtOH	240(4.20)	87-0647-73

Compound	Solvent	$\lambda_{max}(\log \epsilon)$	Ref.
Recedensolide	EtOH	216(4.43),285(4.17), 350(3.48)	102-0185-73
$C_{22}H_{28}O_6$			
Isocalolongic acid	EtOH	275(4.55),301(3.96), 314(3.96),362(2.76)	102-0185-73
Marrubialactone, 20-O-acetyl-	MeCN	208(4.44)	24-2929-73
Pentacyclo[6.2.2.0^{2,7}.0^{3,10}.0^{4,9}]dodecane-5,11-dione, 6,12-diacetoxy-1,2,4,6,9,12-hexamethyl-	EtOH	310(1.95)	5-1675-73
$C_{22}H_{28}O_7$			
Eupacunin	MeOH	211(4.38)	44-2189-73
Eupaserrin	EtOH	210(4.44)(end abs.)	44-1260-73
Eupatocunin	MeOH	212(4.45)(end abs.)	44-2189-73
Isoeupacunin	MeOH	213(4.20)(end abs.)	44-2189-73
Podocarp-7-en-16,17-olactone, 3β-acetoxy-13-(methoxycarbonyl)-13-methyl-6-oxo-	MeOH	240(4.01)	39-2551-73C
$C_{22}H_{28}O_8$			
Coleon D, 3α-acetoxy-	MeOH	270(3.83),333(3.79), 395(3.66)	33-2534-73
Coleon H	MeOH	268(4.14),280s(4.05), 333(3.65),398(3.77)	33-2534-73
3,8-Cyclodecadiyne-1,1,6,6-tetracarboxylic acid, tetraethyl ester	isooctane	203(3.38),273(2.40)	33-0625-73
Eupacunin, 1,10-epoxy-	MeOH	210(4.19)	44-2189-73
Eupacunolin	MeOH	211(4.38)	44-2189-73
Eupacunoxin	MeOH	209(4.23)(end abs.)	44-2189-73
Eupatocunoxin	MeOH	210(4.19)(end abs.)	44-2189-73
Nortrachelogenin, 4-O-ethyl-	EtOH	231(4.20),282(3.84)	94-1108-73
	EtOH-NaOH	248s(4.11),283(3.87), 297s(3.77)	94-1108-73
$C_{22}H_{28}O_{12}$			
2,5-Cyclohexadien-1-one, 4-hydroxy-4-[2-[(2,3,4,6-tetra-O-acetyl-β-D-glucopyranosyl)oxy]ethyl]-	EtOH	227(4.03)	1-0367-73
$C_{22}H_{28}S_4Si_3$			
Silane, bis[5-(dimethyl-2-thienylsilyl)-2-thienyl]dimethyl-	$CHCl_3$	248(4.31)	88-4043-73
$C_{22}H_{29}ClN_2O$			
Cyclohexanamine, N-[4-[(4-chlorophenyl)-methylene]-3-cyclohexyl-2-oxazolidinylidene]-	EtOH	225(4.01),297(4.53)	44-1051-73
$C_{22}H_{29}ClO_4$			
Pregn-4-en-3-one, 20,21-[carbonylbis-(oxy)]-20-chloro-	MeOH	241(4.23)	44-2328-73
$C_{22}H_{29}ClO_8$			
3,8-Decadiyne-1,1,6,6-tetracarboxylic acid, 10-chloro-, tetraethyl ester	isooctane	203(3.40),230s(2.89), 272(2.25)	33-0625-73
$C_{22}H_{29}FO_2$			
Pregna-4,16-diene-3,20-dione, 6α-fluoro-16-methyl-	n.s.g.	240(4.37)	39-0227-73C

Compound	Solvent	λ_{max}(log ε)	Ref.
$C_{22}H_{29}F_3O_3$			
Androst-4-en-3-one, 17-acetoxy-7-(trifluoromethyl)-, (7α,17β)-	MeOH	238(4.20)	44-3670-73
Androst-5-en-7-one, 17-methyl-17-[(trifluoroacetyl)oxy]-, (17β)-	EtOH	237(4.12)	87-0065-73
$C_{22}H_{29}NO_3$			
Androst-4-ene-7-carbonitrile, 17-acetoxy-3-oxo-, (7α,17β)-	MeOH	237(4.20)	44-3670-73
$C_{22}H_{29}NO_3S$			
3,5-Hexadien-1-aminium, N,N,N-trimethyl-6-phenyl-, p-toluenesulfonate	90% EtOH	280(4.20)	78-3797-73
$C_{22}H_{29}NO_6$			
Heteratisine, 19-oxodehydro-	EtOH	310(1.48)	78-3297-73
$C_{22}H_{29}N_3$			
1H-Indole, 3-[3,7-bis(1,1-dimethylethyl)-1H-1,2-diazepin-5-yl]-1-methyl-	EtOH	205(4.64),229(4.39), 333(4.26)	103-0038-73
$C_{22}H_{30}$			
Bi-2,4,6-cycloheptatrien-1-yl, x,x'-bis-(1,1-dimethylethyl)-	EtOH	251(3.89)	18-1785-73
Cyclohepta[de]naphthalene, 2,5-bis(1,1-dimethylethyl)-7,8,9,10-tetrahydro-	n.s.g.	230(4.82),235(4.95), 284(3.74),323(2.79)	35-2940-73
$C_{22}H_{30}ClN_5O_6$			
Propanamide, N-[9-[2-O-acetyl-3-chloro-3-deoxy-5-O-(2,2-dimethyl-1-oxopropyl)-β-D-xylofuranosyl]-9H-purin-6-yl]-2,2-dimethyl-	MeOH	272(3.23)	35-4074-73
$C_{22}H_{30}CuO_4$			
Copper, bis(4,7,7-trimethyl-3-oxobicyclo[2.2.1]heptane-2-carboaldehydato-O,O')-	benzene	320(4.35),650(1.78)	65-0927-73
	MeOH	261(4.08),319(4.21), 660(1.86)	65-0927-73
	$CHCl_3$	262(4.24),318(4.40), 650(1.71)	65-0927-73
	DMF	263(4.11),318(4.29), 680(1.96)	65-0927-73
$C_{22}H_{30}N_2O$			
Cyclohexanamine, N-[3-cyclohexyl-4-(phenylmethylene)-2-oxazolidinylidene]-, (E)-	EtOH	224(4.03),291(4.51)	44-1051-73
$C_{22}H_{30}N_2O_2$			
3,4-Secogardnerine, N_a,N_b-dimethyl-3-hydroxy-	EtOH	221(4.51),284(3.82), 301(3.92)	95-1165-73
Vincadine, N-methyl-, (-)-	MeOH	230(4.60),288(3.93), 296(3.92)	114-0207-73C
$C_{22}H_{30}N_2O_7$			
Azonino[5,4-b]indole-6,12b(1H)-dicarboxylic acid, 8-acetyl-2,3,4,5,6,7,7a,8-octahydro-10,11-dimethoxy-3-methyl-, 6-methyl ester, [6S-(6R*,7aR*,12bR*)]-	EtOH	269(4.05),303(3.88)	44-0215-73

Compound	Solvent	$\lambda_{max}(\log \epsilon)$	Ref.
$C_{22}H_{30}N_4O_2$			
[1,1'-Biphenyl]-2,2'-dicarboxamide, 6,6'-diamino-N,N,N',N'-tetraethyl-	EtOH	212(4.64),303(3.73)	39-2818-73C
$C_{22}H_{30}N_4O_4$			
Benzo[1,2-c:4,5-c']dipyrrole-1,3,5,7-(2H,6H)-tetrone, 4,8-bis(methylamino)-2,6-diphenyl-	80% DMF	606(3.90)	25-1108-73
$C_{22}H_{30}O_2$			
Acetyl dehydroabietate	heptane	267(2.76),276(2.78)	23-3236-73
18-Norpregna-3,5,13-trien-20-one, 3-methoxy-17-methyl-, (17α)-	EtOH	250(4.29)	22-2032-73
19-Norpregna-1,3,5(10)-trien-20-one, 3-methoxy-17α-methyl-	EtOH	219(3.93),279(3.31), 287(3.29)	22-2694-73
9β,10α-Pregn-4-ene-3,20-dione, 6-methylene-	EtOH	258(3.99)	33-2396-73
$C_{22}H_{30}O_3$			
Androsta-9(11),16-dien-12-one, 3-acetoxy-17-methyl-, (3β,5α)-	EtOH	238(4.08)	39-1967-73C
4'H-Androsta-4,16-dieno[16,17-b]pyran-3,4'-dione, 5',6',16,17-tetrahydro-	EtOH	243(4.18),287(2.74)	70-1578-73
2,5-Cyclohexadiene-1,4-dione, 3-hydroxy-5-methyl-2-[(1,4,4a,5,6,7,8,8a-octahydro-2,5,5,8a-tetramethyl-1-naphthalenyl)methyl]-	EtOH	266(4.14),416(3.13)	39-2591-73C
3'H-Cycloprop[15,16]androsta-4,15-dien-3-one, 17-acetoxy-15,16-dihydro-, (15β,16β,17β)-	MeOH	241(4.23)	24-0888-73
18-Norandrosta-8,11,13-trien-11-ol, 3-acetoxy-17,17-dimethyl-, (3β,5α)-	EtOH	286(3.53)	39-1967-73C
Pregn-4-ene-21-carboxylic acid, 17-hydroxy-3-oxo-, γ-lactone, (17α)-	EtOH	239(4.21)	95-0246-73
$C_{22}H_{30}O_4$			
Bertyadionol, dihydrodioxo-, acetate	EtOH	275(4.20)	78-0403-73
Cannabidiolic acid	hexane	225(4.35),270(3.96), 311(3.57)	106-0129-73
	MeOH	224(4.39),266(3.86), 304(3.53)	106-0129-73
Estra-1,3,5(10)-trien-17β-ol, 2,3-dimethoxy-, acetate, Kober test	H_2SO_4	410(3.89),490s(4.15), 508s(4.20),540(4.21)	94-1720-73
Feringin	n.s.g.	263(4.20)	105-0628-73
Gona-1,3,5(10)-trien-17-one, 13β-(2-hydroxyethyl)-3-methoxy-, cyclic 1,2-ethanediyl acetal	EtOH	278(3.30),286(3.26)	94-2427-73
Naphtho[1,8-bc]pyran-3a,6(4H)-diol, 5,6,6a,7,8,9,9a,9b-octahydro-2-(2-methoxyphenyl)-4,7,9b-trimethyl-, (3aα,4β,6α,6aβ,7β,9aα,9bα)-	EtOH	213(4.17),230(4.05), 265(4.27),275(4.27), 300(4.05),311(4.00)	23-3989-73
Pregn-4-en-3-one, 20α,21-[carbonylbis-(oxy)]-	MeOH	240(4.25)	44-2335-73
20β-	MeOH	239(4.24)	44-2335-73
Propanoic acid, 3-(16β,17β-dihydroxy-3-oxoandrost-4-en-17α-yl)-, γ-lactone	MeOH	241(4.16)	87-0839-73
$C_{22}H_{30}O_4S$			
1,3-Dioxa-2-silacyclohexane, 5-ethyl-2-methyl-2-[3-(phenylmethoxy)phenoxy]-4-propyl-	EtOH	209(4.27),275(3.33), 281(3.27)	87-0729-73

Compound	Solvent	λ_{max}(log ϵ)	Ref.
$C_{22}H_{30}O_5$			
Androst-4-ene-7-carboxylic acid, 17-acetoxy-3-oxo-, (7α,17β)-	MeOH	243(4.19)	44-3670-73
7-Oxapregn-4-ene-3,20-dione, 17α-acetoxy-	EtOH	232(4.20)	87-0647-73
1-Phenanthrenecarboxylic acid, 1,2,3,4-4a,9,10,10a-octahydro-5-hydroxy-6-methoxy-1,4a-dimethyl-7-(1-methylethyl)-9-oxo-, methyl ester, [1R-(1α,4aβ,10aα)]-	EtOH	229(4.27),272(4.01), 326(3.52)	78-1237-73
Pregn-4-en-3-one, 17,20β-[carbonylbis-(oxy)]-21-hydroxy-	MeOH	240(4.24)	44-2335-73
Pregn-4-en-3-one, 20α,21-[carbonylbis-(oxy)]-17-hydroxy-	MeOH	240(4.24)	44-2335-73
20β-	MeOH	240(4.22)	44-2335-73
Spiro[7H-furo[3',2':2,3]cyclopenta[1,2-b]pyran-7,1'(2'H)-naphthalene]-2-methanol, 1,2,3',3a,4,4',5,5a,8,9-decahydro-3a,6'-dimethoxy-	EtOH	277(4.19),284(3.03)	94-2202-73
$C_{22}H_{30}O_6$			
Dubiin	n.s.g.	213(3.70)	39-1701-73C
1-Naphthalenecarboxylic acid, 6-(acetoxymethyl)-5-[2-(3-furanyl)ethyl]-3,4,4a,5,6,7,8,8a-octahydro-8a-(hydroxymethyl)-5-methyl-, [4aR-(4aα,5α,6β,8aβ)]-	n.s.g.	210(4.01)	78-2575-73
$C_{22}H_{30}O_7$			
Eupatocunin, 11,13-dihydro-	MeOH	210(4.02)	44-2189-73
Nigakilactone K	MeOH	238s(3.83),270(3.77)	78-1515-73
Nigakilactone L	MeOH	263.5(3.65)	78-1515-73
$C_{22}H_{31}BrO_3$			
Androst-1-en-3-one, 17-acetoxy-4-bromo-1-methyl-, (4α,17β)-	dioxan	247(4.08)	78-1625-73
$C_{22}H_{31}FO_3$			
D-Homoandrost-16-en-17a-one, 3-acetoxy-17-fluoro-, (3β,5α)-	n.s.g.	235(3.88)	35-6655-73
$C_{22}H_{31}NO_2$			
Malouetamide	n.s.g.	244(3.98)	102-1813-73
$C_{22}H_{31}NO_3$			
11-Azapregn-16-ene-3,20-dione, 11-acetyl-, (5α,9β)-	EtOH	235(3.9)	13-0147-73A
$C_{22}H_{31}NO_5$			
Heteratisine, dehydro-	EtOH	270(1.84)	78-3297-73
Isoxazole, 4,5-dihydro-5-(2,2,2',2'-tetramethyl-4,4'-bi-1,3-dioxolan-5-yl)-3-(2,4,6-trimethylphenyl)-	EtOH	214(4.31)	33-1303-73
isomer	EtOH	217(4.38)	33-1303-73
$C_{22}H_{31}NO_6$			
Isoquinoline, 1-[2-(3,4-dimethoxyphenyl)ethyl]-1,2,3,4,5,6,7,8-octahydro-2-methyl-, oxalate	EtOH	229(3.96),280(3.51), 283s(3.47)	4-0217-73

Compound	Solvent	$\lambda_{max}(\log \epsilon)$	Ref.
$C_{22}H_{31}N_3O_4$			
2H-Pyrrole-4-propanoic acid, 2-[[5-carboxy-3-[2-(diethylamino)ethyl]-4-methyl-1H-pyrrol-2-yl)methylene]-3,5-dimethyl-, dihydrobromide	EtOH-HBr	470(4.58)	103-0186-73
$C_{22}H_{32}INO_3$			
Crepidine methiodide	EtOH	211(4.28),215(4.30), 219(4.28),252s(2.42), 258(2.38),265(2.26), 268s(2.04),288(1.48)	1-1907-73
$C_{22}H_{32}N_2O_2$			
2,2'-Bipyridine, 1,1'-diacetyl-4,4'-bis-(1,1-dimethylethyl)-1,1',2,2'-tetrahydro-	MeOH	306(3.54)	78-0391-73
$C_{22}H_{32}N_2O_4$			
2-Propenoic acid, 3,3'-[azinobis(1,2,2-trimethyl-1-cyclopentyl-3-ylidene)]-bis-, cis	EtOH	213(4.58)	39-1658-73C
$C_{22}H_{32}N_2O_5$			
Androst-5-en-3-ol, 16-methoxy-20-(nitroimino)-, acetate	EtOH	276(2.82)	94-1069-73
$C_{22}H_{32}N_2O_{16}S$			
D-glycero-D-galacto-Non-2-enonic acid, 5,5'-[thiobis[(1-oxo-2,1-ethanediyl)-imino]]bis[2,6-anhydro-3,5-dideoxy-	n.s.g.	240(4.07)	49-0402-73
$C_{22}H_{32}N_4$			
2-Tetrazene, 1,4-diethyl-1,4-bis(2,4,6-trimethylphenyl)-	C_6H_{12}	305(4.25)	73-0046-73
	THF	305(4.25)	73-0046-73
$C_{22}H_{32}N_4O_2$			
2-Tetrazene, 1,4-bis(1,1-dimethylethyl)-1,4-bis(3-methoxyphenyl)-	EtOH	237(3.94),277(3.78), 303(3.70)	35-8707-73
$C_{22}H_{32}O_2$			
Androsta-1,3-dien-17-ol, 5-methyl-, acetate, (5α,17β)-	EtOH	266(3.51)	35-3932-73
(5β,17β)-	EtOH	265(3.50)	35-3932-73
3H-Cycloprop[cd]indeno[5,4-f]azulen-7-ol, 2a,4,4a,4b,5,6,7,7a,8,9,9a,9b,9c-9d-tetradecahydro-2a,7a,9b-trimethyl-, acetate	heptane	221(3.59)	35-3932-73
$C_{22}H_{32}O_3$			
Androst-1-en-3-one, 17β-acetoxy-5α-methyl-	EtOH	235(3.95)	35-3932-73
5β-	EtOH	236(3.92)	35-3932-73
2-Cyclopropen-1-one, 2-[(3β,5α,17β)-3,17-dihydroxyandrostan-3-yl]-	n.s.g.	263(1.64)	44-1478-73
2,7-Nonadien-4-yne-1,6-diol, 3,7-dimethyl-9-(2,6,6-trimethyl-1-cyclohexen-1-yl)-, 1-acetate, (E,Z)-	EtOH	205(4.27),229(4.21)	104-1868-73
19-Norpregn-4-ene-3,20-dione, 10β-hydroxy-16α,17α-dimethyl-	n.s.g.	237(4.16)	105-0174-73

Compound	Solvent	λ_{max}(log ϵ)	Ref.
Phenanthro[3,2-b]furan-6-ol, 1,2,3,4,4a-5,6,6a,7,11,11a,11b-dodecahydro-4,4,7,11b-tetramethyl-, acetate, (4aα,6β,6aβ,7α,11aα,11bβ)-	EtOH	218(4.04)	39-0520-73C
Pregna-17(20),20-diene-21-carboxylic acid, 3-hydroxy-, [3β,5α,17(21S)]-	n.s.g.	226(3.98)	44-1478-73
Pregn-4-ene-3,20-dione, 6β-(hydroxy-methyl)-	EtOH	242(4.20)	33-2396-73
(9β,10α)-	EtOH	241(4.20)	33-2396-73
2-Propenoic acid, 3-[[3(S),5α,17β]-17-hydroxyandrostan-3-ylidene]-	n.s.g.	219(3.96)	44-1478-73
$C_{22}H_{32}O_4$			
5α-Androst-8-en-11-one, 3β-acetoxy-17β-hydroxy-17-methyl-	EtOH	255(3.70)	39-1967-73C
5α-Androst-9(11)-en-12-one, 3β-acetoxy-17β-hydroxy-17α-methyl-	EtOH	239(4.14)	39-1967-73C
19-Norpregn-4-ene-3,20-dione, 10β-hy-droperoxy-16α,17α-dimethyl-	n.s.g.	238(4.19)	105-0174-73
$C_{22}H_{32}O_5$			
8-Oxatricyclo[4.3.0.0^{2,5}]non-3-ene-2-carboxylic acid, 3,4,5-tris(1,1-di-methylethyl)-7,9-dioxo-	ether	215(3.51),225(3.22), 235(2.83)	35-8481-73
Pregn-4-ene-3,20-dione, 17,21-dihydroxy-21-methoxy-	MeOH	240(4.23)	44-2335-73
$C_{22}H_{32}O_6$			
2-Phenanthreneacetic acid, tetradeca-hydro-8-(methoxycarbonyl)-2,4b,8-trimethyl-1,10-dioxo-, methyl ester, [2R-(2α,4aα,4bβ,8α,8aα)]-	EtOH EtOH-base	297(3.95) 316(4.25)	39-0853-73C 39-0853-73C
$C_{22}H_{32}O_7$			
Eupacunin, tetrahydro-	MeOH	209(3.56)	44-2189-73
$C_{22}H_{33}FO_2$			
5β-Pregn-17(20)-en-21-one, 3α-hydroxy-20-fluoro-21-methyl-, cis	n.s.g.	252(3.99)	35-6655-73
trans	n.s.g.	250(4.11)	35-6655-73
$C_{22}H_{33}NO_5$			
L-Valine, N-acetyl-, 1,3,4,5,5a,6,7,8-9,9a-decahydro-6,6,9a-trimethyl-3-oxonaphtho[1,2-c]furan-9-yl ester, [5aS-(5aα,9α,9aβ)]- (purpuride)	EtOH	216.5(4.08)	39-0078-73C
$C_{22}H_{33}N_3O_3$			
Bicyclo[3.2.1]octane-2,3-dione, 5,8,8-trimethyl-, 3-[O-[[[3-(cyanomethyl)-2,2,3-trimethylcyclopentyl]amino]-carbonyl]oxime	MeOH	229(3.97)	39-1661-73C
$C_{22}H_{34}N_2O_2$			
6H-Dibenzo[b,d]pyran-1-ol, 3-[[3-(di-methylamino)propyl]methylamino]-6a,7,10,10a-tetrahydro-6,6,9-trimethyl-, (6aR-trans)-	EtOH	224(4.53),257(4.10), 290(3.64)	33-0510-73
Tryptophan, 2-(1,1-dimethylpropyl)-6-(3-methylbutyl)-, methyl ester	EtOH	228(4.54),286(3.83)	32-0141-73

Compound	Solvent	λ_{max}(log ϵ)	Ref.
$C_{22}H_{34}N_4O_4$			
3,5-Hexadien-2-one, 6-(2-isopropyl-5-methylcyclohexyl)-, 2,4-dinitrophenylhydrazone	$CHCl_3$	399(4.69)	22-3071-73
$C_{22}H_{34}O_2$			
Retinoic acid, 7,8-dihydro-, ethyl ester	EtOH	320(4.52)	65-2047-73
$C_{22}H_{34}O_4$			
9β,10α-Androst-4-en-3-one, 17β-hydroxy-17α-methyl-2β,6β-bis(hydroxymethyl)-	EtOH	240.5(4.15)	33-2396-73
9β,10α-Androst-4-en-3-one, 17β-hydroxy-17α-methyl-6,6-bis(hydroxymethyl)-	EtOH	248(4.08)	33-2396-73
Haplopappic acid, dimethyl ester	EtOH	220(4.29)	102-1755-73
Prosta-5,11,13-trien-1-oic acid, 15-hydroxy-8-methyl-9-oxo-, methyl ester	MeOH	235(4.28)	35-8483-73
Rotundifuran	n.s.g.	204.3(3.72)	138-0937-73
$C_{22}H_{35}NO$			
23-Norcon-18(22)-enine, 18-methyl-, 22-oxide, (5α)-	EtOH	237.7(4.03)	22-1814-73
23-Norcon-18(22)-enine, 20-methyl-, 22-oxide, (5α)-	EtOH	243(4.11)	22-1814-73
23-Norcon-20(22)-enine, 18-methyl-, 22-oxide, (18α)-	EtOH	233.7(3.97)	22-1814-73
(18β)-	EtOH	231.7(4.07)	22-1814-73
$C_{22}H_{35}NO_4$			
Acetamide, N-[2,5-dihydro-2-oxo-5-(10-oxo-2-hexadecenyl)-3-furanyl]-, (E)-	EtOH	246(3.73)	44-1253-73
$C_{22}H_{36}N_2O_2$			
5-Benzoxazolol, 6-(butylamino)-4,7-bis-(1,1-dimethylethyl)-2-propyl-	$CHCl_3$	250(3.95),300(3.73)	39-0268-73C
$C_{22}H_{38}O_3$			
Prost-8(12)-en-1-oic acid, 9-oxo-, ethyl ester	EtOH	238(4.16)	32-0031-73

Compound	Solvent	$\lambda_{max}(\log \epsilon)$	Ref.
$C_{23}F_{35}N$			
Pyridine, 3,5-difluoro-2,4,6-tris(undecafluorocyclohexyl)-	C_6H_{12}	273(3.67)	39-1710-73C
$C_{23}H_{11}N_3O$			
14H-Benz[4,5]isoquino[2,1-a]perimidine-10-carbonitrile, 14-oxo-	C_6H_5Cl	508(3.57)	103-1257-73
$C_{23}H_{12}N_2O_3$			
14H-Benz[4,5]isoquino[2,1-a]perimidine-10-carboxylic acid, 14-oxo-	C_6H_5Cl	500(3.68)	103-1257-73
$C_{23}H_{13}NO$			
Fluorantheno[8,9-d]oxazole, 9-phenyl-	EtOH	238(4.5),260(4.1), 275(4.1),322f(4.7)	103-0561-73
$C_{23}H_{13}N_3$			
Pyrido[2,3-a]dibenzo[h,j]phenazine	DMSO	256(4.73),296(4.42), 307(4.56),364(3.90), 383(4.20),405(4.38)	103-0485-73
Pyrido[2,3-b]dibenzo[h,j]phenazine	DMSO	280(4.19)	103-0485-73
$C_{23}H_{14}CrO_7$			
Chromium, pentacarbonyl(6-methoxy-3,4-diphenyl-2H-pyran-2-ylidene)-, (OC-6-21)-	hexane	258(4.36),296(4.06), 350(3.66),528(3.76)	39-2535-73C
$C_{23}H_{14}N_2O_2$			
14H-Benz[4,5]isoquino[2,1-a]perimidin-14-one, 10-methoxy-	C_6H_5Cl	474(3.74)	103-1257-73
Benzo[f]quinoline-1-carboxylic acid, 3-(2-quinolinyl)-	n.s.g.	276(4.73),326(4.35), 366(3.91)	103-0220-73
Cu(I) complex	isoAmOH	535(3.86)	103-0220-73
$C_{23}H_{14}O_3$			
2-Naphthalenecarboxaldehyde, 8-(1,3-dihydro-3-oxonaphtho[1,2-c]furan-1-yl)-	dioxan	241(4.98),250s(4.67), 287(4.19),294(4.18), 315(3.55),331(3.69), 343(3.42)	24-1341-73
$C_{23}H_{15}Br_4P$			
Phosphonium, triphenyl-, 2,3,4,5-tetrabromo-2,4-cyclopentadien-1-ylide	MeCN	225(4.51),268(4.15), 310s(--)	44-3537-73
$C_{23}H_{15}ClO$			
9,10-Ethanoanthracen-11-one, 12-[(4-chlorophenyl)methylene]-9,10-dihydro-	C_6H_{12}	273(4.15),302(4.23), 341s(2.92),362s(2.72), 384s(2.31)	35-6294-73
$C_{23}H_{15}Cl_4P$			
Phosphonium, triphenyl-, 2,3,4,5-tetrachloro-2,4-cyclopentadien-1-ylide	MeCN	268(3.89)	44-3537-73
$C_{23}H_{15}I_4P$			
Phosphonium, triphenyl-, 2,3,4,5-tetraiodo-2,4-cyclopentadien-1-ylide	MeCN	260(4.25),300s(--)	44-3537-73
$C_{23}H_{15}NO_3$			
Isoxazole, 3,5-dibenzoyl-4-phenyl-	EtOH	263(4.41),287s(4.10)	88-2195-73

Compound	Solvent	$\lambda_{max}(\log \epsilon)$	Ref.
$C_{23}H_{15}N_2O_5P$			
Phosphine, (4-methoxyphenyl)bis[(4-nitrophenyl)ethynyl]-	EtOH	310(4.46)	65-2627-73
$C_{23}H_{15}N_2O_6P$			
Phosphine oxide, (4-methoxyphenyl)bis-[(4-nitrophenyl)ethynyl]-	EtOH	288(4.65),360s(3.04)	65-2627-73
$C_{23}H_{15}N_3$			
Pyrido[2,3-f]quinoxaline, 2,3-diphenyl-	DMSO	297(4.40),356(3.93), 367(3.97),414(1.90)	103-0485-73
$C_{23}H_{16}$			
Spiro[indene-2,1'-cycloprop-2'-ene], 1,3-diphenyl-	$CHCl_3$	285(4.23)	5-0214-73
$C_{23}H_{16}BrNO$			
4(1H)-Pyridinone, 1-(4-bromophenyl)-3,5-diphenyl-	EtOH	246(4.37),305(4.40)	4-0665-73
$C_{23}H_{16}BrN_3O$			
Naphtho[2,1-e]-1,2,4-triazine, 3-[2-(5-bromo-2-furanyl)ethenyl]-1,2-dihydro-2-phenyl-	MeOH	282(4.43),314(4.27), 356(4.46),374(4.34), 394(4.18)	103-0145-73
$C_{23}H_{16}ClNO$			
4(1H)-Pyridinone, 1-(4-chlorophenyl)-3,5-diphenyl-	EtOH	246(4.41),303(4.38)	4-0665-73
$C_{23}H_{16}INO$			
4(1H)-Pyridinone, 1-(4-iodophenyl)-3,5-diphenyl-	EtOH	247(4.42),307(4.48)	4-0665-73
$C_{23}H_{16}N_2$			
1H-Pyrido[2,3-b]indole, 2,4-diphenyl-	EtOH	217(4.67),253(4.65), 321(4.53)	103-0968-73
$C_{23}H_{16}N_2O_3$			
2,3,5-Pyrrolidinetrione, 1-phenyl-4-[(phenylamino)phenylmethylene]-	$CHCl_3$	295(4.22),364(4.22)	56-2235-73
$C_{23}H_{16}N_4$			
4H-Imidazo[1,5-a]benzimidazole-3-carbonitrile, 1-phenyl-4-(phenylmethyl)-	EtOH	280(4.34),327(4.12)	103-0366-73
2H-Pyrazolo[3,4-d]pyridazine, 2,4,7-triphenyl-	MeOH	237(4.35),304(4.38)	44-1769-73
Spiro[9H-fluorene-9,3'(2'H)-[1,2,4]triazolo[4,3-a]pyridine], 2'-(2-pyridinyl)-	benzene	270(4.4),288s(4.3), 300(4.2)	5-2088-73
$C_{23}H_{16}N_4O_3$			
Naphtho[2,1-e]-1,2,4-triazine, 1,2-dihydro-3-[2-(5-nitro-2-furanyl)ethenyl]-2-phenyl-	MeOH	286(4.27),304(4.20), 308(4.19),404(4.40), 421(4.45)	103-0145-73
$C_{23}H_{16}O$			
9,10-Ethanoanthracen-11-one, 9,10-dihydro-12-(phenylmethylene)-	C_6H_{12}	271(4.13),298(4.20), 343s(2.82),363s(2.70), 380s(2.32)	35-6294-73

Compound	Solvent	λ_{max}(log ε)	Ref.
$C_{23}H_{16}O_2$			
9(10H)-Anthracenone, 10-(2-oxo-1-phenyl-propylidene)-	hexane	345(3.92)	54-0845-73
2-Naphthalenecarboxaldehyde, 8-[(2-methyl-1-naphthalenyl)carbonyl]-	dioxan	226(4.99),257(4.48), 263(4.46),313(4.07), 348s(3.65)	24-1341-73
1-Propanone, 1-naphtho[1,2,3-kl]xanthen-13-yl-	hexane	228(4.72),262(4.58), 290(4.18),303(4.04), 358(4.08),372(4.11), 391(4.15)	54-0845-73
$C_{23}H_{16}O_3$			
2-Naphthalenecarboxylic acid, 1-(1-naphthalenylcarbonyl)-, methyl ester	MeCN	212(4.72),240(4.79), 290s(3.93),298(3.99), 311(3.97)	24-1341-73
$C_{23}H_{16}O_4$			
Triptycene, 2-carboxy-7-(methoxycarbonyl)-, (+)-	MeOH	207(4.80),240s(4.02), 287(3.77),298(3.82)	18-0605-73
$C_{23}H_{17}ClO$			
Benzeneacetaldehyde, 4-chloro-α-(10,11-dihydro-5H-dibenzo[a,d]cyclohepten-5-ylidene)-	hexane	295(3.90),305(3.83)	54-0845-73
$C_{23}H_{17}ClO_4Se$			
Seleninium, 2,4,6-triphenyl-, perchlorate	MeCN-$HClO_4$	390(4.44)	103-0790-73
$C_{23}H_{17}F_3$			
Phenanthrene, 9,10-dihydro-9-methyl-10-methylene-9-[4-(trifluoromethyl)phenyl]-	hexane	219(4.52),241(4.34), 248(4.34),284(4.07)	104-1057-73
	96% H_2SO_4	271(4.47),333(3.94), 556(3.81)	104-1057-73
	70% $HClO_4$	269(4.49),339(4.00), 556(3.84)	104-1057-73
$C_{23}H_{17}FeN_3O_6$			
Iron, tricarbonyl[2-phenyl-5H,10H-5,10-etheno-5a,9a-(methoxymethano)-1H-[1,2,4]triazolo[1,2-b]phthalazin-1,3(2H)-dione]-	MeCN	218s(4.58),245s(4.27)	78-2373-73
$C_{23}H_{17}N$			
Pyridine, 2,4,6-triphenyl-	EtOH	253(4.68),310(3.99)	35-4891-73
	50%EtOH-HCl	257(4.35),307(4.34)	35-4891-73
$C_{23}H_{17}NO$			
4(1H)-Pyridinone, 1,3,5-triphenyl-	EtOH	244(4.28),302(4.25)	4-0665-73
$C_{23}H_{17}NO_2$			
4(1H)-Pyridinone, 1-(4-hydroxyphenyl)-3,5-diphenyl-	EtOH	244(4.46),303(4.36)	4-0665-73
$C_{23}H_{17}NO_2S_4$			
Thiophene, 2-[2-(5-methyl-2-thienyl)ethenyl]-5-[2-[5-[2-(5-nitro-2-thienyl)-ethenyl]-2-thienyl]ethenyl]-	DMF	284(4.11),433s(--), 505(4.64)	24-0655-73

Compound	Solvent	λ_{max}(log ϵ)	Ref.
$C_{23}H_{17}N_3$			
4-Isoquinolinecarbonitrile, 3-(4-methyl-phenyl)-1-(phenylamino)-	EtOH	223(4.57),262(4.46), 363(4.31)	39-0817-73C
Pyrido[2,3-a]dibenzo[h,j]phenazine, 12,13,14,15-tetrahydro-	CCl_4	257(4.80),335(4.64), 378(3.75),399(3.81), 483(3.26)	103-0485-73
Pyrido[2,3-b]dibenzo[h,j]phenazine, 11,12,13,14-tetrahydro-	DMSO	256(4.63),317(4.29), 380(3.57),462(3.70)	103-0485-73
$C_{23}H_{17}N_3O$			
Naphtho[2,1-e]-1,2,4-triazine, 3-[2-(2-furanyl)ethenyl]-1,2-dihydro-2-phenyl-	MeOH	227(4.51),314(4.27), 334(4.34),367(4.58), 386(4.43)	103-0145-73
Pyrrolo[1,2-a]pyrimidine-8-carbonitrile, 2-benzoyl-6,7-dimethyl-4-phenyl-	MeOH	213(4.46),238(4.41),	4-0287-73
$C_{23}H_{17}N_3O_2$			
3H-Imidazo[4,5-f]quinoline, 2-[2-(2-furanyl)ethenyl]-3-[2-(2-furanyl)-2-propenyl]-	MeOH	259(4.44),310(4.21), 365(4.33)	103-0406-73
$C_{23}H_{17}Se$			
Seleninium, 2,4,6-triphenyl-, perchlorate	MeCN-$HClO_4$	390(4.44)	103-0790-73
$C_{23}H_{18}BrN_5O_3S_2$			
Phenol, 2-[bis(6-methyl-2-benzothiazolyl)amino]methyl]-4-bromo-6-nitro-	benzene	279(4.16),395(4.45)	80-1781-73
	dioxan	229(4.86),276(4.38), 390(4.53)	80-1781-73
	CH_2Cl_2	239(4.42),245(4.40), 277(4.37),393(4.53)	80-1781-73
$C_{23}H_{18}F_3$			
9-Phenanthrenylium, 9,10-dihydro-9,10-dimethyl-10-[4-(trifluoromethyl)-phenyl]-	96% H_2SO_4	271(4.47),333(3.94), 556(3.81)	88-0539-73
	70% $HClO_4$	269(4.49),339(4.00), 556(3.84)	88-0539-73
$C_{23}H_{18}NOP$			
Phosphonium, triphenyl-, 2-nitroso-2,4-cyclopentadien-1-ylide	MeOH	268(3.67),360(3.94)	44-3537-73
$C_{23}H_{18}NO_2P$			
Phosphonium, triphenyl-, 2-nitro-2,4-cyclopentadien-1-ylide	MeCN	222(4.59),266(3.78), 372(4.33)	44-3537-73
$C_{23}H_{18}N_2O_2$			
5(4H)-Oxazolone, 2,4-diphenyl-4-(2-phenyl-2-aziridinyl)-	EtOH	246(4.26)	33-1351-73
2H-Phenanthro[9,10-d]imidazole, 2-methoxy-2-(4-methoxyphenyl)-	n.s.g.	264(3.52),272(3.55), 323(2.76)	78-1185-73
3aH-Phenanthro[9,10-d]imidazole, 3a-methoxy-2-(4-methoxyphenyl)-	n.s.g.	264(3.52),272(3.55), 323(2.76)	78-1185-73
$C_{23}H_{18}N_2O_5S$			
Acetamide, N-[4-[[[4-(4-oxo-4H-1-benzopyran-2-yl)phenyl]amino]sulfonyl]-phenyl]-	dioxan	261(4.41),310(4.44)	83-0299-73

Compound	Solvent	$\lambda_{max}(\log \epsilon)$	Ref.
$C_{23}H_{18}N_2O_6S$			
Acetamide, N-[4-[[[4-(3-hydroxy-4-oxo-4H-1-benzopyran-2-yl)phenyl]amino]-sulfonyl]phenyl]-	dioxan	254(4.49),317(4.16), 355(4.39)	83-0299-73
$C_{23}H_{18}N_4$			
1,2,4-Triazolo[4,3-a]pyridine, 2,3-dihydro-3,3-diphenyl-	benzene	305(4.2),455(3.5)	5-2088-73
$C_{23}H_{18}N_4O$			
2-Propen-1-one, 3-phenyl-3-(phenylamino)-1-(5-phenyl-1H-1,2,3-triazol-4-yl)-	EtOH	227(4.40),380(4.55)	78-3271-73
anion	EtOH	243(4.40),380(4.63)	78-3271-73
$C_{23}H_{18}N_4O_2$			
Benzoic acid, anhydride with N-(5-methyl-4-phenyl-1H-1,2,3-triazol-1-yl)-benzenecarboximidic acid	EtOH	245(4.48),256(4.44), 329(3.48)	78-2119-73
$C_{23}H_{18}N_4O_3$			
Benzamide, N-benzoyl-N-[4-(4-methoxyphenyl)-1H-1,2,3-triazol-1-yl]-	EtOH	239(4.32),295(4.30), 348(4.25)	78-2119-73
$C_{23}H_{18}N_4O_4S$			
Carbamic acid, [5-(dicyanomethylene)-1,3,4,5-tetrahydro-1-[(4-methylphenyl)sulfonyl]benz[cd]indol-4-yl]-, methyl ester	EtOH	238(4.59),282(4.17), 345(3.75)	39-0760-73C
$C_{23}H_{18}O$			
Benzeneacetaldehyde, α-(10,11-dihydro-5H-dibenzo[a,d]cyclohepten-5-ylidene)-	hexane	274(3.97),287s(3.93)	54-0845-73
Methanone, (2-methyl-1-naphthalenyl)(7-methyl-1-naphthalenyl)-	MeCN	223(4.98),245s(4.24), 290s(3.83),322(3.93)	24-1341-73
2-Propanone, 1-(9-anthracenyl)-1-phenyl-	hexane	338(4.18),354(3.95), 372(4.11),393(4.08)	54-0845-73
2-Propanone, 1-(9(10H)-anthracenylidene)-1-phenyl-	hexane	284(4.00)	54-0845-73
$C_{23}H_{18}O_2$			
2-Butanone, 1-phenyl-1-(9H-xanthen-9-ylidene)-	hexane	219(4.72),279(3.98), 329(4.08)	54-0845-73
1,4-Ethenocyclopenta[c]pyran-3(1H)-one, 7-(diphenylmethylene)-4,4a,7,7a-tetrahydro-, (1α,4α,4aβ,7aβ)-	EtOH	236(4.07),287(4.22)	44-3836-73
1H-Inden-1-one, 2,3-dihydro-2-(4-methoxyphenyl)-3-(phenylmethylene)-, cis	EtOH	258(3.61),266(3.67), 275(3.80),283(3.77)	48-0353-73
trans	EtOH	322(4.53),338(4.59), 350(4.37)	48-0353-73
Methanone, [7-(hydroxymethyl)-1-naphthalenyl](2-methyl-1-naphthalenyl)-	dioxan	226(5.02),248(4.34), 294s(3.88),322(3.98)	24-1341-73
2-Naphthalenecarboxylic acid, 1-(1-naphthalenylmethyl)-, methyl ester	MeCN	223(5.01),273(4.08), 283(4.15),290(4.03), 318(3.13)	24-1341-73
$C_{23}H_{18}O_3$			
Benzeneacetic acid, α-(oxodiphenylethylidene)-, methyl ester	EtOH	284(4.4)	2-1333-73

Compound	Solvent	$\lambda_{max}(\log \epsilon)$	Ref.
Triptycene, 2-acetoxy-5-methoxy-	dioxan	217(4.77),261(3.48), 270(3.50),278s(3.59), 288(3.31)	18-0651-73
Triptycene, 2-methoxy-7-(methoxycarbonyl)-	dioxan	210(4.73),215(4.71), 267(3.55),284(3.61), 296(3.58)	18-0611-73
(+)-	MeOH	209(4.83),215s(4.73), 240s(4.14),267(3.54), 283(3.60),296(3.57)	18-0605-73
	dioxan	210(4.73),215(4.71), 267(3.55),284(3.62), 296(3.59)	18-0605-73
Triptycene, 5-methoxy-7-(methoxycarbonyl)-	dioxan	220(4.65),268(3.57), 285(3.67),295(3.63)	18-0611-73
$C_{23}H_{18}O_3S$			
Methanone, (2,4-diphenyl-2H-thiet-2-yl)-(4-methylphenyl)-, S,S-dioxide	EtOH	218(4.35),268(4.35)	18-0667-73
1,4-Oxathiin, 2-(4-methylphenyl)-3,5-diphenyl-, 4,4-dioxide	EtOH	233(4.30),238(4.33)	18-0667-73
$C_{23}H_{18}O_4$			
Benzoic acid, 2,3-dibenzoyl-4-methyl-, methyl ester	EtOH	252(4.5)	22-2856-73
$C_{23}H_{18}O_6$			
4H-1-Benzopyran-4-one, 3-(4,5-dihydroxy-2-methoxyphenyl)-7-(phenylmethoxy)-	EtOH	218(4.57),237s(4.43), 249(4.39),267(4.18), 298(4.28)	39-1277-73C
Stachyoidin, dehydro-	MeOH	218(4.59),232(4.60), 265(4.69)	119-0053-73
$C_{23}H_{18}O_7$			
Chromocyclin, 2-deacetyl-12a-deoxy-, trimethyl ether	EtOH	228(4.37),260(4.46), 327(3.87),404(4.43), 415s(4.41)	105-0498-73
Rotenone	MeOH	261(4.38),268(4.38), 297(4.30),342(3.91)	78-2731-73
$C_{23}H_{19}BF_4N_2OS$			
Benzothiazolium, 2-[(3-ethoxy-1H-phenalen-1-ylidene)amino]-3-methyl-, tetrafluoroborate	MeCN	304(4.05),356(4.12), 395(4.09),517(4.39)	44-2425-73
$C_{23}H_{19}BrN_4O_3S_2$			
Phenol, 2-[bis(6-methoxy-2-benzothiazolyl)amino]methyl]-4-bromo-	benzene	281(4.08),286(4.07), 402(4.30)	80-1781-73
	ether	229(4.52),243(4.43), 278(4.31),284(4.28), 397(4.48)	80-1781-73
	CH_2Cl_2	241(4.49),278(4.37), 402(4.52)	80-1781-73
	EtOH	222(--),276(--), 397(--)	80-1781-73
$C_{23}H_{19}BrN_4S$			
1,2,4-Triazolo[4,3-b][1,3,4]thiadiazin-4-ium, 6-[1,1'-biphenyl]-4-yl-1,7-dihydro-1-(phenylmethyl)-, bromide	EtOH	238(3.91),290s(--), 332(4.20)	48-1131-73

Compound	Solvent	$\lambda_{max}(\log \epsilon)$	Ref.
$C_{23}H_{19}ClN_2O_5S$			
Acetamide, N-[4-[[[4-[3-(5-chloro-2-hydroxyphenyl)-3-oxo-1-propenyl]phenyl]amino]sulfonyl]phenyl]-	dioxan	258(4.47),368(4.40)	83-0299-73
$C_{23}H_{19}FeN_3O_6$			
Iron, tricarbonyl[dihydro-2-phenyl-5H,10H-5,10-etheno-5a,9a-(methoxymethano)-1H-[1,2,4]triazolo[1,2-b]phthalazine-1,3(2H)-dione]-	MeCN	218s(4.56),275s(3.49)	78-2373-73
$C_{23}H_{19}IN_2S$			
Benz[cd]indolium, 1-methyl-2-[3-(3-methyl-2(3H)-benzothiazolylidene)-1-propenyl]-, iodide	EtOH	611(4.72),658(4.82)	103-0314-73
$C_{23}H_{19}NO_2$			
2H-1-Benzopyran-3-carbonitrile, 3,4,5,6-7,8-hexahydro-2-oxo-4-phenyl-8-(phenylmethylene)-	MeOH	288(4.30)	83-0463-73
1-Naphthalenol, 4-[(hydroxyamino)diphenylmethyl]-	n.s.g.	300(3.97),312(3.80)	114-0411-73D
2-Naphthalenol, 1-[(hydroxyamino)diphenylmethyl]-	n.s.g.	273(3.30),285(3.47), 295(3.45),327(3.20), 337(3.25)	114-0411-73D
2(3H)-Oxazolone, 4,5-diphenyl-3-(2-phenylethyl)-	EtOH	288(4.18)	44-3034-73
$C_{23}H_{19}NO_2S$			
1H-Pyrrole, 1-[(4-methylphenyl)sulfonyl]-3,4-diphenyl-	EtOH	223(4.48),243(4.46), 262s(4.28),272s(4.11), 281s(3.84)	24-3824-73
$C_{23}H_{19}N_2OS$			
Benzothiazolium, 2-[(3-ethoxy-1H-phenalen-1-ylidene)amino]-3-methyl-, tetrafluoroborate	MeCN	304(4.05),356(4.12), 395(4.09),517(4.39)	44-2425-73
$C_{23}H_{19}N_3$			
Pyrido[2,3-f]quinoxaline, 7,8,9,10-tetrahydro-2,3-diphenyl-	CCl_4	314(4.65),453(3.23)	103-0485-73
Pyrido[2,3-g]quinoxaline, 6,7,8,9-tetrahydro-2,3-diphenyl-	DMSO	260(4.85),397(3.31)	103-0485-73
$C_{23}H_{19}N_3O$			
1,2-Propanedione, 1-(2-phenyl-1H-indol-3-yl)-, 1-(phenylhydrazone)	EtOH	306(4.44),346s(4.32)	78-3159-73
$C_{23}H_{19}N_3O_2$			
2-Propenamide, 3-(3-hydroxy-1H-indol-2-yl)-N-phenyl-3-(phenylamino)-	EtOH	265(4.40),325(4.20)	95-0964-73
$C_{23}H_{19}N_3O_4$			
L-Alanine, N-benzoyldehydrotryptophyl-	67% MeOH	274(4.04),336(4.27)	105-0273-73
$C_{23}H_{19}N_3O_4S$			
Benzenesulfonamide, N-[1,3-dihydro-1-methyl-3-[(2-nitrophenyl)methylene]-2H-indol-2-ylidene]-4-methyl-, (E)-	n.s.g.	206(4.68),271(4.50), 321(3.73),380s(3.45)	39-1943-73C

Compound	Solvent	$\lambda_{max}(\log \epsilon)$	Ref.
$C_{23}H_{19}N_3O_6$			
Fumaric acid, (3-diazo-5-methyl-2,4-dioxopyrrolidin-1-yl)-, dibenzyl ester	EtOH	240(4.08),292(3.64)	39-2024-73C
Maleic acid, (3-diazo-5-methyl-2,4-dioxopyrrolidin-1-yl)-, dibenzyl ester	EtOH	255(4.00),285(4.10)	39-2024-73C
$C_{23}H_{19}N_4S$			
1,2,4-Triazolo[4,3-b][1,3,4]thiadiazin-4-ium, 6-[1,1'-biphenyl]-4-yl-1,7-dihydro-1-(phenylmethyl)-, bromide	EtOH	238(3.91),290s(--), 332(4.20)	48-1131-73
$C_{23}H_{19}N_5O_2$			
1H-Isoindole-1,3(2H)-dione, 2-[3-[3-amino-6-(1H-indol-3-yl)pyrazinyl]propyl]-	MeOH	232s(4.54),241s(4.32), 273(4.26),289(4.22), 362(3.87)	78-3761-73
$C_{23}H_{19}N_5O_3$			
1H-Isoindole-1,3(2H)-dione, 2-[3-[3-amino-6-(1H-indol-3-yl)pyrazinyl]-propyl]-, oxide	EtOH	231(4.59),240(4.44), 277(4.31),298(4.33), 378(3.68)	78-3761-73
$C_{23}H_{20}$			
Phenanthrene, 9,10-dihydro-9-methyl-10-methylene-9-(4-methylphenyl)-	hexane	217(4.51),245(4.25), 283(4.10)	104-1057-73
	96% H_2SO_4	271(4.54),333(3.98), 407(3.45),561(3.72)	104-1057-73
	70% $HClO_4$	269(4.41),336(3.95), 397(3.50),558(3.70)	104-1057-73
$C_{23}H_{20}AsNO_2$			
Arsonium, triphenyl-, 1-cyano-2-ethoxy-2-oxoethylide	MeOH	223(4.45),264(3.80)	78-1697-73
$C_{23}H_{20}BrNiP$			
Nickel, bromo(η^5-2,4-cyclopentadien-1-yl)(triphenylphosphine)-	C_6H_{12}	344(3.72),518(2.94), 845(1.51)	23-1179-73
$C_{23}H_{20}Br_2N_2O_5$			
6,7-Diazabicyclo[3.2.0]hept-2-ene-6,7-dicarboxylic acid, 1,2-bis(4-bromophenyl)-3,5-dimethyl-4-oxo-, dimethyl ester	MeOH	290(4.14)	44-2043-73
$C_{23}H_{20}ClNO_4$			
5(4H)-Oxazolone, 4-[2-(8-chloro-1,2,3,4-tetrahydro-5-methoxy-1-methyl-4-oxo-2-naphthalenyl)ethylidene]-2-phenyl-, cis	MeCN	222(4.52),242(4.22), 255(4.01),299(4.42)	89-0497-73
$C_{23}H_{20}ClNiO_3P$			
Nickel, chloro(η^5-2,4-cyclopentadien-1-yl)(triphenylphosphite-P)-	MeOH	262(3.63),320(3.12), 475(2.88)	33-1620-73
$C_{23}H_{20}ClNiP$			
Nickel, chloro(η^5-2,4-cyclopentadien-1-yl)(triphenylphosphine)-	C_6H_{12}	331(3.93),512(2.95), 835(1.49)	23-1179-73
$C_{23}H_{20}Cl_3NiPSn$			
Nickel, (η^5-2,4-cyclopentadien-1-yl)-(trichlorostannyl)(triphenylphosphine)-	$CHCl_3$	307s(4.00),340s(3.78), 448(3.08),646(1.78)	23-1179-73

Compound	Solvent	$\lambda_{max}(\log \epsilon)$	Ref.
$C_{23}H_{20}INiP$			
Nickel, (η^5-2,4-cyclopentadien-1-yl)-iodo(triphenylphosphine)-	C_6H_{12}	350s(3.62),527(2.89), 850s(1.53)	23-1179-73
$C_{23}H_{20}NNiO_2P$			
Nickel, (η^5-2,4-cyclopentadien-1-yl)-(nitrito-N)(triphenylphosphine)-	$CHCl_3$	300s(3.98),333s(3.89), 461(3.18),650(1.60)	23-1179-73
$C_{23}H_{20}N_2O$			
1-Naphthalenol, 4-(hydrazinodiphenyl-methyl)-	n.s.g.	300(3.95),310(3.82)	114-0411-73D
2-Naphthalenol, 1-(hydrazinodiphenyl-methyl)-	n.s.g.	274(3.19),285(3.52), 295(3.52),330(3.41), 337(3.49)	114-0411-73D
$C_{23}H_{20}N_2O_2S$			
1H-Pyrazole, 4,5-dihydro-3-[(4-methyl-phenyl)sulfonyl]-4-methylene-5,5-di-phenyl-	EtOH	328(3.90)	22-2746-73
$C_{23}H_{20}N_2O_5S$			
Acetamide, N-[4-[[[4-[3-(2-hydroxyphen-yl)-3-oxo-1-propenyl]phenyl]amino]-sulfonyl]phenyl]-	dioxan	261(4.38),357(4.38)	83-0299-73
1,4,2-Oxathiazole, 5-[2-(4-methoxyphen-yl)ethoxy]-3-(4-nitrophenyl)-5-phenyl-	EtOH	271(4.19),282(4.12), 302(3.95)	39-1574-73C
$C_{23}H_{20}N_2O_6S_2$			
2-Propenoic acid, 3-[1-acetyl-3-[[(4-methylphenyl)sulfonyl]oxy]-1H-indol-2-yl]-2-cyano-3-(methylthio)-, methyl ester	EtOH	230(4.50),270(4.14), 330(4.17)	94-1658-73
$C_{23}H_{20}N_2O_8S$			
2,4(1H,3H)-Pyrimidinedione, 1-[5-[(benz-oyloxy)methyl]-2,5-dihydro-3-[[(4-methylphenyl)sulfonyl]oxy]-2-fur-anyl]-, [R-(R*,S*)]-	EtOH	227(4.42),258(3.95)	44-1283-73
$C_{23}H_{20}N_4$			
3,8-Azo-4,7-methanocyclobuta[b]naphtha-lene, 2a,3,3a,4,7,7a,8,8a-octahydro-3,8-di-2-pyridinyl-	90% EtOH	258(3.85),264(3.89), 270(3.72)	12-0389-73
$C_{23}H_{20}N_4O_2$			
Benzoic acid, 1-methyl-2-phenyl-1,2-eth-anediylidenedihydrazide	EtOH	224(4.42),294(4.43), 356(4.39)	78-2119-73
2H-Pyrazino[1',2':1,5]pyrrolo[2,3-b]in-dole-1,4(3H,6H)-dione, 5a,10b-dihydro-10b-(1H-indol-3-yl)-2,3-dimethyl-	EtOH	220(4.72),237s(4.45), 260(4.20),290(4.00)	39-1819-73C
$C_{23}H_{20}N_4O_3$			
Benzoic acid, 1-(4-methoxyphenyl)-1,2-ethanediylidenedihydrazide	EtOH	218(4.39),290(4.42), 360(4.38)	78-2119-73
$C_{23}H_{20}N_4O_5$			
2,4(1H,3H)-Pteridinedione, 1-(2-deoxy-D-erythro-pentofuranosyl)-6,7-di-phenyl-	pH 3.0	222(4.40),274(4.16), 360(4.11)	24-1401-73
	pH 11.0	220s(4.38),266(4.29), 360(4.19)	24-1401-73

Compound	Solvent	λ_{max}(log ϵ)	Ref.
$C_{23}H_{20}N_4O_6$			
2,4(1H,3H)-Pteridinedione, 6,7-diphenyl-1-β-D-ribofuranosyl-	pH 4.0	221(4.42),273(4.19), 358(4.14)	24-1401-73
	pH 11.0	220s(4.38),265(4.29), 358(4.19)	24-1401-73
2,4(1H,3H)-Pteridinedione, 6,7-diphenyl-3-β-D-ribofuranosyl-	pH 1.0	220s(4.43),272(4.19), 363(4.19)	24-1401-73
	pH 11.0	220s(4.41),240s(4.28), 292(4.39),388(4.07)	24-1401-73
$C_{23}H_{20}O$			
1-Penten-3-one, 1,1,2-triphenyl-	hexane	238(4.26),288(3.96)	54-0845-73
Phenanthrene, 9,10-dihydro-9-(4-methoxyphenyl)-9-methyl-10-methylene-	C_6H_{12}	220(4.52),245(4.42), 281(4.11)	104-1057-73
	96% H_2SO_4	271(4.46),338(3.98), 406(3.42),556(3.73)	104-1057-73
	70% $HClO_4$	269(4.32),337(3.84), 397(3.35),562(3.66)	104-1057-73
$C_{23}H_{20}O_2$			
Benzoic acid, 4-(2,2-diphenylethenyl)-, ethyl ester	EtOH	245(4.25)	104-1511-73
1,5-Pentanedione, 1,3,5-triphenyl-	EtOH	241(4.42)	35-3310-73
$C_{23}H_{20}O_2S$			
2H-Thiopyran, 5,6-dihydro-2,4,6-triphenyl-, 1,1-dioxide, cis	EtOH	223(4.43),244(4.09)	39-0410-73C
$C_{23}H_{20}O_3$			
2-Propen-1-one, 1-[5-methoxy-2-(phenylmethoxy)phenyl]-3-phenyl-	EtOH	228(4.32),309(4.32)	114-0093-73B
$C_{23}H_{20}O_4$			
Methanone, [2-methoxy-6-(phenylmethoxy)-phenyl](3-phenyloxiranyl)-	EtOH	274(3.98)	114-0093-73B
Methanone, [5-methoxy-2-(phenylmethoxy)-phenyl](3-phenyloxiranyl)-	EtOH	260(3.96),350(3.62)	114-0093-73B
$C_{23}H_{20}O_6$			
2H-1-Benzopyran-2-one, 4-methyl-7-[4-[(2-oxo-2H-1-benzopyran-7-yl)oxy]-butoxy]-	CH_2Cl_2	322(4.50)	44-0957-73
2H-1-Benzopyran-2-one, 7,7'-[1,5-pentanediylbis(oxy)]bis-	CH_2Cl_2	324(4.50)	44-0957-73
Deguelin, 6a,12a-dehydro-	MeOH	220(4.45),235(4.50), 260(4.54),312(4.19)	78-2731-73
4H,8H-Furo[3,2-d]benzo[1,2-b:3,4-b']di-pyran-4,11(10H)-dione, 8a,11a-dihydro-5-methoxy-10,10-dimethyl-2-phenyl-, cis (stachyoidin)	MeOH	218(4.52),268(4.55), 308s(4.23)	119-0053-73
Isotachrosin	MeOH	218(4.54),264(4.56), 307(4.38)	119-0064-73
Rotenone, 6a,12a-dehydro-	MeOH	238(4.46),278(4.38), 309(4.26)	78-2731-73
Secorin	EtOH	218s(4.69),247s(4.16), 258(4.13),302s(4.60), 319(4.70)	105-0626-73
Semiglabrin	MeOH	216(4.21),249s(4.23), 256(4.24),274(4.09), 309(4.19)	78-3099-73

Compound	Solvent	λ_{max}(log ε)	Ref.
$C_{23}H_{20}O_7$			
Tephrodinol	MeOH	218(4.49),230s(4.46), 267(4.48),305(4.28)	119-0053-73
$C_{23}H_{20}O_{10}$			
4H-1-Benzopyran-4-one, 7,8-diacetoxy-3-(3-acetoxy-2,4-dimethoxyphenyl)-	MeOH	246(4.22),303(3.86)	102-1157-73
$C_{23}H_{20}Si$			
Silacyclopenta-2,4-diene, 1-methyl-1,2,5-triphenyl-	C_6H_{12}	225(4.12),377(4.26)	6-0123-73
$C_{23}H_{21}$			
9-Phenanthrenylium, 9,10-dihydro-9,10-dimethyl-10-(4-methylphenyl)-	96% H_2SO_4	271(4.54),333(3.98), 407(3.45),561(3.72)	88-0539-73
	70% $HClO_4$	269(4.41),336(3.95), 397(3.50),558(3.70)	88-0539-73
$C_{23}H_{21}AsO_2$			
Arsonium, triphenyl-, 1-acetyl-2-oxo-propylide	MeOH	216(4.41),275(4.20)	78-1697-73
$C_{23}H_{21}NO_2$			
Benzamide, 2-(2,5-dimethylbenzoyl)-N-(4-methylphenyl)-	EtOH	270(3.84)	39-2448-73C
Benzamide, N-phenyl-2-(2,4,6-trimethyl-benzoyl)-	EtOH	214(4.47),247(4.28)	39-1160-73B
$C_{23}H_{21}NO_2S$			
Methanone, [4,5-dihydro-4-phenyl-3-(2,4,6-trimethylphenyl)-5-isoxazolyl]-2-thienyl-, trans	EtOH	268(4.05)	39-1148-73C
$C_{23}H_{21}NO_3$			
Benzene, 1-methoxy-4-[10-(4-nitrophenyl)-1,3,5,7,9-decapentaenyl]-	THF	277(4.01),370(4.49), 442(4.85),455s(--)	18-2828-73
Methanone, [4,5-dihydro-4-phenyl-3-(2,4,6-trimethylphenyl)-5-isoxazolyl]-2-furanyl-, trans	EtOH	280(4.25)	39-1148-73C
Methanone, [5-(2-furanyl)-4,5-dihydro-3-(2,4,6-trimethylphenyl)-4-isoxazolyl]phenyl-	EtOH	245(4.22)	39-1148-73C
$C_{23}H_{21}NO_4S_2$			
Thiopyrano[4,3-b]indole-3,4-dicarboxylic acid, 4a,5-dihydro-5-methyl-1-(methylthio)-4a-phenyl-, dimethyl ester	EtOH	236(4.15),260(4.03), 388(3.72)	94-2770-73
$C_{23}H_{21}NO_5$			
3,4-Pyridinedicarboxylic acid, 1,6-dihydro-6-oxo-2,5-bis(phenylmethyl)-, dimethyl ester	EtOH	266(3.71),312(3.58)	39-0404-73C
$C_{23}H_{21}NO_6$			
1-Cyclohexene-1-acetic acid, 5-(1,3-benzodioxol-5-yl)-6-(benzoylamino)-3-oxo-, methyl ester, trans	MeOH	229(4.42),288(3.66)	88-4587-73
	MeOH-NaOH	225(4.34),288(3.71), 364(4.36)	88-4587-73

Compound	Solvent	λmax(log ε)	Ref.
$C_{23}H_{21}NO_7$			
1,2,3-Benzenetricarboxylic acid, 5-methoxy-4-(8-methyl-2-quinolinyl)-, trimethyl ester	MeOH	240(4.57),263s(4.35), 319(4.05)	39-1338-73C
	MeOH-HClO4	248(4.71),323(4.03)	39-1338-73C
$C_{23}H_{21}N_3$			
1H-Indol-2-amine, 2,3-dihydro-N-(4-methylphenyl)-3-[(4-methylphenyl)imino]-5-methyl-	EtOH	270(4.30),295(4.4), 550(4.0)	95-0008-73
$C_{23}H_{21}N_3OS$			
Benzenepropanethioamide, α-[[4-(dimethylamino)phenyl]imino]-β-oxo-N-phenyl-	MeOH	261(5.12),465(4.68)	19-0893-73
Co complex	MeOH	512(4.19)	19-0893-73
Cu complex	MeOH	537(4.22)	19-0893-73
Ni complex	MeOH	507(4.24)	19-0893-73
$C_{23}H_{21}N_3O_8$			
3a,4,6,6a(3H,4H)-Cyclopentapyrazoletetracarboxylic acid, 5-(2-quinolinyl)-, tetramethyl ester	MeOH	228(4.42),247(4.54), 337(3.99),352s(3.88)	39-1338-73C
$C_{23}H_{21}N_5O_5$			
2(1H)-Pteridinone, 4-amino-6,7-diphenyl-1-β-D-ribofuranosyl-	pH 0.0	222(4.44),282(4.21), 377(4.15)	33-1225-73
	pH 7.0	210(4.68),273(4.38), 371(4.24)	33-1225-73
$C_{23}H_{21}OP$			
Phosphonium, [2-(2-hydroxyphenyl)ethenyl](1-methylethenyl)diphenyl-, hydroxide, inner salt	$CHCl_3$	246(4.85),289(4.23), 254(3.91)	44-1583-73
$C_{23}H_{21}O_5P$			
Phosphoric acid, 3-(4-ethylphenyl)-3-oxo-1-propenyl diphenyl ester	dioxan	268(4.26)	24-0435-73
$C_{23}H_{22}BNO$			
3-Penten-2-one, 4-[(diphenylboryl)phenylamino]-	CH_2Cl_2	260(3.52),331(3.87)	78-3185-73
$C_{23}H_{22}BrNO$			
2-Propen-1-one, 1-(4-bromophenyl)-3-[2-(1-piperidinyl)-1H-inden-3-yl]-	EtOH	281(4.30),499(4.38)	48-1161-73
$C_{23}H_{22}ClNO$			
2-Propen-1-one, 1-(4-chlorophenyl)-3-[2-(1-piperidinyl)-1H-inden-3-yl]-	EtOH	278(4.29),497(4.39)	48-1161-73
$C_{23}H_{22}N_2O$			
Benzamide, N-(1-methylethyl)-2-[phenyl(phenylimino)methyl]-	EtOH	250s(4.23),324(3.46)	103-0701-73
Benzamide, N-[1-phenyl-1-[(1-phenylethylidene)amino]ethyl]-	EtOH	286(4.07)	78-2119-73
Benzamide, 2-[phenyl(phenylimino)methyl]-N-propyl-	EtOH	250s(4.23),324(3.51) (changing)	103-0701-73
$C_{23}H_{22}N_2O_5$			
[3,6'-Bi-1H-indole]-2,2'-dicarboxylic acid, 7-methoxy-, diethyl ester	EtOH	225s(4.53),238(4.61), 292(4.37),314s(4.28), 330s(4.26)	78-1991-73

Compound	Solvent	$\lambda_{max}(\log \epsilon)$	Ref.
[4,6'-Bi-1H-indole]-2,2'-dicarboxylic acid, 7-methoxy-, diethyl ester	EtOH	224(4.54),247(4.64), 297(4.34),342(4.39)	78-1991-73
Cyclopent[e][1,3,4]oxadiazine-1(4aH)-carboxylic acid, 7,7a-dihydro-3-methoxy-6,7a-dimethyl-7-oxo-4a,5-diphenyl-, methyl ester, cis	EtOH	282(4.11)	44-2043-73
2,3-Diazabicyclo[2.2.1]hept-5-ene-2,3-dicarboxylic acid, 1,4-dimethyl-7-oxo-5,6-diphenyl-, dimethyl ester	EtOH	254s(3.96)	44-2043-73
6,7-Diazabicyclo[3.2.0]hept-2-ene-6,7-dicarboxylic acid, 3,5-dimethyl-4-oxo-1,2-diphenyl-, dimethyl ester	EtOH	284(4.11)	44-2043-73
$C_{23}H_{22}N_2O_6$			
Cycloprop[3,4]indeno[2,1-c]pyrazole-3a,3c,6c(3bH)-tricarboxylic acid, 1,6,6a,6b-tetrahydro-1-(phenylmethylene)-, trimethyl ester	EtOH	225s(3.99),280(4.31), 320(2.51)	24-1837-73
geometric isomer	EtOH	225(3.90),286(4.31), 320(2.48)	24-1837-73
$C_{23}H_{22}N_2O_9S$			
2,4(1H,3H)-Pyrimidinedione, 1-[5-O-benzoyl-2-O-[(4-methylphenyl)sulfonyl]-β-D-lyxofuranosyl]-	EtOH	227(4.46),259(4.05)	44-1283-73
2,4(1H,3H)-Pyrimidinedione, 1-[5-O-benzoyl-3-O-[(4-methylphenyl)sulfonyl]-β-D-lyxofuranosyl]-	EtOH	225(4.49),260(4.09)	44-1283-73
$C_{23}H_{22}N_4O_2$			
2H-Pyrazino[1',2':1,5]pyrrolo[2,3-b]indole-1,4(3H,6H)-dione, 5a,10b,11,11a-tetrahydro-10b-(1H-indol-3-yl)-2,3-dimethyl-	EtOH	220(4.37),240s(3.96), 283(3.83),290(3.84)	39-1819-73C
$C_{23}H_{22}N_8O_8$			
4H-3,6a-Methano-1,2-benzodiazocin-4-one, 2-(2,4-dinitrophenyl)-2,3,5,6,7,8,9-10-octahydro-, 2,4-dinitrophenylhydrazone	EtOH	360(4.47)	39-0393-73C
$C_{23}H_{22}O_3S$			
4H-Benzo[3,4]cyclobuta[1,2-b]thiopyran-4-one, 4a,4b,5,6,7,8,8a,8b-octahydro-2,8b-diphenyl-, 1,1-dioxide	EtOH	220(4.21),295(4.03)	18-1007-73
$C_{23}H_{22}O_4$			
Ethanone, 1-[5-methoxy-2,4-bis(phenylmethoxy)phenyl]-	MeOH	234(4.12),270(3.82), 330(3.72)	2-0098-73
1-Propanone, 2-hydroxy-1,2-bis(4-methoxyphenyl)-3-phenyl-	EtOH	276(4.27)	42-0586-73
$C_{23}H_{22}O_5$			
12-Deoxy-$\Delta^{12(12a)}$-dehydrodeguelin	MeOH	258(4.40),291(4.01), 303(4.00),364(4.52), 383(4.45)	78-2731-73
12-Deoxy-$\Delta^{12(12a)}$-dehydrorotenone	MeOH	219(4.47),255(4.17), 264(4.10),362(4.52), 380(4.43)	78-2731-73
Ethanone, 2-hydroxy-2-(2-methoxyphenyl)-1,2-bis(4-methoxyphenyl)-	EtOH	276(4.18)	42-0586-73

Compound	Solvent	$\lambda_{max}(\log \epsilon)$	Ref.
2H,6H-Pyrano[3,2-b]xanthen-6-one, 5-hydroxy-2,2-dimethyl-8-[(3-methyl-2-butenyl)oxy]-	n.s.g.	252(4.56),268(4.58), 328(4.11),384(3.54)	2-0518-73
$C_{23}H_{22}O_6$			
Deguelin	MeOH	238(4.32),250(4.33), 269(4.43),298(3.97)	78-2731-73
Parvisoflavone A, tri-O-methyl-	EtOH	258(4.55),263(4.56)	102-1188-73
Parvisoflavone B, tri-O-methyl-	EtOH	267(4.66)	102-1188-73
Rotenone	MeOH	236(4.16),293(4.25)	78-2731-73
Stachyoidinol	MeOH	213(4.48),250s(4.19), 269(4.41),307(4.03)	119-0053-73
$C_{23}H_{22}O_7$			
Stachyoidinone	MeOH	206(4.27),233(4.21), 288(4.10),372(4.03)	119-0053-73
Sumatrol	MeOH	297(4.36)	78-2731-73
Tephrodindiol	MeOH	214(4.56),248s(4.24), 268(4.44),308(4.11)	119-0053-73
Tephrosin	MeOH	238(4.34),250(4.34), 271(4.40),299(4.00)	78-2731-73
α-Toxicarol	MeOH	228(4.23),235(4.22), 273(4.54),296(4.14)	78-2731-73
$C_{23}H_{22}O_8$			
Pulvinic acid, O-methyl-3,4,4'-trimethoxy-, methyl ester	EtOH	240(4.37),361(4.49)	39-1529-73C
Pulvinic acid, O-methyl-3',4,4'-trimethoxy-, methyl ester	EtOH	241(4.31),265s(4.12), 370(4.45)	39-1529-73C
Tephrodinic acid, 5-O-demethyl-, methyl ester	MeOH	212(4.49),272(4.52), 335s(3.84)	119-0064-73
$C_{23}H_{22}O_{12}$			
Irifloside	EtOH	251s(4.34),274(4.45), 335(3.65)	94-2323-73
	$EtOH-AlCl_3$	249(4.27),283(4.43)	94-2323-73
$C_{23}H_{23}ClN_4O_4$			
1H-Pyrazolo[1,5-a]pyrimidin-8-ium, 7-[2-[4-(dimethylamino)phenyl]ethenyl]-5-methyl-1-phenyl-, (E)-, perchlorate	MeOH	482(4.54)	124-1163-73
$C_{23}H_{23}NO$			
2-Propen-1-one, 1-(4-methylphenyl)-3-[2-(1-pyrrolidinyl)-1H-indol-3-yl]-	EtOH	231(4.12),280(4.27), 481(4.53)	48-1161-73
2-Propen-1-one, 1-phenyl-3-[2-(1-piperidinyl)-1H-inden-3-yl]-	EtOH	232(4.14),270(4.26), 313(4.21),488(4.41)	48-1161-73
$C_{23}H_{23}NO_3$			
2-Butenoic acid, 4-[(4,5-diphenyl-2,4-pentadienyl)amino]-4-oxo-, ethyl ester, (E,E,Z)-	MeOH	208(4.58),224(4.43), 288(4.56),308(4.34)	44-2169-73
1H-Isoindole-4-carboxylic acid, 2,3,3a-4,5,7a-hexahydro-3-oxo-5,6-diphenyl-, ethyl ester, (3aα,4α,5α,7aβ)-	MeOH	242(4.05)	44-2169-73
$C_{23}H_{23}NO_5$			
Isoxazole, 5-phenyl-3-[tetrahydro-2,2-dimethyl-6-(phenylmethoxy)furo[2,3-d]-1,3-dioxol-5-yl]-, [3aR-(3aα,5α,6α,6aα)]-	$CHCl_3$	268(3.58)	136-0311-73D

Compound	Solvent	λ_{max}(log ε)	Ref.
$C_{23}H_{23}NO_6$			
Corynoline, acetyl-	MeOH	236s(3.95),290(3.86)	95-0087-73
Isocorynoline, acetyl-	MeOH	237(3.86),289(3.85)	95-0087-73
$C_{23}H_{23}N_3O_4$			
Benzoic acid, 4-[[2-(4-morpholinyl)-5-phenyl-3-furanyl)azo]-, ethyl ester	CH_2Cl_2	268(4.33),332(4.20), 490(4.58)	39-2523-73C
tetrafluoroborate	CH_2Cl_2	274(4.39),296s(4.23), 478(4.62),500s(4.56)	39-2523-73C
Indolo[2,3-a]quinolizine-3-propanoic acid, 2-(1-cyano-2-methoxy-2-oxoethylidene)-2,3,4,6,7,12-hexahydro-, methyl ester	MeOH	222(4.54),254(4.06), 346(4.04),455(4.66), 481(4.76)	44-2501-73
L-Valine, N-(n-benzoyl-α,β-didehydrotryptophyl)-	67% MeOH	273(4.04),335(4.28)	105-0273-73
$C_{23}H_{23}N_3O_6$			
Cytidine, N-benzoyl-2'-O-(phenylmethyl)-	MeOH	259(4.38),304(4.02)	24-0665-73
Cytidine, N-benzoyl-3'-O-(phenylmethyl)-	MeOH	259(4.27),302(3.88)	24-0665-73
Cytidine, N-benzoyl-5'-O-(phenylmethyl)-	MeOH	258(4.34),304(4.01)	24-0665-73
2-Pyrimidinol, 4-amino-5-(2,4:3,5-di-O-benzylidene-D-allo-pentahydroxypentyl)-	MeOH	272(3.89)	136-0015-73D
D-altro isomer	MeOH	272(3.71)	136-0015-73D
$C_{23}H_{23}N_4$			
1H-Pyrazolo[1,5-a]pyrimidin-8-ium, 7-[2-[4-(dimethylamino)phenyl]ethenyl]-5-methyl-, 1-phenyl-, (E)-, perchlorate	MeOH	482(4.54)	124-1163-73
$C_{23}H_{23}O_3P$			
3H-Naphtho[2,1-e]phosphindol-3-one, 1,2,3a,3b,4,5,11,11a-octahydro-7-methoxy-1-phenyl-, 1-oxide	n.s.g.	262(4.32)	88-3217-73
isomer	n.s.g.	264(4.34)	88-3217-73
3H-Naphtho[2,1-e]phosphindol-3-one, 1,2,3a,4,5,10,11,11a-octahydro-7-methoxy-1-phenyl-, 1-oxide, (3aα,11aβ)-	n.s.g.	272(4.23)	88-3217-73
	acid	295(3.96),360(3.42), 405(3.00)(changing)	88-3217-73
$C_{23}H_{24}$			
Bicyclo[2.2.1]heptane, 7-(diphenylmethylene)-2,2-dimethyl-3-methylene-, (+)-	MeOH	249(4.26)	44-2698-73
	MeOH	248(4.26)	44-2698-73
Bicyclo[3.3.1]nona-2,6-diene, 4,8-dimethyl-2,6-diphenyl-	MeCN	244(4.39),291s(2.56)	5-0844-73
1,4-Methano-1H-fluorene, 2,3,4,4a-tetrahydro-4,10,10-trimethyl-9-phenyl-, (1α,4α,4aβ)-(-)-	MeOH	238(4.30)	44-2698-73
	MeOH	239(4.30)	44-2698-73
Tricyclo[2.2.1.0^{2,6}]heptane, 3-(diphenylmethylene)-1,7,7-trimethyl-	MeOH	259(4.20)	44-2698-73
$C_{23}H_{24}NO_5$			
6H-Benzo[g]-1,3-dioxolo[7,8][1]benzopyrano[3,4,5-ij]quinolizinium, 5,8,12b,13-tetrahydro-9,10-dimethoxy-12b,13-dimethyl-, iodide	EtOH	256(4.11),336(4.22), 394s(3.53)	73-1614-73
$C_{23}H_{24}N_2O_3$			
Acetamide, N-[3,4-dihydro-1-(phenylmethyl)spiro[benz[cd]indole-5(1H),2'-	EtOH	206(4.55),227(4.53), 294(3.88)	39-0760-73C

Compound	Solvent	λ_{max}(log ϵ)	Ref.
[1,3]dioxolan]-4-yl]-N-methyl- (cont.)			
1-Pyrrolidinecarbonitrile, 2-[(3,6,7-trimethoxy-9-phenanthrenyl)methyl]-, (S)-	n.s.g.	257(4.73),285(4.44), 311(3.90),342(2.89), 359(2.31)	33-2882-73
$C_{23}H_{24}N_2O_7$			
Isoxazole, 4,5-dihydro-3-(4-nitrophenyl)-5-[tetrahydro-2,2-dimethyl-6-(phenylmethoxy)furo[2,3-d]-1,3-dioxol-5-yl]-	EtOH	226(4.08),305(4.26)	33-1303-73
$C_{23}H_{24}O_4$			
2H,6H,14H-Dipyrano[2,3-a:2',3'-c]xanthen-14-one, 3,4,7,8-tetrahydro-2,2,6,6-tetramethyl-	MeOH	256(4.60),294(4.42), 341(4.19),376(3.83)	2-1237-73
9H-Xanthen-9-one, 1,3-dihydroxy-2,4-bis-(3-methyl-2-butenyl)-	MeOH	252(4.48),297(4.24)	2-1237-73
$C_{23}H_{24}O_4S_3$			
Ethane, 1,1-bis(p-toluenesulfonyl)-2-(p-toluenethio)-	EtOH	232(4.53),264(3.79), 275(3.61)	44-2600-73
Ethane, 1,2-bis(p-toluenesulfonyl)-1-(p-toluenethio)-	EtOH	228(4.53),258(3.83), 275(3.59)	44-2600-73
$C_{23}H_{24}O_5$			
12-Deoxy-$\Delta^{12(12a)}$-dehydrorotenone, 6',7'-dihydro-	MeOH	219(4.45),256(4.17), 264(4.11),362(4.51), 381(4.42)	78-2731-73
9H-Fluorene-2,7-dibutanoic acid, α-hydroxy-, 7-ethyl ester	EtOH	219(4.50),252(3.73), 260(3.82),292(4.64), 316(4.83)	132-0015-73
9H-Xanthen-9-one, 1,3-dihydroxy-2-(3-methyl-2-butenyl)-7-[(3-methyl-2-butenyl)oxy]-	MeOH	261(4.32),297(4.16), 376(3.71)	2-1233-73
9H-Xanthen-9-one, 1,3,5-trihydroxy-2,4-bis(3-methyl-2-butenyl)-	n.s.g.	252(4.56),268(4.58), 328(4.11),384(3.54)	2-0518-73
9H-Xanthen-9-one, 1,3,7-trihydroxy-2,4-bis(3-methyl-2-butenyl)-	MeOH	262(4.59),301(4.13), 380(3.66)	2-1233-73
$C_{23}H_{24}O_6$			
1,4,6-Heptatrien-3-one, 1,7-bis(3,4-dimethoxyphenyl)-	EtOH	262(4.08),420(4.66)	39-2379-73C
Rot-3'-enonic acid, (6aS,12aS)-	EtOH	217s(4.37),234(4.22), 283(4.21),291s(4.20)	39-1277-73C
	alkali	278(4.07),285(3.96), 322s(4.03),352(4.30)	39-1277-73C
9H-Xanthen-9-one, 1,3,5,6-tetrahydroxy-2,7-bis(3-methyl-2-butenyl)-	n.s.g.	248(4.46),284(4.23), 352(4.20)	2-0518-73
$C_{23}H_{24}O_6S_3$			
Ethane, 1,1,2-tris(p-toluenesulfonyl)-	EtOH	264(3.47),275(3.34)	44-2600-73
$C_{23}H_{24}O_7$			
β-Apoplicatitoxin, trimethyl-	EtOH	281.5(3.61)	23-0482-73
4H-1-Benzopyran-4-one, 2-(3,4-dimethoxyphenyl)-5-hydroxy-3-methoxy-7-[(3-methyl-2-butenyl)oxy]-	EtOH	257(4.12),268s(4.11), 358(4.11)	102-1787-73
Chromocyclin, 2-deacetyl-12a-deoxy-8,10,11-trimethyl-	EtOH	234(4.39),260(4.42), 386(4.27),395(4.26)	105-0498-73
Eriobrucinol, hydroxy-, diacetate	n.s.g.	227(4.07),334(4.00)	78-0903-73

Compound	Solvent	λ_{max}(log ϵ)	Ref.
$C_{23}H_{24}O_9$			
4H-1-Benzopyran-4-one, 7-(β-D-gluco-pyranosyloxy)-3-(4-methoxyphenyl)-2-methyl-	EtOH	248(4.28),293(4.02)	114-0435-73B
Duartin, 8-demethyl-, O-triacetate, (3R)-	MeOH	277(3.8)	102-1157-73
$C_{23}H_{24}O_{10}$			
3-Furancarboxylic acid, tetrahydro-2-(4-hydroxy-3,5-dimethoxyphenyl)-4-[(4-hydroxy-3,5-dimethoxyphenyl)methyl-ene]-5-oxo-, methyl ester, trans-(±)-	EtOH	240(4.20)	12-1571-73
$C_{23}H_{24}O_{12}$			
4H-1-Benzopyran-4-one, 5-hydroxy-2-(4-hydroxy-3-methoxyphenyl)-6-methoxy-7-(β-D-glucopyranosyloxy)-	MeOH	275(4.21),345(4.39)	24-0020-73
$C_{23}H_{25}F_2NO_2$			
1,4-Dioxa-8-azaspiro[4.5]decane, 8-[4,4-bis(4-fluorophenyl)-3-butenyl]-, hydrochloride	MeOH	228(4.10),251(4.15)	73-3879-73
$C_{23}H_{25}NO$			
2,4-Pentadien-1-one, 1-(4-methylphenyl)-4-phenyl-5-(1-piperidinyl)-	EtOH	275(4.14),430(4.68)	48-1161-73
2-Propenamide, N-(4,5-diphenyl-2,4-pen-tadienyl)-N-(1-methylethyl)-, (E,Z)-	MeOH	226(4.20),234(4.19), 289(4.51),308(4.28)	44-2169-73
$C_{23}H_{25}NO_4$			
Tylophorinidine, O-methyl-	EtOH	259(4.70),286(4.42), 312(3.88),340(3.08)	78-0891-73
$C_{23}H_{25}NO_5$			
1H-Indole-1,3-diacetic acid, 2,3-di-hydro-5-methyl-2-oxo-3-phenyl-, diethyl ester	EtOH	258(3.93),288(3.31)	104-0831-73
1H-Indole-1,3-diacetic acid, 2,3-di-hydro-7-methyl-2-oxo-3-phenyl-, diethyl ester	EtOH	258(3.88),287(3.16)	104-0831-73
Isoxazole, 4,5-dihydro-5-phenyl-3-[tetrahydro-2,2-dimethyl-6-(phenyl-methoxy)furo[2,3-d]-1,3-dioxol-5-yl]-, [3aR-[3aα,5α(R*),6α,6aα]]-	EtOH	210(4.15)	136-0311-73D
Benzo[c]phenanthridine, 5,6-dihydro-2,3,6,8,9-pentamethoxy-5-methyl-	$CHCl_3$	281(4.62),310(4.36)	4-0867-73
$C_{23}H_{25}N_3$			
1H-Imidazo[1,2-a]imidazole, 3,6-diphen-yl-2,5-dipropyl-	EtOH	260(4.00),390(3.84)	103-1082-73
$C_{23}H_{25}N_3O_2$			
1-Azulenecarboxylic acid, 2-amino-7-(1-methylethyl)-3-[(4-methylphenyl)azo]-, ethyl ester	MeOH	259(4.16),328(4.56), 345s(4.40),390(4.54), 500(4.05)	18-3266-73
$C_{23}H_{25}N_3O_3$			
Neoechinuline	EtOH	231(4.51),287(4.12), 420(3.99)	32-0141-73

Compound	Solvent	$\lambda_{max}(\log \epsilon)$	Ref.
$C_{23}H_{25}N_3O_4$			
3,4-Secogardnerine, N_b-cyano-3-oxo-, acetate	EtOH	215(4.39),233s(4.06), 261(3.82),269s(3.69), 346(4.37)	95-1165-73
$C_{23}H_{25}N_5O_3$			
Benzoic acid, 4-[2-[3-(4-morpholinyl)-6-phenyl-4-pyridazinyl]hydrazino]-, ethyl ester	CH_2Cl_2	250(4.47),289(4.47)	39-2532-73C
$C_{23}H_{26}Cl_2O_4$			
Pregna-1,4,6-triene-3,20-dione, 17α-acetoxy-4,6-dichloro-	MeOH	235(4.09),306(3.93)	73-2492-73
$C_{23}H_{26}N_2O_4$			
2-Propanone, 1-[4-[2-[4-(acetyloxy)phenyl]-1-ethylbutyl]phenoxy]-3-diazo-	EtOH	268(3.97)	44-3525-73
$C_{23}H_{26}N_2O_5$			
16,19-Secostrychnidine-10,16-dione, 21,22-epoxy-21,22-dihydro-2-methoxy-19-methyl-, (21α,22α)-	EtOH	208(4.37),261(4.23), 299(3.73)	78-4137-73
$C_{23}H_{26}N_2O_6$			
16,19-Secostrychnidine-10,16-dione, 21,22-epoxy-21,22-dihydro-4-hydroxy-3-methoxy-19-methyl-, (21α,22α)-	EtOH	206(4.11),237(4.21), 271(3.81)	78-4137-73
$C_{23}H_{26}N_2O_7S$			
L-Threonine, N-[S-benzoyl-N-[(phenylmethoxy)carbonyl]-L-cysteinyl]-, methyl ester	EtOH	238(4.03),264(3.93)	44-0270-73
$C_{23}H_{26}N_4$			
1H-Imidazo[1,2-a]imidazol-1-amine, 3,6-diphenyl-2,5-dipropyl-	EtOH	290(4.13)	103-1082-73
$C_{23}H_{26}O_4$			
18,19-Dinorpregna-1,3,5(10)-trien-20-yn-6-one, 3-acetoxy-13-ethyl-17-hydroxy-, (17α)-	MeOH	208(4.42),247(4.03), 298(3.34)	24-0723-73
$C_{23}H_{26}O_5$			
1,3-Dioxolane, 4-[1-(3,4-dimethoxyphenyl)-3-(4-methoxyphenyl)-2-propenylidene]-2,2-dimethyl-, (Z,E)-	EtOH	228s(4.25),308(4.49)	39-2359-73C
$C_{23}H_{26}O_6$			
1,3-Dioxolane-4-methanol, α-(3,4-dimethoxyphenyl)-α-[(4-methoxyphenyl)ethynyl]-2,2-dimethyl-	EtOH	255(4.44),282s(3.77), 293(3.12)	39-2359-73C
2(3H)-Furanone, 4-[(3,4-dimethoxyphenyl)methyl]-3-[(4-ethoxy-3-methoxyphenyl)methylene]dihydro-, (R)-	EtOH	232(4.27),288(3.97), 331(4.08)	95-0541-73
1H-Phenalen-1-one, 3-hydroxy-6,7,8,9-tetramethoxy-4-methyl-2-(3-methyl-2-butenyl)-	$CHCl_3$	218(4.59),267(4.59), 353(4.11),390(4.19), 410s(4.17)	39-2388-73C

Compound	Solvent	λmax(log ε)	Ref.
$C_{23}H_{26}O_7$			
4H-1-Benzopyran-4-one, 5-hydroxy-2-(4-hydroxy-3-methoxyphenyl)-3,7-dimethoxy-8-(3-methylbutyl)-	MeOH	277(4.13),340(4.00),415(4.00)	12-0409-73
	MeOH-NaOMe	275(4.16),368(4.05),425(4.09)	12-0409-73
	MeOH-NaOAc	265(4.16),412(4.08)	12-0409-73
	MeOH-AlCl3	272(4.29),356(4.07),418(3.92)	12-0409-73
4H-1-Benzopyran-4-one, 7-hydroxy-3-[5-(3-methoxy-3-methylbutyl)-2-hydroxy-4,6-dimethoxyphenyl]-	EtOH	239(4.33),248(4.33),284(4.07),303s(3.99)	94-1338-73
2(3H)-Furanone, 4-[(3,4-dimethoxyphenyl)methyl]dihydro-3-[(3,4,5-trimethoxyphenyl)methylene]-, (R)-	EtOH	287(4.01),331(4.14)	95-0374-73
2(5H)-Furanone, 4-[(3,4-dimethoxyphenyl)methyl]-3-[(3,4,5-trimethoxyphenyl)methyl]-	EtOH	281(3.63)	95-0374-73
Oxiranecarboxylic acid, 3-(3,4-dimethoxyphenyl)-3-(2,2-dimethyl-1,3-dioxolan-4-yl)-, phenylmethyl ester	EtOH	234(3.90),279(3.43)	39-2359-73C
Phenol, 4-[4-(3,4-dimethoxyphenyl)tetrahydro-1H,3H-furo[3,4-c]furan-1-yl]-2-methoxy-, acetate, (1α,3aα,4α,6aα)-	MeOH	280(3.68)	95-0044-73
$C_{23}H_{26}O_{11}$			
4H-1-Benzopyran-4-one, 5-(β-D-glucopyranosyloxy)-2,3-dihydro-3-hydroxy-7-methoxy-2-(4-methoxyphenyl)-	EtOH	228(3.98),282(3.74)	102-0913-73
$C_{23}H_{27}ClO_4$			
19-Norpregna-4,6-diene-3,20-dione, 17-acetoxy-6-chloro-16-methylene-	MeOH	282(4.37)	87-0649-73
Pregna-1,4,6-triene-3,20-dione, 17α-acetoxy-6-chloro-	MeOH	229(3.96),259(3.96),299(3.97)	94-1295-73
$C_{23}H_{27}ClO_7$			
Benzenepropanoic acid, 5-[3-(5-chloro-2,4-dimethoxyphenyl)-1-oxopropyl]-2,4-dimethoxy-, methyl ester	EtOH	231(4.12),270(3.87),295(3.62),310(3.61)	2-1099-73
$C_{23}H_{27}Cl_3O_4$			
Pregna-4,6-diene-3,20-dione, 17α-acetoxy-4,6,7-trichloro-	MeOH	304(4.20)	73-2492-73
$C_{23}H_{27}F_3O_3$			
3'H-Cyclopropa[6,7]pregna-4,6-diene-3,20-dione, 16,17-epoxy-3',3',6-trifluoro-6,7-dihydro-16-methyl-, (6β,7β,16α)-	n.s.g.	244(4.06)	39-0227-73C
$C_{23}H_{27}NO_2$			
2H-Indol-2-one, 3-[[3,5-bis(1,1-dimethylethyl)-4-hydroxyphenyl]methylene]-1,3-dihydro-	MeOH	211(4.41),254(4.20)	103-0034-73
Murrayazolinine	EtOH	240(3.50),253(3.24),258(3.21),304(3.06)	25-0322-73
$C_{23}H_{27}NO_4$			
Estra-1,3,5(10)-trien-3-ol, 17-acetoxy-2-(3-isoxazolyl)-	EtOH	221(4.28),258(4.00),308(3.74)	12-1763-73

Compound	Solvent	$\lambda_{max}(\log \epsilon)$	Ref.
Estra-1,3,5(10)-trien-3-ol, 17-acetoxy-2-(5-isoxazolyl)-	EtOH	226(4.28),266(4.30), 276(4.21),316(4.02)	12-1763-73
$C_{23}H_{27}NO_5$			
6-Oxomestranol 6-(O-carboxymethyl)oxime	EtOH	258(4.00),308(3.57)	13-0327-73B
$C_{23}H_{27}NO_6$			
6H-Dibenzo[de,g]quinoline-6-carboxylic acid, 4,5,6a,7-tetrahydro-1,3,9,10-tetramethoxy-, ethyl ester	MeOH	278(4.15),307(4.16), 315(4.13)	94-0662-73
$C_{23}H_{27}NO_7$			
Rhoeageninediolmethine, monoacetyl-	EtOH	238(3.93),293(3.92)	73-2799-73
$C_{23}H_{27}N_3O_4$			
3,4-Secohirsutine, N_b-cyano-3-oxo-	EtOH	240(4.38),313(4.22)	95-1165-73
$C_{23}H_{28}BrClO_4$			
Pregna-4,6-diene-3,20-dione, 17α-acetoxy-6-bromo-4-chloro-	MeOH	305(4.14)	73-2492-73
$C_{23}H_{28}N_2O_2$			
1H-Azepine-5-carboxylic acid, 1-benzyl-4-(benzylamino)-2,3,6,7-tetrahydro-, ethyl ester	EtOH	304(4.11)	1-3251-73
$C_{23}H_{28}N_2O_3$			
Gardnerine, N_a-methyl-, acetate	EtOH	233(4.65),281(3.79), 297(3.82)	95-1165-73
$C_{23}H_{28}N_2O_4$			
Formosanan-16-carboxylic acid, 1,2-didehydro-2-ethoxy-19-methyl-, methyl ester	MeOH	213(4.30),246(4.03)	78-2015-73
2-Propanone, 1-[[(17β)-17-acetoxyestra-1,3,5(10)-trien-3-yl]oxy]-3-diazo-	EtOH	270(3.98)	44-3525-73
3,4-Secogardnerine, N_b-methyl-3-oxo-, acetate	EtOH	232(4.12),263(3.84), 345(4.37)	95-1165-73
Δ^{14}-Vincamine, 12-methoxy-	EtOH	228(4.15),271(3.87), 286(3.77),293(3.68)	102-1475-73
$C_{23}H_{28}N_2O_5$			
Cimicidine	EtOH	228(4.38),262(3.86), 293s(3.18)	23-3102-73
	EtOH-NaOH	234(4.34),308(3.69)	23-3102-73
$C_{23}H_{28}N_2O_7$			
4H,5H-1,3-Dioxino[4,5-b][1]benzopyran-4-one, 5a,6,7,8,9,9a-hexahydro-2,2-dimethyl-9a-(4-morpholinyl)-5-(4-nitrophenyl)-	dioxan	254(4.06),282(3.97)	49-0447-73
$C_{23}H_{28}N_3O_4P$			
Phosphonic acid, (9a-ethoxy-9,9a-dihydro-3-methyl-1-phenyl-1H-pyrazolo[3,4-b]quinolin-4-yl)-, diethyl ester	n.s.g.	249(4.36),276(4.36), 337(3.85),365(3.71)	39-1606-73C
Phosphoramidic acid, [2-[(1,5-dihydro-3-methyl-5-oxo-1-phenyl-4H-pyrazol-4-ylidene)methyl]phenyl-, bis(1-methylethyl) ester	EtOH	243(4.40),294(3.80)	39-1606-73C

Compound	Solvent	$\lambda_{max}(\log \epsilon)$	Ref.
$C_{23}H_{28}N_4O_3$			
2H,6H-Indolo[2,3-a]quinolizin-2β-ylacetimidic acid, cyano-3β-(2-methoxycarbonylethyl)-1,3,4,7,12,12b-hexahydro-, methyl ester	MeOH	226(3.86),253(3.82)	44-2501-73
$C_{23}H_{28}O_2$			
1,5-Heptanedione, 4-ethyl-6,6-dimethyl-1,3-diphenyl-	EtOH	242(4.11)	22-0263-73
$C_{23}H_{28}O_3$			
Carda-8,14,16,20(22)-tetraenolide, 3-hydroxy-, (3β,5β)-	MeOH	387(4.30)	102-2737-73
Gona-1,3,5(10),8-tetraen-17-ol, 3-methoxy-13-(2-propenyl)-, acetate, (17α)-(±)-	EtOH	278(4.17)	94-2202-73
$C_{23}H_{28}O_3S$			
2-Naphthalenol, hexahydro-6-phenyl-, 4-methylbenzenesulfonate	MeOH	273(2.66)	44-2077-73
$C_{23}H_{28}O_5$			
Estra-1,3,5(10),16-tetraene-3,17-diol, 11β-methoxy-, diacetate	EtOH	268(2.85),275(2.85)	111-0451-73
	EtOH-NaOH	243(3.97),299(3.46)	111-0451-73
Pregna-1,4,16-triene-3,20-dione, 21-acetoxy-11β-hydroxy-	MeOH	242(4.37)	24-2263-73
Sequirin C, tri-O-methyl-, acetonide, trans	EtOH	265(4.43)	39-2359-73C
$C_{23}H_{28}O_6$			
Estra-1,3,5(10)-triene-3,17β-diol, 16α,17α-epoxy-11β-methoxy-, diacetate	EtOH	268(2.84),275(2.85)	111-0451-73
	EtOH-NaOH	243(3.98),299(3.46)	111-0451-73
2(3H)-Furanone, 3-[(4-ethoxy-3-methoxyphenyl)methyl]dihydro-	EtOH	232(4.23),281(3.81)	95-0541-73
8,14-Secoestra-1,3,5(10),9-tetraen-14-one, 17α-hydroxy-3-methoxy-, racemic hemisuccinate	EtOH	265(4.31)	94-0107-73
$C_{23}H_{28}O_7$			
Epimagnolin	EtOH	231(4.26),279(3.60)	88-0335-73
Erioflorin methacrylate	EtOH	211(4.39)	102-2469-73
$C_{23}H_{28}O_8$			
Flavaspidic acid PB	EtOH	223(4.94),299(4.79), 349(4.93)	102-1493-73
	EtOH-NaOH	239(4.79),317(5.00)	102-1493-73
1,3-Pentadiene-1,2,3,4-tetracarboxylic acid, 5-(dispiro[2.1.2.3]dec-4-ylidene)-, tetramethyl ester	hexane	208(4.02),227(3.38), 310(3.38)	77-0859-73
$C_{23}H_{29}ClO_4$			
19-Norpregn-4-ene-3,20-dione, 17-acetoxy-6β-chloro-16-methylene-	MeOH	238(4.15)	87-0649-73
Pregna-4,6-diene-3,20-dione, 17α-acetoxy-7-chloro-	EtOH	291(4.38)	87-0065-73
Pregna-4,7-diene-3,20-dione, 17α-acetoxy-7-chloro-	EtOH	235(4.22)	87-0065-73
$C_{23}H_{29}ClO_5$			
Pregna-4,6-diene-3,20-dione, 17α-acetoxy-6-chloro-2α-hydroxy-	MeOH	284(3.91)	94-1295-73

Compound	Solvent	λ max(log ε)	Ref.
$C_{23}H_{29}Cl_3N_4O_4S_2$			
3H-Pyrazole-3-c rboxylic acid, 4,5-dihydro-4,4-dimethyl-3-[2-[(2-methylpropyl)dithio]-4-oxo-3-[(phenylacetyl)amino]-1-azetidinyl]-, 2,2,2-trichloroethyl ester	EtOH	334(2.30)	39-1182-73C
more polar epimer	EtOH	334(2.08)	39-1182-73C
$C_{23}H_{29}FO_5$			
Pregna-4,17(20)-dien-21-al, 20-acetoxy-9-fluoro-11β-hydroxy-3-oxo-	MeOH	244(4.43)	24-2263-73
Pregna-4,16-diene-3,20-dione, 21-acetoxy-9-fluoro-11β-hydroxy-	MeOH	239(4.41)	24-2263-73
$C_{23}H_{29}FO_7S$			
Estra-1,3,5(10)-triene-3,6,17-triol, 7-fluoro-, 3,17-diacetate 6-methanesulfonate, (6α,7α,17β)-	$CHCl_3$	269(2.85),276(2.85)	39-1462-73C
$C_{23}H_{29}N_3O_4$			
1H-Azecino[5,4-b]indole-6-acetic acid, 2,3,4,5,6,7,8,9-octahydro-8-hydroxy-α-(methoxymethylene)-, methyl ester, [5R-[5R*,6S*(E),8S*]]-	EtOH	226(4.66),250s(4.10), 284(3.90),293(3.85)	95-1165-73
$C_{23}H_{29}N_3O_7$			
1H-Pyrrolo[2,3-c]pyridine-3-propanoic acid, 4,5,6,7-tetrahydro-2-[[3-(2-methoxy-2-oxoethyl)-4-(3-methoxy-3-oxopropyl)-1H-pyrrol-2-yl-[^{14}C]methyl]-5-oxo-, methyl ester	MeOH	230(4.02)	39-1546-73C
$C_{23}H_{30}N_2O_3$			
Vobasan-17-ol, 11-methoxy-, acetate	EtOH	229(4.49),273(3.58), 299(3.69)	95-1165-73
$C_{23}H_{30}N_2O_4$			
Geissovelline	EtOH	217(4.35),262(4.24), 299(3.02)	44-0215-73
	EtOH-HCl	216(4.34),262(4.16), 297(3.85)	44-0215-73
Vincamine, 12-methoxy-	EtOH	227(4.59),270(3.92), 285(3.79),293(3.76)	102-1475-73
$C_{23}H_{30}N_2O_5$			
Gardneramine oxindole, 17-deoxy-2-deoxo-2,17-epoxy-	MeOH	213(4.57),242s(3.90), 304(3.56)	78-2015-73
$C_{23}H_{30}N_2O_6S$			
2-Pyrrolidinone, 1-[[1,2,3,4-tetrahydro-6,7-dimethoxy-2-(1-piperidinylsulfonyl)-1-naphthalenyl]acetyl]-, didehydro deriv.	EtOH	238(4.27),300s(4.00), 322(4.11)	4-0137-73
$C_{23}H_{30}N_4O_5$			
Spiro[5.11]heptadec-1-ene-3,7-dione, 3-(2,4-dinitrophenylhydrazone)	$CHCl_3$	380(4.46)	39-0393-73C
$C_{23}H_{30}O_3$			
18-Norpregna-3,5,13-trien-20-one, 3-acetoxy-17-methyl-, (17α)-	EtOH	238(4.28)	22-2032-73

Compound	Solvent	$\lambda_{max}(\log \epsilon)$	Ref.
$C_{23}H_{30}O_4$			
Adynerigin, Δ^{16}-dehydro-	MeOH	267(4.28)	102-2737-73
Androsta-1,5-diene-3,11,17-trione, 4,4-dimethyl-, 17-(1,2-ethanediyl acetal)	n.s.g.	224(4.03)	39-2095-73C
1(2H)-Naphthalenone, 5-(formyloxy)-3,4,4a,5,6,8a-hexahydro-8-[2-(2-methoxyphenyl)ethyl]-4,7,8a-trimethyl-, (4α,4aα,5β,8aβ)-	EtOH	224(3.90),273(3.30), 279(3.27)	23-3989-73
19-Norpregn-4-ene-3,20-dione, 17α-acetoxy-16-methylene-	MeOH	240(4.24)	87-0649-73
$C_{23}H_{30}O_5$			
Ankaflavin	dioxan	212(4.16),228(4.21), 382(4.12)	102-2531-73
2H,8H-Benzo[1,2-b:3,4-b']dipyran-2,10-(9H)-dione, 3,4-dihydro-5-methoxy-8,9-dimethyl-6-(3-methyl-2-butenyl)-4-propyl-	EtOH	231(4.38),271(4.03), 327(3.72)	102-0185-73
$C_{23}H_{30}O_6$			
2H,8H-Benzo[1,2-b:3,4-b']dipyran-6-propanoic acid, 3,4-dihydro-5-hydroxy-2,3,8,8-tetramethyl-4-oxo-β-propyl-, methyl ester	EtOH	275(4.55),300(3.97), 312(3.93),366(3.38)	102-0185-73
5β-Pregn-1-ene-3,11,20-trione, 21-acetoxy-17-hydroxy-	n.s.g.	224(3.94)	39-1361-73C
5β-Pregn-2-ene-1,11,20-trione, 21-acetoxy-17-hydroxy-	n.s.g.	225(3.81)	39-1361-73C
$C_{23}H_{30}O_7$			
2(3H)-Furanone, dihydro-3-[hydroxy-(4,5,6,7-tetramethoxy-2-methyl-1-naphthalenyl)methyl]-4,4,5-trimethyl-	EtOH	248(4.70),294s(3.84), 305(3.86)	39-2388-73C
$C_{23}H_{30}O_8$			
Nortrachelogenin, ethyl-methyl-	EtOH	232(4.18),282(3.75)	94-1108-73
$C_{23}H_{31}ClO_4$			
Pregna-5,7-dien-20-one, 17-acetoxy-7-chloro-3β-hydroxy-	EtOH	263(3.85),273(3.97), 283(3.97),295(3.72)	87-0065-73
$C_{23}H_{31}ClO_5$			
Pregna-4,6-dien-20-one, 17-acetoxy-6-chloro-2,3-dihydroxy-, (2α,3β)-	MeOH	237(4.19),244(4.23), 253(4.06)	94-1295-73
(2β,3β)-	MeOH	236(4.24),244(4.31), 252(4.14)	94-1295-73
$C_{23}H_{31}FO_5$			
Androst-4-en-6-one, 17β,19-diacetoxy-3β-fluoro-	EtOH	230(3.83)	22-1098-73
Androst-5-en-4-one, 17β,19-diacetoxy-3β-fluoro-	EtOH	237(3.88)	22-1098-73
Androst-5-en-7-one, 17β,19-diacetoxy-3β-fluoro-	EtOH	235(4.21)	22-1098-73
$C_{23}H_{31}NO$			
5H-Benzocycloheptene-2-methanol, α-[3-(dimethylamino)propyl]-6,7,8,9-tetrahydro-α-phenyl-	MeOH	259(2.75),265(2.77), 274(2.64)	73-2768-73

Compound	Solvent	λmax(log ε)	Ref.
$C_{23}H_{32}Cl_2NO_4P$			
Phosphoric acid, 14,18-dichloro-3,4,5,6-7,8,9,10,11,12-decahydro-2,13-metheno-13H-1-benzazacyclopentadecin-3-yl diethyl ester	EtOH	220(4.46),238(4.72), 317(3.50),332(3.55)	44-0927-73
$C_{23}H_{32}N_2O_4$			
Geissovelline, dihydro-	EtOH	260(4.15),300(3.93)	44-0215-73
	EtOH-HCl	262(4.19),298(3.87)	44-0215-73
	EtOH-KOH	262(4.17),302(4.20)	44-0215-73
$C_{23}H_{32}N_2O_6$			
Geissovelline, dihydrodihydroxy-	EtOH	229(3.94),258(4.14)	44-0215-73
	EtOH-HCl	262(4.15),301(3.85)	44-0215-73
3,5-Methano-3H-dibenzo[a,d]cycloheptene-9-carboxylic acid, 4,4a,5,5a,6,7,8,9-9a,10-decahydro-5a,9-dimethyl-2-(1-methyl-1-nitroethyl)-11-nitro-, methyl ester	EtOH	229(3.83),348(3.79)	23-2323-73
$C_{23}H_{32}N_3$			
1,5-Naphthyridinium, 1-[4-(1,3-dihydro-1,3,3-trimethyl-2H-indol-2-ylidene)-2-butenylidene]decahydro-, trans, perchlorate	EtOH	479(5.07)	104-2606-73
$C_{23}H_{32}O_3$			
5α-Pregna-2,7-dien-6-one, 20β-acetoxy-	EtOH	244(4.00)	13-0609-73A
$C_{23}H_{32}O_4$			
Adynerigenin	MeOH	217(4.22)	102-2737-73
Allocyathin B_3, O-acetyl-, methyl ketal	isooctane	255(3.75)	23-3842-73
Cannabinol, 1β,6β-epoxyhexahydro-, acetate	EtOH	274s(3.29),279(3.31)	78-1615-73
Cannabinol, hexahydro-6-oxo-, acetate	EtOH	223s(3.95),275(3.24), 281(3.29)	78-1615-73
Cyclopenta[c][1]benzopyran-2-carboxaldehyde, 9-acetoxy-1,2,3,3a,4,9b-hexahydro-2,4,4-trimethyl-7-pentyl-, [2S-(2α,3aα,9bβ)]-	EtOH	273(3.28),280(3.33)	78-1615-73
2-Cyclopropen-1-one, 2-[(3β,5α,17β)-17-(formyloxy)-3-hydroxyandrostan-3-yl]-	n.s.g.	266(1.57)	44-1478-73
Pregn-4-ene-3,16-dione, 20α-acetoxy-	EtOH	241(4.23)	78-0823-73
13α-Pregn-4-ene-3,20-dione, 17α-acetoxy-	EtOH	242(4.20)	94-0565-73
13α-Pregn-4-ene-3,20-dione, 17β-acetoxy-	EtOH	243(4.18)	94-0565-73
	n.s.g.	242(4.19),290s(2.19)	70-0611-73
5α-Pregn-16-ene-18,20-dione, 3β-acetoxy-	n.s.g.	218(3.70),243(3.60)	33-2698-73
Pregn-4-ene-3,20-dione, 16α,17α-epoxy-21-(methoxymethyl)-	EtOH	243(4.36)	70-1790-73
$C_{23}H_{32}O_4S$			
12α-Etiojerv-4-en-3-one, 7α-(acetylthio)-17α-acetoxy-	MeOH	237(4.17)	87-0568-73
$C_{23}H_{32}O_4Si$			
1,3-Dioxa-2-silacyclohexane, 2,5-diethyl-2-[3-(phenylmethoxy)phenoxy]-4-propyl-	EtOH	207(4.25),272(3.26), 278(3.20)	87-0729-73

Compound	Solvent	λ_{max}(log ϵ)	Ref.
$C_{23}H_{32}O_5$			
Androst-4-en-3-one, 2α,17β-diacetoxy-	MeOH	241(4.15)	94-1295-73
Androst-4-en-3-one, 2β,17β-diacetoxy-	MeOH	242(4.20)	94-1295-73
Pregn-4-ene-3,20-dione, 17α-acetoxy-6β-hydroxy-	EtOH	236(4.14)	33-2396-73
Pregn-4-ene-3,20-dione, 21-[(methoxycarbonyl)oxy]-	MeOH	240(4.22)	44-2328-73
$C_{23}H_{32}O_6$			
2H-1-Benzopyran-6-propanoic acid, 3,4-dihydro-5-hydroxy-7-methoxy-2,3-dimethyl-8-(3-methyl-2-butenyl)-β-propyl- (recedensic acid)	EtOH	286(4.10),358(3.66)	102-0185-73
$C_{23}H_{33}ClNO_4P$			
Phosphoric acid, 18-chloro-3,4,5,6,7,8-9,10,11,12-decahydro-2,13-metheno-13H-1-benzazacyclopentadecin-3-yl diethyl ester	EtOH	213(4.49),235(4.71)	44-0927-73
$C_{23}H_{33}IO_3$			
Pregn-5-en-20-one, 3β-acetoxy-18-iodo-	EtOH	262(2.71)	22-1456-73
$C_{23}H_{33}NO_3$			
5α-Pregn-17(20)-ene-21-carboxylic acid, 20-cyano-3β-hydroxy-	n.s.g.	224(4.13)	44-1478-73
$C_{23}H_{33}NO_4$			
3,5-Methano-3H-dibenzo[a,d]cycloheptene-9-carboxylic acid, 4,4a,5,5a,6,7,8,9-10,10a-decahydro-5a,9-dimethyl-2-(1-methyl-1-nitroethyl)-, methyl ester, [3R-(3α,4aβ,5α,5aα,9β,9aβ)]-	EtOH	258(3.80),382(3.74)	23-2323-73
$C_{23}H_{33}NO_5$			
3,5-Methano-3H-dibenzo[a,d]cycloheptene-9-carboxylic acid, 4,4a,5,5a,6,7,8,9-9a,10-decahydro-5a,9-dimethyl-2-(1-hydroxy-1-methylethyl)-11-nitro-, methyl ester	EtOH	236(3.80),362(3.75)	23-2323-73
$C_{23}H_{33}NO_6$			
Acetic acid, [[[(3β)-17,17-[1,2-ethanediylbis(oxy)]-3-hydroxyandrost-5-en-7-ylidene]amino]oxy]-	n.s.g.	238(4.04)	13-0723-73A
$C_{23}H_{33}N_3O_3$			
Neoechinuline, hydro-	EtOH	228(4.57),285(3.94), 295(3.82)	32-0141-73
$C_{23}H_{33}N_3O_4$			
5β,14β-Card-20(22)-enolide, 3α-azido-12β,14-dihydroxy-	EtOH	218(4.21)	33-2782-73
5β,14β-Card-20(22)-enolide, 3β-azido-12β,14-dihydroxy-	EtOH	217(4.11)	33-2782-73
5β,14β-Card-20(22)-enolide, 3β-azido-14,16β-dihydroxy-	EtOH	216(4.21)	33-2782-73
$C_{23}H_{34}Br_2O_3$			
Pregnan-6-one, 20β-acetoxy-3β,5α-dibromo-	EtOH	313(2.17)	13-0609-73A

Compound	Solvent	λ_{max}(log ϵ)	Ref.
$C_{23}H_{34}N_2O_3$			
3,4-Secocondyfolan-3-one, 1-ethyl-10,11-dimethoxy-4-methyl-	EtOH	251(3.99),328(3.72)	44-0215-73
	EtOH-HCl	235(3.99),282(3.69)	44-0215-73
$C_{23}H_{34}O_2$			
18-Nor-17α-pregna-3,5,13-trien-20-ol, 3-methoxy-17β,20-dimethyl-	EtOH	250(4.27)	22-2032-73
$C_{23}H_{34}O_3$			
Pregna-17(20),21-diene-21-carboxylic acid, 3-hydroxy-, methyl ester, [3β,5α,17(21)S]-	n.s.g.	222(4.21)	44-1478-73
Pregn-4-ene-3,20-dione, 11-hydroxy-16,17-dimethyl-, (11α,16α)-	EtOH	242(4.19)	105-0039-73
Pregn-4-ene-3,20-dione, 19-hydroxy-16,17-dimethyl-, (16α)-	n.s.g.	242(4.24)	105-0174-73
Pregn-4-en-3-one, 21-acetoxy-	MeOH	241(4.22)	44-2328-73
2-Propenoic acid, 3-[[3(S),5α,17β]-17-hydroxyandrostan-3-ylidene]-, methyl ester	n.s.g.	216(4.16)	44-1478-73
$C_{23}H_{34}O_4$			
5β,14α-Card-20(22)-enolide, 3β,15β-dihydroxy-	EtOH	217.5(4.21)	94-0388-73
5β,14β-Card-20(22)-enolide, 3β,15α-dihydroxy-	EtOH	218.5(4.16)	94-0388-73
5β,14β-Card-20(22)-enolide, 3β,15β-dihydroxy-	EtOH	217(4.21)	94-0388-73
5-Heptenoic acid, 7-[4-(3-hydroxy-1-octenyl)-2-oxobicyclo[3.2.0]hept-3-yl]-, methyl ester	MeOH	280(2.11)	33-0557-73
1(2H)-Phenanthrenone, 7-acetoxy-2-(1-acetyl-2-propenyl)dodecahydro-2,4b-dimethyl-, [2R-(2α,4aα,7β,8aα,10aβ)]-	n.s.g.	283.6(2.31)	33-1078-73
Pregn-4-ene-3,20-dione, 2,6-bis(hydroxymethyl)-	EtOH	241(4.16)	33-2396-73
Pregn-4-ene-3,20-dione, 6,6-bis(hydroxymethyl)-	EtOH	246(4.11)	33-2396-73
5α-Pregn-16-en-20-one, 3β-acetoxy-14β-hydroxy-	n.s.g.	240(4.00)	32-0117-73
Retinoic acid, 11-acetoxy-11,12-dihydro-, methyl ester, 13-cis	EtOH	235(4.18),271(4.11)	32-0117-73
Retinoic acid, 12-carboxy-7,8-dihydro-, dimethyl ester	EtOH	285(4.51)	65-2047-73
$C_{23}H_{34}O_5$			
Pregn-4-en-3-one, 20β-hydroxy-21-[(methoxycarbonyl)oxy]-	MeOH	241(4.23)	44-2335-73
$C_{23}H_{34}O_7$			
11,13-Dihydroheliangininyl 3β,8β-diisobutyrate	EtOH	205(3.69)	102-2469-73
Favescin	EtOH	207(3.20),221(3.26), 297(2.20)	102-2943-73
$C_{23}H_{34}O_{15}$			
Genipin gentiobioside	EtOH	238(4.11)	94-2684-73
$C_{23}H_{35}IO_3$			
Pregn-5-ene-3,20-diol, 18-iodo-, 3-acetate, (20R)-	EtOH	260(2.69)	22-1456-73

Compound	Solvent	$\lambda_{max}(\log \epsilon)$	Ref.
$C_{23}H_{35}N$			
D(17a)-Homo-C,18-dinorpregna-3,5,17(20)-triene-17a-methanamine, N,N-dimethyl-, (13ξ)-	EtOH	236(4.15)	20-0031-73
$C_{23}H_{35}NO_3$			
5α,14β-Card-20(22)-enolide, 3β-amino-14-hydroxy-	EtOH	217(4.16)	33-2782-73
$C_{23}H_{35}NO_4$			
5β,14β-Card-20(22)-enolide, 3α-amino-12β,14-dihydroxy-	EtOH	218(4.20)	33-2782-73
Card-20(22)-enolide, 3β-amino-14,16β-dihydroxy-, hydrochloride	EtOH	216(4.12)	33-2782-73
$C_{23}H_{36}N_2O_2$			
6H-Dibenzo[b,d]pyran, 1-methoxy-3-[methyl(3-dimethylaminopropyl)amino]-6,6,9-trimethyl-6a,10a-trans-6a,7,10,10a-tetrahydro-, (-)-	EtOH	223(4.46),259(4.09), 289(3.25)	33-0510-73
$C_{23}H_{36}N_2O_3$			
Acetic acid, [(3α,5α)-3-(acetyloxy)androstan-17-ylidene]hydrazide	MeOH	231(3.79)	88-2289-73
$C_{23}H_{36}O_3$			
2H-Pyran-2-one, 5-[4-[1-ethyl-2-(4-hydroxycyclohexyl)butyl]cyclohexyl]-	EtOH	297(3.7)	5-2078-73
$C_{23}H_{37}IO_3$			
5α-Pregnane-3,20-diol, 18-iodo-, 3-acetate	EtOH	260(2.74)	22-1456-73
$C_{23}H_{37}NO$			
23-Norcon-18(22)-enine, 18,20-dimethyl-, 22-oxide, (5α)-	EtOH	238(4.06)	22-1814-73
$C_{23}H_{37}NO_2$			
4-Azaandrost-5-en-3-one, 17β-(3-methylbutoxy)-	EtOH	235(4.13)	36-0638-73
$C_{23}H_{39}NO_2$			
Hexadecanamide, N-hydroxy-N-(3-methylphenyl)-	EtOH	254(4.00)	112-0547-73
$C_{23}H_{42}O_5$			
Radiclonic acid, dihydro-, (as dimethyl ester)	MeOH	221(4.11)	88-2333-73

Compound	Solvent	λ_{max}(log ϵ)	Ref.
$C_{24}H_4D_{10}O_2$			
1H-Indene-1,3(2H)-dione, 2-[2,3-di(phenyl-d)-2-cyclopropen-1-ylidene]-	MeCN	232(4.64),250s(4.46), 265s(4.20),287(4.02), 297(4.28),342(4.66)	44-3064-73
$C_{24}H_{10}ClIO_2S_2$			
Naphtho[1,8-bc]thiopyran-3(2H)-one, 2-(9-chloro-3-oxonaphtho[1,2-b]thien-2(3H)-ylidene]-7-iodo-, cis	n.s.g.	506.5(4.15)	103-0960-73
trans	n.s.g.	618(4.45)	103-0960-73
Naphtho[1,8-bc]thiopyran-3(2H)-one, 2-(9-chloro-3-oxonaphtho[2,3-b]thien-2(3H)-ylidene]-7-iodo-, cis	n.s.g.	511(4.23)	103-0960-73
trans	n.s.g.	621(4.52)	103-0960-73
$C_{24}H_{11}Br_2ClN_2$			
Benz[g]indeno[1,2,3-de]phthalazine, 3,11-dibromo-7-(4-chlorophenyl)-	HOAc	260(4.82),302(4.39), 360(4.04),460(3.62)	115-0145-73A
$C_{24}H_{11}Br_2ClO_2$			
7H-Benzo[c]fluoren-7-one, 2,9-dibromo-6-(4-chlorobenzoyl)-	HOAc	254(4.70),286(4.52), 297(4.53),346s(3.66), 450(3.09)	115-0145-73A
$C_{24}H_{11}IO_2S_2$			
Naphtho[1,8-bc]thiopyran-3(2H)-one, 7-iodo-2-(1-oxonaphtho[2,1-b]thien-2(1H)-ylidene)-, cis	n.s.g.	491(4.20)	103-0960-73
trans	n.s.g.	606(4.53)	103-0960-73
$C_{24}H_{12}Br_2N_2$			
Benz[g]indeno[1,2,3-de]phthalazine, 3,11-dibromo-7-phenyl-	HOAc	260(4.41),300(4.02), 400(3.72),455(3.65)	115-0145-73A
$C_{24}H_{12}Br_2N_2O$			
Benz[g]indeno[1,2,3-de]phthalazin-7(6H)-one, 3,11-dibromo-6-phenyl-	HOAc	259(4.73),304(4.47), 380(3.96)	115-0145-73A
$C_{24}H_{12}Br_2O_2$			
7H-Benzo[c]fluoren-7-one, 6-benzoyl-2,9-dibromo-	HOAc	250s(4.63),268(4.49), 288(4.45),296(4.46), 448(3.10)	115-0145-73A
$C_{24}H_{12}N_3O_6P$			
Phosphine, tris[(4-nitrophenyl)ethynyl]-	EtOH	295(4.60)	65-2627-73
$C_{24}H_{12}O_2$			
Benzo[3,4]cyclobuta[1,2-b]naphthacene-6,13-dione	$CHCl_3$	248(4.82),260s(4.45), 320(4.93),353(3.81), 368(4.08),386(4.23), 409(3.73)	39-2267-73C
$C_{24}H_{13}NO_7S$			
1,4-Naphthalenedione, 2-[2,3-dihydro-2-(4-nitrophenyl)-3-oxobenzo[b]thien-2-yl]-, S,S-dioxide	MeOH	252(4.38)	39-1006-73C
$C_{24}H_{14}$			
Triptycene, 9-(1,3-butadiynyl)-	EtOH	198(4.79),211(4.81), 270(3.40),278(3.51)	18-2907-73

Compound	Solvent	λ_{max}(log ϵ)	Ref.
$C_{24}H_{14}Br_2N_2O_2$			
1H-Benz[f]isoindole-1,3(2H)-dione, 6-bromo-4-(4-bromophenyl)-2-(phenylamino)-	EtOH	218(4.68),266(4.76)	115-0145-73A
$C_{24}H_{14}Cl_2N_2$			
Benzo[h]quinazoline, 2,4-bis(4-chlorophenyl)-	EtOH	243(4.47),278(4.64), 319(4.26),353(3.74), 371(3.74)	4-0405-73
$C_{24}H_{14}N_2O$			
Benz[g]indeno[1,2,3-de]phthalazin-7(6H)-one, 6-phenyl-	HOAc	297(4.53),375(4.03)	115-0145-73A
Benz[h]indeno[1,2,3-de]phthalazin-3(2H)-one, 2-phenyl-	n.s.g.	223(4.58),242(4.70), 276(4.63),294(4.67), 330s(4.29)	115-0145-73A
$C_{24}H_{14}N_2O_2S$			
1H-Thieno[2,3-c]pyrazol-4(5H)-one, 3-methyl-5-(2-oxo-1(2H)-acenaphthylidene)-1-phenyl-	EtOH	235(4.48),295(4.25), 330(4.00),470(3.72)	104-2429-73
$C_{24}H_{14}N_2O_3$			
14H-Benz[4,5]isoquino[2,1-a]perimidine-10-carboxylic acid, 14-oxo-, methyl ester	C_6H_5Cl	504(3.70)	103-1257-73
$C_{24}H_{14}O_4$			
Dibenzo[a,j]anthracene-2-carboxylic acid, 7,14-dihydro-7,14-dioxo-, methyl ester	dioxan	225(4.79),286s(4.48), 294s(4.50),303(4.65), 331(3.83),359s(3.57), 408s(3.28)	24-1341-73
$C_{24}H_{14}O_5S$			
1,4-Naphthalenedione, 2-(2,3-dihydro-3-oxo-2-phenylbenzo[b]thien-2-yl)-, S,S-dioxide	MeOH	257(4.41)	39-1006-73C
$C_{24}H_{15}N$			
Benz[c]indeno[1,2,3-kl]acridine, 14-methyl-	C_6H_{12}	226(4.79),241(4.43), 252(4.52),270(4.43), 295(4.65),302(4.70), 335(3.36),350(3.60), 370(3.96),392(4.16), 397(4.15),404(4.20), 415(4.06),430(4.20), 440(3.76)	39-2311-73C
Benz[c]indeno[1,2,3-mn]acridine, 9-methyl-	C_6H_{12}	219(4.55),228(4.46), 239(4.56),242(4.55), 258(4.65),270(4.42), 278(4.50),287(4.42), 295(4.50),300(4.43), 308(4.45),326(3.70), 330(3.70),336(3.50), 390(4.18),402(4.14), 415(4.18),440(3.10)	39-2311-73C
$C_{24}H_{15}N_2S_2$			
10H-Phenothiazinium, 10-(3H-phenothiazin-3-ylidene)-	MeCN	320(4.40),446(4.18), 620(4.33)	39-0264-73B

Compound	Solvent	λ_{max}(log ϵ)	Ref.
$C_{24}H_{15}N_3O_2$			
Acetamide, N-(14-oxo-14H-benz[4,5]isoquino[2,1-a]perimidin-10-yl)-	C_6H_5Cl	480(3.64)	103-1257-73
$C_{24}H_{15}N_3O_3$			
2-Naphthalenol, 1-[(10-nitro-9-anthracenyl)azo]-	$CHCl_3$	255(4.85),270s(4.70), 300s(4.32),430s(3.96), 535(4.23)	22-1305-73
$C_{24}H_{16}$			
[2,2](2,7)Naphthalenophane-1,11-diene	EtOH	239(4.99),283(4.31), 324(3.33),363s(3.20)	77-0806-73
$C_{24}H_{16}Br_2$			
Benzene, 1,1'-(3,5,7,9-dodecatetraene-1,11-diyne-1,12-diyl)bis[4-bromo-, all-E-	benzene	403(5.01),426(4.85)	5-1339-73
(E,E,Z,Z)-	benzene	395(4.94),416s(4.74)	5-1339-73
$C_{24}H_{16}CrO_7$			
Chromium, pentacarbonyl(6-ethoxy-3,4-diphenyl-2H-pyran-2-ylidene)-	hexane	260(4.51),297(4.47), 352(3.81),528(4.00)	39-2535-73C
$C_{24}H_{16}MoO_7$			
Molybdenum, pentacarbonyl(6-ethoxy-3,4-diphenyl-2H-pyran-2-ylidene)-	hexane	258(4.41),295(4.29), 362(3.69),508(4.05)	39-2535-73C
	EtOH	257(4.48),290(4.33), 360(3.80),470(4.01)	39-2535-73C
$C_{24}H_{16}N_2$			
Azuleno[1,2-b]pyrazine, 2,3-diphenyl-	MeOH	291(4.37),354(4.63), 410s(3.95),510(2.29), 555(2.36),605(2.38), 660(2.24),738(1.88)	18-3161-73
Benzo[h]quinazoline, 2,4-diphenyl-	EtOH	240(4.53),266(4.59), 315(4.26),350(3.81), 368(3.81)	4-0405-73
2,2'-Biquinoline, 4-phenyl-, Cu(I) complex	EtOH	550(3.96)	103-1391-73
Naphtho[1,2-b:8,7-b']diquinolizinediium, diperchlorate	MeCN	237(4.89),275(4.27), 310(4.65),344(4.60), 355(4.64),383(3.92), 404(4.08),425(4.14), 449(3.93)	4-0195-73
$C_{24}H_{16}N_2O_5$			
2-Pentene-1,5-dione, 3-(6-nitro-2,1-benzisoxazol-3-yl)-1,5-diphenyl-	MeCN	278(4.33),360(4.11)	44-2834-73
4H-Pyran, 4-[(2,4-dinitrophenyl)methylene]-2,6-diphenyl-	MeCN	250(4.31),315(4.00), 490(4.07)	44-2834-73
Spiro[2H-indole-2,4'-[4'H]pyran]-3(1H)-one, 1-hydroxy-6-nitro-2',6'-diphenyl-	MeCN	250(4.69),380-450(3.30)	44-2834-73
$C_{24}H_{16}N_2S_2$			
3,10'-Bi-10H-phenothiazine	MeCN	258(4.96),318(3.95)	39-0264-73B
$C_{24}H_{16}N_8O_2S$			
1H-Indole-2,3-dione, 3-[[5-[(1,2-dihydro-2-oxo-3H-indol-3-ylidene)hydrazino]-3-phenyl-1,3,4-thiadiazol-2(3H)-ylidene]hydrazone]	EtOH	257(4.34),420(4.30), 505(4.33),540(4.34)	104-2007-73

Compound	Solvent	λ_{max}(log ε)	Ref.
$C_{24}H_{16}O_2$			
Dibenz[a,j]anthracen-7-ol, acetate	MeCN	225(4.67),251(4.36), 287(4.91),299(5.10), 325(4.18)	24-1341-73
$C_{24}H_{16}O_3$			
Dibenz[a,j]anthracene-2-carboxylic acid, 7,14-dihydro-7-oxo-, methyl ester	dioxan	224(4.74),279(4.58), 305s(4.02),355s(3.51)	24-1341-73
$C_{24}H_{16}O_4$			
Benzo[a]pyrene-1,6-diol, diacetate	EtOH	256(4.61),262(4.68), 272(4.45),284(4.62), 297(4.72),337(3.72), 355(4.13),373(4.43), 382(4.31),388(4.37), 393(4.48)	34-0332-73
Benzo[a]pyrene-3,6-diol, diacetate	EtOH	256(4.51),266(4.54), 278(4.26),289(4.54), 302(4.67),337(3.61), 355(3.98),373(4.26), 383(4.15),387(4.20), 394(4.30)	34-0332-73
Benzo[a]pyrene-4,5-diol, diacetate	EtOH	256(4.64),266(4.72), 275(4.46),287(4.69), 298(4.79),333(3.77), 349(4.12),367(4.40), 381(4.28),387(4.47), 394(4.04),403(3.17)	34-0332-73
Benzo[a]pyrene-6,12-diol, diacetate	EtOH	253(4.64),266(4.71), 274(4.51),286(4.68), 297(4.78),337(3.80), 355(4.17),373(4.45), 387(4.37),393(4.50), 407(3.89)	34-0332-73
Dibenz[a,j]anthracene-2-carboxylic acid, 7,14-dihydro-14-hydroxy-7-oxo-, methyl ester	dioxan	223(4.92),235s(4.62), 276(4.74),295s(4.23), 346(3.54)	24-1341-73
2-Naphthalenecarboxylic acid, 8-(1,3-dihydro-3-oxonaphtho[1,2-c]furan-1-yl)-, methyl ester	dioxan	240(5.03),283(4.14), 295(4.11),317(3.49), 331(3.61)	24-1341-73
2-Naphthalenecarboxylic acid, 1-(7-formyl-1-naphthalenyl)carbonyl]-, methyl ester	dioxan	242(4.86),261s(4.53), 289s(4.05),299(4.12), 313(4.10),336(3.88), 349s(3.70)	24-1341-73
$C_{24}H_{16}O_{11}$			
2(3H)-Benzofuranone, 5,6-diacetoxy-3-[4-[4-(acetyloxy)phenyl]-3-hydroxy-5-oxo-2(5H)-furanylidene]-	$CHCl_3$	342s(3.70),440(4.19)	39-1529-73C
$C_{24}H_{17}Cl_4N_3$			
1-Cyclobutene-1-carboximidamide, 3,3-dichloro-4-(dichloromethylene)-N,N'-diphenyl-2-(phenylamino)-, hydrochloride	n.s.g.	290(4.36)	44-1470-73
$C_{24}H_{17}I_2NO_2S$			
1,3-Propanedione, 2-(3-ethyl-2(3H)-benzothiazolylidene)-1,3-bis(4-iodophenyl)-	EtOH	218(4.60),276(4.34), 377(4.45)	73-3616-73

Compound	Solvent	$\lambda_{max}(\log \epsilon)$	Ref.
$C_{24}H_{17}NO$			
Benzo[f]naphtho[2',1':3,4]cyclobuta[1,2-h]isoquinoline, 8c,14b-dihydro-14b-methoxy-	EtOH	248(4.71),280s(4.04), 291(3.88),303(3.89), 328(3.18),343(3.45), 360(3.56)	12-2129-73
Benzo[h]naphtho[1',2':3,4]cyclobuta[1,2-f]isoquinoline, 8c,14b-dihydro-14b-methoxy-	EtOH	228(4.46),247(4.72), 258s(4.57),273s(4.11), 298(3.84),310(3.81), 330(3.00),347(2.63)	12-2129-73
$C_{24}H_{17}NO_2$			
Quinoline, 2,3-dibenzoyl-4-methyl-	MeOH	207(4.62),255(4.54)	44-1769-73
$C_{24}H_{17}NO_3$			
4H-Pyran, 4-[(2-nitrophenyl)methylene]-2,6-diphenyl-	MeCN	248(4.55),272s(4.34), 340(4.39),400(4.09)	44-2834-73
Spiro[2H-indole-2,4'-[4H]pyran]-3(1H)-one, 1-hydroxy-2',6'-diphenyl-	MeCN	238(4.63),330-380(3.30)	44-2834-73
$C_{24}H_{17}NO_3S$			
Benz[a]acridin-5-ol, 4-methylbenzenesulfonate	EtOH	223(4.47),238s(4.31), 243(4.31),248s(4.25), 270s(4.40),280(4.46), 287(4.40),322s(3.62), 332(3.60),348(3.61), 364(3.68),383(3.71), 420(3.25),440(3.25)	12-2315-73
	EtOH-acid	226(4.46),240(4.32), 253(4.26),263(4.24), 283s(4.30),294(4.35), 386s(3.85),401(3.94)	12-2315-73
$C_{24}H_{17}N_3$			
Pyridazino[4,5-b]quinoline, 10-methyl-1,4-diphenyl-	MeOH	212(4.45),255(4.64), 360(3.73)	44-1769-73
$C_{24}H_{17}N_3O_6S$			
1,3-Propanedione, 2-(3-ethyl-2(3H)-benzothiazolylidene)-1,3-bis(4-nitrophenyl)-	EtOH	220(4.59),268(4.41), 378(4.33)	73-3616-73
$C_{24}H_{17}N_3O_6Se$			
1,3-Propanedione, 2-(3-ethyl-2(3H)-benzoselenazolylidene)-1,3-bis(4-nitrophenyl)-	EtOH	216(4.64),270(4.46), 377(4.40)	73-3616-73
$C_{24}H_{18}$			
Azulene, 1-(2,2-diphenylethenyl)-	C_6H_{12}	259(4.56),320(4.42), 403(4.25),643(2.46)	5-0166-73
Benzene, 1,1'-(3,5,7,9-dodecatetraene-1,11-diyne-1,12-diyl)bis-, all-E-	EtOH	391(4.97),411(4.84)	5-1339-73
(E,E,Z,Z)-	EtOH	383(4.92),401s(4.75)	5-1339-73
Cyclopropa[3,4]pentaleno[1,2-b]naphthacene, 2a,2b,4,11,12b,12c-hexahydro-	C_6H_{12}	230(4.95),242s(4.42), 271(3.82),280(3.92), 285(3.90),315(2.93), 318(2.98),330(2.76)	35-4606-73
1,4-Ethenopentacene, 1,4,6,13-tetrahydro-	C_6H_{12}	230(4.95),243(4.23), 270(3.84),279(3.91), 286(3.88),318(2.89), 325(2.63)	35-4606-73

Compound	Solvent	λ_{max}(log ε)	Ref.
1,1'-Spirobi[1H]indene, 3-methyl-	EtOH	206(4.56),236(4.53), 270(3.80)	104-2377-73
$C_{24}H_{18}BrN_3O_4$			
1H-Pyrazole-4-carboxylic acid, 3-(4-bromophenyl)-1-(4-nitrophenyl)-5-phenyl-	EtOH	229(5.52),255(5.42), 308(5.21)	78-0121-73
$C_{24}H_{18}ClN_3O_4$			
1H-Pyrazole-4-carboxylic acid, 3-(2-chlorophenyl)-1-(4-nitrophenyl)-5-phenyl-, ethyl ester	EtOH	302(5.23)	78-0121-73
$C_{24}H_{18}Cl_2N_4$			
Benzenamine, 2,2'-azobis[N-(2-chlorophenyl)-	C_6H_{12}	288(4.61),320(4.43), 504(4.18)	44-0507-73
$C_{24}H_{18}N_2$			
Acenaphtho[1,2-c]cinnoline, 5,6,6a,12b-tetrahydro-5-phenyl-	MeCN	289(4.26)	22-3487-73
1,3-Diazabicyclo[3.1.0]hex-3-ene, 4,5-di-2-naphthalenyl-	C_6H_{12}	226(5.03),245(4.73), 253(4.69),273(4.18), 283(4.21),292(4.09), 341(3.04)	35-1954-73
$C_{24}H_{18}N_2O_3$			
6H-Pyrido[1,2-a]pyrimidin-6-one, 8,9-dibenzoyl-2,4-dimethyl-	MeOH	237(4.35),252(4.41), 391(3.94)	44-3485-73
Pyrrolidine-2,4,5-trione, 1-(4-methylphenyl)-3-[(phenylamino)phenylmethylene]-	$CHCl_3$	296(4.33),364(4.34)	56-2235-73
$C_{24}H_{18}N_2O_4$			
Pyrrolidine-2,4,5-trione, 1-phenyl-3-[(phenylamino)(4-methoxyphenyl)-methylene]-	$CHCl_3$	297(4.26),364(4.37)	56-2235-73
$C_{24}H_{18}N_3O_4P$			
Benzenamine, 4-[bis[(4-nitrophenyl)ethynyl]phosphino]-N,N-dimethyl-	EtOH	288(4.60)	65-2627-73
$C_{24}H_{18}N_3O_5P$			
Benzenamine, 4-[bis[(4-nitrophenyl)ethynyl]phosphinyl]-N,N-dimethyl-	EtOH	293(4.73),350(3.87)	65-2627-73
$C_{24}H_{18}N_4$			
Benzenamine, N,N'-(1,2-di-2-pyridinyl-1,2-ethanediylidene)bis-	EtOH	235(4.38),275(4.27), 325s(3.70)	12-2027-73
Benzenamine, N,N'-(1,2-di-3-pyridinyl-1,2-ethanediylidene)bis-	EtOH	230s(4.38),270s(4.30), 320s(3.87)	12-2027-73
Benzenamine, N,N'-(1,2-di-4-pyridinyl-1,2-ethanediylidene)bis-	EtOH	230(4.46),270s(4.20), 350s(3.70)	12-2027-73
$C_{24}H_{18}N_4O_6$			
1H-Pyrazole-4-carboxylic acid, 1,3-bis-(4-nitrophenyl)-5-phenyl-, ethyl ester	EtOH	302(5.42)	78-0121-73
$C_{24}H_{18}N_5P$			
Pyrido[2,3-e]-1,2,4-triazine, 3-[(triphenylphosphoranylidene)amino]-	EtOH	351(4.29),408(3.61)	4-0575-73

Compound	Solvent	λ_{max}(log ε)	Ref.
$C_{24}H_{18}N_6$			
Diazene, bis[3-(phenylazo)phenyl]-	EtOH	228(4.36),322(4.71), 440(3.06)	7-0727-73
$C_{24}H_{18}N_6S$			
Sulfurdiimide, N,N'-bis[(4-phenylazo)-phenyl]-	C_6H_{12}	331(4.40),472(4.47)	143-0285-73
$C_{24}H_{18}O$			
9,10-Ethanoanthracen-11-one, 9,10-dihydro-12-[(4-methylphenyl)methylene]-	C_6H_{12}	273(4.12),303(4.29), 344s(2.89),361s(2.71), 382s(2.27)	35-6294-73
$C_{24}H_{18}OS_2$			
Methanone, (6-methyl-3,5-diphenyl-1,4-dithiin-2-yl)phenyl-	EtOH	244(4.53),286(4.25)	18-0667-73
$C_{24}H_{18}O_2$			
9(10H)-Anthracenone, 10-(2-oxo-1-phenylbutylidene)-	hexane	249(4.40),269(4.26), 346(3.94)	54-0845-73
Benzeneacetic acid, 3-phenyl-1-naphthalenyl ester	EtOH	255(4.72),291(4.05)	48-0887-73
9,10-Ethanoanthracen-11-one, 9,10-dihydro-12-[(4-methylphenyl)methylene]-	C_6H_{12}	279s(4.01),315(4.36), 364s(2.85),382s(2.37)	35-6294-73
$C_{24}H_{18}O_3$			
Cyclopropane, tribenzoyl-	EtOH	250(4.35)	22-0202-73
2-Naphthalenecarboxylic acid, 1-[(7-formyl-1-naphthalenyl)methyl]-, methyl ester	dioxan	239(4.87),253(4.76), 289(4.18),310(4.17), 337(3.71),351(3.64)	24-1341-73
2-Naphthalenecarboxylic acid, 8-[(2-methyl-1-naphthalenyl)carbonyl]-, methyl ester	dioxan	226(5.06),249(4.49), 313(4.05)	24-1341-73
2-Pentene-1,5-dione, 3-benzoyl-1,5-diphenyl-	EtOH	253(4.31),400(4.30)	22-0202-73
$C_{24}H_{18}O_4$			
2H,8H-Benzo[1,2-b:5,4-b']dipyran-2,8-dione, 3,4,6,7-tetrahydro-4,6-diphenyl- (or isomer)	EtOH	288(3.60)	12-0899-73
2bH-Cycloprop[cd]indene-2,2b-dicarboxylic acid, 5-(diphenylmethylene)-2a,5,5a,5b-tetrahydro-	EtOH	230s(4.26),297(4.29)	24-1837-73
2-Naphthalenecarboxylic acid, 1-[[7-(hydroxymethyl)-1-naphthalenyl]carbonyl]-, methyl ester	dioxan	215(4.82),240(4.85), 288(3.97),299(4.01), 323(4.02)	24-1341-73
Triptycene, 2-acetoxy-7-(methoxycarbonyl)-, (+)-	dioxan	215(4.73),277(3.34), 294(3.58)	18-0611-73
Triptycene, 2,7-diacetoxy-, (+)-	MeOH	214(4.78),240s(3.62), 255s(3.11),262(3.09), 269(3.23),277(3.30)	18-0605-73
Triptycene, 2,5-bis(methoxycarbonyl)-	dioxan	222(4.59),288s(3.82), 298(3.86)	18-0605-73
Triptycene, 5,7-bis(methoxycarbonyl)-	dioxan	222(4.60),286(3.74), 298(3.78)	18-0605-73
$C_{24}H_{18}O_5$			
4,7-Isobenzofurandiol, 1,3-diphenyl-, diacetate	$CHCl_3$	395.0(4.0)	22-1154-73

Compound	Solvent	λ_{max}(log ϵ)	Ref.
1,4-Naphthalenedione, 2-[2-(2,2-dimethyl-1-oxopropyl)-2,3-dihydro-1,3-dioxo-1H-inden-2-yl]-	MeOH	223(4.58),242(4.65), 252s(4.44)	39-1006-73C
$C_{24}H_{18}O_6$			
1(3H)-Isobenzofuranone, 3-(2,4-diacetoxyphenyl)-3-phenyl-	EtOH	320(3.55)	64-0468-73B
$C_{24}H_{18}O_8$			
[2,2'-Binaphthalene]-1,1',4,4'-tetrone, 7,7'-dihydroxy-8,8'-dimethoxy-3,3'-dimethyl-	EtOH	229(4.48),266(4.50), 306s(4.09),313s(4.07), 510(3.55)	2-0507-73
Hexanedioic acid, bis(2-oxo-2H-1-benzopyran-7-yl) ester	CH_2Cl_2	277(4.32),283(4.32), 313(4.24)	44-0957-73
$C_{24}H_{18}S$			
4,11[1',2']-Benzenoanthra[2,3-c]thiophene, 4,11-dihydro-1,3-dimethyl-	C_6H_{12}	226s(4.90),229(4.91), 237(4.88),249(4.59), 267(4.26),276(4.08), 289(3.63),296(3.03), 303(2.94),310(3.22), 316(2.95),324(3.34)	78-1379-73
1,1':2',1"-Terphenyl, 2-(phenylthio)-	EtOH	249(4.37),283(2.16)	35-1285-73
$C_{24}H_{19}BrN_2O_3$			
Spiro[2H-1-benzopyran-2,2'-[2H]indole], 8-bromo-1',3'-dihydro-1',3'-dimethyl-6-nitro-3'-phenyl-	toluene	381(4.65),601(4.95)	103-1098-73
	EtOH	368(4.45),529(4.67)	103-1098-73
	dioxan	372(4.16),587(4.28)	103-1098-73
$C_{24}H_{19}ClN_2O$			
2-Propen-1-one, 1-(4-chlorophenyl)-3-(4,5-dihydro-1,5-diphenyl-1H-pyrazol-3-yl)-	C_6H_{12}	432(4.69)	104-0413-73
	EtOH	452(4.60)	104-0413-73
$C_{24}H_{19}ClO_5$			
Cyclopropenylium, (3-oxo-3-phenylpropyl)diphenyl-, perchlorate	CH_2Cl_2	225(4.37),232(4.36), 246(4.18),292(4.31), 305(4.40),320(4.31)	39-2523-73C
$C_{24}H_{19}Cl_2N_3O_9$			
1H-Imidazole-5-carboxylic acid, 1-[3,5-bis-O-(4-chlorobenzoyl)-2-deoxy-α-D-erythro-pentofuranosyl]-4-nitro-	EtOH	242(3.50)	5-1286-73
$C_{24}H_{19}NO$			
Cyclobuta[a]naphthalene, 2a,8b-dihydro-8b-methoxy-2-phenyl-1-(4-pyridinyl)-	EtOH	236s(4.34),248(4.25), 300s(3.92),310s(3.83)	12-2129-73
1,2,7-Metheno-1H-cyclopropa[b]naphthalene, 1a,2,7,7a-tetrahydro-2-methoxy-1-phenyl-8-(3-pyridinyl)-	EtOH	230(4.21),267s(3.68), 274(3.56)	12-2129-73
1,2,7-Metheno-1H-cyclopropa[b]naphthalene, 1a,2,7,7a-tetrahydro-2-methoxy-8-phenyl-1-(3-pyridinyl)-	EtOH	227s(4.29),274s(3.46), 282s(3.18)	12-2129-73
1,2,7-Metheno-1H-cyclopropa[b]naphthalene, 1a,2,7,7a-tetrahydro-2-methoxy-8-phenyl-1-(4-pyridinyl)-	EtOH	225(4.28),260(4.03)	12-2129-73
Pyridine, 4-(4-methoxyphenyl)-2,6-diphenyl-	EtOH	266(4.58),287s(4.47)	35-4891-73
	50%EtOH-HCl	257(4.24),338(4.54)	35-4891-73
4(1H)-Pyridinone, 1-(4-methylphenyl)-3,5-diphenyl-	EtOH	245(4.36),303(4.35)	4-0665-73

Compound	Solvent	$\lambda_{max}(\log \epsilon)$	Ref.
$C_{24}H_{19}NO_2S$			
1,3-Propanedione, 2-(3-ethyl-2(3H)-benzothiazolylidene)-1,3-diphenyl-	EtOH	218(4.57),250(4.31), 377(4.41)	73-3616-73
$C_{24}H_{19}NO_2Se$			
1,3-Propanedione, 2-(3-ethyl-2(3H)-benzoselenazolylidene)-1,3-diphenyl-	EtOH	220(4.53),249(4.35), 378(4.41)	73-3616-73
$C_{24}H_{19}NO_4$			
3(2H)-Oxazoleacetic acid, 2-oxo-4,5-diphenyl-α-(phenylmethyl)-, (S)-	EtOH	286(4.18)	44-3034-73
$C_{24}H_{19}NS$			
4(1H)-Pyridinethione, 1-methyl-2,3,5-triphenyl-	MeOH	226(4.13),267(3.71), 360(3.96)	77-0833-73
$C_{24}H_{19}N_3O$			
Imidazo[1,5-a]benzimidazole, 3-acetyl-1-phenyl-4-(phenylmethyl)-	EtOH	225(4.36),328(4.52)	103-0366-73
$C_{24}H_{19}N_3O_3$			
2,4,6-Cycloheptatrien-1-one, 5-(4-benzoyl-4-phenyl-1H-1,2,3-triazol-1-yl)-2-ethoxy-	n.s.g.	228(4.46),252(4.49), 328(4.14)	18-1212-73
$C_{24}H_{19}N_3O_4$			
1H-Pyrazole-4-carboxylic acid, 1-(4-nitrophenyl)-3,5-diphenyl-, ethyl ester	EtOH	227(5.48),260s(5.23), 310(5.17)	78-0121-73
$C_{24}H_{19}N_5O_5S$			
8,2'-Thioanhydroadenosine, N^6,$O^{3'}$-dibenzoyl-	EtOH	232(4.44),286s(4.03), 298(4.09)	23-2397-73
$C_{24}H_{19}O$			
Cyclopropenylium, (3-oxo-3-phenylpropyl)diphenyl-, perchlorate	CH_2Cl_2	225(4.37),232(4.36), 246(4.18),292(4.31), 305(4.40),320(4.31)	39-2523-73C
$C_{24}H_{19}OP$			
Phosphonium, triphenyl-, 2-formyl-2,4-cyclopentadien-1-ylide	MeCN	224(4.42),268(4.00), 372(4.31)	44-3537-73
$C_{24}H_{20}$			
Cyclopentadiene, 4-benzyl-1,2-diphenyl-	CH_2Cl_2	238(4.07),334(4.62), 346s(4.59)	78-4307-73
Cyclopentadiene, 1-methyl-2,3,4-triphenyl-	EtOH	237(4.32),320(3.94)	78-4307-73
1,6:11,16-Dimethanocyclobuta[1,2:3,4]-dicycloundecene, 18a,18b-dihydro-	pentane	289(4.36),440(3.94)	35-2357-73
2,7:12,17-Dimethanocyclobuta[1,2:3,4]-dicycloundecene, 9a,9b-dihydro-	pentane	293(4.61),425(4.18)	35-2357-73
[2,2][2,6)Naphthalenophane	C_6H_{12}	220(5.2),240(4.25), 253(3.97),275(3.69), 286(3.66),301(3.43), 321(3.11),336(2.70)	24-2203-73
$C_{24}H_{20}BrN_5O_3$			
Propanenitrile, 3-[[4-[(2-benzoyl-6-bromo-4-nitrophenyl)azo]phenyl]-ethylamino]-	MeOH	503(4.61)	89-0926-73

Compound	Solvent	λ_{max}(log ε)	Ref.
$C_{24}H_{20}ClNO_4$			
Pyridinium, 1-methyl-2,4,6-triphenyl-, perchlorate	EtOH	306(4.13)	103-0333-73
$C_{24}H_{20}Cl_6N_2O_4$			
1,2-Pyridazinedicarboxylic acid, 3,6-dimethyl-4,5-diphenyl-, bis(2,2,2-trichloroethyl) ester	EtOH	245(4.24),295s(3.60)	44-2043-73
$C_{24}H_{20}NNiOP$			
Nickel, (cyanato-N)(η^5-2,4-cyclopentadien-1-yl)(triphenylphosphine)-	$CHCl_3$	317(4.00),486(3.09), 789(1.81)	23-1179-73
$C_{24}H_{20}NNiP$			
Nickel, (η^5-2,4-cyclopentadien-1-yl)-(cyano-C)(triphenylphosphine)-	$CHCl_3$	297(4.12),406(3.00), 607(1.78)	23-1179-73
$C_{24}H_{20}NNiPS$			
Nickel, (η^5-2,4-cyclopentadien-1-yl)-(thiocyanato-N)(triphenylphosphine)-	$CHCl_3$	305(4.02),347s(3.66), 461(3.15),757(1.90)	23-1179-73
$C_{24}H_{20}N_2O$			
2-Propen-1-one, 3-(4,5-dihydro-1,5-diphenyl-1H-pyrazol-3-yl)-1-phenyl-	C_6H_{12}	435(4.39)	104-0413-73
	EtOH	448(4.59)	104-0413-73
$C_{24}H_{20}N_2O_2$			
5H-Benzo[a]pyrido[2,3-g]quinolizine-4,5-dione, 1,4,12b,13-tetrahydro-2-methyl-1-(phenylmethyl)-	EtOH	278(4.47),301(4.27), 408(3.63),430(3.62)	70-1745-73
3aH-Phenanthro[9,10-d]imidazole, 3a-ethoxy-2-(4-methoxyphenyl)-	n.s.g.	261(4.58),317(4.19)	78-1185-73
$C_{24}H_{20}N_2O_3$			
Spiro[2H-1-benzopyran-2,2'-[2H]indole], 1',3'-dihydro-1',3'-dimethyl-6-nitro-3'-phenyl-	toluene	375(4.47),593(4.86)	103-1098-73
	EtOH	369(4.34),540(4.69)	103-1098-73
	dioxan	374(4.21),582(4.55)	103-1098-73
$C_{24}H_{20}N_2O_4S$			
Benzenesulfonamide, N-[3-(1,3-benzodioxol-5-ylmethylene)-1,3-dihydro-1-methyl-2H-indol-2-ylidene]-4-methyl-, (E)-	n.s.g.	210(4.65),325(3.78)	39-1943-73C
Benzenesulfonamide, N-[3-(1,3-dihydro-3-oxo-1-isobenzofuranyl)-1-methyl-1H-indol-2-yl]-4-methyl-	n.s.g.	222(4.74),282(4.09)	39-1943-73C
$C_{24}H_{20}N_4$			
Benzenamine, 2,2'-azobis[N-phenyl-	C_6H_{12}	288(4.51),323(4.02), 500(4.13)	44-0507-73
Benzenamine, N-phenyl-2-[[4-(phenylamino)phenyl]azo]-	C_6H_{12}	290(4.51),325(4.19), 472(3.83)	44-0507-73
1,2-Ethenediamine, N,N'-diphenyl-1,2-di-2-pyridinyl-	EtOH	257(4.39),385(4.15)	12-2027-73
2-Tetrazene, 1,1,4,4-tetraphenyl-	C_6H_{12}	360(4.31)	73-0046-73
	THF	357(4.31)	73-0046-73
$C_{24}H_{20}N_4O_4$			
2-Naphthalenecarboxaldehyde, 3,4-dihydro-3-methyl-1-phenyl-, 2,4-dinitrophenylhydrazone	$CHCl_3$	408(4.21)	39-0308-73C

Compound	Solvent	$\lambda_{max}(\log \epsilon)$	Ref.
$C_{24}H_{20}O$			
3-Oxatricyclo[4.1.0.0^{2,4}]heptane, 4,5,7-triphenyl-, exo-endo-	C_6H_{12}	265(3.08)	88-1045-73
exo-exo-	C_6H_{12}	265(3.11)	88-1045-73
2-Propanone, 1-(10,11-dihydro-5H-dibenzo[a,d]cyclohepten-5-ylidene)-1-phenyl-	hexane	267(4.08)	54-0845-73
$C_{24}H_{20}O_2$			
Benzeneacetaldehyde, α-(10,11-dihydro-5H-dibenzo[a,d]cyclohepten-5-ylidene)-4-methoxy-	hexane	316(3.77),320(3.83)	54-0845-73
9,10-Ethanoanthracene-11-carboxylic acid, 9,10-dihydro-12-phenyl-, methyl ester, cis	C_6H_{12}	252s(2.87),258(3.00), 265(3.12),272(3.13)	35-6294-73
trans	C_6H_{12}	258(2.98),259s(2.88), 265(3.10),272(3.12)	35-6294-73
Ethanone, 1,1'-(5,12-dihydro-5,12-ethanonaphthacene-13,14-diyl)bis-	C_6H_{12}	234(4.90),259(3.84), 267(3.94),272(3.90), 278(3.89),288(3.65), 307(2.87),321(2.77)	78-1379-73
$C_{24}H_{20}O_3$			
2-Naphthalenecarboxylic acid, 1-[[7-(hydroxymethyl)-1-naphthalenyl]methyl]-, methyl ester	dioxan	229(5.01),281s(4.05), 285(4.13),294s(4.06), 321(3.29),333s(3.21)	24-1341-73
$C_{24}H_{20}O_4$			
Benzenebutanoic acid, γ-oxo-α-(2-oxo-2-phenylethyl)-β-phenyl-	MeOH	240(4.64),275(3.90), 320(3.80)	115-0381-73
1H-Phenalene-2-acetic acid, 4-methoxy-α,α-dimethyl-1-oxo-, phenyl ester	EtOH	210(4.45),264(4.44), 310(3.62),321(3.69), 417(4.12),435(4.17)	39-2159-73C
Triptycene, 2,5-dimethoxy-8-(methoxycarbonyl)-	EtOH	204(4.72),226(4.55), 267(3.90),285s(3.77), 292(3.81),303s(3.60)	18-1520-73
$C_{24}H_{20}O_4S$			
4,9[1',2']-Benzenonaphtho[2,3-c]thiophene-1,3-dimethanol, 4,9-dihydro-, diacetate	C_6H_{12}	221(4.89),237(4.35), 253(4.30),273(4.00), 279(4.04),306(2.14), 317(1.97)	78-1379-73
$C_{24}H_{20}O_7$			
4H-1-Benzopyran-4-one, 5,6-dihydroxy-7-methoxy-2-[3-methoxy-4-(phenylmethoxy)phenyl]-	MeOH	222(4.41),250s(3.92), 294(4.21),339(4.40)	24-0020-73
Glabrotephrin	MeOH	218(4.22),247(4.23), 256(4.23),309(4.27)	78-3099-73
Tachrosin, 5-O-demethyl-, 5-O-acetate	MeOH	205(4.76),217(4.73), 265(4.60),302s(4.43)	119-0064-73
$C_{24}H_{20}O_8$			
Tachrosinic acid, 5-O-demethyl-, methyl ester	MeOH	217(4.51),274(4.56), 340s(3.84)	119-0064-73
Tephrodin, 5-O-demethyl-	MeOH	218(4.38),272(4.45), 307(4.16)	119-0053-73

Compound	Solvent	$\lambda_{max}(\log \epsilon)$	Ref.
$C_{24}H_{20}S_3$			
3H-1,2-Dithiole, 3-[(2,2-diphenylethen-yl)thio]-4-(4-methylphenyl)-	C_6H_{12}	230s(4.30),280s(4.08), 310(4.12)	88-1561-73
$C_{24}H_{21}AsO_4$			
Arsonium, triphenyl-, 2,2-dimethyl-4,6-dioxo-1,3-dioxan-5-ylide	MeOH	224(4.43),240s(4.15), 265s(3.61)	78-1697-73
$C_{24}H_{21}BrO_3$			
Spiro[1,3-dioxolane-2,9'-pentacyclo-[4.3.0.0^{2,5}.0^{3,8}.0^{4,7}]nonane-4'-methanol, 1'-bromo-α,α-diphenyl-	EtOH	251(2.70),258(2.75), 264(2.65)	78-0161-73
$C_{24}H_{21}ClO_3$			
Benzoic acid, 3-chloro-, 5-hydroxy-1,4-diphenyl-3-pentenyl ester	MeOH	234(4.24)	39-2030-73C
$C_{24}H_{21}IN_2O$			
Benz[cd]indolium, 2-[3-(3-ethyl-2(3H)-benzoxazolylidene)-1-propenyl]-1-methyl-, iodide	EtOH	580(4.66),625(4.76)	103-0314-73
$C_{24}H_{21}NO$			
1-Naphthalenol, 2-[(methylamino)diphen-ylmethyl]-	n.s.g.	293(3.56),302(3.63), 317(3.61),330(3.56)	114-0411-73D
2-Naphthalenol, 1-[(methylamino)diphen-ylmethyl]-	n.s.g.	277(3.09),285(3.40), 295(3.35),317(3.32), 337(3.40)	114-0411-73D
$C_{24}H_{21}NO_5$			
2-Azabicyclo[3.2.0]hepta-3,6-diene-5,6-dicarboxylic acid, 2-acetyl-4,7-di-phenyl-, dimethyl ester	EtOH	219(4.27),258s(4.18), 270s(4.44),280(4.51), 291s(4.26),299s(4.28)	24-3824-73
7-Azabicyclo[2.2.1]hepta-2,5-diene-2,3-dicarboxylic acid, 7-acetyl-5,6-di-phenyl-, dimethyl ester	EtOH	228(4.36),264s(4.08), 347s(3.26)	24-3824-73
1H-Azepine-4,5-dicarboxylic acid, 1-acetyl-3,6-diphenyl-, dimethyl ester	EtOH	240s(4.39),262s(4.28), 328s(3.18),370s(2.86)	24-3824-73
$C_{24}H_{21}NO_9$			
3-Cyclohexene-1,3-dicarboxylic acid, 6-(1,3-benzodioxol-5-yl)-5-(benzoyl-amino)-4-hydroxy-2-oxo-, dimethyl ester	MeOH-HCl MeOH-NaOH	222(4.37),254(4.27) 222(4.36),276(4.41)	88-4587-73 88-4587-73
$C_{24}H_{21}N_3O_2$			
1H-Indole-3-acetic acid, 2-phenyl-α-(phenylhydrazono)-, ethyl ester	EtOH	306(4.43),340s(4.31)	78-3159-73
$C_{24}H_{21}N_3O_7S_2$			
Benzenesulfonamide, 4-methyl-N-[1-[3-[[(4-methylphenyl)sulfonyl]oxy]-1H-indol-2-yl]-2-nitroethylidene]-	EtOH	223(4.58),385(4.05)	95-0971-73
$C_{24}H_{21}N_5$			
2-Azulenamine, 1,3-bis[(4-methylphenyl)-azo]-	MeOH	254(4.19),355s(4.43), 414(4.72),548(3.85)	18-3266-73
$C_{24}H_{21}N_5O_3$			
Propanenitrile, 3-[[4-[(2-benzoyl-4-ni-trophenyl)azo]phenyl]ethylamino]-	MeOH	482(4.60)	89-0926-73

Compound	Solvent	$\lambda_{max}(\log \epsilon)$	Ref.
$C_{24}H_{22}$			
Cyclobutene, 1,2,3,4-tetramethyl-3,4-bis(phenylethynyl)-, cis	C6H12	242(4.61),257(4.48), 273(3.3),280(3.1)	5-1893-73
trans	C6H12	249(4.5),257(4.69), 273(3.85),280(3.61), 300(3.28)	5-1893-73
1,3,5,7,9,11-Dodecahexaene, 1,12-diphenyl-	81.5% H_2SO_4	445(3.30),550(3.82), 610(4.05),670(3.81), 750s(3.30),800s(3.11)	48-0810-73
	95.8% H_2SO_4	440(3.66),550s(4.43), 600(4.75),670(4.24), 740(4.35)	48-0810-73
	99.9% H_2SO_4	440(3.90),550s(4.02), 630s(4.34),693(4.70), 750(4.94)	48-0810-73
	18% SO_3	390(4.47),630(3.98), 690(4.07)	48-0810-73
	33% SO_3	390(4.92)	48-0810-73
3,5-Octadiene-1,7-diyne, 3,4,5,6-tetramethyl-1,8-diphenyl-, cis-trans	hexane	273(4.48),298(4.31)	5-1893-73
$C_{24}H_{22}FeN_2O$			
Ferrocene, 1-acetyl-1'-[1-[(8-amino-1-naphthalenyl)imino]ethyl]-	EtOH	235(4.69),269(3.85), 350(4.11),463(2.68)	18-3315-73
$C_{24}H_{22}N_2$			
4,4'-Bipyridinium, 1,1'-dimethyl-2,2'-diphenyl-, bis(tetrafluoroborate)	MeCN	258(4.47),334(3.91)	5-1036-73
$C_{24}H_{22}N_2O_3$			
1,3-Butanedione, 1-[1,11b-dihydro-4-oxo-2-[(phenylmethyl)amino]-4H-benzo[a]-quinolizin-3-yl]-	EtOH	243(4.12),262(4.07), 305(4.16)	70-1745-73
$C_{24}H_{22}N_2O_4$			
Propanedioic acid, (7-methylbenzo[a]-phenazin-5(7H)-ylidene)-, diethyl ester	n.s.g.	550s(3.98),596(4.16), 650s(4.08)	103-1407-73
$C_{24}H_{22}N_2O_5S$			
2,3-Dehydrovaline, N-[(2'-phthalimido-2'-benzylthiocarbonyl)vinyl]-, methyl ester	MeOH	219(4.67),312(4.37)	1-0677-73
$C_{24}H_{22}N_2O_5S_3$			
1H-Indole-2-carboximidothioic acid, N-[(4-methylphenyl)sulfonyl]-3-[[(4-methylphenyl)sulfonyl]oxy]-, methyl ester	EtOH	225(4.34),263(4.06), 300(3.95)	95-0971-73
$C_{24}H_{22}N_4O$			
Propanenitrile, 3-[[4-[(2-benzoylphenyl)azo]phenyl]ethylamino]-	MeOH	419(4.56)	89-0926-73
Propanenitrile, 3-[[4-[(4-benzoylphenyl)azo]phenyl]ethylamino]-	MeOH	432(4.63)	89-0926-73
$C_{24}H_{22}N_4O_5$			
2-Naphthalenecarboxaldehyde, 1,2,3,4-tetrahydro-1-hydroxy-3-methyl-1-phenyl-, 2,4-dinitrophenylhydrazone	$CHCl_3$	360(4.35)	39-0308-73C

Compound	Solvent	$\lambda_{max}(\log \epsilon)$	Ref.
$C_{24}H_{22}N_4S_2$			
Cyclopentapyrazole, 3,3'-dithiobis- [2,4,5,6-tetrahydro-2-phenyl-	EtOH	248(4.25),275(4.30)	39-1009-73C
$C_{24}H_{22}N_6O_2$			
Acetamide, N,N'-(7,14-dihydro-7,14-di- methylquinoxalino[2,3-b]phenazine-	EtOH	565(3.87),615(4.33), 670(4.75)	22-1289-73
2,9-diyl)bis-, diperchlorate	EtOH-2% NaOH	505(3.96),545(4.50), 585(4.83)	22-1289-73
$C_{24}H_{22}N_7O_8P$			
Adenosine, N-[(phenylamino)carbonyl]-,	pH 1	284(4.31)	87-1075-73
cyclic 3',5'-(hydrogen phosphate)	pH 7	231(4.26),276(4.34)	87-1075-73
2'-(phenylcarbamate), Na salt	pH 11	233(4.24),276(4.33)	87-1075-73
	pH 13	307(4.46)	87-1075-73
$C_{24}H_{22}O$			
Benzofuran, 4,5,6,7-tetramethyl-2,3-di- phenyl-	MeOH	240(4.19),245s(4.11), 310(4.4),316s(4.32)	5-1893-73
$C_{24}H_{22}O_2$			
Methanone, (3,4,5,6-tetramethyl-1,2- phenylene)bis[phenyl-	EtOH	254(4.5),282(3.8)	5-1893-73
1,5-Pentanedione, 2-methyl-1,3,5-tri- phenyl-	EtOH	244(4.43),278s(3.34)	22-0263-73
$C_{24}H_{22}O_3$			
Methanone, [2-(benzoyloxy)-3,4,5,6- tetramethylphenyl]phenyl-	EtOH	234(4.46),248s(4.39), 275s(3.81),281s(3.78)	5-1893-73
$C_{24}H_{22}O_4$			
2-Propen-1-one, 3-(4-methoxyphenyl)-1- [5-methoxy-2-(phenylmethoxy)phenyl]-	EtOH	231(3.97),340(4.06)	114-0093-73B
$C_{24}H_{22}O_5$			
Methanone, [5-methoxy-2-(phenylmethoxy)- phenyl][3-(4-methoxyphenyl)oxiranyl]-	EtOH	261(3.64),350(3.27)	114-0093-73B
$C_{24}H_{22}O_6$			
2H-1-Benzopyran-2-one, 7,7'-[1,6-hexane- diylbis(oxy)]bis-	CH_2Cl_2	324(4.51)	44-0957-73
[2,2'-Bi-2H-pyran]-6,6'(3H,3'H)-dione, 4,4'-dimethoxy-2,2'-diphenyl-	EtOH	214(3.96),241(3.78)	28-1131-73A
$C_{24}H_{22}O_9$			
Naphtho[2,3-d]-1,3-dioxole-6,7-dicarbox- ylic acid, 5-(3,4,5-trimethoxyphenyl)-, dimethyl ester	EtOH	255(4.60),261(4.60), 292(3.90),305(3.90), 345(3.11)	39-1266-73C
$C_{24}H_{22}O_{10}$			
Naphtho[2,3-d]-1,3-dioxole-6,7-dicarbox- ylic acid, 5-hydroxy-8-(3,4,5-trimeth- oxyphenyl)-, dimethyl ester	EtOH	238(4.40),255s(4.20), 261s(4.30),270(4.60), 275(4.60),303(3.90), 315(3.80),347(3.40), 351(3.40)	39-1266-73C
$C_{24}H_{22}S$			
Benzo[c]thiophene, 4,5,6,7-tetramethyl- 1,3-diphenyl-	EtOH	270s(4.04),373(3.83)	5-1893-73

Compound	Solvent	$\lambda_{max}(\log \epsilon)$	Ref.
$C_{24}H_{23}AsO_3$			
Arsonium, triphenyl-, 1-(ethoxycarbonyl-2-oxopropylide)	MeOH	217(4.37),254(4.10)	78-1697-73
$C_{24}H_{23}NO_7$			
1,2,3-Benzenetricarboxylic acid, 5-hydroxy-4-(4,6,8-trimethyl-2-quinolinyl)-, trimethyl ester	MeOH	216(4.64),251(4.64), 270s(4.47),324s(4.13)	39-1338-73C
	MeOH-acid	213(4.69),252(4.79), 328(4.17)	39-1338-73C
	MeOH-NaOH	230(4.58),247s(4.64), 256(4.68),302(4.28), 343(4.05)	39-1338-73C
$C_{24}H_{23}N_3O_2$			
Acetic acid, α-(1-methyl-2-benzimidazolylamino)-α,α-diphenyl-, ethyl ester	EtOH	250(3.96),286(4.04), 290s(4.03)	94-0981-73
$C_{24}H_{23}N_5O_7$			
Guanosine, N-benzoyl-1-(phenylmethoxy)-	pH 1	235s(4.15),263(4.05), 285(4.05)	44-3046-73
	pH 13	248(4.10),263(4.12), 268(4.12)	44-3046-73
$C_{24}H_{23}N_6O_7PS$			
Adenosine, N-[(phenylamino)carbonyl]-8-[(phenylmethyl)thio]-, cyclic 3',5'-(hydrogen phosphate)	pH 1	308(4.45)	87-1075-73
	pH 7	296(4.49)	87-1075-73
	pH 11	296(4.48)	87-1075-73
	pH 12.75	320(4.52)	87-1075-73
$C_{24}H_{23}NiP$			
Nickel, (η^5-2,4-cyclopentadien-1-yl)-methyl(triphenylphosphine)-	C_6H_{12}	296(4.02),394(3.16), 586(1.81)	23-1179-73
$C_{24}H_{24}BrNO$			
2-Propen-1-one, 1-(4-bromophenyl)-3-[2-(hexahydro-1H-azepin-1-yl)-1H-inden-3-yl]-	EtOH	232(4.15),281(4.31), 494(4.48)	48-1161-73
$C_{24}H_{24}ClNO$			
2-Propen-1-one, 1-(4-chlorophenyl)-3-[2-(hexahydro-1H-azepin-1-yl)-1H-inden-3-yl]-	EtOH	278(4.27),493(4.47)	48-1161-73
$C_{24}H_{24}F_3N_2$			
Methanaminium, N-[4-[[4-(dimethylamino)-2-(trifluoromethyl)phenyl]phenylmethylene]-2,5-cyclohexadien-1-ylidene]-N-methyl-	98% HOAc	431(4.36),604(4.48)	39-1792-73B
$C_{24}H_{24}NO_4$			
11H-Dibenzo[f,h]pyrrolo[1,2-b]isoquinolin-10-ium, 12,13-dihydro-2,3,6,7-tetramethoxy-, chloride	EtOH	284(4.56),330(4.01)	2-1215-73
perchlorate	EtOH	287(4.56),330(4.01)	2-1215-73
$C_{24}H_{24}N_2$			
Triptycene, 2,7-bis(dimethylamino)-, (+)-	MeOH	225(4.62),240s(4.40), 260s(4.19),275s(3.70), 295s(3.18)	18-0605-73

Compound	Solvent	$\lambda_{max}(\log \epsilon)$	Ref.
$C_{24}H_{24}N_2O$			
Benzamide, N-(1,1-dimethylethyl)-2-[phenyl(phenylimino)methyl]-	EtOH	250s(4.23),326(3.52)	103-0701-73
$C_{24}H_{24}N_2O_4$			
Pyrazine, 2,5-bis(carbethoxymethylene)-3,6-diphenyl-	pH 7.38	241(4.11),290(4.03), 307(4.05)	7-0457-73
$C_{24}H_{24}N_2O_5$			
2-Propenoic acid, 2-methyl-, 2-(1',3'-dihydro-3',3'-dimethyl-6-nitrospiro-[2H-1-benzopyran-2,2'-[2H]indol]-1'-yl)ethyl ester	EtOAc	269(4.20),335(3.98)	103-1233-73
2-Propenoic acid, 2-methyl-, 2-[2-(2,3-dihydro-9,9-dimethyloxazolo[3,2-a]indol-9a(9H)-yl)ethenyl]-4-nitrophenyl ester	EtOH	235(4.33)	103-1233-73
$C_{24}H_{24}N_2O_{11}S_2$			
2,4(1H,3H)-Pyrimidinedione, 1-(5-O-benzoyl-3-O-[(4-methylphenyl)sulfonyl]-2-O-(methylsulfonyl)-β-D-lyxofuranosyl]-	EtOH	227(4.45),259(4.00)	44-1283-73
$C_{22}H_{24}N_4$			
2-Tetrazene, 1,4-diethyl-1,4-di-2-naphthalenyl-	C_6H_{12}	353(4.71)	73-0046-73
	THF	352(4.65)	73-0046-73
$C_{24}H_{24}N_4O_9S_2$			
Inosine, 2',3'-bis(4-methylbenzenesulfonate)	EtOH	226(4.42),250s(3.99), 268s(3.82)	44-2896-73
$C_{24}H_{24}N_6O_4$			
L-Threonine, O-(phenylmethyl)-N-[(1H-purin-6-ylamino)carbonyl]-, phenylmethyl ester	pH 1-2	277(4.30)	87-0139-73
	pH 5-7	269(4.26)	87-0139-73
	pH 12	280(4.19)	87-0139-73
$C_{24}H_{24}O$			
Isobenzofuran, 4,7-dihydro-4,5,6,7-tetramethyl-1,3-diphenyl-	MeOH	258(2.88),260(2.86), 264(2.85),280(2.55)	5-1893-73
$C_{24}H_{24}O_2$			
Ethanone, 1,2-diphenyl-2-(2,3,4,5-tetramethylphenoxy)-	MeOH	247(4.19),277s(3.52)	5-1893-73
$C_{24}H_{24}O_4$			
15H-Cyclopenta[a]phenanthrene-3,11-diol, 16,17-dihydro-1,17,17-trimethyl-, diacetate	EtOH	262(4.73),293(4.04), 307(4.08),318(4.11)	39-1967-73C
$C_{24}H_{24}O_8$			
[1]Benzopyrano[3,4-b][1]benzopyran-12(6H)-one, 9-acetoxy-6a,12a-dihydro-2,3-dimethoxy-8-(3-oxobutyl)-	EtOH	217s(4.35),263(3.86), 294(3.33),320(3.18)	39-1277-73C
Tephrodinic acid, methyl ester	MeOH	212(4.53),267(4.49), 324(4.04)	119-0064-73
$C_{24}H_{24}O_9$			
Steganacin	EtOH	255(4.03),285(3.74)	35-1335-73

Compound	Solvent	λmax(log ε)	Ref.
$C_{24}H_{24}O_{12}$			
1,2-Naphthalenedione, 4-[(2,3,4,6-tetra-O-acetyl-β-D-glucopyranosyl)oxy]-	EtOH	205(4.09),250(4.18),335(3.14),396(3.12)	136-0247-73A
$C_{24}H_{25}BrO_3$			
Phenol, 2-[(3-bromo-2-hydroxy-5-methylphenyl)methyl]-6-[(2-hydroxy-3,5-dimethylphenyl)methyl]-4-methyl-	dioxan	288(3.95)	126-0039-73L
$C_{24}H_{25}BrO_4$			
Benzenemethanol, 3-[[3-(3-bromo-2-hydroxy-5-methylphenyl)methyl]-2-hydroxy-5-methylphenyl)methyl]-2-hydroxy-5-methyl-	dioxan	288(3.96)	126-0039-73L
$C_{24}H_{25}FNO_5P$			
[2-(4-Fluorobenzoyl)vinyl]trimethylammonium diphenylphosphate	H_2O	265s(4.01),270(4.03),275s(4.01)	24-0435-73
$C_{24}H_{25}NO$			
2-Propen-1-one, 3-[2-(hexahydro-1H-azepin-1-yl)-1H-inden-3-yl]-1-phenyl-	EtOH	233(4.11),270(4.20),310(4.23),484(4.47)	48-1161-73
2-Propen-1-one, 1-(4-methylphenyl)-3-[2-(1-piperidinyl)-1H-inden-3-yl]-	EtOH	231(4.13),282(4.31),486(4.39)	48-1161-73
$C_{24}H_{25}NO_2S$			
Estra-1,5(10)-diene-3,4,17-trione, 4-(S-phenylthiooxime)	CH_2Cl_2	269(3.94),415(3.99),467(3.94)	39-1031-73C
Estra-1(10),4-diene-2,3,17-trione, 2-(S-phenylthiooxime)-	CH_2Cl_2	265(3.81),410(3.99),462(3.96)	39-1031-73C
$C_{24}H_{25}NO_3$			
1H-Isoindole-4-carboxylic acid, 2,3,3a-4,5,7a-hexahydro-2-methyl-3-oxo-5,6-diphenyl-, ethyl ester	MeOH	242(4.06)	44-2169-73
$C_{24}H_{25}NO_4$			
7H-Pyrano[2,3-c]acridin-7-one, 3,12-dihydro-6,11-dihydroxy-3,3,12-trimeth-	EtOH	239(4.29),272(4.59),296(4.63),323s(4.22),347(4.07),436(3.83)	39-1173-73C
	EtOH-NaOMe	244(--),283(--),299s(--),308s(--),341s(--),460(--)	39-1173-73C
	EtOH-$AlCl_3$	270(--),308(--),367(--),482(--)	39-1173-73C
$C_{24}H_{25}N_3O$			
2-Propenamide, N-methyl-2,3-bis(methylphenylamino)-N-phenyl-, (Z)-	MeOH	255(4.23),304(4.14),346(4.20)	88-2619-73
$C_{24}H_{25}N_5O_8S_2$			
Adenosine, 2',3'-bis(4-methylbenzenesulfonate)	EtOH	226(4.36),260(4.10)	44-2896-73
$C_{24}H_{26}$			
p-Quaterphenyl, 3',4',5',6',1",2",5",6"-octahydro-	n.s.g.	249(4.43)	47-2225-73

Compound	Solvent	$\lambda_{max}(\log \epsilon)$	Ref.
$C_{24}H_{26}BN$			
Dibenz[c,e][1,2]azaborine, 5,6-dihydro-7,9,10-trimethyl-6-(2,4,6-trimethylphenyl)-	C_6H_{12}	338(3.72)	101-0051-73H
$C_{24}H_{26}NO_5P$			
(2-Benzoylvinyl)trimethylammonium diphenylphosphate	H_2O	265(3.94),268(3.94)	24-0435-73
$C_{24}H_{26}N_2$			
Benzeneethanimidamide, N'-(2,6-dimethylphenyl)-N,N-dimethyl-α-phenyl-	C_6H_{12}	226(4.25),245(4.22)	78-4205-73
$C_{24}H_{26}N_2O$			
Estra-1,3,5(10)-trien-17-one, 2,3-dihydroxy-, phenazine	EtOH	214(4.3),257(5.1), 374(4.23)	13-0689-73A
$C_{24}H_{26}N_2O_4S$			
2-Propenoic acid, 3-methyl-2-[[2-(phenylmethyl)carboxamido]-3-(phenylmethylthio)-1-oxo-2-propenyl]amino-, methyl ester	EtOH	299(4.20)	1-0677-73
$C_{24}H_{26}N_2O_5S$			
Spiro[benz[cd]indole-5(1H),2'-[1,3]dioxolan]-4-amine, 3,4-dihydro-N-methyl-1-[(4-methylphenyl)sulfonyl]-N-(2-oxopropyl)-, hydrochloride	EtOH	218(4.48),260(4.19), 284(3.84)	39-0760-73C
$C_{24}H_{26}N_2O_{10}$			
9,14-Diazatricyclo[6.3.2.1^{2,7}]tetradeca-3,5,10,12-tetraene-1,4,5,12-tetracarboxylic acid, 9,14-diacetyl-, tetramethyl ester	MeOH	230s(4.25),248s(4.00), 278s(3.46)	24-3824-73
13,14-Diazatricyclo[6.4.1.1^{2,7}]tetradeca-3,5,9,11-tetraene-4,5,10,11-tetracarboxylic acid, 13,14-diacetyl-, tetramethyl ester	MeCN	227s(4.07),241s(3.94), 274s(3.46)	24-3824-73
$C_{24}H_{26}N_4$			
1,4-Benzenediamine, N,N'-bis[[4-(dimethylamino)phenyl]methylene]-	n.s.g.	392(4.77)	65-1400-73
$C_{24}H_{26}O_3$			
Phenol, 2-[(2-hydroxy-3,5-dimethylphenyl)methyl]-6-[(2-hydroxy-5-methylphenyl)methyl]-4-methyl-	dioxan	287(3.93)	126-0039-73L
$C_{24}H_{26}O_4$			
2,5-Hexanedione, 3,4-bis[(3,4-dimethylphenyl)hydroxymethylene]-	$CHCl_3$	268(4.03),322(4.29)	128-0465-73
1H-Phenalene-1,3(2H)-dione, 9-hydroxy-4-methoxy-2,2-bis(3-methyl-2-butenyl)-	EtOH	208(4.39),248(4.50), 325s(3.97),353(4.10), 364(4.10)	39-2159-73C
1H-Phenalen-1-one, 9-hydroxy-4-methoxy-2-(3-methyl-2-butenyl)-3-[(3-methyl-2-butenyl)oxy]-	EtOH	216(4.50),233s(4.35), 277(4.00),285(3.91), 380(4.20),410(4.18), 431(4.11)	39-2159-73C
2H,12H-Pyrano[2,3-a]xanthen-12-one, 3,4-dihydro-5-methoxy-2,2-dimethyl-6-(3-methyl-2-butenyl)-	MeOH	257(4.52),292(4.39), 356(4.16)	2-1237-73

Compound	Solvent	λ_{max}(log ϵ)	Ref.
$C_{24}H_{26}O_5$			
Licoricone dimethyl ether	EtOH	247(4.38),284(4.10), 304(4.00)	94-1338-73
9H-Xanthen-9-one, 1-hydroxy-3-methoxy-2-(3-methyl-2-butenyl)-7-[(3-methyl-2-butenyl)oxy]-	MeOH	266(4.42),298(4.52), 332(4.23),381(4.01)	2-1233-73
$C_{24}H_{26}O_6$			
1,4,6-Heptatrien-3-one, 1,7-bis(3,4-dimethoxyphenyl)-5-hydroxy-4-methyl-	EtOH	264(4.10),437(4.59)	39-2379-73C
$C_{24}H_{26}O_7$			
2-Butenoic acid, 2-methyl-, 9,10-dihydro-8,8-dimethyl-10-[(3-methyl-1-oxo-2-butenyl)oxy]-2-oxo-2H,8H-benzo[1,2-b:3,4-b']dipyran-9-yl ester, (Z,Z)-	EtOH	221(4.66),255(3.75), 325(4.29)	94-2095-73
Chromocyclin, 2-deacetyl-12a-deoxy-3,8,10,11-tetramethyl- (4λ,3ε)	EtOH	226(4.36),255(4.39), 315(3.76),395(?)	105-0498-73
$C_{24}H_{26}O_8$			
Aglucone A diacetate	MeOH	278(3.69)	95-0044-73
$C_{24}H_{26}O_9$			
4-Cyclopentene-1,3-dione, 2-[3,4-bis-(methoxymethoxy)phenyl]-4-methoxy-5-[4-(methoxymethoxy)phenyl]-	EtOH	230(4.24),248(4.23), 350(3.95)	39-1529-73C
4-Cyclopentene-1,3-dione, 4-[3,4-bis-(methoxymethoxy)phenyl]-5-methoxy-2-[4-(methoxymethoxy)phenyl]-	EtOH	225s(4.19),249(4.12), 269s(3.98),355(3.80)	39-1529-73C
$C_{24}H_{26}S_2$			
Thiophene, 3,3'-(1,2-phenylenedi-2,1-ethenediyl)bis[2,4,5-trimethyl-, cis-cis	C_6H_{12}	227s(4.51),263(4.46), 320(4.34)	39-1136-73C
cis-trans	C_6H_{12}	242(4.35),294(4.33)	39-1136-73C
trans-trans	C_6H_{12}	244(4.42),288(4.40), 315s(4.34)	39-1136-73C
$C_{24}H_{27}NO$			
Morpholine, 4-(7,8-diphenylbicyclo-[4.2.0]oct-7-en-1-yl)-	EtOH	219(4.20),268(4.10)	18-1257-73
2-Propenamide, N-(1,1-dimethylethyl)-N-(4,5-diphenyl-2,4-pentadienyl)-, (E,Z)-	MeOH	224(4.15),234(4.15), 289(4.48),307(4.27)	44-2169-73
$C_{24}H_{27}NO_2S$			
Estra-1,5(10)-diene-3,4-dione, 17β-hydroxy-, 4-(S-phenylthiooxime)	CH_2Cl_2	260(4.82),413(4.00), 468(3.97)	39-1031-73C
Estra-1(10),4-diene-2,3-dione, 17β-hydroxy-, 1-(S-phenylthiooxime)	CH_2Cl_2	270(3.81),408(4.08), 462(4.02)	39-1031-73C
$C_{24}H_{27}NO_4$			
Isotylocrebrine, (+)-	EtOH	262(4.73),285s(4.31), 310s(3.89),344(3.22), 361(3.07)	78-0891-73
$C_{24}H_{27}NO_7$			
5,14-Ethanomorphinan-18,19-dicarboxylic acid, 18,19-didehydro-4-hydroxy-3-methoxy-17-methyl-6-oxo-, dimethyl ester	MeOH	235s(3.90),283(3.51)	78-2383-73

Compound	Solvent	λ_{max}(log ε)	Ref.
$C_{24}H_{27}NO_{12}$			
Benzeneacetonitrile, 3-acetoxy-α-[(2,3,4,6-tetra-O-acetyl-β-D-glucopyranosyl)oxy]-	EtOH	264(2.77),268(2.74)	102-0457-73
$C_{24}H_{27}N_3O_2S$			
Benzenesulfonamide, N-[bis[4-(dimethyl-amino)phenyl]methylene]-4-methyl-	EtOH	225(4.26),392(4.64)	39-2866-73C
$C_{24}H_{27}N_3O_5$			
Codeine salt with tetracyanoethylene and methanol	MeOH	232(4.45),286(3.93)	78-2387-73
$C_{24}H_{27}N_5O_4$			
4,4'-Azoisoxazol-5-one, 3,3'-diphenyl-, triethylamine salt	EtOH	230(4.26),303(2.95), 525(4.19)	32-1045-73
$C_{24}H_{28}BN$			
Boranamine, N-phenyl-1,1-bis(2,4,6-tri-methylphenyl)-	C_6H_{12}	267(4.11)	101-0051-73H
$C_{24}H_{28}BrClO_4$			
Pregna-4,6-diene-3,20-dione, 17α-acet-oxy-6-bromo-4-chloro-16-methylene-	MeOH	301(4.19)	73-2492-73
$C_{24}H_{28}Cl_2O_4$			
Pregna-4,6-diene-3,20-dione, 17α-acet-oxy-4,6-dichloro-16-methylene-	MeOH	299(4.6)	73-2492-73
$C_{24}H_{28}F_6O_5$			
Androst-5-en-7-one, 3β,17β-dihydroxy-17α-methyl-, bis(trifluoroacetate)	EtOH	233(4.11)	87-0257-73
$C_{24}H_{28}N_2O$			
Cyclohexanone, 2,6-bis[[4-(dimethyl-amino)phenyl]methylene]-	CH_2Cl_2	432(4.65)	23-1458-73
$C_{24}H_{28}N_2O_5$			
Novacine	EtOH	216(4.56),267(4.30), 301(4.11)	78-4137-73
$C_{24}H_{28}N_2O_6S$			
Spiro[benz[cd]indole-5(1H),2'-[1,3]diox-olan]-4-amine, N-(2,3-dihydroxy-2-methylpropyl)-3,4-dihydro-1-[(4-methylphenyl)sulfonyl]-	EtOH	220(4.39),260(4.18), 294(3.30)	39-0760-73C
$C_{24}H_{28}N_2O_7$			
16,19-Secostrychnidine-10,16-dione, 21,22-epoxy-21,22-dihydro-14-hydroxy-2,3-dimethoxy-19-methyl-, (21α,22α)-	EtOH	219(4.39),264(4.11), 301(3.91)	78-4137-73
$C_{24}H_{28}N_2O_9$			
Butanedioic acid, (1,5-dihydro-3,5-di-methyl-5-oxo-2H-pyrrol-2-ylidene)-[1,5-dihydro-5-[3-methoxy-1-(methoxy-carbonyl)-3-oxopropylidene]-3,4-di-methyl-2H-pyrrol-2-ylidene]-, di-methyl ester	MeOH	243(4.26),288(4.27), 432(4.46)	24-0812-73

Compound	Solvent	λ_{max}(log ε)	Ref.
$C_{24}H_{28}O_2$			
Cyclohexanone, 3,5,5-trimethyl-2-(3-oxo-1,3-diphenylpropyl)-	EtOH	242(4.13),278(3.04)	22-0263-73
1,3-Dioxolane, 2,4-bis(1,1-dimethylethyl)-5-(9H-fluoren-9-ylidene)-	EtOH	290(4.19),293s(4.19), 315(4.19),318s(4.15)	23-1995-73
$C_{24}H_{28}O_4$			
1,4:5,8-Dimethanobiphenylene-4a,4b-dicarboxylic acid, 1,4,5,8,8a,8b-hexahydro-9,10-bis(1-methylethylidene)-, dimethyl ester, (1α,4α,4aβ,4bα,5β-8β,8aα,8bβ)-	EtOH	245(3.23),282(3.00)	24-1822-73
4,7-Methano-2,3,8-methenocyclopent[a]indene-3,7a-dicarboxylic acid, 2,3,3a-3b,4,7,8,8a-octahydro-1,10-bis(1-methylethylidene)-, dimethyl ester, (2α,3β,3aβ,3bα,4β,7β,7aα,8α,8aβ)-	EtOH	221s(3.95),275(2.68)	24-1822-73
$C_{24}H_{28}O_6$			
19-Norpregna-1,3,5(10)-triene-6,20-dione, 3,17-diacetoxy-	MeOH	247(4.02),297(3.36)	24-0723-73
$C_{24}H_{28}O_7$			
4H-1-Benzopyran-4-one, 2-(3,4-dimethoxyphenyl)-5-hydroxy-3,7-dimethoxy-8-(3-methylbutyl)-	MeOH	252(4.13),257(4.08), 286(4.31),331(4.18), 405(3.90)	12-0409-73
	MeOH-NaOAc	254(4.16),275(4.23), 312(4.13),330(4.11), 370s(3.95)	12-0409-73
	MeOH-$AlCl_3$	242(4.18),282(4.29), 305(4.00),360(4.18), 420(4.10)	12-0409-73
$C_{24}H_{28}O_8$			
Barbatusinone	EtOH	218(4.18),235(4.25), 253s(4.15)	35-0598-73
	EtOH-KOH	224(4.41),275(4.15)	35-0598-73
Trachelogenin, acetylmethyl-	EtOH	232(4.11),280(3.68)	94-1108-73
$C_{24}H_{28}O_8S_2$			
1,2-Cyclohexanedione, 3,6-dimethyl-3,6-bis[[[(4-methylphenyl)sulfonyl]oxy]-methyl-	$CHCl_3$	262(3.08),273(3.01), 400(1.48)	24-2255-73
$C_{24}H_{28}S_3$			
Thiophene, 2,5-dimethyl-3,4-bis[2-(2,4,5-trimethyl-3-thienyl)ethenyl]-, cis-cis	C_6H_{12}	229(4.25),244(4.26), 269s(4.13),304(3.78)	39-1136-73C
cis-trans	C_6H_{12}	231s(4.40),244(4.41), 278(4.35),310(4.16)	39-1136-73C
trans-trans	C_6H_{12}	233s(4.34),248(4.41), 282(4.43),330(4.17)	39-1136-73C
$C_{24}H_{29}BrCl_2O_4$			
Pregn-5-ene-3,20-dione, 17α-acetoxy-6-bromo-4α,7α-dichloro-16-methylene-	MeOH	247(3.63)	73-2492-73
$C_{24}H_{29}ClO_4$			
Pregna-4,6-diene-3,20-dione, 17α-acetoxy-2α-chloro-16-methylene-	MeOH	288(4.39)	73-2492-73

Compound	Solvent	λ_{max}(log ϵ)	Ref.
Pregna-4,6-diene-3,20-dione, 17α-acetoxy-4-chloro-16-methylene-	MeOH	295(4.37)	73-2492-73
$C_{24}H_{29}ClO_5$			
Pregna-4,6-diene-3,20-dione, 6-chloro-17α,19-dihydroxy-16-methylene-, 17-acetate	MeOH	285(4.35)	87-0649-73
$C_{24}H_{29}Cl_3O_4$			
Pregn-5-ene-3,20-dione, 17α-acetoxy-4α,6,7α-trichloro-16-methylene-	MeOH	243(3.68),291(3.79)	73-2492-73
$C_{24}H_{29}FO_5$			
Pregna-1,4,17(20)-trien-21-al, 20-acetoxy-9-fluoro-11β-hydroxy-16α-methyl-3-oxo-	MeOH	247(4.46)	24-2263-73
Pregna-1,4,16-triene-3,20-dione, 21-acetoxy-9-fluoro-11β-hydroxy-16-methyl-	MeOH	243(4.34)	24-2263-73
$C_{24}H_{29}NO_2$			
2H-Indol-2-one, 3-[[3,5-bis(1,1-dimethylethyl)-4-hydroxyphenyl]methylene]-1,3-dihydro-1-methyl-	MeOH	211(4.24),254(3.98)	103-0034-73
$C_{24}H_{29}NO_4$			
Septicine, (+)-	EtOH	238s(4.20),287(3.98)	78-0891-73
$C_{24}H_{29}NO_4S$			
Benzenesulfonamide, N,4-dimethyl-N-(6a,7,10,10a-tetrahydro-1-hydroxy-6,6,9-trimethyl-6H-dibenzo[b,d]pyran-3-yl)-, (6aR-trans)-	EtOH	228s(4.39),287(3.51)	33-0510-73
Benzenesulfonamide, N,4-dimethyl-N-(6a,7,10,10a-tetrahydro-3-hydroxy-6,6,9-trimethyl-6H-dibenzo[b,d]pyran-1-yl)-, (6aR-trans)-	EtOH	239s(4.24),274(3.59), 287(3.57)	33-0510-73
$C_{24}H_{30}$			
Benzene, 1,3,5-tri-1-cyclohexen-1-yl-	MeOH	245(4.37)	32-0849-73
$C_{24}H_{30}BrClNO_3P$			
Phenoxaphosphine, 7-bromo-2-chloro-10-hydroxy-, 10-oxide, dicyclohexylamine salt	EtOH	222(4.66),239s(4.53), 250s(4.32),269(3.33), 294(3.64),303(3.70)	39-1972-73C
$C_{24}H_{30}CuO_8$			
Copper, bis(4,7,7-trimethyl-α,3-dioxobicyclo[2.2.1]heptane-2-acetato)-	benzene	348(4.38),730(1.73)	65-0927-73
	MeOH	338(4.36),732(1.72)	65-0927-73
	$CHCl_3$	348(4.45),730(1.85)	65-0927-73
	DMF	332(4.36),735(1.78)	65-0927-73
polymeric 1:1 chelate	MeOH	235(4.04),327(2.36), 772(1.97)	65-0927-73
3:2 chelate	MeOH	230(4.19),329(4.45), 795(2.11)	65-0927-73
$C_{24}H_{30}N_2$			
Azocyclohexane, 1,1'-diphenyl-	benzene	380(1.74)	24-2890-73
Pyrazine, 1,2-bis(1,1-dimethylethyl)-1,2-dihydro-2,5-diphenyl-	n.s.g.	262(4.29)	39-0683-73C

Compound	Solvent	λ max(log ε)	Ref.
$C_{24}H_{30}N_2O_2$			
Pyrrolidine, 1,1'-[5-[2-(3,4-dimethoxyphenyl)ethenyl]-1,3-phenylene]bis-	EtOH	241(4.31),298(4.29), 330(4.35)	70-1077-73
	EtOH	241(4.57),285(4.31), 298(4.29),330(4.35)	78-1083-73
$C_{24}H_{30}N_2O_5$			
Echitovenaldine	EtOH	246(3.80),328(3.93)	25-1032-73
Vindoline, demethoxy-	EtOH	248(4.05),300(3.50)	2-0007-73
$C_{24}H_{30}N_3O_4P$			
Phosphonic acid, [9a-ethoxy-9,9a-dihydro-3-methyl-1-(3-methylphenyl)-1H-pyrazolo[3,4-b]quinolin-4-yl]-, diethyl ester	n.s.g.	248(4.23),277(4.23), 338(3.70),370(3.60)	39-1606-73C
Phosphonic acid, [9a-ethoxy-9,9a-dihydro-3-methyl-1-(4-methylphenyl)-1H-pyrazolo[3,4-b]quinolin-4-yl]-, diethyl ester	n.s.g.	248(4.51),275(4.47), 338(3.87),374(3.76)	39-1606-73C
$(C_{24}H_{30}N_4O_{11})_n$			
Poly(L-glutamyl-L-glutamyl-L-tyrosyl-L-glutamyl)	0.2M NaOH	243(4.04),294(3.35)	39-1001-73C
$C_{24}H_{30}N_6$			
1,3-Benzenediamine, N^3-[4-(dimethylamino)phenyl]-4-[[4-(dimethylamino)phenyl]azo]-N',N'-dimethyl-	THF	252(4.23),320(4.00), 448(4.50),468(4.52)	44-0507-73
$C_{24}H_{30}O$			
2,5-Cyclohexadien-1-one, 2,3,4,4,5,6-hexa-2-propenyl-	EtOH	255(4.13)	33-0014-73
$C_{24}H_{30}O_2$			
1,5-Heptanedione, 6,6-dimethyl-4-(1-methylethyl)-1,3-diphenyl-	EtOH	242(4.08)	22-0263-73
19-Norpregna-1,3,5(10),6-tetraene-11,20-dione, 3,4,9,14-tetramethyl-	n.s.g.	224(4.28),231s(4.19), 272(3.75)	78-1109-73
$C_{24}H_{30}O_3$			
14-Anhydrobufalin	n.s.g.	300(3.77)	5-0005-73
18-Nor-17α-chola-4,8,11,13-tetraen-24-oic acid, 12-methyl-3-oxo-	EtOH	225(4.18),238(4.07)	78-0021-73
$C_{24}H_{30}O_4$			
Kopeodin	n.s.g.	244(3.62),255(3.61), 327(4.29)	105-0294-73
Moschatol	EtOH	214(4.20),242(3.62), 252(3.51),325(4.14)	105-0399-73
$C_{24}H_{30}O_5$			
Estra-1,3,5(10),8-tetraene-18-carboxylic acid, 17,17-[1,2-ethanediylbis(oxy)]-3-methoxy-, ethyl ester, (±)-	EtOH	280(4.19)	94-2427-73
Galbanic acid	n.s.g.	217(4.17),325(4.25)	105-0400-73
Pregna-1,4,17(20)-trien-21-al, 11β-hydroxy-3-oxo-20-(1-oxopropoxy)-	MeOH	249(4.43)	24-2263-73
Pregna-1,4,16-triene-3,20-dione, 11β-hydroxy-21-(1-oxopropoxy)-	MeOH	242(4.34)	24-2263-73
Pregn-4-ene-3,20-dione, 17α-acetoxy-6β,19-epoxy-16-methylene-	MeOH	237(4.13)	87-0649-73

Compound	Solvent	λ_{max}(log ϵ)	Ref.
$C_{24}H_{30}O_6$			
Argentinogenin	EtOH	288(4.19)	33-2827-73
Estra-1,3,5(10)-triene-3,16α,17β-triol, triacetate, Kober test	H_2SO_4	513(4.50)	94-1720-73
Pregna-4,16-diene-3,11,20-trione, 21-[(ethoxycarbonyl)oxy]-	MeOH	238(4.40)	44-2328-73
$C_{24}H_{30}O_7$			
Heliangin methacrylate	EtOH	212(4.52)	102-2469-73
Naphtho[2,3-d]-1,3-dioxole, 5-(3,4-dimethoxyphenyl)-5,6,7,8-tetrahydro-4-methoxy-6,7-bis(methoxymethyl)-(nirtetralin)	EtOH	226(4.40),284(2.15)	78-1291-73
Talassin B	n.s.g.	251(4.42)	105-0120-73
$C_{24}H_{30}O_8$			
Barbatusin	EtOH	235(4.18)	35-0598-73
	EtOH-base	223(4.43),272s(3.66)	35-0598-73
Diayangambin, (+)-	EtOH	230(4.23),270(3.23)	102-1799-73
$C_{24}H_{30}O_{10}$			
Coleon K	MeOH	270(3.83),333(3.79), 395(3.66)	33-2534-73
$C_{24}H_{30}O_{13}$			
2,5-Cyclohexadien-1-one, 4-acetoxy-4-[2-[(2,3,4,6-tetra-O-acetyl-β-D-glucopyranosyl)oxy]ethyl]-	EtOH	239(3.99)	1-0367-73
2H-Pyran-4-acetic acid, 5-carboxy-3-ethylidene-2-(β-D-glucopyranosyloxy)-3,4-dihydro-2-(3,4-dihydroxyphenyl)ethyl ester, (2α,4β)- (demethyloleoeuropeine)	MeOH	230(3.20),282(2.51)	7-0013-73
$C_{24}H_{30}O_{15}$			
Forsythid tetraacetate	MeOH	232(4.07)	94-0497-73
$C_{24}H_{31}BrO_3$			
19-Norpregna-1,5-diene-3,11,20-trione, 2-bromo-4,4,9,14-tetramethyl-, (9β,10α)-	n.s.g.	255(3.70)	78-1109-73
$C_{24}H_{31}NO$			
Pyridine, 2,6-dicyclohexyl-4-(4-methoxyphenyl)-	EtOH	275(4.34)	35-4891-73
	50%EtOH-HCl	283(4.09),326(4.38)	35-4891-73
$C_{24}H_{31}N_3O_2S$			
7H-Naphtho[2",1":4',5']indeno[1',2':4,5]-pyrido[2,3-d]pyrimidin-7-one, 1,2,3,4-4a,4b,5,6,6a,8,9,10,13,13a,13b,14,15-15a-octadecahydro-2-hydroxy-4a,6a-dimethyl-9-thioxo-, [2S-(2α,4aα,4bβ,6aα-13aβ,13bα,15aβ)]-	EtOH	294(4.28),328(4.06)	27-0212-73
$C_{24}H_{31}N_3O_3$			
1H-Naphtho[2",1":4',5']indeno[1',2':4,5]-pyrido[2,3-d]pyrimidine-7,9(2H,8H)-dione, 3,4,4a,4b,5,6,6a,10,13,13a,13b-14,15,15a-tetradecahydro-2-hydroxy-4a,6a-dimethyl-, [2S-(2α,4aα,4bβ,6aα-13aβ,13bα,15aβ)]-	EtOH	253(3.76),316(3.92)	27-0212-73

Compound	Solvent	λ_{max}(log ϵ)	Ref.
$C_{24}H_{32}N_2O_2$			
Pyrrolidine, 1,1'-[5-[2-(3,4-dimethoxy-phenyl)ethyl]-1,3-phenylene]bis-	EtOH	242(4.61),272(4.10), 289(3.63),315(3.68)	70-1077-73 +78-1083-73
$C_{24}H_{32}N_4O_2$			
7H-Naphth[2",1":4',5']indeno[1',2':4,5]-pyrido[2,3-d]pyrimidin-7-one, 9-amino-1,2,3,4,4a,4b,5,6,6a,8,13,13a,13b,14-15,15a-hexadecahydro-2-hydroxy-4a,6a-dimethyl-, [2S-(2α,4aα,4bβ,6aα,13aβ-13bα,15aβ)]-	EtOH	273(3.78),323(3.48)	27-0212-73
$C_{24}H_{32}N_4O_5$			
Purine, 6-(benzylamino)-7-(1-deoxy-3,4-5,6-di-O-isopropylidene-D-mannitol-1-yl)-	$CHCl_3$	296(4.28)	136-0154-73F
$C_{24}H_{32}N_4O_{13}S$			
Bis[1-(2,3-O-isopropylidene-β-D-ribo-furanosyl)uracil] 5'-sulfite	pH 1	258.5(4.29)	136-0455-73B
	pH 11	259(4.17)	136-0455-73B
$C_{24}H_{32}N_7O_7P$			
Adenosine, 5'-deoxy-5'-[[hydroxy(4-ni-trophenoxy)phosphinyl]octylamino]-, intramol. 5',3'-ester	MeOH	262(4.34)	24-3127-73
diastereoisomer	MeOH	262(4.32)	24-3127-73
$C_{24}H_{32}O_3$			
Androst-4-en-3-one, 17α-ethynyl-16β,17β-dihydroxy-, acetonide	MeOH	240.5(4.18)	87-0839-73
2-Cyclopropen-1-one, 2-[(5α,17β)-17-(acetyloxy)androst-2-en-3-yl]-	n.s.g.	244(4.24)	44-1478-73
19-Nor-pregna-1(10),5-diene-3,11,20-tri-one, 4,4,9,14-tetramethyl-, (9β)-	n.s.g.	239(4.05)	78-1109-73
19-Norpregna-1,3,5(10)-triene-11,20-di-one, 3-hydroxy-2,4,9,14-tetramethyl-, (9β)-	n.s.g.	219(4.01),278(3.28)	78-1109-73
2-Propen-1-one, 1-[(3β)-3-(acetyloxy)-androsta-5,16-dien-17-yl]-	EtOH	260(4.05),333(3.08)	70-1578-73
$C_{24}H_{32}O_4$			
1,3,5-Cyclohexanetrione, 2-acetyl-4,4,6,6-tetra-2-butenyl-	EtOH-acid	237(3.90),282(4.03)	39-2013-73C
	EtOH-base	278(4.25)	39-2013-73C
9β,10α-Pregna-4,6-diene-3,20-dione, 17α-acetoxy-6-methyl-	EtOH	290(4.37)	33-2396-73
9β,10α-Pregn-4-ene-3,20-dione, 17α-acet-oxy-6-methylene-	EtOH	261(3.99)	33-2396-73
Resibufogenin	n.s.g.	300(3.75)	5-0005-73
$C_{24}H_{32}O_5$			
Allocyanthin B_3, O,O-diacetyl-	isooctane	225(3.95),254(3.68), 325(2.14)	23-3842-73
Bufalone, 11α-hydroxy-	EtOH	298(3.75)	39-0725-73C
Kopeolin	n.s.g.	244(3.64),253(3.59), 327(4.13)	105-0294-73
Kopetin	n.s.g.	244(3.56),255(3.42), 327(4.17)	105-0294-73
Naphtho[1,8-bc]pyran-3a,6(4H)-diol, 5,6,6a,7,8,9,9a,9b-octahydro-2-(2-methoxyphenyl)-4,7,9b-trimethyl-, 6-acetate, (3aα,4β,6α,6aβ,7β,9aα,9bα)-	EtOH	213(4.11),230(4.06), 265(4.28),275(4.28), 300(4.03),311(3.95)	23-3989-73

Compound	Solvent	λ_{max}(log ϵ)	Ref.
Pregna-3,5-diene-7,20-dione, 17α-acetoxy-3-methoxy-	EtOH	311(4.47)	87-0065-73
Pregna-4,16-diene-3,20-dione, 21-[(ethoxycarbonyl)oxy]-	MeOH	240(4.43)	44-2328-73
Pregn-4-ene-3,20-dione, 17α,19-dihydroxy-16-methylene-, 17-acetate	MeOH	241(4.17)	87-0649-73
Resibufogenin, 11α-hydroxy-	EtOH	298(3.75)	39-0725-73C
Spiro[1,3-dioxolane-2,1'(2'H)-naphthalene]-5',8'-diol, octahydro-8'-[(2-methoxyphenyl)ethynyl]-4',7',8'a-trimethyl-, (4'α,4'aα,5'β,7'α,8'β,8'aβ)-	EtOH	209(4.31),219(4.26), 247(4.08),257(4.11), 291(3.71),301(3.78)	23-3989-73
$C_{24}H_{32}O_6$			
2(3H)-Furanone, 3-[2-[6-(acetyloxy)-5-(acetyloxy)methyl]decahydro-5,8a-dimethyl-2-methylene-1-naphthalenyl]ethylidene]-, [1R-(1α,4aβ,5α,6α,8aα)]-	n.s.g.	224(3.85),299(3.86)	39-1247-73C
2(5H)-Furanone, 3-[2-[6-(acetyloxy)methyl]decahydro-5,8a-dimethyl-2-methylene-1-naphthalenyl]ethenyl]-, [1R-[1α(E),4aβ,3α,6α,8aα]]-	n.s.g.	246(4.11)	39-1247-73C
Pregn-4-en-3-one, 20-acetoxy-20,21-[carbonylbis(oxy)]-	MeOH	241(4.24)	44-2328-73
isomer	MeOH	241(4.26)	44-2328-73
Pregn-4-en-3-one, 21-acetoxy-17,20β-[carbonylbis(oxy)]-	MeOH	239(4.25)	44-2335-73
$C_{24}H_{32}O_7$			
Niranthin	EtOH	230(4.30),280(1.59)	78-1291-73
$C_{24}H_{32}O_8$			
Hydroxy acid, m. 113-114.5°	EtOH	231(4.35),281(3.86)	94-1108-73
Isoasatone	MeOH	221(3.30)	88-4881-73
$C_{24}H_{32}O_{10}$			
Aloearbonaside, pentaıethyl-	MeOH	284s(--),295(3.99)	94-0149-73
$C_{24}H_{32}O_{12}$			
2,4a,6,8a(4H,4bH)-Biphenylenetetracarboxylic acid, 1,5,8,8b-tetrahydro-3,4b,7,8b-tetrahydroxy-, tetraethyl ester, (4aα,4bβ,8aβ,8bα)-	EtOH	253(4.00)	33-2760-73
$C_{24}H_{33}BrO_4$			
19-Norpregn-5-ene-3,11,20-trione, 1-bromo-2-hydroxy-4,4,9,14-tetramethyl-, (1β,2α,9β,10α)-	n.s.g.	298(3.34)	78-1109-73
$C_{24}H_{33}ClO_4$			
5β-Bufa-20,22-dienolide, 14β-chloro-3β,15α-dihydroxy-	EtOH	300(3.85)	94-0895-73
5β-Bufa-20,22-dienolide, 15α-chloro-3β,14β-dihydroxy-	MeOH	299(3.71)	44-2202-73
$C_{24}H_{33}FO_2$			
Pregna-3,15,16-trien-20-one, 3-ethoxy-6-fluoro-16-methyl-	n.s.g.	242(4.45)	39-0227-73C
$C_{24}H_{33}FO_3$			
Pregna-17(20),20-diene-21-carbonyl fluoride, 3-acetoxy-, [3β,5α,17(21)S]-	n.s.g.	226(4.23)	44-1478-73

Compound	Solvent	λ_{max}(log ϵ)	Ref.
Pregna-3,5-dien-20-one, 16α,17α-epoxy-3-ethoxy-6-fluoro-16β-methyl-	n.s.g.	240(4.30)	39-0227-73C
2-Propenoyl fluoride, 3-[[3(S),5α,17β]-17-(acetyloxy)androstan-3-ylidene]-	n.s.g.	218(4.26)	44-1478-73
$C_{24}H_{33}FO_4$			
A-Homoandrosta-3,4a(5)-diene-4,17-diol, 3-fluoro-, diacetate, (17β)-	n.s.g.	247(3.99),254(4.00)	35-6655-73
$C_{24}H_{33}NO$			
2,5-Cyclohexadien-1-one, 3-(1,1-dimethylethyl)-4-[[4-(1,1-dimethylethyl)-2,6-dimethylphenyl]imino]-2,6-dimethyl-	EtOH	279(4.41),505(2.93)	78-0085-73
$C_{24}H_{33}NO_3$			
Sylvatine	EtOH	259(4.69),305(3.97)	78-0977-73
$C_{24}H_{34}CuO_4$			
Copper, bis[(-)-hydroxyethylidenecamphor]-	benzene	320(4.36),658(1.74)	65-0927-73
	MeOH	258(4.23),320(4.42), 658(1.81)	65-0927-73
	$CHCl_3$	261(4.48),322(4.34), 660(1.69)	65-0927-73
	DMF	315(4.42),658(1.85)	65-0927-73
$C_{24}H_{34}N_2O_{12}$			
1,2,5-Oxadiazole, 3,4-bis(1,2:3,4-di-O-isopropylidene-α-D-galacto-pento-1,5-pyranos-5-yl)-, 2-oxide	EtOH	259(3.53)	136-0311-73D
$C_{24}H_{34}O_4$			
Pregn-4-ene-3,20-dione, 16α,17α-epoxy-21-(ethoxymethyl)-	EtOH	242(4.22)	70-1790-73
2-Propenoic acid, 3-[(5α,17β)-acetoxy-androst-2-en-3-yl]-, (E)-	n.s.g.	262(4.36)	44-1478-73
$C_{24}H_{34}O_5$			
Cyathin A_3, O,O-diacetyl-	isooctane	230s(3.86),323(2.10)	23-3842-73
5β-Pregn-1-ene-3,11-dione, 17-hydroxy-20,21-[(1-methylethylidene)bis(oxy)]-	n.s.g.	225(3.96)	39-1361-73C
5β-Pregn-2-ene-1,11-dione, 17-hydroxy-20,21-[(1-methylethylidene)bis(oxy)]-	n.s.g.	225(3.87)	39-1361-73C
Pregn-4-ene-3,20-dione, 17-acetoxy-6-(hydroxymethyl)-, (6β)-	EtOH	242(4.20)	33-2396-73
(6β,9β,10α)-	EtOH	240(4.20)	33-2396-73
Vouacapane, 6α,7β-diacetoxy-	EtOH	218(4.08)	39-0520-73C
$C_{24}H_{34}O_6$			
Bufa-20,22-dienolide, 3,11,12,14-tetrahydroxy-	EtOH	298(3.75)	33-2827-73
isomer	EtOH	298(3.74)	33-2827-73
2(5H)-Furanone, 3-[2-[6-(acetyloxy)methyl]decahydro-5,8a-dimethyl-2-methylene-1-naphthalenyl]ethyl]-, [1R-(1α,4aβ,5α,6α,8aα)]-	n.s.g.	220(3.93),230(3.64)	39-1247-73C
Pregn-4-en-21-oic acid, 20α-acetoxy-17-hydroxy-3-oxo-, methyl ester	MeOH	240(4.23)	44-2335-73
20β-	MeOH	241(4.23)	44-2335-73

Compound	Solvent	λ_{max}(log ε)	Ref.
$C_{24}H_{35}IO_3$			
Dicyclopenta[3,4:6,7]cycloocta[1,2-d]-1,3-dioxole, 3a,6a,8,9,10,10a,11,11a-octahydro-4-(2-iodo-1-methylethyl)-8-(methoxymethyl)-2,2,6a,11-tetramethyl-, [3aR-[3aα,4(S*),6aα,8α-10aβ,11α,11aβ]]-	n.s.g.	272(3.40)	39-1590-73C
$C_{24}H_{35}NO_2$			
6H-Dibenzo[b,d]pyran-1-ol, 6a,7,10,10a-tetrahydro-6,6,9-trimethyl-3-(1-methyl-3-propyl-3-pyrrolidinyl)-	EtOH	230s(4.82),276(3.98), 283(3.99)	33-0519-73
$C_{24}H_{36}N_2O_5$			
5-Heptenoic acid, 7-[4-(3-acetoxy-2-octenyl)-3,3a,4,5,6,6a-hexahydro-6-oxo-5-cyclopentapyrazolyl]-, methyl ester, [3aR-(3α,4β(1E,3S*),5α(Z),6aα]]-	MeOH	325(2.79)	33-0557-73
$C_{24}H_{36}N_4O_4$			
Frangufoline	EtOH	225s(4.09)	102-0693-73
Frangulanine	EtOH	255s(4.19)	102-0693-73
$C_{24}H_{36}O_3$			
Cyclohexanol, 1,1',1"-(1,3,5-benzenetriyl)tris-	MeOH	262(2.43)	32-0849-73
Dicyclopenta[3,4:6,7]cycloocta[1,2-d]-1,3-dioxole, 3a,6a,8,9,10,10a,11,11a-octahydro-8-(methoxymethyl)-2,2,6a,11-tetramethyl-4-(1-methylethyl)-, [3aR-(3aα,6aα,8α,10aβ,11α,11aβ)]-	n.s.g.	272(3.30)	39-1590-73C
$C_{24}H_{36}O_4$			
1,7,20,26-Tetraoxa[7.0.7.0]paracyclophane	n.s.g.	265(4.15)	18-0263-73
$C_{24}H_{36}O_5$			
Cyathin A_3, diacetyl-	isooctane	290(1.76)	23-3842-73
5-Heptenoic acid, 7-[2-(3-acetoxy-1-octenyl)-4-oxobicyclo[3.1.0]hexan-3-yl]-, methyl ester	MeOH	280s(2.10)	33-0557-73
Pregn-5-en-20-one, 17α-acetoxy-3β-hydroxy-7α-methoxy-	MeOH	199(3.96)	48-0008-73
Prosta-5,10,13-trien-1-oic acid, 15-acetoxy-11-methyl-9-oxo-, methyl ester, (5Z,13E,15S)-	MeOH	226(4.44),316(1.60)	33-0557-73
$C_{24}H_{36}O_6$			
Bicyclo[2.2.0]hexa-2,5-diene-1,2,3-tricarboxylic acid, 4,5,6-tris(1,1-dimethylethyl)-, trimethyl ester	ether	238s(3.45)	35-8481-73
$C_{24}H_{36}O_8$			
Isoasatone, tetrahydro-	MeOH	222(3.32)	88-4881-73
$C_{24}H_{38}N_4O_6S$			
1H-Imidazole-4-hexanoic acid, ε,ε'-thiobis[2,3-dihydro-5-methyl-2-oxo-, diethyl ester	EtOH	214(3.67)	70-2566-73

Compound	Solvent	$\lambda_{max}(\log \epsilon)$	Ref.
$C_{24}H_{38}O_4$			
7H-Benz[e]inden-7-one, 3β-(1,1-dimethylethyl)-1,2,3,3a,4,5,8,9,9aβ,9bα-decahydro-3aβ-methyl-6-[2-(2-methyl-1,3-dioxolan-2-yl)ethyl]-, (±)-	EtOH	248(4.22)	44-3244-73
$C_{24}H_{38}O_5$			
2-Phenanthrenecarboxylic acid, 7-acetoxytetradecahydro-2,4a-dimethyl-1-(2-oxobutyl)-, methyl ester	EtOH	273(1.98)	44-1270-73
$C_{24}H_{38}O_6$			
7-Oxabicyclo[13.2.1]octadeca-10,12-diene-6,14-dione, 8-ethyl-2,4-dihydroxy-16-methoxy-3,9,11,15-tetramethyl-	EtOH	276(4.30)	138-0793-73
$C_{24}H_{38}O_7$			
2,4-Nonadienoic acid, 8-[4-acetoxytetrahydro-6-(2-methoxyethenyl)-3,5-dimethyl-2H-pyran-2-yl]-7-hydroxy-2,6-dimethyl-, methyl ester	EtOH	268(4.37)	33-2287-73
$C_{24}H_{39}NO_3$			
Sylvatine, hexahydro-	EtOH	233(3.88),286(3.81)	78-0977-73
$C_{24}H_{41}NO_2$			
Octadecanamide, N-hydroxy-N-phenyl-	EtOH	253(4.06)	112-0547-73
$C_{24}H_{44}O_5$			
Butanedioic acid, hexadecyloxo-, diethyl ester	MeOH	206(3.07)	83-0366-73

Compound	Solvent	$\lambda_{max}(\log \epsilon)$	Ref.
$C_{25}H_{13}BrO_4$			
1,4-Naphthalenedione, 2-bromo-3-(2,3-dihydro-1,3-dioxo-2-phenyl-1H-inden-2-yl)-	MeOH	225(4.72),247(4.48), 253(4.45),275s(4.11)	39-1006-73C
$C_{25}H_{13}F_{18}N_3O$			
Benzenemethanol, 4-[bis(trifluoromethyl)amino]-α,α-bis[4-[bis(trifluoromethyl)amino]phenyl]-	H_2SO_4	308(3.97),470(4.69)	104-2181-73
$C_{25}H_{13}NO_4$			
1H,3H-Naphtho[1,8-cd]pyran-1,3-dione, 6-[5-(1-naphthalenyl)-2-oxazolyl]-	toluene	308(4.22),410(4.39)	103-1204-73
1H,3H-Naphtho[1,8-cd]pyran-1,3-dione, 6-[5-(2-naphthalenyl)-2-oxazolyl]-	toluene	305(4.19),408(4.38)	103-1204-73
$C_{25}H_{14}Br_2O_2$			
7H-Benzo[c]fluoren-7-one, 2,9-dibromo-6-(4-methylbenzoyl)-	HOAc	252(4.67),265(4.66), 286(4.57),294(4.66), 346s(3.58),450(3.12)	115-0145-73A
$C_{25}H_{14}O_4$			
1,4-Naphthalenedione, 2-(2,3-dihydro-1,3-dioxo-2-phenyl-1H-inden-2-yl)-	MeOH	227(4.63),241(4.52), 246s(4.52),252s(4.44)	39-1006-73C
$C_{25}H_{16}N_2O_2$			
[2,2'-Biquinoline]-4-carboxylic acid, 4'-phenyl-, Cu(I) complex	EtOH	556(4.00)	103-1391-73
$C_{25}H_{17}$			
Cyclopropenylium, 1-(1-azulenyl)-2,3-diphenyl-, perchlorate	50% EtOH	220(4.35),316(4.29), 412(4.19)	5-0166-73
$C_{25}H_{17}F_3O_5$			
Triptycene, 2-methoxy-7-(methoxycarbonyl)-5-(trifluoroacetoxy)-	dioxan	216(4.69),267(3.59), 285(3.69)	18-0651-73
Triptycene, 5-methoxy-7-(methoxycarbonyl)-2-(trifluoroacetoxy)-	dioxan	215(4.69),261(3.55), 268(3.60),288(3.73)	18-0651-73
$C_{25}H_{17}F_3S$			
1,1':2',1"-Terphenyl, 2-(phenylthio)-3"-(trifluoromethyl)-	EtOH	235(4.38),255(4.22), 275(3.89)	35-5288-73
1,1':2',1"-Terphenyl, 2-(phenylthio)-4"-(trifluoromethyl)-	EtOH	235(4.09),248(3.92), 257(3.90),284(3.54)	35-5288-73
$C_{25}H_{17}N_3OS_2$			
4-Thiazolidinone, 3-methyl-5-(9-methyldibenzo[a,c]phenazin-11(9H)-ylidene)-2-thioxo-	$CHCl_3$	770(4.36)	103-1407-73
$C_{25}H_{17}N_3O_2S$			
Benzenesulfonamide, 4-methyl-N-(7-oxo-7H-benzimidazo[2,1-a]benz[de]isoquinolin-1-yl)-	HOAc	297(4.17),341(3.89), 358(3.96),405(4.14), 426s(4.03)	4-0705-73
Benzenesulfonamide, 4-methyl-N-(7-oxo-7H-benzimidazo[2,1-a]benz[de]isoquinolin-6-yl)-	HOAc	301(4.17),346(4.02), 364(4.18),413(4.17), 436s(3.99)	4-0705-73

Compound	Solvent	$\lambda_{max}(\log \epsilon)$	Ref.
$C_{25}H_{18}$			
Azulene, 1-(2,3-diphenyl-1-cyclopropen-1-yl)-	hexane	261(4.39),288(4.47), 321(4.30),350(4.21), 368(4.17),404(4.17), 428(4.09),477(1.90), 581s(2.35),608s(2.40), 633(2.46),698(2.31)	5-0166-73
$C_{25}H_{18}F_{12}N_3$			
Methanaminium, N-[4-[bis[4-[bis(trifluoromethyl)amino]phenyl]methylene]-2,5-cyclohexadien-1-ylidene]-N-methyl-, tetrafluoroborate	$CHCl_3$	448(4.20)	104-2181-73
$C_{25}H_{18}N_2O_5$			
Spiro[2H-indole-2,4'-[4'H]pyran-3(1H)-one, 1-methoxy-6-nitro-2',6'-diphenyl-	MeCN	252(4.67),370-420(3.30)	44-2834-73
$C_{25}H_{18}N_4$			
[1,2,4]Triazolo[4,3-a]quinoline, 1,2-dihydro-1-phenyl-2-(2-quinolinyl)-	benzene	270(4.3),300(4.3), 450(3.8)	5-2088-73
$C_{25}H_{18}O_2$			
Cyclopent[a]indene-1,8-carbolactone, 1,3a,8,8a-tetrahydro-3,8a-diphenyl-	EtOH	253(3.90),273s(3.52), 285s(2.60)	12-0147-73
2,7-Methano-1H-cyclobut[a]indene-8,1-carbolactone, 2,2a,7,7a-tetrahydro-1,7a-diphenyl-	EtOH	260(3.22),263(3.18), 267(3.20),276(3.04)	12-0147-73
$C_{25}H_{18}O_3$			
Dibenz[a,j]anthracene-2-carboxylic acid, 7-methoxy-, methyl ester	dioxan	212(4.57),236(4.67), 254(4.48),262(4.51), 270(4.49),294s(4.61), 303(4.71),315(4.79), 329s(4.29),350(4.19), 364(4.01),381(3.43), 403(3.04)	24-1341-73
$C_{25}H_{18}O_4$			
Naphtho[1,2-c]furan-1(3H)-one, 3-[7-(acetoxymethyl)-1-naphthalenyl]-	dioxan	228(5.02),239s(4.82), 275s(4.04),283(4.11), 294(4.04),316(3.33), 321s(3.24),331(3.41)	24-1341-73
$C_{25}H_{18}O_5$			
2-Naphthalenecarboxylic acid, 1,8'-carbonylbis-, dimethyl ester	dioxan	228s(4.84),242(4.90), 288s(4.03),299(4.10), 313(4.08),339(3.89)	24-1341-73
$C_{25}H_{18}Se$			
9H-Selenoxanthene, 9,9-diphenyl-	EtOH	211(4.60),258(3.70), 286(3.99)	138-0391-73
10H-Selenoxanthene, 9,10-diphenyl-	EtOH	211(4.79),260s(4.05), 274s(3.88),286s(3.84)	138-0391-73
$C_{25}H_{19}NO_3$			
Spiro[2H-indole-2,4'-[4'H]pyran]-3(1H)-one, 1-methoxy-2',6'-diphenyl-	MeCN	238(4.62),330-380(3.26)	44-2834-73

Compound	Solvent	$\lambda_{max}(\log \epsilon)$	Ref.
$C_{25}H_{19}NS_2$			
6H-Bis[1]benzothieno[2,3-c:3',2'-e]azepine, 7,8-dihydro-7-(phenylmethyl)-	EtOH	222(4.71),244(4.58), 271s(3.99),289(3.90), 299(3.98),308(4.02)	44-2814-73
$C_{25}H_{19}N_3S$			
Benzenesulfenamide, N-[4-[(diphenylmethylene)hydrazono]-2,5-cyclohexadien-1-ylidene]-	$CHCl_3$	287(4.19),380(4.14), 463(4.53)	39-1037-73C
$C_{25}H_{19}O_2P$			
Phosphonium, triphenyl-, 2,5-diformyl-2,4-cyclopentadien-1-ylide	MeCN	220(4.29),268(4.21), 310(4.01)	44-3537-73
$C_{25}H_{20}$			
1,1'-Biphenyl, 4,4'-methylenebis-	heptane	257.4(4.61)	101-0353-73C
$C_{25}H_{20}ClNO_2$			
1H-Benzo[f]cyclopenta[c]quinoline-1-carboxylic acid, 4-(4-chlorophenyl)-2,3-dihydro-, ethyl ester	EtOH	260(4.62),280(4.61), 344(3.76),362(3.89)	103-0628-73
$C_{25}H_{20}Cl_6N_2O_5$			
Cyclopent[e][1,3,4]oxadiazine-1(4aH)-carboxylic acid, 7,7a-dihydro-6-methyl-7-oxo-4a,5-diphenyl-3-(2,2,2-trichloroethoxy)-, 2,2,2-trichloroethyl ester, cis	EtOH	280(4.13)	44-2043-73
6,7-Diazabicyclo[3.2.0]hept-2-ene-6,7-dicarboxylic acid, 3,5-dimethyl-4-oxo-1,2-diphenyl-, bis(2,2,2-trichloroethyl) ester	EtOH	283(4.12)	44-2043-73
$C_{25}H_{20}N_2O_6$			
3H-Indol-3-one, 1,2-dihydro-1-methoxy-6-nitro-2,2-bis(2-oxo-2-phenylethyl)-	MeCN	250(4.68),300-420(3.32)	44-2834-73
$C_{25}H_{20}N_4O_{11}S$			
4-Azulenepropanol, 4-nitrobenzenesulfonate, trinitrobenzene complex	CH_2Cl_2	280(4.67),285(4.67), 343(3.72),568(2.63), 605s(--)	44-1106-73
$C_{25}H_{20}O$			
1-Acenaphthylenemethanol, 1,2-dihydro-α,α-diphenyl-	$CHCl_3$	283(3.58),293(3.64), 302s(3.49),308(3.42)	88-1803-73
Benzo[a]cyclopropa[cd]pentalene-2a(2bH)-methanol, 6b,6c-dihydro-1,6c-diphenyl-	EtOH	228(4.20),279(4.10)	12-0147-73
$C_{25}H_{20}OS$			
1,1':2',1"-Terphenyl, 2-[(4-methoxyphenyl)thio]-	EtOH	230(4.33),255(4.06), 283(3.86)	35-5288-73
$C_{25}H_{20}O_2$			
Spiro[cyclopropane-1,1'-[1H]indene]-2-carboxylic acid, 2',3'-diphenyl-, endo	$CHCl_3$	286(3.99)	5-0214-73
exo	$CHCl_3$	289(4.05)	5-0214-73
$C_{25}H_{20}O_4$			
[1,2'-Binaphthalene]-2-carboxylic acid, 4-acetoxy-3-methyl-, methyl ester	CH_2Cl_2	225(5.06),287(4.18), 340(2.95)	48-0375-73

Compound	Solvent	λ_{max}(log ε)	Ref.
2-Naphthalenecarboxylic acid, 1,8'-methylenebis-, dimethyl ester	dioxan	239(4.98),278s(4.02), 288(4.13),298(4.10), 326(3.65),339(3.65)	24-1341-73
2-Phenanthrenecarboxylic acid, 4-acetoxy-3-methyl-1-phenyl-, methyl ester	CH_2Cl_2	260(4.79),293(4.15), 306(4.15),340(2.94)	48-0375-73
$C_{25}H_{20}O_5$			
Isoshinanolone dibenzoate	EtOH	233(4.40),275(3.36), 283(3.38),296(3.24)	102-0175-73
Triptycene, 2-acetoxy-5-methoxy-7-(methoxycarbonyl)-	dioxan	216(4.72),269(3.53), 290(3.75)	18-0651-73
Triptycene, 5-acetoxy-2-methoxy-7-(methoxycarbonyl)-	dioxan	217(4.66),268(3.54), 288(3.75)	18-0651-73
$C_{25}H_{20}O_7$			
[1,2'-Binaphthalene]-1',4',5,8-tetrone, 4,5',8'-trimethoxy-2,3'-dimethyl-	$CHCl_3$	280(4.10),330(3.53), 420(3.89)	102-0175-73
$C_{25}H_{20}O_8$			
Heptanedioic acid, bis(2-oxo-2H-1-benzopyran-7-yl) ester	CH_2Cl_2	277(4.30),283(4.30), 313(4.23)	44-0957-73
$C_{25}H_{20}O_{10}$			
2(5H)-Furanone, 4-acetoxy-3-(4-acetoxyphenyl)-5-[(3,4-diacetoxyphenyl)methylene]-	EtOH	225s(4.04),252s(3.86), 340(4.18)	39-1921-73C
$C_{25}H_{21}Br$			
Cyclopentadiene, 5-bromo-1-ethyl-2,3,4-triphenyl-	EtOH	250(4.37),256s(4.37), 306s(3.91)	78-4307-73
$C_{25}H_{21}Cl_2NO_7$			
2(1H)-Pyridinone, 1-[3,5-bis-O-(4-chlorobenzoyl)-2-deoxy-α-D-erythro-pentofuranosyl]-4-hydroxy-5-methyl-	MeOH	282(3.75)	88-3079-73
β-	MeOH	282(3.67)	88-3079-73
$C_{25}H_{21}NO_2$			
1H-Benzo[f]cyclopenta[c]quinoline-1-carboxylic acid, 2,3-dihydro-4-phenyl-, ethyl ester	EtOH	260(4.64),280(4.60), 342(3.68),360(3.79)	103-0628-73
Pyridine, 2,6-bis(4-methoxyphenyl)-4-phenyl-	EtOH	268(4.65),328(4.03)	35-4891-73
	50%EtOH-HCl	292(4.42),370(4.28)	35-4891-73
$C_{25}H_{21}N_3O$			
2H-Indol-2-one, 3-[1,3-dihydro-5-methyl-3-[(4-methylphenyl)imino]-2H-indol-2-ylidene]-1,3-dihydro-5-methyl-	EtOH	296(4.37),510(4.1)	95-0008-73
$C_{25}H_{21}N_3O_4$			
1H-Pyrazole-4-carboxylic acid, 3-(4-methylphenyl)-1-(4-nitrophenyl)-5-phenyl-, ethyl ester	EtOH	230(5.51),260s(5.32), 315(5.22)	78-0121-73
$C_{25}H_{22}$			
Cyclopentadiene, 1-ethyl-2,3,4-triphenyl-	EtOH	238(4.24),318(3.88)	78-4307-73

Compound	Solvent	λ_{max}(log ϵ)	Ref.
$C_{25}H_{22}BF_4NOS$			
Phenalenylium, 1-ethoxy-3-[(3-ethyl-2(3H)-benzothiazolylidene)methyl]-, tetrafluoroborate	MeCN	282(--),332(--), 402(--),577(4.55)	44-2425-73
$C_{25}H_{22}ClNO_2$			
1H-Benzo[f]cyclopenta[c]quinoline-1-carboxylic acid, 4-(4-chlorophenyl)-2,3,4,5-tetrahydro-, ethyl ester	EtOH	248(4.41),275(4.15), 405(3.61)	103-0628-73
1-Cyclopentene-1-carboxylic acid, 3-[(4-chlorophenyl)methylene]-2-(2-naphthalenylamino)-, ethyl ester	EtOH	275(4.25),330(4.45)	103-0628-73
$C_{25}H_{22}NO$			
Pyrylium, 4-[4-(dimethylamino)phenyl]-2,6-diphenyl-, perchlorate	MeCN	385(4.3),535(4.83)	78-0795-73
$C_{25}H_{22}N_2O_2$			
2-Propen-1-one, 3-(4,5-dihydro-1,5-diphenyl-1H-pyrrol-3-yl)-1-(4-methoxyphenyl)-	C_6H_{12}	425(4.39)	104-0413-73
	EtOH	444(4.54)	104-0413-73
$C_{25}H_{22}N_2O_4$			
1-Cyclopentene-1-carboxylic acid, 2-(2-naphthalenylamino)-3-[(4-nitrophenyl)-methylene]-, ethyl ester	EtOH	243(4.39),320(4.32), 370(4.36)	103-0628-73
Spiro[2H-1-benzopyran-2,2'-[2H]indole], 1',3'-dihydro-8-methoxy-1',3'-dimethyl-6-nitro-3'-phenyl-	toluene	402(4.59),603(4.78)	103-1098-73
	EtOH	392(4.53),565(4.60)	103-1098-73
	dioxan	402(4.71),602(4.82)	103-1098-73
$C_{25}H_{22}N_2O_4S$			
4,5-Imidazolidinedicarboxylic acid, 1,2,3-triphenyl-5-thioxo-, dimethyl ester	EtOH	238(4.32),288(4.16)	22-3437-73
$C_{25}H_{22}N_2O_5$			
4,4-Imidazolidinedicarboxylic acid, 5-oxo-1,2,3-triphenyl-, dimethyl ester	EtOH	237(4.25),280s(--)	22-3437-73
1H-Indeno[1,2-b]quinoxalin-11-ol, 11-(3,4-dimethoxyphenyl)-2,4-dimethoxy-	EtOH	282(4.37),328(4.04), 371(4.30),382(4.32)	78-3337-73
$C_{25}H_{22}N_2O_7$			
[3,6'-Bi-1H-indole]-2,2'-dicarboxylic acid, 3',4-diformyl-7-methoxy-, diethyl ester	EtOH	221(4.66),248(4.57), 253(4.58),257(4.58), 328(4.43),340s(4.42)	78-1991-73
[4,6'-Bi-1H-indole]-2,2'-dicarboxylic acid, 3,3'-diformyl-7-methoxy-, diethyl ester	EtOH	224(4.65),249s(4.44), 251(4.45),259s(4.44), 324s(4.23),341(4.34)	78-1991-73
$C_{25}H_{22}N_2O_9$			
Kinamycin C, isopropylidene-, diacetate	EtOH	261.5(3.47)	94-0931-73
$C_{25}H_{22}N_4O_3$			
Spiro[2H-1-benzopyran-2,2'-[2H]indole], 1',3'-dihydro-1',3',3'-trimethyl-6-[(4-nitrophenyl)azo]-	EtOH	243(4.20),282(4.43), 400(4.26)	103-1463-73
	dioxan	242(4.34),295(4.20), 400(4.29)	103-1463-73
$C_{25}H_{22}O$			
2-Butanone, 1-(10,11-dihydrodibenzo-[a,d]cyclohepten-5-ylidene)-1-phenyl-	hexane	250(4.20)	54-0845-73

Compound	Solvent	λ_{max}(log ε)	Ref.
$C_{25}H_{22}O_5$			
1H-Phenalene-2-acetic acid, 4,9-dimethoxy-α,α-dimethyl-1-oxo-, phenyl ester	EtOH	264(4.44),322(3.69), 417s(4.12),435(4.17)	39-2159-73C
$C_{25}H_{22}O_8$			
4H,8H-Furo[3,2-d]benzo[1,2-b:3,4-b']dipyran-4,11(10H)-dione, 11a-acetoxy-8a,11a-dihydro-5-methoxy-10,10-dimethyl-2-phenyl-, cis-(-)- (tephrodin)	MeOH	223(4.48),266(4.45), 300(4.24)	119-0053-73
Tachrosinic acid, methyl ester	MeOH	217(4.42),268(4.46), 325(3.96)	119-0064-73
$C_{25}H_{23}BF_4N_2O_2S$			
Benzothiazolium, 2-[(4,7-diethoxy-1H-phenalen-1-ylidene)amino]-3-methyl-, tetrafluoroborate	MeCN	327(4.11),436(4.36), 567(4.54)	44-2425-73
$C_{25}H_{23}ClN_2O_3$			
Piperazine, 1-[(4-benzoylphenoxy)acetyl]-4-(4-chlorophenyl)-	EtOH	211(4.61),255(4.60)	111-0574-73
$C_{25}H_{23}F_6N_2$			
Methanaminium, N-[4-[[4-(dimethylamino)-2-(trifluoromethyl)phenyl]phenylmethylene]-3-(trifluoromethyl)-2,5-cyclohexadien-1-ylidene]-N-methyl-	98% HOAc	478(4.20+),678(4.68+)	39-1792-73B
Methanaminium, N-[4-[[4-(dimethylamino)-2-(trifluoromethyl)phenyl][2-(trifluoromethyl)phenyl]methylene]-2,5-cyclohexadien-1-ylidene]-N-methyl-	98% HOAc	416(4.28),613(4.42)	39-1792-73B
Methanaminium, N-[4-[[4-(dimethylamino)-2-(trifluoromethyl)phenyl][4-(trifluoromethyl)phenyl]methylene]-2,5-cyclohexadien-1-ylidene]-N-methyl-	98% HOAc	412(4.15),632(3.56)	39-1792-73B
$C_{25}H_{23}NO$			
1(2H)-Naphthalenone, 3-anilino-2-benzylidene-3,4-dihydro-4,4-dimethyl-	isooctane	270(4.1),305(4.1)	44-4226-73
$C_{25}H_{23}NOS_2$			
Aziridine, 1-benzoyl-2-phenyl-2-(2-phenyl-1,3-dithian-2-yl)-	EtOH	232(4.06)	35-1954-73
$C_{25}H_{23}NO_2$			
1H-Benzo[f]cyclopenta[c]quinoline-1-carboxylic acid, 2,3,4,5-tetrahydro-4-phenyl-, ethyl ester	EtOH	249(4.48),278(4.27), 411(3.70)	103-0628-73
1-Cyclopentene-1-carboxylic acid, 2-(2-naphthalenylamino)-3-(phenylmethylene)-, ethyl ester	EtOH	268(4.29),334(4.46)	103-0628-73
Methanone, [4,5-dihydro-4-phenyl-3-(2,4,6-trimethylphenyl)-5-isoxazolyl]phenyl-	EtOH	248(4.30)	39-1148-73C
$C_{25}H_{23}NO_5$			
4,4-Oxazolidinedicarboxylic acid, 2,3,5-triphenyl-, dimethyl ester	EtOH	240(4.20),289(3.35)	22-3437-73

Compound	Solvent	λmax(log ε)	Ref.
$C_{25}H_{23}NO_6$			
3-Pyridinecarboxylic acid, 6-[3-(3,4-dimethoxyphenyl)-1,3-dioxopropyl]-4-phenyl-, ethyl ester	EtOH	240(4.3),278(4.2), 375(4.6)	103-0212-73
$C_{25}H_{23}N_2O_2S$			
Benzothiazolium, 2-[(4,7-diethoxy-1H-phenalen-1-ylidene)amino]-3-methyl-, tetrafluoroborate	MeCN	327(4.11),436(4.36), 567(4.54)	44-2425-73
$C_{25}H_{23}N_3O$			
Spiro[2H-1-benzopyran-2,2'-[2H]indole], 1',3'-dihydro-1',3',3'-trimethyl-6-(phenylazo)-	EtOH	245(4.10),282(4.28), 358(4.14)	103-1463-73
	dioxan	247(4.22),285(4.38), 360(4.10)	103-1463-73
$C_{25}H_{23}N_5O_7$			
Acetamide, N-phenyl-N-[2-[1,3,4,7-tetrahydro-1,3-dimethyl-2,4-dioxo-7-(tetrahydro-1,3-dimethyl-2,4,6-trioxopyrimidin-5(2H)-ylidene)-2H-pyrano[2,3-d]-pyrimidin-5-yl]ethenyl]-	pyridine	370(4.50),490(4.54)	39-0823-73C
$C_{25}H_{24}$			
Cyclopropene, 1-butyl-1,2,3-triphenyl-	EtOH	228(4.46),310s(4.36), 317(4.44),333(4.36)	35-1285-73
$C_{25}H_{24}BrNO_4$			
1H-[1]Benzoxepino[2,3,4-ij]isoquinoline, 4-bromo-2,3,12,12a-tetrahydro-6,9-dimethoxy-8-(phenylmethoxy)-	EtOH	283(3.63),287(3.61)	95-1094-73
$C_{25}H_{24}Br_2O_3$			
2,4,6,8,10,12,14,16-Heptadecaoctaenoic acid, 17-(3,5-dibromo-4-methoxyphenyl)-, methyl ester, all-E-	$CHCl_3$	429s(4.8),450(4.97), 478(4.92)	1-2574-73
	pyridine	430s(--),450(--), 484(--)	1-2574-73
$C_{25}H_{24}Br_4N_4$			
21H-Biline, 2,3,17,18-tetrabromo-10,24-dihydro-1,7,8,12,13,19-hexamethyl-, dihydrobromide	$CHCl_3$	277(4.78),378(4.35), 466(4.62),504s(4.81), 538(5.15)	39-2281-73C
$C_{25}H_{24}ClF_6N_3O_4$			
Methanaminium, N-[4-[[4-[bis(trifluoromethyl)amino]phenyl][4-(dimethylamino)phenyl]methylene]-2,5-cyclohexadien-1-ylidene]-N-methyl-, perchlorate	EtOH	424(3.76),632(4.60)	104-2181-73
$C_{25}H_{24}ClN_3O_3$			
Piperazine, 1-(4-chlorophenyl)-4-[[4-(hydroxyimino)phenylmethyl]phenoxy]-acetyl]-	EtOH	211(4.65),255(4.61)	111-0574-73
$C_{25}H_{24}N_2$			
1,4-Methanobenzo[c]cinnoline, 1,2,3,4-4a,5,6,10b-octahydro-4a,6-diphenyl-	MeCN	293(4.11)	22-3487-73

Compound	Solvent	λ max(log ε)	Ref.
$C_{25}H_{24}N_2O$			
5-Isoxazoleethanamine, 3-methyl-N,α-diphenyl-β-(phenylmethyl)-	EtOH	248(4.17),296(3.36)	18-3533-73
$C_{25}H_{24}N_2O_4S$			
1,4,2-Oxathiazole-5-ethanol, α-(1-methylethyl)-3-(4-nitrophenyl)-β,5-diphenyl-	EtOH	281(4.16),337(3.64)	39-1580-73C
$C_{25}H_{24}O_5$			
Isosericetin	MeOH	275(4.50),354(3.81)	78-3347-73
$C_{25}H_{24}O_6$			
2H-1-Benzopyran-2-one, 7,7'-[1,7-heptanediylbis(oxy)]bis-	CH_2Cl_2	324(4.50)	44-0957-73
2H-1-Benzopyran-2-one, 7,7'-(1,5-pentanediyl)bis(oxy)bis[4-methyl-	CH_2Cl_2	322(4.50)	44-0957-73
5-Chrysenol, 2,3,8,9-tetramethoxy-12-methyl-, acetate	EtOH	231(4.81),259s(4.60), 279s(5.02),287(5.15), 307(4.54),319(4.34), 334(4.26),362(4.00), 380(4.08)	44-3425-73
$C_{25}H_{24}O_7$			
Galangin, 3-O-methyl-6-(3-methyl-2-butenyl)-, diacetate	MeOH	253(4.23),303(4.18)	12-0641-73
Stachyoidinol acetate	MeOH	213(4.52),247s(4.23), 267(4.42),306(4.09)	119-0053-73
$C_{25}H_{24}O_8$			
Curcumin, diacetyl-	EtOH	255(4.10),402(4.63)	39-2379-73C
$C_{25}H_{25}AsO_4$			
Arsonium, triphenyl-, 2-ethoxy-1-(ethoxycarbonyl)-2-oxoethylide	MeOH	223(4.48),238s(4.23), 270s(3.76)	78-1697-73
$C_{25}H_{25}NO_3$			
Cyclopentanecarboxylic acid, 3-[(2-naphthalenylamino)phenylmethyl]-2-oxo-, ethyl ester	EtOH	224(4.47),270(4.30), 323(3.90)	103-0628-73
$C_{25}H_{25}N_3O_3$			
Indolo[3',2':4,5]pyrrolo[2,1-c][1,4]-benzodiazepine-7,13(5H,12H)-dione, 5-acetyl-14a-(1,1-dimethyl-2-propenyl)-5a,13a,14,14a-tetrahydro-	MeOH	210(4.79),245(4.34), 284s(3.60)	44-4204-73
$C_{25}H_{25}N_7O_7$			
L-Histidine, N-acetyl-2,5-bis[[4-(ethoxycarbonyl)phenyl]azo]-, methyl ester	EtOH	435(4.49)	44-1971-73
$C_{25}H_{25}NiP$			
Nickel, (η^5-2,4-cyclopentadien-1-yl)-ethyl(triphenylphosphine)-	C_6H_{12}	300(4.00),406(3.11), 575(1.90)	23-1179-73
$C_{25}H_{26}Br_6N_4$			
21H-Biline, 2,3,17,18-tetrabromo-10,24-dihydro-1,7,8,12,13,19-hexamethyl-, dihydrobromide	$CHCl_3$	277(4.78),378(4.35), 466(4.62),504s(4.81), 538(5.15)	39-2281-73C

Compound	Solvent	λ_{max}(log ε)	Ref.
$C_{25}H_{26}N_2O_5$			
6,7-Diazabicyclo[3.2.0]hept-2-ene-6,7-dicarboxylic acid, 3,5-dimethyl-4-oxo-1,2-diphenyl-, diethyl ester	EtOH	282(4.11)	44-2043-73
$C_{25}H_{26}N_4O_5$			
2H-Pyran-3-carboxamide, N-(4-morpholinylcarbonyl)-2-oxo-4,6-bis[(phenylmethyl)amino]-	MeCN	249(4.03),312(4.17)	39-2432-73C
$C_{25}H_{26}O_3S$			
4H-Cycloocta[3,4]cyclobuta[1,2-b]thiopyran-4-one, 4a,4b,5,6,7,8,9,10,10a-10b-decahydro-2,10b-diphenyl-, 1,1-dioxide	EtOH	221(4.29),294(4.04)	18-1007-73
$C_{25}H_{26}O_5$			
2H,6H-Benzo[1,2-b:5,4-b']dipyran-6-one, 8-(2,4-dihydroxyphenyl)-7,8-dihydro-2,2-dimethyl-10-(3-methyl-2-butenyl)-, (S)-	EtOH	257(4.48)	94-1192-73
4H-1-Benzopyran-4-one, 5,7-dihydroxy-3-(4-hydroxyphenyl)-6,8-bis(3-methyl-2-butenyl)-	MeOH	272(4.14),368(3.47)	78-3347-73
Flemingin D	EtOH	278(4.05),286(4.05), 375(4.38)	102-2027-73
Methanone, (2,6-dimethoxyphenyl)[6-methoxy-2,4-dimethyl-3-(phenylmethoxy)-phenyl]-	MeOH	211(4.60),226s(4.30), 267(3.88),307(3.67)	24-1198-73
2-Propen-1-one, 3-(2,4-dihydroxyphenyl)-1-[7-hydroxy-2,2-dimethyl-8-(3-methyl-2-butenyl)-2H-1-benzopyran-6-yl]-	EtOH	403(4.49)	94-1192-73
	EtOH-NaOEt	465(4.63)	94-1192-73
	EtOH-$AlCl_3$	470(4.56)	94-1192-73
	EtOH-NaOAc-H_3BO_3	403(4.46)	94-1192-73
$C_{25}H_{26}O_6$			
Flemingin E	EtOH	278(4.09),286(4.08), 375(4.43)	102-2027-73
Flemingin F	EtOH	278(4.11),287(4.11), 375(4.42)	102-2027-73
Lespedeol B	EtOH	275(4.62)	94-2712-73
$C_{25}H_{26}O_7$			
[1]Benzopyrano[3,4-b][1]benzopyran-12(6H)-one, 9-acetoxy-6a,12a-dihydro-2,3-dimethoxy-8-(3-methyl-2-butenyl)-	EtOH	218(4.47),266(4.02), 291(3.76),319(3.61)	39-1277-73C
	EtOH-base	262(3.91),293(3.59), 350(4.08)	39-1277-73C
$C_{25}H_{26}O_9$			
Chromocyclin, 2-deacetyl-12a-deoxy-2-(methoxycarbonyl)-8,10,11-trimethyl-	EtOH	234(4.34),262(4.39), 387(4.08),395(4.02)	105-0498-73
$C_{25}H_{27}BrN_2O_7S_4$			
Benzothiazolium, 2-[3-[3-(2-bromoethyl)-5,6-dimethoxy-2(3H)-benzothiazolylidene]-1-propenyl]-5,6-dimethoxy-3-[2-(sulfothio)ethyl]-, hydroxide, inner salt	MeOH	610(4.80)	18-1509-73

Compound	Solvent	λ_{max}(log ϵ)	Ref.
$C_{25}H_{27}F_3O_4$			
3'H-Cyclopropa[6,7]pregna-1,4,6-triene-3,20-dione, 17-acetoxy-3',3',6-trifluoro-6,7-dihydro-16-methylene-, (6β,7β)-	n.s.g.	244(4.20)	39-0227-73C
$C_{25}H_{27}NO$			
2-Propen-1-one, 3-[3,4-dihydro-2-(1-piperidinyl)-1-naphthalenyl]-1-(4-methylphenyl)-	EtOH	231(4.35),365(4.01), 456(3.82)	48-1161-73
2-Propen-1-one, 3-[2-(hexahydro-1H-azepin-1-yl)-1H-inden-3-yl]-1-(4-methylphenyl)-	EtOH	232(4.12),281(4.27), 483(4.47)	48-1161-73
$C_{25}H_{27}NO_2$			
Pyridine, 4-cyclohexyl-2,6-bis(4-methoxyphenyl)-	EtOH	270(4.51),313s(4.13)	35-4891-73
	50%EtOH-HCl	287(4.22),350(4.37)	35-4891-73
$C_{25}H_{27}NO_4$			
Ancistrocladidine	n.s.g.	233(4.71),248s(4.54), 290s(4.06),308(4.15), 322(4.22),336(4.23)	2-1190-73
Isoquinoline, 1,2,3,4-tetrahydro-6,7-dimethoxy-1-[3-methoxy-4-(phenylmethoxy)phenyl]-	MeOH	206(4.88),230s(4.29), 282(3.85)	78-0031-73
7H-Pyrano[2,3-c]acridin-7-one, 3,12-dihydro-6-hydroxy-11-methoxy-3,3,12-trimethyl-5-(3-methyl-2-butenyl)-	EtOH	241(4.13),272s(4.39), 296(4.50),319s(4.10), 347(3.91),430(3.53)	39-1173-73C
$C_{25}H_{27}NO_8$			
Cephalotaxine, diacetyldemethyl-	EtOH	230s(3.96),295(3.90), 318(3.93)	95-0916-73
$C_{25}H_{27}N_3O_5$			
Codeine derivative, salt with tetracyanoethylene and methanol	MeOH	233(4.37),283(3.28)	78-2387-73
$C_{25}H_{28}ClNO_4$			
Pyrrolidinium, 1-(5,6,10,11-tetrahydro-3,9-dimethoxy-7-oxo-7H,9H,12H-benzo-[1,2]fluoreno[4a,4b-c]furan-12-ylidene)-, chloride	MeOH	273(3.83),298(3.48), 319(3.45),430(4.64)	39-1780-73C
$C_{25}H_{28}ClNO_7$			
6,14-Ethenomorphinan-7,8-dicarboxylic acid, 1-chloro-7,8-didehydro-4,5-epoxy-18,19-dihydro-3,6-dimethoxy-17-methyl-, dimethyl ester	MeOH	288(3.52)	78-2393-73
$C_{25}H_{28}IN_2P$			
Phosphorus(1+), (1,1-dimethylaminato)-(1H-indol-2-ylmethyl)diphenyl-, iodide, (T-4)-	MeOH	272(4.04),278(4.04), 284(4.00),293(3.90)	23-0792-73
$C_{25}H_{28}NO_5P$			
[2-(4-Methylbenzoyl)ethenyl]trimethylammonium diphenylphosphate	H_2O	266s(3.82),273s(3.90), 280(3.94)	24-0435-73

Compound	Solvent	$\lambda_{max}(\log \epsilon)$	Ref.
$C_{25}H_{28}N_2O_8$			
Spiro[1,3-dioxolane-2,6'-[6H]indole-1'-carboxylic acid, 3'a-(3,4-dimethoxyphenyl)octahydro-, 4-nitrophenyl ester, cis-(±)-	MeOH	277(4.13)	33-0347-73
$C_{25}H_{28}O_2$			
Bicyclo[2.2.1]heptan-2-one, 1,7,7-trimethyl-3-(3-oxo-1,3-diphenylpropyl)-	EtOH	241(4.11),278(3.02)	22-0263-73
$C_{25}H_{28}O_3$			
2-Propen-1-one, 3-phenyl-1-(3,4,9,10-tetrahydro-2,2,8,8-tetramethyl-2H,8H-benzo[1,2-b:3,4-b']dipyran-6-yl)-	MeOH	310(4.46),360(4.12)	32-0779-73
$C_{25}H_{28}O_4$			
Benzenemethanol, 2-hydroxy-3-[[2-hydroxy-3-[(2-hydroxy-3,5-dimethylphenyl)methyl]-5-methylphenyl]methyl]-5-methyl-	dioxan	287(3.93)	126-0039-73L
4H-1-Benzopyran-4-one, 2,3-dihydro-7-hydroxy-2-(4-hydroxyphenyl)-6,8-bis(3-methyl-2-butenyl)-	EtOH	284(4.14)	94-1777-73
	EtOH-NaOH	355(--)	94-1777-73
	EtOH-$AlCl_3$	284(--)	94-1777-73
	EtOH-NaOAc	355(--)	94-1777-73
Lespedezin	EtOH	283(3.9),287(3.9)	94-2715-73
	EtOH-base	250(4.3),292(4.1)	94-2715-73
Lespein	EtOH	283(3.8),287(3.8)	94-2715-73
	EtOH-base	250(4.3),292(4.1)	94-2715-73
$C_{25}H_{28}O_5$			
4H-1-Benzopyran-4-one, 2-(2,4-dihydroxyphenyl)-2,3-dihydro-7-hydroxy-6,8-bis(3-methyl-2-butenyl)-, (S)-	EtOH	285(4.19)	94-1192-73
$C_{25}H_{28}O_6$			
[1]Benzopyrano[4,5-bc][1]benzoxepin-7(2H)-one, 1,12a-dihydro-6,8-dihydroxy-1-(1-hydroxy-1-methylethyl)-4-methyl-9-(3-methyl-2-butenyl)-(arugosin C)	EtOH	227(4.34),271(3.94), 293(3.97),309(4.01), 407(3.95)	39-1825-73C
1,6-Heptadiene-3,5-dione, 1,7-bis(3,4-dimethoxyphenyl)-, (E,E)-	EtOH	252(4.09),350(4.34)	39-2379-73C
$C_{25}H_{29}ClN_4NiO_4$			
Nickel(1+), (7,8,12,13-tetradehydro-1,7,8,12,13,19-hexamethylcorrinato-N^{21},N^{22},N^{23},N^{24})-, (SP-4-3)-, perchlorate	n.s.g.	230(4.44),247s(4.37), 325(4.53),336(4.56), 386s(3.76),549(4.30)	39-0991-73C
$C_{25}H_{29}F_3O_4$			
3'H-Cyclopropa[6,7]pregna-4,6-diene-3,20-dione, 17-acetoxy-3',3',6-trifluoro-6,7-dihydro-16-methylene-, (6β,7β)-	n.s.g.	244(4.09)	39-0227-73C
$C_{25}H_{29}F_7O_4$			
Androsta-2,4-diene-3,17-diol, 17-acetate 3-(2,2,3,3,4,4,4-heptafluorobutanoate), (17β)-	dioxan	261(3.79)	78-1591-73

Compound	Solvent	λmax(log ε)	Ref.
Androsta-3,5-diene-3,17-diol, 17-acetate 3-(2,2,3,3,4,4,4-heptafluorobutanoate), (17β)-	dioxan	227(4.21)	78-1591-73
$C_{25}H_{29}NO_4$			
6H,7H,9H-Benzo[1,2]fluoreno[4a,4b-c]furan-7-one, 5,10,11,12-tetrahydro-3,9-dimethoxy-12-(1-pyrrolidinyl)-	MeOH	238(4.04),295s(4.36), 308(4.46),318(4.45)	39-1780-73C
$C_{25}H_{29}NO_6$			
Spiro[2H-indene-2,1'(2'H)-isoquinoline]-5,6'-diol, 1,3,3',4'-tetrahydro-6,7-dimethoxy-1,2'-dimethyl-, diacetate	EtOH	282(3.78),286s(3.77)	78-1265-73
$C_{25}H_{29}NO_7$			
5,14-Ethanomorphinan-18,19-dicarboxylic acid, 18,19-didehydro-4,6-epoxy-3,6-dimethoxy-17-methyl-, dimethyl ester	MeOH	219(4.38),238s(4.10), 283s(3.47)	78-2383-73
$C_{25}H_{29}NO_8$			
Rhoeagenindiolmethine, diacetyldihydro-	EtOH	213(4.30),238(3.89), 291(3.87)	73-2799-73
$C_{25}H_{29}N_4Ni$			
Nickel(1+), (7,8,12,13-tetradehydro-1,7,8,12,13,19-hexamethylcorrinato-N^{21},N^{22},N^{23},N^{24})-, (SP-4-3)-, perchlorate	n.s.g.	230(4.44),247s(4.37), 325(4.53),336(4.56), 386s(3.76),549(4.30)	39-0991-73C
$C_{25}H_{29}N_9O_{12}$			
2,6-Pyridinedicarboxylic acid, bis-[2-(1,2-dihydro-2-oxo-1-β-D-ribofuranosyl-4-pyrimidinyl)hydrazide]	pH 2.8	225s(4.33),282(4.41)	35-1323-73
	pH 6.2	225s(4.33),278(4.39)	35-1323-73
	pH 10.8	242(4.24),335(4.49)	35-1323-73
$C_{25}H_{30}BN$			
Boranamine, N-methyl-N-phenyl-1,1-bis-(2,4,6-trimethylphenyl)-	C_6H_{12}	255(4.06)	101-0051-73H
$C_{25}H_{30}N_2O_6$			
Venenatic acid secolactam	EtOH	226(4.51),268(3.98), 282s(3.85),291(3.78)	2-1057-73
$C_{25}H_{30}N_4O_4$			
1H-Indolo[3,2-e][2]benzazecine-1-carboxylic acid, 6,8a-dicyano-14-ethoxy-2,3,4,4a,5,6,7,8,8a,14,15,15a-dodecahydro-2-hydroxy-, methyl ester	EtOH	230(4.40),274(4.19)	95-1165-73
$C_{25}H_{30}O_7$			
Norkurarinol	EtOH	294(4.22)	94-2733-73
	EtOH-NaOH	336(4.43)	94-2733-73
Talassin A	n.s.g.	248(4.38)	105-0120-73
$C_{25}H_{30}O_8$			
Kadsurin	MeOH	230(4.42),254(4.05), 278(3.54)	88-4257-73
Nortrachelogenin, acetylethylmethyl-	EtOH	232(4.19),281(3.76)	94-1108-73
Trachelogenin, acetylethyl-	EtOH	232(4.29),281(3.90)	94-1108-73

Compound	Solvent	λ_{max}(log ε)	Ref.
$C_{25}H_{30}O_{12}$			
Sugeronin	n.s.g.	273(3.21),277(3.10)	40-0785-73
$C_{25}H_{31}ClO_6$			
Pregna-4,6-diene-3,20-dione, 2α,17α-diacetoxy-6-chloro-	MeOH	287(4.22)	94-1295-73
2β-	MeOH	292.5(4.32)	94-1295-73
$C_{25}H_{31}NO$			
Androst-4-en-3-one, 17-(2-pyridinylmethylene)-	n.s.g.	247(4.51),287(4.02)	19-0887-73
$C_{25}H_{31}NO_2$			
Carbamic acid, methyl[4-phenyl-4-(6,7,8-9-tetrahydro-5H-benzocyclohepten-2-yl)-3-butenyl]-, ethyl ester	MeOH	254(4.17)	73-2768-73
$C_{25}H_{31}NO_4S$			
Benzenesulfonamide, N,4-dimethyl-N-(6a,7,10,10a-tetrahydro-1-methoxy-6,6,9-trimethyl-6H-dibenzo[b,d]-pyran-3-yl)-, (6aR-trans)-	EtOH	213(4.68),227(4.49), 286(3.57)	33-0510-73
$C_{25}H_{31}N_3O_2$			
2-Propenamide, N-[3-[[4-[(1-oxo-3-phenyl-2-propenyl)amino]butyl]amino]phenyl]-3-phenyl-, (E,E)-	n.s.g.	215(4.55),221(4.48), 273(4.70)	33-0474-73
$C_{25}H_{32}N_2O_2$			
4,17a-Diaza-D-homoandrost-5-ene-3,7-dione, 4-(phenylmethyl)-	MeOH	234(4.00)	39-1204-73C
$C_{25}H_{32}O_4$			
Bufa-14,20,22-trienolide, 3-(formyloxy)-, (3β,5β)-	n.s.g.	300(3.78)	5-0005-73
19-Norpregna-1,3,5(10)-trien-20-one, 17-acetoxy-3-ethoxy-16-methylene-	MeOH	278(3.36),288(3.28)	87-0649-73
$C_{25}H_{32}O_5$			
19-Norpregna-3,5-dien-20-one, 3,17α-diacetoxy-16-methylene-	MeOH	235(4.30)	87-0649-73
$C_{25}H_{32}O_7$			
2H,8H-Benzo[1,2-b:3,4-b']dipyran-6-propanoic acid, 5-acetoxy-3,4-dihydro-2,3,8,8-tetramethyl-4-oxo-β-propyl-, methyl ester	EtOH	269(4.36),301(3.86)	102-0185-73
$C_{25}H_{32}O_8$			
Kosin K2	C_6H_{12}	226(4.28),283(4.29)	102-2017-73
Protokosin	n.s.g.	223(4.41),287(4.30)	102-2017-73
$C_{25}H_{32}O_{14}$			
Cornin tetraacetate	EtOH	237(3.97)	1-2581-73
$C_{25}H_{32}O_{15}$			
Cyclopenta[c]pyran-4,7-dicarboxylic acid, 1,4a,5,6,7,7a-hexahydro-1-[(2,3,4,6-tetra-O-acetyl-β-D-glucopyranosyl)oxy]-, 4-methyl ester, [1S-(1α,4aα,7α,7aα)]-	MeOH	234(4.06)	94-0497-73

Compound	Solvent	λmax(log ε)	Ref.
Cyclopenta[c]pyran-4,7-dicarboxylic acid, 1,4a,5,6,7,7a-hexahydro-1-[(2,3,4,6-tetra-O-acetyl-β-D-glucopyranosyl)oxy]-, 7-methyl ester	MeOH	231.5(4.05)	94-0497-73
$C_{25}H_{33}ClO_5$			
Pregna-5,7-dien-20-one, 3β,17α-diacetoxy-7-chloro-	EtOH	263(3.86),273(3.99), 283(3.98),295(3.74)	87-0065-73
$C_{25}H_{33}ClO_6$			
Pregn-4-ene-3,20-dione, 7α,17α-diacetoxy-6β-chloro-	MeOH	237(4.16)	48-0008-73
$C_{25}H_{33}NO$			
Androst-5-en-3β-ol, 17-(2-pyridinylmethylene)-	n.s.g.	251(4.13),286(4.02)	19-0887-73
$C_{25}H_{33}N_3O_4$			
1H-Azecino[5,4-b]indole-6-acetic acid, 3-cyano-8-ethoxy-5-ethyl-2,3,4,5,6,7-8,9-octahydro-α-(methoxymethylene)-, methyl ester, (R)-	EtOH	226(4.65),250(4.08), 285(3.91),293(3.85)	95-1165-73
(S)-	EtOH	226(4.68),250s(4.10), 284(3.92),293(3.84)	95-1165-73
$C_{25}H_{34}O_3$			
4-Isobenzofurancarboxaldehyde, 1,3,3a-4,5,7a-hexahydro-4,7-dimethyl-5-[2-methyl-4-(2,6,6-trimethyl-1-cyclohexen-1-yl)-1,3-butadienyl]-3-oxo-, [3aα,4α,5β(E,E),7aα]-	EtOH	250s(4.19),260(4.21)	39-0590-73C
1,2-Naphthalenedione, 3-(8-cyclohexyloctyl)-4-methoxy-	EtOH	254(4.44),332(3.29), 421(3.22)	136-0247-73A
24-Norchola-5,16,20-trien-22-one, 3β-acetoxy-	EtOH	267(3.26)	19-0809-73
19-Norpregna-1(10),2,5-triene-11,20-dione, 3-methoxy-4,4,9,14-tetramethyl-	n.s.g.	328(4.02)	78-1109-73
$C_{25}H_{34}O_5$			
Furanoeremophilane, 3β-angeloyloxy-9β-senecioyloxy-	MeOH	220(4.51)	18-2840-73
Prostaglandin C_2 tetrahydropyranyl ether	n.s.g.	240(4.0)	88-4730-73
Solidagoic acid B	EtOH	221(3.78)	23-1332-73
$C_{25}H_{34}O_7$			
Androst-14-ene-17-carboxylic acid, 3,12-diacetoxy-11-oxo-, methyl ester	EtOH	293(1.63)	33-2827-73
$C_{25}H_{34}O_9$			
Eupacunin, 11,13-dihydro-13-methoxy-, acetate	MeOH	216(4.04)	44-2189-73
$C_{25}H_{34}O_{13}$			
Cyclopenta[c]pyran-4-carboxylic acid, 1,4a,5,6,7,7a-hexahydro-7-methyl-1-[(tetra-O-acetyl-β-D-glucopyranosyl)oxy]-, methyl ester	EtOH	234(4.22)	94-2684-73

Compound	Solvent	$\lambda_{max}(\log \epsilon)$	Ref.
$C_{25}H_{34}O_{14}$			
Cyclopenta[c]pyran-4-carboxylic acid, 1,4a,5,6,7,7a-hexahydro-5-hydroxy-7-methyl-1-[(tetra-O-acetyl-β-D-glucopyranosyl)oxy]-, methyl ester	EtOH	238(4.05)	1-2581-73
epimer	EtOH	236(4.03)	1-2581-73
$C_{25}H_{35}ClO_6$			
Pregn-4-en-20-one, 7α,17α-diacetoxy-6β-chloro-3β-hydroxy-	MeOH	204(4.01)	48-0008-73
$C_{25}H_{35}NO_4$			
5α-Pregn-17(20)-ene-21-carboxylic acid, 3β-acetoxy-20-cyano-	n.s.g.	223(4.10)	44-1478-73
$C_{25}H_{35}N_3$			
1H-Pyrrole, 3-ethyl-5-[[4-ethyl-2-[(4-ethyl-3,5-dimethyl-1H-pyrrol-2-yl)-methylene]-3-methyl-2H-pyrrol-5-yl]-methyl]-2,4-dimethyl-, hydrobromide	$CHCl_3$	492(4.92)	65-0885-73
$C_{25}H_{35}N_3O_5$			
5β,14β-Card-20(22)-enolide, 3α-azido-14-hydroxy-12β-acetoxy-	EtOH	216(4.22)	33-2782-73
3β-azido-	EtOH	216(4.19)	33-2782-73
5β,14β-Card-20(22)-enolide, 3α-azido-14-hydroxy-16β-acetoxy-	EtOH	215(4.18)	33-2782-73
3β-azido-	EtOH	215(4.10)	33-2782-73
$C_{25}H_{36}O_3$			
24-Norchola-5,16,20-triene-3,22-diol, 3β-acetoxy-22-hydroxy-	EtOH	240(4.01)	19-0809-73
$C_{25}H_{36}O_4$			
1(3H)-Isobenzofuranone, 3a,4,7,7a-tetrahydro-3-hydroxy-4-(hydroxymethyl)-3a,5-dimethyl-7-[2-methyl-4-(2,6,6-trimethyl-1-cyclohexen-1-yl)-1,3-butadienyl]-	EtOH	240(4.22),262(4.25)	39-0590-73C
Pregna-5,16-dien-20-one, 3β-acetoxy-21-(methoxymethyl)-	EtOH	240(3.99),294(2.55)	70-1578-73
Pregn-4-ene-3,20-dione, 16α,17α-epoxy-21-(propoxymethyl)-	EtOH	242(4.23)	70-1790-73
2-Propen-1-one, 1-[(3β,16α,17α)-3-hydroxy-16,17-[(1-methylethylidene)-bis(oxy)androst-5-en-17-yl]-	EtOH	193(3.90),297(2.15)	70-0527-73
$C_{25}H_{36}O_4Si$			
1,3-Dioxa-2-silacyclohexane, 2-butyl-5-ethyl-2-[3-(phenylmethoxy)phenoxy]-4-propyl-	EtOH	207(4.27),273(3.28), 279(3.22)	87-0729-73
$C_{25}H_{36}O_5$			
5α-Androst-2-ene-11α,17β-diol, 3-acetyl-, diacetate	MeOH	233(4.04),300(1.85)	23-3936-73
5β,14α-Card-20(22)-enolide, 3β-acetoxy-15α-hydroxy-	EtOH	216.5(4.25)	94-0388-73
15β-	EtOH	217(4.20)	94-0388-73
5β,14β-Card-20(22)-enolide, 3β-acetoxy-15α-hydroxy-	EtOH	218(4.21)	94-0388-73

Compound	Solvent	λmax(log ε)	Ref.
5β,14β-Card-20(22)-enolide, 3β-acetoxy-15β-hydroxy-	EtOH	216.5(4.22)	94-0388-73
5β,14β,17α-Card-20(22)-enolide, 3β-acetoxy-15α-hydroxy-	EtOH	218(4.18)	94-0388-73
15β-hydroxy-	EtOH	217(4.25)	94-0388-73
Colupulone, 6-hydroxy-	MeOH-acid	240(3.92),284(3.97)	24-1309-73
	MeOH-base	280(4.18)	24-1309-73
Isocohumulone, 5-(3-methyl-2-butenyl)-	MeOH-acid	224(3.96),276(4.03)	24-1309-73
	MeOH-base	254(4.20),279s(4.10)	24-1309-73
1-Propanone, 1-[(3β,16α,17α)-3-acetoxy-16,17-epoxyandrost-5-en-17-yl]-3-methoxy-	EtOH	224(4.01),289s(3.21), 333(2.82)	70-1790-73
$C_{25}H_{36}O_6$			
Pregn-4-ene-3,20-dione, 17α-acetoxy-2α,6β-bis(hydroxymethyl)-	EtOH	243(4.17)	33-2396-73
9β,10α-Pregn-4-ene-3,20-dione, 17α-acetoxy-2β,6β-bis(hydroxymethyl)-	EtOH	241(4.17)	33-2396-73
9β,10α-Pregn-4-ene-3,20-dione, 17α-acetoxy-6,6-bis(hydroxymethyl)-	EtOH	247(4.11)	33-2396-73
Pregn-4-en-3-one, 20β-acetoxy-21-[(methoxycarbonyl)oxy]-	MeOH	241(4.23)	44-2335-73
$C_{25}H_{37}NO_4$			
5α,14β-Card-20(22)-enolide, 3β-(acetylamino)-14-hydroxy-	EtOH	214(4.20)	33-2782-73
$C_{25}H_{37}NO_5$			
5β,14β-Card-20(22)-enolide, 3β-(acetylamino)-12β,14-dihydroxy-	EtOH	218(4.18)	33-2782-73
5β,14β-Card-20(22)-enolide, 3β-(acetylamino)-14,16β-dihydroxy-	EtOH	216(4.13)	33-2782-73
5β,14β-Card-20(22)-enolide, 12β-(acetyloxy)-3β-amino-14-hydroxy-, hydrochloride	EtOH	216(4.14)	33-2782-73
5β,14β-Card-20(22)-enolide, 16β-(acetyloxy)-3α-amino-14-hydroxy-, hydrochloride	EtOH	214(4.16)	33-2782-73
3β-amino-	EtOH	208(4.14)	33-2782-73
	EtOH-HCl	214(4.13)	33-2782-73
$C_{25}H_{38}N_2O_4$			
Acetic acid, acetyl[(3α,5α)-3-(acetyloxy)androstan-17-ylidene)hydrazide	MeOH	231(3.48)	88-2289-73
$C_{25}H_{38}O_5$			
5α-Pregn-16-en-20-one, 3β-acetoxy-18,18-dimethoxy-	n.s.g.	244(3.81)	33-2698-73
$C_{25}H_{38}O_6$			
1H-Benz[e]indene-8α-carboxylic acid, 3β-(1,1-dimethylethoxy)-2,3,3a,4-5,7,8,9,9aβ,9bα-decahydro-3aβ-methyl-6-[2-(2-methyl-1,3-dioxolan-2-yl)ethyl]-7-oxo-, (±)-	EtOH	249(4.16)	44-3244-73
Cyclohept[e]inden-6(2H)-one, 9-acetoxy-8-(acetoxymethyl)-3,3a,4,5,5a,7,8,9-10,10a-decahydro-8-methoxy-3a,5a-dimethyl-1-(1-methylethyl)-	isooctane	282(2.18)	23-3842-73

Compound	Solvent	λ_{max}(log ϵ)	Ref.
$C_{25}H_{38}O_8$			
Prosta-5,13-dien-1-oic acid, 15-hydroxy-8,10-bis(methoxycarbonyl)-9-oxo-, methyl ester, (5Z,8ξ,12ξ,13E)-	NaOH	290(4.18)	88-0451-73
$C_{25}H_{40}O$			
1,3,12,14-Pentadecatetraen-8-ol, 5,11-dimethyl-8-(3-methyl-4,6-heptadienyl)-	heptane	227(5.05)	70-1624-73
$C_{25}H_{40}O_7$			
Prost-13-en-1-oic acid, 11-acetoxy-9,9-[1,2-ethanediylbis(oxy)]-15-oxo-, methyl ester, (11α,13E)-(±)-	MeOH	228(4.15)	78-1447-73
$C_{25}H_{42}$			
Benzene, 1-nonadecenyl-, (E)-	MeOH	251.5(4.29)	24-1612-73
$C_{25}H_{42}O_8$			
2,4-Nonadienoic acid, 8-[4-acetoxy-6-(2,2-dimethoxyethyl)tetrahydro-3,5-dimethyl-2H-pyran-2-yl]-7-hydroxy-2,6-dimethyl-	EtOH	268(4.48)	33-2287-73
$C_{25}H_{43}NO_2$			
Octadecanamide, N-hydroxy-N-(3-methylphenyl)-	EtOH	254(4.00)	112-0547-73
Octadecanamide, N-hydroxy-N-(4-methylphenyl)-	EtOH	250(4.04)	112-0547-73
$C_{25}H_{44}O_5$			
Pentanedioic acid, 2-[6-(hydroxymethyl)-2,4,8,10-tetramethyl-2-dodecenylidene]-4-methyl-, dimethyl ester (radiclonic acid dimethyl ester)	MeOH	232(3.98),250(4.00)	88-2333-73

Compound	Solvent	$\lambda_{max}(\log \epsilon)$	Ref.
$C_{26}H_{13}Cl$			
Dibenzo[cd,lm]perylene, 3-chloro-	toluene	395(4.32),420(4.79), 450(5.02)	104-0379-73
$C_{26}H_{14}Cl_2O_3$			
Dibenzofuran, 2,8-bis(4-chlorobenzoyl)-	EtOH	260(4.66),285(4.37)	40-1505-73
$C_{26}H_{14}N_2OS_2$			
Benzothiazole, 2,2'-(2,8-dibenzofuran-diyl)bis-	THF	321(4.8),340(4.7)	104-2601-73
Benzothiazole, 2,2'-(4,6-dibenzofuran-diyl)bis-	THF	301(4.7),330(4.5), 350(4.5)	104-2601-73
$C_{26}H_{14}O_2$			
6,15-Hexacenedione	$CHCl_3$	330(4.3),343(4.4), 392(3.4),440(3.6), 456(3.6)	22-1154-73
$C_{26}H_{15}Br$			
Hexahelicene, 2-bromo-	$CHCl_3$	260(4.69),268(4.70), 318(4.36),330(4.32), 352(4.01),392(2.79), 414(2.66)	35-0527-73
Hexahelicene, 4-bromo-	$CHCl_3$	257(4.59),270(4.59), 318(4.29),330(4.29), 350(4.00),392(2.66), 414(2.45)	35-0527-73
$C_{26}H_{15}Cl$			
Hexahelicene, 2-chloro-	$CHCl_3$	266(4.72),318(4.39), 330(4.36),351(4.05), 392(2.82),414(2.71)	35-0527-73
Hexahelicene, 4-chloro-	$CHCl_3$	258(4.67),270(4.67), 318(4.38),330(4.38), 351(4.09),392(2.73), 414(2.51)	35-0527-73
$C_{26}H_{15}F$			
Hexahelicene, 2-fluoro-	$CHCl_3$	259(4.69),317(4.42), 328(4.39),349(4.07), 392(2.92),414(2.85)	35-0527-73
Hexahelicene, 4-fluoro-	$CHCl_3$	252(4.67),267(4.65), 317(4.40),329(4.39), 348(4.09),392(2.73), 414(2.54)	35-0527-73
$C_{26}H_{16}$			
Dibenzo[c,p]chrysene	EtOH	213(4.64),276(4.84), 295(4.71),305(4.79), 334(4.09),350(3.87)	44-2783-73
Hexahelicene (phenanthro[3,4-c]phenanthrene)	$CHCl_3$	258(4.73),265(4.74), 317(4.45),328(4.44), 349(4.11),391(2.73), 413(2.52)	35-0527-73
$C_{26}H_{16}F_6$			
Bicyclo[2.2.1]hepta-2,5-diene, 7-(3,4-diphenyl-2,4-cyclopentadien-1-ylidene)-2,3-bis(trifluoromethyl)-	EtOH	230(4.26),255(4.36), 382(3.08)	89-0991-73

Compound	Solvent	$\lambda_{max}(\log \epsilon)$	Ref.
$C_{26}H_{16}F_6S$			
1,1':2',1"-Terphenyl, 3"-(trifluoromethyl)-2-[3-(trifluoromethyl)phenylthio]-	EtOH	235(4.30),255s(4.17), 280(3.85)	35-5288-73
$C_{26}H_{16}N_2O_4$			
Anthracene, 1,9-dinitro-4,5-diphenyl-	EtOH	245(4.48),272(4.65), 426(3.93)	44-1167-73
$C_{26}H_{16}N_4OS$			
Benzoxazole, 2-[5-[2-[6-(2-benzothiazolyl)-3-pyridinyl]ethenyl]-2-pyridinyl]-	n.s.g.	385(4.88)	40-0991-73
Benzoxazole, 2-[6-[2-[6-(2-benzothiazolyl)-3-pyridinyl]ethenyl]-3-pyridinyl]-	n.s.g.	381(4.88)	40-0991-73
$C_{26}H_{16}N_4O_2$			
Benzoxazole, 2-[5-[2-[5-(2-benzoxazolyl)-2-pyridinyl]ethenyl]-2-pyridinyl]-	n.s.g.	379(4.90)	40-0991-73
Benzoxazole, 2,2'-(1,2-ethenediyl)di-5,2-pyridinediyl)bis-	n.s.g.	377(4.91)	40-0991-73
$C_{26}H_{16}N_4S_2$			
Benzothiazole, 2,2'-(1,2-ethenediyldi-5,2-pyridinediyl)bis-	n.s.g.	388(4.94)	40-0991-73
$C_{26}H_{16}O_2S_2$			
9,10-Anthracenedione, 1,8-bis(phenylthio)-	C_6H_{12}	238(4.54),266(4.08), 300(3.92)	35-2565-73
$C_{26}H_{16}O_4$			
1,4-Naphthalenedione, 2-(2,3-dihydro-1,3-dioxo-1-phenyl-1H-inden-2-yl)-3-methyl-	MeOH	227(4.67),246(4.53), 252s(4.50),268s(4.19)	39-1006-73C
$C_{26}H_{16}O_5$			
1,4-Naphthalenedione, 2-[2,3-dihydro-2-(4-methoxyphenyl)-1,3-dioxo-1H-inden-2-yl]-	MeOH	216(4.67),240(4.59)	39-1006-73C
$C_{26}H_{17}Br$			
Benzo[c]phenanthrene, 3-[2-(2-bromophenyl)ethenyl]-, (E)-	$CHCl_3$	273(4.44),312(4.53), 349(4.35)	35-0527-73
Benzo[c]phenanthrene, 3-[2-(4-bromophenyl)ethenyl]-, (E)-	$CHCl_3$	275(4.54),315(4.60), 350(4.50),365(4.42)	35-0527-73
$C_{26}H_{17}Cl$			
Benzo[c]phenanthrene, 3-[2-(2-chlorophenyl)ethenyl]-, (E)-	$CHCl_3$	273(4.49),313(4.58), 349(4.40)	35-0527-73
Benzo[c]phenanthrene, 3-[2-(4-chlorophenyl)ethenyl]-, (E)-	$CHCl_3$	274(4.54),313(4.60), 348(4.49),363(4.41)	35-0527-73
$C_{26}H_{17}F$			
Benzo[c]phenanthrene, 3-[2-(2-fluorophenyl)ethenyl]-, cis	$CHCl_3$	299(4.58)	35-0527-73
trans	$CHCl_3$	271(4.48),314(4.57), 345(4.42),359(4.35)	35-0527-73
Benzo[c]phenanthrene, 3-[2-(4-fluorophenyl)ethenyl]-, trans	$CHCl_3$	271(4.48),312(4.58), 344(4.41),360(4.36)	35-0527-73
$C_{26}H_{17}NO_2$			
Anthracene, 10-nitro-1,8-diphenyl-	EtOH	257(4.86),359s(3.58), 382(3.72),400s(3.68)	44-1167-73

Compound	Solvent	λ max(log ε)	Ref.
$C_{26}H_{17}N_3$			
4-Isoquinolinecarbonitrile, 1-(1-naphthylamino)-3-phenyl-	EtOH	255(4.85),351(4.62)	39-0817-73C
$C_{26}H_{18}$			
Anthracene, 9,10-diphenyl-, radical cation	CH_2Cl_2-TFA	597(4.01),657(4.00), 732(3.93)	39-1594-73B
Benzo[c]phenanthrene, 3-(2-phenylethenyl)-, cis	$CHCl_3$	299(4.39)	35-0527-73
trans	$CHCl_3$	272(4.70),312(4.78), 344(4.63),360(4.56)	35-0527-73
1,1'-Bi-9H-fluorene	C_6H_{12}	267(4.63),289(4.21), 301(4.21)	33-3044-73
4,4'-Bi-9H-fluorene	C_6H_{12}	267(4.50),274s(4.43), 286s(4.25),299(4.12)	33-3044-73
$C_{26}H_{18}N_2$			
Compd., m. 238-9°	CCl_4	294(4.24),305(4.25), 316s(3.98)	23-1995-73
$C_{26}H_{18}N_2O_5$			
6-Isoquinolinecarboxylic acid, 2-benzoyl-5-(benzoyloxy)-1-cyan-1,2-dihydro-, methyl ester	EtOH	238(4.59),293(4.13), 330s(3.80)	78-0857-73
6-Isoquinolinecarboxylic acid, 2-benzoyl-7-(benzoyloxy)-1-cyano-1,2-dihydro-, methyl ester	EtOH	239(4.59),291(4.18), 330s(3.79)	78-0857-73
$C_{26}H_{18}N_4S$			
Imidazo[1,2-a]pyridine, 2,2'-(thiodi-4,1-phenylene)bis-	EtOH	330(4.42)	65-1336-73
$C_{26}H_{18}O_2$			
Cyclobuta[b]naphthalene-3,8-dione, 1,2,2a,8a-tetrahydro-1,2-bis-(phenylmethylene)-	n.s.g.	227(4.63),246s(4.47), 260s(4.37),332s(4.51), 351(4.56),371s(4.54)	35-6688-73
$C_{26}H_{18}O_4$			
Dibenz[a,j]anthracene-2-carboxylic acid, 7-acetoxy-, methyl ester	dioxan	235(4.70),250(4.50), 261(4.52),271(4.51), 290s(4.56),300(4.73), 312(4.82),327s(4.31), 345(4.23),361(4.04), 378(3.18),400(2.66)	24-1341-73
Dibenz[a,j]anthracene-2-carboxylic acid, 14-acetoxy-, methyl ester	dioxan	235(4.65),253(4.45), 260(4.47),273(4.54), 291s(4.54),301(4.74), 313(4.85),330s(4.29), 346(4.20),361(3.99), 346(4.20),361(3.99), 379(3.14),402(2.73)	24-1341-73
1H-Inden-1-one, 2,2'-(1,4-phenylene)bis-[3-methoxy-	EtOH	265(4.6),425(3.5)	104-2400-73
$C_{26}H_{19}NO_3$			
Acetic acid, cyano[3-(diphenylmethylene)-1(3H)-isobenzofuranylidene]-, ethyl ester	EtOH	267s(4.16),288(4.42), 299(4.42),345s(3.95), 402(4.36)	39-1731-73C

Compound	Solvent	λ_{max}(log ϵ)	Ref.
$C_{26}H_{19}N_3O_2$			
Acetic acid, cyano(9-methyldibenzo[a,c]-phenazin-11(9H)-ylidene)-, ethyl ester	n.s.g.	634s(4.21),686(4.39), 748(4.31)	103-1407-73
$C_{26}H_{19}N_3O_6S_2$			
Benzenesulfonamide, N-[2-cyano-9-[[(4-methylphenyl)sulfonyl]oxy]-3-oxo-3H-pyrrolo[1,2-a]indol-1-yl]-4-methyl-	EtOH	224(4.61)	95-0971-73
$C_{26}H_{20}$			
1,3,5-Cycloheptatriene, 1-phenyl-7-(2-phenyl-2,4,6-cycloheptatrien-1-ylidene)-	EtOH	245(4.23),319(4.13)	35-0826-73
Spiro[7H-benzo[c]fluorene-7,1'(2'H)-naphthalene], 3',4'-dihydro-	EtOH	204(4.70),237(4.69), 252s(4.49),306s(3.97), 317(4.10),326(4.05), 342(4.16)	44-2783-73
$C_{26}H_{20}Cl_2N_4$			
Diazene, 1,1'-[1,2-bis(4-chlorophenyl)-1,2-ethanediyl]bis[2-phenyl-	$CHCl_3$	222(4.67),276(4.38), 402(2.70)	78-0101-73
$C_{26}H_{20}N_2$			
Cinnoline, 1,4-dihydro-1,3,4-triphenyl-	MeCN	291(4.07),347(4.05)	22-3487-73
Phenazine, 1,6-bis(phenylmethyl)-	C_6H_{12}	217(4.26),256(5.02), 367(4.15)	56-0943-73
$C_{26}H_{20}N_2O$			
3-Phenanthrenol, 2,7-dimethyl-4,5-di-2-pyridinyl-	MeCN	232(4.67),297(4.39), 316s(4.33),375(3.48), 394(3.54)	44-0407-73
$C_{26}H_{20}N_2O_2$			
1H-Indeno[1,2-b]pyridine-3-carboxamide, 4,5-dihydro-2-methyl-5-oxo-N,4-diphenyl-	EtOH	233(4.40),263(4.38), 301s(3.82),315s(3.70), 345(3.54),475(3.45)	103-0636-73
	EtOH-NaOH	236(4.45),247s(4.42), 281s(4.11),317(3.96), 370s(3.68),530s(3.72)	103-0636-73
8aH-Phenanthro[4',3':4,5]isoxazolo[3,2-a]pyridin-2-ol, 3,8-dimethyl-1-(2-pyridinyl)-	MeOH	258s(4.22),279(4.31), 317s(3.75),383(3.66), 487(3.94)	44-0407-73
Pyridinium, 2,2'-[1,1'-biphenyl]-4,4'-diylbis(2-oxoethylide)	EtOH	269(4.33),440(4.30)	65-1336-73
$C_{26}H_{20}N_2O_2S$			
Pyridinium, 2,2'-(thiodi-4,1-phenylene)-bis(2-oxoethylide)	EtOH	260(4.08),425(4.06)	65-1336-73
$C_{26}H_{20}N_2O_3$			
8aH-Phenanthro[4',3':4,5]isoxazolo[2,3-a]pyridine-2,8a-diol, 3,8-dimethyl-1-(2-pyridinyl)-, hydrochloride	MeOH	261(4.54),360(3.96), 418(3.76),480(4.20)	44-0407-73
Pyrazino[1,2-a:4,3-a']diindole-13,14-dione, 6,7-dihydro-6-(4-methoxyphenyl)-7-methyl-	EtOH	241(3.27),292(3.29), 302(3.36),591(2.22)	95-1643-73
Pyridinium, 2,2'-(oxydi-4,1-phenylene)-bis(2-oxoethylide)	EtOH	261(4.16),423(3.97)	65-1336-73

Compound	Solvent	$\lambda_{max}(\log \epsilon)$	Ref.
$C_{26}H_{20}N_2O_3S$			
Pyridinium, 2,2'-(sulfinyldi-4,1-phenylene)bis(2-oxoethylide)	EtOH	260(4.53),430(3.17)	65-1336-73
$C_{26}H_{20}N_4$			
1,2,4,5-Tetrazine, 1,4-dihydro-1,3,4,6-tetraphenyl-	MeOH	270(4.00),330(4.20)	78-0101-73
$C_{26}H_{20}N_4O$			
3H-Pyrrolo[1,2-a]indole-2-carbonitrile, 3-oxo-1,9-bis(phenylmethyl)amino]-	EtOH	248(4.12),294(3.77), 410(3.82)	95-0964-73
$C_{26}H_{20}O_2$			
Benzhydrol, 4-benzoyl-4'-phenyl-	EtOH	257(4.54)	23-3808-73
Benzhydrol, 4-(4-phenylbenzoyl)-	EtOH	291(4.39)	23-3808-73
Benzo[a]cyclopropa[cd]pentalene-1-carboxylic acid, 2a,2b,6b,6c-tetrahydro-2a,6c-diphenyl-, methyl ester	EtOH	243(4.04),280s(3.85)	12-0147-73
Benzo[a]cyclopropa[cd]pentalene-2a(2bH)-carboxylic acid, 6b,6c-dihydro-1,6c-diphenyl-, methyl ester	EtOH	228(4.22),278(4.08)	12-0147-73
Dibenzo[a,g]cyclooctadecene-7,12-dione, 8,9,10,11,19,20,21,22-octadehydro-1,2,3,4,15,16,17,18-octahydro-, (E,E)-	EtOH	275(3.98),293(4.23), 312(4.46),333(4.47), 460(3.46)	89-0068-73
1,2,7-Metheno-1H-cyclopropa[b]naphthalene-1-carboxylic acid, 1a,2,7,7a-tetrahydro-1a,8-diphenyl-, methyl ester	EtOH	245s(4.04),250s(3.78), 260s(3.60),273(3.20)	12-0147-73
1,2,7-Metheno-1H-cyclopropa[b]naphthalene-1a(2H)-carboxylic acid, 7,7a-dihydro-1,8-diphenyl-, methyl ester	EtOH	248s(4.04),254s(3.92), 260s(3.85),273(3.30)	12-0147-73
$C_{26}H_{20}O_4$			
1,3-Aceanthrylenedicarboxylic acid, 1,2-dihydro-6-phenyl-, dimethyl ester	EtOH	195(4.47),235(4.30), 268(4.90),331(3.40), 350(3.65),370(3.89), 392(3.86),414(3.83)	24-1837-73
Cycloprop[a]indene-1-carboxylic acid, 6-benzoyl-1-formyl-1,1a,6,6a-tetrahydro-6a-phenyl-, methyl ester	EtOH	222(4.15),248(4.18), 278s(3.34),305s(2.60)	12-0147-73
$C_{26}H_{20}O_5$			
Methanone, [2-(diacetoxymethyl)-1-naphthalenyl]-1-naphthalenyl-	dioxan	226(4.94),245s(4.34), 322(3.99)	24-1341-73
$C_{26}H_{21}$			
Cycloheptatrienylium, (triphenylmethyl)-, tetrafluoroborate	2.9M HCl	227(4.67),260s(4.02), 309(3.77)	18-1785-73
$C_{26}H_{21}BrN_2O_2$			
1H-Pyrazole-3-carboxylic acid, 1-(4-bromophenyl)-5-(1,2-diphenylethenyl)-, ethyl ester	C_6H_{12} or EtOH	217(4.52),232s(--), 285(4.26)	4-0015-73
$C_{26}H_{21}ClF_3P$			
Phosphonium, triphenyl[[4-(trifluoromethyl)phenyl]methyl]-	EtOH	267(3.57),274(3.46)	36-0910-73

Compound	Solvent	λ_{max}(log ε)	Ref.
$C_{26}H_{21}ClN_2O_2$			
1H-Pyrazole-3-carboxylic acid, 1-(4-chlorophenyl)-5-(1,2-diphenylethenyl)-, ethyl ester	C_6H_{12} or EtOH	215(4.46),232(4.51), 295(4.27)	4-0015-73
$C_{26}H_{21}ClN_2O_3$			
8aH-Phenanthro[4',3':4,5]isoxazolo[2,3-a]pyridine-2,8a-diol, 3,8-dimethyl-1-(2-pyridinyl)-, hydrochloride	MeOH	261(4.54),360(3.96), 418(3.76),480(4.20)	44-0407-73
$C_{26}H_{21}N_3O_4S$			
Carbamothioic acid, [[2-oxo-4,6-bis-(phenylamino)-2H-pyran-3-yl]carbonyl]-, S-(phenylmethyl) ester	MeCN	251(4.35),328(4.41)	39-2432-73C
$C_{26}H_{22}$			
Benzene, 1,1'-(3,5,7,9-dodecatetraene-1,11-diyne-1,12-diyl)bis[4-methyl-, all-E-	benzene	402(5.00),424(4.85)	5-1339-73
(E,E,Z,Z)-	benzene	391(4.90),415s(4.71)	5-1339-73
Bi-2,4,6-cycloheptatrien-1-yl, x,x'-diphenyl-	EtOH	239(4.57),275s(4.14)	18-1785-73
1,2'-Binaphthalene, 3,3',4,4'-tetrahydro-1'-phenyl-	EtOH	205(4.65),267(3.97)	44-2783-73
Spiro[7H-benzo[c]fluorene-7,1'(2'H)-naphthalene], 3',4',5,6-tetrahydro-	EtOH	203(4.75),238(4.46), 266(3.87),294(3.86)	44-2783-73
$C_{26}H_{22}F_9N_2$			
Methanaminium, N-[4-[[4-(dimethylamino)-2-(trifluoromethyl)phenyl][2-(trifluoromethyl)phenyl]methylene]-3-(trifluoromethyl)-2,5-cyclohexadien-1-ylidene]-N-methyl-	98% HOAc	440(2.93+),677(3.56+)	39-1792-73B
Methanaminium, N-[4-[[4-(dimethylamino)-2-(trifluoromethyl)phenyl][4-(trifluoromethyl)phenyl]methylene]-3-(trifluoromethyl)-2,5-cyclohexadien-1-ylidene]-N-methyl-	98% HOAc	466(3.53+),690(4.00+)	39-1792-73B
$C_{26}H_{22}I_2N_2O_2$			
Pyridinium, 1,1'-[[1,1'-biphenyl]-4,4'-diylbis(2-oxo-2,1-ethanediyl)]bis-, diiodide	EtOH	258(3.53),430(3.05)	65-1336-73
$C_{26}H_{22}I_2N_2O_2S$			
Pyridinium, 1,1'-[thiobis[4,1-phenylene-(2-oxo-2,1-ethanediyl)]bis-, diiodide	EtOH	265(4.06),423(3.92)	65-1336-73
$C_{26}H_{22}I_2N_2O_3$			
Pyridinium, 1,1'-[oxybis[4,1-phenylene-(2-oxo-2,1-ethanediyl)]bis-, diiodide	EtOH	272(4.31),421(3.95)	65-1336-73
$C_{26}H_{22}I_2N_2O_3S$			
Pyridinium, 1,1'-[sulfinylbis[4,1-phenylene(2-oxo-2,1-ethanediyl)]bis-, diiodide	EtOH	254(4.47),420(3.14)	65-1336-73
$C_{26}H_{22}N_2$			
Cinnoline, 1,2,3,4-tetrahydro-1,4,4-triphenyl-	MeCN	293(4.10)	22-3487-73

Compound	Solvent	λ_{max}(log ϵ)	Ref.
$C_{26}H_{22}N_2O$			
Phenol, 3-(phenylmethyl)-4-[[2-(phenylmethyl)phenyl]azo]-	EtOH	240(3.93),245(3.99), 334(4.31),376s(4.19)	23-3827-73
	EtOH-KOH	242(4.05),325(4.11), 441(4.01)	23-3827-73
$C_{26}H_{22}N_4O$			
Benzo[f]quinoline-1-carboxamide, N,N-diethyl-3-(2-quinoxalinyl)-, Cu(I) complex	EtOH	390(4.56),552(3.92)	103-1391-73
$C_{26}H_{22}N_4O_2$			
Benzenamine, N,N-(1,2-di-4-pyridinyl-1,2-ethanediylidene)bis[4-methoxy-	EtOH	235(4.52),283(4.19), 363(4.17)	12-2027-73
2,2'-Bipyridinium, 1,1'-bis(benzoylamino)-4,4'-dimethyl-, dihydroxide bis(inner salt)	dioxan	243(4.45),290(4.00), 353(4.02)	4-0447-73
Pyridinium, 1-(benzoylamino)-2-(1-benzoyl-5-methyl-1H-1,2-diazepin-3-yl)-4-methyl-, hydroxide, inner salt	dioxan	240(4.43),356(3.89)	4-0447-73
$C_{26}H_{22}N_4O_4$			
5,8-Ethenobenzo[3,4]cyclobuta[1,2-d]-pyridazine-6,7-dicarboxylic acid, 4a,4b,5,8,8a,8b-hexahydro-1,4-di-2-pyridinyl-, dimethyl ester	EtOH	251(3.95),260s(--), 267s(--),304(4.07)	12-0389-73
$C_{26}H_{22}O_2$			
Benzo[a]cyclopropa[cd]pentalene-2a(2H)-carboxylic acid, 1,2b,6b,6c-tetrahydro-1,6c-diphenyl-, methyl ester	EtOH	253s(3.11),259s(3.08), 268(3.00),276s(2.78), 278(2.86),280s(2.68)	12-0147-73
1-Penten-4-yn-3-one, 1,1'-(1,3-butadiyne-1,4-diyldi-1-cyclohexene-2,1-diyl)bis-, (E,E)-	EtOH	236(4.36),273(4.17), 332(4.31),372(4.30), 383(4.30),420s(4.16)	89-0068-73
$C_{26}H_{22}O_4$			
Benzo[a]cyclopropa[cd]pentalene-1-carboxylic acid, 1,2,2a,2b,6b,6c-hexahydro-1,2-dihydroxy-2a,6c-diphenyl-, methyl ester	EtOH	228(4.25),260s(3.23), 266(3.18),272(3.15), 282(3.00)	12-0147-73
Benzo[a]cyclopropa[cd]pentalene-2a(2H)-carboxylic acid, 1,2b,6b,6c-tetrahydro-1,2-dihydroxy-1,6c-diphenyl-, methyl ester	C_6H_{12}	253s(3.23),258s(3.11), 264s(2.99),268(2.94), 278(2.86)	12-0147-73
5H-Cycloprop[cd]indene-2,2b(2aH)-dicarboxylic acid, 5-(diphenylmethylene)-5a,5b-dihydro-, dimethyl ester	EtOH	231s(4.25),291(4.29)	24-1837-73
1,2,4-Methenopentalene-1,5-dicarboxylic acid, 3-(diphenylmethylene)-1,2,3,3a-4,6a-hexahydro-, dimethyl ester	EtOH	230(4.26),275(4.20)	24-1822-73
$C_{26}H_{22}O_5$			
2-Naphthalenecarboxylic acid, 1-[[7-(dimethoxymethyl)-1-naphthalenyl]carbonyl]-, methyl ester	dioxan	215(4.78),242(4.85), 288(4.02),299(4.05), 314(4.03)	24-1341-73
$C_{26}H_{22}O_8$			
Octanedioic acid, bis(2-oxo-2H-1-benzopyran-7-yl) ester	CH_2Cl_2	277(4.32),283(4.32), 313(4.24)	44-0957-73

Compound	Solvent	$\lambda_{max}(\log \epsilon)$	Ref.
$C_{26}H_{22}S$			
1,1':2',1"-Terphenyl, 4"-methyl-2-[(4-methylphenyl)thio]-	EtOH	252(4.21),285s(3.97)	35-5288-73
$C_{26}H_{23}IN_2$			
Benz[cd]indolium, 2-[3-(1-ethyl-2(1H)-quinolinylidene)-1-propenyl]-1-methyl-, iodide	EtOH	658(4.94)	103-0314-73
$C_{26}H_{23}NO_3$			
1H-Benzo[f]cyclopenta[c]quinoline-1-carboxylic acid, 2,3-dihydro-4-(4-methoxyphenyl)-, ethyl ester	EtOH	265(4.48),285(4.47), 346(3.73),362(3.78)	103-0628-73
$C_{26}H_{23}NO_4S$			
1,3-Propanedione, 2-(3-ethyl-2(3H)-benzothiazolylidene)-1,3-bis(4-methoxyphenyl)-	EtOH	218(4.56),282(4.29), 380(4.46)	73-3616-73
$C_{26}H_{23}NO_4Se$			
1,3-Propanedione, 2-(3-ethyl-2(3H)-benzoselenazolylidene)-1,3-bis(4-methoxyphenyl)-	EtOH	223(4.60),277(4.34), 384(4.62)	73-3616-73
$C_{26}H_{23}N_3O_8$			
12bH-4a,8b,12c-Triazabenz[a]indeno-[1,2,3-cd]azulene-1,2,3,4-tetracarboxylic acid, 12-methyl-, tetramethyl ester	EtOH	264(3.82),327(3.25), 400(2.92)	88-0597-73
$C_{26}H_{23}N_5O_2$			
1H-Indole, 1,3-bis[2-oxo-1-(phenylhydrazono)propyl]-	EtOH	232(4.47),281(4.06), 351(4.60)	78-3159-73
1,2-Propanedione, 1-(3-acetyl-3a,8a-dihydro-1-phenylpyrazolo[3,4-b]indol-8(1H)-yl)-, 1-(phenylhydrazone)	EtOH	234(4.48),294s(3.96), 350(4.52)	78-3159-73
$C_{26}H_{24}$			
Naphthalene, 1,2,3,4-tetramethyl-5,8-diphenyl-	EtOH	233(4.50),257(4.65), 329(4.17)	118-0783-73
$C_{26}H_{24}I_2N_4O_2$			
Pyridinium, 1,1'-[[1,1'-biphenyl]-4,4'-diylbis(2-oxo-1,2-ethanediyl)]bis-[2-amino-, diiodide	EtOH	275(4.30),335(4.49)	65-1336-73
$C_{26}H_{24}I_2N_4O_2S$			
Pyridinium, 1,1'-[thiobis[4,1-phenylene-(2-oxo-2,1-ethanediyl)]bis[2-amino-, diiodide	EtOH	251(4.61),330(4.39)	65-1336-73
$C_{26}H_{24}I_2N_4O_3$			
Pyridinium, 1,1'-[oxybis[4,1-phenylene-(2-oxo-2,1-ethanediyl)]]bis[2-amino-, diiodide	EtOH	250(4.59),325(4.31)	65-1336-73
$C_{26}H_{24}I_2N_4O_3S$			
Pyridinium, 1,1'-[sulfinylbis[4,1-phenylene(2-oxo-2,1-ethanediyl)]]bis[2-amino-, diiodide	EtOH	260(4.49),330(4.24)	65-1336-73

Compound	Solvent	λ max (log ε)	Ref.
$C_{26}H_{24}N_2$			
Phenazine, 1,2,3,4,6,7,8,9-octahydro-1,5-bis(phenylmethylene)-, (E,E)-	dioxan	230(3.98),295(4.34), 388(4.47)	56-0943-73
$C_{26}H_{24}N_2O_2$			
2-Propen-1-one, 3-(4,5-dihydro-1,5-diphenyl-1H-pyrazol-3-yl)-1-(4-ethoxyphenyl)-	C_6H_{12}	420(4.36)	104-0413-73
	EtOH	444(4.52)	104-0413-73
$C_{26}H_{24}N_2O_3$			
2H-Benzo[a]quinolizin-2-one, 1,6,7,11b-tetrahydro-4-(1,6,7,11b-tetrahydro-2-hydroxy-4-oxo-4H-benzo[a]quinolizin-3-yl)-	EtOH	266(4.00),304(4.10), 405(3.70)	70-1258-73
$C_{26}H_{24}N_4$			
1H-Imidazole-1,2-diamine, N,N'-bis(phenylmethylene)-4-phenyl-5-propyl-	EtOH	255(3.66),267(3.68)	103-1082-73
2-Tetrazene, 1,4-diphenyl-1,4-bis(phenylmethyl)-	C_6H_{12}	347(4.60)	73-0046-73
	THF	352(4.57)	73-0046-73
$C_{26}H_{24}N_4O_4$			
Spiro[2H-1-benzopyran-2,2'-[2H]indole], 1',3'-dihydro-8-methoxy-1',3',3'-trimethyl-6-[(4-nitrophenyl)azo]-	EtOH	242s(3.95),282(4.14), 415(3.92),625(3.09)	103-1463-73
	dioxan	245(4.22),285(4.51), 412(4.22)	103-1463-73
$C_{26}H_{24}N_6O$			
Ajmalan, 1,2,19,20-tetradehydro-1-demethyl-11-[(1-phenyl-1H-tetrazol-5-yl)oxy]-	MeOH	223(4.60)	94-1783-73
$C_{26}H_{24}O$			
4,7-Methano-1H-inden-8-one, 1-ethylidene-3a,4,7,7a-tetrahydro-4,7-dimethyl-5,6-diphenyl-	hexane	247(4.37)	44-3836-73
$C_{26}H_{24}O_2$			
Cyclopenta[a]indene-1-carboxylic acid, 1,2,3,3a,8,8a-hexahydro-3,8a-diphenyl-, methyl ester	EtOH	225(3.45),255s(2.87), 260(2.98),268(3.19), 274(3.18)	12-0147-73
Cyclopenta[a]indene-3-carboxylic acid, 1,2,3,3a,8,8a-hexahydro-1,8a-diphenyl-, methyl ester	EtOH	227(3.43),254s(3.23), 260(3.26),267(3.30), 274(3.30)	12-0147-73
$C_{26}H_{24}O_4$			
2H-Pyran-3(6H)-one, 2-methoxy-6-[(triphenylmethoxy)methyl]-, (2S-trans)-	MeOH	228.2(4.30)	23-3357-73
$C_{26}H_{24}O_7$			
4H-1-Benzopyran-4-one, 5,6,7-trimethoxy-2-[3-methoxy-4-(phenylmethoxy)-phenyl]-	MeOH	245(4.21),330(4.23)	2-0201-73
$C_{26}H_{24}O_{10}$			
Naphtho[2,3-c]furan-1(3H)-one, 7-acetoxy-9-(3,4-diacetoxy-5-methoxyphenyl)-4,9-dihydro-6-methoxy-	EtOH	277.5(3.63)	23-0482-73

Compound	Solvent	$\lambda_{max}(\log \epsilon)$	Ref.
$C_{26}H_{24}Si$			
Silane, bis([1,1'-biphenyl]-4-yl)dimethyl-	heptane	258.8(4.75)	101-0353-73C
$C_{26}H_{25}AsO_2$			
Arsonium, triphenyl-, 4,4-dimethyl-2,6-dioxocyclohexylide	MeOH	213(4.40),265(4.30)	78-1697-73
$C_{26}H_{25}BrO_5$			
Benzoic acid, 4-bromo-, 2-(2,3,5,6,7,7a-hexahydro-7a-methyl-1,5-dioxo-1H-inden-4-yl)-1-(3-methoxyphenyl)ethyl ester, (R*,S*)-(±)-	EtOH	247(4.47)	44-3229-73
$C_{26}H_{25}IN_2$			
Benz[cd]indolium, 2-[3-(1,3-dihydro-1,3,3-trimethyl-2H-indol-2-ylidene)-1-propenyl]-1-methyl-, iodide	EtOH	614(4.80),662(4.93)	103-0314-73
$C_{26}H_{25}NO_3$			
1H-Benzo[f]cyclopenta[c]quinoline-1-carboxylic acid, 2,3,4,5-tetrahydro-4-(4-methoxyphenyl)-, ethyl ester	EtOH	248(4.62),276(4.39), 408(3.79)	103-0628-73
1-Cyclopentene-1-carboxylic acid, 3-[(4-methoxyphenyl)methylene]-2-(2-naphthalenylamino)-, ethyl ester	EtOH	235(4.46),350(4.54)	103-0628-73
$C_{26}H_{25}NO_5$			
Rheadan-8-ol, 16-benzoyl-2,3-dimethoxy-	MeOH	215(4.62),234(4.19), 284(3.63)	77-0740-73
$C_{26}H_{25}NO_6$			
2-Butenedioic acid, 2-[[2,5-bis(phenylmethoxy)phenyl]amino]-, dimethyl ester, (Z)-	$CHCl_3$	245(4.00),270(3.89), 345(4.09)	39-2374-73C
4,4-Oxazolidinedicarboxylic acid, 5-(4-methoxyphenyl)-2,3-diphenyl-, dimethyl ester	EtOH	240(4.24),284(3.69)	22-3437-73
$C_{26}H_{25}N_3O$			
2-Propen-1-one, 3-(4,5-dihydro-1,5-diphenyl-1H-pyrazol-3-yl)-1-[4-(dimethylamino)phenyl]-	C_6H_{12}	415(4.56)	104-0413-73
	EtOH	450(4.67)	104-0413-73
$C_{26}H_{25}N_3O_2$			
Spiro[2H-1-benzopyran-2,2'-[2H]indole], 1',3'-dihydro-8-methoxy-1',3',3'-trimethyl-6-(phenylazo)-	EtOH	242(4.31),290(4.14), 380(4.21),610(3.62)	103-1463-73
	dioxan	248(4.33),285(4.36), 380(4.17)	103-1463-73
$C_{26}H_{26}ClN_3O_4S_2$			
Benzenesulfonamide, 4-chloro-N-[1,2,3-3a,5,9b-hexahydro-5-methyl-9b-[[(4-methylphenyl)sulfonyl]amino]-4H-cyclopenta[c]quinolin-4-ylidene]-	EtOH	224(4.56),283(4.40)	39-1809-73C
$C_{26}H_{26}ClN_3O_8S$			
Benzo[b]pyrido[3,2-f]thiepin, 8-chloro-6-(4-methylpiperazino)-, dimaleate	MeOH	236(4.21),267(4.16), 308(4.02)	73-2778-73

Compound	Solvent	$\lambda_{max}(\log \epsilon)$	Ref.
$C_{26}H_{26}N_4OS$			
N,N'-(Di-4-pyridinylvinylene)dianiline-dimethylsulfoxide adduct	EtOH	265(4.37),435(3.98)	12-2027-73
$C_{26}H_{26}N_4O_4S$			
Benzenecarbothioic acid, S-[2-[[[4-(benzoylamino)-2-methyl-5-pyrimidinyl]-methyl]formylamino]tetrahydro-2-methyl-3-furanyl] ester	EtOH	240(4.34),269(4.29)	94-0785-73
$C_{26}H_{26}N_4O_{11}$			
Norglaucine picrate	EtOH	280(4.17),303(4.20), 315s(4.16),356(4.14)	44-2394-73
$C_{26}H_{26}O_4$			
2-Cyclopenten-1-one, 4-(benzoyloxy)-5-[2-(3,4-dihydro-6-methoxy-1(2H)-naphthalenylidene)ethyl]-5-methyl-	EtOH	265(4.10)	94-0697-73
$C_{26}H_{26}O_5$			
4H,8H-Benzo[1,2-b:3,4-b']dipyran-4-one, 5-hydroxy-3-methoxy-8,8-dimethyl-6-(3-methyl-2-butenyl)-	MeOH	238(4.36),285(3.72), 328(3.79)	12-0641-73
$C_{26}H_{26}O_6$			
2H-1-Benzopyran-2-one, 7,7'-[1,8-octanediylbis(oxy)]bis-	CH_2Cl_2	324(4.50)	44-0957-73
$C_{26}H_{26}O_8$			
[1,1'-Bi-1H-cyclopropa[b]naphthalene]-1,1'-dicarboxylic acid, 1a,1'a,2,2'-2a,2'a,3,3',6,6',6a,6'a,7,7',7a,7'a-tetradecahydro-2,2',7,7'-tetraoxo-, dimethyl ester	EtOH	238s(3.61),253s(3.32), 290(3.02)	104-2389-73
Licoricone, diacetate	EtOH	257(4.59),298(4.06)	94-1338-73
$C_{26}H_{26}O_9$			
Ethanone, 1-[2,4-diacetoxy-3-(3,4-dimethoxyphenyl)-6,7-dimethoxy-1-naphthalenyl]-	EtOH	247(4.75),289s(4.08), 337(3.07)	44-3425-73
$C_{26}H_{26}O_{11}$			
Chromocyclin diacetate	EtOH	224(4.41),272(4.67), 420(3.94)	105-0498-73
$C_{26}H_{27}NO$			
4,7-Methano-1H-inden-1-one, 3a,4,5,6,7-7a-hexahydro-2,3-diphenyl-7a-(1-pyrrolidinyl)-	MeOH	226(4.24),298(4.10)	88-0949-73
$C_{26}H_{27}NO_3$			
4H-Dibenzo[de,g]quinoline, 5,6,6a,7-tetrahydro-2,10-dimethoxy-6-methyl-1-(phenylmethoxy)-, hydrochloride	EtOH	267(4.28),276(4.29), 306(3.88)	2-1086-73
$C_{26}H_{27}N_4S$			
Thiazolo[3,2-a]pyrimidin-4-ium, 5,7-bis[2-[4-(dimethylamino)phenyl]-ethenyl]-, perchlorate	n.s.g.	520(4.84),560(4.80)	124-1151-73

Compound	Solvent	$\lambda_{max}(\log \epsilon)$	Ref.
$C_{26}H_{27}N_5O_4S$			
Benzenecarbothioic acid, S-[2-[formyl-[[2-methyl-4-[[(phenylamino)carbonyl]amino]-5-pyrimidinyl]methyl]amino]-1-(2-hydroxyethyl)-1-propenyl ester	EtOH	244(4.40),278(4.27)	94-0785-73
Benzenecarbothioic acid, S-[2-[formyl-[[2-methyl-4-[[(phenylamino)carbonyl]amino]-5-pyrimidinyl]methyl]amino]tetrahydro-2-methyl-3-furanyl ester	EtOH	248(4.38),275(4.33)	94-0785-73
$C_{26}H_{27}NiP$			
Nickel, (η^5-2,4-cyclopentadien-1-yl)(1-methylethyl)(triphenylphosphine)-	C_6H_{12}	306(3.88),418(3.08), 560(1.93)	23-1179-73
Nickel, (η^5-2,4-cyclopentadien-1-yl)-propyl(triphenylphosphine)-	C_6H_{12}	300(3.88),405(3.00), 575(1.81)	23-1179-73
$C_{26}H_{27}P$			
9-Phosphatricyclo[4.2.1.0^{2,5}]nonane, 9,9-dihydro-9,9,9-triphenyl-, (1α,2α,5α,6α)-	EtOH	228(4.30),255s(3.28), 262(3.38),267(3.44), 275(3.33),320(2.20)	35-4292-73
$C_{26}H_{28}Br_2N_2O_2$			
4aH-Pyrano[3,2-c:5,6-c']dipyridin-4a-ol, 10-(4-bromophenyl)-6-[(4-bromophenyl]-methylene]-1,2,3,4,6,7,8,9,10,10a-decahydro-2,8-dimethyl-, (4aα,10β,10aβ)-	EtOH	296(4.48)	78-4039-73
$C_{26}H_{28}Br_2O_6$			
Benzene, 1,2-bis[(2-bromo-4,5-dimethoxyphenyl)methyl]-4,5-dimethoxy-	n.s.g.	235s(4.46),287(4.03)	39-0891-73C
$C_{26}H_{28}ClNO_2$			
12,13-Benzo-[10](2,4)pyridinophan-1-ol, 16-chloro-, benzoate, anti	EtOH	200(4.40),216(4.48), 236(4.77),311(3.51), 325(3.46)	44-0927-73
syn	EtOH	200(4.39),216(4.52), 236(4.67),312(3.54), 326(3.52)	44-0927-73
$C_{26}H_{28}ClO_2PSe$			
Selenophenium, 1-[2-ethoxy-2-oxo-1-(triphenylphosphoranylidene)ethyl]tetrahydro-, chloride	EtOH	221(4.56),261s(3.86), 265s(3.84),273s(3.76)	104-1778-73
$C_{26}H_{28}Cl_2N_2O_2$			
4aH-Pyrano[3,2-c:5,6-c']dipyridin-4a-ol, 10-(4-chlorophenyl)-6-[(4-chlorophenyl)methylene]-1,2,3,4,6,7,8,9,10,10a-decahydro-2,8-dimethyl-, (4aα,10β,10aα)-	EtOH	295(4.51)	78-4039-73
$C_{26}H_{28}CuFe_2N_6S_2$			
Copper, bis[[1-[(aminothioxomethyl)hydrazono]ethyl]ferrocenato]-	EtOH	261(4.03),328(4.08), 431(3.29)	18-2896-73
$C_{26}H_{28}N_2O_5$			
Isoquinoline, 1,2,3,4-tetrahydro-6-methoxy-1-[(4-methoxy-2-nitrophenyl)methyl]-2-methyl-7-(phenylmethoxy)-	EtOH	282(3.79)	2-1086-73

Compound	Solvent	λ_{max}(log ε)	Ref.
$C_{26}H_{28}N_6$			
1,3,5-Triazine-2,4-diamine, 3,6-dihydro-N,N-dimethyl-N',3-bis(phenylmethyl)-6-[(phenylmethyl)imino]-	MeOH	231(4.33),261(4.71)	114-0419-73C
$C_{26}H_{28}O_5$			
4H-1-Benzopyran-4-one, 5,7-dihydroxy-3-methoxy-6,8-bis(3-methyl-2-butenyl)-2-phenyl-	MeOH	280(4.36),320(3.94)	12-0641-73
2H,6H,12H-Benzo[1,2-b:4,5-b'][5,6-b"]-tripyran-12-one, 3,4,7,8-tetrahydro-11-methoxy-2,2,6,6-tetramethyl-10-phenyl-	MeOH	248(4.28),278(4.54), 320s(4.07)	12-0641-73
$C_{26}H_{28}O_8$			
4H-1-Benzopyran-4-one, 5-acetoxy-2-(3,4-dimethoxyphenyl)-3,7-dimethoxy-8-(3-methyl-2-butenyl)-	MeOH	250(4.30),347(4.23)	12-0409-73
2,3,5-Metheno-1H-cyclopropa[a]pentalene-1,1a,5a-tricarboxylic acid, hexahydro-1-(3a,4,7,7a-tetrahydro-2-methoxy-4,7-methanobenzofuran-3-yl)-, trimethyl ester	EtOH	235s(3.61)	24-1804-73
$C_{26}H_{29}F_3N_3$			
Methanaminium, N-[4-[[4-(dimethylamino)-phenyl][4-(dimethylamino)-2-(trifluoromethyl)phenyl]methylene]-2,5-cyclohexadien-1-ylidene]-N-methyl-	98% HOAc	619(4.06)	39-1792-73B
$C_{26}H_{29}NO_4$			
Isoquinoline, 1,2,3,4-tetrahydro-6,7-dimethoxy-1-[3-methoxy-4-(phenylmethoxy)phenyl]-2-methyl-	MeOH	207(4.87),230s(4.30), 282(3.83)	78-0031-73
$C_{26}H_{29}N_7O_7$			
L-Glutamic acid, N-[[4-[[[2-(acetylamino)-1,4-dihydro-4-oxo-6-pteridinyl]-methylene]amino]phenyl]acetyl]-, diethyl ester	DMF	292(4.27),388(4.39)	87-0697-73
$C_{26}H_{30}ClNO_3S$			
2,13-Metheno-13H-1-benzazacyclopentadecin-3-ol, 18-chloro-3,4,5,6,7,8,9,10-11,12-decahydro-, 4-methylbenzenesulfonate	EtOH	215(4.53),229(4.63), 233(4.65),312(3.50), 326(3.42)	44-0927-73
$C_{26}H_{30}N_2$			
Pyrazine, 1,2-dicyclopentyl-1,2-dihydro-2,5-diphenyl-	n.s.g.	270(4.33)	39-0683-73C
$C_{26}H_{30}N_2O_2$			
Piperazine, 2,5-dimethyl-1,4-bis[(2-phenylcyclopropyl)carbonyl]-, (2R-trans)-	$MeSO_3H$	207(4.42),242(3.95)	44-0804-73
	sulfolane	221(4.36),259(2.70), 267(2.70),274(2.54)	44-0804-73
4aH-Pyrano[3,2-c:5,6-c']dipyridin-4a-ol, 1,2,3,4,6,7,8,9,10,10a-decahydro-2,8-dimethyl-10-phenyl-6-(phenylmethylene)-	EtOH	283(4.42)	78-4039-73

Compound	Solvent	λ_{max}(log ϵ)	Ref.
$C_{26}H_{30}N_2O_3$			
Benzenamine, 5-methoxy-2-[[1,2,3,4-tetrahydro-6-methoxy-2-methyl-7-(phenylmethoxy)-1-isoquinolinyl]-methyl]-	EtOH	286.5(3.83)	2-1086-73
$C_{26}H_{30}N_2O_8$			
Vincoside, 18,19-dihydro-, lactam	MeOH	227(4.45),273(3.91), 281(3.85),290(3.81)	88-4837-73
$C_{26}H_{30}N_4O$			
Phenol, 2,4-bis[[5-methyl-2-(1-methylethyl)phenyl]azo]-	EtOH	243(4.13),345(4.54)	83-0641-73
	EtOH-HCl	320(4.62)	83-0641-73
	EtOH-NaOH	312(4.16),408(4.38)	83-0641-73
$C_{26}H_{30}N_4O_2$			
2,3-Butanedione, 1,4-bis(3-methyl-5-isoxazolyl)-N,N'-bis(4-methylphenyl)-	EtOH	253(4.50),304(3.62)	18-3533-73
4H-Indazol-4-one, 3,3'-(1,4-phenylene)-bis[1,5,6,7-tetrahydro-1,6,6-trimethyl-	MeOH	225(4.39),234s(4.38), 253s(4.19),298(4.24)	24-0450-73
$C_{26}H_{30}O_2$			
1,13-Tetradecadiene-3,12-dione, 1,14-diphenyl-, (E,E)-	EtOH	221(4.23),287(4.52)	12-0183-73
$C_{26}H_{30}O_3$			
Estra-4,14-dien-3-one, 17β-hydroxy-7α-methyl-, benzoate	n.s.g.	253(4.47)	13-0107-73B
$C_{26}H_{30}O_4$			
1,3,8,10-Decanetetrone, 5,5,6,6-tetramethyl-1,10-diphenyl-	EtOH	315(4.49)	22-2692-73
$C_{26}H_{30}O_5$			
Chrysophanol, 1(and 8)-O-β-D-glucopyranosyl-, permethylate	MeOH	221(4.51),258(4.44), 385(3.89)	94-1254-73
$C_{26}H_{30}O_6$			
Arugosin C, mono-O-methyl-	EtOH	212(4.38),264(3.96), 285(3.95),372(3.92)	39-1825-73C
Isokurarinone	EtOH	294(4.26)	94-2733-73
	EtOH-NaOH	335(4.47)	94-2733-73
$C_{26}H_{30}O_7$			
Chromomycinoylmalonic acid, 2-deoxy-6,8,9-trimethyl-, dimethyl ester	EtOH	228(4.30),276(4.72), 325(3.98)	105-0498-73
$C_{26}H_{30}O_8$			
[1,1'-Biphenyl]-3,3'-diol, 2,2',4,4'-tetramethoxy-6,6'-di-2-propenyl-, diacetate	MeOH	227(4.25),277(3.33)	88-4877-73
$C_{26}H_{30}O_9$			
Benzoic acid, 2-hydroxy-4-[[2-hydroxy-4-methoxy-6-(2-oxopentyl)benzoyl]oxy]-6-(2-oxopentyl)-, methyl ester (methyl glomellate)	MeOH	216(4.67),270(4.33), 310(4.16)	102-2993-73

Compound	Solvent	$\lambda_{max}(\log \epsilon)$	Ref.
$C_{26}H_{31}ClO_6$			
Pregna-4,6-diene-3,20-dione, 17α,19-di-acetoxy-6-chloro-16-methylene-	MeOH	285(4.32)	87-0649-73
$C_{26}H_{31}NO_5$			
Isoxazole, 4,5-dihydro-5-[tetrahydro-2,2-dimethyl-6-(phenylmethoxy)furo-[2,3-d]-1,3-dioxol-5-yl]-3-(2,4,6-trimethylphenyl)-	EtOH	214(4.16)	33-1303-73
$C_{26}H_{31}N_6O_7P$			
Benzamide, N-[9-[5,6-dideoxy-6-(diethoxyphosphinyl)-2,3-O-(1-methylethylidene)-β-D-ribofuranurononitrilosyl]-9H-purin-6-yl]-	EtOH	279(4.27)	35-4404-73
$C_{26}H_{32}BN$			
Boranamine, N-(2,6-dimethylphenyl)-1,1-bis(2,4,6-trimethylphenyl)-	C_6H_{12}	254(4.24)	101-0051-73H
$C_{26}H_{32}F_2O_6$			
3'H-Cyclopropa[6,7]pregna-4,6-diene-3,20-dione, 6,17-diacetoxy-3',3'-difluoro-6,7-dihydro-	n.s.g.	248(4.12)	35-6655-73
$C_{26}H_{32}N_3PS_2$			
Phosphinothioic amide, N-[3-cyclohexyl-4-(cyclohexylimino)-1,3-thiazetidin-2-ylidene]-	C_6H_{12}	223(4.81),260s(4.23)	18-2559-73
$C_{26}H_{32}O_6$			
Benz[e]indene-3a-carboxylic acid, 2,3,4,5-tetrahydro-7-methoxy-2-oxo-3,3-bis(3-oxopentyl)-, methyl ester	MeOH	239(3.00),300s(4.28), 318(4.44)	39-1780-73C
2H-1-Benzopyran, 3',4'-dihydro-6,6',7,7'-tetramethoxy-2,2,2',2'-tetramethyl-	n.s.g.	293(3.92),323(3.96)	2-0091-73
Pregna-4,6-diene-3,20-dione, 17α,19-di-acetoxy-16-methylene-	MeOH	282(4.42)	87-0649-73
$C_{26}H_{32}O_7$			
Argentinogenin, 3-O-acetyl-	EtOH	289(4.16)	33-2827-73
Kuraridinol	EtOH	388(4.59)	94-2733-73
	EtOH-NaOEt	449(--)	94-2733-73
Kurarinol	EtOH	287(4.46)	94-2733-73
	EtOH-NaOH	335(--)	94-2733-73
$C_{26}H_{32}O_{11}$			
Matairesinoside	EtOH	229(4.21),281(3.81)	94-0674-73
	EtOH	229(4.33),281(3.79)	94-1114-73
Pinoresinol, β-D-glucoside, (-)-	MeOH	231(4.17),282(3.66)	95-0044-73
$C_{26}H_{32}O_{12}$			
Ethanone, 1-[4-[(4-O-β-D-glucopyranosyl)oxy]phenyl]-2-phenyl-	EtOH	202(4.44),268(4.24)	114-0191-73D
Nortracheloside	EtOH	229s(4.07),282(3.70)	94-1108-73
	EtOH-NaOH	247(4.03),284(3.74), 298(3.73)	94-1108-73

Compound	Solvent	λ_{max}(log ε)	Ref.
$C_{26}H_{32}O_{13}$			
Ethanone, 1-[4-[(4-O-β-D-glucopyranosyl-β-D-glucopyranosyl)oxy]-2-hydroxyphenyl]-2-phenyl-	EtOH	212(4.31),275(4.15), 318(3.82)	114-0191-73D
β-D-Glucopyranoside, 2-(2,4-diacetoxyphenyl)ethyl-, tetraacetate	EtOH	266(2.75),271(2.76)	1-0367-73
β-D-Glucopyranoside, 2-(2,5-diacetoxyphenyl)ethyl]-, tetraacetate	EtOH	267(2.78),272(2.75)	1-0367-73
Ilesugerin	n.s.g.	229(4.35),275(3.36), 280(3.29)	40-0785-73
$C_{26}H_{33}ClO_5$			
5β-Bufa-20,22-dienolide, 3β-acetoxy-14β-chloro-15-oxo-	$CHCl_3$	298(3.88)	94-0895-73
$C_{26}H_{33}NO_{13}$			
Ethylamine, N-acetyl-2-[3-acetoxy-4-(β-D-tetraacetylglucopyranosyloxy)-phenyl]-	EtOH	272(3.1),277(3.1)	102-2243-73
Ethylamine, N-acetyl-2-[4-acetoxy-3-(β-D-tetraacetylglucopyranosyloxy)-phenyl]-	EtOH	270(3.2),276(3.2)	102-2243-73
$C_{26}H_{33}N_3O_3$			
2-Phenanthrenol, 4b,5,6,7,8,8a,9,10-octahydro-4b,8,8-trimethyl-1-(1-methylethyl)-3-[(4-nitrophenyl)azo]-, (4bS-trans)-	EtOH	268s(3.77),368(4.40), 439(4.00)	78-2553-73
$C_{26}H_{34}BrN_5O$			
Pyrido[2',3':3,2]pyrrolo[5,4-c]quinolin-6(5H)-one, 2-bromo-5,7-bis(2-diethylaminoethyl)-5,7-dihydro-, dihydrochloride	MeOH	240(4.68),253s(4.41), 261(4.37),270s(4.17), 279(4.05),303s(4.05), 311(4.11),318s(4.05), 336s(3.95),349(4.09), 366(4.04)	44-3995-73
$C_{26}H_{34}N_2$			
Azocycloheptane, 1,1'-diphenyl-	benzene	370(1.69)	24-2890-73
$C_{26}H_{34}N_2O$			
Androstano[3,2-c]pyrazol-17-ol, 1'-phenyl-, (5α,17β)-	MeOH	212(4.30),268(4.82)	103-0202-73
$C_{26}H_{34}N_2O_6$			
1,11-Dioxadispiro[2.0.5.3]dodec-7-ene-5-acetaldehyde, 6-(hexahydrofuro-[2,3-b]furan-2-yl)-9,12-dihydroxy-6,7-dimethyl-, phenylhydrazone	MeOH	243(4.01),288(3.17)	39-0712-73C
$C_{26}H_{34}O_4$			
24-Norchola-1,20,22-trien-3-one, 14,15-21,23-diepoxy-7-hydroxy-4,4,8-trimethyl- (trichilenone)	EtOH	222(3.99)	39-1047-73C
24-Norchola-2,20,22-trien-1-one, 14,15-21,23-diepoxy-7-hydroxy-4,4,8-trimethyl- (isotrichilenone)	EtOH	220(3.99)	39-1047-73C
$C_{26}H_{34}O_5$			
Resibufogenin acetate	n.s.g.	300(3.75)	5-0005-73

Compound	Solvent	λmax(log ε)	Ref.
$C_{26}H_{34}O_6$			
3,4'-Bi-2H-1-benzopyran, 3,3',4,4'-tetrahydro-6,6',7,7'-tetramethoxy-2,2,2',2'-tetramethyl-	n.s.g.	294(3.98)	2-0091-73
$C_{26}H_{34}O_9$			
Shikokianidin	EtOH	301(1.89)	18-0583-73
$C_{26}H_{34}O_{15}$			
Forsythid, dimethyl ester tetraacetate	MeOH	234.5(4.05)	94-0497-73
$C_{26}H_{35}ClO_5$			
5β-Bufa-20,22-dienolide, 3β-acetoxy-14β-chloro-15α-hydroxy-	EtOH	301(3.82)	94-0895-73
Pregna-4,6-dien-20-one, 17α-acetoxy-6-chloro-2β,3β-[(1-methylethylidene)-bis(oxy)]-	MeOH	237(4.28),244(4.34), 251(5.18)	94-1295-73
$C_{26}H_{35}NO$			
Androst-4-en-17-ol, 17-methyl-3-(2-pyridinylmethylene)-, (17β)-	n.s.g.	312(4.42)	19-0887-73
$C_{26}H_{35}N_5O$			
Pyrido[2',3':3,2]pyrrolo[5,4-c]quinolin-6(5H)-one, 5,7-bis(2-diethylaminoethyl)-5,7-dihydro-, dihydrochloride	MeOH	232(4.59),251(4.43), 257(4.43),274s(3.97), 310(4.13),317s(4.10), 334s(3.92),348(4.04), 364(3.97)	44-3995-73
$C_{26}H_{36}N_2O_6$			
Carbonic acid, 4-[3-[cyclohexyl[(cyclohexylamino)carbonyl]amino]-3-oxo-1-propenyl]-2-methoxyphenyl ethyl ester	MeOH	280(4.05),312s(3.95)	20-0243-73
$C_{26}H_{36}O_4$			
1,3-Benzenediol, 5-methyl-2-[(1,4,4a,5-6,7,8,8a-octahydro-2,5,5,8a-tetramethyl-1-naphthalenyl)methyl]-, diacetate	EtOH	268(2.26),275s(2.55)	39-2591-73C
$C_{26}H_{36}O_5$			
21-Homopregna-5,16-dien-20-one, 3β,21a-diacetoxy-	EtOH	245(4.00)	70-1578-73
$C_{26}H_{36}O_6$			
Gamabufotalin 11-acetate	EtOH	298(3.74)	39-0725-73C
Pregna-5,16-diene-3,20-dione, 21-[(ethoxycarbonyl)oxy]-, 3-(1,2-ethanediyl acetal)	MeOH	240(3.54)	44-2335-73
$C_{26}H_{36}O_9$			
5β-Pregn-16-en-20-one, 7α,11α-diacetoxy-3α,9α-epoxy-14β,18-dihydroxy-3β-methoxy-	n.s.g.	236(4.00)	33-0139-73
$C_{26}H_{36}O_{15}$			
Morroniside, 7-O-methyl-, tetraacetate	EtOH	236(4.22)	95-0030-73
$C_{26}H_{37}N_2O_4$			
Corynoxanium, 1,2,16,17-tetradehydro-2-ethoxy-4-ethyl-17-methoxy-16-(methoxycarbonyl)-, tetrafluoroborate	MeOH	213(4.46),217(4.47), 243(4.19),274(3.41)	78-2015-73

Compound	Solvent	$\lambda_{max}(\log \epsilon)$	Ref.
$C_{26}H_{38}O_4$			
1-Propanone, 1-[(3β)-3-acetoxyandrosta-5,16-dien-17-yl]-3-ethoxy-	EtOH	240(3.99)	70-1578-73
$C_{26}H_{38}O_6$			
Pregn-5-en-20-one, 3β,17α-diacetoxy-7α-methoxy-	MeOH	199(3.93)	48-0008-73
$C_{26}H_{38}O_9$			
Marrubiaside	MeCN	211(4.37),272(3.35)	24-2929-73
$C_{26}H_{39}NO_3$			
1-Propanone, 1-[(3β)-3-acetoxyandrosta-5,16-dien-17-yl]-3-(dimethylamino)-	EtOH	244(4.07)	70-1578-73
$C_{26}H_{40}$			
Tricyclo[4.4.0.0^{2,5}]deca-3,6,8,10-tetraene, 2,4,8,10-tetrakis(1,1-dimethylethyl)-	hexane	273(2.83),282(2.82)	35-0971-73
$C_{26}H_{43}NO$			
6-Azacholest-4-en-7-one	EtOH	235(4.15)	94-1069-73
$C_{26}H_{44}O_4$			
2-Butenoic acid, 4-ethoxy-4-[4-[1-ethyl-2-(4-hydroxycyclohexyl)butyl]cyclohexylidene]-, ethyl ester	EtOH	287(4.3)	5-2078-73

Compound	Solvent	$\lambda_{max}(\log \epsilon)$	Ref.
$C_{27}H_{15}NO_4$			
1,8-Naphthalenedicarboxylic anhydride, 5-[5-(4-biphenylyl)-2-oxazolyl]-	toluene	310(4.31),410(4.39)	103-1204-73
$C_{27}H_{16}N_2O_3$			
1H-Benz[de]isoquinoline-1,3(2H)-dione, 2-phenyl-6-(5-phenyl-2-oxazolyl)-	toluene	295(4.12),398(4.43)	103-1204-73
$C_{27}H_{16}O_6$			
1,4-Naphthalenedione, 2-acetoxy-3-(2,3-dihydro-1,3-dioxo-2-phenyl-1H-inden-2-yl)-	MeOH	224(4.65),240s(4.53), 244s(4.52),250s(4.48)	39-1006-73C
$C_{27}H_{17}BrO_4$			
1,4-Naphthalenedione, 2-bromo-3-(2,3-dihydro-1,3-dioxo-2-phenyl-1H-inden-2-yl)-6,7-dimethyl-	MeOH	220(4.64),247(4.50), 253s(4.48),282s(4.00)	39-1006-73C
$C_{27}H_{17}Br_2ClO_4$			
7H-Benzo[c]fluorene-6-carboxylic acid, 7-acetoxy-2,9-dibromo-7-(4-chlorophenyl)-, methyl ester	EtOH	244(4.73),336(4.22), 352s(4.07)	115-0145-73A
$C_{27}H_{18}$			
9H-Fluorene, 9-(9H-fluoren-9-ylidene)-2-methyl-	benzene	462(4.40)	40-0762-73
Hexahelicene, 2-methyl-	$CHCl_3$	258(4.70),265(4.61), 318(4.40),330(4.35), 350(4.08),392(2.77), 414(2.62)	35-0527-73
Hexahelicene, 4-methyl-	$CHCl_3$	258(4.64),270(4.68), 318(4.42),330(4.40), 350(4.12),392(2.70), 414(2.46)	35-0527-73
$C_{27}H_{18}N_2O_3$			
9,10[1',2']-Benzenoanthracene-13-carboxylic acid, 9,10-dihydro-4-hydroxy-1-(phenylazo)-	EtOH	269(4.01),359(4.25), 466(3.57)	18-0611-73
$C_{27}H_{18}O_2$			
1H-Indene-2,6-dione, 1,1,3-triphenyl-	C_6H_{12}	260(4.5),367(4.7)	18-0275-73
$C_{27}H_{18}O_4$			
1,4-Naphthalenedione, 2-(2,3-dihydro-1,3-dioxo-2-phenyl-1H-inden-2-yl)-6,7-dimethyl-	MeOH	227(4.51),253(4.35), 260(4.31)	39-1006-73C
$C_{27}H_{19}BrClN_3O_6$			
Quinolinium, 2-[[5-[(4-bromophenyl)methylene]tetrahydro-4,6-dioxo-2(1H)-pyrimidinylidene]methyl]-1-phenyl-, perchlorate	EtOH	227(4.43),260(4.17), 315(3.79),383(3.33)	65-1340-73
$C_{27}H_{19}BrClN_3O_7$			
Quinolinium, 2-[[5-[(4-bromophenyl)methylene]tetrahydro-4,6-dioxo-2(1H)-pyrimidinylidene]methyl]-1-(4-hydroxyphenyl)-, perchlorate	EtOH	243(4.11),257(4.19), 310(3.47),390(3.45)	65-1340-73

Compound	Solvent	$\lambda_{max}(\log \epsilon)$	Ref.
$C_{27}H_{19}ClNOP$			
Benzenepropanenitrile, 4-chloro-α-oxo-β-(triphenylphosphoranylidene)-	EtOH	268(3.92),274(3.94), 316(3.94)	39-2241-73C
Benzenepropanenitrile, 4-chloro-β-oxo-α-(triphenylphosphoranylidene)-	EtOH	276(3.91),299(3.90)	39-2241-73C
$C_{27}H_{19}NO$			
Methanone, (1,2-diphenyl-3-indolizinyl)-phenyl-	EtOH	251(4.56),286s(4.25), 400(4.17)	18-0667-73
Methanone, (7-methyl-9-phenyl-2-acridin-yl)phenyl-	EtOH	213(4.39),245(4.64), 257(4.62),273s(4.56), 291(4.60),330(3.67), 348(3.84),367(3.89), 387(3.65),408s(3.58)	39-1259-73C
4(1H)-Pyridinone, 1-(2-naphthalenyl)-3,5-diphenyl-	EtOH	244(4.59),288s(4.34), 309(4.47)	4-0665-73
$C_{27}H_{19}N_3O$			
4-Pyridinecarbonitrile, 2-[3-hydroxy-2,7-dimethyl-5-(2-pyridinyl)-4-phen-anthrenyl]-	MeCN	233(4.67),289(4.37), 318(4.32),395(3.53)	44-0407-73
$C_{27}H_{19}N_3O_2$			
1-Phenanthrenecarbonitrile, 3,6-dihydr-oxy-2,7-dimethyl-4,5-di-2-pyridinyl-	MeCN	242(4.72),318(4.46), 420(3.64)	44-0407-73
$C_{27}H_{20}$			
Allene, tetraphenyl-	C_6H_{12}	246(4.35),267(4.47)	35-2155-73
Benzo[c]phenanthrene, 3-[2-(2-methyl-phenyl)ethenyl]-, (E)-	$CHCl_3$	273(4.59),312(4.70), 348(4.30)	35-0527-73
Benzo[c]phenanthrene, 3-[2-(4-methyl-phenyl)ethenyl]-, (E)-	$CHCl_3$	274(4.48),315(4.58), 348(4.47),364(4.39)	35-0527-73
$C_{27}H_{20}ClN_3O_6$			
Quinolinium, 1-phenyl-2-[[tetrahydro-4,6-dioxo-5-(phenylmethylene)-2(1H)-pyrimidinylidene]methyl]-, perchlor-ate	EtOH	228(4.45),256(4.19), 298(3.44),390(3.88)	65-1340-73
$C_{27}H_{20}ClN_3O_7$			
Quinolinium, 1-(4-hydroxyphenyl)-2-[[tetrahydro-4,6-dioxo-5-(phenylmeth-ylene)-2(1H)-pyrimidinylidene]methyl]-, perchlorate	EtOH	242(4.25),256(4.16), 305(3.62),390(3.70)	65-1340-73
$C_{27}H_{20}N_2$			
2-Propanone, 1,3-di-1H-inden-1-ylidene-, phenylhydrazone	MeOH	256(4.56),413(4.45)	5-0750-73
	MeOH-NaOH	603(4.72)	5-0750-73
	DMSO	432(4.38)	5-0750-73
$C_{27}H_{20}N_2O_2$			
Azuleno[2,1-b]pyrazine-10-carboxylic acid, 2,3-diphenyl-, ethyl ester	MeOH	235(4.41),287(4.50), 361(4.71),410s(5.07), 520s(2.51),560(2.58), 604(2.50)	18-3161-73
$C_{27}H_{20}N_2O_4$			
2,3-Phenazinediol, 5,10-dihydro-5-meth-yl-, dibenzoate	EtOH	230(4.40)	22-1289-73

Compound	Solvent	$\lambda_{max}(\log \epsilon)$	Ref.
$C_{27}H_{20}N_4O_8$			
3,5-Cyclopentadiene-1,3-dicarboxylic acid, 2-[(2,4-dinitrophenyl)hydrazono]-4,5-diphenyl-	MeOH-KOH	252(4.50),596(4.89)	24-3788-73
$C_{27}H_{20}O$			
Anthracene, 9-methoxy-1,8-diphenyl-	EtOH	215(4.50),254s(4.83), 262(5.05),346s(3.52), 369(3.83),384(3.98), 406(3.92)	44-1167-73
$C_{27}H_{20}O_2$			
2H-Inden-2-one, 1,3-dihydro-1-hydroxy-1,3,3-triphenyl-	C_6H_{12}	263(3.31),270(3.34), 278(3.56),320(2.5)	18-0275-73
$C_{27}H_{20}O_6$			
2-Naphthalenecarboxaldehyde, 1-[[7-[bis-(acetyloxy)methyl]-1-naphthalenyl]-carbonyl]-	dioxan	227(4.98),260(4.45), 265(4.45),318(4.07), 350(3.68)	24-1341-73
2-Naphthalenecarboxaldehyde, 8-[[2-[bis-(acetyloxy)methyl]-1-naphthalenyl]-carbonyl]-	dioxan	226(4.98),252(4.44), 259s(4.42),318(4.07), 349s(3.68)	24-1341-73
$C_{27}H_{21}IN_2$			
Benz[cd]indolium, 1-methyl-2-[3-(1-methylbenz[cd]indol-2(1H)-ylidene)-1-propenyl]-, iodide	EtOH	690(4.73),757(5.07)	103-0314-73
$C_{27}H_{21}IN_2S$			
Naphtho[1,2-d]thiazolium, 1-methyl-2-[3-(1-methylbenz[cd]indol-2(1H)-ylidene)-1-propenyl]-, iodide	EtOH	630(4.68),675(4.78)	103-0314-73
$C_{27}H_{21}NOS$			
Sulfilimine, N-(3-oxo-1,3-diphenyl-1-propenyl)-S,S-diphenyl-	EtOH	248s(4.37),380(4.11)	44-4324-73
$C_{27}H_{21}NO_2$			
4,9-Methano-1H-benz[f]isoindole-1,3(2H)-dione, 10-(phenylmethylene)-3a,4,9,9a-tetrahydro-2-methyl-, (3aα,4α,9α,9aα)-	90% EtOH	226(3.88),251(3.07), 269(3.76),274(3.70)	12-1725-73
$C_{27}H_{21}NO_7$			
D-Allonitrile, 2,5-anhydro-, 3,4,6-tribenzoate	MeOH	230(4.54),274(3.45), 288(3.38)	44-1836-73
$C_{27}H_{21}N_3O_2S_2$			
4-Thiazolidinone, 5-(12-methoxy-10,14-dimethyldibenzo[a,c]phenazin-3(14H)-ylidene)-3-methyl-2-thioxo-	n.s.g.	682(4.1),746(4.29)	103-1407-73
$C_{27}H_{21}N_3O_3$			
Acetic acid, cyano(12-methoxy-14-methyldibenzo[a,c]phenazin-3(14H)-ylidene)-, ethyl ester	n.s.g.	594s(4.27),650(4.4), 706(4.32)	103-1407-73
$C_{27}H_{21}O_5P$			
Phosphoric acid, 3-[1,1'-biphenyl]-4-yl-3-oxo-1-propenyl diphenyl ester	dioxan	222s(4.11),297(4.34)	24-0435-73

Compound	Solvent	$\lambda_{max}(\log \epsilon)$	Ref.
$C_{27}H_{22}NO_2P$			
Phosphonium, triphenyl-, 2-(2,5-dioxo-3-pyrrolidinyl)-2,4-cyclopentadien-1-ylide	CH_2Cl_2	269(4.04),295(3.83), 475(1.30)	44-3537-73
$C_{27}H_{22}N_2$			
Azuleno[2,1-b]pyrazine, 8-(1-methylethyl)-2,3-diphenyl-	MeOH	281(4.30),355(4.51), 410s(3.80),440s(3.39), 510s(1.96),560(2.07), 605(2.09),660(1.98), 740s(1.54)	18-3161-73
$C_{27}H_{22}N_2O$			
Benzamide, N-(phenylmethyl)-2-[phenyl(phenylimino)methyl]-	EtOH	250s(4.23),324(3.52) (changing)	103-0701-73
$C_{27}H_{22}N_2O_2$			
Pyridinium, 2,2'-(methylenedi-4,1-phenylene)bis(2-oxoethylide)	EtOH	260(4.35),423(3.94)	65-1336-73
$C_{27}H_{22}N_2O_3$			
8aH-Phenanthro[4',3:4,5]isoxazolo[2,3-a]pyridin-2-ol, 8a-methoxy-3,8-dimethyl-1-(2-pyridinyl)-	MeOH	264(4.47),355(3.90), 480(4.13)	44-0407-73
$C_{27}H_{22}N_2O_4$			
3,5-Cyclopentadiene-1,3-dicarboxylic acid, 4,5-diphenyl-2-(phenylhydrazono)-, dimethyl ester	MeOH	256(4.49),465(4.52)	24-3788-73
	MeOH-NaOEt	267(4.34),488(4.50)	24-3788-73
$C_{27}H_{22}N_2O_8S_2$			
3H-Pyrrolo[1,2-a]indole-2-carboxylic acid, 1-[[(4-methylphenyl)sulfonyl]amino]-9-[[(4-methylphenyl)sulfonyl]oxy]-3-oxo-, methyl ester	EtOH	225(4.54),257(4.34), 320(4.16)	95-0971-73
$C_{27}H_{22}OSi$			
2-Propen-1-one, 1-phenyl-2-(triphenylsilyl)-	C_6H_{12}	248(4.09),322(1.89), 333(2.00),344(2.05), 357(1.95),370(1.68)	23-2024-73
$C_{27}H_{22}O_4$			
6,9-Methanobenzo[h]pentaphene-5,10,15,16-tetrone, 5a,5b,6,7,8,9,9a,9b,15a,15b-decahydro-	$CHCl_3$	256(4.38),307(3.70)	138-0641-73
$C_{27}H_{23}Cl_2N_5O_6$			
7(8H)-Pteridinone, 8-[3,5-bis-O-(4-chlorobenzoyl)-2-deoxy-α-D-erythro-pentofuranosyl]-2-(dimethylamino)-	MeOH	242(4.71),310s(3.81), 365(4.24)	24-0317-73
$C_{27}H_{23}INP$			
Phosphonium, (1H-indol-2-ylmethyl)-triphenyl-	MeOH	271(4.05),278(4.04), 287(3.99),293(3.96)	23-0792-73
$C_{27}H_{23}N_2$			
Benzenaminium, N-[3-(diphenylamino)-2-propenylidene]-N-phenyl-	MeOH	241(4.29),386(4.66)	118-0791-73

Compound	Solvent	$\lambda_{max}(\log \epsilon)$	Ref.
$C_{27}H_{23}N_3O$			
Benzo[f]quinoline-1-carboxamide, N,N-diethyl-3-(2-quinolinyl)-	n.s.g.	280(4.66),328(4.39), 369(3.89)	103-0220-73
Cu(I) complex	isoAmOH	538(3.87)	103-0220-73
$C_{27}H_{23}N_3O_2$			
Benzo[f]quinoline-1-carboxylic acid, 3-(2-quinoxalinyl)-, pentyl ester, Cu(I) complex	EtOH	405(4.56),552(3.89)	103-1391-73
$C_{27}H_{23}N_3O_5S$			
2-Propenoic acid, 2-cyano-3-[3-[[(4-methylphenyl)sulfonyl]oxy]-1H-indol-2-yl]-3-[(phenylmethyl)amino]-, methyl ester	EtOH	302(4.22)	95-0964-73
$C_{27}H_{23}N_3O_7S_2$			
1H-Indole-2-propanoic acid, α-cyano-β-[[(4-methylphenyl)sulfonyl]imino]-3-[[(4-methylphenyl)sulfonyl]oxy]-, methyl ester	EtOH	306(4.13),335(4.13)	95-0971-73
$C_{27}H_{23}N_3O_8S_2$			
Benzenamine, N-methyl-4-[[(4-nitrophenyl)sulfonyl]methyl]-N-[4-[[(4-nitrophenyl)sulfonyl]methyl]phenyl]-	$CHCl_3$	365s(3.24)	23-1187-73
$C_{27}H_{24}IN_5O_5$			
Adenosine, N,1-dibenzoyl-N,6-didehydro-5'-deoxy-1,6-dihydro-5'-iodo-2',3'-O-(1-methylethylidene)-	EtOH	249(4.60),272s(4.31)	35-4404-73
$C_{27}H_{24}I_2N_2O_2$			
Pyridinium, 1,1'-[methylenebis[4,1-phenylene(2-oxo-1,2-ethanediyl)]bis-, diiodide	EtOH	262(4.48),420(3.76)	65-1336-73
$C_{27}H_{24}NO$			
Pyrylium, 4-[2-(dimethylamino)-1-phenylethenyl]-2,6-diphenyl-, perchlorate, (E)-	MeCN	258(4.31),340(4.34), 444(4.64)	78-1031-73
$C_{27}H_{24}N_2O_2$			
1H-Pyrazole-3-carboxylic acid, 5-(1,2-diphenylethenyl)-1-(4-methylphenyl)-, ethyl ester	C_6H_{12} or EtOH	215(4.47),233(4.51), 295(4.27)	4-0015-73
$C_{27}H_{24}N_2O_3$			
2-Furanmethanol, 5-(1,3-diphenyl-2-imidazolidinyl)-, benzoate	MeOH	231(4.50),251(4.58), 281(3.68),290s(3.65)	44-1836-73
$C_{27}H_{24}N_2O_4$			
4,5,7-Metheno-3H-pentaleno[2,1-c]pyrazole-4,7-dicarboxylic acid, 6-(diphenylmethylene)-3a,3b,5,6,6a,7-hexahydro-, dimethyl ester, (3aα,3bβ,4α,5α,6aβ-7α,7aα)-	EtOH	227(4.21),260(4.27), 320(2.56)	24-1822-73
$C_{27}H_{24}N_4$			
1H-Imidazo[1,2-a]imidazol-1-amine, 3,6-diphenyl-N-(phenylmethylene)-5-propyl-	EtOH	245(4.58),290(4.63), 345(4.56)	103-1082-73

Compound	Solvent	$\lambda_{max}(\log \epsilon)$	Ref.
$C_{27}H_{24}N_4O_7$			
2,4(1H,3H)-Pteridinedione, 1-[2-deoxy-3,5-bis-O-(4-methylbenzoyl)-D-erythro-pentofuranosyl]-	MeOH	238(4.61),315(3.79)	24-1401-73
$C_{27}H_{24}O_3$			
1,3,5-Benzenetrimethanol, α,α',α"-tri-phenyl-	MeOH	258(2.42)	32-0849-73
$C_{27}H_{24}O_4$			
2,3,5-Metheno-1H-cyclopropa[a]pentalene-2,5a-dicarboxylic acid, 4-(diphenyl-methylene)hexahydro-, dimethyl ester, (1aα,1bβ,2β,3α,4aβ,5α,5aα)-	EtOH	227s(4.21),261(4.24)	24-1822-73
$C_{27}H_{24}O_8$			
Nonanedioic acid, bis(2-oxo-2H-1-benzo-pyran-7-yl) ester	CH_2Cl_2	277(4.33),283(4.33), 313(4.26)	44-0957-73
$C_{27}H_{25}ClN_2O$			
10H-Azeto[1,2-a:3,4-b']diindole, 10-(4-chlorobenzoyl)-5a,10a,10b,11-tetra-hydro-5a,10a,11,11-tetramethyl-	EtOH	230(4.66),262(4.28), 287(4.24)	88-0365-73
geometric isomer	EtOH	225(4.56),263(4.18), 287(4.11)	88-0365-73
$C_{27}H_{25}NO$			
2-Propenamide, N-(4,5-diphenyl-2,4-pentadienyl)-N-methyl-3-phenyl-	MeOH	213(4.43),223(4.38), 290(4.68)	44-2169-73
$C_{27}H_{25}NO_5$			
4,4-Oxazolidinedicarboxylic acid, 2,3-diphenyl-5-(2-phenylethenyl)-, dimethyl ester	EtOH	253(4.45)	22-3437-73
$C_{27}H_{25}N_5O_6$			
2(1H)-Pteridinone, 4-amino-1-(2-deoxy-3,5-bis-O-(4-methylbenzoyl)-α-D-erythro-pentofuranosyl)-	MeOH	252(4.67),278(3.84), 340(3.92)	33-1225-73
β-	MeOH	252(4.65),278(3.76), 340(3.89)	33-1225-73
$C_{27}H_{26}$			
Naphthalene, 1,2,3,4,6-pentamethyl-5,8-diphenyl-	EtOH	240(4.47),255(4.57), 325(4.03)	118-0783-73
$C_{27}H_{26}BF_4NO_2S$			
Benzothiazolium, 2-[(3,6-diethoxy-1H-phenalen-1-ylidene)methyl]-3-ethyl-, tetrafluoroborate	MeCN	343(4.04),412(3.86), 604(4.64),646(4.60)	44-2425-73
Benzothiazolium, 2-[(3,7-diethoxy-1H-phenalen-1-ylidene)methyl]-3-ethyl-, tetrafluoroborate	MeCN	337(4.14),344(4.14), 367(4.13),425(4.11), 590(4.67),635(4.57)	44-2425-73
Benzothiazolium, 2-[(4,6-diethoxy-1H-phenalen-1-ylidene)methyl]-3-ethyl-, tetrafluoroborate	EtOH	316(4.20),362(4.20), 415(3.68),657f(4.71), 712(4.77)	44-2425-73
Benzothiazolium, 2-[(4,7-diethoxy-1H-phenalen-1-ylidene)methyl]-3-ethyl-, tetrafluoroborate	MeCN	312(4.12),341(4.05), 385(4.14),410(4.16), 642(4.69),700(4.63)	44-2425-73

Compound	Solvent	λmax(log ε)	Ref.
$C_{27}H_{26}I_2N_4O_2$			
Pyridinium, 1,1'-[methylenebis[4,1-phenylene(2-oxo-2,1-ethanediyl)]bis[2-amino-, diiodide	EtOH	250(4.67),325(4.23)	65-1336-73
$C_{27}H_{26}N_2OS$			
1,4,3-Oxathiazin-6-amine, N,N-diethyl-4-(9H-fluoren-9-ylidene)-4,4-dihydro-5-methyl-2-phenyl-	$CHCl_3$	242(4.46),263(4.22), 277(4.10),300(3.70), 310(3.60)	35-0279-73
$C_{27}H_{26}N_2O_3$			
2H-Benzo[a]quinolizine-2,4(3H)-dione, 1,6,7,11b-tetrahydro-3-methyl-3-(1,6,7,11b-tetrahydro-2-oxo-2H-benzo[a]quinolizin-4-yl)-	EtOH	252(4.05),314(4.00)	70-1258-73
$C_{27}H_{26}O$			
4,7-Methano-1H-inden-8-one, 3a,4,7,7a-tetrahydro-4,7-dimethyl-1-(1-methylethylidene)-5,6-diphenyl-, (3aα,4α,7α,7aα)-	hexane	247(4.46)	44-3836-73
1,2,4-Metheno-1H-cyclobuta[cd]pentalen-5(1aH)-one, 4,5a-dimethyl-3-(1-methylethylidene)-1,6-diphenyl-	hexane	224s(4.36),261s(2.81), 304(2.48)	44-3836-73
1-Naphthalenemethanol, 5,6,7,8-tetramethyl-3,4-diphenyl-	MeOH	240s(4.48),260(4.72), 320(4.07)	5-1893-73
$C_{27}H_{26}O_{17}$			
β-D-Glucopyranosiduronic acid, 4-[7-(β-D-glucopyranuronosyloxy)-5-hydroxy-4H-1-benzopyran-2-yl]phenyl-	MeOH	268(4.35),320(4.30)	24-2536-73
$C_{27}H_{27}ClN_2O_3$			
1-Propanone, 3-(1-benzoyl-3-ethenyl-4-piperidinyl)-2-chloro-1-(6-methoxy-4-quinolinyl)- (N-benzoyl-8-chloroquinotoxine)	EtOH	209(4.68),248(3.63)	33-1494-73
$C_{27}H_{27}N_3O_6S_2$			
Morpholine, 4-[[[(4-methylphenyl)sulfonyl]imino][3-[[(4-methylphenyl)sulfonyl]oxy]-1H-indol-2-yl]methyl]-	EtOH	220(4.70),265(4.42)	95-0971-73
$C_{27}H_{27}N_5$			
2-Azulenamine, 5-(1-methylethyl)-1,3-bis[(4-methylphenyl)azo]-	MeOH	235s(4.20),256(4.24), 345s(4.33),355s(4.42), 418(4.75),542(3.86)	18-3266-73
$C_{27}H_{27}N_9O_9S_3$			
1,2,4-Cyclohexanetriol, 3,5,6-triazido-, tris(4-methylbenzenesulfonate), (1α,2α,3β,4α,5β,6β)-	EtOH	227(4.55),263(3.36), 274(3.27)	89-0989-73
$C_{27}H_{27}O_2P$			
Phosphorin, 1-ethoxy-2-ethyl-1,1-dihydro-2,4,6-triphenyl-, 1-oxide	MeOH	232(3.94),325(3.50)	24-1001-73
$C_{27}H_{28}F_6N_3$			
Methanaminium, N-[4-[[4-(dimethylamino)-phenyl][4-(dimethylamino)-2-(trifluo-	98% HOAc	627(3.85)	39-1792-73B

Compound	Solvent	λ_{max}(log ϵ)	Ref.
romethyl)phenyl]methylene]-3-(trifluoromethyl)-2,5-cyclohexadien-1-ylidene]-N-methyl- (cont.)			
$C_{27}H_{28}N_2O_2$			
1H-Pyrrole, 2-[[4,5-dimethyl-3-(phenylmethoxy)-2H-pyrrol-2-ylidene]methyl]-4,5-dimethyl-3-(phenylmethoxy)-, hydrobromide	CH_2Cl_2	468(4.97)	5-0146-73
$C_{27}H_{28}N_2O_3$			
Quinotoxine, N-benzoyl-	MeOH	210(4.73),240s(4.33), 255s(4.06),345(3.66)	33-1485-73
$C_{27}H_{28}N_2O_7S$			
Butanedioic acid, [[[1,3,4,5-tetrahydro-5-oxo-1-[(4-methylphenyl)sulfonyl]-benz[cd]indol-4-yl]amino]methylene]-, diethyl ester	EtOH	229(4.38),292(4.39), 333(3.88)	39-0760-73C
$C_{27}H_{28}N_4O_{12}$			
Menisperine styphnate	MeOH	223(2.66),270(3.07), 307(2.88)	95-0624-73
$C_{27}H_{28}O_4$			
6H-Cyclopenta[a]phenanthren-17-ol, 7,11,12,13,16,17-hexahydro-3,16α-dimethoxy-13-methyl-, benzoate, (±)-	EtOH	313(4.44)	94-0697-73
16β-	EtOH	312(4.32)	94-0697-73
$C_{27}H_{28}O_5$			
D-Allose, 2,5-anhydro-3,4,6-tris(O-phenylmethyl)-	MeOH	229(3.68)	44-1836-73
Metabolite A from Aspergillus terreus	MeOH	243(4.34),371(4.49)	102-2527-73
Metabolite B from Aspergillus terreus	MeOH	243(4.33),374(4.49)	102-2527-73
$C_{27}H_{28}O_6$			
2H-1-Benzopyran-2-one, 7,7'-[1,9-nonanediylbis(oxy)]bis-	CH_2Cl_2	324(4.51)	44-0957-73
Metabolite C from Aspergillus terreus	MeOH	244(4.23),375(4.50)	102-2527-73
Metabolite D from Aspergillus terreus	MeOH	245(4.28),377(4.47)	102-2527-73
$C_{27}H_{28}O_7$			
Metabolite F from Aspergillus terreus	MeOH	242(4.31),375(4.49)	102-2527-73
$C_{27}H_{28}O_8$			
[1]Benzopyrano[3,4-b][1]benzopyran-9,12-diol, 6,6a-dihydro-2,3-dimethoxy-8-(3-methyl-2-butenyl)-, diacetate	EtOH	215(4.39),242s(4.06), 249(4.13),256(4.09), 298(3.92),308s(3.84), 343s(4.15),355(4.35), 372(4.28)	39-1277-73C
$C_{27}H_{28}O_9$			
4H-1-Benzopyran-4-one, 5-acetoxy-2-(4-acetoxy-3-methoxyphenyl)-3,7-dimethoxy-8-(3-methyl-2-butenyl)-	MeOH	300s(3.98),345(3.89)	12-0409-73
2-Butenoic acid, 2-methyl-, 1,3,3a,4,14-14a-hexahydro-6,7,8-trimethoxy-3-oxo-benzo[3,4]furo[3',4':6,7]cycloocta-[1,2-f][1,3]benzodioxol-14-yl ester (steganangin)	EtOH	256(4.03),285(3.71)	35-1335-73

Compound	Solvent	$\lambda_{max}(\log \epsilon)$	Ref.
$C_{27}H_{29}BrN_2O_2$			
1H-Pyrrole, 2-[[4,5-dimethyl-3-(phenylmethoxy)-2H-pyrrol-2-ylidene]methyl]-4,5-dimethyl-3-(phenylmethoxy)-, hydrobromide	CH_2Cl_2	468(4.97)	5-0146-73
$C_{27}H_{29}BrN_4NiO_2$			
Nickel, bromo(octadehydro-1,2,7,8,12,13-18,19-octamethyl-3,17-corrindiolato-N^{21},N^{22},N^{23},N^{24})-, (SP-5-14)-	CH_2Cl_2	265(4.13),349(4.17), 551(3.84)	5-0146-73
$C_{27}H_{29}BrN_4NiO_4$			
Nickel, bromo(2,3,17,18-tetradehydro-3,17-dihydroxy-1,2,8,8,13,13,18,19-octamethyl-7,12-corrindionato-N^{21},N^{22},N^{23},N^{24}]-, (SP-5-15)-	MeOH	327(4.20),465s(3.81), 527(3.85)	5-0146-73
$C_{27}H_{29}NO$			
4,7-Methano-1H-inden-1-one, 3a,4,5,6,7-7a-hexahydro-2,3-diphenyl-7a-(1-piperidinyl)-	MeOH	226(4.23),298(4.07)	88-0949-73
$C_{27}H_{29}NO_2$			
Benzoic acid, 4-(2,2-diphenylethenyl)-, 2-(diethylamino)ethyl ester	EtOH	320(3.95)	104-1511-73
$C_{27}H_{29}NO_6$			
4H-Dibenzo[de,g]quinolin-1-ol, 9-(3,4-dimethoxyphenoxy)-5,6,6a,7-tetrahydro-2,10-dimethoxy-6-methyl-, (±)-	MeOH	268s(4.18),278(4.29), 302(4.25)	35-2995-73
$C_{27}H_{29}NiP$			
Nickel, butyl(η^5-2,4-cyclopentadien-1-yl)(triphenylphosphine)-	C_6H_{12}	301(3.98),406(3.11), 573(1.90)	23-1179-73
Nickel, (η^5-2,4-cyclopentadien-1-yl)(1-methylpropyl)(triphenylphosphine)-	C_6H_{12}	308(3.87),420(3.06), 572(1.85)	23-1179-73
Nickel, (η^5-2,4-cyclopentadien-1-yl)(2-methylpropyl)(triphenylphosphine)-	C_6H_{12}	303(3.95),413(3.03), 589(1.85)	23-1179-73
$C_{27}H_{30}Br_2O_6$			
Benzene, 1-[(2-bromo-4,5-dimethoxyphenyl)methyl]-2-[[(2-bromomethyl)-4,5-dimethoxyphenyl]methyl]-4,5-dimethoxy-	n.s.g.	233(4.47),285(4.01)	39-0891-73C
$C_{27}H_{30}N_2O_7S$			
Butanedioic acid, [[[1,3,4,5-tetrahydro-5-hydroxy-1-[(4-methylphenyl)sulfonyl]benz[cd]indol-4-yl]amino]methylene]-, diethyl ester	EtOH	219(4.52),237(4.20), 267(4.23),289(4.36), 329(3.08)	39-0760-73C
$C_{27}H_{30}N_4O_5S$			
4-Thia-1-azabicyclo[3.2.0]heptane-2-carboxylic acid, 6-[[(2,2-dimethyl-5-oxo-4-phenyl-1-imidazolinyl)phenylacetyl]-amino]-3,3-dimethyl-7-oxo-, [2S-(2α,5α,6β)]-	EtOH-TEA	308(2.53)	4-0265-73
$C_{27}H_{30}N_6O_2$			
Pyrimido[4,5-d]pyridazine, 1,4-dihydro-5,8-dimorpholino-2-phenyl-1-(phenylmethyl)-	EtOH	240(4.41)	95-1043-73

Compound	Solvent	λ_{max}(log ϵ)	Ref.
Pyrimido[4,5-d]pyridazine, 3,4-dihydro-5,8-dimorpholino-2-phenyl-3-(phenylmethyl)-	EtOH	243(4.26),355(3.82)	95-1043-73
$C_{27}H_{30}O_5$			
4H-1-Benzopyran-4-one, 5-hydroxy-3,7-dimethoxy-6,8-bis(3-methyl-2-butenyl)-2-phenyl-	MeOH	280(4.42),305(3.99), 363(4.73)	12-0641-73
$C_{27}H_{30}O_7$			
Arugosin C, mono-O-acetyl-	EtOH	221(4.25),258(3.99), 295(3.99),347(3.77)	39-1825-73C
$C_{27}H_{30}O_8$			
2,3,5-Metheno-1H-cyclopropa[a]pentalene-1,1a,5a-tricarboxylic acid, hexahydro-1-(3a,4,7,7a-tetrahydro-2-hydroxy-4,7-methanobenzofuran-3-yl)-, ethyl trimethyl deriv.	EtOH	210(3.83),226s(3.66)	24-1804-73
$C_{27}H_{30}O_9$			
Benzoic acid, 4-methoxy-, 1-(3,6-dihydro-4-methoxy-6-oxo-2H-pyran-2-yl)-2-propyl-1,2-ethanediyl ester, [6S-[6R*(1R*,2S*)]-	MeOH	225(4.58)	44-3542-73
$C_{27}H_{30}O_{13}$			
4H-1-Benzopyran-4-one, 7-[(4-O-β-D-glucopyranosyl-β-D-glucopyranosyl)-oxy]-3-phenyl-	EtOH	250(4.34),298(3.96)	114-0191-73D
	dioxan	253(4.45),295(3.93), 305(3.95)	114-0365-73D
$C_{27}H_{30}O_{14}$			
Kaempferol 3,7-di-L-rhamnoside	MeOH	230s(--),266(4.43), 320s(--),346(4.26)	105-0526-73
Lobodirin, acetyl-	MeOH	216s(3.90),228(4.20), 244(4.02),261(3.98), 284(3.74)	102-2497-73
$C_{27}H_{31}BrN_4NiO_4$			
Nickel, bromo(2,3,12,13,17,18-hexadehydro-1,2,7,8,12,13,18,19-octamethyl-3,7,8,17-corrintetrolato-N^{21},N^{22},N^{23}-N^{24})-, (SP-5-15)-	MeOH	265(4.04),336(4.04), 526(3.70)	5-0146-73
$C_{27}H_{31}BrO_7$			
Benzenemethanol, 2-[[2-[(2-bromo-4,5-dimethoxyphenyl)methyl]-4,5-dimethoxyphenyl]methyl]-4,5-dimethoxy-	n.s.g.	233(4.43),285(4.00)	39-0891-73C
Benzoic acid, 4-bromo-, 2,3,3a,4,5,6,9-11a-octahydro-6-hydroxy-3,6,10-trimethyl-4-(2-methylene-1-oxobutoxy)-2-oxocyclodeca[b]furan-9-yl ester	EtOH	212(3.80),245(4.27)	44-1853-73
$C_{27}H_{31}F_3O_5$			
3'H-Cyclopropa[6,7]pregna-2,4,6-trien-20-one, 3,17α-diacetoxy-3',3',6-trifluoro-6β,7β-dihydro-16-methylene-	n.s.g.	274(3.81)	39-0227-73C

Compound	Solvent	$\lambda_{max}(\log \epsilon)$	Ref.
$C_{27}H_{31}NO$			
4H-1-Benzopyran-2-amine, N,N-diethyl-5,6,7,8-tetrahydro-3-methyl-4-phenyl-8-(phenylmethylene)-	EtOH	276(4.32)	4-0165-73
$C_{27}H_{31}NO_9$			
Benzenemethanol, 2-[[2-[(4,5-dimethoxy-2-nitrophenyl)methyl]-4,5-dimethoxyphenyl]methyl]-4,5-dimethoxy-	n.s.g.	233s(4.43),284(4.00), 341(3.73)	39-0891-73C
$C_{27}H_{31}N_7O_7$			
L-Glutamic acid, N-[3-[4-[[[2-(acetylamino)-1,4-dihydro-4-oxo-6-pteridinyl]methylene]amino]phenyl]-1-oxopropyl]-, diethyl ester	DMF	296(4.19),373(4.39)	87-0697-73
$C_{27}H_{31}NiPSi$			
Nickel, (η^5-2,4-cyclopentadien-1-yl)-[(trimethylsilyl)methyl](triphenylphosphine)-	C_6H_{12}	309(4.03),421(3.09), 639(1.93)	23-1179-73
$C_{27}H_{32}$			
Propane, 2,2-bis(4-phenylcyclohexen-3-yl)-	n.s.g.	249(4.44)	47-2225-73
$C_{27}H_{32}N_2O_2$			
1H-Pyridp[3,2-c]carbazole-6-carboxylic acid, 4a-ethyl-2,3,4,4a,5,6,7,11c-octahydro-7-methyl-1-(phenylmethyl)-, methyl ester	MeOH	222(4.58),286(3.92)	35-7146-73
$C_{27}H_{32}O_6$			
Arugosin C, di-O-methyl-	EtOH	233(4.17),278(4.08), 342(3.62)	39-1825-73C
1H-Phenalene-1,3(2H)-dione, 4-hydroxy-5,6,7-trimethoxy-9-methyl-2,2-bis(3-methyl-2-butenyl)-	$CHCl_3$	229(4.44),262(4.52), 350(4.04),386s(3.91)	39-2388-73C
$C_{27}H_{32}O_{10}$			
9,10-Anthracenedione, 1,3-dimethoxy-6-methyl-8-[(2,3,4,6-tetra-O-methyl-β-D-glucopyranosyl)oxy]-	MeOH	221(4.63),277(4.39), 400(3.78)	94-1254-73
9,10-Anthracenedione, 1,8-dimethoxy-3-[[(2,3,4,6-tetra-O-methyl-β-D-glucopyranosyl)oxy]methyl]-	MeOH	224(4.68),257(4.41), 275s(4.25),390(3.95)	94-1254-73
$C_{27}H_{33}BrN_4NiO_6$			
Nickel, bromo(2,3,17,18-tetradehydro-1,2,7,8,12,13,18,19-octamethyl-3,7,8,12,13,17-corrinhexolato-N^{21},N^{22},N^{23},N^{24})-, (SP-5-15)-	MeOH	259(4.15),302(4.06), 326(4.08),349s(4.01), 448(3.77),470(3.79)	5-0146-73
$C_{27}H_{33}N_3O_2$			
1'H-Androst-4-eno[3,2-c]pyrazol-17-ol, 1'-(2-aminobenzoyl)-, (17β)-	n.s.g.	234(4.13),276(3.97)	65-0403-73
1'H-Androst-4-eno[3,2-c]pyrazol-17-ol, 1'-(4-aminobenzoyl)-, (17β)-	n.s.g.	226(4.15),274(3.99)	65-0403-73
$C_{27}H_{34}O_7$			
Neokurarinol	EtOH	287(4.26)	94-2733-73
	EtOH-NaOH	334(4.45)	94-2733-73

Compound	Solvent	$\lambda_{max}(\log \epsilon)$	Ref.
$C_{27}H_{34}O_{11}$			
2(3H)-Furanone, 4-[(3,4-dimethoxyphen-yl)methyl]-3-[[4-(β-D-glucopyrano-syloxy)-3-methoxyphenyl]methyl]di-hydro- (arctiin)	EtOH	230(4.13),280(3.67)	94-0674-73
	EtOH	230(4.18),280(3.70)	94-0674-73
	EtOH	230(4.26),280(3.63)	94-1114-73
β-D-Glucopyranoside, 4-[4-(3,4-dimeth-oxyphenyl)tetrahydro-1H,3H-furo[3,4-c]furan-1-yl]-2-methoxyphenyl (1α,3aα,5α,6aα)-	MeOH	231(4.42),280(3.87)	95-0044-73
$C_{27}H_{34}O_{12}$			
Tracheloside	EtOH	230(4.26),280(3.84),	94-0674-73
	EtOH	230(4.21),280(3.76)	94-1114-73
$C_{27}H_{34}O_{14}$			
Ethanone, 1-[4-[(4-O-β-D-glucopyranosyl-β-D-glucopyranosyl)oxy]-2-hydroxyphen-yl]-2-(4-methoxyphenyl)-	EtOH	217(4.40),272(4.17), 320(3.86)	114-0191-73D
$C_{27}H_{34}O_{15}$			
Geniposide pentaacetate	EtOH	235(4.19)	94-2684-73
$C_{27}H_{35}NO_2$			
Androst-5-en-3β-ol, 17-(2-pyridinylmeth-ylene)-, acetate	n.s.g.	251(4.28),288(4.03)	19-0887-73
$C_{27}H_{35}N_2$			
Methanaminium, N-[4-[[4-(dimethylamino)-phenyl]tricyclo[3.3.1.1^{3,7}]dec-1-yl-methylene]-2,5-cyclohexadien-1-ylidene]-N-methyl-	98% HOAc	387(3.67),623(3.43)	39-2151-73B
$C_{27}H_{35}N_3O_2$			
1'H-Androstano[3,2-c]pyrazol-17-ol, 1'-(2-aminobenzoyl)-, (17β)-	n.s.g.	226(4.37),274(4.09)	65-0403-73
1'H-Androstano[3,2-c]pyrazol-17-ol, 1'-(4-aminobenzoyl)-, (17β)-	n.s.g.	230(4.46),279(4.27)	65-0403-73
$C_{27}H_{35}N_3O_3$			
Benzoic acid, 2-amino-, [(17β)-17-hy-droxy-2-(hydroxymethylene)androst-4-en-3-ylidene]hydrazide	n.s.g.	226(4.11),280(4.02)	65-0403-73
Benzoic acid, 4-amino-, [(17β)-17-hy-droxy-2-(hydroxymethylene)androst-4-en-3-ylidene]hydrazide	n.s.g.	225(4.20),272(4.11)	65-0403-73
$C_{27}H_{36}O_4$			
Spirosta-1,4-diene-3,12-dione, (25R)-	MeOH	244(4.11)	39-1940-73C
$C_{27}H_{36}O_4S$			
Retinoic acid, 11,12-dihydro-11-(phenyl-sulfonyl)-, methyl ester	EtOH	217(4.56),265s(--), 272(4.19),283s(--)	22-0746-73
$C_{27}H_{36}O_7$			
18-Norpregna-5,12-diene-3,11,20-trione, 21-acetoxy-17-methyl-, cyclic 3,20-bis(1,2-ethanediyl acetal), (17α)-	MeOH	241(4.02)	44-2328-73
$C_{27}H_{36}O_{15}$			
Cyclopenta[c]pyran-4-carboxylic acid, 5-	EtOH	234(4.07)	1-2581-73

Compound	Solvent	$\lambda_{max}(\log \epsilon)$	Ref.
acetoxy-1,4a,5,6,7,7a-hexahydro-7-methyl-1-[(2,3,4,6-tetra-O-acetyl-β-D-glucopyranosyl)oxy]-, methyl ester (cont.)			
Cyclopenta[c]pyran-4-carboxylic acid, 7-(acetoxymethyl)-1,4a,5,6,7,7a-hexahydro-1-[(2,3,4,6-tetra-O-acetyl-β-D-glucopyranosyl)oxy]-, methyl ester	MeOH	236(4.09)	94-0497-73
Geniposide, dihydro-, acetate	MeOH	234.5(4.06)	94-0497-73
Loganin, pentaacetate	EtOH	233(4.03)	35-0532-73
	EtOH	232.5(4.25)	95-0030-73
$C_{27}H_{36}O_{16}$			
Morroniside pentaacetate	MeOH	238(4.09)	94-0846-73
	EtOH	236(4.32)	95-0030-73
$C_{27}H_{37}AsO_2$			
Arsonium, tributyl-, 1-benzoyl-2-oxo-2-phenylethylide	MeOH	210(4.21),230(4.23), 255s(3.89),318(3.93)	78-1697-73
$C_{27}H_{37}ClO_7$			
Pregn-4-en-20-one, 3β,7α,17α-triacetoxy-6β-chloro-	MeOH	204(4.10)	48-0008-73
$C_{27}H_{37}NO_2$			
Androst-5-en-3β-ol, 17-(2-pyridinylmethyl)-, acetate	n.s.g.	258(3.38),263(3.42), 270(3.29)	19-0887-73
$C_{27}H_{37}N_3O_3$			
Benzoic acid, 2-amino-, [(17β)-17-hydroxy-2-(hydroxymethylene)androstan-3-ylidene]hydrazide	n.s.g.	227(4.49),275(4.18)	65-0403-73
Benzoic acid, 4-amino-, [(17β)-17-hydroxy-2-(hydroxymethylene)androstan-3-ylidene]hydrazide	n.s.g.	229(4.56),270(4.43)	65-0403-73
$C_{27}H_{38}O_4$			
24-Norchola-5,16,20(21)-triene-3,22-diol, diacetate, (3β,22R)-	EtOH	239(4.03)	19-0809-73
(3β,22S)-	EtOH	238(4.03)	19-0809-73
18-Norchola-8,11,13-trien-24-oic acid, 3-acetoxy-12-methyl-, methyl ester (3α,5β,17α)-	C_6H_{12}	220s(4.12),225s(4.07), 261s(2.45),268(2.55), 275s(2.42)	78-0021-73
$C_{27}H_{38}O_6$			
5β,14α-Card-20(22)-enolide, 3β,15α-diacetoxy-	EtOH	215(4.14)	94-0388-73
5β,14α-Card-20(22)-enolide, 3β,15β-diacetoxy-	EtOH	215(4.24)	94-0388-73
5β,14α,17α-Card-20(22)-enolide, 3β,15β-diacetoxy-	EtOH	215.5(4.14)	94-0388-73
5β,14β-Card-20(22)-enolide, 3β,15α-diacetoxy-	EtOH	215.5(4.23)	94-0388-73
5β,14β-Card-20(22)-enolide, 3β,15β-diacetoxy-	EtOH	216(4.22)	94-0388-73
$C_{27}H_{38}O_7$			
5β,14β-Card-20(22)-enolide, 12β-acetoxy-3α,14-dihydroxy-, acetate	EtOH	216(4.17)	33-2782-73
Pregn-5-en-20-one, 3β,7α,17α-triacetoxy-	MeOH	198(4.06)	48-0008-73

Compound	Solvent	λ_{max}(log ε)	Ref.
$C_{27}H_{39}NO_5$			
Androst-2-eno[3,2-b]furan-5'(2'H)-one, 17-acetoxy-3-(4-morpholinyl)-, (5α,17β)-	EtOH	217(4.08)	22-0625-73
$C_{27}H_{39}NO_6$			
5β,14β-Card-20(22)-enolide, 3α-(acetyl-amino)-12β-acetoxy-14-hydroxy-	EtOH	215(4.21)	33-2782-73
3β-(acetylamino)-	EtOH	215(4.17)	33-2782-73
5β,14β-Card-20(22)-enolide, 3α-(acetyl-amino)-16β-acetoxy-14-hydroxy-	EtOH	214(4.14)	33-2782-73
5β,14β-Card-20(22)-enolide, 3β-(acetyl-amino)-16β-acetoxy-14-hydroxy-	EtOH	216(4.14)	33-2782-73
$C_{27}H_{39}N_5O_7$			
Butanoic acid, 3-[(1-oxobutoxy)methyl]-5-[6-[(1-oxobutyl)amino]-9H-purin-9-yl]-1,2-cyclopentanediyl ester, (1α,2α,3β,5β)-(±)-	pH 1	282(4.25)	36-1252-73
$C_{27}H_{40}O_3$			
Isotaondiol	EtOH	298(3.59)	39-2637-73C
Taondiol	EtOH	298(3.59)	78-1605-73
$C_{27}H_{40}O_4$			
1-Propanone, 1-[(3β)-3-(acetyloxy)an-drosta-5,16-dien-17-yl]-3-propoxy-	EtOH	242(3.95)	70-1578-73
$C_{27}H_{40}O_7$			
Cholesta-5,8,14-trien-7-one, 2,3,6,20-22,25-hexahydroxy-, (2β,3β,22R)-(calonysterone)	MeOH	222(4.32),244s(4.13), 294(3.89)	77-0737-73
$C_{27}H_{41}NO_6$			
Acetamide, N-[(3β,5α,20R)-3,20-diacet-oxy-11-oxopregnan-9-yl]-	dioxan	295(1.66)	23-3866-73
$C_{27}H_{41}NO_7$			
Carbamic acid, [(3β,5α,20R)-3,20-di-acetoxy-11-oxopregnan-9-yl]-, methyl ester	dioxan	296(1.64)	23-3866-73
$C_{27}H_{42}$			
Cholesta-2,4,6-triene	C_6H_{12}	297(4.08),308(4.10), 323(3.90)	13-0627-73B
$C_{27}H_{42}N_4O_6$			
Benzenepropanamide, N-[4-[acetyl[3-(acetylamino)propyl]amino]butyl]-N-[3-(acetylamino)propyl]-4-acetoxy-	EtOH	270(3.02)	33-1266-73
$C_{27}H_{42}O$			
Cholesta-2,4-dien-6-one	EtOH	315(3.85)	39-0070-73C
$C_{27}H_{43}BrO$			
Cholest-1-en-3-one, 2-bromo-	EtOH	257(4.10)	18-3155-73
Cholest-4-en-3-one, 2-bromo-	dioxan	248(4.14)	78-1625-73
Cholest-4-en-3-one, 2α-bromo-	dioxan	243(4.18)	78-1625-73
Cholest-4-en-3-one, 4-bromo-	EtOH	263(4.07)	39-1848-73C

Compound	Solvent	λmax(log ε)	Ref.
$C_{27}H_{43}ClO$			
Cholest-1-en-3-one, 2-chloro-	EtOH	249(4.02)	18-3155-73
Cholest-4-en-3-one, 4-chloro-	EtOH	255.5(4.08)	22-1357-73
$C_{27}H_{43}NO$			
6-Aza-B-homocholesta-2,4-dien-7-one	EtOH	239(4.31)	12-0603-73
$C_{27}H_{43}NO_2$			
6-Aza-B-homocholest-4-ene-3,7-dione	EtOH	277(4.17)	12-0603-73
16,28-Secosolanida-5,22(28)-diene-3,15,16-triol	MeOH	241(4.3)	5-2048-73
$C_{27}H_{43}N_5O_4$			
1H-Isoindole-5,6-dicarboxamide, 2,3-dihydro-4,7-bis(methylamino)-1,3-dioxo-N,N',2-tripentyl-	80% DMF	506(3.79),610s(--)	25-1108-73
$C_{27}H_{44}$			
Cholesta-1,3-diene	hexane	262(3.54)	35-3932-73
$C_{27}H_{44}N_2O_2$			
3-Aza-A-homocholest-4a-en-4-one, 3-nitroso-	EtOH	264(4.10),424(2.00)	39-1661-73C
$C_{27}H_{44}O$			
Cholest-2-en-1-one	EtOH	223(3.85)	18-3155-73
Cholest-2-en-4-one	EtOH	226(3.92)	88-4637-73
5α-Cholest-8(14)-en-15-one	n.s.g.	260(4.19)	39-0155-73C
$C_{27}H_{44}O_2$			
Calciferol, 1α-hydroxy-	EtOH	264(4.25)	33-1708-73
Cholestane-2,3-dione, (5β)-	EtOH	270(3.87)	33-2238-73
	EtOH-NaOH	315(3.74)	33-2238-73
Cholestane-3,6-dione, (5α)-	EtOH	286(1.74)	39-1848-73C
Cholest-4-en-3-one, 2α-hydroxy-	EtOH	241(4.12)	33-2238-73
Vitamin D_3, 1α-hydroxy-	ether	265(4.26)	88-3649-73
$C_{27}H_{44}O_3$			
2-Propenoic acid, 3-(4-hydroxyphenyl)-, octadecyl ester	EtOH	205(4.13),230(4.08), 315(4.09)	39-1155-73C
$C_{27}H_{44}O_7$			
Calonysterone, 8,9,14,15-tetrahydro-	MeOH	285(3.97)	77-0737-73
	MeOH-NaOH	340(3.88)	77-0737-73
Cholest-7-en-6-one, 2,3,14,22,25,26-hexahydroxy-, (2β,3β,5β,14α,22R)-	MeOH	245(4.06)	57-0307-73B
$C_{27}H_{44}O_8$			
Photoecdysone from Ajuka turkestanica	EtOH	244(3.95)	105-0125-73
$C_{27}H_{46}ClNO_2$			
16,28-Secosolanidane-3,20-diol, 28-chloro-, (3β,5α,22α)-	EtOH	254(2.71)	48-0739-73
$C_{27}H_{46}ClNO_3$			
16,28-Secosolanidane-3,16,20-triol, 28-chloro-, (3β,5α,16β)-	EtOH	265(3.30)	48-0739-73
(3β,5α,16β,22α,25ξ)-	EtOH	292(2.62)	48-0739-73
(3β,5α,16β,25β)-	EtOH	265(2.14)	48-0739-73

Compound	Solvent	$\lambda_{max}(\log \epsilon)$	Ref.
$C_{27}H_{46}N_2O_3$			
3-Aza-A-norcholestane-5-acetic acid, 3-nitroso-	EtOH	232(3.81)	39-1661-73C
16,28-Secosolanidane-3,20-diol, 28-nitroso-, (3β,5α,22α)-	EtOH	245(3.86),350(2.10)	48-0739-73
$C_{27}H_{46}N_2O_4$			
16,28-Secosolanidane-3,16,20-triol, 28-nitroso-, (3β,5α,16β,25β)-	EtOH	244(3.85),355(2.09)	48-0739-73
$C_{27}H_{46}O_3$			
Benzenepropanoic acid, 4-hydroxy-, octadecyl ester	EtOH	224(3.83),279(3.03)	39-1155-73C

Compound	Solvent	λ_{max}(log ϵ)	Ref.
$C_{28}H_{10}F_{10}$			
Indene, 1,2,3-(pentafluorophenyl)derivative Ia	n.s.g.	217(3.11),253(3.91), 318(3.61)	101-0423-73A
IB	n.s.g.	261(3.81),321(3.48)	101-0423-73A
2	n.s.g.	260(3.90),325(3.69)	101-0423-73A
$(C_{28}H_{14}N_{10})_n$			
Poly(1,2,4-triazolo[4,3-c]quinazoline-5,3-diyl-2,6-pyridinediyl-1,2,4-triazolo[4,3-c]quinazoline-3,5-diyl-2,6-pyridinediyl)	H_2SO_4	283(4.98),355(4.25)	116-0485-73
$C_{28}H_{15}Cl_2NS_2$			
5H-Bisdibenzo[2,3:6,7]thiepino[4,5-b:4',5'-d]pyrrole, 3,7-dichloro-	MeOH	274(4.53),333(4.31)	73-0115-73
$C_{28}H_{16}CrO_6$			
Chromium, pentacarbonyl(3,4,6-triphenyl-2H-pyran-2-ylidene)-, (OC-6-21)-	hexane	247(4.63),323(4.33), 380(3.91),578(3.80)	39-2535-73C
$C_{28}H_{16}F_4O_2$			
9H-Xanthene, 9-[(2,7-difluoro-9H-xanthen-9-ylidene)methyl]-2,7-difluoro-9-methyl-	EtOH	240s(4.38),260s(4.01), 291(3.93),336(4.08)	44-0841-73
$C_{28}H_{16}MoO_6$			
Molybdenum, pentacarbonyl(3,4,6-triphenyl-2H-pyran-2-ylidene)-, (OC-6-21)-	hexane	249(4.72),321(4.28), 372(3.85),553(3.89)	39-2535-73C
$C_{28}H_{16}N_4O_4$			
Diazene, bis(10-nitro-9-anthracenyl)-	$CHCl_3$	248(4.98),290s(4.2), 390(3.68),480(3.76), 580s(3.59)	22-1305-73
$C_{28}H_{16}O_3$			
Anthra[2,3-c]furan-4,11-dione, 1,3-diphenyl-	$CHCl_3$	296(5.7),409(4.2)	22-1154-73
$C_{28}H_{16}O_5$			
Anthra[2,3-c]furan-5,10-dione, 6,9-dihydroxy-1,3-diphenyl-	CH_2Cl_2	287(4.7),519(4.0)	22-2856-73
$C_{28}H_{17}Cl_2N_3O_3$			
Methanone, [3-(2,4-dichlorophenyl)-1-(4-nitrophenyl)-5-phenyl-1H-pyrazol-4-yl]phenyl-	EtOH	236(5.52),290(5.28)	78-0121-73
$C_{28}H_{18}$			
1H-Phenalene, 1,1'-(1,2-ethanediylidene)bis-	THF	233(4.53),280(4.40), 332(3.84),365(3.48), 467(3.68),498(4.28), 536(4.78),581(5.12)	88-3405-73
$C_{28}H_{18}Br_2N_2S_2$			
1H-Indole, 2,2'-dithiobis[3-(4-bromophenyl)-	EtOH	222(4.66),261(4.44), 333(4.02)	94-2739-73
$C_{28}H_{18}ClN_3O_3$			
Methanone, [3-(4-chlorophenyl)-1-(4-nitrophenyl)-5-phenyl-1H-pyrazol-4-yl]phenyl-	EtOH	246(5.97),315(5.24)	78-0121-73

Compound	Solvent	$\lambda_{max}(\log \epsilon)$	Ref.
$C_{28}H_{18}Cl_2N_4O$			
Methanone, [1-(4-chlorophenyl)-4-[(4-chlorophenyl)azo]-5-phenyl-1H-pyrazol-3-yl]phenyl-, cis	EtOH	257(4.73),435(3.49)	138-0455-73
trans	EtOH	244(4.65),344(4.33)	
$C_{28}H_{18}Cl_2N_4O_2$			
Pyrazole, 3-benzoyl-1-(4-chlorophenyl)-4-(4-chlorophenylazoxy)-5-phenyl-, cis	EtOH	260(4.60),355(3.58)	138-0455-73
trans	EtOH	261(4.47),355(4.03)	138-0455-73
$C_{28}H_{18}N_2$			
Benzo[f]quinoline, 3-(4-phenyl-2-quinolinyl)-	n.s.g.	285(4.69),330(4.35), 365(4.07)	103-0220-73
Cu(I) complex	isoAmOH	540(3.97)	103-0220-73
Naphtho[2,3-g]phthalazine, 1,4-diphenyl-	$CHCl_3$	290(5.0),431(3.6), 456(3.8),485(3.7)	22-1154-73
$C_{28}H_{18}N_3P$			
Phosphonium, triphenyl-, 2-(tricyanoethenyl)-2,4-cyclopentadien-1-ylide	MeOH	223(4.55),267(4.02), 462(4.63)	44-3537-73
$C_{28}H_{18}N_4O$			
Benzo[f]quinoline-1-carboxamide, N-phenyl-3-(2-quinoxalinyl)-, Cu(I) complex	EtOH	405(4.53),552(3.84)	103-1391-73
2,4-Pyridinedicarbonitrile, 6-[3-hydroxy-2,7-dimethyl-5-(2-pyridinyl)-4-phenanthrenyl]-	MeCN	227(4.73),236s(4.71), 290(4.42),314s(4.33), 400s(3.49)	44-0407-73
$C_{28}H_{18}N_4O_5$			
Methanone, [3-(3-nitrophenyl)-1-(4-nitrophenyl)-5-phenyl-1H-pyrazol-4-yl]-phenyl-	EtOH	242(5.69),310(5.07)	78-0121-73
$(C_{28}H_{18}N_{10}O_2)_n$			
Poly(2,6-pyridinediyl-1H-1,2,4-triazole-3,5-diyl-1,2-phenyleneiminocarbonyl-2,6-pyridinediylcarbonylimino-1,2-phenylene-1H-1,2,4-triazole-3,5-diyl)	H_2SO_4	260(4.28),295(4.18)	116-0483-73
$C_{28}H_{18}O_6S_2$			
[2,2'-Bibenzo[b]thiophene]-3,3'(2H,2'H)-dione, 2,2'-diphenyl-, 1,1,1',1'-tetraoxide	MeOH	248(4.36)	39-1006-73C
$C_{28}H_{19}N_3O_2$			
Pyrazine, (4-nitrophenyl)triphenyl-	EtOH	226(4.47),261(4.43), 340(4.39)	33-1351-73
Pyrimidine, 2-(4-nitrophenyl)-4,5,6-triphenyl-	EtOH	245s(4.34),265(4.38), 276(4.39),303(4.39), 345s(3.79)	33-1351-73
$C_{28}H_{19}N_3O_3$			
Methanone, [1-(4-nitrophenyl)-3,5-diphenyl-1H-pyrazol-4-yl]phenyl-	EtOH	240(5.60),320(5.27)	78-0121-73

Compound	Solvent	$\lambda_{max}(\log \epsilon)$	Ref.
$C_{28}H_{20}$			
Dibenzo[c,l]chrysene, 3,11-dimethyl-	MeOH	200(4.66),213(4.87), 221(4.89),230s(4.51), 255(4.16),300s(4.74), 310(4.98),340(4.48), 385(2.70),404(2.56)	54-0553-73
9H-Fluorene, 2,2'-(1,2-ethenediyl)bis-	THF	349s(--),363(4.93), 382(4.71)	18-2822-73
9H-Fluorene, 2-methyl-9-(2-methyl-9H-fluoren-9-ylidene)-	benzene	462(4.36)	40-0762-73
Spiro[1H-phenalene-1,1'(2'H)-pyrene], 3',10'a-dihydro-	C_6H_{12}	235(4.84),327(4.36), 343(4.33),396(2.40), 420(2.21)	88-3405-73
Tetrabenzo[a,c,g,i]cyclododecene, (E,E)-	C_6H_{12}	226(4.51),248s(4.38), 266(4.53)	44-0808-73
	C_6H_{12}	225(4.75),266(4.91)	88-1265-73
(Z,Z)-	C_6H_{12}	240(4.50)	44-0808-73
$C_{28}H_{20}ClNO_2$			
Oxeto[2,3-b]indole, 7-(4-chlorobenzoyl)-2,2a,7,7a-tetrahydro-2,2-diphenyl-	n.s.g.	265(3.98)	77-0013B-73
$C_{28}H_{20}N_2$			
Pyrimidine, 2,4,5,6-tetraphenyl-	EtOH	258(4.50)	35-1954-73
$C_{28}H_{20}N_4NiO_2$			
Nickel, benzil-bis-benzoylhydrazone	$CHCl_3$	292(4.32),340(4.23), 358(4.25),392(4.30), 404(4.28),424(4.18)	78-2119-73
$C_{28}H_{20}N_4O_3$			
Spiro[2H-1-benzopyran-2,6'(5'H)-phenanthridine], 5'-methyl-6-(4-nitrophenylazo)-	EtOH	242(4.35),340(3.95), 397(4.09),540s(3.66)	103-1463-73
	dioxan	237(4.57),270s(4.36), 293s(4.20),342s(4.17), 405(4.40)	103-1463-73
$C_{28}H_{20}O$			
9,9'-Bianthryl, 9,9'-epoxy-9,9',10,10'-tetrahydro-	heptane	315(2.81)	3-1794-73
$C_{28}H_{20}O_2$			
9-Anthracenol, 1,8-diphenyl-, acetate	EtOH	213(4.49),261(5.12), 342s(3.52),359(3.81), 378(3.98),398(3.90)	44-1167-73
$C_{28}H_{20}O_2S_2$			
9,10-Anthracenedione, 1,8-bis[(4-methylphenyl)thio]-	C_6H_{12}	238(4.74),268(4.40), 303(4.11)	35-2565-73
$C_{28}H_{20}O_6$			
Dibenz[a,j]anthracene-2-carboxylic acid, 7,14-diacetoxy-, methyl ester	dioxan	212(4.48),236(4.65), 252(4.42),264s(4.48), 273(4.57),292(4.47), 303(4.74),316(4.88), 335s(4.22),351(4.20), 366(4.00),373(3.29), 407(2.91)	24-1341-73

Compound	Solvent	λ_{max}(log ε)	Ref.
$C_{28}H_{20}O_7$			
2,5-Cyclohexadiene-1,4-dione, 5-benzoyl-3-(5-benzoyl-4-hydroxy-2-methoxyphenyl)-2-methoxy-	MeOH	251(4.57),285(4.27), 331(4.01)	18-1498-73
$C_{28}H_{21}NO$			
Acetamide, N-(4,5-diphenyl-9-anthracenyl)-	EtOH	212(4.60),260(5.05), 362(3.84),381(4.02), 401(3.96)	44-1167-73
$C_{28}H_{21}NO_2S$			
Sulfilimine, N-(1-benzoyl-3-oxo-3-phenyl-1-propenyl)-S,S-diphenyl-	EtOH	248(4.13),358(3.96)	44-4324-73
$C_{28}H_{21}NO_4$			
N-Nororientaline, hydrobromide	EtOH	231(4.22),285(3.94)	39-0874-73C
	EtOH-NaOH	247(4.29),301(4.02)	39-0874-73C
$C_{28}H_{21}N_3$			
10bH-2a,6b,10c-Triazabenzo[2,3]pentaleno[1,6-ab]indene, 10-methyl-1,2-diphenyl-	EtOH	241(4.45),258(4.39), 280(4.26),377(3.58)	88-0597-73
$C_{28}H_{21}N_3O$			
Spiro[2H-1-benzopyran-2,6'(5'H)-phenanthridine], 5'-methyl-6-(phenylazo)-	EtOH	240(4.25),267s(4.04), 295s(3.88),365(4.06), 565(2.83)	103-1463-73
	dioxan	245(4.62),266(4.39), 345(4.31),367(4.33)	103-1463-73
$C_{28}H_{21}N_3O_2$			
1,3-Diazabicyclo[3.1.0]hex-3-ene, 2-(4-nitrophenyl)-4,5,6-triphenyl-	EtOH	248(4.35),262s(4.30)	33-1351-73
Pyrimidine, 1,4-dihydro-2-(4-nitrophenyl)-4,5,6-triphenyl-	dioxan	260(4.27),410(3.58)	33-1351-73
$C_{28}H_{22}$			
Anthracene, 9,10-bis(4-methylphenyl)-, radical cation	CH_2Cl_2-TFA	605(4.03),665(4.08)	39-1594-73B
[2.2](4,4')-Biphenylophane	C_6H_{12}	255(4.61),283s(3.95)	24-2190-73
$C_{28}H_{22}AsNO_4$			
Arsonium, triphenyl-, 1-(4-nitrobenzoyl)-2-oxopropylide	MeOH	215(4.48),267(4.38), 325s(3.70)	78-1697-73
$C_{28}H_{22}ClN_3O_7$			
Quinolinium, 1-(4-methoxyphenyl)-2-[[tetrahydro-4,6-dioxo-5-(phenylmethylene)-2(1H)-pyrimidinylidene]-methyl]-, perchlorate	EtOH	245(4.02),255(4.10), 302(3.57),387(3.76)	65-1340-73
Quinolinium, 1-phenyl-2-[[tetrahydro-5-[(4-methoxyphenyl)methylene]-4,6-dioxo-2(1H)-pyrimidinylidene]methyl]-, perchlorate	EtOH	230(4.56),260(4.69), 315(4.06),425(4.34)	65-1340-73
$C_{28}H_{22}ClN_3O_8$			
Quinolinium, 1-(4-hydroxyphenyl)-2-[[tetrahydro-3-[(4-methoxyphenyl)-methylene]-4,6-dioxo-2(1H)-pyrimidinylidene)methyl]-, perchlorate	EtOH	242(4.44),260(4.58), 314(3.98),425(4.26)	65-1340-73

Compound	Solvent	$\lambda_{max}(\log \epsilon)$	Ref.
$C_{28}H_{22}N_2$			
1,3-Diazabicyclo[3.1.0]hex-3-ene, 2,4,5,6-tetraphenyl-, endo	EtOH	238(4.26)	35-1954-73
2,5-Diaza-1,3,5-hexatriene, 1,3,4,6-tetraphenyl-	EtOH	250(4.32),377(4.32)	35-1954-73
$C_{28}H_{22}N_2O_2$			
Diazene, bis(2-[1,1'-biphenyl]-4-ylethenyl)-, 1,2-dioxide	benzene	365(4.5)	48-0796-73
$C_{28}H_{22}N_2O_4$			
3H-Pyrrolo[1,2-c]imidazole-6,7-dicarboxylic acid, 1,3,5-triphenyl-, dimethyl ester	EtOH	265(4.24),290(4.15), 378(4.18)	44-0284-73
$C_{28}H_{22}N_4NiO_2$			
Nickel, bis[benzoic acid (phenylmethylene)hydrazidato]-	$CHCl_3$	250(4.60),315(4.55), 325(4.38),341(4.31), 360(4.44),394(4.19), 402(4.18)	78-2119-73
$C_{28}H_{22}O$			
Benzeneacetaldehyde, α-(2,2-diphenylethenyl)-α-phenyl-	EtOH	252(4.16)	35-2155-73
Furan, 2,3-dihydro-2,3,4,5-tetraphenyl-, trans	EtOH	298(3.97)	35-5416-73
Furan, 2,5-dihydro-2,2,3,4-tetraphenyl-	$CHCl_3$	242(4.00),312(3.97)	44-1583-73
$C_{28}H_{22}O_2$			
Anthracene, 9,10-bis(4-methoxyphenyl)-, radical cation	CH_2Cl_2-TFA	623(4.08),676(4.18)	39-1594-73B
Benzeneacetic acid, α-(2,2-diphenylethenyl)-α-phenyl-	EtOH	253(4.22),293s(2.86)	35-2155-73
Cyclopropanecarboxylic acid, 2,2,3,3-tetraphenyl-	EtOH	223(4.33)	35-2155-73
2,5-Norbornadiene-2-carboxylic acid, 7-benzhydrylidene-3-phenyl-	EtOH	228(4.31),260(4.35)	24-1822-73
$C_{28}H_{22}O_2S$			
Dibenzo[b,f]thiepin-10(11H)-one, 8-(phenylmethoxy)-11-(phenylmethyl)-	MeOH	240(4.43),258s(4.04), 353(3.59)	73-1579-73
Methanone, [thiobis(methylene-4,1-phenylene)]bis[phenyl-	C_6H_{12}	282(4.34),284(4.23), 420(2.42)	39-1574-73C
$C_{28}H_{22}O_6$			
Methanone, (4,4'-dihydroxy-6,6'-dimethoxy[1,1'-biphenyl]-3,3'-diyl)bis-[phenyl-	MeOH	254(4.50),289(4.39), 345(4.10)	18-1498-73
$C_{28}H_{23}AsO_2$			
Arsonium, triphenyl-, 1-benzoyl-2-oxopropylide	MeOH	217(4.43),290(3.96), 325s(3.55)	78-1697-73
$C_{28}H_{23}BrNO_2P$			
2-Propenoic acid, 2-bromo-3-phenyl-3-[(triphenylphosphoranylidene)amino]-, methyl ester	EtOH	314(4.20)	39-0817-73C
$C_{28}H_{23}ClNO_2P$			
2-Propenoic acid, 2-chloro-3-phenyl-3-	EtOH	310(4.09)	39-0817-73C

Compound	Solvent	$\lambda_{max}(\log \epsilon)$	Ref.
[(triphenylphosphoranylidene)amino]-, methyl ester (cont.)			
$C_{28}H_{23}NO$			
Acetamide, N-(9,10-dihydro-4,5-diphenyl-9-anthracenyl)-	EtOH	235s(4.32),260s(3.90)	44-1167-73
$C_{28}H_{23}N_3O_3$			
Benzamide, N-[(2,3-diphenyl-2-aziridinyl)(4-nitrophenyl)methyl]-	EtOH	266(4.11)	33-1351-73
$C_{28}H_{24}$			
Naphthalene, 2,6-bis[2-(4-methylphenyl)-ethenyl]-, cis-cis	benzene	281(4.46),334(4.44)	54-0553-73
cis-trans	benzene	283(4.54),292(4.54), 350(4.69)	54-0553-73
trans-trans	xylene	293(4.49),364(4.84), 383(4.72)	54-0553-73
$C_{28}H_{24}AsNO_2$			
Arsonium, triphenyl-, 2-oxo-1-[(phenylamino)carbonyl]propylide	MeOH	223(4.48),244(4.35), 281(4.27)	78-1697-73
$C_{28}H_{24}N_2O_2$			
Benzo[f]quinoline-1-carboxylic acid, 3-(2-quinolinyl)-, isoamyl ester	n.s.g.	282(4.67),327(4.44), 370(3.97)	103-0220-73
Cu(I) complex	isoAmOH	542(3.89)	103-0220-73
Pyridinium, 2,2'-(1,2-ethanediyldi-4,1-phenylene)bis(2-oxoethylide)	EtOH	255(4.38),425(4.58)	65-1336-73
$C_{28}H_{24}N_2O_3$			
2(1H)-Pyridinone, 3,3'-(1-methyl-3-oxo-1-propene-1,3-diyl)bis[1-(phenylmethyl)-	EtOH	335(3.71)	103-0615-73
$C_{28}H_{24}N_2O_4$			
5,8-Ethenobenzo[3,4]cyclobuta[1,2-d]pyridazine-6,7-dicarboxylic acid, 4a,4b-5,8,8a,8b-hexahydro-1,4-diphenyl-, dimethyl ester	EtOH	322(4.01)	12-0389-73
3H-Pyrrolo[1,2-c]imidazole-6,7-dicarboxylic acid, 7,7a-dihydro-1,3,5-triphenyl-, dimethyl ester	EtOH	240(4.28)	44-0284-73
5H-Pyrrolo[1,2-c]imidazole-6,7-dicarboxylic acid, 6,7-dihydro-1,3,5-triphenyl-, dimethyl ester, (5R*,6R*,7S*)	EtOH	274(4.34)	44-0284-73
5H-Pyrrolo[1,2-c]imidazole-6,7-dicarboxylic acid, 6,7-dihydro-1,3,5-triphenyl-, dimethyl ester, (5R*,6S*,7S*)	EtOH	274(4.33)	44-0284-73
$C_{28}H_{24}N_2O_{12}$			
5H-Benzo[b]carbazole-5-carbonitrile, 1,2,3,4,7-pentaacetoxy-1,2,3,6,11-hexahydro-3-methyl-6,11-dioxo-(diacetylkinamycin C)	EtOH	260(3.94)	94-0931-73
$C_{28}H_{24}O$			
Benzeneethanol, α-(2,2-diphenylethenyl)-α-phenyl-	MeOH	251(4.26)	35-2155-73

Compound	Solvent	$\lambda_{max}(\log \epsilon)$	Ref.
$C_{28}H_{24}OSi$			
3-Buten-2-one, 4-phenyl-3-(triphenylsilyl)-	C_6H_{12}	257(4.20)	23-2024-73
$C_{28}H_{24}O_3$			
Naphtho[1,2-c]furan-1,3-dione, 3a,9b-dihydro-6,7,8,9-tetramethyl-4,5-diphenyl-	EtOH	240s(4.3),295(4.18)	5-1893-73
$C_{28}H_{24}O_6$			
Tetracyclo[4.3.0.0^{2,4}.0^{3,7}]non-8-ene-1,2,8-tricarboxylic acid, 5-(diphenylmethylene)-, trimethyl ester	EtOH	230(4.31),275(4.19)	24-1822-73
Tetracyclo[4.3.0.0^{2,4}.0^{3,7}]non-8-ene-2,8,9-tricarboxylic acid, 5-(diphenylmethylene)-, trimethyl ester	EtOH	231(4.29),276(4.18)	24-1822-73
Tricyclo[4.3.0.0^{2,9}]nona-3,7-diene-1,2,8-tricarboxylic acid, 5-(diphenylmethylene)-, trimethyl ester	EtOH	231s(4.18),289(4.26)	24-1837-73
Tricyclo[4.3.0.0^{2,9}]nona-3,7-diene-2,8,9-tricarboxylic acid, 5-(diphenylmethylene)-, trimethyl ester	EtOH	230s(4.21),295(4.26)	24-1837-73
$C_{28}H_{25}ClN_2O_7$			
2-Naphthacenecarboxamide, 4-(benzoylamino)-7-chloro-1,4,4a,5,5a,6,11,12a-octahydro-3,12-dihydroxy-10-methoxy-N-methyl-1,11-dioxo-	MeOH-borate	218(4.44),242s(4.25), 271(4.02),313(3.85), 441s(4.46),463(4.60), 490(4.49)	88-4907-73
$C_{28}H_{25}ClN_2O_8$			
2-Naphthacenecarboxamide, 4-(benzoylamino)-7-chloro-1,4,4a,5,5a,6,11,12a-octahydro-3,12,12a-trihydroxy-10-methoxy-N-methyl-1,11-dioxo-	MeOH-borate	226(4.42),268(4.23), 337(4.17)	88-4907-73
$C_{28}H_{25}INP$			
Phosphonium, [(1-methyl-1H-indol-2-yl)-methyl]triphenyl-, iodide	MeOH	274(4.10),281(4.09), 283s(4.03),284s(4.02)	23-0792-73
$C_{28}H_{25}IN_4O_5$			
Tubercidin, N^6,N^6-dibenzoyl-5'-deoxy-5'-iodo-2',3'-O-isopropylidene-	MeOH	223(4.32),280(4.08)	18-0618-73
$C_{28}H_{26}$			
1,1'-Biphenyl, 4,4"-(1,2-ethanediyl)-bis[4'-methyl-	C_6H_{12}	258(4.68)	24-2190-73
$C_{28}H_{26}I_2N_2O_2$			
Pyridinium, [1,2-ethanediylbis[4,1-phenylene(2-oxo-2,1-ethanediyl)]bis-, diiodide	EtOH	260(4.48),415(3.53)	65-1336-73
$C_{28}H_{26}N_2O_4$			
3H-Pyrrolo[1,2-c]imidazole-6,7-dicarboxylic acid, 5,6,7,7a-tetrahydro-1,3,5-triphenyl-, dimethyl ester, (3R,5R,6R,7R,7aS)-	EtOH	244(4.19)	44-0284-73
(3R,5R,6R,7S,7aS)-	EtOH	247(4.22)	44-0284-73
(3R,5R,6S,7R,7aS)-	EtOH	245(4.18)	44-0284-73
(3R,5R,6S,7S,7aS)-	EtOH	247(4.20)	44-0284-73

Compound	Solvent	λ max(log ε)	Ref.
3H-Pyrrolo[1,2-c]imidazole-6,7-dicarboxylic acid, 5,6,7,7a-tetrahydro-1,3,5-triphenyl-, dimethyl ester, (3R,5S,6R,7R,7aR)-	EtOH	247(4.21)	44-0284-73
(3R,5S,6S,7R,7aR)	EtOH	247(4.24)	44-0284-73
$C_{28}H_{26}N_4$			
1,2,3,4-Tetrazine, 1,4,5,6-tetrahydro-5,6-diphenyl-1,4-bis(phenylmethyl)-	$CHCl_3$	251(3.84),270s(3.84), 295(4.01)	138-0051-73
$C_{28}H_{26}N_4O_4$			
4H-1,3-Oxazin-6-acetamide, 4-oxo-N-(phenylmethyl)-2-[(phenylmethyl)-amino]-5-[[(phenylmethyl)amino]-carbonyl]-	EtOH	222(4.07)	39-2432-73C
2H-Pyran-3-carboxamide, 2-oxo-4,6-bis-[(phenylmethyl)amino]-N-[[(phenyl-methyl)amino]carbonyl]-	MeCN	252(4.11),312(4.22)	39-2432-73C
$C_{28}H_{26}N_4O_5$			
Tubercidin, N^6,N^6-dibenzoyl-5'-deoxy-2',3'-O-isopropylidene-	MeOH	223(4.53),280s(4.06)	18-0618-73
$C_{28}H_{26}N_6O_5$			
1H,13H-Bis[1,2,4]triazolo[1,2-a:1',2'-a']oxonino[4,3-c:7,8-c']dipyridazine-1,3,13,15(2H,14H)-tetrone, 5,7,9,11-16a,17,18,18a-octahydro-2,14-diphenyl-	MeCN	222(4.57)	78-2373-73
6H,13H-5,13:6,12-Diethano-5a,12a-(methanoxymethano)-1H,5H,8H,12H-[1,2,4]triazolo[1,2-a][1,2,4]triazolo[1',2':1,2]-pyridazino[4,5-d]pyridazine-1,3,8,10-(2H,9H)-tetrone, 2,9-diphenyl-	MeCN	227(4.41),257s(3.13)	78-2373-73
$C_{28}H_{27}F_9N_3$			
Methanaminium, N-[4-[bis[4-(dimethyl-amino)-2-(trifluoromethyl)phenyl]-methylene]-3-(trifluoromethyl)-2,5-cyclohexadiene-1-ylidene]-N-methyl-	98% HOAc	653(3.74)	39-1792-73B
$C_{28}H_{27}NO_{12}$			
Benzo[f]cyclopenta[a]quinolizine-6,7,7a,8,9,10-hexacarboxylic acid, 6,7-dihydro-, hexamethyl ester	MeOH	228s(4.20),319s(3.59), 363(3.99),381(4.12), 452s(3.90),477(4.00), 507(3.93),541s(3.62)	39-1338-73C
	MeOH-acid	247(4.40),263(4.22), 329(4.08),358(4.16)	39-1338-73C
geometric isomer (optical densities in parentheses)	MeOH	231(0.88),284(0.42), 306s(0.32),323(0.25), 349s(0.42),366(0.92), 382(1.26),426s(0.42), 456(0.77),480(0.99), 511(0.87),546s(0.40)	39-1338-73C
	MeOH-acid	252s(0.65),275(1.00), 363(0.89)	39-1338-73C
$C_{28}H_{27}N_5O_4$			
Pyrazolo[3,4-b]indole-8(1H)-acetic acid, 3-(ethoxycarbonyl)-3a,8a-dihydro-1-phenyl-α-(phenylhydrazono)-, ethyl ester, cis	EtOH	232(4.49),291s(4.14), 336(4.52)	78-3159-73

Compound	Solvent	$\lambda_{max}(\log \epsilon)$	Ref.
$C_{28}H_{27}N_7O_2S$			
2,4,7-Pteridinetriamine, 6-(methylsulfonyl)-N,N',N"-tris(phenylmethyl)-	4.5% HCOOH	278(4.30),374(4.22)	4-0133-73
$C_{28}H_{28}$			
Naphthalene, 1,2,3,4,6,7-hexamethyl-5,8-diphenyl-	EtOH	240(4.62),255(4.65), 321(4.04)	118-0783-73
$C_{28}H_{28}INO_4$			
Dibenzo[a,g]quinolizinium, 5,6-dihydro-2,3,10-trimethoxy-13-methyl-11-(phenylmethoxy)-, iodide	MeOH	263(4.48),287(4.60), 305s(4.49)	78-1265-73
Dibenzo[a,g]quinolizinium, 5,6-dihydro-2,3,11-trimethoxy-13-methyl-10-(phenylmethoxy)-, iodide	EtOH	263(4.24),287(4.40), 305s(4.30)	78-1265-73
Dibenzo[a,g]quinolizinium, 5,6-dihydro-2,10,11-trimethoxy-13-methyl-3-(phenylmethoxy)-, iodide	EtOH	264(4.45),287(4.65), 305s(4.54)	78-1265-73
$C_{28}H_{28}I_2N_4O_2$			
Pyridinium, 1,1'-[1,2-ethanediylbis[4,1-phenylene(2-oxo-2,1-ethanediyl)bis[2-amino-, diiodide	EtOH	250(4.73),315(4.19)	65-1336-73
$C_{28}H_{28}N_4$			
2-Tetrazene, 1,1,4,4-tetrakis(phenylmethyl)-	$CHCl_3$	253(3.89),269s(3.94), 290(4.03)	138-0051-73
$C_{28}H_{28}N_4O_5S$			
Benzenecarbothioic acid, S-[2-[[[4-(acetylbenzoyl)amino]-2-methyl-5-pyrimidinyl]methyl]formylamino]tetrahydro-2-methyl-3-furanyl] ester	EtOH	245(4.37),250(4.36)	94-0785-73
$C_{28}H_{28}N_4O_{10}$			
2,4(1H,3H)-Pteridinedione, 6,7-diphenyl-1,3-di-β-D-ribofuranosyl-	pH 5.0	220s(4.40),273(4.20), 361(4.15)	24-1401-73
$C_{28}H_{28}O_2$			
1,2-Naphthalenedimethanol, 5,6,7,8-tetramethyl-3,4-diphenyl-	CH_2Cl_2	238(4.49),263(4.12), 329(3.95)	5-1893-73
$C_{28}H_{28}O_8$			
Colletodiol dibenzoate	MeOH	229(4.56),274(3.31)	39-1487-73C
$C_{28}H_{28}O_9$			
4H-1-Benzopyran-4-one, 2-[3,4-dimethoxy-5-(phenylmethoxy)phenyl]-5,6,7,8-tetramethoxy-	MeOH	274(4.15),321(4.31)	2-0096-73
$C_{28}H_{28}O_{12}$			
Chromocyclin 8,10,12a-triacetate	EtOH	225(4.34),272(4.67), 305s(4.17),392(3.86)	105-0498-73
$C_{28}H_{29}ClO_6$			
1-Propanone, 3-(5-chloro-2,4-dimethoxyphenyl)-1-[(2,4-dimethoxy-3-oxo-3-phenylpropyl)phenyl]-	$CHCl_3$	242(4.33),270(4.15), 295(3.98),309(3.94)	2-1099-73

Compound	Solvent	λ_{max}(log ε)	Ref.
$C_{28}H_{29}NO_6$			
Benzoic acid, 2-[[benzoyl[2-(2-formyl-4,5-dimethoxyphenyl)ethyl]amino]-methyl]-, ethyl ester	MeOH	235(4.56),283(4.09), 315(3.84)	77-0740-73
$C_{28}H_{29}NO_{14}$			
Ethanone, 1-[2-hydroxy-4-[(2,3,4,6-tetra-O-acetyl-β-D-glucopyranosyl)-oxy]phenyl]-2-(4-nitrophenyl)-	EtOH	216(4.16),274(4.25), 310(3.91)	114-0435-73B
$C_{28}H_{30}BN$			
Boranamine, N-1-naphthalenyl-1,1-bis-(2,4,6-trimethylphenyl)-	C_6H_{12}	304(4.02)	101-0051-73H
$C_{28}H_{30}CuO_{10}$			
Copper, bis[dimethyl 2-[(3-methylphenyl)methyl]-3-oxobutanedioato-$O^{1'}$,O^3]-	EtOH	284.5(4.26)	44-0741-73
$C_{28}H_{30}N_4O_8S_2$			
Tubercidin, N^6,5'-O-di-p-toluenesulfonyl-2',3'-O-isopropylidene-	MeOH	223(4.55),291(4.29)	18-0618-73
$C_{28}H_{30}O_5$			
1H-Phenanthro[3,2-b]pyran-4-carboxylic acid, 2,3,4,4a,5,6,8,12b-octahydro-10-(4-methoxyphenyl)-4,12b-dimethyl-8-oxo-, methyl ester, [4S-(4α,4aβ,12α)]-	EtOH	225(3.98),262(3.77), 325(4.07)	12-1763-73
$C_{28}H_{30}O_6$			
2H-1-Benzopyran-2-one, 7,7'-[1,10-decanediylbis(oxy)]bis-	CH_2Cl_2	324(4.50)	44-0957-73
$C_{28}H_{30}O_{11}$			
Bruceantarin	EtOH	231(4.02),278(3.85)	44-0178-73
	EtOH-NaOH	230(3.96),330(3.65)	44-0178-73
Ethanone, 2-phenyl-1-[4-(2,3,4,6-tetra-O-acetyl-β-D-glucopyranosyl)oxy]-phenyl]-	EtOH	212(4.08),264(4.13)	114-0435-73B
$C_{28}H_{30}O_{12}$			
Ethanone, 1-[2-hydroxy-4-[(2,3,4,6-tetra-O-acetyl-β-D-glucopyranosyl)-oxy]phenyl]-2-phenyl-	EtOH	216(4.16),270(4.12), 320(3.80)	114-0435-73B
$C_{28}H_{31}NO$			
4,7-Methanoazulen-1(3aH)-one, 4,5,6,7-8,8a-hexahydro-2,3-diphenyl-8a-(1-piperidinyl)-	MeOH	226(4.21),297(4.01)	88-0949-73
Piperidine, 1-(3-bicyclo[2.2.2]oct-2-en-2-yl-1-oxo-2,3-diphenyl-2-propenyl)-	MeOH	231(4.27),290(4.09)	88-0949-73
Piperidine, 1-(3-bicyclo[3.2.1]oct-2-en-3-yl-1-oxo-2,3-diphenyl-2-propenyl)-	MeOH	228(4.28),283(4.01)	88-0949-73
$C_{28}H_{31}NO_6$			
4H-Dibenzo[de,g]quinoline, 9-(3,4-dimethoxyphenoxy)-5,6,6a,7-tetrahydro-1,2,10-trimethoxy-6-methyl-, hydrobromide	MeOH	280(4.25),300(4.18), 316s(4.04)	35-2995-73

Compound	Solvent	$\lambda_{max}(\log \epsilon)$	Ref.
$C_{28}H_{31}NO_{12}$			
Benzo[f]cyclopenta[a]quinolizine-6,7,7a,8,9,10-hexacarboxylic acid, 6,7,9,10,11,12-hexahydro-, hexamethyl ester	MeOH	271(4.17),282(4.20)	39-1338-73C
	MeOH-$HClO_4$	240s(3.79),271(3.87), 288(3.96)	39-1338-73C
$C_{28}H_{31}NiP$			
Nickel, (η^5-2,4-cyclopentadien-1-yl)-(2,2-dimethylpropyl)(triphenyl-phosphine)-	C_6H_{12}	305(3.84),424(2.90), 600(1.88)	23-1179-73
$C_{28}H_{32}BrNO_6$			
4H-Dibenzo[de,g]quinoline, 9-(3,4-di-methoxyphenoxy)-5,6,6a,7-tetrahydro-1,2,10-trimethoxy-6-methyl-, hydro-bromide	MeOH	280(4.25),300(4.18), 316s(4.04)	35-2995-73
$C_{28}H_{32}N_2O_3$			
4aH-Pyrano[3,2-c:5,6-c']dipyridin-4a-ol, 1,2,3,4,6,7,8,9,10,10a-decahydro-2,8-dimethyl-10-phenyl-6-(phenylmethyl-ene)-, acetate	EtOH	227s(4.04),235s(3.94), 287(4.49)	78-4039-73
$C_{28}H_{32}N_4O_{10}$			
Poly(L-tyrosyl-L-glutamyl-L-tyrosyl-L-glutamyl)	0.2M NaOH	243(4.00),294(3.34)	39-1001-73C
$C_{28}H_{32}O$			
Spiro[2.5]octa-4,7-dien-6-one, 5,7-bis-(1,1-dimethylethyl)-1,2-diphenyl-, trans	n.s.g.	280(4.31)	70-1998-73
$C_{28}H_{32}O_3$			
Colletodiol, tetrahydro-, dibenzoate	EtOH	229(4.29),273(3.01)	39-1487-73C
$C_{28}H_{32}O_5$			
1-Phenanthrenecarboxylic acid, 1,2,3,4-4a,9,10,10a-octahydro-6-hydroxy-7-[3-(4-methoxyphenyl)-1-oxo-2-prop-enyl]-1,4a-dimethyl-, methyl ester	EtOH	294(3.78),306(3.77), 365(4.21)	12-1763-73
$C_{28}H_{32}O_{11}$			
Satratoxin G	MeOH	256(3.81)	57-0758-73C
$C_{28}H_{32}O_{14}$			
Isoflavone, 7-(β-cellobiosyloxy)-4'-methoxy-	EtOH	261(4.47),306(3.98)	114-0191-73D
	dioxan	263(4.46),303s(3.84)	114-0365-73D
Linarin	EtOH	271(4.30),330(4.36)	95-0707-73
$C_{28}H_{32}O_{15}$			
Unranin	EtOH	287(4.36),335(4.43)	95-0707-73
$C_{28}H_{33}NO_{12}$			
Benzo[f]cyclopenta[a]quinolizine-6,7,7a,8,9,10(8H)-hexacarboxylic acid, 6,7,9,10,10a,10b,11,12-octahydro-, hexamethyl ester	MeOH and MeOH-acid	259(3.95),299(3.26)	39-1338-73C
$C_{28}H_{33}N_7O_5$			
Carbamic acid, [2-[[3-[6-(dimethylami-no)-9H-purin-9-yl]-2-hydroxypropyl]-	pH 1	270(4.29)	87-0037-73

Compound	Solvent	λ_{max}(log ε)	Ref.
amino]-1-[(4-methoxyphenyl)methyl]-2-oxoethyl]-, phenylmethyl ester (cont.)			
$C_{28}H_{34}ClN_4O_4$			
2H-Isoindole-2-propanaminium, N-(2-chloroethyl)-N-[2-[[3-(1,3-dihydro-1,3-dioxo-2H-isoindol-2-yl)propyl]methylamino]ethyl]-N-methyl-, chloride, hydrochloride	pH 1	300(3.68)	103-0383-73
$C_{28}H_{34}N_2$			
Pyrazine, 1,2-dicyclohexyl-1,2-dihydro-2,5-diphenyl-	n.s.g.	269(4.29)	39-0683-73C
$C_{28}H_{34}N_2O_6$			
Benzenamine, 4-(3,4-dimethoxyphenoxy)-5-methoxy-2-[(1,2,3,4-tetrahydro-6,7-dimethoxy-2-methyl-1-isoquinolinyl)methyl]-, (±)-	$CHCl_3$	238(4.32),291(4.04)	35-2995-73
$C_{28}H_{34}O_6$			
1H-Phenalene-1,3(2H)-dione, 4,5,6,7-tetramethoxy-9-methyl-2,2-bis(3-methyl-2-butenyl)-	EtOH	221(4.35),255(4.50), 350(3.95)	39-2388-73C
$C_{28}H_{34}O_8$			
Allocyathin B_3, O,O-diacetyl-, maleic anhydride adduct	dioxan	230s(3.72),319(2.04)	23-3842-73
Argentinogenin, di-O-acetyl-	EtOH	248(4.03),294(3.73)	33-2827-73
$C_{28}H_{35}ClO_8$			
Pregn-4-ene-3,20-dione, 7α,17α,19-triacetoxy-6β-chloro-16-methylene-	MeOH	235(4.18)	87-0649-73
$C_{28}H_{35}N_3O_2$			
1'H-Androst-4-eno[3,2-c]pyrazol-17-ol, 1'-(2-aminobenzoyl)-17-methyl-, (17β)-	n.s.g.	230(4.00),276(4.06)	65-0403-73
1'H-Androst-4-eno[3,2-c]pyrazol-17-ol, 1'-(4-aminobenzoyl)-17-methyl-, (17β)-	n.s.g.	234(4.15),280(4.26)	65-0403-73
$C_{28}H_{35}N_4O_5$			
2H-Isoindole-2-propanaminium, N-[2-[[3-(1,3-dihydro-1,3-dioxo-2H-isoindol-2-yl)propyl]methylamino]ethyl]-N-(2-hydroxyethyl)-N-methyl-, chloride, hydrochloride	pH 1	300(3.68)	103-0383-73
$C_{28}H_{35}O_3$			
Pyrylium, 4-methyl-2,6-bis[4-(pentyloxy)phenyl]-	CH_2Cl_2	238(4.2),284(4.2), 323(4.3),362(4.2), 475(4.63)	78-0795-73
$C_{28}H_{36}N_2O_2$			
1'H-Androstano[3,2-c]pyrazol-17-ol, 1'-phenyl-, acetate, (5α,17β)-	MeOH	212(4.43),270(4.63)	103-0202-73
$C_{28}H_{36}N_4$			
2H,21H-Porphine, 3,7,12,13,17,18-hexahydro-2,2,7,7,12,12,17,17-octamethyl-,	EtOH-CF_3COOH	295(4.66),321s(4.59), 332(4.62),346(4.59),	89-0914-73

Compound	Solvent	λ max (log ε)	Ref.
bromide, hydrobromide (cont.)		381s(3.84),404(3.65), 530(4.22)	89-0914-73
monoperchlorate mono(trifluoroacetate)	CF_3COOH	290s(4.15),308s(3.54), 321(4.88),340s(4.71), 353(4.96),376(4.57), 393(4.49),500(.00)	89-0914-73
$C_{28}H_{36}O_3$			
D:A-Friedo-24,30-dinoroleana-1(10),3,5-7-tetraene-2,21-dione, 3-hydroxy-, (20β)- (tingenone)	MeOH	252s(3.95),425(4.11)	39-2721-73C
	$CHCl_3$	250(3.98),262s(3.89), 345s(3.22),422(4.19)	39-2725-73C
Tingenin A	MeOH	253s(3.87),290s(3.34), 420(3.98)	35-6473-73
$C_{28}H_{36}O_4$			
Ergosta-2,5,8(14),24-tetraen-26-oic acid, 20,22-dihydroxy-1-oxo-, δ-lactone, (22R)-	EtOH	223(4.29)	78-1353-73
Ergosta-2,5,14,24-tetraen-26-oic acid, 20,22-dihydroxy-1-oxo-, δ-lactone	EtOH	220s(4.27)	78-1353-73
Tingenin B	MeOH	255s(3.83),287(3.11), 420(4.00)	35-6473-73
Tingenone, 20-hydroxy-	EtOH	256s(3.97),426(4.05)	39-2721-73C
$C_{28}H_{36}O_5$			
Ergosta-2,5,8(14),24-tetraen-26-oic acid, 17,20,22-trihydroxy-1-oxo-, δ-lactone (Withanolide J)	EtOH	224(4.26)	78-1353-73
Ergosta-2,5,14,24-tetraen-26-oic acid, 17,20,22-trihydroxy-1-oxo-, δ-lactone (Withanolide L)	EtOH	220s(4.27)	78-1353-73
Ergosta-3,5,8(14),24-tetraen-26-oic acid, 17,20,22-trihydroxy-1-oxo-, δ-lactone (Withanolide K)	EtOH	231(4.40)	78-1353-73
$C_{28}H_{36}O_6$			
Ergosta-2,24-dien-26-oic acid, 5,6:14,15-diepoxy-20,22-dihydroxy-1-oxo-, δ-lactone, (5α,6α,15α,22R)-	EtOH	226(4.26)	78-1353-73
(5β,6β,15α,22R)-	EtOH	226(4.27)	78-1353-73
Ergosta-2,5,24-trien-26-oic acid, 14,15-epoxy-17,20,22-trihydroxy-1-oxo-, δ-lactone, (15α,22R)-	EtOH	225(4.28)	78-1353-73
$C_{28}H_{36}O_7$			
5β-Bufa-20,22-dienolide, 3β,11α-diacetoxy-14,15β-epoxy-	EtOH	298(3.72)	39-0725-73C
$C_{28}H_{36}O_9$			
19-Norcarda-1,3,5(10),20(22)-tetraenolide, 3-(β-D-glucopyranosyloxy)-14β-hydroxy-	MeOH	203(4.66),218(4.42), 275(3.16)	5-0224-73
5β-Pregna-14,16-dien-20-one, 7α,11α,18-triacetoxy-3α,9α-epoxy-3β-methoxy-	n.s.g.	309(4.04)	33-0139-73
$C_{28}H_{36}O_{10}$			
5β-Pregn-16-en-20-one, 7α,11α,18-triacetoxy-3α,9α:14β,15β-diepoxy-3β-methoxy-	n.s.g.	244(3.89)	33-0139-73

Compound	Solvent	$\lambda_{max}(\log \epsilon)$	Ref.
$C_{28}H_{36}O_{11}$			
Bruceantin	EtOH	221(4.15),280(3.81)	44-0178-73
	EtOH-NaOH	221(4.19),328(3.63)	44-0178-73
$C_{28}H_{37}ClO_6$			
5β-Bufa-20,22-dienolide, 3β,15α-diacetoxy-14β-chloro-	MeOH	295(3.64)	94-0895-73
$C_{28}H_{37}NO$			
2,5-Cyclohexadien-1-one, 3-cyclohexyl-4-[(4-cyclohexyl-2,6-dimethylphenyl)imino]-2,6-dimethyl-	EtOH	220(4.24),278(4.16)	78-0085-73
$C_{28}H_{37}NO_9$			
Isoharringtonine	EtOH	241(3.56),290(3.62)	95-0916-73
$C_{28}H_{37}N_3O_2$			
1'H-Androstano[3,2-c]pyrazol-17-ol, 1'-(2-aminobenzoyl)-17-methyl-, (17β)-	n.s.g.	231(3.84)	65-0403-73
1'H-Androstano[3,2-c]pyrazol-17-ol, 1'-(4-aminobenzoyl)-17-methyl-, (17β)-	n.s.g.	225(4.35),297(4.05)	65-0403-73
$C_{28}H_{37}N_3O_3$			
Benzoic acid, 2-amino-, [(17β)-17-hydroxy-2-(hydroxymethylene)-17-methylandrost-4-en-3-ylidene]hydrazide	n.s.g.	229(3.90),264(4.01)	65-0403-73
Benzoic acid, 4-amino-, [(17β)-17-hydroxy-2-(hydroxymethylene)-17-methylandrost-4-en-3-ylidene]hydrazide	n.s.g.	226(4.09),275(4.10)	65-0403-73
$C_{28}H_{37}N_3O_4$			
1H-Pyrrole-3-propanoic acid, 2-[[2-[(4-ethyl-3,5-dimethyl-1H-pyrrol-2-yl)methylene]-4-(3-methoxy-3-oxopropyl)-3-methyl-2H-pyrrol-5-yl]methyl]-4-methyl-, methyl ester, hydrobromide	$CHCl_3$	496(4.86)	103-1059-73
$C_{28}H_{37}N_5O_{13}$			
Adenosine, 2',3',5'-tris-O-(2,4,4-trimethyl-5-oxo-1,3-dioxolan-2-yl)-	MeOH	259(4.17)	35-4025-73
$C_{28}H_{38}CuO_8$			
Copper, bis(ethyl 4,7,7-trimethyl-α,3-dioxobicyclo[2.2.1]heptane-2-acetato)-	benzene	331(4.38),672(1.77)	65-0927-73
	MeOH	262(3.98),329(4.30),675(1.81)	65-0927-73
	$CHCl_3$	269(4.23),333(4.40),670(1.76)	65-0927-73
	DMF	260(4.09),320(4.34),675(1.82)	65-0927-73
$C_{28}H_{38}N_2$			
Diazene, bis(4-cyclohexyl-2,6-dimethylphenyl)-	EtOH	220(4.24),278(4.16)	78-0085-73
$C_{28}H_{38}N_6O_5$			
6H,13H-5,13:6,12-Diethano-5a,12a-(methanoxymethano)-1H,5H,8H,12H-[1,2,4]triazolo[1,2-a][1,2,4]triazolo[1',2':1,2]pyridazino[4,5-d]pyridazine-1,3,8,10-(2H,9H)-tetrone, 2,9-dicyclohexyl-	MeCN	230(3.76),233(3.77)	78-2373-73

Compound	Solvent	$\lambda_{max}(\log \epsilon)$	Ref.
$C_{28}H_{38}O_4$			
Ergosta-5,14,24-trien-26-oic acid, 20,22-dihydroxy-1-oxo-, δ-lactone, (22R)-	EtOH	224s(4.00)	78-1353-73
$C_{28}H_{38}O_4S$			
Retinoic acid, 11,12-dihydro-11-(phenylsulfonyl)-, ethyl ester	EtOH	272(4.13)	22-0746-73
$C_{28}H_{38}O_6$			
Ergost-24-en-26-oic acid, 5,6:14,15-diepoxy-20,22-dihydroxy-1-oxo-, δ-lactone	EtOH	225(3.95)	78-1353-73
$C_{28}H_{38}O_9$			
Pregn-16-en-20-one, 7,11,18-triacetoxy-3,9-epoxy-3-methoxy-, (3α,5β,7α,11α)-	n.s.g.	235(3.93)	33-0139-73
$C_{28}H_{38}O_{10}$			
4a,7a-Epoxy-5H-cyclopenta[a]cyclopropa-[f]cycloundecen-4(1H)-one, 2,7,10,11-tetraacetoxy-1a,2,3,6,7,10,11,11a-octahydro-1,1,3,6,9-pentamethyl-	n.s.g.	198(4.13),227(3.47), 297(1.64)	88-3611-73
Pregn-16-en-20-one, 7,11,18-triacetoxy-3,9-epoxy-3-methoxy-, (3α,5β,7α,11α-14β)-	n.s.g.	236(3.99)	33-0139-73
$C_{28}H_{39}N_3O_3$			
Benzoic acid, 2-amino-, [(17β)-17-hydroxy-2-(hydroxymethylene)-17-methylandrostan-3-ylidene]hydrazide	n.s.g.	226(4.11),275(3.68)	65-0403-73
Benzoic acid, 4-amino-, [(17β)-17-hydroxy-2-(hydroxymethylene)-17-methylandrostan-3-ylidene]hydrazide	n.s.g.	229(4.09),273(3.92)	65-0403-73
$C_{28}H_{40}O_5$			
21-Norchola-5,22-dien-20-one, 3-acetoxy-16,17-[(1-methylethylidene)bis(oxy)]-, (3β,16α)-	EtOH	233(3.81),323(2.27)	70-1083-73
$C_{28}H_{40}O_7$			
Ergost-2-en-26-oic acid, 24,25-epoxy-5,6,22,27-tetrahydroxy-1-oxo-, δ-lactone, (5α,6β,22R,24S,25S)-	n.s.g.	225(3.82)	24-0576-73
$C_{28}H_{40}O_{10}$			
4a,7a-Epoxy-5H-cyclopenta[a]cyclopropa-[f]cycloundecene-2,4,7,10,11-pentol, 1,1a,2,3,4,6,7,10,11,11a-decahydro-1,1,3,6,9-pentamethyl-, 2,7,10,11-tetraacetate	n.s.g.	204(4.04)	88-3611-73
$C_{28}H_{42}O_8$			
7-Oxabicyclo[13.2.1]octadeca-10,12-diene-6,14-dione, 2,4-diacetoxy-8-ethyl-16-methoxy-3,9,11,15-tetramethyl-	EtOH	275(4.26)	138-0793-73
$C_{28}H_{43}BrO$			
A-Homocholesta-3,5-dien-2-one, 3-bromo-	EtOH	259(3.54)	73-0565-73

Compound	Solvent	λ max(log ε)	Ref.
$C_{28}H_{43}NO_4$			
4-Azaspirost-5-en-3-one, 4-(2-hydroxyethyl)-, (25R)-	MeOH	237(4.01)	2-1254-73
$C_{28}H_{44}O$			
5,7β-Cyclo-B-homo-5β-cholest-2-en-4-one	EtOH	222(3.92)	73-2760-73
5,7α-Cyclo-B-homo-5α-cholest-3-en-2-one	EtOH	265(3.97)	73-2760-73
5,7β-Cyclo-B-homo-5β-cholest-3-en-2-one	EtOH	267(3.83)	73-2760-73
Ergosta-5,7,24(28)-trien-3-ol, (3β)-	hexane	262(3.99),272(4.14), 282(3.93)	35-5747-73
A-Homocholesta-3,5-dien-2-one	EtOH	226(3.85)	73-0565-73
$C_{28}H_{44}OS_2$			
Cholest-2-eno[2,3-d][1,3]oxathiole-2'-thione	MeOH	238(3.36),275(3.47)	44-4211-73
$C_{28}H_{44}O_2$			
Cholesta-1,4-dien-3-one, 4-methoxy-	C_6H_{12}	234(4.01),270(3.82), 352s(2.01)	88-4637-73
Cholestan-3-one, 1,2-epoxy-4-methylene-, (1α,2α,5α)-	EtOH	234(3.75)	78-0353-73
(1β,2β,5α)-	EtOH	225(3.40)	78-0353-73
(1β,2β,5β)-	EtOH	240(3.65)	78-0353-73
1,5-Cyclocholest-3-en-2-one, 1-methoxy-	C H	242(3.65),285s(3.13)	88-4637-73
19-Norcholesta-1(10),5-dien-3-ol, acetate, (3β)-	EtOH	240(4.15)	77-0752-73
$C_{28}H_{44}O_3$			
19-Norcholest-5(10)-en-6-one, 3-acetoxy-, (3β)-	EtOH	247(3.63)	77-0752-73
$C_{28}H_{45}NO_3$			
19-Norcholest-5(10)-en-6-one, 3-acetoxy-, 6-oxime, (3β)-	EtOH	242(4.23)	77-0752-73
$C_{28}H_{46}O$			
5,7α-Cyclo-B-homo-5α-cholestan-4-one	EtOH	215(3.59)	73-2760-73
5,7β-Cyclo-B-homo-5β-cholestan-4-one	EtOH	212(3.19)	73-2760-73
B-Homocholest-5-en-7-one	EtOH	247(3.86)	73-0913-73
1,2-Seco-5α-cholest-2-yn-1-ol, 4-methylene-	EtOH	223(3.99),231s(--)	78-0353-73
$C_{28}H_{46}O_2$			
Cholest-5-en-4-one, 3 -methoxy-	EtOH	242(3.86)	78-0239-73
4'H-Cholest-2-eno[3,2-b]oxet-4-one, 2,3-dihydro-	C_6H_{12}	216(2.28),279(2.01)	88-4637-73
1,5-Cyclocholestan-2-one, 1-methoxy-	C_6H_{12}	227(3.54)	88-4637-73
$C_{28}H_{46}O_3$			
2,5-Cyclohexadiene-1,4-dione, 2-methoxy-6-methyl-3-(3,7,11,15-tetramethyl-2-hexadecenyl)-	EtOH	264(4.10)	65-2038-73
2-Propenoic acid, 3-(4-methoxyphenyl)-, octadecyl ester	EtOH	227(4.17),309(4.41)	39-1155-73C
$C_{28}H_{46}O_7$			
Makisterone A	EtOH	242(4.07)	12-1805-73
$C_{28}H_{46}O_8$			
Dacrysterone	EtOH	240(4.06)	12-1805-73

Compound	Solvent	$\lambda_{max}(\log \epsilon)$	Ref.
Glycosarcostin, 12β-O-cinnamoyl-20-O-acetyl-	MeOH	217(4.20),223(4.15), 278(4.36)	88-4735-73
$C_{28}H_{48}O_4Si$			
Prosta-5,11,13-trien-1-oic acid, 15-[[(1,1-dimethylethyl)dimethylsilyl]-oxy]-9-oxo-, methyl ester	MeOH	235(4.28)	35-8483-73
$C_{28}H_{49}NO_2$			
Docosanamide, N-hydroxy-N-phenyl-	EtOH	253(4.07)	112-0547-73

Compound	Solvent	$\lambda_{max}(\log \epsilon)$	Ref.
$(C_{29}H_{15}N_9)n$			
Poly(1,2,4-triazolo[4,3-c]quinazoline-3,5-diyl-2,6-pyridinediyl-1,2,4-triazolo[4,3-c]quinazoline-5,3-diyl-1,3-phenylene)	H_2SO_4	282(5.02),342(4.4), 362(4.46)	116-0483-73
Poly(1,2,4-triazolo[4,3-c]quinazoline-3,5-diyl-2,6-pyridinediyl-1,2,4-triazolo[4,3-c]quinazoline-5,3-diyl-1,4-phenylene)	H_2SO_4	290(4.96),355(4.85)	116-0483-73
Poly(1,2,4-triazolo[4,3-c]quinazoline-5,3-diyl-2,6-pyridinediyl-1,2,4-triazolo[4,3-c]quinazoline-3,5-diyl-1,3-phenylene)	H_2SO_4	275(4.46),340(4.12)	116-0483-73
Poly(1,2,4-triazolo[4,3-c]quinazoline-5,3-diyl-2,6-pyridinediyl-1,2,4-triazolo[4,3-c]quinazoline-3,5-diyl-1,4-phenylene)	H_2SO_4	270(4.84),340(4.38)	116-0483-73
$C_{29}H_{16}O_4$			
1,4-Naphthalenedione, 2-[2,3-dihydro-2-(1-naphthalenyl)-1,3-dioxo-1H-inden-2-yl]-	MeOH	220(4.83),245(4.54), 252s(4.50),287(4.11)	39-1006-73C
$C_{29}H_{18}BrN_5O_3S_2$			
Phenol, 2-[bis(naphtho[2,3-d]thiazol-2-ylamino)methyl]-4-bromo-6-nitro-	benzene	290(4.26),312(4.04), 335(3.88),349(3.91), 410(4.12)	80-1781-73
	CH_2Cl_2	255(4.89),264(4.85), 287(4.46),311(4.22), 333(4.10),348(4.13), 407(4.29)	80-1781-73
	ether	258(4.91),266(4.93), 288(4.54),313(4.30), 403(4.37)	80-1781-73
(also qualitative spectrum in EtOH)	MeCN	230(--),257(--), 264(--),290(--), 299(--),311(--), 332(--),344(--), 402(--)	80-1781-73
$C_{29}H_{18}Br_2N_2O_2$			
Pyrazole, 4,5-dibenzoyl-1-(2,4-dibromophenyl)-3-phenyl-	MeOH	242s(4.41),302(4.08)	44-1769-73
$C_{29}H_{18}Br_2N_4$			
1H-Pyrazolo[3,4-d]pyridazine, 1-(2,4-dibromophenyl)-3,4,7-triphenyl-	MeOH	224s(4.69),305(4.14)	44-1769-73
$C_{29}H_{18}N_2O_2$			
Benzo[f]quinoline-1-carboxylic acid, 3-(4-phenyl-2-quinolinyl)-	n.s.g.	281(4.81),330(4.37), 368(3.99)	103-0220-73
Cu(I) complex	isoAmOH	538(3.97)	103-0220-73
$C_{29}H_{18}O_2$			
4H-Phenanthro[9,10-b]pyran-4-one, 2,3-diphenyl-	$CHCl_3$	264(3.48),293(3.28), 337(2.70),352(2.48)	35-0463-73
$C_{29}H_{19}N_3O$			
Benzo[f]quinoline-1-carboxamide, N-phenyl-3-(2-quinolinyl)-	n.s.g.	280(4.75),327(4.45), 368(3.99)	103-0220-73

Compound	Solvent	$\lambda_{max}(\log \epsilon)$	Ref.
Benzo[f]quinoline-1-carboxamide, N-phenyl-3-(2-quinolinyl)-, Cu(I) complex	isoAmOH	538(3.92)	103-0220-73
$(C_{29}H_{19}N_9O_2)n$			
Poly(2,6-pyridinediyl-1H-1,2,4-triazolo-3,5-diyl-1,2-phenyleneiminocarbonyl-1,4-phenylenecarbonylimino-1,2-phenylene-1H-1,2,4-triazole-3,5-diyl)	H_2SO_4	290(4.47)	116-0483-73
isomer	H_2SO_4	275(4.76),352(4.4)	116-0483-73
isomer	H_2SO_4	282(4.95),346(4.27)	116-0483-73
isomer	H_2SO_4	275(5.11),355(4.66)	116-0483-73
$C_{29}H_{20}Cl_2N_8O$			
Urea, N,N'-bis[5-(4-chlorophenyl)-1-phenyl-1H-1,2,3-triazol-4-yl]-	EtOH	248(4.34)	42-0589-73
$C_{29}H_{20}O_3$			
2H-Naphtho[1,2-b]pyran-2-one, 3,4-dihydro-4-(4-hydroxy-1-naphthalenyl)-3-phenyl-	MeOH	239(4.7),296(4.1), 327(3.7)	88-4203-73
$C_{29}H_{21}BrO_3$			
3-Furancarboxylic acid, 4-bromo-2,5-dihydro-2,2,5,5-tetraphenyl-	EtOH	238s(4.09),258s(3.72), 264s(3.54),268s(3.38)	18-1733-73
$C_{29}H_{21}NO$			
1H-Pyrrole, 1-benzoyl-2,3,5-triphenyl-	EtOH	206(4.55),257(4.41), 273s(4.36)	1-0271-73
Pyrrole, 3-benzoyl-2,4,5-triphenyl-	EtOH	207(4.57),243(4.35), 283(4.32)	1-0271-73
$C_{29}H_{21}NO_2$			
Methanone, (5'-methylspiro[2H-1-benzopyran-2,6'(5'H)-phenanthridin]-6-yl)-phenyl-	EtOH	245(4.18),260s(4.12), 320(3.75),515(2.85)	103-1463-73
	dioxan	247(4.66),267s(4.56), 317(4.15)	103-1463-73
$C_{29}H_{22}Br_2N_2O$			
1,4-Pentadien-3-one, 1,5-bis[(4-bromophenyl)amino]-2,4-diphenyl-	EtOH	240s(4.35),300(4.43), 415(4.64)	4-0665-73
$C_{29}H_{22}Cl_2N_2O$			
1,4-Pentadien-3-one, 1,5-bis[(4-chlorophenyl)amino]-2,4-diphenyl-	EtOH	237s(4.19),300(4.33), 417(4.55)	4-0665-73
$C_{29}H_{22}INO_3$			
Benzo[f]quinolinium, 3-(1,3-benzodioxol-5-yl)-1-[2-(2-hydroxyphenyl)ethenyl]-4-methyl-, iodide	EtOH	369(4.45),413(4.40)	103-0633-73
Benzo[f]quinolinium, 3-(1,3-benzodioxol-5-yl)-1-[2-(4-hydroxyphenyl)ethenyl]-4-methyl-, iodide	EtOH	407(4.73)	103-0633-73
$C_{29}H_{22}INO_4$			
Benzo[f]quinolinium, 3-(1,3-benzodioxol-5-yl)-1-[2-(2,4-dihydroxyphenyl)ethenyl]-4-methyl-, iodide	EtOH	483(4.87),598(4.14)	103-0633-73
Benzo[f]quinolinium, 3-(1,3-benzodioxol-5-yl)-1-[2-(3,4-dihydroxyphenyl)ethenyl]-4-methyl-, iodide	EtOH	456(4.18),640(3.58)	103-0633-73

Compound	Solvent	λ max(log ε)	Ref.
$C_{29}H_{22}I_2N_2O$			
1,4-Pentadien-3-one, 1,5-bis[(4-iodophenyl)amino]-2,4-diphenyl-	EtOH	256(4.35),305(4.36), 420(4.56)	4-0665-73
$C_{29}H_{22}N_2O_2$			
5(4H)-Oxazolone, 4-(2,3-diphenyl-2-aziridinyl)-2,4-diphenyl-	EtOH	232(4.27),244(4.30)	33-1351-73
$C_{29}H_{22}N_4O_4$			
Spiro[2H-1-benzopyran-2,6'(5'H)-phenanthridine], 8-methoxy-5'-methyl-6-[(4-nitrophenyl)azo]-	EtOH	250(4.25),265s(4.20), 320(3.84),400(3.84), 510(4.06),590(4.07)	103-1463-73
	dioxan	268(4.47),420(4.37)	103-1463-73
$C_{29}H_{22}N_8O$			
Urea, N,N'-bis(1,5-diphenyl-1H-1,2,3-triazol-4-yl)-	EtOH	241(4.34)	42-0589-73
$C_{29}H_{22}O_7$			
4H-1-Benzopyran-4-one, 5,6-dihydroxy-2-[3-hydroxy-4-(phenylmethoxy)phenyl]-7-(phenylmethoxy)-	MeOH	245(3.82),283(4.17), 340(4.36)	24-0020-73
$C_{29}H_{23}N_3O_2$			
Spiro[2H-1-benzopyran-2,6'(5'H)-phenanthridine], 8-methoxy-5'-methyl-6-(phenylazo)-	EtOH	245(4.60),265s(4.53), 390(4.35),450s(4.11), 610(3.85)	103-1463-73
	dioxan	242(4.61),260s(4.47), 385(4.36)	103-1463-73
$C_{29}H_{23}N_3O_8S$			
1,2,4-Triazin-5(2H)-one, 3,4-dihydro-3-thioxo-2-(2,3,5-tri-O-benzoyl-β-D-ribofuranosyl)-	pH 13	228(4.7),271(4.4)	24-3039-73
	MeOH	205(4.4),228(4.7), 271(4.3)	24-3039-73
$C_{29}H_{24}$			
Bicyclo[2.1.0]pentane, 2,2,5,5-tetraphenyl-	hexane	263(3.03),273(2.88)	35-2957-73
Cyclopropane, 1,1-diphenyl-2-(2,2-diphenylethenyl)-	MeOH	268(4.28)	35-2957-73
1,4-Pentadiene, 1,1,5,5-tetraphenyl-	MeOH	263(4.41)	35-2957-73
$C_{29}H_{24}ClN_3O_8$			
Quinolinium, 6-methoxy-1-(4-methoxyphenyl)-2-[[tetrahydro-4,6-dioxo-5-(phenylmethylene)-2(1H)-pyrimidinylidene]methyl]-, perchlorate	EtOH	225(4.31),258(4.04), 310(3.81),398(4.07)	65-1340-73
Quinolinium, 1-(4-methoxyphenyl)-2-[[tetrahydro-5-[(4-methoxyphenyl)methylene]-4,6-dioxo-2(1H)-pyrimidinylidene]methyl]-, perchlorate	EtOH	222(4.32),260(4.27), 315(3.65),424(3.87)	65-1340-73
$C_{29}H_{24}IP$			
Phosphonium, (1-azulenylmethyl)triphenyl-, iodide	EtOH	237(4.34),280(4.59), 290(4.52),343(3.75), 355(3.68),359(3.74), 537(2.60),625(2.54), 680(2.11)	5-0166-73

Compound	Solvent	$\lambda_{max}(\log \epsilon)$	Ref.
$C_{29}H_{24}N_2$			
Indeno[1,2-b]azirine, 1-benzyl-6-(benzylimino)-1,1a,6,6a-tetrahydro-1a-phenyl-	isooctane	254(4.16)	44-0654-73
$C_{29}H_{24}N_2O$			
1-Naphthalenol, 4-[diphenyl(2-phenylhydrazino)methyl]-	n.s.g.	300(4.08),310(4.00)	114-0411-73D
2-Naphthalenol, 1-[diphenyl(2-phenylhydrazino)methyl]-	n.s.g.	285(3.73),327(3.29), 337(3.33)	114-0411-73D
1,4-Pentadien-3-one, 2,4-diphenyl-1,5-bis(phenylamino)-	EtOH	238(4.28),293(4.26), 308s(4.21),415(4.51)	4-0665-73
$C_{29}H_{24}O_2$			
3-Butenoic acid, 2,2,4,4-tetraphenyl-, methyl ester	EtOH	253(4.23),293s(2.87)	35-2155-73
$C_{29}H_{24}O_7$			
Methanone, [2-(acetoxymethyl)-1-naphthalenyl][7-(diacetoxymethyl)-1-naphthalenyl]-	dioxan	226(4.99),245s(4.42), 315(4.02)	24-1341-73
Methanone, [7-(acetoxymethyl)-1-naphthalenyl][2-(diacetoxymethyl)-1-naphthalenyl]-	dioxan	225(4.99),246s(4.37), 322(4.01)	24-1341-73
$C_{29}H_{24}O_8$			
1-Cyclohexene-1-carboxylic acid, 3,4,5-tris(benzoyloxy)-, methyl ester	isooctane	229(4.65),268s(3.48), 282(3.42)	35-7821-73
$C_{29}H_{25}AsO_3$			
Arsonium, triphenyl-, 1-benzoyl-2-ethoxy-2-oxoethylide	MeOH	221(4.50),272(4.11), 300(3.86)	78-1697-73
$C_{29}H_{25}BrNO_2P$			
2-Propenoic acid, 2-bromo-3-(4-methylphenyl)-3-[(triphenylphosphoranylidene)amino]-, methyl ester	EtOH	313(4.30)	39-0817-73C
2-Propenoic acid, 2-bromo-3-phenyl-3-[(triphenylphosphoranylidene)amino]-, ethyl ester	EtOH	313(4.28)	39-0817-73C
$C_{29}H_{25}ClNO_2P$			
2-Propenoic acid, 2-chloro-3-phenyl-3-[(triphenylphosphoranylidene)amino]-, ethyl ester	EtOH	309(4.30)	39-0817-73C
$C_{29}H_{25}NO_6S$			
7-Azabicyclo[2.2.1]hepta-2,5-diene-2,3-dicarboxylic acid, 7-[(4-methylphenyl)sulfonyl]-5,6-diphenyl-, dimethyl ester	EtOH	227(4.49),250s(4.29), 266s(4.16),283s(3.97), 353(3.23)	24-3824-73
1H-Azepine-4,5-dicarboxylic acid, 1-[(4-methylphenyl)sulfonyl]-3,6-diphenyl-, dimethyl ester	EtOH	240s(4.45),261s(4.32), 330s(3.26)	24-3824-73
Phthalic acid, 4-[(4-methylphenyl)sulfonamido]-3,6-diphenyl-, dimethyl ester	MeOH	243(4.54),260s(4.34), 275s(4.06),294s(2.48)	24-3824-73
$C_{29}H_{25}N_3O$			
[2,2'-Biquinoline]-4-carboxamide, N,N-diethyl-4'-phenyl-, Cu(I) complex	EtOH	550(3.98)	103-1391-73

Compound	Solvent	λ_{max}(log ϵ)	Ref.
$C_{29}H_{25}N_5O_5$			
2(1H)-Pteridinone, 6,7-diphenyl-4-(phenylamino)-1-β-D-ribofuranosyl-	MeOH	229(4.53),280(4.22), 385(4.27)	33-1225-73
$C_{29}H_{25}NiP$			
Nickel, (η^5-2,4-cyclopentadien-1-yl)-phenyl(triphenylphosphine)-	C_6H_{12}	305(4.01),408(3.08), 559(1.98)	23-1179-73
$C_{29}H_{26}N_2$			
1H-Carbazole, 9-(2,6-diphenyl-4-pyridinyl)-2,3,4,4a,9,9a-hexahydro-	MeOH	210(4.43),235(4.20), 327(3.09)	103-0321-73
$C_{29}H_{26}N_2O_6$			
Cycloprop[3,4]indeno[2,1-c]pyrazole-3a,3c,6c(3bH)-tricarboxylic acid, 1-(diphenylmethylene)-1,6,6a,6b-tetrahydro-, trimethyl ester	EtOH	233s(4.06),289(4.19), 320(2.18)	24-1837-73
$C_{29}H_{26}N_2O_7$			
6-Isoquinolinecarboxylic acid, 2-benzoyl-1-cyano-1,2-dihydro-5-hydroxy-1-[(3,4,5-trimethoxyphenyl)methyl]-, methyl ester	EtOH	239(4.46),260(4.44), 367(3.89)	78-0857-73
6-Isoquinolinecarboxylic acid, 2-benzoyl-1-cyano-1,2-dihydro-7-hydroxy-1-[(3,4,5-trimethoxyphenyl)methyl]-, methyl ester	EtOH	238(3.49),305(4.14)	78-0857-73
$C_{29}H_{27}ClN_2O_4S$			
3H-Indolium, 2-[3-(3,4-diphenyl-2(3H)-thiazolylidene)-1-propenyl]-1,3,3-trimethyl-, perchlorate	EtOH	542(5.03)	124-0913-73
	$CHCl_3$	543(5.00)	124-0913-73
3H-Indolium, 2-[3-(3,5-diphenyl-2(3H)-thiazolylidene)-1-propenyl]-1,3,3-trimethyl-, perchlorate	EtOH	562(5.10)	124-0913-73
	$CHCl_3$	568(5.06)	124-0913-73
$C_{29}H_{27}INOP$			
Phosphonium, [[3-(2-hydroxyethyl)-1H-indol-2-yl]methyl]-, iodide	MeOH	262s(3.56),268s(3.62), 276(3.63),285s(3.58), 294s(3.53)	23-0792-73
$C_{29}H_{27}N_3O_2S_2$			
Thiopyrano[4,3-b]indole-3,4-dicarboxamide, 4a,5-dihydro-4a-methyl-1-(methylthio)-N,N'-bis(phenylmethyl)-	EtOH	259(4.85),315(4.59)	94-2770-73
$C_{29}H_{27}N_3O_3$			
Propanoic acid, 3-[[2-(2,2-di-1H-indol-3-ylethyl)phenyl]amino]-3-oxo-, ethyl ester	EtOH	275(4.03),283(4.05), 292(4.00)	78-3761-73
$C_{29}H_{28}$			
Cyclopentadiene, 1-cyclohexyl-2,3,4-triphenyl-	EtOH	237(4.35),319(4.00)	78-4307-73
$C_{29}H_{28}IN_2P$			
Phosphonium, [4-(dimethylamino)phenyl]-(1H-indol-2-ylmethyl)diphenyl-, iodide	MeOH	297(4.48),304(4.47)	23-0792-73

Compound	Solvent	λmax(log ε)	Ref.
$C_{29}H_{28}N_2O_8S_2$			
1H-Indole-2-propanoic acid, α-acetyl-β-[[(4-methylphenyl)sulfonyl]imino]-3-[[(4-methylphenyl)sulfonyl]oxy]-	EtOH	342(4.25)	95-0971-73
$C_{29}H_{28}N_4O_7$			
2,4(1H,3H)-Pteridinedione, 1-[2-deoxy-3,5-bis-O-(4-methylbenzoyl)-D-ribofuranosyl]-6,7-dimethyl-	MeOH	238(4.66),325(3.97)	24-1401-73
2,4(1H,3H)-Pteridinedione, 3-[2-deoxy-3,5-bis-O-(4-methylbenzoyl)-D-ribofuranosyl]-6,7-dimethyl-	MeOH	239(4.62),330(3.97)	24-1401-73
$C_{29}H_{28}N_4O_8S$			
Tubercidin, N^6,N^6-dibenzoyl-2',3'-O-isopropylidene-5'-O-methanesulfonyl-	MeOH	222(4.52),240s(4.43),280s(4.05)	18-0618-73
$C_{29}H_{28}O$			
4,7-Methano-1H-inden-8-one, 1-cyclopentylidene-3a,4,7,7a-tetrahydro-4,7-dimethyl-5,6-diphenyl-	hexane	253(4.31)	44-3836-73
$C_{29}H_{28}O_2$			
1-Naphthalenecarboxylic acid, 5,6,7,8-tetramethyl-3,4-diphenyl-, ethyl ester	EtOH	232(4.42),263(4.72),332(3.99)	5-1893-73
2-Naphthalenecarboxylic acid, 5,6,7,8-tetramethyl-1,4-diphenyl-, ethyl ester	EtOH	237s(4.41),265(4.71),329(4.02)	118-0783-73
$C_{29}H_{28}O_{12}$			
4H-1-Benzopyran-4-one, 3-phenyl-7-[(2,3,4,6-tetra-O-acetyl-β-D-glucopyranosyl)oxy]-	EtOH	248(4.41),296(3.90)	114-0435-73B
	dioxan	250(4.48),294(3.89),303(3.91)	114-0365-73D
$C_{29}H_{29}NO_{12}$			
Benzo[f]cyclopenta[a]quinolizine-6,7,7a,8,9,10(8H)-hexacarboxylic acid, 6,7-dihydro-4-methyl-, hexamethyl ester	MeOH	266(3.97),327s(3.38),366(3.62),383(3.81),448s(3.76),472s(3.88),501(3.84),534(3.54)	39-1338-73C
	$MeOH-HClO_4$	258(4.06),275s(4.00),281(4.04),288(4.04),331s(3.68),368(3.86)	39-1338-73C
Cyclobut[4,5]azepino[1,2-a]quinoline-7,7a,8,9,9a,10-hexacarboxylic acid, 10,11-dihydro-1-methyl-, hexamethyl ester	MeOH	233(4.29),256s(4.14),356(3.84),404(3.85)	39-1338-73C
	$MeOH-HClO_4$	232(4.25),253(4.24),361(3.90),400(3.86)	39-1338-73C
isomer	MeOH	238(4.35),259(4.10),339(3.58),362(3.76),407(3.81)	39-1338-73C
	$MeOH-HClO_4$	228s(4.31),254(4.21),358(3.95),374(3.11),413(3.85)	39-1338-73C
$C_{29}H_{29}N_2O$			
Quinolinium, 3-acetyl-4-[2-[4-(dimethylamino)phenyl]ethenyl]-6-methyl-1-(4-methylphenyl)-, perchlorate	MeOH	546(3.40)	65-0877-73

Compound	Solvent	λ_{max}(log ε)	Ref.
$C_{29}H_{29}N_2O_3$			
Quinolinium, 3-acetyl-4-[2-[4-(dimethylamino)phenyl]ethenyl]-6-methoxy-1-(4-methoxyphenyl)-, perchlorate	MeOH	548(3.49)	65-0877-73
$C_{29}H_{30}N_4O_3$			
Pyrimido[1",2":1,2;3",4":1',2']dipyrido-[3,4-b:3',4'-b']diindole-6-butanoic acid, 5,5b,6,7,9,10,15,15b,17,18-decahydro-γ-oxo-, methyl ester	EtOH	225(4.85),275(4.23), 282(4.24),290(4.16)	22-2705-73
$C_{29}H_{30}O_8$			
9H-Xanthen-9-one, 1,3,7-triacetoxy-2,4-bis(3-methyl-2-butenyl)-	MeOH	266(4.28),308(4.42), 364(4.16)	2-1233-73
$C_{29}H_{31}BrO_8$			
Eupacunin 2-bromobenzoate	MeOH	284(3.00)	44-2189-73
$C_{29}H_{31}CoN_4$			
Cobalt, [1,2,3,7,8,12,13,17,18,19-decadehydro-8,12-diethyl-21,22-dihydro-2,3,7,13,17,18-hexamethylcorrinato-N^{21},N^{22},N^{23},N^{24}]-, (SP-4-3)-, hydrobromide	$CHCl_3$	356(4.83),403(4.40), 422(4.49),462s(3.72), 650(3.57)	39-2281-73C
$C_{29}H_{31}FeN_4$			
Iron, [1,2,3,7,8,12,13,17,18,19-decadehydro-8,12-diethyl-21,22-dihydro-2,3,7,13,17,18-hexamethylcorrinato-(3-)-N^{21},N^{22},N^{23},N^{24}]-, (SP-4-3)-	$CHCl_3$	380(4.88),505(4.15)	39-2281-73C
$C_{29}H_{31}NO_5$			
2H-Pyran, 3,6-dihydro-3-nitro-2,4,6-triphenyl-2,6-dipropoxy-	EtOH	248(4.10)	88-2195-73
$C_{29}H_{31}NO_7S$			
8H-Dibenzo[a,g]quinolizidinium, 13,14-didehydro-5,6-dihydro-1,9,10-trimethoxy-N-methyl-2,3-(methylenedioxy)-, p-toluenesulfonate	EtOH	220(4.56),244s(4.18), 343(4.36)	73-1614-73
$C_{29}H_{31}NO_{11}$			
Evonine, 1,2-dideacetoxy-10-(deacetoxymethyl)-1,2,9,10-tetradehydro-	EtOH	225(3.90),287(4.17)	78-1773-73
$C_{29}H_{31}NO_{12}$			
Evonine, O^9-deacetyl-1-deacetoxy-10-(deacetoxymethyl)-1,2,9,10-tetradehydro-	dioxan	325(4.31)	78-1795-73
$C_{29}H_{32}BN$			
Boranamine, N-methyl-N-1-naphthalenyl-1,1-bis(2,4,6-trimethylphenyl)-	C_6H_{12}	294(3.94)	101-0051-73H
$C_{29}H_{32}CuN_4O_4$			
Copper, [19-ethoxy-18,23-dihydro-2,2,7,8,12,13,18,18-octamethyl-21H-biline-1,3,17(2H)-trionato(2-)-N^{21},N^{22},N^{23},N^{24}]-	CH_2Cl_2	292(4.21),395(4.51), 666(4.06),732(4.43)	5-1067-73

Compound	Solvent	$\lambda_{max}(\log \epsilon)$	Ref.
$C_{29}H_{32}INO_4$			
6H-Dibenzo[a,g]quinolizinium, 5,8-dihydro-2,3,10-trimethoxy-7,13-dimethyl-11-(phenylmethoxy)-, iodide	EtOH	264(4.07),293s(4.12), 326(4.34)	78-1265-73
6H-Dibenzo[a,g]quinolizinium, 5,8-dihydro-2,3,11-trimethoxy-7,13-dimethyl-10-(phenylmethoxy)-, iodide	EtOH	264(4.04),292s(4.09), 327(4.35)	78-1265-73
6H-Dibenzo[a,g]quinolizinium, 5,8-dihydro-2,10,11-trimethoxy-7,13-dimethyl-3-(phenylmethoxy)-, iodide	EtOH	293s(4.13),327(4.39)	78-1265-73
$C_{29}H_{32}N_2O_9$			
Benzaldehyde, 4,5-dimethoxy-2-[2-methoxy-4-nitro-5-[(1,2,3,4-tetrahydro-6,7-dimethoxy-2-methyl-1-isoquinolinyl)methyl]phenoxy]-, (±)-	MeOH	279(4.16),327(3.99)	35-2995-73
$C_{29}H_{32}N_4O_4$			
21H-Biline-1,3,19(2H)-trione, 17-ethynyl-17,18,22,24-tetrahydro-17-hydroxy-2,2,7,8,12,13,18,18-octamethyl-	acetone	365(4.35),557s(4.21), 584(4.29)	5-1067-73
$C_{29}H_{32}O_2$			
1,5-Pentanedione, 1,5-bis(2,4,6-trimethylphenyl)-3-phenyl-	EtOH	250(3.77)	35-3310-73
$C_{29}H_{32}O_6$			
Benzeneacetic acid, α-methoxy-, 3-(6-carboxyhexyl)-4-oxo-2-(2-phenylethenyl)-2-cyclopenten-1-yl ester	MeOH	325(4.54)	35-2664-73
2H-1-Benzopyran-2-one, 7,7'-[1,11-undecenediylbis(oxy)]bis-	CH_2Cl_2	324(4.50)	44-0957-73
$C_{29}H_{32}O_8$			
Angustidienolide	MeOH	212(3.90),283(4.08)	39-1599-73C
Arugosin C, di-O-acetyl-	EtOH	223(4.07),256(3.76), 297(3.76),347(3.62)	39-1825-73C
$C_{29}H_{32}O_{13}$			
Ethanone, 1-[2-hydroxy-4-[(2,3,4,6-tetra-O-acetyl-β-D-glucopyranosyl)oxy]phenyl]-2-(4-methoxyphenyl)-	EtOH	224(4.16),270(4.14), 318(3.82)	114-0435-73B
$C_{29}H_{32}O_{15}$			
Aloearbonaside, pentaacetyl-	MeOH	225s(--),284(4.02)	94-0149-73
$C_{29}H_{33}BrO_8$			
Benzenemethanol, 2-[[2-[(2-bromo-4,5-dimethoxyphenyl)methyl]-4,5-dimethoxyphenyl]methyl]-4,5-dimethoxy-, acetate	n.s.g.	235(4.53),285(4.07)	39-0891-73C
$C_{29}H_{33}NO_{10}$			
Benzenemethanol, 2-[[2-[(4,5-dimethoxy-2-nitrophenyl)methyl]-4,5-dimethoxyphenyl]methyl]-4,5-dimethoxy-, acetate	n.s.g.	236(4.42),284(3.98), 343(3.75)	39-0891-73C

Compound	Solvent	λ_{max}(log ϵ)	Ref.
$C_{29}H_{33}N_3O_7S_2$			
1H-Indole-2-carboximidamide, N-(2,2-diethoxyethyl)-N'-[(4-methylphenyl)sulfonyl]-3-[[(4-methylphenyl)sulfonyl]-oxy]-	EtOH	220(4.91),310(4.59)	95-0971-73
$C_{29}H_{34}O_4$			
1,3,5-Cyclohexanetrione, 6-benzoyl-2,2,4,4-tetra-2-butenyl-	EtOH-acid	254(4.05),284(4.12)	39-2013-73C
	EtOH-base	254(4.12),280(4.23)	39-2013-73C
$C_{29}H_{34}O_5$			
[1,1'-Biphenyl]-4-carboxylic acid, 3-(2-methoxy-2-oxoethyl)-2-(3-oxo-1-octen-yl)cyclopentyl ester	n.s.g.	274(4.38)	138-1073-73
9H-Xanthen-9-one, 1-hydroxy-3-methoxy-2,4-bis(3-methyl-2-butenyl)-7-[(3-methyl-2-butenyl)oxy]-	MeOH	264(4.62),310(4.32), 346(4.44),380(4.06)	2-1233-73
$C_{29}H_{34}O_8$			
Melioca-8,14-dienoic acid, 3β-acetoxy-1-oxo-, methyl ester	MeOH	212(3.95),285(4.26)	39-1599-73C
$C_{29}H_{35}NO$			
Androst-5-en-3β-ol, 17-(2-quinolinyl-methylene)-	n.s.g.	208(3.31),214(3.31)	19-0887-73
$C_{29}H_{35}NO_3$			
Protophomin	EtOH	207(4.15),245(4.12)	33-2387-73
$C_{29}H_{36}O$			
1H-Naphtho[1,8a-c]furan, 7-(3,3-diphen-yl-2-propenyl)octahydro-7,8-dimethyl-	n.s.g.	252(4.48)	78-2575-73
$C_{29}H_{36}O_9$			
Satratoxin H	MeOH	225(4.17),255(4.02)	57-0758-73C
$C_{29}H_{37}NO_2$			
1H-Cyclotridec[d]isoindole-1,17(2H)-dione, 3,3a,6,6a,9,10,11,12,13,14-deca-hydro-4,5,10-trimethyl-3-(phenylmeth-yl)- (proxiphomin)	EtOH	206(4.36),217(4.09), 243(4.03)	33-2387-73
[13]Cytochalasa-6,13,21-triene-1,23-dione, 16-methyl-10-phenyl-	EtOH	205(4.41),218(4.13), 239(4.04)	33-2387-73
$C_{29}H_{37}NO_4$			
[13]Cytochalasa-6(12),13,21-triene-1,23-dione, 7,20-dihydroxy-16-methyl-10-phenyl- (deoxaphomin)	MeOH	217(4.15),234(3.94)	33-0966-73
$C_{29}H_{37}N_3O_5$			
1H-Pyrrole-3-propanoic acid, 2-[[2-[(4-ethyl-3,5-dimethyl-1H-pyrrol-2-yl)-methylene]-4-(3-methoxy-3-oxopropyl)-3-methyl-2H-pyrrol-5-yl]methyl]-5-formyl-4-methyl-, methyl ester, hydrobromide	$CHCl_3$	492(5.04)	103-1059-73
$C_{29}H_{38}N_5NiO$			
Nickel(1+), (1,2,3,7,8,12,13,17,18,19-decahydro-1,2,2,7,7,12,12,17,17-nona-	EtOH	275(4.27),339(4.12), 399(3.52),492(4.01)	89-0914-73

Compound	Solvent	$\lambda_{max}(\log \epsilon)$	Ref.
methyl-19-oxo-21H-biline-1-carbonitrilato-N^{21},N^{22},N^{23},N^{24})-, perchlorate (cont.)			
$C_{29}H_{38}O_2$			
1H-Naphtho[1,8a-c]furan-7-propanol, decahydro-7,8-dimethyl-α,α-diphenyl-	n.s.g.	258(2.70)	78-2575-73
$C_{29}H_{39}ClN_4NiO_4$			
Nickel(1+), (2,3-didehydro-1,2,3,7,8-12,13,17,18,19-decamethylcorrinato-N^{21},N^{22},N^{23},N^{24})-, (SP-4-2-)-, perchlorate	n.s.g.	262(4.15),278(4.11), 315(3.82),426(4.02)	39-0991-73C
$C_{29}H_{39}NO_6$			
1H-Pyrrole-2-propanoic acid, 2,5-dihydro-3-hydroxy-4-(15-hydroxy-12,16-dimethyl-1-oxo-2,4,6,8,10,12-heptadecahexaenyl)-β,1-dimethyl-5-oxo-, methyl ester	EtOH	415.5(4.80)	88-3643-73
$C_{29}H_{39}NO_9$			
Homoharringtonine	EtOH	241(3.54),290(3.61)	95-0916-73
$C_{29}H_{40}O_3$			
30-Noroleana-9(11),13(18),20-triene-12,19-dione, 3β-hydroxy-	EtOH	250(4+),260(4+), 290(4+)	104-1696-73
	EtOH-KOH	261(4.08)	104-1696-73
$C_{29}H_{40}O_4$			
24-Nor-18β-olean-12-en-30,22β-olactone, 3,11-dioxo-	dioxan	245(4.03)	39-2076-73C
$C_{29}H_{40}O_9$			
Pregn-16-en-20-one, 7,11-diacetoxy-3,9-epoxy-3-methoxy-14,18-[(1-methylethylidene)bis(oxy)]-, (3α,5β,7α,11α,14β)-	n.s.g.	236(3.98)	33-0139-73
$C_{29}H_{42}O_2$			
30-Noroleana-11,13(18)-diene-3,21-dione	EtOH	242(4.3),250(4.4), 262(4.1)	104-1696-73
$C_{29}H_{42}O_4$			
1,3,5-Cyclohexanetrione, 2,2,4,4-tetrakis(3-methyl-2-butenyl)-6-propionyl-	EtOH-acid	233(4.02),283(4.08)	39-2013-73C
	EtOH-base	280(4.21)	39-2013-73C
$C_{29}H_{42}O_5$			
Stigmasta-5,24(28)-dien-29-oic acid, 3,22,23-trihydroxy-7-oxo-, δ-lactone, (3β,22R,23S)-	EtOH	230(4.22)	23-1223-73
$C_{29}H_{42}O_6$			
21-Norchol-4-ene-3,20-dione, 16,17:22,23-bis[(1-methylethylidene)bis(oxy)]-, (16α)-	EtOH	238(4.29)	70-1083-73
$C_{29}H_{43}BrO_7$			
Cholan-24-oic acid, 3α,7α-diacetoxy-11α-bromo-12-oxo-, methyl ester	EtOH	274(2.00)	44-2587-73
11β-	EtOH	310(2.04)	44-2587-73

Compound	Solvent	λ_{max}(log ϵ)	Ref.
$C_{29}H_{43}ClN_4NiO_4$			
Nickel(1+), (8,12-diethyl-15,16-dihydro-1,3,7,13,17,19-hexamethylcorrinato-N^{21},N^{22},N^{23},N^{24})-, (SP-4-3)-, perchlorate	n.s.g.	264(3.98),278s(3.95), 300(4.08),347(3.62), 386s(3.95),408(4.18)	39-0991-73C
$C_{29}H_{43}O_2$			
Pyrylium, 4-[3-[2,6-bis(1,1-dimethylethyl)-4H-pyran-4-ylidene]-1-propenyl]-2,6-bis(1,1-dimethylethyl)-, perchlorate, (E)-	MeOH	598(5.43)	78-0795-73
$C_{29}H_{44}O$			
1,10-Secocholesta-5,7,9,14-tetraen-2-one, 1,1-dimethyl-	EtOH	217(4.33),267(4.26)	88-0813-73
$C_{29}H_{44}O_2$			
Taondiol, 2-deoxy-9,11-dimethyl-	EtOH	194(3.49)	39-2637-73C
$C_{29}H_{44}O_4$			
24-Norolean-12-en-29-oic acid, 3-hydroxy-11-oxo-, (3β,4α,20β)-	dioxan	245(4.06)	39-2076-73C
Stigmasta-5,24(28)-dien-29-oic acid, 3,22,23-trihydroxy-, δ-lactone, (3β,22R,23S)-	EtOH	210(4.07)	23-1223-73
$C_{29}H_{44}O_6$			
20,23-Cyclo-5α,20ξ-cholanic acid, 3β-hydroxy-21-oxo-23-(ethoxycarbonyl)-, ethyl ester	C_6H_{12}	205(3.47)	23-3263-73
$C_{29}H_{45}FO_3$			
Cholest-4-en-6-one, 19-acetoxy-3β-fluoro-	EtOH	230(3.70)	22-1098-73
Cholest-5-en-7-one, 19-acetoxy-3β-fluoro-	EtOH	234(4.10)	22-1098-73
$C_{29}H_{45}NO_4$			
Veralosidinine	n.s.g.	248(2.44)	105-0472-73
$C_{29}H_{46}$			
29-Noroleana-11,13(18)-diene, (20β)-	EtOH	242(4.5),250(4.6), 260(4.4)	104-1696-73
$C_{29}H_{46}N_2O_4$			
1'H-Cholest-6-eno[6,7-b]azirin-3-ol, 5,6-epoxy-6,7-dihydro-1'-nitroso-, acetate	EtOH	225(3.80),292(3.83)	94-1287-73
$C_{29}H_{46}O$			
9,19-Cycloergost-4-en-3-one, 14-methyl-	EtOH	275(4.10)	78-0569-73
$C_{29}H_{46}O_3$			
Cholestane-3,6-dione, 5,7-epoxy-4,4-dimethyl-, (5α,7α)-	EtOH	294(1.86)	78-2297-73
Cholest-4-en-6-one, 3β-acetoxy-	EtOH	236(3.78)	39-0070-73C
B-Norcholest-5-ene-6-carboxaldehyde, 3β-acetoxy-	EtOH	253.5(4.02)	94-1287-73

Compound	Solvent	$\lambda_{max}(\log \epsilon)$	Ref.
$C_{29}H_{46}O_4$			
2-Propenoic acid, 3-(4-acetoxyphenyl)-, octadecyl ester	EtOH	221(4.14),284(4.33)	39-1155-73C
$C_{29}H_{47}BrO_4$			
Cholestan-6-one, 3-acetoxy-7-bromo-5-hydroxy-, (3β,5α,7α)-	EtOH	300(1.73)	78-2297-73
$C_{29}H_{47}NO_3$			
5(10→1βH)-abeo-5α-Cholestan-3-one, N-acetyl-5α,10α-iminooxy-	EtOH	236(3.66)	78-2683-73
$C_{29}H_{48}ClNO_3$			
5α-Cholestan-20-ol, 3β-acetoxy-22,26-(chloroepimino)-, (20R,22R,25R)-	EtOH	275(2.26)	48-0739-73
(20R,22R,25S)-	EtOH	278(2.67)	48-0739-73
(20R,22S,25R)-	EtOH	262(3.25)	48-0739-73
(20R,22S,25S)-	EtOH	295(2.54)	48-0739-73
$C_{29}H_{48}O$			
Stigmasterol	EtOH	206(3.70)	102-1755-73
$C_{29}H_{48}O_2$			
Cholest-4-en-3-one, 6β-ethoxy-	EtOH	237(4.15)	39-1848-73C
$C_{29}H_{49}NO_3$			
5(10→1βH)-abeo-5α-Cholestan-3-ol, N-acetyl-5α,10α-iminooxy-	EtOH	234(3.64)	78-2683-73
$C_{29}H_{51}NO_2$			
Docosanamide, N-hydroxy-N-(3-methylphenyl)-	EtOH	254(4.01)	112-0547-73
$C_{29}H_{51}NO_6$			
1H-Pyrrole-2-propanoic acid, 2,5-dihydro-3-hydroxy-4-(15-hydroxy-12,16-dimethyl-1-oxoheptadecyl)- ,1-dimethyl-5-oxo-, methyl ester	EtOH	245(4.09),285(4.14)	88-3643-73
$C_{29}H_{60}Si_4$			
Silane, 3,4-pentadien-1-yne-1,3-diyl-5-ylidenetetrakis[(1,1-dimethylethyl)-dimethyl-	EtOH	264(4.23)	35-3324-73

Compound	Solvent	λ_{max}(log ϵ)	Ref.
$C_{30}H_{14}Cl_2O_3$			
Naphtho[2,1,8-qra]naphthacene-7,12-dione, 1,3-dichloro-6-phenoxy-	C_6H_5Cl	482(4.0)	104-2405-73
after irradiation	C_6H_5Cl	482(3.7),606(4.0), 662(4.2)	104-2405-73
$C_{30}H_{16}Br_2Cl_2O_2$			
Naphtho[2,3-c]furan-1(3H)-one, 7-bromo-9-(4-bromophenyl)-3,3-bis(4-chlorophenyl)-	n.s.g.	225(4.81),255(4.93), 292(4.07),358(3.68)	115-0145-73A
$(C_{30}H_{16}N_8)n$			
Poly(1,2,4-triazolo[4,3-c]quinazoline-3,5-diyl-1,3-phenylene-1,2,4-triazolo-[4,3-c]quinazoline-5,3-diyl-1,4-phenylene)	H_2SO_4	293(5.04),345(4.56)	116-0483-73
Poly(1,2,4-triazolo[4,3-c]quinazoline-3,5-diyl-1,4-phenylene-1,2,4-triazolo-[4,3-c]quinazoline-5,3-diyl-1,4-phenylene)	H_2SO_4	296(5.48),355(4.76)	116-0483-73
isomer	H_2SO_4	277(4.75),353(4.28)	116-0483-73
isomer	H_2SO_4	277(5.0),354(4.4)	116-0483-73
$C_{30}H_{16}O_4$			
9,10-Anthracenedione, 1,1'-(1,2-ethenediyl)bis-	H_2SO_4	267(4.86),308(4.42), 410(4.29),486(3.76)	39-0850-73C
9,10-Anthracenedione, 2,2'-(1,2-ethenediyl)bis-	H_2SO_4	256(4.51),328(4.51), 430(4.13),572(4.47)	39-0850-73C
$C_{30}H_{18}Br_2O_2$			
Naphtho[2,3-c]furan-1(3H)-one, 7-bromo-9-(4-bromophenyl)-3,3-diphenyl-	n.s.g.	254(4.98),292(4.12), 355(3.71)	115-0145-73A
$C_{30}H_{18}O_3$			
9-Anthracenecarboxylic acid anhydride	CH_2Cl_2	249s(5.03),255(5.05), 320s(3.36),335s(3.69), 352s(3.94),367(4.11), 387(4.10)	5-0844-73
$C_{30}H_{18}O_4$			
5,12-Naphthacenedione, 1,4-dihydroxy-6,11-diphenyl-	CH_2Cl_2	300(4.3),468(4.0)	22-2856-73
$C_{30}H_{19}N_3OS_2$			
4-Thiazolidinone, 3-methyl-5-(9-phenyldibenzo[a,c]phenazin-11(9H)-ylidene)-2-thioxo-	$CHCl_3$	700s(4.29),764(4.42)	103-1407-73
$C_{30}H_{20}$			
Phenanthrene, 2,2'-(1,2-ethenediyl)bis-	THF	277(4.80),285(4.91), 299(4.90),337s(--), 348(4.89),360s(--), 375s(--)	18-0909-73
Phenanthrene, 3,3'-(1,2-ethenediyl)bis-	THF	252(4.81),273(4.68), 279s(--),291s(--), 305(4.23),345s(--), 357(4.75),379(4.62)	18-0909-73
Phenanthrene, 9,9'-(1,2-ethenediyl)bis-	benzene	301(4.27),340(4.30)	18-0909-73

Compound	Solvent	λ_{max}(log ε)	Ref.
$C_{30}H_{20}F_4O_2$			
9H-Xanthene, 9-[1-(2,7-difluoro-9H-xanthen-9-ylidene)ethyl]-9-ethyl-2,7-difluoro-	EtOH	248(4.28),288(3.90), 307(4.09)	44-0841-73
$C_{30}H_{20}N_2O$			
Furo[2,3-d]pyridazine, tetraphenyl-	MeOH	222s(4.35),274(4.25), 310(4.27)	44-1769-73
$C_{30}H_{20}N_2O_2$			
Benz[a]anthracene-7,12-dione, 8,11-bis-(phenylamino)-	benzene	640(4.23),674(4.23)	40-1328-73
Phenanthro[4,3-c]pyrido[1,2-b][1,2]benzisoxazolium, 14-hydroxy-6,15-dimethyl-13-(2-pyridinyl)-, hydroxide, inner salt	MeCN	253(4.63),342(4.31), 372s(4.18),584(3.72)	4-0195-73
1H,5H-Pyrazolo[1,2-a]pyrazole-1,5-dione, 2,3,6,7-tetraphenyl-	n.s.g.	262(4.39)	39-0221-73C
$(C_{30}H_{20}N_8O_2)_n$			
Poly(1H-1,2,4-triazole-3,5-diyl-1,3-phenylene-1H-1,2,4-triazole-3,5-diyl-1,2-phenyleneiminocarbonyl-1,3-phenylenecarbonylimino-1,2-phenylene)	H_2SO_4	275(4.92),352(4.45)	116-0483-73
Poly(1H-1,2,4-triazole-3,5-diyl-1,4-phenylene-1H-1,2,4-triazole-3,5-diyl-1,2-phenyleneiminocarbonyl-1,4-phenylenecarbonylimino-1,2-phenylene)	H_2SO_4	282(4.96),370(4.41)	116-0483-73
isomer	H_2SO_4	236(4.35),294(4.48)	116-0483-73
isomer	H_2SO_4	248(4.45),296(4.67)	116-0483-73
$C_{30}H_{20}O_2S$			
Thiophene, 3,4-dibenzoyl-2,5-diphenyl-	MeOH	198(4.81),262(4.66)	35-2750-73
	dioxan	270(4.81)	35-2561-73
$C_{30}H_{20}O_3$			
Furan, 2,3-dibenzoyl-4,5-diphenyl-	MeOH	256(4.19),342(3.68)	44-1769-73
Naphtho[2,3-c]furan-1,3-dione, 3a,4-dihydro-4,4,9-triphenyl-	$CHCl_3$	315(4.09),340s(3.87)	18-1737-73
$C_{30}H_{20}S_2$			
Thieno[3,4-c]thiophene-5-S^{IV}, 1,3,4,6-tetraphenyl-	$C_2H_4Cl_2$	265(4.44),295(4.42), 553(4.04)	35-2561-73
	$CHCl_3$	258(4.30),262s(4.27), 292(4.15),551(3.92)	35-2750-73
$C_{30}H_{21}ClO_2$			
3-Cyclobutene-1,2-dione, 3-(chlorodiphenylmethyl)-4-(diphenylmethyl)-	EtOH	243s(3.76),259s(3.57), 266s(3.52),273s(3.46)	18-1733-73
$C_{30}H_{21}NO$			
Benzeneacetonitrile, α-(2,2,5-triphenyl-3(2H)-furanylidene)-	$CHCl_3$	257(4.07),380(4.19)	5-0375-73
$C_{30}H_{22}$			
9H-Fluorene, 2,2'-(1,3-butadiene-1,4-diyl)bis-	THF	364(4.86),380(4.99), 404(4.63)	18-2822-73
$C_{30}H_{22}Br_2N_2S_2$			
1H-Indole, 2,2'-dithiobis[3-(4-bromophenyl)-1-methyl-	EtOH	224(4.67),267(4.52), 355(4.07)	94-2739-73

Compound	Solvent	λ_{max}(log ε)	Ref.
$C_{30}H_{22}Br_2O_{10}$			
Rugulosin, dibromodehydrotetrahydro-, (+)-	dioxan	225(4.40),279s(4.03), 289(4.22),346(3.86)	78-3703-73
$C_{30}H_{22}INO_4$			
Benzo[f]quinolinium, 3-(1,3-benzodioxol-5-yl)-1-[2-(1,3-benzodioxol-5-yl)ethenyl]-4-methyl-, iodide	EtOH	429(5.71)	103-0633-73
$C_{30}H_{22}N_2$			
Benzene, 1,1',1"-[5-diazo-4-(phenylmethyl)-1,3-cyclopentadiene-1,2,3-triyl]-tris-	EtOH	241(4.36),325(4.01)	78-4307-73
Benzene, 1-(5-diazo-2,3,4-triphenyl-1,3-cyclopentadien-1-yl)-4-methyl-	CH_2Cl_2	251(4.64),335(4.58)	78-4307-73
$C_{30}H_{22}N_2O_2$			
Benzo[c]phenanthrene-2,11-diol, 3,10-dimethyl-1,12-di-2-pyridinyl-	n.s.g.	225(4.8),295(4.7), 360(4.0),395(3.9), 420(3.9)	4-0195-73
$C_{30}H_{22}OS_2$			
Bis(3-phenylthiochromen-2-yl) ether	EtOH	259(4.56),302(4.49), 335(4.07)	7-0527-73
	96% H_2SO_4	250(4.01),281(4.57), 310(3.36),432(3.56)	7-0527-73
Bis(4-phenylthiochromen-2-yl) ether	EtOH	234(4.70),270(3.97), 312(3.61)	7-0527-73
	96% H_2SO_4	264(4.41),338(3.80), 362(3.85),422(4.04)	7-0527-73
1H,3H-Thieno[3,4-c]thiophene, 1,3,4,6-tetraphenyl-, 2-oxide, cis	dioxan	230(4.30),320(4.21)	35-2561-73
$C_{30}H_{22}O_2$			
Ethanone, 1-phenyl-2-(2,2,5-trimethyl-3(2H)-furanylidene)-	$CHCl_3$	255(4.13),400(4.28)	5-0375-73
$C_{30}H_{22}O_3$			
3-Cyclobutene-1,2-dione, 3-(diphenylmethyl)-4-(hydroxyphenylmethyl)-	EtOH	258s(4.02),265s(3.95), 275s(3.85)	18-1733-73
$C_{30}H_{22}O_4$			
4-Furanol, 2,3-dibenzoyl-4,5-dihydro-4,5-diphenyl-	MeOH	255(4.19),305s(3.80)	44-1769-73
$C_{30}H_{22}O_5$			
2,5-Furandione, 3,4-bis(hydroxydiphenylmethyl)-	EtOH	212(4.39),255(3.83), 285s(3.54)	18-1733-73
$C_{30}H_{22}O_6$			
1H-Indene-1,3(2H)-dione, 2,2'-(1,4-phenylene)bis[2-(2-oxopropyl)-	EtOH	240(4.9),300s(3.7)	104-2400-73
$C_{30}H_{22}O_{10}$			
Rhusflavanone	MeOH	208(4.68),223(4.65), 294(4.49),336(3.80)	88-4747-73
	MeOH-NaOAc	257(4.38),271(4.42), 300(4.36),320(4.36)	88-4747-73
	MeOH-AlCl$_3$	224(4.76),256(4.25), 315(4.63),384(3.88)	88-4747-73

Compound	Solvent	λ max (log ε)	Ref.
$C_{30}H_{22}O_{11}$			
Deoxyrubroskyrin, (-)-	dioxan	280(4.89),369(4.00), 380(4.00),510(4.93), 531(3.92),570(3.63)	78-3703-73
$C_{30}H_{22}S_2$			
1H,3H-Thieno[3,4-c]thiophene, 1,3,4,6-tetraphenyl-, cis	dioxan	225(4.37),240s(4.21), 317(4.29)	35-2561-73
$C_{30}H_{23}Br$			
Benzene, 1,1',1"-[5-bromo-4-(phenylmethyl)-1,3-cyclopentadiene-1,2,3-triyl]tris-	EtOH	245(4.39),260s(4.34), 345(3.99)	78-4307-73
$C_{30}H_{23}N$			
1-Naphthalenamine, N-benzylidene-4-(diphenylmethyl)-	n.s.g.	295(4.00),350(4.00), 395(3.50)	114-0411-73D
$C_{30}H_{23}NO$			
4(1H)-Pyridinone, 1-methyl-2,3,5,6-tetraphenyl-	MeOH	236s(4.36),276(4.12)	77-0833-73
$C_{30}H_{23}NS$			
4(1H)-Pyridinethione, 1-methyl-2,3,5,6-tetraphenyl-	MeOH	238(4.18),272s(3.80), 360(4.18)	77-0833-73
$C_{30}H_{24}$			
Benzene, 1,1',1"-[4-(phenylmethyl)-1,3-cyclopentadiene-1,2,3-triyl]tris-	EtOH	239(4.41),320(4.00)	78-4307-73
10,13:14,17-Dietheno-1,20:4,7-dimethenobenzocycloeicosene, 8,9,18,19-tetrahydro-	C_6H_{12}	240s(4.46),258(4.85), 280s(4.23),295s(3.95)	24-2190-73
$C_{30}H_{24}INO_3$			
Benzo[f]quinolinium, 3-(1,3-benzodioxol-5-yl)-1-[2-(4-methoxyphenyl)ethenyl]-4-methyl-, iodide	EtOH	413(4.75)	103-0633-73
$C_{30}H_{24}INO_4$			
Benzo[f]quinolinium, 3-(1,3-benzodioxol-5-yl)-1-[2-(2-hydroxy-3-methoxyphenyl)ethenyl]-4-methyl-, iodide	EtOH	412(4.79),623(3.25)	103-0633-73
$C_{30}H_{24}N_2O$			
2-Propen-1-one, 1-[1,1'-biphenyl]-4-yl-3-(4,5-dihydro-1,5-diphenyl-1H-pyrazol-3-yl)-	C_6H_{12}	430(4.15)	104-0413-73
	EtOH	450(4.28)	104-0413-73
$C_{30}H_{24}N_2O_2S_2$			
1H-Indole, 2,2'-dithiobis[3-(4-methoxyphenyl)-	EtOH	226(4.65),255(4.54), 333(4.05)	94-2739-73
$C_{30}H_{24}N_2S$			
1H-Indole, 2,2'-thiobis[3-(phenylmethyl)-	EtOH	293(4.42),301(4.44)	94-2739-73
$C_{30}H_{24}N_2S_2$			
1H-Indole, 2,2'-dithiobis[1-methyl-3-phenyl-	EtOH	227(4.59),258(4.43), 283s(4.19),360(4.00)	94-2739-73
1H-Indole, 2,2'-dithiobis[3-(phenylmethyl)-	EtOH	299(4.09),340(4.13)	94-2739-73

Compound	Solvent	λ_{max}(log ϵ)	Ref.
$C_{30}H_{24}O_2$			
1,3-Dioxolane, 4-(9H-fluoren-9-ylidene)-2,5-bis(4-methylphenyl)-	EtOH	287s(4.31),299(4.33), 318(4.24),331(4.31)	23-1995-73
$C_{30}H_{24}O_4$			
Dehydrotectol	EtOH	271(4.53),340(3.09)	102-0942-73
$C_{30}H_{24}O_9$			
2,5-Cyclohexadiene-1,4-dione, 3-[4-hydroxy-2-methoxy-5-(4-methoxybenzoyl)-phenyl]-2-methoxy-5-(4-methoxybenzoyl)-	MeOH	244(4.49),292(4.54), 331(4.26)	18-1498-73
$C_{30}H_{24}O_{10}$			
Flavoskyrin, (-)-	dioxan	267(4.64),303(4.04), 312(4.04),328(3.92), 368(4.01),414(3.89), 433s(3.85)	78-3721-73
$C_{30}H_{24}O_{12}$			
Rubroskyrin, dihydro-, (-)-	EtOH	280(5.08),400(3.89), 510(3.80),534(3.78), 574(3.46)	78-3703-73
$C_{30}H_{24}S$			
2H-Thiopyran, 2,4,6-triphenyl-2-(phenylmethyl)-	n.s.g.	249(4.34),350(3.60)	104-2190-73
4H-Thiopyran, 2,4,6-triphenyl-4-(phenylmethyl)-	n.s.g.	236(4.45)	104-2190-73
$C_{30}H_{25}N_3O$			
Phenol, 2-[4,5-dihydro-5-(1-methyl-1H-indol-3-yl)-1,3-diphenyl-1H-pyrazol-5-yl]-	EtOH	212(4.64),252(4.59), 270(4.60)	103-0038-73
$C_{30}H_{25}OP$			
Phosphonium, triphenyl-, 2-(hydroxyphenylmethyl)-2,4-cyclopentadien-1-ylide	MeOH	267(3.6),315(3.4), 520(2.8)	44-3537-73
$C_{30}H_{26}$			
10,13:14,17-Dietheno-1,20:4,7-dimethenobenzocycloeicosene, 2,3,8,9,18,19-hexahydro-	C_6H_{12}	267(4.57),285s(4.09), 313s(3.54)	24-2190-73
$C_{30}H_{26}ClN_3O_9$			
Quinolinium, 6-methoxy-1-(4-methoxyphenyl)-2-[[tetrahydro-5-[(4-methoxyphenyl)methylene]-4,6-dioxo-2(1H)-pyrimidinylidene]methyl]-, perchlorate	EtOH	224(4.20),260(4.25), 335(3.82),430(3.89)	65-1340-73
$C_{30}H_{26}N_2$			
Pyrazine, 1,2-dihydro-2,5-diphenyl-1,2-bis(phenylmethyl)-	n.s.g.	251(4.14),392(2.45)	39-0683-73C
$C_{30}H_{26}N_2O_2$			
Azuleno[1,2-b]pyrazine-10-carboxylic acid, 8-(1-methylethyl)-2,3-diphenyl-, ethyl ester	MeOH	237(4.41),291(4.51), 364(4.72),410s(4.15), 430s(3.91),565(2.63), 620(2.55)	18-3161-73
Benzamide, N-benzoyl-N-[1-phenyl-1-[(1-phenylethylidene)amino]ethyl]-	EtOH	230(4.25),280(4.15), 292(4.09)	78-2119-73

Compound	Solvent	λ_{max}(log ϵ)	Ref.
[2,2'-Biquinoline]-4-carboxylic acid, 4'-phenyl-, pentyl ester, Cu(I) complex	EtOH	570(4.01)	103-1391-73
$C_{30}H_{26}N_2S_2$			
Bis[1]benzothieno[2,3-b:2',3'-f[[1,5]-diazocine, 1,2,3,4,8,9,10,11-octahydro-7,14-diphenyl-	MeOH	274(4.18)	88-2279-73
$C_{30}H_{26}N_4NiO_2$			
Nickel, bis[benzoic acid[(4-methylphenyl)methylene]hydrazidato]-	$CHCl_3$	251(4.58),315(4.58), 327(4.38),342(4.33), 358(4.32),395(4.23), 408(4.21)	78-2119-73
$C_{30}H_{26}N_4NiO_4$			
Nickel, bis[benzoic acid[(2-methoxyphenyl)methylene]hydrazidato]-	$CHCl_3$	250(4.51),310(4.38), 317(4.38),324(4.31), 340(4.34),355(4.36), 369(4.37),404(4.31), 411(4.31)	78-2119-73
Nickel, bis[benzoic acid[(4-methoxyphenyl)methylene]hydrazidato]-	$CHCl_3$	248(4.55),314(4.54), 320(4.57),325(4.43), 343(4.39),353(4.43), 398(4.45),412(4.43)	78-2119-73
$C_{30}H_{26}O_8$			
Methanone, (4,4'-dihydroxy-6,6'-dimethoxy[1,1'-biphenyl]-3,3'-diylbis[(4-methoxyphenyl)-	MeOH	226(4.48),260(4.54), 296(4.57),350(4.30)	18-1498-73
$C_{30}H_{26}Si_2$			
Silane, 1,4-phenylenebis[diphenyl-	heptane	278.8(1.84)	70-1825-73
$C_{30}H_{27}N_3O_5S_2$			
1H-Indole-2-carboximidamide, N-[(4-methylphenyl)sulfonyl]-3-[[(4-methylphenyl)sulfonyl]oxy]-N'-(phenylmethyl)-	EtOH	305(4.27)	95-0971-73
$C_{30}H_{27}N_3S$			
[1]Benzothieno[2,3-d]pyrimidine, 5,6,7-8-tetrahydro-4-phenyl-2-(4,5,6,7-tetrahydro-2-phenyl-1H-indol-3-yl)-	MeOH	239(4.45),272(4.38)	88-2279-73
$C_{30}H_{27}N_5O_9$			
Isoquinoline, 1-m-toluidino-3,4-dihydro-6,7-dimethoxy-3-phenyl-, picrate	EtOH	265(4.19),300(4.09)	106-0364-73
	EtOH-acid	285(4.18),323(4.10)	106-0364-73
$C_{30}H_{27}NiP$			
Nickel, (η^5-2,4-cyclopentadien-1-yl)-(phenylmethyl)(triphenylphosphine)-	C_6H_{12}	306(3.75),446(3.31), 629(1.93)	23-1179-73
$C_{30}H_{28}N_2$			
2-Biphenylamine, N-2-(2-biphenylaminomethylene)cyclohexylidene-	MeOH	212(3.40),225s(2.93), 376(1.40)	88-2821-73
	MeOH-$HClO_4$	212(3.27),234(2.25), 392(2.09)	88-2821-73
$C_{30}H_{28}N_6O_6S_4$			
Chetocin, 19,19'-dideoxy-6,6'-dihydroxy-(verticillin A)	dioxan	306(3.78)	39-1819-73C

Compound	Solvent	λ_{max}(log ε)	Ref.
$C_{30}H_{28}N_6O_7S_4$			
Verticillin B	dioxan	306(3.75)	39-1819-73C
$C_{30}H_{28}N_6O_7S_5$			
Verticillin C	dioxan	303(3.74)	39-1819-73C
$C_{30}H_{28}O_4$			
1,2-Naphthalenedicarboxylic acid, 5,6,7,8-tetramethyl-3,4-diphenyl-, dimethyl ester	EtOH	231(4.38),266(4.72), 340(3.78)	5-1893-73
2,3-Naphthalenedicarboxylic acid, 5,6,7,8-tetramethyl-1,4-diphenyl-, dimethyl ester	EtOH	238s(4.46),266(4.74), 331(3.95)	118-0783-73
1,5,18,22-Tetraoxa[5.0.5.0]paracyclophane	n.s.g.	263(4.04)	18-0263-73
$C_{30}H_{29}NO_{11}$			
1,2,3-Benzenetricarboxylic acid, 5-[(3-methoxy-1-(methoxycarbonyl)-3-oxo-1-propenyl]oxy]-4-(4,6,8-trimethyl-2-quinolinyl)-, trimethyl ester, (E)-	MeOH	233(4.65),267s(4.42), 317(4.07)	39-1338-73C
	MeOH-$HClO_4$	252(4.68),328(4.06)	39-1338-73C
$C_{30}H_{29}N_3O_5$			
Cytidine, N-acetyl-2'-deoxy-5'-O-(triphenylmethyl)-	EtOH	248(4.14),300(--)	39-0290-73C
$C_{30}H_{29}N_3O_6$			
Cytidine, 3'-O-(carboxymethyl)-2'-deoxy-5'-O-(triphenylmethyl)-	EtOH	271(3.94)	39-0290-73C
$C_{30}H_{30}$			
Benzene, 1,1'-(3,5,7,9-dodecatetraene-1,11-diyne-1,12-diyl)bis[2,4,6-trimethyl-, (all-E)-	benzene	410(5.00),434(4.83)	5-1339-73
(E,E,Z,Z)-	benzene	401(4.85),425s(4.63)	5-1339-73
$C_{30}H_{30}BN$			
Dibenz[c,e][1,2]azaborine, 5,6-dihydro-7,9,10-trimethyl-5-phenyl-6-(2,4,6-trimethylphenyl)-	C_6H_{12}	343(3.76)	101-0051-73H
$C_{30}H_{30}N_2O_4$			
13H,28H-8,12:23,27-Dinitrilo-7H,22H-dibenzo[c,p][1,6,14,19]tetraoxacyclohexacosin, 5,15,20,30-tetrahydro-	$CHCl_3$	265(3.94)	77-0831-73
$C_{30}H_{30}N_4$			
1H-Imidazo[1,2-a]imidazol-1-amine, 3,6-diphenyl-N-(phenylmethylene)-2,5-dipropyl-	EtOH	245(3.88),285(3.65), 345(3.89)	103-1082-73
$C_{30}H_{30}N_6O_5$			
Chetocin, 2,5:2',5'-bis[de(epidithio)]-5,6-didehydro-19,19'-dideoxy-6'-hydroxy-	EtOH	240(4.42),297(3.81)	39-1819-73C
$C_{30}H_{30}O_7$			
Isocycloheterophyllin	EtOH	292(4.43),385(4.32)	2-0298-73

Compound	Solvent	λmax(log ε)	Ref.
$C_{30}H_{30}O_{13}$			
4H-1-Benzopyran-4-one, 3-(4-methoxyphen-yl)-7-[(2,3,4,6-tetra-O-acetyl-β-D-glucopyranosyl)oxy]-	EtOH	260(4.43),300(3.88)	114-0435-73B
	dioxan	263(4.50),303s(3.86)	114-0365-73D
$C_{30}H_{31}NO_{11}$			
1,2,3-Benzenetricarboxylic acid, 5-[3-methoxy-1-(methoxycarbonyl)-3-oxopro-poxy]-4-(4,6,8-trimethyl-2-quinolin-yl)-, trimethyl ester	MeOH	241(4.16),265s(3.97), 320(3.67)	39-1338-73C
	MeOH-HClO4	252(4.31),328(4.06)	39-1338-73C
$C_{30}H_{31}NO_{12}$			
Benzo[f]cyclopenta[a]quinolizine-6,7,7a-8,9,10(8H)-hexacarboxylic acid, 6,7-dihydro-2,4-dimethyl-, hexamethyl ester	MeOH	240(4.19),285(3.83), 318(3.74),332(3.79), 368(4.14),384(4.33), 453s(4.11),479(4.31), 509(4.33),545(4.05)	39-1338-73C
	MeOH-HClO4	296(4.40),369s(4.24), 375(4.28)	39-1338-73C
isomer	MeOH	240(4.18),261(4.17), 360s(3.99),384(4.16), 451s(4.04),475(4.19), 506(4.18),540s(3.91)	39-1338-73C
	MeOH-HClO4	260(4.17),286s(4.30), 292(4.33),339s(3.85), 372(4.16)	39-1338-73C
$C_{30}H_{32}BN$			
Boranamine, N,N-diphenyl-1,1-bis(2,4,6-trimethylphenyl)-	C_6H_{12}	282(3.75)	101-0051-73H
$C_{30}H_{32}N_2O_5$			
D-Ribitol, 1,4-anhydro-1-C-(1,3-diphen-yl-2-imidazolidinyl)-2,3-O-(1-methyl-ethylidene)-, 5-benzoate, (S)-	MeOH	253(4.54),283(3.63), 292(3.64)	44-1836-73
$C_{30}H_{32}N_6O_5$			
Chetocin, 2,5:2',5'-bis[de(epidithio)-19,19'-dideoxy-6-hydroxy-	EtOH	243(4.10),302(3.72)	39-1819-73C
$C_{30}H_{32}N_6O_6$			
Tetradethioverticillin A	EtOH	243(4.05),303(3.66)	39-1819-73C
isomer	EtOH	243(4.07),302(3.71)	39-1819-73C
$C_{30}H_{32}O_2$			
Pentacyclo[6.2.2.0^{3,10}.0^{4,9}]dodecane-5,11-dione, 6,12-dibenzyl-1,4,6,12-tetramethyl-	dioxan	260f(2.7),303(2.4), 313(2.4)	5-1675-73
$C_{30}H_{32}O_7$			
4H-1-Benzopyran-4-one, 5,7-diacetoxy-3a-methoxy-6,8-bis(3-methyl-2-butenyl)-2-phenyl-	MeOH	257(3.8)	12-0641-73
$C_{30}H_{32}S_6Si_3$			
Silane, bis[5'-(dimethyl-2-thienylsil-yl)[2,2'-bithiophene]-5-yl]dimethyl-	$CHCl_3$	244(4.24),326(4.30)	88-4043-73
$C_{30}H_{33}NO_2$			
1(4H)-Pyridinecarboxylic acid, 3-[4-(2-	$CHCl_3$	300s(4.49),315(4.71),	89-0411-73

Compound	Solvent	λ max (log ε)	Ref.
ethynyl-1-cyclohexen-1-yl)-1,3-buta-dienyl]-5-[2-(2-ethynyl-1-cyclohexen-1-yl)ethenyl]-, ethyl ester (cont.)		328(4.76),390(4.28), 414s(4.00)	89-0411-73
$C_{30}H_{34}N_2O_{10}$			
Furazan, 3,4-bis[tetrahydro-2,2-dimeth-yl-6-(phenylmethoxy)furo[2,3-d]-1,3-dioxol-5-yl]-, 2-oxide, [3aR-(3aα,5α-6α,6aα)][3'aR-(3'aα,5'α,6'α,6'aα)]-	EtOH	260(3.58)	136-0311-73D
$C_{30}H_{34}N_5O_9P$			
9H-Purine-6-carbamic acid, 9-(2,3-iso-propylidene-5'-dibenzylphosphoryl-β-D-ribofuranosyl)-, ethyl ester	pH 1	276(4.22)	87-0956-73
	pH 13	292(4.36)	87-0956-73
	20% EtOH	268(4.23)	87-0956-73
$C_{30}H_{34}O_5$			
2H-1-Benzopyran-2,5,7(6H,8H)-trione, 4-hydroxy-6,8,8-tris(3-methyl-2-butenyl)-3-phenyl-	MeOH	254(4.20),304(4.44)	2-0106-73
$C_{30}H_{35}NO_{13}$			
8,9-Secoevonin-8-oic acid, 1,9-bis[de-(acetyloxy)]-10-de[(acetyloxy)methyl]-1,10-didehydro-9-oxo-, methyl ester	EtOH	223(3.89),265(3.49)	78-1773-73
$C_{30}H_{36}N_2$			
18-Norandrosta-2,13-diene-2-carboni-trile, 17,17-dimethyl-3-(2-methyl-1H-indol-3-yl)-	MeOH	224(4.50),282(3.90)	103-0205-73
$C_{30}H_{36}N_6$			
1,3,5-Triazine-2,4-diamine, 3,6-dihydro-N,N-bis(1-methylethyl)-N',3-bis(phen-ylmethyl)-6-[(phenylmethyl)imino]-	MeOH	251(4.43)	114-0419-73C
$C_{30}H_{36}O_5$			
4H-1-Benzopyran-4-one, 2-[3,4-dihydro-3-hydroxy-2,2-dimethyl-8-(3-methyl-2-butenyl)-2H-1-benzopyran-6-yl]-2,3-dihydro-7-hydroxy-8-(3-methyl-2-butenyl)-	EtOH	285(4.17)	94-1436-73
	EtOH-NaOH	345(4.46)	94-1436-73
4H-1-Benzopyran-4-one, 2-[2.3-dihydro-2-(1-hydroxy-1-methylethyl)-7-(3-methyl-2-butenyl)-5-benzofuranyl]-2,3-dihydro-7-hydroxy-8-(3-methyl-2-butenyl)-	EtOH	285(4.21)	94-1436-73
	EtOH-NaOH	346(4.46)	94-1436-73
$C_{30}H_{36}O_{11}$			
Kadsuranin	MeOH	231(4.48),255(4.03), 280(3.51)	88-4257-73
$C_{30}H_{38}$			
1,1'-Bicyclopropene, 1,1'-diphenyl-2,2',3,3'-tetrapropyl-	EtOH	240(3.97),273s(3.04), 280(2.88)	18-3881-73
$C_{30}H_{38}N_2$			
Pyrazine, 1,2-dicycloheptyl-1,2-dihydro-2,5-diphenyl-	n.s.g.	267(4.18)	39-0683-73C

Compound	Solvent	$\lambda_{max}(\log \epsilon)$	Ref.
$C_{30}H_{38}N_2O$			
Androst-2-ene-2-carbonitrile, 17-hydroxy-17-methyl-3-(2-methyl-1H-indol-3-yl)-, (17β)-	MeOH	224(4.73),283(4.13)	103-0205-73
$C_{30}H_{38}N_2O_{18}S_3$			
β-D-Glucopyranoside, 1,3,4-thiadiazole-2,5-diyl bis[1-thio-, 2,2',3,3',4,4'-6,6'-tetraacetate	n.s.g.	281(3.89)	48-0915-73
1,3,4-Thiadiazole-2(3H)-thione, 3-(2,3,4,6-tetra-O-acetyl-β-D-glucopyranosyl)-5-[(2,3,4,6-tetra-O-acetyl-β-D-glucopyranosyl)thio]-	n.s.g.	321(4.10)	48-0915-73
$C_{30}H_{38}O_4$			
[1,1'-Bi-1H-cyclopropa[b]naphthalene]-2,2',7,7'-tetrone, 1,1'-dibutyl-1a,1'a,2a,2'a,3,3',6,6',6a,6'a,7a,7'a-dodecahydro-	EtOH	240s(3.39),291s(2.89)	104-2389-73
Tingenone, mono-O-acetyl-	$CHCl_3$	245(2.95),267(2.74), 275(2.70)	39-2725-73C
$C_{30}H_{38}O_6$			
Ergosta-2,5,8(14),22-tetraen-26-oic acid, 20,22-dihydroxy-1-oxo-, δ-lactone, (22R)-	EtOH	220(4.24)	78-1353-73
1,13-Tetradecadiene-3,12-dione, 1,14-bis(3,5-dimethoxyphenyl)-, (E,E)-	EtOH	295(4.10)	12-0183-73
$C_{30}H_{39}Cl_2NO_{13}$			
2H-Pyran-2-one, 5-[[2,6-dideoxy-4-O-(3,5-dichloro-2,4-dimethoxy-6-methylbenzoyl)-3-O-(2,3,6-trideoxy-3-C-methyl-4-O-methyl-3-nitro-α-L-ribo-hexopyranosyl)-β-D-arabino-hexopyranosyl]-oxy]-5,6-dihydro-6-methyl-, (6S-trans)	n.s.g.	208(4.66),287(3.00)	35-0942-73
$C_{30}H_{40}N_2O_2S$			
Thiobinupharidine, 6-hydroxy-	EtOH-acid	209(4.35),292(3.51)	35-6342-73
$C_{30}H_{40}N_2O_8$			
De-N-methylgoldinamine methyl ester acetate	pH 1	237(4.55),290s(4.17), 331(4.60)	35-8449-73
	pH 7	237(4.52),290s(4.18), 335(4.60)	35-8449-73
	pH 13	237(4.52),290s(4.18), 335(4.60)	35-8449-73
$C_{30}H_{40}O_4$			
Pristimerin	n.s.g.	420(4)	102-0945-73
$C_{30}H_{40}O_5$			
Dispermoquinone	EtOH	318(4.28),328(4.26), 414(3.36)	78-2997-73
Olean-19-en-29-oic acid, 18-hydroxy-3,11,21-trioxo-, γ-lactone, (18α,20α)-	EtOH	235(3.4)	104-1696-73
$C_{30}H_{40}O_{12}$			
Filixic acid ABB	EtOH	224(4.43),299(4.28), 345(4.28)	102-2055-73
	EtOH-NaOH	241(4.37),314(4.33)	102-2055-73

Compound	Solvent	λ_{max}(log ε)	Ref.
Filixic acid PBP	EtOH	225(4.42),297(4.24), 345(4.12)	102-1493-73
	EtOH-NaOH	242(4.37),315(4.26)	102-1493-73
$C_{30}H_{41}Cl_2NO_{14}$			
D-ribo-Hexonic acid, O-2,3,6-trideoxy-3-C-methyl-4-O-methyl-3-nitro-α-L-ribohexopyranosyl-(1→3)-O-2,6-dideoxy-4-O-(3,5-dichloro-2,4-dimethoxy-6-methylbenzoyl)-β-D-arabinohexopyranosyl-(1→4)-2,6-dideoxy-, δ-lactone	n.s.g.	210(4.56),287(2.99)	35-0942-73
$C_{30}H_{41}NO_3$			
24-Nor-2,3-secooleana-3,12-dien-29-oic acid, 2-cyano-22-hydroxy-11-oxo-, γ-lactone, (20β,22β)-	dioxan	246(4.08)	39-2076-73C
$C_{30}H_{41}NO_4$			
24-Nor-2,3-secoolean-12-en-29-oic acid, 2-cyano-3,4-epoxy-22-hydroxy-11-oxo-, γ-lactone, (20β,22β)-	dioxan	246(4.06)	39-2076-73C
$C_{30}H_{42}BrNO$			
9-Phenanthrenemethanol, 6-bromo-α-[(diheptylamino)methyl]-, hydrochloride	$CHCl_3$	282(4.49),294(4.55), 327(3.49),343(3.42)	87-0940-73
$C_{30}H_{42}BrNO_4S$			
9-Phenanthrenemethanol, 6-bromo-α-[(diheptylamino)methyl]-, hydrogen sulfate	$CHCl_3$	282(4.49),294(4.55), 327(3.49),343(3.42)	87-0940-73
$C_{30}H_{42}N_2O_2S$			
Thiobinupharidine	EtOH	215s(4.11)	35-6342-73
	EtOH-acid	215s(4.11)	35-6342-73
Thionuphlutine B	EtOH	210s(4.48)	35-6342-73
	EtOH-acid	217s(4.18)	35-6342-73
$C_{30}H_{42}O_7$			
Δ^{16}-Dehydroadynerigenin D-diginoside	MeOH	267(4.23)	102-2737-73
Havanensin 3,7-diacetate	EtOH	212(3.58)	39-1047-73C
$C_{30}H_{42}O_8$			
Δ^{16}-Dehydroadynerigenin D-digitaloside	MeOH	267(4.16)	102-2737-73
$C_{30}H_{42}O_{10}$			
Kopeoside	n.s.g.	244(3.34),253(3.12), 327(4.12)	105-0294-73
$C_{30}H_{43}BrO_3$			
5α-Lanosta-8,24-diene-3,7,11-trione, 24-bromo-	EtOH	270(3.82)	39-1583-73C
$C_{30}H_{44}O_2$			
D:C-Friedooleana-5,8-diene-1,7-dione	EtOH	255(3.20)	78-3909-73
$C_{30}H_{44}O_4$			
1,3,5-Cyclohexanetrione, 2-butanoyl-4,4,6,6-tetrakis(3-methyl-2-butenyl)-	EtOH-acid	232(4.03),283(4.14)	39-2013-73C
	EtOH-base	280(4.24)	39-2013-73C
24-Norolean-12-en-29-oic acid, 3,11-dioxo-, methyl ester, (4α,20β)-	dioxan	246(4.11)	39-2076-73C

Compound	Solvent	$\lambda_{max}(\log \epsilon)$	Ref.
$C_{30}H_{44}O_6$			
A(1),30-Dinorolean-12-ene-3,20-dicarboxylic acid, 3-hydroxy-11-oxo-. (3β,20β)-	EtOH	250(4.03)	36-1557-73
$C_{30}H_{44}O_7$			
Adynerin	MeOH	217(4.08)	102-2737-73
2,3-Secoolean-12-ene-2,3,29-tricarboxylic acid, 11-oxo-	EtOH	249(4.10)	36-1557-73
$C_{30}H_{44}O_8$			
Bufa-4,20(22)-dienolide, 3-[(6-deoxy-α-L-mannopyranosyl)oxy]-14-hydroxy-, (3β)-	H_2O	196(4.28)	97-0013-73
Bufa-4,22-dienolide, 3-[(6-deoxy-α-L-mannopyranosyl)oxy]-14-hydroxy-, (3β,20ξ)-	EtOH	219(3.70)	97-0013-73
$C_{30}H_{45}BrO$			
5α-Lanosta-7,9(11),24-trien-3-one, 24-bromo-	EtOH	236(4.15),243(4.21), 252(4.09)	39-1583-73C
$C_{30}H_{45}BrO_3$			
5α-Lanosta-8,24-diene-7,11-dione, 24-bromo-3β-hydroxy-	EtOH	270(3.85)	39-1583-73C
$C_{30}H_{46}N_2S$			
Cholest-2-eno[2,3-b]thiophene-4-carbonitrile, 5-amino-	$CHCl_3$	242(3.74),290(3.73)	44-4211-73
$C_{30}H_{46}O$			
5α-Lanosta-7,9(11),24-trien-3-one	EtOH	236(4.22),243(4.28), 252(4.11)	39-1583-73C
$C_{30}H_{46}O_2$			
5α-Ergosta-7,22,24(28)-trien-3β-ol, acetate	EtOH	232(4.52)	35-5747-73
Ergosta-8,22,24(28)-trien-3β-ol, acetate	EtOH	230(4.45),240s(4.23)	35-5747-73
D:A-Friedoolean-1-en-3-one, 24,25-epoxy-	EtOH	235(3.82)	78-1365-73
Lup-20(29)-ene-3,11-dione	n.s.g.	290(2.04)	102-1125-73
$C_{30}H_{46}O_3$			
D:A-Friedooleanan-24-al, 1,3-dioxo-	EtOH	261(3.66)	78-1365-73
	70%EtOH-NaOH	290(4.30)	78-1365-73
D:A-Friedooleanane-1,3-dione, 24,25-epoxy-	EtOH	261(3.70)	78-1365-73
	70%EtOH-NaOH	290(4.32)	78-1365-73
$C_{30}H_{46}O_4$			
D:A-Friedooleanan-24-oic acid, 1,3-dioxo-	EtOH	261(3.49)	78-1365-73
	70%EtOH-NaOH	284(4.16)	78-1365-73
24-Norolean-12-en-29-oic acid, 3β-hydroxy-11-oxo-	dioxan	245(4.05)	39-2076-73C
$C_{30}H_{46}O_7$			
Jaligonic acid	EtOH	204(3.65)	100-0326-73

Compound	Solvent	λ max (log ε)	Ref.
$C_{30}H_{47}BrO$			
5α-Lanosta-7,9(11),24-trien-3β-ol, 24-bromo-	EtOH	236(4.11),243(4.20), 252(4.07)	39-1583-73C
$C_{30}H_{48}$			
D:B-Friedooleana-1,5(10)-diene	EtOH	274(3.89)	78-3909-73
D:B-Friedooleana-1(10),5-diene	EtOH	233(4.42),238(4.37), 248(4.30)	78-3909-73
A-Neo-18,20αH-ursa-3(5),6-diene	n.s.g.	246(4.28),255(4.42), 265(4.24)	7-0439-73
10-Nor-A:B-neo-18,20αH-ursa-5(10),9(11)-diene, 3β-methyl-	n.s.g.	233(4.27),237(4.37), 246(4.42),255(4.22)	7-0439-73
$C_{30}H_{48}O$			
Glut-5(10)-en-1-one	EtOH	218(3.87)	78-3909-73
5α-Lanosta-7,9(11),24-trien-3β-ol	EtOH	236(4.24),243(4.29), 252(4.13)	39-1583-73C
$C_{30}H_{48}O_2$			
D:A-Friedooleanane-1,3-dione	EtOH	261(3.63)	78-1365-73
	70%EtOH-NaOH	290(4.30)	78-1365-73
$C_{30}H_{48}O_3$			
D:A-Friedooleanane-1,3-dione, 24-hydroxy-	EtOH	261(3.56)	78-1365-73
	70%EtOH-NaOH	290(4.33)	78-1365-73
D:A-Friedooleane-1,3-dione, 7-hydroxy-, (7α)-	EtOH	261(3.56)	78-1365-73
	70%EtOH-NaOH	284(4.33)	78-1365-73
A-Homocholest-5-en-7-one, 4β-acetoxy-	EtOH	238(4.00)	73-2976-73
Oleana-11,13(18)-diene-3β,21α,29-triol	EtOH	242(4.41),250(4.5), 260(4.3)	104-1696-73
Oleanolic acid (astrantiagenin C)	MeOH	220(2.83)	106-0391-73
$C_{30}H_{48}O_4$			
Astrantiagenin E	MeOH	220(2.83)	106-0391-73
$C_{30}H_{50}O_3Si$			
Silane, (1,1-dimethylethyl)dimethyl-[(17β)-17-[(tetrahydro-2H-pyran-2-yl)oxy]androsta-2,4-dien-3-yl]oxy]-	ether	278(3.58)	77-0564-73
$C_{30}H_{54}I_2MoN_6$			
Molybdenum(1+), iodohexakis(2-isocyano-2-methylpropane)-, iodide	MeOH	218(4.62),240s(--), 275(4.34),406(2.61)	77-0202-73

Compound	Solvent	$\lambda_{max}(\log \epsilon)$	Ref.
$C_{31}H_{16}O_7$			
1,4-Naphthalenedione, 2-[2-[(1,4-dihydro-1,4-dioxo-2-naphthalenyl)acetyl]-2,3-dihydro-1,3-dioxo-1H-inden-2-yl]-	MeOH	224(4.81),243(4.80), 252s(4.66)	39-1006-73C
$C_{31}H_{18}N_2O_3$			
1H-Benz[de]isoquinoline-1,3(2H)-dione, 6-[5-(1-naphthalenyl)-2-oxazolyl]-2-phenyl-	toluene	305(4.30),405(4.50)	103-1204-73
1H-Benz[de]isoquinoline-1,3(2H)-dione, 6-[5-(2-naphthalenyl)-2-oxazolyl]-2-phenyl-	toluene	305(4.24),405(4.43)	103-1204-73
$C_{31}H_{19}Br_2N_3O_2$			
Acetic acid, cyano(3,6-dibromo-9-phenyldibenzo[a,c]phenazin-11(9H)-ylidene)-, ethyl ester	n.s.g.	640s(4.35),696(4.50), 756s(4.36)	103-1407-73
$C_{31}H_{20}$			
Benzo[m]hexahelicene, 4-methyl-	CH_2Cl_2	240(4.61),246s(4.59), 271(4.85),285s(4.61), 326(4.48),334(4.48), 350s(4.18),390s(3.21), 415s(2.95)	54-0651-73
Naphtho[1,2-a]naphtho[2,1-h]anthracene, 1-methyl-	CH_2Cl_2	228(4.61),249s(4.51), 258(4.46),266(4.44), 283s(4.29),293s(4.44), 305s(4.74),317(5.01), 330(5.03),350s(4.12), 362(4.09),380(4.05), 393(3.96),399s(3.88), 417(3.58)	54-0651-73
$C_{31}H_{21}NO$			
Pyrrolo[2,1-a]isoquinoline, 3-benzoyl-1,2-diphenyl-	EtOH	270(4.57),296(4.19), 336(3.94),398(4.23)	18-0667-73
Pyrrolo[1,2-a]quinoline, 1-benzoyl-2,3-diphenyl-	EtOH	266(4.59),292s(4.15), 332(3.92),380(4.11), 394(4.18)	18-0667-73
$C_{31}H_{21}N_3O$			
[2,2'-Biquinoline]-4-carboxamide, N,4'-diphenyl-, Cu(I) complex	EtOH	560(4.08)	103-1391-73
$C_{31}H_{21}N_3O_2$			
Acetic acid, cyano(9-phenyldibenzo[a,c]phenazin-11(9H)-ylidene)-, ethyl ester	n.s.g.	634s(4.4),690(4.57), 756s(4.47)	103-1407-73
$C_{31}H_{22}$			
Benzo[c]phenanthrene, 2-[2-(8-methyl-1-naphthalenyl)ethenyl]-, cis	MeOH	223(4.74),236(4.63), 257s(4.42),289(4.62), 310s(4.35),320s(4.28), 336s(4.13)	54-0651-73
trans	MeOH	205(4.98),221(4.77), 237(4.71),248s(4.62), 254s(4.54),260s(4.49), 289(4.65),309s(4.44), 322s(4.38),336s(4.27), 445(3.79)	54-0651-73

Compound	Solvent	λ_{max}(log ε)	Ref.
$C_{31}H_{22}ClN_3O_6$			
Benzo[f]quinolinium, 4-phenyl-3-[[tetrahydro-4,6-dioxo-5-(phenylmethylene)-2(1H)-pyrimidinylidene]methyl]-, perchlorate	EtOH	238(4.38),269(3.97), 290(4.02),320(3.87), 408(4.11)	65-1340-73
$C_{31}H_{22}O_4$			
5H-Cyclopenta-1,4-dioxin-5,7(1H)-dione, 2,3-dihydro-2,3,6,6-tetraphenyl-	EtOH	299(3.91)	95-0001-73
$C_{31}H_{23}BrN_2O_{11}$			
Benzoic acid, 4-bromo-, 1,2,4-triacetoxy-5-cyano-2,3,4,5,6,11-hexahydro-3-hydroxy-3-methyl-6,11-dioxo-1H-benzo[b]indazol-7-yl ester (kinamycin C p-bromobenzoate)	EtOH	249(4.04)	94-0931-73
$C_{31}H_{23}BrO_4$			
3-Furanacetic acid, 4-bromo-2,5-dihydro-α-oxo-2,2,5,5-tetraphenyl-, methyl ester	$CHCl_3$	266(3.90),275s(3.88)	18-1733-73
$C_{31}H_{23}NO_4$			
3H-Oxazolo[4,3-a]isoquinolin-3-one, 1-[3,4-bis(phenylmethoxy)phenyl]-	EtOH	243(4.36),258(4.18), 277(4.13),553(4.10)	44-2291-73
$C_{31}H_{24}$			
Benzene, 1,1',1"-[4-methyl-5-(phenylmethylene)-1,3-cyclopentadiene-1,2,3-triyl]tris-	EtOH	243s(4.27),270(4.34), 325(4.31)	78-4307-73
$C_{31}H_{24}Cl_2N_4O_3$			
2-Propenamide, N,N'-carbonylbis(imino-2,1-phenylene)]bis[3-(4-chlorophenyl)-	HOAc	310(4.66)	48-1152-73
$C_{31}H_{24}N_6O_7$			
2-Propenamide, N,N'-[carbonylbis(imino-2,1-phenylene)]bis[3-(2-nitrophenyl)-	HOAc	250(4.55)	48-1152-73
2-Propenamide, N,N'-[carbonylbis(imino-2,1-phenylene)]bis[3-(4-nitrophenyl)-	HOAc	336(4.55)	48-1152-73
$C_{31}H_{24}O$			
Bicyclo[2.2.0]hexa-2,5-diene, 1-methoxy-2,3,5,6-tetraphenyl-	$CHCl_3$	290(4.40)	89-0152-73
$C_{31}H_{24}O_3$			
3-Cyclobutene-1,2-dione, 3-(diphenylmethyl)-4-(methoxydiphenylmethyl)-	EtOH	259s(4.02),265s(3.96), 274s(3.89)	18-1733-73
$C_{31}H_{24}O_6$			
Phenanthro[4,5-def][1,3]dioxepin, 2,2'-[methylenebis(oxy)]bis[10,11-dihydro-	n.s.g.	275s(4.39),283(4.40), 293s(4.18),309(4.16)	39-1263-73C
$C_{31}H_{25}AsO_4S_2$			
Arsonium, triphenyl-, bis(phenylsulfonyl)methylide	MeOH	217(4.54),265(4.03), 285(3.77)	78-1697-73
$C_{31}H_{25}BF_4N_4OS_2$			
Benzothiazolium, 2-[[7-ethoxy-4-[(3-methyl-2(1H)-benzothiazolylidene)-	MeCN	302(4.42),327(4.42), 420(3.88),520(4.40),	44-2425-73

Compound	Solvent	$\lambda_{max}(\log \epsilon)$	Ref.
amino]-1H-phenalen-1-ylidene]amino]-3-methyl-, tetrafluoroborate (cont.)		625(4.78)	44-2425-73
$C_{31}H_{25}N_3O_{11}$			
1H-Imidazole-5-carboxylic acid, 4-nitro-1-(2,3,5-tri-O-benzoyl-β-D-xylo-furanosyl)-, methyl ester	EtOH	232(4.58),276(3.74), 281s(3.71)	5-1286-73
$C_{31}H_{26}ClN_2O$			
Benzo[f]quinolinium, 2-acetyl-4-(4-chlorophenyl)-1-[2-[4-(dimethyl-amino)phenyl]ethenyl]-, perchlorate	MeOH	550(3.57)	65-0877-73
$C_{31}H_{26}INO_4$			
Benzo[f]quinolinium, 3-(1,3-benzodioxol-5-yl)-1-[2-(3,4-dimethoxyphenyl)ethen-yl]-4-methyl-, iodide	EtOH	417(4.76)	103-0633-73
$C_{31}H_{26}N_3O_3$			
Benzo[f]quinolinium, 2-acetyl-1-[2-[4-(dimethylamino)phenyl]ethenyl]-4-(4-nitrophenyl)-, perchlorate	MeOH	535(3.40)	65-0877-73
$C_{31}H_{26}O$			
4,7-Methano-1H-inden-8-one, 3a,4,7,7a-tetrahydro-4,7-dimethyl-5,6-diphenyl-1-(phenylmethylene)-	hexane	278(4.28)	44-3836-73
$C_{31}H_{26}O_2$			
2-Naphthalenecarboxylic acid, 1,2-di-hydro-3-methyl-1,1,4-triphenyl-, methyl ester	EtOH	228(4.27),285(3.84)	18-1737-73
$C_{31}H_{26}O_6$			
2-Propen-1-one, 3-(1,3-benzodioxol-5-yl)-1-[5-methoxy-2,4-bis(phenylmeth-oxy)phenyl]-	MeOH	240(4.2),365(4.4)	2-0098-73
2-Propen-1-one, 1-[2,4-bis(phenylmeth-oxy)phenyl]-3-(6-methoxy-1,3-benzo-dioxol-5-yl)-	MeOH	208(4.86),247(4.2), 313(4.4),392(4.38)	39-1737-73C
$C_{31}H_{26}O_7$			
4H-1-Benzopyran-4-one, 5-hydroxy-6-meth-oxy-2-[3-methoxy-4-(phenylmethyl)phen-yl]-7-(phenylmethoxy)-	MeOH	243(4.01),277(4.17), 338(4.47)	24-0020-73
Methanone, [3-(1,3-benzodioxol-5-yl)-oxiranyl][5-methoxy-2,4-bis(phenyl-methoxy)phenyl]-	MeOH	240(4.3),280(4.12), 340(4.0)	2-0098-73
$C_{31}H_{26}O_9$			
Methanone, [2-[bis(acetyloxy)methyl]-1-naphthalenyl][7-[bis(acetyloxy)-methyl]-1-naphthalenyl]-	dioxan	226(4.99),243s(4.43), 250s(4.41),315(4.04)	24-1341-73
$C_{31}H_{26}Si$			
Silacyclopenta-2,4-diene, 1-ethenyl-1-methyl-2,3,4,5-tetraphenyl-	C_6H_{12}	250(4.43),360(3.94)	78-2395-73

Compound	Solvent	$\lambda_{max}(\log \epsilon)$	Ref.
$C_{31}H_{27}IN_2O_2$			
Benzo[f]quinolinium, 3-(1,3-benzodioxol-5-yl)-1-[2-[4-(dimethylamino)phenyl]ethenyl]-4-methyl-, iodide	EtOH	549(4.72)	103-0633-73
$C_{31}H_{27}N_2O$			
Benzo[f]quinolinium, 2-acetyl-1-[2-[4-(dimethylamino)phenyl]ethenyl]-4-phenyl-, perchlorate	MeOH	560(3.60)	65-0877-73
$C_{31}H_{27}N_7NaO_8PS$			
Adenosine, N-[(phenylamino)carbonyl]-8-[(phenylmethyl)thio]-, cyclic 3',5'-(hydrogen phosphate) 2'-(phenylcarbamate)-, sodium salt	pH 1	309(4.24)	87-1075-73
	pH 7	295(4.30)	87-1075-73
	pH 11	298(4.39)	87-1075-73
	pH 12.8	321(4.49)	87-1075-73
$C_{31}H_{28}$			
Cyclopropane, 1,1,2,2-tetraphenyl-3-(2-methylpropenyl)-	C_6H_{12}	225(4.44),269(3.26), 275(3.00)	35-2155-73
Cyclopropane, 1,1,2,3-tetraphenyl-2-(2-methylpropenyl)-	C_6H_{12}	228(4.47),267s(3.21), 274s(2.96)	35-2155-73
1,4-Hexadiene, 5-methyl-1,1,3,3-tetraphenyl-	C_6H_{12}	255(4.26)	35-2155-73
$C_{31}H_{28}N_2O$			
1,4-Pentadien-3-one, 1,5-bis[(4-methylphenyl)amino]-2,4-diphenyl-	EtOH	236(4.20),297(4.20), 421(4.41)	4-0665-73
$C_{31}H_{28}N_2O_4$			
4,4-Imidazolidinedicarboxylic acid, 1,2,3,5-tetraphenyl-, dimethyl ester	EtOH	247(4.34),287(3.67)	22-3437-73
$C_{31}H_{28}O_5$			
2-Propen-1-one, 1-[2,4-bis(phenylmethoxy)phenyl]-3-(2,4-dimethoxyphenyl)-	MeOH	207(4.8),245(4.2), 360(4.14)	39-1737-73C
$C_{31}H_{28}O_6$			
4-Phenanthrenol, 7,7'-[methylenebis(oxy)]bis[9,10-dihydro-5-methoxy-	n.s.g.	268s(4.37),273(4.39), 300(4.15)	39-1263-73C
$C_{31}H_{29}N_2O_5$			
Quinolinium, 3-acetyl-6-acetoxy-1-(4-acetoxyphenyl)-4-[2-[4-(dimethylamino)phenyl]ethenyl]-, chloride	MeOH	546(3.30)	65-0877-73
$C_{31}H_{29}N_3O$			
1,3-Propanediamine, 2-(3-methyl-5-isoxazolyl)-N,N',1,3-tetraphenyl-	EtOH	246(4.40),295(3.56)	18-3533-73
$C_{31}H_{29}O_4P$			
Phosphonium, triphenyl-, 2-[3-ethoxy-1-(ethoxycarbonyl)-3-oxo-1-propenyl]-2,4-cyclopentadien-1-ylide	MeOH	225(4.56),269(4.04), 394(4.23)	44-3537-73
$C_{31}H_{30}O$			
4,7-Methano-1H-inden-8-one, 1-(dicyclopropylmethylene)-3a,4,7,7a-tetrahydro-4,7-dimethyl-5,6-diphenyl-	hexane	261(4.40)	44-3836-73

Compound	Solvent	λ_{max}(log ϵ)	Ref.
$C_{31}H_{30}O_3$			
Phenol, 4-(1-methyl-1-phenylethyl)-, carbonate (2:1)	$C_2H_4Cl_2$	264(3.20),270(3.11)	116-0305-73
$C_{31}H_{30}O_5$			
Phenol, 4,4'-(1-methylethylidene)bis-, carbonate (2:1)	$C_2H_4Cl_2$	277(3.63),284(3.54)	116-0305-73
$C_{31}H_{31}N_3O_2S$			
Benzenesulfonamide, 4-methyl-N-(2,2',3-3',4,4',9,9'-octahydro-[1,9'-bi-1H-carbazol]-1'-yl)-	$CHCl_3$	240(4.49),286(4.20), 293(4.17),340(2.60)	39-1809-73C
$C_{31}H_{32}O_8S_4$			
Propane, 1,1,3,3-tetrakis(p-toluene-sulfonyl)-	EtOH	267(3.59),275(3.50)	44-2600-73
$C_{31}H_{32}O_{16}$			
7-Oxabicyclo[2.2.1]hepta-2,5-diene-1,2-3,6-tetracarboxylic acid, 4-methoxy-5-[octahydro-1,1a,5a-tris(methoxycarb-onyl)-2,3,5-metheno-1H-cyclopropa[a]-pentalen-1-yl]-, tetramethyl ester	EtOH	225(4.12),285s(3.08)	24-1804-73
$C_{31}H_{33}Br_2NO_8$			
2(1H)-Isoquinolinecarboxylic acid, 5-bromo-1-[[2-bromo-4-methoxy-3-[(phen-ylmethoxy)phenyl]methyl]-8-[(ethoxy-carbonyl)oxy]-3,4-dihydro-7-methoxy-, ethyl ester	EtOH	281(3.71),286(3.72)	95-1094-73
$C_{31}H_{33}NO_{12}$			
Cyclobut[4,5]azepino[1,2-a]quinoline-7,7a,8,9,9a,10-hexacarboxylic acid, 10,11-dihydro-1,3,5-trimethyl-, hexamethyl ester	MeOH	236(4.25),256s(4.12), 285s(3.89),350(3.86), 409(3.82)	39-1338-73C
	$MeOH-HClO_4$	236(4.24),255(4.17), 359(3.91),416(3.89)	39-1338-73C
$C_{31}H_{33}N_5O_4S_2$			
4,6(1H,5H)-Pyrimidinedione, 5-[1,3-di-ethyl-5-[(1-ethyl-2(1H)-quinolinyli-dene)methyl]-1,2,3,4-tetrahydro-4-oxo-2-thioxo-7H-pyrano[2,3-d]pyrimidin-7-ylidene]-1,3-diethyldihydro-2-thioxo-	pyridine	432(4.51),590(4.78)	39-0823-73C
$C_{31}H_{33}N_5O_6$			
2,4,6(1H,3H,5H)-Pyrimidinetrione, 5-[1,3-diethyl-5-[(1-ethyl-2(1H)-quino-linylidene)methyl]-1,2,3,4-tetrahydro-2,4-dioxo-7H-pyrano[2,3-d]pyrimidin-7-ylidene]-1,3-diethyl-	EtOH	403(4.23),550(4.59)	39-0823-73C
	pyridine	420(4.36),585(4.69)	39-0823-73C
$C_{31}H_{33}N_5O_7$			
2,4,6(1H,3H,5H)-Pyrimidinetrione, 5-[1,3-diethyl-5-[3-(3-ethyl-2(3H)-benzoxazolylidene)-1-propenyl]-1,2,3,4-tetrahydro-2,4-dioxo-7H-pyrano[2,3-d]pyrimidin-7-ylidene]-1,3-diethyl-	acetone	42(4.58),612(5.16)	39-0823-73C
	pyridine	448(4.55),622(5.15)	39-0823-73C

Compound	Solvent	$\lambda_{max}(\log \epsilon)$	Ref.
$C_{31}H_{34}N_2O$			
Phenol, 4-[di(1H-indol-3-yl)methyl]-2,6-bis(1,1-dimethylethyl)-	MeOH	225(4.51),284(3.83)	103-0034-73
$C_{31}H_{35}CoN_4$			
Cobalt, bis(cyano-C)(octadehydro-1,2,3-7,8,12,13,17,18,19-decamethylcorrin-ato-N^{21},N^{22},N^{23},N^{24})-, (OC-6-34)-	CHCl	383(5.02),503(4.11), 649(3.61),724s(3.23)	39-2281-73C
	pyridine	427(4.93),502(3.72), 539(4.04),580(4.72)	39-2281-73C
$C_{31}H_{35}N_3O_9$			
1H-Pyrrolo[2,3-c]pyridine-5-propanoic acid, 4,5,6,7-tetrahydro-2-[5-(phenyl-methoxy)carbonyl]-3-(2-methoxycarbon-ylethyl)-4-(methoxycarbonylmethyl)-1H-pyrrol-2-yl-^{14}C]methyl]-5-oxo-, methyl ester	MeOH	287(4.31)	39-1546-73C
$C_{31}H_{36}N_4O_4$			
2H-Biline-1,17-dione, 19-ethoxy-3-ethyn-yl-2,3,18,23-tetrahydro-3-hydroxy-2,2,7,8,12,13,18,18-octamethyl-	CH_2Cl_2	280(4.19),303(4.11), 318(4.11),364(4.28), 562s(4.12),593(4.24)	5-1067-73
$C_{31}H_{36}O_6$			
2H-1-Benzopyran-2,5,7(6H,8H)-trione, 4-hydroxy-3-(4-methoxyphenyl)-6,8,8-tris(3-methyl-2-butenyl)-	MeOH	306(4.33)	2-0106-73
$C_{31}H_{37}NO_2$			
Androst-5-en-3β-ol, 17-(2-quinolinyl-methylene)-, acetate	n.s.g.	208(3.73),214(3.72)	19-0887-73
$C_{31}H_{40}N_4O_5$			
Chaenorhine	EtOH	264(4.00),280s(3.84)	33-1266-73
	EtOH-HCl	219(4.28),233s(4.23), 255(4.21),276s(3.95)	33-1266-73
$C_{31}H_{40}O_6$			
Phenol, 2,2',2"-methylidynetris[6-meth-oxy-4-propyl-	EtOH	281(3.98),286(3.99)	12-1337-73
	EtOH-KOH	285(4.07),300(3.71)	12-1337-73
$C_{31}H_{40}O_{12}$			
Clerodendrin A, 2-deoxy-2-oxo-	MeOH	278(1.85)	39-0712-73C
$C_{31}H_{42}N_2O_8$			
Goldinamine methyl ether acetate	pH 1	210(4.64),238(4.53), 298s(4.28),336(4.60)	35-8449-73
	pH 7	210(4.64),238(4.52), 298s(4.27),336(4.59)	35-8449-73
	pH 13	238(4.53),298s(4.27), 336(4.60)	35-8449-73
$C_{31}H_{42}N_4O_5$			
Chaenorhine, 13,14-dihydro-	EtOH	235s(4.05),270(3.52)	33-1266-73
$C_{31}H_{42}O_{12}$			
Clerodendrin A (under nitrogen)	MeOH	203(4.03)	39-0712-73C
$C_{31}H_{43}ClN_4NiO_4$			
Nickel(1+), (2,3,16,17-tetradehydro-	n.s.g.	261(4.40),277(4.35),	39-0991-73C

Compound	Solvent	λ_{max}(log ε)	Ref.
8,12-diethyl-1,2,3,7,13,17,18,19-octamethylcorrinato-N^{21},N^{22},N^{23},N^{24})-, (SP-4-2)-, perchlorate (cont.)		315(4.03),358s(3.93), 425(4.21),498s(3.32)	39-0991-73C
$C_{31}H_{44}N_2O_5$			
Pregn-4-ene-3,20-dione, 17-[(10-diazo-1,9-dioxodecyl)oxy]-	MeOH	242(4.38),275s(3.87)	13-0139-73B
$C_{31}H_{44}N_4O_3$			
Chaenorhine, 12,34-dideoxo-	EtOH	250s(4.1)	33-1266-73
$C_{31}H_{44}N_4O_5$			
1,5,9,13-Tetraazacycloheptadecan-6-one, 13-acetyl-1-[3-(4-hydroxyphenyl)-1-oxopropyl]-8-(4-methoxyphenyl)-, (S)-	EtOH	277(3.42),282s(3.37)	33-1266-73
	EtOH-NaOH	246(4.03),277(3.46), 284(3.49),298(3.48)	33-1266-73
$C_{31}H_{44}O_4$			
Macedonic acid, dioxo-, methyl ester	EtOH	242(4.4),251(4.5), 260(4.3)	104-1696-73
$C_{31}H_{44}O_7$			
A spirost-4-ene	EtOH	235(3.94)	105-0534-73
$C_{31}H_{44}O_8$			
Pregn-4-ene-3,11,20-trione, 21-hydroxy-17-[(9-methoxy-1,9-dioxononyl)oxy]-	MeOH	238(4.19)	13-0139-73B
$C_{31}H_{44}O_{12}$			
Clerodendrin A, dihydro- (under nitrogen)	MeOH	203(3.71)	39-0712-73C
$C_{31}H_{45}BrO_5$			
Pregn-4-ene-3,20-dione, 17-[(10-bromo-1,9-dioxodecyl)oxy]-	MeOH	240(4.18)	13-0139-73B
$C_{31}H_{45}ClN_4NiO_4$			
Nickel, 8,12-diethyl-1,2,3,7,13,17,18-19-octamethylisocorrin perchlorate	n.s.g.	251(4.24),263(4.19), 275s(4.13),286s(4.11), 297(4.11),343(3.88), 410(4.32)	39-0991-73C
$C_{31}H_{45}ClO_5$			
Pregn-4-ene-3,20-dione, 17-[(10-chloro-1,9-dioxodecyl)oxy]-	MeOH	241(4.22)	13-0139-73B
$C_{31}H_{45}NO_4$			
24-Nor-2,3-secoolean-12-en-29-oic acid, 2-cyano-3,4-epoxy-11-oxo-, methyl ester, (20β)-	dioxan	247(4.12)	39-2076-73C
$C_{31}H_{46}N_4O_2$			
Chaenorhine, 12,29,34-trideoxo-	EtOH	258s(4.05)	33-1266-73
$C_{31}H_{46}O_4$			
1,3,5-Cyclohexanetrione, 2-pentanoyl-4,4,6,6-tetrakis(3-methyl-2-butenyl)-	EtOH-acid	230(4.01),283(4.14)	39-2013-73C
	EtOH-base	281(4.22)	39-2013-73C
4-Cyclohexene-1,3-diol, 5-[[1-(1,5-dimethylhexyl)-2,3,3a,6,7,7a-hexahydro-7a-methyl-1H-inden-4-yl]ethynyl]-4-methyl-, diacetate	EtOH	273(4.30)	88-3649-73

Compound	Solvent	$\lambda_{max}(\log \epsilon)$	Ref.
Macedonic acid, hydroxyoxo-, methyl ester	EtOH	242(4.2),251(4.2), 260(4.1)	104-1696-73
$C_{31}H_{46}O_5$			
5α-Cholesta-9(11),24-dien-23-one, 3β,6α-diacetoxy-	EtOH	237(4.05)	39-1745-73C
$C_{31}H_{46}O_6$			
Pregn-4-ene-3,20-dione, 17-[(10-hydroxy-1,9-dioxodecyl)oxy]-	MeOH	240(4.19)	13-0139-73B
$C_{31}H_{48}N_2O_4$			
Olean-12-en-28-oic acid, 2,3-bis(hydroxyimino)-, methyl ester	EtOH-NaOH	283(3.84)	95-0296-73
$C_{31}H_{48}N_2O_5$			
Hydromanumycin	MeOH	210(4.48),256(4.37)	88-4995-73
$C_{31}H_{48}N_4O_2$			
Chaenorhine, 13,14-dihydro-12,29,34-trideoxo-	EtOH	215(4.47),239s(4.16), 274(3.69),287s(3.53)	33-1266-73
$C_{31}H_{48}O_3$			
Cyclograndisolide	MeOH	209(4.33)	78-0013-73
Epicyclograndisolide	MeOH	210(4.15)	78-0013-73
D:A-Friedoolean-1-en-3-one, 24,25-epoxy-1-methoxy-	EtOH	258(4.14)	78-1365-73
D:A-Friedoolean-2-en-1-one, 24,25-epoxy-3-methoxy-	EtOH	256(4.14)	78-1365-73
19-Norcholesta-1(10),8-dien-6-one, 3-acetoxy-4,4,5-trimethyl-	n.s.g.	248(4.22)	88-3349-73
19-Norcholesta-7,9(11)-dien-6-one, 3-acetoxy-4,4,5-trimethyl-	n.s.g.	297(4.17)	88-3349-73
$C_{31}H_{48}O_4$			
4-Cyclohexene-1,3-diol, 5-[2-[1-(1,5-dimethylhexyl)-2,3,3a,6,7,7a-hexahydro-7a-methyl-1H-inden-4-yl)ethenyl]-4-methyl-, diacetate	ether	260(3.94)	88-3649-73
$C_{31}H_{50}O_2$			
D:A-Friedoolean-1-en-3-one, 1-methoxy-	EtOH	258(4.12)	78-1365-73
D:A-Friedoolean-2-en-1-one, 3-methoxy-	EtOH	253(4.13)	78-1365-73
$C_{31}H_{50}O_3$			
D:A-Friedoolean-1-en-3-one, 24-hydroxy-1-methoxy-	EtOH	258(4.17)	78-1365-73
D:A-Friedoolean-2-en-1-one, 24-hydroxy-3-methoxy-	EtOH	253(4.13)	78-1365-73
Testosterone laurate	hexane	232(4.24)	10-0528-73F
$C_{31}H_{50}O_4$			
Cholestan-6-one, 3-acetoxy-5,7-epoxy-4,4-dimethyl-, (3β,5α,7α)-	$CHCl_3$	295(1.58)	78-2297-73
$C_{31}H_{50}O_5$			
5α-Cholestan-6-one, 3β,7α-diacetoxy-	EtOH	300(1.98)	39-0070-73C

Compound	Solvent	$\lambda_{max}(\log \epsilon)$	Ref.
$C_{31}H_{51}NO_9$			
6,15,16-Trioxatricyclo[10.2.1.1^{1,4}]hexadec-2-en-7-one, 11-[[2-O-acetyl-3,4,6-trideoxy-3-(dimethylamino)-β-D-xylo-hexopyranosyl]oxy]-5-ethyl-9-hydroxy-2,4,8,10,12,14-hexamethyl-	EtOH	278(4.29)	138-0793-73
$C_{31}H_{52}O$			
Cyclotrichosantol	EtOH	195(3.85)	44-3688-73

Compound	Solvent	λ_{max}(log ε)	Ref.
$C_{32}H_{16}NS$			
18H-Difluoreno[1,9-ab:9',1'-ij]pheno-thiazin-18-yl	$C_6H_3Cl_3$	354(4.63),465(4.13), 548(4.39),562(4.39), 580(4.58)	24-1711-73
$C_{32}H_{16}N_2$			
Difluoreno[1,9-ab:1',9'-hi]phenazine	benzene	310(4.50)	24-1711-73
	$C_6H_3Cl_3$	342(4.76),369(4.47), 387(4.36),410(4.41), 435(4.66)	24-1711-73
$C_{32}H_{18}O_3$			
Naphthaceno[2,3-c]furan-4,13-dione, 1,3-diphenyl-	$CHCl_3$	325(--),338(4.6), 405(4.0),430(4.1), 455(4.2)	22-1154-73
Naphthaceno[2,3-c]furan-5,12-dione, 1,3-diphenyl-	$CHCl_3$	305(4.0),501(4.3)	22-1154-73
$C_{32}H_{20}O_4$			
9,10-Anthracenedione, 2,2'-(1,2-dimeth-yl-1,2-ethenediyl)bis-, (E)-	$CHCl_3$	260(5.11),280s(4.68), 332(4.23)	39-0850-73C
$C_{32}H_{21}NO_2$			
1H-Isoindole-1,3(2H)-dione, 4,5,6,7-tetraphenyl-	dioxan	252s(4.43),322(3.72)	47-2143-73
$C_{32}H_{21}N_3$			
2-Butenenitrile, 2-[2-(9-acridinyl)eth-enyl]-4-[9(10H)-acridinylidene]-	EtOH	250(4.9),318(4.0), 570(4.5)	18-0283-73
$C_{32}H_{22}$			
Anthracene, 1,8,10-triphenyl-	EtOH	214(4.65),261(5.00), 343s(3.56),361(3.89), 380(4.07),400(4.01)	44-1167-73
Phenanthrene, 2,2'-(1,3-butadiene-1,4-diyl)bis-	THF	287(4.67),295(4.65), 354(4.88),371(5.01), 392(4.89)	18-0909-73
Phenanthrene, 3,3'-(1,3-butadiene-1,4-diyl)bis-	THF	253s(--),280(4.53), 299(4.33),314(4.24), 360(4.79),378(4.91), 399(4.82)	18-0909-73
Phenanthrene, 9,9'-(1,3-butadiene-1,4-diyl)bis-	benzene	367(4.56)	18-0909-73
$C_{32}H_{22}Br_2O_2$			
Naphtho[2,3-c]furan-1(3H)-one, 7-bromo-9-(4-bromophenyl)-3,3-bis(2-methyl-phenyl)-	n.s.g.	255(4.90),292(4.04), 356(3.65)	115-0145-73A
Naphtho[2,3-c]furan-1(3H)-one, 7-bromo-9-(4-bromophenyl)-3,3-bis(3-methyl-phenyl)-	n.s.g.	254(4.92),293(4.05), 355(3.68)	115-0145-73A
Naphtho[2,3-c]furan-1(3H)-one, 7-bromo-9-(4-bromophenyl)-3,3-bis(4-methyl-phenyl)-	n.s.g.	255(4.84),293(4.08), 355(3.68)	115-0145-73A
Naphtho[2,3-c]furan-1(3H)-one, 7-bromo-9-(4-bromophenyl)-3,3-bis(phenyl-methyl)-	n.s.g.	244(4.80),295(4.16)	115-0145-73A
$C_{32}H_{22}Br_2O_4$			
Naphtho[2,3-c]furan-1(3H)-one, 7-bromo-	n.s.g.	230(4.82),253(4.91),	115-0145-73A

Compound	Solvent	λmax(log ε)	Ref.
9-(4-bromophenyl)-3,3-bis(4-methoxyphenyl)-		357(3.65)	115-0145-73A
$C_{32}H_{22}N_4$			
Triptycene, 2,7-bis(phenylazo)-, (-)-	MeOH	212(4.73),232(4.45), 240s(4.38),242s(4.28), 253s(4.10),258s(4.03), 325(4.52),440(3.20)	18-0605-73
$C_{32}H_{22}O_2$			
9(10H)-Anthracenone, 10-hydroxy-1,8,10-triphenyl-	EtOH	222s(4.63),291(4.01)	44-1167-73
1,4-Naphthacenedione, 8,9-dimethyl-6,11-diphenyl-	CH_2Cl_2	278(5.2),341(4.2), 357(4.4),414(3.7), 436(3.8),504(3.9)	22-2856-73
$C_{32}H_{22}O_4$			
9,10-Anthracenedione, 2,2'-(1,2-dimethyl-1,2-ethanediyl)bis-	$CHCl_3$	260(5.13),280s(4.71), 332(4.26)	39-0850-73C
5,12-Naphthacenedione, 1,4-dihydroxy-8,9-dimethyl-6,11-diphenyl-	CH_2Cl_2	280(4.4),312(4.5), 466(4.1)	22-2856-73
$C_{32}H_{23}NO_2$			
1H-Isoindole-1,3(2H)-dione, 3a,7a-dihydro-4,5,6,7-tetraphenyl-	dioxan	232s(4.30),320(4.08)	47-2143-73
$C_{32}H_{23}N_2O_3$			
Phenanthro[4,3-e]pyrido[1,2-b][1,2]benzisoxazolium, 14-acetoxy-6,15-dimethyl-13-(2-pyridinyl)-, perchlorate	MeCN	250(4.64),255(4.65), 319(4.11),395(3.75)	4-0195-73
$C_{32}H_{24}$			
[2.2](9,10)-Anthracenophane	CH_2Cl_2	257(5.18),270s(4.48), 280(4.46),307(3.51), 315s(3.49),342s(3.35), 365s(3.72),375s(3.88), 382(3.96),388s(3.90), 419(3.66),455s(2.81)	5-0844-73
1,3,5-Hexatriene, 1,6-di-2-fluorenyl-	THF	263s(--),380(4.89), 399(5.04),424(4.91)	18-2822-73
Phenanthrene, 2,2'-(1,2-ethenediyl)bis-[7-methyl-, (E)-	dioxan	220(4.63),285(4.83), 297(4.82),336s(4.76), 348(4.85),365s(4.67), 374s(4.49)	24-2190-73
[2.2](2,7)-Phenanthrophane	C_6H_{12}	233(4.82),252(4.95), 298s(3.79)	24-2190-73
$C_{32}H_{24}ClN_3O_6$			
Benzo[f]quinolinium, 4-(4-methylphenyl)-3-[[tetrahydro-4,6-dioxo-5-(phenylmethylene)-2(1H)-pyrimidinylidene]methyl]-, perchlorate	EtOH	240(4.22),255(4.19), 289(3.76),320(3.67), 405(3.75)	65-1340-73
$C_{32}H_{24}ClN_3O_7$			
Benzo[f]quinolinium, 4-phenyl-3-[[tetrahydro-5-[(4-methoxyphenyl)methylene]-4,6-dioxo-2(1H)-pyrimidinylidene]methyl]-, perchlorate	EtOH	239(4.37),264(3.97), 285(4.02),321(3.58), 428(3.96)	65-1340-73
1H-Pyrazolo[3,4-b]pyridine, 4-chloro-1-(2,3,5-tri-O-benzoyl-β-D-ribo-	EtOH	219(4.70),230(4.68), 272(3.92),282(3.90),	104-1294-73

Compound	Solvent	λ_{max}(log ε)	Ref.
furanosyl)- (cont.)		292(3.87),297(3.86), 304s(3.75)	104-1294-73
$C_{32}H_{24}Cl_2N_2O_2$			
Dispiro[2H-indole-2,1'-cyclobutane-2',2"-[2H]indole]-3,3"(1H,1"H)-dione, 3',4'-bis(2-chlorophenyl)-1,1"-dimethyl-	dioxan	240(4.94),420(3.54)	39-2804-73C
Dispiro[2H-indole-2,1'-cyclobutane-2',2"-[2H]indole]-3,3"-(1H,1"H)-dione, 3',4'-bis(4-chlorophenyl)-1,1"-dimethyl-	dioxan	240(4.94),418(3.54)	39-2804-73C
$C_{32}H_{24}N_4O_8$			
7(8H)-Pteridinone, 8-(2,3,5-tri-O-benzoyl-β-D-ribofuranosyl)-	MeOH	228(4.68),272s(3.84), 282(3.89),300(3.92)	24-0317-73
$C_{32}H_{24}N_4O_9$			
2,4(1H,3H)-Pteridinedione, 1-(2,3,5-tri-O-benzoyl-β-D-ribofuranosyl)-	MeOH	231(4.71),315(3.84)	24-1401-73
$C_{32}H_{24}O_2$			
Tricyclo[3.1.0.0^{2,4}]hexane-3,6-dicarboxaldehyde, 1,2,4,5-tetraphenyl-, anti	EtOH	220(4.49),267(3.65)	104-0963-73
$C_{32}H_{25}N_5O_8$			
2(1H)-Pteridinone, 4-amino-1-(2,3,5-tri-O-benzoyl-β-D-ribofuranosyl)-	MeOH	246(4.12),287(3.62), 338(3.97)	33-1225-73
$C_{32}H_{25}N_5O_9$			
4,7(3H,8H)-Pteridinedione, 2-amino-8-(2,3,5-tri-O-benzoyl-β-D-ribofuranosyl)-	MeOH	228(4.66),282(3.97), 350(4.08)	24-1952-73
$C_{32}H_{26}$			
Fulvene, 1-ethyl-2,3,4,6-tetraphenyl-	EtOH	243s(4.27),260(4.33), 322(4.29)	78-4307-73
$C_{32}H_{26}N_2O$			
2,3-Diazabicyclo[5.1.0]octa-2,4-dien-6-one, 8,8-dimethyl-1,4,5,7-tetraphenyl-	EtOH	290s(3.91),398(3.68)	107-0249-73
1,2-Diazocin-4(7H)-one, 7,7-dimethyl-3,5,6,8-tetraphenyl-	EtOH	245(4.22),316(3.71)	107-0249-73
$C_{32}H_{26}N_2O_2$			
Dispiro[2H-indole-2,1'-cyclobutane-2',2"-[2H]indole]-3,3"(1H,1"H)-dione, 1,1"-dimethyl-3',4'-diphenyl-	dioxan	240(4.80),307(3.82), 419(3.48)	39-2804-73C
$C_{32}H_{26}O_3$			
3-Cyclobutene-1,2-dione, 3-(diphenylmethyl)-4-(ethoxydiphenylmethyl)-	EtOH	260s(4.01),266s(3.96), 273s(3.89)	18-1733-73
2H-Indeno[1,2-b]furan, 3-(diphenylmethylene)-3,8b-dihydro-2,8b-dimethoxy-4-phenyl-	EtOH	237(4.31),294(3.90)	18-1737-73
$C_{32}H_{26}O_4$			
Tetracyclo[4.3.0.0^{2,4}.0^{2,7}]non-8-ene-2,8-dicarboxylic acid, 5-(diphenylmethylene)-, dimethyl ester	EtOH	228(4.31),285(4.31)	24-1822-73

Compound	Solvent	λ_{max}(log ϵ)	Ref.
Tetracyclo[4.3.0.0^{2,4}.0^{3,7}]non-8-ene-2,9-dicarboxylic acid, 5-(diphenylmethylene)-, dimethyl ester	EtOH	228(4.33),285(4.31)	24-1822-73
Tricyclo[4.3.0.0^{2,9}]nona-3,7-diene-2,8-dicarboxylic acid, 5-(diphenylmethylene)-, dimethyl ester	EtOH	242(4.38),294(4.28)	24-1837-73
Tricyclo[4.3.0.0^{2,9}]nona-3,7-diene-2,9-dicarboxylic acid, 5-(diphenylmethylene)-, dimethyl ester	EtOH	242(4.39),297(4.37)	24-1837-73
$C_{32}H_{26}O_8$			
Methanone, (4,4'-diacetoxy-6,6'-dimethoxy-[1,1'-biphenyl]-3,3'-diyl)bis-[phenyl-	MeOH	254(4.60),284s(4.36)	18-1498-73
$C_{32}H_{26}O_9$			
[2,2'-Bianthracene]-9,9'(10H,10'H)-dione, 1,1',5,8,8'-pentahydroxy-3,3'-dimethoxy-6,6'-dimethyl-	$CHCl_3$	240(4.49),264(4.48), 273(4.47),365(4.42)	64-0255-73C
$C_{32}H_{26}O_{10}$			
Candicanin	EtOH	250(4.54),300(4.36)	2-0410-73
$C_{32}H_{27}N_3O_8S$			
4H-Pyrrolo[2,3-d]pyrimidin-4-one, 3,5,6,7-tetrahydro-2-[(2,3,5-tri-O-benzoylribofuranosyl)thio]-	EtOH	228(4.73),272(3.94)	104-1995-73
$C_{32}H_{28}$			
Naphthalene, 1,2,3,4-tetramethyl-5,6,8-triphenyl-	MeOH	263(4.7),337(4.15)	5-1893-73
	EtOH	239s(4.47),264(4.69), 334(4.08)	118-0783-73
[2.2](2,7)-Phenanthrenophane, 5,6,17,18-tetrahydro-	C_6H_{12}	268s(4.53),277(4.59), 318(3.84)	24-2190-73
$C_{32}H_{28}NO$			
Pyridinium, 4-ethoxy-1-methyl-2,3,5,6-tetraphenyl-, tetrafluoroborate	MeOH	243(4.41),290s(3.94)	77-0833-73
$C_{32}H_{28}NP$			
[1,1'-Biphenyl]-2-amine, 2',6-dimethyl-N-(triphenylphosphoranylidene)-	MeOH	214(4.62),265s(3.88)	39-2818-73C
$C_{32}H_{28}N_2O_2S_2$			
1H-Indole, 2,2'-dithiobis[3-(4-methoxyphenyl)-1-methyl-	EtOH	230(4.64),255s(4.53), 331(4.00)	94-2739-73
$C_{32}H_{28}N_2O_3$			
2H-Indol-2-one, 1,3-dihydro-3-(4-methoxyphenyl)-3-[3-(4-methoxyphenyl)-1-methyl-1H-indol-2-yl]-1-methyl-	EtOH	228(4.36),286s(3.86)	94-2739-73
$C_{32}H_{28}O$			
4,7-Methano-1H-inden-8-one, 3a,4,7,7a-tetrahydro-4,7-dimethyl-5,6-diphenyl-1-(1-phenylethylidene)-	hexane	258(4.59)	44-3836-73
$C_{32}H_{28}O_4$			
1,2-Cyclobutanedicarboxylic acid, 3,3,4,4-tetraphenyl-, dimethyl ester	EtOH	262(3.04),269(3.04), 275(2.85)	18-1737-73

Compound	Solvent	λ_{max}(log ϵ)	Ref.
$C_{32}H_{28}S_2$			
Dibenzo[5,6:13,14]cyclohexadeca[1,2-c:9,10-c']dithiophene, 1,3,12,14-tetramethyl-	EtOH	249s(4.23),280(4.18), 350(3.42)	39-1136-73C
$C_{32}H_{29}NO_5$			
4,4-Oxazolidinedicarboxylic acid, 5-(diphenylmethyl)-2,3-diphenyl-, dimethyl ester	EtOH	290(3.33)	22-3437-73
$C_{32}H_{29}N_2O$			
Benzo[f]quinolinium, 2-acetyl-1-[2-[4-(dimethylamino)phenyl]ethenyl]-4-(4-methylphenyl)-, perchlorate	MeOH	551(3.52)	65-0877-73
$C_{32}H_{29}N_2O_2$			
Benzo[f]quinolinium, 2-acetyl-1-[2-[4-(dimethylamino)phenyl]ethenyl]-4-(4-methoxyphenyl)-, perchlorate	MeOH	542(3.38)	65-0877-73
$C_{32}H_{29}N_5O_6S$			
8,2'-Thioanhydroguanosine, N^2-acetyl-5'-O-monomethoxytrityl-	EtOH	229s(4.29),270(4.33), 293s(4.11)	23-2397-73
$C_{32}H_{30}N_2O_2$			
Benzamide, N-benzoyl-N-[1-phenyl-1-[(1-phenylpropylidene]amino]propyl]-	C_6H_{12}	223(4.53),286(4.16), 295(4.15)	78-2119-73
$C_{32}H_{30}O_8$			
Methanone, (4,4',6,6'-tetramethoxy-[1,1'-biphenyl]-3,3'-diyl)bis[(4-methoxyphenyl)-	MeOH	259(4.50),288(4.61)	18-1498-73
$C_{32}H_{30}O_{11}$			
[2,2'-Bianthracene]-8,8'(5H,5'H)-dione, 6,6',7,7'-tetrahydro-1,1',5,6,6',9,9'-hexahydroxy-3,3'-dimethoxy-6,6'-dimethyl-	EtOH	233(4.49),279(4.82), 319(4.10),330s(4.00), 407(4.34)	64-0255-73C
$C_{32}H_{30}O_{14}$			
Secalonic acid E	dioxan	265(4.37),338(4.64)	39-2440-73C +77-0464-73
$C_{32}H_{32}N_6O_{10}$			
α-D-Glucopyranoside, methyl 6-[2,6-bis-(benzoylamino)-9H-purin-9-yl]-6-deoxy-, 2,3,4-triacetate	MeOH	248(4.28),304(3.94), 345(4.06)	18-3165-73
$C_{32}H_{32}O_4$			
1,6,19,24-Tetraoxa[6.0.6.0]paracyclophane	n.s.g.	264(4.11)	18-0263-73
$C_{32}H_{33}BrO_4$			
Phenol, 2-[(3-bromo-2-hydroxy-5-methylphenyl)methyl]-6-[[2-hydroxy-3-[(2-hydroxy-3,5-dimethylphenyl)methyl]-5-methylphenyl]methyl]-4-methyl-	dioxan	288(4.09)	126-0039-73L
$C_{32}H_{33}BrO_5$			
Benzenemethanol, 3-[[3-[[3-[(3-bromo-2-	dioxan	288(4.09)	126-0039-73L

Compound	Solvent	λmax(log ε)	Ref.
hydroxy-5-methylphenyl)methyl]-2-hydroxy-5-methylphenyl)methyl]-2-hydroxy-5-methylphenyl)methyl]-2-hydroxy-5-methyl- (cont.)			126-0039-73L
$C_{32}H_{33}ClN_2O_7$			
2-Naphthacenecarboxamide, 4-(benzoylamino)-7-chloro-N-(1,1-dimethylethyl)-1,4,4a,5,5a,6,11,12a-octahydro-3,12-dihydroxy-10-methoxy-6-methyl-1,11-dioxo-	MeOH-HCl	220(4.47),268(4.38), 356(4.18)	89-0497-73
	MeOH-NaOH	218(4.46),268(4.28), 367(3.96)	89-0497-73
	MeOH-borate	218(4.48),269(4.24), 338(4.11)	89-0497-73
$C_{32}H_{33}ClN_2O_8$			
2-Naphthacenecarboxamide, 4-(benzoylamino)-7-chloro-N-(1,1-dimethylethyl)-1,4,4a,5,5a,6,11,1′a-octahydro-3,12,12a-trihydroxy-10-methoxy-6-methyl-1,11-dioxo-	MeOH-HCl	266(4.49),277(4.63), 360(4.32)	88-3513-73
$C_{32}H_{33}NO_2$			
9,13-Methano-11H-dibenzo[h,n]azacycloheneicosine-11-carboxylic acid, 22,23,24,25-tetradehydro-1,2,3,4-18,19,20,21-octahydro-, ethyl ester	$CHCl_3$	346(4.92),380s(4.57), 406s(4.23),429(4.20), 452(4.08),510s(3.45)	89-0410-73
$C_{32}H_{34}O_4$			
Phenol, 2-[(2-hydroxy-3,5-dimethylphenyl)methyl]-6-[[2-hydroxy-3-[(2-hydroxy-5-methylphenyl)methyl]-5-methylphenyl]methyl]-4-methyl-	dioxan	287(4.05)	126-0039-73L
$C_{32}H_{35}NO_2$			
1(4H)-Pyridinecarboxylic acid, 3,5-bis-[4-(2-ethynyl-1-cyclohexen-1-yl)-1,3-butadienyl]-, ethyl ester	$CHCl_3$	329(4.90),339(4.93), 380(4.38),398(4.40), 424s(4.15)	89-0410-73
$C_{32}H_{36}N_2O_5$			
Chaetoglobosin A	EtOH	223(4.61),245s(3.96), 274(3.82),282(3.82), 292(3.73)	88-2109-73
Chaetoglobosin B	EtOH	222(4.64),245s(3.99), 274(3.90),281(3.90), 290(3.83)	88-2109-73
$C_{32}H_{37}N_4O_4Tl$			
Thallium, aquahydroxy[methyl 8,13-diethyl-3,7,12,14-tetramethyl-21H,23H-porphine-2-propanoato(2-)-N^{21},N^{22},N^{23}-N^{24}]-, (OC-6-24)-	CH_2Cl_2	415(4.38),543(4.10), 580(3.86)	39-2142-73C
$C_{32}H_{38}N_4$			
1,2-Ethanediamine, N,N'-bis[4-(1,3-dihydro-1,3,3-trimethyl-2H-indol-2-ylidene)-2-butenylidene]-, diperchlorate	n.s.g.	438(5.05),498(5.19)	104-1286-73
$C_{32}H_{38}S_4$			
Disulfide, 2,2'-bis[2-(phenylthio)adamantyl]-	C_6H_{12}	223(4.36),277(3.61)	39-2862-73C

Compound	Solvent	$\lambda_{max}(\log \epsilon)$	Ref.
$C_{32}H_{39}NO_{15}$			
Evonine, O^9,O^{15}-dideacetyl-	EtOH	224(3.80),266(3.50)	102-0703-73
$C_{32}H_{39}N_4O_2Tl$			
Thallium, aquahydroxy(2,3,5,8-tetraethyl-1,4,6,7-tetramethylporphinato)-	CH_2Cl_2	415(5.53),542(4.27), 580(4.15)	39-2142-73C
Thallium, aquahydroxy(2,3,6,7-tetraethyl-1,4,5,18-tetramethylporphinato)-	CH_2Cl_2	415(5.56),542(4.30), 580(4.16)	39-2142-73C
Thallium, aquahydroxy(2,4,6,8-tetraethyl-1,3,5,7-tetramethylporphinato)-	CH_2Cl_2	415(5.46),542(4.23), 580(4.09)	39-2142-73C
$C_{32}H_{40}N_8O_8$			
Tetrapyrido[4,3-b:4',3'-f:4",3"-j:4"'-3"'-n][1,5,9,13]tetraazacyclohexadecine-6,12,18,24(2H,8H,14H,20H)-tetrone, 4a,5,10a,11,16a,17,22a,23-octahydro-2,8,14,20-tetrakis(methoxymethyl)-	$CHCl_3$	327.5(4.471)	64-0471-73B
$C_{32}H_{40}O_5$			
Isotingenone, di-O-acetyl-	EtOH	250(4.90),290(4.04)	39-2725-73C
$C_{32}H_{42}N_2$			
Pyrazine, 1,2-dicyclooctyl-1,2-dihydro-2,5-diphenyl-	n.s.g.	259(4.30)	39-0683-73C
$C_{32}H_{42}N_4O_4$			
22H-Biline-3,17-dione, 1,19-diethoxy-2,10,18,23-tetrahydro-2,2,7,8,10-12,13,18,18-nonamethyl-, (E,E)-	CH_2Cl_2	290(4.23),422(4.49), 460(4.43)	5-1067-73
(Z,Z)-	CH_2Cl_2	390(--),420(--)	5-1067-73
$C_{32}H_{42}N_4O_5$			
Chaenorhine, N(2)-methyl-	EtOH	213(4.39),260(4.03), 279s(3.87)	33-1266-73
$C_{32}H_{42}O_5$			
Tingenone, di-O-acetyldihydro-	EtOH	266(3.13),274(3.11)	39-2725-73C
$C_{32}H_{42}O_{16}$			
Matairesinol, 4,4'-di-O-β-D-glucopyranoside	EtOH	225(4.09),279(3.65)	23-1050-73
	EtOH	225(4.09),279(3.65)	94-1114-73
$C_{32}H_{42}O_{17}$			
Nortrachelogenin, 4,4'-di-O-β-D-glucopyranoside	EtOH	224(4.19),279(3.75)	94-1114-73
$C_{32}H_{43}Cl_2NO_{15}$			
D-ribo-Hexonic acid, O-2,3,6-trideoxy-3-C-methyl-4-O-methyl-3-nitro-α-L-ribo-hexopyranosyl-(1→3)-O-2,6'-dideoxy-4-O-(3,5-dichloro-2,4-dimethoxy-6-methylbenzoyl)-β-D-arabino-hexopyranosyl-(1→4)-2,6-dideoxy-, δ-lactone, 3-acetate	n.s.g.	208(4.56),287(2.97)	35-0942-73
$C_{32}H_{44}O_8$			
Datiscacin	$CHCl_3$	231(3.98),268(3.73)	44-1420-73
Havanensin triacetate	EtOH	212(4.57)	39-1047-73C

Compound	Solvent	$\lambda_{max}(\log \epsilon)$	Ref.
$C_{32}H_{46}ClN_5O_8$			
2-Pentenoic acid, 3-(2,2-dimethyl-1-oxo-propoxy)-4,4-dimethyl-, ester with N-[9-[3-chloro-3-deoxy-5-O-(2,2-dimethyl-1-oxopropyl)-β-D-xylofuranosyl]-9H-purin-6-yl]-2,2-dimethylpropanamide	MeOH	272(3.23)	35-4074-73
$C_{32}H_{47}BrO_4$			
5α-Lanosta-8,24-diene-7,11-dione, 3β-acetoxy-24-bromo-	EtOH	270(3.85)	39-1583-73C
$C_{32}H_{48}Br_2O_4$			
5α-Lanost-8-ene-7,11-dione, 3-acetoxy-24,25-dibromo-	EtOH	271(3.98)	39-1583-73C
$C_{32}H_{48}N_8O_8$			
Tetrapyrido[4,3-b:4',3'-f:4",3"-j:4'"-3"'-n][1,5,9,13]tetraazacyclohexadecine-6,12,18,24(2H,8H,14H,20H)-tetrone, 3,4,4a,5,9,10,10a,11,15,16,16a,17,21-22,22a,23-hexadecahydro-2,8,14,20-tetrakis(methoxymethyl)-	$CHCl_3$	296(4.656)	64-0471-73B
$C_{32}H_{48}O_3$			
Lanosta-8,22,25-trien-24-one, 3β-acetoxy-	EtOH	244(4.12)	39-0806-73C
$C_{32}H_{48}O_4$			
D:A-Friedooleanan-2-en-24-al, 3-acetoxy-	EtOH	238(3.96)	78-1365-73
D:A-Friedoolean-2-en-1-one, 3-acetoxy-24,25-epoxy-	EtOH	239(3.97)	78-1365-73
Olean-12-en-28-oic acid, 2-(hydroxymethylene)-3-oxo-, methyl ester	EtOH	294(3.92)	95-0296-73
$C_{32}H_{48}O_8$			
Cucurbitacin Q1	n.s.g.	230(4.03)	102-2741-73
acetonide	MeOH	230(4.03)	102-2741-73
$C_{32}H_{49}BrO_2$			
5α-Lanosta-7,9(11),24-trien-3β-ol, 24-bromo-, acetate	EtOH	236(4.17),243(4.24), 252(4.10)	39-1583-73C
$C_{32}H_{50}Br_2O_2$			
5α-Lanosta-7,9(11)-dien-3β-ol, 24,25-dibromo-, acetate	EtOH	236(4.24),243(4.31), 252(4.13)	39-1583-73C
isomer B	EtOH	236(4.24),243(4.31), 252(4.13)	39-1583-73C
$C_{32}H_{50}O_2$			
D:C-Friedooleana-7,9(11)-dien-16-ol, acetate, (16β)-	EtOH	235s(--),241(4.04), 248s(--)	88-1987-73
5α-Lanosta-7,9(11),24-trien-3β-ol, acetate	EtOH	236(4.19),243(4.26), 252(4.09)	39-1583-73C
$C_{32}H_{50}O_3$			
D:A-Friedoolean-2-en-1-one, 3-acetoxy-	EtOH	237(4.44)	78-1365-73
D:A-Friedoolean-2-en-1-one, 24-acetoxy-	EtOH	230(3.76)	78-1365-73
Lup-12-en-11-one, 3β-acetoxy-	n.s.g.	246(3.95)	102-1125-73
30-Oxataraxast-20-en-3β-ol, acetate	C_6H_{12}	232(4.06)	2-0977-73

Compound	Solvent	λ_{max}(log ε)	Ref.
$C_{32}H_{50}O_4$			
D:A-Friedoolean-2-en-1-one, 3-acetoxy-24-hydroxy-	EtOH	237(3.85)	78-1365-73
	EtOH-NaOH	290(4.05)	78-1365-73
$C_{32}H_{50}O_5$			
1,5-Cyclo-19-nor-1,10-secocholest-9(11)-en-12-one, 2,6-diacetoxy-10-ethyl-	EtOH	237(4.05)	39-0900-73C
$C_{32}H_{50}O_7$			
Jaligonic acid, dimethyl ester	EtOH	204(3.66)	100-0326-73
$C_{32}H_{51}NO_2$			
Acetic acid, [(5α)-cholestan-3-ylidene]-cyano-, ethyl ester	EtOH	244(4.12)	22-0622-73
$C_{32}H_{52}O_2$			
A triterpene acetate	EtOH	209(3.27)	102-0451-73

Compound	Solvent	$\lambda_{max}(\log \epsilon)$	Ref.
$C_{33}H_{18}O_9$			
5,6,11,12,17,18-Trinaphthylenehexone, 1,7,13-trihydroxy-3,9,15-trimethyl-	dioxan	273(4.49),299(4.52), 423(4.16)	88-3695-73
$C_{33}H_{20}N_2O_3$			
1H-Benz[de]isoquinoline-1,3(2H)-dione, 6-(5-[1,1'-biphenyl]-4-yl-2-oxazol-yl)-2-phenyl-	toluene	310(4.41),405(4.53)	103-1204-73
$C_{33}H_{24}Br_2N_2O_4$			
Propanedioic acid, (3,6-dibromo-9-phen-yldibenzo[a,c]phenazin-11(9H)-yli-dene)-, diethyl ester	n.s.g.	620s(4.33),668(4.37), 736s(4.14)	103-1407-73
$C_{33}H_{24}ClN_2P$			
Benzeneacetonitrile, 4-chloro-α-[phenyl-[(triphenylphosphoranylidene)amino]-methylene]-	EtOH	331(4.11)	39-0817-73C
$C_{33}H_{24}INO_3$			
Benzo[f]quinolinium, 3-(1,3-benzodioxol-5-yl)-1-[2-(2-hydroxy-1-naphthalenyl)-ethenyl]-4-methyl-, iodide	EtOH	412(4.44),477(4.52)	103-0633-73
$C_{33}H_{24}N_2O$			
3-Penten-2-one, 3-[2-(9-acridinyl)ethen-yl]-5-[9(10H)-acridinylidene]-	EtOH	249(5.1),346(4.1), 525(4.3)	18-0283-73
$C_{33}H_{24}N_4O_7$			
Cyclopent[e][1,3,4]oxadiazin-7(1H)-one, 4a,7a-dihydro-6,7a-dimethyl-1-(4-ni-trobenzoyl)-3-(4-nitrophenyl)-4a,5-diphenyl-, cis	EtOH	247(4.23),281(4.37), 335(4.04)	44-2043-73
$C_{33}H_{25}AsO_2$			
Arsonium, triphenyl-, 1-benzoyl-2-oxo-2-phenylethylide	MeOH	222(4.56),315(3.95), 350s(3.59)	78-1697-73
$C_{33}H_{25}N_2P$			
Benzeneacetonitrile, α-[phenyl(triphen-ylphosphoranylidene)amino]methylene]-	EtOH	324(4.12)	39-0817-73C
$C_{33}H_{26}ClN_3O_7$			
Benzo[f]quinolinium, 4-(4-methylphenyl)-3-[[tetrahydro-5-[(4-methoxyphenyl)-methylene]-4,6-dioxo-2(1H)-pyrimidin-ylidene]methyl]-, perchlorate	EtOH	242(4.24),267(3.88), 294(3.97),320(3.73), 430(4.12)	65-1340-73
$C_{33}H_{26}N_2O_3$			
Cyclopent[e][1,3,4]oxadiazin-7(1H)-one, 1-benzoyl-4a,7a-dihydro-6,7a-dimethyl-3,4a,5-triphenyl-, cis	EtOH	280(4.40)	44-2043-73
$C_{33}H_{26}N_2O_4$			
Propanedioic acid, (9-phenyldibenzo-[a,c]phenazin-11(9H)-ylidene)-, diethyl ester	n.s.g.	620s(4.37),670(4.41), 740s(4.19)	103-1407-73
$C_{33}H_{26}N_2O_5$			
Cyclopent[e][1,3,4]oxadiazine-1-carbox-	EtOH	284(4.11)	44-2043-73

Compound	Solvent	λ_{max}(log ε)	Ref.
ylic acid, 1,4a,7,7a-tetrahydro-6,7a-dimethyl-7-oxo-3-phenoxy-4a,5-diphenyl-, phenyl ester (cont.)			
2,3-Diazabicyclo[2.2.1]hept-5-ene-2,3-dicarboxylic acid, 1,4-dimethyl-7-oxo-5,6-diphenyl-, diphenyl ester	EtOH	283(4.13)	44-2043-73
$C_{33}H_{26}N_4O_7$			
2-Propenamide, N,N'-[carbonylbis(imino-2,1-phenylene)]bis[3-(1,3-benzodioxol-5-yl)-	HOAc	336(4.69)	48-1152-73
$C_{33}H_{26}OSi$			
2-Propen-1-one, 1,3-diphenyl-2-(triphenylsilyl)-	C_6H_{12}	248(4.38),267(4.21), 330(2.54),345s(2.54), 359(2.44),377(2.05)	23-2024-73
$C_{33}H_{27}N_3O$			
Benzo[f]quinoline-1-carboxamide, N,N-diethyl-3-(4-phenyl-2-quinolinyl)-	n.s.g.	280(4.82),328(4.45), 369(4.00)	103-0220-73
Cu(I) complex	isoAmOH	540(3.98)	103-0220-73
$C_{33}H_{27}N_5O_9$			
7(8H)-Pteridinone, 2-amino-4-methoxy-8-(2,3,5-tri-O-benzoyl-β-D-ribofuranosyl)-	MeOH	207s(4.62),230(4.69), 275(3.85),350(4.16)	24-1952-73
β-D-Ribofuranoside, 2-amino-4-methoxy-7-pteridinyl, 2,3,5-tribenzoate	MeOH	229(4.80),270(4.04), 347(4.13)	24-1952-73
$C_{33}H_{28}O_{10}$			
4H-1-Benzopyran-4-one, 2-[3-[2,3-dihydro-5-hydroxy-2-(3-hydroxy-4-methoxyphenyl)-4-oxo-4H-1-benzopyran-8-yl]-4-methoxyphenyl]-2,3-dihydro-5-hydroxy-7-methoxy-	EtOH	226(4.93),288(4.75), 331(3.40)	102-0671-73
[2,9'-Bianthracene]-4',9,10(1'H)-trione, 2',3'-dihydro-1,2',8,10'-tetrahydroxy-3,5',7'-trimethoxy-2',6-dimethyl-	EtOH	225(4.47),272(4.60), 310s(4.05),330s(3.77), 401(3.99),432s(3.90), 449s(3.86)	64-0354-73C
	EtOH-NaOH	228(4.47),265(4.62), 312s(4.08),372(3.87), 389s(3.86),523(3.80)	64-0354-73C
$C_{33}H_{29}NSi$			
7-Silabicyclo[2.2.1]hept-5-ene-2-nitrile, 7,7-dimethyl-1,4,5,6-tetraphenyl-	n.s.g.	218(4.29),254(3.98)	78-2395-73
$C_{33}H_{29}N_2O_3$			
Benzo[f]quinolinium, 2-acetyl-4-(4-acetoxyphenyl)-1-[2-[4-(dimethylamino)-phenyl]ethenyl]-, perchlorate	MeOH	552(3.40)	65-0877-73
$C_{33}H_{30}N_2O_9$			
Uridine, 5-(1-methylethyl)-, 2',3',5'-tribenzoate	pH 13	268(3.92)	56-1205-73
$C_{33}H_{30}N_4O_4$			
5,10-Azo-1,4-etheno-6,9-methanobenzo[b]-biphenylene-2,3-dicarboxylic acid,	EtOH	257(3.86),263(3.87), 270(3.73)	12-0389-73

Compound	Solvent	$\lambda_{max}(\log \epsilon)$	Ref.
1,4,4a,4b,5,5a,6,9,9a,10,10a,10b-dodecahydro-5,10-di-2-pyridinyl-, dimethyl ester (cont.)			
$C_{33}H_{30}N_4O_5$			
2-Propenamide, N,N'-[carbonylbis(imino-2,1-phenylene)]bis[3-(4-methoxyphenyl)-	HOAc	332(4.63)	48-1152-73
$C_{33}H_{30}O$			
1,4:9,10-Dimethanoanthracen-12-one, 1,4-4a,9,9a,10-hexahydro-1,4-dimethyl-11-(1-methylethylidene)-2,3-diphenyl-	90% EtOH	231(4.22),262(4.03), 268(4.04),275(4.01)	12-1725-73
$C_{33}H_{31}Cl_3N_2O_7$			
Thymidine, 3'-O-[2-oxo-2-(2,2,2-trichloroethoxy)ethyl]-5'-O-(triphenylmethyl)-	EtOH	232(--),266(3.98)	39-0290-73C
$C_{33}H_{32}O_{10}$			
[2,9'-Bianthracene]-4',8'(1H,5H)-dione, 2',3',6,7-tetrahydro-1,2',6,9,10'-pentahydroxy-3,5',7'-trimethoxy-2',6-dimethyl-	EtOH	234(4.66),274(5.02), 314s(4.14),330s(4.03), 397(4.35)	64-0354-73C
$C_{33}H_{32}O_{16}$			
4H-1-Benzopyran-4-one, 5,7-diacetoxy-3-[4-[(2,3,4,6-tetra-O-acetyl-β-D-glucopyranosyl)oxy]phenyl]-	dioxan	253(4.53),300s(3.75)	114-0365-73D
$C_{33}H_{33}N_3O$			
1,3-Propanediamine, 2-(3-methyl-5-isoxazolyl)-N,N'-bis(4-methylphenyl)-1,3-diphenyl-	EtOH	249(4.43),304(3.56)	18-3533-73
$C_{33}H_{34}N_4O_5$			
21H,23H-Porphine-2-propanoic acid, 13-ethyl-8-formyl-18-(methoxycarbonyl)-3,7,12,17-tetramethyl-, methyl ester	CH_2Cl_2	413(5.62),427s(4.93), 521(3.80),566(4.31),	5-1329-73
	CH_2Cl_2-CF_3COOH	418(5.48),532s(3.54), 552s(3.83),570(3.94), 602s(3.79),624(4.15)	5-1329-73
$C_{33}H_{34}N_6O_4$			
Adenosine, 2'-deoxy-N-[(dimethylamino)-methylene]-5'-O-[(4-methoxyphenyl)-diphenylmethyl]-	EtOH	232(--),312(4.54)	39-0290-73C
$C_{33}H_{35}CuN_5$			
Copper, [2,7,12,17-tetraethyl-3,8,13,18-tetramethyl-21H,23H-porphine-5-carbonitrilato(2-)-N^{21},N^{22},N^{23},N^{24}]-, (SP-4-2)-	CHCl	409(5.18),547(3.65), 588(4.08)	103-1065-73
$C_{33}H_{35}N_5O_5$			
Ergotamine	H_2O	313(3.89)	39-1312-73B
	EtOH	311(3.93)	39-1312-73B
Ergotaminine	EtOH	313(3.92)	39-1312-73B
$C_{33}H_{35}N_5O_7$			
2,4,6(1H,3H,5H)-Pyrimidinetrione, 5-[1,3-diethyl-5-[5-(3-ethyl-2(3H)-	$CHCl_3$	475(4.45),700(5.15)	39-0823-73C
	pyridine	480(4.37),707(5.14)	39-0823-73C

Compound	Solvent	$\lambda_{max}(\log \epsilon)$	Ref.
benzoxazolylidene)-1,3-pentadienyl]-1,2,3,4-tetrahydro-2,4-dioxo-7H-pyrano[2,3-d]pyrimidin-7-ylidene]-1,3-diethyl- (cont.)			39-0823-73C
$C_{33}H_{35}N_6O_8P$			
Adenosine, N,N-dibenzoyl-5'-deoxy-5'-(diethoxyphos-hinyl)cyanomethyl-2',3'-O-isopropylidene-	EtOH	249(4.60),272s(4.32)	35-4404-73
$C_{33}H_{35}NiPSi$			
Nickel, (η^5-2,4-cyclopentadien-1-yl)-[phenyl(trimethylsilyl)methyl](triphenylphosphine)-	C_6H_{12}	373(3.67),464(3.14), 674(2.00)	23-1179-73
$C_{33}H_{36}ClN_3O_3$			
Cyclopropenylium, tris[4-(4-morpholinyl)phenyl]-, chloride	MeCN	434(4.06)	64-0535-73B
$C_{33}H_{36}CuN_4O$			
Copper, [2.6.12,17-tetraethyl-3,8,13,18-tetramethyl-21H,23H-porphine-5-carboxaldehydato(2-)-N^{21},N^{22},N^{23},N^{24}]-, (SP-4-2)-	$CHCl_3$	406(5.28),530(3.95), 566(4.12),640(3.60)	103-1065-73
$C_{33}H_{36}N_4O_4$			
21H,23H-Porphine-2-propanoic acid, 18-carboxy-8,13-diethyl-3,7,12,17-tetramethyl-, 2-methyl ester	n.s.g.	260(4.05),403(5.20), 506(3.97),544(4.07), 573(3.81),632(3.32)	5-1741-73
$C_{33}H_{36}O_5$			
Benzenemethanol, 2-hydroxy-3-[2 hydroxy-3-[(2-hydroxy-3,5-dimethylphenyl)methyl]-5-methylphenyl]-5-methylphenyl]-5-methyl-	dioxan	287(4.07)	126-0039-73L
$C_{33}H_{36}O_{16}$			
4H-1-Benzopyran-4-one, 3-acetoxy-2,3-dihydro-7-methoxy-2-(4-methoxyphenyl)-5-[(2,3,4,6-tetra-O-acetyl-β-D-glucopyranosyl)oxy]-	EtOH	230(4.50),280(4.26)	102-0913-73
$C_{33}H_{37}ClN_2O_8$			
3-Cyclohexene-1-carboxylic acid, 5-(benzoylamino)-6-[(8-chloro-1,2,3,4-tetrahydro-5-methoxy-1-methyl-4-oxo-2-naphthalenyl)methyl]-3-[[(1,1-dimethylethyl)amino]carbonyl]-4-hydroxy-2-oxo-, methyl ester	MeOH-NaOH	227(4.50),278(4.20), 326(3.57)	89-0497-73
$C_{33}H_{37}CuN_5O$			
Copper, [2,7,12,17-tetraethyl-3,8,13,18-tetramethyl-21H,23H-porphine-5-carboxaldehyde oximato(2-)-N^{21},N^{22},N^{23},N^{24}]-, (SP-4-2)-	$CHCl_3$	405(5.47),530(4.07), 566(4.27)	103-1065-73
$C_{33}H_{37}N_5O_7$			
Adenosine, 5'-O-(1-ethoxyethyl)-N,N-bis-(4-methylbenzoyl)-2',3'-O-(1-methylethylidene)-	MeOH	262(4.45),270s(4.44)	18-3228-73

Compound	Solvent	λ max(log ε)	Ref.
$C_{33}H_{38}CuN_4O$			
Copper, [2,7,12,17-tetraethyl-3,8,13,18-tetramethyl-21H,23H-porphine-5-methanolato(2-)-N^{21},N^{22},N^{23},N^{24}]-, (SP-4-2)-	$CHCl_3$	405(5.12),533(4.04), 570(4.20)	103-1065-73
$C_{33}H_{38}N_2O$			
Phenol, 4-[bis(2-methyl-1H-indol-3-yl)-methyl]-2,6-bis(1,1-dimethylethyl)-	MeOH	211(4.37),229(4.41), 284(3.81)	103-0034-73
$C_{33}H_{38}N_2O$			
Retinol, 4-(phenylazo)benzoate, (11-cis-13-cis)-	EtOH	317(4.72)	104-1868-73
$C_{33}H_{39}CoN_4$			
Cobalt, 1,2,3,7,8,12,13,17,18,19-decadehydro-2,7,8,12,13,18-hexaethyl-21,22-dihydro-3,17-dimethylcorrinato(3-)-N^{21},N^{22},N^{23},N^{24}]-, (SP-4-3)-	$CHCl_3$	385(5.01),473s(4.00), 498(4.16),653(3.51)	39-2281-73C
$C_{33}H_{39}N_4O_4Tl$			
Thallium, aquahydroxy[methyl 8,13-diethyl-3,7,12,17,20-pentamethyl-21H,23H-porphine-2-propanoato(2-)-N^{21},N^{22},N^{23},N^{24}]-, (OC-6-24)-	CH_2Cl_2	420(5.51),549(4.19), 579(3.54),591(3.48)	39-2142-73C
$C_{33}H_{40}N_4$			
1,3-Propanediamine, N,N'-bis[4-(1,3-dihydro-1,3,3-trimethyl-2H-indol-2-ylidene)-2-butenylidene]-, diperchlorate	n.s.g.	443(5.04),489(5.22)	104-1286-73
$C_{33}H_{41}CoN_6O_4$			
Cobalt, bis(nitrito-O)(octadehydro-2,8,12,18-tetraethyl-1,3,7,13,17,19-hexamethylcorrinato-N^{21},N^{22},N^{23},N^{24})-	$CHCl_3$	280(4.49),283(4.42), 626(4.00),676(4.13)	39-0775-73C
$C_{33}H_{41}CoN_{10}$			
Cobalt, diazido(octadehydro-2,8,12,18-tetraethyl-1,3,7,13,17,19-hexamethylcorrinato-N^{21},N^{22},N^{23},N^{24})-	$CHCl_3$	286(4.49),364(4.42), 688(4.00)	39-0775-73C
$C_{33}H_{41}N_2O_{13}P$			
3'-Uridylic acid, 2',5'-bis-O-(tetrahydro-4-methoxy-2H-pyran-4-yl)-, diphenyl ester	EtOH	260(4.09)	39-2513-73C
$C_{33}H_{42}N_4O_6$			
Chaenorhine, N(2)-acetyl-	n.s.g.	217(4.46),263(4.06), 279s(3.94)	33-1266-73
$C_{33}H_{42}O_4$			
1,3,5-Cyclohexanetrione, 2-benzoyl-4,4,6,6-tetrakis(3-methyl-2-butenyl)-	EtOH-acid	247(3.99),282(4.03)	39-2013-73C
	EtOH-base	251(4.07),277(4.10)	39-2013-73C
$C_{33}H_{44}N_2O_3$			
Dendrocrepine	EtOH	252s(2.96),258(2.89), 264(2.75)	1-1907-73
Isodendrocrepine	EtOH	252(2.70),258(2.68), 264(2.54),267(2.34)	1-1907-73

Compound	Solvent	λ_{max}(log ε)	Ref.
$C_{33}H_{44}O_{16}$			
2(3H)-Furanone, 4-[(3,4-dimethoxyphenyl)methyl]-3-[[4-[(6-O-β-D-glucopyranosyl-β-D-glucopyranosyl)oxy]-3-methoxyphenyl]methyl]dihydro- (arctigenin 4'-β-gentiobioside)	EtOH	230(4.20),280(3.79)	31-0017-73 +94-0639-73 +94-0674-73
	EtOH	230(4.22),280(3.75)	94-2778-73
$C_{33}H_{45}NO_3$			
4-Azaspirost-5-en-3-one, 4-(phenylmethyl)-, (25R)-	MeOH	236(4.04)	2-1254-73
$C_{33}H_{46}O_9$			
Pregn-4-ene-3,11,20-trione, 21-acetoxy-17-[(9-methoxy-1,9-dioxononyl)oxy]-	MeOH	238(4.20)	13-0139-73B
$C_{33}H_{47}N_3O_2$			
Cholesta-1,4-dien-3-one, (4-nitrophenylhydrazone)	EtOH	248(3.90),420(4.48)	39-1565-73C
$C_{33}H_{47}N_3O_6S$			
C-Nor-9,11-secospirostan-3-one, 9-azido-11-[[(4-methylphenyl)sulfonyl]oxy]-	EtOH	225(4.2)	13-0147-73A
$C_{33}H_{48}O$			
A-Nor-5α-cholestan-2-one, 3-(phenylmethylene)-, (E)-	EtOH	286(4.22)	22-1376-73
(Z)-	EtOH	299(4.15)	22-1376-73
$C_{33}H_{48}O_2$			
Spiro[A-norcholestane-3,2'-oxiran]-2-one, 3'-phenyl-	C_6H_{12}	316(1.78)	22-1376-73
isomer	C_6H_{12}	316(2.33)	22-1376-73
isomer	C_6H_{12}	316(1.95)	22-1376-73
isomer	C_6H_{12}	314(2.41)	22-1376-73
$C_{33}H_{48}O_6S$			
11-Oxaspirostan-3-ol, 4-methylbenzenesulfonate	EtOH	225(4.15)	13-0147-73A
$C_{33}H_{48}O_7$			
Pregn-4-ene-3,20-dione, 17-[(10-acetoxy-1,9-dioxodecyl)oxy]-	MeOH	240(4.20)	13-0139-73B
$C_{33}H_{49}N_3O_2$			
5α-Cholest-1-en-3-one, 4-nitrophenylhydrazone	EtOH	237(3.59),289(3.56), 321(3.51),402(4.11)	39-1565-73C
Diazene, [(5α)-cholest-2-en-3-yl](4-nitrophenyl)-	EtOH	328(4.40)	39-1565-73C
$C_{33}H_{50}O_3$			
A tetracyclic steroid from Colletin spinosissima	EtOH	224(4.16)	102-0893-73
$C_{33}H_{50}O_4$			
30-Norlupa-18,20(29)-diene-3β,28-diol, diacetate	C_6H_{12}	240(4.26),247(4.31), 256(4.13)	73-1179-73
$C_{33}H_{50}O_5$			
30-Norlup-18-en-21-one, 3β,28-diacetoxy-	C_6H_{12}	235(4.22)	73-1179-73

Compound	Solvent	λ_{max}(log ϵ)	Ref.
Stigmasta-5,24(28)-dien-29-oic acid, 3-acetoxy-22,23-epoxy-, ethyl ester, (3β,22S,23S,24Z)-	EtOH	231(4.17)	23-1223-73
$C_{33}H_{52}O_2$			
Cholesteryl sorbate	n.s.g.	259.4(4.39)	35-0240-73
$C_{33}H_{52}O_6$			
Cholestan-6-one, 2,3-diacetoxy-5,7-epoxy-4,4-dimethyl-, (2β,3β,5α,7α)-	EtOH	283(2.00)	78-2297-73
$C_{33}H_{53}NO_5$			
Lanost-6-eno[6,7-d]oxazole-2',11(3'H)-dione, 3-acetoxy-6,7-dihydro-	EtOH	296(1.53)	23-3866-73
	dioxan	296(1.48)	23-3866-73
$C_{33}H_{55}NO_5$			
Lanostan-11-one, 3-acetoxy-7-[(amino-carbonyl)oxy]-, (3β,7α)-	EtOH	293(1.71)	23-3866-73
	dioxan	295(1.59)	23-3866-73

Compound	Solvent	$\lambda_{max}(\log \epsilon)$	Ref.
$C_{34}H_{18}N_4O_8S_2$			
Naphth[1,2-d]oxazole-5-sulfonic acid, 2,2'-(2,7-phenazinediyl)bis-	DMF	345(3.97),440(4.05)	115-0027-73A
$C_{34}H_{20}$			
Pyrene, 2,2'-(1,2-ethenediyl)bis-	THF	251(4.77),310(4.87), 324(5.03),342(4.12), 359s(--),392(3.39), 415(3.27)	18-2822-73
$C_{34}H_{20}N_4O_8S_2$			
Naphth[1,2-d]oxazole-5-sulfonic acid, 2,2'-(azodi-4,1-phenylene)bis-	DMF	420(3.94)	115-0027-73A
$C_{34}H_{20}O_2$			
5,14-Pentacenedione, 1,4-diphenyl-	$CHCl_3$	275(4.9),330(4.5), 345(4.6),455(4.0)	22-1154-73
$C_{34}H_{20}O_2S_2$			
4H,8H-Benzo[1,2-c:4,5-c']dithiophene-4,8-dione, 1,3,5,7-tetraphenyl-	$C_2H_4Cl_2$	275(4.52),348(3.96)	44-3975-73
$C_{34}H_{22}O_2$			
Benzo[1,2-b:4,3-b']difuran, 1,2,7,8-tetraphenyl-	$CHCl_3$	333(4.4),346(4.5), 359(4.3)	22-1154-73
Benzo[1,2-b:4,5-b']difuran, 2,3,6,7-tetraphenyl-	$CHCl_3$	344(4.23),359(4.45), 372(4.38)	22-1154-73
$C_{34}H_{22}O_4$			
1(3H)-Isobenzofuranone, 5,6-dibenzoyl-4,7-diphenyl-	EtOH	250(4.6)	22-2856-73
$C_{34}H_{24}$			
1,3,5-Hexatriene, 1,6-di-2-phenanthrenyl-	THF	285(4.56),296(4.55), 312(4.26),371(4.93), 390(5.08),414(4.95)	18-0909-73
1,3,5-Hexatriene, 1,6-di-3-phenanthrenyl-	THF	255s(--),279(4.40), 289(4.41),309(4.24), 324(4.27),359s(--), 377(4.87),396(5.02), 420(4.91)	18-0909-73
1,3,5-Hexatriene, 1,6-di-9-phenanthrenyl-	benzene	384(4.67)	18-0909-73
$C_{34}H_{24}Br_2O_2$			
p-Terphenyl, 5,6-bis(bromomethyl)-2,3-dibenzoyl-	EtOH	247(4.6)	22-2856-73
$C_{34}H_{24}N_2$			
4,4'-Bipyridinium, 2,2',6,6'-tetraphenyl-	MeCN	244(4.87),270s(--), 290s(--),318(4.22)	5-1036-73
$C_{34}H_{24}O_2$			
4,4'-Bipyrrylium, 2,2',6,6'-tetraphenyl-, bis(tetrafluoroborate)	MeCN	221(4.37),254(4.36), 293(4.67),357(4.29), 463(4.54)	5-1036-73
4H-Pyran, 4-(2,6-diphenyl-4H-pyran-4-ylidene)-2,6-diphenyl-	dioxan	270s(4.52),276(4.53), 437(4.57),458(4.70)	78-2005-73
radical cation tetrafluoroborate	MeCN	233(4.35),257(4.37), 282(4.38),316(4.43),	5-1036-73

Compound	Solvent	$\lambda_{max}(\log \epsilon)$	Ref.
radical cation tetrafluoroborate (cont.)		340(4.36),411(4.38), 499(4.26),702(4.33), 785(4.35)	5-1036-73
$C_{34}H_{24}S_2$			
4H,8H-Benzo[1,2-c:4,5-c']dithiophene, 1,3,5,7-tetraphenyl-	$C_2H_4Cl_2$	262(4.53),306(4.50)	44-3975-73
4,4'-Bithiopyrylium, 2,2',6,6'-tetra-phenyl-, bis(tetrafluoroborate)	MeCN	229(4.46),282(4.61), 305(4.67),448(4.82)	5-1036-73
radical cation perchlorate	MeCN	253(4.51),335(4.18), 348(4.19),458(4.40), 868(4.32)	5-1036-73
4H-Thiopyran, 4-(2,6-diphenyl-4H-thio-pyran-4-ylidene)-2,6-diphenyl-	dioxan	258(4.63),265(4.41), 476(4.63)	78-2005-73
$C_{34}H_{26}$			
1,3-Butadiene, 1,1,2,4,4-pentaphenyl-	EtOH	244(4.23),341(4.06)	44-0322-73
1,3,5,7-Octatetraene, 1,8-di-2-fluor-enyl-	THF	275(4.21),394(4.95), 432(5.10),461(5.00)	18-2822-73
$C_{34}H_{26}N_2$			
Phthalazine, 6,7-dimethyl-1,4,5,8-tetra-phenyl-	CH_2Cl_2	316(4.1)	22-2856-73
$C_{34}H_{26}O$			
3-Buten-2-one, 1,1,1,4,4-pentaphenyl-	EtOH	272(3.78),308(3.95)	44-0322-73
$C_{34}H_{26}O_2$			
p-Terphenyl, 2,3-dibenzoyl-5,6-dimethyl-	EtOH	241(4.6)	22-2856-73
$C_{34}H_{26}O_3$			
5,6-Isobenzofurandimethanol, 1,3,4,7-tetraphenyl-	CH_2Cl_2	322(4.4),387(4.2)	22-2856-73
$C_{34}H_{26}O_4$			
9,10-Anthracenedione, 2,2'-(1,1,2,2-tetramethyl-1,2-ethanediyl)bis-	$CHCl_3$	260(4.81),280s(4.40), 334(3.08)	39-0850-73C
p-Terphenyl, 2,3-dibenzoyl-5,6-bis(hy-droxymethyl)-	EtOH	254(4.7)	22-2856-73
$C_{34}H_{26}O_6$			
9H-Xanthen-9-one, 1-hydroxy-3,5,6-tris-(phenylmethoxy)-	$CHCl_3$	249(4.78),286s(4.08), 319(4.48),345s(4.01)	39-1329-73C
$C_{34}H_{27}N_2$			
Quinolinium, 1-(phenylmethyl)-2-[3-(1-phenyl-2(1H)-quinolinylidene)-1-pro-penyl]-, perchlorate	n.s.g.	614(5.17)	104-2195-73
$C_{34}H_{27}N_2P$			
Benzeneacetonitrile, α-[(4-methylphen-yl)[(triphenylphosphoranylidene)-amino]methylene]-	EtOH	329(4.30)	39-0817-73C
$C_{34}H_{28}N_2O_2$			
Benzo[f]quinoline-1-carboxylic acid, 3-(4-phenyl-2-quinolinyl)-, pentyl ester	n.s.g.	285(4.70),331(4.37), 370(3.91)	103-0220-73
Cu(I) complex	isoAmOH	548(3.98)	103-0220-73

Compound	Solvent	λ_{max}(log ε)	Ref.
$C_{34}H_{28}N_4O_9$			
2,4(1H,3H)-Pteridinedione, 6,7-dimethyl-1-(2,3,5-tri-O-benzoyl-β-D-ribofuranosyl)-	MeOH	229(4.75),326(4.01)	24-1401-73
$C_{34}H_{28}O_3$			
2-Propanone, 1-[3-(diphenylmethylene)-3,8b-dihydro-8b-methoxy-4-phenyl-2H-indeno[1,2-b]furan-2-yl]-	$CHCl_3$	249(4.45),297(4.01)	18-1737-73
$C_{34}H_{28}O_3Si$			
4,7-Silanoisobenzofuran-1,3-dione, 3a,4,7,7a-tetrahydro-8,8-dimethyl-4,5,6,7-tetraphenyl-	n.s.g.	227(4.45),272(4.00)	78-2395-73
$C_{34}H_{28}O_4$			
Tricyclo[3.1.0.0^{2,4}]hexane-3,6-dicarboxylic acid, 1,2,4,5-tetraphenyl-, dimethyl ester, anti	EtOH	220(4.52),267(3.70)	104-0963-73
$C_{34}H_{28}O_8$			
Bicyclo[2.2.1]hepta-2,5-diene-2,3-dicarboxylic acid, 7-[2,3-bis(methoxycarbonyl)bicyclo[2.2.1]hepta-2,5-dien-7-ylidene]-5,6-diphenyl-, dimethyl ester	EtOH	230(4.47),265s(4.11), 347s(3.49)	89-0991-73
$C_{34}H_{29}ClN_2S_2$			
Benzothiazolium, 3-ethyl-2-[6-[3-ethyl-2(3H)-benzothiazolylidene)methyl]-3-methyl-1H-phenalen-1-ylidene]methyl]-, chloride	MeCN	327(4.52),348(4.50), 430(3.63),510(3.83), 905(5.10)	44-2425-73
$C_{34}H_{29}NSi$			
7-Silabicyclo[2.2.1]hept-5-ene-2-carbonitrile, 7-ethenyl-7-methyl-1,4,5,6-tetraphenyl-	n.s.g.	232(4.34),276(3.95)	78-2395-73
$C_{34}H_{29}N_4O_2PS$			
Benzenesulfonamide, N-[1,3-dihydro-1-methyl-3-[(triphenylphosphoranylidene)hydrazono]-2H-indol-2-ylidene]-4-methyl-	$CHCl_3$	242(4.07),278(4.38), 302(3.66),345(3.87), 400s(3.50)	39-1943-73C
$C_{34}H_{29}N_5O_8$			
2(1H)-Pteridinone, 4-(dimethylamino)-1-(2,3,5-tri-O-benzoyl-β-D-ribofuranosyl)-	MeOH	228(4.72),283(3.76), 335(3.98)	33-1225-73
7(8H)-Pteridinone, 2-(dimethylamino)-8-(2,3,5-tri-O-benzoyl-β-D-ribofuranosyl)-	MeOH	228(4.76),272(3.89), 282s(3.84),363(4.23)	24-0317-73
$C_{34}H_{30}N_2$			
6,6'-Biquinolinium, 2,2'-dimethyl-1,1'-bis(phenylmethyl)-, diperchlorate	n.s.g.	260(5.08),335(4.35)	104-2195-73
$C_{34}H_{30}N_2O$			
Quinolinium, 6,6'-oxybis[2-methyl-1-(phenylmethyl)-, diperchlorate	n.s.g.	256(5.24),325(4.03)	104-2195-73

Compound	Solvent	λ_{max}(log ε)	Ref.
$C_{34}H_{30}N_2O_4$			
Dispiro[2H-indole-2,1'-cyclobutane-2',2"-[2H]indole]-3,3'-(1H,1"H)-dione, 3',4'-bis(2-methoxyphenyl)-1,1"-dimethyl-	dioxan	240(4.86),307(3.83), 418(3.48)	39-2804-73C
Dispiro[2H-indole-2,1'-cyclobutane-2',2"-[2H]indole]-3,3"(1H,1"H)-dione, 3',4'-bis(4-methoxyphenyl)-1,1"-dimethyl-	dioxan	238(4.96),421(3.53)	39-2804-73C
$C_{34}H_{30}N_2S$			
Quinolinium, 6,6'-thiobis[2-methyl-1-(phenylmethyl)-, diperchlorate	n.s.g.	255(5.36),325(4.22)	104-2195-73
$C_{34}H_{30}N_2S_2$			
Quinolinium, 6,6'-dithiobis[2-methyl-1-(phenylmethyl)-, diperchlorate	n.s.g.	248(5.40),342(3.96)	104-2195-73
$C_{34}H_{30}N_6O_8$			
7(8H)-Pteridinone, 2-amino-4-(dimethylamino)-8-(2,3,5-tri-O-benzoyl-α-D-ribofuranosyl)-	MeOH	228(4.74),276(4.32), 369(4.22)	24-0317-73
7(8H)-Pteridinone, 2-amino-4-(dimethylamino)-8-(2,3,5-tri-O-benzoyl-β-D-ribofuranosyl)-	MeOH	228(4.67),277(4.27), 370(4.14)	24-0317-73
$C_{34}H_{30}O_4$			
1H-Phenalene, 1,1'-(1,2-ethanediylidene)bis[3-ethoxy-7-methoxy-	$CHCl_3$	535f(4.15),573(4.49), 626(4.78)	44-2425-73
$C_{34}H_{30}O_8$			
4H-1-Benzopyran-4-one, 8-[5-(3,4-dihydro-7-methoxy-4-oxo-2H-1-benzopyran-2-yl)-2-methoxyphenyl]-2,3-dihydro-7-methoxy-2-(4-methoxyphenyl)-	EtOH	232(4.92),292(4.63), 330(4.26)	102-0671-73
$C_{34}H_{30}O_{10}$			
4H-1-Benzopyran-4-one, 2-[3-[2-(3,4-dimethoxyphenyl)-3,4-dihydro-5-hydroxy-4-oxo-2H-1-benzopyran-8-yl]-4-methoxyphenyl]-2,3-dihydro-5-hydroxy-7-methoxy-	EtOH	226(4.93),288(4.74), 331(3.40)	102-0671-73
Methanone, (4,4'-diacetoxy-6,6'-dimethoxy-[1,1'-biphenyl]-3,3'-diyl)bis[(4-methoxyphenyl)-	MeOH	256s(4.43),292(4.62)	18-1498-73
$C_{34}H_{30}O_{18}$			
1,2,3-Benzenetriol, 5-[2,6-diacetoxy-4-(2,4,6-triacetoxyphenoxy]phenoxy]-, triacetate	n.s.g.	233(4.41),273(3.67)	88-4277-73
$C_{34}H_{31}Br_3O_{14}$			
4aH-Xanthene-4a-carboxylic acid, 4-acetoxy-7-bromo-5-[5-bromo-3-[[[3-bromo-2-(methoxycarbonyl)-6-methyl-4-oxo-2-cyclohexen-1-yl]oxy]carbonyl]-2,4-dihydroxyphenyl]-1,2,3,4,9,9a-hexahydro-7-hydroxy-6-methyl-, methyl ester	dioxan	264(4.40),362(3.92)	78-0519-73

Compound	Solvent	λ_{max}(log ϵ)	Ref.
$C_{34}H_{31}N_5O_8S$			
Adenosine, N,1-dibenzoyl-N,6-didehydro-1,6-dihydro-2',3'-O-(1-methylethylidene)-, 5'-(4-methylbenzenesulfonate)	EtOH	247(4.60),272s(4.31)	35-4404-73
$C_{34}H_{32}INO_4$			
Dibenzo[a,g]quinolizinium, 5,6-dihydro-2,11-dimethoxy-13-methyl-3,10-bis-(phenylmethoxy)-, iodide	MeOH	264(4.50),287(4.66), 305s(4.56)	78-1265-73
$C_{34}H_{32}N_2O_5$			
Tricordatine	MeOH	227(4.60),275s(3.69), 284(3.71),304s(3.44)	102-2509-73
$C_{34}H_{32}N_2O_6$			
[1,1'-Biphenyl]-2,2'-dicarboxylic acid, 6,6'-bis[[(1-phenylethyl)amino]carbonyl]-, dimethyl ester	EtOH	286(3.27)	33-2255-73
$C_{34}H_{32}N_2O_8$			
Compound 19	EtOH	213s(4.65),242(4.10), 294(3.69),301s(3.63)	95-1165-73
$C_{34}H_{32}N_2O_9$			
Uridine, 5-(1,1-dimethylethyl)-, 2',3'.5'-tribenzoate	pH 1	235(4.48)	56-1205-73
	pH 13	320(4.47)	56-1205-73
$C_{34}H_{32}O_9$			
4H-1-Benzopyran-4-one, 5,6,7,8-tetramethoxy-2-[4-methoxy-3,5-bis(phenylmethoxy)phenyl]-	MeOH	271(4.36),317(4.44)	2-1092-73
$C_{34}H_{32}O_{15}$			
Eumitrin A_1	dioxan	272(3.99),281(4.02), 286(4.02),334(4.51)	78-0519-73
$C_{34}H_{34}N_4O_4$			
Phylloerythrin, 10-oxo-, methyl ester	CH_2Cl_2	416(5.05),519s(3.62), 562(3.91),585(4.00), 637(3.41)	39-2517-73C
	CH_2Cl_2 + CF_3COOH	418(5.28),564(4.00), 599(3.67),613s(3.64)	39-2517-73C
$C_{34}H_{34}O_7$			
2H-1-Benzopyran, 4,4'-oxybis[3,4-dihydro-5,7-dimethoxy-2-phenyl-	MeOH	260(3.50)	2-0120-73
$C_{34}H_{34}O_{14}$			
Eumitrin A_2	dioxan	262(4.17),278(4.26), 298(4.05),335(4.39)	78-0519-73
Eumitrin B	dioxan	253(3.79),275(4.02), 295(3.72),336(4.17)	78-0519-73
$C_{34}H_{35}BrN_4NiO_2$			
Nickel, bromo[octadehydro-1,2,7,8,12-13,18,19-octamethyl-17-(phenylmethoxy)-3-corrolato-N^{21},N^{22},N^{23},N^{24}]-, (SP-5-15)-	CH_2Cl_2	275(4.24),353(4.29), 560(3.99)	5-0146-73

Compound	Solvent	λmax(log ε)	Ref.
$C_{34}H_{36}F_3N_4O_2Tl$			
Thallium, [2,7,12,17-tetraethyl-3,8,13-18-tetramethyl-21H,23H-porphinato(2-)-N^{21},N^{22},N^{23},N^{24}](trifluoroacetato-O)-, (SP-5-12)-	CH_2Cl_2	414(5.55),542(4.28), 580(4.15)	39-2142-73C
$C_{34}H_{36}N_4O_5$			
21H,23H-Porphine-2-propanoic acid, 13-ethyl-18-(methoxycarbonyl)-3,7,12,17-tetramethyl-8-(2-oxoethyl)-	CH_2Cl_2	407(5.32),510(3.96), 548(4.20),574(3.92), 633(3.04)	5-1329-73
	CH_2Cl_2 + CF_3COOH	411(5.50),555(4.08), 607(3.95)	5-1329-73
$C_{34}H_{36}N_6O_2$			
Pyrimido[4,5-d]pyridazine, 3,4-dihydro-5,8-dimorpholino-2-phenyl-3,4-bis-(phenylmethyl)-	EtOH	238(4.44)	95-1043-73
$C_{34}H_{37}BrN_4NiO_4$			
Nickel, bromo(3-benzyloxy-7,8,17-tri-hydroxy-1,2,7,8,12,13,18,19-octa-methyltridehydrocorrinato)-	MeOH	269(4.12),338(4.12), 524(3.78)	5-0146-73
Nickel, bromo(17-benzyloxy-3,7,8-tri-hydroxy-1,2,7,8,12,13,18,19-octa-methyltridehydrocorrinato)-	MeOH	268(4.06),338(4.17), 526(3.76)	5-0146-73
$C_{34}H_{37}BrN_4O_3$			
3-Phorbinepropanoic acid, 6-bromo-9,14-diethyl-4,8,13,18-tetramethyl-20-oxo-, methyl ester, (13S-trans)-	CH_2Cl_2	414(5.01),516(3.86), 548(4.10),613(3.73), 672(4.58)	39-2517-73C
	CH_2Cl_2 + CF_3COOH	422(5.12),540(3.64), 563(3.80),612(3.82), 664(4.49)	39-2517-73C
$C_{34}H_{37}BrN_4O_4$			
21H,23H-Porphine-2-propanoic acid, 8-(2-bromoethyl)-13-ethyl-18-(methoxycarbo-nyl)-3,7,12,17-tetramethyl-	CH_2Cl_2	504(5.27),510(3.98), 547(4.14),575(3.90), 633(3.00)	5-1329-73
	CH_2Cl_2 + CF_3COOH	412(5.49),557(4.11), 604(3.93)	5-1329-73
$C_{34}H_{38}CuO_4$			
Copper, bis(3-benzoyl-1,7,7-trimethyl-bicyclo[2.2.1]heptan-2-onato-O,O')-	benzene	335(4.51),662(1.80)	65-0927-73
	MeOH	258(4.32),330(4.45)	65-0927-73
	$CHCl_3$	271(4.40),334(4.56), 660(1.79)	65-0927-73
	DMF	270(4.28),332(4.42), 680(1.96)	65-0927-73
$C_{34}H_{38}N_4O_4$			
Rhodoporphyrin XV, dimethyl ester	n.s.g.	260(4.12),404(5.28), 505(4.01),544(4.14), 572(3.87),631(3.35)	5-1741-73
$C_{34}H_{38}N_4O_6$			
Porphine, 4-ethyl-2-(1,2-dihydroxyethyl)-6-(methoxycarbonyl)-7-(2-methoxycarbo-nylethyl)-1,3,5,8-tetramethyl-	CH_2Cl_2	404(5.34),510(3.98), 548(4.22),575(3.91), 632(3.08)	5-1329-73
	CH_2Cl_2 + CF_3COOH	413(5.50),558(4.08), 609(3.96)	5-1329-73

Compound	Solvent	$\lambda_{max}(\log \epsilon)$	Ref.
$C_{34}H_{39}BrN_4NiO_6$			
Nickel, bromo[2,3,17,18-tetradehydro-1,2,7,8,12,13,18,19-octamethyl-17-(phenylmethoxy)-3,7,8,12,13-corrin-pentolato]-, (SP-5-15)-	MeOH	300(4.16),328(4.01),353s(3.94),452s(3.73),473(3.78)	5-0146-73
$C_{34}H_{41}NO_{16}$			
Evonine, 2-deacetyl-	EtOH	224(4.00),268(3.58)	102-0703-73
Neoevonine	EtOH	224(3.74),265(3.51)	78-1773-73
$C_{34}H_{41}N_5O_{19}$			
2(1H)-Pteridinone, 1-(2,3,4,6-tetra-O-acetyl-β-D-glucopyranosyl)-4-[(2,3,4,6-tetra-O-acetyl-β-D-glucopyranosyl)amino]-	MeOH	240(4.06),320(3.87)	24-2982-73
$C_{34}H_{42}N_2O_4$			
β-Belladonnine	n.s.g.	254(2.63),259(2.67),263(2.66)	105-0657-73
$C_{34}H_{42}N_4$			
1,4-Butanediamine, N,N'-bis[4-(1,3-dihydro-1,3,3-trimethyl-2H-indol-2-ylidene)-2-butenylidene]-, diperchlorate	n.s.g.	452(5.08),484(5.24)	104-1286-73
Piperazinium, 1,4-bis[4-(1,3-dihydro-1,3,3-trimethyl-2H-indol-2-ylidene)-2-butenylidene]-, diperchlorate	n.s.g.	448(4.28),515(5.40)	104-1286-73
$C_{34}H_{44}O_6$			
2,4,6,8,10-Tetradecapentaenoic acid, 1a,2,5,5a,6,9,10,10a-octahydro-5,5a-dihydroxy-4-(hydroxymethyl)-1,1,7,9-tetramethyl-11-oxo-1H-2,8a-methano-cyclopenta[a]cyclopropa[e]cyclodecen-6-yl ester	MeOH	222(4.28),365(4.63)	88-0881-73
$C_{34}H_{44}S_6Si_5$			
Silane, bis[5-[[5-(dimethyl-2-thienyl-silyl)-2-thienyl]dimethylsilyl]-2-thienyl]dimethyl-	$CHCl_3$	249(4.34)	88-4043-73
$C_{34}H_{46}O_6$			
Tingenol, tri-O-acetyl-	$CHCl_3$	240(3.14),266(2.89),276(2.88)	39-2725-73C
$C_{34}H_{46}O_{13}$			
Marrubiaside, 2',3',4',6'-tetra-O-acetyl-	MeCN	208.5(4.36)	24-2929-73
$C_{34}H_{47}NO_9$			
Oleficin	EtOH	418.5(4.80)	88-3643-73
$C_{34}H_{48}N_2O_4$			
6H-5a,14b-Etheno-5aH-benzo[c]cyclopenta-[h]pyridazino[1,2-a]cinnoline-1,4-di-one, 7-acetoxy-7,8,9,9a,9b,10,11,11a-12,13,14,14a-dodecahydro-9a,11a-di-methyl-12-(1,4,5-trimethyl-2-hexenyl)-	ether	225(3.93)	39-0888-73C

Compound	Solvent	λ max(log ε)	Ref.
$C_{34}H_{48}O_4$			
30-Norolean-12-en-11-one, 3-acetoxy-20-(1-oxo-2-propynyl)-, (3β,20β)-	EtOH	249(4.05),308(2.42)	78-2327-73
$C_{34}H_{48}O_6$			
Oleana-9(11),13(18)-diene-12,19-dione, 3β,6β-diacetoxy-	EtOH	278(3.96)	44-3685-73
$C_{34}H_{48}O_7$			
Isoglabrolide, 21α-hydroxy-, diacetate	EtOH	237(3.09)	104-1696-73
$C_{34}H_{48}O_9$			
Fabacein	$CHCl_3$	230(4.00)	44-1055-73
$C_{34}H_{49}ClO_2S$			
Cholest-5-en-3β-ol, O-(4-chlorophenyl)-carbonothioate	CH_2Cl_2	240(3.89),277(3.00), 308(1.90)	39-1567-73C
$C_{34}H_{50}N_2$			
1'H-Cholestano[3,2-c]pyrazole, 1'-phenyl-	MeOH	212(4.60),270(4.83)	103-0202-73
$C_{34}H_{50}N_2O_4$			
6H-5a,14b-Etheno-5aH-benzo[c]cyclopenta-[h]pyridazino[1,2-a]cinnoline-1,4-dione, 7-acetoxy-2,3,7,8,9,9a,9b,10,11-11a,12,13,14,14a-tetradecahydro-9a,11a-dimethyl-12-(1,4,5-trimethyl-2-hexenyl)-	EtOH	225(3.62),255(3.56)	39-0888-73C
$C_{34}H_{50}OS$			
Cholest-5-ene-3-thiol, benzoate	C_6H_{12}	256(3.85),288(3.90), 420(2.15)	39-1567-73C
$C_{34}H_{52}OS$			
Cholestan-3-ol, benzenecarbothioate, (3β,5α)-	EtOH	251(3.85),289(3.88)	39-1567-73C
$C_{34}H_{52}O_4$			
Oleana-11,13(18)-diene-3,6-diol, diacetate, (3β,6β)-	EtOH	243(4.37),250(4.40), 260(4.20)	44-3685-73
$C_{34}H_{52}O_5$			
D:A-Friedooleanane-1,3-dione, 2-acetyl-7-acetoxy-, (7α)-	EtOH	234(3.98),281(4.01)	78-1365-73
D:A-Friedoolean-2-en-1-one, 3,7-diacetoxy-, (7α)-	EtOH	238(3.97)	78-1365-73
D:A-Friedoolean-2-en-1-one, 3,24-diacetoxy-	EtOH	237(3.97)	78-1365-73
	EtOH-NaOH	290(4.15)	78-1365-73

Compound	Solvent	$\lambda_{max}(\log \epsilon)$	Ref.
$(C_{35}H_{19}N_9)_n$			
Poly(1,2,4-triazolo[4,3-c]quinazoline-5,3-diyl-2,6-pyridinediyl-1,2,4-triazolo[4,3-c]quinazoline-3,5-diyl-[1,1'-biphenyl]-4,4'-diyl)	H_2SO_4	268(5.18),315(4.68)	116-0483-73
$(C_{35}H_{19}N_9O)_n$			
Poly(1,2,4-triazolo[4,3-c]quinazoline-5,3-diyl-2,6-pyridinediyl-1,2,4-triazolo[4,3-c]quinazoline-3,5-diyl-1,4-phenyleneoxy-1,4-phenylene)	H_2SO_4	283(5.09),347(4.47)	116-0483-73
$C_{35}H_{21}N_9$			
1,2,4-Triazolo[4,3-c]quinazoline, 3,3'-(2,6-pyridinediyl)bis[5-phenyl-	H_2SO_4	261(4.91),288(5.00), 340(4.4)	116-0483-73
1,2,4-Triazolo[4,3-c]quinazoline, 5,5'-(2,6-pyridinediyl)bis[3-phenyl-	H_2SO_4	276(5.2),370(4.6)	116-0483-73
$C_{35}H_{22}$			
Benzo[c]phenanthro[3,4-l]chrysene, 15-methyl-	MeOH	204(4.78),221(4.80), 234s(4.63),257(4.51)	54-0553-73
$C_{35}H_{23}N_3$			
2H-Isoindole-5,6-dicarbonitrile, 2-methyl-1,3,4,7-tetraphenyl-	$CHCl_3$	245(4.58),269(4.51), 408(3.31)	35-2749-73
$C_{35}H_{23}N_3O$			
Benzo[f]quinoline-1-carboxamide, N-phenyl-3-(4-phenyl-2-quinolinyl)-	n.s.g.	283(4.76),330(4.39), 370(3.93)	103-0220-73
Cu(I) complex	isoAmOH	550(4.01)	103-0220-73
$(C_{35}H_{23}N_9O_2)_n$			
Poly(2,6-pyridinediyl-1H-1,2,4-triazole-3,5-diyl-1,2-phenyleneiminocarbonyl-[1,1'-biphenyl]-4,4'-diylcarbonylimino-1,2-phenylene-1H-1,2,4-triazole-3,5-diyl)	H_2SO_4	260(4.84),300(4.80)	116-0483-73
$(C_{35}H_{23}N_9O_3)_n$			
Poly(2,6-pyridinediyl-1H-1,2,4-triazole-3,5-diyl-1,2-phenyleneiminocarbonyl-1,4-phenyleneoxy-1,4-phenylenecarbonylimino-1,2-phenylene-1H-1,2,4-triazole-3,5-diyl)	H_2SO_4	273(4.84)	116-0483-73
$(C_{35}H_{23}N_9O_4S)_n$			
Poly(2,6-pyridinediyl-1H-1,2,4-triazole-3,5-diyl-1,2-phenyleneiminocarbonyl-1,4-phenylenesulfonyl-1,4-phenylenecarbonylimino-1,2-phenylene-1H-1,2,4-triazole-3,5-diyl) (1λ,2ε)	H_2SO_4	272(4.78),?(4.48)	116-0483-73
$C_{35}H_{24}ClN_3O_4S$			
Dibenzo[a,c]phenazinium, 11-[(3-methyl-2(3H)-benzothiazolylidene)methyl]-9-phenyl-, perchlorate	$CHCl_3$	750(5.68)	103-1407-73
$C_{35}H_{24}N_2$			
2-Propanone, 1,3-di-9H-fluoren-9-ylidene-, phenylhydrazone	MeOH	245s(4.42),256s(4.37), 294s(3.14),358(3.19), 428(3.92)	5-0750-73

Compound	Solvent	$\lambda_{max}(\log \epsilon)$	Ref.
$C_{35}H_{24}O_9$			
Cryptosporin, tribenzoate	CH_2Cl_2	233(4.70),275(4.21), 345(3.57)	33-0619-73
$C_{35}H_{25}N_3S$			
Benzo[c]thiophen-4,7-imine-5,6-dicarbonitrile, 4,5,6,7-tetrahydro-8-methyl-1,3,4,7-tetraphenyl-	$CHCl_3$	288(4.27)	35-2749-73
4,7-Epithio-2H-isoindole-5,6-dicarbonitrile, 4,5,6,7-tetrahydro-2-methyl-1,3,4,7-tetraphenyl-	MeOH	278(4.06)	35-2749-73
$C_{35}H_{25}N_9O_2$			
Benzamide, N,N'-[2,6-pyridinediylbis-[1H-1,2,4-triazole-5,3-diyl-2,1-phenylene]]bis-	H_2SO_4	257(4.8)	116-0483-73
$C_{35}H_{25}O_2$			
Pyrylium, 4-[(2,6-diphenyl-4H-pyran-4-ylidene)methyl]-2,6-diphenyl-, perchlorate	MeOH	384(4.44),551(5.11)	78-0795-73
$C_{35}H_{26}$			
7H-Benzocycloheptene, 5,6,7,8-tetraphenyl-	MeCN	275(4.53)	35-3818-73
Spiro[4.6]undeca-1,3,6,8,10-pentaene, 1,2,3,4-tetraphenyl-	EtOH	250(4.52),275s(4.22)	78-4307-73
$C_{35}H_{26}O_{10}$			
D-arabino-Hept-2-enonic acid, 3-deoxy-, γ-lactone, tetrabenzoate	MeOH	232(4.57)	136-0431-73A
$C_{35}H_{28}O_3Si$			
4,7-Silanoisobenzofuran-1,3-dione, 8-ethenyl-3a,4,7,7a-tetrahydro-8-methyl-4,5,6,7-tetraphenyl-	n.s.g.	226(4.51),277(3.95), 287(3.90)	78-2395-73
$C_{35}H_{28}O_6$			
9H-Xanthen-9-one, 1-methoxy-3,5,6-tris-(phenylmethoxy)-	$CHCl_3$	249(4.77),290s(4.26), 305(4.44),325s(4.15)	39-1329-73C
$C_{35}H_{29}CrN_2O_3P$			
Chromium, tricarbonyl[α-methyl-N-(2-pyridinylmethylene)benzenemethanamin-N,N'](triphenylphosphine)-	acetone	624(3.79)	101-0183-73K
$C_{35}H_{29}MoN_2O_3P$			
Molybdenum, tricarbonyl[α-methyl-N-(2-pyridinylmethylene)benzenemethanamine-N,N'](triphenylphosphine)-	acetone	573(3.81)	101-0183-73K
$C_{35}H_{29}N_2O$			
Benzo[f]quinolinium, 2-acetyl-1-[2-[4-(dimethylamino)phenyl]ethenyl]-4-(2-naphthalenyl)-, perchlorate	MeOH	553(3.45)	65-0877-73
$C_{35}H_{29}N_2O_3W$			
Tungsten, tricarbonyl[α-methyl-N-(2-pyridinylmethylene)benzenemethanamine-N,N'](triphenylphosphine)-	acetone	595(3.78)	101-0183-73K

Compound	Solvent	$\lambda_{max}(\log \epsilon)$	Ref.
$C_{35}H_{30}N_4O_7$			
Benzamide, N-benzoyl-N-[7-[5-O-benzoyl-2,3-O-(1-methylethylidene)-β-D-ribofuranosyl]-7H-pyrrolo[2,3-d]pyrimidin-4-yl]-	MeOH	226(4.63),273(4.08), 281(4.06)	18-0618-73
$C_{35}H_{31}N_2OS_2$			
Benzothiazolium, 2-[[3-ethoxy-6-[(3-ethyl-2(3H)-benzothiazolylidene)methyl]-1H-phenalen-1-ylidene]methyl]-3-ethyl-, tetrafluoroborate	MeCN	340(4.60),400(3.89), 840(5.03)	44-2425-73
Benzothiazolium, 2-[[3-ethoxy-7-[(3-ethyl-2(3H)-benzothiazolylidene)methyl]-1H-phenalen-1-ylidene]methyl]-3-ethyl-, tetrafluoroborate	MeCN	398(4.32),558(4.26), 812(4.99)	44-2425-73
Benzothiazolium, 2-[[6-ethoxy-3-[(3-ethyl-2(3H)-benzothiazolylidene)methyl]-1H-phenalen-1-ylidene]methyl]-3-ethyl-, tetrafluoroborate	MeCN	291(4.32),362(4.36), 573(4.72),757(4.60)	44-2425-73
Benzothiazolium, 2-[[7-ethoxy-4-[(3-ethyl-2(3H)-benzothiazolylidene)methyl]-1H-phenalen-1-ylidene]methyl]-3-ethyl-, tetrafluoroborate	MeCN	335(4.30),417(4.42), 572(4.35),845(4.97)	44-2425-73
$C_{35}H_{31}N_5O_8$			
7(8H)-Pteridinone, 2-(dimethylamino)-6-methyl-8-(2,3,5-tri-O-benzoyl-β-D-ribofuranosyl)-	MeOH	226(4.70),271(3.85), 279(3.82),315s(3.87), 360(4.20)	24-0317-73
α-D-Ribofuranoside, 2-(dimethylamino)-6-methyl-7-pteridinyl, 2,3,5-tribenzoate	MeOH	230(4.72),272(4.19), 279(4.18),385(4.07)	24-0317-73
β-	MeOH	230(4.72),272(4.19), 279(4.18),385(4.07)	24-0317-73
$C_{35}H_{31}N_5O_9$			
7(8H)-Pteridinone, 2-(dimethylamino)-4-methoxy-8-(2,3,5-tri-O-benzoyl-β-D-ribofuranosyl)-	MeOH	230(4.82),272(3.83), 277(3.81),364(4.21)	24-1952-73
β-D-Ribofuranoside, 2-amino-4-(1-methylethoxy)-7-pteridinyl, 2,3,5-tribenzoate	MeOH	229(4.77),270(3.99), 347(4.08)	24-1952-73
β-D-Ribofuranoside, 2-(dimethylamino)-4-methoxy-7-pteridinyl, 2,3,5-tribenzoate	MeOH	232(4.82),280(4.22), 367(4.17)	24-1952-73
$C_{35}H_{32}N_2$			
Quinolinium, 6,6'-methylenebis[2-methyl-1-(phenylmethyl)-, diperchlorate	n.s.g.	242(5.06),323(4.13)	104-2195-73
$C_{35}H_{34}N_2O_5$			
Nortiliacorine A	MeOH	215(4.80),235s(4.69), 293(4.00)	102-0203-73
Nortiliacorinine A	MeOH	212(4.75),236s(4.67), 292(3.99)	102-0203-73
Trigelletine	MeOH	234(4.72),275s(3.73), 289(3.77),307s(3.58)	102-2509-73
$C_{35}H_{34}O_2Si$			
7-Silabicyclo[2.2.1]hept-5-ene-2-carboxylic acid, 7,7-dimethyl-1,4,5,6-tetraphenyl-, ethyl ester	n.s.g.	235(4.45),279(4.05)	78-2395-73

Compound	Solvent	$\lambda_{max}(\log \epsilon)$	Ref.
$C_{35}H_{35}NO_{16}$			
Benzo[f]cyclopenta[a]quinolizine-6,7,7a,8,9,10(8H)-hexacarboxylic acid, 6,7-dihydro-12-[4-methoxy-2-(methoxycarbonyl)-4-oxo-2-butenyl]-, hexamethyl ester	MeOH	234(4.35),323(4.00), 368(4.36),384(4.49), 502s(4.20)	39-1338-73C
	MeOH-$HClO_4$	280(4.38),367(4.32)	39-1338-73C
$C_{35}H_{35}N_3O_7$			
Thymidine, (3,4-dihydro-1(2H)-quinolin-yl)-, 3',5'-bis(4-methylbenzoate)	EtOH	222(4.30),245(4.34), 252(4.34),260(4.34), 301(3.42)	69-2879-73
$C_{35}H_{36}CoN_4$			
Cobalt, [1,2,3,7,8,12,13,17,18,19-deca-dehydro-8,12-diethyl-21,22-dihydro-2,3,7,13,17,18-hexamethyl-21-phenyl-corrinato(2-)-N^{21},N^{22},N^{23},N^{24}]-, (SP-4-2)-	$CHCl_3$	376(4.68),625(3.40), 681(3.62)	39-2281-73C
$C_{35}H_{36}INO_4$			
6H-Dibenzo[a,g]quinolizinium, 5,8-di-hydro-2,11-dimethoxy-7,13-dimethyl-3,10-bis(phenylmethoxy)-, iodide	EtOH	264s(4.14),270s(4.11), 293s(4.14),327(4.36)	78-1265-73
$C_{35}H_{36}N_2O_6$			
Cycleacurine	EtOH	284(3.83)	44-1846-73
$C_{35}H_{38}CoN_7O_2$			
Cobalt, (octadehydro-2,8,12,18-tetra-ethyl-1,3,7,13,17,19-hexamethyl-10-nitro-5,15-corrindicarbonitrilato-N^{21},N^{22},N^{23},N^{24})-, (SP-4-4)-	$CHCl_3$	270(4.38),340(4.49), 490(3.88),550(4.27)	39-0775-73C
$C_{35}H_{39}CoN_6$			
Cobalt, (octadehydro-2,8,12,18-tetraeth-yl-1,3,7,13,17,19-hexamethyl-5,15-cor-rindicarbonitrilato-N^{21},N^{22},N^{23},N^{24})-, (SP-4-3)-	$CHCl_3$	270(4.31),341(4.54), 373s(4.22),403s(4.10), 480(3.69),542(4.19)	39-0775-73C
Cobalt(1+), (octadehydro-2,8,12,18-tetraethyl-1,3,7,13,17,19-hexamethyl-5,15-corrindicarbonitrilato-N^{21},N^{22}-N^{23},N^{24})-, (SP-4-3)-, perchlorate	$CHCl_3$	285(4.39),330(4.31), 520(4.19),613(4.20)	39-0775-73C
	$CHCl_3$-NaBr	291(4.40),337(4.46), 540(4.31),616(3.93)	39-0775-73C
$C_{35}H_{39}N_5O_5$			
Ergocristine	H_2O	316(3.89)	39-1312-73B
	EtOH	312(3.94)	39-1312-73B
Ergocristinine	EtOH	314(3.95)	39-1312-73B
	5% EtOH	313(3.88)	
$C_{35}H_{40}N_5O_{10}P$			
β-D-ribo-Heptofuranuronic acid, 1-[1-benzoyl-6-(benzoylimino)-1,6-dihydro-9H-purin-9-yl]-1,5,6-trideoxy-6-(di-ethoxyphosphinyl)-2,3-O-(1-methyleth-ylidene)-, ethyl ester	EtOH	247(4.59),272(4.31)	35-4404-73
$C_{35}H_{41}CoN_6$			
Cobalt, bis(cyano-C)(octadehydro-2,8,12-18-tetraethyl-1,3,7,13,17,19-hexameth-ylcorrinato-N^{21},N^{22},N^{23},N^{24}]-, (OC-6-34)-	$CHCl_3$	276(4.98),301(4.21), 361(3.92),405(4.01), 503(3.41),538(3.06), 620s(3.16),682(3.76),	39-0775-73C

Compound	Solvent	$\lambda_{max}(\log \epsilon)$	Ref.
(cont.)		754(4.19)	39-0775-73C
$C_{35}H_{41}NO_{11}$			
Rifamycin, 25-deacetoxy-1,4-dideoxy-	EtOH-HCl	213(4.52),274(4.43), 331(3.92),386(3.71)	33-2323-73
$C_{35}H_{42}Cl_2CuN_5O_2P$			
Copper, [(dimethylamino)(2,7,12,17-tetraethyl-3,8,13,18-tetramethyl-21H,23H-porphin-5-yl)methyl phosphorodichloridato(2-)-N^{21},N^{22},N^{23}-N^{24}]-, (SP-4-2)-	$CHCl_3$	401(5.14),440(4.88), 535(3.88),575(4.04)	103-1065-73
$C_{35}H_{42}O_5$			
2H-1-Benzopyran-2,5,7(6H,8H)-trione, 4-hydroxy-6,6,8,8-tetrakis(3-methyl-2-butenyl)-3-phenyl-	MeOH	258(4.10),303(4.31)	2-0106-73
$C_{35}H_{42}O_{15}$			
Lignan B glucoside tetraacetate	MeOH	230(4.39),280(3.80)	95-0044-73
$C_{35}H_{43}CuN_5$			
Copper, [2,7,12,17-tetraethyl-N,N,3,8-13,18-hexamethyl-21H,23H-porphine-5-methanaminato(2-)-N^{21},N^{22},N^{23},N^{24}]-, (SP-4-2)-	$CHCl_3$	408(5.11),542(4.00), 585(4.10)	103-1065-73
$C_{35}H_{43}NO_{11}$			
Rifamycin, 25-O-deacetyl-1,4-dideoxy-1,4-dihydro-1,4-dioxo-	EtOH	277(4.42),328(3.94), 389(3.70)	33-2323-73
$C_{35}H_{44}N_4$			
1,5-Pentanediamine, N,N'-bis[4-(1,3-dihydro-1,3,3-trimethyl-2H-indol-2-ylidene)-2-butenylidene]-, diperchlorate	n.s.g.	480(5.23)	104-1286-73
$C_{35}H_{45}NO_{11}$			
Rifamycin, 25-O-deacetyl-11-deoxo-1,4-deoxy-1,4-dihydro-11-hydroxy-1,4-dioxo-	EtOH	229(4.54),269(4.35), 327(4.17),410(3.72)	33-2323-73
$C_{35}H_{46}N_4O_2$			
21H-Biline-1,19-dione, 2,3,7,8,12,13,17-18-octaethyl-22,24-dihydro-	CH_2Cl_2	366(4.76),645(4.18)	39-2149-73C
$C_{35}H_{48}N_4O_2$			
21H-Biline-1,19-dione, 2,3,7,8,12,13,17-18-octaethyl-2,3,22,24-tetrahydro-, trans	CH_2Cl_2	347(4.65),591(4.26)	39-2149-73C
$C_{35}H_{48}N_4O_7$			
1,5,9,13-Tetraazacycloheptadecan-6-one, 9,13-diacetyl-1-[3-[4-(acetyloxy)-phenyl]-1-oxopropyk]-8-(4-methoxy-phenyl)-, (S)-	EtOH	268s(3.13),274(3.19), 283(3.04)	33-1266-73
$C_{35}H_{48}O_8$			
Oleana-9(11),13(18)-dien-29-oic acid, 3β,21α-diacetoxy-12,19-dioxo-, methyl ester	EtOH	283(4.1)	104-1696-73

Compound	Solvent	λ max(log ε)	Ref.
$C_{35}H_{49}NO_{11}$			
Rifamycin, 25-O-acetoxy-1,4-dideoxy-1,4,12,13,14,15,28,29-octahydro-1,4-dioxo-	EtOH	235(4.38),277(4.30),305(4.15),398(3.60)	33-2323-73
$C_{35}H_{50}N_4O_6$			
B-Norcholest-5-ene-6-carboxaldehyde, 3β-acetoxy-, 6-(2,4-dinitrophenylhydrazone)	EtOH	384(4.41)	94-1287-73
$C_{35}H_{50}O_8S$			
C-Nor-9,11-secospirostan-3-one, 11-acetoxy-9-[[(4-methylphenyl)sulfonyl]-oxy]-, (5α,9β,25R)-	EtOH	226(4.2)	13-0147-73A
$C_{35}H_{52}O_2S$			
Cholest-5-en-3-ol, (3β)-, 4-methoxybenzenecarbothioate	EtOH	228(4.07),234(4.05),266(4.22),313(3.89),419(2.20)	39-1567-73C
$C_{35}H_{63}MoN_7$			
Molybdenum(2+), heptakis(2-isocyano-2-methylpropane)-, bis[hexafluorophosphate(1-)]-	MeOH	248(4.53),275(4.42),413(3.02)	77-0202-73

Compound	Solvent	$\lambda_{max}(\log \epsilon)$	Ref.
$(C_{36}H_{19}N_9O)_n$			
Poly(1,2,4-triazolo[4,3-c]quinazoline-5,3-diyl-2,6-pyridinediyl-1,2,4-triazolo[4,3-c]quinazoline-3,5-diyl-1,4-phenylenecarbonyl-1,4-phenylene)	H_2SO_4	285(5.09),350(4.63)	116-0483-73
$(C_{36}H_{20}N_8)_n$			
Poly(1,2,4-triazolo[4,3-c]quinazoline-5,3-diyl-1,3-phenylene-1,2,4-triazolo[4,3-c]quinazoline-3,5-diyl-[1,1'-biphenyl]-4,4'-diyl)	H_2SO_4	289(5.04),346(4.46)	116-0483-73
Poly(1,2,4-triazolo[4,3-c]quinazoline-5,3-diyl-1,4-phenylene-1,2,4-triazolo[4,3-c]quinazoline-3,5-diyl-[1,1'-biphenyl]-4,4'-diyl)	H_2SO_4	264(4.96),398(4.76)	116-0483-73
$(C_{36}H_{20}N_8O)_n$			
Poly(1,2,4-triazolo[4,3-c]quinazoline-5,3-diyl-1,3-phenylene-1,2,4-triazolo[4,3-c]quinazoline-3,5-diyl-1,4-phenyleneoxy-1,4-phenylene)	H_2SO_4	237(4.72),288(5.34), 404(4.35)	116-0483-73
Poly(1,2,4-triazolo[4,3-c]quinazoline-5,3-diyl-1,4-phenylene-1,2,4-triazolo[4,3-c]quinazoline-3,5-diyl-1,4-phenyleneoxy-1,4-phenylene)-	H_2SO_4	273(5.02),394(4.54)	116-0483-73
$(C_{36}H_{20}N_8O_2S)_n$			
Poly(1,2,4-triazolo[4,3-c]quinazoline-5,3-diyl-1,3-phenylene-1,2,4-triazolo[4,3-c]quinazoline-3,5-diyl-1,4-phenylenesulfonyl-1,4-phenylene)	H_2SO_4	292(4.95),345(4.47)	116-0483-73
Poly(1,2,4-triazolo[4,3-c]quinazoline-5,3-diyl-1,4-phenylene-1,2,4-triazolo[4,3-c]quinazoline-3,5-diyl-1,4-phenylenesulfonyl-1,4-phenylene)	H_2SO_4	285(4.3),355(4.1)	116-0483-73
$C_{36}H_{22}$			
1,3-Butadiene, 1,4-di-2-pyrenyl-	THF	249s(--),258(4.54), 268s(--),314s(--), 333(5.03),344(5.25), 365(4.96),385(4.78), 399s(--),424(3.59)	18-2822-73
$C_{36}H_{22}N_8$			
1,2,4-Triazolo[4,3-c]quinazoline, 3,3'-(1,3-phenylene)bis[5-phenyl-	H_2SO_4	269(4.73),283(4.75), 352(4.87)	116-0483-73
1,2,4-Triazolo[4,3-c]quinazoline, 3,3'-(1,4-phenylene)bis[5-phenyl-	H_2SO_4	265(4.2),285(4.3)	116-0483-73
1,2,4-Triazolo[4,3-c]quinazoline, 5,5'-(1,3-phenylene)bis[3-phenyl-	H_2SO_4	289(5.04),345(4.5)	116-0483-73
1,2,4-Triazolo[4,3-c]quinazoline, 5,5'-(1,4-phenylene)bis[3-phenyl-	H_2SO_4	289(5.02),345(4.4)	116-0483-73
$(C_{36}H_{24}N_8O_2)_n$			
Poly(1H-1,2,4-triazole-3,5-diyl-1,3-phenylene-1H-1,2,4-triazole-3,5-diyl-1,2-phenyleneiminocarbonyl[1,1'-biphenyl]-4,4'-diylcarbonylimino-1,2-phenylene)	H_2SO_4	274(4.87),390(4.64)	116-0483-73

Compound	Solvent	λmax(log ε)	Ref.
Poly(1H-1,2,4-triazole-3,5-diyl-1,4-phenylene-1H-1,2,4-triazole-3,5-diyl-1,2-phenyleneiminocarbonyl[1,1'-biphenyl]-4,4'-diylcarbonylimino-1,2-phenylene)	H_2SO_4	305(4.65)	116-0483-73
$(C_{36}H_{24}N_8O_3)_n$			
Poly(1H-1,2,4-triazole-3,5-diyl-1,3-phenylene-1H-1,2,4-triazole-3,5-diyl-1,2-phenyleneiminocarbonyl-1,4-phenyleneoxy-1,4-phenylenecarbonylimino-1,2-phenylene)	H_2SO_4	236(4.73),290(4.72)	116-0483-73
Poly(1H-1,2,4-triazole-3,5-diyl-1,4-phenylene-1H-1,2,4-triazole-3,5-diyl-1,2-phenyleneiminocarbonyl-1,4-phenyleneoxy-1,4-phenylenecarbonylimino-1,2-phenylene)	H_2SO_4	273(4.95),392(4.36)	116-0483-73
$(C_{36}H_{24}N_8O_4S)_n$			
Poly(1H-1,2,4-triazole-3,5-diyl-1,4-phenylene-1H-1,2,4-triazole-3,5-diyl-1,2-phenyleneiminocarbonyl-1,4-phenylenesulfonyl-1,4-phenylenecarbonylimino-1,2-phenylene)	H_2SO_4	292(4.55)	116-0483-73
$C_{36}H_{24}O$			
9,14-Epoxynaphtho[2',3':3,4]cyclobuta[1,2-d]phenanthrene, 8c,9,14,14a-tetrahydro-9,14-diphenyl-	$C_2H_4Cl_2$	253(4.68),260(4.73), 272s(4.46),285(4.23), 298(4.25),310(4.24)	88-0043-73
$C_{36}H_{25}NO_2$			
1H-Pyrrole, 1,3-dibenzoyl-2,4,5-triphenyl-	EtOH	210(4.73),259(4.63), 280(4.46)	1-0271-73
$C_{36}H_{26}$			
1,3,5,7-Octatetraene, 1,8-di-2-phenanthrenyl-	THF	255(4.60),284(4.47), 294(4.53),319(4.24), 371s(--),388(4.99), 408(5.15),436(5.06)	18-0909-73
1,3,5,7-Octatetraene, 1,8-di-3-phenanthrenyl-	THF	253(4.89),296(4.32), 319(4.18),334(4.30), 372s(4.69),391(4.93), 414(5.09),440(5.00)	18-0909-73
1,3,5,7-Octatetraene, 1,8-di-9-phenanthrenyl-	benzene	296(4.52),403(4.83)	18-0909-73
$C_{36}H_{26}N_2$			
Cyclobuta[b]quinoxaline, 1-(diphenylmethyl)-2-(diphenylmethylene)-1,2-dihydro-	$CHCl_3$	275(4.23),385(4.28)	18-1733-73
Pyrazine, 1,2-dihydro-1,2-di-2-naphthalenyl-2,5-diphenyl-	n.s.g.	259(4.49),268(4.56), 311(4.35)	39-0683-73C
$C_{36}H_{26}N_4$			
5,10-Methanobenzo[g]phthalazine, 11-(diphenylmethylene)-4a,5,10,10a-tetrahydro-1,4-di-2-pyridinyl-	90% EtOH	222(4.04),247(3.96), 271(3.83),313(3.85)	12-1725-73

Compound	Solvent	$\lambda_{max}(\log \epsilon)$	Ref.
$C_{36}H_{26}N_8O_2$			
Benzamide, N,N'-[1,3-phenylenebis(1H-1,2,4-triazole-5,3-diyl-2,1-phenylene)]bis-	H_2SO_4	261(4.83)	116-0483-73
Benzamide, N,N'-[1,4-phenylenebis(1H-1,2,4-triazole-5,3-diyl-2,1-phenylene)]bis-	H_2SO_4	254(4.7),298(4.8)	116-0483-73
1,3-Benzenedicarboxamide, N,N'-bis[2-(5-phenyl-1H-1,2,4-triazol-3-yl)phenyl]-	H_2SO_4	285(4.87),342(4.13)	116-0483-73
1,4-Benzenedicarboxamide, N,N'-bis[2-(5-phenyl-1H-1,2,4-triazol-3-yl)phenyl]-	H_2SO_4	285(4.78),348(4.28)	116-0483-73
$C_{36}H_{26}O_2$			
Ethanone, 1-phenyl-2-(2,2,4,5-tetraphenyl-3(2H)-furanylidene)-	$CHCl_3$	250(4.08),400(4.31)	5-0375-73
$C_{36}H_{26}O_4S$			
Benzo[c]thiophene-5,6-dicarboxylic acid, 1,3,4,7-tetraphenyl-, dimethyl ester	dioxan	273(5.01),390(4.00)	35-2561-73
$C_{36}H_{27}O_2$			
Pyrylium, 4-[1-(2,6-diphenyl-4H-pyran-4-ylidene)ethyl]-2,6-diphenyl-, perchlorate	MeCN	385(4.44),604(4.82)	78-0795-73
$C_{36}H_{28}$			
1,3,5,7,9-Decapentaene, 1,10-di-2-fluorenyl-	THF	388s(--),409(5.00), 432(5.16),461(5.09)	18-2822-73
$C_{36}H_{28}O_4$			
1,4-Naphthacenediol, 8,9-dimethyl-6,11-diphenyl-, diacetate	CH_2Cl_2	386(3.0),413(3.3), 437(3.7),464(4.0), 496(4.0)	22-2856-73
$C_{36}H_{30}N_2$			
4,4'-Bipyridinium, 1,1'-dimethyl-2,2',6,6'-tetraphenyl-, bis-(tetrafluoroborate)	MeCN	260(4.59),334(4.20)	5-1036-73
4,4'-Bipyridinyl, 1,1'-dihydro-1,1'-dimethyl-2,2',6,6'-tetraphenyl-	MeCN	250(4.32),488(4.38)	5-1036-73
Pyridiniumyl, 1,4-dihydro-1-methyl-4-(1-methyl-2,6-diphenyl-4(1H)-pyridinylidene)-2,6-diphenyl- (semiquinone)	MeCN	254(4.36),375(4.23), 655(4.10),695(4.13), 770(3.92)	5-1036-73
$C_{36}H_{30}O_4$			
[2,2'-Bifuran]-5,5'(2H,2'H)-dione, 2,2,4,4-tetrakis(4-methylphenyl)-	n.s.g.	285(4.38)	88-4221-73
$C_{36}H_{32}N_2$			
Quinolinium, 6,6'-(1,2-ethenediyl)bis-[2-methyl-1-(phenylmethyl)-, diperchlorate	n.s.g.	256(5.42),328(4.16)	104-2195-73
$C_{36}H_{32}O_4$			
1,3,5-Cyclohexanetrione, 6-acetyl-2,2,4,4-tetrakis(phenylmethyl)-	EtOH-acid	288(3.85)	39-2013-73C
	EtOH-base	279(4.08)	39-2013-73C
$C_{36}H_{33}N_3O_9$			
1H-Isoindole-1,3(2H)-dione, 2,2',2"-(1,3,5-trioxane-2,4,6-triyltri-3,1-propanediyl)tris-	EtOH	232(4.12),241(3.95), 291(3.31)	78-3761-73

Compound	Solvent	$\lambda_{max}(\log \epsilon)$	Ref.
$C_{36}H_{34}$			
Benzene, 1,1',1",1"'-(3,3'-dipropyl[bi-cyclopropen-1-yl]-1,1',2,2'-tetrayl)-tetrakis-	EtOH	267(4.21)	18-3881-73
$C_{36}H_{34}N_2$			
Quinolinium, 6,6'-(1,2-ethanediyl)bis-[2-methyl-1-(phenylmethyl)-, diper-chlorate	n.s.g.	240(5.17),322(3.96)	104-2195-73
$C_{36}H_{34}O_2Si$			
7-Silabicyclo[2.2.1]hept-5-ene-2-carb-oxylic acid, 7-ethenyl-7-methyl-1,4,5,6-tetraphenyl-, ethyl ester	n.s.g.	234(4.41),278(3.94), 290(3.90)	78-2395-73
$C_{36}H_{36}N_4O_2$			
Dispiro[2H-indole-2,1'-cyclobutane-2',2"-[2H]indole]-3,3"(1H,1"H)-dione, 3',4'-bis[4-(dimethylamino)-phenyl]-1,1'-dimethyl-	dioxan	242(4.86),418(3.47)	39-2804-73C
$C_{36}H_{38}N_4O_4$			
21H,23H-Porphine-2,7-dipropanoic acid, 12,17-diethenyl-3,8,13,18-tetrameth-yl-, dimethyl ester	CH_2Cl_2	406(5.19),506(4.12), 539(4.02),576(3.76), 629(3.60)	39-2478-73C
	CH_2Cl_2+ CF_3COOH	412(5.38),556(4.19), 599(3.81)	39-2478-73C
21H,23H-Porphine-5-^{13}C-2,18-dipropanoic acid, 8,13-diethenyl-3,7,12,17-tetra-methyl-, dimethyl ester	$CHCl_3$	408(5.22),507(4.24), 540(4.12),577(3.93), 631(3.82)	39-2923-73C
$C_{36}H_{38}O_9$			
2H-1-Benzopyran, 4,4'-oxybis[3,4-di-hydro-5,7-dimethoxy-2-(4-methoxy-phenyl)-	MeOH	215(4.64),273(3.49)	2-0120-73
$C_{36}H_{39}BrN_4O_5$			
3-Phorbinepropanoic acid, 6-bromo-9,14-diethyl-21-(methoxycarbonyl)-4,8,13,18-tetramethyl-20-oxo-, methyl ester, [3S-(3α,4β,21β)]-	CH_2Cl_2	413(5.03),482(3.48), 515(3.91),546(4.14), 613(3.80),673(4.61)	39-2517-73C
	CH_2Cl_2+ CF_3COOH	419(5.06),538(3.66), 579(3.88),612(3.88), 666(4.57)	39-2517-73C
$C_{36}H_{40}Br_2N_4O_4$			
21H,23H-Porphine-2,18-dipropanoic acid, 7,12-bis(2-bromoethyl)-3,8,13,17-tetramethyl-, dimethyl ester	CH_2Cl_2	403(5.28),501(4.17), 535(4.01),569(3.79), 626(3.64)	5-1329-73
	CH_2Cl_2+ CF_3COOH	408(5.56),549(3.69), 595(3.90)	5-1329-73
$C_{36}H_{40}Cl_2N_4O_4$			
21H,23H-Porphine-2,7-dipropanoic acid, 12,17-bis(2-chloroethyl)-3,8,13,18-tetramethyl-, dimethyl ester	CH_2Cl_2	399(5.23),499(4.15), 532(3.90),569(3.74),	39-2478-73C
	CH_2Cl_2+ CF_3COOH	404(5.51),551(4.18), 593(3.78)	39-2478-73C
$C_{36}H_{40}CuN_4O_4$			
Mesoporphyrin III dimethyl ester, copper complex	$CHCl_3$	400(5.52),526(4.10), 562(4.34)	65-0885-73

Compound	Solvent	$\lambda_{max}(\log \epsilon)$	Ref.
Mesoporphyrin IX dimethyl ester, copper complex	$CHCl_3$	399(5.56),527(5.09), 563(4.36)	65-0885-73
$C_{36}H_{41}NO_{11}$			
Rifamycin, 2,7-demethoxy-1,4,23-tri-deoxy-23,27-epoxy-1,4-dihydro-1,4-dioxo-	EtOH	275(4.44),330s(--), 390(3.68)	33-2323-73
$C_{36}H_{42}N_4O_6$			
21H,23H-Porphine-2,7-dipropanoic acid, 12,17-bis(2-hydroxyethyl)-3,8,13,18-tetramethyl-	CH_2Cl_2	399(5.30),498(4.15), 531(3.95),568(3.78), 621(3.60)	39-2478-73C
	CH_2Cl_2+ CF_3COOH	407(5.50),551(4.20), 593(3.78)	39-2478-73C
21H,23H-Porphine-2-propanoic acid, 8-(2,2-dimethoxyethyl)-13-ethyl-18-(methoxycarbonyl)-3,7,12,17-tetra-methyl-, methyl ester	CH_2Cl_2	406(5.28),509(3.99), 547(4.16),575(3.90), 632(3.08)	5-1329-73
	CH_2Cl_2+ CF_3COOH	411(5.52),556(4.11), 606(3.93)	5-1329-73
$C_{36}H_{42}O_{16}$			
Lignan A glucoside pentaacetate	MeOH	280(3.75)	95-0044-73
$C_{36}H_{43}NO_{10}$			
Rifarubin A	EtOH	247(4.46),275(4.47), 318(4.16),510(3.86)	33-2323-73
Rifarubin B	EtOH	245(4.41),271(4.41), 320(4.11),510(3.78)	33-2323-73
$C_{36}H_{43}NO_{16}$			
Evonoline	EtOH	222(3.90),265(3.56)	73-2132-73
$C_{36}H_{43}NO_{17}$			
Evonine	EtOH	222(3.90),265(3.56)	73-2132-73
	EtOH	227(3.79),267(3.51)	78-1773-73
Isoevonine	EtOH	224(4.04),271(3.59)	73-2132-73
$C_{36}H_{44}IN_4Tl$			
Thallium, iodo[2,3,7,8,12,13,17,18-octaethyl-21H,23H-porphinato(2-)-N^{21},N^{22},N^{23},N^{24}]-, (SP-5-12)-	CH_2Cl_2	421(5.46),546(4.26), 584(4.10)	39-2142-73C
$C_{36}H_{44}N_4OZn$			
Zinc, [2,3,7,8,12,13,17,18-octaethyl-21H,23H-porphin-5-olato(2-)-N^{21},N^{22},N^{23},N^{24}]-, (SP-4-2)-	CH_2Cl_2	406(5.34),534(4.10), 568(3.82)	39-0691-73C
$C_{36}H_{44}N_4O_2$			
7α,15α-(Tetracyanoethano)ergosta-5,8(14),22-trien-3β-ol, acetate	C_6H_{12}	220(3.68),284(2.70)	44-0237-73
$C_{36}H_{44}N_4O_6$			
21H-Biline-3,7-dipropanoic acid, 13,18-diacetyl-5,15,23,24-tetrahydro-2,8,12,17,19-pentamethyl-, dimethyl ester	$CHCl_3$	487(4.38)	65-1583-73
	$CHCl_3$-HBr	484(4.47)	65-1583-73
$C_{36}H_{44}O_6$			
2H-1-Benzopyran-2,5,7(6H,8H)-trione, 4-hydroxy-3-(4-methoxyphenyl)-6,6,8,8-tetrakis(3-methyl-2-butenyl)-	MeOH	254(4.17),308(4.29)	2-0106-73

Compound	Solvent	$\lambda_{max}(\log \epsilon)$	Ref.
$C_{36}H_{44}O_{12}$			
1-Butanone, 1-[3,5-bis[[2,4-dihydroxy-6-methoxy-5-methyl-3-(1-oxobutyl)-phenyl]methyl]-2,4,6-trihydroxy-phenyl]- (kosin K1)	C_6H_{12}	229(4.59),284(4.60)	102-2017-73
$C_{36}H_{44}O_{13}$			
19-Norcarda-1,3,5(10),20(22)-tetraeno-lide, 14β-hydroxy-3-[(2,3,4,6-tetra-O-acetyl-β-D-glucopyranosyl)oxy]-	MeOH	202(4.67),217(4.40), 273(3.16)	5-0224-73
$C_{36}H_{45}NO_{10}$			
Rifarubin SV, 29-deoxo-1,4-dideoxy-1,4-dihydro-29-hydroxy-1,4-dioxo- (dihydrorifarubin A)	EtOH	246(4.47),274(4.48), 317(4.17),510(3.89)	33-2323-73
$C_{36}H_{45}NO_{11}$			
Rifamycin, 27-demethoxy-1,4,23-trideoxy-23,27-epoxy-14,16,17,18,19-hexahydro-1,4-dioxo-	EtOH	234(4.35),277(4.32), 390(3.62)	33-2323-73
$C_{36}H_{46}N_4$			
1,6-Hexanediamine, N,N'-bis[4-(1,3-di-hydro-1,3,3-trimethyl-2H-indol-2-yl-idene)-2-butenylidene]-, dipicrate	n.s.g.	475(5.27)	104-1286-73
21H,23H-Porphine, 2,3,7,8,12,13,17,18-octaethyl-, dihydrochloride	$CHCl_3$	419(5.25),554(4.18), 559(4.17),577(3.78), 599(3.98)	78-3241-73
dihydroiodide	$CHCl_3$	404(5.37),563(3.98), 587(3.70),605(3.56)	78-3241-73
diperchlorate	$CHCl_3$	408(5.55),551(4.17), 554(4.16),576(3.74), 597(3.92)	78-3241-73
bis(tetrafluoroborate)	$CHCl_3$	405(5.50),550(4.17), 554(4.16),575(3.75), 595(3.89)	78-3241-73
$C_{36}H_{46}N_4Zn$			
Zinc, [2,3,7,8,12,13,17,18-octaethyl-7,8-dihydro-21H,23H-porphinato(2-)-N^{21},N^{22},N^{23},N^{24}]-, [SP-4-2-(trans)]-	CH_2Cl_2	397(5.15),500(3.76), 536(3.63),569(3.81), 616(4.58)	39-2149-73C
$C_{36}H_{46}O_4$			
Metabolite a from estradiol oxidation	EtOH	280(3.63)	10-0001-73F
Metabolite b from estradiol oxidation	EtOH	296(3.37)	10-0001-73F
$C_{36}H_{47}I_3N_4$			
21H,23H-Porphine, 2,3,7,8,12,13,17,18-octaethyl-, monohydroiodide mono-(hydrogen triiodide)	$CHCl_3$	397(5.24),534(3.95), 560(4.08),572(3.98), 604(3.58)	78-3241-73
$C_{36}H_{47}N_4O_2Tl$			
Thallium, aquahydroxy[2,3,7,8,12,13,17-18-octaethyl-21H,23H-porphinato(2-)-N^{21},N^{22},N^{23},N^{24}]-, (OC-6-23)-	CH_2Cl_2	415(5.52),543(4.26), 581(4.15)	39-2142-73C
$C_{36}H_{48}$			
1,12:2,11:3,10:4,9-Tetrabutanodibenzo-[a,g]cyclododecene, 5,6,7,8,13,14,15-16-octahydro-	hexane	273(3.0)	44-2261-73

Compound	Solvent	λmax(log ε)	Ref.
$C_{36}H_{49}NO_{10}$ Rifarubin SV, 1,4-dideoxy-1,4,16,17,18-19-hexahydro-1,4-dioxo-	EtOH	234(4.48),271(4.08), 326(4.13),425(3.65)	33-2323-73
$C_{36}H_{49}N_4O_2Tl$ Thallium, aquahydroxy[2,3,7,8,12,13,17-18-octaethyl-21H,23H-porphinato(2-)-N^{21},N^{22},N^{23},N^{24}]-, [OC-6-24-(trans)]-	CH_2Cl_2	408(5.21),512(3.72), 577(3.76),625(4.65)	39-2149-73C
$C_{36}H_{50}N_2$ Cholest-2-ene-2-carbonitrile, 3-(1H-indol-3-yl)-	MeOH	220(4.49),290(3.95)	103-0205-73
$C_{36}H_{50}N_4O_4$ 21H-Biline-1,5,19(2H)-trione, 2,3,7,8-12,13,17,18-octaethyl-3,4,22,24-tetrahydro-4-methoxy-	CH_2Cl_2	326(4.72),505(4.40), 536(4.42)	39-2149-73C
$C_{36}H_{52}O_{10}$ Jaligonic acid triacetate	EtOH	204(3.72)	100-0326-73
$C_{36}H_{53}N_3O_2$ 5α-Lanosta-1,8-dien-3-one, (4-nitrophenylhydrazone), (3E)-	EtOH	240(3.95),295(3.65), 328(3.60),404(3.40)	39-1565-73C
$C_{36}H_{54}OS$ Cholest-5-en-3-ol, 4,4-dimethyl-, benzenecarbothioate, (3β)-	EtOH	253(4.02),290(4.02)	39-1567-73C
$C_{36}H_{55}N_3O_2$ 5α-Lanost-8-en-3-one, (4-nitrophenylhydrazone)	EtOH	250(4.02),395(4.38)	39-1565-73C
$C_{36}H_{60}N_4$ 2-Tetrazene, 1,4-bis[3,5-bis(1,1-dimethylethyl)phenyl]-1,4-bis(1,1-dimethylethyl)-	EtOH	248(4.30),310(3.00)	35-8707-73

Compound	Solvent	λmax(log ε)	Ref.
$(C_{37}H_{20}N_8O)_n$			
Poly(1,2,4-triazolo[4,3-c]quinazoline-5,3-diyl-1,3-phenylene-1,2,4-triazolo[4,3-c]quinazoline-3,5-diyl-1,4-phenylenecarbonyl-1,4-phenylene)	H_2SO_4	286(4.96),401(4.33)	116-0483-73
$C_{37}H_{23}N_3O_3$			
9,15-Methano-11H-dibenzo[f,h][1,2,4]triazolo[1,2-b]phthalazine-11,13,16(12H)-trione, 9,15-dihydro-9,12,15-triphenyl-, endo	$CHCl_3$	263(5.11),300(4.41), 313(4.39),340(2.64), 348(2.39),357(2.23)	5-0129-73
exo	$CHCl_3$	260(4.95),299(4.30), 311(4.37),336(2.68), 344(2.52),353(2.38)	5-0129-73
$(C_{37}H_{24}N_8O_3)_n$			
Poly(1H-1,2,4-triazole-3,5-diyl-1,3-phenylene-1H-1,2,4-triazole-3,5-diyl-1,2-phenyleneiminocarbonyl-1,4-phenylenecarbonyl-1,4-phenylenecarbonylimino-1,2-phenylene)	H_2SO_4	280(4.55)	116-0483-73
isomer	H_2SO_4	283(4.96),347(4.65)	116-0483-73
$C_{37}H_{26}N_2$			
Pyrazolo[1,5-a]pyridine, 2,4,5,6,7-pentaphenyl-	dioxan	286(4.47),324(4.00)	39-0221-73C
$C_{37}H_{27}BF_4N_6S_3$			
Benzothiazolium, 2-[[4,7-bis[(3-methyl-2(3H)-benzothiazolylidene)amino]-1H-phenalen-1-ylidene]amino]-, tetrafluoroborate	MeCN	332(4.30),635(4.61)	44-2425-73
$C_{37}H_{27}NO_2$			
1H-Benz[f]isoindole-1,3(2H)-dione, 3a,4-dihydro-4,9-diphenyl-2-(phenylmethyl)-	$CHCl_3$	310(4.23),340s(3.94)	18-1737-73
2,5-Pyrrolidinedione, 2,4-bis(diphenylmethylene)-1-(phenylmethyl)-	EtOH	252(4.46),309(4.34), 400(4.05)	18-1737-73
$C_{37}H_{27}O_2$			
Pyrylium, 4-[3-(2,6-diphenyl-4H-pyran-4-ylidene)-1-propenyl]-2,6-diphenyl-, perchlorate	MeCN	385(4.10),686(5.07)	78-0795-73
$C_{37}H_{28}N_2O$			
1,4-Pentadien-3-one, 1,5-bis(2-naphthalenylamino)-2,4-diphenyl-	EtOH	235s(4.27),284(4.47), 315(4.38),452(4.64)	4-0665-73
$C_{37}H_{28}O_2$			
Ethanone, 2-[5-(4-methylphenyl)-2,2,4-triphenyl-3(2H)-furanylidene]-1-phenyl-	$CHCl_3$	265(4.13),410(4.30)	5-0375-73
$C_{37}H_{29}BrN_2O$			
Spiro[acridine-9(10H),2'-[2H-1]benzopyran], 6'-bromo-3',4'-dihydro-10-methyl-4'-[(10-methyl-9(10H)-acridinylidene)methyl]-	dioxan	229(4.85),268(4.38), 284(4.39),369(4.00)	103-0496-73
	HOAc	361(4.45),428(4.00)	103-0496-73
Spiro[acridine-9(10H),2'-[2H-1]benzopyran], 8'-bromo-3',4'-dihydro-10-methyl-4'-[(10-methyl-9(10H)-acri-	dioxan	228(4.81),268(4.37), 283(4.36),368(4.00)	103-0496-73
	HOAc	362(4.43),428(3.98)	103-0496-73

Compound	Solvent	λ_{max}(log ϵ)	Ref.
dinylidene)methyl]- (cont.)			103-0496-73
$C_{37}H_{29}Cl_2N_5O_6S_2$			
Benzenesulfonamide, N,N'-[[(4-nitrophenyl)methylene]bis(1-methyl-1H-indole-3,2-diyl)]bis[4-chloro-	$CHCl_3$	241(4.52),282(4.53)	39-1943-73C
	n.s.g.	223(4.37),280(4.08)	39-1943-73C
$C_{37}H_{29}CoN_4P$			
Corrole, Co(III)(triphenylphosphine)-	$CHCl_3$	291(4.25),362(4.68), 391(4.53),512s(3.83), 536(3.94),566(4.01)	39-2281-73C
$C_{37}H_{29}N_3O_3$			
Spiro[acridine-9(10H),2'-[2H-1]benzopyran], 3',4'-dihydro-10-methyl-4'-[(10-methyl-9(10H)-acridinylidene)methyl]-6'-nitro-	dioxan	229(4.71),267(4.41), 285(4.42),366(4.03)	103-0496-73
	HOAc	347(4.32),361(4.49), 427(4.01)	103-0496-73
$C_{37}H_{29}N_3O_9$			
2-Pyrimidinol, 4-benzamido-5-(2,3,5-tri-O-benzoyl-α-D-ribofuranosyl)-	EtOH	230(4.62),266(4.06), 322(4.34)	136-0015-73
β-	EtOH	231(4.63),238(3.83)	136-0015-73D
$C_{37}H_{30}Cl_2N_4O_9S_2$			
Benzenesulfonamide, N,N'-[(phenylmethylene)bis(1-methyl-1H-indole-3,2-diyl)]-bis[4-chloro-	n.s.g.	223(4.76),283(4.45)	39-1943-73C
$C_{37}H_{30}N_2O$			
Spiro[acridine-9(10H),2'-[2H-1]benzopyran], 3',4'-dihydro-10-methyl-4'-[(10-methyl-9(10H)-acridinylidene)methyl]-	$CHCl_3$	278(4.41),368(4.01)	103-0496-73
	HOAc	360(4.39),426(3.94)	103-0496-73
$C_{37}H_{30}O$			
4,7-Methano-1H-inden-8-one, 1-(diphenylmethylene)-3a,4,7,7a-tetrahydro-4,7-dimethyl-5,6-diphenyl-	hexane	273(4.26)	44-3836-73
$C_{37}H_{31}N_5O_5S$			
Benzamide, N-[6a,7,8,9a-tetrahydro-7-hydroxy-8-[[(4-methoxyphenyl)diphenylmethoxy]methyl]furo[2',3':4,5]thiazolo[3,2-e]purin-4-yl]-	EtOH	235(4.47),285s(4.15), 298(4.27)	23-2397-73
$C_{37}H_{35}N_5O_7$			
Adenosine, N,N-bis(4-methylbenzoyl)-2',3'-O-(1-methylethylidene)-, 5'-(4-methylbenzoate)	MeOH	247(4.56),270s(4.51)	18-3228-73
$C_{37}H_{35}N_5O_9$			
7(8H)-Pteridinone, 2-amino-4-(pentyloxy)-8-(2,3,5-tri-O-benzoyl-β-D-ribofuranosyl)-	MeOH	207s(4.58),230(4.67), 277(3.84),350(4.16)	24-1952-73
β-D-Ribofuranoside, 2-amino-4-(pentyloxy)-7-pteridinyl, 2,3,5-tribenzoate	MeOH	229(4.76),270(3.92), 345(4.04)	24-1952-73
$C_{37}H_{36}N_2O_6$			
Trigilletine, O-acetyl-	MeOH	207(4.76),232(4.63), 267s(3.55),275s(3.60), 283(3.62)	102-2509-73

Compound	Solvent	λ_{max}(log ε)	Ref.
$C_{37}H_{36}O_{10}$			
2-Propen-1-one, 3-[2'-hydroxy-4',6,6'-trimethoxy-3'-[3-(4-methoxyphenyl)-1-oxo-2-propenyl][1,1'-biphenyl]-3-yl]-1-(2,4,6-trimethoxyphenyl)-	EtOH	300(4.40),353(4.69)	102-0671-73
$C_{37}H_{38}N_2O_5$			
Oxyacanthan, 6',7-epoxy-12'-ethoxy-6-methoxy-2,2'-dimethyl- (O-ethyltrigilletine)	MeOH	206(4.78),235(4.63),274s(3.63),286(3.66),304s(3.52)	102-2509-73
$C_{37}H_{38}N_2O_6$			
Isoquinoline, 1-[[4-[5-[(3,4-dihydro-6,7-dimethoxy-1-isoquinolinyl)methyl]-2-methoxyphenoxy]phenylmethyl]-3,4-dihydro-6,7-dimethoxy-	MeOH	276(4.17),309(4.04)	87-0913-73
$C_{37}H_{38}N_3O$			
Quinolinium, 3-acetyl-4-[[2,2-bis[4-(dimethylamino)phenyl]ethenyl]-6-methyl-1-(4-methylphenyl)-, perchlorate	MeOH	600(4.04)	65-0877-73
$C_{37}H_{38}N_3O_3$			
Quinolinium, 3-acetyl-4-[2,2-bis[4-(dimethylamino)phenyl]ethenyl]-6-methoxy-1-(4-methoxyphenyl)-, perchlorate	MeOH	594(3.97)	65-0877-73
$C_{37}H_{38}N_4O_7$			
3-Phorbinepropanoic acid, 9-acetyl-3,4-didehydro-14-ethyl-21-methoxy-21-(methoxycarbonyl)-4,8,13,18-tetramethyl-20-oxo-, methyl ester, (S)-	dioxan	231(4.21),280(4.45),419(5.46),527(3.87),571(4.26),592(4.23),640(3.50)	5-1710-73
$C_{37}H_{38}N_4O_8$			
Haplophytine, 10-oxo-	EtOH	220(4.71),268(4.19),307(3.60)	23-3102-73
$C_{37}H_{40}CoN_4$			
Cobalt, [1,2,3,7,8,12,13,17,18,19-decadehydro-2,8,12,18-tetraethyl-21,22-dihydro-3,7,13,17-tetramethyl-21-phenylcorrinato(2-)-N^{21},N^{22},N^{23},N^{24}]-, (SP-4-2)-	$CHCl_3$	374(4.66),422s(3.88),625(3.38),680(3.57)	39-2281-73C
	$CHCl_3$+ CF_3COOH	347(4.67),394(3.91),642(3.16)	39-2281-73C
$C_{37}H_{40}N_2O_6$			
Cycleadrine	EtOH	282(3.81)	44-1846-73
Cycleanorine	EtOH	282(4.01)	44-1846-73
Cycleapeltine	EtOH	282(3.72)	44-1846-73
Nemuarine	n.s.g.	211(4.87),284(3.98)	12-0455-73
Thaligine	EtOH	282(3.94)	31-0517-73
$C_{37}H_{40}N_4O_7$			
Haplophytine	EtOH	220(4.69),265(4.16),305(3.65)	35-7842-73
3-Phorbinepropanoic acid, 3,4-didehydro-14-ethyl-9-(1-hydroxyethyl)-21-methoxy-21-(methoxycarbonyl)-4,8,13,18-tetramethyl-20-oxo-, methyl ester	dioxan	249(4.14),274(4.21),306(4.33),395s(4.78),418(5.35),520(3.96),562(4.23),579(4.15),631(3.13)	5-1710-73

Compound	Solvent	λ_{max}(log ε)	Ref.
$C_{37}H_{40}O_6$			
Carbonic acid, (1-methylethylidene)di-4,1-phenylene bis[4-(1,1-dimethylethyl)phenyl] ester	$C_2H_4Cl_2$	264(3.26),270(3.17)	116-0305-73
$C_{37}H_{41}NO_{12}$			
Rifamycin, 1,4,21,23-tetradeoxy-1,4-dihydro-1,4,21,23-tetraoxo-	EtOH	270(4.38),312(4.30), 400(3.60),522(3.41)	33-2323-73
$C_{37}H_{42}N_4O_6$			
21H,23H-Porphine-2,18-dipropanoic acid, 7,12-diethyl-α^2-methoxy-3,8,13,17-tetramethyl-β^2-oxo-, dimethyl ester	dioxan	505(4.16),543(4.23), 572(4.04),628(3.37)	5-1741-73
$C_{37}H_{44}N_4O_4$			
22H-Biline-3,17-dione, 1,19-diethoxy-2,2,7,8,12,13,18,18-octamethyl-10-phenyl-2,10,18,23-tetrahydro-, (E,E)-	CH_2Cl_2	287(4.25),425(4.50), 440s(4.49)	5-1067-73
$C_{37}H_{44}N_5Tl$			
Thallium, (cyano-C)[2,3,7,8,12,13,17,18-octaethyl-21H,23H-porphinato(2-)-N^{21},N^{22},N^{23},N^{24}]-, (SP-5-31)-	CH_2Cl_2	416(5.56),545(4.27), 583(4.08)	39-2142-73C
$C_{37}H_{44}O_6S_2$			
Benzenecarbothioic acid, O-[3a,6,6a,10-11,11a,12,12a-octahydro-2,2,6a,12-tetramethyl-4-[1-methyl-2-[[(4-methylphenyl)sulfonyl]oxy]ethyl]-5H-benzo-[6,7]cyclopenta[3,4]cycloocta[1,2-d]-1,3-dioxol-6-yl] ester	C_6H_{12}	235(4.20),240(4.15), 255(4.04),283(3.78)	39-1590-73C
$C_{37}H_{45}NO_{11}$			
Rifamycin, N,15-didehydro-15-deoxo-1-deoxy-1,15-epoxy-	EtOH-HCl	220(4.53),273(4.38), 293s(--),420(4.31), 437(4.38)	33-2348-73
$C_{37}H_{45}NO_{12}$			
Rifamycin, 25-O-deacetyl-1,4-dideoxy-1,4-dihydro-1,4-dioxo-, 8-acetate	EtOH	223(4.48),258(4.41), 297(4.24)	33-2323-73
Rifamycin, 25-O-deacetyl-1,4-dideoxy-1,4-dihydro-1,4-dioxo-, 21-acetate	EtOH	223(4.61),275(4.47), 307(4.27),392(3.73), 530(3.30)	33-2323-73
Rifamycin S	EtOH-HCl	219(4.51),281(4.48), 340(3.92),410(3.72)	33-2287-73
$C_{37}H_{45}NO_{13}$			
Rifamycin S, 16,17-epoxy-	EtOH	239(4.37),277(4.33), 397(3.62)	33-2323-73
Rifamycin S, 18,19-epoxy-	EtOH	240(4.35),277(4.35), 397(3.67)	33-2323-73
$C_{37}H_{45}NO_{14}$			
Rifamycin S, 16,17:18,19-diepoxy-	EtOH	240(4.35),278(4.30), 400(3.58)	33-2323-73
$C_{37}H_{45}N_3O_{11}$			
7,1-(Epoxypentadeca[1,11,13]trieno)-1H-furo[3',2':5,6]naphtho[1,2-d]-1,2,3-triazole-8,26(7H)-dione, 16-acetoxy-	EtOH	220(4.62),275(4.36), 403(4.29),422(4.30)	33-2348-73
	EtOH-HCl	220(4.61),274(4.37),	33-2348-73

Compound	Solvent	λ_{max}(log ϵ)	Ref.
4,9,18,20-tetrahydroxy-14-methoxy-5,7,15,17,19,21,25-heptamethyl- (cont.)		358(4.08),385(4.08),401(4.10)	33-2348-73
Rifamycin, 1,4-dideoxy-4-diazo-1,4-dihydro-1-oxo-	EtOH	230(4.59),285(4.41),318(4.38),408(4.13)	33-2287-73
$C_{37}H_{46}N_2O_3$			
Phenol, 4-[bis(5-methoxy-1,2-dimethyl-3-indolyl)methyl]-2,6-bis(1,1-dimethylethyl)-	MeOH	212(4.44),288(3.9)	103-0034-73
$C_{37}H_{46}N_2O_{10}$			
7,2-(Epoxytetradeca[1,11,13]trieno)-1H-furo[3',2':5,6]naphth[1,2-d]imidazol-8(7H)-one, 16-acetoxy-4,9,18,20-tetrahydroxy-14-methoxy-5,7,15,17,19,21,25-heptamethyl-	EtOH	223(4.65),275(4.34),325(4.11),438(4.43)	33-2348-73
	EtOH-HCl	223(4.78),275(4.49),358(4.19),408(4.22)	33-2348-73
$C_{37}H_{46}N_2O_{11}$			
Rifamycin S, 1-deoxo-1-imino-	EtOH	225(4.54),267(4.31),312(4.23),390(3.66),412(3.66),435s(--)	33-2348-73
	EtOH-HCl	225(4.66),280(4.38),425(4.07)	33-2348-73
$C_{37}H_{46}N_2O_{12}$			
Rifamycin S, 3-amino-	EtOH	226(4.48),265(4.49),311(4.10),365(3.87),520(3.05)	33-2348-73
$C_{37}H_{46}O_{22}$			
Ethanone, 1-[6-methoxy-2,4-bis[(2,3,4,6-tetra-O-acetyl-β-D-glucopyranosyl)oxy]phenyl]-	n.s.g.	275(3.14)	40-0785-73
$C_{37}H_{47}AlN_4O$			
Aluminum, methoxy[2,3,7,8,12,13,17,18-octaethyl-21H,23H-porphinato(2-)-N^{21},N^{22},N^{23},N^{24}]-, (SP-5-12)-	CH_2Cl_2	330(4.26),380s(4.81),399(5.26),470s(2.89),484s(3.19),500s(3.28),533(4.12),571(4.32)	24-2710-73
$C_{37}H_{47}FeN_4O$			
Iron, methoxy[2,3,7,8,12,13,17,18-octaethyl-21H,23H-porphinato(2-)-N^{21},N^{22},N^{23},N^{24}]oxo-, (OC-6-23)-	CH_2Cl_2-10% MeOH	356(4.74),396(5.02),477(4.07),512s(3.93),592(3.93)	64-0433-73B
$C_{37}H_{47}MoN_4O_2$			
Molybdenum, [methoxy[2,3,7,8,12,13,17-18-octaethyl-21H,23H-porphinato(2-)-N^{21},N^{22},N^{23},N^{24}]oxo-, (OC-6-23)-	CH_2Cl_2	342(4.73),443(4.94),512s(3.55),562(4.18),595(4.00)	24-2710-73
$C_{37}H_{47}NO_{12}$			
Rifamycinol	EtOH	230(4.54),270(4.27),327(4.09),423(3.73)	33-2323-73
$C_{37}H_{47}N_4O_2W$			
Tungsten, [methoxy[2,3,7,8,12,13,17,18-octaethyl-21H,23H-porphinato(2-)-N^{21},N^{22},N^{23},N^{24}]oxo-, (OC-6-23)-	CH_2Cl_2	360(4.38),432(5.13),557(3.94),594(3.73)	24-2710-73

Compound	Solvent	$\lambda_{max}(\log \epsilon)$	Ref.
$C_{37}H_{48}N_2O_{11}$			
Rifamycin SV, 1-amino-1-deoxy-	EtOH	218(4.60),298(4.22), 414(4.17)	33-2348-73
$C_{37}H_{49}NO_{12}$			
Rifamycin S, tetrahydro-	EtOH-HCl	235(4.35),280(4.32), 340(3.92),415(3.67)	33-2287-73
$C_{37}H_{51}BrO_2S$			
30-Norolean-12-en-11-one, 20-[2-[(4-bromophenyl)thio]ethenyl]-3-hydroxy-, [3β,20β(E)]-	EtOH	251(4.30),274(4.24)	78-2327-73
$C_{37}H_{51}NO_{11}$			
Rifamycin SV, 4-deoxytetrahydro-	EtOH	217(4.36),239(4.36), 290(4.32),325s(3.79), 409(4.09)	33-2287-73
$C_{37}H_{51}NO_{12}$			
Rifamycin S, hexahydro-	EtOH-HCl	236(4.41),272(4.36), 337(3.97),410(3.61)	33-2287-73
Rifamycinol S, 16,17,18,19-tetrahydro-	EtOH	237(4.41),270(4.06), 326(4.09),424(3.63)	33-2323-73
$C_{37}H_{52}N_2$			
Cholest-2-ene-2-carbonitrile, 3-(2-methyl-1H-indol-3-yl)-	MeOH	225(4.58),283(3.99)	103-0205-73
$C_{37}H_{52}O$			
D:B-Friedoolean-5(10)-en-1-one, 2-(phenylmethylene)-	EtOH	228(4.31),292(4.66)	78-3909-73
$C_{37}H_{56}O_9S$			
C-Nor-9,11-secospirostane-9,11-diol, 3,3-dimethoxy-, 11-acetate 9-(4-methylbenzenesulfonate)-, (5α,9β,25R)-	EtOH	225(4.4)	13-0147-73A
$C_{37}H_{59}NO_{12}$			
Antibiotic B-58941	EtOH	240(4.21)	138-0799-73
$C_{37}H_{62}O_3$			
Testosterone stearate	hexane	232(4.24)	10-0528-73F
$C_{37}H_{67}NO_{13}$			
Erythromycin B, 8-hydroxy-, (8S)-	MeOH	280(1.56)	33-1557-73
Erythromycin B, 8-hydroxy-, 8-epi-(8R)-	MeOH	280s(1.65)	33-1557-73

Compound	Solvent	λmax(log ε)	Ref.
$C_{38}H_{22}Br_2O_2$			
Naphtho[2,3-c]furan-1(3H)-one, 7-bromo-9-(4-bromophenyl)-3,3-di-1-naphthalenyl-	n.s.g.	224(5.19),254(4.87), 284(4.50),355(3.70)	115-0145-73A
$C_{38}H_{22}O_4$			
4H,10H-Naphtho[2,3-c:6,7-c']difuran-4,10-dione, 1,3,6,8-tetraphenyl-	$CHCl_3$	293(4.6),375(4.4), 485(4.3)	22-1154-73
$C_{38}H_{24}$			
1,3,5-Hexatriene, 1,6-di-2-pyrenyl-	THF	265(4.48),285(4.20), 328(4.79),345(5.07), 358(4.96),386(5.05), 410(4.51),431(4.07)	18-2822-73
$C_{38}H_{25}NO_2$			
1H-Isoindole-1,3(2H)-dione, 2,4,5,6,7-pentaphenyl-	dioxan	253(4.68),320s(3.65)	47-2143-73
$C_{38}H_{26}$			
Anthracene, 1,8,9,10-tetraphenyl-	EtOH	229s(4.53),270(4.85), 369s(3.89),391(4.07), 409(4.04)	44-1167-73
$C_{38}H_{27}NO_2$			
1H-Isoindole-1,3(2H)-dione, 3a,7a-dihydro-2,4,5,6,7-pentaphenyl-	dioxan	230(4.53),322(4.05)	47-2143-73
$C_{38}H_{28}$			
1,3,5,7,9-Decapentaene, 1,10-di-2-phenanthrenyl-	THF	260(4.90),266(4.84), 297(4.46),382s(--), 404(5.05),426(5.18), 455(5.10)	18-0909-73
1,3,5,7,9-Decapentaene, 1,10-di-3-phenanthrenyl-	THF	255(4.89),301(4.28), 329(4.26),345(4.42), 375(4.66),407(4.92), 428(5.07),458(5.00)	18-0909-73
1,3,5,7,9-Decapentaene, 1,10-di-9-phenanthrenyl-	benzene	305(4.43),420(4.81)	18-0909-73
$C_{38}H_{28}ClN_3O_4$			
Dibenzo[a,c]phenazinium, 11-[(1-ethyl-2(1H)-quinolinylidene)methyl]-9-phenyl-, perchlorate	$CHCl_3$	408(5.15),500(4.98), 780(5.49)	103-1407-73
$C_{38}H_{28}Cl_2O$			
Acenaphthylene, 5,5'-[oxybis(2-chlorophenyl)methylene]bis[1,2-dihydro-	H_2SO_4	388(--),590(4.53)	94-0383-73
Acenaphthylene, 5,5'-[oxybis(4-chlorophenyl)methylene]bis[1,2-dihydro-	H_2SO_4	398(--),603(4.53)	94-0383-73
$C_{38}H_{28}O_2$			
9,10-Anthracenediol, 9,10-dihydro-1,8,9,10-tetraphenyl-, cis	EtOH	223s(4.68),265s(3.89)	44-1167-73
trans	EtOH	222s(4.73)	44-1167-73
$C_{38}H_{30}$			
1,3,5,7,9,11-Dodecahexaene, 1,12-di-2-fluorenyl-	THF	296(4.37),423(5.06), 446(5.20),477(5.13)	18-2822-73

Compound	Solvent	λ_{max}(log ε)	Ref.
$C_{38}H_{30}O$			
Acenaphthylene, 5,5'-[oxybis(phenylmethylene)]bis[1,2-dihydro-	H_2SO_4	383(--),588(4.92)	94-0383-73
$C_{38}H_{30}O_2$			
1,5-Acenaphthylenedimethanol, 1,2-dihydro-α,α,α',α'-tetraphenyl-	$CHCl_3$	252(3.15),284(3.83), 295(3.91),303s(3.80), 324(3.00)	88-1803-73
$C_{38}H_{30}O_6$			
p-Terphenyl, 5,6-bis(acetoxymethyl)-2,3-dibenzoyl-	EtOH	257(4.7)	22-2856-73
$C_{38}H_{31}N_5O_7$			
7H-Purin-6-amine, N-(phenylmethyl)-7-(2,3,5-tri-O-benzoyl-β-D-ribofuranosyl)-	EtOH	277s(3.86),285s(3.92), 300(3.97)	18-3858-73
$C_{38}H_{31}P$			
Phosphorin, 4-(diphenylmethylene)-1,4-dihydro-1-[(4-methylphenyl)methyl]-2,6-diphenyl-	EtOH	255(4.36),303(4.05), 383(4.30)	88-0223-73
Phosphorin, 4-[2-(4-methylphenyl)-1,1-diphenylethyl]-2,6-diphenyl-	EtOH	267(4.54)	88-0223-73
$C_{38}H_{32}$			
Naphthalene, 1,2,3,4-tetramethyl-5,6,7,8-tetraphenyl-	EtOH	238s(4.52),262(4.63), 329(4.00)	118-0783-73
$C_{38}H_{32}N_2O$			
Spiro[acridine-9(10H),2'-[2H-1]benzopyran], 3',4'-dihydro-6',10-dimethyl-4'-[(10-methyl-9(10H)-acridinylidene)methyl]-, (S)-	dioxan	228(4.85),267(4.41), 283(4.42),368(4.03)	103-0496-73
	HOAc	361(4.39),428(3.95)	103-0496-73
$C_{38}H_{32}N_2O_2$			
Spiro[acridine-9(10H),2'-[2H-1]benzopyran], 3',4'-dihydro-6'-methoxy-10-methyl-4'-[(10-methyl-9(10H)-acridinylidene)methyl]-, (S)-	dioxan	225(4.86),267(4.35), 286(4.37),368(3.97)	103-0496-73
	HOAc	361(4.32),428(3.84)	103-0496-73
Spiro[acridine-9(10H),2'-[2H-1]benzopyran], 3',4'-dihydro-8'-methoxy-10-methyl-4'-[(10-methyl-9(10H)-acridinylidene)methyl]-, (S)-	dioxan	225(4.87),267(4.36), 368(3.95)	103-0496-73
	HOAc	361(4.38),428(3.92)	103-0496-73
$C_{38}H_{32}O_4$			
2-Propenoic acid, 3,3'-(1,2,4,5-tetraphenyltricyclo[3.1.0.0^{2,4}]hexane-3,6-diyl)bis-, dimethyl ester	EtOH	226(3.25)	104-0963-73
$C_{38}H_{34}CuO_4$			
Copper, bis[3,4-dihydro-7-methyl-2-(phenylacetyl)-1(2H)-naphthalenonato-O,O']-	MeOH	211(4.61),254(4.58), 260(4.55),334(4.01), 339(3.49),410(3.40)	18-2908-73
$C_{38}H_{36}N_4O_7$			
Benzoic acid, 4-methyl-, ester with 4-methyl-N-(4-methylbenzoyl)-N-[7-[2,3-O-(1-methylethylidene)-β-D-ribofuranosyl]-7H-pyrrolo[2,3-d]pyrimidin-4-yl]benzamide	MeOH	240(4.68)	18-3228-73

Compound	Solvent	λ_{max}(log ε)	Ref.
$C_{38}H_{38}O_7$			
Gibba-1,3,4a(10a),4b-tetraene-10-carboxylic acid, 6,6'-oxybis[1,7-dimethyl-8-oxo-, dimethyl ester, (6α,7β,9aβ-10β)-(6'α,7'β,9'aβ,10'β)-	n.s.g.	267s(4.21),276(4.28), 288(3.92),300(3.77)	39-1476-73C
$C_{38}H_{40}N_4$			
Nordihydrotoxiferine	EtOH	293(4.41),323(4.34)	32-0543-73
$C_{38}H_{40}N_6O_4$			
21H,23H-Porphine-2,18-dipropanoic acid, 7,12-bis(2-cyanoethyl)-3,8,13,17-tetramethyl-, dimethyl ester	CH_2Cl_2	401(5.26),498(4.19), 533(3.99),565(3.86), 595(3.32)	5-1329-73
	CH_2Cl_2 + CF_3COOH	404(5.61),549(4.21), 592(3.84)	5-1329-73
$C_{38}H_{42}CoN_4$			
Cobalt(III), 8,12-diethyl-2,3,7,13,17-18-hexamethylcorrole, N(21)-p-tolyl-deriv.	$CHCl_3$	376(4.69),425s(3.90), 626(3.30),682(3.96)	39-2281-73C
$C_{38}H_{42}N_2O_5$			
Pakistanine, 1-O-methyl-10-deoxy-	EtOH	228(4.55),281(4.36), 299s(4.06)	35-5742-73
$C_{38}H_{42}N_2O_6$			
Funiferine	MeOH	233s(4.64),286(4.15), 292s(4.12)	100-0066-73
Pakistanine, 1-O-methyl-	EtOH	207(4.88),225s(4.75), 270s(4.28),277(4.37), 304(4.16)	35-5742-73
$C_{38}H_{42}N_4O_7$			
Haplophytine, O-methyl-	EtOH	221(4.67),265(4.09), 300(3.54)	35-7842-73
$C_{38}H_{42}O_3$			
Estra-1,3,5,7,9-pentaene, 17,17'-oxybis-[3-methoxy-	EtOH	268(4.03),282(4.01), 292(3.89),324(3.71), 340(3.89)	70-1574-73
$C_{38}H_{42}O_{11}$			
2H-1-Benzopyran, 4,4'-oxybis[2-(3,4-dimethoxyphenyl)-3,4-dihydro-5,7-dimethoxy-	MeOH	278(3.65)	2-0120-73
$C_{38}H_{43}F_3N_4O_2Zn$			
Zinc, [2,3,7,8,12,13,17,18-octaethyl-21H,23H-porphin-5-yl trifluoroacetato(2-)-N^{21},N^{22},N^{23},N^{24}]-, (SP-4-2)-	CH_2Cl_2	404(5.52),533(4.20), 571(4.20)	39-0691-73C
$C_{38}H_{44}F_3N_4O_2Tl$			
Thallium, [2,3,7,8,12,13,17,18-octaethyl-21H,23H-porphinato(2-)-N^{21},N^{22},N^{23},N^{24}](trifluoroacetato-O)-, (SP-5-12)-	CH_2Cl_2	412(5.43),541(4.20), 578(4.13)	39-2142-73C
$C_{38}H_{44}N_2O_6$			
Pakistanamine, 11,12-dihydro-	EtOH	206(4.71),225s(4.41), 279(3.94),310s(3.50)	35-5742-73

Compound	Solvent	λ_{max}(log ε)	Ref.
$C_{38}H_{45}F_3N_4O_2$			
Acetic acid, trifluoro-, 2,3,7,8,12,13-17,18-octaethyl-21H,23H-porphin-5-yl ester	CH_2Cl_2	399(5.19),500(4.16),533(3.87),625(3.42)	39-0691-73C
	CH_2Cl_2 + CF_3COOH	411(5.51),555(4.20),599(3.72)	39-0691-73C
$C_{38}H_{45}F_3N_4O_2Zn$			
Zinc, [2,3,7,8,12,13,17,18-octaethyl-7,8-dihydro-21H,23H-porphin-5-yl trifluoroacetato(2-)-N^{21},N^{22},N^{23},N^{24}]-, [SP-4-2-(trans)]-	CH_2Cl_2	399(5.19),501(3.70),536(3.48),572(3.88),617(4.69)	39-2149-73C
$C_{38}H_{45}NO_{11}$			
Rifamycin S, 25-deacetoxy-25-oxo-, 21,23-acetonide	EtOH	228(4.58),270(4.31),312(4.28),394(3.55),523(3.40)	33-2323-73
Rifamycin S, 21-deoxy-21-oxo-25-O-deacetyl-, 23,25-acetonide	EtOH	231(4.56),275(4.37),305s(--),385(3.62),520s(--)	33-2323-73
$C_{38}H_{45}NO_{13}$			
Rifamycin S, 21-O-formyl-	EtOH	228(4.48),277(4.34),390(3.62)	33-2323-73
$C_{38}H_{46}N_2O_{14}$			
Rifamycin S, 3-(nitromethyl)-	EtOH	275(4.40),390(3.72)	33-2348-73
$C_{38}H_{46}N_6O_6$			
Adenosine, 2'-deoxy-3'-O-(carboxymethyl)-5'-O-(4-methoxyphenyldiphenylmethyl)-, triethylamine salt	EtOH	234(--),260(4.16)	39-0290-73C
$C_{38}H_{47}FeN_4O_2$			
Iron, (acetato-O)[2,3,7,8,12,13,17,18-octaethyl-21H,23H-porphinato(2-)-N^{21},N^{22},N^{23},N^{24}]-, (SP-5-12)-	CH_2Cl_2-1% HOAc	372s(4.93),396(4.99),458s(3.81),503(3.93),533(3.93),580s(3.50),627(3.67)	64-0433-73B
$C_{38}H_{47}NO_{11}$			
Rifamycin S, 25-O-deacetyl-, 21,23-acetonide	EtOH	226(4.47),269(4.27),315(4.27),400(3.20),530(3.26)	33-2323-73
Rifamycin S, 25-O-deacetyl-, 23,25-acetonide	EtOH	270(4.37),313(4.27),395s(--),520(3.30)	33-2323-73
$C_{38}H_{47}NO_{12}$			
Rifamycin S, 25-O-deacetyl-25-O-propionyl-	EtOH-HCl	218(4.51),276(4.46),335(3.91),390(3.73)	33-2323-73
Rifamycin S, iminomethyl ether	EtOH	221(4.61),279(4.41),337(3.93),405(3.65)	33-2287-73
Rifamycin S, 8-O-methyl-	EtOH	220(4.48),264(4.40),297s(4.26),347s(3.88)	33-2287-73
$C_{38}H_{47}NO_{18}$			
Euonine	EtOH	230(3.88),270(3.52)	88-0113-73
$C_{38}H_{47}N_4O_3Tl$			
Thallium, acetato[2,3,7,8,12,13,17,18-octaethyl-21H,23H-porphinato(2-)-N^{21},N^{22},N^{23},N^{24}]-, hydrate, (OC-6-12)-	CH_2Cl_2	415(5.54),544(4.26),580(4.13)	39-2142-73C

Compound	Solvent	λ_{max}(log ϵ)	Ref.
$C_{38}H_{47}N_5O_4$			
21H,23H-Porphine-2,18-dipropanoic acid, 7-[2-(diethylamino)ethyl]-3,8,13,17-tetramethyl-, dimethyl ester	$CHCl_3$	401(5.23),499(4.11), 534(3.91),569(3.77), 625(3.50)	103-0186-73
$C_{38}H_{48}N_2O_{12}$			
Rifamycin, 1,4-dideoxy-1,4-dihydro-3-(methylamino)-1,4-dioxo-	EtOH	234(4.49),267(4.47), 319(4.13),370(3.88), 530(3.16)	33-2348-73
$C_{38}H_{48}N_4$			
1,5-Naphthyridinium, 1,5-bis[4-(1,3-dihydro-1,3,3-trimethyl-2H-indol-2-ylidene)-2-butenylidene]decahydro-, trans, diperchlorate	EtOH	505(5.36)	104-2606-73
1,6-Naphthyridinium, 1,6-bis[4-(1,3-dihydro-1,3,3-trimethyl-2H-indol-2-ylidene)-2-butenylidene]decahydro-, trans, diperchlorate	EtOH	451(5.04),497(5.27)	104-2606-73
1,8-Naphthyridinium, 1,8-bis[4-(1,3-dihydro-1,3,3-trimethyl-2H-indol-2-ylidene)-2-butenylidene]decahydro-, trans, diperchlorate	EtOH	450(5.29)	104-2606-73
Quinoxalinium, 1,4-bis[4-(1,3-dihydro-1,3,3-trimethyl-2H-indol-2-ylidene)-2-butenylidene]decahydro-, trans, diperchlorate	EtOH	447(4.66),513(5.33)	104-2606-73
$C_{38}H_{49}NO_{11}$			
Rifarubin A dimethylacetal	EtOH	209(4.46),244(4.46), 270(4.47),315(4.16), 510(3.79)	33-2323-73
$C_{38}H_{50}GeN_4O_2$			
Germanium, dimethoxy[2,3,7,8,12,13,17-18-octaethyl-21H,23H-porphinato(2-)-N^{21},N^{22},N^{23},N^{24}]-, (OC-6-12)-	benzene	341(4.41),389s(4.72), 410(5.58),475s(2.82), 502s(3.26),538(4.26), 574(4.27)	24-2710-73
$C_{38}H_{50}N_2O_{10}S_2$			
Dibenzo[b,f]thiepin, 10,11-dihydro-8-(methylthio)-10-[4-(3-capryloyloxypropyl)piperazino]-, dihydrogen maleate	MeOH	276(4.11)	73-1190-73
$C_{38}H_{50}N_4O_2Si$			
Silicon, dimethoxy[2,3,7,8,12,13,17,18-octaethyl-21H,23H-porphinato(2-)-N^{21},N^{22},N^{23},N^{24}]-, (OC-6-12)-	benzene	337(4.29),390s(4.63), 408(5.45),502s(3.08), 538(4.10),573(4.16)	24-2710-73
$C_{38}H_{50}N_4O_2Sn$			
Tin, dimethoxy[2,3,7,8,12,13,17,18-octaethyl-21H,23H-porphinato(2-)-N^{21},N^{22},N^{23},N^{24}]-, (OC-6-12)-	benzene	354(4.45),390s(4.74), 410(5.50),480s(2.87), 504s(3.31),542(4.31), 578(4.26)	24-2710-73
$C_{38}H_{50}O_6$			
Xanthochymol	C_6H_{12}	264(4.09),364(3.99)	88-4977-73

Compound	Solvent	$\lambda_{max}(\log \epsilon)$	Ref.
$C_{38}H_{50}O_{12}$			
1,2-Naphthalenedione, 3-(8-cyclohexyl-octyl)-4-[(2,3,6,7-tetra-O-acetyl-β-D-glucopyranosyl)oxy]-	EtOH	242(4.08),252(4.09), 331(3.11),408(2.89)	136-0247-73A
$C_{38}H_{54}N_2$			
Cholest-2-ene-2-carbonitrile, 3-(1,2-di-methyl-1H-indol-3-yl)-	MeOH	227(4.60),292(3.99)	103-0205-73
$C_{38}H_{55}NO_6$			
Avenamine B	EtOH	222(4.37),253(3.82), 355(3.65)	78-0629-73
$C_{38}H_{55}NO_7$			
Avenamine A	EtOH	222(4.36),253(3.85), 355(3.68)	78-0629-73
$C_{38}H_{60}N_2O_2$			
Androstan-17-one, 3-hydroxy-, [(3α,5α)-androstan-17-ylidene]hydrazone, (3α,5α)-	MeOH	210(4.18),228(3.57)	88-2289-73

Compound	Solvent	λ_{max}(log ε)	Ref.
$C_{39}H_{30}N_4O_7$			
Tubercidin, N6,N6,5'-O-tribenzoyl-2',3'-O-(phenylmethylene)-	MeOH	224(4.67),280s(4.08)	18-3228-73
$C_{39}H_{30}O_3Si$			
4,7-Silanoisobenzofuran-1,3-dione, 3a,4,7,7a-tetrahydro-8-methyl-4,5,6,7,8-pentaphenyl-	n.s.g.	218(4.52),266(3.94), 291(3.86)	78-2395-73
$C_{39}H_{31}N_5O_9$			
7(8H)-Pteridinone, 2-amino-4-(phenylmethoxy)-8-(2,3,5-tri-O-benzoyl-β-D-ribofuranosyl)-	MeOH	229(4.75),275(4.02), 281(4.01),351(4.22)	24-1952-73
β-D-Ribofuranoside, 2-amino-4-(phenylmethoxy)-7-pteridinyl, 2,3,5-tribenzoate	MeOH	230(4.78),272(4.07), 350(4.12)	24-1952-73
$C_{39}H_{31}O_2$			
Pyrylium, 4-[3-(2,6-diphenyl-4H-pyran-4-ylidene)-1-methyl-1-butenyl]-2,6-2,6-diphenyl-, perchlorate	MeCN	385(4.49),724(5.14)	78-0795-73
$C_{39}H_{32}N_4O_7$			
2,4(1H,3H)-Pteridinedione, 1-[2-deoxy-3,5-bis-O-(4-methylbenzoyl)-D-ribofuranosyl]-6,7-diphenyl-	MeOH	236(4.67),272(4.24), 358(4.11)	24-1401-73
$C_{39}H_{34}O_3$			
4,7-Methano-1H-inden-8-one, 1-[bis(4-methoxyphenyl)methylene]-3a,4,7,7a-tetrahydro-4,7-dimethyl-5,6-diphenyl-, (3aα,4α,7α,7aα)-	hexane	284(4.20)	44-3836-73
$C_{39}H_{35}ClN_3O$			
Benzo[f]quinolinium, 2-acetyl-1-[2,2-bis[4-(dimethylamino)phenyl]ethenyl]-4-(4-chlorophenyl)-, perchlorate	MeOH	578(3.59)	65-0877-73
$C_{39}H_{35}N_4O_3$			
Benzo[f]quinolinium, 2-acetyl-1-[2,2-bis[4-(dimethylamino)phenyl]ethenyl]-4-(4-methylphenyl)-, perchlorate	MeOH	610(3.78)	65-0877-73
$C_{39}H_{36}N_3O$			
Benzo[f]quinolinium, 2-acetyl-1-[2,2-bis[4-(dimethylamino)phenyl]ethenyl]-4-phenyl-, perchlorate	MeOH	600(3.65)	65-0877-73
$C_{39}H_{36}N_4O_4S_2$			
Benzenesulfonamide, N,N'-[(phenylmethylene)bis(1-methyl-1H-indole-3,2-diyl)-bis[4-methyl-	n.s.g.	223(4.76),283(4.45)	39-1943-73C
$C_{39}H_{38}N_2O_7$			
Nortiliacorine A, N,O-diacetyl-	MeOH	208(4.79),233s(4.65), 291(3.77)	102-0203-73
$C_{39}H_{38}N_3O_5$			
Quinolinium, 3-acetyl-6-acetoxy-1-(4-acetoxyphenyl)-4-[2,2-bis[4-(dimethylamino)phenyl]ethenyl]-, perchlorate	MeOH	590(3.85)	65-0877-73

Compound	Solvent	λmax(log ε)	Ref.
$C_{39}H_{40}N_4O_9$			
Haplophytine, O-acetyl-10-oxo-	EtOH	219(4.73),263(4.14), 304(3.58)	23-3102-73
$C_{39}H_{42}CoN_5$			
Cobalt, [1,2,3,7,8,12,13,17,18,19-decadehydro-2,8,16,18-tetraethyl-21,22-dihydro-3,7,13,17-tetramethylcorrinato(3-)-N^{21},N^{22},N^{23},N^{24}](1-isocyano-4-methylbenzene)-, (SP-5-53)-	$CHCl_3$	510(4.84),532s(4.66), 652(3.54),680(4.18), 712(4.42)	39-2281-73C
$C_{39}H_{42}N_4O_8$			
3-Phorbinepropanoic acid, 9-[1-(acetyloxy)ethyl]-3,4-didehydro-14-ethyl-21-methoxy-21-(methoxycarbonyl)-4,8,13-18-tetramethyl-20-oxo-, methyl ester	dioxan	249(4.28),274(4.40), 304(4.39),370s(4.57), 417(5.40),520(3.98), 562(4.27),578(4.18), 631(3.18)	5-1710-73
$C_{39}H_{44}N_2O_6$			
Funiferine, O-methyl-	MeOH	231s(4.60),286(4.03), 292s(3.97)	100-0066-73
Pakistanine, 1,10-di-O-methyl-	EtOH	215(4.60),270s(4.27), 277(4.29),301(4.09)	35-5742-73
$C_{39}H_{44}N_2O_8$			
Thalictrogamine	EtOH	230s(4.39),277(4.11), 298s(3.98),307s(3.82)	88-0775-73
$C_{39}H_{44}O_{10}$			
Spiro[10b,4-(epoxymethano)-5a,8-methenocyclobuta[5,6]benz[1,2-a]azulene-2(1H)-8'(9'H)-[5H-7,9a]methanobenz[a]azulene-5,10'-dicarboxylic acid, 2a,3,4,4a,4'b-5,6,6',7,7',8,9,10,10',10a,10c-hexadecahydro-2',7',8-trihydroxy-1',4-dimethyl-7-methylene-3,12-dioxo-, dimethyl ester	MeOH	213(3.80),231s(3.62), 286(3.18)	78-3177-73
isomer	MeOH	219(3.70),234(3.59), 286(3.26)	78-3177-73
$C_{39}H_{45}ClN_2O_6$			
Cycleahomine chloride	EtOH	284(4.08)	44-1846-73
$C_{39}H_{45}IN_2O_6$			
Tetrandrine monomethiodide	EtOH	281(4.10)	44-1846-73
$C_{39}H_{46}N_2O_6$			
Dauricine, O-methyl-, (±)-	MeOH	284(4.04)	87-0913-73
$C_{39}H_{46}N_2O_8$			
1,23:6,9-Dietheno-11,15-metheno-2H,15H-benzo[19,20][1,11]dioxacycloeicosino-[5,4-b]pyridin-21-ol, 3,4,4a,5,16,17-hexahydro-17-(2-hydroxyethoxy)-12,20,25-trimethoxy-4-methyl-18-[2-(methylamino)ethyl]-	EtOH	284(4.08)	44-1846-73
$C_{39}H_{46}O_{11}$			
Kosin K3	C_6H_{12}	224(4.42),282(4.45)	102-2017-73

Compound	Solvent	$\lambda_{max}(\log \epsilon)$	Ref.
$C_{39}H_{47}NO_{13}$			
Rifamycin S, 8-O-acetyl-	EtOH	223(4.50),259(4.40), 297(4.23)	33-2323-73
Rifamycin S, 21(or 23)-O-acetyl-	EtOH	227(4.55),276(4.40), 390(3.70)	33-2323-73
$C_{39}H_{50}N_2O_{12}$			
2,7-(Epoxypentadeca[1,11,13]trieno)-7H-furo[3',2':5,6]naphth[2,3-d]imidazole-1,11(2H)-dione, 21-acetoxy-8,9-dihydro-5,6,10,17,19-pentahydroxy-23-methoxy-2,4,9,12,16,18,20,22-octamethyl-	EtOH-HCl	223(4.50),254(4.40), 290(4.41),325s(--), 455(3.95)	33-2348-73
Rifamycin S, 3-(dimethylamino)-	EtOH	217(4.45),270(4.46), 327(4.13),370s(--), 550(3.30)	33-2348-73
Rifamycin S, 3-(ethylamino)-	EtOH	233(4.43),267(4.42), 320(4.08),370(3.82), 530(3.15)	33-2348-73
$C_{39}H_{50}N_2O_{12}$			
Rifamycin S, 3-(2-hydroxyethylamino)-	EtOH	233(4.44),260(4.45), 320(4.16),375s(--), 530(2.95)	33-2348-73
$C_{39}H_{50}O_{12}$			
Kosin K4	C_6H_{12}	224(4.54),285(4.56)	102-2017-73
$C_{39}H_{50}O_{23}$			
Genipin gentiobioside octaacetate	EtOH	235(4.22)	94-2684-73
$C_{39}H_{51}NO_{12}$			
Rifamycin, 1,4-dideoxy-1,4-dimethoxy-	EtOH	230(4.60),305(4.33), 440(3.60)	33-2287-73
$C_{39}H_{55}NO_{12}$			
Rifamycin SV, 1,4,8-tri-O-methyl-, methanolysis	EtOH	223(4.60),288(4.52), 405(3.74)	33-2287-73
$C_{39}H_{60}O_{15}$			
Pregna-5,16-dien-20-one, 3-[(O-6-deoxy-α-L-mannopyranosyl-(1→2)-O-[6-deoxy-α-L-mannopyranosyl-(1→4)-β-D-glucopyranosyl)oxy]-, (3β)-	EtOH	239(3.86)	94-1240-73
$C_{39}H_{70}O_5$			
2H-Pyran-6-acetic acid, α,3-dihexadecyl-4-hydroxy-2-oxo-	EtOH	210(4.11),292(3.95)	44-2540-73

Compound	Solvent	λmax(log ε)	Ref.
$C_{40}H_{24}N_8$			
1,2,4-Triazolo[4,3-c]quinazoline, 5,5'-(2,6-naphthalenediyl)bis[3-phenyl-	H_2SO_4	278(4.75),400(4.68)	116-0483-73
$C_{40}H_{24}O_3$			
Anthra[2,3-c]furan-5,10-dione, 1,3,6,9-tetraphenyl-	CHCl	330s(--),502(4.2)	22-1154-73
$C_{40}H_{26}$			
Benzo[b]biphenylene, 6,7,8,9-tetraphenyl-	C_6H_{12}	251(4.44),274(4.71), 282(4.82),296(4.63), 309(4.74),341(3.86), 353(3.71),373(3.81), 394(3.81)	44-3812-73
$C_{40}H_{28}N_4$			
2-Tetrazene, 1,1,4,4-tetra-2-naphthalenyl-	THF	352(4.61)	73-0046-73
$C_{40}H_{30}$			
1,3,5,7,9,11-Dodecahexaene, 1,12-di-2-phenanthrenyl-	THF	270(4.82),292s(--), 350(4.20),417(4.99), 441(5.16),472(5.09)	18-0909-73
1,3,5,7,9,11-Dodecahexaene, 1,12-di-3-phenanthrenyl-	THF	356(4.40),421(5.01), 443(5.13),474(5.03)	18-0909-73
1,3,5,7,9,11-Dodecahexaene, 1,12-di-9-phenanthrenyl-	benzene	314(4.35),434(5.17)	18-0909-73
$C_{40}H_{30}N_2O_2$			
Benzamide, N-benzoyl-N-[(diphenylmethylene)amino]diphenylmethyl]-	C_6H_{12}	230(4.52),313(3.85)	78-2119-73
Unknown compd. from 2,4,6-triphenyl-1,4-oxazine acid hydrolysis	EtOH	240s(4.24),330(4.56)	44-3433-73
$C_{40}H_{32}N_2$			
Phenazine, 1,2,3,4,6,7,8,9-octahydro-1,4,6,9-tetrakis(phenylmethylene)-, all-E	dioxan	237(4.39),350(4.64), 430(4.20)	56-0943-73
Phenazine, 1,4,6,9-tetrakis(phenylmethyl)-	C_6H_{12}	216(4.70),266(5.03), 368(4.15)	56-0943-73
$C_{40}H_{33}N_5O_9$			
β-D-Ribofuranoside, 2-amino-6-methyl-4-(phenylmethoxy)-7-pteridinyl, 2,3,5-tribenzoate	MeOH	230(4.78),268(4.11), 348(4.11)	24-1952-73
$C_{40}H_{35}P$			
Phosphorin, 2,6-bis(4-methylphenyl)-4-[2-(4-methylphenyl)-1,1-diphenylethyl]-	EtOH	273(4.59)	88-0223-73
$C_{40}H_{36}Cl_4N_4O_5$			
Phylloerythrin, 10,10-(tetrachloro-o-phenylenedioxy)-, methyl ester	CH_2Cl_2	419(5.32),531(3.92), 577(4.33),626(3.38)	39-2517-73C
	CH_2Cl_2 + CF_3COOH	416(5.37),553(4.18), 591(4.14)	39-2517-73C
	1:1 CH_2Cl_2-CF_3COOH	414(5.52),549(4.00), 566(4.08),594(3.71), 617(3.89)	39-2517-73C

Compound	Solvent	$\lambda_{max}(\log \epsilon)$	Ref.
$C_{40}H_{36}N_4O_6S_2$			
Benzenesulfonamide, N,N'-[(1,3-benzodioxol-5-ylmethylene)bis(1-methyl-1H-indole-3,2-diyl)]bis[4-methyl-	$CHCl_3$	242(4.40),288(4.41)	39-1943-73C
	n.s.g.	223(4.70),280(4.44)	39-1943-73C
$C_{40}H_{36}O_2Si$			
7-Silabicyclo[2.2.1]hept-5-ene-2-carboxylic acid, 7-methyl-1,4,5,6,7-pentaphenyl-, ethyl ester	n.s.g.	234(4.42),276(3.97), 293(3.91)	78-2395-73
$C_{40}H_{38}N_3O$			
Benzo[f]quinolinium, 2-acetyl-1-[2,2-bis[4-(dimethylamino)phenyl]ethenyl]-4-(4-methylphenyl)-, perchlorate	MeOH	606(3.92)	65-0877-73
$C_{40}H_{38}N_3O_2$			
Benzo[f]quinolinium, 2-acetyl-1-[2,2-bis[4-(dimethylamino)phenyl]ethenyl]-4-(4-methoxyphenyl)-, perchlorate	MeOH	604(3.84)	65-0877-73
$C_{40}H_{38}Si_2$			
Silane, [1,1'-biphenyl]-4,4'-diylbis-[[1,1'-biphenyl]-4-yldimethyl-	heptane	262.0(4.84)	101-0353-73C
$C_{40}H_{40}N_2O_8$			
Isoquinoline, 1,1'-[(4,4',5,5'-tetramethoxy[1,1'-biphenyl]-2,2'-diyl)-bis(methylene)]bis[6,7-dimethoxy-	EtOH	239(5.06),284(4.14), 314(3.85),328(3.91)	35-6861-73
$C_{40}H_{40}N_2O_9$			
Oxothalicarpine	$CHCl_3$	246s(5.67),272(5.58), 292(5.49),318(5.11)	35-2995-73
$C_{40}H_{41}BrO_5$			
Phenol, 2-[[3-[(3-bromo-2-hydroxy-5-methylphenyl)methyl]-2-hydroxy-5-methylphenyl]methyl]-6-[[2-hydroxy-3-[(2-hydroxy-3,5-dimethylphenyl)-methyl]-5-methylphenyl]methyl]-4-methyl-	dioxan	288(4.18)	126-0039-73L
$C_{40}H_{41}BrO_6$			
Benzenemethanol, 3-[[3-[[3-[[3-[(3-bromo-2-hydroxy-5-methylphenyl)-methyl]-2-hydroxy-5-methylphenyl]-methyl]-2-hydroxy-5-methylphenyl]-methyl]-2-hydroxy-5-methylphenyl]-methyl]-2-hydroxy-5-methyl-	dioxan	288(4.19)	126-0039-73L
$C_{40}H_{42}O_5$			
Phenol, 2-[[2-hydroxy-3-[(2-hydroxy-3,5-dimethylphenyl)methyl]-5-methylphenyl]methyl]-6-[[2-hydroxy-3-[(2-hydroxy-5-methylphenyl)methyl]-5-methylphenyl]methyl]-4-methyl-	dioxan	287(4.16)	126-0039-73L
$C_{40}H_{44}N_2O_7$			
Pakistanine, 10-O-acetyl-1-O-methyl-	EtOH	207(4.78),230s(4.53), 270s(4.30),280(4.37), 290s(4.25),300s(4.08)	35-5742-73

Compound	Solvent	λ_{max}(log ϵ)	Ref.
$C_{40}H_{44}N_4O_8$			
21H,23H-Porphine-2,7,18-tripropanoic acid, 12-ethenyl-8-(2-methoxy-2-oxoethyl)-3,13,17-trimethyl-, trimethyl ester	$CHCl_3$	407(5.26),506(4.18), 540(4.04),576(3.87), 629(3.69)	12-2697-73
$C_{40}H_{44}N_4O_9$			
21H,23H-Porphine-2,7,18-tripropanoic acid, 12-acetyl-8-(2-methoxy-2-oxoethyl)-3,13,17-trimethyl-, trimethyl ester	$CHCl_3$	412(5.28),511(4.09), 549(4.06),580(3.90), 636(3.40)	12-2697-73
$C_{40}H_{44}O_{12}$			
Spiro[4a,1-(epoxymethano)-7,9a-methanobenz[a]azulene-8(9H),2'(1'H)-[10b,4]-(epoxymethano)[5a,8]methanocyclobuta-[5,6]benz[1,2-a]azulene]-5',10-dicarboxylic acid, 1,2,2'a,3',4',4'a,4b,5,5'-6,6',7,7',8',9',10,10',10a,10'a,10'c-eicosahydro-7,8'-dihydroxy-1,4'-dimethyl-7'-methylene-2,3',12'-trioxo-, dimethyl ester	MeOH	227(3.84),285(2.36), 325(1.90)	78-3177-73
Spiro[4a,8-(epoxymethano)-7,9a-methanobenz[a]azulene-8(9H),2'(1'H)-[10b,4]-(epoxymethano)[5a,8]methanocyclobuta-[5,6]benz[1,2-a]azulene-5',10-dicarboxylic acid, 1,2,2'a,3',4',4'a,4b,5,5'-6,6',7,7',8',9',10,10',10a,10'a,10'c-eicosahydro-7,8'-dihydroxy-1,4'-dimethyl-2,3',11,11'-tetraoxo-, dimethyl ester	MeOH	227(3.78),281(2.38), 326(1.81)	78-3177-73
$C_{40}H_{46}INO_8$			
1,23:6,9-Dietheno-11,15-metheno-2H,15H-benzo[19,20][1,11]dioxacycloeicosino-[5,4-b]pyridinium, 18-ethenyl-3,4,4a-5,16,17-hexahydro-17-(2-hydroxyethoxy)-12,20,21,25-tetramethoxy-4,4-dimethyl-, iodide	EtOH	263(4.21),292(3.92)	44-1846-73
$C_{40}H_{46}N_2O_8$			
Thalictropine	MeOH	225(4.46),278(4.12), 298s(3.88),310s(3.70)	88-0775-73
	MeOH-base	281(--),300s(--), 340(--)	88-0775-73
Thalidoxine	MeOH	275(4.23),296s(4.08), 310s(4.02)	88-1859-73
$C_{40}H_{46}N_4O_4$			
Criophylline	EtOH	214(4.26),228(4.06), 257(3.93),299(4.08), 327(4.28)	88-5081-73
$C_{40}H_{46}N_4O_8$			
21H,23H-Porphine-2,7-dipropanoic acid, 12,17-bis[2-(acetyloxy)ethyl]-3,8,13,18-tetramethyl-, dimethyl ester	CH_2Cl_2	398(5.20),497(4.13), 531(3.95),567(3.76), 621(3.54)	39-2478-73C
	CH_2Cl_2 - CF_3COOH	405(5.56),550(4.19), 592(3.78)	39-2478-73C

Compound	Solvent	λ_{max}(log ε)	Ref.
21H,23H-Porphine-2,7,18-tripropanoic acid, 12-ethyl-8-(2-methoxy-2-oxoethyl)-3,13,17-trimethyl-, trimethyl ester	$CHCl_3$	404(5.30),502(4.12), 538(4.06),569(3.90), 624(3.53)	12-2697-73
$C_{40}H_{46}N_4O_9$			
21H,23H-Porphine-2,7,18-tripropanoic acid, 12-(1-hydroxyethyl)-8-(2-methoxy-2-oxoethyl)-3,13,17-trimethyl-, trimethyl ester	$CHCl_3$	405(5.31),501(4.20), 535(4.01),571(3.88), 625(3.67)	12-2697-73
$C_{40}H_{46}O_{13}$			
2H-1-Benzopyran, 4-[[3,4-dihydro-5,7-dimethoxy-2-(3,4,5-trimethoxyphenyl)-2H-1-benzopyran-4-yl]oxy]-3,4-dihydro-5,6-dimethoxy-2-(3,4,5-trimethoxyphenyl)-	MeOH	269(3.689)	2-0120-73
$C_{40}H_{46}O_{19}$			
Ethanone, 2-phenyl-1-[4-[[2,3,6-tri-O-acetyl-4-O-(2,3,4,6-tetra-O-acetyl-β-D-glucopyranosyl)-β-D-glucopyranosyl]oxy]phenyl]-	EtOH	202(4.39),263(4.23)	114-0191-73D
$C_{40}H_{46}O_{20}$			
Ethanone, 1-[2-hydroxy-4-[[2,3,6-tri-O-acetyl-4-O-(2,3,4,6-tetra-O-acetyl-β-D-glucopyranosyl)-β-D-glucopyranosyl]oxy]phenyl]-2-phenyl-	EtOH	214(4.33),270(4.16), 318(3.83)	114-0191-73D
$C_{40}H_{47}N_4O_{10}Tl$			
Thallium, aquahydroxy[tetramethyl 3,7,13,17-tetramethyl-21H,23H-porphine-2,8,12,18-tetrapropanoato(2-)-N^{21},N^{22},N^{23},N^{24}]-, (OC-6-23)-	CH_2Cl_2	417(5.54),544(4.27), 582(4.09)	78-0553-73
Thallium, aquahydroxy[tetramethyl 3,8,12,17-tetramethyl-21H,23H-porphine-2,7,13,18-tetrapropanoato(2-)-N^{21},N^{22},N^{23},N^{24}]-, (OC-6-23)-	CH_2Cl_2	417(5.56),544(4.28), 582(4.08)	78-0553-73
$C_{40}H_{48}$			
Octadecanonaene, 1,18-bis(2,4,5-trimethylphenyl)-3,7,12,16-tetramethyl-, all-E	benzene	490(5.1),525(5.0)	18-1553-73
Octadecanonaene, 1,18-bis(2,4,6-trimethylphenyl)-3,7,12,16-tetramethyl-, all-E	benzene	471(5.0),500(4.9)	18-1553-73
Octadecanonaene, 1,18-bis(3,4,5-trimethylphenyl)-3,7,12,16-tetramethyl-, all-E	benzene	460(4.9),491(5.1), 525(5.0)	18-1553-73
$C_{40}H_{48}N_2O_8$			
Ethanol, 2-[[2,3,13,14,25,28a-hexahydro-5,6,9,21-tetramethoxy-1-methyl-11-[2-(methylamino)ethyl]-1H-15,18-etheno-8,12:20,24-dimetheno-12H-[1,11]dioxacyclodocosino[2,3,4-ij]isoquinolin-13-yl]oxy]-	EtOH	283(3.83)	44-1846-73

Compound	Solvent	$\lambda_{max}(\log \epsilon)$	Ref.
$C_{40}H_{49}NO_{12}$			
Rifamycin S, 21,23-acetonide	EtOH	228(4.59),274(4.41), 305(4.28),395(3.83)	33-2323-73
$C_{40}H_{50}N_2O_{12}$			
Rifamycin S, 3-(cyclopropylamino)-	EtOH	232(4.45),267(4.45), 319(4.12),370(3.83), 530(3.26)	33-2348-73
$C_{40}H_{50}N_4O_8$			
21H,23H-Porphine-2,18-dipropanoic acid, 7,12-bis(2,2-dimethoxyethyl)- 3,8,13,17-tetramethyl-, dimethyl ester	CH_2Cl_2	399(5.23),498(4.09), 535(3.90),569(3.74), 623(3.52)	5-1329-73
	CH_2Cl_2 - CF_3COOH	405(5.57),549(4.18), 593(3.70)	5-1329-73
$C_{40}H_{51}NO_{12}$			
Rifamycin, 25-O-deacetyl-1,4-dideoxy-1,4-dihydro-1,4-dioxo-, 21-(2,2-dimethylpropanoate)	EtOH	275(4.44),333(3.92), 390(3.72)	33-2323-73
Rifamycin, 25-O-deacetyl-1,4-dideoxy-25-O-(2,2-dimethyl-1-oxopropyl)-1,4-dihydro-1,4-dioxo-	EtOH	277(4.30),400(3.63)	33-2323-73
$C_{40}H_{52}N_2O_{12}$			
Rifamycin S, 3-(isopropylamino)-	EtOH	231(4.48),267(4.47), 319(4.13),370(3.86), 530(3.23)	33-2348-73
$C_{40}H_{52}N_4O_2$			
21H,23H-Porphine-8-acetic acid, 2,3,7,8-12,13,17,18-octaethyl-, ethyl ester	$CHCl_3$	402(5.24),502(4.00), 535(3.72),571(3.65), 623(3.28)	39-1424-73C
$C_{40}H_{53}NO_{12}$			
Rifamycin, 1,4,8-tri-O-methyl-	EtOH	228(4.65),295(4.50), 410(3.70)	33-2287-73
$C_{40}H_{54}N_2O_{13}$			
Rifamycin, 3-[(2-hydroxyethyl)methylamino]-	EtOH-HCl	244(4.47),262(4.49), 333(4.25),408(3.83)	33-2348-73
$C_{40}H_{55}N_3O_8S_2$			
C-Nor-9,11-secospirostan-3,9-diol, 11-azido-, bis(4-methylbenzenesulfonate), (3β,5α,9β25R)-	EtOH	225(4.4)	13-0147-73A
$C_{40}H_{56}$			
α-Carotene	dioxan	269(5.00),334(3.95), 430(5.00),452(5.19), 480(5.13)	33-1124-73
δ-Carotene	isooctane	271s(4.45),279(4.62), 344(4.07),410(4.77), 428(5.06),455(5.25), 487(5.20)	33-1124-73
$C_{40}H_{56}O_4$			
Triphasiaxanthin	$CHCl_3$	480(4.99),510(4.93)	114-0315-73C

Compound	Solvent	λ_{max}(log ε)	Ref.
$C_{40}H_{56}O_9S_2$			
C-Nor-9,11-secospirostan-3,9,11-triol, 3,11-bis(4-methylbenzenesulfonate), (3β,5α,9β,25R)-	EtOH	225(4.43)	13-0147-73A
$C_{40}H_{58}N_2$			
Pyrazine, 1,2-dicyclododecyl-1,2-dihydro-2,5-diphenyl-	n.s.g.	267(4.33)	39-0683-73C
$C_{40}H_{60}O_2$			
Kitol	EtOH	295(4.69)	39-0590-73C
	EtOH	296(4.70)	39-0590-73C
$C_{40}H_{63}NO_{13}$			
4-Oxabicyclo[12.2.1]heptadeca-7,9-diene-17-carboxaldehyde, 15-[[3,6-dideoxy-4-O-[2,6-dideoxy-3-C-methyl-4-O-(3-methyl-1-oxobutyl)-α-L-ribohexopyranosyl]-3-(dimethylamino)-β-D-glucopyranosyl]-oxy]-11-hydroxy-16-methoxy-5,12-dimethyl-3-oxo-	MeOH	215(4.26)	138-0799-73
isomer	MeOH	215(4.24)	138-0799-73

Compound	Solvent	$\lambda_{max}(\log \epsilon)$	Ref.
$C_{41}H_{29}N$ 1-Benzazocine, 2,3,4,5,6-pentaphenyl-	CHCl	254(4.56)	77-0019-73
$C_{41}H_{35}NiPPb$ Nickel, (η^5-2,4-cyclopentadien-1-yl)-(triphenylphosphine)(triphenyl-plumbyl)-	C_6H_{12}	386(4.04),440s(3.48), 568(1.90)	23-1179-73
$C_{41}H_{35}NiPSn$ Nickel, (η^5-2,4-cyclopentadien-1-yl)-(triphenylphosphine)(triphenyl-stannyl)-	C_6H_{12}	347(3.84),405s(3.27), 568(1.85)	23-1179-73
$C_{41}H_{35}NiP_2$ Nickel(1+), (η^5-2,4-cyclopentadien-1-yl)bis(triphenylphosphine)-, tetra-fluoroborate	C_6H_{12}	340s(3.87),441(3.11), 553(2.00)	23-1179-73
$C_{41}H_{36}N_2O_7$ D-Ribitol, 1,4-anhydro-1-C-(1,3-diphen-yl-2-imidazolidinyl)-, 2,3,5-tribenz-oate, (S)-	n.s.g.	232(4.68),252(4.54), 282(3.77)	44-1836-73
$C_{41}H_{38}N_3O_3$ Benzo[f]quinolinium, 2-acetyl-4-[4-(acetyloxy)phenyl]-1-[2,2-bis[4-(dimethylamino)phenyl]ethenyl]-, perchlorate	MeOH	609(3.71)	65-0877-73
$C_{41}H_{41}BrCoN_4O_2$ Cobalt, bromo[octadehydro-1,2,7,8,12,13-18,19-octamethyl-3,7-bis(phenylmeth-oxy)corrinato-N^{21},N^{22},N^{23},N^{24}]-, (SP-5-13)-	CH_2Cl_2	280(4.45),320(4.45), 344s(4.32),494(4.22), 566(3.80)	5-0146-73
$C_{41}H_{41}BrN_4NiO_2$ Nickel, bromo[octadehydro-1,2,7,8,12,13-18,19-octamethyl-3,7-bis(phenylmeth-oxy)corrinato-N^{21},N^{22},N^{23},N^{24}]-, (SP-5-13)-	CH_2Cl_2	277(4.44),355(4.50), 460s(3.68),563(4.15)	5-0146-73
$C_{41}H_{42}N_2O_4$ β-D-Ribofuranose, 1-deoxy-1-(1,3-di-phenyl-2-imidazolidinyl)-2,3,5-tris-O-(phenylmethyl)-	MeOH	254(4.52),294(3.63)	44-1836-73
$C_{41}H_{43}BrCoN_4O_4$ Cobalt, bromo[7,8,12,13,17,19-hexadehy-dro-1,2,7,8,12,13,18,19-octamethyl-3,17-bis(phenylmethoxy)-7,8-corrin-diolato-N^{21},N^{22},N^{23},N^{24}]-, (SP-5-15)-	CH_2Cl_2	345(4.16),460(3.79), 530(3.70)	5-0146-73
$C_{41}H_{43}BrN_4O_4Ni$ Nickel, bromo[7,8,12,13,17,19-hexadehy-dro-1,2,7,8,12,13,18,19-octamethyl-3,17-bis(phenylmethoxy)-7,8-corrin-diolato-N^{21},N^{22},N^{23},N^{24}]-, (SP-5-15)-	CH_2Cl_2	276(4.18),346(4.22), 535(3.93)	5-0146-73
$C_{41}H_{44}N_2O_8$ Pakistanine, 1,10-di-O-acetyl-	EtOH	215(4.53),275(4.23), 305(3.89)	35-5742-73

Compound	Solvent	$\lambda_{max}(\log \epsilon)$	Ref.
$C_{41}H_{44}N_4O_7S$			
21H,23H-Porphine-2-propanoic acid, 13-ethyl-18-(methoxycarbonyl)-3,7,12,17-tetramethyl-8-[2-[(4-methylphenyl)-sulfonyl]oxy]ethyl]-, methyl ester	CH_2Cl_2	404(5.30),501(3.96), 547(4.20),576(3.91), 632(3.04)	5-1329-73
	CH_2Cl_2-CF_3COOH	412(5.55),558(4.12), 604(3.93)	5-1329-73
$C_{41}H_{44}O_6$			
Benzenemethanol, 2-hydroxy-3-[[2-hydroxy-3-[[2-hydroxy-3-[[2-hydroxy-3-[(2-hydroxy-3,5-dimethylphenyl)-methyl]-5-methylphenyl]methyl]-5-methylphenyl]methyl]-5-methylphenyl]methyl]-5-methyl-	dioxan	287(4.17)	126-0039-73L
$C_{41}H_{44}O_{20}$			
4H-1-Benzopyran-4-one, 3-phenyl-7-[(2,3,6-tri-O-acetyl-4-O-(2,3,4,6-tetra-O-acetyl-β-D-glucopyranosyl)-β-D-glucopyranosyl]oxy]-	EtOH	248(4.40),296(3.96)	114-0191-73D
$C_{41}H_{45}BrCoN_4O_6$			
Cobalt, bromo[2,3,17,18-tetradehydro-1,2,7,8,12,13,18,19-octamethyl-3,17-bis(phenylmethoxy)-7,8,12,13-corrintetrolato-N^{21},N^{22},N^{23},N^{24}]-, (SP-5-15)-	CH_2Cl_2	304(4.25),440(3.72)	5-0146-73
$C_{41}H_{45}BrN_4NiO_6$			
Nickel, bromo[2,3,17,18-tetradehydro-1,2,7,8,12,13,18,19-octamethyl-3,17-bis(phenylmethoxy)-7,8,12,13-corrintetrolato-N^{21},N^{22},N^{23},N^{24}]-, (SP-5-15)-	CH_2Cl_2	265(4.18),302(4.23), 331(4.22),360s(4.07), 456s(3.90),478(3.98)	5-0146-73
$C_{41}H_{46}BrNO_{16}$			
Evonine, O^6-[(4-bromophenyl)methyl]-O^6-deacetyl-	EtOH	222(4.18),264(3.50)	102-0703-73
$C_{41}H_{46}INO_{16}$			
Evonine, O^6-deacetyl-O^6-[(4-iodophenyl)-methyl]-	EtOH	233(4.32),262(3.62)	102-0703-73
$C_{41}H_{48}O_{21}$			
Ethanone, 1-[2-hydroxy-4-[[2,3,6-tri-O-acetyl-4-O-(2,3,4,6-tetra-O-acetyl-β-D-glucopyranosyl)-β-D-glucopyranosyl]oxy]phenyl]-2-(4-methoxyphenyl)-	EtOH	217(4.44),270(4.22), 319(3.88)	114-0191-73D
$C_{41}H_{49}CoN_4O_6$			
Cobalt(1+), (diethyl octadehydro-2,17-diethenyl-1,19-diethoxy-3,7,13,18-tetramethyl-8,12-corrindipropanoato-N^{21},N^{22},N^{23},N^{24})-, (SP-4-3)-, perchlorate	CH_2Cl_2	285(4.35),367(4.35), 465(3.89),560(4.05)	5-0141-73
$C_{41}H_{49}NO_{14}$			
Rifamycin, 1,4-dideoxy-1,4-dihydro-1,4-dioxo-, 8,21(or 23)-diacetate	EtOH	224(4.49),257(4.37), 300(4.20)	33-2323-73
Rifamycin, 1,4-dideoxy-1,4-dihydro-1,4-dioxo-, 21,23-diacetate	EtOH	225(4.55),275(4.41), 390(3.68)	33-2323-73

Compound	Solvent	λ_{max}(log ϵ)	Ref.
$C_{41}H_{49}N_4NiO_6$			
Nickel(1+), (diethyl octadehydro-2,17-diethenyl-1,19-diethoxy-3,7,13,18-tetramethyl-8,12-corrindipropanoato-N^{21},N^{22},N^{23},N^{24})-, (SP-4-3)-, perchlorate	CH_2Cl_2	284(4.40),366(4.40), 464(3.83),560(4.11)	5-0141-73
$C_{41}H_{50}N_2O_8$			
Ethanol, 2-[[11-[2-(dimethylamino)ethyl]-2,3,13,14,25,25a-hexahydro-5,6,9-21-tetramethoxy-1-methyl-1H-15,18-etheno-8,12:20,24-dimetheno-12H-[1,11]-dioxacyclodocosino[2,3,4-ij]isoquinolin-13-yl]oxy]-	EtOH	282(3.90)	44-1846-73
$C_{41}H_{52}N_2O_{12}$			
2,7-(Epoxypentadeca[1,11,13]trieno)-7H-furo[3',2':5,6]naphth[2,3-d]imidazole-1,6,10,11(2H)-tetrone, 21-acetoxy-9-ethyl-8,9-dihydro-5,17,19-trihydroxy-23-methoxy-2,4,8,12,16,18,20,22-octamethyl-	EtOH	230(4.50),254(4.41), 270(4.41),344(4.12),	33-2348-73
Rifamycin S, 3-pyrrolidino-	EtOH	263(4.49),330(4.19), 370s(--),545(3.40)	33-2348-73
$C_{41}H_{52}N_2O_{13}$			
Rifamycin S, 3-morpholino-	EtOH	220(4.48),273(4.48), 322(4.17),550(3.38)	33-2348-73
$C_{41}H_{53}NO_{13}$			
9,4-(Epoxypentadeca[1,11,13]trienimino)-naphtho[1,2-b:7,8-b']difuran-10,26-(9H)-dione, 16-acetoxy-2,3-dihydro-2,5,6,18,20-pentahydroxy-14-methoxy-3,5,7,9,15,17,19,21,25-nonamethyl-	EtOH	230(4.64),250(4.45), 300(4.28),315(4.29), 445(3.97)	33-2348-73
$C_{41}H_{54}N_2O_{12}$			
2,7-(Epoxypentadeca[1,11,13]trieno-7H-furo[3',2':5,6]naphth[2,3-d]imidazole-1,11(2H)-dione, 21-acetoxy-9-ethyl-8,9-dihydro-5,6,10,17,19-pentahydroxy-23-methoxy-2,4,8,12,16,18,20,22-octamethyl-	EtOH-HCl	225(4.42),293(4.41), 457(3.97)	33-2348-73
Rifamycin S, 3-(diethylamino)-	EtOH	270(4.49),327(4.16), 540(3.38)	33-2348-73
$C_{41}H_{54}N_2O_{13}$			
Rifamycin, 3-morpholino-	EtOH-HCl	223(4.62),296(4.34), 441(3.95)	33-2348-73
$C_{41}H_{55}N_3O_{12}$			
Rifamycin, 3-piperazino-	EtOH-HCl	225(4.52),295(4.25), 435(3.88)	33-2348-73
$C_{41}H_{56}N_2O_{13}$			
Rifamycin, 3-[ethyl(2-hydroxyethyl)-amino]-	EtOH-HCl	245(4.47),263(4.49), 334(4.25),408(3.95)	33-2348-73
$C_{41}H_{56}N_2O_{14}$			
Rifamycin, 3-[bis(2-hydroxyethyl)amino]-	EtOH-HCl	223(4.60),295(4.33), 435(4.00)	33-2348-73

Compound	Solvent	$\lambda_{max}(\log \epsilon)$	Ref.
$C_{41}H_{56}N_4O_4$			
Secamine, tetrahydro-	MeOH	223(4.76),285(4.20), 292(4.17)	95-0483-73
$C_{41}H_{63}NO_{14}$			
Antibiotic B-58941, diacetate	EtOH	240(4.18)	138-0799-73
$C_{41}H_{74}O_5$			
Octadecanoic acid, 6-ethoxy-3-hexadecyl-2-oxo-2H-pyran-4-yl ester	EtOH	227(3.76),315(3.94)	44-2540-73

Compound	Solvent	$\lambda_{max}(\log \epsilon)$	Ref.
$C_{42}H_{24}$			
Diphenanthro[3,2-c:3',2'-l]chrysene	benzene	270(4.17),291(4.43), 303(4.43),322(4.49), 337(4.73),353(4.91), 366s(4.60),385(4.41), 400s(4.00),433(3.07)	54-0553-73
Diphenanthro[3,2-c:3',4'-l]chrysene	CH_2Cl_2	239(4.90),274(4.71), 310(4.85),334s(4.72), 350(4.78),379(4.61), 433s(2.98),450s(2.42)	54-0553-73
Diphenanthro[3,4-c:3',4'-l]chrysene, (±)-	CH_2Cl_2	242(4.80),259(4.82), 277(4.82),312(4.61), 338(4.59),354(4.60), 375(4.46),407s(3.58), 431s(3.01)	54-0553-73
meso-	CH_2Cl_2	228(4.81),259(4.90), 276(4.93),321s(4.49), 336(4.59),348(4.59), 360(4.54),383(4.32), 406s(3.79),432(3.38)	54-0553-73
$C_{42}H_{24}Br_4Cl_2N_4$			
Imidazolyl, 4,5-bis(4-bromophenyl)-2-(3-chlorophenyl)-, dimer	EtOH	280(4.43)	103-0085-73
$C_{42}H_{24}Br_4N_6O_4$			
Imidazolyl, 4,5-bis(4-bromophenyl)-2-(4-nitrophenyl)-, dimer	EtOH	275(4.53)	103-0085-73
$C_{42}H_{24}Br_6N_4$			
Imidazolyl, 2,4,5-tris(4-bromophenyl)-, dimer	EtOH	280(4.52)	103-0085-73
$C_{42}H_{26}$			
Benzo[c]phenanthro[3,4-l]chrysene, 15-(2-phenylethenyl)-	CH_2Cl_2	227(4.17),233s(4.66), 273(4.82),315s(4.63), 330(4.68),355(4.65), 375s(4.54)	54-0553-73
$C_{42}H_{26}Br_4N_4$			
Imidazolyl, 4,5-bis(4-bromophenyl)-2-phenyl-, dimer	EtOH	280(4.61)	103-0085-73
$C_{42}H_{26}N_8$			
1,2,4-Triazolo[4,3-c]quinazoline, 5,5'-[1,1'-biphenyl]-4,4'-diylbis[3-phenyl-	H_2SO_4	262(4.87),288(4.82), 342(4.34)	116-0483-73
$C_{42}H_{26}N_8O$			
1,2,4-Triazolo[4,3-c]quinazoline, 5,5'-(oxydi-4,1-phenylene)bis[3-phenyl-	H_2SO_4	277(5.16),400(4.68)	116-0483-73
$C_{42}H_{26}N_8O_2S$			
1,2,4-Triazolo[4,3-c]quinazoline, 5,5'-(sulfonyldi-4,1-phenylene)bis[3-phenyl-	H_2SO_4	289(4.94),346(4.46)	116-0483-73
$C_{42}H_{26}O_4$			
5,12-Naphthacenedione, 1,4-dihydroxy-6,8,9,11-tetraphenyl-	CH_2Cl_2	266(5.0),325(4.6), 470(4.2)	22-2856-73

Compound	Solvent	$\lambda_{max}(\log \epsilon)$	Ref.
$C_{42}H_{28}$			
Dibenzo[c,l]chrysene, 3,11-bis(2-phenyl-ethenyl)-	CH_2Cl_2	285(4.71),333(4.86), 351(4.78),378(4.63)	54-0553-73
Phenanthrene, 3,3'-(2,6-naphthalenediyl-di-2,1-ethenediyl)bis-, cis-cis	xylene	289(4.58),303s(4.40), 350s(4.73),358(4.75), 372s(4.67)	54-0553-73
$C_{42}H_{30}$			
Anthra[2,3-j]heptaphene, 5,8,13,16,21-24-hexahydro-	CH_2Cl_2	254s(4.70),261(4.96), 271(5.18),285s(4.51), 296(4.46),310s(4.30), 324(4.30)	24-2058-73
$C_{42}H_{30}N_8O_2$			
[1,1'-Biphenyl]-4,4'-dicarboxamide, N,N'-bis[2-(5-phenyl-1H-1,2,4-triazol-3-yl)phenyl]-	H_2SO_4	279(4.89),328(4.75)	116-0483-73
$C_{42}H_{30}N_8O_3$			
Benzamide, 4,4'-oxybis[N-[2-(5-phenyl-1H-1,2,4-triazol-3-yl)phenyl]-	H_2SO_4	239(4.35),275(4.75)	116-0483-73
$C_{42}H_{30}N_8O_4S$			
Benzamide, 4,4'-sulfonylbis[N-[2-(5-phenyl-1H-1,2,4-triazol-3-yl)phenyl]-	H_2SO_4	285(4.9),340(4.22)	116-0483-73
$C_{42}H_{30}O_2S$			
Benzene, 1, 1',1",1'"-[sulfonylbis(3-phenyl-1-cyclopropene-3,1,2-triyl)-tetrakis-	$CHCl_3$	314(4.62)	88-4827-73
$C_{42}H_{32}$			
1,4-Cyclohexadiene, 1,2,3,4,5,6-hexa-phenyl-	$CHCl_3$	267(3.7),273(3.6)	35-0861-73
$C_{42}H_{34}$			
1,1'-Biphenyl, 2,2'-bis[2-(2'-methyl-[1,1'-biphenyl]-2-yl)ethenyl]-, (Z,Z)-	C_6H_{12}	290(4.36)	44-0808-73
$C_{42}H_{34}N_4$			
3H-Cyclobut-2-eno[b]quinoxaline, 2-(di-phenylmethyl)-1-(diphenylmethylene)-, 1,2-phenylenediamine addition compd.	$CHCl_3$	304(3.76)	18-1733-73
1H-Pyrazole, 1,1'-[1,1'-biphenyl]-4,4'-diylbis[4,5-dihydro-3,5-diphenyl-	toluene	394(4.76)	48-0549-73
$C_{42}H_{34}O_2P_2$			
6,11-Phosphinidene-2H-naphth[2,3-e]iso-phosphindole, 5a,6,11,11a-tetrahydro-2,12-dimethyl-1,3,6,11-tetraphenyl-, 2,12-dioxide	EtOH	384(3.73)	39-0927-73C
$C_{42}H_{34}Si$			
Silacyclopenta-2,4-diene, 1,1,x,x'-tetraphenyl-y,y'-bis(4-methylphenyl)-	C_6H_{12}	208(4.99),255(4.48), 367(3.93)	101-0381-73C
$C_{42}H_{36}O_4P_2$			
6,11-Phosphi idene-2H-naphth[2,3-e]iso-phosphindole-4,5-diol, 4,5,5a,6,11,11a-hexahydro-2,12-dimethyl-1,3,6,11-tetraphenyl-, 2,12-dioxide	EtOH	368(3.86)	39-0927-73C

Compound	Solvent	λmax(log ε)	Ref.
$C_{42}H_{37}N_5O_8$			
Adenosine, N,N-bis(4-methylbenzoyl)-	MeOH	244(4.71),270s(4.55)	18-3228-73
$C_{42}H_{38}O_3$			
Acenaphthylene, 5,5'-[oxybis(2-ethoxyphenyl)methylene]bis[1,2-dihydro-	H_2SO_4	618(5.96)	94-0383-73
$C_{42}H_{40}N_4O_{10}Tc_2$			
Technetium, hexacarbonyl[μ-[dimethyl-7,12-diethyl-3,4,13,17-tetramethyl-21H,23H-porphine-2,18-dipropanoato-(2-)]di-	CH_2Cl_2	370s(4.03),396(4.43), 480s(3.59),507(3.93)	138-0941-73
$C_{42}H_{46}O_{21}$			
4H-1-Benzopyran-4-one, 3-(4-methoxyphenyl)-7-[[2,3,6-tri-O-acetyl-4-O-(2,3,4,6-tetra-O-acetyl-β-D-glucopyranosyl)-β-D-glucopyranosyl]oxy]-	EtOH	258(4.49),306(3.94)	114-0191-73D
$C_{42}H_{48}$			
Anthra[2,3-j]heptaphene, 1,2,3,4,4a,5-8,8a,9,10,11,12,12a,13,16,16a,17,18-19,20,20a,21,22,22a-tetracosahydro-	CH_2Cl_2	263(4.74),267(4.76), 271(4.88),285(4.43), 294(4.36),312(4.00), 325(3.70)	24-2058-73
$C_{42}H_{48}N_4O_4$			
Anhydromacralstonine, N'$_a$-demethyl-	EtOH	230(4.83),285(4.28), 305(4.02),318(3.75)	102-1467-73
$C_{42}H_{48}N_4O_6$			
Alkaloid F from Voacanga thouarsii	EtOH	223(4.57),261(4), 301(4.13),325(4.21)	102-2039-73
$C_{42}H_{48}N_4O_{10}$			
21H,23H-Porphine-2,7-dipropanoic acid, 10-acetoxy-12,17-bis(2-acetoxyethyl)-3,8,13,18-tetramethyl-, dimethyl ester	CH_2Cl_2	401(5.26),500(4.18), 532(3.73),572(3.77), 625(3.13)	39-2478-73C
	CH_2Cl_2-CF_3COOH	413(5.52),558(4.08), 595(3.51)	39-2478-73C
$C_{42}H_{48}N_4O_{11}$			
Rifamycin S, 2,3-diaminopyridine reaction product	EtOH-NaOH	227(4.62),260(4.52), 321(4.66),500(3.98)	33-2348-73
$C_{42}H_{48}O_{22}$			
Ilesugerin octaacetate	n.s.g.	229(4.28),275(3.39), 280(3.28)	40-0785-73
$C_{42}H_{49}FeN_4O$			
Iron, [2,3,7,8,12,13,17,18-octaethyl-21H,23H-porphinato(2-)-N^{21},N^{22},N^{23}-N^{24}]phenoxy-, (SP-5-12)-	benzene	350s(4.71),395(5.00), 487(4.10),518s(4.03), 600(3.96)	64-0433-73B
$C_{42}H_{49}GaN_4O$			
Gallium, [2,3,7,8,12,13,17,18-octaethyl-21H,23H-porphinato(2-)-N^{21},N^{22},N^{23}-N^{24}]phenoxy-, (SP-5-12)-	benzene	340(4.29),386s(4.77), 404(5.43),486s(3.12), 500(3.29),537(4.21), 574(4.34)	24-2710-73

Compound	Solvent	$\lambda_{max}(\log \epsilon)$	Ref.
$C_{42}H_{49}MnN_4O$			
Manganese, [2,3,7,8,12,13,17,18-octaethyl-21H,23H-porphinato(2-)-N^{21},N^{22},N^{23}-N^{24}]phenoxy-, (SP-5-12)-	benzene	355(4.69),437(4.62), 462(4.31),557(3.95), 758(2.80)	24-2710-73
$C_{42}H_{49}MoN_4O_2$			
Molybdenum, [2,3,7,8,12,13,17,18-octaethyl-21H,23H-porphinato(2-)-N^{21},N^{22}-N^{23},N^{24}]oxyphenoxy-, (OC-6-23)-	benzene	343(4.77),454(4.84), 573(4.15),606(3.91)	24-2710-73
$C_{42}H_{49}N_4O_2Re$			
Rhenium, [2,3,7,8,12,13,17,18-octaethyl-21H,23H-porphinato(2-)-N^{21},N^{22},N^{23}-N^{24}]oxyphenoxy-, (OC-6-23)-	benzene	337(4.81),454(4.79), 578(3.98),596(3.93)	24-2710-73
$C_{42}H_{49}N_4O_2W$			
Tungsten, [2,3,7,8,12,13,17,18-octaethyl-21H,23H-porphinato(2-)-N^{21},N^{22}-N^{23},N^{24}]oxyphenoxy-, (OC-6-23)-	benzene	356(4.26),433(5.28), 562(4.09),598(3.90)	24-2710-73
$C_{42}H_{49}N_4O_{11}Tl$			
Thallium, (acetato-O)aqua[tetramethyl 3,8,13,18-tetramethyl-21H,23H-porphine-2,7,12,17-tetrapropanoato(2-)-N^{21},N^{22},N^{23},N^{24}]-, (OC-6-23)-	CH_2Cl_2	416(5.58),544(4.30), 581(4.11)	39-2142-73C
$C_{42}H_{50}N_4O_5$			
Alkaloid H from Voacanga thouarsii	EtOH	221(4.63),260(4.29), 298(3.70)	102-2039-73
$C_{42}H_{51}NO_{14}$			
Rifamycin, 3-(1-acetyl-2-oxopropyl)-1,4-dideoxy-1,4-dihydro-1,4-dioxo-	EtOH	215(4.51),276(4.49), 380s(--)	33-2348-73
$C_{42}H_{54}N_2O_{12}$			
Rifamycin S, 3-piperidino-	EtOH	217(4.45),268(4.43), 321(4.15),545(3.42)	33-2348-73
$C_{42}H_{54}N_4O_{10}$			
Alkaloid C from Voacanga thouarsii	EtOH	223(4.57),263(4.1), 299(4.17),328(4.21)	102-2039-73
$C_{42}H_{55}N_3O_{12}$			
Rifamycin S, 3-(2-methylpiperazinyl)-	EtOH	217(4.50),271(4.45), 322(4.19),550(3.48)	33-2348-73
$C_{42}H_{56}N_2O_{12}$			
Rifamycin, 3-(3-methyl-1-pyrrolidinyl)-	EtOH-HCl	227(4.56),290(4.25), 320s(--),444(4.06)	33-2348-73
$C_{42}H_{56}N_2O_{13}$			
Rifamycin, 3-(3-hydroxy-1-piperidinyl)-	EtOH-HCl	224(4.57),295(4.28), 320s(--),440(3.98)	33-2348-73
Rifamycin, 3-(4-hydroxy-1-piperidinyl)-	EtOH-HCl	220(4.60),295(4.28), 320s(--),442(3.95)	33-2348-73
$C_{42}H_{56}N_2O_{14}$			
Rifamycin S, 3-[(2,2-dimethoxyethyl)-methylamino]-	EtOH	223(4.50),265(4.45), 319(4.22),375s(--), 550(3.08)	33-2348-73

Compound	Solvent	λ_{max}(log ε)	Ref.
$C_{42}H_{56}N_4O_{24}$			
α-D-Glucopyranoside, 2,3-dihydroxy-1-[1-(3-hydroxyphenyl)-1H-pyrazolo-[3,4-b]quinoxalin-3-yl]propyl O-α-D-glucopyranosyl-(1→4)-O-α-D-gluco-pyranosyl-(1→4)-O-α-D-glucopyrano-syl-(1→4)-	pH 2.5	257(4.53),335(4.01), 404(3.57)	48-0517-73
	pH 10.2	248(4.61),304(3.83), 335(4.02),404(3.57)	48-0517-73
$C_{42}H_{57}N_3O_{12}$			
Rifamycin, 3-(N-methyl-1-piperazinyl)-	EtOH-HCl	226(4.54),317(4.29), 448(4.08)	33-2348-73
$C_{42}H_{59}BrN_6O_4$			
21H-Biline-8,12-dipropanoic acid, 1-bro-mo-3,18-bis[2-(diethylamino)ethyl]-10,24-dihydro-2,7,13,17,19-penta-methyl-, tetrahydrobromide	EtOH-HBr	455(4.61),524(4.92)	103-0186-73
$C_{42}H_{70}O_{11}$			
Salinomycin	67% EtOH	284(2.10)	88-4955-73

Compound	Solvent	$\lambda_{max}(\log \epsilon)$	Ref.
$C_{43}H_{26}N_8O$			
Methanone, bis[4-(3-phenyl-1,2,4-triazolo[4,3-c]quinazolin-5-yl)phenyl]-	H_2SO_4	294(5.01),351(4.68)	116-0483-73
$C_{43}H_{30}N_2$			
Pyrazolo[1,5-a]pyridine, 2,3,4,5,6,7-hexaphenyl-	n.s.g.	258(4.43),274(4.43), 325(3.60)	39-0221-73C
$C_{43}H_{30}N_8O_3$			
Benzamide, 4,4'-carbonylbis[N-[2-(5-phenyl-1H-1,2,4-triazol-3-yl)phenyl]-	H_2SO_4	280(4.0),340(4.31)	116-0483-73
$C_{43}H_{30}S$			
Methanethione, bis(1,2,3-triphenyl-2-cyclopropen-1-yl)-	EtOH	225(4.68),302(4.48), 326s(4.26)	35-1285-73
$C_{43}H_{33}NSi$			
7-Silabicyclo[2.2.1]hept-5-ene-2-carbonitrile, 1,4,5,6,7,7-hexaphenyl-, endo	n.s.g.	226(4.59),278(3.99), 287(3.86),297(3.81)	78-2395-73
$C_{43}H_{34}O$			
1,4:9,10-Dimethanoanthracen-12-one, 11-(diphenylmethylene)-1,4,4a,9,9a,10-hexahydro-1,4-dimethyl-2,3-diphenyl-	90% EtOH	224(4.54),269(4.30), 277(4.23)	12-1725-73
$C_{43}H_{38}N_3O$			
Benzo[f]quinolinium, 2-acetyl-1-[2,2-bis[4-(dimethylamino)phenyl]ethenyl]-4-(2-naphthalenyl)-, perchlorate	MeOH	590(3.64)	65-0877-73
$C_{43}H_{41}CoN_6O_2$			
Cobalt, bis(cyano-C)[octadehydro-1,2,7,8,12,13,18,19-octamethyl-3,17-bis(phenylmethoxy)corrinato-N^{21},N^{22},N^{23},N^{24}]-, (OC-6-34)-	CH_2Cl_2	276(4.31),296s(4.25), 375s(4.04),404(4.08), 504s(3.50),632s(3.32), 696(3.80),787(4.17)	5-0146-73
$C_{43}H_{45}CoN_6O_6$			
Cobalt, bis(cyano-C)[2,3,17,18-tetradehydro-7,8,12,13-tetrahydroxy-1,2,7,8,12,13,18,19-octamethyl-3,17-bis(phenylmethoxy)corrinato-N^{21},N^{22},N^{23},N^{24}]-, (OC-6-43)-	CH_2Cl_2	327(4.10),387(3.98), 558(3.79),594(3.84)	5-0146-73
$C_{43}H_{46}N_4O_7$			
Alkaloid H from Voacanga thouarsii	EtOH	220(4.72),263(4.29), 295(4.39),328(4.49)	102-2039-73
$C_{43}H_{47}ClN_2O_{12}$			
Rifamycin VIII, 4'-chloro-1,4-didehydro-1-deoxy-1',4-dihydro-1-oxo-	EtOH-NaOH	230(4.68),304(4.31), 316(4.31),406(4.07), 517(3.82)	33-2348-73
$C_{43}H_{47}N_3O_9$			
Milliamine C	MeOH	228(4.62),260(4.28), 315(4.15)	88-0881-73
$C_{43}H_{48}ClN_3O_{11}$			
Rifazine, 39(or 40)-chloro-	EtOH-NaOH	247(4.75),285s(--), 345(4.49),535(3.91)	33-2348-73

Compound	Solvent	λ_{max}(log ε)	Ref.
$C_{43}H_{48}N_2O_{12}$			
Rifamycin VIII, 1',4-didehydro-1-deoxy-1,4-dihydro-1-oxo-	EtOH	229(4.73),305(4.30), 315(4.30),402(4.13), 510(3.88)	33-2348-73
$C_{43}H_{48}N_4O_6$			
Alkaloid from Voacanga thouarsii	EtOH	223(4.40),265(3.97), 298(4.04),328(4.68)	102-2039-73
$C_{43}H_{48}N_4O_7$			
Alkaloid A from Voacanga thouarsii	EtOH	220(4.49),263(4), 292(4.14),328(4.18)	102-2039-73
$C_{43}H_{48}N_4O_8$			
Alkaloid B from Voacanga thouarsii	EtOH	222(4.78),263(4.07), 297(4.18),327(4.25)	102-2039-73
$C_{43}H_{48}O_{12}$			
Spiro[10b,4-(epoxymethano)-5a,8-methanocyclobuta[5,6]benz[1,2-a]azulene-2-(1H),8'(9'H)-[5H-7,9a]methanobenz[a]-azulene-5,10'-dicarboxylic acid, 2',8-diacetoxy-2a,3,4,4a,4'b,5,6,6',7,7',8-9,10,10',10a,10c-hexadecahydro-7-hydroxy-1',4-dimethyl-7-methylene-3,12-dioxo-, dimethyl ester	MeOH	215(4.08),270(3.34)	78-3177-73
$C_{43}H_{48}O_{16}$			
Dryocrassin	EtOH	222(4.62),306(4.43), 351(4.42)	102-1491B-73
$C_{43}H_{49}N_3O_{11}$			
Rifazine	EtOH-NaOH	247(4.77),285s(--), 342(4.53),527(3.92)	33-2348-73
$C_{43}H_{50}N_2O_{12}$			
Rifamycin, 1,4-dideoxy-1,4-dihydro-1,4-dioxo-3-(phenylamino)-	EtOH	261(4.43),325(4.47), 388(3.77),580(3.66)	33-2348-73
Rifamycin, 1,4-dideoxy-1,4-dihydro-4-[(2-hydroxyphenyl)imino]-1-oxo-	EtOH	225(4.64),323(4.25), 400s(--),500(3.80)	33-2348-73
Rifamycin VIII, didehydrodihydro-	EtOH	227(4.50),335(4.10), 500(3.58)	33-2348-73
$C_{43}H_{50}N_4O_7$			
Alkaloid E from Voacanga thouarsii	EtOH	225(4.66),265(4.08), 283s(3.96),291s(3.90)	102-2039-73
$C_{43}H_{50}O_9$			
Pregna-4,16-diene-3,11,20-trione, 21,21'-[carbonylbis(oxy)]bis-	MeOH	238(4.69)	44-2328-73
$C_{43}H_{51}NO_{12}$			
2,7-(Epoxypentadeca[1,11,13]trieno)-7H-benzofuro[5,4-b]carbazole-1,6,12,13-(2H)-tetrone, 23-acetoxy-8,9,10,11-tetrahydro-5,19,21-trihydroxy-25-methoxy-2,4,14,18,20,22,24-heptamethyl-	EtOH	279(4.41),301(4.39), 375(3.76),480(3.63)	33-2348-73

Compound	Solvent	$\lambda_{max}(\log \epsilon)$	Ref.
$C_{43}H_{51}NO_{15}$			
Rifamycin S, 8,21,23-triacetate	EtOH	225(4.44),258(4.34), 303(4.15)	33-2323-73
$C_{43}H_{52}N_2O_{12}$			
Rifamycin VIII, 1',4-didehydro-1-deoxy-1,4,16,17,18,19-hexahydro-1-oxo-	EtOH	228(4.59),317(4.32), 400(4.13),505(3.88)	33-2348-73
$C_{43}H_{52}N_2O_{13}$			
Rifamycin S, 3-[(2-furanylmethyl)methyl-amino]-	EtOH	220(4.48),260s(--), 320(4.19),446(3.64)	33-2348-73
$C_{43}H_{52}N_4O_6$			
Voacorine	EtOH	230(4.45),285(3.90), 295(3.93)	102-0451-73
stereoisomer	EtOH	232(4.52),285(4.10), 293(4.09)	102-0451-73
$C_{43}H_{53}NO_{12}$			
2,7-(Epoxypentadeca[1,11,13]trieno)-7H-benzofuro[5,4-b]carbazole-1,13(2H)-di-one, 23-acetoxy-8,9,10,11-tetrahydro-5,6,12,19,21-pentahydroxy-25-methoxy-2,4,14,18,20,22,24-heptamethyl-	EtOH	240(4.55),302(4.27), 495(4.08)	33-2348-73
$C_{43}H_{53}NO_{15}$			
Rifamycin, triacetyl deriv.	EtOH	229(4.50),300(4.26), 360(3.38),421(3.56)	33-2287-73
$C_{43}H_{53}N_3O_{11}$			
Rifazine, 16,17,18,19-tetrahydro-	EtOH-NaOH	247(4.62),282(4.41), 343(4.47),530(3.88)	33-2348-73
$C_{43}H_{54}N_2O_{12}$			
Rifamycin, 1,4-dideoxy-1,4,16,17,18,19-hexahydro-4-[(2-hydroxyphenyl)imino]-1-oxo-	EtOH	283(4.34),318(4.26), 543(3.85)	33-2348-73
$C_{43}H_{54}O_7$			
Pregna-4,16-diene-3,20-dione, 21,21'-[carbonylbis(oxy)]bis-	MeOH	240(4.65)	44-2328-73
$C_{43}H_{55}NO_{15}$			
Acetic acid, (3-rifamycinyl)-, ethyl ester	EtOH	227(4.60),320(4.29), 453(4.18)	33-2348-73
	EtOH-HCl	274(4.47),350(3.79)	33-2348-73
$C_{43}H_{56}N_2O_{12}$			
Rifamycin S, 3-(cyclohexylamino)-	EtOH	226(4.47),267(4.42), 320(4.31),375(3.80), 520(3.38)	33-2348-73
Rifamycin S, 3-(2-methyl-1-piperidinyl)-	EtOH	243s(--),269(4.56), 324(4.18),527(3.46)	33-2348-73
Rifamycin S, 3-(3-methyl-1-piperidinyl)-	EtOH	222(4.50),274(4.47), 327(4.19),550(3.45)	33-2348-73
Rifamycin S, 3-(4-methyl-1-piperidinyl)-	EtOH	219(4.41),270(4.40), 324(4.13),550(3.32)	33-2348-73

Compound	Solvent	$\lambda_{max}(\log \epsilon)$	Ref.
$C_{43}H_{56}N_2O_{13}$			
Rifamycin S, 3-(3,5-dimethyl-4-morpholinyl)-	EtOH	222(4.47),272(4.43), 323(4.18),390s(--), 550(3.45)	33-2348-73
$C_{43}H_{57}N_3O_{13}$			
Rifamycin, 3-[4-(aminocarbonyl)-1-piperidinyl]-	EtOH-HCl	222(4.53),280s(--), 325s(--),440(3.86)	33-2348-73
Rifamycin S, 3-[3-(2-aminoethyl)-4-morpholinyl]-	EtOH	235(4.43),267(4.43), 320(4.13),370(3.85), 530(3.26)	33-2348-73
$C_{43}H_{58}N_2O_{12}$			
9,4-(Epoxypentadeca[1,11,13]trienimino)-naphtho[1,2-b:7,8-b']difuran-10,26-(9H)-dione, 16-acetoxy-2-(dimethyl-amino)-2,3-dihydro-5,6,18,20-tetra-hydroxy-14-methoxy-3,3,7,9,15,17,19,21,25-nonamethyl-	EtOH	230(4.62),250(4.42), 300(4.25),318(4.29), 450(3.98)	33-2348-73
$C_{43}H_{58}N_2O_{12}S$			
Rifamycin, 3-(3,5-dimethyl-4-thiomorpholinyl)-	EtOH-HCl	220(4.55),282(4.32), 320s(--),440(3.89)	33-2348-73
$C_{43}H_{58}N_2O_{13}$			
Rifamycin, 3-[4-(hydroxymethyl)-1-piperidinyl]-	EtOH-HCl	223(4.40),295(4.12), 320s(--),442(3.81)	33-2348-73
$C_{43}H_{58}N_2O_{14}$			
Rifamycin S, 3-[(2,2-diethoxyethyl)-amino]-	EtOH	230(4.47),267(4.47), 317(4.15),370(3.87), 525(3.23)	33-2348-73
$C_{43}H_{59}N_3O_{12}$			
Rifamycin S, 3-[2-(diethylamino)ethyl-amino]-	EtOH	260(4.57),322(4.47), 380(3.75),490(3.57)	33-2348-73
$C_{43}H_{60}N_2O_{12}$			
Mocimycin (component 3)	MeOH	209s(4.16),234(4.82), 318(3.89)	88-5173-73
$C_{43}H_{62}O_5$			
Pregn-4-en-3-one, 21,21'-[carbonylbis-(oxy)]bis-	MeOH	241(4.51)	44-2328-73

Compound	Solvent	λmax(log ε)	Ref.
$C_{44}H_{30}Br_4N_4$			
Imidazolyl, 4,5-bis(4-bromophenyl)-2-(3-methylphenyl)-, dimer	EtOH	280(4.36)	103-0085-73
Imidazolyl, 4,5-bis(4-bromophenyl)-2-(4-methylphenyl)-, dimer	EtOH	285(4.52)	103-0085-73
$C_{44}H_{30}N_4$			
21H,23H-Porphine, 5,10,15,20-tetraphenyl-	benzene	419(5.67),481(3.53), 515(4.28),548(3.90), 593(3.72),649(3.53)	88-2887-73
$C_{44}H_{30}N_8NiO_4$			
Nickel, bis(benzoic acid [phenyl(5-phenyl-1,3,4-oxadiazol-2-yl)methylene]hydrazidato]-	$CHCl_3$	288(4.53),426(4.95)	78-2119-73
$C_{44}H_{31}N_4O_2Tl$			
Thallium, aquahydroxy[5,10,15,20-tetraphenyl-21H,23H-porphinato-(2-)-N^{21},N^{22},N^{23},N^{24}]-, (OC-6-23)	CH_2Cl_2	433(5.72),567(4.27), 607(4.00)	39-2142-73C
$C_{44}H_{32}Cl_2N_2O_2$			
Dispiro[2H-indole-2,1'-cyclobutane-2',2"-[2H]indole]-3,3"(1H,1"H)-dione, 3',4'-bis(2-chlorophenyl)-1,1"-bis(phenylmethyl)-	dioxan	239(4.90),415(3.54)	39-2804-73C
$C_{44}H_{32}N_4O_9$			
2,4(1H,3H)-Pteridinedione, 6,7-diphenyl-1-(2,3,5-tri-O-benzoyl-β-D-ribofuranosyl)-	MeOH	228(4.84),272(4.35), 358(4.16)	24-1401-73
2,4(1H,3H)-Pteridinedione, 6,7-diphenyl-3-(2,3,5-tri-O-benzoyl-β-D-ribofuranosyl)-	MeOH	229(4.83),273(4.30), 364(4.21)	24-1401-73
$C_{44}H_{32}O_2$			
Methanone, (1,2,4,5-tetraphenyltricyclo-[3.1.0.0^{2,4}]hexane-3,6-diyl)bis[phenyl-	EtOH	222(4.50),250(4.38)	104-0963-73
$C_{44}H_{32}O_3$			
Spiro[1,3-dioxolane-2,12'-[6,11]methano-[2H]cyclopent[a]anthracen]-2'-one, 5'a,6',11',11'a-tetrahydro-1',3',6',11'-tetraphenyl-	EtOH	269(4.40),336(3.66), 493(3.29)	39-0927-73C
$C_{44}H_{33}N_5O_8$			
2(1H)-Pteridinone, 4-amino-6,7-diphenyl-1-(2,3,5-tri-O-benzoyl-β-D-ribofuranosyl)-	MeOH	228(4.85),274(4.44), 370(4.20)	33-1225-73
$C_{44}H_{34}N_2O_2$			
Dispiro[2H-indole-2,1'-cyclobutane-2',2"-[2H]indole]-3,3"(1H,1"H)-dione, 3',4'-diphenyl-1,1"-bis(phenylmethyl)-, (1'α,2'α,3'α,4'β)-	dioxan	239(4.95),417(3.54)	39-2804-73C
$C_{44}H_{36}O_4$			
4,7-Methano-2,3,8-methenocyclopent[a]indene-3,7a-dicarboxylic acid, 1,7-bis-diphenylmethylene)-1,2,3a,3b,4,7,8,8a-	EtOH	218s(4.31),225s(4.27), 250(4.29)	24-1822-73

Compound	Solvent	$\lambda_{max}(\log \epsilon)$	Ref.
octahydro-, dimethyl ester (cont.)			24-1822-73
exo-exo	EtOH	219s(4.31),225(4.27), 250(4.29)	24-1822-73
$C_{44}H_{38}Si$			
Silacyclopenta-2,4-diene, 2,3,4,5-tetrakis(4-methylphenyl)-1,1-diphenyl-	C_6H_{12}	206(4.96),255s(4.46), 372(3.95)	101-0381-73C
$C_{44}H_{42}O_{20}$			
Secalonic acid E, dimethyl ester, hexaacetate	n.s.g.	244(4.27),275(4.26), 335(3.58)	39-2440-73C
$C_{44}H_{50}N_2O_{12}$			
Rifamycin VIII, 1',4'-didehydro-1-deoxy-1,4-dihydro-4'-methyl-1-oxo-	EtOH-NaOH	229(4.70),304(4.26), 324(4.30),405(4.09), 522(3.90)	33-2348-73
Rifamycin VIII, 1',4'-didehydro-1-deoxy-1,4-dihydro-5'-methyl-1-oxo-	EtOH-NaOH	230(4.65),303(4.22), 323(4.22),408(4.11), 515(3.95)	33-2348-73
Rifamycin VIII, 1',4'-didehydro-1-deoxy-1,4-dihydro-6'-methyl-1-oxo-	EtOH-NaOH	228(4.66),300(4.27), 323(4.27),401(4.12), 515(3.88)	33-2348-73
$C_{44}H_{50}O_7S_3$			
Benzenecarbothioic acid, O,O'-[3a,6,6a-8,9,10,11,11a,12,12a-decahydro-2,2,6a-12-tetramethyl-4-[1-methyl-2-[[(4-methylphenyl)sulfonyl]oxy]ethyl]-5H-benzo[6,7]cyclopenta[3,4]cycloocta-[1,2-d]-1,3-dioxole-6,9-diyl ester	n.s.g.	253(4.28),285(4.34)	39-1590-73C
$C_{44}H_{51}N_3O_{11}$			
Rifamycin S, 2,3-diaminotoluene product, isomer 1	EtOH-NaOH	247(4.80),290s(--), 343(4.53),520(4.03)	33-2348-73
isomer s	EtOH-NaOH	246(4.82),290s(--), 341(4.57),520(4.06)	33-2348-73
Rifamycin S, 3,4-diaminotoluene product, isomer 1	EtOH-NaOH	246(4.69),285s(--), 345(4.43),520(3.94)	33-2348-73
isomer s	EtOH-NaOH	246(4.79),290s(--), 343(4.53),520(4.03)	33-2348-73
$C_{44}H_{52}N_2O_{11}$			
Rifamycin, 1-deoxy-1-[(phenylmethylene)-amino]-	EtOH	228(4.64),308(4.28), 460(3.90)	33-2348-73
$C_{44}H_{52}N_2O_{12}$			
Rifamycin, 1,4-dideoxy-1,4-dihydro-4-[(2-methoxyphenyl)imino]-1-oxo-	EtOH	254(4.48),324(4.26), 405(3.84),520(3.85)	33-2348-73
$C_{44}H_{52}N_2O_{13}$			
Rifamycin, 1,4-dideoxy-1,4-dihydro-3-[(2-methoxyphenyl)amino]-1,4-dioxo-	EtOH	262(4.42),331(4.14), 400s(--),580(3.45)	33-2348-73
$C_{44}H_{54}N_2O_{11}$			
Rifamycin, 1-deoxy-1-[(phenylmethyl)-amino]-	EtOH	217(4.66),297(4.25), 345s(--),395s(--), 413(4.17)	33-2348-73
$C_{44}H_{55}NO_{16}$			
Rifamycin, 3-[2-ethoxy-1-(ethoxycarbonyl)-	EtOH	277(4.47),400(3.70)	33-2348-73

Compound	Solvent	λmax(log ε)	Ref.
$C_{44}H_{58}I_2N_2O_8$			
1,23:6,9-Dietheno-11,15-metheno-2H,15H-benzo[19,20][1,11]dioxacycloeicosino-[5,4-b]pyridinium, 3,4,4a,5,6,17-hexahydro-12,20,21,25-tetramethoxy-17-(2-methoxyethoxy)-4,4-dimethyl-18-[2-(trimethylammonio)ethyl]-, diiodide	EtOH	281(3.39)	44-1846-73
1H-15,18-Etheno-8,12:20,24-dimetheno-12H-[1,11]dioxacyclodocosino[2,3,4-ij]isoquinolinium, 2,3,13,14,25,25c-hexahydro-5,6,9,21-tetramethoxy-13-(2-methoxyethoxy)-1,1-dimethyl-11-[2-(trimethylammonio)ethyl]-, diiodide	EtOH	280(4.17)	44-1846-73
$C_{44}H_{58}N_2O_{12}$			
Rifamycin S, 3-(4,4-dimethyl-1-piperidinyl)-	EtOH	270(4.42),324(4.12),550(3.35)	33-2348-73
$C_{44}H_{60}N_2O_{12}$			
Rifamycin, 3-(cycloheptylamino)-	EtOH-HCl	226(4.59),275s(--),312(4.22),444(4.09)	33-2348-73
Rifamycin, 3-(3,3-dimethyl-1-piperidinyl)-	EtOH-HCl	221(4.45),296(4.17),325s(--),444(3.86)	33-2348-73
Rifamycin, 3-(3,4-dimethyl-1-piperidinyl)-, isomer A, m. 238°	EtOH-HCl	220(4.55),290s(--),315(4.18),444(3.91)	33-2348-73
isomer B	EtOH-HCl	220(4.50),271(4.43),324(4.16),450s(--)	33-2348-73
Rifamycin, 3-(3,5-dimethyl-1-piperidinyl)-	EtOH-HCl	227(4.48),268(4.48),324(4.20),550(3.48)	33-2348-73
Rifamycin, 3-(3-ethyl-1-piperidinyl)-	EtOH-HCl	223(4.55),290(4.25),320s(--),444(3.95)	33-2348-73
Rifamycin, 3-(4-ethyl-1-piperidinyl)-	EtOH-HCl	220(4.56),295(4.29),320s(--),445(3.99)	33-2348-73
$C_{44}H_{60}N_6O_4$			
21H,23H-Porphine-2,18-dipropanoic acid, 7,12-bis[2-(diethylamino)ethyl]-3,8-13,17-tetramethyl-, dimethyl ester	$CHCl_3$	401(5.18),499(4.08),534(3.94),567(3.78),621(3.57)	103-0186-73
$C_{44}H_{62}N_2O_{12}$			
Mocimycin methyl ether	pH 1	207(4.71),231(4.77),290s(4.21),334(4.59)	35-8449-73
	pH 7	207(4.71),232(4.78),290s(4.21),335(4.59)	35-8449-73
	pH 13	232(4.80),290s(4.22),329(4.61)	35-8449-73

Compound	Solvent	$\lambda_{max}(\log \epsilon)$	Ref.
$C_{45}H_{38}O_2Si$			
7-Silabicyclo[2.2.1]hept-5-ene-2-carboxylic acid, 1,4,5,6,7,7-hexaphenyl-, ethyl ester	n.s.g.	233(4.50),278(4.05), 295(3.89)	78-2395-73
$C_{45}H_{42}CoN_4P$			
Cobalt, [1,2,3,7,8,12,13,17,18,19-decadehydro-21,23-dihydro-2,3,7,8,12,13-17,18-octamethylcorrinato(3-)-N^{21},N^{22}-N^{23},N^{24}](triphenylphosphine)-, (SP-5-14)-	$CHCl_3$	358(4.76),378s(4.68), 495s(3.63),530s(3.85), 560(4.30)	39-2281-73C
$C_{45}H_{45}N_3O_6$			
13H,28H,43H-8,12:23,27:38,42-Trinitrilo-7H,22H,37H-tribenzo[c,p,c][1,6,14,19-27,32]hexaoxacyclononatriacontin, 5,15,20,30,35,45-hexahydro-	$CHCl_3$	265(4.13)	77-0831-73
$C_{45}H_{53}N_3O_{11}$			
Rifazine, 39,40-dimethyl-	EtOH-NaOH	246(4.78),290s(--), 345(4.50),515(3.98)	33-2348-73
Rifazine, 38-ethyl-, 1-isomer	EtOH-NaOH	247(4.70),290s(--), 343(4.45),515(3.87)	33-2348-73
s-isomer	EtOH-NaOH	245(4.76),290s(--), 340(4.51),515(3.92)	33-2348-73
$C_{45}H_{56}N_2O_{12}$			
Rifamycin, 3-[methyl(phenylmethyl)-amino]-	EtOH-HCl	220(4.66),292(4.35), 325s(--),440(3.98)	33-2348-73
$C_{45}H_{60}N_2O_{14}$			
Rifamycin, 3-[4-(ethoxycarbonyl)-1-piperidinyl]-	EtOH-HCl	223(4.55),295(4.30), 320s(--),442(3.81)	33-2348-73
$C_{45}H_{62}N_2O_{12}$			
Rifamycin, 3-(3-ethyl-4-methyl-1-piperidinyl)-	EtOH-HCl	224(4.56),293(4.28), 320s(--),444(3.99)	33-2348-73
Rifamycin, 3-[4-(1-methylethyl)-1-piperidinyl]-	EtOH-HCl	222(4.54),290s(--), 315(4.17),446(3.90)	33-2348-73
$C_{45}H_{64}N_2O_{12}$			
Mocimycin dimethyl ether	pH 1	211(4.73),233(4.77), 298s(4.27),336(4.60)	35-8449-73
	pH 7	211(4.74),233(4.77), 298s(4.27),336(4.60)	35-8449-73
	pH 13	233(4.77),298s(4.27), 336(4.60)	35-8449-73
$C_{45}H_{73}NO_{16}$			
Solasonine	94% H_2SO_4	260(4.1),325(4.34), 412(3.86)	105-0659-73

Compound	Solvent	$\lambda_{max}(\log \epsilon)$	Ref.
$C_{46}H_{30}O_2S$			
Methanone, (1,3,4,7-tetraphenylbenzo-[c]thiophene-5,6-diyl)bis[phenyl-	dioxan	240(4.37),261(4.58), 280(4.35),400(3.92)	44-3975-73
$C_{46}H_{30}S_2$			
Benzo[1,2-c:4,5-c']dithiophene-6-S^{IV}, 1,3,4,5,7,8-hexaphenyl-	$CHCl_3$	245(4.59),259s(4.50), 316(4.38),370s(3.48), 793(4.06),877(3.25)	35-2750-73
$C_{46}H_{32}S_2$			
4H,8H-Benzo[1,2-c:4,5-c']dithiophene, hexaphenyl-	$C_2H_4Cl_2$	233(4.31),258(4.32), 300(4.34)	44-3975-73
$C_{46}H_{33}N_4O_3Tl$			
Thallium, (acetato-O)aqua[5,10,15,20-tetraphenyl-21H,23H-porphinato(2-)-N^{21},N^{22},N^{23},N^{24}]-, (OC-6-23)-	CH_2Cl_2	433(5.72),567(4.30), 607(4.02)	39-2142-73C
$C_{46}H_{34}N_8NiO_6$			
Nickel, bis[benzoic acid [(4-methoxy-phenyl)(5-phenyl-1,3,4-oxadiazol-2-yl)methylene]hydrazidato]-	$CHCl_3$	306(4.58),432(4.73)	78-2119-73
$C_{46}H_{34}O$			
Acenaphthylene, 5,5'-[oxybis(1-naphtha-lenylmethylene)]bis[1,2-dihydro-	H_2SO_4	658(5.27)	94-0383-73
Acenaphthylene, 5,5'-[oxybis(2-naphtha-lenylmethylene)]bis[1,2-dihydro-	H_2SO_4	623(5.27)	4-0383-73
$C_{46}H_{36}O_2Si$			
Methanone, 7,7-dimethyl-1,4,5,6-tetra-phenyl-7-silabicyclo[2.2.1]hepta-2,5-diene-2,3-diylbis[phenyl-	n.s.g.	228(4.50),286(4.15), 296(4.14),390(4.01)	78-2395-73
$C_{46}H_{36}O_4$			
Dispiro[1,3-dioxolane-2,2'-[6,11]meth-ano[2H]cyclopent[a]anthracene-12',2"-[1,3]dioxolane], 5'a,6',11',11'a-tetrahydro-1',3',6',11'-tetraphenyl-	EtOH	350(3.81)	39-0927-73C
$C_{46}H_{36}O_6P_2$			
Phosphorin, 4,4'-dioxybis[1,4-dihydro-1-hydroxy-1-oxo-2,4,6-triphenyl-, 1,1'-dioxide	MeOH	245(4.56)	24-1001-73
$C_{46}H_{54}N_2O_{12}$			
13H-2,7-(Epoxypentadeca[1,11,13]trieno)-furo[3",2":5',6']naphth[2',3':4,5]-imidazo[2,1-a]isoquinoline-1,16(2H)-dione, 26-acetoxy-7a,12-dihydro-5,6,15,22,24-pentahydroxy-28-methoxy-2,4,17,21,23,25,27-heptamethyl-	EtOH-HCl	232(4.56),264(4.52), 324(4.21),410s(--)	33-2348-73
$C_{46}H_{56}N_2O_{12}$			
Rifamycin, 3-(3,4-dihydro-2(1H)-isoquin-olinyl)-	EtOH-HCl	230s(--),269(4.48), 325(4.17),420s(--), 540(3.20)	33-2348-73
$C_{46}H_{60}N_2O_{12}$			
2H-2,7-(Epoxypentadeca[1,11,13]trieno)-	EtOH	316(4.29),448(4.14)	33-2348-73

Compound	Solvent	λmax(log ε)	Ref.
benzofuro[4,5-f]cyclopent[b]indole-1-12(7aH)-dione, 22-acetoxy-8,9,10,10a-tetrahydro-5,6,11,18,20-pentahydroxy-24-methoxy-2,4,13,17,19,21,23-heptamethyl-7a-(1-pyrrolidinyl)-	EtOH-HCl	276(4.47),340(3.93)	33-2348-73
$C_{46}H_{62}O_{18}$			
Sinapoylerysimoside	EtOH	218(4.37),330(3.97)	105-0718-73
$C_{46}H_{64}N_2O_{12}$			
Rifamycin, 3-[4-(1,1-dimethylethyl)-1-piperidinyl]-	EtOH-HCl	221(4.54),290(4.28), 320s(--),442(3.94)	33-2348-73
$C_{47}H_{33}NO_2S$			
Methanone, (4,7-dihydro-8-methyl-1,3,4-7-tetraphenylbenzo[c]thiophen-4,7-imine-5,6-diyl)bis[phenyl-	$CHCl_3$	264(4.54),273s(4.48), 284s(4.45)	35-2749-73
$C_{47}H_{41}N_3O_5$			
Cytidine, 2',5'-bis-O-(triphenylmethyl)-	MeOH	265(3.86)	24-0665-73
Cytidine, 3',5'-bis-O-(triphenylmethyl)-	MeOH	267(3.94)	24-0665-73
$C_{47}H_{47}O_4$			
Pyrylium, 4-[3-(2,6-diphenyl-4H-pyran-4-ylidene)-1-propenyl]-2,6-bis[4-(pentyloxy)phenyl]-, perchlorate, (E)-	CH_2Cl_2	385(4.33),470(4.28), 694(5.36)	78-0795-73
$C_{47}H_{50}N_2O_{12}$			
Rifamycin VII, 1',4-didehydro-1-deoxy-1,4-dihydro-1-oxo-	EtOH-NaOH	285s(--),332(4.24), 440(4.03),560(4.09)	33-2348-73
$C_{47}H_{51}N_3O_{11}$			
Rifamycin IX	EtOH-NaOH	254(4.67),294(4.55), 357(4.49),520(4.04)	33-2348-73
$C_{47}H_{55}N_3O_{11}$			
Rifamycin IX, 5',6',7',8'-tetrahydro-	EtOH-NaOH	248(4.88),345(4.62), 510(4.16)	33-2348-73
$C_{47}H_{58}O_{23}$			
2(3H)-Furanone, 4-[(3,4-dimethoxyphenyl)methyl]dihydro-3-[[3-methoxy-4-[[2,3,4-tri-O-acetyl-6-O-(2,3,4,6-tetra-O-acetyl-β-D-glucopyranosyl)-β-D-glucopyranosyl]oxy]phenyl]methyl]-	EtOH	229(4.22),279(3.81)	31-0017-73 +94-0639-73
	EtOH	229(4.18),280(3.77)	94-2778-73
$C_{47}H_{62}O_{11}S_3$			
C-Nor-9,11-secospirostan-3,9,11-triol, tris(4-methylbenzenesulfonate)-, (3β,5α,9β,22R)-	EtOH	226(4.75)	13-0147-73A
$C_{48}H_{38}N_{12}O_4$			
25H,27H-Dibenzo[b,g]porphine-9,13-dipropanoic acid, 1,1,2,2,18,18,19,19-octacyano-1,2,3,17a,18,19,20,24a-octahydro-8,14,17a,24a-tetramethyl-, dimethyl ester	$CHCl_3$	409(5.12),502(4.13), 537(3.97),543(3.97), 576(3.92),604s(3.78), 640(3.82),663(4.14), 724s(3.57)	39-1424-73C
$C_{48}H_{42}O_9$			
7,9,19,21,31,33-Hexaoxaheptacyclo[32.2-	$C_2H_4Cl_2$	265(3.47),272(3.42)	116-0305-73

Compound	Solvent	λ max (log ε)	Ref.
2.2^3,6^.2^10,10^.2^16,18^.2^22,25^2^27,30^]-octatetraconta-3,5,10,12,15,17,22-24,27,29,34,36,37,39,41,43,45,47-octadecaene-8,20,32-trione, 2,2,14-14,26,26-hexamethyl- (cont.)			116-0305-73
$C_{48}H_{44}$			
Dibenzo[a,e]cyclooctene, 1,2,3,4,7,8,9-10-octamethyl-5,6,11,12-tetraphenyl-	dioxan	230(4.79),305(4.36)	5-1893-73
$C_{48}H_{44}N_4O_{12}$			
2,4(1H,3H)-Pteridinedione, 1,3-bis(2-deoxy-3,5-bis-O-(4-methylbenzoyl)-D-ribofuranosyl)-	MeOH	239(4.88),316(3.86)	24-1401-73
$C_{48}H_{46}N_4O_4$			
[1,1'-Biphenyl]-2,2',6,6'-tetracarboxamide, N,N',N",N'"-tetrakis(1-phenylethyl)-	hexane	185(5.34),212s(--)	33-2255-73
$C_{48}H_{49}BrO_6$			
Phenol, 2-[[3-[(3-bromo-2-hydroxy-5-methylphenyl)methyl]-2-hydroxy-5-methylphenyl]methyl]-6-[[2-hydroxy-3-[[2-hydroxy-3-[(2-hydroxy-3,5-dimethylphenyl)methyl]-5-methylphenyl]-methyl]-5-methylphenyl]methyl]-4-methyl-	dioxan	288(4.27)	126-0039-73L
$C_{48}H_{50}N_4O_{12}$			
25H,27H-Dibenzo[b,g]porphine-1,2,18,19-tetracarboxylic acid, 3,17a,20,24a-tetrahydro-9,13-bis(3-methoxy-3-oxopropyl)-8,14,17a,24a-tetramethyl-, tetramethyl ester	$CHCl_3$	412(4.96),507(3.99), 542(3.87),550(3.87), 579(3.70),609s(3.54), 649s(3.61),666(3.96)	39-1424-73C
$C_{48}H_{50}O_6$			
Phenol, 2-[[2-hydroxy-3-[[2-hydroxy-3-[(2-hydroxy-3,5-dimethylphenyl)methyl]-5-methylphenyl]methyl]-5-methylphenyl]methyl]-6-[[2-hydroxy-3-[(2-hydroxy-5-methylphenyl)methyl]-5-methylphenyl]methyl]-4-methyl-	dioxan	287(4.25)	126-0039-73L
$C_{48}H_{54}GeN_4O_2$			
Germanium, [2,3,7,8,12,13,17,18-octaethyl-21H,23H-porphinato(2-)-N^21^-N^22^,N^23^,N^24^]diphenoxy-, (OC-6-12)-	benzene	341(4.37),390(4.73), 409(5.46),470s(2.98), 500(3.25),537(4.25), 573(4.39)	24-2710-73
$C_{48}H_{54}N_4O_2Si$			
Silicon, [2,3,7,8,12,13,17,18-octaethyl-21H,23H-porphinato(2-)-N^21^,N^22^,N^23^-N^24^]diphenoxy-, (OC-6-12)-	benzene	337(4.43),390s(4.79), 408(5.50),505s(3.27), 538(4.18),574(4.31)	24-2710-73
$C_{48}H_{54}N_4O_2Sn$			
Tin, [2,3,7,8,12,13,17,18-octaethyl-21H,23H-porphinato(2-)-N^21^,N^22^,N^23^-N^24^]-, (OC-6-12)-	benzene	348s(4.28),406(5.29), 503(3.34),541(4.28), 578(4.29)	24-2710-73

Compound	Solvent	λ max (log ε)	Ref.
$C_{48}H_{55}CrN_4O_2$ Chromium, [2,3,7,8,12,13,17,18-octaethyl-21H,23H-porphinato(2-)-N^{21},N^{22},N^{23}-N^{24}](phenol)phenoxy-, (OC-6-23)-	benzene	350(4.41),370(4.41), 386(4.43),425(5.20), 544(4.05),576(3.98), 654(2.59)	24-2710-73
$C_{48}H_{58}O_{24}$ 2(3H)-Furanone, dihydro-3,4-bis[[3-methoxy-4-[(2,3,4,6-tetra-O-acetyl-β-D-glucopyranosyl)oxy]phenyl]methyl]-, (3R-trans)-	EtOH	227s(4.11),279(3.66)	23-1050-73
	EtOH	227s(4.11),279(3.66)	94-1114-73
$C_{48}H_{58}O_{25}$ Nortrachelogenin-4,4'-di-O-β-D-glucopyranoside octaacetate	EtOH	226s(4.15),279(3.76)	94-1114-73
$C_{48}H_{60}N_2O_{12}$ Rifamycin, 3-(4-phenyl-1-piperidinyl)-	EtOH-HCl	213(4.62),230s(--), 290(4.32),320s(--), 440(3.92)	33-2348-73
$C_{48}H_{64}N_2O_{12}$ 2H-2,7-(Epoxypentadeca[1,11,13]trieno)-benzofuro[4,5-f]cyclopent[b]indole-1,12(7aH)-dione, 22-acetoxy-7a-(hexahydro-1H-azepin-1-yl)-8,9,10,10a-tetrahydro-5,6,11,18,20-pentahydroxy-24-methoxy-2,4,13,17,19,21,23-heptamethyl-	EtOH-HCl	217(4.57),270(4.31), 300s(--),440(3.95)	33-2348-73
$C_{48}H_{64}O_{21}$ Chromocyclomycin	EtOH	229(4.54),283(4.74), 322(4.21),335(4.13), 420(4.02)	105-0492-73
$C_{48}H_{66}N_2O_{12}$ Rifamycin, 3-(4-cyclohexyl-1-piperidinyl)-	EtOH-HCl	224(4.55),295(4.24), 320s(--),445(3.99)	33-2348-73
$C_{48}H_{84}O_3$ 2,5-Cyclohexadiene-1,4-dione, 2-methoxy-5-methyl-3,6-bis(3,7,11,15-tetramethyl-2-hexadecenyl)- (mixture with 5 and 6 substituents interchanged)	EtOH	273(4.02)	65-2038-73
$C_{49}H_{46}CoN_4O_2P$ Cobalt, [1,2,3,7,8,12,13,17,18,19-decadehydro-2,8,12,18-tetraethyl-21,23-dihydro-7,13-dimethyl-3,17-corrindicarboxaldehydato(3-)-N^{21},N^{22},N^{23},N^{24}]-(triphenylphosphine)-, (SP-5-14)-	$CHCl_3$	370(4.43),465s(4.27), 550(4.49),592(4.15), 633(4.40)	39-2281-73C
$C_{49}H_{50}CoN_4P$ Cobalt, [1,2,3,7,8,12,13,17,18,19-decadehydro-2,8,12,18-tetraethyl-21,23-dihydro-3,7,13,17-tetramethylcorrinato(3-)-N^{21},N^{22},N^{23},N^{24}](triphenylphosphine)-, (SP-5-14)-	$CHCl_3$	358(4.75),378s(4.68), 494s(3.64),530s(3.85), 559(4.28)	39-2281-73C

Compound	Solvent	λmax(log ε)	Ref.
$C_{49}H_{62}N_2O_{12}$			
Rifamycin, 3-[4-(phenylmethyl)-1-piperidinyl]-	EtOH-HCl	213(4.61),230s(--), 295(4.28),320s(--), 443(4.00)	33-2348-73
$C_{49}H_{68}N_2O_{12}$			
Rifamycin, 3-[4-(cyclohexylmethyl)-1-piperidinyl]-	EtOH-HCl	223(4.59),296(4.28), 320s(--),444(4.03)	33-2348-73
$C_{49}H_{75}CoN_{11}O_8$			
Cobinamide, methyl-	pH 8	305f(4.3),460f(4.0)	10-0526-73E
$C_{50}H_{28}$			
Benzo[c]phenanthro[2,1-b]pyrene, 8-(benzo[c]phenanthrenyl)-	CH_2Cl_2	235(4.77),273(4.85), 314(4.57),330(4.57), 356(4.57),416(3.95), 450s(3.19)	54-0651-73
Hexaheliceno[3,4-c]hexahelicene	CH_2Cl_2	238s(4.67),275(4.83), 327s(4.57),344s(4.61), 359(4.67),370s(4.62)	54-0651-73
$C_{50}H_{30}$			
Phenanthro[3,4-c]chrysene, 3-(2-benzo[c]phenanthren-2-ylethenyl)-, (E)-	CH_2Cl_2	270(4.87),327(4.62), 344(4.63),358s(4.60), 447(3.20)	54-0651-73
$C_{50}H_{44}O_6P_2$			
Phosphorin, 4,4'-dioxybis[1-ethoxy-1,4-dihydro-2,4,6-triphenyl-, P,P'-dioxide	C_6H_{12}	255(4.51)	24-1001-73
isomers	C_6H_{12}	255(4.45)	24-1001-73
$C_{50}H_{48}N_4O_{12}$			
2,4(1H,3H)-Pteridinedione, 1,3-bis[2-deoxy-3,5-bis-O-(4-methylbenzoyl)-D-ribofuranosyl]-6,7-dimethyl-	MeOH	239(4.87),326(3.95)	24-1401-73
$C_{50}H_{56}N_8$			
5,22[1',2']:11,16[1",2"]-Dibenzdinaphtho[2,3-f:2',3'-m][1,2,4,5,8,9,11,12]-octaazacyclotetradecine, 5,7,11,16,18-22-hexahydro-8,19-dioctyl-	$CHCl_3$	257(4.73),339(4.69)	35-5757-73
$C_{50}H_{75}NO_{16}$			
Avenacin B	EtOH	222(4.19),253(3.58), 355(3.28)	78-0629-73
$C_{51}H_{38}O_2Si$			
Methanone, (7-methyl-1,4,5,6,7-pentaphenyl-7-silabicyclo[2.2.1]hepta-2,5-diene-2,3-diyl)bis[phenyl-, syn	n.s.g.	284(4.15),386(3.80)	78-2395-73
$C_{51}H_{50}CoN_4O_2P$			
Cobalt, [1,2,3,7,8,12,13,17,18,19-decadehydro-2,7,8,12,13,18-hexaethyl-21,23-dihydro-3,17-corrindicarboxaldehydato(3-)-N^{21},N^{22},N^{23},N^{24}]-(triphenylphosphine)-, (SP-5-14)-	$CHCl_3$	371(4.45),465s(4.28), 550(4.11),593(4.16), 635(4.42)	39-2281-73C

Compound	Solvent	λmax(log ε)	Ref.
$C_{51}H_{54}CoN_4P$			
Cobalt, [1,2,3,7,8,12,13,17,18,19-decadehydro-2,7,8,12,13,18-hexaethyl-21,23-dihydro-3,17-dimethylcorrin-ato(3-)-N[21],N[22],N[23],N[24]](triphenyl-phosphine)-, (SP-5-14)-	$CHCl_3$	358(4.76),378s(4.67), 494s(3.65),530s(3.88), 559(4.29)	39-2281-73C
$C_{51}H_{72}N_2O_{12}$			
Rifamycin, 3-[4-(3-cyclohexylpropyl)-1-piperidinyl]-	EtOH-HCl	225(4.58),296(4.28), 325s(--),444(4.03)	33-2348-73
$C_{52}H_{38}N_6$			
Octabenzo[c,f,j,l,p,s,w,y][1,5,9,14,18-22]hexaazacyclohexacosine, 11,32-di-hydro-	CCl_4	370s(4.20),408(4.21)	78-1399-73
	MeCN	243(4.77),258s(4.74), 400(4.20)	78-1399-73
$C_{52}H_{38}O_2P_2$			
6,11-Phosphinidene-2H-naphth[2,3-e]iso-phosphindole, 5a,6,11,11a-tetrahydro-1,2,3,6,11,12-hexaphenyl-, 2,12-di-oxide	EtOH	395(3.83)	39-0927-73C
$C_{52}H_{40}O_4P_2$			
4,9-Phosphinidenebenz[5,6]indeno[1,2-c]-phosphole-9a(3bH)-carboxaldehyde, 2,4,9,10-tetrahydro-10-hydroxy-1,2,3,4,9,11-hexaphenyl-, 2,11-dioxide	EtOH	375(3.78)	39-0927-73C
$C_{52}H_{42}$			
Bi-2,4,6-cycloheptatrien-1-yl, x,x'-bis-(triphenylmethyl)-	EtOH	261(4.00)	18-1785-73
$C_{52}H_{48}N_4S_2$			
3H-Indolium, 2,2'-[1,3-phenylenebis[(4-phenylthiazol-3(2H)-yl-2-ylidene)-1-propen-1-yl-3-ylidene]]bis[1,3,3-tri-methyl-, diperchlorate	EtOH	515(5.03),550(5.18)	124-0913-73
	$CHCl_3$	526(5.11),546(5.07)	124-0913-73
3H-Indolium, 2,2'-[1,3-phenylenebis[(5-phenylthiazol-3(2H)-yl-2-ylidene)-1-propen-1-yl-3-ylidene]]bis[1,3,3-tri-methyl-, diperchlorate	EtOH	539(5.19),571(5.27)	124-0913-73
	$CHCl_3$	545(5.21),578(5.31)	124-0913-73
3H-Indolium, 2,2'-[1,4-phenylenebis[(4-phenylthiazol-3(2H)-yl-2-ylidene)-1-propen-1-yl-3-ylidene]]bis[1,3,3-tri-methyl-, diperchlorate	EtOH	518(5.26),548(5.24)	124-0913-73
	$CHCl_3$	526(5.34),548(5.23)	124-0913-73
3H-Indolium, 2,2'-[1,4-phenylenebis[(5-phenylthiazol-3(2H)-yl-2-ylidene)-1-propen-1-yl-3-ylidene]]bis[1,3,3-tri-methyl-, diperchlorate	EtOH	540(5.09),572(5.18)	124-0913-73
	$CHCl_3$	547(5.04),583(5.30)	124-0913-73
$C_{52}H_{48}N_8O_4$			
Tetracondensation product of 1-benzyl-3-carbamoylpyridinium chloride	$CHCl_3$	338.5(4.863)	64-0471-73B
$C_{53}H_{62}N_6O_8$			
21H-Biline-8,12-dipropanoic acid, 2,18-diacetyl-1,19-bis[(4-acetyl-3,5-di-methyl-1H-pyrrol-2-yl)methyl]-10,24-dihydro-3,7,13,17-tetramethyl-, di-methyl ester, dihydrobromide	MeOH-HBr	450(4.68),526(4.72)	65-1583-73

Compound	Solvent	λ_{max}(log ε)	Ref.
$C_{53}H_{70}N_6O_4$			
22H-Biline-8,12-dipropanoic acid, 2,18-diethyl-1,19-bis[(4-ethyl-3,5-dimethyl-1H-pyrrol-2-yl)methyl]-10,23-dihydro-3,7,13,17-tetramethyl-, dimethyl ester, dihydrochloride	$CHCl_3$	462(4.54),528(5.04)	65-0885-73
dihydrobromide	$CHCl_3$	467(4.56),526(5.07)	65-0885-73
$C_{54}H_{36}O_{12}$			
Anthra[2,3-j]heptaphene-6,7,14,15,22,23-hexol, hexaacetate	CH_2Cl_2	244(4.65),280(4.99), 337(5.11)	24-2058-73
$C_{54}H_{45}N_3O_6$			
Cytidine, N-benzoyl-2',5'-bis-O-(triphenylmethyl)-	MeOH	261(4.32),307(3.87)	24-0665-73
Cytidine, N-benzoyl-3',5'-bis-O-(triphenylmethyl)-	MeOH	260(4.37),305(4.00)	24-0665-73
$C_{54}H_{47}N_3O_5$			
Cytidine, 2'-O-(phenylmethyl)-3',5'-bis-O-(triphenylmethyl)-	MeOH	267(4.02)	24-0665-73
Cytidine, 3'-O-(phenylmethyl)-2',5'-bis-O-(triphenylmethyl)-	MeOH	265(3.91)	24-0665-73
$C_{54}H_{84}O_3$			
Cholesta-4,6-dien-3-one, 4-[(3-oxocholest-4-en-4-yl)oxy]-	EtOH	313(4.36)	39-1848-73C
$C_{55}H_{65}O_6$			
Pyrylium, 4-[(2,6-bis[4-(pentyloxy)phenyl]-4H-pyran-4-ylidene]methyl]-2,6-bis[4-(pentyloxy)phenyl]-, perchlorate	MeCN	435(4.53),567(5.21)	78-0795-73
$C_{55}H_{83}NO_{21}$			
Avenacin A	EtOH	222(4.42),255(3.91), 356(3.77)	78-0629-73
$C_{56}H_{40}O_2Si$			
Methanone, (1,4,5,6,7,7-hexaphenyl-7-silabicyclo[2.2.1]hepta-2,5-diene-2,3-diyl)bis[phenyl-	n.s.g.	233(4.63),294(4.12), 387(4.69)	78-2395-73
$C_{56}H_{56}N_8O_8$			
Tetrapyrido[4,3-b:4',3'-f:4",3"-j:4"'-3"'-n][1,5,9,13]tetraazacyclohexadecine-6,12,18,24(2H,8H,14H,20H)-tetrone, 4a,5,10a,11,16a,17,22a,23-octahydro-2,8,14,20-tetrakis[(phenylmethoxy)-methyl]-	$CHCl_3$	328(4.413)	64-0471-73B
$C_{57}H_{72}N_6O_8$			
21H-Biline-3,7,13,17-tetrapropanoic acid, 1-[(4-ethyl-3,5-dimethyl-2H-pyrrol-2-ylidene)methyl]-19-[(4-ethyl-3,5-dimethyl-1H-pyrrol-2-yl)-methylene]-5,15,19,23-tetrahydro-2,8,12,18-tetramethyl-, trihydrobromide	$CHCl_3$	451(4.66),492(4.92), 551(5.18)	103-1059-73

Compound	Solvent	$\lambda_{max}(\log \epsilon)$	Ref.
$C_{57}H_{89}Cl_2NO_{31}$			
Everheptose	n.s.g.	208(4.41)	35-0942-73
$C_{58}H_{44}N_4O_{16}$			
2,4(1H,3H)-Pteridinedione, 1,3-bis-(2,3,5-tri-O-benzoyl-β-D-ribo-furanosyl)-	MeOH	229(4.95),315(3.96)	24-1401-73
$C_{58}H_{65}N_5O_{14}$			
Aminosidin, penta-N-benzylidene-	MeOH	250(4.89)	94-0609-73
$C_{58}H_{65}N_5O_{19}$			
Aminosidin, penta-N-salicylidene-	MeOH	237(4.45),257(4.40)	94-0609-73
$C_{58}H_{75}N_5O_{14}$			
Aminosidin, penta-N-benzyl-	MeOH	252(3.16),259(3.06),265(3.03),269(2.72)	94-0609-73
$C_{59}H_{108}O_6$			
2H-Pyran-6-acetic acid, α,3-dihexadecyl-2-oxo-4-[(1-oxooctadecyl)oxy]-, ethyl ester	EtOH	210(3.95),300(4.01)	44-2540-73
$C_{60}H_{48}N_4O_{16}$			
2,4(1H,3H)-Pteridinedione, 6,7-dimethyl-1,3-bis(2,3,5-tri-O-benzoyl-β-D-ribo-furanosyl)-	MeOH	229(5.02),323(4.09)	24-1401-73
$C_{60}H_{52}N_4O_{12}$			
2,4(1H,3H)-Pteridinedione, 6,7-diphenyl-1,3-bis[2-deoxy-3,5-bis-O-(4-methyl-benzoyl)-erythro-pentofuranosyl]-	MeOH	237(4.90),270(4.35),461(4.18)	24-1401-73
$C_{60}H_{60}N_4O_8$			
13H,28H,43H,58H-8,12:23,27:38,42:53,57-Tetranitrilo-7H,22H,37H,52H-tetraben-zo[c,p,c_1,p_1][1,6,14,19,27,32,40,45]-octaoxacyclodopentacontin, 5,15,20-30,35,45,50,60-octahydro-	CHCl	266(4.25)	77-0831-73
$C_{60}H_{86}N_2O_{23}$			
Olean-12-en-29-oic acid, 3-[[3,4-di-O-acetyl-N-(2-ethoxy-2-oxoethyl)-2-O-[2,3,4-tri-O-acetyl-N-(2-ethoxy-2-oxo-ethyl)-β-D-glucopyranuronamidosyl]-β-D-glucopyranuronamidosyl]oxy]-11-oxo-, (3β,20β)-	EtOH	250(4.1)	65-0688-73
$C_{61}H_{51}N_3O_6$			
Cytidine, N-benzoyl-2'-O-(phenylmethyl)-3',5'-bis-O-(triphenylmethyl)-	MeOH	260(4.36),305(3.94)	24-0665-73
Cytidine, N-benzoyl-3'-O-(phenylmethyl)-2',5'-bis-O-(triphenylmethyl)-	MeOH	260(4.39),305(3.96)	24-0665-73
$C_{61}H_{51}N_5O_8$			
Adenosine, N,N-bis(4-methylbenzoyl)-5'-O-(triphenylmethyl)-2',5'-bis(4-meth-ylbenzoate)	MeOH	242(4.65),270s(4.46)	18-3228-73

Compound	Solvent	$\lambda_{max}(\log \epsilon)$	Ref.
$C_{62}H_{82}N_4$			
1,1,2,2-Ethanetetracarbonitrile, 1,2-di-ergosta-3,5,7,23-tetraen-7-yl-	$CHCl_3$	306(4.72),313(4.68)	44-0237-73
$C_{62}H_{84}N_{12}O_{17}$			
Actinomycin Z_5	MeOH	442(1.24)	88-2567-73
$C_{63}H_{75}N_5O_{19}$			
Aminosidin, penta-N-anisylidene-	MeOH	272(4.94),280(4.88), 288(4.78)	94-0609-73
$C_{63}H_{85}N_5O_{14}$			
Aminosidin, penta(N-benzyl-N-methyl)-	EtOH	253(3.26),259(3.17), 265(3.02),269(2.84)	94-0609-73
$C_{63}H_{91}CoN_{13}O_{14}P$			
Cobalamine, methyl-	pH 1	305f(4.3),460f(3.9)	10-0526-73E
	pH 7.4	340f(4.1),525f(3.9)	10-0526-73E
$C_{64}H_{56}O_{12}$			
7,9,19,21,31,33,43,45-Octaoxanonacyclo-[$44.2.2.2^{3,6}.2^{10,23}.2^{15,18}.2^{25,28}.2^{27,30}.2^{34,37}.2^{39,42}$]tetrahexaconta-3,5,10,12,15,17,22,24,27,29,34,36,39-41,46,48,49,51,53,55,57,59,61,63-tetracosaene-8,20,32,33-tetrone, 2,2,14,14,26,26,38,38-octamethyl-	$C_2H_4Cl_2$	265(3.60),272(3.54)	116-0305-73
$C_{65}H_{95}CoN_{13}O_{14}P$			
Cobalamine, propyl-	9;1 $PhCH_2OH$-EtOH	382(4.0),440(3.9)	10-0526-73E
$C_{66}H_{55}N_3O_5$			
Cytidine, 2',3',5'-tri-O-(triphenyl-methyl)-	MeOH	265(3.96)	24-0665-73
$C_{67}H_{120}O_2$			
2,5-Cyclohexadiene-1,4-dione, 2-methyl-3,5,6-tris(3,7,11,15-tetramethyl-2-hexadecenyl)-	hexane	260(4.16),269(4.16)	65-2038-73
$C_{68}H_{52}N_4$			
6,6'-Biquinolinium, 1,1'-bis(phenyl-methyl)-2,2'-bis[3-(1-phenyl-2(1H)-quinolinylidene)-1-propenyl]-, di-perchlorate	n.s.g.	630(5.53)	104-2195-73
$C_{68}H_{52}N_4O$			
Quinolinium, 6,6'-oxybis[1-(phenylmeth-yl)-2-[3-(1-phenyl-2(1H)-quinolinyli-dene]-1-propenyl-, diperchlorate	n.s.g.	628(5.54)	104-2195-73
$C_{68}H_{52}N_4S$			
Quinolinium, 6,6'-thiobis[1-(phenylmeth-yl)-2-[3-(1-phenyl-2(1H)-quinolinyli-dene]-1-propenyl]-, diperchlorate	n.s.g.	632(5.54)	104-2195-73
$C_{68}H_{52}N_4S_2$			
Quinolinium, 6,6'-dithiobis[1-(phenyl-methyl)-2-[3-(1-phenyl-2(1H)-quinolin-ylidene]-1-propenyl]-, diperchlorate	n.s.g.	627(5.49)	104-2195-73

Compound	Solvent	$\lambda_{max}(\log \epsilon)$	Ref.
$C_{69}H_{54}N_4$			
Quinolinium, 6,6'-methylenebis[1-(phenylmethyl)-2-[3-(1-phenyl-2(1H)-quinolinylidene)-1-propenyl]-, diperchlorate	n.s.g.	620(5.09)	104-2195-73
$C_{70}H_{44}N_2O_4$			
1H-Isoindole-1,3(2H)-dione, 2,2'-(1,2-phenylenebis[4,5,6,7-tetraphenyl-	dioxan	252(4.89),325(3.89)	47-2143-73
1H-Isoindole-1,3(2H)-dione, 2,2'-(1,3-phenylenebis[4,5,6,7-tetraphenyl-	dioxan	253(4.94),320(3.96)	47-2143-73
1H-Isoindole-1,3(2H)-dione, 2,2'-(1,4-phenylenebis[4,5,6,7-tetraphenyl-	dioxan	263(4.87),322s(4.01)	47-2143-73
$C_{70}H_{48}N_2O_4$			
1H-Isoindole-1,3(2H)-dione, 2,2'-(1,2-phenylenebis[3a,7a-dihydro-4,5,6,7-tetraphenyl-	dioxan	228s(4.70),320(4.33)	47-2143-73
1H-Isoindole-1,3(2H)-dione, 2,2'-(1,3-phenylenebis[3a,7a-dihydro-4,5,6,7-tetraphenyl-	dioxan	230s(4.75),320(4.33)	47-2143-73
1H-Isoindole-1,3(2H)-dione, 2,2'-(1,4-phenylenebis[3a,7a-dihydro-4,5,6,7-tetraphenyl-	dioxan	235(4.78),322(4.33)	47-2143-73
$C_{70}H_{52}N_4O_{16}$			
2,4(1H,3H)-Pteridinedione, 6,7-diphenyl-1,3-bis(2,3,5-tri-O-benzoyl-β-D-ribofuranosyl)-	MeOH	229(4.98),273(4.32), 360(4.13)	24-1401-73
$C_{70}H_{54}N_4$			
Quinolinium, 6,6'-(1,2-ethenediyl)bis-[1-(phenylmethyl)-2-[3-(1-phenyl-2(1H)-quinolinylidene)-1-propenyl]-, diperchlorate	n.s.g.	638(5.68)	104-2195-73
$C_{70}H_{56}N_4$			
Quinolinium, 6,6'-(1,2-ethanediyl)bis-[1-(phenylmethyl)-2-[3-(1-phenyl-2(1H)-quinolinylidene)-1-propenyl]-, diperchlorate	n.s.g.	618(5.10)	104-2195-73
$C_{70}H_{104}O_{32}$			
Senegin II	EtOH	317(4.28)	94-0791-73
$C_{72}H_{88}Fe_2N_8O$			
Iron, bis[2,3,7,8,12,13,17,18-octaethyl-21H,23H-porphinato(2-)-N^{21},N^{22},N^{23}-N^{24}]-μ-oxodi-	benzene	343(4.89),388(5.08), 563(4.16),590(4.07)	64-0433-73B
$C_{72}H_{88}N_8OSc_2$			
Scandium, bis[2,3,7,8,12,13,17,18-octaethyl-21H,23H-porphinato(2-)-N^{21},N^{22},N^{23},N^{24}]-μ-oxodi-	CH_2Cl_2	335(4.65),392(5.58), 404(5.58),502s(3.59), 538(4.37),576(4.50)	64-0433-73B
$C_{73}H_{59}N_3O_6$			
Cytidine, N-benzoyl-2',3',5'-tris-O-(triphenylmethyl)-	MeOH	261(4.31),305s(3.81)	24-0665-73

Compound	Solvent	λ_{max}(log ϵ)	Ref.
$C_{75}H_{75}N_5O_{10}$			
13H,28H,43H,58H,73H-8,12:23,27:38,42-53,57:68,72-Pentanitrilo-7H,22H,37H-52H,67H-pentabenzo[c,p,c_1,p_1,c_2][1-6,14,19,27,32,40,45,53,58]decaoxa-cyclopentahexacontin, 5,15,20,30-35,45,50,60,65,75-decahydro-	$CHCl_3$	265(4.35)	77-0831-73
$C_{75}H_{112}O_{35}$			
Senegin III	EtOH	315(4.30)	94-1564-73
$C_{75}H_{120}O_8$			
HOC, tetraethoxyethyl ether	MeOH	272(3.53),278(3.49)	78-1659-73
$C_{77}H_{96}N_8O_{12}$			
21H-Biline-2,8,12,18-tetrapropanoic acid, 19-[[5-[(4-ethyl-3,5-dimethyl-2H-pyrrol-2-ylidene)methyl]-3-(3-methoxy-3-oxopropyl)-4-methyl-1H-pyrrol-2-yl]methyl]-1-[[2-[(4-ethyl-3,5-dimethyl-1H-pyrrol-2-yl)methylene]-4-(3-methoxy-3-oxopropyl)-3-methyl-2H-pyrrol-5-yl]methyl]-10,23-dihydro-3,7,13,17-tetramethyl-, tetramethyl ester, tetrahydrobromide	$CHCl_3$	450(4.73),470(4.83), 513(5.02),559(5.38)	103-1059-73
$C_{81}H_{104}N_6O_{19}$			
Glycyrrhizic acid, tripeptide with tryptophan ethyl ester	EtOH	223(4.85),250(4.19), 273(4.16),282(4.14), 291(4.09)	65-0688-73
$C_{81}H_{122}O_{39}$			
Senegin IV	EtOH	315(4.30)	94-1564-73
$C_{84}H_{65}N_5O_{23}$			
7(8H)-Pteridinone, 8-(2,3,5-tri-O-benzoyl-β-D-ribofuranosyl)-2-[(2,3,5-tri-O-benzoyl-β-D-ribofuranosyl)amino]-4-[(2,3,5-tri-O-benzoyl-β-D-ribofuranosyl)oxy]-	MeOH	229(5.12),272(4.13), 282(4.13),348(4.11)	24-1952-73
$C_{96}H_{96}CuN_8$			
Copper, [3,6,14,17,25,28,36,39-octakis-(1,1-dimethylethyl)-45H,47H-tetraphenanthro[9,10-b:9',10'-g:9",10"-1:9"'-10"'-q]porphyrazinato(2-)-N^{45},N^{46},N^{47} N^{48}]-, (SP-4-1)-	$C_6H_4Cl_2$	360(4.79),477(4.38), 635(4.42),700(5.13)	65-2010-73
$C_{96}H_{96}MgN_8$			
Magnesium, [3,6,14,17,25,28,36,39-octakis(1,1-dimethylethyl)-45H,47H-tetraphenanthro[9,10-b:9',10'-g:9",10"-1-9"',10"'-q]porphyrazinato(2-)-N^{45},N^{46},N^{47},N^{48}]-, (SP-4-1)-	$CHCl_3$	380(4.89),470(4.24), 630(4.59),697(5.30)	65-2010-73
$C_{96}H_{106}N_8$			
21H,23H-Porphyrazine, 2,3,7,8,12,13,17-18-octakis[4-(1,1-dimethylethyl)phenyl]-	heptane	268(4.53),362(4.97), 450(4.51),562s(4.34), 595(4.69),666(4.90)	65-2010-73

Compound	Solvent	λ_{max}(log ε)	Ref.
21H,23H-Porphyrazine, 2,3,7,8,12,13,17-18-octakis[4-(1,1-dimethylethyl)phenyl]-, cobalt complex (cont.)	heptane	342(4.69),382s(4.39), 437(4.29),562(4.27), 610(4.59)	65-2010-73
copper complex	heptane	360(4.88),450(4.40), 575(4.36),625(5.00)	65-2010-73
ferrous complex	heptane	345(4.85),455(4.38), 595(4.30),635(4.41)	65-2010-73
magnesium complex	heptane	380(4.93),460(4.14), 595s(4.36),646(4.98)	65-2010-73
palladium complex	heptane	340(4.70),450(4.17), 535(4.20),615(4.61)	65-2010-73
vanadyl complex	heptane	364(4.87),470(4.48), 585(4.30),640(5.07)	65-2010-73
$C_{108}H_{184}O_{28}$			
3,6,9,12,15-Pentaoxaheptadecan-1-ol, 17,17',17",17"'-[[5,11,17,23-tetrakis-(1,1,3,3-tetramethylbutyl)pentacyclo-[19.3.1.1^{3,7}.1^{9,13},1^{15,19}]octacosa-1(25),3,5,7(28),9,11,13(27),15,17-19(26),21,23-dodecaene-25,26,27,28-tetrayl]tetrakis(oxy)tetrakis-	MeOH	272(3.60)	78-1659-73
$C_{190}H_{288}I_2N_{40}O_{50}S_4$			
L-Proline, N-butoxycarbonyl-L-seryl-L-tyrosyl-L-seryl-L-methionyl-γ-tert-butyl-L-glutamyl-L-histidyl-L-phenylalanyl-L-arginyl-L-tryptophylglycyl-N$^{\varepsilon}$-butoxycarbonyl-L-lysyl-L-prolyl-L-valylglycyl-N$^{\varepsilon}$-butoxycarbonyl-L-lysyl-N$^{\varepsilon}$-butoxycarbonyl-L-lysyl-L-arginyl-L-arginyl-L-prolyl-L-valyl-N$^{\varepsilon}$-butoxycarbonyl-L-lysyl-L-valyl-L-3,5-diiodotyrosyl-, tert-butyl ester, tritosylate	MeOH-NaOH	283(3.87),290(3.88)	39-2875-73C

1- -73, Acta Chem. Scand., 27 (1973)
0209 G. Kjellin and J. Sandström
0258 I. Wennerbeck
0271 C.L. Pedersen and O. Buchardt
0367 S.R. Jensen et al.
0433 S. Brandänge et al.
0595 K. Undheim and R. Lie
0600 G. Sundström
0677 O.J.K. Kovacs et al.
1059 K. Undheim and G.A. Ulsaker
1109 G. Sundström
1183 G. Isaksson and J. Sandström
1390 K. Undheim and G.A. Ulsaker
1573 G. Magnusson and S. Thoren
1735 A. Skancke
1749 K. Undheim and R. Lie
1763 P.E. Fjeldstad and K. Undheim
1891 B.G. Pring and C.G. Swahn
1907 M. Elander et al.
1914 O. Ceder et al.
1923 O. Ceder and U. Stenhede
1982 U. Ekevag et al.
2095 O. Ceder and M.L. Samuelsson
2107 A.J. Aasen et al.
2221 O. Ceder and U. Stenhede
2485 T. Liljefors et al.
2574 A.G. Andrewes
2581 S.R. Jensen et al.
2710 J. Sierankiewicz and S. Gatenbeck
2802 P. Krogsgaard-Larsen et al.
3121 M. Moron et al.
3133 S. Pennanen
3211 N. Jacobsen and K. Torssell
3251 P. Krugsgaard-Larsen et al.
3259 O. Ceder and K. Vernmark
3264 O. Ceder and M.L. Samuelsson
3499 D. Alexandersson and N. Vannerberg
3632 P. Juvvik and B. Sundby
3641 P. Juvvik and B. Sundby
3647 J. Møller et al.

2- -73, Indian J. Chem., 11 (1973)
0007 A. Chatterjee et al.
0009 S.C. Agarwal et al.
0085 K.N.N. Ayengar et al.
0091 T.R. Kasturi et al.
0096 A.J. Kalra et al.
0098 A.C. Jain et al.
0100 B.S. Bajwa et al.
0104 O.P. Vig et al.
0106 A.C. Jain and S.M. Jain
0115 M. Darbarwar et al.
0120 M.S. Kamat et al.
0131 A.S. Sarma
0134 M.M. Aly
0201 M. Krishnamurti et al.
0203 A.S.R. Anjaneyulu et al.
0207 B. Vig et al.
0209 P.G. Naik Satam and N.V. Bringi
0298 A.V. RamaRao et al.
0301 P.R. Vijayasarathy and G.S. Krishna Rao
0313 P.P. Paranjpe and G. Bagavant
0342 J.R. Merchant and H.K. Desai
0403 A.V. Rama Rao and M. Varadan
0407 A. Chatterjee, S.C. Basa and D. Basu
0410 M. Bandopadhyay et al.
0413 P.G. Deshmukh et al.
0433 J.R. Merchant and H.K. Desai
0446 A. Chatterjee and B. Bandyopadhyay
0499 K.N. Mehrotva and T. Singh
0507 G.S. Sidhu et al.
0509 C.P. Dutta et al.
0518 V.S. Deshpande et al.
0528 Y.N. Shukla et al.
0530 M. Bandopadhyay et al.
0541 S.S. Kumari et al.
0577 S. Mukherjee et al.
0611 P.B. Talukdar et al.
0621 K.B. Prasad and S.C. Shaw
0628 V.P. Arya and S.J. Shenoy
0631 S.N. Bannore and J.I. Bose
0707 A.K. Das Gupta and R.M. Chatterje
0744 V.P. Arya et al.
0825 V. Seshadri et al.
0847 S.R. Ramadas and J. Radhakrishnan
0863 V.A. Pol and A.B. Kulkarni
0882 N. Guruswamy et al.
0884 N. Singh and K. Krishan
0974 V. Viswanatha and G.S. Krishna Rao
0977 S.K. Talapatra et al.
0991 S.V. Eswaran et al.
1047B K. Nagarajan and R.K. Shah
1057 A. Banerji et al.
1074 A. KrishnaMurty et al.
1084 M.S. Pramila and B.R. Pai
1086 B.R. Pai and C.S. Swaminathan
1088 V.N. Ramachandran et al.
1092 A.J. Kalra et al.
1099 T.R. Kasturi and E.M. Abraham
1126 S. Mahey et al.
1142 M.S. El-Ezaby et al.
1187 J.R. Merchant and R.G. Jadhav
1190 T.R. Govindachari et al.
1203 D.L. Dhane and K.A. Noras
1215 T.R. Govindachuri et al.
1225 R.N. Khanna et al.
1233 S.M. Anand and A.C. Jain
1237 S.M. Anand and A.C. Jain
1245 A.K. Das Gupta and K.R. Das
1254 H. Singh et al.
1257 P.B. Talukdar et al.
1333 B.H. Patwardhan and G. Bagavant
1334 D.K. Khanna and Vishwapaul

3- -73, Anal. Chem., 45 (1973)
0415 W.L. Paul and S.G. Schulman
1794 S.A. Carlson and D.M. Hercules

4- -73. J. Heterocyclic Chem., 10 (1973)
0015 H. El Khadem et al.
0021 M. Nagata et al.
0031 T. Kametani et al.
0051 E.E. Garcia et al.
0059 S.K. Sengupta et al.
0071 A.W. Chow et al.
0077 T. Kametani et al.
0085 K-Y. Zee-Cheng and C.C. Cheng
0095 H. Zinnes and J. Shavel, Jr.
0115 J.E. Douglass and H.D. Fortner
0123 H.L. Yale et al.
0133 W.D. Johnston et al.

0137 K.D. Paull and C.C. Cheng
0139 H.N. Al-Jalb and F.W. Al-Azawi
0143 H.L. Yale and J.T. Sheehan
0165 P.L. Myers and J.W. Lewis
0181 E. Abushanab et al.
0191 A. Arcoria et al.
0195 D.L. Fields and T.H. Regan
0209 M. Israel and N. Muhammad
0217 R.R. Wittekind and S. Lazarus
0225 R. Madhav et al.
0249 J.A. Skorcz et al.
0261 S. Plescia et al.
0265 N. Muhammad and D.L. Mays
0267 R. Weber and M. Renson
0287 J. W. Sowell and C.D. Blanton, Jr.
0307 W. V. Curran
0347 R. F. Abdulla
0357 B. Cavalleri et al.
0399 P.C. Unangst and P.L. Southwick
0403 L.J. Chinn
0405 W.J. Houlihan and A.J. Pieroni
0411 J. Elguero et al.
0413 A.H. Albert et al.
0417 B. Rayner et al.
0425 M. Chaykovsky et al.
0443 E.A. Abu-Mustafa et al.
0447 Y. Tamura et al.
0459 J.M. Kamenka and M.N. Alam
0469 J. Diez et al.
0487 R.A. Coburn and R.A. Glennon
0519 W.T. Comer et al.
0575 A. Messmer et al.
0601 Y.F. Shealy et al.
0623 G. Brancaccio et al.
0643 A. Arcoria et al.
0665 I.E. El-Kholy et al.
0687 C.L. Schmidt and L.B. Townsend
0689 D. Misiti et al.
0705 P.H. Grayshan and A.T. Peters
0779 S. Nesnow and C. Heidelberger
0807 P.D. Cook and R.N. Castle
0821 K.T. Potts et al.
0835 T. Novinson et al.
0843 P.F. Crain et al.
0867 K.Y. Zee-Cheng and C.C. Cheng
0871 L.H. Klemm and H. Lund
0883 A. Walser and G. Silverman
0885 A.H. Albert et al.
0887 T. Novinson et al.
0935 K.H. Dudley et al.
0947 Y. Tamura et al.
0989 M. Golfier and R. Milcent
1007 G. Guanti et al.
1015 P. Sohar and G.H. Denny
1021 R.P. Rao et al.
1043 E. Dyer et al.
1051 H.S. El Khadem and E.S. El Ashry
1055 J.W.A.M. Janssen et al.

5- -73, Ann. Chem. Liebigs (1973)
0005 W. Haede et al.
0103 H.-J. Willenbrock et al.
0129 W. Ried and S.-H. Lim
0141 H.H. Inhoffen et al.
0146 H.H. Inhoffen et al.
0166 J.O. Currie, Jr., et al.
0207 A. Treibs et al.
0214 H. Dürr et al.
0224 H. Kubinyi et al.
0310 S. Hünig et al.
0324 S. Hünig et al.
0339 S. Hünig et al.
0375 W. Ried and E. König
0407 R. Tschesche et al.
0432 G. Rücker and K.H. Kahrs
0531 R. Jeck and G. Wilhelm
0636 W. Walter and M. Radke
0650 G. Kresze and H. Härtner
0750 C. Reichardt and P. Miederer
0844 G. Kaupp
0879 F. Asinger et al.
0961 R. Jeck et al.
1036 S. Hünig et al.
1067 H.H. Inhoffen et al.
1112 O. Dann et al.
1237 W.H. Gündel and I. Hagedorn
1286 H. Guglielmi
1329 G.W. Kenner et al.
1339 H. Straub et al.
1388 S. Ghisla et al.
1545 F. Ziegler et al.
1675 H.-D. Becker
1710 H. Wolf and H. Scheer
1741 H. Scheer and H. Wolf
1893 A. Huth et al.
1943 A. Klemer et al.
1955 H. Neunhoeffer and G. Werner
1963 H. Neunhoeffer amd G. Frey
2025 A. Roedig et al.
2048 G. Adam and K. Schreiber
2078 W. Kreiser and H.-U. Warnecke
2088 E. Fahr et al.

6- -73, Ann. Chim.(Paris), 8 (1973)
0123 J.C. Brunet and N. Demey
0217 L. Korejzl and J. Wiemann
0329 A. Yanagida and C. Gansser
0397 A. Meyer

7- -73, Ann. chim.(Rome), 63 (1973)
0013 E. Ragazzi et al.
0045 F. Duro et al.
0050 S. Fisichella et al.
0055 S. Fisichella et al.
0255 G. Pappalardo et al.
0269 O. Caputo et al.
0319 I. Degani and R. Fochi
0363 C. Calzolari et al.
0373 E. Barni and G. DiModica
0379 E. Barni and G. DiModica
0439 S. Bertozzi et al.
0457 S. Ceriani and G. Tarzia
0527 I. Degani, R. Fochi and G. Spunta
0613 S. Mangiavacchi and M. Scotton
0619 E. Abignente et al.
0635 M. Ghelardoni and V. Pestellini
0727 L. Pentimalli and G. Milani
0779 S. Fisichella et al.

8- -73, Manufacturing Chemists Assoc. Research Project, Nos. 157-215 (1973)

10- -73D, Arch. Biochem. Biophys., 157 (1973)
0083 C.-Y. Lee and J. Everse

10- -73E, Arch. Biochem. Biophys., 158 (1973)
0526 R.T. Taylor and M.L. Hanna

10- -73F, Arch. Biochem. Biophys., 159 (1973)
0001 G. Lugaro et al.
0240 V. Ulrich and K.H. Schnabel
0528 Y. Kishimoto

12- -73, Australian J. Chem., 26 (1973)
0147 G. Sugowdz et al.
0183 S. Nimgirawath et al.
0201 F. Yuste and F. Walls
0209 R.M. Carman et al.
0389 R.N. Warrener et al.
0409 J.T. Pinhey and I.A. Southwell
0415 C.G. Begg et al.
0437 J.B. Bremner and P. Wiriyachitra
0455 I.R.C. Bick et al.
0571 R.M. Carman and B.N. Venzke
0595 G.W.K. Cavill and R.J. Quinn
0603 M.S. Ahmad and N.K. Pillai
0619 B. Halton and A.D. Woolhouse
0641 A.C. Jain and M.K. Zutshi
0687 E.R. Krajniak et al.
0845 E.V. Lassak et al.
0883 R.M. Carman et al.
0889 L.A. Summers
0893 K.G. Lewis
0899 E.R. Krajniak et al.
1031 C.S. Barnes et al.
1051 E.V. Lassak et al.
1059 W.J. Davidson and J.A. Elix
1069 H.J.T. Chan and J.A. Elix
1079 J.A. Elix and B.A. Ferguson
1093 J.A. Elix and D. Tronson
1111 K. Picker et al.
1121 J. Mock et al.
1147 M.A. Khan and J.B. Polya
1239 A. Meisters and T. Mole
1251 K.G. Boto and F.G. Thomas
1283 R.M. Carman and B.N. Venzke
1337 E.R. Krajniak et al.
1377 I.R.C. Bick and A.J. Blakman
1551 J.W. Ducker and M.J. Gunter
1571 A.F.A. Wallis
1585 J.B. Polya and M. Woodruff
1689 D.J. Brown and R.K. Lynn
1725 P.L. Watson and R.N. Warrener
1763 G.D. Beresford et al.
1805 G.B. Russell and J.G. Fraser
1911 R.S. Dickson and H.P. Kirsch
1977 R.M. Carman and B.N. Venzke
2027 C.S. Barnes et al.
2035 G.Y. Moltrasio et al.
2065 D.R. Baigent and I.R.C. Bick
2129 T. Teitei et al.
2153 J.T. Baker and C.C. Duke
2159 D. St.C. Black and K.G. Watson
2213 R.F.C. Brown et al.
2221 L. Breen et al.
2235 R.M. Carman and B.N. Venzke
2257 J.R. Cannon et al.
2291 F.N. Lahey and R.V. Stick
2311 F.N. Lahey and R.V. Stick
2315 J. Mock et al.
2459 B.S. Balgir et al.
2473 D.St.C. Black and K.G. Watson
2491 D.St.C. Black and K.G. Watson
2555 D.D. Evans
2567 J.W. Ducker and M.J. Gunter
2671 A.J. Birch et al.
2697 P.S. Clezy and V. Diakin
2723 L.A. Summers

13- -73A, Steroids, 21 (1973)
0147 R.C. Rastogi et al.
0609 W.B. Smith et al.
0689 H.P. Gelbke and R. Knuppen
0723 R.S. Rosenfeld et al.

13- -73B, Steroids, 22 1973)
0107 G.H. Rasmusson and G.E. Arth
0139 R.H. Purdy et al.
0327 N. Kundu
0627 L.L. Smith et al.
0763 A.K. Lala and A.B. Kulkarni

18- -73, Bull. Chem. Soc. Japan, 46 (1973)
0166 K. Isobe et al.
0194 S. Yamamoto et al.
0199 K. Imafuku and H. Matsumura
0244 S. Kato et al.
0253 T. Nishino et al.
0263 J. Nishikido et al.
0275 A. Oku et al.
0283 O. Tsuge and A. Torii
0299 S. Yanagida et al.
0337 E. Kaji and S. Zen
0540 T. Sasaki et al.
0544 K. Imafuku and H. Matsumura
0550 H. Komura et al.
0572 N. Nishi and J. Noguchi
0577 T. Sekiba
0580 T. Nishino et al.
0583 T. Isobe et al.
0600 K. Takahashi et al.
0605 M. Kuritani et al.
0611 Y. Sakata et al.
0618 K. Anzoi and M. Matsui
0643 Y. Okamoto and H. Sakurai
0651 F. Ogura and M. Nakagawa
0667 Y. Hayasi et al.
0690 H. Takeshita et al.
0693 S. Sekiguchi and T. Shiojima
0699 M. Yokoyama and S. Hongo
0880 H. Takeshita and S. Tanno
0888 K. Naemura and M. Nakazaki
0909 Y. Takeuchi et al.
0915 H. Tatemitsu et al.
0939 K. Sugiura and M. Goto
0942 N. Hata et al.
0964 T. Shiba and H. Kato
1007 H. Aoyama et al.
1008 T. Asao et al.
1009 Y. Ogata et al.
1212 H. Horino and T. Toda
1250 T. Isida et al.
1257 M. Miyamoto and H. Nozaki
1366 M. Mashima and F. Ikeda

1371 M. Mashima and F. Ikeda
1437 T. Matsuo et al.
1498 K. Kurosawa et al.
1509 M. Yamamoto et al.
1520 Y. Shimizu et al.
1546 S. Watanabe et al.
1553 T. Hamasaki et al.
1563 T. Seita et al.
1572 T. Seita et al.
1579 S. Fujita et al.
1733 F. Toda and N. Doi
1737 F. Toda et al.
1762 T. Seita et al.
1772 T. Shimizu et al.
1785 K. Okamoto et al.
1803 T. Osaki et al.
1816 Y. Kobayashi and S. Wakamatsu
1851 T. Akiyama et al.
1890 M. Hattori et al.
2112 E. Sekido et al.
2181 K. Ohga and T. Matsuo
2187 Y. Murakami et al.
2253 T. Nishio et al.
2421 M. Otomo and K. Kodama
2498 I. Hirao, Y. Kato and S. Kozakura
2504 K. Yamada et al.
2559 I. Ojima et al.
2562 T. Suami et al.
2565 K. Muneyuki et al.
2804 K. Yamagiya et al.
2822 Y. Takeuchi et al.
2828 Y. Takeuchi et al.
2840 H. Nagano et al.
2892 H. Satonaka et al.
2896 Y. Omote et al.
2907 S. Akiyama et al.
2908 M. Iwata and S. Emoto
2915 H. Takeshita et al.
2918 H. Shirasaki et al.
3139 S. Yamamoto
3155 J.Y. Satoh et al.
3161 T. Nozoe et al.
3165 S. Fukatsu et al.
3198 I. Saito et al.
3228 K. Anzai and M. Matsui
3266 T. Nozoe et al.
3275 I. Nakagawa and T. Hata
3315 Y. Omote et al.
3316 K. Mizuno, C. Pac and H. Sakurai
3319 A.G. Giumanini et al.
3462 Y. Kobayashi
3467 Y. Kobayashi
3517 S. Ito et al.
3533 C. Kashima and Y. Tsuda
3603 T. Sone and Y. Abe
3858 N. Nakazaki et al.
3876 C. Shin et al.
3881 K. Okamoto et al.
3898 H. Kawamoto et al.

19- -73, Bull. Acad. Polon. Sci., 21 (1973)
0009 K. Gawecka and S. Nejer
0091 A.R. Daniewski et al.
0257 L. Strekowski et al.
0351 J. Kochany and H. Piotrowska
0593 W. Libus et al.
0785 W.M. Daniewski et al.
0809 M. Kocor and W. Wojciechowska
0849 L. Skulski and G. Adamska
0881 K. Kochany and H. Piotrowska
0887 W. Gustowski et al.
0893 J. Mirek et al.

20- -73, Bull. soc. chim. Belges, 82 (1973)
0031 G. Van de Woude and L. van Hove
0215 A. Maquestiau et al.
0243 H. De Pooter et al.
0259 H. De Pooter et al.
0299 C. Van de Sande and M. Vandewalle
0699 B. Tursch et al.
0705 C. Van de Sande and M. Vandewalle

22- -73, Bull. soc. chim. France (1973)
0202 E. Elkik and H. Assadi-Far
0249 J. Laureillard et al.
0263 L. Gorrichon-Guigon and Y. Maroni-Barnaud
0335 G. Muraro et al.
0343 G. Muraro et al.
0359 G. Bauduin et al.
0549 M. Rivière-Baudet and J. Satgé
0622 D. Kontonassios et al.
0625 J. Schreiber et al.
0630 M. Nastasi and J. Streith
0635 M. Nastasi and J. Streith
0691 F. Plenat et al.
0724 G. Le Guillanton and A. Daver
0743 M. Julia and D. Arnould
0746 M. Julia and D. Arnould
0971 R.A. Bafford et al.
1032 R. Pinel and Y. Mollier
1049 C. Metge and C. Bertrand
1098 A. Guida and M. Mousseron-Canet
1109 G. Dana et al.
1154 A. Verine et al.
1225 J.-C. Halle et al.
1285 H. Wahl et al.
1289 H. Wahl et al.
1305 J. Rigaudy et al.
1351 M.M. El Gaied and Y. Bessiere-Chretien
1357 R. Lorne and S. Julia
1376 J. Muzart and J.-P. Pete
1390 A. Belly et al.
1395 A. Belly et al.
1409 R. Gelin et al.
1433 J.P. Gesson et al.
1442 R. Martin and G. Coton
1454 C. Maignan and F. Rouessac
1456 P. Choay et al.
1517 G. Descotes et al.
1553 J.C. Halle
1659 C. Lemarie-Retour et al.
1676 G. Dana et al.
1760 J.P. Girault et al.
1781 M. Hauteville et al.
1784 M. Hauteville et al.
1800 M. Bertrand and C. Santelli-Rouvier
1814 J.-P. Alazard and X. Lusinchi
1849 J.-L. Barascut et al.
1854 R.M. Claramunt et al.
2029 G. Leclerc

2032 J. Schmitt et al.
2039 Y. Bessiere-Chretien and H. Serne
2046 M. Julia and J.-Y. Lallemand
2058 M. Julia and J.-Y. Lallemand
2065 H. Ledon et al.
2071 H. Ledon et al.
2086 J.-F. Biellman and G. Branlant
2093 J. Andrieux
2098 J.M. Coustard and J.-C. Jacquesy
2121 P. Courtot and J.-C. Clement
2126 J. Daunis
2209 J.-M. Carpentier
2214 J.-M. Carpentier
2231 R. Gallardo-Herrero et al.
2301 C. Dumont and M. Vidal
2320 M. Lasperas and E. Casadevall
2331 M. Santelli- and M. Bertrand
2429 M. Cossu-Jouve et al.
2472 M. de Botton
2482 P. Bouchet et al.
2493 J. Daunis and C. Pigiere
2506 R. Baudouy et al.
2638 M. Deneux et al.
2692 R. Gelin et al.
2694 R. Joly et al.
2705 T. Imbert et al.
2715 L. Pichat et al.
2719 L. Pichat et al.
2739 G. Guillerm et al.
2746 L. Veniard and G. Pourcelot
2818 J. Daunis and C. Pigiere
2836 S. Geribaldi et al.
2843 J. Perronnet and P. Girault
2847 J. Streith and B. Willig
2856 M. Peyrot and Y. Lepage
3044 M. Pays and M. Beljean
3067 P. Caubere and G. Coudert
3071 M. de Botton
3087 R. Martin
3159 P. Bouchet and C. Coquelet
3178 J. Daunis and M. Follet
3187 J. Barjot et al.
3303 J. Elguero et al.
3324 M. Beljean and M. Pays
3334 N. Kim Son et al.
3397 G. Tsatsaronis and T. Soulis
3416 R. Gelin et al.
3437 F. Texier and R. Carrié
3442 R. Mertz et al.
3458 G. LeGuillanton
3487 G. Cauquis et al.
3493 P. Caubere et al.

23- -73, Can. J. Chem., 51 (1973)
0338 M.J. Nye and W.P. Tang
0388 G.O. Aspinall et al.
0394 G.O. Aspinall and R.R. King
0468 K.R. Kopecky et al.
0482 B.F. MacDonald and G.M. Barton
0748 M. Gordon et al.
0760 T.J. Danielson and E.M. Hawes
0792 J.A. Eenkhoorn et al.
0811 G. Manoussakis et al.
1050 S. Nishibe et al.
1089 J.K. Groves et al.
1179 J. Thomson and M.C. Baird
1187 R. Van Est-Stammer and J. Engberds
1223 C.R. Popplestone and A.M. Unrau
1267 P. Yates and D.J. MacGregor
1313 M.J. Robins et al.
1332 T.A.Anthonsen et al.
1346 M.S. Henderson et al.
1359 G.O. Aspinall et al.
1378 T.R. Lynch et al.
1458 P.J. Smith et al.
1598 L.R.C. Barclay et al.
1617 J.A. Findlay and D. Kwan
1724 P. de Mayo and M.C. Usselman
1741 A. Taurins and V.T. Khuow
1812 H.H. Baer and S.-H.L. Chiu
1995 Y.-N. Kuo and M.J. Nye
2024 A.G. Brook and J.M. Duff
2166 E. Piers and M.B. Geraghty
2207 G.L. Lange and E. Neidert
2215 G.L. Lange and E. Neidert
2323 W.A. Ayer and P.D. Deshpande
2338 E.W. Warnhoff and P. Reynolds-Warnhoff
2349 D.E. Horning and J.M. Muchowski
2397 K. K. Ogilvie and L.A. Slotin
2578 T.R. Chamberlain and J.J. McCullough
2821 H. Roigt and R.M. Leblanc
3102 M.P. Cava et al.
3143 R.A. Cox and E. Buncel
3157 W.A. Ayer and L.L. Carstens
3161 M.J. Robins and G.L. Basom
3173 P.G. Khazanie and E. Lee-Ruff
3177 E. Kiehlmann et al.
3236 R.F. Severson and W.H. Schuller
3263 C.R. Engel et al.
3299 J.A. Findlay and D. Kwan
3357 N.L. Holder and B. Fraser-Reid
3486 C.O. Bender and H.D. Burgess
3539 M.F. Mayahi and M.F. El-Bermani
3620 C. Schmidt and J. Thazhuthaveetil
3756 C.C. Leznoff and J.Y. Wong
3808 D.P. Thiemann et al.
3827 D.J.W. Goon et al.
3842 W.A. Ayer and H. Taube
3866 O.E. Edwards and Z. Paryzek
3936 J.P. Guthrie and Y. Ueda
3950 B. Fraser-Reid et al.
3989 L. Scmidt

24- 73, Chem. Ber., 106 (1973)
0008 R. Askani and J.P. Chesick
0020 H. Wagner et al.
0317 W. Pfleiderer et al.
0355 S. Blechert et al.
0368 S. Blechert et al.
0382 F. Bohlmann et al.
0388 D.V. Rao et al.
0435 G.W. Fischer and P. Schneider
0450 W. Sucrow et al.
0497 F. Bohlmann and W. Skuballa
0570 R. Hansel and J. Schulz
0576 K. Annen et al.
0655 G. Manecke and M. Hartel
0665 W. Hutzenlaub and W. Pfleiderer
0674 H.J. Kuhn and K. Gollnick
0723 H. Hofmeister et al.
0745 W. Sucrow et al.

0803 H. Brockmann, Jr. and G. Knobloch
0812 S.A. Khan et al.
0845 F. Bohlmann and C. Zdero
0857 R. Criegee et al.
0888 R. Wiechert et al.
1001 A. Hettche and K. Dimroth
1116 G. Manecke and U. Rotter
1172 H. Möhrle and R. Engelsing
1182 B. Franck and U. Zeidler
1198 B. Franck et al.
1303 H. Wieglepp et al.
1309 W. Reininger
1328 F. Bohlmann and C. Zdero
1337 F. Bohlmann and C. Zdero
1341 G. Snatzke and K. Kunde
1389 K. Eistetter and W. Pfleiderer
1401 G. Ritzmann and W. Pfleiderer
1423 H. Bartfeld and W. Flitsch
1459 P. Rosenmund et al.
1474 P. Rosenmund et al.
1589 F.A. Neugebauer and H. Fischer
1612 T. Kauffmann et al.
1628 K. Zauer et al.
1661 C. Reichardt and K. Halbritter
1678 G. Ege and G. Jooss
1711 J. Brandt et al.
1758 R.W. Hoffmann et al.
1804 H. Prinzbach and D. Hunkler
1822 H. Prinzbach et al.
1837 H. Prinzbach et al.
1952 H. Schmid et al.
2058 H. Brockmann and H. Laatsch
2070 J. Reisch and W.F. Ossenkop
2087 F. Bohlmann and C. Wesdemiotis
2140 F. Bohlmann and C. Zdero
2190 H.A. Staab and M. Haenel
2203 M. Haenel and H.A. Staab
2255 H.R. Krüger et al.
2263 H. Hofmeister et al.
2427 F. Umland et al.
2530 F.A. Neugebauer et al.
2536 H. Wagner et al.
2710 J.W. Buchler et al.
2745 F. Bohlmann et al.
2755 F. Bohlmann et al.
2890 J. Bonnekessel and C. Rüchardt
2929 R. Tschesche and H.-U. Plenio
2943 T. Severin and K.H. Brautigam
2982 W. Pfleiderer et al.
3035 F. Bohlmann and N. Rao
3039 H. Vorbrüggen and P. Strehlke
3097 R. Kreher and H. Wissmann
3127 A. Murayama et al.
3149 W. Pfleiderer and W. Hutzenlaub
3175 H. Yamamoto et al.
3203 W. Hutzenlaub et al.
3223 H. Besl et al.
3240 E. Wille and W. Lüttke
3432 W. Sucrow et al.
3533 J. Lehmann and H. Wamhoff
3544 G. Buhr
3621 F. Bohlmann and P.-D. Hopf
3636 J. Ruppert et al.
3743 H. Bredereck et al.
3772 F. Bohlmann and P.-D. Hopf
3775 F. Bohlmann et al.
3779 F. Bohlmann and C. Zdero
3788 T.J. Arackal and B. Eistert
3817 D. Stusche and H. Prinzbach
3824 H. Prinzbach et al.

25- -73, Chem. and Ind.(London) (1973)
0041 T. Uyehara et al.
0089 O. Korver et al.
0229 B. Zsadon
0275 I.F. Eckhard et al.
0322 D.P. Chakraborty et al.
0478 Z. Vesely et al.
0695 I.J. Smith and B.J. Tighe
0792 S.C. Das et al.
0952 Y. Tamura et al.
1032 P.L. Majumder et al.
1066 R.N. Butler
1108 W.H. Gumprecht
1111 P.A. Crooks and R. Szyndler
1162 H. Ullah and P. Sykes

27- -73, Chimia, 27 (1973)
0073 M. Neuenschwander et al.
0099 U. Stauss et al.
0212 G. Bouchon et al.

28- -73A, Compt. rend., 276 (1973)
0519 P. Duhamel et al.
0803 J. Ficini and J. D'Angelo
0883 J. Ficini et al.
0959 A. Frankowski and J. Streith
1033 G. Leclerc
1035 J.-L. Piette et al.
1115 J. Sotiropoulos and A.M. Lamazonere
1131 G. LeGuillanton
1215 J. Rigaudy et al.
1319 P. Duhamel et al.
1327 F. LeGoffic et al.
1457 P. Souchay et al.
1799 B. Mompon et al.

28- -73B, Compt. rend., 277 (1973)
0247 F. Venien et al.
0407 P. Decock et al.

30- -73, Doklady Akad. Nauk S.S.S.R., 208-213 (1973)(English translation pagination)
0001 A.V. Belotsvetov et al.
0061 L.A. Karamysheva et al.
0139 M.K. Yusupov et al.
0207 L.M. Yagupol'skii et al.
0234 A.A. Akhrem et al.
0394 B.N. Laskorin et al.
0445 A.A. Akhrem et al.
0486 A.A. Akhrem et al.
0521 V.N. Nezavibat'ko et al.
0676 Y.A. Zhdanov et al.
0767 D.P. Del'tsova et al.
0828 I.Y. Postovskii et al.
0932 V.I. Sokolov et al.
0941 M.G. Voronkov et al.

31- -73, Experientia, 29 (1973)
0017 S. Nishibe et al.

0517 M. Shamma and S.Y. Yao
0518 J. Kunitomo et al.

32- -73, Gazz. chim. ital., 103 (1973)
0003 G. Adembri et al.
0031 O. Attanasi et al.
0037 S. Auricchio and A. Ricca
0047 G. Bailo et al.
0117 G. Cainelli et al.
0127 B. Cardillo et al.
0141 G. Casnati et al.
0309 E. Belgodere et al.
0543 R. Marini-Bettolo and F.D. Monache
0649 F. DeSantis and F. Stegel
0681 F. Montanari et al.
0709 S. Trovato et al.
0723 P. Beltrame and P. Carniti
0755 A. Fravolini et al.
0771 O.G. deLima et al.
0779 F.D. Monache et al.
0849 P. Bicev et al.
1045 M. Croci et al.
1057 A. Fravolini et al.
1063 A. Fravolini et al.
1073 A. Fravolini et al.
1083 V. Tortorella et al.
1271 M. Adinolfi et al.

33- -73, Helv. Chim. Acta, 56 (1973)
0014 J. Borgulya et al.
0075 U. Widmer et al.
0139 R. Imhof et al.
0239 H.J. Wüthrich
0265 E. Demole et al.
0347 P. Pfäffli and H. Hauth
0374 F. Troxler
0474 G. Englert et al.
0478 H. Scheurer et al.
0510 T. Petrzilka and W.G. Lusuardi
0519 T. Petrzilka et al.
0545 H.R. Pfaendler and H. Tanida
0553 S. Teitel et al.
0557 P. Vogel and P. Crabbé
0597 G. Calzaferri et al.
0619 A. Closse and H.-P. Sigg
0625 A. Etournaud and H. Wyler
0681 P. Gilgen et al.
0723 J.E. Heller and A.S. Dreiding
0759 F. Schneider et al.
0875 H. Schlossarczyk et al.
0944 A. Niederhauser et al.
0966 M. Binder and C. Tamm
0983 K. Kokkinos and R. Wizinger
1046 M. Geisel et al.
1062 H.A. Wolf and M.P. Zink
1078 F. Marti et al.
1083 C.W. Jefford et al.
1124 R. Buchecker and C.H. Eugster
1129 P. Ruedi and C.H. Eugster
1225 K. Harzer and W. Pfleiderer
1266 H.O. Bernhard et al.
1303 J.M.J. Tronchet et al.
1310 J.M.J. Tronchet et al.
1318 A. Niederhauser and M. Neuenschwander
1351 N.S. Narasimhan et al.
1457 N. Sarcevic et al.
1483 G. Doucet-Baudry and M.R. Perrot
1485 G. Grethe et al.
1494 J. Gutzwiller and M.R. Uskokovic
1557 P. Kurath et al.
1620 V. Harder and H. Werner
1679 W. Sieber et al.
1708 A. Fürst et al.
1741 H.-U. Gonzenbach et al.
1752 H. Christen and E. Kloster-Jensen
1763 H.W. Gschwend
1787 H. Maag and B.K. Manukian
1812 W. Oppolzer
1819 M. Visconitini and Y. Furuta
1882 L. Re, B. Maurer and G. Ohloff
1908 C. Heizmann et al.
1948 B.R. von Wartburg et al.
1956 B.R. von Wartburg et al.
2007 A. Orahovats et al.
2025 W. Skorianetz and G. Ohloff
2028 K.H. Schulte-Elte
2107 W. Klötzer and W.E. Oberhäusli
2151 W. Skorianetz and G. Ohloff
2227 N. Baumann
2238 R. Sandmeier and C. Tamm
2255 G. Helmchen et al.
2287 W. Oppolzer and V. Prelog
2323 W. Kump and H. Bickel
2348 W. Kump and H. Bickel
2387 M. Binder and C. Tamm
2396 F. Schneider et al.
2405 R. Roulet et al.
2450 R. Baumeler et al.
2479 H. Greuter et al.
2534 M. Moir et al.
2588 H. Giezendanner et al.
2611 H. Giezendanner et al.
2628 B. Winkler-Lardelli
2689 J.M.J. Tronchet and R. Graf
2694 A. Closse and D. Hauser
2698 F. Marti et al.
2719 M. Pinar et al.
2760 J. Sinnreich and H. Batzer
2782 E. Hauser et al.
2796 J. Peter-Katalinic et al.
2827 S. Spengel et al.
2834 M.R. Uskokovic et al.
2882 L. Faber and W. Wiegrebe
2691 S. Shatzmiller et al.
2975 S. Shatzmiller and A. Eschenmoser
2981 U. Koch-Pomeranz et al.
3004 D. Bellus et al.
3044 L. Chardonnens et al.

34- -73, J. Chem. Eng. Data, 18 (1973)
0099 G.Y. Sarkis and S. Al-Azawe
0102 G.Y. Sarkis and S. Al-Azawe
0109 S. Al-Azawe and G.Y. Sarkis
0332 C.R. Raha et al.

35- -73. J. Am. Chem. Soc., 95 (1973)
0137 J. Put and F.C. De Schryver
0146 P.D. Bartlett et al.
0239 M. Koreeda et al.
0240 N. Harada
0250 M.E. Garst and T.A. Spencer
0274 R.C. De Selms and F. Delay

0279 E.M. Burgess and H.R. Penton, Jr.
0463 N. Ishibe, M. Sunami and. M. Odani
0468 W.G. Dauben et al.
0527 W.J. Bernstein et al.
0532 J.J. Partridge et al.
0540 G. Buchi et al.
0598 A.H.-J. Wang et al.
0620 E.L. Allred and K.J. Voorhees
0621 K. Mislow et al.
0682 J.C. Hemminger et al.
0721 A.V. Pocius and J.T. Yardley
0811 H.E. Smith et al.
0826 W.M. Jones et al.
0861 C.D. DeBoer et al.
0942 A.K. Ganguly et al.
0971 W.L. Mandella and R.W. Franck
0980 P.G. Gassman and W.J. Greenlee
1217 J.H. Brewster and R.T. Prudence
1229 R.K. Hill and D.A. Cullison
1253 T. Okuyama et al.
1274 H.E. Zimmerman and M. Viriot-Villaume
1285 B.M. Trost, R.C. Atkins and L. Hoffman
1323 J.R. Barrio and N.J. Leonard
1335 S.M. Kupchan et al.
1342 C.B. Quinn and J.R. Wiseman
1350 T. Sasaki et al.
1429 J.D. Scott and B.R. Russell
1553 D.J. Pasto, A.F. Chen and G. Binsch
1586 H. Tanida and H. Matsumura
1602 R.R. Lii and S.I. Miller
1621 V. Raso and B.D. Stollar
1673 P.Y. Bruice et al.
1676 C.J. Sih et al.
1677 E.F. Ullman et al.
1874 S.F. Nelsen and J.P. Gillespie
1889 R.G. Salomon and J.K. Kochi
1908 S.L. Nickol and J.A. Kampmeier
1945 A. Padwa et al.
1954 A. Padwa et al.
2058 A. Elgavi et al.
2155 H.E. Zimmerman et al.
2230 L.A. Paquette et al.
2303 E.J. Corey and D.S. Watt
2320 N.J. Leonard et al.
2357 P.H. Gebert et al.
2359 R.A. LaBar and W.M. Jones
2379 A.G. Anastassiou and R.C. Griffith
2390 W.M. Horspool et al.
2561 M.P. Cava et al.
2565 R.J. Basaly and J.C. Martin
2603 W. Weyler, Jr. et al.
2664 M. Miyano and C.R. Dorn
2677 A. Vincze et al.
2695 W.A. Sheppard and D.W. Webster
2748 D.H.R. Barton et al.
2749 K.T. Potts and D. McKeough
2750 K.T. Potts and D. McKeough
2940 S.F. Nelsen and J.P. Gillespie
2957 H.E. Zimmerman and J.A. Pincock
2971 R.D. Guthrie and J. Littedrick
2995 S.M. Kupchan et al.
3000 G.M. Strunz and A.S. Court
3019 N.P.B. Dudman and B. Zerner
3043 Z. Yoshida et al.
3070 R.A. Moss and G.M. Love
3201 V. Boekelheide and R.A. Hollins
3239 R.C. Kerber et al.
3246 H.E. Zimmerman and J.A. Pincock
3289 K.E. Hine and R.F. Childs
3310 H.O. House et al.
3324 T.L. Chwang and R. West
3400 T.F. Spande and G.G. Glenner
3415 J.C. Sheehan and R.R. Kurtz
3425 K.G. Hancock and J.D. Kramer
3678 M.M. Cook and C. Djerassi
3692 J.H. Dopper et al.
3818 H. Durr et al.
3932 W.G. Dauben et al.
3947 D.R. Morton and N.J. Turro
3957 T.H. Koch, R.J. Sluski and R.H. Moseley
3970 H.E. Zimmerman and W. Eberbach
3977 H.E. Zimmerman and D.R. Amick
3994 R. Hershfield and G.L. Schmir
4010 N.J. Leonard and K. Ito
4016 S. Greenberg and J.G. Moffatt
4025 A.F. Russell et al.
4054 M. Ikehara and T. Tezuka
4062 S.M. Kupchan and A.J. Liepa
4074 M.J. Robins et al.
4081 H. Hayashi and K. Nakanishi
4096 H. Hart and M. Kuzuya
4099 W.E. Billups and W.Y. Chow
4103 R. Moyori et al.
4292 E.W. Turnblom and T.J. Katz
4320 J. Metcalfe and E.K.C. Lee
4346 R.L. Cargill et al.
4356 J.M. Patterson et al.
4361 N.A. Porter and L.J. Marnett
4379 H.D. Hartzler
4404 A. Hampton et al.
4426 W.E. Truce and C. Lin
4489 S.J. Rehfeld
4565 W.J. Evans et al.
4582 P.J. Garratt et al.
4592 H. Hart and G.M. Love
4599 D.R. Arnold and R.J. Birtwell
4606 H.E. Zimmerman et al.
4611 P.J. Kropp
4647 L.A. Paquette et al.
4687 Y. Ogata and Y. Sawaki
4692 Y. Ogata and Y. Sawaki
4891 M. deC.G. Barrio et al.
4924 T. Hosokawa and P.M. Maitlis
5003 R.M. Forbis and K.L. Rinehart, Jr.
5048 E. Block and J. O'Connor
5072 R.A.G. Smith and J.R. Knowles
5086 O.L. Chapman et al.
5088 W.G. Dauben and J. Ipaktschi
5098 M.A. Wuonola and R.B. Woodward
5288 B.M. Trost and H.C. Arndt
5298 B.M. Trost and M.J. Bogdanowicz
5416 L.T. Scott and W.D. Cotton
5417 E. Sonveaus and L. Ghosez
5604 P.J. Wagner et al.
5632 T. Sasaki et al.
5649 D.A. Buckingham et al.
5662 A. Krantz and C.Y. Lin
5677 W.C. Jones, Jr. et al.
5700 R.A. Johnson and S. Seltzer
5742 M. Shamma et al.

5747 M. Fryberg et al.
5757 J.E. Baldwin and J. Huff
5788 K. Isono et al.
5824 P.M. McCurry, Jr. and K. Abe
5825 E.A. Truesdale and D.J. Cram
5833 C.P. Casey and T.J. Burkhardt
6120 C.B. Quinn and J.R. Wiseman
6197 J. Cornelisse et al.
6277 W.T. Ford and M. Newcomb
6294 H. Hart, D.L. Dean and D.N. Buchanan
6342 R.T. LaLonde et al.
6407 E.C. Taylor et al.
6413 E.C. Taylor et al.
6473 K. Nakanishi et al.
6478 R.J. Boyd et al.
6655 P. Crabbe et al.
6685 C.A. Lewis and R. Wolfenden
6688 R. Breslow et al.
6709 W.I. Ferree, Jr. and B.F. Plummer
6717 L.A. Paquette and M.J. Epstein
6723 R.C. Hahn and D.W. Kurtz
6770 E. Vedejs, M.F. Salomon and P.D. Weeks
6792 C.K. Sauers et al.
6861 S.M. Kupchan et al.
6928 D.B. Larson et al.
7009 M.M. Exner et al.
7101 G. Biggi et al.
7146 F.E. Ziegler and E.B. Spitzner
7161 W.K. Anderson and R.H. Dewey
7174 C.R. Frihart and N.J. Leonard
7320 S.R. Tanny and F.W. Fowler
7325 M.F. Semmelhack, J.S. Foos and S. Katz
7345 A. Bienvenue
7391 J. Kolc and J. Michl
7458 F.E. Ziegler and G.B. Bennett
7501 P.A. Bartlett and W.S. Johnson
7731 C.K. Sauers and H.M. Relles
7752 P.D. McDonald and G.A. Hamilton
7813 B.M. Trost et al.
7821 C.D. Snyder and H. Rapoport
7842 P. Yates et al.
7914 J.W. Pavlik and J. Kwong
7917 D. Arigoni et al.
7925 T. Beetz and R.M. Kellogg
8073 T. Koizuni and P. Haake
8080 G.W. Allen and P. Haake
8114 E.E. Waali and W.M. Jones
8118 L.S. Trzupek
8209 A.D. Wolf and M. Jones, Jr.
8250 V.Y. Merritt et al.
8308 R.T. Borchardt and L.A. Cohen
8313 R.T. Borchardt and L.A. Cohen
8319 R.T. Bor hardt and L.A. Cohen
8380 S.F. Nelsen et al.
8389 K.L. Kirk et al.
8407 L.R. Fedor and B.S.R. Murty
8414 S.J. Benkovic et al.
8427 E. Wenkert et al.
8449 H. Maehr et al.
8468 R.D. Miller et al.
8481 S. Masamune et al.
8483 E.J. Corey and H.S. Sachdev
8512 F.I. Carroll and A. Sobti
8658 G. Wulfsberg et al.
8670 P.S. Mariano and J.-K. Ko
8692 D.G. Farnum et al.
8707 S.F. Nelsen and R.T. Landis,II
8737 R.P. Panzica and L.B. Townsend

36- -73, <u>J. Pharm. Sci.</u>, <u>62</u> (1973)
0510 C.M. Lai and W.D. Mason
0638 N.J. Doorenbos and W.E. Solomons
0910 J. Novotny et al.
0926 S. Ghosal et al.
0937 G.F. Thompson and J.M. Collins
1199 W.E. Meyer et al.
1206 R.M. Wiedhopf
1252 Y.F. Shealy and J.D. Clayton
1381 G.M. Steinberg et al.
1432 Y.F. Shealy and J.D. Clayton
1557 M.H.A. Elgamal
1879 T.O. Soine et al.
1885 J. Philip and D.H. Szulczewski
1897 A.U. De and B.P. Saha
1899 D.D. Gardner and L.R. Garson

39- -73B, <u>J. Chem. Soc., Perkin Trans. II</u>, 1973)
0050 G. Gaviraghi and G. Pagani
0055 S. Del Cima et al.
0063 P. Beltrame et al.
0084 K.L. Cook and A.J. Waring
0095 E.D. Owen and D.M. Allen
0107 S. Kovac et al.
0160 F.T. Boyle and R.A.Y. Jones
0237 A. Fischer and J.N. Ramsay
0264 P. Hanson and R.O.C. Norman
0278 I.H. Sadler and J.A.G. Stewart
0301 Z. Rappoport and A. Gal
0374 J. Bertram et al.
0447 A.G. Evans et al.
0514 M. Rabinovitz and A. Grinvald
0548 A.H. Jackson and B. Naidoo
0599 J. Klein and J.Y. Becker
0616 Z. Rappoport and P. Peled
0710 M.R. Crampton and H.A. Khan
0786 W.J. Bover and P. Zuman
0808 E. Pelizzetti and C. Verdi
0872 R. Iyer et al.
0878 R. Iyer et al.
0885 C.W.N. Cumper et al.
0918 B.C. Challis and A.J. Lawson
1045 Z. Rappoport and D. Ladkani
1101 A. Albert amd H. Taguchi
1125 I.W. Jones and J.C. Tebby
1155 J. Griffiths and M. Lockwood
1160 M.V. Bhatt and M. Ravindranathan
1184 G. Pagani
1312 A. Bowd et al.
1430 P. Carniti et al.
1594 U. Svanholm and V.D. Parker
1729 D. Lloyd et al.
1792 D.E. Grocock et al.
1796 J. Simpson and G.B. Porter
1922 P. De Maria et al.
2075 R.A. Shaw and P. Ward
2111 S.-O. Chua et al.
2151 G.S. Dodd and G. Hallas

39- -73, J. Chem. Soc., Perkin Trans. I, (1973)
0001 R.E. Bowman et al.
0013 T.Y. Au et al.
0022 J. Kitchin and R.J. Stoodley
0026 G. Jones and R.K. Jones
0044 W. Carruthers et al.
0047 G.I. Gregory et al.
0051 W. Carruthers and M.I. Qureshi
0070 P.E. Georghiou and G. Just
0073 B. Zwanenburg et al.
0078 T.J. King et al.
0138 T. Miyamoto et al.
0140 R.K. Bentley et al.
0145 S.O. Badanyan et al.
0155 I. Midgley and C. Djerassi
0163 S. Bradamante and G. Pagani
0167 F.T. Boyle and R.A.Y. Jones
0194 R.I. Crane et al.
0221 C.W. Rees and M. Yelland
0227 H. Carpio, P. Crabbe and J.H. Fried
0235 G. Read and V.M. Ruiz
0244 R.P. Panzica and L.B. Townsend
0268 I. Baxter and W.R. Phillips
0290 M.D. Edge et al.
0308 E. Block and R. Stevenson
0349 G.Y. Moltrasio et al.
0351 J. Ackrell and A.J. Boulton
0368 G. Read and V.M. Ruiz
0391 K. Yamauchi and M. Kinoshita
0393 V. Dave and J.S. Whitehurst
0404 P.J. Machin et al.
0410 D.A. Pulman and D.A. Whiting
0419 E. Collins and P.V.R. Shannon
0453 M.W. Partridge and A. Smith
0456 A. Clader et al.
0465 D.C. Cook and A. Lawson
0469 P.D. Hobbs and P.D. Magnus
0471 T. Kametani et al.
0493 R.G.F. Giles et al.
0509 W.S. Powell and R.A. Heacock
0520 J.R. Mahajan and M.B. Monteiro
0529 K.L. Cook and A.J. Waring
0581 B.V. Burger et al.
0584 B.V. Burger et al.
0590 B.V. Burger and C.F. Garbers
0606 N.R. Barot and J.A. Elvidge
0615 M.H. Tankard and J.S. Whitehurst
0657 R.K. Mackie et al.
0683 J.W. Lown and M.H. Akhtar
0691 G.H. Barnett et al.
0702 R. Fielden et al.
0712 N. Kato et al.
0720 J.S. Cowie et al.
0725 G.R. Pettit and Y. Kamano
0734 P. Jacquignon et al.
0736 J.D. Connolly and I.M.S. Thornton
0739 M. Kleiner
0743 A.G. Fallis et al.
0760 R.E. Bowman et al.
0775 C.M. Elson et al.
0806 L.H. Briggs et al.
0810 P. Crabbe, G.A. Garcia and C. Rius
0817 T. Nishiwaki and F. Fujiyama
0823 J. Bailey and J. Elvidge
0832 D.B. Baird et al.
0850 D.G. Davies, P. Hodge and P. Yates
0853 J.P. Johnston and K.H. Overton
0874 D.H.R. Barton et al.
0881 R. Bonnett and A.F. McDonagh
0888 P.E. Georghiou and G. Just
0891 T. Sato and K. Uno
0900 G. Guest and B.A. Marples
0907 B. Shankar Joshi and V.N. Kamat
0914 K. Ishikawa and T.B.H. McMurry
0927 J.M. Holland and D.W. Jones
0943 D.R. Sutherland et al.
0965 D.M.X. Donnelly et al.
0968 G. Jones et al.
0991 A.W. Johnson et al.
0998 P. Lakshminarayana et al.
1001 Y. Trudelle
1006 K. Buggle et al.
1009 T. Takeshima et al.
1022 F.M. Dean, J. Goodchild and A.W. Hill
1031 D.H.R. Barton et al.
1037 D.H.R. Barton et al.
1041 C.J. Cattanach et al.
1047 W.R. Chan, J.A. Gibbs and D.R. Taylor
1066 D.H. Coy et al.
1079 F.R. Atherton and R.W. Lambert
1089 S. Bien, D. Amith and M. Ber
1108 Z.T. Fomum et al.
1121 J.M. Birchall et al.
1134 G. Gallina et al.
1136 W. Carruthers and M.G. Pellatt
1148 G. Bianchi et al.
1155 A.A.L. Gunatilake and M.U. Sultanbawa
1173 A.W. Fraser and J.R. Lewis
1179 R.M. Letcher and L.R.M. Nhamo
1181 W. Carruthers and R. Pooranamoorthy
1182 R.D. Allan et al.
1187 I. Ager et al.
1204 H. Singh et al.
1209 T. Hirata et al.
1221 A.E. Opara and G. Read
1223 G. Read and V.M. Ruiz
1247 A. Balmain and J.D. Connolly
1251 M.M. Coombs and T.S. Bhatt
1255 M.M. Coombs and M. Hall
1259 J.M. Binhall and M.T. Clark
1263 R.M. Letcher and L.R.M. Nhamo
1266 B.J. Arnold et al.
1277 L. Crombie et al.
1297 G. Brooks, M.A. Shah and G.A. Taylor
1310 H. McNab and D.M. Smith
1314 R.J. Grout et al.
1321 D.M. Brunwin and G. Lowe
1329 A.J. Quillinan and F. Scheinmann
1338 R.M. Acheson and D.F. Nisbet
1349 D.K. Black et al.
1352 M. Moir and R.H. Thomson
1357 R.N. Butler et al.
1361 J.J. Schneider
1366 Y.A. Hirsch and L.Y. Lin
1374 R.S. Jaret et al.
1405 R.D. Chambers and M.Y. Gribble
1411 R.D. Chambers and M.Y. Gribble

1416 Y. Badar et al.
1424 H.J. Callott et al.
1462 M. Neeman, Y. Osawa and T. Mukai
1476 B.E. Cross and R.E. Markwell
1487 J. MacMillan and T.J. Simpson
1493 J.W. Browne et al.
1511 W. Carruthers and D. Whitmarsh
1529 R.L. Edwards and M. Gill
1538 R.L. Edwards and N. Gill
1542 M.G. Barlow et al.
1546 A.R. Battersby et al.
1556 M. Moir and R.H. Thomson
1565 D.H.R. Barton et al.
1567 S. Achmatowicz et al.
1571 D.H.R. Barton et al.
1574 D.H.R. Barton et al.
1580 D.H.R. Barton et al.
1583 R.B. Boar, D.A. Lewis and J.F. Mc-Ghie
1588 D.W. Dunwell and D. Evans
1590 K.D. Barrow et al.
1599 D.A.H. Taylor and F.W. Wehrli
1602 A.S. Bailey and A.J. Buckley
1606 T. Nishiwaki et al.
1615 A. Albert and H. Mizuno
1620 A. Albert and W. Pendergast
1625 A. Albert and W. Pendergast
1629 A. Albert and H. Taguchi
1634 A. Albert
1653 I. Fleming and R.B. Woodward
1658 E.H. Billett and I. Fleming
1661 E.H. Billett et al.
1682 B.G. Gunn and M.F.G. Stevens
1701 G.A. Eagle and D.E.A. Rivett
1710 R.D. Chambers et al.
1720 N.J. Cusack et al.
1731 G.V. Boyd
1737 D.M.X. Donnelly et al.
1745 D.S.H. Smith et al.
1754 D. Nasipuri et al.
1757 A.J. Birch and E.G. Hutchinson
1780 S.K. Roy
1786 T.M. Cresp and M.V. Sargent
1798 M.G. Barlow et al.
1802 A.K. Das Gupta and R.M. Chatterje
1809 A.S. Bailey et al.
1819 H. Minato et al.
1825 J.A. Ballantine
1830 R.D. Burnett and D.N. Kirk
1840 H. Heaney et al.
1843 N. Fukamiya, M. Kato and A. Yoshi-koshi
1848 T. Koga and M. Tomoeda
1855 C.V.Z. Smith et al.
1865 P.B. Desai
1882 A.J. Birch et al.
1903 S.M. Hecht and D. Werner
1913 R.K. Bramely, J. Caldwell and R. Grigg
1921 R.L. Edwards and M. Gill
1940 R. Howe et al.
1943 A.S. Bailey and A.J. Buckley
1958 R.M. Harrison and J.D. Hobson
1960 R.M. Harrison et al.
1967 C.L. Hewwett et al.
1972 I. Granoth et al.
1974 A. Albert and H. Mizuno
1983 D. Kidd and B.V. Swingland
1985 J. Kitchin and R.J. Stoodley
1989 E.W. Colvin et al.
2013 M. Collins and D.R.J. Laws
2016 C.F. Garbers et al.
2019 M. Kleiner
2022 G.R. Brown
2024 G. Lowe and D.D. Ridley
2030 J.A. Donnelly et al.
2037 A. Albert and H. Taguchi
2046 H. McKennis, Jr. et al.
2049 R. Lie and K. Undheim
2076 K.F. Cohen et al.
2083 D. Mukherjee et al.
2091 Y. Tamura, Y. Sumida and M. Ikeda
2095 R.V. Cooms et al.
2105 R.J. Stoodley and N.S. Watson
2113 G.L. Hodgson et al.
2137 A.S. Clegg et al.
2142 R.J. Abraham et al.
2149 J.A.S. Cavaleiro and K.M. Smith
2159 D.A. Frost and G.A. Morrison
2202 G.M. Iskander
2209 C.A. Elliger et al.
2212 K. Takeda, I. Horibe and H. Minato
2220 P. Crabbe et al.
2236 M.M. Coombs et al.
2241 J.A. Claisse et al.
2253 P.J. Garratt et al.
2267 B.E. Ayres et al.
2281 M. Conlon et al.
2319 N. Bosworth and P. Magnus
2327 D.J. Chadwick et al.
2345 C.G. Beddows and D.V. Wilson
2351 J.G. Dingwall et al.
2359 R.V. Davies et al.
2374 I. Baxter and W.R. Phillips
2379 P.J. Roughley and D.A. Whiting
2388 D.A. Frost and G.A. Morrison
2404 G.L. Buchanan and G.A.R. Young
2420 V.M. Kapoor amd A.M. Mehta
2432 J.M.A. Al-Rawi and J.A. Elvidge
2440 C.C. Howard amd R.A.W. Johnstone
2445 D. Lichtenberg et al.
2448 F.G. Baddar et al.
2454 T.K. Sarkar
2460 J. Kitchin and R.J. Stoodley
2478 J.A.S. Cavaleiro et al.
2485 W. Cocker et al.
2499 J.K. Chakrabarti et al.
2506 K. Yamauchi and M. Kinoshita
2513 J.H. van Boom et al.
2517 G.W. Kenner et al.
2523 G.V. Boyd and K. Heatherington
2532 G.V. Boyd and K. Heatherington
2535 T.L. Gilchrist et al.
2551 P. Mussini et al.
2563 D.S.R. East et al.
2569 B. Hankinson et al.
2580 Y. Tamura et al.
2591 K. Ima-Ye and H. Kakisawa
2600 G.M. Strunz et al.
2618 N. Ishibe and Y. Yamaguchi
2637 A.G. Gonzalez et al.
2642 I.W. Farrell et al.

2647 U. Reichman et al.
2659 A. Albert
2671 K.J. Crowley et al.
2707 R.A. Burrell, J.M. Cox and E.G. Savins
2721 P.M. Brown et al.
2725 F.D. Monache et al.
2769 W.K. Warburton et al.
2785 M.T.W. Hearn et al.
2789 M.F. Ansell and S.A. Mahmud
2804 M. Hooper and W.N. Pitkethly
2814 W.L.F. Armarego and B.A. Milley
2818 D.E. A.es et al.
2830 M.J. Begley and N. Whittaker
2853 C.H. Hassall and B.A. Morgan
2862 M.M. Campbell and D.M. Evgenios
2866 M.M. Campbell and D.M. Evgenios
2875 D.E. Brundish and R. Wade
2885 J.E. Dickeson et al.
2901 H.E. Foster and J. Hurst
2907 G. Lowe and H.W. Yeung
2923 A.R. Battersby et al.
2949 R. Muthukrishnan et al.
2975 B.E. Cross and L.J. Zammitt

40- -73, Nippon Kagaku Kaishi, (1973)
0118 K. Konishi et al.
0137 M. Nakayama et al.
0762 S. Kajigaeshi et al.
0771 M. Tabata et al.
0785 M. Ichikawa et al.
0991 A. Yamaguchi et al.
1314 S. Kwon et al.
1328 M. Matsuoka et al.
1505 T. Keumi et al.
1519 M. Takahashi et al.
1738 S. Kuroiwa and S. Ogasawara
1944 S. Kwon et al.
2152 T. Tokumitsu and T. Hayashi
2347 K. Takahashi et al.

42- -73, J. Indian Chem. Soc., 50 (1973)
0129 D.N. Dhar and R.K. Singh
0154 P.B. Talukdar et al.
0260 D. Sen and P. Sengupta
0277 N. Singh and K. Krishan
0329 O.P. Vig et al.
0430 B.H. Patwardhan
0586 F.G. Baddar et al.
0589 F.G. Baddar et al.
0620 D.D. Nanavati
0694 N. Singh and K. Krishan

44- -73, J. Org. Chem., 38 (1973)
0020 T.R. Williams and D.J. Cram
0060 M.P. Cava and I. Noguchi
0095 R.A. Kretchmer and W.M. Schafer
0123 G. Buchi, E. Demole and A.F. Thomas
0146 C.V. Greco and V.G. Grosso
0151 S.M. Kupchan et al.
0153 G.A. Ungefug and C.W. Roberts
0165 Y. Yost and H.R. Gutmann
0178 S.M. Kupchan et al.
0183 S.L. Goldstein and E. McNelis
0187 B. Berrang et al.
0193 A. Rosenthal and D.A. Baker
0198 A. Rosenthal and D.A. Baker
0215 R.E. Moore and H. Rapoport
0237 A.L. Andrews et al.
0264 J.D. Fissekis and F. Sweet
0270 D.G. Clark and E.H. Cordes
0277 J.W. Wilt and T.P. Malloy
0284 A. Padwa and E. Glazer
0322 P. Tomboulian et al.
0338 I. Lalezari et al.
0399 F.S. Prout
0407 D.L. Fields et al.
0431 J.J. Eisch et al.
0437 N. Finch and G.W. Gemenden
0449 A. Walser et al.
0475 D.M. Gale and S.C. Cherkofsky
0507 V. Kalyanaraman and M.V. George
0514 H.O. House et al.
0551 K. Sato et al.
0560 D. De Filippo et al.
0585 H. Chikamatsu and W. Herz
0593 D.H. Shannahoff and R.A. Sanchez
0598 T. Sasaki et al.
0632 E.T. McBee et al.
0639 R.R. Sauers and A.M. De Paolis
0654 D.L. Garling and N.H. Cromwell
0703 Tzoong-Chyh Lee
0728 A.G. Hortmann et al.
0741 H.O. House et al.
0802 M. Yokoyama, Y. Sawachi and T. Isso
0804 G. Montaudo and C.G. Overberger
0808 K. Grohmann et al.
0813 A.J. Lin and A.C. Sartorelli
0815 M.D. Grove and D. Weisleder
0825 A.S. Katner
0831 G. Brancaccio et al.
0841 I. Granoth and A. Kalir
0864 P.J. Garratt et al.
0896 P.J. Wittek et al.
0927 W.E. Parham et al.
0937 T.C. Owen, J.M. Fayadh and S. Chen
0957 L.H. Leenders et al.
0967 D. Caine et al.
0990 J. Zemlicka et al.
1000 H.O. House and M.J. Umen
1015 D.J. Pasto et al.
1051 B.A. Pawson and S. Gurbaxani
1055 S.M. Kupchan and G. Tsou
1095 C. Temple, Jr. et al.
1106 R.N. McDonald, N.L. Wolfe and H.E. Petty
1157 J.S. Swenton et al.
1167 H.O. House, D. Koepsell and W. Jaeger
1178 E. Vedejs et al.
1207 W.E. Parham et al.
1215 N.P. Peet and R.L. Cargill
1218 N.P. Peet et al.
1222 N.P. Peet et al.
1249 E.M. Burgess and W.M. Williams
1253 J.F. Bagli et al.
1260 S.M. Kupchan et al.
1270 F.B. Hirschmann and H. Hirschmann
1283 T. Sasaki et al.
1306 D. Redmore
1316 F.J. Weigert
1325 S.S. Mirvish et al.

1333 A. Padwa et al.
1340 E.T. McBee and K.J. Sienkowski
1367 W.L. Collier and R.S. Macomber
1398 H.O. House and D.G. Melillo
1420 S.M. Kupchan et al.
1439 A.G. Anderson, Jr. et al.
1445 A.G. Anderson, Jr. et al.
1451 H.H. Wasserman et al.
1470 D. Kristol and R. Shapiro
1478 P. Crabbe et al.
1483 D.R. Coulson
1504 R. Littell and G.R. Allen, Jr.
1559 J.R. Grunwell et al.
1562 T.E. Young and L.J. Heitz
1583 E.E. Schweizer et al.
1588 M.M. Martin and J.M. King
1591 T.R. Bosin et al.
1641 R.R. Wittekind et al.
1648 T. Sasaki et al.
1697 A. Wissner and J. Meinwald
1703 V. Usieli and S. Sarel
1726 W.J. Gensler and P.H. Solomon
1743 G.M. Laidlow et al.
1749 T.J. Clark
1751 W.J. Middleton et al.
1759 M. Salmon, E. Diaz and A. Ortega
1762 T. Kubota and H. Sakurai
1767 A.T. Bottini et al.
1769 K.T. Potts and A.J. Elliott
1782 J. Zrilichovsky and U. Fotadar
1824 B. Frydman et al.
1836 H.P. Albrecht et al.
1841 G. Trummlitz and J.G. Moffatt
1846 S.M. Kupchan et al.
1853 S.M. Kupchan et al.
1886 L.A. Paquette and M.J. Broadhurst
1893 L.A. Paquette and M.J. Broadhurst
1933 D.F. Barringer, Jr. et al.
1944 J. Cason et al.
1959 A.G. Anastassiou et al.
1971 W. Nagai, K.L. Kirk and L.A. Cohen
1993 B.A.M. Oude-Alink et al.
2043 D. MacKay et al.
2049 E. Abushanab et al.
2066 U. Reichman et al.
2073 A. Rosowsky and K.N. Chen
2077 H. Tanida et al.
2093 J.G. Whitney and K.T. Lee
2099 F.R. Stermitz and D.K. Williams
2117 G.L. Lange et al.
2125 R.L. Cargill and T.E. Jackson
2156 G.E. Wilson, Jr. and R. Albert
2169 H.W. Gschwend et al.
2189 S.M. Kupchan et al.
2202 Y. Kamano and G.R. Pettit
2236 H.A. Brandman and R.T. Conley
2238 E.C. Taylor et al.
2249 C. Lin et al.
2254 H. Newman
2257 B. Gorewit and M. Rosenblum
2261 R.D. Stephens
2281 V.M. Csizmadia et al.
2287 M. Ohoka et al.
2291 J.L. Neumeyer and C.B. Boyce
2294 M.L. Casey et al.
2328 M.L. Lewbart
2335 M.L. Lewbart
2351 D.E. Portlock et al.
2355 M. Frangopol et al.
2383 W. Fenical et al.
2394 M.P. Cava, I. Noguchi and K.T. Buck
2397 F.L. Lam and J.C. Parham
2421 A.G. Anastassiou and E. Reichmanis
2425 J.K. Elwood
2430 J.K. Elwood
2478 C.W. Spangler et al.
2501 L. Toke et al.
2540 E.S. Rothman, G.G. Moore and S.S. Hecht
2544 W.F. Winecoff et al.
2587 Y. Yanuka and G. Halperin
2590 G. Lepore et al.
2600 L.A. Carpino et al.
2604 L. De Vries
2614 R. Richter and H. Ulrich
2623 V.J. Traynelis et al.
2629 V.J. Tranelis et al.
2698 J.P. Morizur et al.
2728 D.P. Chakraborty et al.
2732 J.W. Huffman and J.J. Gibbs
2756 D.R. Dimmel
2783 J.W. Burnham et al.
2809 F.A. Davis et al.
2814 H. Wynberg and M. Cabell
2821 J.E. McMurry and A.P. Coppolino
2831 G.W. Gribble and R.B. Nelson
2834 J.A. Van Allan et al.
2838 C.F. Bernasconi et al.
2870 S.R. Wilson and R.B. Turner
2882 L.J. Dolby and S.J. Nelson
2896 T. Sasaki et al.
2913 J.G. Cannon et al.
2939 J.A. Moore et al.
2945 F.B. Culp et al.
2949 F. Bartow, A. Nabeya and J.A. Moore
2954 A. Nabeya et al.
2982 J.H. MacMillan and S.S. Washburne
3034 J.C. Sheehan and F.S. Guziec, Jr.
3046 A.A. Watson et al.
3051 J. Beeby and P.J. Garratt
3064 I. Agranat et al.
3073 N.H. Fischer and H.-N. Lin
3077 A. Walser et al.
3087 K.T. Potts and J. Kane
3094 G.R. Krow et al.
3122 C.K. Fay et al.
3136 S.R. Alpha
3145 J. Haywood-Farmer et al.
3149 R. Curci et al.
3179 T.C. Jain et al.
3226 J.R. Obst and J.M. Harkin
3229 N. Cohen et al.
3239 Z.G. Hajos and D.R. Parrish
3244 Z.G. Hajos and D.R. Parrish
3250 L.A. Paquette et al.
3257 L.A. Paquette et al.
3277 G.L. Szekeres et al.
3302 J.P. Ferris amd T.J. Ryan
3311 R.A. Abramovitch and T. Takaya
3324 R.J. Sundberg and H.F. Russell

3350 F.J. McEvoy and G.R. Allen, Jr.
3367 U. Reichman et al.
3375 D.P. Weeks and F.H. Field
3383 D.P. Weeks et al.
3418 H. Hart, M. Verma and I. Wang
3425 I.W. Elliott, Jr. and S.L. Evans
3428 T.A. Bryson
3431 J.W. Westley et al.
3433 J. Correia
3485 K.T. Potts and R.K.C. Hsia
3487 R.J. Friary et al.
3502 A. Walser et al.
3507 P.D. Halphen and T.C. Owen
3525 J.A. Katzenellenbogen et al.
3537 Z. Yoshida et al.
3542 W.J. McGahren et al.
3592 S.F. Nelsen and J.P. Gillespie
3615 J.L. Isidor and R.L. McKee
3663 D. Caine and F.N. Tuller
3670 G.H. Rasmusson, A. Chen and G.E. Arth
3685 M. Kocor et al.
3688 M. Kocor and J. St. Pyrek
3704 L.M. Lerner
3797 E.P. Burrows, S.L. Jones and H.E. Smith
3805 R.K. Mrogan, Jr., et al.
3812 F. Hasan and J. Rocek
3829 R.L. Cargill et al.
3832 W.K. Anderson and E.J. LaVoie
3836 K. Houk and L.J. Luskus
3868 R.A. Coburn and B. Bhooshan
3872 M.K. Eberle et al.
3874 D.T. Connor and M. von Strandtmann
3878 I.L. Doerr and R.E. Willette
3893 H.O. House and M.J. Umen
3928 V. Boekelheide and P.H. Anderson
3937 S.J. Valenty and P.S. Skell
3975 M.P. Cava and M.A. Sprecker
3990 Z.-I. Yoshida et al.
3993 R.H. Reuss and L.H. Winters
3995 R.Y. Ning et al.
4007 A. Padwa and W. Koehn
4044 F.J. McEvoy and G.R. Allen, Jr.
4068 E. Wenkert et al.
4087 P.Y. Johnson et al.
4100 T. Sasaki et al.
4167 C.K. Bradsher and L.S. Davies
4204 G.A. Ellestad et al.
4206 R.Y. Ning et al.
4211 S.K. Roy
4226 G. Glaros and N.H. Cromwell
4259 P.R. Farina and H. Tieckelmann
4281 N.P. Peet and R.L. Cargill
4295 A. Pocker
4305 E. Wenkert et al.
4324 Y. Tamura et al.
4342 N. Carrasco et al.
4348 G. Buchi et al.
4383 C.O. Okafor
4386 C.O. Okafor
4402 E.S. Lewis and E.C. Nie
4404 W.C. Fleming et al.
4412 N. Finch et al.
4440 T.S. Dobashi et al.
4457 T.M. Harris, J.V. Hay and E. Quarterman

46- -73, J. Phys. Chem., 77 (1973)
0482 J.C. Nnadi et al.
0831 G.M. Wyman and B.M. Zarnegar
0910 P.A. Mullen and M.K. Orloff
1830 M. O'Sullivan and A.C. Testa
2160 K. Akagane et al.
2520 K. Kimura et al.
2652 E.V. Patton and R. West

47- -73, J. Polymer Sci., Pt. A-1, 11 (1973)
0119 J. Lal and E.F. Devlin
1107 D.R. Parnell and D.P. Macaione
2143 F.W. Harris and S.O. Norris
2225 H.M. Relles

48- -73, J. prakt. Chem., 315 (1973)
0008 G. Langbein et al.
0039 K. Gewald and J. Schael
0044 K. Gewald et al.
0097 H.G.O. Becker et al.
0144 H. Hartmann and I. Reuther
0149 D. Cech et al.
0185 T.R. Vakula et al.
0202 N.A. Ibrahim et al.
0300 N.R. El-Rayyes
0353 S.M.R. Omran and N.S. Harb
0375 S.M. Abdel-Wahhab et al.
0382 H. Dorn
0419 N. Latif et al.
0492 A.R.A. Raouf
0497 H. Hartmann et al.
0517 B. Teichmann et al.
0539 K. Gewald et al.
0549 F. Pragst
0649 K. Issleib and H.-P. Abicht
0679 K. Gewald et al.
0711 M. Schulz and G. West
0717 M. Augustin et al.
0725 H. Böttcher et al.
0739 G. Adam et al.
0779 K. Gewald and H.-J. Jänsch
0796 I. Hahnemann and W. Pritzkow
0810 S. Dähne and F. Schob
0887 C. Kipping et al.
0895 G. Kowollik et al.
0915 G. Wagner and B. Dietzsch
0993 T.P. Ivanov and D.M. Mondeshka
1105 M. Scholz et al.
1131 H.G.O. Becker et al.
1152 W.I. Awad et al.
1161 G.W. Fischer and P. Schneider

49- -73, Monatsh. Chem., 104 (1973)
0274 J. Paul and K. Schlögl
0312 M. Pailer and H. Grünhaus
0402 P. Meindl and H. Tuppy
0415 W. Klötzer et al.
0447 S. Penades et al.
0633 P. Shammugam et al.
0644 E. Langer and H. Lehner
0911 F. Kuffer et al.
1008 H. Griengl and W. Sieber
1224 P. Hrnciar and R. Sokolova
1315 V. Bohmer et al.

54- -73, Rec. trav. chim., 92 (1973)
0237 H. DeKoning et al.
0553 W.H. Laarhoven and T. Cuppen
0651 W.H. Laarhoven and M.H. De Jong
0683 H. DeKoning et al.
0705 W.H. Dekker
0762 W. Hagens et al.
0845 H. Polman et al.
0985 P.C. Traas and H. Boelens
1169 H. Kolind-Andersen et al.
1267 C.C. Bolt and F.J. Zeelen
1377 P.A. LeClerg et al.

56- -73, Roczniki Chem., 47 (1973)
0181 L. Musial and A.B. Bojarska
0415 J. Gronowska and E. Pilat
0943 W.E. Hahn and B. Muszkiet
1053 T. Lesiak and S. Nilek
1191 J. Gronowska et al.
1205 M. Draminski and B. Fiszer
1275 J. Ciba et al.
1281 B. Sila et al.
1645 L. Strekowski
1735 B. Macierewicz
1943 F. Kazmierczak et al.
1949 J. Gronowska et al.
2101 J. Gronowska et al.
2235 W. Zankowska-Jasinska and J. Eilmes
2361 W. Czuba and M. Wozniak

57- -73B, Science, 180 (1973)
0307 J.N. Kaplanis et al.

57- -73C, Science, 181 (1973)
0758 R.M. Eppley and W.J. Bailey

59- -73, Spectrochim. Acta, 29A (1973)
0139 C. Klofutar et al.
0161 A. Arcoria et al.
0365 S.P. Moulik et al.
0803 T.J. Sekuur and P. Kranenburg
0807 T.J. Sekuur and P. Kranenburg
0981 V.P. Senthilnathan and S. Singh
1069 C. Klofutar et al.
1601 A. Arcoria et al.

60- -73, J. Chem. Soc., Faraday Trans I, (1973)
0555 G.V. Buxton and R.M. Sellers

61- -73, Ber. Bunsengesellschaft. Phys. Chem., 77 (1973)
0281 H. Rau and H. Bisle

62- -73, Z. phys. Chem. (Leipzig), 253 (1973)
0289 I.M. Issa et al.

63- -73, Z. physiol. Chem., 354 (1973)
0421 M. Schonharting et al.
1307 W. Schaefer and E. Bauer
1611 G. Swoboda and W. Hasselbach

64- -73B, Z. Naturforsch., 28b (1973)
0196 P. Shanmugam and R. Palaniappan
0433 J.W. Buchler and H.H. Schneehage
0468 R. Gopal et al.
0471 W.H. Gündel et al.
0535 T. Eicher and R. Graf
0610 A.H. Abou El Ela et al.
0662 H.D. Scharf and H. Leismann

64- -73C, Z.Naturforsch., 28c (1973)
0255 W. Steglich and E. Topfer-Petersen
0260 A. Guiotto et al.
0354 W. Steglich et al.
0436 S. Imre
0675 G. Walter and E. Hecker

65- -73, Zhur. Obshchei Khim., 43 (1973) (English translation pagination)
0087 S.V. Krivun et al.
0121 V.N. Aleksandrov et al.
0403 L.N. Volovel'skii and I.I. Kuz'menko
0409 L.N. Polyachenko et al.
0638 V.D. Orlov et al.
0663 E.V. Popova and G.S. Grinenko
0688 G.A. Tolstikov et al.
0877 B.M. Gutsulyak and P.D. Romanko
0885 L.I. Fleiderman et al.
0918 V.M. Berezovskii and L.M. Mel'nikova
0923 V.M. Potapov et al.
0927 V.M. Potapov et al.
1118 O.P. Shitov et al.
1226 A.N. Pudovik et al.
1336 I.N. Chernyuk et al.
1340 G.T. Pilyugin et al.
1397 M.G. Voronkov and S.F. Pavlov
1400 V.A. Izmail'skii and O.I. Lobova
1574 G.D. Glebova and V.M. Berezovskii
1578 G.D. Glebova and V.M. Berezovskii
1583 V.D. Rumyantseva et al.
1587 A.F. Mironov et al.
1593 V.D. Rumyantseva et al.
1699 M.V. Kashutina
2005 V.V. Zverev et al.
2010 L.E. Marinina et al.
2038 O.I. Volkova et al.
2047 L.P. Davydova et al.
2058 G.A. Tolstikov et al.
2164 V.V. Dorokhova et al.
2285 L.S. Tul'chinskaya et al.
2301 A.A. Apsit et al.
2627 B.I. Stepanov et al.
2718 Y.A. Maletin et al.

67- -73, J. Structural Chem. U.S.S.R., (1973)(English translation)
0061 E.N. Kharlamova et al.

69- -73, Biochemistry, 12 (1973)
0194 J.T. Kuzmierek et al.
1010 J.P. Miller et al.
1520 D.T. Gibson et al.
1845 L.J. Bowie et al.
2011 J.F. Brandts and L.J. Kaplan
2179 M.J. Robins and E.M. Trip
2879 R.S. Wilson and M.P. Mertes
3023 J. Bieth et al.
3328 A. Hampton et al.
3938 L. Votila

3956 G.N. Bennett et al.
3962 P.F. Torrence et al.
4074 D.J. Brunswick and B.S. Cooperman
4154 E.N. Hudson and G. Weber
4790 F. Ishikawa et al.
4992 E.F. Elstner et al.
5084 G. Stohrer et al.
5310 J.P. Miller et al.

70- -73, Izvest. Akad. Nauk S.S.S.R., 22 (1973)(English translation)
0034 V.A. Mironov and A.A. Akhrem
0088 A.V. Zakharychev et al.
0155 N.Y. Grigor'eva et al.
0212 S.L. Ioffe et al.
0346 V.A. Mironov et al.
0357 V.A. Mironov et al.
0527 A.A. Akhrem et al.
0611 A.A. Akhrem et al.
0811 A.A. Akhrem et al.
1029 E.A. El'perina et al.
1033 B.P. Gusev et al.
1042 N.K. Levchenko et al.
1057 N.S. Padyukova et al.
1077 A.A. Akhrem et al.
1083 A.A. Akhrem et al.
1237 M.V. Mavrov and V.F. Kucherov
1258 A.A. Akhrem et al.
1263 A.A. Akhrem et al.
1271 V.S. Oseledehik et al.
1380 S.I. Zav'yalov et al.
1574 S.N. Ananchenko et al.
1578 A.A. Akhrem et al.
1617 V.P. Yur'ev et al.
1624 V.P. Yur'ev et al.
1641 S.I. Zav'yalov et al.
1745 A.A. Akhrem et al.
1790 A.A. Akhrem et al.
1794 A.A. Akhrem et al.
1825 V.A. Kuznetsov et al.
1859 S.I. Zav'yalov et al.
1959 Z.A. Krasnaya et al.
1963 E.P. Prokof'ev et al.
1984 V.A. Mironov et al.
1998 B.D. Sviridov et al.
2006 V.M. Belikov et al.
2017 Y.L. Gol'dfarb and M.A. Kalik
2027 V.N. Piottukh-Peletskii et al.
2036 S.I. Zav'yalov et al.
2301 Z.A. Krasnaya et al.
2308 S.I. Zav'yalov and G.V. Pokhvisneva
2318 A.Y. Tikhanov and L.B. Volodarskii
2478 Z.A. Krasnaya et al.
2505 S.I. Zav'yalov et al.
2566 S.I. Zav'yalov et al.
2593 E.I. Bagrii et al.
2717 I.P. Romm et al.

73- -73, Coll. Czech. Chem. Comm., 38 (1973)
0046 M. Bleha and D. Lim
0115 J.O. Jilek et al.
0224 J. Durmis et al.
0289 M. Uher and J. Jendrichovsky
0565 V. Cerny et al.
0599 J.O. Jilek et al.
0620 M. Uher and J. Jendrichovsky
0739 L. Novotny et al.
0913 L. Kohout and J. Fajkos
1084 V. Benesova et al.
1091 V. Zikan et al.
1168 Z. Arnold
1179 E. Klintova et al.
1190 J.O. Jilek et al.
1381 R. Wightman and A. Holy
1398 J. Joska et al.
1438 R. Kotva et al.
1571 A. Rybar and L. Stibranyi
1579 K. Sindelar et al.
1596 V. Bartl et al.
1602 M. Rajsner et al.
1609 K. Antos et al.
1614 V. Simmek and A. Klasek
1693 V. Bartl et al.
1700 R. Kada et al.
1705 A. Jurasek and J. Kovac
1712 F. Santavy and L. Hruban
1804 M. Holub et al.
1809 R. Frimm et al.
2132 L. Dubravkova et al.
2137 K. Sindelar et al.
2301 V. Bartl et al.
2484 K. Sindelar et al.
2492 R. Mickova
2504 A. Klasek et al.
2633 Z. Arnold et al.
2641 Z. Arnold and J. Sauliova
2760 L. Kohout
2768 Z.J. Vejdelek et al.
2778 V. Bartl et al.
2788 J. Bielavsky and F. Ornst
2799 J. Hrbek, Jr. et al.
2976 H. Velgova and V. Cerny
2989 Z.J. Vejdelek et al.
3181 H. Hrebabecky et al.
3312 K. Haisova et al.
3321 K. Sindelar et al.
3479 J. Kuthan et al.
3514 J. Slavik and L. Dolejs
3616 A. Mistr et al.
3879 K. Sindelar et al.
3912 A. Holy

77- -73, J. Chem. Soc., Chem. Comm. (1973)
0013B D.R. Juliano and G.D. Tringham
0019 B.M. Adger et al.
0035 J.P. Cress and D.M. Forkey
0078 E.E. Garcia et al.
0099 L. Cariello et al.
0119 P. Crabbé et al.
0150 G.G. Abott and D. Leaver
0202 M. Novotny and S.J. Lippard
0229 G. Biggi and F. Pietra
0265 L. Crombie et al.
0330 D. Bryce-Smith et al.
0344 J.E. Baldwin and O.W. Lever, Jr.
0409 L.A. Paquette and M.J. Kukla
0464 C.C. Howard et al.
0492 K. Hori et al.
0495 V. Skaic and M. Hohnjec
0501 R.G. Carlson et al.
0523 G. Biggi et al.
0526 I.G. Guest et al.

0539 M. Maeda and M. Kojima
0555 R. Marchelli and L.C. Vining
0564 M. Tanabe and D.F. Crowe
0566 M.N. Galbraith and D.H.S. Horn
0579 J.J. Artus et al.
0601 A.G. Anastassiou and R.L. Elliott
0614 N.S. Bhacca et al.
0642 D.L. Trepanier et al.
0665 R.M. Acheson and G. Paglietti
0684 J.L. Wong and M.F. Zady
0686 R.G.S. Ritchie et al.
0703 R. Miura et al.
0706 W.J. Evans and M.F. Hawthorne
0737 L. Canonica et al.
0740 M. Shamma and L. Toke
0752 Y. Watanabe and Y. Mizuhara
0806 J.R. Davy and J.A. Reiss
0812 R.M. McGrath et al.
0831 G.R. Newkome and J.M. Robinson
0833 K.T. Potts and J. Baum
0859 S. Sarel et al.
0881 R.K. Murray, Jr. and D.L. Goff
0910 V. Mark
0917 T. Fujii et al.
0926 K. Nagarajan and R.K. Shah
0937 R.E. Moore and G. Yost

78- -73, Tetrahedron, 29 (1973)
0013 J.P. Kutney et al.
0021 J. Meney et al.
0031 J.F. Blount et al.
0057 M. Sekiya et al.
0085 P.B. Baker et al.
0101 M.K. Saxena, M.N. Gudi and M.V. George
0107 P.S. Steyn
0121 A.S. Shawali and H.M. Hassaneen
0161 A.J.H. Klunder and B. Zwanenburg
0205 R.A. Corral et al.
0213 S.F. Dyke et al.
0221 M. Kamel et al.
0239 T.H. Campion and G.A. Morrison
0245 P.K. Grant et al.
0253 G. Seitz and W. Klein
0275 H. Sato et al.
0279 N.L. Weinberg and B. Belleau
0309 S.K. Das Gupta and A.S. Sarma
0321 N.O. Vesterager et al.
0353 M. Weissenberg et al.
0359 B.A. Brady et al.
0391 P.M. Atlani et al.
0403 E.L. Ghisalberti et al.
0413 J.P. Girault, P. Scribe and G. Dana
0419 S.V. Kessar and G.S. Joshi
0519 Dun-Mei Yang et al.
0529 T. Sasaki et al.
0533 H. Ogawa, N. Shimojo and H. Kato
0553 R.J. Abraham et al.
0569 A.S. Narula and S. Dev
0603 C.A. Mudry and A.R. Fraca
0629 R. Tschesche et al.
0639 G. Doleschall and K. Lempert
0669 G.F. Smith and D.A. Taylor
0683 S.N. Balasubrahmanyam and M. Balasubramanian
0715 T.R. Kasturi et al.
0795 J.R. Wilt et al.
0809 H. Ogawa and M. Kubo
0823 E. Kondo and T. Mitsugi
0857 S.F. Dyke et al.
0867 C.M. Lok et al.
0879 R. Addink and W. Berends
0891 T.R. Govindachari et al.
0903 P.R. Jefferies and G.K. Worth
0921 U. Kucklander
0935 J.R. Martin et al.
0977 A. Banerji and P.C. Ghosh
1031 R. Michelot and H. Khedija
1037 J.A. Donnelly et al.
1063 Y. Tamura et al.
1083 A.A. Akhrem et al.
1109 J.R. Bull and A.J. Hodgkinson
1119 G. Mehta, U.R. Nayak and Sukh Dev
1131 J. Brunton et al.
1169 K. Utimoto, M. Tamura and K. Sisido
1185 Y. Sakaino et al.
1215 R. Storer and D.W. Young
1217 R. Storer and D.W. Young
1227 J.F. Biellmann et al.
1237 J.F. Biellmann et al.
1243 J.L. Montero and F. Winternitz
1265 M. Shamma and J.F. Nugent
1285 T. Tanaka and I. Iijima
1291 A.S.R. Anjaneyulu et al.
1321 R.S.D. Mittal et al.
1353 E. Glotter et al.
1365 B.S. Joshi et al.
1379 J. DeWit and H. Wynberg
1393 P.J. Vroegop et al.
1399 I. Agranat
1429 B. Robinson and M. Uppal Zubair
1441 D.F. Zinkel and B.P. Spalding
1447 D. Taub et al.
1465 W.A. Slusarchyk et al.
1515 T. Murae et al.
1591 L. Dehennin and R. Scholler
1605 A.G. Gonzalez et al.
1611 C.H. Evans, A.S. Jones and R.T. Walker
1615 R. Mecholam et al.
1621 G. Magnusson et al.
1625 V. Calo et al.
1659 J.W. Cornforth et al.
1691 A.W.J.D. Dekkers et al.
1697 I. Gosney and D. Lloyd
1721 R. Storer et al.
1745 C.P. Ivanov and D.M. Mondeshka
1773 Y. Shizuri et al.
1795 Y. Shizuri et al.
1801 T. Kondo, H. Nakai and T. Goto
1833 L. Schrader
1843 P. Caubere et al.
1851 P. Caubere et al.
1857 P. Caubere et al.
1865 E. Casadevall et al.
1949 M. Shamma et al.
1975 A.T. Bottini et al.
1991 H. Ishii et al.
2005 N. Ishibe, M. Sunami and M. Odani
2015 N. Aimi et al.
2027 T. Kametani et al.

2047 R. Caputo et al.
2065 J. Quintana et al.
2077 L. Dalgaard et al.
2087 L. Bang et al.
2097 L. Bang and G. Ourisson
2119 K.S. Balachandran and M.V. George
2135 J. Kool, H. Wynberg and R.M. Kellogg
2153 R. Fuks
2245 M.P. Cava et al.
2293 A.S. Jones, P. Lewis and S.F. Withers
2297 R. Hanna et al.
2327 S. Rozen et al.
2337 S. Smolinski et al.
2343 J. Geigert et al.
2359 Y. Tamura et al.
2373 M. Korat and D. Ginsburg
2383 R. Rubinstein et al.
2387 R. Giger et al.
2393 R. Giger et al.
2395 R. Balasubramanian and M.V. George
2405 G. Bianchi et al.
2449 J. Fabian
2553 J.D. Martin
2561 T.A. Modro and A. Piekos
2565 G. Cimino et al.
2575 T.G. Payne and P.R. Jefferies
2645 J.P. Kutney et al.
2683 M.L. Mihailovic et al.
2699 P.-T. Cheng et al.
2703 J. Geigert et al.
2715 M.D. Grove et al.
2731 D.G. Carlson et al.
2781 E. Koltai et al.
2783 E. Koltai et al.
2795 E. Koltai and K. Lempert
2807 A.H. Haines
2811 S.K. Talapatra et al.
2821 H. Monti and M. Bertrand
2943 D. Mowat and R.D.H. Murray
2973 A.G. Anderson, Jr. and D.R. Fagerburg
2997 J.D. Martin
3023 J. Kitchin and R.J. Stoodley
3091 T.R. Govindachari et al.
3099 T.M. Smalberger et al.
3159 M. Ruccia et al.
3173 G. Subrahmanyam and T. Dutta Roy
3177 G. Adam
3185 I. Bally et al.
3241 H. Ogoshi et al.
3271 Y. Tanaka et al.
3297 R. Aneja et al.
3337 T. Matsuura et al.
3347 A.C. Jain and M.K. Zutshi
3357 F. LeGoffic et al.
3379 S.F. Khoo et al.
3399 C. Guimon et al.
3425 N.S. Kobrina et al.
3497 S. Mannen and H.A. Itano
3553 G. Rio, D. Bricout and L. Lacombe
3571 G.Y. Simig et al.
3579 T. Bolsman and T.J. DeBoer
3599 D. Gonbeau et al.
3609 H. Ledon et al.
3631 J.P. Gesson and J.C. Jacquesy
3687 S. Huneck et al.
3699 G.L. Bartolini et al.
3703 N. Takeda et al.
3721 S. Seo et al.
3761 T.P. Karpetsky and E.H. White
3781 E.N. Marvell et al.
3797 E.N. Marvell et al.
3813 M. Ogawa, M. Takagi and T. Matsuda
3819 N. Miyamoto and H. Nozaki
3833 J. Goldman et al.
3881 S.F. Dyke et al.
3903 R. Grigg and J.L. Jackson
3909 L.R. Row et al.
3929 T. Bolsam and T.J. DeBoer
4013 M. Keller and G. Snatzke
4039 G.G. Lyle et al.
4045 M.K. Eberle et al.
4049 M.K. Eberle and G.G. Kahle
4053 J. Pataki
4071 K.L. Stuart et al.
4103 T.R. Kasturi et al.
4111 D.A. Ben-Efraim
4137 N.G. Bisset, B.C. Das and J. Parello
4153 M. Barczai-Beke et al.
4159 R.K. Bramley et al.
4205 E.B. Pedersen and S.-O. Lawesson
4225 G. Bauduin and Y. Pietrasanta
4241 H. Martens et al.
4251 A. Svendsen and P.M. Boll
4259 F. Cafieri et al.
4263 S.A.G. DeGraaf and U.K. Pandit
4271 G. Prota and E. Ponsiglione
4307 B.H. Freeman et al.

80- -73, <u>Revue Roumaine Chim.</u>, <u>18</u> (1973)
0263 M. Iovu and A. Angelescu
0589 P. Spagu and E. Ivan
0677 D. Sugiu
0685 I. Simiti et al.
0723 L. Beu and J. Russu
0883 M. Iovu and G. Cimpeanu
1005 M. Raileanu and I. Radulian
1379 S. Majer and E.L. Eliel
1617 I. Nicullescu-Duvaz et al.
1777 S. Sugiu and Z. Gyorfi
1781 S. Arramovici et al.

82- -73B, <u>J. Mol. Spectr.</u>, <u>46</u> (1973)
0419 E.R. Farnsworth and G.W. King

82- -73C, <u>J. Mol. Spectr.</u>, <u>47</u> (1973)
0469 D.B. Larson and S.P. McGlynn

83- -73, <u>Arch. Pharm.</u>, <u>306</u> (1973)
0152 D. Suciu
0257 H.J. Kallmayer
0299 G. Wurm
0360 J. Schnekenburger
0366 E. Graf and K.C. Liu
0389 G. Seitz and H. Mönnighoff
0446 F. Eiden and U. Kuckländer
0463 H.H. Otto
0481 H. Auterhoff and W. Wiemann
0500 J. Knabe and R. Saggau
0592 J. Knabe and A. Frie

0641 C.H. Brieskorn and H.H. Fröhlich
0648 J. Knabe and A. Frie
0784 J. Knabe and R. Dörr
0813 B. Unterhalt and U. Pindur
0857 K.E. Schulte et al.
0872 F. Eiden and J. Iwan
0881 H. Auterhoff and J. Bertram

87- -73, J. Med. Chem., 16 (1973)
0034 S.E. Parker and J. Weinstock
0037 R. Vince and R.G. Isakson
0044 H. Zinnes et al.
0065 R.W. Guthrie et al.
0139 C. Il Hong et al.
0176 E.J. Glamkowski et al.
0183 P.T. Berkowitz et al.
0254 C.F. Schwender et al.
0257 R.W. Guthrie et al.
0289 C.N. Eaton et al.
0294 A. Bloch et al.
0352 J.F. Blount et al.
0358 K. Kikugawa et al.
0365 A. Giner-Sorolla et al.
0407 T. Jen et al.
0416 G. Firnau et al.
0429 J. Fried and C.H. Lin
0499 I.C. Calder et al.
0512 J. Scott and A. Boris
0524 S. Nesnow et al.
0557 B. Cavalleri et al.
0568 W.F. Johns and L.M. Hofmann
0592 M.A. Iorio et al.
0638 W. Korytnyk and S.C. Srivastava
0643 R.A. Sharma et al.
0647 R.A. LeMahieu et al.
0649 E.L. Shapiro et al.
0671 M. Gotz et al.
0697 E.C. Roberts and Y.F. Shealy
0839 L.J. Chinn and L.M. Hofmann
0869 A. Rosowsky et al.
0913 S.M. Kupchan and H.W. Altland
0940 R.E. Haron et al.
0956 C.I. Hong and G.H. Chheda
0984 A. Giner-Sorolla et al.
1042 D.L. Klayman et al.
1056 G. Alonso et al.
1075 K.H. Boswell et al.
1096 W. Korytnyk et al.
1188 G.R. Gough et al.
1223 J.L. Neumeyer et al.
1228 J.L. Neumeyer et al.
1256 R.B. Moffett and A.D. Rudzik
1272 G.J. Durant et al.
1296 H. Berner et al.

88- -73, Tetrahedron Letters, (1973)
0001 R.D. Allan et al.
0007 R.D. Allan et al.
0009 M.D. Gheorghiu et al.
0017 T. Norin et al.
0029 G. Massiot et al.
0037 A. Ichihara et al.
0043 T. Miyamoto and Y. Odaira
0047 I. Murata and K. Nakasuji
0113 K. Sugiura et al.
0139 E.T. Tinelli et al.
0159 C.V. Ristagno and R.G. Lawler
0197 H.D. Becker and T. Bremholt
0209 P.M. Greaves et al.
0223 G. Markl and D.E. Fischer
0299 G.E. Van Lear et al.
0313 W. Fenical et al.
0335 C. Nishino and T. Mitsui
0361 H. Ogawa et al.
0365 K. Takayama et al.
0411 S. Ranganathan and H. Raman
0451 N.A. Abraham
0539 G.I. Borodkin et al.
0597 O. Tsuge and H. Samura
0603 J.J. Koenig and C.G. Wermuth
0669 E. Dunkelblum and S. Brenner
0775 M. Shamma and J.L. Moniot
0803 C. Tani et al.
0813 H. deNijs and W.N. Speckamp
0821 F. Serratosa and P. Sole
0861 G. Maier and B. Hoppe
0865 G. Tuchscherer et al.
0877 I. Kawamoto et al.
0881 D. Uemura and Y. Hirata
0891 P. Bouchet et al.
0903 A. Picot and X. Lusinchi
0911 R. West et al.
0945 R.W. Pero, D. Harvan and M.C. Blois
0949 M.H. Rosen et al.
0991 S. Chandrasekaran et al.
0999 D. Belue and C.D. Weis
1001 F. du R. Volsteedt et al.
1019 P.D. Landor et al.
1041 A. Marchesini et al.
1045 A. Padwa and L. Brodsky
1073 H. Yanagawa et al.
1089 M.J. Goldstein and S.A. Kline
1135 C. Gallina and A. Liberatori
1147 A. Holy
1151 R.D. Miller and D. Dolce
1199 G. Fukata et al.
1213 A. Steigel and J. Sauer
1265 I. Agranat et al.
1307 A.S. Kende et al.
1319 P. Crabbe and A. Cerbantes
1349 V. Usieli and S. Sarel
1425 P. Rasoanaivo et al.
1447 W. Trommer and H. Blume
1553 K. Reiff et al.
1561 P. de Mayo and H.Y. Ng
1591 I. Murata and K. Nakasuji
1623 R.K. Razdan et al.
1649 L.G. Schroff et al.
1687 M. Iguchi et al.
1737 S. Ito et al.
1757 F. Khuong-Huu et al.
1803 T.S. Cantrell
1835 T. Mukai and H. Sukawa
1859 M. Shamma et al.
1871 G. Cignarelli and G. Cordella
1987 T. Kikuchi et al.
2015 Z. Rappoport et al.
2031 G. Köbrich and B. Rösner
2059 W. Friedrichsen and R. Epbinder
2109 S. Sekita et al.
2149 R.C. Hahn and R.P. Johnson

2159 R.B. Morin et al.
2163 R.B. Morin et al.
2195 C.L. Pedersen et al.
2213 F. Van Hulle et al.
2221 P. Caubere et al.
2279 R. Heckendorn and A.R. Gagneu
2283 T. Matssura and Y. Ito
2289 H. Suginome and T. Uchida
2313 J.B. Heather et al.
2333 T. Sassa et al.
2351 Y. Tamura et al.
2361 Y. Gaoni
2365 S. Sadeh and Y. Gaoni
2375 R. Bishop and W. Parker
2381 A.G. Gonzalez et al.
2385 G. Mehta and S.K. Kapoor
2397 H.G. de Graaf et al.
2401 G.R. Cliff et al.
2487 S. Brenner and E. Dunkelblum
2567 H. Brockmann and E.A. Stahler
2587 H. Singh et al.
2615 C. Shin and J. Yoshimura
2619 Z. Yoshida et al.
2627 T. Machiguchi et al.
2655 A.A. Akhrem et al.
2671 S. Yanagida et al.
2675 B.M. Trost and P.L. Kinson
2731 T. Sasaki et al.
2737 S. Ito et al.
2759 M. Iguchi et al.
2795 B. Nalliah et al.
2807 L.N. Yakhontov and M.F. Marshalkin
2811 V.N. Rekunova et al.
2821 R.M. Acheson and R.G. Bolton
2823 C. Vos and P.E.J. Verwiel
2871 J.R. Scheffer et al.
2875 M. Franck-Neumann and C. Buchecker
2887 G.H. Barnett et al.
2923 S.V. Kessar et al.
2939 J.O. Polazzi and M.P. Kotick
2955 K.L. Stevens et al.
2963 U. Shimomura and F.H. Johnson
2971 A. Kolb et al.
2989 R.J.S. Beer and A. Naylor
2993 H. Junek et al.
3009 Y. Okuno et al.
3039 D. Jeremic et al.
3059 P.C. Billot et al.
3067 A.G. Anastassiou and R.C. Griffith
3079 R.L. Shone
3103 A.G. Anastassiou et al.
3131 K. Kawazu et al.
3149 T. Novinson et al.
3153 E.J. Corey and R.D. Balanson
3181 C.M. Bowes et al.
3187 J.J. Artus et al.
3217 Y. Kashman and O. Awerbouch
3251 J. Torri and M. Azzaro
3337 L.H. Zalkow et al.
3349 R. Hanna
3401 I. Murata et al.
3405 I. Murata et al.
3409 R. Gompper and U. Jersak
3441 F. Weisbuch et al.
3493 M. Bobek et al.
3513 W. Martin et al.
3537 S. Iwasaki et al.
3611 H.J. Opferkuch and E. Hecker
3623 Z. Goldscmidt and A. Worchel
3625 A.G. Gonzalez et al.
3643 G. Horvath et al.
3649 R.G. Harrison et al.
3695 H. Brockmann and H. Laatsch
3747 H. Hogeveen and P.W. Kwant
3759 Z. Goldscmidt et al.
3805 A.G. Anastassiou et al.
3883 N. Abe et al.
3891 M. Kuzuya and H. Hart
3947 L.R.C. Barclay et al.
3999 M. Tada and T. Takahashi
4017 J.F. Haley, Jr. and P.M. Keehn
4037 C.H. Brieskorn and R. Ahlborn
4043 T. Kauffmann and H.-H. Kniese
4059 J.V. Greenhill and M. Ramli
4079 I. Agranat and M.R. Pick
4135 E. Kurosawa et al.
4163 J.P. Luttringer and J. Streith
4167 B. Willig and J. Streith
4189 H. Ishii et al.
4203 A.K. Das Gupta et al.
4221 T. Sato et al.
4229 V. Dave et al.
4257 Y.P. Chen et al.
4263 M. Matsui et al.
4277 K. Glombitza and E. Sattler
4295 A. Gelleri and A. Messmer
4319 L. Dalgaard and S.-O. Lawesson
4321 R. Helder and H. Wynberg
4325 H. Hogeveen and T.B. Middelkoop
4335 A. Cornelis et al.
4339 V. Viswanatha and G.S. KrishnaRao
4391 W.G. Duncan et al.
4403 R.D. Miller and D.L. Dolce
4425 W.G. Dauben et al.
4503 G. Markl and C. Martin
4553 J.P. Marino and J.M. Samanen
4569 I. Kouno et al.
4587 H. Muxfeldt et al.
4591 R.B. Reinarz and G.J. Fonken
4595 R.B. Reinarz and G.J. Fonken
4637 J.P. Pete and J.L. Wolfhugel
4701 R.A. Moss and G.M. Love
4730 P. Crabbe et al.
4735 T. Yamagishi et al.
4747 Y. Lin and F. Chen
4827 R. Weiss et al.
4837 R.T. Brown and A.A. Charalambides
4841 D.C. Wigfield and K. Taymaz
4869 Y. Fukuyama et al.
4873 T. Fujii et al.
4877 S. Yamamura et al.
4881 K. Sasaki et al.
4885 K. Saito and T. Mukai
4907 H. Urbach et al.
4955 H. Kinashi et al.
4967 K. Yamada et al.
4977 C.G. Karanjgoakar et al.
4995 K. Schröder and A. Zeeck
5005 S.K. Talapatra et al.
5065 H. Ogawa et al.
5077 J.O. Folayan and D.W. Hutchinson
5081 A. Cavé et al.

5095 P. Stütz and P.A. Stadler
5099 I.R.C. Bick et al.
5101 K. Hafner and F. Schmidt
5105 K. Hafner and F. Schmidt
5123 J.A. Lenoir and B.L. Johnson
5153 S. Kurata et al.
5173 C. Vos and P.E.J. Verwiel
5213 R.B. Morin et al.

89- -73, Angew. Chem., 12 (1973)(International Edition)
0068 K. Yamamoto and F. Sondheimer
0070 G. Baschang and V. Krita
0072 T. Iwakuma et al.
0074 Z. Janousek and H.G. Viehe
0076 S. Kuroda et al.
0081 M.T. Reetz et al.
0152 R. Weiss and S. Andrae
0224 H. Rau
0240 M. Franck-Neumann and C. Buchecker
0325 G. Schröder et al.
0328 G. Schröder et al.
0334 L..Fitjer and J.-M. Conia
0335 R. Kaiser and K. Hafner
0337 K. Hafner et al.
0410 P.J. Beeby and F. Sondheimer
0411 P.J. Beeby and F. Sondheimer
0418 K. Hafner and F. Schmidt
0495 D. Seebach et al.
0497 H. Muxfeldt et al.
0505B W. Grimme and H.-J. Rother
0570 H. Günther et al.
0572 H.-D. Martin and M. Hekman
0575 K. Hafner and H.U. Süss
0577 H. Dürr et al.
0580 H. Klein et al.
0655 W. Ahrens and A. Berndt
0660 M. Christl
0840 F. Klärner and E. Vogel
0910 E. Götschi et al.
0912 E. Götschi and A. Eschenmoser
0914 P.M. Müller et al.
0926 E. Hoyer et al.
0931 G. Märkl and F. Kneidl
0989 R. Schwesinger and H. Prinzbach
0991 H. Sauter et al.

93- -73, J. Applied Chem. S.S.S.R., (1973) (English translation)
2424 T.N. Kuz'micheva

94- -73, Chem. Pharm. Bull.(Japan), 21 (1973)
0034 H. Uno et al.
0054 K. Hiroi and S. Yamada
0062 M. Nagano et al.
0074 M. Nagano et al.
0107 T. Asako et al.
0118 K. Kohashi et al.
0125 H. Igeta et al.
0149 K. Makino et al.
0209 T. Fujii et al.
0241 Y. Maki et al.
0256 H. Uno, A.Irie and K. Hino
0279 H. Nagase et al.
0296 K. Yamakawa et al.
0329 F. Takami et al.
0335 T. Komeno and H. Itani
0383 T. Ueda et al.
0388 M. Okada and Y. Saito
0478 M. Furukawa et al.
0487 T. Ohsawo et al.
0497 H. Inouye and T. Nishioka
0528 S. Oida et al.
0565 T. Nambara et al.
0600 N. Morita et al.
0609 H. Taniyama et al.
0639 S. Nishibe et al.
0662 T. Kametani et al.
0674 S. Nishibe et al.
0692 A. Yamazaki et al.
0697 T. Asako et al.
0703 T. Asako et al.
0712 M. Yamazaki et al.
0742 A. Terada et al.
0785 A. Takamizawa et al.
0791 Y. Tsukitani et al.
0807 A. Terada et al.
0837 Y. Kondo and T. Takemoto
0846 H. Inouye et al.
0895 Y. Kamano and G.R. Pettit
0903 K. Nagasawa and H. Yoshidome
0921 G. Kobayashi et al.
0931 S. Omura et al.
0981 Y. Shiokawa and S. Ohki
1020 G. Nonaka et al.
1047 T. Kato, Y. Yamamoto and S. Takeda
1069 M. Kobayashi and H. Mitsuhashi
1080 H. Yanagisawa et al.
1090 K. Hirai et al.
1108 S. Nishibe et al.
1114 S. Nishibe et al.
1118 Y. Kobayashi et al.
1132 H. Nagase
1139 Y. Tamura et al.
1143 A. Yamazaki et al.
1155 S. Nishibe et al.
1164 Y. Sato et al.
1192 K. Kyogoku et al.
1213 M. Sekiya et al.
1240 T. Nohara et al.
1254 H. Okabe et al.
1287 M. Onda and K. Takeuchi
1295 T. Abe and A. Kambegawa
1300 A. Takamizawa and S. Matsumoto
1305 K. Hirai et al.
1338 M. Kaneda et al.
1342 S. Kubota and M. Uda
1372 Y. Tamura et al.
1382 M. Muraoka and T. Ueda
1404 A. Terada et al.
1410 G. Nonaka and I. Nishioka
1431 M. Kurumi et al.
1436 K. Kyogoku et al.
1451 T. Ueda and H. Ohtsuka
1481 H. Ishii et al.
1530 T. Ueda and H. Ohtsuka
1547 I. Yosioka et al.
1564 Y. Tsukitani and J. Shoji
1601 M. Kumagaya et al.
1658 Y. Tominaga et al.
1667 M. Sone et al.
1676 T. Fujii et al.

1720 M. Kimura et al.
1741 M. Kimura et al.
1777 K. Kyogoku et al.
1783 S. Sakai et al.
1835 T. Fujii et al.
1851 T. Murakami et al.
1868 M. Shibasaki et al.
1914 Y. Kikugawa et al.
1927 Y. Kikugawa et al.
1943 T. Higashino et al.
1954 T. Fujii and T. Saito
2014 H. Ogura and M. Sakaguchi
2019 H. Ogura, M. Kiwano and T. Itoh
2026 H. Ogura et al.
2048 M. Onda et al.
2051 H. Ogura et al.
2070 Y. Taniguchi and H. Kato
2095 K. Sano et al.
2112 G. Otani and S. Yamada
2168 T. Kabeya et al.
2187 K. Kohashi et al.
2195 K. Yoshioka et al.
2202 K. Yoshioka et al.
2224 K. Hirai and H. Sugimoto
2286 C. Takahashi et al.
2323 M. Arisawa et al.
2344 G. Kobayashi et al.
2346 H. Ishii et al.
2349 T. Fujii and T. Nishitani
2366 K. Meguro et al.
2375 K. Meguro and Y. Kuwada
2396 M. Nagano et al.
2408 M. Nagano et al.
2427 K. Yoshioka et al.
2452 T. Nambara et al.
2562 M. Arisawa et al.
2571 T. Murata et al.
2585 H. Tomisawa and R. Fujita
2590 H. Tomisawa et al.
2639 N. Shoji et al.
2643 T. Higashino and E. Hayashi
2684 T. Endo and H. Taguchi
2695 T. Fujii et al.
2705 N. Kondo et al.
2712 A. Ueno et al.
2715 A. Ueno et al.
2733 K. Kyogoku et al.
2739 T. Hino et al.
2770 Y. Tominaga et al.
2778 S. Nishibe et al.
2786 T. Hino et al.
2806 K. Hayashi et al.

95- -73, J. Pharm. Soc. Japan, 93 (1973)
0001 T. Yamazaki and T. Takizawa
0008 T. Ozawa and N. Kinae
0020 H. Shirai and T. Hayazaki
0030 T. Endo and H. Taguchi
0033 K. Tsuji et al.
0044 H. Inouye et al.
0073 T. Kato et al.
0087 G. Nonaka et al.
0094 T. Higashino et al.
0202 K. Kinoshita and S. Murase
0207 I. Ito and T. Ueda
0223 M. Ogawa et al.
0246 T. Asako et al.
0261 S. Takahashi and M. Takido
0296 M. Yasue et al.
0304 T. Ozawa et al.
0322 G. Kobayashi et al.
0330 T. Koyama et al.
0374 S. Nishibe et al.
0409 E. Hayashi et al.
0422 M. Fujira et al.
0448 J. Haginiwa et al.
0483 S. Sakai et al.
0541 S. Nishibe et al.
0566 T. Asako et al.
0612 G. Kobayashi et al.
0619 H. Hikino et al.
0624 F. Abe et al.
0642 S. Yurugi et al.
0648 Y. Tamura et al.
0707 K. Takahashi et al.
0729 H. Inoue et al.
0817 N. Oda, Y. Kanie and I. Ito
0836 G. Kobayashi et al.
0893 M. Sakamoto et al.
0896 S. Fukushima et al.
0916 S. Asada
0925 K. Kigazawa et al.
0964 G. Kobayashi et al.
0971 Y. Tominaga et al.
0977 T. Matsui et al.
0982 S. Tanaka and K. Hashimoto
0997 S. Tanaka et al.
1008 M. Sone et al.
1043 S. Yurugi et al.
1064 S. Furukawa et al.
1084 T. Kato and T. Hozumi
1087 M. Nagai et al.
1094 T. Kametani et al.
1100 Y. Takai et al.
1165 S. Sakai et al.
1183 K. Yoshioka et al.
1211 K. Ito et al.
1215 K. Ito et al.
1218 K. Ito et al.
1231 I. Imagaki et al.
1253 K. Meguro et al.
1263 K. Meguro and Y. Kuwada
1302 M. Mori et al.
1371 H. Shirai et al.
1406 K. Matoba and T. Yamazaki
1433 Y. Tominaga et al.
1437 T. Kato et al.
1514 S. Fukushima et al.
1520 Y. Tominaga et al.
1523 Y. Tominaga et al.
1542 M. Ohnishi et al.
1581 S. Kimoto et al.
1617 K. Ito et al.
1643 M. Sakamoto et al.
1685 T. Kato et al.

97- -73, Z. Chemie, 13 (1973)
0013 P. Berlin and K.R.H. Repke
0026 J. Fabian
0072 H. Böhland and R. Müller
0132 J. Liebscher and H. Hartmann
0342 J. Liebscher and H. Hartmann

0465 W. Schroth et al.

98- -73, J. Agr. Food Chem., 21 (1973)
0354 C.A. Henrick et al.
0676 T. Kurata et al.
0792 G.G. Ecke
0927 R.J. Cole and J.W. Kirksey

99- -73, Theor. Exptl. Chem., 9 (1973)
0417 V.T. Grachev et al.

100- -73, Lloydia, 36 (1973)
0066 A.N. Tackie et al.
0326 W.S. Woo
0333 K. Szendrei et al.
0422 L.A. Mitscher et al.

101- -73A, J. Organometallic Chem., 47 (1973)
0423 M.R. Wiles and A.G. Massey

101- -73C, J. Organometallic Chem., 49 (1973)
0243 C. Moberg and M. Nilsson
0353 F. Correa-Duran et al.
0381 J.C. Brunet and C. Lemahieu

101- -73H, J. Organometallic Chem., 54 (1973)
0C19 M. Pierce-Butler and G.R. Willey
0001 C.T. Viswanathan and C.A. Wilkie
0051 M.E. Glogowski et al.
0239 V.G. Shubin et al.

101- -73I, J. Organometallic Chem., 55 (1973)
0111 J.A. Connor et al.
0121 S. Kato et al.
0153 J. Deberitz and H. Noth

101- -73J, J. Organometallic Chem., 56 (1973)
0323 E.W. Neuse

101- -73K, J. Organometallic Chem., 57 (1973)
0183 H. Brunner and W.A. Herrmann

101- -73M, J. Organometallic Chem., 59 (1973)
0207 G. Matsubayashi et al.

101- -73N, J. Organometallic Chem., 60 (1973)
0077 J.A. Connor and E.M. Jones

102- -73, Phytochemistry, 12 (1973)
0025 F. Skoog et al.
0169 M. Naim et al.
0175 M. Tezuka et al.
0185 E. Guerreiro et al.
0193 S. Ghosal and R.S. Srivastava
0199 N. Peube-Locou et al.
0203 A.N. Tackie et al.
0228 J. Reisch et al.
0236 S.K. Talapatra et al.
0238 B.M. Krishna and R.B. Chaganty
0413 C.J. Aiba et al.
0417 R. Braz Filho et al.
0425 N. Adityachaudhury and P.K. Gupta
0429 W. Herz and I. Wahlberg
0433 M.A. Ferreira et al.
0447 R.C. Mollan et al.
0451 M.B. Patel et al.
0457 R. Gmelin et al.
0671 N.S. Prakasa Rao et al.
0693 D.W. Bishay et al.
0703 L. Crombie et al.
0726 F. Bohlmann and H. Franke
0731 A. Zane
0883 M. Silva et al.
0893 P. Pacheco et al.
0913 O.A. Lima and J. Polonsky
0929 A. Kjaer and A. Schuster
0942 K.C. Joshi et al.
0945 J.M. Edwards and A.E. Schwarting
0947 R. Braz Filho et al.
0948 F. Baralle et al.
1125 E.L. Ghisalberti et al.
1157 D.M.X. Donnelly et al.
1163 C.J. Aiba et al.
1167 S.P. Majumdar et al.
1182 N.C. Franca et al.
1184 R. Braz Filho et al.
1188 R.M.V. Assumpcao and O.R. Gottlieb
1191 J.P. Chapelle et al.
1415 W. Herz et al.
1421 W. Herz and I. Wahlberg
1427 M. Bittner et al.
1455 A.C. Jain and B.N. Sharma
1467 D.E. Burke et al.
1475 J. Bruneton et al.
1491B Y. Noro et al.
1493 S. Hisada et al.
1505 M. Shamma and S.S. Salgar
1509 K. Kaneko et al.
1755 M. Silva and P.G. Sammes
1787 A.W. Fraser and J.R. Lewis
1797 F.H. Stodola et al.
1799 G.B. Russell and P.G. Fenemore
1805 M.V. von Bulow et al.
1813 F. Khuong-Huu et al.
1822 G.A. Miana
1831B P. Bhattacharyya and D.P. Chakraborty
1881 D.T. Coxon et al.
2017 M. Lounasmaa et al.
2027 B. Cardillo et al.
2039 Y. Rolland et al.
2055 S. Hisada et al.
2058 E. Grossmann et al.
2071 A. Shoeb et al.
2073 M.N.S. Nayar et al.
2087 J.H. Rogozinska et al.
2243 P.O. Larsen et al.
2279 Y. Arai et al.
2312 S.K. Talapatra et al.
2315 F.G. Torto et al.
2317 S. Imre et al.
2389 J. Stockig et al.
2469 S. Gnecco et al.
2497 S. Huneck et al.
2501 M. Moir and R.H. Thomson
2509 A.N. Tackie et al.
2513 V. Preininger et al.
2521 B. Danieli et al.
2527 N. Ojima et al.
2531 P.S. Manchand et al.
2542 S. Ahmad et al.
2544 K. Ogiyama and M. Yasue

2552 J. Reisch et al.
2555 J.R. Hlubucek et al.
2717 G. Mellows et al.
2737 T. Yamauchi et al.
2741 Atta-Ur-Rahman et al.
2789 R.M. Letcher
2931 K. Hayashi et al.
2943 A.G. Duff et al.
2987 R.G. Powell and K.L. Mikolajczak
2993 S. Huneck and G. Follmann
2997 A.G. Gonzalez et al.
3010 M.K. Bhan
3014 M. Pinar

103- -73, Khim. Geterosikl. Soedin, 9 (1973) (English translation)
0001 A.D. Voitenko et al.
0026 I.I. Grandberg and V.I. Sorokin
0031 I.I. Grandberg et al.
0034 G.I. Zhungietu et al.
0038 G.I. Zhungietu et al.
0051 V.T. Grachev et al.
0055 P.B. Terent'ev et al.
0069 I.G. Il'ina et al.
0076 V.N. Antonova and E.R. Zakhs
0083 V.I. Nifontov et al.
0085 L.G. Tikhonova et al.
0112 K.N. Zelenin et al.
0117 M. Y. Lidak et al.
0120 S.A. Amitina and L.B. Volodarskii
0123 T.K. Sevast'yanova and L.B. Voldarskii
0137 N.F. Kucherova et al.
0141 V.A. Bren' et al.
0145 L.Y. Oleinikova and F.T. Pozharskii
0186 G.V. Ponomarev
0196 I.I. Grandberg and N.I. Bovrova
0202 G.I. Zhungietu et al.
0205 G.I. Zhungietu and L.M. Reulets
0207 B.E. Zaitsev et al.
0212 N.S. Prostakov et al.
0220 A.L. Gershuns and P.Y. Pustovar
0226 B.Y. Karele et al.
0247 L.G. Timoshinina and V.M. Vvedenskii
0253 N.E. Britikova et al.
0256 R.P. Bokaldere and A.Y. Liepin'
0300 S.M. Khripak et al.
0306 A.N. Kost et al.
0311 L.M. Zorin et al.
0314 Y.B. Shteinberg
0321 G.I. Zhungietu et al.
0323 N.S. Prostakov et al.
0333 V.G. Tishchenko et al.
0349 Y.B. Kurbatov et al.
0352 S.V. Abdullaev et al.
0366 V.M. Aryuzina and M.N. Shchukina
0369 N.M. Kaganskii et al.
0374 N.O. Saldabol et al.
0377 N.I. Grineva and T.S. Lomakina
0383 N.I. Grineva and T.S. Lomakina
0403 A.F. Oleinik et al.
0406 F.T. Pozharskii and L.Y. Oleinikova
0416 G.N. Dorofeenko et al.
0435 N.I. Chernova et al.
0441 I.S. Slyusarenko et al.
0456 A.N. Kost et al.
0467 I.Y. Kvitko and E.A. Pantilova
0471 G.A. Golubeva et al.
0481 D.I. Biskupskaya and A.V. Voropaeva
0485 I.G. Il'ina et al,
0488 M.E. Konshin
0490 M.E. Konshin and D.I. Uvarov
0496 E.R. Zakhs et al.
0503 G.A. Golubeva et al.
0510 B.Y. Karele et al.
0513 T.G. Koksharova et al.
0518 A.D. Sinegibskaya et al.
0521 I.Y. Kvitko and N.B. Sokolova
0525 S.M. Khripak et al.
0531 R.M. Bystrova and Y.M. Yutilov
0546 N.N. Borisova and V.G. Kul'nevich
0552 F.A. Trofimov et al.
0561 M.I. Shenbor and V.I. Tikhonov
0588 M.A. Mosto lavskii et al.
0598 Y.N. Portnov et al.
0615 Z.A. Krasnaya et al.
0621 L.G. Levkovskaya and T.S. Safonova
0628 N.S. Kozlov and G.V. Vorob'eva
0633 N.S. Kozlov et al.
0636 Y.R. Uldrikis et al.
0639 K.A. Nuridzhanyan and G.V. Kuznetsova
0659 I.Y. Kvitko et al.
0687 O.V. Moreiko and E.D. Sych
0701 R.E. Valter
0717 B.L. Moldaver et al.
0726 V.A. Anisimova et al.
0740 Y.V. Koshchienko and A.M. Simonov
0785 V.D. Romanenko and S.I. Burmistrov
0790 M.A. Kudinova et al.
0792 V.A. Azimov and L.N. Yakhontov
0802 Z.N. Nazarova et al.
0816 V.L. Savel'ev et al.
0850 F.A. Mikhailenko et al.
0880 V.G. Granik et al.
0888 K.M. Dyumaev et al.
0911 A.S. Vitvitskaya et al.
0917 L.I. Kolobushkina et al.
0922 N.M. Starshikov and F.T. Pozharskii
0925 V.P. Chekhun et al.
0939 Z.N. Nazarova et al.
0942 A.A. Akhrem et al.
0944 G.N. Dorofeenko et al.
0960 M.O. Mostoslavskii et al.
0968 R.S. Sagitullin et al.
0974 A.N. Kost et al.
0994 G.Y. Dubur et al.
1005 D.I. Uvarov and M.E. Konshin
1008 V.S. Kobrin et al.
1028 I.G. Il'ina et al.
1048 A.Y. Lazaris et al.
1056 L.I. Kolobushkina et al.
1059 L.I. Fleiderman et al.
1065 G.N. Ponomarev and B.V. Rozynov
1078 E.D. Sych and O.V. Moreiko
1082 V.M. Dziomko and A.V. Ivashchenko
1098 M.A. Gal'bershtam and N.P. Samoilova
1108 T.V. Troepol'skaya and Y.P. Kitaev
1119 A.F. Pozharskii et al.
1138 E.D. Sych et al.

1145 T.S. Safonova et al.
1152 G.I. Zhungietu et al.
1154 T.V. Mel'nikova et al.
1173 V.I. Ofitserov et al.
1204 S.E. Kovalev et al.
1216 A.V. Lazaris et al.
1233 E.L. Zaitseva et al.
1253 I.F. Tishchenkova and L.E. Kholodov
1257 V.I. Tikhonov and V.I. Rogovik
1280 T.S. Leonova et al.
1284 T.G. Koksharova et al.
1307 N.N. Magdesieva et al.
1327 I.S. Slyusarenko et al.
1355 M.I. Struchkova et al.
1367 N.N. Suvorov et al.
1391 A.L. Gershans et al.
1407 V.N. Rudenko and Y. Il'chenko
1423 V.P. Shchipanov
1463 E.R. Zakhs
1473 V.I. Shvedov et al.
1490 E.Y. Zinchenko et al.
1497 N.A. Kogan and M.I. Vlasova
1507 P.B. Terent'ev et al.
1517 N.N. Chipanina et al.
1532 N.V. Sazonov and T.S. Safonova
1535 N.B. Karpova and Y.S.Tsizin
1542 Y.A. Sedov et al.

104- -73, Zhur. Organ. Khim., 9 (1973) (English translation)
0044 A.N. Gafarov et al.
0074 O.A. Shavrygina et al.
0165 V.L. Plakidin and P.P. Gnatyuk
0208 A.L. Fridam et al.
0352 V.M. Neplyuev et al.
0379 N.S. Dokunikhin et al.
0394 G.N. Dorofeenko et al.
0407 M.E. Galanov and L.A. Pavlova
0413 V.G. Tishchenko and M.M. Fetisova
0477 S.M. Kvitko et al.
0578 N.G. Kostina and V.D. Shteingarts
0611 M.N. Preobrazhenskaya et al.
0686 V.N. Odinokov et al.
0732 T.N. Grigorova et al.
0793 A.Y. Tikhonov and L.B. Voladarskii
0831 P.A. Petyunin and V.V. Bolotov
0835 V.I. Sladkov et al.
0852 M.M. Kul'chitskii et al.
0861 P.A. Petyunin and V.V. Bolotov
0882 I.A. Korbukh et al.
0887 A.E. Kulikova et al.
0908 R.Y. Popova et al.
0922 S.L. Ioffe
0931 S.L. Ioffe et al.
0963 M.I. Komendantov and I.N. Domnin
1027 A.Y. Tsimanis et al.
1057 V.G. Shubin et al.
1082 N.I. Aboskalova et al.
1091 G.I. Bystritskii et al.
1200 K.A. Nuridzhanyan and G.V. Kuznetsova
1246 N.E. Akhmetova et al.
1275 N.P. Kostyuchenko et al.
1286 A.I. Kiprianov and V.Y. Buryak
1291 L.M. Kryakova et al.
1294 I.A. Korbukh et al.
1308 A.V. El'sov et al.
1316 K.L. Muravich-Aleksandr et al.
1449 M.I. Komendantov et al.
1511 K.G. Tashchuk et al.
1523 L.B. Krasnova et al.
1565 A.B. Tomchin et al.
1696 A.D. Zorina et al.
1729 G.G. Yakobson et al.
1739 M.S. Korobov et al.
1766 A.Y. Il-chenko
1776 A.D. Bulat and V.N. Mikhailova
1778 N.N. Magdesieva and R.A. Kyandzhetsian
1792 S.P. Mal'tseva and B.I. Stepanov
1815 Y.M. Slobodin and I.Z. Egenburg
1822 S.I. Radchenko and V.A. Naumov
1830 T.S. Kuznetsova et al.
1834 T.I. Temnikova et al.
1868 V.L. Khristoforov et al.
1927 M.B. Braude et al.
1986 V.S. Sorokina and L.A. Pavlova
1990 L.B. Volodarskii et al.
1995 V.S. Martybov and M.N. Preobrazhenskaya
2006 O.P. Shelyapin
2007 A.B. Tomchin et al.
2034 O.A. Erastov et al.
2106 S.S. Gitis et al.
2111 S.V. Bogatkov et al.
2119 S. Goszczynski and W. Zielinski
2144 V.M. Potapov et al.
2149 V.M. Potapov et al.
2172 V.A. Koptyug and A.V. Golounin
2181 M.I. Dronkina and L.M. Yagupol'skii
2190 V.G. Kharchenko and A.A. Rassudova
2195 I.N. Chernyuk et al.
2202 M.Y. Kornilov and E.M. Ruban
2213 B.A. Ivin et al.
2216 Y.N. Koshelev et al.
2223 M.I. Preobrazhenskaya et al.
2245 S.M. Kvitko et al.
2317 V.N. Odinokov et al.
2331 O.V. Kul'bitskaya et al.
2360 R.R. Kostikov et al.
2377 A.V. Golounin and V.A. Koptyug
2389 E.P. Serebryakov et al.
2400 E.Y. Markava et al.
2405 Y.E. Gerasimenko and N.T. Poteleshchenko
2418 B.A. Ivin et al.
2429 L.N. Zakharov et al.
2473 R.R. Kostikov et al.
2527 R.B. Zhurin and V.B. Vainer
2534 V.P. Yur'ev et al.
2542 A.V. El'tsov et al.
2560 V.A. Ivanov et al.
2580 Y.P. Khilya et al.
2596 M.Y. Kornilov et al.
2601 E.M. Ruban and M.Y. Kornilov
2606 A.I. Kiprianov and G.A. Lezenko
2622 A.V. El'tsov and V.E. Lopatin
2631 M.B. Kolesova et al.

105- -73, Khim. Prirodn. Soedin, 9 (1973)
0007 L.A. Golvina and G.K. Nikonov

0025 A.I. Saidkhodzhaer and G.K. Nikonov
0027 D.P. Popa and A.M. Reinbol'd
0039 L.S. Morozova et al.
0043 I.F. Makarevich
0095 A.S. Kadyrov and G.K. Nikonov
0118 Z.V. Dubovenko et al.
0120 O.A. Konovalova et al.
0125 B.Z. Usmanov et al.
0127 V.A. Kompantsev and A.L. Shinkarenko
0137 S. Khakindzhanov et al.
0139 A.N. Ban'kovskaya et al.
0162 G.P. Moiseeva et al.
0165 D.P. Popa et al.
0174 V.I. Bayunova and G.S. Grinenko
0183 R.M. Lagidze et al.
0191 N.Y. Novgorodova et al.
0223 A.S. Mezensev et al.
0252 V.G. Leont'eva et al.
0273 M. Bakhra et al.
0283 A.A. Savina and M.E. Perel'son
0294 K.M. Kamilov and G.N. Nikonov
0341 V.T. Ivanov et al.
0390 B. Akyev et al.
0397 Y.E. Sklyar et al.
0399 Y.E. Sklyar et al.
0400 V.N. Borisov et al.
0402 M.I. Yusupov and G.P. Sidyakin
0407 M.V. Artem'eva et al.
0421 V.G. Khodzhaev et al.
0465 M.V. Artem'eva et al.
0472 R. Shakirov and S.Y. Yunusov
0475 R. Ziyaev et al.
0492 Y.A. Berlin et al.
0498 Y.A. Berlin et al.
0512 E.F. Nesmelova and G.P. Sidyakin
0521 G.G. Zapesochnaya and T.T. Pangarova
0526 G.P. Shnyakina and G.G. Zapesochnaya
0534 M.V. Gorovits et al.
0583 T.K. Khasanov et al.
0586 M.V. Artem'eva et al.
0613 T.N. Il'inskaya
0626 L.I. Dukhovlinova et al.
0628 S.V. Serkerov
0640 A.I. Syrchina et al.
0644 G.P. Shnyakina and G.G. Zapesochnaya
0646 V.N. Borisov et al.
0652 I.N. Sokol'skii
0655 R.T. Mirzamatov et al.
0657 M.S. Khalmirzhaev et al.
0659 E.N. Novruzov et al.
0660 K.S. Umarov et al.
0661 L.D. Yakhontova et al.
0664 L.D. Yakhontova et al.
0672 L.R. Golovine and G.K. Nikonov
0718 A.M. Navruzova et al.
0727 R. Ziyaev et al.

106- -73, Die Pharmazie, 28 (1973)
0103 D. Heller and G. Wagner
0129 Z.I. El-Darawy et al.
0364 A.A.B. Hazzaa et al.
0391 K. Hiller et al.
0409 K. Hiller et al.
0641 D. Heller and G. Wagner

107- -73, Synthetic Comm., 3 (1973)
0013 J.K. Crandall et al.
0025 H. deKoning et al.
0073 E. Wenkert et al.
0129 R.B. Miller and B.F. Smith
0181 K. Yamada et al.
0219 C.C. Cook and P.M. Rimmer
0225 H. Iida et al.
0249 T. Sasaki et al.
0355 J.A. Findlay and F.Y. Shum
0369 T. Sasaki et al.
0393 R.K. Hill and R.V. Shetty
0397 E.E. Garcia

108- -73, Israel J. Chem.. 11 (1973)
0557 E. Dunkelblum
0723 J. Almog and E.D. Bergmann
0791 A.Y. Meyer and A. Goldblum
0819 D.S. Malament

110- -73, Russian J. Phys. Chem., 47 (1973)
0627 G.L. Ryzhova and A.M. Pogaleeva
1210 G.A. Chmutova et al.

111- -73, Chim. ther., 8 (1973)
0290 E. Ravina et al.
0346 R. Albrecht and G.A. Hoyer
0451 G. Azadian-Boulanger and D. Bertin
0545 B. Ronot
0574 P. de Cointet et al.

112- -73, Spectroscopy Letters, 6 (1973)
0007 P.J. Kovi et al.
0547 Y.K. Agrawal and S.G. Tandon
0621 E.A. Romanenko et al.

114- -73A, Acta Chim. Acad. Sci. Hung., 76 (1973)
0081 Z. Csürös

114- -73B, Acta Chim. Acad. Sci. Hung., 77 (1973)
0035 E. Moharos and A.I. Kiss
0069 A. Toth and E. Dudar
0093 G. Litkei and R. Bognar
0435 R. Bognar and A. Levai

114- -73C, Acta Chim. Acad. Sci. Hung., 78 (1973)
0039 G. Zlatos et al.
0207 B. Zsadon et al.
0315 J. Szabolcs and L. Timar
0419 Z. Csürös

114- -73D, Acta Chim. Acad. Sci. Hung., 79 (1973)
0105 K. Horvath-Dora et al.
0191 A. Levai and R. Bognar
0365 A. Levai et al.
0411 M.A.F. Elkaschef

115- -73, Egyptian J. Chem., 16 (1973)
0297 W.I. Awad and A.I. Hashem
0381 A. Sammour and M. Elhashash

115- -73A, Egyptian J. Chem., Special Issue (1973)
0027 A.M. Osman et al.
0067 I.M. Issa et al.
0077 R. Abu-Eittah and A. El-Shahawy
0145 F.G. Baddar et al.

116- -73, Macromolecules, 6 (1973)
0305 J.S. Humphrey, Jr. et al.
0483 V.V. Korshak et al.
0517 R. Boni and A.S. Verdini
0571 A. Cosani et al.

117- 73, Org. Preps. Procedures, 5 (1973)
0017 C.A. Mudry and A.R. Frasca
0075 T. Sasaki et al.
0095 T. Hisano et al.

118- -73, Synthesis, 5 (1973)
0106 W.J. LeNoble and W.S. Chang
0149 G. Dauphin et al.
0159B Y. Tamura et al.
0164 J. Almog and B.A. Weissman
0213 D.K. Banerjee and G. Subramanyam
0225 G. Entenmann
0308 D. Nasipuri and R. Bhattacharya
0313B K. Srinivasan et al.
0363 T. Nishiwaki and T. Takahashi
0414 H.G.O. Becker et al.
0542 D.N. Dhar and R.C. Manjal
0546 J. Lehmann and H. Wamhoff
0611 L.E. Friedrich and R.A. Fioto
0667 H.-D. Martin and M. Hekman
0783 H. Straub et al.
0791 D. Lloyd et al.

119- -73, S. African Chem. Inst. J., 26 (1973)
0053 R. Vleggaar et al.
0064 R. Vleggaar et al.
0071 R. Vleggaar et al.
0132 P.E.J. Kruger and R.R. Arndt

120- -73, Pakistan J. Sci. Ind. Research, 16 (1973)
0096 M.S. Hussain et al.

121- -73, J. Macromol. Sci., 7 (1973)
1297 T. Seita et al.

124- -73, Ukrain. Khim. Zhur., 39 (1973)
0215 V.N. Skopenko et al.
0353 M.Y. Kornilov et al.
0703 A.V. Stetsenko et al.
0913 I.L. Mushkalo et al.
0922 V.A. Chuihuk
1036 V.E. Pashinnik et al.
1151 S.M. Shulga and V.A. Chuihuk
1163 Y.M. Volovenko et al.
1265 E.E. Milliaresi and V.E. Ruchkin

126- -73B, Makromol. Chem., 164 (1973)
0007 T. Seita et al.
0025 H. Kammerer and V. Steiner

126- -73D, Makromol. Chem., 166 (1973)
0311 K. Sugiyama et al.

126- -73G, Makromol. Chem., 169 (1973)
0327 K. Takemoto et al.

126- -73J, Makromol. Chem., 172 (1973)
0019 T. Seita et al.

126- -73L, Makromol. Chem., 174 (1973)
0007 K. Kondo et al.
0039 H. Kammerer and W. Niemann

128- -73, Croatica Chim. Acta, 45 (1973)
0357 D. Bilovic and V. Skaric
0465 M. Lacan et al.
0495 V. Skaric et al.

129- -73, Synthesis Inorg. Metal-Org. Chem., 3 (1973)
0291 J. Plesek et al.

130- -73, Bioorganic Chem., 2 (1973). (Issues 2-4)
0124 A.I. Scott et al.
0191 W.S. Powell and R.A. Heacock
0197 L. Davis

131- -73, J. Mol. Structure, 19 (1973)
0255 D. Simov and S. Stojanov

132- -73, Anales Assoc. Quim. Argentina, 61 (1973)
0015 A. Rahman and O.L. Tombesi
0051 J.M. Agoff et al.
0113 H.S.E. Gatica
0153 M.C. Teglia and R.A. Cadenas
0233 M.A. Ruveda et al.
0279 A. Rahman and N.N. Ferraccutti

133- -73, Pharm. Acta Helv., 48 (1973)
0157 G.D. Rees and J.K. Sugden
0389 B. Testa

135- -73, J. Appl. Spectroscopy S.S.S.R., 19 (1973)
1154 M.G. Voronkov et al.
1299 T.Y. Paperno et al.
1521 S.I. Radchenko

136- -73A, Carbohydrate Research, 26 (1973)
0071 S.R. Jenkins and E. Walton
0247 P.N. Cote and L. Goodman
0255 A.S. Jones and R.T. Walker
0377 M.C. Teglia and R.A. Cadenas
0431 M.I. Litter and R.M. de Lederkremer

136- -73B, Carbohydrate Research, 27 (1973)
0149 H. Iwamura et al.
0225 T.E. Walker et al.
0243 G. Giovanninetti et al.
0455 P.C. Srivastava and R.J. Rousseau
0468 K. Antonakis and M. Arvor-Egron

136- -73C, Carbohydrate Research, 28 (1973)
0125 S. David and C. Auge
0129 J.M.J. Tronchet et al.
0201 D. Horton et al.

0339 J.W. Llewellyn and J.M. Williams
0378 A.J. Freestone et al.

136- -73D, Carbohydrate Research, 29 (1973)
0015 S. David and A. Lubineau
0165 M.L. Sharma and E. Newbrun
0259 S.F. Quadri et al.
0297 J.M.J. Tronchet et al.
0311 J.M.J. Tronchet and N. LeHong

136- -73E, Carbohydrate Research, 30 (1973)
0133 M.J. Taylor et al.
0165 H.S. El Khadem et al.
0192 K. Antonakis and M. Bessodes
0225 D.M. Vyas and W.A. Szarek
0395 J.M.J. Tronchet and D. Schwarzenbach

136- -73F, Carbohydrate Research, 31 (1973)
0101 E.W. Thomas
0154 H. Komura et al.
0159 J.M.J. Tronchet and E. Mihaly
0245 M.W. Winkley
0347 H.H. Baer and C.-W. Chiu

138- -73, Chemistry Letters, (1973)
0003 R. Noyori et al.
0051 S. Mataka and J.P. Anselme
0063 Y. Hayashi et al.
0067 N. Morita et al.
0111 T. Sato et al.
0133 Y. Naya and Y. Hirose
0187 C. Pac et al.
0245 M. Takasugi et al.
0255 K. Hirotsu et al.
0309 K. Mizuno et al.
0321 T. Matsumoto et al.
0391 M. Hori et al.
0413 I. Murata and K. Yamamoto
0455 A. Matsumoto et al.
0491 T. Sakai and Y. Hirose
0561 I. Murata et al.
0641 K. Maruyama et al.
0727 Y. Naya and Y. Hirose
0793 T. Suzuki et al.
0799 T. Suzuki
0859 T. Hata and T. Kurihara
0915 H. Obara et al.
0917 T. Fuchigami and K. Odo
0929 T. Tatee and T. Takahashi
0937 Y. Asaka et al.
0941 M. Tsutsui and C.P. Hrung
0967 K. Kondo et al.
1073 A. Guzman and P. Crabbe
1111 J. Furukawa and K. Omura
1117 T. Matsumoto et al.
1169 Y. Kayama et al.

139- 73A, Phosphorus, 2 (1973)
0209 I.J. Borowitz and R.K. Crouch

139- -73B, Phosphorus, 3 (1973)
0037 G. Aksnes and F.Y. Khalil
0109 G. Aksnes and F.Y. Khalil

140- -73, J. Anal. Chem. S.S.S.R.,(1973) (English translation)
0005 S.I. Gusev et al.
0008 S.P. Mushtakova et al.
0087 Z.E. Mel'chekova and V.I. Murashova
0395 V.M. Ivanov et al.
0971 A.V. Dolgorev
1973 N.S. Ershova et al.

141- -73, Acta Univ. Palackianae Olomucensis Fac. Med., Suppl. XIII (1973)
0001 F. Santavy et al.

142- -73, Heterocycles, 1 (1973)
0021 M. Nitta and T. Mukai
0031 M. Shamma and D.Y. Hwang
0043 D. McNeil and K.L. Stuart
0251 N. Shoji et al.

143- -73, Int. J. Sulfur Chem., 8 (1973)
0019 E. Chiellini et al.
0205 J.R. Shelton and K.E. Davis
0217 J.R. Shelton and K.E. Davis
0273 I.D. Rae
0285 R. Mayer and U. Pleiss
0359 S. Kato et al.
0427 N. Kito and A. Ohno
0437 S. Kato et al.
0519 I.D. Rae and M.J. Wade
0539 L. Field and J.E. White